P9-CSB-150

the physiological basis
of medical practice

the physiological basis

Eighth Edition

With 49 contributors under the general editorship of NORMAN BURKE TAYLOR

John V. Basmajian
Ronald A. Bergman
Robert W. Berliner
Charles H. Best
H. K. F. Blaschko
E. Raymond Borun
Louis L. Boyarsky
K. Brown-Grant
Paul C. Bucy
Fergus W. Campbell
James Campbell
Donald W. Clarke
Jay D. Coffman
Paul D. Coleman
James A. Dauphinee
B. T. Donovan
Lionel E. Dorfman

Joseph Engelberg
Donald E. Gregg
Reginald E. Haist
G. W. Harris
Joseph E. Hawkins, Jr.
N. C. Hightower, Jr.
Joseph B. Houpt
Andrew Huvos
Albert A. Kattus
William K. Kerr
W. Milo Keynes
Dorothy C. H. Ley
Colin C. Lucas
Robert L. MacMillan
E. A. McCulloch
F. C. Monkhouse

William C. North
Jessie H. Ridout
James M. Salter
John W. Scott
Nathan W. Shock
Arthur A. Siebens
Fritiof S. Sjöstrand
Durwood J. Smith
William E. Stone
Norman B. Taylor
Klaus Thurau
Marthe Vogt
Donald G. Walker
E. N. Willmer
W. B. Youmans
James F. Zolman

A TEXT IN APPLIED PHYSIOLOGY

of medical practice

CHARLES HERBERT BEST

C.B.E., M.A., M.D., D.Sc. (Lond.), F.R.C.S., F.R.C.P. (Canada),
Professor and Lately Head of Department of Physiology,
Director of the Banting-Best Department
of Medical Research, University of Toronto

NORMAN BURKE TAYLOR

V.D., M.D., F.R.S. (Canada), F.R.C.S., (Edin.),
F.R.C.P. (Canada), M.R.C.S. (Eng.), L.R.C.P. (Lond.)
Lately Professor of the History of Medicine
and Medical Literature, University of
Western Ontario, London, Canada;
formerly Professor of Physiology, University of Toronto

Baltimore · 1966 **The Williams & Wilkins Company**

Copyright ©, 1966
THE WILLIAMS & WILKINS COMPANY

FIRST EDITION, JANUARY, 1937
Reprinted, March, 1937; August, 1937; October, 1937; January, 1939
SECOND EDITION, SEPTEMBER, 1939
Reprinted, May, 1940; April, 1941; May, 1942
THIRD EDITION, MARCH, 1943
Reprinted, June, 1943, February, 1944
FOURTH EDITION, NOVEMBER, 1945
Reprinted, April, 1946; August, 1946; March, 1947; December, 1947; March, 1948; July, 1949
FIFTH EDITION, JANUARY, 1950
Reprinted, May, 1950; July, 1950; February, 1951; January, 1952; February, 1953
SIXTH EDITION, JANUARY, 1955
Reprinted, July, 1956; June, 1957; October, 1958; November, 1959; May, 1960
SEVENTH EDITION, JANUARY, 1961
Reprinted, April, 1965
FIRST SPANISH EDITION, 1939
SECOND SPANISH EDITION, 1941
THIRD SPANISH EDITION, 1943
FOURTH SPANISH EDITION, 1947
FIFTH SPANISH EDITION, 1954
FIRST PORTUGESE EDITION, 1940
SECOND PORTUGESE EDITION, 1945
FIRST ITALIAN EDITION, 1955
SECOND ITALIAN EDITION, 1959
FIRST POLISH EDITION, 1960
FIRST RUMANIAN EDITION, 1958
EIGHTH EDITION, DECEMBER, 1966
Reprinted, October, 1967

Library of Congress Catalog Card Number 66-24510

COMPOSED AND PRINTED AT THE WAVERLY PRESS, INC., BALTIMORE, MD. 21202 U.S.A.

Preface to the Eighth Edition

Some major changes and additions have been made in this edition and a number of new contributors enlisted. Professor Joseph Engelberg has written an introductory chapter on The Cell. The section on The Nervous System has been moved from its old position to the beginning of the book. Professor Louis Boyarsky has rewritten some of the chapters of this section and revised others. Professor Paul Coleman has revised chapter 8, The Cerebral Cortex.

Dr. James Zolman is the author of an entirely new chapter on Conditioning and Learning which replaces the chapter on Conditioned Reflexes in the last edition. Professor Fritiof Sjöstrand has contributed a new chapter on the Physiology of Muscle to which Professor John Basmajian has added an article on Electromyography, and Professor Ronald Bergman one titled The Gross Organization and Function of Whole Skeletal Muscle.

Many of the chapters of section IV have been revised by Dr. Dorothy Ley, a new contributor. Three other new authors in this section are; Dr. Ernest McCulloch who has completely rewritten chapter 32, Dr. Robert MacMillan who has collaborated with Dr. Frank Monkhouse in the revision of chapter 33, and Professor James Dauphinee who has written a chapter titled The Regulation of the Hydrogen Ion Concentration of the Body Fluids, which entirely replaces the old chapter on this subject.

Chapters 53 and 54 in Respiration have again been revised by Professor W. B. Youmans, while the revision of chapter 50 has been taken over by Professor William Stone and chapters 51 and 52 by Professor A. A. Siebens.

Professor Donald Walker is the author of chapter 55, a new and welcome one titled The Cytoarchitecture of Protein Secretory and Active Transport Cells. Professor N. C. Hightower has rewritten the section on Digestion. Chapter 66, The Metabolism of the Purine Bases, has been revised and largely rewritten by Dr. Joseph Houpt.

The Endocrine section introduces four authors eminent in their chosen fields, Drs. H. Blaschko, K. Brown-Grant, W. M. Keynes and Marthe Vogt.

We are indebted to Drs. William Kerr and Lionel Dorfman for the article on The Urinary Bladder at the end of chapter 80 which takes the place of the corresponding chapter in the 7th Edition.

To all contributors, old and new, we extend our very grateful acknowledgment.

Preface to First Edition

Physiology is a science in its own right and the laboratory worker who pursues his researches quite detached from medical problems need offer no apology for his academic outlook. Indeed some of the most valuable contributions to medical science have been the outcome of laboratory studies whose applications could not have been foreseen. Nevertheless, we feel that the teacher of physiology in a medical school owes it to his students, whose ultimate interest it must be conceded is in the diagnosis and treatment of disease, to emphasize those aspects of the subject which will throw light upon disorders of function. The physiologist can in this way play a part in giving the student and practitioner a vantage point from which he may gain a rational view of pathological processes.

We have endeavored to write a book which will serve to link the laboratory and the clinic, and which will therefore promote continuity of physiological teaching throughout the pre-clinical and clinical years of the under-graduate course. It is hoped that when the principles underlying diseased states are pointed out to the medical student, and he is shown how a knowledge of such principles aids in the interpretation of symptoms or in directing treatment, he will take a keener interest in physiological studies. When such studies are restricted to the classical aspects of the subject, apparently remote from clinical application, the student is likely to regard them only as a task which his teachers in their inscrutable wisdom have condemned him to perform. Too often he gains the idea, from such a course, that physiology is of very limited utility and comes to believe that, having once passed into the clinical years, most of what he has "crammed" for examination purposes may be forgotten without detriment to his more purely medical studies. Unfortunately, he does not always realize at this stage in his education how great has been the part which physiological discoveries have played in the progress of medicine, and that the practice of today has evolved from the "theories" of yesterday.

Many physiological problems can be approached only through animal experimentation. Advances in many fields, most notably in those of carbohydrate metabolism, nutrition, and endocrinology, bear witness to the fertility of this method of research. On the other hand, many problems can be elucidated only by observations upon man, and physiology has gained much from clinical research. The normal human subject as an experimental animal possesses unique advantages for many types of investigation; and in disease, nature produces abnormalities of structure and function which the physiological laboratory can imitate only in the crudest way. Within recent years the clinical physiologist, fully realizing these advantages and the opportunities afforded by the hospital wards, has contributed very largely to physiological knowledge. In many instances, clinical research has not only revealed the true nature of the underlying process in disease, but has cast a light into some dark corner of physiology as well; several examples of clinical investigation which have pointed the way to the physiologist could be cited. In the last century, knowledge of the processes of disease was sought mainly in studies of morbid *anatomy*; biochemistry was in its infancy and many of the procedures now commonly employed for the investigation of the human subject had not been devised. Today, the student of scientific medicine is directing his attention more and more to the study of morbid *physiology* in his efforts to solve clinical problems. This newer outlook has borne fruit in many fields. It has had the beneficent result of drawing the clinic and the physiological and biochemical laboratories onto common ground from which it has often been possible to launch a joint attack upon disease. We feel that this modern trend in the field of research should be reflected in the teaching of medical students, and have therefore given greater prominence to clinical aspects of the subject than is usual in physiological texts.

In order to understand the function of an organ it is usually essential to have a knowledge of its structure. For this reason we have followed the plan of preceding the account of the physiology of a part by a short description of its morphology and, in many instances, of its nerve and blood supply. The architecture and functions of the central nervous system are so intimately related that some space has been devoted to a description of the more important fiber tracts and grey masses of the cerebrum, cerebellum, and spinal cord.

We wish to thank our colleagues in physiology, biochemistry and anatomy whom we have drawn upon on so many occasions for information and advice; without their generous help the undertaking would have been an almost impossible one. We are also deeply grateful for the unstinted assistance which we have received from our friends on the clinical staff, several of whom have read parts of the text in manuscript or in proof. We wish especially to acknowledge our indebtedness to Professor A. M. Wynne who has written the section on the oxidizing systems of living cells, to Dr. J. K. W. Ferguson for his collaboration in the preparation of Chapter 33, and to Professor C. B. Weld and Dr. E. T. Waters whose stimulating criticisms and sound counsel have been invaluable.

Finally, we wish to thank our secretaries, Miss Mabel Cory and Miss Dudley Martin, who have spent so many tedious hours in preparing the manuscript for the press, in checking the references and in compiling the index.

October 15, 1936   C. H. B.
                                                               N. B. T.

Contributors

John V. Basmajian, M.D. Professor and Head, Department of Anatomy, Queen's University, Kingston, Ontario, Canada

Ronald A. Bergman, Ph.D. Assistant Professor of Anatomy, The Johns Hopkins University School of Medicine, Baltimore, Maryland

Robert W. Berliner, M.D. Director, Intramural Research, National Heart Institute, National Institutes of Health, Bethesda, Maryland

Charles H. Best, M.A., M.D., D.Sc. (Lond.), F.R.S., F.R.C.P. (Canada) Director of the Banting-Best Department of Medical Research, University of Toronto

H. K. F. Blaschko, F.R.S. Reader in Biochemical Pharmacology at Oxford University, Oxford, England

E. Raymond Borun. Department of Medicine, Center for the Health Sciences, University of California at Los Angeles, Los Angeles, California

Louis L. Boyarsky, Ph.D. Professor of Physiology and Biophysics, Department of Physiology and Biophysics, University of Kentucky, Lexington, Kentucky

K. Brown-Grant, M.D., Sc.D. Locke Research Fellow of the Royal Society, Department of Human Anatomy, University of Oxford, Oxford, England

Paul C. Bucy, M.D., B.S., M.S. Professor of Surgery, Northwestern University Medical School. Director, Section on Neurological Surgery, Chicago Wesley Memorial Hospital

Fergus W. Campbell, M.D., Ph.D., The Physiological Laboratory, University of Cambridge, Cambridge, England

James Campbell, M.A., Ph.D. Department of Physiology, University of Toronto, Canada

Donald W. Clarke, B.Sc., M.Sc., Ph.D. Banting & Best Department of Medical Research and Department of Physiology, University of Toronto, Canada

Jay D. Coffman, M.D. Assistant Professor of Medicine, Boston University School of Medicine and Physician-in-charge, Peripheral Vascular Laboratory, University Hospital, Boston University Medical Center, Boston, Massachusetts

Paul D. Coleman, Ph.D. Associate Professor of Physiology, University of Maryland School of Medicine, Baltimore, Maryland

James A. Dauphinee, Ph.D., M.D., F.R.C.P. (C) Professor of Pathological Chemistry, University of Toronto, Canada

B. T. Donovan, Ph.D. Department of Neuroendocrinology, Institute of Psychiatry, The Maudsley Hospital, Denmark Hill, London, England

Lionel E. Dorfman, M.D., Department of Surgery, University of Toronto, Canada

Joseph Engelberg, Ph.D. Department of Physiology and Biophysics, University of Kentucky, Lexington, Kentucky

Donald E. Gregg, Ph.D., M.D. Chief, Department of Cardiorespiratory Diseases, Walter Reed Army Institute of Research, Walter Reed Army Medical Center, Washington, D. C.

Reginald E. Haist, M.A., M.D., Ph.D., F.R.S.C. Chairman, Department of Physiology, University of Toronto, Toronto, Ontario, Canada

Professor G. W. Harris, F.R.S. Dr. Lee's Professor of Anatomy, University of Oxford, Oxford, England

Joseph E. Hawkins, Jr., M.A. (Oxon.), Ph.D. (Harv.) Professor of Physiological Acoustics, Kresge Hearing Research Institute, Department of Otorhinolaryngology, University of Michigan Medical School, Ann Arbor, Michigan

Dr. N. C. Hightower, Jr. Director, Department of Clinical Physiology, Scott and White Clinic, Scott and White Memorial Hospital, Sherwood and Brindley Foundation, Temple, Texas

Joseph B. Houpt, M.D., F.R.C.P. (C) Clinical Teacher, Department of Medicine, University of Toronto; Physician, New Mount Sinai Hospital, Toronto; Consultant, Arthritis Service, Sunnybrook Hospital, Toronto, Ontario, Canada

Dr. *Andrew Huvos*   Associate in Medicine, Boston University School of Medicine, Boston, Massachusetts

Albert A. Kattus, M.D.   Professor of Medicine (Cardiology), UCLA Center for the Health Sciences, Los Angeles, California

William K. Kerr, M.D.   Associate, Department of Surgery, University of Toronto, Canada

W. Milo Keynes, M.D., M.Chir. (Cambridge), F.R.C.S. (England)   Nuffield Department of Surgery, The Radcliffe Infirmary, Oxford, Ehgland

Dorothy C. H. Ley, M.D., B.Sc. (Med.), F.R.C.P. (C), F.A.C.P.   Director of Haematology, Toronto Western Hospital; Associate in Medicine, University of Toronto, Canada

Colin C. Lucas, M.A.Sc., Ph.D., D.Sc., F.R.S.C., F.C.I.C.   Banting and Best Department of Medical Research, University of Toronto, Canada

Robert L. MacMillan, M.D., M.R.C.P. (Lond.), F.R.C.P. (Canada), F.A.C.P., Assistant Professor, Department of Medicine, University of Toronto, Canada.

E. A. McCulloch, M.D., F.R.C.P. (C)   Associate Professor, Department of Medical Biophysics, University of Toronto; Associate, Department of Medicine, University of Toronto; Head, Subdivision of Hematology, Division of Biological Research, The Ontario Cancer Institute, Toronto, Canada

Dr. *F. C. Monkhouse*   Professor of Physiology and Director of Teaching Laboratories, University of Toronto, Canada

William C. North, M.D., Ph.D.   Professor of Anesthesiology and Pharmacology, University of Tennessee College of Medicine, Memphis, Tennessee

Jessie H. Ridout, M.A., Ph.D.   Banting-Best Department of Medical Research, University of Toronto, Canada

James M. Salter, M.A., Ph.D., Banting Best Department of Medical Research, University of Toronto, Canada

John W. Scott, M.A., M.D.   Professor of Physiology, University of Toronto, Canada

Nathan W. Shock, Ph.D.   Chief, Gerontology Branch, National Institute of Child Health and Human Development and the Baltimore City Hospitals, Baltimore, Maryland

Arthur A. Siebens, M.D.   Professor of Physiology and Pediatrics, Director of Rehabilitation Center, University of Wisconsin School of Medicine, Madison, Wisconsin

Fritiof S. Sjöstrand   Professor of Zoology, University of California at Los Angeles, Los Angeles, California

Durwood J. Smith, M.D.   Professor and Chairman, Department of Pharmacology, The University of Vermont, College of Medicine, Burlington, Vermont

William E. Stone, Ph.D., Professor of Physiology, University of Wisconsin Medical School, Madison, Wisconsin

Norman B. Taylor, V.D., M.D., F.R.S., (Canada), F.R.C.S. (Edin.), F.R.C.P. (Canada), M.R.C.S. (Eng.), L.R.C.P. (Lond.), formerly Professor of Physiology, University of Toronto, and Professor of the History of Medicine and Medical Literature, University of Western Ontario, Canada.

Klaus Thurau, M.D., Department of Physiology, University of Munich, Munich, West Germany

Marthe Vogt, F.R.S.   Agricultural Research Council Institute of Animal Physiology, Babraham, Cambridge, England.

Donald G. Walker, Ph.D.   Professor of Anatomy, Department of Anatomy, The Johns Hopkins University School of Medicine, Baltimore, Maryland

E. N. Willmer, M.A., M.Sc., Sc.D., F.R.S.   Professor of Histology, University of Cambridge, Fellow of Clare College, Cambridge, England

W. B. Youmans, M.D., Ph.D.   Professor and Chairman, Department of Physiology, University of Wisconsin Medical School, Madison, Wisconsin

James F. Zolman, Ph.D.   Department of Physiology and Biophysics, College of Medicine, University of Kentucky, Lexington, Kentucky

CONTENTS

SECTION IV. THE BLOOD AND LYMPH

SECTION V. CIRCULATION

SECTION VI.   RESPIRATION

SPECIAL CHAPTER

SECTION VII.   DIGESTION

SECTION VIII. METABOLISM AND NUTRITION

SECTION IX. THE DUCTLESS GLANDS OR ENDOCRINES

SECTION X. THE EXCRETION OF URINE

CHAPTER 1

By Way of Introduction—The Cell

Levels of Organization

A multicellular organism is a society of cells. The cellular units manifest, as do the units of any complex society, division of labor, specialization, mutual interaction according to a set of rules and centralized control. Consider the levels of organization of the human organism. *Atoms* are combined in different ways to yield the *monomers* (amino acids, nucleotides, sugars), which are the building blocks of biological *macromolecules* (proteins, nucleic acids, polysaccharides). Macromolecules are combined with smaller molecules to form cell *organelles* (the cell membrane, mitochondria, lysosomes, endoplasmic reticulum). The organelles are combined to form *cells*, the cells to form *tissues*, the tissues to form *organs*, and the organs to form the *organism*.

The study of mammalian physiology, being the study of the dynamic interrelationships amongst tissues and organs, lies by and large, at the organismal level. The organismal level is also the operational level of the practicing physician. This may be seen from the following example. It is a truism that only the individual cells in an organism are "alive." It is also certainly true that when all the cells in an organism are dead that the organism itself is dead. Yet death as we know it in the human sphere is not usually the result of cellular death. Consider a person who receives a fatal blow on his head. The examining physician notes that respiration, heart action, and the reflexes of the eye have ceased and issues a death certificate. Yet, in fact, at that moment nearly all the cells in the body, perhaps with the exception of some cells which may have been killed at the site of impact, are likely to be alive and fully competent. Cell samples taken from different organs could undoubtedly be grown or maintained in tissue culture. Why then is an individual dead when virtually all of his living parts are still viable and competent? It is evident that here death is the result of a disturbance among the relationships existing *between* cells. The central nervous system is disorganized and ceases to send appropriate impulses to the cardiac and respiratory machinery; the resulting reduction in the supply of oxygen to the brain causes the central nervous system to deteriorate. A chain reaction has started leading, in the long run, to the destruction of individual cells. A "death certificate" is a prediction, based upon past experience, of cellular death.

From this it is evident, that molecular and cellular biology play a supporting role to mammalian physiology but are not a major province in its domain. For this reason it is not our aim, in this chapter, to outline the discipline known as cell physiology. Instead, we wish to present a number of powerful generalizations from this field to illuminate and clarify certain facets of organismal physiology.

Cell Structure

Every existing cell has, for all practical purposes, a definite *boundary*. By boundary we mean that on one side of the boundary we have intracellular material and on the other side extracellular material.[1] Every cell is bounded by a *membrane*. The words boundary and membrane are not synonyms. It is easy to think of a cell-like system which is bounded, though not bounded by a membrane. A piece of gelatin, for example, has a definite boundary, yet it is not bounded by a membrane. Permeability and electrical studies carried out over the past eighty years had suggested that cells are bounded by a membrane. The cell membrane, however, remained somewhat of a hypothetical entity, named the *plasma membrane*, until relatively recently when electron microscope studies provided the first direct evidence of its existence. Membranes of similar thickness and appearance as the cell membrane have, since then, also been found at the boundary or interior of a large number of subcellular particles and organelles. J. D. Robertson, who has effected a profound synthesis of ideas in this field, calls this ubiquitous membrane the *unit membrane*. We proceed to use this unifying structure as a vantage point from which to view the structure and properties of cells.

[1] It is conceivable that at the time of the origin of life self-replicating molecules were not partitioned from one another so that an unequivocal boundary could not be assigned at that time to an "organism."

Fɪɢ. 1.1a

Fɪɢ. 1.1

(a) Electron micrograph of portion of a human red blood cell. The unit membrane structure bounding the cell is shown. (Permanganate fixation, magnification: 280,000 ×. Courtesy of J. David Robertson.)

(b) The unit membrane: Appearance in high-resolution electron micrographs.

(c) The unit membrane: Postulated molecular structure. Rod-like lipid molecules (*L*) are arranged in a two-dimensional, double-layered structure. The hydrophilic and hydrophobic moieties of the lipid molecules are labeled, respectively, *i* and *o*. Unfolded macromolecules (*M*) form the surfaces of the membrane. (After J. David Robertson.)

Tʜᴇ Uɴɪᴛ Mᴇᴍʙʀᴀɴᴇ

Universality as a Cell Membrane

In fig. 1.1a we have an electron micrograph of a section of a human red blood cell. The cell is bounded at its very edge by a unit membrane which appears as two dark bands on either side of a light band. An electron-microscopically observable unit membrane has been found at the boundary of the cytoplasm of all animal and plant cells, protozoa, bacteria and even the tiny pleuro-pneumonia-like-organisms (PPLO). Viruses, in general, are not bounded by a membrane. Some of the larger mammalian cell viruses, however, are bounded by a unit membrane which appears to be derived from the cell membrane of the host cell. In plant cells and bacteria the unit membrane lies below the rigid, polysaccharide cell wall and bounds the *protoplast*, i.e. the cell *sans* cell wall. We have an important biological generalization in the fact that the same type of

structure is found at the cytoplasmic boundary of all cell types.

Dimensions

As measured on electron-micrographs, the unit membrane has an average thickness of 75 Å (fig. 1.1b), though membrane thicknesses as low as 50 Å and above 100 Å have been observed. Some of the variation can, no doubt, be ascribed to shrinkage and swelling attendant on the fixing and staining of cellular material prior to electron-micrography. To this, however, will be added the variations in membrane thickness resulting from differences in the specific molecular species incorporated into the different membranes.

Asymmetry

An interesting and important property of the unit membrane is an apparent asymmetry between its two sides. The two sides of the membrane appear to have different properties. This is

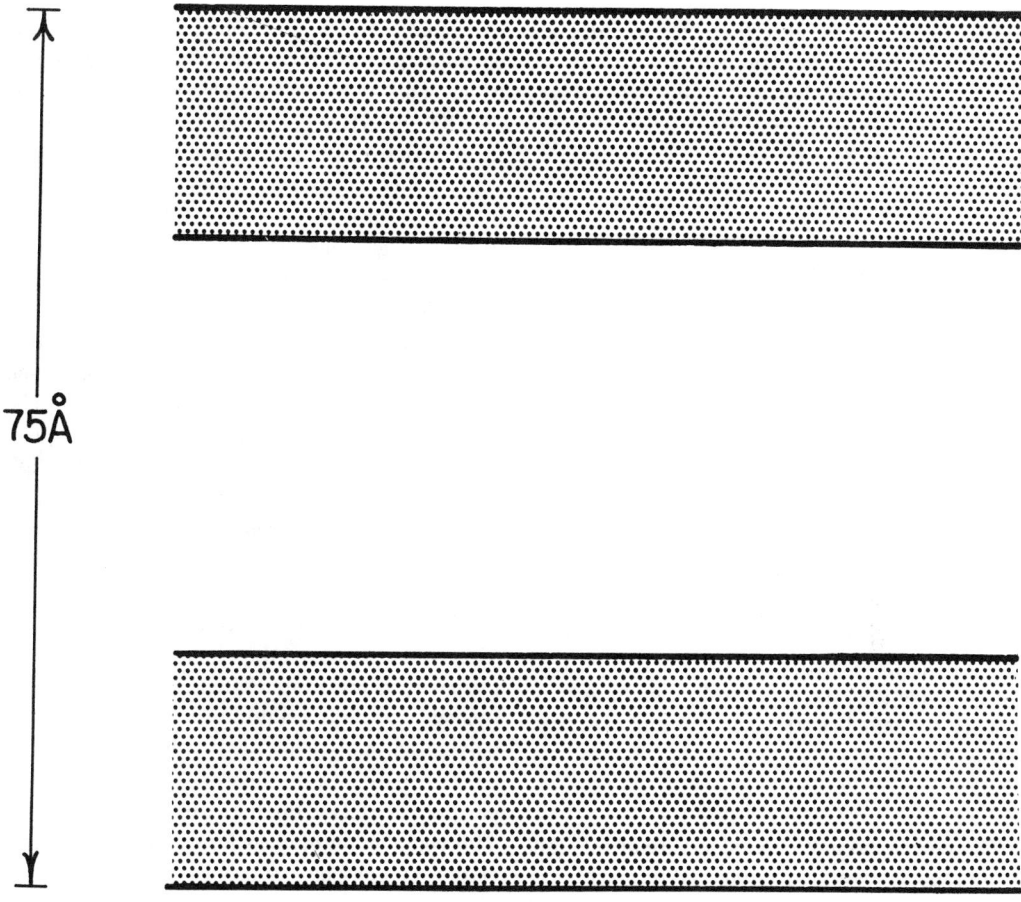

75Å

FIG. 1.1b

shown by the appearance in electron micrographs of cross-sectional views of both the myelin sheath peripheral, mammalian nerve and the membranes of chloroplasts in plant cells. It is useful at this time to provisionally label the two sides of the membranes as *outside* and *inside* (*cytoplasmic*) surfaces. In the case of the cell membrane the "outside" surface is in contact with the cell environment, the "inside" surface is in contact with the cytoplasm. Some simple applications of these ideas will be given below in reference to the structure of other cell organelles.

Electrical Properties

Even before the universal nature of the unit membrane had been demonstrated by electron microscopy, electrical measurements gave rise to the interesting generalization that the boundaries of all kinds of cells shared a common property: The capacitance per unit area of the cell boundary material was about 1 microfarad/cm². This figure can be combined with the 75 Å dimension of the unit membrane in an interesting manner. The cell membrane of *resting nerve* can be pictured to the first approximation, to be the dielectric material of a charged condenser. The charge is negative on the inside surface, positive on the outside surface resulting in a difference of potential across the membrane on the order of 0.06 volts. The intensity of an electric field is usually expressed in the dimensions volts per meter. Thus, the electric field within the cell membrane of resting nerve is on the order of

$$\frac{(0.06 \text{ volts})}{(75 \times 10^{-10} \text{ meters})} \cong 10,000,000 \text{ volts/meter.}$$

The dielectric strength of a commercial insulator is the maximum volts/meter which the material can stand without breaking down. The highest dielectric strength for a good commercial insulator such as rubber is about 1,000,000 volts/meter. We see then that the cell membrane material looked at as an electrical insulator must be credited with a very high dielectric strength, one which of necessity lies in excess of 10,000,000 volts/meter.

A second number of interest which we are able to estimate is the dielectric constant, κ, of the cell membrane material. The capacitance of a condenser is a measure of the amount of charge which can be stored in the plates of the condenser when a certain voltage is impressed across these plates. The capacitance, C, is directly proportional to the cross-sectional area, A, of the condenser, and to the dielectric constant, κ, of the insulator between the condenser plates; the capacitance is inversely proportional to the thickness of the dielectric, d, that is, the distance between the condenser plates. In M.K.S. units $C = \epsilon_0 \kappa A / d$, where ϵ_0 is the constant 9×10^{-12} farads/meter. Solving for κ and substituting we find that

$$\kappa = Cd/\epsilon_0 A$$
$$= \frac{(10^{-6}\,\text{farad})\,(75 \times 10^{-10}\text{m})}{(9 \times 10^{-12}\,\text{farads/meter})\,(10^{-4}\text{m}^2)}$$
$$\cong 8.$$

Again compared to commercial electrical insulators a dielectric constant of 8 is relatively high. We conclude that the nerve (cell) membrane has a relatively high dielectric constant and dielectric strength.

Molecular Structure

The postulated molecular structure of the unit membrane is best understood in terms of the hydrophilic and hydrophobic nature of certain chemical groups. Hydrophilic groups are those which ionize and bear an electrical charge (e.g. $-COO^-$, $-NH_3^+$), or groups which participate in hydrogen bonding (e.g. $-OH$, $-NH$). Substances containing these groups tend to dissolve in water, since these groups interact with the dipolar water molecule by means of a polar bond or a hydrogen bond. Amino acids and sugar molecules, for example, are hydrophilic. The long-chain hydrocarbons, (e.g. long-chain fatty acids) on the other hand, are *hydrophobic*. Such molecules are relatively insoluble in water. The aggregation of hydrophobic molecules in the presence of water has been recently explained as follows. The structure of water is in an ordered, ice-like state in the vicinity of non-polar molecules. When non-polar molecules leave the water phase and form an aggregate, the degree of order of the water phase is decreased; the entropy (degree of disorder) of the whole system is thereby increased. Since systems tend to change spontaneously towards a state in which the entropy is maximized, non-polar (hydrophobic) molecules tend to separate from the water phase and to aggregate, i.e., they do not "dissolve" in water. This complex set of ideas for explaining the association of non-polar molecules is represented in

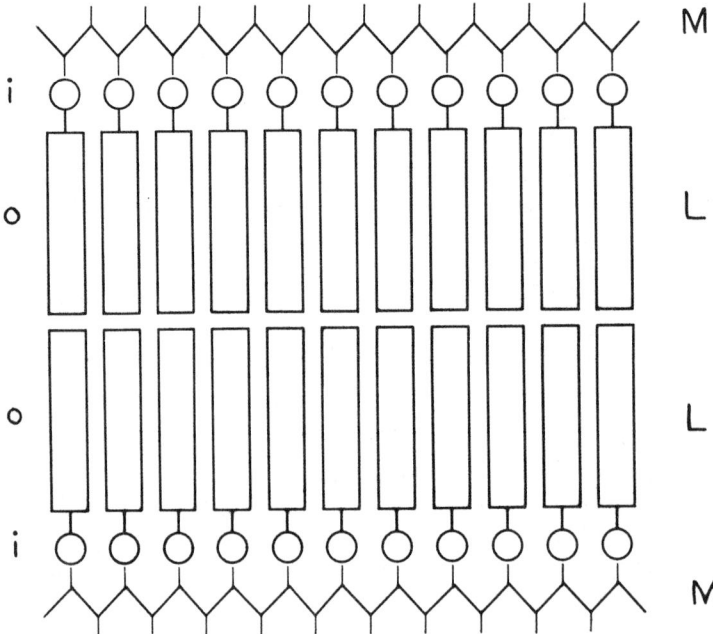

Fig. 1.1c

the current literature by the words "hydrophobic bond."

Consider now a molecule, a long-chain fatty acid, for example. This molecule is hydrophobic for the most part but bears a hydrophilic group at one end. The ionized carboxyl group at the end of the fatty acid is hydrophilic, though the rest of the molecule is hydrophobic. When hydrophobia exceeds hydrophilia, such a substance does not appreciably dissolve molecule-by-molecule in water. If enough molecules of this kind are present, however, these can enter the water phase and simultaneously satisfy hydrophobic and hydrophilic tendencies, by forming spherical or lamellar *micelles*. A micelle is a multimolecular structure having the hydrophilic parts of the constituent molecules at its surface and in contact with water, while the hydrophobic parts are on the interior in a milieu of other hydrophobic groups.

A contemporary model of the unit membrane pictures it to be a lamellar micelle consisting of two rows of phospholipid molecules (fig. 1.1c). The hydrophilic ionized phosphate groups of the lipid are at the surface of the micelle. The hydrophobic hydrocarbon chains are on the interior. The two surfaces of the micelle are covered by a macromolecular material. The previously referred to asymmetry of the unit membrane is attributed to differences in the macromolecular materials which line the two surfaces of the micelle.

Cell Organelles

The unit membrane concept provides a natural approach to the structure of the cell and to many of its organelles (table 1.1).

Cell Nucleus

The nucleus is bounded by the *nuclear membrane*. This membrane differs from the cell membrane in a number of important ways.

1. The nuclear membrane is made up of two unit membrane layers which are separated from one another by a distance of about 150 Å (fig. 1.2a). By contrast, the cell membrane consists of a single unit membrane layer. The region between the two layers of unit membrane is the *perinuclear space*. In terms of our unit membrane asymmetry convention, the inner (perinuclear) surface of the two unit membrane layers corresponds to the "extracellular" side of the unit membrane; the outer surface of the nuclear membrane which touches on cytoplasm, nuclear pores and nucleus corresponds to the "cytoplasmic" side of the unit membrane.

2. The nuclear membrane is perforated. It is pierced by a large number of large pores (diameter ~1000 Å) which seemingly provide continuity between the cytoplasm and the intranuclear material. The existence of a perforated nuclear membrane is consistent with the lack of osmotic activity and low electrical resistance of many nuclei.

Mitochondria

It is convenient to think of a mitochondrion as being generated from a football-like structure made up of two layers of unit membrane (table 1.1). The folding of the inner unit membrane layer generates the cristae (the transverse partitions in the mitochondrion) and leads to an increase in total membrane surface area (fig. 1.2b). In the mitochondrion many of the important reactants (enzymes, electron transport chain constituents) appear to be attached to the membranes and thus do not float free in solution. The folded inner mitochondrial membrane provides a larger reactive surface area per unit volume of organelle. The mitochondrion is the site in the cell where gaseous oxygen interacts with electrons derived from sugar, fat, and protein degradation products. The process which is coupled to this highly exergonic interaction generates biologically available energy in the form of ATP (adenosine triphosphate). As much as 95% of the energy utilized by cellular activities in the mammalian organism is derived from the interaction of oxygen with the electron transport system in the mitochondrion. For this reason physiological phenomena involving the uptake of oxygen, the liberation of heat, and the production of energy-rich substances involved in muscle contraction and nerve impulse conduction can, and should be, related on the cellular level to mitochondrial function.

Endoplasmic Reticulum

This cytoplasmic membrane system (table 1.1) is particularly conspicuous in the cytoplasm of liver and glandular tissue cells, where much protein synthesis goes on. The membranes of the endoplasmic reticulum are arranged in the form of rather flat, interconnected vesicles, each vesicle being bounded by a single layer of unit membrane material. The interior of these vesicles (the "extracellular" side of the bounding membrane) has been shown in some instances to be continuous with the perinuclear space of the

TABLE 1.1

Organelles of the Mammalian Cell: Representative Shapes, Dimensions and Composition

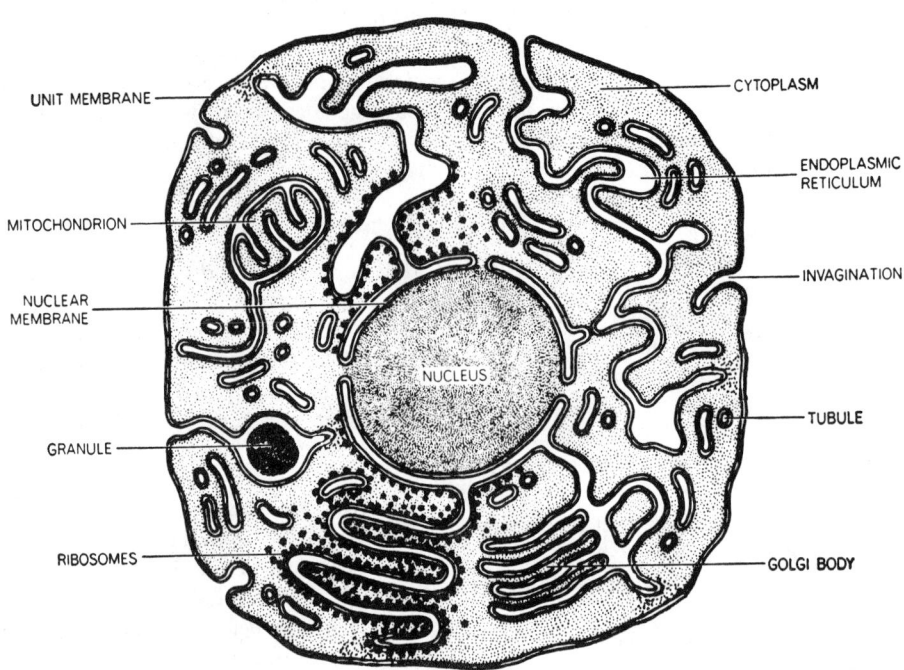

A schematic, idealized and speculative diagram of a generalized cell drawn by J. David Robertson. The cell is represented as a three-phase system: membranes, cytoplasm and intranuclear material, and endoplasmic reticulum cisternal content.

ORGANELLE	COMPOSITION/STRUCTURE		FUNCTION
CELL ⊢ 20μ ⊣	Water	85%	

	Per cent dry weight:
	  Protein
	  Lipid
	  DNA
	  RNA
		
		65
		15
		3
		5	

	Bounded by single unit membrane		
NUCLEUS (One or more per cell) ⊢ 10μ ⊣ ⊢300Å Pore dia. 1,000 Å	Water	80%	

	Per cent dry weight:
	  Protein
	  DNA
	  RNA
	  Protein
		
		80%
		18%
		2%
		$\left\{\begin{array}{l}\frac{1}{2}\text{ histone}\\\frac{1}{2}\text{ non-hist.}\end{array}\right\}$	

1,000 to 10,000 pores per nucleus	Bounded by two layers of unit membrane		

ORGANELLE	COMPOSITION/STRUCTURE	FUNCTION
MITOCHONDRIA (1000 per cell)	Water 75% <hr> Per cent dry weight: Protein 75% Lipid 25% RNA <1% DNA <1% <hr> Contains: 1. Krebs cycle enzymes 2. Electron transport chain (inner membrane?) 3. Enzymes for synthetic reactions which require ATP <hr> Bounded by two layers of unit membrane	Generates 95% of the energy (ATP) used by an aerobic cell
ENDOPLASMIC RETICULUM Rough Smooth	1. Membranes contain: Lipids Protein (enzymes) RNA (?) 2. The interior canals of the endoplasmic reticulum are believed to be continuous with the perinuclear space. The endoplasmic reticulum membranes are sometimes seen to be continuous with the outer nuclear unit membrane. <hr> Bounded by a single unit membrane	An intracellular "circulatory system"?
RIBOSOMES (10^8 per liver cell)	RNA 50% Protein 50% <hr> Not bounded by unit membrane	Site of cytoplasmic protein synthesis: Here amino acids are ordered into a polypeptide chain along a messenger-RNA template.
NUCLEOLUS (One or more per cell)	1. Organelle having the highest density. (ribosomal?) 2. Rich in (ribosomal?) RNA 3. Composed of a reticular network of helically coiled fibrils. <hr> Not bounded by a unit membrane	Function not known

ORGANELLE	COMPOSITION/STRUCTURE	FUNCTION

CHROMOSOMES (46 per human diploid cell)
 1–5µ
	1. Site of nuclear DNA
	 2. Liver cell chromosomes:
	    DNA 25%
	    Histone 25%
	    RNA 10%
	    Residual protein 40%
	
	 Not bounded by a unit membrane
		Specifies nucleotide sequence in messenger-RNA

CENTRIOLE 0.2µ End view: Centrioles always found in pairs	Not bounded by a unit membrane	Involved in cell motion 1. Found at center of mitotic poles. 2. Found at base of all cilia and flagella. 3. Centromere (kinetochore) of chromosomes believed to be related to centriole.
LYSOSOMES 0.5µ	Contain a set of hydrolytic enzymes Bounded by a single unit membrane	Involved in phagocytosis, autolysis, wound healing
GOLGI APPARATUS	A system of unit membrane bounded flattened sacs associated with vesicles and vacuoles of various sizes.	Appears to be involved in the formation of secretory (zymogen) granules.

nuclear membrane (fig. 1.2a).[2] The membranes themselves are continuous with the outer nuclear membrane layer and with the cell membrane. The system of channels consisting of the interior of the endoplasmic reticulum has been likened to an intracellular circulatory system.

Ribosomes

These ribonucleoprotein particles form the physical substrate on which protein synthesis

[2] It has been suggested on the basis of rather indirect evidence that the perinuclear space of the nuclear membrane, and the interior (the cisternae) of the endoplasmic reticulum are continuous with the extracellular space which surrounds the cell. If this proves correct then it is possible for an extracellular substance to enter the nucleus without first traversing the cytoplasm of the cell.

takes place. Ribosomes may be attached to the "cytoplasmic" side of the endoplasmic reticulum membranes yielding the so-called "rough" endoplasmic reticulum, or they may be free in the cytoplasm. Though protein synthesis takes place in the nucleus, as well as in the cytoplasm, there is some controversy, at present, as to whether ribosomal particles, as such, exist in the nucleus. The ribosomes are the sites where amino acids are ordered to form the polypeptide chains of protein molecules. The amino acid sequence of a given protein is stored in the nucleotide sequence of nuclear DNA. Copies of this nucleotide sequence, in the form of messenger—RNA, attach to the ribosomes and act as templates specifying the order in which amino acids are to be incorporated into the newly made proteins. Physiological phenomena involving the synthesis and elabora-

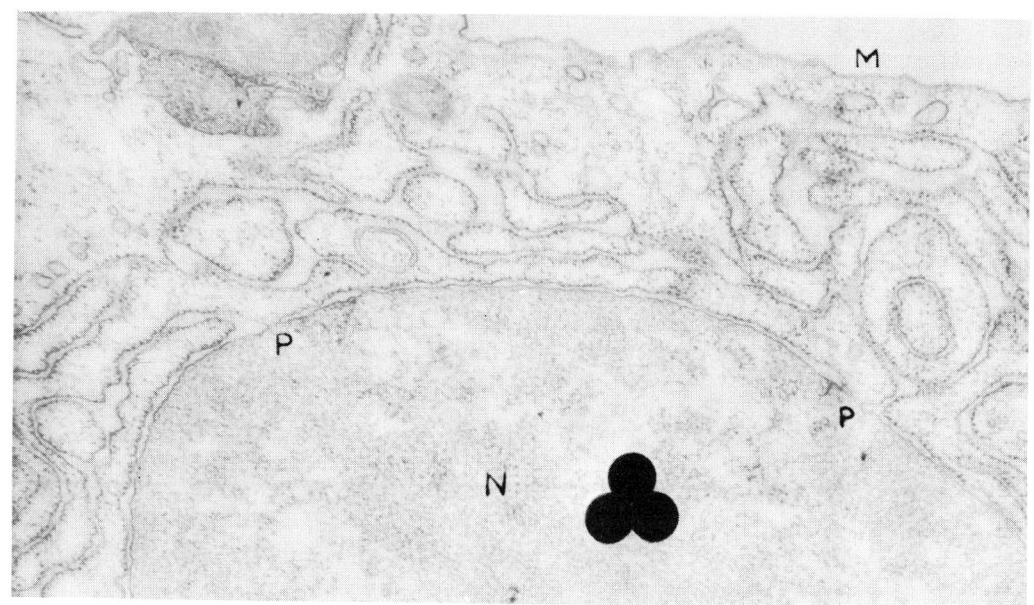

A

B

FIG. 1.2

(a) Nuclear membrane and endoplasmic reticulum (25,000 ×, osmic acid fixation). Acinous cell from the parotid gland of the mouse. The nucleus, N, is bounded by a double membrane. Two nuclear pores, P, can be seen. The ribosome-studded endoplasmic reticulum membranes can be seen in the cytoplasm. The outer layer of the unit membrane invaginates at two places (near the pores) to form the cisternae of the endoplasmic reticulum. The cell membrane, M, is seen at the top. The three black circles are polystyrene spheres (diameter 0.25 μ). (Courtesy of Harold F. Parks.)

(b) Mitochondria (100,000 ×). Note the unit membrane pattern and the formation of cristae by the infolding of the inner membrane. (Courtesy of J. David Robertson.)

tion of specific polypeptides and proteins should, when possible, be referred back to the subcellular events described here.

Myelin Sheath

The sheath of a myelinated nerve fiber consists of many layers of unit membrane tightly wrapped around the surface of the filamentous nerve axone. The myelin sheath is formed when a Schwann cell adheres to the surface of the axone at one point, and then wraps itself around the axone in a continuous circular movement. The cell membrane of the Schwann cell which lies next to the axone becomes the myelin sheath. Each time the Schwann cell circles around the axone two layers of unit membrane are added to the myelin sheath.

THE CELL MEMBRANE

The biological role played by the cell membrane can best be interpreted from the point of view of evolution. It is unlikely that at the time of the origin of life the first organism was already equipped with a bounding membrane. It is more likely that this early organism was a relatively simple, self-replicating molecule. With the rise in biological complexity, however, a cell organelle arose which isolated the organism from its environment. This organelle, the cell membrane, had selective value since it tended to reduce the influx of injurious molecules from the environment while tending to preserve useful molecules for the exclusive use of the organism.

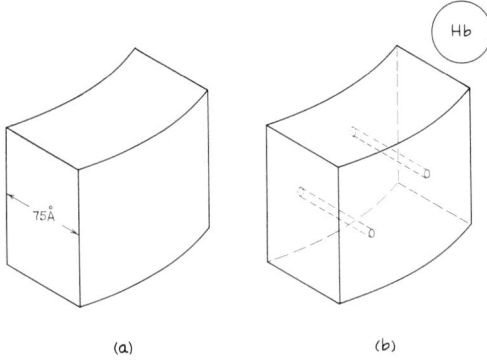

(a)   (b)

FIG. 1.3. Simple models of cell membrane.
(a) First approximation. Oil film 75 Å thick.
(b) Second approximation. 75 Å thick oilfilm perforated by pores. Assuming 7 Å for the average diameter of a pore, each pore is about ten pore diameters long. The diameter of a hemoglobin molecule (Hb) is shown to the same scale.

From this point of view the cell membrane should be thought of as a barrier to diffusion. Basically the cell membrane should be considered to be an impermeable rather than a permeable structure. In fact, as we shall see, the cell membrane is relatively (as compared to an equal thickness of water) impermeable to *all* molecules.

We have considered the unit membrane to be basically a lipid micelle. To the *first approximation*, indeed, it is convenient to treat the cell membrane as if it were a thin oil film (fig. 1.3a). This crude approximation suffices to explain a number of important permeability and electrical properties of the cell membrane. To this approximation the movement of a substance across the cell membrane takes place as follows: Each individual molecule of the substance leaves the aqueous phase on one side of the membrane and dissolves in the oil film. The molecule then diffuses across the oil film and enters the aqueous phase on the other side.

A slightly more sophisticated model of the cell membrane is required to explain a number of experimental findings, which can best be interpreted by assuming that some molecules can pass through the membrane without leaving the aqueous phase. In other words to the *second approximation* the cell membrane behaves as if it were an oil film pierced by pores (fig. 1.3b). The aqueous phase is continuous across the membrane through the pores. These pores need not necessarily be of a permanent nature; they may be statistical in nature, that is, temporary holes in the oil film created by thermal agitation. From osmotic studies on the human erythrocyte it has been inferred that the effective diameter of individual pores is about 7 Å and that the total pore area is only about 0.0001 of the total surface area of the cell. From the small size of the pores it is evident that the smaller particles (water, Na^+, K^+, Cl^-) can cross the cell membrane via the pores. Larger molecules will have to cross the membrane in the region which we have referred to as the "oil film." For the purposes of our survey, then, we shall find it useful to view the cell membrane as a perforated oil film. To this simple model more complex features (carrier molecules, enzymes, virus attachment sites) can be added as needed.

We now proceed with a brief discussion of in what manner and at what relative rates substances of biological significance cross the cell membrane. Several modes of transport will be discussed; these are:

a. *Bulk flow.* In this mode water molecules do not pass through the membrane by dissolving in it and diffusing across one by one; rather, the motion of each molecule is correlated with that of neighboring water molecules, that is, water flows through the pores in the membrane as it does through a pipe.

b. *Diffusion.* Solute and water molecules dissolve in and cross the membrane individually as a consequence of their thermal (Brownian) motion.

c. *Carrier-mediated diffusion.* Solute molecules combine with membrane-bound *carrier* molecules. The carrier-solute complex diffuses or otherwise moves across the membrane.

d. *Active transport.* The movement of molecules across the membrane by a carrier-mediated process which requires an input of energy.

Transport

PHYSICAL BASIS OF DIFFUSION

Consider a tube which is divided into two parts by a thin, removeable partition. The tube contains an aqueous solution of some substance. The concentration of this substance is higher to the right of the partition than to the left. After the partition is carefully withdrawn it is found that the concentration on the left increases with time and that on the right decreases with time. Ultimately the concentration becomes the same throughout the tube. In this example was there a "force" which moved the solute molecules from the region of high concentration on the right to the region of low concentration on the left? The answer is "no." The physical explanation of this phenomenon is quite simple. Every solute molecule is under constant bombardment from adjacent solute and solvent molecules. As a result a given solute molecule follows an erratic path through the liquid. At one instant it may move to the left and a little later to the right. This is a kind of *Brownian motion* in which the particle which moves is an atom or molecule rather than a large, microscopically observable object. At any given instant half the molecules, on the average, move to the right and half to the left. Since there are initially more solute molecules at the right of our tube than at the left it is evident that at any given time more solute molecules move from right to left than from left to right. With time the solute concentration in the whole tube is equalized. Thus, we have the interesting result that though each individual solute molecule minds its own business and moves this way and that way, when looking at the average motion of a large collection of such molecules one observes a net flow of solute from a region of high concentration into a region of low concentration.

DIFFUSION THROUGH A MEMBRANE

In view of our interest in the diffusion of molecules through the cell membrane we shall define a number, the *permeability coefficient*, which is descriptive of the ease with which a *given solute* can diffuse through a *given membrane*. Clearly this number will be a function both of the nature of the membrane and of the nature of the solute molecule.

Consider a tube which is divided into two parts by a fixed membrane (fig. 1.4). The tube is filled with a solution containing a solute which is at concentration C_1 to the right of the membrane and at concentration C_2 to the left. Assuming that C_1 is greater than C_2 there will be a net transfer of solute across the membrane from right to left. To simplify the mathematics we assume that over the period of observation the concentrations C_1 and C_2 (in moles/cm^3) remain constant with time. These restrictions can be approximated in a real system by taking measurements over a sufficiently short period so that the concentrations do not change appreciably, and by stirring the solutions on each side of the membrane. Under these conditions there will be a net *rate of flow*, Q (moles/sec), of solute across the membrane. What is Q proportional to? We know that when the concentration is equal on both sides, that is, when $C_1 = C_2$, that Q is zero. From this we would expect the flow rate Q to be proportional to the *concentration gradient*,

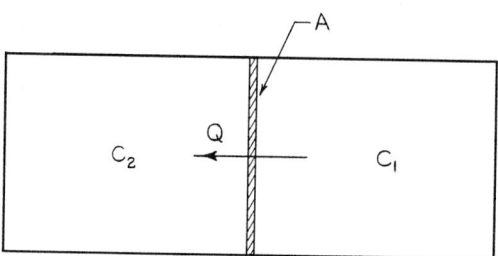

FIG. 1.4. Permeability. Chamber divided by a thin membrane of area A. The concentration of a given substance is C_1 on the right and C_2 on the left. The rate, Q, in moles/sec., with which the substance diffuses from right to left is

$$Q = kA (C_1 - C_2),$$

where k is the permeability coefficient of the membrane for the given substance.

$(C_1 - C_2)$. Q may be also expected to be proportional to the area, A (cm²), of the membrane, the greater the area the greater the flow rate. Introducing the proportionality constant, k, we obtain the equation

$$Q = kA \ (C_1 - C_2). \qquad (1)$$

What are the dimensions of k? Solving for k,

$$k = \frac{Q}{A(C_1 - C_2)} = \frac{\text{moles/sec}}{(\text{cm}^2)(\text{moles/cm}^3)} = \frac{\text{cm}}{\text{sec}} \qquad (2)$$

we find it to have the dimensions centimeters per second. k is defined to *be the permeability coefficient* for the given solute and membrane, the greater k, the greater the rate with which the solute diffuses across the membrane. From equation (2) observe that the permeability coefficient k is the flow rate of solute per unit membrane area when a unit concentration gradient of solute is maintained across the membrane.

PHYLOGENETIC VARIABILITY

In our discussions of membranous systems we have emphasized the remarkable unity of various biological phenomena when seen from the point of view of the unit membrane concept. It is appropriate at this point to temper this view by taking note of the great diversity of properties manifested by biological membranes. In table 1.2 we note a hundred-fold difference in permeability to water of the cell membranes of *Ameba proteus* and the human erythrocyte. Even, comparisons within the class of erythrocytes, however, shows such marked differences. The permeabilities to glycerol of the cell membranes of erythrocytes of two evolutionary cousins, the rat and the ox, differ by a factor of more than one hundred. In the coming pages we will be discussing a number of generalizations relating the chemical structure of a solute molecule to its permeability coefficient. These generalizations were derived from studies on a variety of cells, often plant cells.

TABLE 1.2

Permeability to Water of Some Cell Membranes
(Prosser and Brown, 1961)

Species	Extracellular Fluid	Permeability
		(μ³ water/μ² surface area/atm.)
Ameba proteus	Fresh water	0.03
Arbacia egg	Sea water	0.4
Human erythrocyte	Serum	3.0

TABLE 1.3

Orders of Magnitude of the Permeability Coefficients of Erythrocyte Membranes
(For references see Davson, 1964)

Substance	Oil/Water Partition Coefficient	Permeability Coefficient (cm/sec)	Species
Water	10^{-3}	10^{-2}	Ox
Urea	10^{-4}	10^{-4}	Ox
Cl⁻	—	10^{-4}	Man
K⁺	—	10^{-8}	Man
Na⁺	—	10^{-10}	Man

When these generalizations are applied to specific mammalian cells one must, as a rule, expect to find many exceptions.

MOVEMENT OF WATER ACROSS THE CELL MEMBRANE

Because of the special role which water plays in biological systems and because of the unique physical characteristics of this molecule we shall treat the diffusion of water across the cell membrane as a special case. Compared to other molecules water diffuses across the cell membrane at a very rapid rate. The permeability coefficient of water is 400 times greater than that of urea (table 1.3), though the latter molecule itself has a very high permeability constant as compared to other molecules of biological significance. As a result, the water within an erythrocyte turns over with water from outside the erythrocyte in a small fraction of one second (see Problem 6). An observer stationed at the cell membrane would see not a trickle of water but a torrent of water surging in and out of the cell across the cell membrane. Yet the impermeability of the cell membrane is strikingly demonstrated by the fact that a water layer of equal thickness would have a permeability to water 10,000 to 100,000 times larger. Thus, when we say that the cell membrane is very permeable to water we are speaking in relative terms.

Osmotic phenomena arise as a consequence of the high rate, as compared to other cell constituents, with which water crosses the cell membrane. Insight into osmotic phenomena can be most easily obtained, as is usually the case in physical chemistry, by studying a comparable system of ideal gases.

Consider a container (fig. 1.5a) which is divided into two equal parts by a partition. There are an equal number of ideal gas molecules on each side of the partition. What distinguishes the two sides is that on the left there are 12 big molecules (marbles) and 4 small molecules (dots), a total of 16 molecules, which on the right there are 16 small molecules. (In the biological system the dots correspond to water molecules, the marbles to molecules in the cell or extracellular fluid which penetrate the cell membrane very slowly, if at all.) Now it is a characteristic of the ideal gas that its pressure depends only on the *number* of particles and *not* on the *nature* (large or small molecule) of the gas. Hence, the pressure is the same on each side of the partition. Let us now drill holes through the partition of a size such that the dots can pass through but the marbles cannot (fig. 1.5b). What happens next is a consequence of the fact that in a mixture of ideal gases each component behaves as if the other components did not exist. Thus, dots migrate through the partition until the number of dots on the left equals the number of dots on the right (fig. 1.5c). More generally, we can say that the migration will occur in a direction to equalize the number of dots per unit volume (concentration) on both sides of the partition. The migration can be prevented by decreasing the volume on the left side of the chamber so as to equalize the initial concentration of dots on both sides of the *semi-permeable* partition (fig. 1.5d). The decrease in volume is accompanied by an increase in the pressure of the gas in the left chamber. This increase in pressure, π, required (fig. 1.5d) to prevent the net flow of "solvent" (dots) between the two chambers is defined to be the *osmotic pressure* of the "solution" (marbles dissolved in dots) with respect to the pure "solvent" (dots).

To transpose this problem back to the cell. The perforated partition corresponds (in its osmotic properties) to the semipermeable cell membrane. The small particles (dots) correspond to the solvent (water), the large particles (marbles) to the solute. As compared to water the marbles represent solute molecules which penetrate the cell membrane slowly, if at all. For an aqueous solution the osmotic pressure, π (in atmospheres), can be estimated from the equation

$$\pi V = n_0 RT. \tag{7}$$

In this equation V is the volume (in liters) of the solution, n_0 is the number of moles of solute particles in this volume, T is the absolute temperature (°K) and R is the universal gas constant (8.2×10^{-2} $(1 \times \text{atm})/(\text{mole} \times \text{°K})$). If the

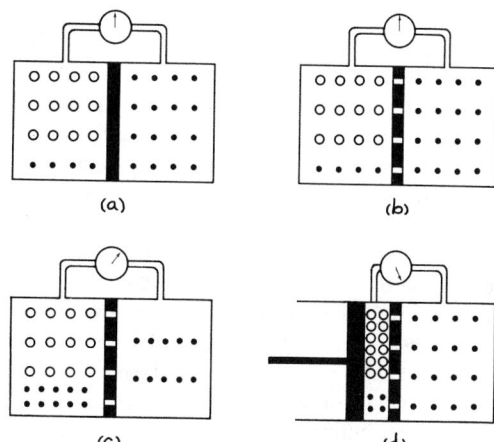

Fig. 1.5. Ideal gas model of osmosis.
(a) An equal number of particles on each side of the partition leads to a zero pressure difference between the two compartments.
(b) Holes are drilled through the partition. These are of such size that the dots, but not the marbles, can pass from one compartment to the next.
(c) At equilibrium the concentration of dots is the same on both sides of the partition. Due to the presence of the marbles, the pressure is higher on the left than it is on the right.
(d) The net flow of dots from right to left is averted by decreasing the volume of the left compartment and thereby increasing the concentration of dots on the left. The pressure difference between the two compartments when the net flow of dots is zero is the osmotic pressure, π.

fluid which bathes a cell has the same osmotic pressure as the cell interior then there is no *net* flow of water between these compartments and the cell does not swell or shrink. Mammalian cells do not swell or shrink when placed in 0.9% NaCl (M.W. 58.5). The molarity of this solution is $9/58.5 = 0.15$M in NaCl. The NaCl is, however, almost completely ionized so that there are approximately 2 (more precisely 1.87) osmotically active particles (Na^+ and Cl^-) for every NaCl molecule. Hence, $n_0 = 2 \times 0.15 = 0.3$ moles (per liter), $V = 1$ liter, $T = 310°$ (at body temperature) and the osmotic pressure of the interior of the mammalian cell is, approximately,

$$\pi = n_0 RT/V = (0.3)\ (8.2 \times 10^{-2})\ (3.1 \times 10^2)/1$$
$$= 7.5 \text{ atmospheres.}$$

Any system, such as the cell or the mitochondrion, which is bounded by a semipermeable membrane manifests osmotic properties. Nuclear pores would lead one to expect the nuclear membrane to be a permeable, rather than a semipermeable membrane. Indeed, when HeLa cells (cells in tissue culture originally derived from a cervical carcinoma) are placed in a hypotonic solution, the cell diameter increases but the nuclear diameter does not change appreciably. There is at present one puzzling aspect about the permeability of the nuclear membrane. The larger protein molecules, such as ovalbumin and gamma-globulin, are not able to pass through the nuclear membrane even though these molecules are smaller than the nuclear pores.

In the mammalian organism the osmotic pressure of the blood and extracellular fluids is regulated very precisely so that net water exchanges between cells and extracellular fluid are minimal. In the ameba, a fresh water organism, there is a constant influx of water into the organism. It takes a continuing energy expenditure on the part of this organism to pump the water out again. This may account for the relatively low permeability to water of the ameba as compared with the human erythrocyte (table 1.2).

Physico-chemical Criteria for Rates of Diffusion Across Cell Membranes

Lipid Solubility

Consider a vessel in which there are two fluid phases, water and oil, in contact at an interface. A third substance is introduced and dissolves in the two phases. When equilibrium is reached the concentration, C, of the substance in each phase is determined. The oil-water *partition coefficient*, B, of the solute substance is defined by

$$B = \frac{C_{oil}}{C_{water}}.$$

Insight into the significance of the partition coefficient can be obtained by examining its kinetic basis. Even after equilibrium is reached molecules of solute move from the oil phase into the water phase as well as in the reverse direction. At any given instant the rate of flow of substance, $Q_{o \to w}$, from oil into water is proportional to the concentration (more precisely, the chemical potential) of the substance in the oil phase. Thus, $Q_{o \to w} = K_{o \to w} C_{oil}$. Similarly, $Q_{w \to o} = K_{w \to o} C_{water}$, where the K's are the rate (proportionality) constants. At equilibrium the two flow rates must be equal; hence

$$K_{o \to w} C_{oil} = K_{w \to o} C_{water} \quad \text{(at equilibrium)}$$

and

$$B = \frac{C_{oil}}{C_{water}} = \frac{K_{w \to o}}{K_{o \to w}}$$

We see that the partition coefficient can also be defined as the ratio of the rate constants. A low partition coefficient, for example, implies that

the solute substance has a greater tendency to leave the oil phase and enter the water, than it has to leave the water and enter the oil.

To return to our study of diffusion across the cell membrane. For a substance to pass *through* the cell membrane (we do not here consider movement through pores) it is necessary for it to (1) enter the membrane (oil phase), (2) diffuse across the membrane and (3) reenter the waterphase. For many substances of biological interest the partition coefficient is a number very small compared to one (table 1.3). Such substances have trouble getting into the cell membrane but get out of it with relative ease. For this class of substances the movement of substance from the water phase into the membrane phase is the rate-limiting step for diffusion across the membrane. Hence, for these substances in general, though with notable exceptions, *the greater the partition coefficient of the substance, the greater its permeability coefficient (Overton's rule).* For large, fatty molecules (tristearin, cholesterol, lecithin) the problem is opposite to the one we have discussed. Here the partition coefficient is high; the molecule presumably enters the cell membrane readily but has difficulty reentering the water phase. Thus, it is likely that fats cross the cell membrane by means other than simple diffusion.

Hydrophilia

Chemical groups are said to be *polar* when the positive nuclei and negative electrons are so unevenly arrayed that the local net electrical charge does not average to zero. Let us consider some examples. Ionized groups, that is groups which have lost or gained electrons, are polar. Groups in which there has not been a net gain or loss of charge, but where a displacement of charge within the group has led to a concentration of negative charge in one region, and positive charge in another, are also polar. The alcoholic hydroxyl group is polar because the two valence electrons shared by the hydrogen and oxygen atoms are attracted toward the more electronegative oxygen atom ($-\overset{-}{O}\overset{+}{H}$). This is also why water is a highly polar substance.

The strong electrical interaction between the dipolar water molecule and other polar molecules makes the latter hydrophilic. The greater the number of hydroxyl groups on an organic molecule, for example, the greater the hydrophilia. As one would expect from the lipid (hydrophobic) constitution of unit membranes, the permeability of the cell membrane is inversely related to the hydrophilic nature of the diffusing substance. From this it is to be expected that hydrophilic substances, such as sodium ions, potassium ions, sugars, and amino acids, will penetrate the cell membrane only very slowly by passive diffusion. In table 1.3 note that the permeability constant of sodium ion, Na^+, is only about one hundred millionth that of water. It is equally evident, however, that from the point of view of the economy of the cell certain hydrophilic substances must be brought into the cell in appreciable quantities. As we shall see such substances are transported into the cell by a process which involves membrane bound carrier molecules. While it is generally true that electrically charged particles penetrate the cell membrane only very slowly by passive diffusion, it is to be noted that in the case of the mammalian red blood cell, the anions OH^-, Cl^- (table 1.3), and HCO_3^- as well as the cation H^+ have permeabilities which are very high compared to that of the cations Na^+ and K^+. It is believed that these electrolytes passively diffuse across the cell membrane via the pores. The electrical charge distribution in the walls of the pores apparently favors the diffusion of one ion over another.

Molecular Size

In general it may be said for a series of homologous substances that the greater the molecular weight, the smaller the permeability constant. This follows from the fact that the larger a particle the slower its Brownian motion and, consequently, the smaller its rate of diffusion. For polar macromolecules such as proteins, nucleic acids and viruses the permeability constant, as estimated from theory, is infinitesimally small. Such particles cross the cell membrane but not by means of passive diffusion. Again, we must seek a special transport mechanism.

CARRIER-MEDIATED TRANSPORT

The Carrier Model

We have noted that many substances, such as amino acids and sugars, which are vital to the economy of the cell can be expected to cross the cell membrane by simple diffusion only at low rates. A considerable body of experimental evidence which has accumulated suggests the following method of transport. These substances combine with specific, membrane-bound *carrier molecules* and cross the cell membrane as part of a substance-carrier molecular complex. The car-

rier molecules are assumed to be confined to the membrane and to shuttle back and forth from one side of the membrane to the other. The carrier is like a ferryboat—it accelerates the rate of transport across a barrier. Presumably the carrier reduces the thermal energy needed by a molecule to leave the aqueous phase and to enter the membrane phase. Consider a sugar molecule which is strongly bound to the surrounding water by hydrogen bonds. For this molecule to enter the non-aqueous phase, the membrane, it is necessary for the molecule to await a thermal collision of sufficient magnitude to break the hydrogen bonds. Suppose there exists, however, a carrier molecule in the membrane to which the sugar can attach by hydrogen bonding. Then the thermal energy needed by the sugar to enter the membrane is thereby decreased and the entry of the molecule into the membrane is greatly facilitated. As this is being written, however, no carrier molecule has been isolated. The structures and modes of operation of carrier molecules involved in membrane transport are, therefore, unknown. For the time being the carrier is a hypothetical, but useful and powerful construct in the interpretation of biological transport phenomena.

How does one know when one is dealing with carrier-mediated transport rather than with simple diffusion? Carrier-mediated transport is defined operationally by the following criteria:

Saturation. When there is no carrier equation 1 tells us that for simple diffusion the rate of transport is proportional to the concentration gradient $(C_1–C_2)$. If the gradient doubles the rate of transport doubles. This is not the case for carrier-mediated transport. Here concentrations will be reached at which most carrier molecules are in constant use. Further increases in concentration will not appreciably increase the rate of transport since few unoccupied carriers are available. The carrier system is saturated and the carrier-mediated transport operates at the maximum possible rate.

Competition. Two substances *A* and *B* which attach to the same carrier *compete* for the carrier system. If *B* is added to the extracellular fluid the uptake of *A* is decreased because *B* molecules now occupy carrier molecules which were previously all available for the transport of *A*. The competition, of course, is mutual and *A* reduces the rate of uptake of *B*.

Specificity. One carrier molecule may transport one amino acid or group of amino acids, whilst another transports one sugar or group of sugars. If the addition of a substance X does not decrease the carrier-mediated uptake of a substance A then A and X do not share the same carrier system. The chemical specificity of the substance-carrier interaction if thereby shown. This specificity is never perfect and a given carrier may carry, with varying efficiencies, a number of substances of related chemical structure.

Inhibition. This is a special case of competition. A substance I may combine with a carrier strongly and irreversibly so that the carrier cannot combine with its usual substrate A. Here even though I is not being transported the transport of A is inhibited.

The carrier-mediated transport of a substance along a concentration gradient (i.e. in the direction of normal, passive diffusion) is called *facilitated diffusion*. On the level of the organism a beautiful analogy to facilitated diffusion may be found in the transport of oxygen from the lungs to the tissues. The *carrier* is the hemoglobin molecule. The carrier manifests *specificity*—it combines with oxygen but not with nitrogen, *saturation*—an increase in alveolar oxygen tension beyond certain levels does not yield a proportional increase in oxygen transport, *competition*—carbon dioxide competes with oxygen for the same carrier, and *inhibition*—carbon monoxide combines tenaciously with the carrier and prevents the uptake of oxygen. This analogy also illustrates downhill active transport (described below) since the transport of oxygen and carbon dioxide between the lungs and tissues requires energy. This energy (needed to move the blood) is derived predominantly from the muscle cells of the heart.

Transport Which Requires Energy

ACTIVE TRANSPORT

The transport processes which we have discussed so far have dealt with the movement of molecules from regions of high concentration to regions of low concentration. (For the sake of generality and scientific precision we should really say from regions of high electrochemical potential to regions of low electrochemical potential.) Such transport processes are thermodynamically spontaneous and do not require an expenditure of energy on the part of the cell.[3] In every cell,

[3] A transport process in which the net flow of substance is from a region of high electrochemical potential into a region of low electrochemical potential can be, but need not be spontaneous. An

TABLE 1.4

Concentrations (meq./lH₂O) of Certain Ions in Human Plasma and Erythrocytes

(After Davson, 1964)

	K^+	Na^+	Ca^{++}	Mg^{++}	Cl^-	HCO_3^-
Plasma	5	140	3	1	110	28
Erythro-cytes	150	15	Trace	3	70	27
Ratio (P/E)	0.03	9	—	0.3	1.6	~1

however, there exist mechanisms whereby substances can be transported across membranes from regions of low concentration to regions of high concentration. Every mole of substance moved against an electrochemical potential gradient must be paid for by the expenditure of certain amount of energy, the payment being porportional to the magnitude of the opposed gradient. The required energy for this *active transport* is derived from the breaking of chemical bonds of energy-rich substances such as adenosine triphosphate (ATP), or possibly in some cases, from direct oxidative processes which involve the electron transport chain.

In mammalian cells the existence of active transport processes for sodium and potassium ions can be readily inferred from the concentrations of these ions in the intracellular and extracellular fluids (table 1.4). In general, though with exceptions, the concentration of K^+ is greater in the cell than it is in the extracellular fluid, while the concentration of Na^+ is lower in the cell than it is in the extracellular fluid. From the magnitudes of the permeabilities of cell membranes to these ions (table 1.3) it can be

energy source might be coupled to such a process, for example, so as to accelerate the net rate of flow of substance over what it would be in the case of passive diffusion. Ussing has suggested the name "downhill active transport" for this case. He suggests that passive diffusion can be distinguished from active transport by comparing the flux ratios in both directions across the membrane, as follows. Let the concentration of substance be C_1 and C_2 on the two sides of the membrane. For passive transport the rate of flow of substance from region 1 to region 2, $Q_{1\to 2}$, is given by $Q_{1\to 2} = KC_1$ and the flow in the opposite direction by $Q_{2\to 1} = KC_2$, where K is a constant. Thus for the case of passive, i.e. spontaneous, transport

$$Q_{1\to 2}/C_1 = Q_{2\to 1}/C_2 = K$$

and the two flux ratios are equal. When the two flux ratios are not equal, $Q_{1\to 2}/C_1 \neq Q_{2\to 1}/C_2$, then the transport is active rather than passive. The two flux ratios can be measured by having isotopically labeled substance on one side of the membrane and unlabeled substance on the other.

shown (Problem 7) that the intra- and extra-cellular concentrations would equalize by passive diffusion over a period of time equal to several hours. It follows that *in vivo* concentration gradients of these ions are maintained across the cell membrane by an active transport process which pumps the ions across the membrane at rates equal and opposite to those with which they leak out.

Active transport is a carrier-mediated transport. The criteria which define it therefore include: (1) saturation, (2) competition, (3) specificity and (4) inhibition. A new criterion which must be added for active transport is (5) the requirement for energy. Since this is an energy-coupled process, active transport can propel molecules against an electrochemical gradient. These criteria are illustrated in Problem 9.

The new feature which emerges in active transport is the requirement for energy. Thermodynamically a substance can be made to move against a concentration gradient only by the expenditure of energy. If the energy supply is blocked, active transport ceases. As an example we may take the human erythrocyte which under normal circumstances has a potassium concentration which is higher in the cell than it is in the serum. When erythrocytes are refrigerated, active transport ceases and potassium ions diffuse slowly and passively out of the cells until the intracellular and extracellular potassium concentrations are equal. When refrigerated blood is returned to 37°C. active transport resumes, providing there is an energy source such as glucose in the serum, and the intracellular potassium concentration increases towards normal levels.

A useful model for active transport is shown in fig. 1.6. In addition to the carrier, there is an enzyme, ϵ, and an energy source, W. The substance to be transported combines reversibly with a carrier molecule. The substance-carrier complex diffuses to the intracellular side of the cell membrane where the complex dissociates and the substance discharges into the cell. In this model an enzyme ϵ which is localized on the intracellular side of the membrane degrades the carrier molecule into an inactive form, that is, a form which does not combine with the substance. The degradative process is enzymatic and does not require an input of energy. The inactivated carrier passes to the extracellular side of the membrane where it is converted to its active state by an energy-requiring process. The cycle

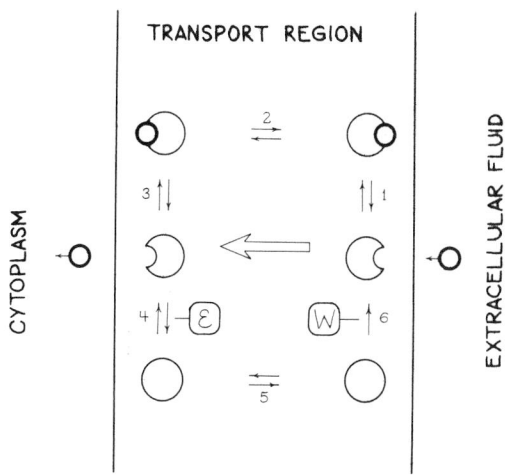

FIG. 1.6. Model for active transport (after Heinz and Walsh, 1958). The carrier molecules (large circles) are confined to the membrane region. There is a net transport of substance (small circles) from the extracellular fluid to the cytoplasm. The large arrow indicates the direction of transport.

(1) Substance combines with carrier.
(2) Substance-carrier complex passes to cytoplasmic side.
(3) Substance-carrier complex dissociates. Substance discharged into cytoplasm.
(4) Carrier is enzymatically degraded into an inactive form.
(5) Inactive carrier passes to extracellular side.
(6) Carrier is activated by an energy-requiring process.

then repeats. It should be pointed out that there exists no direct evidence for this model. The postulated carrier molecule, the enzyme and the carrier activating system have not been isolated or biochemically defined. Nevertheless, the model shown in fig. 1.6 is exceedingly helpful in discussing a wide range of experimental findings related to active transport.

It might be thought that active transport should give rise to a continuously increasing concentration gradient. This is not the case for two reasons: First, as the concentration gradient increases, passive diffusion in a direction opposite to that of active transport increases. A steady-state will be reached at which the rate of active transport equals the counter-current rate of passive diffusion. Second, as the intracellular concentration of substance increases the probability of a loaded carrier molecule returning from the intracellular to the extracellular side increases; that is, the equilibrium is driven in a direction opposite to the one where the carrier is inactivated and reactivated (fig. 1.6). Thus, when active transport is operative a steady-state may be reached at which the ratio of intracellular to extracellular concentration of substance remains constant with time.

The adaptive value and evolutionary significance of active transport is clear: The total amount of an amino acid in the environment of a microorganism, for example, may be very large though its concentration and rate of entry into the cell may be too small to sustain an adequate level of protein synthesis. In the presence of an energy-coupled carrier system the amino acid can be concentrated within the cell. Such a system should not be thought of as operating only between the cell and its outside. It can operate at the level of any membrane system, making it possible for a cell organelle to concentrate some constituent. This is the case for the mitochondrion in which magnesium ion is concentrated. The general features of active transport and facilitated diffusion hold true for a wide range of transport phenomena. Active transport processes for amino acids, sugars and ions (Na^+, K^+, Cl^-, Mg^{++}, etc.) have been shown to exist. The terminology varies. In the nerve one speaks of the "sodium and potassium pump"; in the kidney of "active secretion and reabsorption"; it is likely that a unitary process is involved.

PINOCYTOSIS

In discussing the relationship between permeability and molecular size it was pointed out that as regards to passive diffusion the permeability of the cell membrane to large molecules, such as proteins, is negligible. Yet, the passage of undegraded macromolecules into cells is well documented. As examples we cite: (a) the genetic transformation of bacteria by transforming principle (deoxyribonucleic acid), (b) the infection of cells by viruses, and (c) the entrance into cells of fluorescent, labeled antibodies. The mechanism whereby these macromolecules enter the cell is not known. It is suspected however that it is related to *pinocytosis* (cell drinking) a phenomenon prevalent in ameboid cells. This phenomenon is related to phagocytosis. In both phenomena a unit membrane bounded vacuole which engulfs extracellular fluid is formed by the cell (fig. 1.7). The vacuole travels into the interior of the cell. The contents of the vacuole face the "outside" surface of the unit membrane. Thus, from the point of view of the asymmetry of the unit membrane the vacuolar content lies outside the cytoplasm, just as the contents of the gastrointestinal tract lies, in reality, outside of an organism. However, in pinocytosis the unit membrane appears to have properties in the cell interior which are different from those which it had on the cell surface. The cell membrane of the ameba, for example, is highly impermeable to glucose. When pinocytosis is stimulated, however, glucose uptake from the extracellular fluid becomes considerable. It is not known how macromolecules pass from the interior of the pinocytotic vacuole into the cytoplasm. It is suspected that the vacuolar membrane breaks down in the cell interior and liberates its contents. This mech-

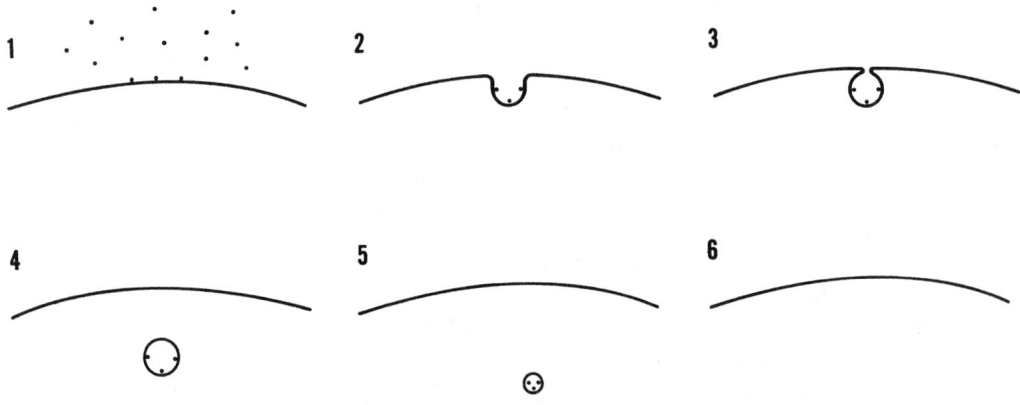

FIG. 1.7. Pinocytosis. Molecules which stimulate pinocytosis are indicated by dots.
(1) Molecules adsorb to the outer surface of the cell membrane.
(2) The membrane invaginates in the region of adsorption.
(3) A vacuole forms.
(4) The vacuole travels inwards.
(5) During its inward journey the vacuole shrinks.
(6) The membrane disappears and the adsorbed molecules spill into the cytoplasm.
(After Bennett, 1956.)

anism has been proposed but has not been experimentally substantiated.

Pinocytosis, however, is not simply the entrapment of a volume of extracellular fluid with the subsequent uptake of solutes from the fluid. In the ameba the actual uptake of protein exceeds by many times the protein content in the extracellular fluid taken up in pinocytosis. This anomaly was explained when it was shown that the protein was adsorbed to the cell membrane prior to the formation of the pinocytotic vacuole. It thus appears likely that the transport process involved in pinocytosis is primarily one of cell membrane movement into the interior of the cell, and that the ingestion of the extracellular fluid which is trapped in the vacuole is a by-product of the process. Pinocytosis is an active transport process in which the carrier is the unit membrane.

PROBLEMS

The problems which follow demonstrate that it is possible, by the use of simple reasoning and elementary mathematics (arithmetic and algebra), to obtain quite profound results concerning exceedingly complex physiological systems. It requires some courage, however, on your part, the courage to simplify, to discard those elements which your intuition tells you have only a small effect on the result you seek. It also implies an openess to the attainable and approximate in the face of the impossibility of the precise. We hope that in solving these problems you will rely on your mind and on pencil and paper, not on books. "It is better to light a candle than to walk in darkness."

Data

1. Treat the mammalian cell as a cube 20μ on edge.
2. $1 \text{ m} = 10^2 \text{ cm} = 10^3 \text{ mm} = 10^6 \mu = 10^9 \text{ m}\mu = 10^{10} \text{ Å}$.
3. Definition of logarithm: $e^{\ln x} = x; \therefore 2^y = e^{(\ln 2)y}$
4. Definition of pH: $[\text{H}^+] = 10^{-\text{pH}}$, where $[\text{H}^+]$ is the hydrogen ion concentration in moles/liter.
5. 6×10^{23} particles $= 1$ mole of particles.

Problems

1. Assume the density of mammalian tissues to be about 1 gm/cm³. Without recourse to the literature (use a ruler, if necessary);
   (a) Estimate the volume, in cm³, of (1) your body, (2) your brain.
   (b) Estimate the total number of cells (1) in your body, (2) your brain.
   (c) Estimate the total number of generations

required between the fertilized egg and the adult organism. (Every time the cell number doubles this constitutes one generation.)

2. The structure shown below appears in an electron micrograph at a magnification of 25,000 X. Is it a single unit membrane or an organelle bounded by unit membranes?

$$\Vert$$

3. Following J. D. Robertson let us denote with respect to the unit membrane the extracellular space by "X" and the cytoplasmic space by "Y". In terms of this notation a complete section through a lysosome (table 1.1) can be denoted by YXY. By this we mean that the scalpel which makes the section starts in the cytoplasm (Y), passes through the lysosome interior (X) and reemerges in the cytoplasm (Y). Encode sections passing through the following organelles:
   (a) The cell. (Ignore organelles in cell interior).
   (b) An endoplasmic reticulum vesicle.
   (c) A mitochondrion: A complete transverse section which passes parallel to the cristae but which does not pass through any of them.
   (d) A mitochondrion: A complete transverse section which passes through one of the cristae.
   (e) A nucleus.
   (f) A pinocytosis vacuole.

4. It has been estimated that the hormone thyroxine may be physiologically active at blood concentrations of $10^{-11} M$ and that thyroxine acts on the cell membrane. Calculate the number of thyroxine molecules per cell membrane assuming that the thyroxine levels in blood and cell membrane are the same.

5. Treat the mitochondrion as if it were a box 2.5 μ long, having a square cross-section 0.5 to 0.5 μ. If the intramitochondrial pH is 7.0 how many hydrogen ions will be found, on the average, in one mitochondrion?

6. The cell membrane is very permeable to water. Thus, water continuously exchanges between the inside and the outside of the cell. This exchange cannot be detected by ordinary means since, on the average, for every molecule of water that enters the cell another molecule leaves. The exchange can be detected, however, by placing a cell in heavy water and measuring the rate with which heavy water appears in the cell. Villegas, Barton and Solomon (J. Gen. Physiol. **42**, 355, 1958) find that heavy water enters the bovine erythrocyte at the rate 5×10^{-9} cm³/sec. Estimate the time (in seconds) for the water in a typical

mammalian cell to completely exchange with the outside.

7. Obtain a rough estimate of the order of magnitude (seconds, hours, or days) of the time required for the human erythrocyte to lose most of its K^+ ions after the active transport of K^+ is abolished by refrigeration. (Use data from Tables 1.3 and 1.4. For the purpose of this calculation assume some average K^+ concentration gradient.) Reference: J. E. Harris (1941). "The Reversible Nature of the Potassium Loss from Erythrocytes during Storage of Blood at 2–5°C." Biol. Bull. **79**, 373.

8. Mammalian cells are placed in a 0.3 M urea solution. The cells swell considerably. Can you explain this phenomenon?

9. List five criteria for active transport and illustrate each by means of the following data for a mammalian cell:

Experiment No.	Extracellular Medium	Relative rate with which glucose crosses into cell
1	40mM glucose	1.0
2	80mM glucose	1.4
3	120mM glucose	1.6
4	40mM glucose + dinitrophenol	0.1
5	40 mM glucose + 40mM galactose	0.5
6	40 mM glucose + 40mM fructose	1.0
7	40mM glucose + 0.1mM phlorizin	0.2

Dinitrophenol uncouples oxidative phosphorylation and reduces the supply of ATP.

10. Heinz and Walsh (1958) have put forth a very useful, but necessarily speculative, molecular model of active transport. Since the details of this process are not known consider, with regard to Fig. 1.5, the following possibilities:
    (a) The positions in the cycle of the energy source and enzyme are interchanged. That is, $W: 6 \rightarrow 4$ and $\epsilon: 4 \rightarrow 6$.
    (b) $\epsilon: 4 \rightarrow 3$, W remains where it is. The enzyme aids in the dissociation of the complex *and* inactivates the carrier.
    (c) $W: 6 \rightarrow 3$ and $\epsilon: 4 \rightarrow 6$. The system which is coupled to the energy source dissociates the complex *and* inactivates the carrier. The enzyme catalyzes the conversion of inactive carrier to carrier.

    Can you think of experimental tests which would distinguish these four possibilities?

11. The human red blood cell is biconcave and (in the wet state) about 8 μ in diameter, 1 μ thick at the center and 2.4 μ thick at its thickest point. We are interested in the following question: Is blood: (a) a suspension of red blood cells in serum, or (b) is it a densely packed aggregate of red blood cells with

serum poured into the interstices? To distinguish these two possibilities we will estimate the number of cells which could be neatly stacked into a cubical container of dimensions 1 mm × 1 mm × 1 mm. The estimate obtained will be compared with red cell counts of 6×10^6 per mm³ which are not unusual for young males. In this calculation it is convenient to treat the red cell as a box of dimensions 8 μ × 8 μ × 2.4 μ.
    (a) Calculate approximately how many such boxes can be packed in a single 2.4 μ thick layer at the bottom of the container, i.e., over an area 1 mm × 1 mm.
    (b) Calculate how many such layers fit into the container.
    (c) How many red cells fit into the 1 mm × 1 mm × 1 mm container?
    (d) Interpret the result.
    (e) How do you reconcile your result with the fact that when blood is centrifuged the packed volume of red cells is about 47% of the blood volume?

12. *Solvent Drag.* Andersen and Ussing (Acta Physiol. Scand. 1957, **39**, 228) have measured the permeability coefficients, k, for the passage of thiourea and acetamide through isolated toad skin. The thiourea (M.W. 76) and acetamide (M.W. 59) were dissolved in salt solutions, the concentrations of the salts being adjusted to provide an appropriate total osmotic pressure. For each substance two measurements of the permeability coefficient were made: (1) k_{in} was obtained when the concentration gradient was such that the net movement of substance by diffusion was in the direction from outside to inside. (2) k_{out} was obtained with the movement of substance in the opposite direction. (See figure below.) The two measurements for each substance were carried out under two conditions: (1) In the absence of an osmotic flow of water. (2) In the presence of an osmotic flow of water resulting from the outside solution having a lower osmotic pressure than the inside solution. The following results were obtained:

Solute	(Ratio: k_{in}/k_{out})	
	No osmotic flow	With osmotic flow
Thiourea	1.0	1.3
Acetamide	1.1	2.0

    (a) In what direction does the water flow due to the osmotic differential?
    (b) What conclusion can you reach from these

data as to whether there are "pores" (i.e. water filled channels) through the toad skin?

REFERENCES

BENNETT, H. S. The concepts of membrane flow and membrane vesiculation as mechanics for active transport and ion pumping. J. Biophys. Biochem. Cyt., 2 (Suppl.), 99, 1956.

BRACHET, J. AND MIRSKY, A. E., The Cell. Vol. II: "Cells and their Component Parts." Academic Press, New York, 1961.

CHRISTENSEN, H. N. Biological Transport. W. A. Benjamin, New York, 1962.

COLLANDER, R. Cell Membranes: Their Resistance to Penetration and Their Capacity for Transport, in Plant Physiology, F. C. Steward, Ed., Vol. II, Academic Press, New York, 1959.

CSÁKY, T. Z. Transport through biological membranes. Ann. Rev. Physiol., 27, 415, 1965.

DAVSON, H. A Textbook of General Physiology, 3rd ed. Little, Brown and Company, Boston, 1964.

DAVSON, H. AND DANIELLI, J. F. The Permeability of Natural Membranes. Cambridge, 1952.

DE REUCK, A. V. S. AND CAMERON, M. P. (eds.). Lysosomes. Ciba Foundation Symposium. Little, Brown and Co., Boston, 1963.

DICK, D. A. T. Osmotic properties of living cells. Internat. Rev. Cyt., 8, 388, 1959.

EINSTEIN, A. Investigations on the Theory of the Brownian Movement. Dover, New York, 1956.

FISHMAN, A. P. (ed.). Symposium on the plasma membrane. Circulation, 26, 983, 1962.

HARRIS, E. J. (ed.). Transport and accumulation in biological systems. Academic Press, New York, 1956.

HEINZ, E. AND WALSH, P. M. Exchange diffusion, transport and intracellular level of amino acids in Ehrlich carcinoma cells. J. Biol. Chem., 233, 1488, 1958.

HOLTER, H. Pinocytosis. Internat. Rev. Cyt., 8, 481, 1959.

LEHNINGER, A. L. The Mitochondrion. W. A. Benjamin, New York, 1964.

PROSSER, C. L. AND BROWN, F. A., JR. Comparative animal physiology, 2nd ed., W. B. Saunders, Philadelphia, 1962.

ROBERTSON, J. D. Unit membranes: A review with recent new studies of experimental alterations and a new subunit structure in synaptic membranes, in Cellular Membranes in Development, M. LOCKE (ed.), Academic Press, New York, 1964.

SCHACHMAN, H. K. Considerations on the tertiary structure of proteins. Symp. Quant. Biol., 28, 409, 1963.

TOWER, D. B. Molecular transport across neural and non-neural membranes, in Properties of Membranes, Springer, 1962.

VILLEGAS, R., BARTON, T. C. AND SOLOMON, A. K. The entrance of water into beef and dog red cells. J. Gen. Physiol., 42, 355, 1958.

I

THE NERVOUS SYSTEM

under the editorship of
Louis L. Boyarsky

CHAPTER 2

The Structure and Physiological Properties of Nerve

The Structure of Nervous Tissue

The structural unit of the nervous system is the *nerve cell* or *neuron*. Other elements—*neuroglial cells*—lying among the nerve cells provide a supporting framework.

THE NEURON

The neuron consists of a *body* or *soma*, and two types of process—the *dendrite* and the *axon (axis-cylinder process*, fig. 2.1). In vertebrates, the bodies of the nerve cells lie within the gray matter of the central nervous system or in outlying ganglia, e.g., posterior spinal root, cranial or sympathetic ganglia. The white matter of the brain and spinal cord and of the peripheral nerves is composed of bundles of nerve fibers. The core of each nerve fiber is formed by a process of a nerve cell, and many of them are surrounded by a sheath of myelin which gives them a white appearance. The gray matter receives a rich blood supply from the vessels of the pia mater (1000 mm/mm³ of capillaries); the blood supply to the white substance is much less profuse (300 mm/mm³ of capillaries).

There are a number of different types of nerve cell; those in which axon and dendrite arise by a common stem are called *unipolar*, and those in which the axon and the dendrite or dendrites spring from opposite or at least different parts of the soma are called *bipolar* or *multipolar*. The cell bodies or somata are of various sizes and forms—stellate, round, pyramidal, fusiform, etc.

After fixation and staining by special techniques, various structures are seen in the cytoplasm or *perikaryon* of the nerve cell body: (a) *neurofibrils*, (b) *Nissl bodies* or *tigroid* substance, (c) *Golgi* apparatus, (d) *mitochondria*, (e) *ribosomes* and (f) the *endoplasmic reticulum* (see also ch. 1). Electron microscopy has revealed much of the detailed structure of these intracellular structures. Their structure and function appear to be the same in all cells studied so far. Mitochondria are found along the entire length of the axis cylinder. These bodies contain all the enzymes required for the respiratory activity of the cell and are therefore responsible for those functions dependent upon aerobic metabolism. The neuro-

fibrils appear as fine filaments which stream through the cytoplasm from dendrites to axon (fig. 2.2); they enter the latter process and extend to its terminations. The Nissl bodies are granular masses stainable with basic dyes. They give a striped or *tigroid* appearance to the cell. They are absent from the region of origin of the axon and vary in size the number with the state of the neuron; they undergo disintegration (chromatolysis) in a fatigued or injured cell or in one whose axon has been sectioned (p. 27). The internal reticular apparatus of Golgi is a coarse network seen within the cells when special methods—e.g., impregnation with silver chromate—are employed which leave the Nissl bodies and the neurofibrils invisible. It is a debatable question whether the Nissl substance is present in the living cell in the particulate form observed, or whether the latter represents the precipitation from colloidal solution of some material, probably a nucleoprotein, by the methods of fixation employed.

The *nucleus* of the nerve cell contains one and sometimes two *nucleoli* but, as a rule, no *centrosome*. The nuclei of most nerve cells stain poorly, owing apparently to their chromatin paucity. The absence of a centrosome indicates that the highly specialized nerve cell has lost its power of division. Nerve cells once destroyed are replaced merely by neuroglia.

The linking together of neurons to form conducting pathways is effected by the contact (but not union) of the axon terminal of one nerve cell with the body or dendritic process of another. Such a function, without anatomical continuity, is called a *synapse* (ch. 4).

Though the nerve cell frequently possesses more than one dendrite the axon is single. The axon may be long and contribute to one of the tracts of the central nervous system forming the white matter, or terminate as a peripheral nerve fiber. Such cells are referred to as *Golgi I type*. In the *Golgi II* type cell, the axon is short and ends within the gray matter by making contact with another neuron. The axon arises from a small elevation on the surface of the cell body—the *axon hillock*. It may give off short collateral branches or run as an unbranched fiber, not dividing until it has reached its destination. The

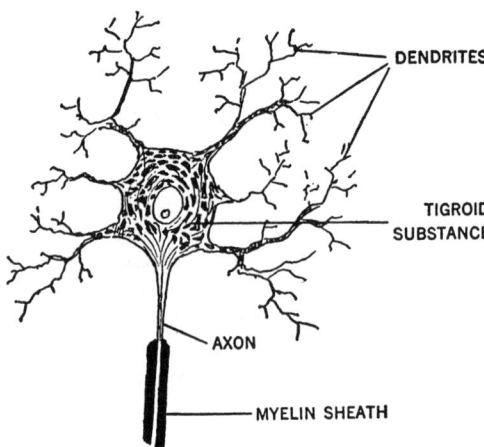

FIG. 2.1. Showing different parts of the neuron.

dendrite is the receptive process of the neuron, the axon is the discharging process, i.e., the former transmits the impulse toward the latter, away from the cell body. Within the central nervous system the dendrite is usually short and possesses many branches, but in the peripheral nerves (sensory nerve fiber) it is comparable in length with an axon. Nerve fibers which carry impulses to the central nervous system are termed *afferent;* those conveying impulses from the central nervous system to the periphery are called *efferent.* Purely sensory (afferent) nerves are therefore composed, strictly speaking, of dendrites, and purely motor (efferent) nerves are composed of axons. A mixed nerve contains fibers of both types. This unidirectional conduction is due to the properties of synapses, for nerve fibers can be made to conduct in either direction.

As with other cells the cytoplasm of the soma is enveloped by a *plasma* or *unit membrane,* composed of lipoprotein, a bimolecular leaflet of lipid material covered by a layer of protein. This extends over the processes of the nerve cell. The electrical properties of nerve depend upon the plasma membrane.

The Nerve Fiber

The white matter of the central nervous system and the peripheral nerves are composed of thousands of individual nerve fibers. Within the gray matter the axis cylinders are enclosed only by the plasma membrane; but upon leaving the gray substance they acquire a sheath of lipid material called *myelin.* The *myelin sheath* is prolonged over the fibers of the somatic nerves but not over those of autonomic nerves. Hence we speak of

myelinated and *unmyelinated* (or *medullated* and *unmedullated*) nerves. Myelinated fibers are usually larger than 1 micron in diameter and conduct faster than the smaller unmyelinated fibers.

The myelin sheath of the somatic nerves is enveloped in turn by a delicate membrane of flat cells called the *neurilemma* or *sheath of Schwann;* its cells are known as Schwann cells. Myelinated nerves appear as if constricted at regular intervals along their course. This appearance is due to the absence of myelin at these points and the dipping inwards of the neurilemma; they are known as the *nodes of Ranvier.* The segments between the nodes vary in length in different nerves, but the usual internodal distance is about 1 mm. Each internodalal segment of the neurilemma consists of a single Schwann cell. The fibers forming the white matter of the central nervous system have no neurilemma; this membrane is also absent from the fibers of the optic nerve.

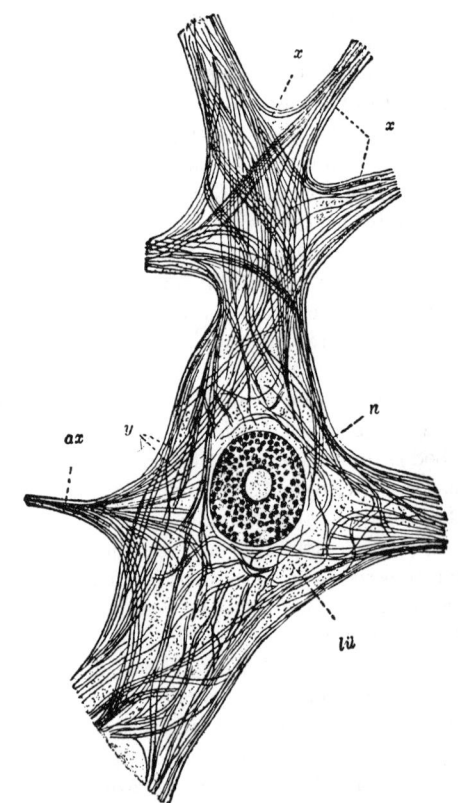

FIG. 2.2. Showing neurofibrils in a cell from the anterior gray column of the human spinal cord. *ax,* axon; *lii,* interfibrillar spaces; *n,* nucleus; *x,* neurofibrils passing from one dendrite to another; *y,* neurofibrils passing through the body of the cell (from Ranson after Bethe and Heidenhain).

Compared with the myelin sheath the neurilemma in the region of the node of Ranvier is highly permeable to ions. There is good evidence that the conduction of the impulse along a myelinated nerve is a "leaping" from node to node over the intersegmental regions rather than a continuous process. This type of conduction is called *saltatory* (Latin *saltus*, a leaping).

Myelination of Fiber Tracts in the Central Nervous System

The nerve fibers in the various conducting pathways receive their myelin sheaths at different ages and it is generally believed that the myelination of a given tract and the time at which it commences to function coincide. The sensory tracts become myelinated first, those of the posterior columns of the spinal cord between the fourth and fifth months of fetal life (human). The spinocerebellar tracts are myelinated later and the motor paths, e.g., corticospinal (pyramidal) tracts do not commence to receive their myelin sheaths until the second month of life and are not completely myelinated until about the second year, or about the time when the child has learned to walk. The fibers of association paths, for the most part, myelinate at still later dates. The function of the myelin sheath is not known, but the high insulating property of myelin suggests that it acts to confine the nerve impulse to individual fibers and thus to prevent cross stimulation of adjacent axons.

The *neuroglia* or "*glia*" (Greek, glue) is a special type of interstitial tissue. Its cells are of three kinds; *astrocytes*, *oligodendrocytes* and *microglia*. The microglia appear to have a phago-

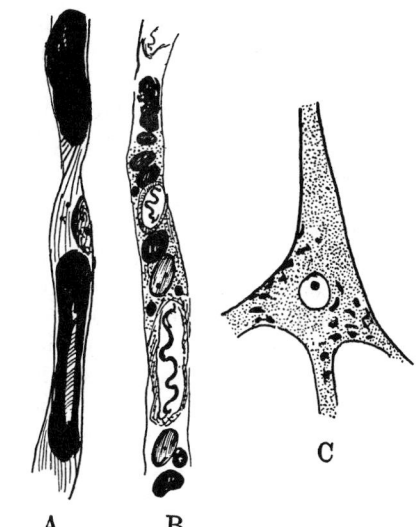

FIG. 2.4. Degenerating nerve stained with osmic acid. A, shows appearance of distal segment of nerve fiber 2 days after section, note large masses of myelin derived from medullary sheath; B, 5 days after section, smaller myelin particles together with droplets of fatty acids and fragmented neurofibrils; C, retrograde degeneration in cell body, disintegration of Nissl bodies.

cytic role since they wander into the central nervous system from the meninges and blood vessels, and increase in number during inflammatory processes (fig. 2.3). The astrocytes are found surrounding blood vessels and are thought by some to make up the blood-brain barrier. Evidence has been obtained that the oligodendroglia are involved in the formation of the myelin layers around axons within the central nervous system. Since it has been shown that the extracellular space of the central nervous system is very small, the glia may have permeability properties which enables them to function as a special kind of extracellular "space."

Degeneration and Regeneration of Nerve

When a peripheral nerve is cut, the part of the nerve separated from the cell body shows a series of chemical and physical degenerative changes. At the same time the fibers of the proximal stump of the nerve, those still attached to their cell bodies, grow distally toward the separated part of the nerve; these changes constitute the process of regeneration (fig. 2.4).

DEGENERATION

The degenerative period may be divided into an early and late phase. Shortly after the nerve

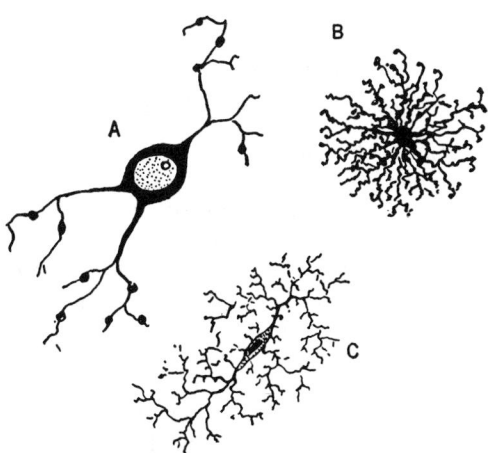

FIG. 2.3. Three types of neuroglial cell. A, oligodendroglia; B, astrocyte; C, microglia.

has been sectioned, the axis cylinder swells, the myelin sheath begins to form bead-like structures and a series of enlargements (round, fatty fragments) appear (fig. 2.3). The axon breaks up and its parts are devoured by macrophages. Up to three days after section, the nerve will continue to conduct an impulse. Changes in the action potential can be observed as early as two days after section. After the third day, the ability of the nerve to conduct has seriously deterioriated and after the fifth day, an impulse can no longer be evoked. The earliest fibers to fail are in the B group; The A fail next and the C last. The first period (3–5 days) is one in which the changes in nerve are largely physical. Changes in the ultrastructure of the myelin sheath can be shown to occur during this period, as well as changes in the endoplasmic reticulum, mitochondria, neurofibrils and the plasma membrane.

Up to the eighth day, little or no changes in lipid histochemistry may be detected although changes in nerve cholinesterase and failure in the ability to synthesize acetylcholine have been demonstrated about the third day. The lipids appear to maintain their original chemical structure. From the 8th to the 32nd day after section, the myelin gradually disappears, while Schwann cells and macrophages have both increased greatly in number. Why the meylin breaks down is not clear. It has been suggested that the macrophages and Schwann cells secrete enzymes which aid in the destruction of myelin. The principal myelin lipids are free cholesterol, and two lipids containing sphingosine, cerebroside and sphingomyelin. At the time of the disappearance of the myelin, cholesterol esters appear in large quantities and free cholesterol disappears.

The changes just described are generally known as Wallerian degeneration after Augustus Waller, an English phsyiologist, who first described them. But changes not recognized by Waller also occur in the neuron on the proximal side of the section (*retrograde degeneration*). The nerve fiber as far centrally as the first node of Ranvier shows changes similar in nature to those just described. In the cell body itself, swelling of the cytoplasm and nucleus occurs and the Nissl granules undergo disintegration (*chromatolysis*). Atrophy of the cell body may ultimately result.

REGENERATION

Following section of a nerve, the fibers in the central stump begin to send out branches consisting of outgrowths of the axon near the cut tip. Up to fifty branches may sprout from a cut axon. At the same time, there is a rapid proliferation of the Schwann cells. If a gap larger than 3 mm exists between the central and peripheral stumps, the fibers tend to intermesh and form a tumor-like swelling called a *neuroma*. In such an event regeneration will probably never occur. For this reason it is necessary to join accurately by suture the proximal and peripheral stumps. If the neuroma is composed of sensory fibers it may be very painful to pressure, often a troublesome complication following amputation. When peripheral degeneration has proceeded for enough time so that the peripheral stump contains only empty neurilemmal tubes, one of the outgrowing sprouts enters a tube and grows to form a new axon. Only one of the many sprouts enters an empty tube. The ability of axons to grow down into a peripheral stump has led some observers to invoke a special chemical attraction between the nerve fiber and the terminal organ. This is the doctrine of *neurotropism*. No direct evidence exists for such an attractive force. This is not to gainsay that the nerve which enters muscle may not have an influence on the properties of the muscle. Eccles and coworkers have recently shown that exchanging the nerve fibers to slow and fast muscles will cause the slow muscle to become a fast one and vice versa. The explanation of this phenomenon is at present unknown.

The rate of growth of regenerating nerve is from 1–4 mm per day. It has been established, in a variety of experiments, that there is a flow of axoplasm down normal nerve at about the same rate. This axoplasmic flow is accompanied by the movement of protein and nucleoprotein. It is not known what role axoplasmic flow has in the regeneration of nerve.

Principles of Bioelectricity

The Concept of Electrical Potential

Some preliminary considerations are required regarding the physics of electric charge and potential which will be necessary for understanding the phenomena of bioelectricity. Electric charge is responsible for the repulsion of similarly charged bodies and the attraction of oppositely-charged bodies. (1) Two kinds of charge exist, negative and positive. The unit of negative charge is that found on the electron; the unit of positive charge is the same as that for the negative. (2) These charges are always found in multiples of the fundamental unit which cannot be subdivided into smaller amounts. The charge on the electron is too small to serve as a practical unit; the amount of charge carried by 6.2×10^{17} electrons, the *coulomb*, is used as the practical unit. A positive charge results from a deficiency in charge caused by the removal of electrons from a neutral body. For example, a positive sodium ion results when one electron is removed from the neutral sodium atom.

The concept of potential arises from the energy stored in areas where electric charge is present. If electric charge is present, an electric *field* exists in the space around the charge extending to infinity. Its strength is measured by the force which would be exerted on a unit positive charge placed at a point in the field. The intensity of the field decreases inversely as the square of the distance from the charge (Coulomb's Law). In order to move a charge in the field, work must be performed against the field. Thus, it takes work to move a positive charge up to a region where another positive charge is situated since work is defined as the product of force by the distance moved. The potential at a point in the field is defined as the work that must be done on a unit positive charge to move it up to that point from an infinite distance. This is the absolute definition of potential which is seldom necessary in practice. The significant quantity in experimental work is the difference in potential between two points. The potential difference between two points is defined as the work necessary to move a unit charge from one point to the other. The work is measured in the *joules*. The practical unit of potential difference is the *volt*, i.e., the potential difference against which one joule of work is done in the transference of one coulomb.

The Origin of Potentials

A difference in potential is produced when a current flows in a medium. The difference in potential so produced may be calculated from Ohm's Law. If E is the potential difference in volts, I the current in amperes (coulombs/sec.) and R the resistance in ohms, then $E = IR$. The potentials recorded from biological tissues vary from 50 microvolts to several millivolts (action potentials) for externally recorded potentials.

Such current flows require sources of energy since the movement of ions in matter is always against the opposition of resistance of the medium; in all ionic flows heat and energy are lost. In order to produce currents, special sources of electrical energy are available such as the battery and generator. Such sources of energy are said to produce an electromotive force or *emf*. In solutions, electrical energy is produced by chemical reactions which result in the separation of charge at electrodes. Other sources of energy produce separation of charge by the flow of ions from solutions of high concentration into a solution of lower concentration. All such sources store the energy as a separation of charge. The separation of charge is manifest as a difference in electrical potential between two electrodes on which the charge separation occurs.

Two sources of energy are important in understanding the origin of biological potentials; these sources give rise to emfs called electrode or *concentration* potentials and *diffusion* or *membrane* potentials. Concentration potentials arise in every measurement of potential difference in solution and are generally to be avoided in biological measurements. They arise whenever an electrode consisting of an electrolytic salt is dipped into a solution containing an ion in common with the electrode. Thus, an electrode made of silver and coated with silver chloride inserted into a solution of sodium chloride will produce a potential difference between the electrode and the solution. The silver dissolves in the solution as silver ion, Ag^+, leaving the electrode negative. The positive Ag^+ ion remains at the electrode, forming a double layer of charge with the negative electrode. Charge is therefore separated at the electrodes. If two such electrodes are set up, each dipping into a different concentration of sodium chloride (a concentration cell) double layers will be set up at each electrode, but the double layer at one electrode will be more densely charged. When two such electrodes are connected by a wire a current will flow. The emf produced between the two electrodes can be calculated from the Nernst equation for the concentration cell.

$$E = 2.303 \frac{RT}{F} \log \frac{C_1}{C_2}$$

where R is the gas constant (1.99 cal/mole/°C), T the absolute temperature (°K), F the Faraday, (23,050 cal/volt/mol, 96,494 coulombs/mole), C_1 and C_2 are the concentrations of electrolyte in each solution. Note, that according to the formula if the concentrations are equal in each solution, the emf is zero. The method of producing a concentration cell is shown in figure 2.5.

Diffusion Potentials

Let us place two solutions containing different amounts of NaCl in contact by means of mem-

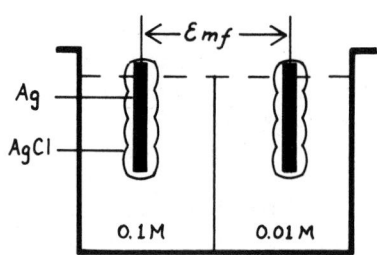

FIG. 2.5. A concentration cell. Both solutions contain sodium chloride. The partition between the compartments is freely permeable to water and salt.

$$E = \frac{u - v}{u + v} \, 2.303 \, \frac{RT}{F} \log \frac{C_1}{C_2}$$

where u and v are the mobilities of the cation and anion respectively, i.e., the rates at which ions move under unit field strength in solution. The remaining symbols are the same as those in the Nernst equation. Note that when the anion and cation mobilities are equal, $u = v$, and the emf is zero.

THE MEASUREMENT OF BIOELECTRIC POTENTIALS

Injury and Resting Potentials

brane freely permeable to the electrolyte. An emf whose origin is quite different from that of the electrode potentials we have discussed will arise at the membrane. The potential difference arises from the diffusion of ions across the membrane or at any junction between such solutions. They are therefore called variously, *diffusion, membrane* or *junction* potentials. The sodium chloride in the solution near the membrane tends to diffuse across into the other solution; the sodium ion diffusing faster than the chloride ion. The emf at the membrane depends upon the rates (mobilities) at which the sodium and chloride ions move and the relative concentration of sodium chloride. Since Na^+ diffuses faster than Cl^-, a separation of charge is produced; the solution into which a net Na^+ flow occurs becoming positive. At biological membranes, somewhat special hindrances to the movement of ions are present. Potassium and chloride usually diffuse at the same rate in solution; however, the ability of chloride to move across the cell membrane is more limited than that of potassium. Under these circumstances, potassium diffuses ahead of chloride and an excess of potassium ions appears on one side of the membrane. Although the excess is small, it is sufficient to set up an emf or potential difference so that the solution containing the lesser concentration of potassium chloride becomes positive to that containing the higher concentration. There is, in effect, a greater loss of potassium from the more concentrated to the less concentrated solution. The more concentrated solution becomes negative since it has lost positive charge. The concentration of K^+ increases until the emf has become sufficiently negative to keep any further K^+ from diffusing across the membrane. The diffusion potential at a membrane is given by a formula similar to the Nernst equation in which the latter has been modified to take into account the mobilities of the ions. The equation is

A potential difference exists between the inside and outside of all cells. The potential difference has been most intensively studied in nerve and muscle because of the close connection between the potentials and the mechanism of excitation and propagation. In order to measure this potential difference accurately, however, special methods must be employed. Classically, the emf of a nerve trunk or whole muscle determined by measuring the difference in potential between intact tissue and an injured region by means of a galvanometer or sensitive potentiometer. Under these experimental conditions, a potential difference between intact and injured tissue is detected with the injured tissue negative to the uninjured region. In making such measurements it is necessary to ascertain that the electrodes themselves do not set up potentials when current passes through them. The electrodes must therefore be of the "non-polarizable" type, such as silver-silver chloride. The current which flows through the galvanometer is known as the *current of injury*, a term happily no longer in use. The potential determined in this way is called a *resting potential*, since it is obtained when the nerve or muscle is not being stimulated. The injury potential is usually of the order of several millivolts; the exact magnitude depending upon the type of injury. The existence of an injury potential may be explained as follows. The injury exposes the interior of one end of the nerve or muscle to the electrode. An emf exists at the membrane of the intact part of the tissue; this emf acts as a battery to send current through the galvanometer and the injured region which has been rendered permeable. The direction of current flow is always in a direction which demonstrates that the interior of the cells is negative (fig. 2.6). The potentials and currents are small because what is actually measured is the IR fall along the outside of the nerve caused by current flow from the intact region to the injured region. If there is a considerable amount of saline around the tissue, the *IR* drop is small since the resistance of the solution is low. Substitution of a non-electrolyte of high resistance, such as sucrose, for saline enables the recording of higher value of potential.

An additional precaution is necessary in the measurement of bioelectric potentials. The silver-silver chloride electrodes should not be in direct contact with the tissue. It is necessary to place potassium chloride bridges between the electrode and the tissue. The potassium chloride bridges are tubes of glass filled with a saturated solution of potassium chloride. The silver-silver chloride electrodes are placed in contact with one end of the bridge; the other end of the bridge is in contact with the tissue. The arrangement of electrodes and bridges is shown in fig. 2.7. The reason for using this arrangement is to eliminate the concentration potentials set up at the electrodes due to the chloride in the extracellular space of the tissue. By placing saturated potassium chloride around the silver-silver chloride electrodes, the local concentration cells are eliminated. The electrodes are not in contact with the cells. The only effective potential which is recordable is that which arises at the tissue

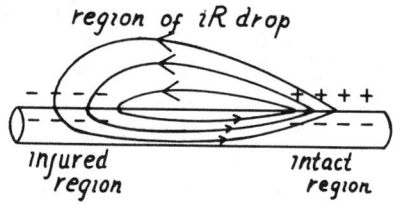

Fig. 2.6. The flow of currents in injured tissue. Conventional current flows externally from the intact region, into the injured region, and back to the intact region through the inside of the cell.

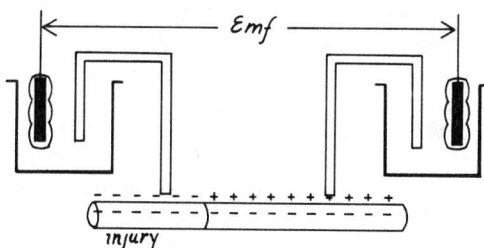

Fig. 2.7. Method for measurement of injury potentials. The silver-silver chloride electrodes are connected to the tissue by means of the KCl bridges, which are shown as tubes touching the nerve.

TABLE 2.1
Resting and Action Potentials
(m*V*)

Tissue	Resting Potential	Action Potential
Loligo axon	61	96
Sepia axon	62	122
Carcinus axon	82	134
Frog myelinated nerve fiber	71	116
Frog striated muscle fiber	88	119
Frog cardiac muscle fiber	70	90
Dog cardiac muscle fiber	90	121
Kid cardiac muscle fiber	94	135

membrane itself. The potential between the saturated KCl and the tissue is essentially zero because the junction or diffusion potential of the KCl bridges is zero. Thus the membrane potential of the tissue is the only source of emf in such an arrangement.

Transmembrane Potentials

In recent years, methods have been developed for measuring the potential difference present across the cell membrane—the *membrane* or *transmembrane potential*. It is, of course, a resting potential. In some cells, such as the giant axon of the squid, it is possible to insert an electrode into the body of the axon down its length and, by placing another electrode outside the cell, to measure the transmembrane potential directly. In other cells, where this technique is not feasible, another method is used. A glass capillary is drawn out to a fine tip less than 1 micron in diameter. The capillary is filled with saturated KCl or NaCl and serves as a microelectrode. It is inserted directly into the soma, muscle fiber or even peripheral nerve fiber and the potential difference measured between the microelectrode and a large, nonpolarizable electrode (connected via a KCl bridge) located outside the cell; this is the transmembrane potential. Such a method always involves the possibility that the injury caused by the puncture will result in a gradual fall in the potential and death of the cell. The membrane potentials of a variety of cells are shown in table 2.1; they range from 61 to 94 millivolts.

Theory of the Membrane Potential

The original theory of the membrane potential, largely valid today in broad outline, was first

TABLE 2.2

Ionic Content of Nerve and Muscle Cells

(mM kg⁻¹ intra-cellular water)

Tissue	Sodium			Potassium			Chloride		
	In	Out	Ratio	In	Out	Ratio	In	Out	Ratio
Carcinus nerve		460		380	10	38		540	
Carcinus nerve		460		230	10	23		540	
Frog nerve (Nov.)	37	120	0.31	110	2.5	44		120	
Frog nerve (Mar.)				170		68			
Frog sartorius muscle	15	120	0.12	125	2.5	50	1.2	120	0.01
Frog sartorius muscle	26	120	0.22	115	2.5	46	11	120	0.092
Rat cardiac muscle	13	150	0.087	140	2.7	52		140	
Dog skeletal muscle	12	150	0.08	140	2.7	48		140	

Ionic Fluxes of Resting Membrane

(μμ mol. cm⁻² sec⁻¹)

Tissue	In	Out		In	Out				
Sepia axon	61	31		17	58				
				(11)	(33)				
Carcinus axon				19	22				
Frog sartorius muscle	13	16		7	5				
Frog sartorius muscle		5–10			20				
Frog abdominal muscle		5		10	10				
Frog ext. long. dig. IV muscle				4	5				

enunciated by Bernstein at the turn of this century. It is well-known that the concentration of potassium is much higher inside cells than outside. Table 2.2 gives the value of the ratio of inside to outside concentrations for potassium and other important ions in various tissues. The ratios vary from 2.5 to 10. Bernstein maintained that the membrane potential was the result of the outward diffusion of potassium ions from the cells. Since the resting potential is a diffusion potential in which the mobility of the chloride anion was taken as zero and sodium was also presumed to be unable to penetrate the cell, the magnitude of the membrane potential can be calculated from the formula for the diffusion potential in which $v = 0$. The formula reduces to that of Nernst,

$$E = 2.3 \frac{RT}{F} \log \frac{K_{outside}}{K_{inside}}.$$

Verification for this theory has been obtained by Hodgkin and Huxley in several experiments in which the external potassium concentration was varied and the resting potential of the squid axon measured. It was shown that the resting potential varied directly with the logarithm of the external concentration of potassium over a wide range. Table 2.2 shows that the sodium is largely present outside cells. The independence of the resting potential from the concentration of sodium was shown in a series of experiments in which varying the external sodium concentration over a wide range had no effect on the resting potential of the squid axon. Similar results have been demonstrated for frog cardiac and skeletal muscle. The mechanism by which the ionic concentration differences are maintained will be discussed later in the section on active transport processes in nerve.

Ionic Distributions and the Membrane Potential

If no other ion but potassium could penetrate the membrane, the membrane potential would be given by the equation for a diffusion potential in which the anion mobility was zero. The resulting equation is then equal to the Nernst equation for a concentration cell. Actually, however, potassium does not pass through the membrane alone since there is always some flux from the sodium and chloride ions. Two equations for the membrane potential have been proposed to take into account the flow of several ionic species through the membrane. These are the Goldman equation and the Hodgkin-Huxley equivalent circuit for the resting membrane. Tests of these equations are usually made by plotting the membrane potential against the external potassium concentration and observing how closely the equations agree with the experimentally derived curve. All the equations, the Nernst relation included, are satisfactory over some range of potassium concentrations. We wish now to show how the Nernst equation is obtained.

In order to move an ion in a solution in which a potential difference is present, work must be done with or against two forces; the electrical field, and any concentration difference in the ions. Thus both "electrical" and "concentration" work must be performed. The electrical work, in joules, necessary to move a mole of ion against a potential difference, E, in volts, is given by the expression, work $= FE$, where F is the Faraday (96,494 coulombs/mole). The concentration work required to move a mole of ion from a concentration C_1 to a concentration C_2, where C_2 is higher than C_1, is given by the expression $2.303\ RT \log C_2/C_1$ where R is the gas constant and T the absolute temperature. If the ion is moving with the gradient, then energy is obtained from the concentration difference. The total work is given by the sum of the electrical and the concentration work, or work $= FE + 2.303\ RT \log C_2/C_1$. When the system is at equilibrium, the total work required is zero (this is the definition of thermodynamic equilibrium) and the potential difference is given by the Nernst equation,

$$E = 2.303\ \frac{RT}{F} \log \frac{C_1}{C_2}$$

The physical interpretation of this equation is that the tendency of an ion to diffuse down its concentration gradient is countered by the build-up of an electric field at the junction of the two solutions. The direction of the field is such as to hold back the ion from further movement. Note also that it is only necessary to move a very minute number of ions in order to produce the restraint required to obtain equilibrium of electric and concentration gradients. As an example of how the Nernst equation may be used we calculate

the potential which might exist in frog muscle where the internal concentration of potassium is 155 meq/L and the external concentration 4 meq/L. Substituting these values into the Nernst equation at a temperature of 27° C we obtain for the potential difference,

$$E = \frac{2.303\ (8.2)\ (300)}{96,500} \log \frac{4}{155}$$

$$= -95\ \text{mv}.$$

The Goldman equation will not be derived here. However, in the derivation, the assumptions are made that the total flow of current through the membrane is zero, that is, that the flow of negative charges is equal to the flow of positive charges, and also that the drop in potential across the membrane is linear. Using these assumptions it can be shown that the resting potential will be given by the relation

$$E = 2.303\ \frac{RT}{F} \log \frac{P_K C_K^0 + P_{Na} C_{Na}^0 + P_{Cl} C_{Cl}}{P_K C_K + P_{Na} C_{Na} + P_{Cl}^0 C_{Cl}^0}.$$

In this equation R, T, and F have their usual significance. P represents the permeability of the membrane to the ion and the superscript "0" above the concentration, i.e., C^0, represents the concentration outside the cell, the unlabeled C, the concentration within the cell. When the permeabilities to Na and Cl are taken to be zero, the equation reduces to the Nernst equation. If permeabilities are assumed to have the ratio $P_K:P_{Na}:P_{Cl}::1:0.04:.045$ the emf of the membrane as given by the equation agrees rather well with the value measured in the squid axon and the resting membrane potential agrees well with the calculated value over a more than fifty-fold variation of concentration of external potassium.

A third approximation to the membrane potential is the Hodgkin-Huxley equivalent circuit for the nerve membrane. The membrane is assumed to contain separate channels through which each of the ions pass without interference from the others. The total electrical current flow through the membrane is again assumed to be zero. Each ion in passing through the channel encounters resistance to flow in the membrane which is symbolized in a diagram as an electrical resistance (fig. 2.8). There are three such channels, one for each ion; each is represented by a battery (equilibrium potential) whose emf is calculated from the Nernst relation and whose opposition to current flow is shown as a resistance.

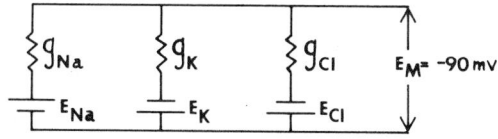

FIG. 2.8. The Hodgkin-Huxley equivalent circuit for the membrane. The symbols E represent the "equilibrium" potentials as determined for each ion from the Nernst equation. The symbol g represents the conductance of each ion.

Often the reciprocal of the resistance, the conductance g, is used to represent the channel permeability. If the total current from the membrane is zero, it can be shown that the membrane potential, E, resulting from the three emf's in parallel is given by the equation

$$E = \frac{E_K g_K + E_{Na} g_{Na} + E_{Cl} g_{Cl}}{g_{Na} + g_K + g_{Cl}}$$

The g's represent the conductance of the membrane; they correspond approximately to the permeabilities to each ion. The emfs are the equilibrium potentials for each ion. Thus in frog muscle the equilibrium potential for potassium is -95 mv, for sodium $+65$ mv, and for chloride -90 mv; values which have been calculated for each ion from the Nernst equation and the concentration of ions inside and outside the cell. Assuming further that $g_K = 100\ g_{Na} = 100\ g_{Cl}$, which is approximately true for frog muscle, we obtain for the emf across the membrane,

$$\frac{-95(g) + 65(g/100) + (-90)\ (g/100)}{g + g/100 + g/100}$$

or -95 mv, a value very close to the actual membrane potential. The Hodgkin-Huxley equivalent circuit will prove very important in discussing the mechanism of the action potential in later sections.

Physiological Properties of the Nerve Fiber

EXCITABILITY AND CONDUCTIVITY

The function of nerve is to transmit information from one region of the organism to another. In order to do this, the neuron must be stimulated or excited; a process which is termed *excitation*. Once the neuron has been excited, it transmits an impulse in the form of a wave of electricity (charge) along the nerve fiber. Because the impulse is conducted along the nerve fiber, nerve is said to possess the property of *conductivity*. This property must not be confused, however, with the electrical conductivity of a wire, for which the same term is used, since conduction in nerve and in a wire differ in many ways. In a wire the conduction of electricity is by way of electrons; the effects are propagated essentially with the velocity of light. But in nerve, propagation is ionic and the velocity is much slower— of the order of magnitude of one-third the speed of sound in air. We must also distinguish between the events of excitation and propagation in

nerve. When a nerve is stimulated events occur in the membrane during excitation in the vicinity of the electrodes which are non-propagated. As soon as excitation has occurred, the impulse proceeds away from the site of excitation much as a wave travels in a string. It is fundamental that nerve may be excited anywhere along its length and propagation is away from the point of stimulation in both directions. Wherever a junction (synapse) intervenes between nerve fibers in the mammalian nervous system, propagation can only continue in one direction.

Excitation

Many different kinds of stimuli may be utilized to excite nerve or muscle (electrical, thermal, mechanical and chemical). The sensory termination of nerve fibers, the receptor, is specialized to respond to only one or two of such types of stimulus to the exclusion of others. Since electrical stimuli of any intensity, shape and duration may be easily produced both accurately and repetitively, electrical stimuli are universally used to study the phenomena of excitation and propagation. Moreover, the nerve impulse is electrical in nature and many of its effects as an excitatory agent can be simulated by the electrical stimulus.

Characteristics of the Stimulus

Nerve responds to electrical stimulation provided that the electrical stimulus fulfills certain specific criteria. First, the stimulus must be sufficiently intense. The intensity of current of a stimulus just adequate to cause an impulse is called the *threshold*. Intensities below threshold are referred to as *subliminal*. In a compound nerve trunk, in which the nerve fibers have different thresholds, an average threshold, representing an intensity causing fifty percent of the fibers to respond, is often used. The threshold varies only slightly if the temperature and external ionic composition are maintained constant.

A second characteristic of the stimulus is its rate of rise. If the current is increased too slowly the nerve will not respond. Figure 2.9 shows two linearly rising currents one of which is able to reach threshold. The other current rises too slowly and the nerve is able to accommodate to the passage of the current. *Accommodation*, therefore, consists of a rise in threshold of the tissue during stimulation. To minimize accommodation, it is convenient to employ as stimuli currents which rise extremely rapidly. Two such stimuli are shown in fig. 2.10, the square wave and the exponential pulse.

The third characteristic which the stimulus must possess is sufficient duration. The pulses of fig. 2.10, if too short in duration would not result in an impulse. The two properties, intensity and duration obviously interact and it is therefore important to discuss the relationship between the threshold stimulus intensity and the duration of the stimulus—the *strength-duration* relationship.

For this purpose, the following kind of experiment is usually performed. A stimulus of a fixed duration, e.g., 1 millisecond, is applied to a nerve through two electrodes one of which is the cathode (−), the other the anode (+). The threshold is determined by increasing the current until a response is obtained—at the particular duration selected. A series of other durations are selected and the thresholds determined. The thresholds obtained at each duration are plotted as a function of the duration. The curve so obtained is called the *strength-duration* relationship for nerve (fig. 2.11).

The curve is accurately described over most of its course by the empirical relationship $I = I_0 (1 - e^{-kt})^{-1}$, where I_0 and k are constants, t is the duration and I the threshold current. For short durations the relation is approximated by the equation $It = $ constant. The latter equation is obtained for short durations of the stimulus in which accommodation is presumably slight. This relationship may be given a simple but important interpretation. The current I is the charge per unit time which is placed on the membrane in a time t. The product of the current and time, is, therefore, equivalent to a constant charge. The equation implies that a critical amount of charge must be placed on the membrane, whatever the current or duration.

What is the meaning of this critical constant

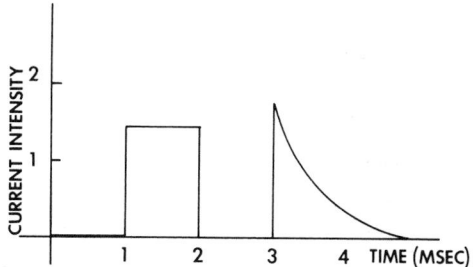

FIG. 2.10. Two commonly used stimuli; a rectangular pulse (*left*) and an exponential pulse (*right*).

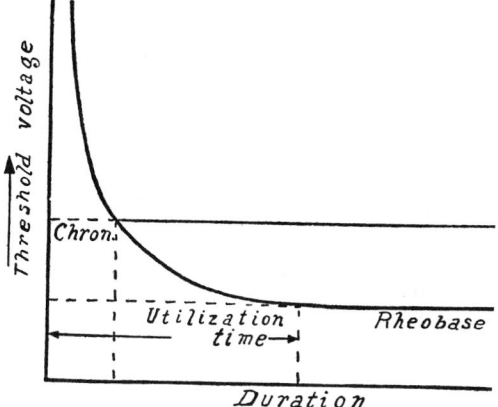

FIG. 2.11. Strength-duration curve; chron., chronaxie.

charge? We have already discussed the membrane potential and its origin. Placing a charge on the membrane is equivalent to reducing the net charge on the membrane; part of the charge on the membrane is neutralized. Such a partial neutralization of charge is equivalent to a *depolarization* of the membrane or to a reduction in the membrane potential from its resting value. Increased polarization or *hyperpolarization* results in an increase in the membrane potential. Depolarization decreases the stability of the membrane; hyperpolarization increases its stability.

Anodal and Cathodal Phenomena

A feature of excitation discovered quite early was that the impulse originated at the stimulating electrode which was the cathode, i.e., at the negative electrode. Figure 2.12 illustrates the lines of current flow into and out of the electrodes. At the cathode, the lines of current flow pass outwards through the membrane; at the anode, where current is flowing inward, excitation is hindered. Continuous current flowing into the nerve depolarizes the membrane in the vicinity of

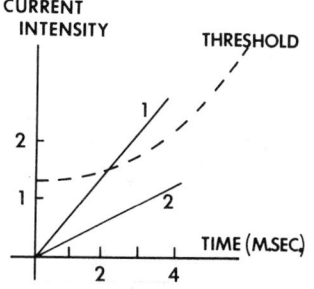

FIG. 2.9. A schematic representation of the effect of rate of rise of current. Curves 1 and 2 represent two stimuli with different rates of rise. Stimulus 2 never reaches threshold (dotted line). Stimulus 1 attains threshold.

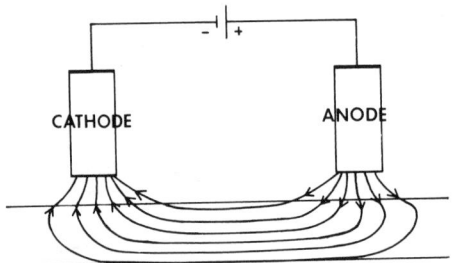

FIG. 2.12. Illustrating the passage of direct current through tissue. Anode is defined as the electrode which sends current *into* tissue.

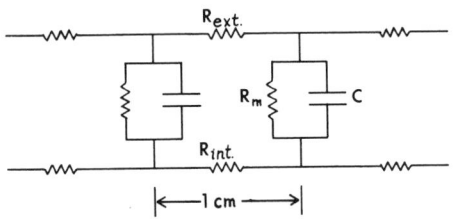

FIG. 2.13. Equivalent circuit of a nerve (radius $1\ \mu$) considered as an electric cable. R_{ext} is the resistance of one cm. of the external medium; generally low. R_{int} is the resistance of one cm. of the internal axoplasm ($10^7\ \Omega$) and R_m is the resistance of one cm. of the membrane to radial currents—of the order of $10^{10}\ \Omega$. The capacity, C, is $10^{-7}\ \mu$fd. for one cm. of nerve.

the cathode and hyperpolarizes it in the vicinity of the anode. Thus it is easier to stimulate a nerve in the vicinity of the cathode because the membrane potential has been lowered; conversely, at the anode, the membrane potential is increased and higher currents are required to excite tissue. The effects of direct current on the excitability of nerve and muscle are referred to as electrotonic phenomena; the depolarization at the cathode is called *catalectrotonus*, that at the anode *anelectrotonus*.

Summation and the Local Excitatory State

The application of a brief subthreshold stimulus has a residual effect on nerve even though an impulse has not been evoked. If a second stimulus follows the first within one millisecond, a second sufficiently intense subthreshold stimulus may result in a response. The longer the interval between the two stimuli, however, the more intense the second stimulus must be to yield a response. The stimuli sum their effect on the nerve membrane so that a response occurs.

The interpretation which is given to this experiment is that the first subthreshold stimulus produces a change in the membrane potential which lasts for a millisecond or more. This change facilitates the effect of a second stimulus. The

change in the membrane caused by the first stimulus is referred to as the "local excitatory state" in the vicinity of the electrode. It is a non-propagated response of the membrane which will be identified later with the depolarization of the membrane in the region of the cathode.

The Local Excitatory State

The experiments on subthreshold summation and the electrotonic properties of nerve led to the theory that the membrane potential should be decreased in the vicinity of the cathode. Direct evidence that such a depolarization occurs has been obtained from experiments demonstrating that potential changes occur in the vicinity of the cathode and anode in agreement with the theory.

First, however, the purely passive changes in the membrane potential must be discussed, i.e., those changes which result from the fact that nerve has the properties of an electric cable, possessing electrical capacitance and resistance. The nerve membrane can store charge; it therefore has the property of capacitance. The capacitance C is defined as the charge, Q, which must be placed on two surfaces in order to produce a unit potential difference V between them ($C = Q/V$). The units of C are in farads when Q is in coulombs and V in volts. The capacitance of the nerve membrane is 1 microfarad/cm².

For each unit length of nerve there is also an external electrical resistance and an internal resistance. The membrane resistance constitutes a third electrical resistance. Each centimeter length of nerve may be considered as an electrical cable (fig. 2.13) consisting of these resistances and the capacitance. If a stimulating current is passed through a section of nerve, the condensers will charge but the most distant ones will be least charged since more external and internal resistance is included between them and the source of current. If one were to measure the charging process at any moment, the voltage at the electrodes would be highest at the electrodes and would decrease exponentially as one proceeded away from the stimulating electrodes (fig. 2.14). This charging process is almost instantaneous

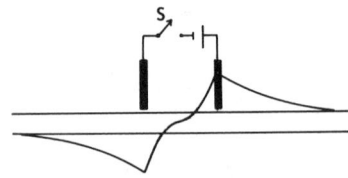

FIG. 2.14. Illustrating the passive, electrotonic potential along the nerve resulting from the passage of direct current into the nerve.

and represents a non-propagated build-up of charge along the nerve. It extends for some distance along the nerve but it is never propagated as a wave.

When nerve is stimulated, two electrical events take place. The membrane charges passively as a cable and, at the same time, the nerve begins to react physiologically at the cathode. Events at the anode are purely passive since excitation does not occur there; the time course of charging at the anode may be taken as that for the passive or physical charging of nerve. At the cathode, both passive charging occurs and, in addition, an active process which we have called the local excitatory process. If the passive process at the cathode is subtracted graphically from the overall recorded response, the local excitatory process should be obtained. The passive, physical process at the anode and cathode are linear, that is they are proportional to the stimulating current. In order to measure the local responses an experiment is performed in which the potential difference between electrodes placed at the anode and cathode is measured with respect to a distant electrode. Figure 2.14 shows the results of the potential measurements and also the result of subtracting the passive response from the overall response to obtain the local potential which corresponds to an active non-linear process at the electrode.

The significance of the local potential is that it demonstrates the time course of the depolarization at the cathode. When the depolarization at this electrode reaches a critical value, corresponding to a constant amount of charge on the membrane, an action potential will be initiated which will propagate away from the electrode. Such local responses consisting of a depolarization can be found in many tissues. For example, receptors must be depolarized before they give rise to an action potential; the potential representing the local excitatory state of the receptor is called the generator potential. An active process also occurs at the neuromuscular end-plate which is called the end-plate potential; a depolarization which initiates the propagated action potential of muscle. At the synapses of neurons, a local, non-propagated potential called the excitatory post-synaptic potential (EPSP) may be recorded which gives rise to the nerve impulse of the neuron. The critical event in the excitation of all these cells is the local, non-propagated depolarization. When this depolarization becomes of critical magnitude, the explosive, propagated activity called the nerve impulse is set off.

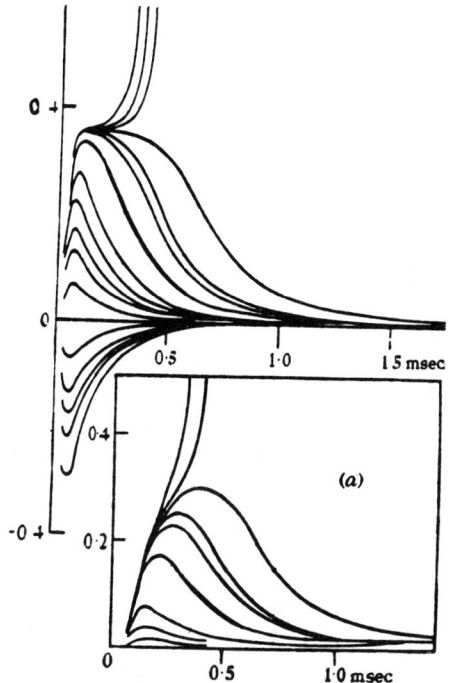

FIG. 2.15. Electrical changes at stimulating electrode produced by shocks with relative strengths, successively from above, 1.00 (upper 6 curves), 0.96, 0.85, 0.71, 0.57, 0.43, 0.21, −0.21, −0.43, −0.57, −0.71, −1.00. The ordinate scale gives the potential as a fraction of the propagated spike, which was about 40 mV in amplitude. The 0.96 curve is thicker than the others, because the local response had begun to fluctuate very slightly at this strength. The width of the line indicates the extent of fluctuation. (Inset) Responses produced by shocks with strengths, successively from above, 1.00 (upper 5 curves), 0.96, 0.85, 0.71, 0.57; obtained from curves in upper figure by subtracting anodic changes from corresponding cathodic curves. Ordinate as above. (From A. L. Hodgkin, Proc. Roy. Soc. Lond. (1938–39), 126, 87–121.

The Action Potential

The external recorded action potential may be obtained by stimulating a nerve at one end and picking up the response of the nerve some distance away with two recording electrodes and a recording device. Figure 2.15 shows the arrangement by which the action potential of nerve is usually recorded. Such recording is called external recording. One may either record the action potential by means of a very fast galvanometer, as was done in the classical days, or as at present with a cathode ray oscilloscope.

Unlike any instrument previously employed for this purpose, e.g., the string galvanometer or the capillary electrometer, the moving part of this instrument—a stream of electrons—processes practically no mass and has in consequence no inertia. It is therefore capable of recording very

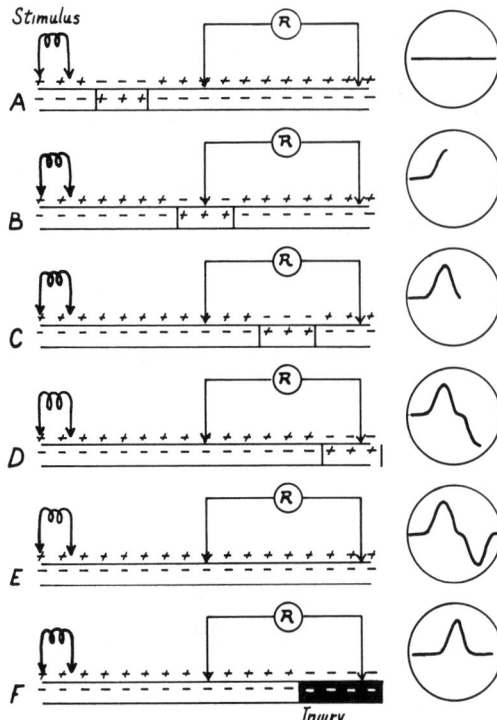

FIG. 2.16. Passage of action potential down a nerve. Stimulus is applied at left. Cathode ray oscilloscope is indicated at *R*. The recorded potential is shown at the face of the cathode ray oscilloscope at the extreme right of each figure. A monophasic potential is shown in figure *F*.

rapid changes in electrical potential. The instrument consists of an evacuated tube; an electron stream from a hot cathode strikes a fluorescent screen upon which it produces a spot of light. On either side of the electron stream is placed a vertical plate. A potential difference is created between the pair of plates; the electric field set up across the path of the stream deflects it horizontally, and sweeps it across the screen. The spot of light is converted into a horizontal streak. By means of a sweep oscillator the horizontal deflections are repeated many times per second. A second pair of horizontal plates is placed one above, the other below, the electron stream. These are connected with the nerve whose action current is timed to reach them at the instant the stream is deflected horizontally by the vertical plates. A vertical deflection of the electron stream results with production of a standing wave which is photographed and a permanent record thus obtained. The speed of the horizontal movement of the spot of light enables the time scale to be calculated, and can be varied by altering the potential applied to the horizontal pair of plates;

the horizontal movement corresponds to the movement of a kymograph, though of course its rate is very many times faster. The upward deflection is analogous to the rise of a muscle lever. The magnitude of the action potential is determined from the height of the wave. Before reaching the recording system the action current is amplified several thousand times by passing it through an amplifier. This is necessary because the electron stream requires about 50 volts to cause a deflection of 1 cm on the face of the tube.

The response on the cathode ray oscilloscope or the galvanometer shows up as a diphasic variation of potential. The cathode ray oscilloscope records the potential under one recording electrode as a function of time with respect to the other recording electrode. The interpretation of such a recorded potential is that when the nerve is stimulated, an electrical impulse is sent down the nerve. This electrical impulse hitting the first electrode causes a response of the oscilloscope beam in one direction. When the impulse passes between the electrodes, no recorded potential is observed. But when the impulse reaches the distant electrode, a potential is recorded which has the opposite direction of the first. We therefore say that there are two phases present in the action potential. It is quite clear that one can eliminate the second phase of the action potential by preventing the negativity of the impulse from reaching the second electrode. This can be done by either making a crush in the region of the nerve between the two electrodes or crushing directly under the distant electrode. Of course, if the crush is at the first electrode, no potential will be recorded at all, since the action potential cannot pass a dead region of nerve. The potential recorded when the nerve is crushed at the second electrode is called a monophasic potential and is shown also in the accompanying figure.

The Compound Nature of the Action Current Recorded from a Nerve Trunk

Erlanger, and Gasser studied the action potential of mixed nerve trunks by means of the cathode ray oscillograph. Upon analysis of the electrical potentials of mammalian nerves, they showed that the "spike" is actually compound and represents the fusion of the potentials of three main types of nerve fiber, which are referred to as the A, B, and C groups (fig. 2.17). Several properties of nerve are correlated with the diameters of the fibers, the larger the fiber diameter, the higher is the conduction velocity and the lower the threshold of excitation, the greater the magnitude of electrical response, but the shorter its duration and refractory period. The relationship of conduction velocity to diameter of the nerve fiber is a linear one (fig. 2.18). The amplitude of the externally recorded potential is also linearly related to the fiber diameter.

The A group is composed of the largest fibers, 1 to 20 micra in diameter, with conduction rates from 5 m. per sec. or less for the smallest fiber to 100 m. per sec. for the largest. The fibers of the A group are all myelinated, are both sensory and motor in function and are found in such somatic nerves as the sciatic and saphenous nerves.

The B fibers are myelinated and have diameters from 1 to 3 micra, and conduction velocities from about 3 m. per sec. to 14 m. per sec. The B fibers are found solely in autonomic (preganglionic and in some myelinated postganglionic) nerves. The C group, composed of the smallest fibers (less than 1 micron in diameter), are unmyelinated and have a conduction rate of around 2 m. per sec. or less; many are found in cutaneous and visceral nerves. They have a high threshold, thirty-fold that of the A group. The A group of fibers make by far the greatest contribution to the compound spike potential, and the C group least. The electrical potentials recorded from both A and C fibers show slow variations in potential following the action potential, negative and positive after-potentials, but the B group shows no negative after-potential with a single response, though it appears upon repetitive stimulation. The B fibers are the most susceptible to asphyxia, the C fibers the least so.

The linear relationship between fiber diameter and conduction velocity holds also for growing nerves of young animals (Hursh). During growth the diameters of the nerve fibers in the nerve of the leg, for example, increase as the nerve lengthens. Conduction velocity increases proportionately so that the time taken for an impulse to travel from the toes of a kitten a few days old to the spinal cord is the same as for a full grown cat. Thus the kitten and the cat react to stimulation with about equal promptness.

The diameters of the regenerating fibers in a sectioned or crushed nerve also enlarge gradually and conduction velocities increase accordingly; the relationship again being a linear one. The maximum conduction velocity is not reached until maximum diameter of the fiber is attained. If the axons of the nerve alone are interrupted, the

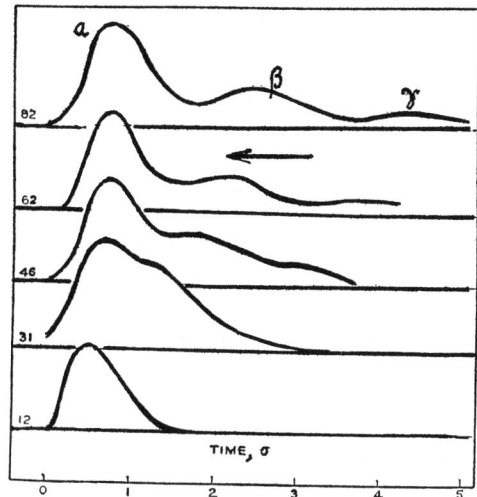

FIG. 2.17. Cathode ray oscillograph records of the action currents in the sciatic nerve of the bull-frog after conduction from the point of stimulation through the distances (in millimeters) shown at the left. The action potentials might be compared to runners in a race who become separated along the course as the faster contestants outstrip the slower; thus in a record at 82 mm. from the point of stimulation three waves are shown, whereas at 12 mm. the potentials are fused, and only one large wave appears. (Modified from Erlanger, Bishop and Gasser.)

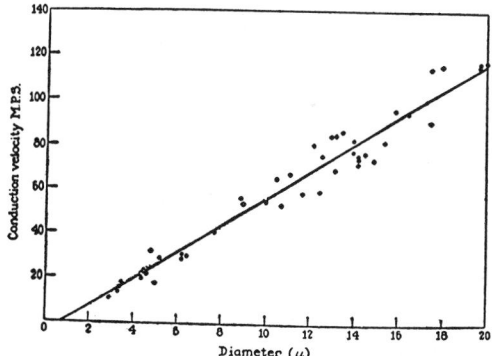

FIG. 2.18. Linear relation between diameter and conduction velocity of mammalian nerve fibers. Each point represents a determination of the maximum conduction velocity of meters per sec. and of the diameter in micra of the largest fiber of an individual nerve. Dots = adult nerves. Circles = immature nerves. (After Hursh.)

sheaths of the nerve fibers remaining intact, the diameters and conduction velocities may reach those of the normal nerve; this rarely occurs if the nerve has been completely severed.

Action Currents and Excitation

The externally recorded action potential represents a potential variation along the nerve. An alternate way of looking at the nerve impulse

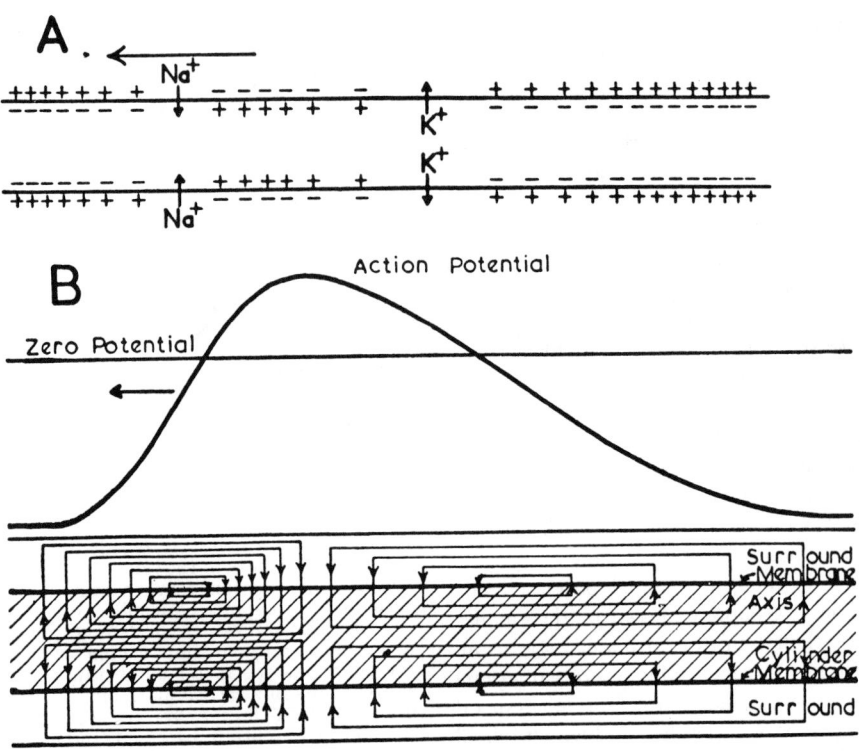

FIG. 2.19. (A) The movement of sodium and potassium during the action potential, travelling in the direction of the arrow. The charge in each region is also shown. (B) Upper curve shows the potential distribution of the impulse along the nerve. The lower part shows the flow of currents in the external medium and within the fiber. There is a reversal of potential during the spike. (After Eccles.)

is as a set of currents flowing out of the membrane ahead of the area of greatest depolarization. A nerve impulse consists, then, of the movements of these currents along the nerve (fig. 2.19). The term action current is as appropriate as action potential. The advantage of considering the currents of nerve instead of the potential is that one can then understand how the self-exciting properties of the nerve impulse arise. The analogy is often made that the nerve acts like a fuse along which ignition progresses. It is the currents themselves which act to depolarize the nerve. Ahead of the region of depolarization, action currents leave the nerve. These currents, therefore, act as a virtual cathode since they have the direction of currents flowing into a cathodal electrode. The hypothesis that action currents act to depolarize the region ahead of them was substantiated by the experiments of Hodgkin. He showed that if action currents were allowed to enter but not to excite a region beyond a narcotized stretch of nerve, then the action currents give rise to two phenomena beyond the blocked region; an increase in excitability and a depolarization of the fiber. Neither the increase in excitability nor the

depolarization were large enough to set up an impulse; the block diminished the intensity of the currents but it was clear from this experiment that action currents could cause depolarization and therefore a change in excitability.

Another hypothesis which was part of the general theory of self-excitation was that in order for self-excitation by a propagated nerve impulse to occur, not only was a depolarization necessary, but there had to occur also an increase in permeability to ions at the depolarized region. In this way, depolarization would lead to increased ion flow through the membrane ahead of the depolarized region which was not yet excited. In other words, during the action potential a path had to be opened in the membrane through which the charge from resting membrane could flow. By discharging resting membrane ahead of itself, the action potential became self-propagating. Evidence for this characteristic of self-propagating activity was obtained by Curtis and Cole who showed that there was an increased permeability to ions during activity. This was demonstrated as a decrease in transverse resistance of the membrane from a resting value of

1000 Ω-cm² to one of 25 Ω-cm² during the rise of the action potential in the squid axon. Decreases in membrane resistance have also been demonstrated in other tissues such as muscle during propagated activity.

Conduction Rates

The velocity of the nerve impulse varies in different nerve fibers in accordance with their diameters, the thicker fibers conducting more rapidly than those of smaller diameter. In the large motor fibers of the mammal the rate is from 80 to 120 meters per second. Sensory nerves of the skin being of smaller diameter have slower conduction rates. Nonmedullated fibers conduct more slowly than medullated. Some of the fibers subserving pain sensation and those of the sympathetic nervous system have a very slow conduction rate (see also ch. 3).

The following table from Hill gives the conduction rates in the nerves of several different animals.

Medullated nerve, mammal, 37° C, about 120 m. per sec.

Medullated nerve, dogfish, 20° C, about 35 m. per sec.

Medullated nerve, frog, 20° C, about 30 m. per sec.

Nonmedullated nerve, crab, 22° C, about 1.5 m. per sec.

Nonmedullated nerve, mammal, 37° C, about 1 m. per sec.

Nonmedullated nerve, olfactory of pike, 20° C, 0.2 m. per sec.

Nonmedullated nerve, in fishing filament of *Physalia*, 26° C, average 0.12 m. per sec.

Nonmedullated nerve, in Anadon, 0.05 m. per sec.

Compare the velocity of sound in air at 0° C., 331 m. per sec.

By an indirect method of measurement Carmichael and his associates found the rates of conduction in various human postganglionic sympathetic nerves to be from 0.85 to 2.30 m. per sec. The lower figures were obtained for the nerves of the leg, the higher ones for the nerves of the chest.

The "All or None" Principle

A stimulus which is just capable of exciting a nerve fiber (threshold stimulus) sets up an impulse which is no different from one set up by a much stronger stimulus. The impulse set up by the weak stimulus is conducted just as rapidly and is just as strong, as one set up by the strong stimulus when judged by the action current developed or the mechanical response of the muscle. Briefly, the propagated disturbance set up in a single nerve fiber cannot be graded by grading the intensity or duration of the stimulus —the nerve fiber gives a maximal response or none at all. To make use again of the train of gunpowder analogy—the flame of a match applied to the powder fuse will start a traveling spark no less intense than one started by the flame of a torch. The restoration of the strength of the impulse to its original value after passing from a narcotized region into normal nerve also shows the "all or none" nature of nervous conduction. The well known fact that a strong stimulus applied to a nerve trunk causes an action current of greater amplitude, and a greater muscular response than a weaker stimulus is due to the fact that the nerve trunk is composed of many fibers each of which supplies a group of muscle fibers. The weak stimulus excites only a proportion of the units of the nerve, a maximal stimulus excites them all. For example, the *cutaneous dorsi muscle* of the frog is supplied by a nerve which contains only 8 or 9 fibers; each of these innervates about 20 muscle fibers. Keith Lucas found that when the nerve was stimulated by shocks, gradually increasing in intensity, the muscular responses did not show a similar continuous rise in amplitude; on the contrary, the responses of the muscle increased in a series of well-defined steps; that is, increasing the stimulus intensity produced no effect for a time upon the amplitude of the muscular response, but then a slight increase in strength of stimulus produced a sudden rise in amplitude. The steps were never greater in number than the number of fibers, and were due, it was concluded, to additional fibers becoming excited as the strength of stimulus reached a certain value.

It must also be remembered that the all or none principle applies only for the condition of the nerve at the point where, and the moment when, the impulse arises. A stimulus which will give rise to a response of a certain magnitude under one condition of the nerve may give a much smaller response under other conditions, e.g., during the relative refractory period (see below), narcosis, oxygen lack, etc.

The Absolute and Relative Refractory Periods of Nerve

For a brief interval following the passage of an impulse along the nerve fiber, a second stimulus,

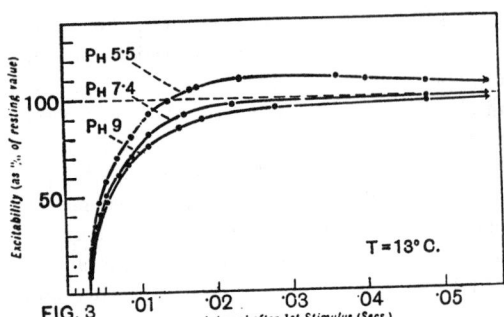

FIG. 2.20. Recovery of excitability in nerve perfused with fluids of different pH. (After Adrian.)

however strong, is unable to evoke a response. This interval is called the absolute refractory period. In a frog's sciatic nerve at a temperature of about 15° C the absolute refractory period has a duration of between 2 and 3 msec. Its duration is roughly the same as the action potential "spike" (p. 43). It is much shorter in mammalian nerve (1.0 to 0.4 msec. in large medullated nerve fibers).

The period during which the nerve is absolutely refractory is succeeded by one in which the nerve, though it will not respond to a stimulus of the same strength as it did before the passage of the impulse, will respond to a somewhat stronger one. The excitability of the nerve gradually increases and the strength of stimulus necessary for excitability becomes progressively less (fig. 2.20). In the end, the restoration of excitability is complete and the nerve responds to a stimulus of no greater strength than that which is capable of exciting a resting nerve. The period following the absolute refractory phase and during which the excitability gradually rises to normal is called the *relative refractory period*. It lasts for from 10 to 30 msec. or at any rate until the excitability of the nerve has returned to about 95 per cent of the resting value (full recovery may not be attained until the lapse of 100 msec.). It should be pointed out that the failure of the nerve to conduct a second impulse is not due simply to lowered excitability at the *point in the nerve where the original stimulus was applied,* for during the absolute refractory period a stimulus applied to any other point upon the nerve likewise fails to set up an impulse. The passage of the impulse along the nerve leaves in its wake a change of state like a trail of ash after the ignition of a powder fuse. For the moment the impulse consumes the entire resources of the nerve fiber (Adrian). The burned fuse must have its store of energy replenished by laying a fresh train of

powder grains before a second spark can transverse the path of the first. So also, a certain time is required for the changes associated with the passage of the impulse to become reversed and the nerve restored to its resting condition (polarized state, see also p. 44).

The refractory period renders a continuous excitatory state of the nerve impossible just as the corresponding period in cardiac muscle assures rhythmical contractions and prevents summation and tetanus. Fusion or summation of impulses does not occur. The refractory period obviously must also limit the frequency of the impulses. In the mammal the absolute refractory period is about 0.5 msec. The intervals between impulses cannot be shorter than the absolute refractory period; the maximum impulse frequency is therefore around 1000 per sec. At this rate the impulses are travelling in the *relative* refractory period of their predecessors and are weaker and more slowly conducted. In frog nerve with its refractory period of from 2 to 3 msec., the maximal impulse frequency is between 250 and 300 per second.

Volume Conduction

The propagation of the nerve impulse has been discussed in situations in which the recording of the action potential has been quite ideal; the nerves were considered to be in air and the potential recorded was a simple diphasic wave. When an action potential arises in nerve which is surrounded by tissue, however, the situation is more complicated since the tissue acts as a conductor. The form of the action potential recorded under such circumstances will not necessarily be a simple diphasic negative wave but, may, indeed, be triphasic. It may appear strange that the potential recorded will change, but this may be understood rather broadly in the following terms. Electrodes which are external to a tissue actually record the potential difference caused by the current which flows in the tissue between the two recording electrodes. The current flow produces an "*IR*" drop in the tissue. In a nerve which is in air the current flowing between two electrodes is largely longitudinal (fig. 2.20). The nerve scarcely records the potential resulting from the currents coming out at right angles to the membrane. The potential drop observed along the nerve results from current flow in the extracellular fluid. In air, the current lines are highly dense longitudinally and they produce a drop in potential along the nerve which is most negative at the origin of the action potential (fig. 2.21). The

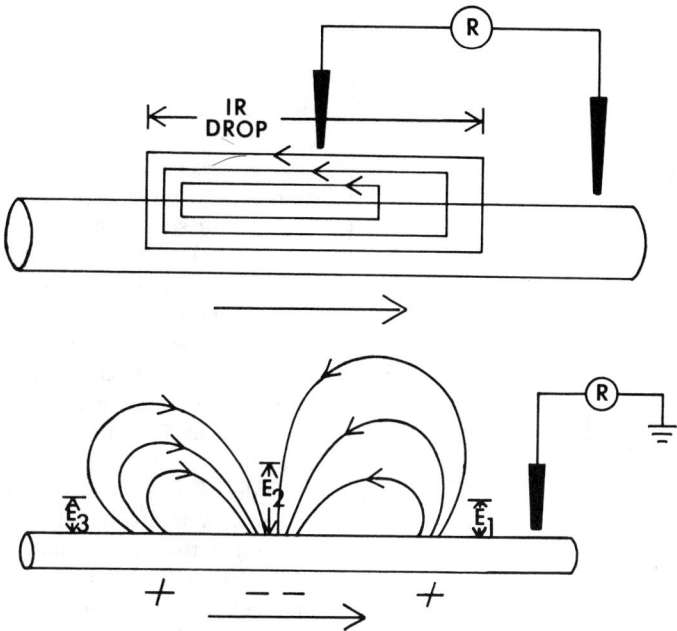

Fɪɢ. 2.21. Upper figure illustrates the recording of the action potential from a nerve in air. The arrow shows the direction of travel of the nerve impulse (leading egde). The lower figure shows the potential recorded from an action potential in a conducting medium. The recording electrode registers the potentials E_1, E_2 and E_3 in that order. The potential is thus equivalent to two dipoles back to back.

action potential between one electrode anywhere on the nerve and another at the injured end is a monophasic potential since the potential variation along the nerve falls away from the center of negativity.

When a nerve is placed in a volume conductor, that is, in a medium with the conductivity of saline, the situation is much altered. The membrane current enters and leaves the membrane at the same points as in air, but the current now spreads out into the medium. The most intense current flows are no longer longitudinal; current density is highest at the points where the current enters and leaves the nerve (fig. 2.20). The drops in potential now occur principally at three regions: a region ahead of the nerve where current is leaving (E_1); a region where current is entering the nerve, at the maximum depolarization of the action potential (E_2); and a region where the action potential is decreasing, recovery is occurring, and current is again leaving (E_3). If one now records the potential between an electrode on the nerve and one located at a distant point in the medium where the potential is constant, a triphasic potential variation will be found. An initial positive phase is recorded when the first IR drop, E_1, reaches the electrode; a second negative phase is recorded when the second IR drop, E_2, reaches the electrode; a

third negative phase is recorded when the third IR, E_3, drop reaches the electrode.

The system of IR drops in the medium, acting between a recording electrode and a distant point may be considered to be equivalent to two travelling dipoles, placed back to back (fig. 2.21). A travelling wave of depolarization acts like a dipole facing the direction of travel; a wave of repolarization acts therefore in an opposite sense with the negativity facing the direction of travel. When two such phenomena are separate in time the initial wave of depolarization and repolarization may be recorded separately as in cardiac tissue (ch. 35). In nerve however, the wave of repolarization follows immediately after the depolarization and a triphasic wave is recorded. The magnitude of the potential recorded in a volume conductor will depend upon how close the recording electrode is placed to the sources of potential. If the electrode is five mm. or so away from the nerve, very little potential variation will be detected.

The Classical Mechanism of the Action Potential

The action potential has been described in part as a travelling wave of currents accompanying the action potential. The mechanism by which these currents were produced was not examined but the role of the currents in exciting a region

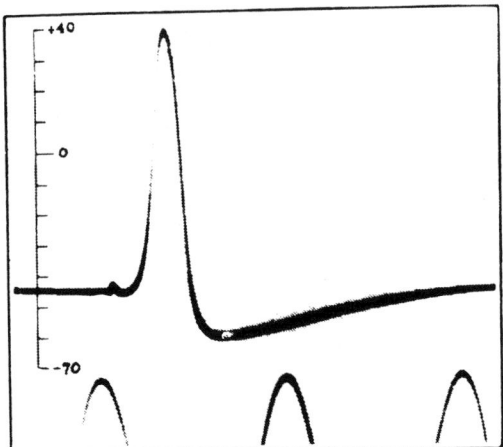

Fig. 2.22. Action potential recorded with an internal electrode from a squid giant axon. The scale shows the internal potential in mv., relative to the outside bath. Time marks are in 2 msec. intervals. (After Hodgkin and Huxley.)

ahead of the approaching nerve impulse was discussed. It is now necessary to discuss the origin of the action potential in terms of the prevalent ions, namely, sodium and potassium. The resting potential was shown to arise from a diffusion of potassium ions across the cell membrane. The action potential has a more complex origin. Recent experimental investigations have demonstrated that the action potential results chiefly from the movement of sodium ions inward during the early, rising, part of the nerve impulse and that there is a movement outward of potassium ions, later, during the fall of the action potential.

At the turn of the century, the action potential was attributed to a complete depolarization of the membrane in the region of the action potential; an area more negative than other parts of the nerve and into which the ionic currents flowed. This concept, first enunciated by Bernstein, could not be tested with the methods and tissues available until 1940. At that time two groups, one in England, the other in America, performed the critical experiments which led to a reexamination of the Bernstein concept. The experiments consisted of utilizing the giant axon of the squid to make a direct measurement of the transmembrane potential. The axon is 0.1 mm in diameter so that it is possible to insert an electrode directly within the axon along its length and to place another, larger electrode outside. The resting potential was measured and the nerve stimulated to obtain an action potential. The results of such an experiment are illustrated in fig. 2.22. According to classical concepts, the action potential arose from

the fall of the membrane potential toward zero; and when the membrane potential was zero, the nerve was completely depolarized. In the case of the squid axon instead of a simple depolarization of the membrane, an "overshoot" of the potential past the zero baseline occurred. Such an overshoot represents a reversal of the potential from the resting state so that during the peak of the action potential, the inside of the cell becomes about 50–60 mv positive to the outside (fig. 2.22). This is an astonishing result for at the first sight there does not appear to be any mechanism by which the potential difference could invert. Bernstein considered the resting potential a diffusion potential resulting from the permeability of nerve to potassium and the impermeability to sodium and chloride. The ionic events during the action potential were attributed to an increased flow of ions other than potassium so that the diffusion potential across the membrane disappeared when the sodium and chloride flows were permitted to take place. (In a diffusion cell the emf is proportional to the difference of the mobilities of cations and anions and if these are equal, the emf is zero.) This hypothesis, while showing how the membrane potential could become zero, did not appear to contain an explanation of how the reversal might arise.

The Modern Concept of the Action Potential

Closer consideration of the details of ionic flow pointed to sodium as the ion which might give rise to the reversal of potential. Since the concentration of sodium is higher outside than inside nerve, a flow of sodium inwards would tend to make the inside positive with respect to the outside. The experimental result establishing that sodium is the most important cation involved in both the production of the action potential and of the overshoot is simple. The squid axon is normally surrounded by sea water osmotically equivalent to a 0.3M sodium chloride solution. If the concentration of the sodium in the sea water is changed so that less sodium is present, the amplitude of the action potential will diminish. In such experiments, the resting potential is unaffected by altering the sodium concentration. It may be concluded that sodium is essential to the production of the action potential and, therefore, indirectly of the overshoot. Figure 2.23 illustrates the type of result obtained from such substitution experiments. Note that in applying half sea water, the osmotic lack of sodium is balanced by substituting an osmotically equivalent amount of a non-electrolyte such as sucrose or an electrolyte such as choline chloride.

A variety of experiments were carried out to determine the dependence of the sodium and potassium ionic currents on the membrane potential. Unfortunately, it is not possible to measure the flows directly during a depolarization of nerve independently of one another. The changes in current flow affect the membrane potential which in turn affects the current flow. This concept of a mutual influence of current and potential is important for the understanding of the mechanism of the action potential but it is necessary to eliminate the interaction if one wishes to study the effect of a change in membrane potential on the ionic fluxes. The principle of the method by which independence of current and potential is achieved is to depolarize the membrane to a given value and to subsequently maintain the potential at the original value. The membrane potential remains constant but the currents through the membrane continue to change once the membrane potential has been changed. It is therefore possible to investigate the ionic flow resulting from a given amount of depolarization. The method is referred to as the *Voltage Clamp* method because the membrane potential is "clamped" or fixed at an invariant value. The procedure involves complicated electronic devices for maintaining the potential constant but it is unnecessary here to enter into a discussion of the apparatus. Note that once the potential has been clamped there will be no flow of current into the capacitive element of the membrane since to put charge on a condenser requires a changing potential. The current flow is purely resistive and ionic. The current, however, may change while the depolarization is being maintained. This appears to violate Ohm's Law which states that the current flow in a system depends upon the voltage ($I = E/R$), and the voltage across the membrane is held constant in these experiments. However, the resistance or permeability of the membrane changes during a voltage clamp experiment and thus, although the potential is constant, extensive changes in current may take place.

The effect of a small clamp on the current flow through the membrane is shown in fig. 2.24. The depolarizing clamp causes a diphasic current which is first inward, then outward. If a solution which lacks sodium is substituted, the initial inward current disappears but the outward current remains unaffected. The early, inward

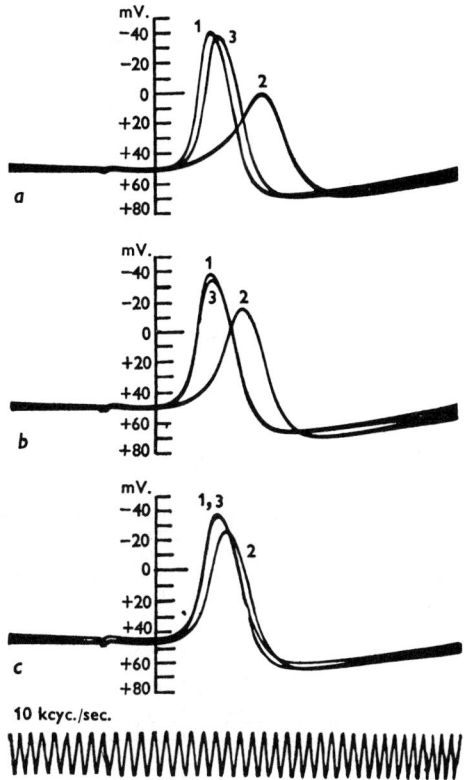

Fig. 2.23. Single action potentials recorded from a squid giant axon.
(1) Normal action potential in sea water.
(2) Action potential after equilibration in medium with altered sodium.
(3) Action potential after return to normal sodium solution. *a* is 0.33 times normal, *b* is 0.5 times normal and *c* is 0.71 times normal in concentration.

current is, therefore, attributed to sodium inflow. The dependence of the sodium current on the amount of depolarization can be ascertained by an experiment in which progressively greater amounts of depolarization are used. As the membrane potential is decreased (greater clamp voltage), the inward current increases. With further increases in the depolarization, however, the sodium current decreases in magnitude and ultimately disappears.

The results of a brief depolarization or clamp may now be outlined: (1) There occurs, initially, a brief inward current resulting from an inward movement of sodium ions, followed by an outward flow of potassium ions. (2) The amount of sodium flowing depends upon the extent of depolarization; the greater the depolarization, the larger the sodium current. (3) The potassium current is unaffected by the depolarization but is affected by a hyperpolarization of the membrane.

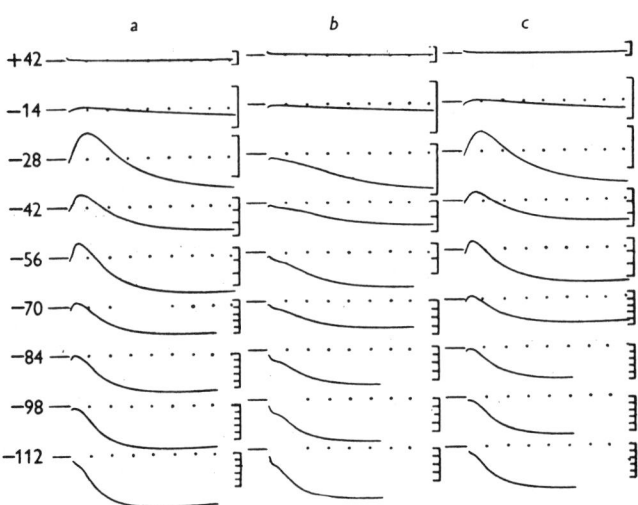

FIG. 2.24. Currents flowing through squid giant axon membrane during a steady voltage clamp. Figures on left are clamped values of the membrane potential in mv. relative to resting potential (outside minus inside). Minus values represent depolarizations. Columns *a* and *c*, axon in sea water. Column *b*, axon in choline sea water without sodium. Vertical scale, 1 div. = 0.5 ma./cm.². Time dots are 1 msec. apart. (After Hodgkin and Huxley.)

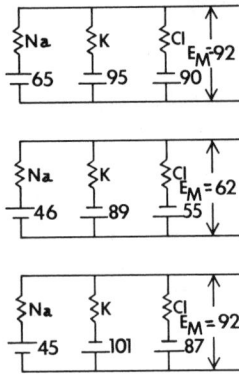

FIG. 2.25. Equivalent circuits for three membranes. Upper is for mammalian skeletal muscle fiber, middle is for squid giant axon, and lower is for frog sartorius muscle fiber. E_m is resting potential; all values are in mv.

Increasing the membrane potential from, for example, -60 to -80 mv increases the potassium current.

To understand the mechanism of the action potential, it is necessary to combine the results of the clamp experiments with a detailed theory evolved by A. Hodgkin and A. F. Huxley in 1955—a theory which explains all the known phenomena of excitation and conduction in nerve and muscle. According to this theory, the nerve membrane is represented as containing three channels through which sodium, potassium and chloride ions may move independently. The individual ions are considered to be forced through the membrane by an electromotive force produced by the concentration difference of each ion. A schematic circuit representing the three channel hypothesis is shown in fig. 2.25. The value of each emf is given by the Nernst equation and the three emf's are equivalent to the three "equilibrium" potentials discussed in the section devoted to the membrane potential. It is important to understand that the network is only an electrical "equivalent" and that the channels are not physically located one next to the other. Each of the channels represents a group of many identical channels in a unit area of the membrane lumped together schematically as one channel. The resistance signifies the opposition encountered by each ion in the unit area of membrane. The reciprocal of the resistance is proportional to the permeability of the membrane to the ion.

The sequence of ionic events in an action potential may now be described as follows. A depolarizing voltage in the form of a brief stimulus is applied to the membrane and the sodium influx increases. If this influx is greater than the flow of potassium and chloride which go in the opposite direction, then a net amount of sodium enters the fiber in the direction of its concentration gradient. This small amount of sodium causes a change in the membrane potential. But as we discussed above, the change in potential across the membrane leads to an increased sodium influx, which, in turn leads to a further decrease in the membrane potential. Therefore the influx of sodium builds up quite rapidly. This process of a mutual effect of the sodium influx on the membrane potential is termed the *regenerative factor* in impulse transmission. In terms of the equivalent circuit, the action potential develops in the following way. The increase in permeability to sodium is essentially a decrease in resistance. The potential difference across the membrane which is the resultant of the three emfs in parallel will approach that which has the lowest resistance in series with it. The resistance to potassium and chloride does not change. The membrane potential therefore tends to approach the potential given by the equilibrium potential of the sodium ion which is, in volts,

$$E_{Na} = 0.058 \log \frac{Na_{outside}}{Na_{inside}}.$$

The equilibrium potential of the sodium ion is also approximately the value of the overshoot but this value is never quite reached. It is possible that an increased efflux of potassium plus an active process pumping out sodium may contribute to the difference between the theoretical and experimental values of the overshoot.

The rapid rise in sodium current does not continue for very long (as the clamp experiments show the sodium currents are rapidly followed by a potassium efflux from the axon). The sodium influx is terminated by a process called sodium inactivation which develops during the increase in sodium flux. That such an inactivation process exists can be demonstrated by clamp experiments of another type. If a clamp voltage (of the order of 10 millivolts) is applied which is insufficient to cause a sodium influx, it can nevertheless set into action the process of inactivation. If, following the small depolarization, a larger one of about 40 mv is applied it is observed that the large clamp voltage does not give the magnitude of sodium current it would have given had the smaller voltage not been applied. The small voltage has resulted in the larger being less effective. By following the small voltage by the larger clamp voltage at various intervals, the time course of development of the inactivation can be obtained. The sodium current is turned off by this process. Figure 2.26 shows the time course of the inactivation process.

A second process also aids in the restoration of the membrane potential. We observed that a potassium influx followed the sodium influx. The time course of efflux of potassium corresponds to the fall of the action potential. The increase in conductance to potassium means that the po-

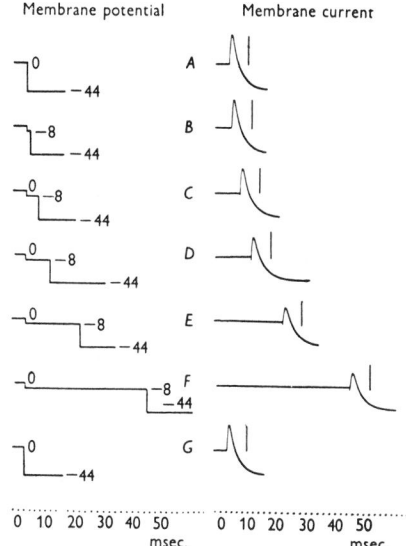

Membrane potential   Membrane current

Fig. 2.26. Development of "inactivation" during constant depolarization of 8 mv. Left column: displacement of membrane potential from the resting value in mv. Right column: membrane currents as a function of time for the displacement in the left column. The vertical lines show the sodium current expected in the absence of the conditioning step. (After Hodgkin and Huxley.)

tential across the membrane now tries to approach the potential given by the equilibrium potential for potassium. This is negative inside to outside. The increased permeability to potassium tends to restore the membrane potential to an internally negative state. Figure 2.27 shows the time course of the increase in conductance of potassium in relation to the inactivation process.

Both the sodium and potassium flows during the phase of increased permeability are in the direction of their concentration gradients. The flow of ions during the action potential is purely passive and depends only upon the concentration gradient. The production of a nerve impulse should therefore be independent of metabolism. This deduction is substantiated by experiments in which both aerobic and anerobic processes are blocked by inhibitors. Nerves may continue to conduct for hours, even when stimulated at high rates under the influence of metabolic inhibitors. The increased permeability to sodium and potassium persists although the means for pumping sodium and potassium have been cut off. This is not to say that transport processes are not important for maintaining the ionic inequalities. If nerve is continually stimulated while being treated with an inhibitor, it fails to pump out the sodium which accumulates inside the nerve by both passive influx and the small amount

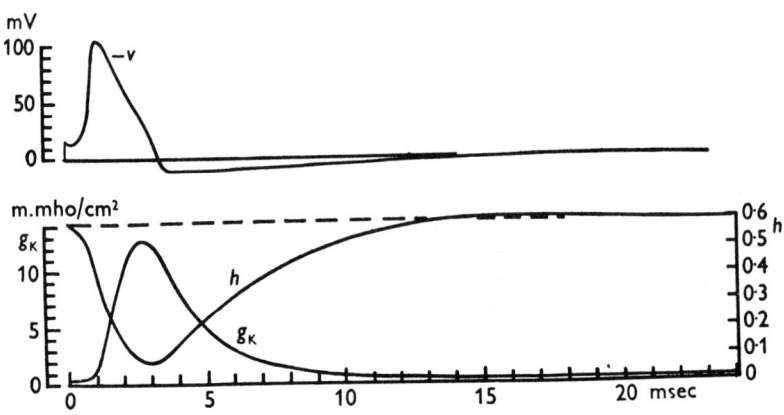

Fig. 2.27. Time course of inactivation (h) and potassium conductance (g_K) during a non-propagated action potential. Upper curve is action potential in response to a 15 mg. initial depolarization. (After Hodgkin and Huxley.)

which passes inward during excitation. Ultimately the nerve will depolarize as the result of potassium loss or sodium influx. The metabolic activity which maintains the ionic concentration by pumping out sodium from nerve is necessary in the long run but both the resting and the action potential do not appear to depend upon metabolism for their production.

How does this theory of nerve explain other important phenomena of nerve such as refractoriness and accommodation? The absolute refractory period is the result of the inability of nerve to respond to a stimulus no matter how intense. This inability corresponds to the period during the action potential when sodium influx is completely inactivated. It is impossible to turn on the sodium influx machinery while the process is inactivated. During the relative refractory period, the nerve is under the influence of both sodium inactivation and the increased potassium efflux. The potassium influx tends to maintain the membrane potential at the original unexcited level. The restorative processes of sodium inactivation and potassium efflux must be opposed by very large depolarizations in order to get sufficient sodium influx to start regeneration. Similarly, accommodation, which is a rise in threshold during the persistent application of a linearly rising current, may be explained as the result of growth of inactivation at the cathode of an exciting current, much as inactivation proceeded in the clamp experiments which demonstrated the existence of the process.

Nerve Metabolism

Intermediary Metabolism

As is well-known, tissues contain three metabolic schemes whose function is to manufacture and store energy in the form of 'high-energy' phosphate bonds. Nerve is no different than other tissues in this respect, containing all the apparatus necessary for the production of the principle high energy compound, adenosine-triphosphate (ATP). The three interconnected parts of the metabolic scheme are: (1) The Embden-Meyerhoff pathway of glycolysis, (2) The Krebs tricarboxylic acid cycle, and (3) The electron transport system. The pathway of glycolysis is concerned with the breakdown of glucose to pyruvate and/or lactate. Only a small amount of ATP is produced in this pathway which is anaerobic. The Krebs cycle converts the pyruvate formed in the glycolytic pathway to carbon dioxide and water and requires the presence of oxygen in order to function. The oxygen unites with the hydrogen from the pyruvate by means of the electron transport scheme which contains coenzymes consisting of cytochromes and flavoproteins. The major part of the ATP is produced in the anaerobic portion of the metabolic pathway—the Krebs cycle and the electron transport scheme.

There is no question of the existence of glycolysis in nerve. This tissue consumes glucose and forms lactate in equivalent amounts in nitrogen, i.e., anaerobically. Little lactic acid is produced at rest in oxygen. Although older experiments appeared to demonstrate no increase of lactate with stimulation, more recent experiments have shown that lactate is increased by stimulation at 100/sec in air. Nerve continues to conduct when placed in nitrogen; this is to be anticipated from the discussion on the mechanism of the action potential where it was shown that the action potential does not depend immediately upon metabolism. Failure in nitrogen is the result of the accumulation of ions which causes a depolarization of nerve.

Further evidence for the existence of glycolytic systems in nerve comes from the effect of metabolic inhibitors on nerve metabolism. Iodoacetic acid, which interferes with glycolysis, causes a decrease in the oxygen consumption of nerve. At the same time the effects of the inhibitor may be slowed by the administration of sodium lactate; the latter possibly forming pyruvate which is then oxidized. The enzymes necessary for the formation of lactic acid, diphosphopyridine nucleotide (DPN or NAD), is found in frog nerve. It has also been shown that the administration of glucose partially prevents the loss of potassium and gain of sodium resulting from anoxia of nerve.

Evidence for the presence of the Krebs cycle in nerve comes from the effect of inhibitors on the oxygen consumption of frog nerve. Methylfluoracetate, an inhibitor which acts in the Krebs cycle, inhibits the rate of oxygen uptake and ultimately causes a failure of conduction. If the nerve is pre-equilibrated with sodium fumarate or sodium succinate, the inhibition is overcome and the nerve regains its ability to conduct and to consume oxygen. Fumarate and succinate are intermediates in the Krebs cycle and serve to keep going the portion of the cycle devoted to converting succinate or fumarate to carbon dioxide and water.

The importance of the electron transport scheme has been demonstrated by experiments in which the cytochrome oxidase of nerve has been inactivated by carbon monoxide. When nerve is poisoned with carbon monoxide, the cytochrome oxidase fails to function and oxygen does not react to form water. The nerve behaves as though it were in nitrogen. However, it is possible to dissociate the carbon monoxide from the cytochrome oxidase by shining visible light on the nerve. The nerve then regains its ability to consume oxygen and will conduct an action potential.

Resting and Active Metabolism

The metabolism of nerve, like that of muscle is divided into a resting (unstimulated) and active (stimulated) state. In the resting state, the oxygen consumption of frog sciatic nerve is quite low, 30–40 mm^3/g wet weight/hr. That of mammalian nerve is higher, about 200–300 mm^3/g/hr. These values may be compared with those for brain which is of the order of 2000 mm^3/g/hr. Corresponding to the consumption of oxygen, there is

a resting release of heat by nerve which is 0.15 cal/g/hr for frog sciatic nerve.

The oxygen consumption of nerve is accompanied by a release of carbon dixoide to the extent that the respiratory quotient (moles CO_2/moles O_2) is 0.8. This value indicates that the fuel of nerve may not be exclusively glucose which would yield a respiratory quotient of 1. During excitation the respiratory quotient of the extra oxygen consumption of nerve changes to 0.9, strongly suggesting that the recovery processes following excitation use a different substrate than during the resting state. But the principle substrate of nerve is as yet unknown. Carbohydrate disappears from resting, excised nerve but the addition of carbohydrate does not increase the rate of respiration. Apparently nerve contains substrate stores that can be used either with or without carbohydrate.

How much of the resting heat production of nerve can be attributed to the heat production of the process pumping Na^+ out of nerve and K^+ into the cell during the resting state? One can calculate the energy required to extrude sodium against both the electrical forces in the membrane and the concentration gradient. A similar calculation may be made for potassium uptake. If the process is assumed to be inefficient and to produce heat equal to the work done (50% mechanical efficiency) an estimate of the heat production can be obtained. In the case of sodium, it is necessary to pump the ion against both the electric field and the concentration gradient since the ion is positive and it must be forced out against the negative attraction of the interior. The electric work required is given by EF (ionic flux). The concentration work is obtained from the relationship (flux) $RT \log C_1/C_2$, where the symbols have their usual significance (p. 29). Substituting the values for frog nerve of $E = 0.070$ volt, $F = 23$, 050 cal/volt/mole, $C_1/C_2 = 3$ (sodium), and a sodium flux of 10^{-5} mole/g/hr, one obtains an electrical work of 0.015 cal/g/hr and a concentration work of 0.007 cal/g/hr. The total work to pump sodium is therefore the sum of these i.e. 0.022 cal/g/hr. A similar calculation for potassium shows that the energy necessary to pump this ion into nerve is 0.019 cal/g/hr. The work necessary to pump both sodium and potassium is 0.041 calories. If the pump has a mechanical efficiency (work/work + heat) of 50% then the heat production equals the work done and accounts for about 50% of the total heat production (0.15 cal/g/hr).

When nerve is stimulated, there is an increase

in the oxygen consumption and an increased loss of heat. The extra oxygen consumption may double. The increase in heat production and oxygen consumption parallel one another and depend upon the frequency of stimulation. The increase in oxygen consumption rises gradually with increase in frequency of stimulation, levelling off at about 100 impulses per sec. The extra heat which accompanies short tetanic stimulation has been shown by Hill and coworkers to consist of two phases; an early one lasting only 2–3 seconds, called the *initial heat* which amounts to a few percent of the total extra heat followed by the remainder of the heat production which is called the *delayed* heat. The latter is presumably concerned with the recovery processes in nerve involving the pumping of ions. The extra oxygen consumption of nerve may be eliminated by inhibitors (azide and methylfluoracetate) which have no effect on the action potential.

Abbott, Hill and Howarth, using improved thermal methods have been able to measure the heat output resulting from a single shock to a crab nerve. They found that the initial heat accompanying an action potential occurred in two phases, an early, rapid portion, 1 millisecond in duration which was positive (exothermic) and a delayed, negative (endothermic) heat of absorption. The actual heats during an impulse were $+14 \times 10^{-16}$ and -12×10^{-16} cal/g/impulse. The difference gives the net initial heat production. Calculations by Hodgkin indicate that the initial heat can be accounted for by the heat production (Joule heat) of the action currents flowing within and without the nerve. But other processes such as heat produced by the mixing of sodium entering nerve may also account for the initial heat.

GENERAL REFERENCES

ADRIAN, E. D. (1935) The Mechanism of Nervous Action. Univ. of Penn., Phila.

BISHOP, G. H. (1956) Natural History of the Nerve Impulse. Physiol. Rev., 36: 376.

CONNELLY, C. M. (1959) Recovery Processes and Metabolism of Nerve, In ONVLEY, J. L. (ed.) Biophysical Science. Chap. 51, John Wiley and Sons, New York.

DAVSON, H. (1959) Textbook of General Physiology. 2d ed., Little, Brown & Company, Boston.

ECCLES, J. C. (1952) The Neurophysiological Basis of Mind. Oxford, London.

ELLIOT, K. A. C., PAGE, I. H., AND QUASTEL, J. H. (eds.). Neurochemistry. 2d ed., C. C Thomas, Springfield.

ERLANGER, J. AND GASSER, H. S. (1937) Electrical Signs of Nervous Activity, Univ. of Penn. Press, Phila.

GERARD, R. W. (1932) Nerve metabolism. Physiol. Rev., 12: 469.

HILL, A. V. (1959) The heat production of muscle and nerve. Ann. Rev. Physiol., 21: 1.

HODGKIN, A. L. (1951) The ionic basis of electrical activity in nerve and muscle. Biol. Rev., 26: 339.

KATZ, B. (1939) Electric Excitation of Nerve. Oxford Univ. Press, London.

MACINNES, D. A. (1939) The Principles of Electrochemistry. Reinhold Publishing Corp., New York.

MONNIER, A. M. (1934) L'Excitation Electrique des Tissues. Hermann, Paris.

RICHTER, D. (1957) Metabolism of the Nervous System, Pergamon, N. Y.

TASAKI, I. (1953) Nervous Transmission. Thomas, Springfield.

YOUNG, J. Z. (1942) The functional repair of nervous tissue. Physiol. Rev., 22: 318.

Literature

ABBOTT, B. C., HILL, A. V., AND HOWARTH, J. V. (1958) The positive and negative heat production associated with a nerve impulse. Proc. Roy. Soc., 148B, 149.

CALDWELL, P. C., HODGKIN, A. L., KEYNES, R. D., AND SHAW, T. L. (1960) The effects of injecting 'energy-rich' phosphate compounds on the active transport of ions in the giant axons of Loligo. J. Physiol., 152, 561.

COLE, K. S. AND MOORE, J. W. (1960) Ionic current measurements in the squid giant axon membrane. J. Gen. Physiol., 44, 123.

CONNELLY, C. M. (1959) Recovery processes and metabolism of nerve, in Biophysical Science, Oncley, J. L. (ed.), John Wiley & Sons, Inc., New York.

COLE, K. S. AND CURTIS, H. J. (1939) Electric impedance of the squid giant axon during activity. J. Gen. Physiol., 22, 649.

CURTIS, H. J. AND COLE, K. S. (1938) Transverse electric impedance of the squid giant axon. J. Gen. Physiol., 21, 757.

GEREN, B. B. (1954) The formation from the Schwann cell surface of myelin in the peripheral nerves of chick embryos. Exper. Cell Res., 7, 558.

HODGKIN, A. L. (1937) Evidence for electrical transmission in nerve. I. J. Physiol., 90: 183.

HODGKIN, A. L. (1937) Evidence for electrical transmission in nerve. II. J. Physiol., 90, 211.

HODGKIN, A. L. (1938) The subthreshold potentials in a crustacean nerve fiber. Proc. Roy. Soc., London, S. B., 126, 87.

HODGKIN, A. L. (1957) Ionic movements and electrical activity in giant nerve fibers. Proc. Roy. Soc., B., 148, 1.

HODGKIN, A. L. AND HUXLEY, A. F. (1945) Resting and action potentials in single nerve fibers. J. Physiol., 104, 176.

HODGKIN, A. L., HUXLEY, A. F., AND KATZ, B. (1952) Measurement of current-voltage relations in the membrane of the giant axon of Loligo. J. Physiol., 116, 424.

HODGKIN, A. L. AND HUXLEY, A. F. (1952) Currents carried by sodium and potassium ions through the membrane of the giant axon of Loligo. J. Physiol., 116, 449.

HODGKIN, A. L. AND HUXLEY, A. F. (1952) The

components of membrane conductance in the giant axon of Loligo. J. Physiol., 116, 473.

HODGKIN, A. L. AND HUXLEY, A. F. (1952) The dual effect of membrane potential on sodium conductance in the giant axon of Loligo. J. Physiol., 116, 497.

HODGKIN, A. L. AND HUXLEY, A. F. (1952) A quantitative description of membrane current and its application to conduction and excitation in nerve. J. Physiol., 117, 500.

HODGKIN, A. L. AND KEYNES, R. D. (1953) The mobility and diffusion coefficient of potassium in giant axons from sepia. J. Physiol., 119, 513.

HODGKIN, A. L. AND KEYNES, R. D. (1955) Active transport of cations in giant axons from sepia and loligo. J. Physiol., 128: 28.

HODGKIN, A. L. AND KEYNES, R. D. (1956) Experiments on the injection of substances into squid giant axons by means of a microsyringe. J. Physiol., 121: 592.

HURSH, J. B. (1939) Conduction velocity and diameter of nerve fibers. Am. J. Physiol., 127, 131.

HUXLEY, A. F. (1954) Electrical Processes in Nerve Conduction. In CLARKE, H. T. AND NACHMANSOHN, D., (eds.), Ion Transport Across Membranes, New York.

HUXLEY, A. F. AND STAMPFLI, R. (1949) Evidence for saltatory conduction in peripheral myelinated nerve fibers. J. Physiol., 108, 315.

HUXLEY, A. F. AND STAMPFLI, R. (1951) Direct determination of membrane resting potential and action potential in single myelinated nerve fibers. J. Physiol., 112: 476.

KEYNES, R. D. (1951) The ionic movements during nervous activity. J. Physiol., 114, 119.

NASTUK, W. L. AND HODGKIN, A. L. (1950) The electrical activity in single muscle fibers, J. Cell Comp. Physiol., 35, 39.

NERNST, W. (1908) Zur Theorie des elektrischen Reizes. Pflüg. Arch., 122, 275.

ROBERTSON, J. D. (1957) New observations on the ultrastructure of the membranes of frog peripheral nerve fibers. J. Biophys. &. Biochem. Cytol., 3, 1043.

CHAPTER 3

Receptor Organs and Sensation

The Receptor Organs

The afferent fibers end peripherally either as bare unmyelinated filaments or in accessory structures called *receptors* (fig. 3.1). These are specialized to respond most effectively to one or other type of stimulus. When stimulated appropriately an impulse or a series of impulses is sent along the afferent fiber. Receptors are situated in the skin, muscles, tendons, etc., and in such special organs as those of sight, hearing, smell and taste. They are also contained in the walls of the respiratory and digestive tracts, mesentery, carotid sinus and other internal structures. Through receptors in these various situations messages (nerve impulses) are continually being transmitted over somatic and autonomic pathways to the central nervous system.

Those receptors which respond to stimuli arising outside the body, e.g., in the skin, eye, ear, etc., are called *exteroceptors*. Of these, ones which make perception at a distince possible, i.e., those situated in the visual, auditory or olfactory sense organs, are sometimes referred to as *distance receptors* (telereceptors). Receptors lying in the mucous linings of the respiratory or digestive tracts are spoken of as *interoceptors. Proprioceptors* are those which respond to stimuli originating within the body itself, e.g., in the skeletal muscles, (p. 58) tendons, joints, heart, carotid sinus, gastrointestinal wall, etc. Though each variety of receptor responds most readily to one particular type of stimulus—*adequate stimulus*—many will respond in some degree to stimuli of other types. The retina, for instance, can be stimulated mechanically or electrically and the receptors of taste, though responding most effectively to chemical stimuli, may also be stimulated by an electric shock applied to the tongue. A terminology based upon the type of stimulus which excites them adequately is sometimes used to designate different varieties of reception organ. Thus, *tango-* (touch), *chemo-* (taste, smell and the receptors of the carotid and aortic bodies) and *photo-* (light) *receptors* are spoken of.

Analysis of Sensation

The problems of the senses have been studied by two approaches. First, by using human sub-jects much can be learned by investigating what physical and chemical events they are able to detect and discriminate, but this involves much more than the sense organs; for example, a subjective threshold may depend on the state of the central nervous system as much as on the sensory receptors concerned. Secondly, objective methods of analysis can be used. Investigation of the action of receptors in setting up nerve impulses has received a great impetus in the last forty years by the improved methods of detecting nervous activity electrically. Much of this has been done in animal experiment, but structural similarities of sense organs in man and animals make it possible to apply this knowledge to interpret human sensory problems.

Cutaneous Sensations

The sensations which may be aroused by stimulation of the skin are *touch, cold, warmth* and *pain* Each of these sensations, except the last, is evoked from regions where sense organs possessing distinctive structural features are found. Small areas are mapped out upon the skin which are specific for one or other sensation. The areas are called touch, cold, heat or pain "spots" respectively in accordance with the sensation which their stimulation arouses (fig. 3.2). It must be emphasized that these spots are outlined by subjective methods, and maps vary from time to time in the same individual. They must not be confused with objectively demonstrable nerve endings. The latter are the basis from which 'spots' reach consciousness, but the central nervous system may select or reject components of the sensory discharge during transmission to the cortex. It must, also, be pointed out that it has recently been demonstrated that parts of the human skin which contain few endings that can be differentiated histologically, nevertheless have a wide range of subjective sensation that can be evoked by appropriate stimulation. It is possible that the site of the nerve ending within the skin may confer some specificity on it or that as yet unrecognised features of its structure may be concerned; but the elaborate encapsulated endings are found in skin surfaces of high sensory significance, e.g. finger tips etc.

If the mixed *nerve* supplying receptor organs is excited *directly* by the application of the type of stimulus, e.g., touch, heat, etc., for which the receptor itself is adapted to respond, the characteristic sensation is not, as a rule, aroused; a painful sensation usually results. Moreover, reflexes can usually be elicited much more readily by stimulating the receptors than by applying the stimulus directly to the afferent nerve, and certain reflexes cannot be evoked at all by direct excitation of the nerve fiber. Pressure upon the pad of the hind foot of the "spinal dog", for example, causes a strong extension of the whole limb—the *extensor thrust*—whereas no form of stimulus applied directly to the afferent nerve itself will produce this reflex (Sherrington). The afferent fiber before terminating in the receptor organ or as a free nerve filament loses its myelin sheath and neurilemma and ends as a naked axis cylinder often branched or convoluted.

LIGHT TOUCH. Tactile sensation—the sensation aroused by light contact—has been associated with three types of receptor, *Meissner's corpuscles*, *Merkel's disks* and a basketlike arrangement of nerve fibers surrounding the base of hair follicle (fig. 3.3). Meissner's corpuscles are situated in the papillae of the skin, just beneath the epidermis. They are unevenly distributed, being sparsely scattered over such a region as the volar aspect of the forearm but numerous in the skin of the hand, foot, nipple and lips, and in the mucous membrane of the tip of the tongue. They are well organized structures, consisting of irregularly coiled nerve endings with capsules of connective tissue. *Merkel's disks* consist of groups of three or more cup-shaped disks with a reticulated appearance (fig. 3.3F). The nerve fiber upon approaching a group of such structures breaks up into branches, one going to each disk. Merkel's disks are found in the skin of the snouts of pigs and other mammals

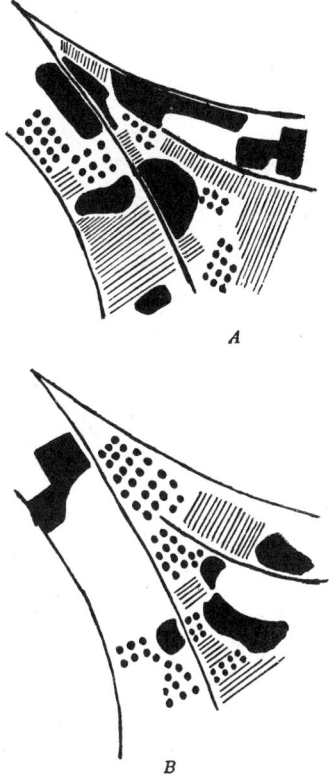

A

B

FIG. 3.2. Showing cold spots (A) and hot spots (B) within an area on the palm of the hand. The sensation in each case was most intense in the black areas, less intense in the lined and mildest in the dotted areas. In the blank portions no definite sensation was aroused (after Goldscheider).

and in the fingertips, lips and mouth of man. The basketlike arrangement, surrounding the base of a hair follicle consists of a number of short, vertical, nerve filaments which end in small bulbous expansions. They are stimulated by any slight movements of the hairs.

Inequality of pressure with consequent deformation of the skin surface is the essential factor in the stimulation of touch receptors. If the pressure is distributed equally, and, therefore, no deformation of the skin occurs, a tactile sensation is not experienced; when, for example, a finger is dipped into mercury a sensation is aroused only in the narrow band of skin where it is deformed as a result of unequal pressures at the interface between the mercury and air.

The sensation of light touch is tested by bringing a wisp of absorbent cotton in contact with the skin, or by the use of von Frey's esthesiometers. These consist of a series of hairs of graded thickness attached at right angles to wooden holders. The pressure in grams required to bend each hair

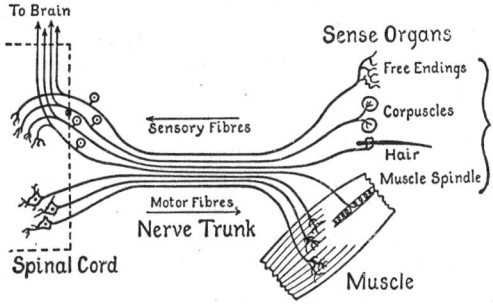

FIG. 3.1. Diagram to show the nervous connections between the central nervous system and the periphery (muscle and cutaneous receptors) (from Adrian, *The Basis of Sensation*).

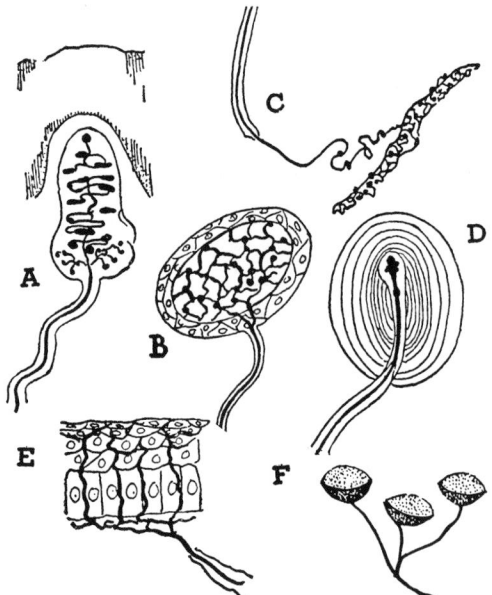

FIG. 3.3. Cutaneous receptors. A, Meissner's corpuscle (touch); B, Krause's end bulb (cold); C, Ruffini's end organs (warmth); D, Pacinian corpuscle (deep pressure); E, bare nerve endings in cornea (pain); F, Merkel's disks (touch) (in part from Bainbridge and Menzie, *Essentials of Physiology*, Longmann, Green and Co.).

is known. In order, therefore, to express the sensitivity of the skin to touch in terms of pressure the hair is found by trial which, when pressed vertically upon the skin until bending occurs, causes the sensation. The sensitivity of the skin to touch varies widely in different regions. The minimal pressures required are given in table 3.1. When hairy parts, such as the back of the hand, are lightly brushed with a tuft of cotton wool the hairs serving as levers deform the skin, and thus cause stimulation of touch receptors situated in the neighborhood of the hair follicles. Shaving the hairs over such parts greatly reduces the sensitivity to touch. Other regions quite devoid of hairs such as the finger tips and lips, on the other hand, possess tactile sensibility.

TACTILE LOCALIZATION. When a tactile stimulus is applied to a point upon the skin the normal subject is capable of recognizing the location of the stimulus with a high degree of accuracy. This faculty is termed *topognosia*. A tactile sensation has, thus, associated with it a localizing quality in addition to its specific characteristic, which has been called "local sign". Though there is a neural basis for point to point projection of skin areas to the cerebral cortex, the actual faculty of locating the point touched appears to be acquired by experience and not inborn. Localization is much

more precise over some regions, such as lips and tips of the fingers, than over others, such as the forearm or thigh. In some nervous diseases this localization is grossly impaired. In certain lesions of the cerebral cortex the subject usually, according to Horsley, when asked to locate the stimulus indicates a point some distance from it on the *proximal* side. In some diseases, notably hysteria, the subject feels the stimulus at a corresponding point on the opposite side of the body; or in a limb on the side opposite to that to which the stimulus was applied; this phenomenon is called *allocheiria*.

The localization of a cold, hot or painful sensation is very inaccurate unless the stimulating agent actually touches the skin. Thus, heat radiated from a small object about 1 mm. from the cutaneous surface gives rise to a diffuse sensation. The more accurate localization when contact is made with the skin is evident though the subject experiences no sensation of touch. It is likely, nevertheless, that the tactile receptors are excited, that the failure to appreciate touch is due to masking by the stronger stimulus, and that impulses arising in the touch endings are responsible for the more accurate localization of the other types of stimulus when these are applied directly to the skin.

TACTILE DISCRIMINATION (TWO-POINT SENSIBILITY, COMPASS TEST). If two stimuli are applied simultaneously, two distinct sensations are felt, provided the distance between the two stimulated points is sufficiently great. Thus, when the points of a pair of compasses are blunted or covered with cotton wool and applied to the finger tip, the subject recognizes the duality of the stimulus if the points are more than about 2.3 mm. apart. When they are separated by a shorter distance a single sensation is experienced. The minimal distance at which the recognition of two stimuli is possible varies in different regions, as shown in table 3.2.

In the case of the limbs the power of discrimination diminishes progressively from the distal to the more proximal segments, and hairless regions in general have a higher discriminating ability than those covered with hair.

A correspondence is also exhibited between the mobility of a part and its discriminating ability. For example, the minimal distance necessary for two stimuli to give rise to a double sensation is less for the fingers and hand than for the arm, shoulder and back, and diminishes progressively over the skin of the face from the region of the ear to the lips.

It should be pointed out that the values given

in the foregoing table do not represent the distances separating individual touch receptors, and tactile sensation can be evoked from single stimuli applied successively from points only 0.1 mm. apart. The density of receptors in the surface is only one of the factors enabling the central nervous system to discriminate characteristics of the stimulus.

TICKLING AND ITCHING. There has been much discussion concerning the origins of these sensations. The *tickling* sensation caused by light stimulation of the skin, as by a straw, appears to be due to the summed effects of stimulating both touch and pain endings. Section of the lateral spinothalamic tract (which conveys pain impulses) results in the loss of the appreciation of pain but retention of the sense of touch; a tickling sensation cannot be aroused over the analgesic skin. On the other hand, the sense of touch is lost while that of pain is retained, when the skin is rendered moderately ischemic; again, the tickling sensation cannot be elicited. The *itchiness* which is experienced in the region adjacent to a slight injury, or during the healing of a more severe injury when the skin is rubbed, is also dependent upon impulses travelling by both tactile and pain fibers, but the *spontaneous* itching (i.e., in the absence of any external stimulus) which is felt under the same circumstances, may be due to the mild stimulation of pain endings alone. This type of itchiness is affected relatively little by ischemia. Both types of itching are attributed to a chemical stimulator acting upon nerve endings and liberated by the damaged cells of the skin. This sub-

TABLE 3.1

The minimal pressures required for the elicitation of the sensation of touch from various cutaneous regions

(After Meyers)

Region	Grams per Square Millimeter
Nose	2
Lips	2.5
Tip of finger	3
Back of finger	5
Upper arm, inner surface of thigh	7
Back of hand	12
Calf, shoulder	16
Abdomen	26
Front of leg, sole of foot	28
Back of forearm	33
Loin	48

TABLE 3.2

Different cutaneous areas compared with regard to the minimal distance which must separate two stimulated points in order to arouse a double sensation

(After Meyers)

Region	Minimal Distance
	mm.
Volar surface of finger tip	2.3
Dorsal surface of third phalanx	6.8
Palm of hand	11.3
Sole of foot	16.0
Back of hand	31.6
Back of neck	54.0
Middle of back, upper arm and thigh	67.1

stance appears to be the same as that which causes the triple response. An extract of skin showing this response when injected into normal skin induces both types of itching. Histamine introduced into the skin has a similar effect. Rothman believes that itching is mediated by the C group of nerve fibers.

The sensation of *cold* has been associated with the end organs of Krause (fig. 3.3B) and *warmth* with the end organs of Ruffini (fig. 3.3C). Mechanical or electrical stimulation, as well as the application of heat itself, will stimulate the latter end organs and give rise to the sensation of warmth. The end organ of Ruffini is situated in close proximity to the deep plexus of blood vessels; when these latter dilate the endings are stimulated by the warmer blood coming from deeper regions. The cold receptors are also stimulated at temperatures above 112°F. giving rise to a sensation, not of heat but of cold. Cold, of course, is a negative quality—the sensation being due to the withdrawal of heat. It would be more correct, therefore, to say that the cold receptors are stimulated at extremes of temperature, above 112°F. or below that at which the warm receptors respond. When mapped on the skin, cold and touch spots are much less numerous than touch and pain spots.

PRESSURE upon the skin considerably greater than that which elicits the sensation of touch stimulates the more deeply lying receptors including the *Pacinian corpuscles* (fig. 3.3D). The sensation of pressure is not, however, a true cutaneous sensation; the Pacinian corpuscles are situated in the subcutaneous tissues or inner layers of the dermis as well as in tendons, periosteum and other deep-seated structures; their nerve fibers run chiefly, not in the cutaneous nerves, but in the sensory fibers of mixed nerves supplying muscles, tendons, joints and blood vessels. Since the sense of deep pressure is preserved after sectioning the cutaneous nerves, the loss of light touch, a purely cutaneous sense, may, therefore, be undetected in a lesion affecting this sensation, unless the contact is made very lightly, as by a wisp of cotton wool, with the skin; otherwise receptors in the subcutaneous tissues may be stimulated.

PAIN is subserved by naked nerve endings, consisting mostly of non-medullated fibers which terminate in the superficial layers of the dermis in delicate loops lying parallel to the skin surface, or as long naked neurofibrillae. Only occasionally do fibrils penetrate the epidermis. Bare nerve endings mediating pain are also present in the cornea (fig. 3.3E) and in serous surfaces (peritoneum, pleura, etc.); touch, cold and warm endings are absent and the corresponding sensations cannot be aroused from these locations. It has been the general belief that the cornea contains only pain endings and that any stimulus, if intense enough to evoke a response at all, causes pain. The sensation of cold can, however, be elicited from the cornea, and, the sensation of touch without pain can be aroused by a very mild stimulus such as a jet of isotonic saline. Certain structures, e.g., the tooth pulp, the middle meningeal artery, the arteries at the base of the brain and some of the vessels of the scalp contain no sensory fibers except those which give rise to pain. Other structures, on the contrary, e.g., the substance of the brain and the mucosa of the cheek opposite the second lower molar tooth, are insensitive to pain.

Most of the pain impulses arising in the skin travel to the central nervous system in the somatic nerves, but some of those from deeper structures join autonomic nerves. All enter the central nervous system by the lateral divisions of the posterior spinal nerve roots or the cranial nerves.

The pain endings do not respond selectively to one variety of stimulus but to any type whether mechanical, chemical or thermal, provided it is sufficiently intense. The pain stimulus, whatever it may be, has one property in common, namely, that it is of a nature to cause injury. The sensation of pain therefore serves a protective purpose, giving warning of injurious stimuli. Stimuli which arouse painful sensations also provoke reflex actions which have the following features. (a) They comprise movements for *protection* or *defense*, or for the withdrawal of the part from the noxious agent. (b) They are *prepotent*, other less urgent

reflexes being for the time inhibited. (c) They are *imperative* and can override voluntary control. Such reflexes are called *nociceptive*.

Perception of and Reaction to Pain

Pain thresholds. A distinction should be drawn between the *perception of pain* and the *reaction* which results, e.g., contraction of facial muscles, vocalization, narrowing of eyelids, changes in pulse rate or rise in blood pressure, sweating, and vasomotor responses. The threshold can be conveniently measured by focussing heat from a lamp on the forehead for 3 sec. and measuring the intensity which becomes painful. The subject indicates the perception threshold verbally and the reactivity threshold may be found by detecting when a change of skin resistance occurs by a wheatstone bridge and galvanometer.

In man the *perception threshold*, under similar conditions, remains remarkably constant between normal persons, and for the same person from day to day, or from hour to hour of the day. The threshold is altered, however, by such extraneous influences as a loud noise, gripping some object or clenching the jaws, which may raise it by 40 per cent. The threshold may be definitely raised by a placebo, and some distraction, such as pain or discomfort, in one situation may reduce the perception of pain in another. The twitch applied to a horse's nose during a minor operation is a familiar example. Even other sensations, e.g., touch, pressure (rubbing), warmth, etc., may raise the pain threshold. The analgesic action of counterirritation is, in some instances, dependent upon such an effect. Hypnosis also raises very considerably the perception threshold, as do alcohol and, of course, other analgesic drugs.

The *threshold of reaction* to pain varies widely between different subjects. Alcohol and analgesic drugs raise the reaction threshold to a greater degree than they do the perception threshold (Wolff and Haryd).

Cutaneous pain. A blindfolded subject is unable to distinguish between the pain caused by a pin prick, a hot point, a punctate electrical stimulus or the plucking of a hair, provided no associated nonpainful sensation gives the patient a clue as to the nature of the stimulating agent. These pains would all be described as sharp, "bright" or pricking. A burning pain is experienced when the sensation is more prolonged, whether caused by heat or ulta-violet light or by a chemical or mechanical irritant. There is no spatial summation of pain stimuli, i.e., the threshold for pain is not influenced by the extent of the area stimulated. Nor, in contrast to stimulation by touch or warmth, adaptation to a painful stimulus does not occur; pain continues to be felt as long as the stimulus is applied. The biological significance of this is obvious.

Dissociation of cutaneous sensations. In disease, the several modalities of sensation, touch, cold, warmth, and pain may be lost separately, or they may be temporarily dissociated by artificial means as by asphyxia, cocaine or the application of cold. Thus, the cutaneous sensations, touch, cold, warmth and pain are lost in this order when the skin is made ischemic. If the skin is cocainized, the appreciation of cold is lost first; then follow in order the senses of warmth, pain and touch. Cooling the skin causes first, failure of cold sensations, then in succession the sensations of touch, pain and warmth are lost. Also, after section of a cutaneous nerve, the area of pain loss is smaller than that of touch; there is thus a boundary zone from which a response to a painful stimulus, such as that of a pin prick, can be obtained but which is insensitive to light touch.

Deep sensibility. Pain in the deep structures, muscles, bones and joints, etc., the sense of pressure in the subcutaneous tissues, and sense of position and movement (e.g., kinesthetic sense) of joints, come in to the category of deep sensibility. Deep sensibility is mediated by afferent fibers in the mixed nerves. Pain arising in deep structures differs in certain respects from superficial pain. It is poorly localized (ch. 62), and is often of a dull, aching or "sickening" character as compared with superficial pain which tends more usually to have a "bright," sharp or burning quality. Deep pain is more often accompanied by nausea and vomiting, slowing of the pulse, and a fall in blood pressure, whereas cutaneous pain is more commonly associated with a quickening of the pulse and a rise in blood pressure.

Muscles, tendons and fasciae are especially susceptible to painful stimulation by chemical agents. The injection of a few drops of a 6 per cent saline solution into one of these structures causes pain. Muscle is relatively insensitive to pricking or cutting but pain is aroused by pressure, e.g., pinching or squeezing, or by exercising under ischemic conditions (p. 62). Severe tension acts also as a pain stimulus for muscle, tendon or fascia. Pain occurring in ischemic muscle during activity is due to a chemical irritant produced by active tissues and which accumulates and stimulates the pain endings when the circulation to the part is arrested or considerably reduced. This substance is referred to as factor P by Lewis and his associates. The soreness of healthy muscles which comes on some hours after exercise may be of the same nature.

Periosteum and cancellous bone are very sensitive to the various types of mechanical stimulation, but compact bone is insensitive to drilling or sawing. The arteries give rise to painful sensations when pricked, but the walls of the veins, except the larger intracranial veins, are usually insensitive.

Visceral pain and *referred pain* are dealt with in chapter 62, *central pain* in chapters 7 and 8, and *headache* in chapter 7.

Hyperalgesia. In many persons an area of tenderness develops around even a small cutaneous injury and spreads for a considerable distance in all directions. The soreness starts within a few seconds, increases to a maximum in from 15 to 30 minutes and lasts for hours or, with a more severe injury, for days. The threshold for pain as tested by a needle prick is lowered only slightly over the area, but the pain when aroused is diffuse, and unusually intense and prolonged. This phenomenon has been studied by Lewis and his associates. Injury was produced by prolonged faradic stimulation of the skin, by crushing a small cutaneous fold with forceps or by direct stimulation of a cutaneous nerve trunk or one of its branches. A similar area of cutaneous hyperalgesia may result from an injury or an inflammatory process involving deep-lying tissue or mucous membrane. Thus, stimulation of a dental nerve or of the mucous membrane of the maxillary antrum is followed by tenderness of the overlying skin of the cheek. Lewis' experiments point to a specific system of nerves in the skin as being responsible for the hyperalgesia. They are not sympathetic filaments, for the phenomenon is observed in skin completely deprived of its sympathetic innervation. Lewis concluded that the nerve fibers responsible were distinct from pain fibers and suggested a separate innervation of 'nocifensor' fibers; this has not been supported by more recent work such as that of Weddel on the distribution and sensitivity of fibers in human skin. It is now thought that the nocifensor fibers are the same as the fine branching fibers subserving slow pain. Impulses arising in the damaged region spread via branching fibers to release a chemical excitant in neighboring areas; this alters the responsiveness of the endings of other fibers round the area of damage.

A similar process has been demonstrated in animal experiments by recording the action potentials from small skin nerves.

Vibration sense, pallesthesia. This is the ability

to perceive stimuli of a vibratory nature applied
to the body surface, as by means of a low-pitched
tuning fork, or other vibrating instrument. They
arise if the stimulus is applied to bone tendon and
muscle and are therefore part of the system of
deep sensibility. Pollock has shown that the vibration sense is retained though the superficial sensations have been lost, which indicates that it is
conveyed by fibers other than those mediating
the latter sensations, namely by the deep system.
Receptors for vibration sense are probably also
situated in the deeper layers of the skin, and in the
subcutaneous tissues. Though the sense is usually
elicited by placing a vibrating tuning fork upon
a bone, e.g. the shin or some other superficial
bone, it can be aroused by applying the instrument to the soft tissues. The structures which respond to vibration are the proprioceptors of
tendon and muscle. The basis of this sense is
probably the stimulation of receptors by rapid
mechanical changes in pressure which will cause
many receptors to set up impulses together in
time with the tuning fork.

Testing the vibration sense is an important
diagnostic aid in neurological conditions. It is impaired or lost (and often before the sensation of
touch or kinesthetic sense is affected) in lesions of
the peripheral nerves, or of the posterior columns
of the cord, but is not affected if both tactile and
kinesthetic senses are intact—a fact that supports
the view that it is mediated by the same receptors
which subserve both of these sensations.

Stereognosis (G. *sterio*, solid + *gnosis*, knowledge), *stereognostic perception.* This is the ability
to recognize, with the eyes closed, the size, weight
and shape of objects placed in the hand or upon
some other part. The absence of this sense is called
astereognosis. When placed in the hand of a normal
person while his eyes are closed, a coin, button,
chain, ball or cube is easily identified from its size,
weight, shape, texture (fur, wool, mesh) etc. Recognition may be made, though less readily, even
if the object is laid upon the foot or pressed

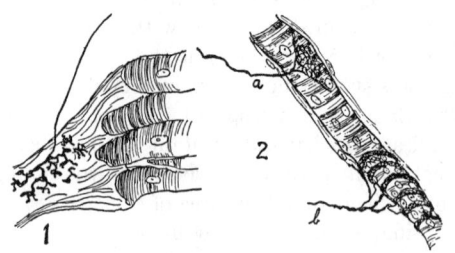

Fig. 3.4. 1. Golgi ending in tendon; 2. intrafusal fiber showing, *a*, muscle flower-spray and *b*,
annulo-spiral endings.

against the toes. Stereognosis is not a separate
sense, but depends upon the senses of touch,
spatial discrimination, cutaneous localization, and
the kinesthetic sense. It is impaired or lost in lesions of the peripheral nerves or posterior columns
of the cord, or of the somesthetic area of the
cerebral cortex.

The Proprioceptors of Muscles, Tendons and Joints

The receptors situated in skeletal muscles and
in the tendons and joints furnish information to
the central nervous system concerning the movements and positions of the limbs and other parts.
Afferent fibers carrying this information make up
from $\frac{1}{3}$ to $\frac{1}{2}$ of the fibers in a so-called motor nerve.
As a result of the messages received by the nerv-
ous centers, the contractions of individual muscles
and groups of muscles are coördinated to produce
smooth, finely adjusted and effective movements
which would be impossible in the absence of such
guidance from the periphery. For this reason the
term *kinesthetic* is applied to this group of receptors. A proportion of these afferent impulses
arouse no sensation, their information being delivered to centers lying beneath consciousness. To
others are due the sensations grouped in the section under deep sensibility. The receptors in the
situations mentioned respond to mechanical stimulation, e.g., pressure or stretch. These types of
stimulus are furnished by the strains and stresses
set up in the muscles, tendons and joints during
muscular contraction.

The sensory endings in the various situations
mentioned above are of four main types: (1) *muscle spindles*, (2) *Golgi corpuscles*, (3) *Pacinian corpuscles*, and (4) *unencapsulated nerve endings.*

(1) *The muscle spindle* is a fusiform body from
0.75 to 4 mm. long and from 0.1 to 0.2 mm. broad
lying parallel to and between the muscle fibers
(fig. 3.4). It is constituted of a bundle of from
3 to 10 muscle fibers (*intrafusal fibers*) enclosed
in a fibrous capsule. The latter is separated from
the intrafusal fibers by a lymph space bridged
across by delicate septa. The intrafusal fibers
differ from the ordinary fibers of the muscle in
being smaller and more circular on cross section,
and in having a greater number of nuclei and
coarser striations. The nerve supply of the spindle
is double—afferent and efferent. The former
enters the spindle about its center, the latter more
toward one or other end. The efferent fibers are
mostly small (7 to 10 μ) and go to end plates on
the intrafusal muscle fibers. They are designated

γ fibers to distinguish them from the larger α motor fibers supplying the rest of a muscle. The afferent fibers end in two ways. The large (17–18 μ) fibers coil round the middle of an intrafusal fiber to form an annulospinal ending. Smaller fibers go towards the ends of the spindle and ramify to form endings, called from their appearance, flower spray endings of Ruffini.

(2) *The Golgi corpuscles* (fig. 3.4) are situated in tendons and consist of a bundle of tendinous fibers surrounded by a lymph space and enclosed within a fibrous capsule. Afferent nerve fibers enter the organ near its center and ramify upon its constituent fibers. Tension is the adequate stimulus for these receptors.

(3) *The Pacinian corpuscles* are oval bodies composed of concentric laminae, like the "skins" of a sectioned onion. The afferent fiber penetrates to the center of the corpuscle. Pressure is the adequate stimulus. These receptor organs are found in tendons, joints, periosteum, especially beneath tendinous insertions, in fasciae covering muscles and in subcutaneous tissues (fig. 3.3D). They are also found in the mesentery.

(4) *Free nerve endings* lie between the muscle fibers, in tendons and in the fasciae and joints. They mediate deep pain.

The Response of Receptors

The electrical response of a receptor may be studied by isolating a single fiber from a sensory nerve trunk and applying the appropriate stimulus to the end organ. Receptors respond to the application of a constant stimulus with a series of repetitive impulses. Figure 3.5 shows the responses obtained from receptors responding to different sensory inputs. At the onset of the stimulus, which may consist simply of a change in intensity, there occurs a series of closely-spaced impulses representing a high rate of discharge. In most such discharges, depending upon the modality involved, the initial high rate gradually declines to a lower value. The diminution in frequency of discharge during the application of a constant stimulus is called *adaptation*. Figure 3.6 shows the time course of adaptation of a muscle spindle to a suddenly applied weight. Adaptation corresponds to the familiar psychological observation that one gradually becomes less aware of a continuing stimulus such as touch or odor. An increase in the intensity of the stimulus has a two-fold effect. It causes an increase in the initial rate of firing at the onset of the stimulus and it results in an increase in the rate of the steady-state discharge.

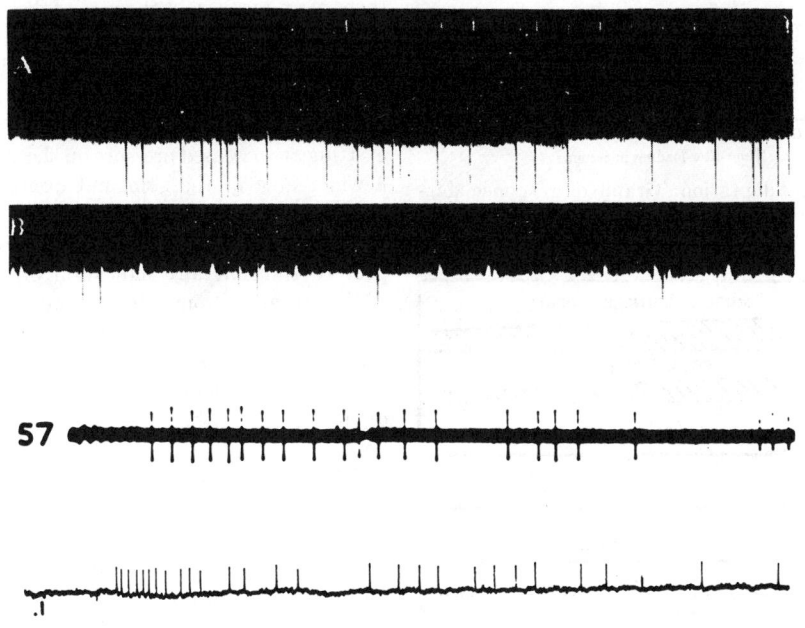

FIG. 3.5
Upper panel: Discharges in dorsal cutaneous nerves of frog. *A* shows responses to touch. *B* are the responses to 2% acetic acid on skin. (after Adrian).
Middle panel: response of non-myelinated fiber of cat to heat applied to skin. Temperature 57° C. (After Iggo.)
Bottom panel: response of a single fiber of the rat chorda tympani nerve to 0.1 M NaCl applied to tongue. (After Pfaffmann.)

The amount of adaptation differs greatly among the different fiber types (fig. 3.7). The most rapidly adapting receptor is that for light touch whereas, the muscle spindle and the free nerve endings involved in the perception of pain show but slight adaptation.

The initial response and the steady-state (baseline) response probably subserve different functions in the organism. The detection of the presence of a new signal in the environment can be associated with the initial high-frequency response of the receptor. On the other hand, the baseline discharge in the steady state is probably concerned with the regulation of the internal state of the organism. For example, the receptor response to a thermal stimulus shows the typical initial rise in frequency followed by a decline to

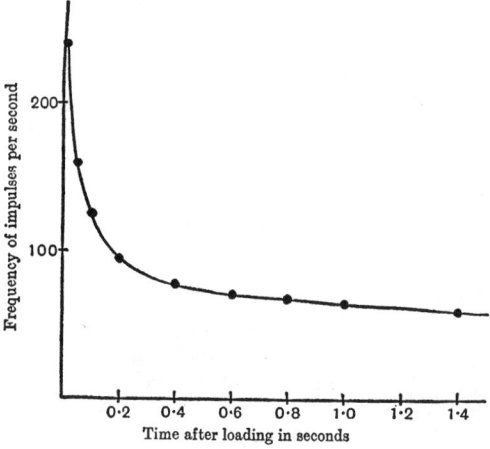

Fig. 3.6. Adaptation. Graph of response during first second after sudden loading with a large load. 100 gm. Temperature 14°C. (After Matthews).

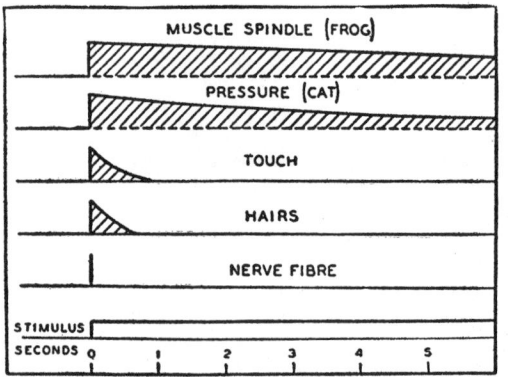

Fig 3.7. Showing the response of nerve fiber and of different types of receptor to a continued stimulus. Adaptation is most rapid in the nerve fiber and slowest in the muscle spindle (from Adrian, *The Basis of Sensation*, Christophers, London).

TABLE 3.3

Receptor	Onset Frequency sec-1	Baseline Frequency sec-1
Joint	30	18
Touch	43	20
Muscle spindle	400	200
	250	90
Thermal		
Cold	50	15
	2	0
Heat	—	0–5
	—	12–35
Olfaction	—	100

a baseline level. The new baseline is higher than the initial baseline and remains so. The initial transient rise indicates the presence of a change in temperature and the direction of the temperature change. The altered baseline discharge, however, is very likely used by the organism to assist in the regulation of its internal temperature. The baseline discharges from an enormous number of thermal receptors are averaged by the central nervous system to give an indication of the average skin temperature of the body.

One aspect of the code for intensity consists, then, of an increase in the rate of discharge to an increased stimulus intensity. A second determinant of subjective intensity is unquestionably the recruitment of additional receptors as the intensity of stimulation is increased. For example, exerting an increased pressure on the skin, distorts a wider area of the skin and excites a greater number of receptors.

The frequency of the discharge does not appear to transmit any indication of the quality of the sensation from skin and muscle. Table 3.3 lists a number of receptor types together with a sampling of the discharge frequencies to an onset of the stimulus, and the baseline or steady-state discharge. Note that in this restricted sample both touch and cold receptors may be found which have approximately the same rates of discharge. The series of impulses from any given receptor does not show any regularity or pattern which would distinguish it from the discharge in any other receptor. The code for skin sensation appears to rely heavily upon a "place" mechanism, i.e., there are special fibers which carry the impulses which give rise to each sensation. But some exceptions must be noted. There are fiber types which respond to at least two kinds of stimuli. For example, touch receptors have been discovered whose baseline frequency of discharge may be increased or decreased by altering the temperature of the skin in the region of contact. Some investigators believe that the characteristics of sensation can only be explained by a theory in which the response of many receptors gives a complex pattern in time and space corresponding to each sensation.

THE GENERATOR POTENTIAL

We have discussed the discharge of impulses when the appropriate receptor in the skin has been stimulated. But what mechanism accounts for the repetitive nature of the discharge? In several special nerve preparations, it has been demonstrated that the application of a constant current or indeed of any constant stimulus which will depolarize a nerve may lead to repetitive firing. These experiments suggested that there may exist depolarizing processes in the receptor which could act as a constant stimulus and give rise to a repetitive discharge. Indeed, in all receptors where it has been experimentally feasible

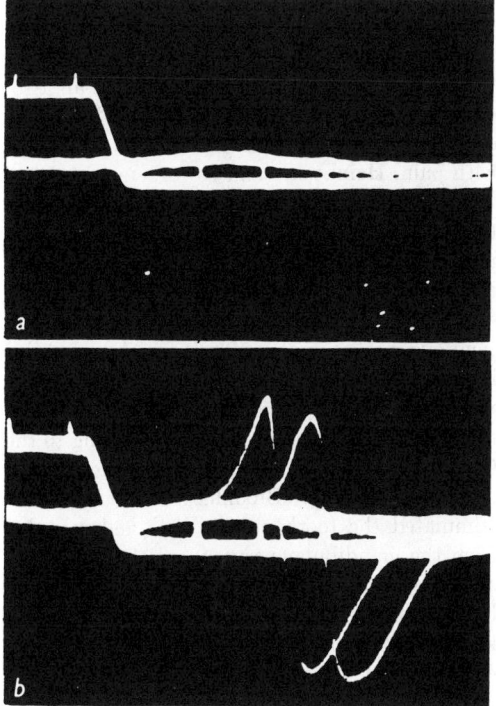

FIG. 3.8. Generator potentials and spikes from Pacinian corpuscle.

a. Generator potential (lower record) to an inadequate mechanical stimulus (upper record).

b. A just threshold mechanical stimulus applied successively giving rise to a generator potential (solid line) and occasionally to two spikes (after Gray and Sato).

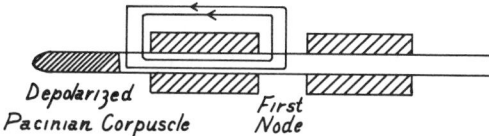

FIG. 3.9. Mechanism of action of Pacinian corpuscle. Currents flow from depolarized region internally to exit at the first node. Corpuscle has been removed.

to investigate this question, it has been found that the application of the adequate stimulus leads to a depolarization of the axon. This depolarization of the receptor is given a special name—*the generator potential*. It is so called because it acts to generate the nerve impulse. Figure 3.8 illustrates the generator potential obtained from a Pacinian corpuscle preparation to which a constant weight has been applied. A potential difference appears between the encapsulated unmyelinated region of the axon and a distant region. The potential is monophasic to an abrupt stimulus and therefore is non-propagating.[1] The depolarization can be graded, i.e., if increasing weights are applied to the receptor, greater amounts of depolarization are produced. If the depolarization is sufficiently intense, a series of impulses will appear on the rising depolarization in some receptors which will continue so long as the depolarization exceeds a critical level.

It is not the depolarization itself that causes excitation of the axon. Figure 3.9 demonstrates the true mechanism of activation. When the unmyelinated region which is enclosed by the capsule becomes depolarized, currents flow from the depolarized region into the first node. The currents passing through the first node then act like the leading edge of an action potential in that they pass outwards through the membrane in the vicinity of the node. They, therefore, have a depolarizing effect on the membrane within the node by appearing to enter a cathode. The intensity of these currents will depend upon the amount of depolarization which, in turn, depends upon the strength of the stimulus. It has also been shown that the frequency of discharge

[1] The non-propagated character of the generator potential is indicated by several facts. The potential is monophasic; the absence of a second phase indicates that the negativity of the impulse is not striking the distant electrode. The latency of response is very short—that to be anticipated from a wave which is essentially spreading electrotonically through the resistance-capacitance network of the axon and finally, the potential can be graded, a property not possessed by the all-or-none propagated action potential.

is a function of the amount of depolarization of the membrane; the greater the depolarization, the greater the frequency of discharge.

Sensory Coding in the Nerve Trunk

A number of studies have been carried out in an effort to correlate a given sensation with a specific type of nerve fiber. This has been performed by relating certain elevations in the compound, spread-out action potential of nerve to specific sensations such as touch and cold. The compound action potential consists of groups of fibers each group of which has approximately the same diameter. Such fibers have approximately the same velocity of travel so that the individual impulses from nerves of about the same diameter tend to stay together as they propagate along the nerve. An example of recording from a pure sensory nerve, the saphenous of the cat, is shown in fig. 3.10. The recording electrodes were placed 5 cm. from the stimulating electrodes. This distance enabled the slower fibers to fall behind the faster. Each hump of the action potential represents a group of fibers with a certain range of diameters and velocities. The elevations are labeled A-α, and A-δ. C fibers, consisting of axons with diameters less than 1 μ are present in the saphenous but are not shown in the figure; a B elevation is not present in the saphenous.

It has been possible to analyze the function of each elevation by blocking the propagation of each group selectively with either asphyxia (ischemia) or local anesthetics such as cocaine. By placing an air-cuff around the arm and inflating it, ischemia is produced and a loss in sensation follows. Touch and pain (fast) disap-

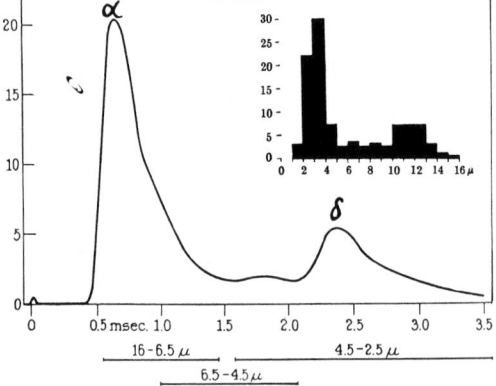

Fig. 3.10. Action potential in human sensory nerve. Fiber groups are shown in insert. The inflections in the falling phase are artifacts of recording (after Gasser).

pear first followed by cold and warmth; finally so-called "second" pain disappears. (It is maintained by many workers that there are two distinguishable sensations to a painful stimulus—an early, bright, sharp pain called "first" pain which is followed in one second or so by a second type of pain which is duller in quality. The latter is called "second" pain). If a similar experiment is carried out on an excised nerve so that the disappearance of the potentials may be observed, it is noted that the A elevation disappears first, followed closely by the A-δ and the remainder of the groups in turn. The C fibers are the last to fail. Touch and pain are therefore associated with the fast A and the A-δ groups.

Confirmatory results have been obtained using cocaine. The order of disappearance of sensation, however, is different. Usually, the order of disappearance of sensation is: slow pain, cold, warmth, fast pain and touch. In the isolated nerve experiments, the C group was blocked first but the A elevation groups disappeared in the same order as in the asphyxia experiments.

It appears clear that there is an association of large fibers with the sensation of touch. In addition there is a clear association of the A-δ fibers with first pain and in many experiments an association of C fibers with second pain. The better-established correlation is that of the A-δ fibers with pain. Heinbecker and coworkers stimulated an isolated nerve in the leg of a patient who was to have an operation for gangrene. They then recorded from the nerve of the amputated limb and obtained a record of the elevations at each stimulus intensity. They observed that the patient did not compalin of pain until a stimulus intensity was reached which gave rise to an elevation in the action potential corresponding to the A-δ group. No elevation corresponding to the C group was observed unless the stimuli were extremely intense. Brookhart and coworkers stimulated the tooth pulp in cats and recorded from the mandibular nerve. Since the pulp gives only a sensation of pain, they were able to correlate the strength-duration curves with those for known fiber groups. That from the tooth pulp corresponded to the A-δ elevation as studied in the saphenous nerve.

The association of C fibers with pain is a matter of some dispute since there is considerable dubiety about the existence of second pain as a reproducible psychological phenomenon. There is considerable evidence, however, from experiments to be described later, that the C group is concerned with the transmission of many sensations and that intense nociceptive stimuli may give rise to pain which is transmitted by the C group.

THE CODING OF SKIN SENSATION

The basic problem in the psychophysiology of sensation is the method by which the central nervous system makes a distinction among the various modalities of sensation. In previous sections the role of special endings within the skin as determinants of specificity has been discused. The individual sensations must be subserved at least in part by specialized, encapsulated endings such as Meissner's and Pacinian corpuscles for touch and the Krause end bulb for cold, among others. The sensation of pain is mediated by the free nerve endings which were not associated with the transmission of any other sensory modality. The clear-cut division of receptors into encapsulated and free nerve endings both histologically and functionally cannot at present be entirely substantiated experimentally and there is considerable difference of opinion in this area. The concept of a relation between encapsulation and function has been challenged by Wedell and co-workers at Oxford and they have put forth the idea that free nerve endings may act as receptors for many functions.

The classical evidence for establishing that specific nerve endings are involved in the perception of sensation was given above. But Wedell and and others have pointed out the difficulty of obtaining reproducible results when mapping sensory skin sites. Day-to-day variations occur which would not be anticipated if specific nerve endings alone determined the quality of sensation. The classic concept that encapsulated endings exist has also been challenged with the following observations by the Oxford group. Firstly, in glabrous or non-hairy skin all types of sensation can be evoked with the appropriate stimulus although the presence of specialized nerve endings cannot be unequivocally demonstrated in these areas histologically. These workers have gone further and denied the very existence of specialized nerve endings in skin, maintaining that the encapsulated endings which are seen, are artifacts of histological origin. Secondly, the cornea, which contains only free nerve endings, can yield sensations of touch, warmth, cold, itch, and tickle. The appropriate conclusion, at present, is not that specific nerve endings do not exist, but that free nerve endings can serve as receptors for

many sensations. It may, indeed, prove true that there exist a variety of different types of free nerve endings whose membranes are different at the molecular level, thus accounting for the variety of responses possible with free nerve endings.

The point of view that free nerve endings may be involved in many sensations is supported by the work of several laboratories. For example, Iggo has investigated the response from single, cutaneous, unmyelinated C fibers which comprise about 80% of all cutaneous fibers in the cat saphenous nerve. These fibers which are presumably connected to free nerve endings in the skin respond to very slight stimuli such as touch whereas other such fibers respond to temperature changes. Other workers have demonstrated that in the toad skin, unmyelinated fibers exhibited discharges when either heat, cold or touch was applied to the skin. Similar results have been obtained for fibers in the lingual nerve associated with sensation from the tongue.

Iggo, recording from single unmyelinated fibers, found a group of high threshold fibers which he called nocifensor. These are fibers which carry impulses from receptors which respond to warmth and cold as well as pressure but only to intensities which are intense enough to cause injury to the skin. They therefore correspond well to a group of fibers within the C group which will respond to a painful stimulus, whatever the modality, providing the stimulus is intense enough. This, then, is the best evidence that the C fibers are involved in the transmission of painful excitation.

REFERENCES

General

BRINK, F. (1956) Nerve Metabolism, in Metabolism of the Nervous System, D. RICHTER (ed.) Pergamon, New York.

CREESE, R. (ed.) (1963) Recent Advances in Physiology. 8th ed. Ch. 3, Electrophysiology (R. CREESE). Ch. 4, Motor unit in reflex action (A. J. BULLER). Little, Brown and Co., Boston.

ELDRED, E., GRANIT, R. AND MERTON, P. A. (1953) J. Physiol., **122:** 498.

KEELE, C. A. AND SMITH, R. (eds.) (1962) The Assessment of Pain in Man and Animals. Latimer, Trend & Company, Plymouth.

ZOTTERMAN, Y. (1959) Thermal sensations. Ch. 18 in Handbook of Physiology, Sec. 1, Vol. 1, Am. Physiol. Soc., Wash., D.C.

Literature

ADRIAN, E. D. AND BRONK, D. W. (1928) The discharge of impulses in motor nerve fibers. I. J. Physiol., **66,** 81.

ADRIAN, E. D. AND ZOTTERMAN, Y. (1926) The impulses produced by sensory nerve endings II. J. Physiol., 61, 151.

ADRIAN, E. D. AND ZOTTERMAN Y. (1926) The impulses produced by the sensory nerve endings. III. J.Physiol., 61, 465.

ALVAREZ-BUYLLA, R. AND RAMIREZ DE ARELLANO, J. (1953) Local responses in Pacinian corpuscles. Am. J. Physiol., 172, 237.

BISHOP, G. H. (1943) Responses to electrical stimulation of single sensory units of skin. J. Neurophysiol., 6, 361.

BRONK, D. W. AND STELLA, G. (1935) The response to steady pressure of single end organs in the isolated carotid sinus. Am. J. Physiol., 110, 708.

EYZAGUIRRE, C. AND KUFFLER, S. W. (1955) Processes of excitation in the dendrites and in the soma of single isolated sensory nerve cells, the lobster and crayfish. J. Gen. Physiol., 39, 87.

GASSER, H. S. (1960) Effect of method of leading on the recording of the nerve fiber spectrum. J. Gen. Physiol., 43, 927.

GASSER, H. AND ERLANGER, J. (1929) The role of fiber size in the establishment of a nerve block by pressure or cocaine. Am. J. Physiol., 88, 581.

GRAY, J. A. B. AND SATO, M. (1953) Properties of the receptor potential in Pacinian corpuscles. J. Physiol., 122, 610.

HARTLINE, H. K. AND GRAHAM, C. H. (1932) Nerve impulses from single receptors in the eye. J. Cell Comp. Physiol., 1, 277.

HENSEL, H. AND ZOTTERMAN, Y. (1951) The response of mechanoreceptors to thermal stimulation. J. Physiol., 115, 16.

JONES, M. H. (1956). Second pain; fact or artifact? Science, 124, 442.

KATZ, B. (1950) Depolarization of sensory terminals and the initiation of impulses in the muscle spindle. J. Physiol., 111, 261.

LELE, P. AND SINCLAIR, D. C. (1955) Observations on the reaction time to cutaneous thermal stimuli. J. Neurol. Neurosurgery and Psychiat., 18, 120.

LELE, P. AND WEDDELL, G. (1956). The relationship between neuro-histology and corneal sensibility. Brain, 79, 119.

LELE, P. P., WEDDELL, G., AND WILLIAMS, C. (1954) The relationship between heat transfer, skin temperature and cutaneous sensibility. J. Physiol., 126, 206.

LOEWENSTEIN, W. R. (1959) The generation of electric activity in a nerve ending. Ann. N. Y. Acad. Sci., 81, 367.

LOEWENSTEIN, W. R. AND RATHKAMP, R. (1958) The sites for mechano-electric conversion in a Pacinian corpuscle. J. Gen. Physiol., 41, 1245.

MATTHEWS, B. H. C. (1931) The response of a single end organ. J. Physiol., 71, 64.

MATTHEWS, B. H. C. (1933) Nerve endings in mammalian muscle. J. Physiol., 78, 1.

O'LEARY, J. P., HEINBECKER, P., AND BISHOP, G. H. (1935) Analysis of a function of nerve to muscle. Am. J. Physiol., 110, 636.

SINCLAIR, D. C., WEDDELL, G., AND ZANDER, E. (1952) The relationship of cutaneous sensibility to neurohistology in the human pinna. J. Anat., 86, 402.

TOWER, S. S. (1940) Units for sensory reception in cornea; with notes on nerve impulses from sclera, iris and lens. J. Neurophysiol., 3, 486.

WEDDELL, G., SINCLAIR, D. C., AND FEINDEL, W. H. (1948) An anatomical basis for alteration in quality of pain sensibility. J. Neurophysiol., 11, 99.

ZOTTERMAN, Y. (1933) Studies in the peripheral neuron mechanism of pain. Acta. Med. Scandinavica, 80, 185.

CHAPTER 4

Physiological and Electrical Characteristics of Reflex Activity

The most primitive multicellular organisms do not possess an elaborate nervous organization for integrating their responses to external stimuli. In an organism such as Hydra, cells have become specialized to respond directly to the environmental stimulus. Epithelio-muscular cells in the vicinity of the mouth can respond directly to changes in acidity and alkalinity of the water in which the animals live so that the mouth contracts when a sufficient number of aboral cells are stimulated. In this animal the most primitive form of neural organization, the nerve net, may also be found. This diffuse network of nerves with no breaks or junctions serves to connect one part with another so that a stimulus in one part of the organism can spread to another region. This organism is capable of retracting its parts away from sources of danger and thus exhibits a basic form of reflex activity.

In more complex forms, a form of neural activity called the reflex has arisen. The principal characteristic of such activity is the evocation of a prompt and unique response to a given stimulus. For example, shining light on the eye causes a contraction of the pupil. A different stimulus applied to the organism such as a pinch will lead to dilatation of the pupil. Contraction of the pupil has adaptive value in that it prevents excessive amounts of light from entering the eye; the withdrawal of the foot from a painful stimulus avoids the effects of a damaging stimulus. The development of such reflex activity has enabled the organism to respond immediately and directly to certain important stimuli in the environment. It has also relegated important regions of neural activity to a highly protected internal region of the organism. In the course of evolution the pathways over which reflex activity may take place have become centralized, and the separate reflexes have integrated, one with the other to produce more complex forms of behavior. Much of the behavior of lower forms, such as insects, may be understood as an elaboration of unit reflex activity into more and more complex patterns and arrangements. Man also manifests considerable reflex and innate behavior in infancy; activities such as the grasp reflex and the startle reflex gradually disappear and are replaced by complex and flexible forms of behavior such as learning. Such complexity appears to be the result of the diversity, number and complexity of the neural networks within the central nervous system. The simplest form of neural net or circuit is the reflex arc to be discussed next.

The Reflex Arc

The anatomical basis of reflex action is the reflex arc which in its simplest form consists of: (a) An afferent limb composed of the receptor organ, which upon excitation, gives rise to nerve impulses and the neuron whose processes transmit the impulse to the central nervous system. In the case of the spinal reflex arc, the cell bodies of the afferent neurons are situated in the posterior root ganglia. (b) An efferent limb constituted of a motor neuron which conducts impulses from the central nervous system to an effector organ-muscle or gland. In the case of motor spinal reflex arcs, the axons of the efferent neurons leave the cord by the anterior nerve roots and travel in the peripheral nerves; their cell bodies are situated in the anterior horns. (c) A center situated in the gray matter of the central nervous system and consisting of the cell body and dendrites of the efferent neuron and its junction (synapse) with the central process of the afferent neuron.

The afferent and efferent limbs may connect directly in the center, but usually one or more nerve cells may be interposed between the two. These are spoken of as connector, internuncial, or intercalated neurons (fig. 4.1). The stretch reflex (pp. 68 and 84) as shown by Lloyd is carried out through a reflex arc of only two neurons, but the great majority of the spinal reflex arcs in higher animals consist of several neurons, and in most reflexes each afferent neuron makes connection through collateral branches and internuncial neurons with a large number of motoneurons.

Injury, leading to loss of function of any one part of the reflex arc, is sufficient to destroy the function of the whole.

Historical survey. Because the subject of reflex activity is so complicated, it is well to obtain a general perspective on the historical development of the entire field. Apart from occasional clinical

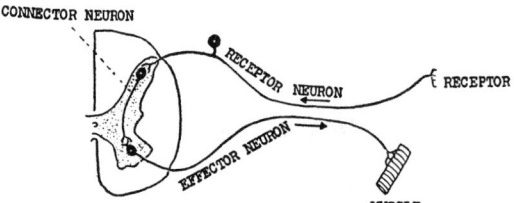

FIG. 4.1. Diagram of a simple reflex arc

observations, the scientific study of reflexes may be said to have begun in the 1830's when Bell in England and Magendie in France, established the functions of the dorsal and ventral roots of the spinal cord. By the beginning of the present century, Sherrington at Oxford had begun a detailed, quantitative investigation of the properties of extensor and flexor reflexes. At about the same time, the Spanish histo-anatomist Ramon y Cajàl had argued cogently for the neuron doctrine, asserting that sensory and motor neurons were contiguous and not continuous. But neurophysiological investigations of reflex activity did not penetrate to the synaptic level until the introduction of electrophysiological methods. The use of such methods was pioneered in the years 1920–1926 by Gasser and Erlanger who made extensive employment of the cathode ray oscilloscope for the study of the electrical responses of nerve and spinal cord.

At this time electrophysiological methods were also introduced by Adrian for the investigation of receptor responses. After the properties of the compound action potential had been thoroughly studied, Lloyd made a definitive study of spinal reflexes in the 1940's investigating in the ventral root the electrical correlates of the phenomena studied by Sherrington. The introduction of glass electrodes in 1946 by Ling and Gerard enabled workers like Eccles to examine the events of excitation and inhibition at the neuronal level. The advances in this area were greatly aided by the analysis of the action potential by Hodgkin, Huxley and Katz between 1950 and 1955. Modern studies employ both intra- and extracellular microelectrodes in detailed investigations of the electrical responses of individual cells in the cord and higher centers.

Classification of Reflexes

Reflexes may be classified with respect to the extent of involvement of regions of the spinal cord into segmental, inter-segmental and suprasegmental reflexes. Those reflexes whose arcs pass through only one anatomical segmental arc are called segmental reflexes. An example of this type is the patellar reflex (the knee jerk). Intersegmental reflexes involve more than one segment.

Thus, pinching the hind limb of a cat may lead to flexion of a contralateral forelimb. Suprasegmental reflexes involve interactions between nuclei above the cord and the segments of the cord itself. Such reflexes are exemplified by movements of the head causing extension of the limbs in a spinal animal. The principal reflexes utilized for investigating the properties of the synapse have been the segmental. The segmental reflexes are further divided into two kinds: flexor and stretch reflexes. The latter reflexes are the basis of most of our information on the nature of the reflex and the synapse.

Another classification of reflexes has proved useful in clinical work. Reflexes are classified into four categories: superficial, deep, visceral and pathological. Superficial reflexes are those elicited from mucous membranes or skin, i.e., the surface of the body. Examples of such reflexes are the corneal reflex, or blinking of the eye when the cornea is touched, and the plantar reflex, a flexion of the toes when the sole of the foot is stroked. Deep reflexes are stretch reflexes in which extension of a muscle is obtained by striking the tendon of a given muscle. The patellar reflex (knee jerk), triceps and biceps reflexes are examples of this type of reflex. Visceral reflexes are elicited from deep-lying structures: examples of such reflexes are the pupillary reflex, i.e., constriction of the pupil when light is shined in the eye and the carotid sinus reflex, in which pressure on the carotid sinus causes a fall in blood pressure. Finally, the pathological reflexes consist of those which are present only as an abnormality. An example of this type is the Babinski reflex which consists of a spreading of the toes when the plantar surface of the foot is stroked. This reflex may be evoked from humans in which lesions of the upper motor pathways of the spinal cord are present.

The Reflex Preparation

Two animal preparations have usually been employed to study the properties of spinal reflexes; the spinal and the decerebrate animal. The spinal animal is prepared by sectioning the cord at the first cervical level; the decerebrate animal is prepared by transecting the brain stem in the region of the superior and inferior colliculi. Immediately after the transection, the spinal animal is in a condition called *spinal shock* in which there is complete absence of reflexes below the level of the section. Within an hour or two there is a return of the flexion and extension reflexes in the cat and dog; in the human the return may take weeks or more. Spinal shock does not occur in the decerebrate animal; on the contrary, the stretch reflexes are exaggerated; there is considerable rigidity of the limbs; and hyperextension and arching of the back (opisthotonus) are present. The blood pressure of the spinal animal tends to fall immediately after the section, but if the animal is properly maintained on artificial respiration, oxygenation is satisfactory, acid-base balance of the blood is achieved, and the blood pressure returns to normal values. The usefulness of such preparations is obvious since reflexes may be studied under experimental conditions without anesthesia which depresses reflex activity.

Sherrington employed the reflexes occurring in flexor and extensor muscles as prototypes of synaptic activity. The individual muscle was isolated and attached to a strain gage so that tension could be recorded. It was also necessary to cut the nerves going to muscles other than those being investigated in order to avoid the afferent stimuli which might arise reflexly during activation of other muscles than those being studied. The flexor reflexes which consist of the withdrawal of a limb are evoked by any noxious stimulus such as pinching the skin; the stretch reflexes are evoked by stretching a muscle, causing the muscle itself to contract reflexly. Although the extensor reflexes are simpler anatomically, it is experimentally easier to investigate the general properties of reflexes using the flexor response. It is easier to evoke a flexor response by isolating a skin nerve and applying a single shock

than to apply a quick stretch to an extensor muscle in order to activate a group of afferent nerves synchronously. For this reason, the study of reflexes will begin with a discussion of the flexor reflex.

The Flexor Reflex

The flexor reflex is investigated by stimulating a nerve arising in the skin with a strong shock and measuring the tension developed in a flexor muscle. The stimulus may be applied to the saphenous nerve of the hind limb and the tension recorded from the semitendinosus, a flexor, which is attached to a strain gage. The adequate stimulus for evoking a flexor response is therefore a noxious stimulus. Either a single shock may be used, in which case the response is a twitch (fig. 4.2), or a series of repetitive stimuli are employed and the response is a reflex tetanus. Use of a single shock shows that the response may be graded; increasing the intensity of shock results in a greater response up to a maximum. Other properties which are general characteristics of reflexes may be demonstrated with the flexor reflex. The property of *spatial summation* may be demonstrated by stimulating two skin nerves simultaneously each of which alone is capable of giving flexor reflex. If the stimuli are just subthreshold and stimuli are delivered simultaneously, the individual effect of each stimulus will summate and the reflex response will occur. This experiment demonstrates the property of *summation*. Both summation and the *subliminal fringe* are demonstrable in a slightly different experiment. Suppose a flexor reflex has a minimum

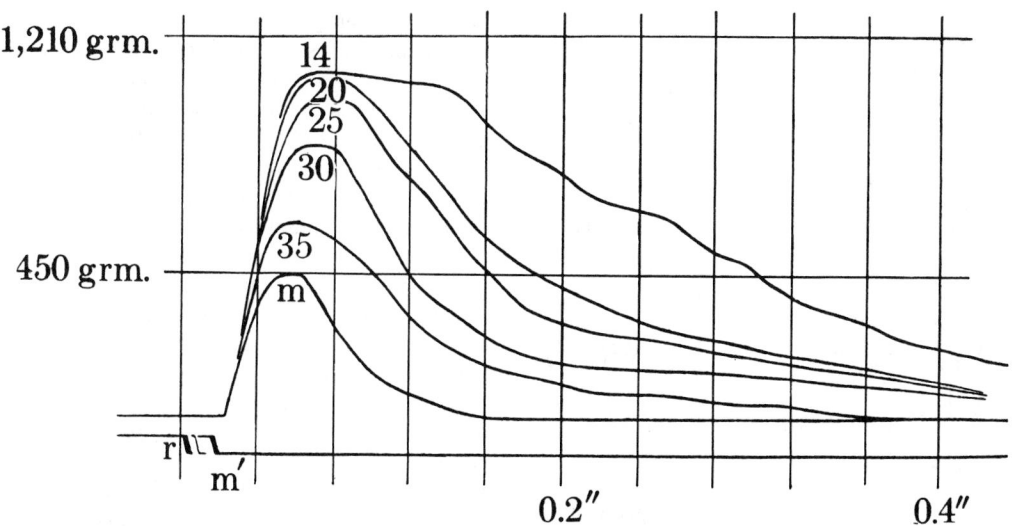

Fig. 4.2. Tracings of flexor reflex myograms of tibialis anticus muscle of spinal cat. Curve *m* is for a maximal motor nerve twitch of the same muscle. Reflexes were obtained by increasing the intensity of the single shock to the ipsilateral popliteal nerve. (After Sherrington.)

tension (5 kg.) to each of two afferent volleys in different nerves. The stimuli are then adjusted so that 1 kg. tension is obtained separately. If the two stimuli are now applied together a response of 3 kg. tension is obtained. Under these circumstances the response (3 kg.) is greater than was anticipated from the sum of the individual responses (2 kg.). The interpretation of this experiment is that each input nerve is connected to motoneurons which do not fire if one nerve is stimulated, but fire when both nerves are stimulated together (fig. 4.3). Neurons which fire only when both inputs are stimulated are said to be in the *subliminal* (subthreshold) *fringe*. These neurons are partially excited but do not fire when only one input is stimulated. The partially excited neurons in the subliminal fringe are said to exhibit the phenomenon of *facilitation*. The neurons which are activated by a stimulus and give a reflex response are said to be in the *discharge zone*. Neurons can be brought out of the subliminal fringe into the discharge zone by increasing the strength of stimulus so that more afferent fibers impinge on the neurons of the subliminal fringe; or they may be excited by stimulating nerves which are synergistic in function but which do not necessarily give rise to a reflex response themselves. Note that when neurons in the subliminal fringe are activated, *convergence* of input fibers on the output motoneuron is taking place.

Another important concept is that of *occlusion* (fig. 4.3). A slight modification of the experiment described above may be utilized to demonstrate this phenomenon. The experiment is now arranged so that each stimulus gives a maximum reflex response of 10 kg. tension. If the two stimuli are now applied together a tension of only 16 kg. results. This is less than the sum of the reflex responses obtained separately (20 kg.). The interpretation of this experiment is that there are neurons in the discharge zone which are common

to both inputs; therefore, when both stimuli are applied the response cannot be 20 kg. but will be less by an amount determined by those neurons which are occluded or hidden, (20 − 16 = 4 kg.). Another way to state this is that when stimuli are such as to give maximum reflex responses, the discharge zones of each input will overlap.

One of the significant ways in which reflexes differ is in central delay or latency. This is defined as the time between the arrival of the input volley at the first synapse and the beginning of the response of the motoneuron. This delay time may be calculated by measuring first the total time from stimulus to response and subtracting from this time, the total afferent and efferent conduction times to and from the cord along the nerves. The central latency obtained by this method is between 3 and 5.5 msec. for the flexor reflex. A more accurate measurement of central delay will be discussed later when electrophysiological methods are introduced.

THE STRETCH REFLEXES

The adequate stimulus which elicits this reflex is a stretch of the muscle. If the stretch is performed rapidly a nearly synchronous volley of impulses enters the cord; the reflex response is abrupt and occurs without any apparent central delay. The prototype of these reflexes is the patellar reflex or knee jerk in which a sharp tap on the patellar tendon produces a contraction of the quadriceps muscle. The receptors involved in this reflex are the annulospiral endings of the muscle spindle. The reflex shows no *after-discharge;* that is the response ceases immediately after the stimulus terminates. The measurement of central latency is difficult to achieve by myographic methods since the latency is so short and the input volley not quite synchronous. The electrophysiological method to be described below gives a period of about 0.5 msec. for the central latency of the patellar reflex.

In addition to investigating the responses to a rapid stretch of muscle, it is possible to study the reflex response to a continuous stretch of extensor muscles. Since two types of response exist to stretching extensor muscles, the response to a quick stretch is termed the phasic response whereas the response to continuing stretch is called the tonic response. Sherrington employed decerebrate animals in the study of the stretch reflexes. The animal was securely attached to a table which could be suddenly lowered by a given amount. An extensor muscle (quadriceps) which was to be studied was isolated and its tendon

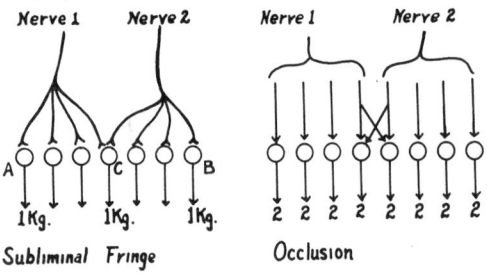

FIG. 4.3. Schematic circuits to explain subliminal fringe and occlusion. Circles represent motoneurons. (See text.)

attached to a myographic lever. All other muscles
in the limb were denervated. By lowering the
table to which the animal was securely fixed, the
muscle was stretched a few millimeters and a large
isometric tension developed. Two components of
the reflex response can be observed in the myographic response (fig. 4.4); an initial, rapidly
rising component which is phasic and a sustained,
slowly-falling tension which is the tonic component of the reflex. The true course of the
reflex, however, can only be determined by
excluding the passive tension developed by the
muscle. This is secured by cutting the nerve to
the muscle and repeating the experiment. A curve
of passively developed tension (fig. 4.4) is obtained which can be subtracted from the tension
developed when the nerve was intact. That the
response is reflex in nature can easily be proved
by sectioning the dorsal roots; whereby the reflex
tension disappears.

The tonic component of the stretch reflex is
clearly important in maintaining posture. Extension of the muscle, as by swaying away from
the center of gravity, activates the stretch reflex
and restores the muscle to its initial length. The
concept of such reflex standing arose from observations on decerebrate animals in which the
limbs are hyperextended. Here "reflex standing"
appears to be taking place. The extensor muscles
are reflexly activated by any slight stretch of the
muscle. Other factors play a role such as a release
from inhibiting influences from higher centers but
the reflex nature of the rigidity is demonstrable
by sectioning the dorsal roots of a single limb;
the rigidity then disappears.

Another fundamental phenomenon can be
observed in these experiments. Stretching of
antagonist muscles such as the semitendinosus or
biceps causes a decrease in reflex tension. Indeed,
stretching of the biceps caused complete disappearance of the myotatic reflex evoked by sustained stretch to the level given by passive tension
alone (curve P) (fig. 4.4). Such a depression of
reflex activity caused by stimulation of specific
nerves, in this case the ipsilateral antagonists,
is known as *inhibition* and will be studied in
greater detail later. Inhibition does not simply
consist of a lack of reflex activity or a capturing of
the motor pathways by the inhibiting nerve. It
will be shown later that the inhibiting neurons
cause a change in the membrane potential of the
motoneuron tending to stabilize the motoneuron
against responding reflexly.

The *Principle of Reciprocal Innervation* is one
of the broad generalizations about spinal reflex

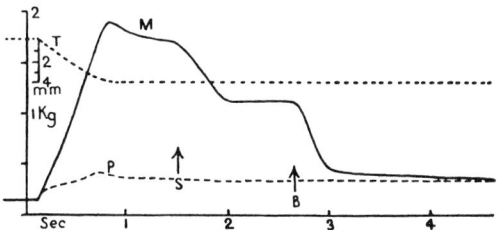

FIG. 4.4. Response of quadriceps to stretch *T*
of 4 mm., before *M*, and after *P*, severance of its
nerve. During the response *M*, a stretch of semitendinosus begins approximately at *S*, followed by
a stretch of biceps at *B*. (After Creed, Denny-
Brown et al., *Reflex Activity of the Spinal Cord*,
Clarendon Press, Oxford.)

activity which resulted from Sherrington's early
work on excitation and inhibition. The principle
states that the flexors and extensor reflexes of
the same limb cannot be simultaneously active; if
a flexor reflex is evoked, the extensor is inhibited
and vice versa. For instance, the afferent nerves
evoking an extensor reflex have connections
going to the flexor motoneurons of the same limb
causing them to be inhibited. When a flexor
reflex is elicited, its connections on the extensor
motoneurons cause the extensor reflexes to be
inhibited. The extent of inhibition in all such
cases is proportional to the reflex activity taking
place so that a primitive form of organization is
taking place at the segmental level and on one
side of the limb. But at the same time the evocation of a reflex on one side causes opposite effects
on the motoneuron pools of the opposite limb.
Thus when a flexor reflex is obtained on one side
of the animal, the flexors of the opposite limb
are inhibited and the extensors are facilitated.
Two examples of such integrated contralateral
activity are the crossed extensor reflex and
Phillipson's reflex. The *crossed extensor reflex*, is
obtained by pinching the limb of a spinal or
decerebrate animal. The pinched limb withdraws
but the contralateral limb extends. Similarly
Phillipson's reflex is obtained from the extended
limb of a spinal or decerebrate animal. Flexing the
limb forcibly produces the clasp-knife reflex
(cf. *the muscle spindle* pp. 58 and 79) and causes
the opposite limb to extend. Reciprocal innervation is very useful in more elaborate activities
such as walking where it is obviously necessary to
have complete synchronization of flexor and extensor activity. The presence of reciprocal innervation ensures that accidental evocation of
simultaneous reflex antagonist activity does not
occur; when one reflex is active, the other is
inhibited.

Electrophysiological Investigations

We noted that it was difficult to investigate the properties of the stretch reflex quantitatively by classical methods. Nor did the methods of Sherrington for the investigation of reflexes succeed in giving information about the details of synaptic action such as synaptic delay or the quantitative relationship between nerve input and reflex output. The electrophysiological method is so designed that appropriate nerves are stimulated and the electrical response recorded from the ventral root. The electrical potentials which are recorded from the ventral root are referred to as reflex responses as were the myographic recordings of tension. If a nerve from a muscle is stimulated and the ventral root discharge simultaneously recorded, two responses are observed to be present in the discharge (fig. 4.5). An early, large spike lasting 1 msec. appears after a short latency, followed by a series of irregular discharges lasting for about 10 msec. The first discharge can be evoked along by a quick stretch of an extensor muscle, so that it is the electrical counterpart of the stretch reflex. The later, irregular discharge can be evoked alone by stimulating a purely sensory skin nerve such as the saphenous and is the electrical counterpart of the flexor reflex.

As a result of electrophysiological studies on reflexes an alternate classification of nerve fiber types has come into use. Afferent nerves are divided into four categories in accordance with their fiber diameter and velocity of conduction; group I, 12–21 μ, group II, 6–12 μ and group III, 1–6 μ. Group IV consists of C fibers less than 1 μ in diameter. Groups I, II, and III$_a$ correspond to fibers in the A category; group III corresponds to A delta. All somatic nerve trunks contain the afferent groups II, III, and IV. Group I, containing the fastest afferent fibers is present only in nerves from muscles and is associated with afferents from the muscle spindle (group I$_a$) and the Golgi tendon organ (group I$_b$).

Motor nerves consist of two groups of fibers. One group, the α motoneuron innervates the striated muscle fiber, is 9–13 μ in diameter and constitutes about 70% of all the efferent fibers; the second group are the γ efferents, 3–6 μ in diameter and are the efferent fibers to the intrafusal muscles of the spindle.

THE MONOSYNAPTIC REFLEX

The rapid reflex response of short latency is elicited by exciting type I$_a$ fibers. The latency of the reflex, if measured by stimulating a dorsal root and recording from a ventral root is exceedingly short; the shortest latencies being around 0.5 msec. This appears to be the delay corresponding to the time necessary to traverse a synapse. A precise measurement of the synaptic delay may be performed by stimulating neurons directly within the spinal cord in the region of the motoneurons (fig. 4.6). At low stimulus intensities, interneurons within the cord are fired; at higher stimulus strengths the motoneuron itself is excited. The difference in time between the interneuronal and the motoneuron response is a measure of the synaptic delay. By this direct method, the delay is found to be 0.5 msec. It may therefore be concluded that the early spike

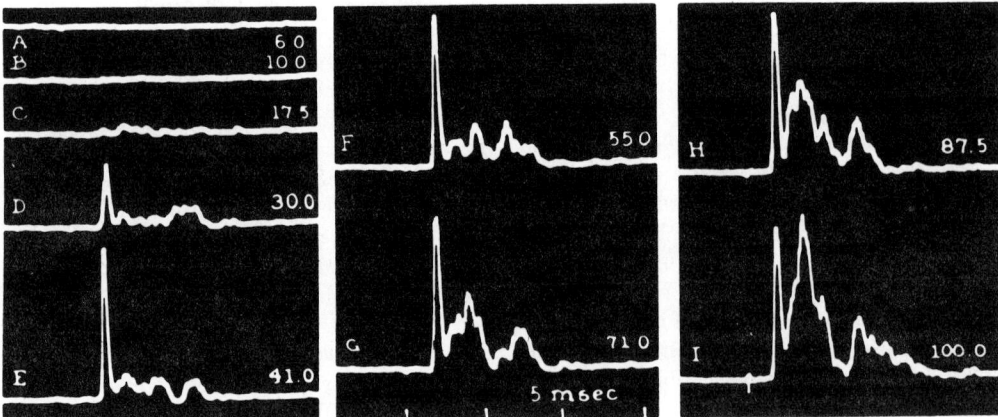

FIG. 4.5. Dorsal root-ventral reflex discharges from the first sacral segment. The successive records illustrate the growth of the reflex discharge as the afferent (dorsal root) volley is increased in size. The figures to the right hand of each observation give the relative size of the afferent volley employed for that observation. Time = 5 msec. (After Lloyd.)

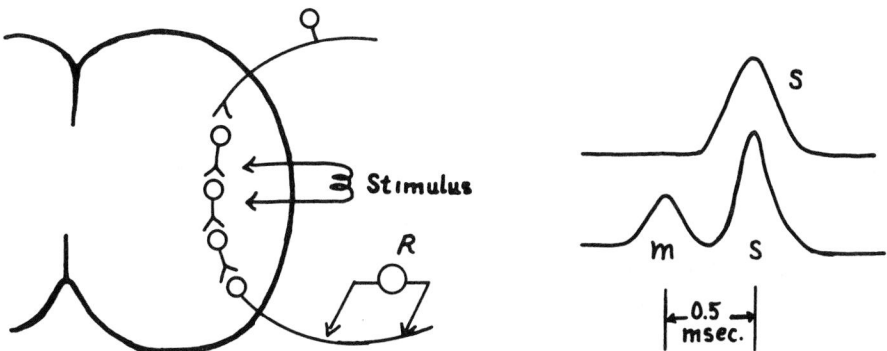

FIG. 4.6. Measurement of synaptic delay of spinal cord synapse. Response *s* represents motoneurons of internuncial pool responding to weak shock; *m* is the response of the motoneuron. The difference in time, 0.5 msec., represents the synaptic delay. (After Renshaw.)

of the reflex discharge arises from a reflex arc in which only one synapse is present between the afferent and efferent neurons; no internuncial neurons are interposed between these. For this reason, the electrical reflex is referred to as *monosynaptic reflex*.

The Polysynaptic Reflex

The electrical discharge which corresponds to the flexor reflex has a long latency—of the order of 3 to 5 msec. It must therefore contain more than one synapse. The neurons which are interposed between the input and output are called interneurons or internuncials. The afferent nerves involved in evoking the reflex are members of groups II, III, and IV. Assuming that each synaptic delay is about 0.5 msec. and that the transit time over the short interneuronal axons is negligible the number of neurons probably involved in the reflex is between six and ten (reflex latency/synaptic delay). The electrical discharge therefore corresponds to the after-discharge which occurs in the flexor reflex, and results from persistent activity over delay pathways between the input and the final motoneuron. At least two basic circuits exist which may give rise to an after-discharge (fig. 4.7). One arrangement of neurons consists of a series of delay pathways in parallel without any feedback from a subsequent to a preceding neuron. This is called a *multiple chain network*. A second neural configuration consists of a chain of neurons so arranged that some of the neurons further down in the chain may feedback to earlier neurons and reexcite them. Such chains are called *reverberatory networks* for they give rise to activity which reverberates back to the first cells in the chain. At present, the relative contribution of each network to after-discharge in polysynaptic reflexes is unknown.

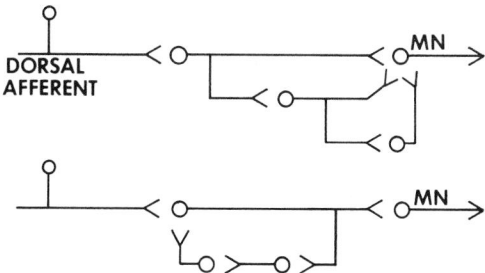

FIG. 4.7. Circuits which may give rise to after-discharge. Upper is multiple chain, lower is reverberating circuit.

Facilitation and Temporal Summation

The experimental basis of spatial summation has been discussed in relation to the flexor reflex. In such experiments, two submaximal stimuli were applied simultaneously over different pathways and a reflex response occurred. The interpretation of such an experiment was that the two input pathways contained nerve fibers which terminated on the same neuron. The response arose because the effects of two spatially different fibers summed on the same motoneuron. The first or conditioning stimulus is applied to the nerve from one head of the gastrocnemius muscle; the second or test stimulus, which is strong enough to evoke a reflex is applied to the nerve from the other head of the muscle. If the two stimuli are applied simultaneously, an augmentation of the response by as much as 300% may occur (fig. 4.8). If, however, the conditioning volley is separated from the test volley, it gradually loses its effectiveness so that when they are 10 msec. apart the effect has almost disappeared. It is clear from these experiments that a conditioning volley which causes no reflex response may give rise to facilitatory effects which may last for as long as 10 msec. or more. This

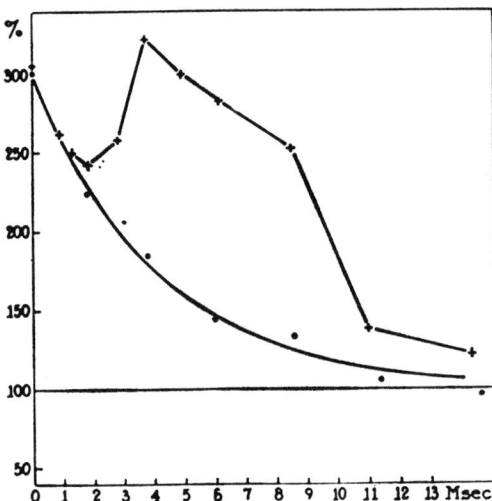

FIG.4.8. Facilitation of biceps reflex by afferent volleys in semitendinosus nerve. Amplitude of the test reflex, expressed as per cent of control amplitude, is plotted as function of the time interval between conditioning and test volleys. To obtain the curve represented by dots, conditioning volleys of near reflex threshold strength were used. Stronger conditioning volleys caused the appearance of a second period of facilitation (crosses). (After Lloyd.)

kind of *residual facilitation* can occur in pathways where no internuncials are apparently present as in extensor nuclei of the cord; or the same results can be obtained in the flexor nuclei of the cord (fig. 4.8). The explanation of how a facilitation independent of internuncial delay networks can occur will be explained later in terms of the effects of the afferent volley on the potential changes occurring in the motoneuron. These experiments raise the question of whether temporal summation is possible in the nervous system. Lorente de Nó had demonstrated in the oculomotor nucleus that temporal summation could occur. He applied two stimuli in close succession to this nucleus and measured the reflex response of ocular motoneurons. The stimuli had to be delivered within 0.1 msec. of each other in order to obtain summation. This experiment appeared to remove the possibility of any kind of temporal summation. But the experiments on residual facilitation in monosynaptic systems reopen this question.

The Electrical Response of the Motoneuron

THE EXCITATORY POSTSYNAPTIC POTENTIAL (EPSP)

In previous discussions the activity of the synapse has been investigated by external record-

ing techniques. Another method has proven very productive in exploring the detailed mechanism of synaptic action. Utilized chiefly by Eccles and coworkers, this method consists of inserting finely drawn-out microelectrodes made of glass and filled with KCl or NaCl into the cell body of motoneurons of the spinal cord. When the microelectrode is inserted, a resting potential of about -70 mv. is observed, with the interior of the cell negative to the outside. If the motoneuron is antidromically excited, i.e., by stimulating the axon of the motoneuron, the motoneuron is excited without the intervention of the synapse. An action potential with an overshoot of about 20 mv. appears. Thus antidromic excitation gives rise to an action potential in the postsynaptic cell, the motoneuron, which is no different in its general characteristics than that obtained from squid axon or the muscle fiber. The slight inflections which appear on the rise do not enter into the present discussion.

The events of interest in synaptic excitation, however, occur when excitation is delivered orthodromically, i.e., to the afferent neuron of the dorsal root, so that the presynaptic endings of this neuron are excited. In such experiments in which a synapse is present, an additional potential appears in recording from the postsynaptic cell which is a sign of synaptic depolarization. Figure 4.9 shows the response of the motoneuron to a presynaptic volley. The slow potential which appears just before the action potential is called the excitatory postsynaptic potential or EPSP. It consists of a depolarization of the membrane which may last for 20 msec. and can best be seen when the extent of depolarization is insufficient to give rise to an action potential. When the membrane potential falls to a critical value of about -60 mv., the motoneuron fires and an action potential appears on the EPSP. Temporal summation of such EPSP is also possible. If two subliminal volleys are sent in over the same nerve, each volley produces an effect which is manifested by an EPSP. The EPSP's will then sum and if the critical level of depolarization is reached, an impulse will be set off.

The EPSP is monophasic and non-propagating; it represents a depolarization which is localized to the soma of the motoneuron. Unlike the action potential, the EPSP is a potential which is not all-or-none in character since it can be augmented simply by increasing the intensity of the input volley. Moreover, the EPSP's of different inputs can sum on a postsynaptic cell to produce a greater depolarization. These characteristics show that the EPSP is produced in a process which is fundamentally different from that of the action potential.

Several lines of evidence indicate that the EPSP arises from a depolarization of the post-synaptic membrane and an influx of *all* ions into the cell. One group of experiments concerns setting the membrane at a given membrane potential by passing current across the membrane. A double-barreled microelectrode was inserted into a motoneuron. One electrode was used to depolarize or hyperpolarize the neuron with a direct current; the other to record the EPSP. When the membrane potential was increased, the

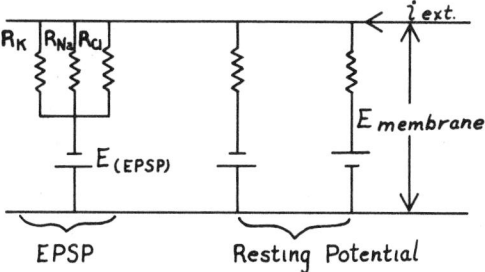

FIG. 4.10. Equivalent circuit of motoneuron membrane for EPSP. Left circuit represents channels giving rise to EPSP. Right circuits represent circuit of polarized membrane.

amplitude and rate of rise of the EPSP increased. Conversely when the membrane potential was decreased, the EPSP decreased. There was a reversal of the direction of the EPSP when the membrane potential was set at zero volts. The explanation of this effect goes back to the experiments on the squid axon. We recall that when the axon was clamped at the equilibrium potential of an ion, a reversal of current flow occurred through the membrane above and below this value of clamp voltage. We may imagine that the motoneuron membrane contains channels through which ions can flow to cause the development of an EPSP. These channels are supposed to be additional to those serving as producers of the action potential. A diagram of the equivalent circuit for such channels is shown in fig. 4.10. When the membrane potential is set at the equilibrium potential of the EPSP, a change in resistance of this channel can have no effect on the recorded potential. No EPSP will develop. Under normal circumstances the membrane potential is determined by the equilibrium potential for potassium but when the EPSP channels decrease in resistance, the potential recorded tends to approach the equilibrium potential for the EPSP. Now the only process which can have an equilibrium potential of zero is one in which the membrane is freely permeable to all ions. This process will have an equilibrium potential of zero because it is a diffusion potential and the value of the emf developed in a diffusion potential depends directly upon the difference of mobilities of the cations and anions. During the production of the EPSP it is presumed that the mobilities are equal so that the process has an equilibrium potential of zero.

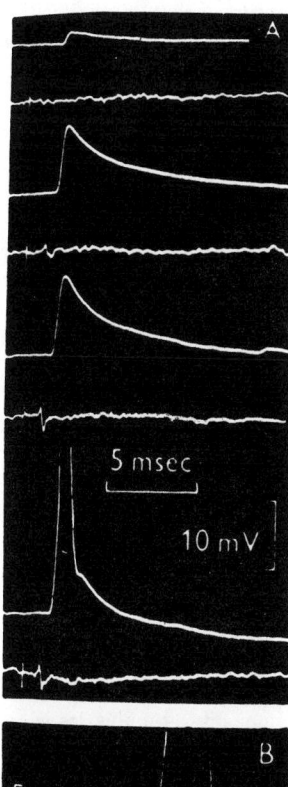

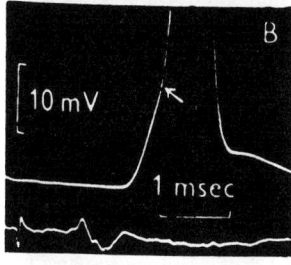

FIG. 4.9. Intracellular potentials set up in a biceps-semitendinosus neuron by various sizes of volleys in the afferent nerve (lower records). *A* shows synaptic potentials (upper records) of graded size, the largest setting up and action potential. In *B* a faster record of this response is shown. Note spike arising at arrow from more slowly rising synaptic potential. (Brock, Coombs and Eccles).

The Inhibitory Potentials

If a monosynaptic reflex is evoked by orthodromic excitation, an inhibition of the reflex can be produced by stimulating an ipsilateral antagonist nerve as described more fully in the section on inhibition. The effect of the inhibitory stimulus is to cause a hyperpolarization of the postsynaptic membrane in a direction opposite to that of the EPSP (fig. 4.11). This hyperpolarization consequent upon an inhibitory stimulus is called the inhibitory postsynaptic potential or IPSP. Its time course is the same as that of EPSP, of the order of 20 msec., and corresponds to the curve of inhibition obtained from reflex studies. Indeed the IPSP is a mere image of the EPSP in the same motoneuron. The IPSP causes a hyperpolarization of the membrane and renders it less excitable according to the principles of peripheral neurophysiology. Any EPSP which occurs during an IPSP will generate currents which will be less effective in causing excitation of the cell.

The problem of determining the nature of the currents responsible for the IPSP has been attacked by the same procedures described for the EPSP. Using doubled-barrelled microelectrodes, it is found that setting the membrane potential at −80 mv. will cause the disappearance of the IPSP. The potential −80 mv. is the average of that determined by potassium (−70) and chloride (−90) suggesting that the IPSP results from an increased flow of K+ and Cl− making the inside more negative. Further evidence however, points to chloride as the principal ion involved in producing the EPSP. The method of electrophoretic injection has been used to demonstrate this. One barrel of a double microelectrode is filled with KCl and made negative so that this electrode effectively drives chloride ions into the cell; it is a hyperpolarizing current since it is internally negative. The other barrel electrode records the IPSP. It is found that the injection of chloride into the cell converts the IPSP elicited by a group I_a afferent volley from a hyperpolarization to a depolarization (EPSP). The injection of chloride caused an increased internal concentration of chloride. The transmitter causing inhibition (see Electrical and Chemical Transmission)

results in an increased permeability to chloride, but the chloride ionic gradient is now opposite to its normal direction so that a depolarization will occur instead of a hyperpolarization if the membrane is especially permeable to chloride. Chloride now flows out and makes the inside of the cell less negative. A number of anions were injected internally and all those which were less than a certain hydrated ion diameter caused a reversal of the IPSP to an EPSP. Apparently the inhibitory substance opens pores which allow ions below a certain size to pass. Since chloride is the only anion which exists in a high enough concentration to flow out during such an inhibition, it is presumed that chloride is the main contributor to the inhibitory currents which flow.

TYPES OF INHIBITION

Some restraint must be placed upon the ability of muscle and neural circuits to respond. In reaching for an object, for example, the muscle must be controlled if the movement is to be accurate and the muscle is not to overshoot the mark. Certainly reciprocal innervation of some type must often be employed so that when a muscle is activated its antagonist will be inhibited; otherwise persistent opposition of an undesired sort will be encountered. These two reasons give some indication of the usefulness of inhibition in motor movement. A third less obvious necessity for inhibition arises from the very complexity of neural activity in which some form of "negative feedback" or inhibition is necessary in order to keep the complex neural networks from over-activity. An abnormal form of such activity is observed, for example, in strychnine poisoning in which inhibitory neurons have been shown to be inactivated. In a strychninized animal any stimulus leads to persistent neural activity and convulsion. Again, in the disorder known as Parkinsonism, periodic activity in the form of tremor of a limb manifests itself, presumably as a result of injury to inhibitory systems which restrain normal motor activity.

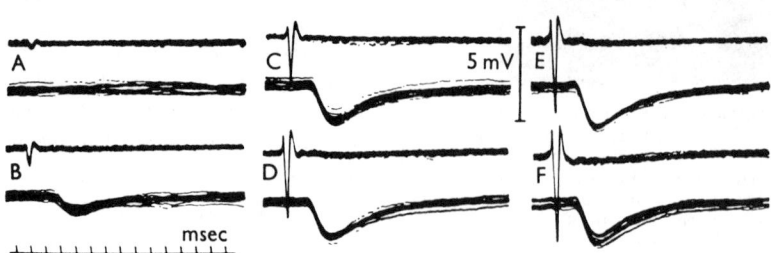

FIG. 4.11

Three kinds of inhibition have been extensively studied: (a) *direct*, (b) *pre-synaptic*, and (c) *Renshaw cell or recurrent inhibition*. A fourth type of inhibition, called indirect inhibition and extensively discussed by Sherrington is not now considered to be inhibition per se but a form of occlusion.

The direct form of inhibition can be observed by evoking a monosynaptic reflex and then depressing the amplitude of the reflex by stimulating an ipsilateral skin nerve (type II fibers). It is necessary to stimulate the inhibitory nerve shortly before eliciting the reflex. By varying the interval between the inhibitory and excitatory stimulus, the time course of direct inhibition can be obtained. The inhibitory nerve is stimulated first. A curve of the form of fig. 4.12 is obtained in which maximum inhibition is obtained at an interval of 0.5 msec. between the two stimuli and with a delay lasting for about 10 msec. The interval 0.5 msec., is equivalent to one synaptic delay so that at least one inhibitory interneuron is interposed between the afferent neuron and the motoneuron. It is believed at present that this interneuron in the inhibitory pathway possesses the ability to secrete a substance at its terminals which depolarizes the membrane and leads to an IPSP. Thus a neuron which is normally excitatory to other neurons may exert an inhibitory action by the interposition of an inhibitory neuron. Other mechanisms which have been proposed include terminating the neuron on a special region of the postsynaptic neuron so that it can have inhibitory effects on special regions of the postsynaptic cell.

Direct inhibition is very susceptible to strychnine injection which can completely abolish it. This effect of strychnine is the basis for the explanation of its convulsant activity—all inhibition of the direct type having been removed, the slightest stimulus causes a tremendous extensor response.

Presynaptic Inhibition

Early in the studies of the electrical responses evoked by reflex action, electrodes were placed on the surface of the spinal cord or on dorsal roots and large potentials which were positive to distant regions, called P waves were recorded. It was suspected that this positivity might be the sign of some inhibitory presynaptic activity going on in the cord. To demonstrate presynaptic inhibition, a reflex response is elicited in extensor motoneurons. This reflex will be inhibited if it is preceded by stimuli from any nerve entering the cord. Group I_a and I_b fibers are most effective in causing the inhibition but groups II and III will also serve. The time course of such an inhibition is shown in fig. 4.13. Unlike direct inhibition, maximum inhibition is observed when the inhibitory stimulus precedes the excitatory by about 20 msec. The inhibition may endure for as long as 200–300 msec. and is extremely resistant to strychnine.

Several lines of evidence indicate that this inhibition is presynaptic. Recording within the motoneuron at the time that inhibition is produced shows no changes in the membrane potential. Neither a hyperpolarization or a depolarization is produced by an inhibitory volley. Instead,

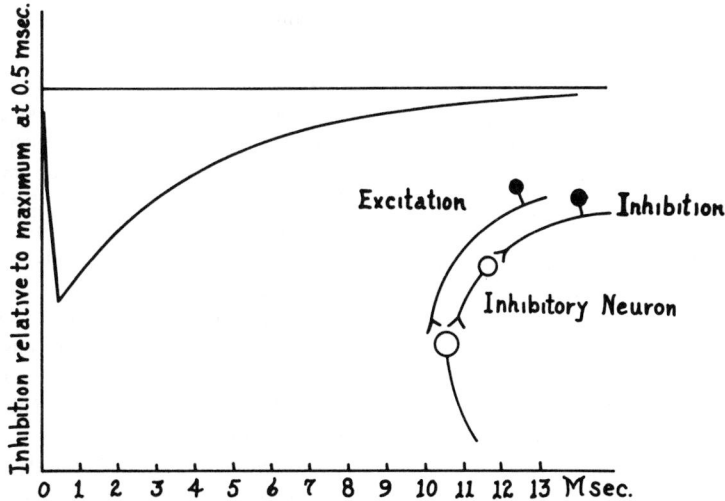

FIG. 4.12. Time course of direct inhibition. Insert shows circuit containing inhibitory neuron (after Lloyd).

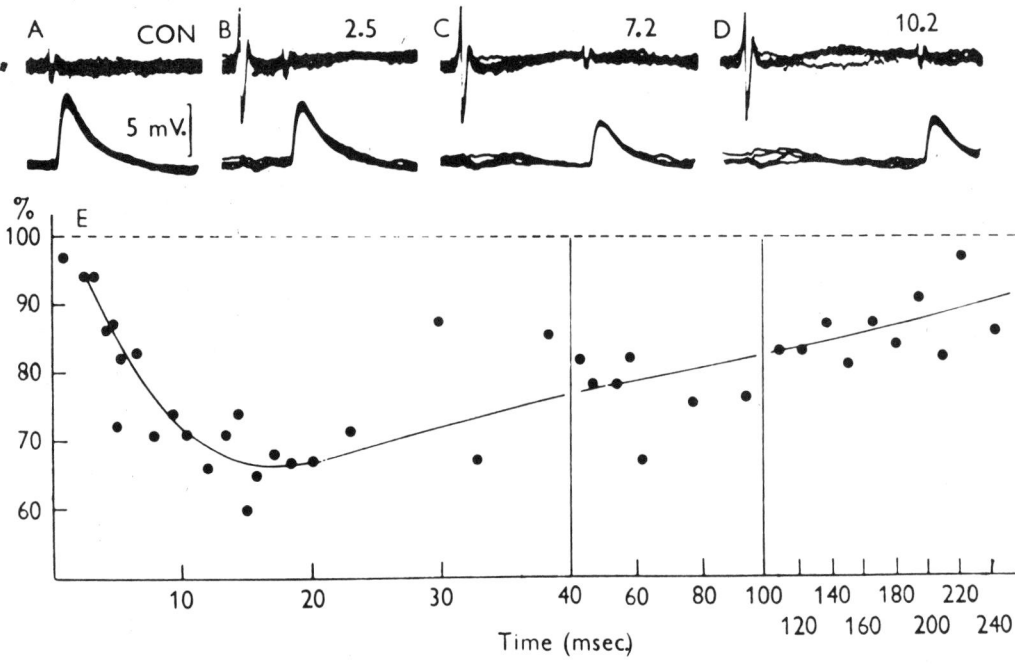

FIG. 4.13. Time course of presynaptic inhibition (*E*). Inhibitory stimulus is maximal group I volley in biceps-semitendinosus nerve. Monosynaptic EPSP's were evoked at various intervals after the inhibitory stimulus by stimulating the gastrocnemius-soleus nerve maximally. *A* shows control EPSP; *B*, *C*, and *D* are the EPSP's at intervals marked above the records.

it is noted that the magnitude of the EPSP which is set up by the reflex volley is diminished by the inhibitory stimulus and that the magnitude of the EPSP parallels the curve of inhibition (fig. 4.13). It has also been shown that there is a depolarization of the presynaptic fine terminals entering the dorsal region of the cord. Microelectrodes are inserted into and just outside a nerve fibre. The undesirable potential of neighboring neurons which is recorded inside a nerve fibre together with the membrane potential, may be obviated by subtracting the externally recorded potential from the internally recorded to obtain the true membrane potential. It is found that the time course of the depolarization produced by inhibitory volleys parallels the time course of inhibition. Presynaptic depolarization may affect the amount of transmitter released from the presynaptic terminals. Since long delays are involved in presynaptic inhibition, many interneurons are interposed between the first and last neurons of the chain.

Renshaw Cell Inhibition

In 1941 Renshaw discovered that a volley of impulses delivered to motor axons causes an inhibition of all types of motoneurons at the segmental level. This type of inhibition has therefore been called antidromic because the inhibition may be evoked by firing backwards over the

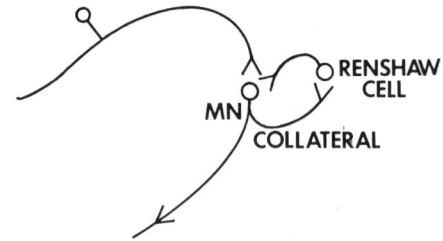

FIG. 4.14. Schematic drawing of recurrent inhibition.

motor roots into the spinal cord. When such antidromic excitation was used, an after-discharge of quite high frequency was present in the recording from a ventral root. It was shown by microelectrode recording that the discharge did not occur in the motoneuron but in neighboring cells near the motoneuron—in cells which discharge with a high frequency when the antidromic excitation occurs. At the same time the motoneuron is inhibited. These neighboring cells are therefore believed to cause the inhibition. The motoneuron displays a hyperpolarization which has all the characteristics of an inhibitory postsynaptic potential and the IPSP lasts for the period of time corresponding to the discharge in the neighboring cells which are called Renshaw cells. An anatomical pathway has been suggested to explain these results (fig. 4.14). The motoneuron gives off a

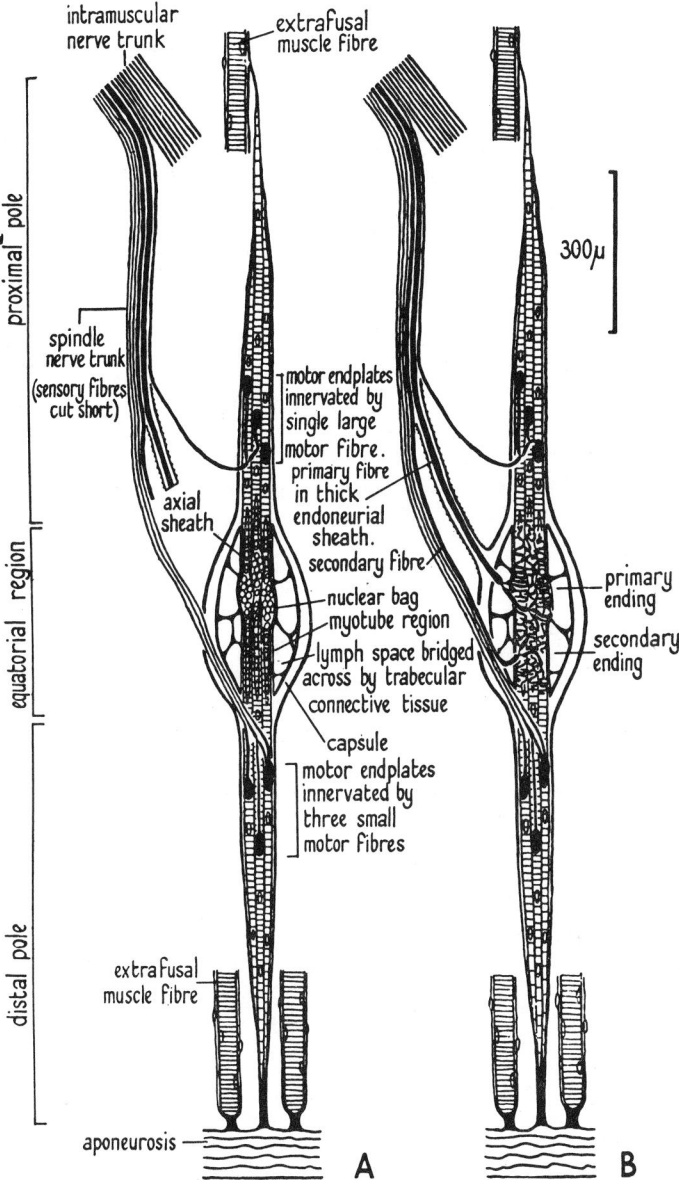

intramuscular
nerve trunk

extrafusal
muscle fibre

proximal pole

300μ

spindle
nerve trunk
(sensory fibres
cut short)

motor endplates
innervated by
single large
motor fibre.
primary fibre
in thick
endoneurial
sheath.
secondary fibre

axial
sheath

equatorial region

nuclear bag
myotube region

lymph space bridged
across by trabecular
connective tissue

primary
ending

secondary
ending

capsule

motor endplates
innervated by
three small
motor fibres

distal pole

extrafusal
muscle fibre

aponeurosis

A   B

FIG. 4.15. Diagram of an idealized rabbit's muscle spindle. In *A* the efferent innervation by the fine nerve fibers is shown (the afferent innervation is omitted). *B* shows the spindle complete with afferent innervation. (After Barker).

parallel with the muscle. The sensory role of the spindle is subserved by nerve endings in the nuclear bag. The nerve fibers are type I_a ; larger than 12 μ in diameter with conduction velocities of more than 90 m./sec. Another group of afferents originates outside the nuclear bag in the myotube region; these endings are flower spray in type and their nerves are in group II. The principle motor nerve of the spindle going to the intrafusal fiber is a large fiber called a γ efferent; three smaller fibers also innervate the intrafusal fibers.

The Golgi tendon organ arises from the tendon of the muscle and is anatomically in series with the muscle. When the muscle is stretched, the Golgi tendon organ is stretched and stimulated and when the muscle contracts, the Golgi tendon organ is compressed and stimulated. The Golgi organ gives rise to afferent fibers which are classified as I_b with a modal velocity of about 80 m./sec., somewhat slower than the I_a group. The extent of stretch necessary to evoke a response from the Golgi tendon organ is greater than for the annulospiral ending.

The anatomical difference between the annulo-spiral and Golgi tendon organ is paralleled by a similar difference in their reflex responses to stretch. The annulospiral endings are in parallel with the extrafusal fibers. Therefore, when a muscle containing such an ending is stretched, the annulospinal endings respond with an afferent volley in the I_a fibers and a reflex myotatic discharge occurs in the extensor muscle. These endings respond only to stretch and cease firing when the muscle shortens or relaxes. On the other hand, the Golgi tendon organ responds to both shortening or extension of muscle. However, it is necessary to stretch muscles considerably before any effective discharge occurs. The reflex response in which the Golgi tendon organ is involved is called the *inverse myotatic reflex* or *clasp-knife reflex*. The limbs of a decerebrate animal are extended and stiff. If such an extended limb is flexed forcibly, considerable resistance is met until at a certain extension the limb suddenly gives way to the force. By stretching the extensor muscles much beyond their normal position during the flexion, we activate the Golgi tendon organs and inhibit the extensor reflexes. This type of inhibition is called *autogenic* since it arises from the very muscle from which the reflex itself was obtained.

The properties of the muscle spindle which are significant for the maintenance of a fixed length of muscle are the following. (a) A passive stretch of the muscle and its spindles causes the spindles to discharge and send impulses to the cord over group I_a fibers. The discharge rate is high at the beginning of the stretch but falls off to reach a steady maintained, tonic rate. The frequency of discharge of the spindle in the steady state is proportional to the extent to which the muscle has been stretched. (b) Adaptation of the spindle discharge is slight. The tonic discharge continues indefinitely as long as the muscle is kept stretched. (c) Contraction of the muscle (shortening of the muscle fibers) causes cessation of firing. Shortening releases the spindle from the tension caused by

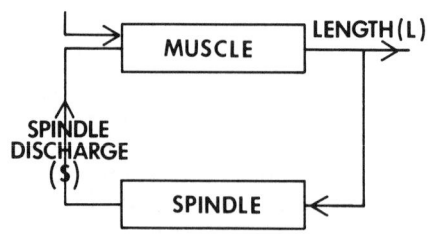

Fig. 4.16. The muscle-muscle spindle feedback loop.

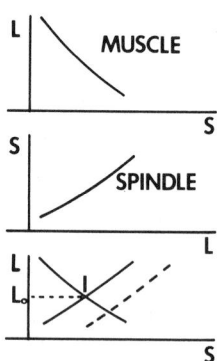

Fig. 4.17. Explanation of constant length servo loop. (See text.)

extension, and the spindle is no longer mechanically excited. This experimental finding demonstrates that the spindles are functionally in parallel with the extrafusal muscle fibers. (d) Contraction of the intrafusal fibers of the motor spindle results in an acceleration of the discharge from the spindle. By stimulating the intrafusal fiber, the annulospiral endings are placed under stress and the endings are stimulated. Contraction of the intrafusal fibers is equivalent to taking up the slack on the intrafusal fibers and placing the annulospiral endings under some degree of tension. It is therefore the same effectively as passively stretching the muscle. All these properties are important when the spindle acts as part of the reflex arc to maintain a constant length of muscle. The feedback loop is shown in fig. 4.16.

Using a block type of schematic we may diagram the relationship between the length of the muscle and the spindle discharge in maintaining the length of the muscle constant. The excitation for the reflex discharge of the muscle comes from the spindle. The relationship between the muscle length (L) and incoming spindle excitation (S) is an inverse one; the greater the discharge from the spindle, the shorter the length of muscle (fig. 4.17). We must also consider the relationship in the feedback loop that has as its input the length of the muscle and its output the spindle discharge. In this case the spindle discharge (S) is proportional to the extension of the muscle (L). This function is also shown in fig. 4.17. In the steady-state, the length is maintained constant at the value given by the intersection of the two curves. Let us see how this system works. If the spindle discharge should increase the muscle will shorten thus decreasing the discharge. When the discharge diminishes, the muscle relaxes and lengthens, the spindle is again stretched and the discharge rate is increased. The dashed line represents a shift of the spindle discharge transfer function as a result of γ efferent activity. The intrafusal fibers shorten putting more tension on the annulospiral endings at a given length of muscle and effecting a higher spindle discharge rate. The entire curve shifts to the right. The steady-state point is also shifted to an intersection where a greater spindle discharge rate is necessary to maintain the muscle at a shorter length.

What of a rapid shortening muscle as during a voluntary movement? Such movement can occur in either of two ways; a direct activation of the motoneuron via the corticospinal pathway or excitation of the motoneuron indirectly through the γ-efferent system. The γ efferents may be activated by stimulating the descending reticular formation. Such stimulation will cause shortening of the intrafusal fibers, stretching of the annulospinal endings and an immediate spindle discharge. The spindle discharge will then elicit a phasic reflex response of the extensor motoneuron. Thus, a rapid voluntary movement may be evoked by intrafusal excitation.

The Descending Reticular Formation

We have briefly mentioned the role of the reticular formation above. The reticular formation consists of a mass of cells and axon fibers surrounding the central canal of the brain stem, which extends from the medulla to the beginning of the thalamus. Definite groups of cells as nuclei can be observed throughout the reticular formation and it is nowadays considered to connect upper regions of the brain with the spinal cord in both directions. We may therefore speak of a descending and an ascending reticular formation. The descending reticular system with which we are concerned at this time, consists of one central or medial region and two lateral areas. Fibers originating from the motor cortex, the caudate nucleus and the vestibular nuclei of the cerebellum pass to the descending system (fig. 4.18). The reticular formation sends fibers in turn to the motoneurons of the spinal cord where they influence the activity of the flexor and extensor motoneuron pools. Within the reticular formation itself there are excitatory and inhibitory areas. The lateral areas of the reticular formation are facilitatory to extensor reflexes and inhibitory to flexor reflexes; the areas in the midline have the opposite effect-inhibiting extensors and facilitating flexor reflexes.

The reticular formation is part of the system controlling efferent activity; the efferents are excited by reticular stimulation. The lateral reticular system acts on the γ-efferent neurons to increase the rate of firing from the spindle. It thus facilitates extensor reflexes. A similar effect can be obtained by stimulating the vestibulo-spinal pathway. Conversely, stimulation of the bulbar

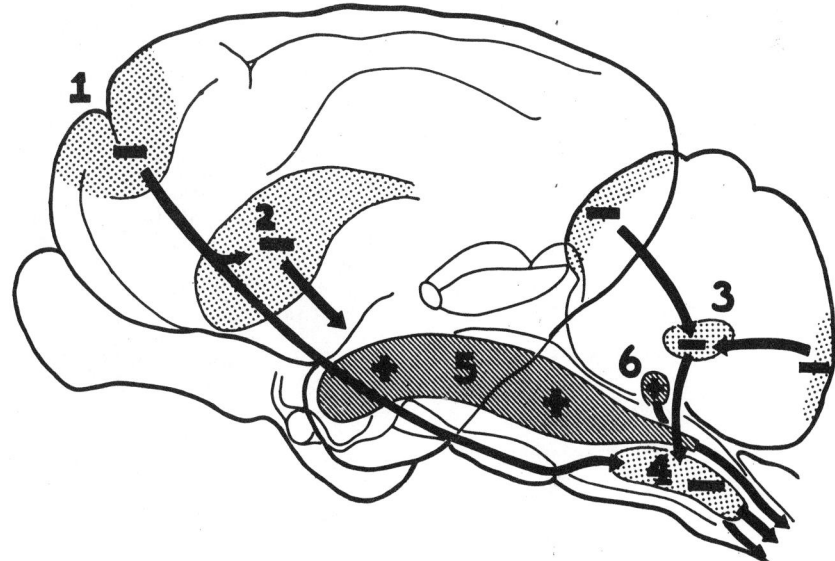

Fig. 4.18. A reconstruction of the cat brain, showing the suppressor and facilitatory systems acting on the descending reticular formation. Suppressor pathways are: (1) cortico-bulbar-reticular, (2) caudato-spinal, (3) cerebello-reticular, and (4) reticulo-spinal. Facilitatory pathways are: (5) reticulo-spinal and (6) vestibulo-spinal. (After Lindsley, Schreiner and Magoun.)

reticular formation in the midline will decrease spindle discharge and inhibit the knee jerk reflex.

Decerebrate rigidity consists of a continuous spasm of the extensor muscles leading to a rigidity in all limbs and a dorsiflexion of the back and head. This posture results from transection of the brain in the region of the colliculi; the extensor rigidity from an enormous facilitation of the extensor reflexes. The vestibulo-spinal and facilitatory regions of the reticular formation are intact in such an animal. These centers and the spinal motoneurons have been released from any inhibitory influences exerted by the cortico-spinal and caudato-spinal pathways by the section of the brain stem.

REFERENCES

General

CREED, R. S., DENNY-BROWN, D., ECCLES, J. C., LIDDELL, E. G. T. AND SHERRINGTON, C. S. (1932) Reflex Activity of the Spinal Cord. Oxford University Press, London.

CROSBY, E. C., HUMPHREY, T. AND LAUER, E. W. (1962) Correlative Anatomy of the Nervous System. MacMillan, N.Y.

ECCLES, J. C. (1957) The Physiology of Nerve Cells. Johns Hopkins Press, Baltimore.

ECCLES, J. C. (1964) The Physiology of Synapses. Academic Press, N.Y.

FULTON, J. F. (1926) Muscular Contraction and the Reflex Control of Movement. Williams & Wilkins Co., Baltimore.

KUFFLER, S. W. (1948) Physiology of neuromuscular junctions: Electrical Aspects. Fed. Proc., 7, 437.

LLOYD, D. P. C. (1959) Spinal Mechanisms Involved in Somatic Activities. Handbook of Physiology, Vol. II, 929.

McLENNAN, HUGH (1963) Synaptic Transmission. W. B. Saunders Co., Philadelphia, London.

SHERRINGTON, C. S. (1906) The Integrative Action of the Nervous System. Yale University Press, New Haven.

Literature

BARKER, D. (1948) The innervation of the motor spindle. Quart J. Microsc. Science, 89, 143.

BARRON, D. H. AND MATTHEWS, B. H. C. (1938) The Interpretation of Potential Changes in the Spinal Cord. J. Physiol., 92, 276.

BROCK, L. G., COOMBS, J. S. AND ECCLES, J. C. (1952) The recording of potentials from motoneurones with an intracellular electrode. J. Physiol., 117, 431.

BROWN, G. L. AND FELDBERG, W. (1937) The acetylcholine metabolism of a sympathetic ganglion. J. Physiol., 88, 265.

COOMBS, J. S., CURTIS, D. R. AND ECCLES, J. C. (1957) The generation of impulses in motoneurones. J. Physiol., 139, 232.

COOMBS, J. S., CURTIS, D. R. AND ECCLES, J. C. (1957) The interpretation of spike potentials of motoneurones. J. Physiol., 139, 198.

COOMBS, J. S., CURTIS, D. R. AND ECCLES, J. C. (1956) "Time courses of motoneuronal responses. Nature, London, 178, 1049.

COOMBS, J. S., ECCLES, J. C. AND FATT, P. (1955) Excitatory synaptic action in motoneurones. J. Physiol., 130, 374.

COOMBS, J. S., ECCLES, J. C. AND FATT, P. (1955) The specific ionic conductances and the ionic movements across the motoneural membrane that produce the inhibitory postsynaptic potential. J. Physiol., 130, 326.

COOPER, S. D. E. DENNY-BROWN AND SHERRINGTON, S. (1927) Interaction between ipsilateral spinal reflexes acting on the flexor muscles of the hindlimb. Proc. Roy. Soc., 101B, 262.

DE ROBERTIS, E. AND FRANCHI, C. M. (1937) Electron microscope observations on synaptic vesicles in synapses of the retinal rods and cones. J. Biophysics and Biochem. Cytol., 2, 319.

ECCLES, J. C., ECCLES, R. M. AND MAYNE, F. (1961) Central inhibitory action attributable to presynaptic depolarization produced by muscle afferent volleys. J. Physiol., 159, 147.

ECCLES, J. C., FATT, P. AND KOKETSO, K. (1954). Cholinergic and inhibitory synapses in a pathway from motor-axon collaterals to motoneurons. J. Physiol. 126, 524.

ECCLES, R. M. (1951) Intracellular potentials recorded from a mammalian sympathetic ganglion. J. Physiol., 115, 74.

FRANK, K. AND FUORTES, M. G. F. (1957) Presynaptic and postsynaptic inhibition of monosynaptic reflexes. Fed. Proc. 16, 39.

FRANK, K. (1959) Basic mechanisms of synaptic transmission in the central nervous system. I.R.E., Tr. Med. Electron., ME-6, 85.

HAGIWARA, S. AND TASAKI, I. (1958) A study of the mechanism of impulse transmission across the giant synapse of the squid. J. Physiol. 143, 114.

LLOYD, D. P. C. (1941) A direct central inhibitory action of dromically conducted impulses. J. Neurophysiol., 4, 184.

LLOYD, D. P. C. (1943) Reflex action in relation to pattern and peripheral source of afferent stimulation. J. Neurophysiol., 6, 111.

LLOYD, D. P. C. (1943) Neuron patterns controlling transmission of ipsilateral hind limb reflexes in cat. J. Neurophysiol., 6, 293.

LLOYD, D. P. C. (1946) Facilitation and inhibition of spinal motoneurones. J. Neurophysiol., 9, 421.

LLOYD, D. P. C. (1957) Temporal summation in rhythmically active monosynaptic reflex pathways. J. Gen. Physiol., 40, 427.

LORENTE DE NO, R. (1938) Limits of variation of the synaptic delay of motoneurons. J. Neurophysiol., 1, 187.

LORENTE DE NO, R. (1938) Synaptic stimulation of motoneurones as a local process. J. Neurophysiol., 1, 195.

MERTON, P. A. (1951) The silent period in a muscle of the human hand. J. Physiol., 114, 183.

PALAY, S. L. (1958) The morphology of synapses in the central nervous system. Exper. Cell Res. (supp.), 5, 275.

PERRY, W. L. M. (1953) Acetylcholine release in the cat's superior cervical ganglion. J. Physiol., 119, 439.

RENSHAW, B. (1941) Influence of discharge of motoneurons upon excitation of neighboring motoneurons. J. Neurophysiol., 4, 167.

RENSHAW, B. AND THERMAN, P. O. (1941) Excitation of intraspinal mammalian axons by nerve impulses in adjacent axons. Am. J. Physiol., 133, 96.

CHAPTER 5

The Physiological Mechanisms Governing Posture and Equilibrium

Stretch or Myotatic Reflexes

The basic reflex for posture is the stretch reflex. It is present in all healthy skeletal muscles, but it is more pronounced and more readily elicited in some muscles than in others. When a resting muscle is stretched it responds by contracting. This is the stretch reflex. Pulling on the muscles stimulates the muscle-spindles (ch. 3 and 4) which are specialized sensory end-organs lying among the muscle fibers. These spindles send afferent nervous impulses up the sensory fibers of the muscular nerve and into the spinal cord over the posterior spinal roots. Within the spinal cord these impulses are transferred over a single synapse to the α motor cells of the anterior gray column of the spinal cord. These α cells, in turn, send impulses out over the anterior spinal roots, down the motor fibers and into the skeletal muscle where they cause the muscle to contract. This reflex is normally present and serves particularly to maintain the body of the animal in an upright position. Such reflexes are, therefore, more pronounced in the extensor muscles. These reflexes become exaggerated after the cerebrum is removed by transecting the brainstem through the mesencephalon (decerebration). This produces a state known as *decerebrate rigidity*, in which stretch reflexes are more easily elicited; these stretch-reflexes are commonly studied under the abnormal circumstances of decerebrate rigidity. Naturally, section of either the related anterior or posterior spinal roots, or dividing the muscular nerve, or destroying the related portion of the spinal cord interrupts the reflex arc and abolishes the response. The muscular response is proportionate, within limits, to the stretching force, and persists so long as the stretching is maintained. The muscular contraction ceases as soon as the stretching force is withdrawn, i.e., there is no after-discharge. The latent period of the stretch reflex is short—less than 20 msec. This reflex is readily inhibited by stimuli to the extremity which would ordinarily be painful (nociceptive stimuli), or by stimulation of the afferent nerves from the skin, or by stretching the antagonistic flexor muscles, or by applying excessive stretching force to the muscle itself or to its tendon. This latter inhibition gives rise to the lengthening reaction (see below). These forms of inhibition are largely devices to protect the muscle from overextension, and the animal from injury. In figure 5.1 are the graphic results of the classical experiments of Liddell and Sherrington demonstrating some of these points.

As noted above the stretch reflex is enhanced by decerebration. Such transection of the midbrain abolishes controlling inhibitory impulses from the cerebral cortex, the basal ganglia and the anterior lobe of the cerebellum which are transmitted down the spinal cord from the bulbar reticular formation, while leaving intact the facilitatory mechanism in the more caudal portions of the reticular formation. Even with fixed lesions of the central nervous system the intensity of the muscular responses to the stretch reflex wax and wane under varying circumstances. This modulation of the reflex response may be brought about by changes in these facilitatory impulses which affect the stretch reflex directly, or by descending impulses which vary the response of the muscle spindle to stretch. This latter effect is produced over small neurons known as gamma efferents which arise in the anterior gray columns of the spinal cord and innervate the intrafusal muscle fibers within the muscle spindle. This control of the responsiveness of the peripheral sensory end-organ is in considerable measure exercised by the reticular formation of the brain stem. By varying the tension within the muscle spindle, its response to stretch is varied and, in turn, the reflex muscular contraction.

The afferent fibers of the myotatic reflex arcs are large-caliber, myelinated, rapidly conducting fibers of the A group. The red muscle fibers of the extensors, upon which the maintenance of posture depends, are also more plentifully supplied with large diameter nerve fibers than are the pale fibers of flexor muscles. The stretch reflexes show reciprocal innervation; when a muscle reacts to a stretching force by contraction, its antagonist relaxes: the *myotatic unit*, which consists of mus-

84

cle receptor, afferent nerve fiber, spinal center and motoneuron, "exhibits within itself in full measure the elementary mechanism of reciprocal innervation" (Lloyd).

THE KNEE AND ANKLE JERKS

A sharp tap upon the patellar tendon, when the knee joint is semi-flexed, stretches the quadriceps extensor muscle and causes it to contract. Similarly a blow upon the tendo Achillis causes a quick contraction of the calf muscles. These brief contractions or jerks, as well as those described below for the upper limb, are "fractional examples of the stretch reflex" and are not due to stimulation of the tendon but to stretching of the muscle, a stretch of 0.05 mm. or less in $\frac{1}{20}$ second, sufficient to elicit the response. A voluntary action, such as clasping the hands together, reinforces the reflex and increases the force of the jerk. The center for the knee jerk in the human subject lies in the 2nd, 3rd and 4th lumbar segments of the cord; it is innervated through the anterior crural nerve. The center for the ankle jerk is situated in the 1st sacral segment; the peripheral nerve is the sciatic. Lloyd has shown that only two neurons are involved in the reflex arc of the knee and ankle jerks, and of other myotatic reflexes, i.e., the impulse passes from afferent fiber to motor neuron without traversing an internuncial neuron (see also ch. 3).

Any condition, such as decerebration or injury to the descending motor pathways (ch. 6), which enhances the stretch reflexes increases the tendon jerks.[1] They are abolished by an injury or disease involving the efferent or afferent limb of the reflex arc or the center itself (anterior horn cells). On account of its brief twitchlike character the knee jerk is sometimes spoken of as the "phasic reaction" of the stretch reflex. The sustained contraction which results from a continuous pull upon the tendon and is concerned in the maintenance of posture is referred to as the "static or postural reaction" of the stretch reflex. The knee jerk is less affected by abnormal states, e.g., spinal transection, anesthetics, circulatory failures, etc., than are the postural reactions. In an animal

[1] When the electrical responses are recorded from the muscle of an animal during the elicitation of a tendon jerk, cessation of the action currents is found to occur during the actual contraction of the muscle. This, the so-called *"silent period"*, is probably due to the muscle spindles being relieved of stretch as the muscle shortens. An additional factor is the synchronous nature of the discharge down the motoneurons, for the latter, being all excited in unison, pass also simultaneously into the subnormal phase.

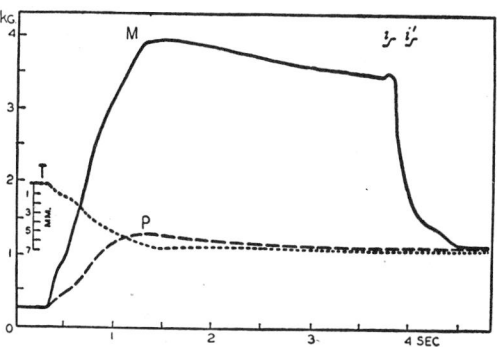

FIG. 5.1. The stretch reflex of the quadriceps (cat). Muscular response (M) before and (P) after cutting nerve to the muscle. T is a record of the table-fall which stretches the muscle. At the right is shown the effect of reflex inhibition, evoked between *i* and *i'* by stimulation of afferent fibers in the ipsilateral peroneopopliteal nerve (from Liddell and Sherrington).

such as the dog or rabbit, the knee jerk returns in a few minutes after spinal transection, in the monkey only after some days. In man, though postural reflex activity is entirely lost and the muscles are quite flaccid, the knee jerk is elicitable in some degree within 3 weeks after a complete transverse lesion of the spinal cord (see ch. 6).

The smooth and steady character of the contractions brought about through the stretch reflexes concerned with the maintenance of posture is due to the asynchronous sensory impulses set up by the numerous stretch receptors and the resulting asynchronous reflex discharge of motor impulses to the muscles. The muscle fibers are, therefore, never all relaxed nor all contracted at the same time. The sharp contraction of the quadriceps characteristic of the knee jerk, on the contrary, is brought about by the discharge of a volley of synchronous impulses which causes the fibers of the muscle to contract in unison.

Clonus. Under certain conditions a muscle or group of muscles instead of contracting smoothly and continuously may do so rhythmically in a series of rapidly repeated movements or jerks. Thus, in lesions of the central nervous system associated with hypertonus, sharp passive dorsiflexion at the ankle joint with maintenance of the foot in the dorsiflexed position by light pressure upon the sole, evokes a stretch reflex which consists of a series of rhythmical contractions of the stretched muscles (ankle clonus). The sudden dorsiflexion causes a sufficient number of stretch receptors to discharge a synchronous volley of impulses along the afferent nerve to the spinal centers and a synchronous efferent volley to be discharged to the muscles. The continued stretch of the muscle caused by keeping the ankle in the dorsiflexed position sets up another synchronous volley as soon as the motoneurons have recovered each time from the subnormal phase of the preceding one. Thus, the clonic movements continue so long as the muscles are kept upon the stretch. Clonus can be evoked in a similar fashion in other situations.

Some Other Stretch Reflexes (Deep or Tendon Reflexes) of Clinical Importance

The *jaw jerk*. Tapping the chin with the mouth partly open, and jaw supported, stretches the masseters, which contract and jerk the jaw. The reflex center is in the pons.

The *biceps jerk* is elicited by a sharp tap upon the biceps tendon in front of the elbow joint; the response consists of a quick contraction of the biceps with flexion of the elbow. The center for the reflex is situated in the 5th and 6th cervical segments of the cord; it is innervated through the musculocutaneous nerve.

The *triceps jerk* is evoked by a blow upon the triceps muscle just above the olecranon process of the ulna; contraction of the muscle and extension of the elbow result. The center for the response lies in the 6th and 7th cervical segments; the peripheral nerve is the musculospiral (radial).

The *supinator jerk* consists of contraction of the supinator muscle and flexion of the elbow; it follows a blow upon the styloid process of the radius. The center lies in the 5th and 6th cervical segments of the cord; the peripheral nerve is the musculospiral.

Rossolimo's reflex which is seen with hyperactivity of the stretch reflexes in the lower extremity, consists of flexion of the toes, including the hallux, when the toes are flicked on their plantar surfaces. A similar response (*Hoffmann's reflex*), which consists of a sudden flexion of the terminal phalanx of the thumb, can be evoked by flicking the finger tips.

The Tone of Skeletal Muscle

As a result chiefly of the work of the Sherrington school the word "tone" or "tonus" as applied to skeletal muscle has acquired a clearly defined meaning. Muscle tone is the steady reflex contraction of the muscles concerned in maintaining the posture characteristic of a given animal species. To use Sherrington's words "reflex tonus is postural contraction." Tonus has its basis in the

"static reactions" of the stretch reflexes, and its seat is therefore mainly in the *antigravity muscles*. In most mammals these are extensor muscles and in decerebrate rigidity the animal exhibits an attitude which is a caricature of standing, due to an exaggeration of the tone of the extensors.

In man the antigravity muscles and consequently those which exhibit the greatest degree of tone are the retractors of the neck, the elevators of the jaw (masseters), the supraspinatus, the extensors of the back, the ventral muscles of the abdominal wall (probably), and the extensors of the knee and ankle (vastocrureus, gastrocnemius and soleus). When these muscles are completely relaxed, as in an unconscious person, the body collapses. In the healthy conscious person, stretch reflexes are largely instrumental in preventing this occurrence.

Though the fundamental basis of tonus in voluntary muscle is the myotatic reflex centered in the spinal cord, the tonic state is influenced profoundly by higher centers. Impulses from labyrinthine and neck muscle receptors (pp. 88 and 92) exert their influence upon this background of tonus established through lower spinal centers. Similarly, pathways from cerebellar, midbrain and cerebral centers convey impulses which, impinging upon the final common path, are capable of altering the degree of tonus, or effecting finer adjustments in the tonic state and of maintaining its normal distribution between groups of muscles (fig. 5.8, p. 95). The tone of a given group of muscles may also be influenced through the spinal centers by impulses arising in other muscle groups (e.g., neck muscles and the muscles of the digits, ankle and wrist, as in the positive supporting reaction) and in skin receptors.

When the spinal centers are separated from higher centers there is an areflexic state of muscular flaccidity. Gradually this gives way to a state of hyperreflexia. The extensor tone, however, never is as pronounced as in decerebrate rigidity, whereas the flexor reflexes are more active.

A feature of tonic contraction is its economy in the expenditure of energy. Posture is maintained for long periods with little or no evidence of fatigue, e.g., in decerebrate rigidity; in the maintained closure of the jaws, standing or sitting in the normal person; and in the clasping reflex of the frog. The increase in metabolism is less than in the case of those ordinary contractions which result in movement, though the difference is not as great as was once supposed.[2] The work of

[2] In the normal human subject postural con-

Forbes and of Adrian and their associates indicates that the economy of energy is effected through different groups of muscle fibers contracting in relays, only a proportion of the total number of fiber groups of the muscle being active at any moment. Thus, active fiber groups mingled with inactive groups are scattered throughout the muscle. The alternating periods of rest and activity of the muscle groups explain how the tonic contraction can be maintained for so long without showing fatigue.

RED AND WHITE MUSCLE

The skeletal muscles of many animals, e.g., birds, rabbit, cat, etc., can be clearly divided into two types, (a) *red or dark*, and (b) *white or pale*. The former, as compared with the latter, are composed of smaller fibers having a granular and more opaque appearance, possessing more distinct longitudinal striations but less pronounced cross striations, and containing a larger proportion of sarcoplasm.[3] These *red* fibers contract more slowly, fatigue less readily, and are tetanized at a slower rate of stimulation than are the pale fibers. The *pale* fibers are translucent, show prominent cross striations and a small quantity of sarcoplasm. Those muscles which execute rapid movements are usually, though not invariably, of the pale variety, whereas the slower movements are carried out chiefly by the dark muscles. It is probable that all muscles are a mixture of the two types of fiber, but that in some the red, in others the pale type, predominates. The segregation of the two types of fiber in different muscles is much more pronounced in some animals, e.g., the fowl and rabbit, than in others. In birds capable of soaring or of long flight the wing muscles are mainly of the red type. In man and the monkey the two kinds of muscle can be distinguished with the naked eye, though the differences are not very pronounced. The predominance of one or other type of fiber, can, however, be readily made out under the microscope. The rapidly contracting flexor muscles are largely composed of the pale fibers, whereas each of the extensors usually has a superficially placed, rapidly contracting, pale component (or head) and a deep, slowly acting dark head. No hard and fast line, however, can be drawn, since both types of extensor muscle exhibit

tractions cause a rise of from 50 to 70 per cent in the basal metabolism. In certain nervous states, in which the body is maintained in fixed attitudes for long periods (catatonia), the increase in metabolism resulting from the tonic contraction of the muscles is less (20 per cent) than in the normal subject. The circulatory effects of sustained posture are also less pronounced in the pathological cases.

[3] They resemble the intrafusal fibers of the muscle spindle (p. 58).

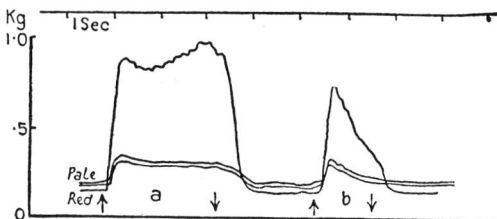

FIG. 5.2. The reflex effect of the labyrinthine and neck reflexes on red and pale muscle. Preparation with section of brain-stem slightly anterior to superior colliculi. M. triceps, short lateral head (pale), double traced line; short medial head (red), single line. Neck dorsiflexed at ↑ and ventriflexed at ↓. Labyrinth in intermediate position in each neck posture. (From Creed, Denny-Brown, Eccles, Liddell and Sherrington *Reflex Activity of the Spinal Cord*, Clarendon Press.)

FIG. 5.3. A suspended decerebrate cat showing extensor rigidity. In A, the labyrinths are intact. B, a decerebrate and labyrinthectomized animal. As a result of the destruction of the labyrinths the head has dropped; this position of the head induces reflex flexion of the forelimbs and extension of the hindlimbs (tonic neck reflexes, p. 93). (After Pollock and Davis.)

tone, and both take part in phasic contractions (fig. 5.2).

Decerebrate Rigidity

This is the term applied to the sustained contraction of the extensor muscles which supervenes upon transection of the brain stem at any level between the superior colliculi and the vestibular nuclei.[4] It was first studied and described in detail by Sherrington. The animal assumes a characteristic attitude with limbs stiffly extended,

[4] Decerebration can also be produced by tying the common carotids and the basilar artery at the center of the pons and thereby depriving the forebrain of its blood supply.

head retracted, jaws closed, and tail horizontal or erect. When placed upon its feet the limbs support the weight of the body (fig. 5.3.A). *The position is a caricature of the normal standing position.* The knee jerk and other stretch reflexes are exaggerated. The righting reflexes are abolished; tonic neck and labyrinthine reflexes are retained.

In some instances there is increased reflex excitability of the flexor muscles as well, but the characteristic feature of decerebrate rigidity is the tonic contraction of the muscles which maintain the posture of the body against gravity, the *antigravity muscles*. I may be pointed out that in the frog, whose natural posture is squatting with flexed thighs, legs and arms, it is the flexor muscles which are the site of decerebrate rigidity. Also in the sloth, whose habit it is to remain for long periods suspended from a tree branch, flexor rigidity is the characteristic result of decerebration. In the pigeon the flexor muscles which maintain the resting (folded) position of the wing exhibit rigidity, and in the ape the muscles which hold the elbow semiflexed when the body is erect show increased tone. In man abolition of the function of the cerebral motor cortex results in a state of increased tone in the flexors of the arms and in the extensors in the lower extremities, whereas decerebration at the mesencephalic level is associated with extensor spasticity in all four extremities.

TONIC LABYRINTHINE AND NECK REFLEXES IN THE DECEREBRATE PREPARATION (SEE ALSO P. 73)

Labyrinthine proprioceptors are responsible for the tone of the neck extensors; consequently, after destruction of the labyrinths in the decerebrate preparation the head is no longer held erect but falls into the fully flexed position. The rigidity in the forelimbs in turn is maintained through proprioceptive reflexes initiated in the extended neck muscles as well as directly through labyrinthine reflexes (p. 93). After labyrinthectomy, therefore, the flexed position assumed by the head sets up proprioceptive impulses from the neck muscles which lead to a reduction in the extensor tone of the forelimbs; these then become strongly flexed upon the chest (fig. 5.3B). If the neck muscles of the labyrinthectomized animal are deafferented, movements of the head are without effect upon the extensor muscles of either fore or hind limbs.

LENGTHENING AND SHORTENING REACTIONS

Attempts at passive flexion of the extended limb of the decerebrate (or chronic spinal) prepa-

ration are met by considerable resistance. If the force is increased beyond a certain point the stretch reflex (upon which the resistance depends) is inhibited and the limb gives way suddenly (*clasp-knife effect*). It may then be easily flexed to any degree and remains in the new position. The elongation of the extensor muscles which permits the flexion of the limb is called the *"lengthening reaction."* Upon moving the limb again into the extended position, the extensor muscle shortens adaptively, and again resists the limb being bent. This is the *"shortening reaction"*. These reactions give the muscles a certain plastic quality. The giving way of the extensor contraction in the lengthening reaction has been ascribed to inhibitory impulses from the tendon and the muscle that are set up when the stretch stimulus reaches a certain intensity. With inhibition of the extensor of the forcibly flexed knee, the knee extensor of the opposite leg is excited; this is known as *Phillipson's reflex*, a special instance of the principle of reciprocal innervation.

A CONSIDERATION OF THE CENTRAL MECHANISMS CONCERNED IN THE PRODUCTION OF DECEREBRATE RIGIDITY

Bazett and Penfield succeeded in keeping animals (cats) alive for two to three weeks after aseptic section through the midbrain. The animals showed extensor rigidity up to the day of death, though as time elapsed the condition tended to be less constant, intervals of reduced extensor tone and increased flexor tone alternating with periods showing the typical decerebrate posture. The fact that extensor rigidity was present so long after operation makes it clear that the condition is not due to the irritation of fibers at the plane of section, for these must have undergone degeneration before the end of the survival period. In a more recent investigation Bard and Macht demonstrated that if the hypothalamus is left intact, even though severed from the midbrain and bulb, and if the animals are given intensive care, they may recover some useful movement of their extremities following transection through the upper mesencephalon.

Decerebrate rigidity is evidently due to the release from higher control of a center or centers situated below the level of the transection. This control of the stretch reflex (postural reflexes; muscular tone) is complex. The precentral motor cortex exerts the most marked inhibitory effect upon these reflex muscular activities. In this portion of the cerebral cortex a narrow strip originally described by Marion Hines and commonly

known as 4s is particularly active in this regard.
Area 4s lies just anterior to area 4, or the area
gigantopyramidalis, which contains the Betz cells,
and immediately behind area 6, an agranular
precentral area which contains no Betz cells.
Neighboring cortical areas are probably also similarly although less effectively active. The opinion
once held, that this inhibitory effect over the postural reflexes is exerted by the giant pyramidal
cells of Betz in area 4 of the precentral gyrus and
the corticospinal or "pyramidal" tract, which
arises from the precentral gyrus, is certainly
erroneous. There is also evidence that some of the
basal ganglia exercise a certain controlling influence, probably both inhibitory and facilitatory,
over the postural reflexes, but detailed information regarding the anatomy and physiology of this
mechanism is lacking. In animals the anterior
lobe of the cerebellum exercises an inhibitory control over the stretch reflexes. Destruction of this
portion of the cerebellum in the cat results in a
state akin to decerebrate rigidity, whereas electrical stimulation of this portion of the cerebellum
in a decerebrate cat causes a pronounced relaxation of the decerebrate rigidity. In man it appears
that this cerebellar inhibitory mechanism is far
less effective than in animals or is absent altogether, for no one has ever demonstrated any
human cases in which cerebellar lesions have resulted in spasticity. The only alteration in muscular tone seen in human beings with cerebellar lesions is hypotonia.

In any consideration of the control of muscular
activity by the central nervous system one is repeatedly impressed with the important differences
between the organization of the nervous system
of man as compared with lower animals. If one
removes the precentral motor cortex (areas 4 and
6, or the frontal agranular cortex) from man, a
severe and enduring spastic paralysis of the contralateral extremities develops. If, on the other
hand, the "motor" cortex or the cortex of the sigmoid gyrus is removed from the cat, or even if the
entire cerebral cortex is removed, any paralysis is
fleeting and slight, and any alteration in the tonic
state of the skeletal musculature is of little moment. These facts illustrate the constant care
which must be exerted in interpreting any facts
demonstrated in animal experiments in explanation of phenomena observed in man.

Area 4s exercises its *inhibitory* influence over
muscular activity by transmitting impulses to a
centrally placed bulbar portion of the reticular
formation. It is likely that the basal ganglia and

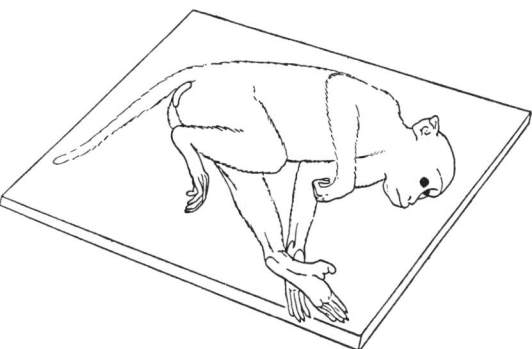

FIG. 5.4. Showing posture of a "thalamus"
monkey. The underneath limbs are extended and
the uppermost flexed. When the animal is turned
over, the previously extended limbs (being now
uppermost) are flexed, and those which were
flexed (now underneath) are extended. (After Bie-
ber and Fulton.)

the cerebellum also send their impulses there. The
reticular formation also contains a laterally placed
facilitatory mechanism which is capable of *enhancing* the postural reflexes. This facilitatory
mechanism is connected with various other central neural structures, but most notably with the
vestibular apparatus and the vestibular nuclei.
These nuclei may augment reflex activity either
directly over the vestibulo-spinal pathways or by
way of the reticular formation. It is obvious then
that the reticular formation, which contains both
inhibitory and facilitatory mechanisms, is capable
of acting as a center for the regulation of the
stretch and other postural reflexes and of muscular activity in general.

The view that spasticity is not merely the result of excessive spinal reflex activity released by
the removal of suprasegmental inhibitory control but is due to an imbalance of the reticular
formation between inhibition and facilitation is a
distinct advance in our physiological thinking,
but it represents an incomplete understanding of
the problem and ignores many clinical facts. Some
of the most striking examples of muscular spasticity from disturbances in the human central
nervous system are seen in patients with traumatic or neoplastic lesions of the spinal cord. In
such cases the entire brain, including the reticular
formation of the brain-stem, has been excluded
from the control of the skeletal musculature which
is innervated by the spinal cord below the level of
the lesion. Obviously the spasticity must therefore be of spinal origin only, representing a
removal of descending inhibitory influences and
a release of spinal mechanisms from suprasegmental control.

Decerebrate Rigidity in Man

In certain neurological disorders in man one encounters disturbances in muscular tone and in the postural reflexes, including the stretch reflex. With lesions in the region of the midbrain one sees a state very akin to the decerebrate rigidity of laboratory animals. All four extremities are rigidly extended. The forearms are pronated. The muscles show the lengthening and shortening reactions, and the tonic neck and labyrinthine reflexes can be elicited. When the head is flexed on the neck the legs are rigidly extended and the arms are flexed at the elbows. When the head is rotated to one side the extremities on that side become rigidly extended while those on the opposite side relax or flex. When the head is rotated to the opposite side the pattern is reversed (fig. 5.4). With decortication rather than decerebration the picture is somewhat different. The lower extremity is still usually spastic in extension but the upper extremity is usually flexed at the elbow, wrist and fingers. This is the situation usually seen in patients with a spastic hemiplegia caused by a destructive lesion in the internal capsule.

Diseases affecting the basal ganglia are commonly associated with increased muscular tone. This differs from spasticity in that it affects both flexors and extensors more nearly equally, and the degree of resistance to passive manipulation is more nearly constant throughout the range of motion. This rigidity seems to be dependent upon proprioceptive afferent impulses, as it disappears

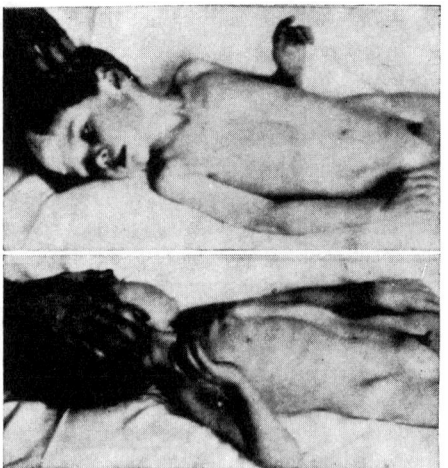

FIG. 5.5. Decerebrate child. Suprasellar cyst causing interruption of descending pathways at the level of the midbrain. Turning the head to one side causes extension of the arm of that side and increased flexion of the opposite arm. (Modified after L. E. Davis.)

when the posterior spinal roots are divided. In this respect it resembles the spasticity of decerebrate rigidity, which is dependent upon the stretch reflex for its existence.

The Spinal State

Transection of the cord produces an immediate flaccid paralysis of the muscles below the point of section. Immediately after section in the lower cervical region the limbs hang limply, the muscles being quite toneless. The stretch reflexes and other extensor responses cannot be elicited and the knee jerk is abolished. The blood pressure falls and vascular and visceral reflexes are unobtainable. This condition is called *spinal shock*. Its duration varies from species to species. The higher the position of the animal in the phylogenetic scale the more profound is the shock and the slower is the recovery. In the frog the duration of spinal shock is brief. In the rabbit, the knee jerk returns within a few minutes, in the cat within an hour, and in the dog somewhat more slowly. In the monkey it does not reappear for several days. Other extensor reflexes remain in abeyance for a much longer time. In the cat and dog the picture immediately following spinal transection is different from that seen after decerebration. The extensor stretch reflexes are less active, while the flexor responses to nociceptive stimuli are more easily elicited. Consequently, if the spinal cord of a decerebrate preparation is sectioned, the exaggerated extensor tone is replaced (below the section) by an imbalance in the sense of an increased flexor tone.

Spinal shock also follows section through the medulla below the vestibular nuclei (*decapitate preparation*).

In the cat and dog recovery from spinal shock gradually takes place in a few days. The blood pressure is restored to normal and the vascular reflexes can again be obtained. The reactions of the extensor muscles return, and the animal is able, though imperfectly and very briefly, to support the weight of the body when placed upon its feet (chronic spinal animal).

Spinal shock is attributed to the removal of impulses which in the intact animal descend from higher centers to reinforce the spinal centers. That it is due to this and not simply to an inhibitory effect of the local injury itself seems clear from the fact that after an animal has recovered from spinal shock, a second transection made behind (lower than the original one) does not cause a return of the shock state. In *the cat and dog* the flexor reflexes are evidently dependent only to a minor extent upon the higher centers, since they are capable of being executed by the spinal centers alone and are seen in their most exaggerated form in animals or human beings with a complete transection of the spinal cord. The fact that the extensor stretch reflexes are less active in the spinal animal is due to the loss of facilitatory impulses from the reticular formation and the vestibular nuclei, but these reactions can eventually also be carried out by the spinal centers. In *primates* in which a greater degree of motor function is represented in the cerebral cortex, the immediate effect of cord section upon reflex activity is much more profound than in the cat or dog. Recovery of reflex activity following transection of the spinal cord is in considerable measure dependent upon the condition of the animal or patient. Infection or impaired nutrition greatly retard recovery.

The "Thalamus" Animal

This term is given to an animal whose cerebral hemispheres have been removed, leaving the optic thalami intact (see fig. 5.9, Section I). Such preparations retain their righting reflexes and can regulate their body temperature. They are also capable of carrying out coordinated reflex acts and show, often to an exaggerated degree, reactions which in the intact animal are associated with emotional states (fright, anger). Such reactions, which are termed pseudoaffective, are also exhibited by an animal whose cortex alone has been ablated (e.g. "sham rage", see ch. 7). In contrast to the decerebrate animal, the distribution of muscular tone in the thalamic cat or dog shows little departure from the normal, though pronounced extensor rigidity becomes evident when the animal is held suspended in mid-air.

Primates, on the contrary, are usually unable to walk after bilateral decortication, and they show profound alterations in the muscular tone of the limbs. Such an animal generally assumes a characteristic attitude. When it lies upon its side the limbs that are underneath are extended and those that are uppermost are flexed. The limbs that are uppermost show a pronounced grasp reflex. Turning the animal on to its opposite side reverses the picture. The limbs which were underneath and extended are now flexed and show the grasp reflex, while the limbs that previously were uppermost, being now underneath, are extended. Righting reflexes (except those dependent upon vision) and the tonic labyrinthine and neck reflexes of Magnus and de Kleijn are shown in a striking fashion (fig. 5.5).

If the extirpation of the cerebral cortex is carried out piecemeal over a considerable period of time, and if the animal is given meticulous care as to nutrition and manipulation of its extremities, it may be able to stand briefly and awkwardly and may even take a few steps, but in general such an animal is quite disabled. The disability is much more profound than that seen in a decorticate cat.

Static and Statokinetic Reflexes of Magnus and de Kleijn

The reflex mechanisms governing the orientation of the head in space, the position of the head in relation to the trunk and the appropriate adjustments of limbs and eyes to the position of the head, are called into action by afferent impulses discharged from receptors situated in (a) the vestibular apparatus (semicircular canals or utricle), (b) the neck muscles, (c) the retina, and (d) in the body wall or limb muscles.

These are complex reflexes concerned with the posture of the extremities and the trunk as influenced by movements of other extremities, of the trunk and of the head and neck. They aid in maintaining the position of the body in space, in restoring the body to an upright position when its position has been disturbed, in forward progression, etc. A more detailed account of these postural reflexes follows.

General Static Reflexes

THE RIGHTING REFLEXES

The orientation of the head in space, and the ability to maintain the body in a certain definite (normal) relation to the head is a characteristic of animal life. A cat held back downwards and then allowed to fall through the air lands upon its feet, its head and body assuming, in a flash, the normal attitude. A fish resists any attempt to turn it from its natural position and if placed in the water upon its back flips almost instantly into the normal swimming position. Even a crayfish rights itself when placed on its back.[5] These righting reactions are complex and involve five separate types of reflex.

[5] The otocyst of the crayfish and lobster is the homologue of the utricle of mammals. It is open to the exterior and at moulting time its lining is shed. The otoliths consist of grains of sand which the animal itself introduces into the otocyst. If, after moulting, the animal is placed in a dish containing fine iron filings, these are inserted and various forced movements of the head and body can be induced by bringing a magnet into relation with the ear.

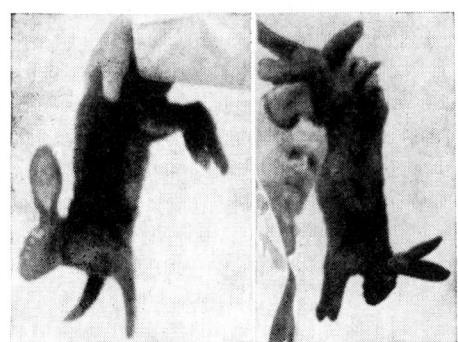

FIG. 5.6. On left, position taken up by a thalamus rabbit with intact labyrinths. As it possesses the labyrinthine righting reflexes, it carries its head in the normal position. On the right, position taken up by a rabbit like the preceding but deprived of its labyrinths. The head is not raised towards the normal position. (After Magnus.)

(a) Labyrinthine righting reflexes acting upon the neck muscles.

(b) Neck righting reflexes acting upon the body.

(c) Body righting reflexes acting upon the head.

(d) Body righting reflexes acting upon the body.

(e) Optical righting reflexes.

The first four of these are demonstrated best upon a "thalamus" animal (p. 91). When a "thalamus" rabbit or a blindfold normal animal is suspended by the pelvis (fig. 5.6) the head turns until it assumes its normal position in space i.e., into the position it would occupy were the animal in its natural position. The maintenance of the head in the new position is due to *labyrinthine righting reflexes* acting upon the neck muscles. Turning the body of the animal through the air into different positions is followed by compensatory movements of the head, its orientation in space being thereby maintained. After extirpation of the labyrinths or destruction of the utricle alone, the head shows no compensatory movements when the rabbit is suspended; it hangs limply like that of a dead rabbit.

When the blindfold or thalamic animal is laid resting upon its side on a table, the head is raised into the usual upright position as a result of the labyrinthine reflexes just mentioned. The contraction of the neck muscles which rotate the head sets up, in turn, proprioceptive impulses, which through a center in the upper cervical cord exert an influence upon the muscles of the body which rotate it (thorax first, then pelvis) into the normal relationship to the head. This is the *neck righting reflex acting upon the body*. A labyrinthectomized animal when laid upon its side behaves in a some-

what similar manner. The reaction under the latter circumstances is due, however, to the asymmetrical stimulation (pressure of one side of the body upon the table) of exteroceptors in the body wall, and the reflex contraction of the neck muscles. This is the *body righting reflex acting upon the head*. If a board of a weight equal to that of the animal is laid upon its upper surface, the pressure being thereby disposed equally on the two sides, the compensatory movement of the head does not occur.

Again, when a blindfold animal or one which has been decorticated is laid upon its side, and its head held down to the table, to eliminate the righting reflexes of labyrinthine and cervical origins, as well as the body righting reflex acting upon the head, the body nevertheless attempts to right itself by raising the hindquarters. This must be due to the asymmetrical pressure upon the body exerting a reflex effect upon the skeletal musculature, i.e., a *body righting reflex acting upon the body*.

This reflex is well shown by the labyrinthectomized dogfish, especially if blinded. When placed in the water (pressure being equal on all sides) upon its side or back, the fish deprived of its labyrinths swims away in the false position. When, however, it comes into contact with the bottom or side of the tank (pressure then being exerted unequally) it immediately rights itself. Even worms possess this means of orientation.

The *optical righting reflexes* are initiated through retinal impressions. They are absent in the thalamic animal since their center is cortical (occipital lobes). Visual impressions play a prominent role in the orientation of the head in some animals, such as the monkey, dog and cat. If a labyrinthectomized dog is held in the air in order to exclude the body righting reflexes, it is capable of orienting the head, but is not able to do so if blindfolded. The optical righting reflexes are of minor importance as compared with the labyrinthine in animals such as the rabbit and guinea pig whose cortical development is more rudimentary, and who depend to a large extent upon subcortical visual centers. In the more intelligent animals the optical righting reflexes are abolished by decortication. Yet even the crayfish deprived of its otocyst is able to right itself, though with less facility than normally, when placed upside down in water. In this medium righting reflexes due to unequally distributed pressures upon the body surface must obviously be in abeyance; the righting reaction, then, is apparently entirely of ocular origin. That this is so is proved by blinding the animal; then the righting reaction is lost completely.

To sum up, the righting reflexes may now be given in their natural sequence. When the animal is placed upon its back the labyrinthine reflex acting upon the neck muscles turns the head into its normal relationship to the dimensions of space; the proprioceptive reflexes of the neck muscles then bring the body into its normal relation to the head. When resting upon a rigid support these reflexes are reinforced by body righting reflexes (on head and body). When the animal falls through air or water, these latter reflexes of course do not come into play. A labyrinthectomized but otherwise normal animal, such as the cat or dog, may attempt to recover its upright position when falling through the air, by the operation of the optical righting reactions (however, see fig. 5.18). The righting effort is absent if the eyes are covered with a hood. Furthermore, an air-breathing animal deprived of its labyrinths, though a good swimmer, drowns if thrown into deep water, since it cannot orient itself by the sight of surrounding objects. Persons with congenital defects of the labyrinths, though able to swim, may become disoriented and drown if they fall or dive into deep water.

Righting reflexes may be demonstrated in the human subject. A baby a few weeks old, for example, when lying prone raises the head into a nearly vertical position. When blindfolded and held by the pelvis in different positions in the air, it moves the head toward the normal position.

Local and Segmental Static Reactions. Supporting Reactions

Magnus speaks of the simultaneous reflex contractions of both extensor and flexor muscles and other opposing muscles, whereby the joints are fixed and the limbs converted into rigid pillars for the support of the body against gravity, as the *positive supporting reaction*. This reaction is initiated by:—

(a) Impulses discharged from the proprioceptors of the flexor muscles of the terminal segments of the limbs—digits and ankle or wrist; the pressure of an animal's paw upon the ground by stretching these muscles provides the adequate stimulus which calls forth simultaneous reflex contractions of the flexors and extensors of the knee (or elbow).

(b) Myotatic reflexes set up in the flexors of ankle and toes (plantar flexors), and of the corresponding forelimb joints; excessive extension at these joints is thus counteracted. Any tendency

toward over-extension at the knee or elbow is also provided against through the reflex set up when the flexors of these joints are stretched. Similarly, any tendency of the knee or elbow to bend under the weight of the body calls forth a myotatic reflex from the extensors, which prevents any weakening of the supporting action of the limb.

(c) Impulses set up in the pressure receptors in the deeper layers of the skin of the sole when in contact with the ground; thus exteroceptive reflexes reinforce those of proprioceptive origin. The exteroceptor element is well shown in a decerebellated dog. When such a preparation is placed upon its back and the head strongly flexed, the hindlimbs are flexed in all joints. Light pressure with the finger upon the toe pad then causes an extension of the limb, and if the finger be moved with the limb as it extends so that only very light pressure upon the pad is maintained, one has the sensation of the limb being drawn out by the finger. For this reason the movement has been called the "magnet reaction."

The relaxation of the muscles and the unfixing of the joints which enables the limb to be flexed and moved to a new position is called the *negative supporting reaction*. It is brought about by raising the pad off the ground and plantar flexing the toes and ankle. The exteroceptive stimulus and the stretch stimulus to the *plantar flexors* are thus removed. The reflex "unlocking" of the limb is not, however, simply due to the removal of these stimuli, but has in addition a positive element, namely, the stimulus provided by plantar flexion and the consequent stretching of the dorsi-flexors of the toes and ankle—relaxation of the extensors of the knee or elbow and contraction of the flexors result.

The supporting reactions, though seen best in a decerebellate animal, can also be demonstrated in the decorticate preparation or in one whose brainstem has been divided above the medulla oblongata. Segmental static reactions, e.g., the combination of flexion reflex and crossed extension reflex, have been described in chapter 4.

Statotonic or Attitudinal Reflexes

(1) *Tonic labyrinthine and neck reflexes acting upon the limbs.* These reflexes influence the tone of the skeletal muscles and thereby maintain the different parts of the body in an attitude appropriate to a given position of the head. They are investigated best in the decerebrate animal (p. 1165), the righting reflexes being then largely abolished. The proprioceptors concerned are in:
(a) the *labyrinth* (tonic labyrinthine, i.e., utricu-

lar, reflexes) which are brought into play by alterations in the position of the head in space, (b) the *neck muscles* (tonic neck reflexes) which come into action when the position of the head is altered with respect to the body. In order to study separately the part played by each of these reflexes in any given reaction, the following procedures are adopted.

A. To exclude the neck reflexes:

(a) Immobilization of the neck of an animal by means of a plaster of Paris bandage in order to prevent movement of the head in relation to the trunk. Any tonic effects resulting from a change in the animal's position must then be due solely to alterations in the position of the head in space (labyrinthine reflexes); or (b) section of the posterior roots of the first three of four pairs of cervical nerves.

B. To exclude tonic labyrinthine reflexes:

(a) Fixation of the head alone in some suitable apparatus. The tonic effect resulting from movement of the body must then be due to an alteration in the position of the body in relation to the head, i.e., to movements of the neck; or (b) destruction of the labyrinths or section of the 8th cranial nerves.

The labyrinthine reflexes exert an influence upon the tone of the extensor muscles which is in the *same* direction (increase or decrease) in all four limbs. The influence of the neck reflexes, on the other hand, is usually in *opposite* directions in the fore and hind pairs of limbs. The greatest degree of extensor tone is exerted through the labyrinth mechanism when the animal is supine and the mouth cleft inclined at an angle of 45° (fig. 5.7) above the horizontal plane. Extensor tone diminishes as the angle increases; it is minimal in

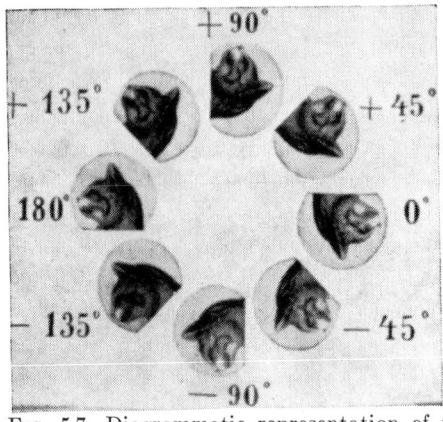

Fig. 5.7. Diagrammatic representation of the positions of an animal's head, each marked with the angle which the mouth cleft makes with the horizontal plane. (After Magnus.)

the prone position with the mouth cleft at an angle of 45° below the horizontal plane.

In an animal on all fours the labyrinthine effect is, therefore, to increase or decrease the extensor tone in the muscles of all four limbs when the head is strongly extended or flexed, respectively. In the decerebrate labyrinthectomized animal, with the neck reflexes alone operating, flexion of the forelimbs and extension of the hindlimbs occur when the neck is flexed toward the sternum (ventriflexion) (see fig. 5.3, p. 87). Extension of the neck (dorsiflexion) produces the converse picture, i.e., extension of the forelimbs and flexion of the hindlimbs. When, therefore, the neck is ventriflexed in the decerebrate animal with intact labyrinths, the neck reflexes reinforce the tonic labyrinthine effect upon the forelimbs but antagonize that upon the hindlimbs; the usual result is relaxation of the forelimbs with strong extension of the hindlimbs. When the neck is extended the neck reflexes reinforce the labyrinthine effect upon the tone of the forelimbs but antagonize that upon the hindlimbs. The effect of the neck reflexes upon the extensor tone of the latter again predominates; the extension of the forelimbs is maintained but definite relaxation of the hindlimbs occurs.

Rotation of an animal's head (turning in the frontal plane of the skull) causes increased extensor tone of the fore and hindlimbs on the side of the body toward which the jaw is rotated (*jaw limbs*) and reduces the extensor tone of the opposite limbs (*skull limbs*).[6] Inclination of the head toward one shoulder (lateral flexion) as when an animal turns a corner is accompanied by similar effects—extension of the limbs on the side of the body toward which the jaw (or snout) is inclined (jaw limbs) and flexion of the limbs on the opposite side (skull limbs).

Pressure upon the last cervical vertebra reduces the tone in all four limbs (*vertebra prominens reflex*).

The significance of these reflexes and their importance in the coördination of the postural muscles may be realized when the attitudes of the intact animal are observed. Thus when an animal turns to one side, the limbs of that side are stiffened in order to support the body's weight. A cat looking upwards to a bird in a tree extends the forelimbs and flexes the hindlimbs, thus giving

[6] Magnus has introduced the term *jaw limbs* to indicate the limbs toward which the chin of man or the jaw of animals is rotated or inclined. The opposite limbs, i.e., the limbs to which the vertex of the skull is rotated, are called *skull limbs*.

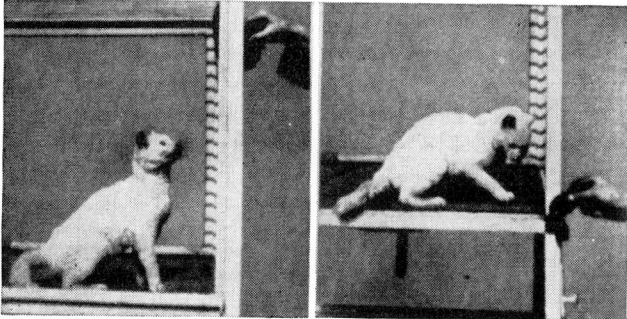

FIG. 5.8. Photographs of a normal cat, showing the animal's posture (on left) when its attention is attracted by an object placed above it. Photograph of the same animal (on right) when its attention is drawn to an object below it. The difference between the two positions of the forelimbs is very marked, because in them the neck and labyrinthine reflexes reinforce one another; the hindlimbs are in much the same position in both cases, since the two sets of reflexes cancel one another. (After Magnus.)

the back a suitable inclination which improves the position of the head and eyes, and places the body in a position preparatory for a spring (fig. 5.8). When looking into a hole or beneath a cupboard the flexion of the forelimbs and extension of the hindquarters gives an opposite but no less advantageous inclination to the body. Depression of the back in the region of the last cervical vertebra brings the animal into a crouching attitude.

Stato-tonic effects may be demonstrated in certain lesions of the central nervous system associated with a state analogous to decerebrate rigidity of animals (pp. 87, 90). Turning the head to one side, for example, causes an increased tone in the extensors of the jaw limbs and decreased tone in the limb muscles of the opposite side.[7] When the head is in the position for maximal labyrinthine tone, i.e., when the patient is supine and the neck extended, the extensor tone of the paralyzed limbs increases, but it decreases in the prone position.

(2) *Tonic labyrinthine and cervical reflexes acting upon the eyes.* Tonic effects upon the eye muscles, analogous to those described for the skeletal muscles, result from changes in the position of the head. Labyrinthine and neck reflexes are responsible. Alteration in the position of the head with neck immobilized, or movement of the head in relation to the body after labyrinthectomy, is followed by compensatory eye movements. Turning the head downwards causes an upward movement of the eyes, which are held in this position so long as the head position is maintained, the tone of the superior recti and inferior oblique being increased while that of the inferior recti and superior oblique is reduced. A corresponding compensatory

[7] This, according to Magnus, can also be shown in a certain percentage of normal infants, and in hydrocephalus it may be well marked.

movement of the eyes occurs when the head is turned upward. Similarly, when the head is turned to one side the internal and external recti of the two eyes cooperate to deviate the eyes outward or inward in relation to the head. Briefly, the eyes are moved in a direction opposite to that taken by the head; thus they tend to maintain their original position in space and with it the visual field as it was prior to the head movement. It should be pointed out that the actual *movement* of the eyes is a stato-kinetic reflex (p. 96) and is due to a different mechanism (semicircular canals) from that which maintains the eye *position* while the head is held in the altered attitude. The latter is a stato-tonic reflex, dependent upon the utricle.

SUMMARY OF THE CENTERS FOR GENERAL STATIC REFLEXES

Magnus found that all the static reactions mentioned in the foregoing section could be obtained unaltered after removal of the cerebellum, as could also most of the stato-kinetic reflexes to be described in the next section. Nevertheless, this rather surprising fact does not necessarily imply that in the normal intact animal the cerebellum plays no part in these reactions. A contrary conclusion must be drawn from anatomical considerations and from observations in cerebellar disease in which disturbances referable to the labyrinth (e.g., abnormal positions of head, falling, etc.) are manifest. Moreover, numerous connections between the labyrinths, the vestibular nuclei and the cerebellum have been demonstrated.

(a) *The righting reflexes.* All the labyrinthine righting reflexes, as well as the body righting reflexes acting upon the head, have their centers in the midbrain. The center for the optical righting reflexes is cortical, that for the body righting reflexes acting upon the head is in the midbrain.

(b) *The stato-tonic labyrinthine reflexes* acting upon the skeletal muscles have their center in the vestibular nuclei.

(c) *The neck reflexes* are centered in the upper two or three cervical segments of the spinal cord (see fig. 5.9).

(d) The centers for the *tonic labyrinthine and cervical reflexes acting upon the eyes* are situated between the vestibular nuclei and the oculomotor nuclei.

Placing and hopping reactions. These have been thoroughly investigated by Bard and his associates. Bard and Brooks describe five *placing reactions:*

(1) If a cat is held in mid-air with legs dependent and chin held up so that it cannot see anything below or in front, contact of the backs of the forepaws with the edge of the table is followed by a quick movement of the limbs which brings the paws, pads down, precisely upon the surface of the table. (2) If the forelimbs of a cat are held down while the chin is brought in contact with the table near its edge, the forepaws when released are instantly raised and placed upon the table beside the chin. This movement is usually followed by extension of the limbs and the assumption of a standing position. (3) If the fore-or hindlimbs of a cat standing or sitting upon a table are pushed over the table's edge, they are immediately lifted and placed in their original positions. (4) If one abducts, without holding, the limb of a standing cat, it is instantly returned to its previous position. (5) If a blindfolded cat is suspended in the air with forelimbs free, and its head brought toward some obstacle, at the instant that the vibrissae come into contact with the object the forepaws are raised and accurately planted upon the surface of the object. The first three of these reactions are due to stimulation of receptors upon the body surface (exteroceptors) and probably also of proprioceptors in muscles and tendons. The fourth is a purely proprioceptive reflex; the last is initiated from tactile receptors.

The *hopping reactions* consist of limb movements which serve to maintain the standing position against any force acting upon it in a horizontal plane. When, for example, a cat is held so that its body is supported upon one fore- or hindlimb and is then pushed in one or other direction, the supporting limb hops quickly in the direction of the displacement, the foot being kept directly under the corresponding shoulder or hip. The hopping reactions are probably dependent upon myotatic (stretch) reflexes (pp. 68 and 84).

The placing and hopping reactions are controlled from the sensorimotor area of the cerebral cortex. Bard and Brooks found that removal of this region from both cerebral hemispheres abolished

the placing reactions, and produced an extreme degree of deficiency in the hopping reactions. Decortication (complete removal of the neocortex) produce no greater deficiency. The control exerted by the cerebral cortex is entirely contralateral, i.e., the component movements of the reactions on one side of the body are governed solely by the opposite side of the brain.

Kinetic, Statokinetic or Acceleratory Reflexes

The term kinetic is attached to these labyrinthine reflexes because they are caused by the *movement* of the head, but since it is not the movement itself, but *acceleration* above a certain rate, either angular (rotatory) or linear (progressive), that is the adequate stimulus, *acceleratory reflexes* is a better name.

ANATOMY OF THE LABYRINTH

The nature of the specialized end organs of the labyrinth which initiate the static and acceleratory reflexes regulating and modifying posture and equilibrium must now be considered. They consist of five discrete areas of highly differentiated neuroepithelium, innervated by the fibers of the vestibular division of the eighth cranial nerve: three *cristae* (i.e. 'crests') and two *maculae* (i.e. 'spots'). These structures occupy special positions within the *membranous labyrinth*, a system of interconnected, fluid-filled ducts and sacs, viz. the three *semicircular canals*, the *utricle*, and the *saccule*. The membranous labyrinth in turn is enclosed by the *bony labyrinth*, a series of passages in the petrous portion of the temporal bone. These consist of the three corresponding bony semicircular canals, each of which opens at either end into an expanded ovoid chamber, the *vestibule*, in which lie the utricle and saccule (fig. 5.10 and 5.11).

The bony *cochlea*, containing the membranous *cochlear duct* with the end organ of hearing, is also a part of this system. It is customary, therefore, to differentiate between the *auditory* and the *non-auditory labyrinth*. Although it is with the latter, often referred to simply as the *labyrinth* or the *vestibular apparatus*, that we are concerned here, the reader should refer also to the description of cochlear anatomy in ch. 17, in order to get a clearer understanding of the relations of these complicated structures one to another.

The labyrinthine fluids. The entire membranous labyrinth is filled with a clear fluid, the *endolymph* or *otic fluid*, which resembles intracellular fluid in its ionic composition, having a far greater concentration of potassium than of sodium. In the space between the membranous labyrinth and the walls of the bony labyrinth is the *perilymph* or *periotic fluid*, which has approximately the same

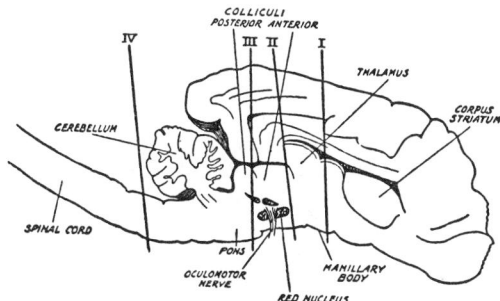

FIG. 5.9. Diagram to illustrate the effects of sections through cat's brain at various levels. Line I, thalamic animal, righting, tonic labyrinthine and neck reflexes retained; little disturbance of muscular tone; Lines II and III, decerebrate rigidity; Line IV, behind vestibular nucleus, decapitate animal, extensor rigidity less marked, tonic neck reflexes retained. Section at level of second or third cervical segment of the cord—spinal animal—abolishes the tonic neck reflexes (after Magnus); III indicates Sherrington's original section.

composition as the cerebrospinal liquor and other interstitial fluids. For a discussion of the origin, circulation, and fate of these labyrinthine fluids and an analysis of their composition, see ch. 17.

The semicircular canals. Each canal has an expanded end, the *ampulla* in which is located the *crista ampullaris,* the specific sense organ. The canals lie in planes approximately at right angles to one another and are called, respectively: the *horizontal, lateral,* or *external;* the *superior* or *anterior* (vertical); and the *posterior* (vertical). (fig. 5.10). Note that the ampulla of the horizontal canal is located at its anterior end, with the ampulla of the superior canal close beside it. Both open into the utricle near the macula, whereas the ampulla of the posterior canal is directed away from the other two and opens into the opposite end of the utricle, near the narrow end of the horizontal canal. The narrow ends of the two vertical canals unite to form the *common crus,* through which they communicate with the utricle. Al-

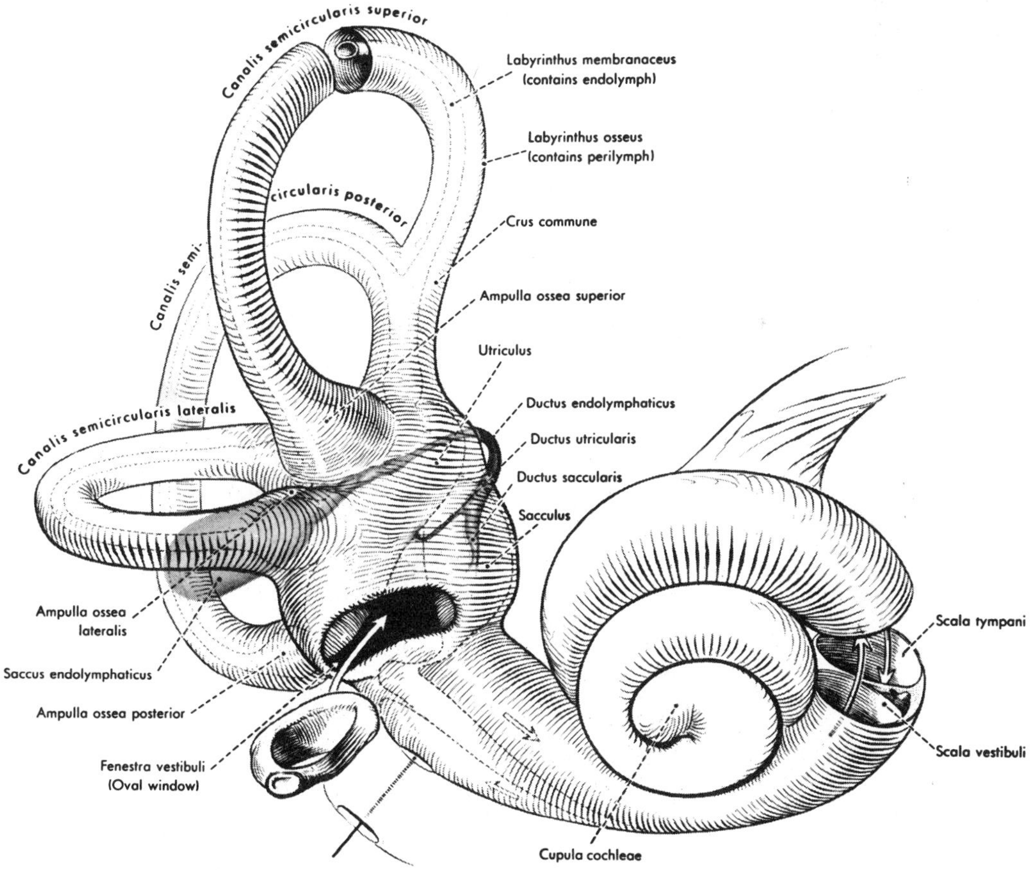

FIG. 5.10. The bony labyrinth (human, right side) with the position of the membranous labyrinth indicated, including the endolymphatic duct and sac. The stapes has been removed from the oval window to reveal the interior of the vestibule, and the cochlea has been opened in the first coil to show the cochlear duct in cross-section. (From a drawing by Biaggio J. Melloni, reproduced by permission of Abbott Laboratories, North Chicago, Illinois.)

though the canals themselves are semicircular, it can readily be seen that the utricle completes the 'circle' for each of them.

The horizontal canals of the two sides lie in the same plane, with their convexities directed outwards and backwards. When the head is in the erect position these canals are only approximately horizontal; they are, in fact, inclined downwards and backwards at an angle of about 30° to the horizontal plane. Their position may be illustrated by holding the clenched fists, representing the two ampullae, in front of the face, with the elbows half-flexed and raised to shoulder height.

The planes of the vertical (anterior and posterior) canals both make an angle of about 45° with the frontal and the sagittal planes of the skull. The anterior canal of one ear is therefore nearly in the same plane as the posterior canal of the other ear, whereas the posterior or anterior canal of one ear is at right angles to its fellow of the opposite side as well as to the other two canals of the same ear (fig. 5.12).

The crista ampullaris. The receptor organ of each semicircular canal is located in the ampulla athwart the canal. It consists of a ridge of neuroepithelium which is surrounded at its base by a secretory epithelium, the *planum semilunatum.* The neuroepithelium contains two types of sensory *hair cells,* one flask-shaped and surrounded by an afferent nerve-chalice (type I of Wersäll), the other cylindrical, with afferent and efferent nerve endings at its base (type II). Each hair cell bears 40 to 60 hairs (*stereocilia*), the rootlets of which are embedded in a cuticular plate at the apex of the cell, and a single *kinocilium* (resembling the motile cilia of the trachea, for example), with its basal body surrounded by a small cuticle-free area of the cell surface. The stereocilia are drawn up in orderly rows and graded according to length, the longest (40–75 μ) next to the kinocilium (fig. 5.13). Between the hair cells are the *supporting cells,* with nuclei near the basement membrane and microvilli on their apical surfaces (fig. 5.14). Extending from the crista to the roof of the ampulla is a gelatinous, dome-like structure, the *cupula,* enclosing the long sensory hairs in fine, parallel channels. The cupula, an elusive entity, was long regarded as an artifact of histological preparation but it is now recognized as the essential moving part in the stimulation of the hair cells. It appears to be a secretion of the supporting cells of the crista and to consist largely of mucopolysaccharides.

The otolith organs: utricle, and saccule. The utricle communicates with the saccule by way of the *utriculo-saccular duct,* and the saccule with the cochlear duct by way of the *ductus reuniens* (Hensen). From the utriculo-saccular duct arises the *endolymphatic duct,* which extends through the bony *vestibular aqueduct* to end in the blind *endo-lymphatic sac,* lying on the intracranial surface of the petrous bone, between the periosteum and the dura (fig. 5.10).

The *maculae* of the utricle and saccule are patches of neuroepithelium closely resembling the cristae in cytoarchitecture, with hair cells of type I and type II and supporting cells. Instead of bearing a cupula, each macula is covered by an *otolithic membrane* into which the short (5–7 μ) sensory hairs extend. This is also a gelatinous structure, but it contains in addition an abundance of *otokonia,* crystals of calcium carbonate in the form of *calcite.* These otokonia, with a specific gravity of 2.93–2.95, make a substantial contribution to the total mass of the otolithic membrane (fig. 5.15).

The macula of the utricle is located on the inferior and anterior walls of the sac, its posterior two-thirds sloping back at an angle of 30°, parallel with the horizontal canal, and its anterior one-third turned up at an obtuse angle like the tip of a ski. The right and left utricular maculae lie in the same approximately horizontal plane. Their positions can be illustrated by holding the hands forward, palms up, with the fingers slightly flexed. The macula of the saccule is situated on the medial wall of the saccule, overlying the bone, in a more or less vertical antero-posterior plane. The positions of the right and left saccular maculae can be illustrated by crossing the hands in front of one, with the palms in the vertical plane and the fingers partially flexed.

THE NERVOUS CONNECTIONS OF THE LABYRINTH

The central connections of the vestibular mechanism are very widely distributed throughout the central nervous system, and are far from being fully known, but the following connections are fairly well established.

The impulses from the proprioceptors of the different parts of the non-auditory labyrinth are conveyed to the medulla by the fibers of the vestibular division of the 8th nerve. The cell bodies of the vestibular neurons lie in Scarpa's ganglion situated in the internal auditory meatus. These cells are bipolar. Their afferent processes (dendrites) are distributed to the sense organs of the utricle, saccule and semicircular canals, and terminate synaptically on the bodies of the hair cells. The fibers ending on type I cells (chalices) are generally of larger caliber than those on type II cells. Their axons pass for the most part to the *superior, lateral, medial* and *inferior vestibular nuclei* in the medulla (a few go directly to the flocculo-nodular lobe and the fastigial nuclei of the cerebellum) from which relay fibers follow three pathways. Thus there are:

(a) Ascending fibers from the superior vestibular nucleus which join the medial longitudinal bundle of the same side. From the medial vestibu-

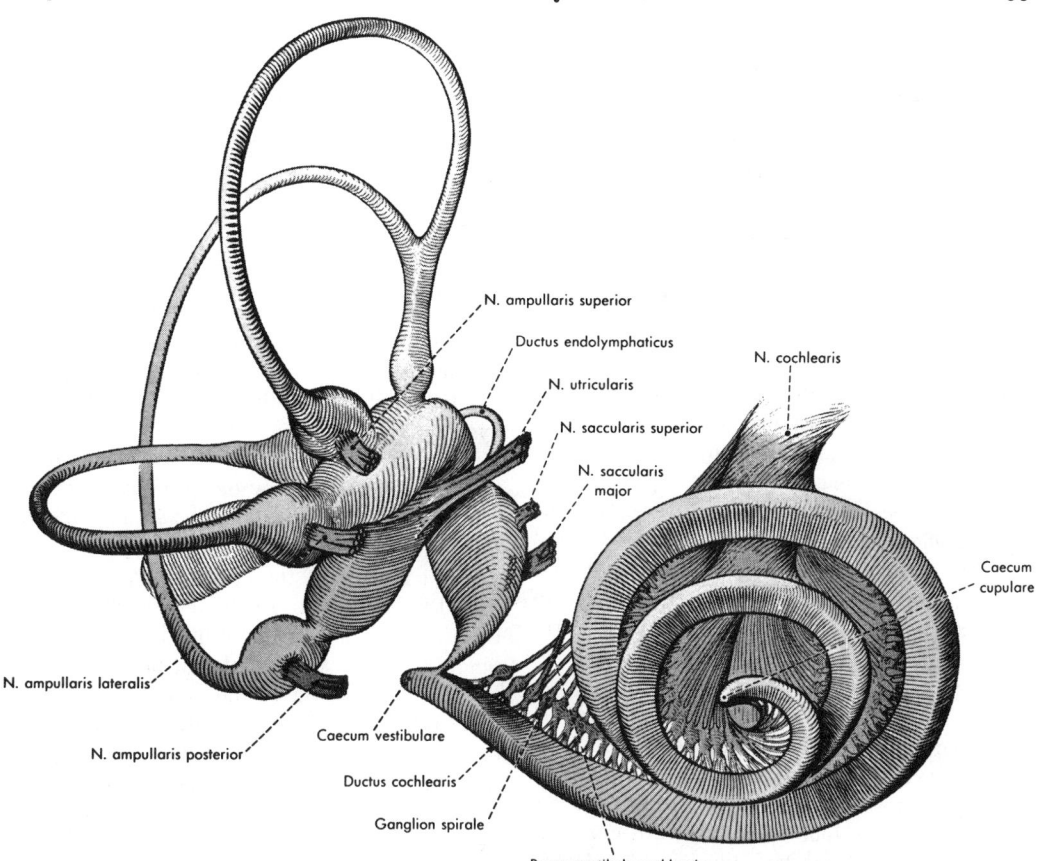

FIG. 5.11. The membranous labyrinth (human, right side) showing the innervation of the vestibular end organs and the organ of Corti. (From a drawing by Biaggio J. Melloni, reproduced by permission of Abbott Laboratories, North Chicago, Illinois.)

lar nucleus impulses are relayed to the medial longitudinal fasciculus of the opposite side; from the inferior vestibular nucleus fibers ascend in the medial longitudinal fasciculus of both sides. The fibers from these nuclei terminate in the nuclei of the 3rd, 4th and 6th cranial nerves and constitute the vesibulo-ocular tract. Through these connections, remarkably precise reflex movements of the eyes are brought about (fig. 5.16).

(b) Fibers descend from the lateral (Deiter's) and the inferior vestibular nuclei. Those from the lateral nucleus constitute the vestibulospinal tract (ch. 6), while those from the inferior nucleus descend in the spinal extension of the medial longitudinal fasciculus as far as the upper cervical region of the cord, where they synapse with the anterior horn cells. Through these connections impulses are conveyed to the muscles of the neck, trunk and limbs (fig. 5.17A).

(c) Fibers pass via the inferior cerebellar peduncle mainly to the flocculonodular lobe of the cerebellum on the same side, but also to the fastigial nucleus of the same side. These constitute the vestibulo-cerebellar tract (fig. 5.17B).

(d) Numerous connections exist between the vestibular nuclei and the reticular formation, which constitutes an internuncial relay between the vestibular nuclei of both sides and the motor neurons of the spinal cord (via the reticulospinal tract). In it impulses from both labyrinths are reorganized, in accordance with the principle of reciprocal innervation, into excitatory and inhibitory impulses influencing the flexors and extensors of the limbs.

(e) Vestibular connections to the temporal cortex, which apparently follow much the same path as the auditory fibers, have been described in the dog, cat, and monkey.

(f) Efferent fibers from the lateral vestibular nucleus which follow the same course as the fibers of the olivocochlear bundle have been described by Gacek. They end on the hair cells of the neuroepithelia as large, densely-granulated endings (Wersäll). A diagram showing the course of the vestibular efferents is given in fig. 17.12A.

EFFECTS OF LABYRINTHECTOMY

The first systematic study of the results of surgical injury to the semicircular canals was

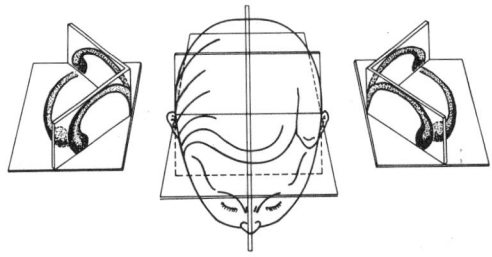

FIG. 5.12. Relations of the semicircular canals to the median sagittal, transverse frontal, and horizontal planes of the head.

made by Flourens (1824) in the pigeon. Upon cutting each of the canals, he observed forced movements of the head and conjugate deviations of the eyes in the plane of the injured canal. Thus, Flourens demonstrated for the first time the significance of the three-dimensional anatomical arrangement of the canals. In similar experiments on the rabbit he was also able to produce convulsive eye movements and disturbances of equilibrium. Ewald (1892) further analyzed the effects of labyrinthectomy in the pigeon. Immediately after operation he observed profound muscle weakness and loss of ability to fly. Later the weakness gradually disappeared, but the power of flight did not return. Severe loss of muscular tone after labyrinthectomy is also seen in the frog. McNally and Tait (1925) showed that this weakness depends upon destruction of the utricle rather than the semicircular canals.

Unilateral labyrinthectomy. The immediate effect of surgical ablation of one labyrinth in laboratory animals is to produce striking asymmetry of posture and body movements. These changes may be summarized as follows:

(1) *Ocular.* Both eyes are turned toward the side of the operation. The eye of the operated side also shows downward deviation, whereas the eye of the sound side turns upwards (skew deviation). *Horizontal nystagmus* (rapid, rhythmical, fast and slow alternating movements of the eyes) is present, with the fast movements toward the normal side.

(2) *Lateral flexion and rotation of the occiput* is toward the operated side, together with flexion of the thorax on the pelvis.

(3) *The extensor tone of the limb muscles* is greater on the sound side than on the operated side, the limbs of this side being flexed and adducted, whereas those of the opposite side are extended and abducted.

(4) *Spontaneous movements.* These are all toward the operated side and consist of (a) circling,

i.e., turning of the body around a vertical axis; (b) rolling, i.e., rotation around a horizontal axis (in the rabbit the rolling movements are very violent); (c) side-to-side movements of the head (head nystagmus); (d) falling to operated side.

In the normal animal, the actions of the right and left labyrinths are in part synergistic, but to a great extent they are antagonistic. Symmetrical posture and normal movements of head, eyes, trunk, and limbs depend, therefore, on the interplay between the two labyrinths, acting both in concert and in opposition. Many of the features of unilateral labyrinthectomy, especially the nystagmus, the asymmetry of posture, and the rolling and circling movements, are results of the unopposed tonic activity of the remaining labyrinth, producing continuously acting righting reflexes. Irritative effects on the fibers of the vestibular nerve of the operated side appear to be of less importance. Bilateral destruction of the labyrinths by surgery or ototoxic drugs causes diminished muscle tone, ataxia, and loss of the ability to perform complicated coordinated movements, e.g., those of flight, as in the pigeon, or those of righting the body while falling through the air, as in the cat. There is a slow improvement in the posture and gait of a cat or dog after destruction of one or both labyrinths, largely through compensation by ocular and proprioceptive reflexes, but even after several months deficiency phenomena can still be observed.

In man, intracranial section of the vestibular nerve is not followed by the violent disturbance of equilibrium that occurs after labyrinthectomy in animals (Dandy). Admittedly, the two cases are hardly comparable, since section of the eighth nerve has been carried out only in patients already suffering from the profound dysfunction and destruction of the vestibular end organs that can occur in Menière's syndrome.

Opening the labyrinth, as in the operation of fenestration of the horizontal canal to improve hearing in otosclerosis, causes vertigo (false sense of rotation) and other symptoms of vestibular disturbance, which usually subside after a week or two. After stapedectomy for otosclerosis, in which the vestibule is opened for a short time at the oval window, the vertigo is less severe, but most patients experience it for a few days, and in some individuals it may persist.

Degeneration of the vestibular neuroepithelia caused by prolonged administration of the ototoxic antibiotic *streptomycin* is usually bilateral and may produce a profound deficit of vestibular function in man and laboratory animals (fig. 5.18). In tuberculous patients, who usually receive prolonged therapy, the manifestations have ranged from a mild, transient vertigo to a complete loss of vestibular responses ("dead labyrinth"), with or without persistent, disabling ataxia. Since these effects occur in patients whose labyrinths were intact before they received treatment with the antibiotic, they demonstrate that the loss of vestibular function can be a far more serious matter for the human being than it was once thought to be. In most patients with streptomycin intoxication of the labyrinths, ocular and proprioceptive reflexes eventually compensate in large measure for the vestibular loss, but these patients may still have difficulty in walking in the dark, or even in an open field or on rough ground.

LABYRINTHINE FUNCTION

The semicircular canals are organs of dynamic sense, whereas the otolithic organs subserve both dynamic and static senses. The hair cells of the ampullar cristae of the canals respond to angular acceleration (rotation). The hair cells of the macula of the utricle, and probably those of the macula of the saccule as well, are stimulated mainly by changes in position of the head, and by linear acceleration. They are sometimes called *gravity receptors.*[8]

The semicircular canals. The receptors of the cristae respond and give rise to a sensation at the commencement and at the cessation of a rapid rotatory movement. Though impulses at low frequency are continuously discharged along the nerve fibers while the head is at rest, a sharp increase in impulse frequency occurs at the commencement of the rotation, and again at its end. The rapid discharge lasts for 20–25 seconds. The receptors of the cristae, therefore, give no information of a continuous rotatory motion of constant speed, though any change in speed of rotation (i.e., positive or negative angular acceleration) is signalled to the central nervous system. The reason for this will be evident upon consideration of the stimulating mechanism.

Stimulation of the sensitive hair cells of the cristae is brought about through the effect which the movement of the head exerts upon the endolymph within the canals, the particular canal being stimulated depending upon the plane in which the rotation occurs. The canals are of capil-

[8] Breuer (1874 to 1891) was the first to point out the difference in function between the semicircular canals and the utricle.

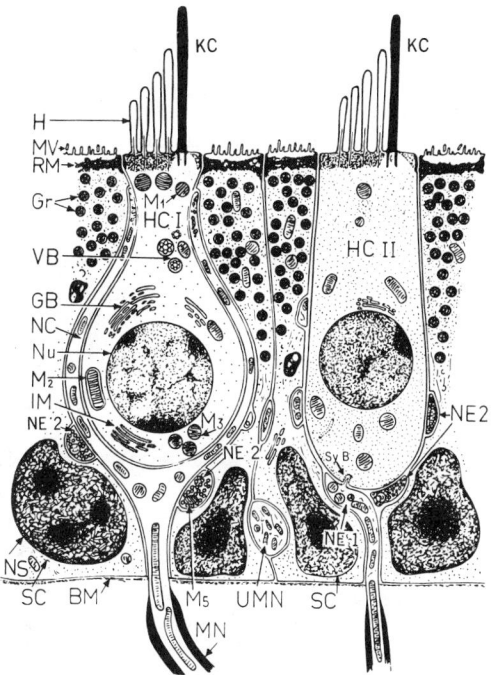

FIG. 5.13. Schematic drawings of the two types of vestibular sensory cells (HC I and HC II) and their supporting cells, SC. KC, kinocilium; H, stereocilia; MV, microvilli; RM, reticular membrane; Gr, granules; M_1-M_5, mitochondria; VB, vesiculated body; GB, Golgi complex; NC, nerve chalice; Nu, nucleus; IM, intracellular membranes; NE_1, afferent nerve ending with synaptic bar, SyB; NE_2, efferent nerve ending; UMN, unmyelinated nerve fiber; MN, myelinated nerve fiber; NB, nucleus of supporting cell; BM, basement membrane. (From Engström, Ades and Hawkins, in *Modern Trends in Neuromorphology*, Lenhossék Memorial Volume, Symp. Biol. Hung. 1965, 5: 21.)

lary diameter (0.1 to 0.2 mm. in man). The membranous labyrinth is essentially a closed system and is supported on the outside by connective tissue strands, by perilymph, and by the unyielding walls of the osseous labyrinth.

When the head turns quickly from a position of rest, say to the right (see fig. 5.19 and table 5.1), i.e., in a clockwise direction, and in the plane of the horizontal canals (around a vertical axis), the endolymph within the canal, owing to its inertia, does not move at first with the walls of the canal. This lag is equivalent to a movement or flow of endolymph to the left—counter clockwise —in both canals. But owing to the relative positions of the two ampullae such a flow of endolymph is toward the ampulla (*ampullopetal*) in the right canal and away from the ampulla (*ampullofugal*) in the left. It causes the cupula— the gelatinous dome surmounting the crista, in

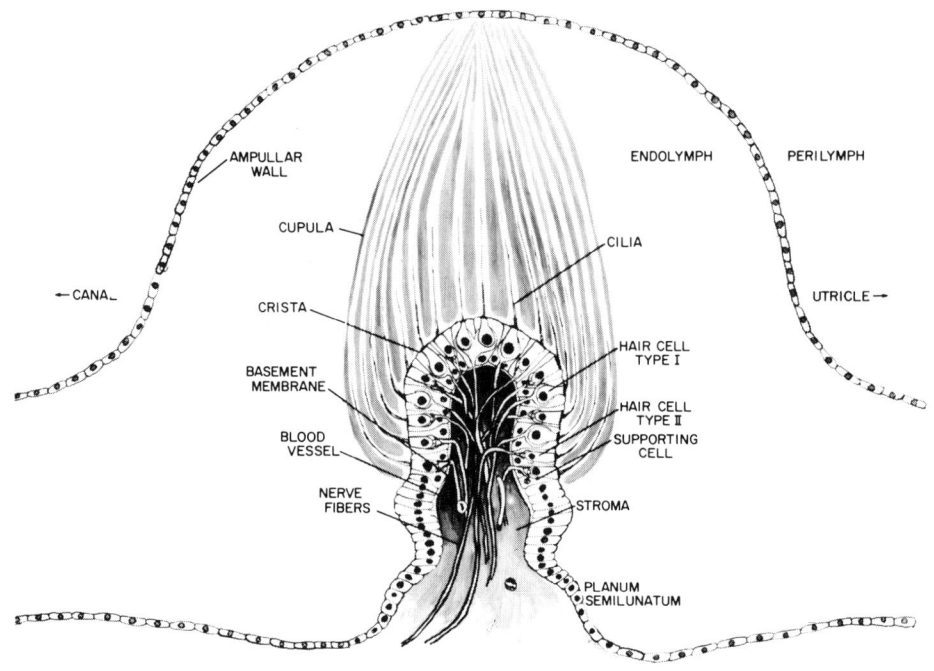

FIG. 5.14. Diagram showing the structure of an ampullar crista and cupula

TABLE 5.1

Semicircular Canal	Rotation About the:					
	Longitudinal axis		Transverse axis		Vertical axis	
	Right	Left	Forwards	Backwards	Clockwise	Anticlockwise
Right ant. vert......	●	⊗	●	⊗	⊗	●
Left ant. vert........	⊗	●	●	⊗	●	⊗
Right post. vert.....	●	⊗	⊗	●	●	⊗
Left post. vert.......	⊗	●	⊗	●	⊗	●
Right horizontal.....	○	○	○	○	●	⊗
Left horizontal......	○	○	○	○	⊗	●

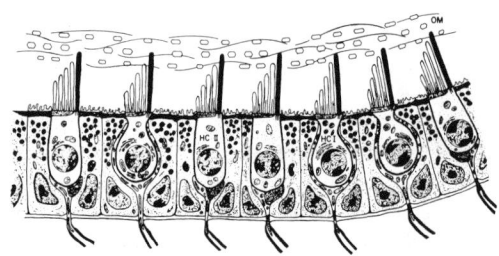

FIG. 5.15. Diagram of the neuroepithelium of the macula of the utricle, with otolithic membrane and otokonia.

which the hairs are embedded—to swing toward the utricle in the right ampulla and away from the utricle in the left ampulla. Deflection of the cupula causes, in turn, bending of the hairs which acts as a more effective stimulus to the hair cells when the swing is toward the utricle (right) than when it is away from the utricle (left). These events are reversed when the rotation is to the left—counterclockwise.

Thus, a clockwise rotary movement of the head (e.g., a quick turn) around a vertical axis stimulates the right horizontal canal; a counterclockwise motion excites the left, or, put in another way, the receptors of the horizontal canal are stimulated only when the flow of endolymph is ampullopetal.

Responses of the six semicircular canals (of fish, the thornback ray) to rotation. ● excited; ⊗ inhibited; ○ unaffected. ant. vert. = anterior vertical; post. vert. = posterior vertical. (After Lowenstein and Sand.)

The receptors of the vertical canals, on the other hand, are stimulated only when the flow of endolymph is ampullofugal. Until recently there was no satisfactory explanation for this difference between the horizontal and vertical canals, which was first pointed out by Ewald, and is generally referred to as Ewald's Law.

It has now been shown that there is a mor-

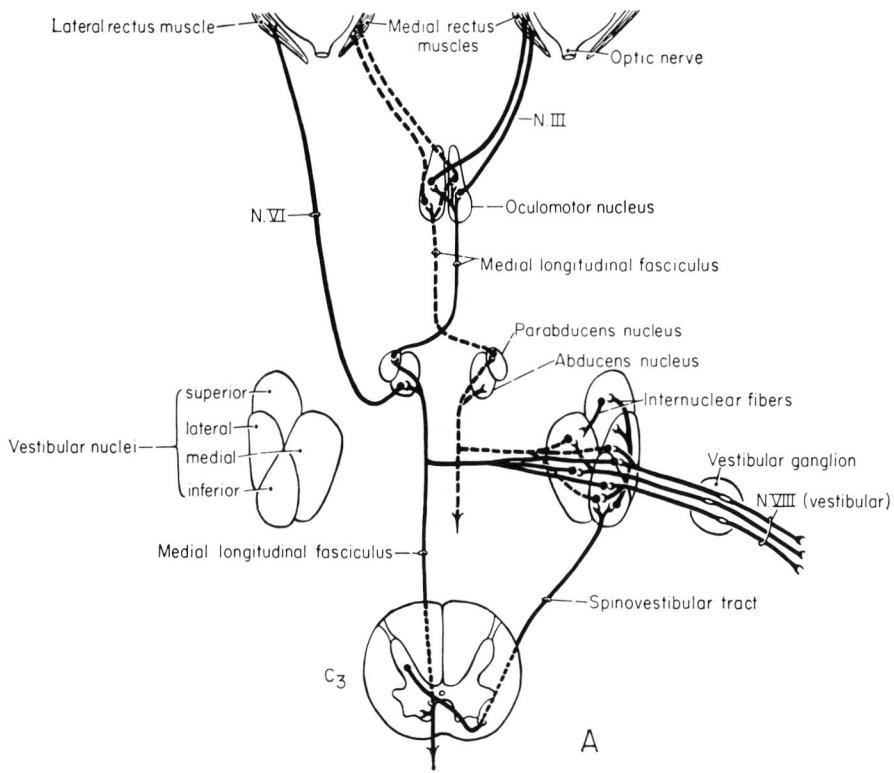

FIG. 5.16. Diagram showing the relation of the vestibular nuclei to the medial longitudinal fasciculus and the motor nuclei of the eye muscles for movements in the horizontal plane. (From E. C. Crosby, T. Humphrey, and E. W. Lauer, *Correlative Anatomy of the Nervous System*, The Macmillan Company, New York, 1962. Reproduced by permission.)

phological polarization of the hair cells of the cristae, corresponding to the functional polarization described by Ewald's Law. The bundles of cilia on the hair cells show a consistent arrangement, with the kinocilium always located at the periphery of the hair bundle. In the crista of the horizontal canal, the kinocilium is always on the side of the bundle *toward* the utricle, whereas in the vertical canals it is always on the side *away from* the utricle. (Lowenstein and others). Flock and Wersäll have postulated that bending of the hairs toward the kinocilium depolarizes the cell and thus increases the rate of discharge in the afferent nerve fibers which innervate it; bending of the hairs in the opposite direction causes hyperpolarization and a diminished rate of nerve impulses (fig. 5.20).

The maximal response is given by a canal when it is rotated in its own plane. This is a statement of the principle discovered by Fluorens, sometimes referred to as Flourens' Law. No response is aroused from a horizontal canal by rotation in a plane at right angles to this. But a vertical canal, though most effectvely stimulated by

rotation in its own plane (diagonal) also gives a lesser response when rotated in other planes. Thus a quick tilt of the head, forward or backward (rotation around a transverse axis), or laterally toward a shoulder (rotation around an anteroposterior axis) stimulates the vertical canals.

Furthermore, since the vertical canals are placed diagonally in the head, and the anterior vertical canal of one side is in the same plane with the posterior canal of the opposite side, a *diagonal* rotatory movement forward will maximally stimulate an anterior canal and suppress the activity in the opposite posterior canal. A backward rotatory movement will act in the opposite way.

When any rotational stimulus lasts for longer than a few seconds, and the inertia of the endolymph is overcome, the cupula is restored to its resting position; at the cessation of the movement the momentum of the fluid causes bending of the cupula in a direction opposite to that at the commencement of the movement. This is why no sensation occurs during prolonged

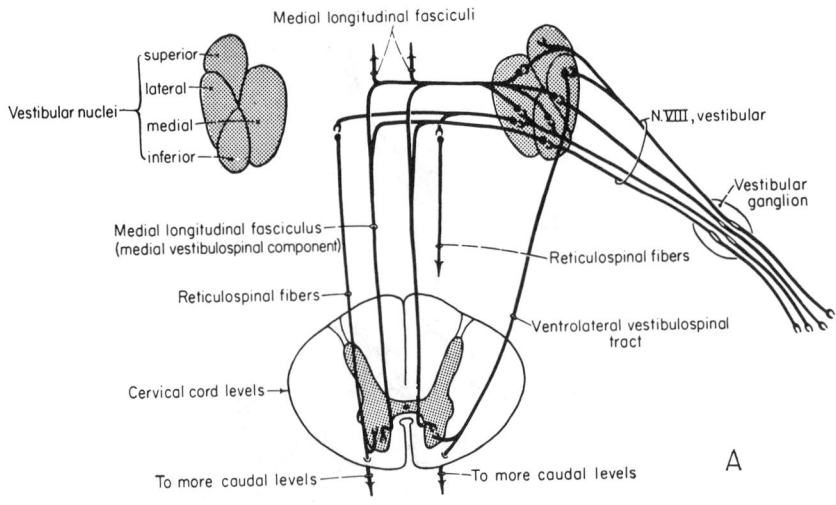

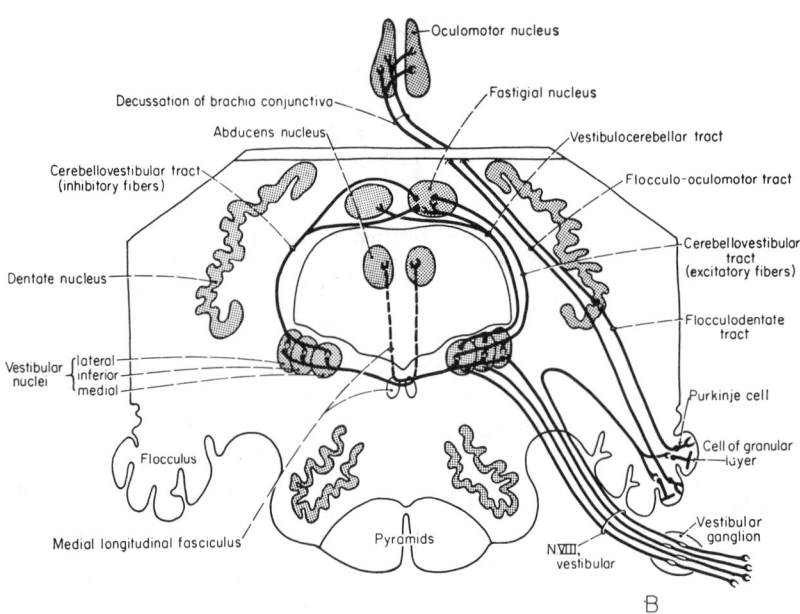

FIG. 5.17. A. Connections between the vestibular nuclei and the ventral horns of the spinal cord. B. Connections between the vestibular nuclei and the cerebellum. (From E. C. Crosby, T. Humphrey, and E. W. Lauer, *Correlative Anatomy of the Nervous System*, The Macmillan Company, New York, 1962. Reproduced by permission.)

rotation, but a sensation of turning in the opposite direction is felt during deceleration or when the rotation suddenly ceases.

The mechanism of the semicircular canals is admirably suited to signal rapid turns of the head, i.e., a rotatory movement in one or other plane. But it is poorly adapted to report continuous rotation at a constant speed (for, as Adrian points out, this is a movement to which the body throughout its life is rarely if ever subjected, and the body has therefore not developed suitable

receptors to record it). Continuous rotation tends to confuse rather than to inform, and also, because of the swing of the cupula in the reverse direction when the rotary movement ceases, an illusion of rotation (in the opposite direction) is created. The ballet dancer avoids the confusion in a pirouette by making a series of alternating accelerations and decelerations of the head, fixing the gaze for as long as possible on the same point during each rotation.

A brief outline of the experiments on vestibular

function. The foregoing account of vestibular mechanisms is based upon the work of many investigators. Some of the basic experiments will be briefly outlined.

Tait and McNally studied the effect on frogs of tilting and rotation after denervation of one or more canals in various combinations, and after destruction of the utricle or saccule. Steinhausen elucidated especially the movements of the cupula in the canals of the pike. The labyrinth can be visualized in the living fish after the introduction of India ink, the cupula showing up clearly against the darker background. He demonstrated that it completely partitions the cavity of the ampulla, being in contact everywhere around its free circumference with the membranous wall. It moves during caloric stimulation as well as during angular acceleration, but not during electrical stimulation. Later, similar studies were made by Dohlman which confirmed Steinhausen's findings. Dohlman followed the endolymph movements by means of a drop of oil introduced into a canal. Ross employed the *right half* of a frog's head held in an apparatus, whereby the labyrinth could be turned and fixed in any desired plane,

and subjected to rotation. The electrical changes were recorded from a filament of the auditory nerve. Clockwise rotation caused a response from the horizontal canal, whereas an anticlockwise movement was ineffective. Steinhausen's conception of a deflected cupula caused by an endolymph movement was verified. Lowenstein and Sand employed the surviving isolated labyrinth of the elasmobranch, *Raja clavata*, and recorded the electrical potentials from individual canals. They found that the nerve endings of the cristae discharged impulses continuously at a low rate during rest, but at increased frequency during angular acceleration or deceleration, depending upon the direction of rotation. Adrian, experimenting with cats, recorded the potentials from single units by means of a fine wire electrode inserted into the medulla in close proximity to the vestibular nuclei. The main findings of others in cold-blooded animals were confirmed.

Cupulae resembling those of the semicircular canals are found in the *lateral line system* of fish and amphibia. From the developmental as well as the morphological point of view, these end organs are closely related to those of the labyrinth, so that one often speaks of them together as belong-

Fig. 5.18. Righting reactions of the cat while falling. Left, normal cat, dropped in supine position, immediately rights itself in air and lands on its feet. Right, cat with labyrinthine neuroepithelia destroyed by streptomycin makes no attempt to right itself in air and lands on the cushion on its back.

ing to the *acustico-lateralis* system. It is not surprising that their physiological mechanisms of excitation are similar. All show characteristic electrical responses to stimulation, the *microphonic potentials*. In the ampullar cristae and in the cochlea these potentials reproduce the frequency of the stimulus. (See ch. 18) In the lateral line, on the other hand, the response frequency is twice that of the stimulus. Flock and Wersäll have shown that the cristae of the lateral line, unlike those of the ampulla, have approximately half of their hair cells with kinocilia on one side of the hair bundle, and the other half with kinocilia on the opposite side. The cristae therefore have bidirectional polarization and respond to movements of the cupula in both directions, giving rise to the frequency doubling in the microphonic potentials.

EFFECTS OF STIMULATION OF THE SEMICIRCULAR CANALS

The semicircular canals respond to any one of the following forms of stimulation: (1) *Rotation* (angular acceleration) of the head about a vertical, transverse or anteroposterior axis. (2) *Caloric* —syringing the ear with hot or cold water. (3)

Galvanic i.e. passage of a direct current through the labyrinth. (4) *Mechanical*.

Rotation

The effects produced by rotation are: (a) *Nystagmus*, (b) *vertigo*, (c) *reactions of the neck and limb muscles*, (d) *reactions of the autonomic nervous system*.

(a) *Nystagmus*. When an animal's head is turned sharply about a vertical axis, i.e., in the plane of the horizontal canals, the eyes deviate in the opposite direction, and then return with a quick jerk to the original forward-looking position.

If the horizontal rotation is continued, a rhythmical, jerky, to-and-fro movement of the eyes occurs, which is called *nystagmus* (from the Greek *nystazein*, to nod or doze). It is present during rotation (*per-rotational* nystagmus) and again immediately after rotation (*post-rotational* nystagmus). During rotation with the eyes open, the nystagmus consists of two components: *optokinetic nystagmus* in response to the movement of images across the retina, and *vestibular nystagmus* in response to the stimulation of the semicircular canals. The optokinetic component, which lasts so long as rotation is continued, can be excluded by the simple expedient of closing or covering the eyes. When the apparent movement of the environment is no longer seen, only the vestibular component remains. It lasts for about 20 sec., i.e., during the displacement of the cupula in response to the angular acceleration.

Post-rotational vestibular nystagmus can easily be demonstrated in man by rotating the subject with eyes closed, in a revolving chair (Bárány chair), at a rate of about 10 complete turns in 20 sec. (30 r.p.m.). In order to stimulate the horizontal canals maximally, the head should be inclined forward about 30°, so that the horizontal canals are almost exactly in the plane of rotation. When the rotation is suddenly stopped (angular deceleration), and the subject opens his eyes, the rapid to-and-fro motion of the eyes is seen. It consists of a slow deviation to one side, and a quick return to the normal position. This post-rotatory nystagmus lasts for about 20 sec. in a normal person; its quick component is in a direction opposite to that of the rotatory movement. By convention *the direction of the quick movement is taken to designate the direction of nystagmus from whatever cause*. Thus a right horizontal per-rotational nystagmus is caused by

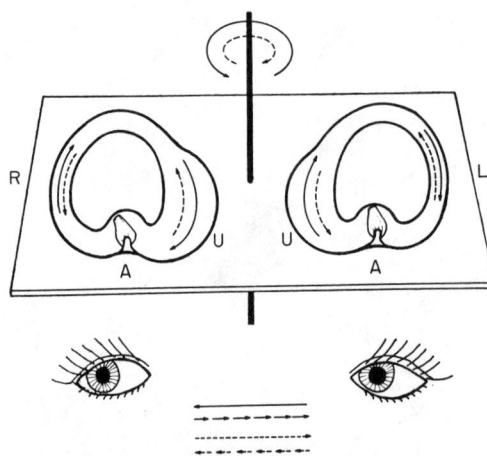

FIG. 5.19. Direction of fluid movement and cupular displacement in the horizontal canals during and after rotation to the left. Solid arrows represent per-rotational displacement, interrupted arrows post-rotational. Below, the long arrows give the direction of the slow component of nystagmus, the short arrows that of the fast component. (Adapted from Portmann.)

rotation to the right. At the end of rotation to the right, the nystagmus reverses its direction, and becomes a left horizontal post-rotational nystagmus.

When the eyes are kept open during rotation, the optokinetic and vestibular components of nystagmus are in the same direction and thus synergistic. During deceleration they are in opposite directions and thus antagonistic, since the optokinetic nystagmus does not reverse its direction.

There are two other forms of nystagmus—*vertical* and *rotatory*—in which the eyes oscillate up and down, and round and anteroposterior axis, respectively. These types result from the simultaneous excitation of both vertical canals. Vertical nystagmus is induced when the canals are stimulated with the sagittal plane of the head in the plane of rotation, that is with the head inclined about 90° to one or other shoulder. The rotatory type follows when the frontal plane of the head is bent forward 90° or more, or backward 30° to 60°. In each instance the post-rotational nystagmus is observed after the head has been brought upright (fig. 5.21).

Central connections responsible for nystagmus. The slow phase of vestibular nystagmus is initiated from the semicircular canals and has its center in the vestibular nuclei, from which impulses are discharged, in part at least, through the medial longitudinal bundle to the motor nuclei for the eye muscles. The quick component is entirely central, but the nervous pathways upon which it depends are uncertain. However, its neural mechanism must lie in the brain stem between and including the nuclei for the third nerves and the vestibuli nuclei, for nystagmus occurs after transections of the brain above and below these levels, respectively. It is not abolished by ablation of the cerebellum. Even the nuclei of the 3rd and 4th nerves may not be necessary, for in the rabbit nystagmus can be induced after section just above the abducens nucleus. Lorente de Nó has located the center for the rapid phase in the formatio reticularis in the region of the abducens nucleus. He also found that nystagmus could still be produced after section of both medial longitudinal bundles. There may be a double pathway from the vestibular nucleus to the nuclei of the ocular nerves—through the medial longitudinal bundle and through the reticular formation.

Optokinetic nystagmus is initiated from the retina. Impulses reach the medial longitudinal bundle and the eye muscle nuclei by way of the optic nerve and tract and the superior colliculus.

(b) *Vertigo.* True vertigo consists of a sensa-

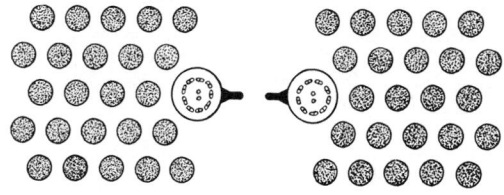

FIG. 5.20. Schematic representation of two vestibular hair bundles cut transversely in a plane parallel to the cuticular surface of the neuroepithelium. The position of the basal foot of the kinocilium is indicated to illustrate the morphological asymmetry of this structure. On the left, displacement in the direction of the arrow is excitatory, on the right, inhibitory. (After Lowenstein, Osborne, and Wersäll.)

tion that the environment is whirling, or that one is whirling oneself. *Dizziness* is a more general term, indicating a feeling of unsteadiness and disequilibrium. In either case the disturbance of equilibrium may be so severe that the individual staggers and falls. When a subject is rotated with the head 30° forward, he experiences true vertigo during deceleration, a false sense of spinning in the opposite direction in the horizontal plane (sensation of counter-rotation).

If the subject is rotated with the head bowed forward at an angle of about 120°, in order to stimulate the vertical canals, and the head is maintained in this position after rotation, the sensation is the same as if the head position had been upright during rotation, i.e., one of counter-rotation in the horizontal plane. If, however, the head is brought upright after rotation there is then a sensation of falling to one or the other side, i.e., of rotation of the body in the frontal plane; the sensation is one of falling to the side away from that toward which the body had been rotated. Rotation with the head bent backwards to an angle of 60° and then brought upright gives a sensation of falling to the same side as that toward which the body had been rotated (see table 5.2). A sensation of falling forward or backward (i.e., rotation in the sagittal plane) results from rotation with the head flexed on one shoulder and then brought upright.

Vertigo and dizziness arise from other causes than rotation. They are common symptoms in disease, constitutional or neurological, and occur in alcoholic intoxication, seasickness, swinging, etc. Also, just as the labyrinth influences the movements of the ocular muscles, so, conversely, labyrinthine function may be disturbed and vertigo or dizziness produced as a result of some unusual or abnormal action of the eye muscles. Vertigo and its associated phenomena are, therefore, common effects of eye strain or of viewing

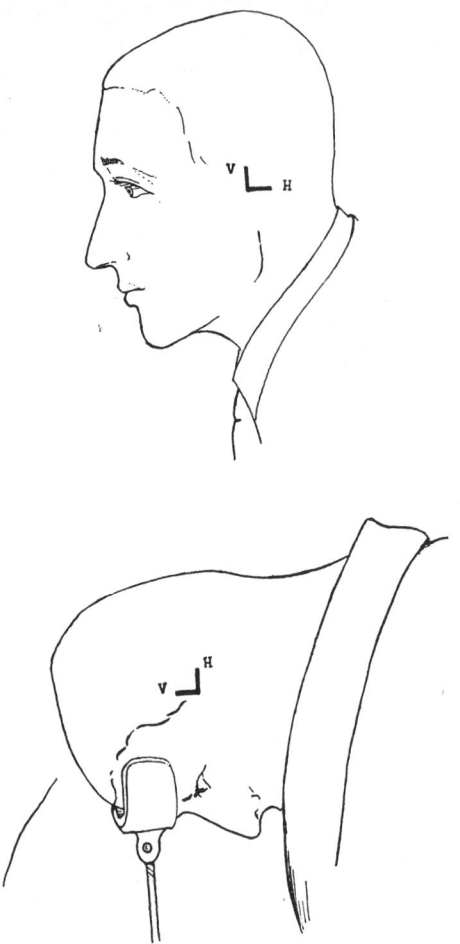

FIG. 5.21. Positions during rotation. Upper head inclined 30° forward, horizontal canals in plane of rotation. Lower, head inclined 120° forward, vertical canals in plane of rotation. V, vertical canals; H, horizontal canals.

the landscape from a moving train; an ocular element is also an important contributory factor in the causation of seasickness. For example, if one sees, in a motion picture, events which if actually experienced would cause giddiness, a sensation of vertigo may be aroused. But with whatever condition vertigo is associated, whether cardiovascular, renal, toxic, gastrointestinal or neurological, its immediate cause is excitation of the semicircular canals or of their central connections.

(c) *Reactions of the neck and limb muscles.* In animals stimulation of the horizontal canals by a rotatory motion causes alterations in tone and movements on both sides of the body which tend to resist the rotatory movement, and enable the animal to maintain its balance. When, for ex-

ample, a frog is rotated on a round table, say to the *left*, the tone of the neck muscles is increased on the right side and reduced on the left, the head turning to the *right*. The limbs, especially the hindlimb on the left, are extended; those on the right are flexed. The animal may move around to the right. Cessation of the rotary motion causes a reversal of these effects upon the neck and limbs. In the snake, lizard, and reptiles with very long necks, the head may deviate to one or other side by as much as 100° or more. Sometimes a quick return to the normal position occurs, as in nystagmus. A *head nystagmus*, with alternating slow and fast movements, can easily be demonstrated by rotating a guinea pig about a vertical axis.

Dusser de Barenne, who first described these reflexes, cites a simple means for their demonstration. When a frog is rotated, say to the left, around its long axis by suspending it by a thread fixed to its jaw, and giving the thread a twist between the finger and thumb, the animal's right hindlimb is extended and abducted, and the toes spread, while the left hindlimb is bent at knee and ankle, and the toes flexed. As the movement to the left comes to an end, and turning to the right begins the limb movements are reversed. Similar movements may occur in the forelimbs.

Corresponding effects follow rotation, e.g., a quick tilt, in the plane of a vertical canal. Tait and McNally described the respective vertical canals as affecting the limb muscles on one or other "corner" of the body. Thus, stimulation of the right anterior vertical canal by a quick tilt diagonally forward and to the right causes contraction of the right forelimb: stimulation of the left anterior vertical canal by tilting forward and to the left causes a corresponding movement of the left forelimb. Backward tilting to right or left

FIG. 5.22. So-called 'discobolus' position resulting from caloric or galvanic excitation of the labyrinth. (From Camis after Wodak and Fischer.)

causes, respectively, contraction of the muscles of the right and of the left hindlimbs.

The past-pointing test of Bárány. Under ordinary circumstances if a normal person places his finger upon a certain spot he has no difficulty in hitting the mark again with his eyes closed. After rotation, though able to place his finger upon a mark with his eyes open, he cannot find it again when his eyes are closed. The finger *deviates* or *past-points* to one or other side, or above or below the mark, the direction of the miss-aim being dependent upon the direction of the previous rotation and upon the position of the head during rotation (see table 5.2). Past-pointing is not reflex in nature but is a voluntary motor act, the error in judgment is the result of the associated subjective phenomenon, an unconscious correction being made in the opposite direction for the false sensation. The past-pointing and the vertigo are in opposite directions.

Other post-rotational reactions. If the body is rotated in the plane of the horizontal canals and the rotation stopped, the head (eyes closed) then turns in the direction of the rotation. If rotation is carried out with the head in one or other plane of the vertical canals and the head after rotation is brought upright while the eyes are closed, the body leans to one or other side, backward or forward, according to the position of the head during rotation. The subject may actually fall in the direction to which the body leans. The phenom-

enon is virtually a past-pointing of the entire body. The actual fall is, therefore, opposite in direction to the vertiginous sensation of falling. That is, the subject has the illusion that he is leaning to one side (i.e., a sense of being rotated in the frontal plane of the skull), and in order to correct his supposed false position and retain his balance, leans actually in the *opposite* direction. If he attempts to walk, he falls.

One particularly interesting reaction resulting from excitation of the semicircular canals is that which has been appropriately called the *discus throwing* or *discobolus* attitude (fig. 5.22). Though occurring after rotation it is evoked most readily by caloric (especially cold) or galvanic stimulation of the canals. A stimulus applied, say, to the left ear causes a twisting of the thorax upon the pelvis and rotation of the head to the stimulated side. When the arms are raised they are also turned toward this side with the left limb lower than the right. After a short time the attitude is reversed, the body swings round and takes up a position in the opposite direction. The attitude may reverse its direction several times. It is due to reflex alterations in tone of the musculature on the two sides of the body.

(d) *Reactions of the autonomic nervous system.* Excitation of the semicircular canals in man is not uncommonly followed by nausea, vomiting and pallor. A fall in blood pressure of 10 mm. or so may occur, together with slowing of the heart by

TABLE 5.2

Stimulation of the semicircular canals in man

The table summarizes the major subjective and somatic effects of rotational, caloric, and galvanic stimulation of the semicircular canals. With stimuli opposite in sign to those indicated, the reactions are reversed.

The results of any given stimulation of the semicircular canals in a normal subject can be predicted by considering a) the positions of the individual canals and their ampullae in relation to the stimulus; b) the direction of the fluid movement and cupular displacement produced by the stimulus; and c) the excitatory effect of that displacement in accordance with the laws of Ewald and Flourens. A detailed and well-illustrated account of vestibular testing is found in Portmann's *Diseases of the Ear, Nose, and Throat.*

Position of Head	Stimulus	Type and Direction of Post-rotational Nystagmus (Fast Component)	Sensation of Vertigo, Head Upright after Rotation	Past-Pointing	Falling (after Bringing Head Upright)*
Upright or 30° forward	Rotation right	Horizontal, left	Turning left	To right	To right
Forward 120°	Rotation right	Rotary, left	Falling to left	To right	To right
Backward 60°	Rotation right	Rotary, right	Falling to right	To left	To left
Inclined 90° to right shoulder	Rotation right	Vertical, downward	Falling forward	Upward	Backward
Inclined 90° to left shoulder	Rotation right	Vertical, upward	Falling backward	Downward	Forward
Backward right	Caloric 44° C. to ear or 30° C. to left	Horizontal, right	Falling to right	To left	To left
Forward 120°	Caloric 44° C. to left ear or 30° C. to right	Horizontal, left	Falling to left	To right	To right
Upright	Galvanic (up to 15 ma.) Cathode on right	Mixture of horizontal and rotary, right	Turning right	To left	To left

* *NOTE.* After stimulation of the vertical canals the subject cannot control his fall when his head is brought into the upright position. The observer must be prepared to catch him to prevent injury.

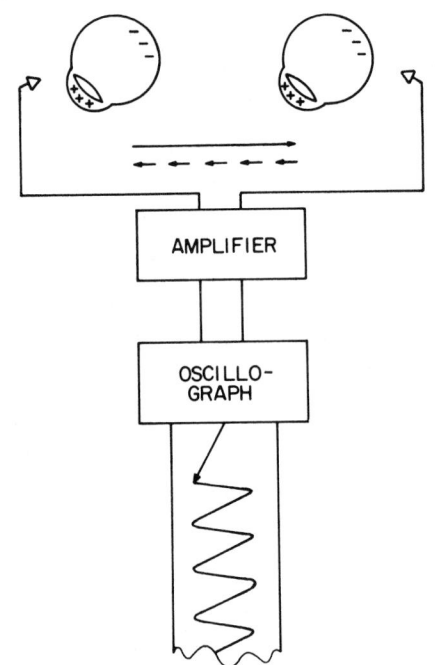

Fig. 5.23. Diagram illustrating nystagmography. The DC potential difference (corneo-retinal potential) between the two electrodes on the skin near the outer canthi varies as the eyes move from side to side in nystagmus. The variations are amplified and recorded as the electronystagmogram.

8 or 10 beats per min. In the rabbit, syringing the ear causes vasodilatation and a fall in blood pressure. During rotation the pupil constricts; pupillary dilatation occurs upon cessation of the rotary movement.

Anti-motion sickness drugs usually act on the autonomic system and not on the semicircular canals or the vestibular pathways. Small doses of barbiturates, however, can be shown to suppress both optokinetic and vestibular nystagmus.

Caloric Stimulation

The effects of caloric stimulation are not unlike those following rotation, but the caloric method possesses an advantage in that one labyrinth can be examined at a time. The ear to be tested is syringed with warm or cool water. In clinical practice ice water is often used. When the head is bent backward through 60° the horizontal canals are vertical with the ampulae upward. The douche causes a greater change in the temperature of the endolymph in the part of the canal lying nearer to the external meatus than in the part more deeply situated. Convection currents are set up which cause a displacement of the cupula, and horizontal nystagmus and vertigo result. The change in temperature in the canal follows the irrigation of the external meatus by about 3 seconds. The direction of the convection currents, which of course are due to changes in the specific gravity of the endolymph resulting from heating or cooling, is determined by the temperature of the douche fluid. Thus a cold douche causes currents away from the ampulla, whereas a hot douche causes flow toward the ampulla (see table 5.2). Caloric stimulation of the vertical canals is effected by douching with the head upright and elicits a rotatory nystagmus.

In the caloric test according to Fitzgerald, Cawthorne, and Hallpike, the ear canal is douched with about 240 ml. of water at 30° C., and again at 44° C., for 40 sec. each. The duration of the nystagmus is recorded, and the results for each ear are plotted as a *calorigram*. In normal subjects the nystagmus usually lasts for 90 to 130 sec. In streptomycin intoxication with damage to the ampullar cristae, the duration is reduced or absent.

Galvanic Stimulation

For galvanic stimulation of the labyrinths, electrodes are placed on the two mastoid processes and a weak direct current is passed between them. Alternatively, the cathode may be placed on either mastoid process and the anode on an indifferent part of the body. As the current is slowly increased from zero to 10 or 15 ma., there is first a sensation of vertigo, then a bending of the head and trunk away from the cathode, and finally nystagmus of the combined horizontal and rotary type, with the fast component toward the cathode. Past-pointing can be demonstrated, and nausea and vomiting may occur.

Although all of the vestibular end organs appear to be involved in the response to the galvanic current, it is the nerve fibers rather than the hair cells that are excited directly. Steinhausen showed that there is no movement of the cupula during this form of stimulation. Furthermore, after destruction of the neuroepithelium by streptomycin, the current is still able to elicit nystagmus, even though rotation and caloric stimulation are ineffective. Because of uncertainties of interpretation and lack of specificity, the galvanic test has not found wide application in the clinical evaluation of vestibular function. Nevertheless, it does offer the possibility of by-passing the end organs while testing the vestibular nerve and its central connections.

Cupulometry and Electronystagmography

Cupulometry is a form of quantitative test of the function of the semicircular canals employing a motor-driven rotating chair with carefully controlled acceleration and speed of turning, and a hydraulic brake to permit abrupt stops. The subject is seated in the axis of rotation, with the head bent forward 30° for optimal stimulation of the horizontal canals. Acceleration is subliminal at 0.5°/sec.², so that there is no deflection of the cupula until the chair is suddenly stopped. After a short period of rotation at a constant velocity of 15, 30, or 60°/sec., the brake is applied and the durations of the resulting post-rotational nystagmus and vertigo are recorded. A plot showing these durations of the objective and the subjective after-effects as functions of the velocity of turning (an indirect measure of the force applied to the cupula by sudden deceleration to a stop) is called a *cupulogram.* (van Egmond, Groen, and Jongkees; Daly and Cohen).

Electronystagmography consists in recording the eye movements in nystagmus by means of the *corneo-retinal potential* (fig. 5.23). This is the strong dc resting potential of the eye, with cornae positive and retina negative. When the eyes are turned to the right, an electrode on the skin at the right outer canthus becomes positive, an electrode at the left outer canthus negative. As the eyes swing back to the left, the difference is reversed. By means of an amplifier with an appropriately long time-constant and an oscillograph (or electroencephalograph), these potentials can be recorded as an *electronystagmogram.* (fig. 5.24) With a suitable commutator on the revolving chair, per-rotational nystagmus can be recorded as well as post-rotational. Accurate measures of rate and amplitude of nystagmus and speed of the slow and fast components can be obtained which may be much more informative than the conventional measure of nystagmus duration alone. Electronystagmography is appropriate for monitoring spontaneous nystagmus and for caloric testing, as well as for studies of semicircular canal function in experimental animals.

Mechanical Stimulation

Ewald cemented a metal cylinder over a hole made in the bony wall of the horizontal canal. A piston fitted into the cylinder could be operated by air pressure. During the descent and ascent of the pneumatic hammer the membranous canal was alternately compressed and decompressed. The endolymph during compression and decompression moved, respectively, toward and away from the ampulla. An endolymph movement toward the ampulla caused a movement of the head and eyes to the opposite side. Decompression caused a weaker movement in the reverse direction.

Mechanical stimulation of the semicircular canals is the basis of the pneumatic test for a fistula in the labyrinth. Compression and decompression of the air in the external meatus by means of a Politzer bulb or a pneumatic otoscope causes a flow of endolymph between the fistula and the round window, with stimulation of the ampullar cristae. Either a slow movement of the eyes or a mixed rotary and horizontal nystagmus is seen (Lucoe's sign).

Acoustical stimulation of the vestibular end organs can occur in the presence of a fistula or in special circumstances after fenestration of the horizontal canal in otosclerotic patients. In such cases the patient experiences giddiness or vertigo whenever an intense sound reaches his ear. This is the *Tullio phenomenon.*

The otolithic organs (utricle and saccule, gravity receptors). The role played by the utricle in the static reflexes has been dealt with in previous sections (see righting reflexes). The gravity receptors respond also to linear acceleration, that is, to movements in a straight line forward, backward, up or down, or laterally, as well as to slow tilting of the head on its transverse or its antero-posterior axis. The gravity receptors are also stimulated by a sudden cessation of a linear movement (deceleration), or a sharp change in the speed of such a movement. It is possible that bending the hairs also acts as a stimulus. The utricular organs are also stimulated by centrifugal force, and under certain conditions by angular acceleration.

The effective stimulus to the utricular hair cells seems to be the bending of the cilia by the weight of the otoliths. The hair cells show definite patterns of directional polarization, the significance of which is not yet clear. We may assume, however, that the patterns of nerve impulses from the two utricles are continously being monitored and compared in the vestibular centers of the medulla, and the position of the head constantly readjusted to minimize these differences.

In the cat, when the head is level the receptors cause a discharge of impulses at a relatively low frequency (at about 6 per sec.). When the head is tilted laterally (on its antero-posterior axis—cheek down) from the level position to an angle of 20°, the impulse frequency increases up to 95 per sec. in the nerve on the side to which the head is tilted, but the resting discharge on the opposite side ceases. Thus, in a lateral tilt to the right the otoliths on that side (cheek down) are dependent

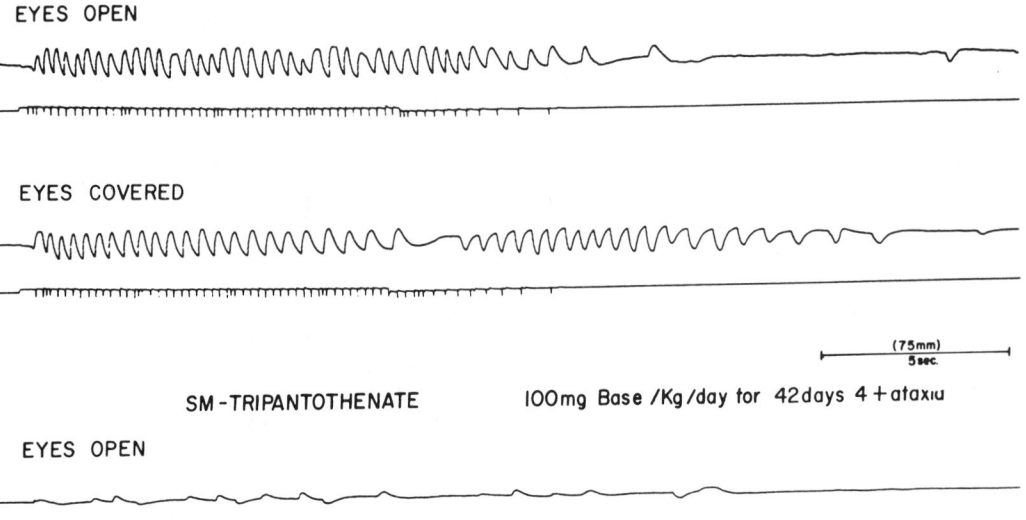

FIG. 5.24. Electronystagmograms of a cat rotated clockwise for 10 sec. at 25 r.p.m. before and after streptomycin intoxication. With the eyes open, the horizontal nystagmus is of both optokinetic and vestibular origin, and no post-rotational nystagmus appears. With the eyes covered, the nystagmus is of vestibular origin only, and there is a strong post-rotational nystagmus. After destruction of the neuroepithelium of the cristae by streptomycin, the optokinetic response is minimal, and the vestibular response is absent.

and presumably exert a gravitational pull, whereas those on the opposite side are *resting* on the maculae. The greater the degree of downward tilt from the level position the higher is the impulse frequency (see fig. 5.25). If the head is held in the tilted position the impulse frequency declines slowly, for the gravity receptors are of the slow-adapting type. Tilting around a transverse axis (snout up or down) also evokes a response, though less readily than does a lateral tilt.

The saccule. The role played by the saccule in the responses just described has not been settled unequivocally. Though anatomically and cytoarchitecturally this structure appears to be part of the vestibular mechanism, it has been thought by many to have auditory rather than vestibular function. McNally and Tait observed no loss of vestibular function in the frog after denervation of the saccules. The auditory nerve from a frog's labyrinth which has been denervated except for the saccule does not respond to vestibular stimuli

by a discharge of impulses, but gives a response when a vibrating tuning fork is brought near it. Lorente de Nó, on the other hand, traced saccular fibers to the vestibular nucleus, but could find no fibers connecting the saccular macula with the cochlear nuclei. It is not unlikely that the saccule has auditory function in lower forms which it loses in higher animals with the development of the cochlea.

VESTIBULAR REACTIONS IN DISEASE

Abnormal vestibular reactions are seen in various diseased conditions involving (a) the labyrinth, (b) the vestibular nerve, or (c) the vestibular centers or central pathways (e.g., Deiters' nucleus, medial longitudinal bundle, cerebellum). Normally, some slight nystagmus may occur upon looking for a time to the right or left, but if nystagmus is present when looking forward or if pronounced when the eyes are turned to one side, it is pathological. A spontaneous vertical nystagmus suggests a lesion of the brain-stem; it is not seen in disease of the labyrinth itself or of the vestibular nerve. The phenomenon of past-pointing, unless induced artificially, is always pathological and suggests a cerebellar lesion. Spontaneous vertigo most commonly occurs as a result of labyrinthine disease but may be seen with disorders of the medulla oblongata. Disturbance of equilibrium may be seen with diseases of the labyrinth, the brain-stem or the cerebellum. On the other hand, a lesion in one or other of these situations may cause a failure of the usual reactions following rotary or caloric stimulation. In deaf mutes, the labyrinthine reactions, as a rule, are absent. Again, the reactions to artificial stimulation may be abnormal; for example, in a lesion of the brain-stem vertical nystagmus may occur in response to a stimulus which normally causes nystagmus of the horizontal type.

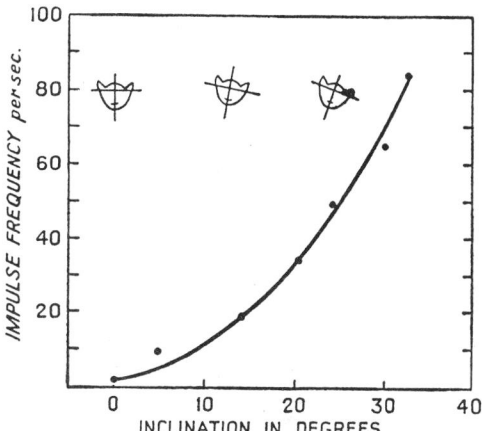

Fig. 5.25. Response of gravity receptor (otolith organ), showing the relationship between degree of tilt of head and frequency of impulses in vestibular nerve. (After Adrian.)

MENIÈRE'S SYNDROME

This distressing condition is characterized by paroxysmal attacks of vertigo, subjective noise in the ears (*tinnitus aurium*), and a progressive impairment of hearing of the sensori-neural type (ch. 19). The neuroepithelium of the cochlea (organ of Corti) is affected as well as that of the semicircular canals. There are various pathological processes in the ears which may give rise to this symptom complex, but it is generally attributed to a disturbance of the fluid balance in the inner ear, since distension of the cochlear duct (labyrinthine hydrops) has been observed *post mortem*. Reducing the sodium content of the body by a low-salt diet is often effective in relieving the victims of Menière's syndrome. In intractable cases, when surgical treatment is indicated it may take the form of destructive labyrinthotomy, intracranial section of the vestibular division of the VIIIth nerve (Dandy), or destruction of the vestibular end organs with ultrasonic irradiation (Arslan).

VESTIBULAR REACTIONS IN SPACE FLIGHT

Normal postural equilibrium and orientation depend upon the processing and interpretation of sensory information from the eyes, the otolith organs, the semicircular canals, and the proprioceptors of the neck, trunk, and limbs. These sensory systems are adapted for responding within an appropriate context and dynamic range. When they are exposed to unusual environments and new combinations of forces the information they deliver may be conflicting or

false. For an aircraft pilot or astronaut such confusing or illusory impressions of his position and motion can lead to disastrous errors of judgment. It is therefore little wonder that the normal and abnormal reactions of the vestibular system are matters of vital interest to those concerned with space travel.

The effects of prolonged exposure to a zero-gravity environment, in which the otolith organs are deprived of the stimulation to which they are otherwise exposed at all times, remain to be explored. The weightless condition can be reproduced on earth only during brief periods of parabolic flight. A second matter of concern is the *Coriolis reaction*, which occurs when a subject exposed to angular rotation at a constant speed (as on a rotating space platform) tilts his head about an axis perpendicular to the axis of rotation. The tilting can produce a sudden, strong vestibular disturbance, with vertigo, nystagmus, disorientation, nausea, and vomiting. The mechanism of the Coriolis reaction is not fully understood, but it is supposed to be due to shifting one pair of canals out of the plane of rotation and another pair into it. It would also appear to be closely related to the violent responses that occur, as described earlier, when the head is brought upright immediately after rotational stimulation of the vertical canals in the Bárány chair.

REFERENCES

ADRIAN, E. D. Discharges from vestibular receptors in the cat. J. Physiol., 1943, **101**, 389.

ARSLAN, M. An improved technique of the ultrasonic irradiation of the vestibular apparatus by Menière's disease. Acta oto-laryng. (Stockholm), 1962, **55**, 467.

ASCHAN, G., BERGSTEDT, M., AND STAHLE, J. Nystagmography. Recording of nystagmus in clinical neuro-otological examinations. Acta oto-laryng. (Stockholm), 1956, Suppl. **129**.

ATKINSON, M. Menière's original papers. Reprinted with an English translation together with commentaries and biographical sketch. Acta oto-laryng. (Stockholm), 1961, Suppl. **162**.

BARD, P. AND MACHT, M. B. The behavior of chronically decerebrate cats. Ciba Foundation Symposium on the Neurological Basis of Behavior. (Ed. by G. E. W. WOLSTENHOLME AND C. M. O'CONNOR), pp. 55–75. Little, Brown & Co., Boston, 1958.

BAST, T. H. AND ANSON, B. J. The temporal bone and the ear. Charles C Thomas, Springfield, Ill., 1949.

BAZETT, H. C. AND PENFIELD, W. G. A study of the Sherringtonian decerebrate animal in the chronic as well as in the acute condition. Brain, 1922, **45**, 185.

CAMIS, M. The physiology of the vestibular apparatus. (Transl. by R. S. Creed) Clarendon Press, Oxford, 1930.

CARLSTRÖM, D. A crystallographic study of vertebrate otoliths. Biol. Bull., 1963, **125**, 441.

CREED, R. S., DENNY-BROWN, D., ECCLES, J. C., LIDDELL, E. G. T., AND SHERRINGTON, C. S. Reflex Activity of the Spinal Cord. Clarendon Press, Oxford, 1932.

CROSBY, E. C. Nystagmus as a sign of central nervous system involvement. Ann. Otol., Rhinol., & Laryngol., 1953, **62**, 1117.

DALY, J. F. AND COHEN, N. Cupulometry as an investigative tool. Arch. Otolaryng., 1965, **81**, 340. Viomycin ototoxicity in man: a cupulometric study. Ann. Otol., Rhinol., & Laryngol., 1965, **74**, 521.

DANDY, W. E. Treatment of Menière's disease by section of only the vestibular portion of the acoustic nerve. Bull. Johns Hopkins Hosp., 1933, **53**, 52.

DAVIS, L. E. Decerebrate rigidity in man. Arch. Neurol. Psychiat., 1925, **13**, 569.

DOHLMAN, G. Some practical and theoretical points in labyrinthology. Proc. Roy. Soc. Med., 1935, **28**, 1371.

VAN EGMOND, A. L. J., GROEN, J. J., AND JONGKEES, L. B. W. The turning test with small regulable stimuli. J. Laryng. & Otol., 1948, **62**, 63.

ENGSTRÖM, H., ADES, H. W., AND HAWKINS, J. E., JR. Structure and function of the sensory hairs of the inner ear. J. Acoust. Soc. Am., 1962, **34**, 1356.

FERNÁNDEZ, C., ALZATE, R., AND LINDSAY, J. R. Experimental Observations on postural nystagmus in the cat. Ann. Otol., Rhinol., & Laryngol., 1959, **68**, 816.

FITZGERALD, G., CAWTHORNE, T. E., AND HALLPIKE, C. S. Studies in human vestibular function. I. Observations on the directional preponderance of caloric nystagmus resulting from cerebral lesions. Brain, 1942, **65**, 115.

FLOCK, Å. Electron microscopic and electrophysiological studies on the lateral line canal organ. Acta oto-laryng. (Stockholm) 1965, Suppl. **199**.

GERNANDT, B. E. Vestibular mechanisms. Chap. XXII in Handbook of Physiology. Section 1: Neurophysiology, Vol. I. American Physiological Society, Washington, D. C., 1959.

GUEDRY, F. E., JR. Physiological studies of vestibular function. In Contributions to Sensory Physiology, Vol. 1 (W. D. Neff, ed.) Academic Press, New York and London, 1965.

GRAYBIEL, A. The importance of the otolithic organs in man based upon a specific test for utricular function. Ann. Otol., Rhinol., & Laryngol., 1956, **65**, 470.

HAWKINS, J. E., JR. Antibiotics and the inner ear. Trans. Amer. Acad. Ophthalmol. and Otolaryng., 1959, **63**, 206.

DE KLEIJN, A. Experimental physiology of the labyrinth. J. Laryng. & Otol., 1923, **38**, 646.

DE KLEIJN, A. AND VERSTEEGH, C. Some remarks upon the present position of the physiology of the labyrinth. J. Laryng. & Otol., 1927, **42**, 649.

KUIPER, J. W. The microphonic effect of the lateral line organ. Natuurkundig Laboratorium, Groningen, 1956.

LIDDELL, E. G. T. AND SHERRINGTON, C. S. Reflexes in response to stretch (myotatic reflexes). Proc. Roy. Soc. London, ser. B, 1924, **96**, 212.

LIDDELL, E. G. T. AND SHERRINGTON, C. S. Further observations on myotatic reflexes. Proc. Roy. Soc. London, ser. B, 1925, **97**, 267.

LINDSAY, J. R. Postural vertigo and positional nystagmus. Ann. Otol., Rhinol., & Laryngo., 1951, **60**, 1134.

LLOYD, D. P. C. Activity in neurons of the bulbospinal correlation system. J. Neurophysiol., 1941, **4**, 115.

LOWENSTEIN, O. AND SAND, A. The individual and integrated activity of the semicircular canals of the elasmobranch labyrinth. J. Physiol., 1940, **99**, 89.

LOWENSTEIN, O., OSBORNE, M. P., AND WERSÄLL, J. Structure and innervation of the sensory epithelia of the labyrinth in the Thornback ray (*Raja clavata*). Proc. Roy. Soc. London, ser. B, 1964, **160**, 1.

MACKENZIE, K. G. Intracranial division of the vestibular portion of the auditory nerve for Menière's disease. Canad. M. A. J., 1936, **34**, 369.

McNALLY, W. J. AND STEWART, E. A. Physiology of labyrinth reviewed in relation to seasickness and other forms of motion sickness. War Med., 1942, **2**, 683.

McNALLY, W. J. AND TAIT, J. Ablation experiments on the labyrinth of the frog. Am. J. Physiol., 1925, **75**, 155.

MAGNUS, R. Körperstellung. Springer Verlag, Berlin, 1924.

MAGNUS, R. Animal posture. Proc. Roy. Soc. London, ser. B, 1925, **98**, 339.

MAGNUS, R. Studies on the physiology of posture. Lancet, 1926, **2**, 531.

PENFIELD, W. Vestibular sensation and the cerebral cortex. Ann. Otol., Rhinol., & Laryngol., 1957, **66**, 691.

POLLOCK, L. J. AND DAVIS, L. E. The reflex activities of a decerebrate animal. J. Comp. Neurol., 1930, 50, 377.

POLLOCK, L. J. AND DAVIS, L. E. Studies in decerebration. VI. The effect of deafferentiation upon decerebrate rigidity. Am. J. Physiol., 1931, 98, 1931.

PORTMANN, G. Diseases of the ear, nose, and throat. (Transl. from the French by F. Montreuil and J. G. Waltner.) Williams & Wilkins Co., Baltimore, 1951.

RETZIUS, G. Das Gehörorgan der Wirbelthiere. Samson & Wallin, Stockholm. Vol. I, 1881; Vol. II, 1884.

ROSS, D. A. Electrical studies on the frog's labyrinth. J. Physiol., 1936, 86, 117.

SHERRINGTON, C. S. Decerebrate rigidity, and reflex co-ordination of movements. J. Physiol., 1898, 22, 319.

SJÖBERG, A., STAHLE, J., JOHNSON, S., AND SAHL, R. Treatment of Menière's disease by ultrasonic irradiation. Acta oto-laryng. (Stockholm), Suppl. 178, 1963.

SMITH, CATHERINE A. Microscopic structure of the utricle. Ann. Otol., Rhinol., & Laryngol., 1956, 65, 450.

STAHLE, J. Electronystagmography in the caloric and rotatory tests. Acta oto-laryng. (Stockholm), 1958, Suppl. 137.

STEINHAUSEN, W. Über Sichtbarmachung und Funktionsprüfung der Cupula terminalis in den Bogengangsampullen des Labyrinthes. Arch. ges. Physiol., 1927, 217, 747; Über den experimentellen Nachweis der Ablenkung der Cupula terminalis in der intakten Bogengangsampulle des Labyrinthes bei der thermischen und adäquaten rotatorischen Reizung. Z. f. Hals-, Nasen-, u. Ohrenheilk., 1931, 29, 211; Über die Funktion der Cupula in den Bogengangsampullen des Labyrinthes. Z. f. Hals-, Nasen-, u. Ohrenheilk., 1933, 34, 201.

TAIT, J. Is all hearing cochlear? Ann. Otol., Rhinol., & Laryngol., 1932, 41, 681.

TAIT, J. AND McNALLY, W. J. Some results of section of particular nerve branches to the ampullae of the four vertical semicircular canals of the frog. Quart. J. Exper. Physiol., 1933, 23, 147.

WERSÄLL, J. Studies on the structure and innervation of the sensory epithelium of the cristae ampullares in the guinea pig. Acta oto-laryng. (Stockholm), 1956, Suppl. 126.

WERSÄLL, J. AND FLOCK, Å. Functional anatomy of the vestibular and lateral line organs. In Contributions to sensory physiology, Vol. 1 (W. D. NEFF, ed.) Academic Press, New York and London, 1965.

CHAPTER 6

The Spinal Cord and Brain Stem (*Medulla Oblongata, Pons and Midbrain*) and the Reticular Formation

Outline of the Internal Structure of the Spinal Cord

In figure 6.1 the spinal cords is shown in cross-section. The *gray matter*, centrally placed, is in the form roughly of an H or the two wings of a butterfly. It is composed of a mass of nerve cell bodies and nerve fibers (dendrons and axons), mostly unmyelinated, supported by a framework of neuroglia. The ventral and dorsal portions of each lateral half of the gray mass (i.e., each arm of the H) are commonly referred to, respectively, as the ventral (or anterior) and dorsal (or posterior) horns; but since the gray matter extends throughout the length of the cord "column" is a more suitable term than "horn." In the ventral columns are situated the large bodies (100 μ in diameter) of the motor neurons whose axons leave the cord by the ventral roots. Each axon ends in a group of skeletal muscle fibers—the neuromuscular structure constituting the so-called motor unit. The large multipolar cells are known as α cells and innervate the ordinary striated muscle fibers. The small γ cells innervate the intrafusal fibers of the muscle spindles and thus regulate the threshold of these important proprioceptive end-organs (see ch. 3). In the thoracic and upper lumbar segments, the gray mass lying between the ventral and dorsal columns shows a small lateral projection. This is the lateral column or horn; it contains a cluster of nerve cells (the *intermediolateral cell column*) they give origin to sympathetic (preganglionic) fibers which leave the cord by the anterior (ventral) nerve roots. The well defined collection of cells occupying the inner part of the base of the posterior horn is known as *Clarke's column;* this group, since it is confined almost entirely to the thoracic region of the cord, is also known as the *dorsal nucleus*. It is homologous with the nucleus cuneatus of the medulla oblongata (p. 123). To the outer side of the base of the posterior column is an area where strands of white matter and prolongations from the main mass of gray matter intermingle to form a delicate interlacement. This is known as the *reticular formation* (formatio reticularis) and is most prominent in the cervical region. It is continuous with the reticular formation of the medulla oblongata and pons. At the apex of the dorsal horn is a cap of gelatinous material containing groups of small nerve cells possessing many dendrites and named the *substantia gelatinosa of Rolando*. It is believed to receive the finest fibers (myelinated and unmyelinated) of the posterior roots. The remaining part of the substance of the dorsal horns constitutes the *chief sensory nucleus*. A canal pierces the bar or isthmus connecting the two lateral masses of gray matter across the midline; it is known as the *central canal*. The gray isthmus itself is called the *gray commissure*. Sometimes the parts in front and behind the central canal are referred to as the anterior and posterior gray commissures, respectively (fig. 6.2).

The *white matter*, which completely surrounds the gray matter is composed of bundles of fibers both myelinated and unmyelinated, the former predominating. A deep cleft on the ventral aspect of the spinal cord (the *anterior median fissure*) and a septum on the dorsal aspect (*posterior median septum*) together, incompletely divide the white matter into two lateral halves. The bands of white matter lying in front of the gray commissure are called the *anterior (ventral) white commissure;* a few strands of white matter lying behind or within the posterior part of the gray commissure are sometimes called the *posterior (dorsal) white commissure*. Each half is further marked out, by the fibers of the ventral and dorsal nerve roots, into three white columns or funiculi, ventral (anterior), lateral and dorsal (posterior). The *anterior (ventral) funiculus* lies between the anterior median fisure on the one hand, and the ventral gray column (anterior horn) and the fibers of the ventral roots on the other. Bounded in front and medially by the last two structures, and postero-medially by the dorsal gray column and the fibers of the dorsal roots lies the *lateral funiculus*. The *dorsal funiculus* is situated between the dorsal gray column (posterior horn) and the dorsal root fibers which form its anterolateral boundary, and the posterior median septum.

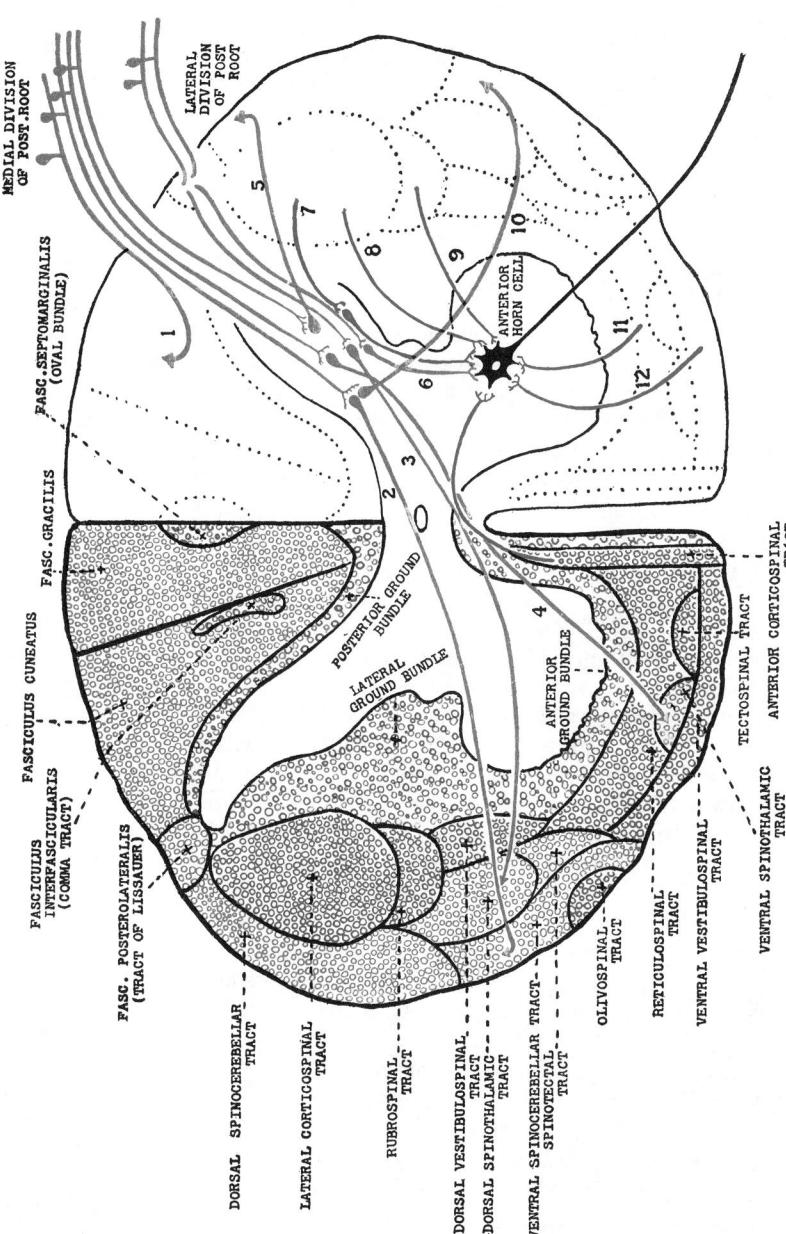

Fig. 6.1. Diagram to show tracts of the cord. Ascending fibers shown in blue, descending in red, spinal motoneuron in black. 1, represents fibers ascending in posterior columns (mediating sensations of touch, spatial discrimination, and of position and movement); 2 and 10, represent fibers entering the contralateral and homolateral ventral spinocerebellar tracts, respectively; 3, represents fibers entering dorsal spinothalamic tract of the opposite side (mediating pain and thermal sensations); 4, represents fibers entering ventral spinothalamic tract of the opposite side (mediating touch and tactile localization); 5, fiber entering dorsal spinocerebellar tract; 6, internuncial neuron connecting a posterior root fiber with anterior horn cell (reflex arc); 7 and 8, crossed corticospinal fibers connecting, respectively, through an internuncial neuron and directly, with anterior horn cell; fiber of anterior corticospinal tract (not numbered) also shown; 9, rubrospinal fiber; 11, reticulospinal fiber; 12, vestibulospinal fiber. The student must recognize that this is a very schematic representation of the fiber systems in the spinal cord. These various bundles of fibers do not occupy such circumscribed compartments as this diagram might lead one to believe.

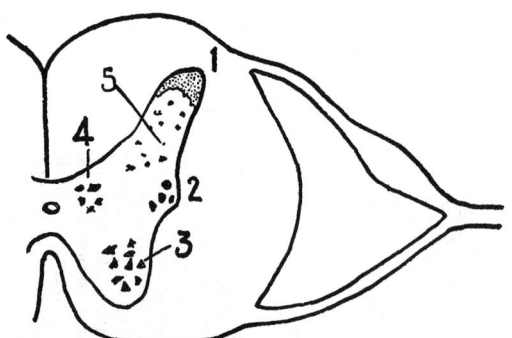

FIG. 6.2. Main cell groups in the thoracic region of the spinal cord. 1, substantia gelatinosa of Rolando; 2, intermedio-lateral cell column (sympathetic); 3, cells (motoneurons) of anterior horn; 4, Clarke's column (dorsal nucleus) of posterior horn; 5, chief sensory nucleus.

The Spinal Nerve Roots

There are 31 pairs of spinal nerve roots, a pair from each spinal segment. The anterior and posterior roots join within the vertebral canal just beyond the posterior root ganglion to form a corresponding number of spinal nerves.

The *anterior roots* of the spinal nerves are composed entirely of efferent fibers (p. 26).[1] These are (a) coarse, heavily myelinated, the axons of cells of the anterior horns, which are conveyed in the peripheral nerves to the skeletal muscles, and (b) fine, lightly myelinated fibers, in the thoracic and lumbar regions; these are preganglionic fibers of the sympathetic nervous system. The *posterior roots* are constituted of afferent fibers from the skin, muscles and viscera. They are the central processes of the large unipolar cells of the spinal ganglia. There is no important evidence that they contain efferent fibers. These statements regard-

[1] Although doubt has been expressed from time to time concerning the purely efferent nature of the fibers composing the anterior roots, no substantial evidence has been ever brought forward to show that this is not so. It is true that stimulation of the central end of an anterior root sometimes gives rise to pain, but this is due to the presence of recurrent fibers from the posterior roots and in no way invalidates the Bell-Magendie law. Neurons have been found in the anterior roots resembling those of the posterior root ganglia, but there is no evidence that they are sensory in function. Some authors have been led to believe that the anterior roots transmit sensory impulses because pain is not always relieved by section of the posterior roots. There are three possible reasons for the failure of this operation. In the first place, the pain may arise within the central nervous system itself, a filament of a posterior root may have escaped division, or innervation from adjacent spinal segments may overlap to an unusual extent; pain would then continue to be registered from the area innervated by the severed roots.

ing the efferent and afferent nature, respectively, of the anterior and posterior roots are called the Bell-Magendie law. Two divisions of the posterior root, a medial and a lateral, are distinguished. The lateral division is largely composed of small unmyelinated fibers; these, after entering the cord form the small trianglular area at the tip of the posterior horn known as Lissauer's tract. The fibers of the medial division enter the posterior columns of the cord (see fig. 6.1).

The Segmental Distribution of the Spinal Nerves

In the young mammalian embryo and in certain adult lower forms, e.g., fishes, the body is demarcated into a regular series of transverse segments or *metameres*. The muscles (*myotomes*), skin (*dermatomes*) and viscera of each of these primitive blocks eventually receive innervation from the nerve roots of a corresponding spinal segment. The anterior root of each spinal nerve supplies motor fibers to the respective myotome, and autonomic fibers to the viscera and skin; the posterior root supplies sensory fibers to the corresponding dermatome as well as to the muscles and viscera. As a result of the outgrowth of the embryonic limbs the orderly arrangement of the metameres from before backwards becomes altered. In the adult mammal, the primitive metameric disposition is observed only in the trunk. The fibers of the spinal nerves supplying the limbs have joined to form the brachial and lumbosacral plexuses and, after intermingling freely, issue again as the peripheral nerves. The latter, in consequence, are composed of fibers derived from two or more spinal segments, and fibers from a given segment pass into several peripheral nerves. The muscles supplied by a given spinal segment do not necessarily lie in close proximity to one another (the coracobrachialis, for example, is innervated by the same segments as those which supply the muscles of the thumb) and a single muscle may derive its nerve supply from more than one spinal segment. As development proceeds and the limbs grow out from the trunk, the dermatomes become arranged in a series of narrow areas lying for the most part in the long axis of the limb (fig. 6.3). The skin and muscles of the limbs also tend to move away from the visceral structures with which they were originally associated and, in the adult, structures innervated by a common spinal segment may be widely separated. Thus, the diaphragm is innervated (through the phrenic) from the 3, 4 and 5

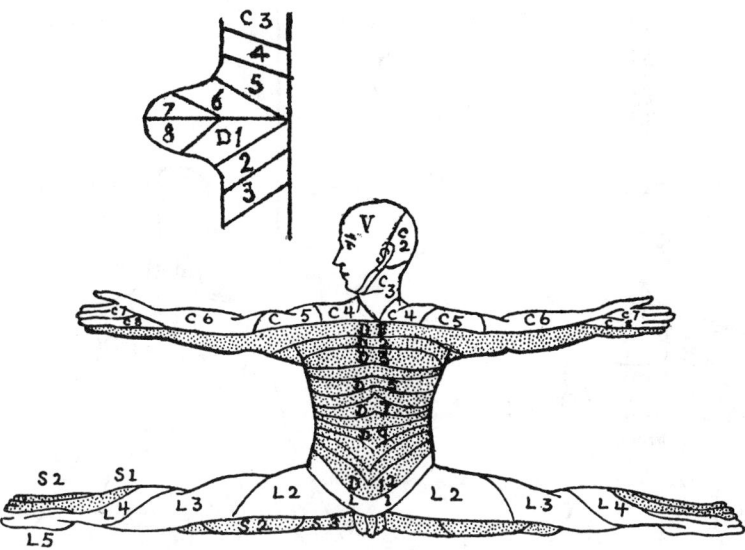

Fig. 6.3. *Upper:* Showing the drawing out of the metameres of the embryo with the development of the upper limb-bud. *Lower:* Showing the segmental arrangement of the dermatomes. (From Strong and Elwyn, after Luciani.)

cervical segments which also supply skin and muscle in the region of the neck and shoulder. The heart receives sensory and autonomic fibers from the upper thoracic segments; these segments also supply sensory fibers to the skin over the inner aspect of the arm and hand and upper part of the thorax. The distribution of the dermatomes and cutaneous nerves in the human subject are shown in figure 6.4.

Several methods have been employed by different investigators in mapping out the dermatomes in animals and in the human subject. The *anatomical* method is laborious and consists in tracing the fibers of a spinal root to their terminations in the skin. A *physiological* method ("isolation" or "sensory remainder" method) was employed by Sherrington in cats and monkeys and Foerster in man. The area of skin supplied by a given segment was demarcated by dividing the sensory roots above and below it. The sensitive area of skin bounded above and below by an anesthetic zone indicated the area of distribution of the undivided roots. Owing to the overlap of fibers from adjacen-segments, it is not possible to produce an anesthetic area by the division of the sensory roots of a single segment (fig. 6.5). Head mapped out the segmental distribution of the cutaneous nerves in the human subject from studies of cases of herpes zoster, a condition due to a lesion of the ganglion cells of the posterior roots. Within more recent years Foerster, using Sherrington's method has mapped out the dermatomes in man. He also

stimulated the posterior roots at operation and used the resulting vascular reaction (vasodilatation) as the means of demarcating the dermatomes.

The Tracts of the Spinal Cord

The fiber tracts of the cord are divisible into two main groups. (a) *Long tracts* (projection tracts) connect the cord with other parts of the central nervous system. Some of these (ascending tracts) carry impulses to higher centers; other tracts (descending) conduct in the reverse direction—from higher centers to spinal neurons. (b) *Short tracts* (intersegmental or association tracts, ground bundles) begin and end within the spinal cord and connect different segments. The fiber tracts making up the substance of the respective funiculi are listed in table 6.1 and shown diagrammatically in figure 6.6.

Ascending Tracts of the Spinal Cord

1. DORSOLATERAL FASCICULUS (TRACT OF LISSAUER). This is seen in cross section as a small area lying between the tip of the posterior horn and the periphery of the spinal cord (fig. 6.6). It is composed of fibers derived from the lateral division of the posterior nerve roots. These fibers upon entering the spinal cord connect immediately, or after a very short upward or downward course, with cells occupying the tip of the posterior horn, i.e., in the substantia gelatinosa of Rolando (p. 116). The fibers of this tract are

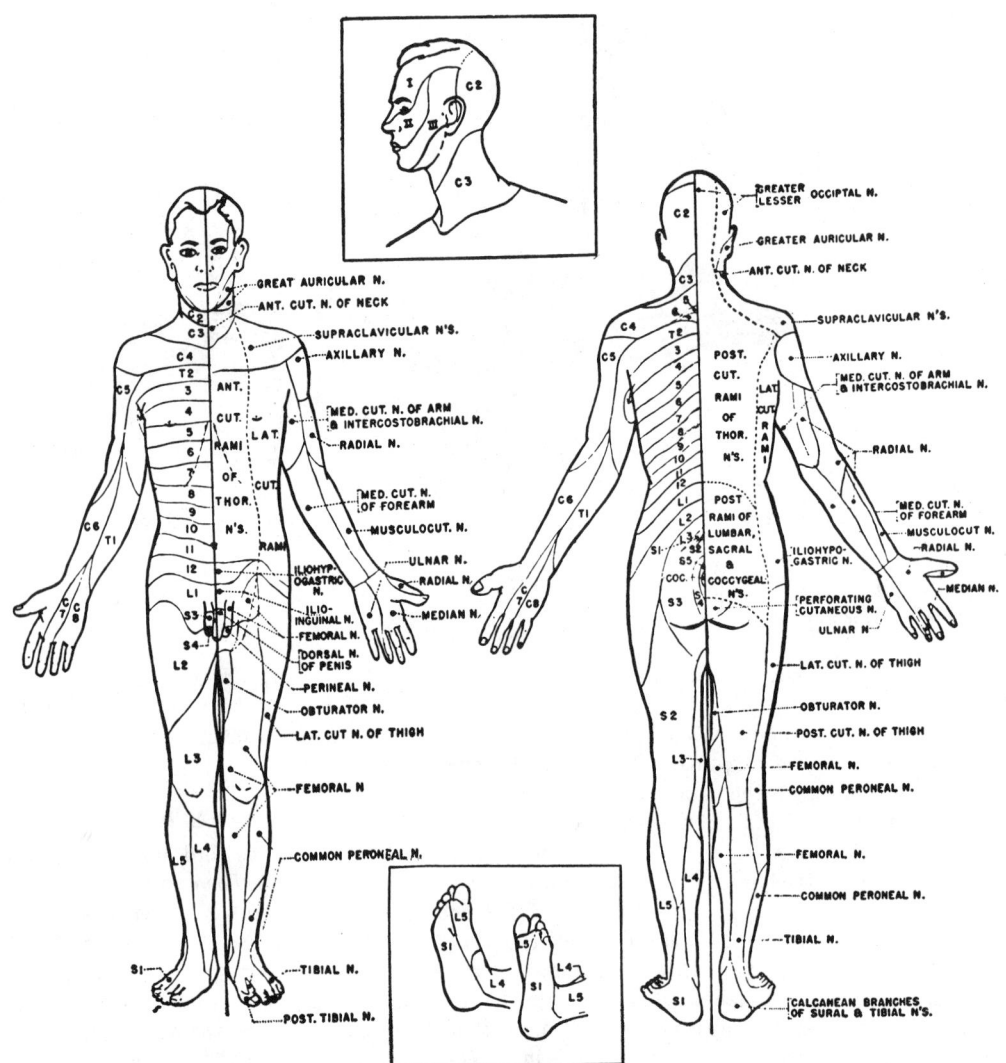

FIG. 6.4. Showing distribution of cutaneous nerves (right halves of figures) and the dermatomes (left halves). (After Wolff.) The student must recognize that these are schematic outlines and that the actual areas of innervation vary considerably from person to person.

mostly of small diameter and for the most part unmyelinated, and from both pathological and experimental evidence there is little doubt but that they constitute the primary neurons in the pathway for pain and crude thermal sensations. The axons of the secondary neurons (axons of the cells in the substantia gelatinosa of Rolando just mentioned) go to form the lateral spinothalamic tract of the opposite side, to be immediately described.

2. ANTEROLATERAL AND VENTRAL (ANTERIOR) SPINOTHALAMIC TRACTS. These tracts occupy, respectively, the lateral and ventral columns of the cord. The fibers of the *lateral* tract arise, as mentioned above, from cells in the substantia

gelatinosa of Rolando; of the opposite side of the cord. Those of the *ventral* tract are the axons of cells in the chief sensory nucleus of the opposite dorsal horn of gray matter.

In order to reach the ventral spinothalamic tract of the opposite side, the fibers arising from the chief sensory nucleus ascend in the posterior columns for two or three spinal segments, and then cross in the anterior white commissure. This tract is a crossed pathway for the sensations of *touch*, and probably also for *tactile localization*. These sensations have, therefore, a double path to consciousness for they are also conveyed uncrossed in the posterior columns of the cord.

The fibers going to form the lateral spinothalamic tract (secondary neurons from cells of substantia gelatinosa of Rolando of the opposite side) ascend for a short way (within a single segment), and then cross in the anterior white commissure. This tract transmits impulses aroused by all forms of thermal and painful stimuli.

The two tracts—anterior and lateral—come together in the medulla oblongata to constitute the spinal lemniscus which joins the medial lemniscus in the upper part of the medulla oblongata to enter the thalamus (ch. 7).

3. SPINOTECTAL TRACT. This is placed in the lateral column ventral to the lateral spinothalamic tract. Its fibers arise from cells in the posterior horn of the opposite side and terminate in the superior colliculus. It subserves spinovisual reflexes.

4. SPINO-OLIVARY TRACT. The fibers of this tract are the axons of cells in the dorsal horn of gray matter; they run with olivospinal fibers and

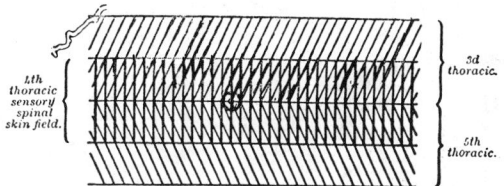

FIG. 6.5. Diagram showing the overlapping of the skin area innervated through the fourth thoracic spinal nerve root by those supplied by the third and fifth. The small circle indicates the position of the nipple. (After Sherrington.)

end in the inferior olivary nucleus of the opposite side. They probably transmit proprioceptive impulses which are relayed from the olivary nucleus to the cerebellum. Some anatomists have expressed doubts as to the existence of an olivospinal tract.

5. SPINOCEREBELLAR TRACTS. (a) The *dorsal (posterior) spinocerebellar tract* (direct cerebellar or tract of Flechsig) is situated in the posterior part of the lateral funiculus to the outer side of the lateral corticospinal tract. It is composed of the axons of the cells of Clarke's column (p. 116) of the same side and, possibly, to some extent of the opposite side. The direct cerebellar tract reaches the cerebellum via the inferior cerebellar peduncle; its fibers end mainly in the cortex of the anterior and posterior lobes of the cerebellum (ch. 10). (b) The *ventral (anterior or indirect) spinocerebellar tract* arises from cells in the base of the dorsal horn, mainly of the same side, but also of the opposite side of the cord. It ascends in front of the dorsal spinocerebellar tract and is continued upwards through the brain stem as far as the midbrain where it arches backwards (arciform fibers) to reach the cerebellum via its superior peduncle. Its constituent fibers end in the cortex of the anterior and posterior cerebellar lobes. The spinocerebellar tracts carry impulses arising in the proprioceptors of the muscles, tendons and joints. The information thus conveyed to the cerebellum is essential for the latter's

TABLE 6.1

Funiculus	Ascending Tracts	Descending Tracts	Intersegmental Tracts (Ground Bundles)
Ventral (anterior)	Ventral (anterior) spino-thalamic	Ventral (anterior) corti-cospinal Ventral vestibulospinal Ventral (anterior) tecto-spinal Reticulospinal	Ventral (anterior) inter-segmental fasciculus
Lateral	Lateral spinothalamic Dorsal (posterior) spino-cerebellar (Flechsig) Ventral (anterior) spino-cerebellar Spinotectal Dorsolateral (posterolateral) fasciculus (Lissauer)	Lateral corticospinal Rubrospinal Olivospinal (Helweg) Dorsal tectospinal Lateral vestibulospinal	Lateral intersegmental fasciculus
Dorsal (posterior)	Fasciculus gracilis Fasciculus cuneatus		Septomarginal fasciculus Dorsal (posterior) inter-segmental fasciculus

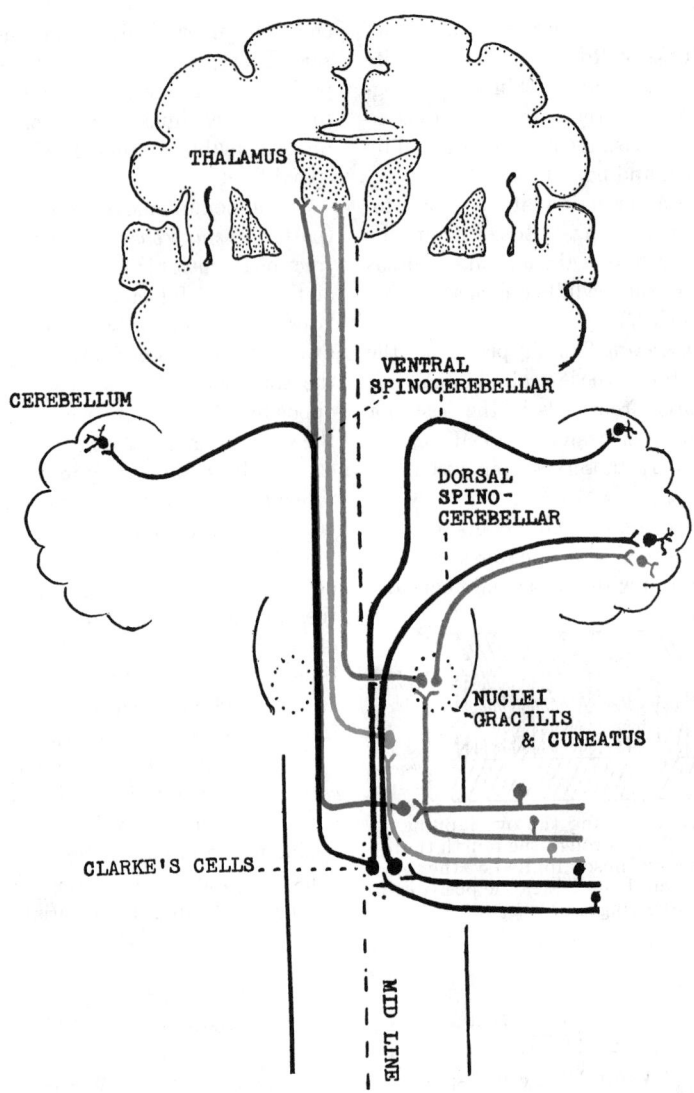

FIG. 6.6. Diagram showing the course of afferent impulses after their entrance into the cord. *Red*, pathway for pain and thermal sensations (ascend in ventrolateral spinothalamic tract of opposite side). *Blue*, pathway for touch, sense of position and movement, and spatial discrimination (ascend in posterior columns); external arcuate fibers from posterior column nuclei to cerebellum also shown. *Green*, pathway for touch, and tactile localization (after travelling for variable distances in posterior columns, fibers cross to ventral spinothalamic tract of opposite side). *Black*, ventral and dorsal spinocerebellar tracts, some fibers of latter (not shown) also cross to opposite side.

function in adjusting the tone of the skeletal muscles and synergizing their movements (ch. 10).

6. FASCICULI GRACILIS (TRACT OF GOLL) AND CUNEATUS (TRACT OF BURDACH). These occupy the dorsal (posterior) funiculus of the spinal cord. In the upper part of the spinal cord the former tract lies on the medial side of the latter.

Both tracts are composed of heavily myelinated fibers which are the continuation upwards of the fibers of the medial division of the posterior nerve roots of the same side. The nerve cell bodies from which these fibers arise lie outside of the spinal cord in the posterior root ganglia. The fasciculus gracilis commences in the lowest level of the spinal cord. After their entrance into the cord, its fibers divide into long ascending and short descending branches. A few of the former fibers and all the latter, after a short course, enter the gray matter. The long divisions become displaced medially as they ascend, with the result that fibers arising at lower levels (e.g., sacral region) come to lie nearer the midline than those entering the spinal cord higher up: the fasciculus cuneatus first appears in the midthoracic region. Therefore, from the midthoracic region upwards, the more medially placed tract (fasciculus gracilis) is derived from the lower thoracic, and the lumbar and sacral nerve roots, in this order, from the lateral to the medial border of the tract. The ascending fibers of both tracts pass uncrossed to the medulla oblongata, ending, respectively, in the nucleus gracilis and the nucleus cuneatus. However, this division into two tracts and two nuclei is an artificial one. We are dealing here with only one tract with fibers serving different parts of the body. From the nuclei gracilis and cuneatus the axons of secondary neurons emerge and, passing medially as the *internal arcuate fibers*, decussate with those of the opposite side (sensory decussation). They ascend through the brain stem as the *medial lemniscus* (see below) to terminate in the posteroventral part of the lateral nucleus of the thalamus. Other fibers (*external arcuate*) from the nuclei gracilis and cuneatus relay impulses to the cerebellum from these same posterior columns. They are concerned with reflex activity and not with sensory perception.

Summary of the Principal Pathways Ascending through the Spinal Cord

1. SENSORY (conveying impulses to consciousness). (a) The fibers mediating thermal and painful sensations enter the cord in the lateral divisions of the posterior nerve roots. According to Ranson they are unmyelinated. Within the spinal cord they constitute Lissauer's tract. Immediately, or after a very short upward or downward course, they enter the dorsal horn and connect with nerve cells in the substantia gelatinosa of Rolando. The axons of the latter secondary neurons cross to the opposite side in the white commissures and ascend as the ventrolateral spinothalamic tract. This tract occupies a position in the brain stem lateral to the medial lemniscus and ends in the posterolateral part of the ventral nucleus of the thalamus (cf. figs. 6.1 and 6.6).

(b) The fibers conveying all other sensory impulses, e.g., from the muscles and joints (sense of movement and position), and those mediating the senses of vibration, touch, pressure, tactile localization and spatial discrimination (compass test), enter the cord in the medial division of the posterior roots and ascend in the fasciculus gracilis and fasciculus cuneatus. The fibers mediating all these sensations, except *some* of those concerned with touch and probably with tactile localization, pass without crossing to the nuclei in the medulla oblongata where they connect with secondary neurons. The axons of the latter constitute the *internal arcuate* fibers; they decussate with those of the opposite side and ascend to the thalamus as the medial lemniscus (or fillet). Tertiary neurons convey the impulses to the cerebral cortex.

In a transverse spinal lesion interrupting solely the posterior fasciculi, vibratory and position senses are lost but the sensation of touch is retained, since the fibers which have entered the gray matter and crossed below the level of the lesion to ascend in the ventral spinothalamic tract have escaped injury. Likewise, although a hemisection of the spinal cord destroys vibratory and position senses on the same side and pain and temperature sensibilities on the opposite side it does not abolish tactile sensibility as this is conveyed in both crossed and uncrossed pathways (see hemisection of the cord).

2. NONSENSORY impulses from the muscles, tendons and joints as well as nonsensory impulses aroused by a tactile stimulus, are conveyed into the spinal cord by fibers composing the medial divisions of the posterior roots. These fibers connect immediately with the cells of Clarke's column and are continued upwards in the dorsal (direct) and ventral (indirect) cerebellar tracts of the same side, mainly, but also of the opposite side. Some of these impulses, viz., those which enter the cervical cord, are conveyed by fibers of the cuneate fasciculus to the cuneate nucleus, to be relayed by secondary neurons (*external arcuate fibers*) via the inferior peduncles to the cerebellum (see fig. 6.6).

Sensory Paths in the Brain Stem (Medulla Oblongata, Pons and Midbrain)

The *medial lemniscus* (or fillet) is composed of fibers arising in the nuclei gracilis and cuneatus. The fibers leave the ventral aspects of these nuclei and arch forward and medially (as *internal arcuate fibers*) to the midline where they cross with corresponding fibers of the opposite side (*sensory decussation*). They then turn upwards as a compact bundle known as the medial lemniscus or fillet. This ascends through the medulla oblongata and pons dorsal to the corticospinal tracts, and through the tegmentum of the midbrain.

The *spinal lemniscus* (or fillet) is formed by the fusion of the anterior and lateral spinothalamic tracts and is therefore a crossed path for impulses aroused by light touch, pressure, pain, heat and cold. In the upper part of the medulla oblongata the spinal lemniscus joins the medial lemniscus on its outer side, and is joined in the pons by the trigeminal lemniscus.

The *trigeminal lemniscus* (or fillet) conveys impulses from the area of distribution of the trigeminal nerve of the opposite side (p. 127).

The fibers of the medial, spinal and trigeminal lemnisci terminate in the thalamus, from where tertiary neurons pass to the cerebral cortex (see fig. 6.7).

The *lateral lemniscus* constitutes the pathway for auditory impulses from the cochlear nuclei to the inferior colliculus and the medial geniculate body.

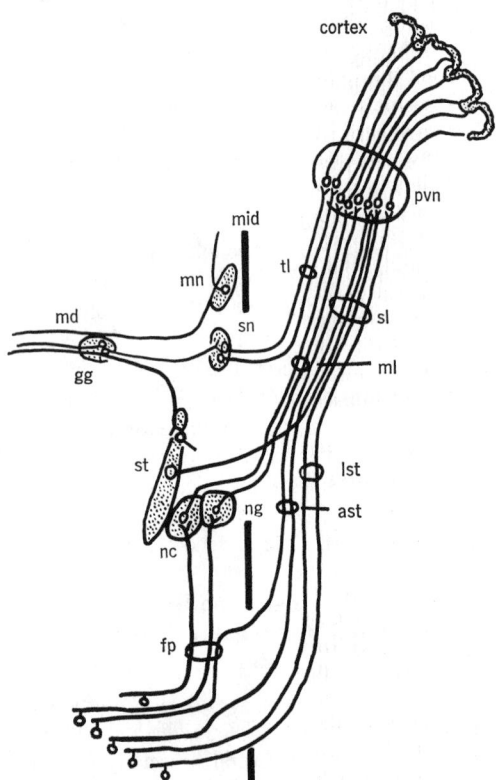

FIG. 6.7. Diagram of the trigeminal, medial and spinal lemnisci. *mn*, mesencephalic motor nucleus of trigeminal nerve; *sn*, sensory nuc. of trigeminal; *st*, spinal tract and nucleus of trigeminal; *md*, motor fibers passing into mandibular nerve; *gg*. gasserian ganglion; *nc*, nuc. cuneatus; *fp*, posterior columns of the cord; *ng*, nuc. gracillis; *tl*, trigeminal lemniscus; *pvn*, posterior ventral nuc. of the thalamus; *sl*, spinal lemniscus; *ml*, medial lemniscus; *lst*, lateral spinothalamic tract; *ast*, anterior spinothalamic tract; *mid*, midline. The trigeminal is on the medial side of the medial lemniscus, only in the medulla; it comes to lie on the outer side in the pons, and in close relation to the spinal lemniscus.

The sensory pathways are constituted of three neurons. For example, the pathway traversed by the sensory impulses for touch or kinesthetic sense consists of a primary neuron whose cell body lies in the posterior root ganglion, a secondary neuron originating in a posterior column nucleus (gracilis or cuneatus) and a tertiary neuron arising in the thalamus which convey impulses to the somesthetic area of the cerebral cortex (ch. 8). The cells of the gasserian ganglia are the primary neurons of the trigeminal pathway; secondary neurons lie in the sensory nucleus and in the spinal nucleus of the nerve (p. 128); tertiary neuron fibers ascend to the cortex from the thalamus. In the upper part of the pons and in the midbrain these several sensory pathways become fused together into a compact bundle. But a lesion in the lower part of the brain stem may involve one of the sensory pathways exclusively of the others. Thus an injury localized to the outer part of the lower pons or of the medulla oblongata may by injuring the spinal lemniscus cause loss of sensation to pain, heat and cold over the *opposite half* of the body leaving muscle sense and tactile discrimination intact. Sensory loss of this nature accompanied by ipsilateral cerebellar symptoms occurs as a result of the occlusion (as by thrombosis or embolism) of the posterior inferior cerebellar artery. Usually also, as a result of the involvement of the bulbospinal tract of the trigeminal nerve (p. 128) the face on the *same side* as the occluded vessel shows a loss of pain and temperature sensibilities whereas tactile sensation which is transmitted by the main sensory nucleus is largely unaffected. A lesion more centrally placed may, by implicating the medial lemniscus alone, cause the converse type of dissociated sensory defect, namely, loss of the sense of position of the limbs and of spatial discrimination with retention of sensibility to pain, heat and cold. In lesions at higher levels in the brain stem all forms of sensation are likely to be involved more or less equally.

Descending Tracts of the Spinal Cord

1. CORTICOSPINAL (CEREBROSPINAL) TRACTS. From their origins in the cerebral cortex these tracts descend through the cerebrum and brain stem on each side to the lower border of the medulla oblongata. Here each tract divides into two bundles of unequal size, the larger of which crosses to the opposite side and descends in the posterior part of the lateral funiculus of the cord as the *lateral corticospinal tract*. The remaining fibers uncrossed, descend in the anterior funiculus as the *anterior corticospinal tract*. In most in-

stances the direct or anterior corticospinal tract is but a small part of the total number of cortico-spinal fibers (usually not over 10 per cent), but the number of fibers in the anterior tract varies and in rare instances most of the corticospinal fibers lie in this position. In most cases these anteriorly placed fibers descend only as far as the cervical spinal cord. Even these fibers cross to the opposite side before terminating on the ganglion cells of the anterior gray column (*cf.* figs. 6.1 and 6.8). There are also direct corticospinal fibers lying in the lateral columns of the spinal cord which do not cross to the opposite side. Through these the precentral motor cortex sends impulses to ipsi-lateral skeletal muscles.

All corticospinal fibers whether crossed or un-crossed connect with the large motor cells of the ventral gray columns (anterior horn cells). The connections are of two types, (a) direct synapses (20 to 30 per cent) with the motor neurons, (b) in-direct connections with these cells through an internuncial neuron whose cell body is also in communication with a posterior root fiber on each side. It has been estimated that from 75 to 90 per cent of the corticospinal fibers terminate in the cervical (55 per cent) and thoracic (20 per cent) regions of the spinal cord, and about 25 per cent in the lumbar and sacral regions.

For many years an erroneous belief was enter-tained that all of the fibers in the pyramids on the ventral surface of the medulla oblongata arose from the Betz cells of the precentral gyrus and were responsible for all voluntary activity of the skeletal musculature. It is now known that this concept contains many errors. Only a very small percentage of the corticospinal fibers arise from the gigantic Betz cells of the precentral gyrus, approximately 3 to 4 per cent. The remainder of the corticospinal fibers arise from other cells in the precentral gyrus, from cells in the parietal

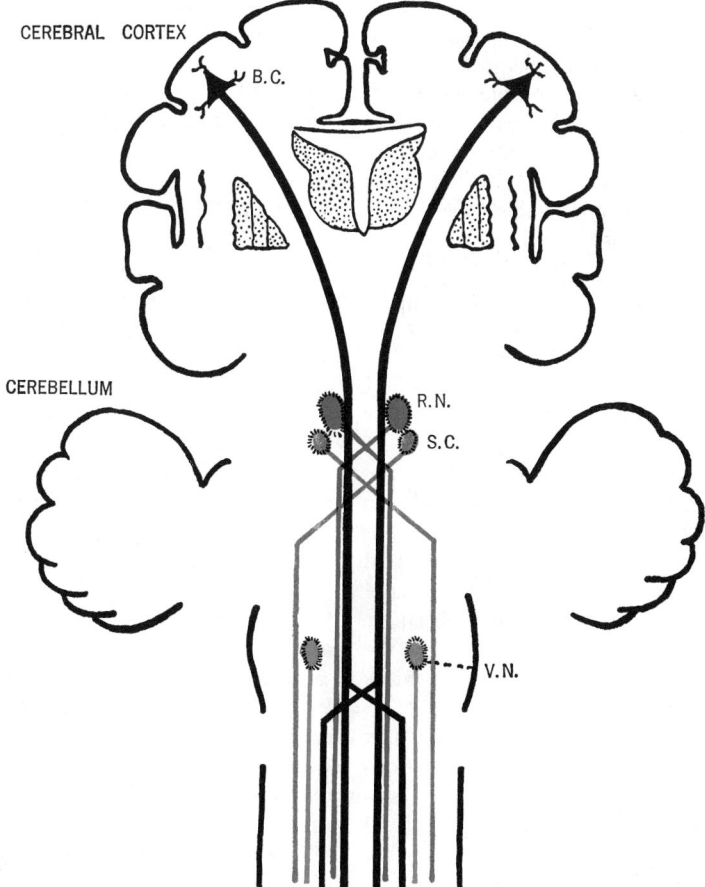

Fɪɢ. 6.8. Diagram of the descending tracts of the cord showing corticospinal tracts (black), rubro-spinal tracts (red), tectospinal tracts (blue) and vestibulospinal tracts (green). B.C., Betz cell of motor cortex; R.N., red nucleus; S.C., superior colliculus; V.N., vestibular nucleus. The implication of this figure that the corticospinal tract arises exclusively from the Betz cells is erroneous.

cortex and perhaps other areas. There is a question as to whether all of the fibers in the medullary pyramids are of cortical origin, and some investigators have even questioned as to whether they are all descending fibers. Certainly all voluntary muscular activity is not achieved exclusively by corticospinal fibers or by fibers contained in the medullary pyramids. There are multisynaptic fiber pathways from the cortex down to the anterior horn cells of the spinal cord which are also capable of producing voluntary movement.

2. VESTIBULOSPINAL TRACTS. Two tracts, a ventral and a lateral, are commonly designated, although there is no evidence that they serve different functions or that there is any significant difference between them. The *ventral vestibulospinal tract* arises predominantly from the spinal or inferior vestibular nucleus (in the cat) and descends in the forepart of the anterior funiculus of the spinal cord just lateral to the anterior corticospinal tract. It is a downward extension of the medial longitudinal fasciculus of the brain stem. The *lateral vestibulospinal tract* is a prominent descending pathway lying in the anterolateral part of the spinal cord. It arises from the lateral vestibular or Deiter's nucleus and extends throughout the entire length of the spinal cord. Most of its fibers are uncrossed although a few arise from the contralateral lateral vestibular nucleus. The vestibulospinal fibers terminate either upon the anterior horn cells or upon small internuncial neurons which in turn form synapses with the motor cells of the anterior gray horns of the spinal cord.

3. TECTOSPINAL TRACTS of each spinal half arise from the contralateral superior and inferior colliculi and descend at first as a single compact bundle through the reticular formation of the brain stem. Upon reaching the cord the fibers are segregated into two fasciculi, a ventral and a dorsal, which descend in the ventral and lateral white columns respectively. The fibers synapse with the spinal motonureons, either directly or through internuncial neurons, especially in the cervical region, wherein are situated the centers for the neck muscles. Impulses from the retina are received by the superior colliculus which through such impulses, and its spinal connections serves as a center for the integration of visual impressions with body movement, especially of the head (*visuospinal reflexes*). This center is probably of less importance in man, with his highly developed visual cortex, than in animals. Auditory reflexes may also be mediated by this tract and the inferior colliculus.

4. RUBROSPINAL TRACT arises from the large cells (nucleus magnocellularis) in the posterior part of the red nucleus (p. 144). The fibers immediately upon leaving the red nucleus cross to the opposite side (*Forel's decussation*) and descend through the reticular formation of the pons and medulla to enter the lateral funiculus of the cord ventral to the lateral corticospinal tract. In carnivorous animals, e.g., cat and dog, the rubrospinal tract is large and important. In the primates, particularly in man, the rubrospinal tract is so small that its existence has been questioned; at any rate it has little if any functional significance.

5. OLIVOSPINAL (BULBOSPINAL) TRACT OF HELWEG. Its fibers are presumed to arise from cells in the neighborhood of the inferior olivary nucleus and descend in the ventral and lateral part of the lateral funiculus. However, its existence has been seriously questioned. It descends no farther than the cervical region. The fibers synapse with motor neurons. The functions of this tract are unknown. It and the thalamo-olivary tract constitute a possible path whereby impulses from the thalamus may reach the spinal centers.

6. RETICULOSPINAL TRACTS arise from cells scattered through the reticular formation of the brain stem. They are two in number, one in which crossed fibers predominate descends in the anterior funiculus, the other composed mainly of uncrossed fibers, in the lateral funiculus. They connect with the motor neurons in the anterior horns and probably with cells in the lateral horn. Impulses conveyed over this complex pathway are concerned with the regulation of the reflex activity of the skeletal musculature, the control of the vegetative nervous system, adjustment of the threshold of peripheral end-organs such as the muscle spindles and of the sensory pathways.

Intersegmental Tracts of the Spinal Cord

There is in each funiculus of the cord lying close to the gray matter an intersegmental fasciculus or ground bundle. These, as already mentioned serve to link spinal segments of different levels Their fibers arise from cells in the gray matter and after an ascending or descending course of variable length end around cells of the same or of the opposite side at a higher or a lower level. A proportion of the fibers constituting the intersegmental fasciculus of the lateral column of the spinal cord (*lateral intersegmental fasciculus* or *lateral ground bundle*) are continued upwards into the medial longitudinal fasciculus (or bundle) of the brain stem. The ground bundle of the anterior funiculus (*anterior intersegmental* or *sulcomarginal fasciculus*) is composed of fibers which connect the anterior horn cells of one side with those of the opposite side both at the same and at different levels. In the cervical region, it is composed largely of the spinal fibers of the medial longitudinal fasciculus.

The posterior funiculus contains (a) the septo-marginal fasciculus and (b) the posterior interseg-mental fasciculus (or posterior ground bundle).

The *septomarginal fasciculus* is composed of (a) intersegmental fibers which arise from cells of the posterior horn and synapse with corresponding cells at lower levels and (b) descending fibers of the medial divisions of the posterior nerve roots. Septomarginal fasciculus is a term applicable to these fibers only in the lumbar region where they abut on each side against the posterior median septum. They are also known here as the *oval area* or *bundle of Fleichsig*. These fibers form areas of different sizes and shapes on cross section at various spinal levels. In the cervical and upper thoracic regions the fibers appear on section as a crescentic area at about the center of the posterior funiculus. Here they are spoken of as the *comma tract of Schultz*, or *tractus interfascicularis*. In the lower thoracic region they form a narrow zone bounding the posterior aspect of the cord and are known as the *dorsal peripheral strand*. In the sacral region this tract lies against the posterior part of the median septum and is called the tri-angular area of Philippe-Gombault. The descend-ing fibers of the branches of the medial division of the posterior roots as they descend also, like the long ascending branches, become displaced toward the midline.

The *posterior intersegmental fasciculus* is seen in cross section as a small area lying behind the posterior gray commissure. Its fibers connect the posterior horn cells of different segments (see fig. 6.1).

The Longitudinal Fasciculus (or Bundle)

The medial (posterior) longitudinal fasciculus (or bundle) is a tract of great physiological im-portance and is present in all vertebrates. It is composed of fibers which connect the 3rd, 4th and 6th cranial nerves with one another and with the vestibular nuclei, and makes connections with the motoneurons of the cervical segments of the spinal cord (fig. 6.15). The tract lies near the midline and extends from the cervical segments of the spinal cord, where it is continuous with the an-terior intersegmental fasciculus (anterior ground bundle) to the floor of the 3rd ventricle. In the

medulla oblongata it lies immediately subjacent to the floor of the 4th ventricle; in the pons it courses through the formatio reticularis, and in the midbrain, lies in relation to the gray matter of the floor of the Sylvian (cerebral) aqueduct. It also received fibers from the lateral lemniscus (au-ditory path, p. 124) and from the superior col-liculus, through which it is in communication with the optic pathway (ch. 16). The essential function of the medial longitudinal bundle is the coordination of reflex movements of the ocular and neck muscles in response to labyrinthine, auditory and visual stimuli.

The Central Connections of the Trigeminal, Facial, Glossopharyngeal, Vagus, Acces-sory and Hypoglossal Nerves

The Trigeminal Pathway

The trigeminal nerve appears on the lateral surface of the pons. The nerve has three roots (a) a large *sensory*, (b) a small *motor*, and (c) a *mesen-cephalic* (fig. 6.9).

The fibers of the *sensory root* convey impulses from the anterior part of the scalp, from the skin of the forehead and face, with the exception of an area over the lower border of the mandible. It also supplies the mucous membrane of the mouth, anterior two-thirds of tongue and nose, the cornea and conjunctivae and part of the intracranial dura mater. This root arises from the cells of the gasserian (semilunar) ganglion, which corresponds to a spinal posterior root ganglion. The processes of the ganglion cells di-vide into peripheral and central branches. The

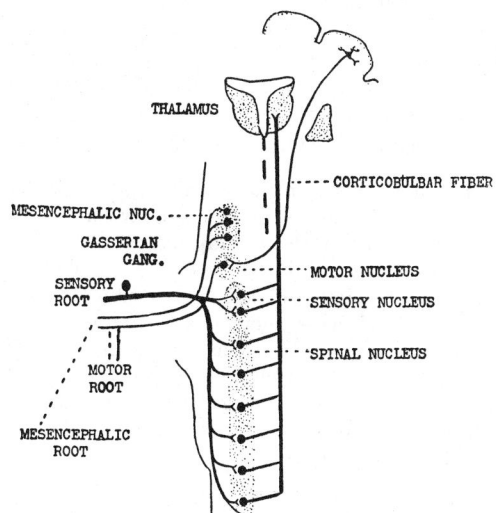

Fig. 6.9. Diagram of the central connections of the trigeminal nerve.

former enter into the composition of the peripheral divisions (ophthalmic, maxillary and mandibular) of the nerve; the central branches (which constitute the sensory root of the nerve) enter the pons in close association with the fibers of the motor root and divide into an ascending and a descending group in a manner homologous with a spinal root fiber. The *ascending fibers* convey impulses of light touch, tactile discrimination and localization, and of the sense of position and passive movement. They end in a nucleus (*main or upper sensory nucleus of the trigeminal nerve*) situated in the pons, deep and lateral to the motor nucleus. The axons of cells in this nucleus ascend with those from the spinal nucleus of the trigeminal nerve (see below) to form the *trigeminal lemniscus*. The *descending fibers* constitute the *bulbospinal tract of the trigeminal nerve*. They subserve sensations of pain and temperature over the entire trigeminal area. They descend through the pons and medulla oblongata and may be traced as far as the 2nd cervical segment. This tract dwindles gradually in its descent, its fibers terminating around cells in the substantia gelatinosa of Rolando which in this situation is referred to as the *spinal nucleus of the trigeminal nerve*. From the spinal nucleus the axons of secondary neurons swing downward in the spinal tract of the trigeminal nerve as far as the upper cervical spinal cord. They then cross the midline and turn upward. In the upper part of the medulla oblongata they join fibers arising from the upper sensory nucleus to form the *trigeminal lemniscus* (or fillet). The trigeminal lemniscus lies in close association with the medial and the spinal lemnisci (spinothalamic tracts) (p. 120); its fibers terminate in the posteroventral nucleus of the thalamus.

A number of reflexes are mediated through the afferent fibers of the trigeminal nerve, e.g., corneal, winking, sneezing and oculocardiac.

The main sensory nucleus of the trigeminal corresponds to the nuclei of the posterior columns of the spinal cord (nuclei gracilis and cuneatus) and like the latter sends fibers to the cerebellum through the inferior cerebellar peduncle. The spinal tract of the trigeminal nerve may be looked upon as corresponding to the tract of Lissauer (p. 1189), and the spinal nucleus as an extension upwards of the substantia gelatinosa of Rolando whose cells, as we have seen, give rise to the lateral spinothalamic tract.

The *motor root* fibers arise from a nucleus in the upper part of the pons underlying the lateral part of the floor of the 4th ventricle. The nucleus receives fibers from the corticobulbar tract of the opposite side and also probably from the same side. The motor root after its emergence from the brain stem, travels peripherally with the sensory root and, passing deep to the gasserian ganglion, joins the mandibular (3rd) division of the trigeminal nerve to supply the muscles of mastication (temporal, masseter and pterygoids).

The *mesencephalic root* consists of a small bundle of fibers which run in company with the fibers of the motor root. Entering the pons they ascend to the *mesencephalic nucleus* of the trigeminal, an elongated collection of nerve cells extending from the level of the motor nucleus to the upper region of the midbrain. It was thought at one time that the mesencephalic root and nucleus were motor in function, but it is now generally admitted that they are composed of afferent neurons. The nucleus is looked upon as a group of cells homologous with the gasserian (semilunar) ganglion and the posterior root ganglia of the spinal nerves, but which has migrated or been "drawn" into the brain stem at an early period of phylogenetic development. It is believed to receive proprioceptive impulses from the muscles of mastication and possibly from the ocular muscles.

LESIONS INVOLVING THE TRIGEMINAL PATHWAYS. Either the peripheral portions or the central connections of the nerve may be the seat of disease. A lesion of the nerve peripheral to the ganglion is more likely to involve only one of its three divisions. Pain, or loss of sensibility over the distribution of the division affected, may result. If the gasserian ganglion is involved the disturbance of sensation usually involves the area of distribution of more than one division, often of the entire nerve. If as a result the eye is rendered anesthetic the patient may develop an ulceration of the cornea and an inflammation of the cornea and conjunctiva. This has often been referred to as a neuroparalytic keratitis anb has been attributed to the loss of some obscure trophic influence of the nerve. Actually it results from the fact that the eye is anesthetic and can be injured easily by a foreign body or by scratching without any discomfort to the patient. The eye is then likely to be neglected by the patient because it is not painful. As a result he may lose his sight or even his eye.

Herpetic eruptions may result from the involvement of the gasserian ganglion. Spontaneous herpes zoster usually involves the area of distribution of the ophthalmic division and is often serious because the lesions on the cornea may lead to corneal opacity and loss of vision. Such herpes is also commonly followed by a very distressing post-herpetic neuralgia which is very difficult to treat satisfactorily.

Paralysis of the muscles of mastication with reduction in the strength of the bite on the affected side and deviation of the mandible toward the paralyzed side when it is opened occurs when the motor division is involved. Such paralysis is commonly seen in association with affections of the mandibular division which the motor root joins, or of the gasserian ganglion which lies directly over the motor root.

Loss of sensation of taste (as well as of ordinary sensibility) over the anterior two-thirds of the tongue on the corresponding side is a common accompaniment of degenerative changes affecting the mandibular division of the 5th nerve. The taste fibers to this part of the tongue are derived from the chorda tympani branch of the facial, but travel via the lingual branch of the mandibular division of the trigeminal nerve. Removal of the gasserian ganglion does not result in a loss of taste.

Lesions (e.g., tumors, vascular changes) in the pons, medulla or upper cervical spinal cord may injure the upper sensory nucleus, the motor nucleus, the trigeminal lemniscus (crossed) or the bulbospinal tract of the nerve. When the motor nucleus is involved weakness and wasting of the muscles of mastication result; implication of the ascending sensory fibers, or of the main sensory nucleus in the pons, is followed by loss of the sensation of light touch and the discriminative aspects of cutaneous sensibility over the same side of the face, but the retention of sensibility to pain, heat and cold. The neighboring spinothalamic tract (crossed) may suffer coincidently with the ascending sensory fibers, when thermanesthesia and analgesia over the trunk and limbs of the opposite side combined with loss of tactile sensation over the face of the same side will result (see also p. 123). Syringomyelia extending into the upper cervical region or into the bulb (syringobulbia) is likely to cause, as a result of pressure upon the spinal tract of the nerve, a loss of the appreciation of pain and changes in temperature, with retention of tactile sensibility.

The trigeminal nerve, or one of its divisions, is sometimes the seat of a severe and intractable type of pain which recurs in paroxysms (*trigeminal neuralgia; tic douloureux*). The cause of the affection is unknown. In treating the condition, injections of alcohol into the division of the nerve involved are sometimes employed. The injection is made into the nerve at the infraorbital foramen in the case of involvement of the maxillary division, and at the foramen ovale of the sphenoid or at the supraorbital notch, respectively, in disease of the mandibular or ophthalmic division. Injection or section of the peripheral branches result in only temporary remission of the pain whereas the section of the nerve between the gasserian ganglion and the pons provides permanent relief. The motor root can be spared in such an operation.

THE FACIAL NERVE

The facial nerve consists of a large *motor* and a small *sensory* portion. The two portions or roots appear at the lower border of the pons and enter the internal auditory meatus in company with the auditory nerve.

The *sensory* root of the facial, which is also known as the *nervus intermedius of Wrisberg*, contains not only afferent fibers but secretory and vasodilator (parasympathetic) fibers as well.

The *sensory fibers* arise from the cells of the geniculate ganglion (fig. 6.10). The peripheral processes of these cells are distributed through the chorda tympani branch of the facial nerve to the taste buds and mucous membrane of the anterior two-thirds of the tongue, and through the nerve to the pterygoid canal (formed by the union of the greater superficial petrosal and the deep petrosal nerves), and the sphenopalatine ganglion to the lacrimal gland and the mucosa of the soft palate and posterior part of the nose. The chorda tympani branch joins the trunk of the lingual nerve through which it is conveyed to the floor of the mouth.[2] The central processes of the ganglion cells end in the *sensory nucleus* situated in the upper part of the tractus solitarius. Fibers arise from the latter and ascend in the medial fillet of the opposite side to reach the thalamus.

The *parasympathetic fibers* arise from the *superior salivatory nucleus* which lies in close relation to the motor nucleus of the facial. After leaving the brain stem in the sensory root

[2] The nervus intermedius, the geniculate ganglion, the chorda tympani and part of the great superficial petrosal nerve are sometimes grouped together under the name *glossopalatine nerve*. The origin and distribution of the secretory and sensory fibers of which this nerve is composed are closely similar to those of the glossopharyngeal, and it is considered by some as an aberrant part of the latter nerve.

A small proportion of taste fibers may take an alternative route, namely, via the chorda tympani to the otic ganglion and thence by way of the internal sphenoidal and great superficial petrosal nerves, genicular ganglion and nervus intermedius to the brain stem (Schwartz and Weddell).

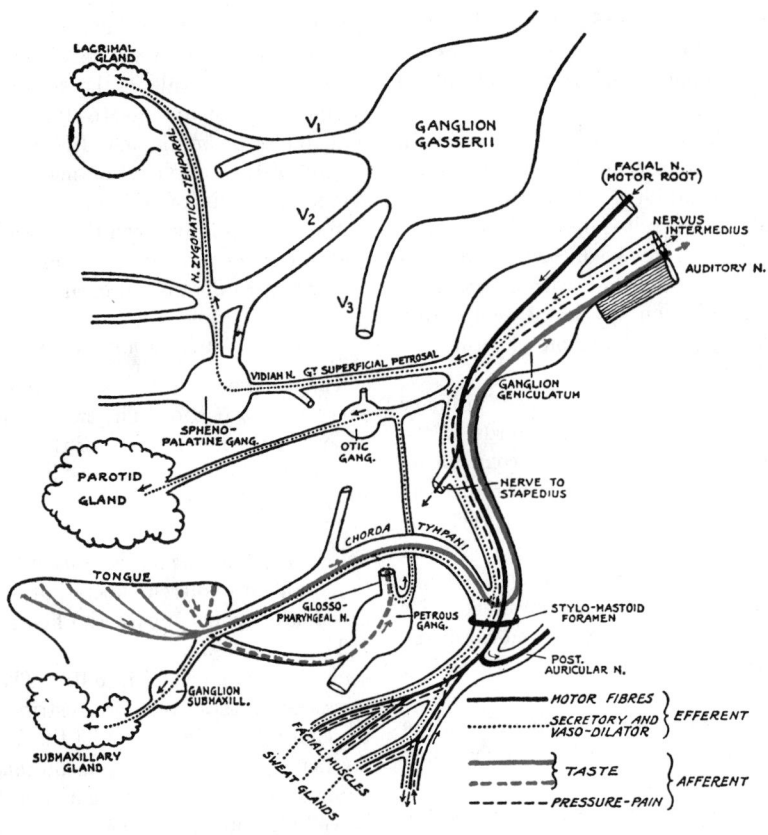

FIG. 6.10. Diagram of the facial nerve; afferent and efferent paths, including taste (red) and secretory fibers (dotted lines). (After Purves-Stewart.)

the parasympathetic secretory and vasodilator fibers pass via the *great superficial petrosal* nerve and *nerve to pterygoid canal* (formed by the union of the great superficial and deep petrosal nerves) to the *sphenopalatine ganglion* from where they are relayed to the lacrymal gland, and to the vessels and glands of the palate and posterior part of the nose. The secretory and vasodilator fibers to the submaxillary and sublingual glands leave the facial with the taste fibers in the chorda tympani branch.

The *motor part* of the facial is conveyed through the facial canal of the temporal bone to the stylomastoid foramen. After its emergence from the latter it is distributed to muscles of the face, auricle, and forehead. The motor fibers arise from a nucleus in the lower part of the pons and pass backwards to the lower end of the nucleus of the abducent nerve. Then ascending to the upper end of the latter they bend and sweep downwards and forward to where they leave the brain. As the facial fibers take this arched course to the point of their emergence from the brain stem, they, together with the abducent nucleus, form a prom-

inence in the floor of the 4th ventricle, known as the *facial colliculus.*

Connections: the motor nucleus of the facial nerve receives:

1. Fibers from the corticobulbar tract of the same and of the opposite side.
2. Fibers from the lateral, trigeminal and medial lemnisci, and from the spinothalamic tracts. Through these connections reflex facial movements in animals may be initiated from various receptive areas of the body.

FACIAL PARALYSIS. The effects of interruption of the facial pathway vary in certain important features according to the level at which the injury occurs. The nature of the motor loss following a lesion of the supranuclear (corticobulbar) fibers is described on pages 133 and 134. In the paralysis resulting from division to the trunk of the facial nerve all the muscles of the affected side of the face are completely paralyzed. The subject is unable to close the eye owing to paralysis of the orbicularis oculi, or to frown; the eyebrow droops. The mouth is drawn over to the sound side by the unparalyzed muscles and the muscles of the affected side do not take part in the facial expression of emotional states, e.g., laughing or crying.

Facial paralysis may result from a lesion involving:

1. The motor nucleus or the intra-pontine course of the motor fibers (tumors, hemorrhage, etc.).

2. The nerve as it crosses the posterior fossa of the skull to reach the internal auditory meatus, as in fractures of the skull or tumors in this situation; the sensory portion and the auditory nerve are commonly involved as well, when loss of the sensation of taste over the anterior two-thirds of the tongue, and deafness on the affected side will result.

3. The nerve in its course through the temporal bone as in fracture of the skull or in otitis media; inflammation of the nerve within the facial canal (aqueduct of Fallopius)—*Bell's palsy*—may occur.

4. The nerve after its emergence from the stylomastoid foramen, as it lies behind the angle of the jaw; inflammation, parotid tumors, or accidental injuries may implicate the nerve in this situation.

The Glossopharyngeal Nerve

The glossopharyngeal nerve contains motor, secretory, vasodilator and sensory fibers. The nerve emerges from the side of the upper part of the medulla oblongata in the groove between the olive and the restiform body. The motor fibers are distributed almost entirely to the stylopharyngeus muscle; a few terminate in the circular and longitudinal muscle of the upper part of the pharynx. However, division of the glossopharyngeal nerve which is done for glossopharyngeal neuralgia produces no motor disability so far as the patient is concerned. The secretory and vasodilator fibers (via its tympanic branch, the tympanic plexus, the small superficial petrosal nerve and the otic ganglion) supply the parotid gland. The *sensory* fibers arise from cells in the superior (jugular) and inferior (petrous) ganglia of the glossopharyngeal nerve. The peripheral processes of the cells of the latter ganglion supply the taste buds of the posterior third of the tongue. Those from cells of the *superior* ganglion mediate *ordinary sensations* (touch, thermal, etc.), from this part of the tongue and the mucosa of the pharynx and posterior part of the mouth; the central processes (superior ganglion) terminate in the *dorsal nucleus* of the vagus and (inferior ganglion) in the lower part of the *tractus solitarius*. Fibers (secondary neurons) pass from the latter nucleus and, crossing to the medial

fillet of the opposite side, ascend to the thalamus, from where axons of tertiary neurons pass to the cortical area for taste. The motor fibers arise from the upper part of the *nucleus ambiguus* situated in the reticular formation of the medulla oblongata. Secretory fibers are the axons of cells lying in the *inferior salivatory* nucleus which lies below the superior nucleus of the same name. The carotid sinus nerve is another important afferent branch of the glossopharyngeal nerve. It is concerned with the conduction of impulses from the carotid body and the carotid sinus to the medulla oblongata. These impulses and their frequency are determined by chemical changes in the blood which are detected by the carotid body and by changes in the blood pressure which are detected by the carotid sinus. These afferent impulses are concerned in reflex activities which take part in controlling the pulse rate, the respiratory rate and the blood pressure.

The Vagus Nerve

The vagus nerve contains motor, secretory, vasodilator and sensory fibers. The secretory and vasodilator fibers and the fibers to the involuntary muscle of the bronchi, heart, esophagus, stomach, small intestine, gall-bladder, etc. (parasympathetic fibers, ch. 12) arise from cells in the *dorsal nucleus of the vagus* (principal autonomic nucleus). This gray mass extends upwards from the lower, closed part of the medulla oblongata to beneath the floor of the 4th ventricle at the level of the striae medullares. The voluntary motor fibers arise in close relationship with the motor fibers of the glossopharyngeal nerve, namely, from the cells of the *nucleus ambiguus* lying below the glossopharyngeal neurons. They supply (through the superior laryngeal branch) the cricothyroid and arytenoid muscles of the larynx, and the inferior constrictor of the pharynx. The pharyngeal and recurrent laryngeal branches of the vagus also convey voluntary motor fibers many of which are derived from the bulbar nucleus of the accessory nerve (see below) to the pharyngeal muscles (with the exception of the stylopharyngeus), and to the muscles of the soft palate (except the tensor palati) and larynx (except the cricothyroid). The cell bodies of the *sensory fibers* lie in the inferior ganglion of the vagus (ganglion nodosum). The peripheral processes of these cells convey impulses from the lungs, heart, larynx, pharynx, esophagus, stomach, small intestine and gall-bladder. They also, through the anterior laryngeal branch, innervate the taste buds of the epiglottis and valleculae (the depressions lying at the sides of the fold running from the epiglottis to the base of the tongue). The taste fibers end centrally by synapsing with cells in the *gustatory nucleus* lying in the upper and medial part of the *tractus solitarius*. These impulses are relayed upwards along the same paths as those conveying other taste impulses. Afferent vagal fibers from visceral structures terminate in the dorsal nucleus. This latter is, therefore, both motor and sensory in function and constitutes an important visceral reflex center. It contains the cardio-inhibitory and vomiting centers.

Vagal afferent filaments travelling in Arnold's nerve mediate the general sensations of the skin lining the external auditory meatus and a small area behind the auricle. Irritation of these fibers may cause reflex coughing. These sensory fibers have their cell stations in the jugular ganglion.

THE SPINAL ACCESSORY NERVE

The spinal accessory nerve is entirely motor and is made up of a bulbar and a spinal root. The *bulbar* root arises from the lower (caudal) end of the nucleus ambiguous from cells situated below those which give origin to the motor fibers of the vagus. The bulbar fibers join the vagus within and below the jugular foramen and are distributed, as already mentioned, in the pharyngeal and recurrent branches of the latter nerve; these fibers of the spinal accessory nerve innervate the muscles of the larynx, with the exception of the cricothyroid, the muscles of the pharynx and those of the soft palate, with the exception of the tensor palati (which is supplied by the 5th cranial nerve). The *spinal* root is composed of the axons of a group of cells in the anterior gray column of the spinal cord extending from the 1st to the 4th or 5th cervical segment inclusive. These fibers supply the sternocleidomastoid and trapezius muscles. The spinal part of the nerve exchanges fibers with the bulbar part in the jugular foramen.

THE HYPOGLOSSAL NERVE

The hypoglossal nerve is also purely motor. Its fibers are derived from a nucleus situated near the midline in the floor of the posterior part of the 4th ventricle and medial to the nucleus ambiguus. It supplies the thyrohyoid, styloglossus, hyoglossus and genioglossus muscles, and the intrinsic muscles of the tongue.

THE PATHWAYS FOR THE CONTROL OF MUSCULAR ACTIVITY

The neural mechanism controlling the activity of the skeletal musculature is extremely complex and as yet incompletely understood. Voluntary movements are dependent in primates (monkeys, apes and man) upon the precentral motor cortex. The same is not true for lower animals. Birds and reptiles have practically no cerebral cortex and their well organized movements are controlled by nuclear masses more or less comparable to the basal ganglia of the primate brain. In higher animal forms such as rodents the cerebral cortex is present but of relatively little importance so far as muscular activity is concerned. In the carnivores, e.g., cat and dog, a specialized portion of the cerebral cortex (the sigmoid gyrus) has developed into a "motor" cortex. If it is stimulated electrically movements can be produced in the contralateral extremities and if the sigmoid gyrus is removed a transitory contralateral paralysis ensues. However, the cerebral cortex is not essential for useful movement of the skeletal musculature. The sigmoid gyri can be removed from both sides with only a temporary paralysis. In fact, the entire cortex can be removed and the animal still be able to sit, stand, walk or run. In primates the situation is quite different. Here the cerebral cortex is much more important but there still exists a considerable difference between the various animals. If one removes the precentral motor cortex or even the entire cortex from one cerebral hemisphere in a monkey, a complete paralysis of the opposite side of the face and of the opposite arm and leg will result. Useful movement will soon begin to return and in a few weeks the animal will be running about, climbing the walls of his cage and hopping about on his trapeze in an agile fashion, although a partial paralysis of the involved arm and leg will be obvious. The ape, too, will recover, though not as completely as the monkey, whereas removal of the precentral motor cortex in man will result in a contralateral paralysis which, though it will improve, will always be severely disabling. After such an operation a man will become able to walk, although with a limping gait dragging and circumducting his leg. He will never recover useful movement in his upper extremity and will probably have no movement at all in his hand and fingers.

The recovery in primates following removal of the precentral motor cortex is due almost entirely to ipsilateral innervation from the intact cerebral hemisphere, for if the remaining precentral motor cortex is removed a severe and enduring paralysis *in all four extremities* is the immediate result. It is true that if the cortex is removed piecemeal in several operations over months of time and if the animal is given very special care occasionally it is possible to produce a bilaterally decorticate monkey that has a few awkward but very limited voluntary movements. At best such an animal is almost completely disabled. In most instances he is totally paralyzed except for a few useless stereotyped grasping movements. In view of the demonstrably greater importance of the precentral motor cortex in man as compared with the motor cortex of cats it is obvious that in the human being the production of useful voluntary movements is dependent upon this important area of the cerebral cortex. It is evident that the subcortical centers (basal ganglia, red nucleus, substantia nigra, reticular formation, cerebellum and spinal cord) are important in the production of well coordinated, useful muscular activity, but in man these centers cannot function adequately in the absence of the precentral motor cortex.

The precentral motor cortex gives rise to corticospinal fibers which arise from the precentral gyrus and descend to the anterior gray horns of the spinal cord. These fibers are concerned with voluntary muscular activity and primarily with delicate, precise, well coordinated movements of the distal parts of the extremities, particularly the digits. The relationship of the corticospinal fibers which arise in the parietal cortex to voluntary muscular activity is unkuown. It is certain, however, that this parietal component of the corticospinal system is not capable of producing useful coordinated movements independent of the precentral motor cortex.

The precentral motor cortex gives rise to many more descending fibers with motor functions than just the corticospinal fibers. There are fibers to the basal ganglia, the red nucleus, the substantia nigra, the reticular formation and the pontine nuclei (and through them impulses pass to the cerebellum). These, too, are concerned with the production of voluntary muscular activity. In the absence of the corticospinal tract such movement is apt to be cruder and less delicate but still useful. Exactly which of these many fiber systems —corticocaudate; corticopallidal; corticonigral; corticopontine, etc.—is concerned in the production of voluntary muscular activity is unknown.

This neural mechanism is also concerned with other functions of great concern in the organization of muscular activity. These include (1) the control by inhibition and facilitation of the various postural reflexes (see ch. 64); (2) the control of various automatic and associated movements, such as swinging of the arms when walking; (3) various visceral and vasomotor activities such as respiratory movements, blood pressure, pulse rate, the vascular bed, gastrointestinal motility, etc.

Corticobulbar Fibers

The fibers passing from the lower part of the motor area of the cortex to the cranial nuclei constitute the important *corticobular tract*. These bear precisely the same relationship to the cells of the cranial motor nuclei as does the corticospinal tract to the anterior horn cells of the cord. The corticobulbar fibers, however, cross at various levels throughout the brain stem.

The Internal Capsule

In a horizontal section of the cerebrum, the internal capsule is seen as a compact band of white matter lying between the thalamus and caudate nucleus on its inner aspect and the lenticular nucleus on its lateral aspect (cf. fig. 6.11). It is the broad highway of communication in both directions between the cerebral cortex and subcortical and spinal centers. In addition to the corticospinal and corticobulbar tracts the following are the principal tracts which compose it:

I. *Descending*
   a. *Corticopontine tracts* consisting of three bundles of fibers, *frontopontine, parietopontine* and *occipitopontine* from the corresponding areas of the cerebral cortex to the nuclei of the pons.
   b. *Corticorubral tract*, from the frontal lobe to the red nucleus.
   c. *Corticothalamic* from almost all areas of the cortex to various nuclei of the thalamus.
   d. *Corticostriatal fibers* from the precentral area of the cortex to the caudate nucleus and the globus pallidus.
   e. *Occipitotectal fibers* from the para- and peristriate cortex to the tectum of the midbrain.
   f. *Corticonigral fibers* from the precentral and temporal areas to the substantia nigra.
II. *Ascending*
   a. *Thalamic radiations* consist of four bundles ascending from the thalamus, *anterior, superior, posterior* and *inferior*, which

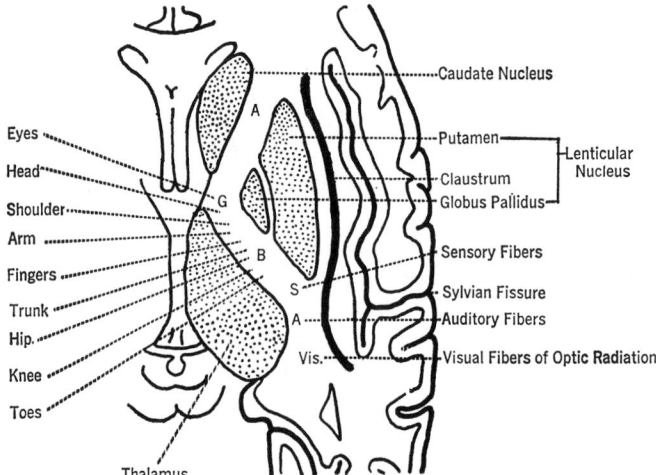

Fig. 6.11. Horizontal section of right hemisphere, showing corticobulbar and corticospinal fibers, and the location of the visual and sensory fibers. A, anterior limb of capsule; B, posterior limb; G, genu.

connect the thalamus with various parts of the cerebral cortex. The anterior group terminate in prefrontal areas, and the superior group in the somesthetic area (postcentral gyrus).

b. *Auditory radiation fibers* ascending from the medial geniculate body to the temporal cortex (geniculo-temporal fibers).

c. *Optic radiation fibers* ascending from the lateral geniculate body to the visual area in the occipital cortex (geniculocalcarine) fibers.

d. *Rubrocortical fibers* from the red nucleus to the cortex.

The internal capsule is bent in the horizontal plane to form a convexity directed medially. The region of the angle so produced is called the *knee* (*genu*); the portions in front and behind this are known, respectively, as the *anterior* and *posterior limbs*. The shorter anterior limb lies between the caudate nucleus and the lenticular nucleus; the posterior limb between the lenticular nucleus and the thalamus. The extension backwards of the posterior limb is known as the *retrolenticular part*.

The anterior limb is occupied by the *fronto-pontine* fibers and the *anterior thalamic radiation* (thalamofrontal fibers), the *frontothalamic tract*, *corticostriatal* and *corticorubral tracts*. In the anterior three-fifths of the posterior limb are transmitted the *corticobulbar* and *corticospinal* fibers. The fibers of these two tracts are organized in accordance with the portions of the body which they innervate, those carrying impulses for the eye muscles, the muscles of the tongue, and face and upper and lower extremities arranged in this order from before backwards; and those trans-

mitting impulses destined for the proximal part of an extremity are placed in front of those for the more distal muscles. The remaining part of the posterior limb, and the retrolenticular part carry in anteroposterior order the *superior* and *posterior thalamic radiations*, the *auditory* (*geniculotemporal*), and the *inferior thalamic radiations*, *corticothalamic*, and *parietopontine* fibers, and the *optic* (*geniculo-occipital*) *radiations*.

The internal capsule is supplied with blood through the lateral striate branches of the middle cerebral artery, by the recurrent artery of Hubner from the anterior cerebral artery, and the anterior choriodal artery from the internal carotid artery.

A Comparison of the Effects Produced by Injury of Supraspinal Paths with Those of the Spinal Centers or Peripheral Nerves (Motoneurons)

It is obvious that lesions at various points in the nervous system are likely to produce different manifestations. This is particularly true in the field of muscular activity. In view of the intricacy of the neural mechanism responsible for muscular activity which has been briefly outlined above, it must be obvious that the patterns of muscular disturbances which may develop can vary through a wide range. There are no simple syndromes upon which the student may rely. Rather he must familiarize himself, as completely as is possible in our present state of knowledge and ignorance, with the neural mechanisms responsible for muscular activity and then must attempt to understand and interpret what he finds in the patient in the light of that knowledge.

Destruction of the peripheral nerves supplying a skeletal muscle produces an easily understood clinical picture. The muscle is (1) totally paralyzed, it is beyond the patient's control and he cannot move it; (2) no reflex activity of any sort is possible, although in the early stages the muscle may still contract in response to direct percussion or direct stimulation with a galvanic current; and (3) the muscle wastes away to a useless fibrous cord because it is devoid of innervation and completely without use. Involvement of this sort is often spoken of as a "lower motor neuron" paralysis and it may develop following destruction of the anterior horn cells in the spinal cord, or following division of the anterior spinal roots or of the muscular nerve. One must never forget, however, that not all paralyses are complete. Some innervation may remain and then the muscle is weakened but not completely paralyzed, the reflexes are diminished but not abolished and the wasting is incomplete.

Although the term "lower motor neuron" paralysis is accurate for the condition described above, it has the disadvantage that it implies that there is a counterpart, an "upper motor neuron" paralysis. This is misleading for there is no constant reliable entity which can be so designated. The manifestations of involvement of the many neurons which lie above the anterior horn cell which are responsible in one way or another for some phase of muscular activity vary widely depending upon which such neurons or groups of neurons are involved. Thus we may have a severe paralysis with spasticity and hyperactivity of the stretch reflexes if the descending motor pathways in the internal capsule are involved. If on the other hand the lesion is limited to the corticospinal fibers in the central portion of the cerebral peduncle one sees a loss of some fineness and delicacy of movement with little or no spasticity and little increase in tendon reflexes. Lesions of the globus pallidus combined with destruction of the substantia nigra are, on the other hand, characterized by increased resistance to passive manipulation of the extremities, with a generalized rigidity of the body and a loss of the facial movements of expression and of many automatic associated muscular movements but with little or no true paralysis and little if any change in the tendon reflexes. As we have noted before a paralysis arising from a lesion in the internal capsule is commonly associated with a flexor spasticity in the upper extremity and an extensor spasticity in the lower extremity, whereas a severe lesion in the mesencephalon is likely to produce a paralysis with extensor spasticity in all four extremities. In contrast with this a paralysis due to a transverse lesion of the spinal cord will produce a complete paralysis of the skeletal musculature below the level of the lesion with a variable reflex pattern. In some cases, or even only at some times in a given case, the paralyzed extremities may show a severe extensor spasm while at other times a severe flexor pattern may develop. In contrast with "lower motor neuron" lesions, paralysis due to involvement of motor neurons above the anterior horn cells are almost always associated with some type of reflex activity. Often this reflex activity is exaggerated beyond that which one would expect in normal muscles. However, the nature and pattern of the reflex activity will vary depending upon the location of the lesion and the pathways which are involved. One reflex seems to have its own specific significance—the *sign of Babinski*. This reflex is elicited by stroking the outer margin of the sole of the foot from the heel toward the little toe. Normally, such stimulation is associated with a flexion of all of the toes. However, if the corticospinal fibers from the "foot" area of the upper part of the precentral gyrus are interrupted the great toe will extend or dorsiflex. The other toes may or may not "fan" outward laterally. It must be remembered that such a "positive" response is dependent upon an intact peripheral mechanism. Regardless of the nature or location of the central lesion the sign of Babinski will not be elicited if the great toe is ankylosed, if the extensor tendon is severed or the extensor hallucis muscle destroyed, or the muscular nerve to this muscle interrupted or the related anterior spinal root or anterior horn cells seriously damaged. It must also be remembered that this is a sign only of interruption of the corticospinal fibers which innervate the musculature of the great toe. It is not a sign of damage to any other corticospinal fibers.

Both "upper" and "lower" motor neuron paralyses may be associated with atrophy or wasting of the involved muscles. Muscular wasting is in general proportionate to the degree of loss of use of the muscle rather than to loss of innervation. Because the paralysis resulting from a complete "lower" motor neuron lesion is complete both as to voluntary and reflex activity the atrophy is likewise complete. Wasting from "upper motor neuron" lesions is never that severe because even with a complete paralysis of voluntary activity some reflex activity persists.

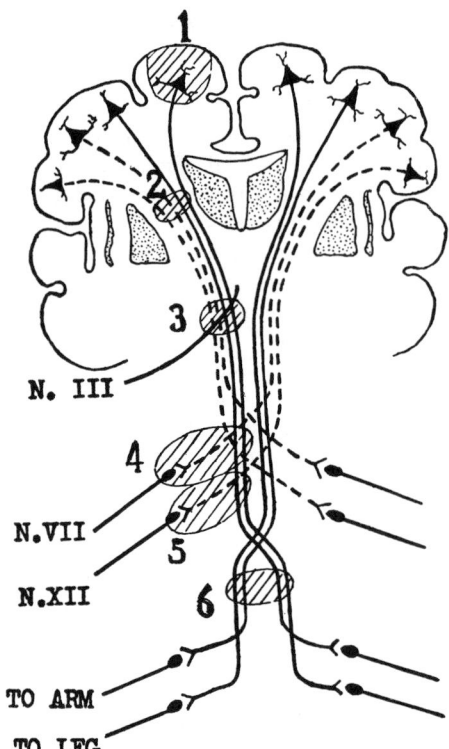

FIG. 6.12. Diagram illustrating the effects of lesions at various levels. 1, lesion of cerebral cortex causing monoplegia or hemiplegia, depending upon its extent; 2, lesion of internal capsule, hemiplegia; 3, lesion of midbrain involving descending motor fibers and nucleus or tract of the third nerve (Weber's paralysis); 4, lesion in pons destroying descending motor fibers and nucleus of facial nerve, crossed hemiplegia with homolateral facial paralysis; 5, lesion in medulla oblongata involving descending motor fibers and the hypoglossal nucleus, crossed hemiplegia and homolateral paralysis of lingual muscles; 6, transection of spinal cord, paraplegia. (In part from Villiger and from Ranson.)

Lesions at various levels are likely to involve other structures and thus indicate their location by the nature of the other clinical manifestations which the patient develops (fig. 6.12). Thus a massive lesion of the internal capsule will produce a contralateral hemihypesthesia and possibly a homonymous hemianopia as well as a hemiplegia. A unilateral lesion in the midbrain often will produce a third cranial nerve palsy (with a ptosis of the upper eyelid, a paralysis of several ocular muscles, a dilatation of the pupil and a loss of the pupillary light reflex) on the side of involvement in addition to a contralateral spastic hemiplegia. Lesions involving one half of the lower brain stem may be associated with a paralysis of one or more cranial nerves (e.g., facial, vagus or hypoglossal) on that side of the body and a hemiplegia and

hemianesthesia on the opposite side of the body. In contrast with this unilateral lesions of the spinal cord produce what is known as a Brown-Sequard syndrome—a paralysis of the skeletal muscles of the trunk and extremities and a loss of position and vibratory sensibilities below the level of the lesion and on the same side with a loss of pain and thermal sensibilities on the opposite side (fig. 6.13). Obviously the possible combinations of symptoms and signs are numerous and cannot all be discussed in detail here. Their recognition and proper interpretation are dependent upon a thorough understanding of the structure and function of the nervous system.

It is evident that the paralysis is more likely to be bilateral if the lesion is situated in a region where, as in the brain stem or spinal cord, the descending motor tracts of the two sides are approximated, than if it is located at a level where these tracts are widely separated, as in the corona radiata or internal capsule; then unilateral effects are usual. Complete interruption of the spinal cord will of course result in paralysis on both sides of the body below the level of the lesion—*paraplegia* (p. 139).

FUNCTIONAL, MORPHOLOGICAL AND CHEMICAL CHANGES IN DENERVATED MUSCLE

A lesion which involves any part of the lower motor neuron—anterior horn cell—such as may result from anterior poliomyelitis or peripheral nerve injury, is followed by degenerative changes which extend to and include the nerve terminals within the muscle. A muscle thus completely denervated exhibits constant, fine, rapid, rhyth-

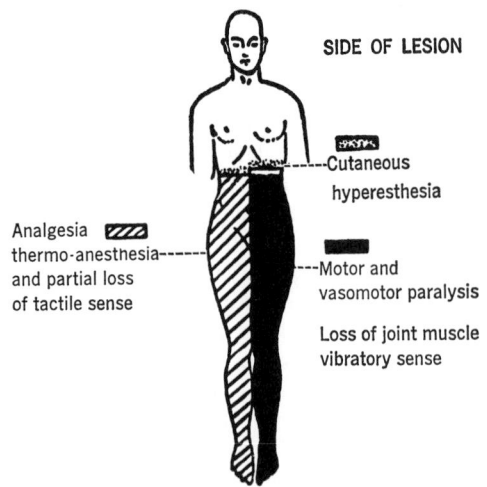

FIG. 6.13. Diagram showing effects following hemisection of the spinal cord in the lower thoracic region. Narrow white band at level of lesion indicates total anesthesia and analgesia.

mical contractions. This so-called fibrillation of the denervated muscle does not appear until several days after the abnormal electrical reactions (reaction of degeneration, ch. 2) have already developed and complete degeneration of the nerve has occurred. The muscle fibers contract asynchronously; the contractions involve only a part of the length (0.5 to 1 mm.) of the fiber and give rise to small irregular action potentials. The fibrillation can sometimes, though not commonly, be seen through the skin. Having once appeared, fibrillation persists for a year or more and until the contractile elements have undergone complete atrophy. According to Denny-Brown, a reduction in tension developed by the muscle when stimulated maximally can be detected within 2 minutes after section of the nerve, but other investigators have been unable to observe any loss of contractile force until after a much longer interval (30 to 40 hours). An outstanding functional effect of denervation is the great increase in the sensitivity of the muscle to the intravenous or intra-arterial injection of acetylcholine. Normal muscle is excited by the intra-arterial injection of from 0.2 to 2.0 mg. of acetylcholine, whereas denervated muscle responds to a dose of from 0.002 to 0.02 γ. It is generally believed that this hypersensitivity to acetylcholine is responsible for the Vulpian and Sherrington effects, and most probably also for the "fright reaction" described by Bender. The denervated muscle is also hyperexcitable, though to a less pronounced degree, to potassium chloride.

The denervated muscle soon commences to atrophy, reduction in its bulk becoming apparent within a few days after section of the nerve. Atrophy progresses rapidly and is followed by degeneration of the contractile elements. Microscopic changes in the muscle fibers consist of swelling and vesiculation of the nuclei, a reduction in sarcoplasm, and fading, followed by disappearance of the striations of the myofibrillae. Ultimately all contractile tissue disappears and is replaced by fibrous tissue and fat. As these morphological changes are occurring, the muscle gradually loses its plastic or ductile quality, flexors and adductors shorten and become more or less "set" in their new positions. The antagonistic muscles lengthen adaptively. This state of the muscles is called *contracture*. This disappearance of the denervated muscle fibers and their replacement by fibrous tissue is important in considering when a divided muscular nerve should be sutured or replaced by transplantation of another nerve. Obviously if such operations are delayed until only fibrous tissue remains they will be unsuccessful. If they are to succeed they should be performed within a year after the muscular nerve has been damaged.

The chemical changes in denervated muscle comprise a reduction in glycogen, phosphocreatine and adenosine triphosphate, but they do not become pronounced until the onset of fibrillation. The breakdown and subsequent resynthesis of glycogen by the denervated muscle during a work period is normal for a time following nerve section but when fibrillation supervenes, the ability of the muscle to restore its glycogen after contraction is greatly impaired. The atrophying muscle shows a large increase in calcium, a smaller increase in chloride, and a decrease in potassium. The changes in chloride and potassium can be accounted for by the reduction in muscle mass and its replacement by interstitial tissue and fluid. The increase in calcium is too great, however, to be explained entirely in this way.

The cause of fibrillation in denervated muscle is unknown, but it is not improbable that it is a manifestation of its hypersensitivity to acetylcholine. The observation of Magladery and Solandt that quinidine, which abolishes acetylcholine hypersensitivity, also suppresses fibrillation is highly suggestive; yet as Dale and his associates have shown, direct stimulation of denervated muscle does not cause the release of acetylcholine. It follows, therefore, that if the stimulating effect of this agent is responsible for fibrillation it must be carried to the muscle in the blood stream. The increased sensitivity to acetylcholine may be due to a lack of cholinesterase for, according to Marnay and Nachmansohn, this enzyme, which normally is concentrated in the neighborhood of the nerve endings in skeletal muscle, disappears after denervation. The lack of cholinesterase might also explain the failure of eserine to cause anything more than a transient augmentation of fibrillation.

SYRINGOMYELIA

This condition is characterized by a cavitation of the spinal cord surrounded by an area of gliosis. The disease process involves the central gray matter primarily and the surrounding white matter to a variable degree. The process may extend for considerable distances up and down the spinal cord. The lower cervical and upper thoracic regions are most commonly affected. The disease may extend into the bulb (syringobulbia) when signs of implication of the nuclei of the cranial nerves appear.

A loss of pain and temperature sensibilities, muscular weakness and changes due to involvement of the central sympathetic fibers are among the characteristic features of the disease. Owing to the site of the changes, the fibers mediating pain, heat and cold, where they make connections with the cells of the posterior horns, are first destroyed. If the lesion is unilateral, thermoanesthesia and analgesia of the skin supplied by, and on the same side as the diseased segments result. Other sensations, e.g., touch, muscle sense, are unaffected until later in the disease. Involvement of the spinal nucleus of the trigeminal results in the characteristic sensory loss over the face. When the disease involves both dorsal horns or the anterior gray commissure where the fibers subserving pain and temperature sensibilities cross the thermoanesthesia and analgesia are bilateral. The muscles innervated by the anterior horn cells of the diseased segments become weak and wasted; these effects often appear first in the small muscles of the hand. So long as the disease does not cause injury to the white matter, the sensory and motor effects are limited and have a segmental distribution. Involvement of the descending motor pathways will result in a spastic paralysis below the level of the lesion, while pressure upon the spinothalamic tracts and dorsal columns will be followed by sensory loss below the level of the lesion. The degree of sensory loss, its type and distribution and whether homolateral or contralateral vary according to the extent to which the individual tracts are affected by the disease. As a result of the loss of the protective sensations (pain and (temperature), patients with syringomyelia are prone to suffer injuries which, not being perceived at the time, are neglected and ultimately lead to serious lesions, e.g., painless burns or the disorganization of a joint (arthropathy, Charcot's joint). Involvement of the sympathetic centers in the lateral columns leads to vasomotor disturbances, excessive sweating or absence of sweating, cyanosis, etc. So-called trophic disturbances, e.g., ulcers, whitlows, gangrene, etc., are largely the result of vasomotor abnormalities and the loss of sensation which, as just mentioned, permits an injury, trivial perhaps at first, to be disregarded.

SUBACUTE COMBINED DEGENERATION OF THE SPINAL CORD

This condition involves the white matter of the cord and is almost always associated sooner or later with pernicious anemia. The degenerative process consists of a breakdown of the myelin sheaths, subsequent destruction of the axons and their replacement by newly formed glial tissue. The changes are most pronounced in the corticospinal and cerebellar tracts and in the posterior columns. The chief clinical features are, therefore: (a) muscular weakness and spasticity, (b) impairment of the sense of position and of passive movement of the limbs with consequent ataxia and a positive Romberg sign, (c) loss or impairment of spatial discrimination, and vibratory sensibility. The relative extent to which these sensations are lost is variable. Paresthesias (tingling, pricking and burning sensations) frequently precede the sensory loss, and are usually the result of an associated peripheral neuropathy. The reflexes vary. The tendon jerks are frequently exaggerated as a result of involvement of the descending motor

pathways, but they may disappear as the disease progresses if the peripheral neuropathy becomes sufficiently severe. The plantar response is usually of the "extensor" type.

The severity of the nervous manifestations do not always run parallel with that of the blood picture; the neurological features may be pronounced though the anemia is of mild degree, or vice versa. Subacute combined degeneration of the cord, though associated with pernicious anemia, is not due to the anemia itself. This is shown by the well recognized fact that the blood picture may be restored to normal by the administration of folic acid, but the neurological condition progresses unchecked, whereas the latter is arrested by the hematinic principle (vitamin B_{12}). See also chapter 30.

TABES DORSALIS, LOCOMOTOR ATAXIA

In this condition, which is the result of syphilis, the fibers of the dorsal roots at their point of entry into the spinal cord (i.e., the central processes of the primary sensory neurons) are attacked. The ganglion cell bodies of the dorsal roots, as a rule, are not affected. The essential lesion within the spinal cord, therefore, involves the entrance zone of the lateral division of the dorsal roots (dorsolateral fasciculus of Lissauer), and the dorsal fasciculi (gracilis and cuneatus). The endogenous fibers of the spinal cord escape, but although it is those tracts composed of exogenous fibers which are specifically attacked by the disease, the functions of the cerebellar and spinothalamic tracts are also seriously disturbed as a result of degeneration of the primary neurons leading to them. The descending tracts remain as a rule practically unaffected. The reason for the selective destruction of the exogenous fibers of the cord is unknown; possibly it is compression of the fibers by proliferation or inflammatory swelling of the meninges at the point of entrance of the posterior root.

The sensory changes are those which might be expected to result from a gradual degeneration of dorsal root fibers. Somewhat similar effects are produced in monkeys by section of the posterior nerve roots.

The chief manifestations are as follows: (a) During the degenerative process paresthesias of various types, hyperesthesia and stabbing pains are common. (b) Impairment, or loss to a variable degree, of all forms of sensation follows. Loss of the rapid conduction component of deep pain occurs early. Loss of the sense of position and of passive movement, and blockage of afferent cerebellar impulses result in marked incoördination of the muscles—ataxia. Movements are jerky, exaggerated and imperfectly controlled, the subject being unable to move his feet in the desired direction or to assume a given position at will, e.g., placing the heel of one foot upon the toes of the other. The gait is ataxic, the feet are kept wide apart, raised unnecessarily high and brought down in a stamping fashion; the patient may learn to overcome this tendency by shuffling.

The loss of sense of position is in large measure responsible for the patient's difficulties. When standing with the eyes closed the patient, being thus deprived of an important aid in maintaining his equilibrium, tends to sway and may fall (Romberg's sign). (c) The interruption of the pathways for proprioceptive impulses from the skeletal muscles results in extreme *hypotonia*, but there is no true paralysis. (d) The *tendon reflexes* are abolished as a result of the destruction of the afferent limb of the proprioceptive reflex arc. The abdominal reflexes may or may not be present. (e) *"Lightning pains"* and *trophic disturbances*. The former are severe stabbing paroxysmal pains usually localized to an area supplied by one or more spinal segments. They are commonly in the abdomen or in the lower extremities. Vasodilatation, small hemorrhages or herpes zoster may occur in the painful area. These vascular and cutaneous effects have been attributed to antidromic impulses reaching the periphery via sensory fibers. The skin of the affected area may break down with the formation of so-called trophic ulcers. Painless destruction of joints (Charcot's joint) is not uncommon in tabes. The loss of the sense of pain which causes the patient to suffer injuries of which he is unaware, the extreme hypotonia of the muscles which normally support the joint, and the vascular disturbances resulting from damage to autonomic fibers combine to produce such joint conditions. They are usually classed among the trophic disturbances, the term implying that the interruption of trophic impulses is responsible. However, the existence of true trophic fibers, i.e., specific fibers which preside over the nutrition of the peripheral tissues, is questionable. (f) *Tabetic crises*. These are apparently the result of the involvement of afferent autonomic fibers which enter the spinal cord by the dorsal roots. They consist of paroxysmal attacks of pain and functional disturbances in one or other of the viscera. Gastric crises are the commonest. They consist of severe epigastric pain and vomiting. *Rectal crises* consisting of pain in and increased activity of the rectum, *vesical crises* with bladder pain and difficult urination or *laryngeal crises*, in which spasm of the adductors of the larynx with dyspnea may occur. (g) *Ocular signs*. The pupils are as a rule constricted and often unequal. The Argyll-Robertson pupil (ch. 16) in which the reflex to accommodation is retained but the reaction to light is lost, is a characteristic ocular feature of tabes dorsalis. The pupil also frequently fails to respond by dilatation to stimulation of the skin of the neck (ciliospinal reflex). The loss of this reflex is usually attributed to degeneration of the central sympathetic pathway

through which the dilator pupillae muscle is innervated. Some drooping of the upper lid (ptosis) may also result from the blockage of sympathetic pathways which normally transmit impulses to the smooth muscle in this situation; compensatory contraction of the frontalis muscle with wrinkling of the skin of the forehead results. Damage to the fibers of the 3rd, 4th or 6th nerves results in paralysis of the ocular muscles, the external rectus most commonly. Squint and double vision (diplopia (ch. 16)) are consequences. Primary optic atrophy often occurs.

Disseminated (Multiple) Sclerosis

This is a chronic disease of the nervous system characterized anatomically by the occurrence of small patches of demyelination followed by overgrowth of glial tissue throughout the white substance of the brain (especially in the regions beneath the lateral ventricles), and spinal cord. The lesions in the cord are most numerous in the corticospinal tracts and in the posterior columns. Clinically, the disease is marked by an insidious onset, irregular course, with remissions and relapses of unpredictable duration, and a great variability of signs and symptoms between individual cases. Progressive spastic weakness of the muscles of the legs, with increased tendon jerks, "extensor" plantar response (Babinski) and loss of abdominal reflexes, is a common manifestation of this disease. Many patients also complain of paresthesias and have a loss of vibration and muscle senses from lesions in the posterior columns. The loss of tactile and pain and thermal sensibilities are seldom striking and rarely of an enduring nature. Impairment of vision, or even blindness, may result from involvement of the optic nerve, chiasma or tract. Nystagmus, slurring of speech and intention tremor, once regarded as diagnostic of the disease, appear late if at all and are manifestations of involvement of cerebellar pathways.

Complete Transverse Division of the Spinal Cord

A sudden, or rapidly progressive, complete interruption of the continuity of the cord may result from injury (e.g., gunshot wound, fracture-dislocation of the spine, etc.) or from acute inflammation (e.g., transverse myelitis). Immediate and complete loss of voluntary power below the level of the lesion results. Paralysis of both lower limbs resulting from this or any other nervous lesion is spoken of as *paraplegia*. Complete division of the cord in the lower cervical region will result in paralysis of all four limbs, *quadriplegia*. A lesion of this nature in the upper cervical region is of course rapidly fatal since the diaphragm and other respiratory muscles are isolated from the respiratory center.

Stage of spinal shock. Immediately following the injury there are complete loss of visceral and somatic sensations, and flaccid paralysis below the level of the lesion. The skeletal muscles are quite toneless. The tendon jerks, plantar response and abdominal reflexes are abolished. The cremasteric and bulbocavernosus reflexes, though absent as a rule, may at times be elicited. The anal reflex is present. A zone of heightened sensitivity (hyperesthesia) immediately above the level of the lesion may be present and spontaneous pains in this region, or a feeling of tightness encircling the body may be experienced by the patient. There is retention of urine and feces. This stage is analogous to the state of spinal shock in lower animals but is much more severe and prolonged (ch. 8). In man spinal shock lasts for from one to three weeks.

Stage of reflex activity. After a variable period of time, depending largely upon the general health of the patient, reflex activity begins to return to the isolated spinal cord below the level of the lesion. The first reflex to appear is usually the sign of Babinski, the extensor response of the great toe to stimulation of the sole of the foot. This reflex is actually a part of the flexor reflex pattern of the lower extremities. Both exaggerated extensor and flexor reflex patterns are usually present with lesions of the descending motor pathways. They vary in intensity and in relation to each other. If the lesion lies above the pons the extensor reflexes usually predominate. If the lesion is in the spinal cord the flexor reflexes are usually more prominent than when the lesion lies at higher levels and they may exceed the extensor reflexes in intensity. Then a paraplegia in flexion is present. However, this balance between extensor and flexor reflexes fluctuates from time to time in the same patient and is quite variable from one patient to another. After the sign of Babinski has become elicitable other flexor reflexes, dorsiflexion of the foot, flexion of the knee and hip gradually become more marked and more easily elicited. At first they are usually seen only with stimuli which except for the interruption of the pain pathways in the spinal cord would be painful, i.e., nociceptive stimuli. Later less intense stimuli such as passive flexion of the toes or mere touching of the foot or leg may be sufficient to provoke a violent flexion of the leg. When this stage is reached the patient usually has a paraplegia in flexion. The extensor reflexes begin to return after variable periods. At first the only demonstrable reflex of this type may be the patellar tendon reflex (knee jerk). Later the Achilles tendon reflex (ankle jerk) will return, ankle and patellar clonus may be elicited. At times the patient may develop severe extensor spasms and the muscles may be involved by severe clonic contractions with little or no external stimulation. At other times the extremities may lie quietly without either extensor or flexor reflexes causing any striking disturbances. Elicitation of the flexor reflexes will immediately result in a subsidence of ankle clonus or other manifestations of the extensor reflexes, and *vice versa.* This inhibition of the one when the other is produced is due to reciprocal innervation. On occasion elicitation of the flexor reflexes will be associated with evacuation of the bowel and bladder. This Head and Riddock termed the *"mass reflex."* However, reflex or automatic evacuation of the bowel and bladder need not be associated with a violent flexion of both lower extremities. Such reflex evacuation may result from distention of the bladder or rectum as the case may be, or may be induced by the patient. He may produce emptying of the bladder by stimulating the skin on the inner aspect of the upper thigh or reflex defecation by stimulating the rectal musoca at and just above the anal ring. These reflexes are often used to great advantage by the paraplegic patient. The time of development of these various reflexes and their vigor depend in large measure upon the condition of the patient and his paralyzed extremities. A poor state of nutrition or the presence of infection in the urinary tract or in decubitus ulcers, the development of severe muscular wasting or of fibrous changes in the muscles or about the joints will all mitigate against the development of active reflex activity.

INCOMPLETE INTERRUPTION OF THE CORD

A bilateral lesion of gradual onset which impairs the activity of the descending motor pathways usually causes *paraplegia in extension.* The muscles are spastic and extensor activity predominates. The tendon jerks are exaggerated and patellar and ankle clonus can be readily elicited. Paraplegia in extension is more or less comparable to decerebrate extensor rigidity. The "extensor" plantar response, which is in reality a part of the flexor reflex pattern, is present, but much less intense than in paraplegia in flexion. It is associated with much less contraction in other flexor muscles and may be accompanied by a crossed extensor reflex. The mass reflex is absent. The abdominal reflexes are lost.

The Plantar Reflexes

This is the most appropriate place to consider these and other superficial reflexes.

The *normal plantar response* to a light scratch applied to the skin of the sole is plantar flexion of the four outer toes with no movement, or, more usually, plantar flexion of the great toe. The center for the reflex lies in the first sacral segment; its physiological significance is unknown. With a lesion of the corticospinal fibers from the precentral region to the foot (see also p. 135) at any level above the first sacral segment, the normal response is replaced by one in which *dorsiflexion* of the great toe and often spreading or fanning of the outer toes occurs. It is elicited best from the outer border of the sole. This response is called after its discoverer the *sign of Babinski* (fig. 6.14). From the dorsiflexion of the great toe, which is due to the contraction of the extensor longus hallucis, this reflex is also frequently referred to as the extensor response.[3] This term, however, is incorrect since the upward movement of the great toe is part of a general flexor response homologous with the flexor reflex elicitable from the hind limb of a lower animal (p. 67) (see Walshe). The dorsiflexors of the toes, although classed anatomically as extensors must, when compared physiologically with similar muscles in the limb of an animal such as the dog, be included among the flexors. In lesions of descending spinal tracts in which extensor reflex activity overshadows the flexor reactions, the so-called extensor plantar response is less active and less readily elicited than when flexor patterns predominate. Nevertheless the flexor nature of the reflex is shown by the associated contraction of the hamstrings, i.e., semitendinosus, semimembranosus and biceps femoris, which usually occurs (see also p. 140). Its flexor nature is also indicated by the fact that an undoubted extensor reflex such as ankle clonus is readily inhibited by evoking the Babinski reaction (reciprocal inhibition).

In the restricted forms of the extensor response as seen in hemiplegia, the receptive field of the reflex is also strictly circumscribed, being elicitable only from the sole—the outer border especially.

---

[3] An "extensor" plantar response is present normally in infants up to the first year or so, i.e., to the age of walking, and is then probably due to the undeveloped state of the corticospinal tracts. It is also present in normal adults during deep sleep and in the apneic stage of Cheyne-Stokes respiration, being apparently due in the latter instance, to anoxemia of the motor cortex.

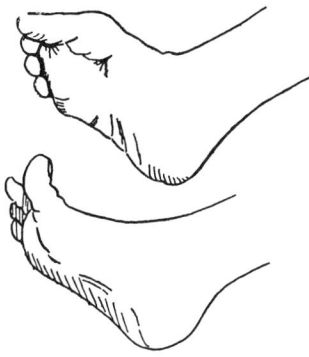

Fig. 6.14. Upper drawing, normal plantar response, lower drawing, Babinski response.

In paraplegia-in-flexion in which flexor activity predominates the so-called "extensor" response is maximal and, as we have seen, is simply part of a widespread flexor reaction. The receptive field of the reflex is extensive and the application of a stimulus is followed by contraction not only of the extensor longus hallucis (with dorsiflexion of the hallux) and hamstrings but by an associated contraction of the true flexors of the lower limb, the extensor longus digitorum, tibialis anticus, gracilis, sartorius, rectus femoris and iliopsoas.

Other Superficial Reflexes

1. *Oppenheim's reflex* is simply a modified Babinski response; it is associated with the same conditions as the latter and has a similar significance. It consists in dorsiflexion of the hallux which results when a firm downward sliding pressure is applied to the skin over the anterior border of the tibia. The Gordon, Chaddock and Gonda reflexes are other modifications of the Babinski response.

2. *Abdominal reflexes.* Lightly scratching the skin of the abdomen of a normal person causes a reflex contraction of the abdominal muscles. They do not appear until between the 6th and 8th months of age when the infant can sit up unsupported. These reflexes are, of course, abolished by any lesion which interrupts afferent conduction from the skin of the abdomen or destroys the anterior horn cells or the motor pathways concerned with the abdominal musculature. These reflexes also are often abolished by a lesion which interrupts the corticospinal pathways above the 7th thoracic segment, but they are *not* permanently abolished by extirpation of the precentral gyrus. These confusing facts have thrown serious doubt on all current physiological explanations of the abdominal reflexes.

3. *Cremasteric reflex* consists of contraction of the cremaster muscle and elevation of testicle which results from a light stroke applied to the skin on the inner aspect of the upper part of the

thigh. It is often abolished by corticospinal lesions or as a result of destruction of the center in the 1st or 2nd lumbar segment.

4. *Bulbocavernosus reflex* has its center in the 3rd and 4th sacral segments. It consists of contraction of the bulbocavernosus muscle (detected by palpation) in response to stimulation of the glans penis. It is absent in a lesion involving any part of its reflex arc, motor or sensory limb, or center.

5. *Anal reflex* is the contraction of the external anal sphincter in response to scratching the neighboring skin. Its center is situated in the 4th and 5th sacral segments and the coccygeal segment; it is lost after interruption of its reflex arc.

6. *Gluteal reflex*. Scratching the skin of the buttock causes contraction of the gluteal muscles. It depends upon the integrity of the 4th and 5th lumbar and upper sacral segments.

The *deep* or *tendon reflexes,* such as the knee jerk, ankle jerk, etc., have been discussed in chapters 4 and 5.

The Reticular Formation

The central portion of the brain stem is occupied by a diffuse ill defined mass of nerve cells and fibers known as the *reticular formation*. It extends downward into the spinal cord and upward into the thalamus and subthalamus. In the following discussion we shall not be concerned with the spinal reticular formation. The reticular formation in the brain stem can be subdivided into numerous nuclei or cell masses. However, as these have not been shown to have functional significance no cognizance of these cellular groups will be taken here. The reticular formation has been defined (see Segundo, 1956) as including all areas within the brain stem (excepting primary afferent pathways) which when stimulated will produce "arousal." This includes the bulbar reticular formation, the pontomesencephalic tegmentum, the hypothalamus, the subthalamus, and the ventromedial portion (including the intralaminar nuclei) and the reticular nucleus of the thalamus. There appears to be little doubt but that the reticular formation constitutes one, if not the most important regulatory mechanism within the central nervous system. As will be discussed below it is concerned with such general effects as the arousal of the entire organism, alerting the animal, maintaining attention, or, on the other hand, with the production of sleep or in cases of injury to the reticular formation the development of stupor or coma. It is also concerned with such specific effects as the control of muscular activity, the regulation of the receptivity of peripheral sensory endorgans, the control of the threshold of central

sensory pathways, the regulation of vegetative visceral and vasomotor responses and of emotional expression. (The reader who is interested in the extensive literature concerning the reticular formation. and in more detailed information is referred to the summarizing articles by Segundo (1956) and French (1958) and to the Henry Ford Hospital symposium on the reticular formation of the brain (1958)).

The reticular formation is subject to a wide variety of afferent impulses. Every afferent pathway bearing information to the brain concerning the outside world, its relation to the organism itself and activities within the organism also sends afferents into the reticular formation. These connections are by means of both direct afferent fibers and collaterals from the main afferent pathways to the cerebellum and thalamus. Thus the reticular formation receives afferent impulses from the optic, the olfactory, the auditory and the gustatory systems as well as from the spinal and trigeminal pathways which bear impulses concerned with tactile, painful, thermal and vibratory sensibilities and sensations from the muscles, joints and tendons, and afferent impulses from the viscera and other internal structures of the body. In addition afferent fibers converge on the reticular formation from the cerebellum, the basal ganglia, the thalamus, the rhinencephalon and the cerebral cortex. Peculiarly, only certain specific portions of the cerebral neocortex seem to send afferent impulses to the reticular formation. These are the orbital, oculomotor, sensorimotor and posterior parietal cortices, the superior temporal and cingular gyri and the temporal pole. In addition the activity of the reticular formation is influenced by certain hormonal and chemical changes (adrenalin, acetylcholine, carbon dioxide, etc.) and by many drugs (barbiturates, anesthetics, tranquilizing compounds, etc.).

In turn, efferent impulses from the reticular formation are conducted cephalad into the brain, particularly to all parts of the cerebral cortex, and caudad into the spinal cord. Because of the multisynaptic character of the pathways to and from the reticular formation and the small caliber of many of the fibers connected with it reticulocortical conduction is much slower than in the primary sensory system. The reticulospinal fibers run bilaterally in the lateral and ventral white columns of the spinal cord and transmission in this system is thought to be quite rapid.

One of the first effects shown to result from excitation of the reticular formation was that of arousal. This may be demonstrated in two ways, electroencephalographically and by the animal's behavior. In general these two parallel one another but that is not invariably true. There are circumstances under which the electroencephalographic pattern may be changed from that characteristic of the waking state (desynchronized, irregular waves of low amplitude), to that characteristic of sleep (slow, regular waves of high amplitude) without the animal's actually going to sleep, e.g., in the atropinized animal. The changes characteristic of arousal which are induced by stimulation of the reticular formation are the same as those brought about by physiological stimuli. In addition to actual arousal from sleep, stimulation of the reticular formation also has a very definite effect upon the awake animal in that it appears to "alert" him for possible changes in his environment, or serves to make him more attentive to such changes. Thus it may be said that the reticular formation is indispensable for the initiation and maintenance of wakefulness. On the other hand, lesions of the reticular formation impair the wakefulness of the organism. Experimental lesions in the cephalic end of the reticular formation in the mesencephalic tegmentum and basal proeion of the diencephalon of the cat produces sleep while destructive lesions in this same portion of the human brain result in coma. Likewise, small lesions in this same portion of the reticular formation of the cat are associated with a state which Ingram, Barris and Ranson referred to as "catalepsy."

The reticular formation is also concerned with more specific activities. Early Magoun and Rhines showed that the bulbar reticular formation is capable of inhibiting the spinal mechanism responsible for the stretch reflex of the skeletal muscles. It is through this mechanism in the brain stem that the cortical inhibitory mechanism finds expression. In addition the reticular formation is also capable of facilitation of the more peripheral motor mechanism. These effects are produced through the large motor cells of the anterior gray column of the spinal cord, the alpha cells, which innervate the ordinary striated muscle fibers, and also by controlling the receptivity of the muscle spindle (the sensory end-organ within skeletal muscle which responds to stretching) through the small gamma cells of the anterior horn.

In addition to controlling the receptivity of the stretch receptors in skeletal muscles, it also appears that the reticular formation is able to control the sensitivity of certain other sensory receptors such as those in the retina and the cochlea, and of tactile receptors, and is capable of modifying conduction along various sensory pathways, in the thalamus and in the sensory cortex. In this way the reticular formation is able to regulate the threshold of sensory perception and to control the level of attention to sensory stimuli. In all likelihood the reticular formation is not the only neural mechanism concerned in such control but it appears to be an important one.

The reticular formation is also capable of exerting extensive influence over many autonomic, or viscerovascular vegetative functions, such as cardiac, vascular, respiratory, gastrointestinal, metabolic and the control of the temperature of the body.

REFERENCES

FOERSTER, O. Brain, 1933, **56**, 1.

FRENCH, J. D.　J. Neurosurg., 1958, **15**, 97.

HEAD, H. Brain, 1893, **16**, 339. Brain, 1894, **17**, 339. Brain, 1896, **19**, 153.

INGRAM, W. R., BARRIS, R. W., AND RANSOM, S. W. Arch. Neurol. & Psychiat., 1936, **35**, 1175.

MAGLADERY, J. W. AND SOLANDT, D. Y. Neurophysiology, 1942, **5**, 357.

MAGOUN, H. W. AND RHINES, R. J. Neurophysiol., 1946, **9**, 165.

MARNAY, A. AND NACHMANSOHN, D. J. Phisoly., 1932, **92**, 37.

SEGUNDO, J. P. Acta Neurol. Latinoam., 1956, **3**, 245.

SWARTZ, H. G. AND WEDDELL, G. Brain, 1938, **61**, 99.

WALSHE, F. M. R. Brain, 1956, **79**, 529.

Monographs and Reviews

FULTON, J. F. AND KELLER, A. D. The sign of Babinski: a study of the evolution of cortical dominance in primates. Charles C Thomas, Springfield, Ill., 1932.

HARRIS, W. Brain, 1927, **50**, 399.

JASPER, H. H., PROCTOR, L. D., KNIGHTON, R. S., NOSHAY, W. C., AND COSTELLO, R. T. (Eds.) Reticular formation of the brain. Henry Ford Hospital International Symposium. Little, Brown & Co., Boston, 1958.

RANSON, S. W. The anatomy of the nervous system from the standpoint of development and function. W. B. Saunders Co., Philadelphia, 1928.

TOWER, S. S. Physiol. Rev., 1939, **19**, 1.

CHAPTER 7

The Basal Ganglia. The Thalamus and Hypothalamus

The Basal Ganglia

The basal ganglia form a large and prominent part of the human brain, and in lower animal forms are a very important part of the nervous mechanism controlling muscular activity. Destructive lesions in the human basal ganglia are associated with several well known, common, severe motor disorders which are fairly constant in their clinical pattern, yet our knowledge of the nervous connections and of the functional activity of the human basal ganglia is grossly deficient. At one time it was denied (erroneously) that the basal ganglia had any connections with the cerebral cortex or that there was any functional or somatotopic localization within them. The thalamic connections are imperfectly understood. There is no known *direct* connection by which afferent impulses from the various sense organs can send information regarding the outside world or the body itself to the basal ganglia. Experimental stimulation or destruction of the basal ganglia in laboratory animals produces very little effect. Then, what is the function of the basal ganglia in the human brain? What do they do and how? Are they merely vestigial remnants from earlier animal forms? That seems most unlikely. They form a large part of the brain and they have grown proportionately from the lower primates to man, so that whereas the globus pallidus, putamen and caudate nucleus occupy 980 cu. mm. in the rhesus monkey, they measure 2775 cu. mm. in the chimpanzee and have a volume of 14,912 cu. mm. in man (Harman and Carpenter, 1950). There have been some discussions of the possibility that the basal ganglia may be related to perceptual functions (Mettler, 1955) but the evidence in support of such a possibility is most tenuous. There also is some reason to believe that the basal ganglia may be related to vegetative or autonomic functions but the evidence is inadequate to establish such a relationship or to permit us to understand it if it exists. At this time we have reliable evidence only that the basal ganglia are intimately concerned in the activity of the skeletal musculature. At present no one can answer the question as to what the basal ganglia do or how

they do it in man. It may prove profitable, however, to summarize what we do know.

The term "basal ganglia" is a loose one which defies accurate definition. There certainly is no uniformity of opinion even as to what the term includes. Perhaps the term is meaningless in modern neurology and will be discarded shortly, but for the moment it is so deeply embedded in our literature and in our thinking that it cannot be discarded. For the purpose of this discussion the term will include the *caudate nucleus*, the *putamen*, the *globus pallidus*, the *subthalamic body of Luys*, the *red nucleus* and the *substantia nigra*. (The caudate nucleus and putamen are often referred to as the *striatum* and the globus pallidus as the *pallidum*. The putamen and globus pallidus are sometimes referred to as the *lenticular nucleus*.) The *claustrum* should also be included in the basal ganglia but as practically nothing is known of its connections or functions it need not be considered further. It might be argued that the subthalamic body, the red nucleus and the substantia nigra should not be included; but their anatomical relationships, their numerous connections and their apparent close functional relationships with the other nuclei of the basal ganglia make their inclusion natural and reasonable. One might also include the substantia reticularis of the brain stem, the pontine nuclei, the inferior olive, the cerebellum and the amygdala. They certainly form part of this subcortical motor mechanism. But the reticular formation is related not only to muscular activities as are the basal ganglia (Magoun and Rhines, 1947) but it also has what are perhaps even more important functions concerned with the alerting reaction, the control of spinal reflexes, of sensory threshold and of visceral regulation (Magoun and his coworkers). The pontine nuclei, inferior olive, and cerebellum, although related in an important fashion to muscular activity (Bailey, 1949) are too far removed to be included in the term "basal ganglia." The amygdala has no known connections with the functions of the skeletal muscular system and seems more likely to be related to vegetative activities.

The cytology of the various nuclei under discussion offers little assistance in understanding their functional activity. For the most part the nuclei seem to be divided into two groups—the small-celled and the large-celled parts. As is true of the cerebral cortex the small-celled parts appear to be the receptive divisions of the basal ganglia, whereas the large-celled parts have a predominantly motor function. The caudate nucleus and the putamen constitute the receptive portion and so far as is known at this time receive their afferent innervation from the precentral motor cortex (areas 4, 4s, and 6), the suppressor strips of Dusser de Barenne and his coworkers (areas 4s, 8, 2, and 24), (Fig. 7.1) and in a small way from the thalamus. In turn the caudate nucleus and putamen send their efferent fibers mainly to the large-celled or "motor" portion of the lenticular nucleus, the globus pallidus, (Fig. 7.2) with a much smaller group of efferent fibers going to the substantia nigra. Similarly the substantia nigra is divided into a large-celled (pigmented) dorsal portion and a small-celled (unpigmented) ventral portion which lies just above the cerebral peduncle. And the red nucleus is divided into a small-celled anterior portion and a large-celled posterior portion which gives rise to the rubrospinal tract. Here we must call attention to the fact that a material change has occurred in the red nucleus in primates as compared with that in the carnivora. In the dog and cat the magnocellular portion of the red nucleus and the rubrospinal tract are large and presumably important structures, whereas in the primates this portion of the red nucleus and the rubrospinal tract which arises from it are small and apparently insignificant (Stern, 1936). It is obvious that the experimental evidence which has indicated a place of great importance for the magnocellular portion of the red nucleus and the rubro-

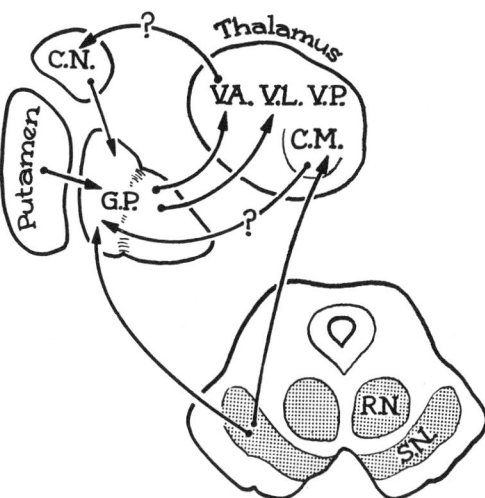

FIG. 7.2. Some of the intrinsic connections within the basal ganglia.

spinal tract in the neural mechanism controlling muscular tone in the carnivora (Rademaker, 1926) is not applicable to the monkey, the ape or man. Another structure, the reticular formation of the brain stem, has apparently taken over that function. In fact, the reticular formation and the inferior olive are probably the principal effector or efferent structures of the subcortical motor system in primates.

Within the basal ganglia almost all parts are connected with all other parts (Fig. 7.2), i.e., the globus pallidus sends fibers to the red nucleus, the substantia nigra and the subthalamic nucleus; the substantia nigra sends fibers to the red nucleus, the globus pallidus and the subthalamic nucleus; the subthalamic nucleus sends fibers to the globus pallidus, red nucleus and the substantia nigra. Within the basal ganglia there are also circular systems, such as the projection from the caudate nucleus to the globus pallidus, the globus pallidus to the ventral anterior nucleus of the thalamus, and from this thalamic nucleus back to the caudate nucleus (Fig. 7.2). Two parts of the basal ganglia, however, remain more or less aloof from this intranuclear activity. They are the caudate nucleus and putamen, and the red nucleus. The caudate nucleus and putamen on the one hand receive their afferent innervation largely from the cerebral cortex (with additional afferent connections from the substantia nigra (Ranson and Ranson, 1939) and from the ventral anterior nucleus of the thalamus), and they distribute their efferents to the globus pallidus and the substantia nigra. The red nu-

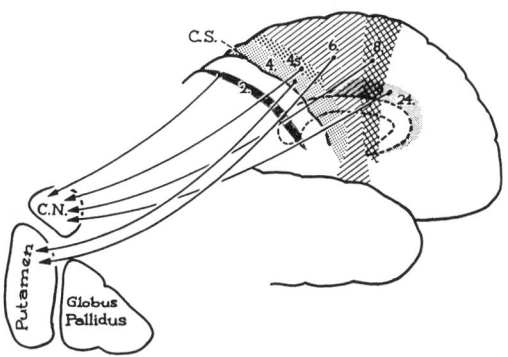

FIG. 7.1. The connections from the cerebral cortex to the caudate nucleus and putamen.

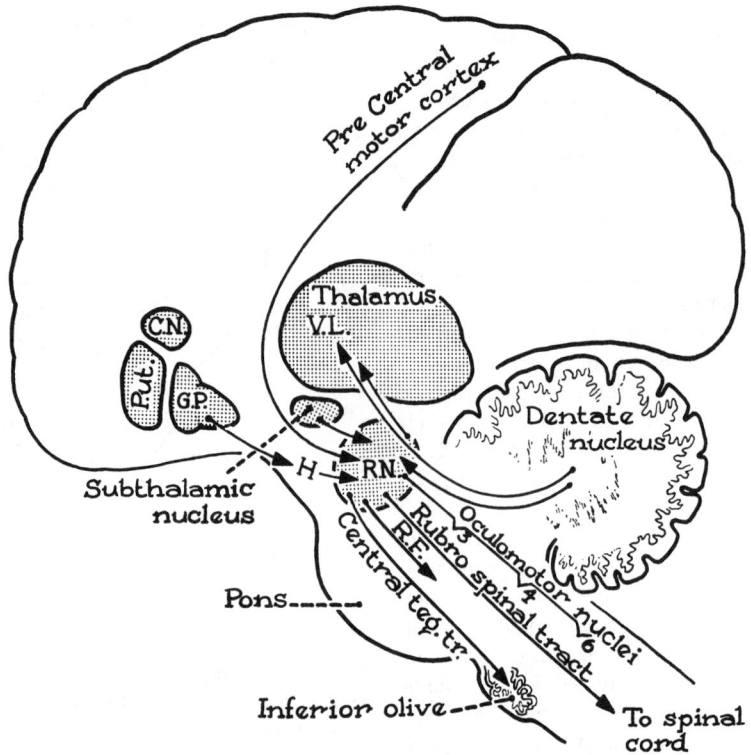

FIG. 7.3. Connections of the red nucleus.

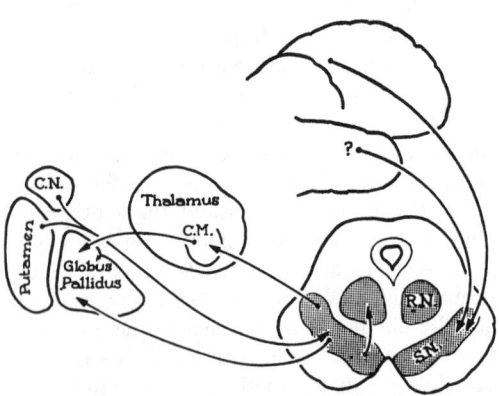

FIG. 7.4. Some connections of the substantia nigra with other parts of the basal ganglia.

cleus receives from all of the other nuclei of the basal ganglia (and from the precentral motor cortex and the cerebellum) but sends all of its efferent fibers to structures outside of the basal ganglia, to the spinal cord, the reticular substance of the brain stem, the ventrolateral nucleus of the thalamus, the inferior olive and the oculomotor nuclei (Fig. 7.3). Thus the caudate nucleus and the putamen appear to be acting as the primary receiving station of the basal ganglia whereas the red nucleus and the globus pallidus

are acting as the principal sending stations. In addition to their efferent fibers there are fibers from the substantia nigra and the subthalamic nucleus to the substantia reticularis and the center-median nucleus of the thalamus (Ranson, Ranson and Ranson, 1941; Glees, 1945; Brodal, 1948) (Fig. 7.4).

FUNCTION

What do the basal ganglia do with this complicated neural mechanism? Here again our knowledge is very incomplete. The location of the basal ganglia in the interior of the cerebral hemisphere, covered with the cerebral cortex and white matter, in very intimate relationship with the Island of Reil, the internal capsule, the thalamus and the hypothalamus has made discrete stimulation or destruction difficult. In any event the many experiments carried out on the basal ganglia have shed surprisingly little light on their activity. Furthermore, in man the functional activity of the basal ganglia is apparently quite different from the lower animal forms, even monkeys. Whether this or some other factors are the reason, it is a fact that it has been almost impossible to duplicate in animals the clinical pictures associated with diseases of the basal ganglia in man. The only exception is the intention tremor produced in both man and monkey by section of the superior cerebellar peduncle (Walker and Botterell, 1937). It is true that Richter (1945) produced a parkinsonianlike state in monkeys by destruction of the globus pallidus and substantia nigra by chronic intoxication with carbon disulfide. But as Richter noted, the experimentally produced state was not the same as that seen in man because, "The characteristic tremor, in particular, is lacking." As a result we must turn to the experiments conducted in man by nature herself for what limited knowledge we have of the functions of the human basal ganglia.

It has been repeatedly said that there is no localization of function, somatotopic or otherwise, in the basal ganglia. Clinical experience leaves no doubt that this statement is untrue. Disease in different parts of the basal ganglia give rise to vastly different clinical pictures. Destruction at any point in the dentato-rubrothalamic projection (Fig. 7.5) causes an inten-

tion tremor. Lesions of the substantia nigra and globus pallidus are associated with parkinsonism and a tremor at rest. Destruction of the caudate nucleus and putamen is seen in patients with choreoathetosis. Obviously there must be some functional differences between these various nuclei. Every clinical neurologist is aware of how the tremor of parkinsonism may begin in the head and neck, or in the foot, or in a finger, and then later gradually spread to other parts of the body on the same or opposite side. Obviously there is somatotopic localization in the basal ganglia in man, otherwise such localized manifestations of disease would not be possible.

What are the specific manifestations of disease of the basal ganglia and what do they signify in terms of normal physiological activity? Diseases of the basal ganglia and experimental studies indicate at least four principal functions of the basal ganglia: (a) the production of useful voluntary muscular activity; (b) the control of reflex muscular activity; (c) the production of automatic associated movements; and (d) the

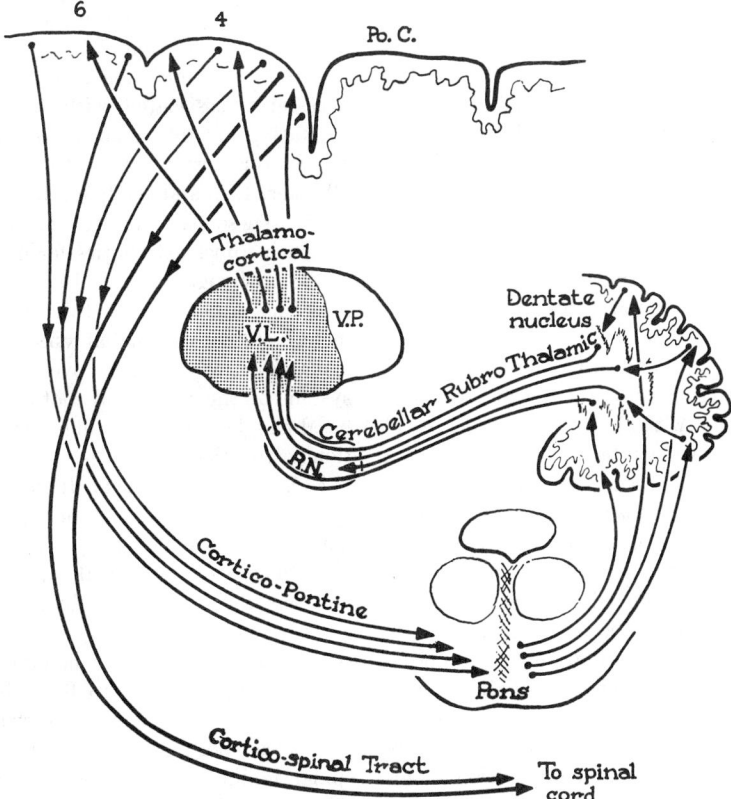

Fig. 7.5. A circular pathway involving the cerebral cortex and the cerebellum. Interruption of this pathway between the dentate nucleus, red nucleus and thalamus results in the appearance of an intention tremor. This probably is the result of the loss of controlling impulses from the cerebellum to the precentral motor cortex.

control of the precentral motor cortex in its function of producing muscular activity.

Voluntary muscular activity. For years it was thought that the production of voluntary muscular activity occurred exclusively as the result of the activity of the corticospinal tract. It is now obvious that that is incorrect. In the birds and reptiles there is no "motor cortex" (Ariens Kappers, 1929). The basal ganglia function as the "head ganglia" of the neural mechanism controlling movement; it is a detailed and exquisite control, as one can see by studying a bird in the air. In the dog and cat there is a "motor" cortex but if it (or even the entire cerebral cortex) is removed the animal still sits, stands and walks. It appears that the animal does this largely with its basal ganglia but even if the basal ganglia and the diencephalon are removed useful movements are not completely abolished in cats. Bard and Macht (1958) decerebrated a small series of cats. In some animals the transection was immediately above the pons, in others it was through the mesencephalon producing a "low mesencephalic cat," whereas in the remainder it was through the upper midbrain producing a "high mesencephalic cat." The "pontile cats" never stood or walked. The "low mesencephalic cats" never walked spontaneously but unsteady walking could be induced by "strong" stimulation. The "high mesencephalic cats" spontaneously assumed a crouching or sitting position and walked in response to such stimuli as a light slap, a whistle or a tweak of the tail. One such animal "frequently" walked spontaneously. Unfortunately we are not supplied with detailed information regarding the character of the walking and other muscular activities, nor do we know how the activity of these animals compared with that of a decorticate cat with the basal ganglia intact. That there was a considerable difference seems obvious.

In primates the situation is quite different from what it is in the carnivora and other lower animal forms. If the precentral motor cortex (areas 4 and 6) is removed from both cerebral hemispheres the animal becomes almost totally paralyzed. Such voluntary movement as an occasional animal may reacquire is possible only if the cortex is removed piecemeal over months of time and if the animal is given painstaking care in retraining and repeated manipulation of his extremities. Even under the most optimum circumstances the movement which is recovered is very limited and stereotyped (Bucy and Fulton, 1933; Woolsey and Bard, 1943; Travis and Woolsey, 1956). Does this mean that in primates the basal ganglia and other subcortical centers have lost their ability to produce useful voluntary movements? This seems unlikely, but it does appear that they have lost their ability to produce such movements in the absence of the precentral motor cortex. Area 4 of the precentral cortex gives rise to corticospinal fibers whereas area 6 does not (Verhaart and Kennard, 1940). If we remove area 4 from the precentral motor cortex of monkeys bilaterally, leaving area 6 on one or both sides, the animal is still able to walk, sit, climb and feed himself but the movements are limited and awkward and reside more about the proximal joints than in the digits (Bucy and Fulton, 1933). Similarly, if the medullary pyramids on the under surface of the medulla oblongata are sectioned in the monkey, the fine, delicate, precise movements of the digits are lost but crude awkward movements of the extremities, particularly those which are more stereotyped and which are related to standing, to progression, etc., are retained (Tower, 1940). Likewise, and somewhat surprisingly, destruction of the corticospinal fibers in the cerebral peduncle in man does not completely paralyze the contralateral extremities, nor is such an operation necessarily associated with the severely incapacitating hemiplegia of a destructive lesion in the motor cortex or in the internal capsule (Walker, 1949 and 1952; White; Swanson; Bucy, 1957). These patients are able to walk and to use their upper extremities for many useful purposes. Although final decisive proof is lacking it seems probable that these voluntary movements present in the absence of the corticospinal fibers are produced over the multisynaptic system of the precentral motor cortex and the basal ganglia and other subcortical centers functioning together.

Reflex muscular activity. Rigidity is one of the characteristics of disease of the basal ganglia, notably Parkinson's paralysis agitans. Clinicians frequently attempt to make a sharp distinction between the rigidity of diseases of the basal ganglia and the spasticity associated with decerebration and capsular hemiplegia. However, the differences appear to be rather superficial. As Fulton and his coworkers were the first to emphasize, both result from the loss of supraspinal inhibition which is not concerned with the corticospinal fibers. Furthermore, as Foerster (1921), Walshe (1924), and Pollock and Davis (1930) have shown, the rigidity of paralysis agitans, like the spasticity of decerebration, is abolished by interrupting afferent impulses from the involved muscle to the spinal cord. This demonstrates that both rigidity and spasticity result primarily from activity of the local, spinal reflex arc which is released to hyperactivity by removal of descending, inhibitory influences. Thus it appears likely that the basal ganglia as well as the precentral motor cortex, area 4s and the bulbar reticular formation, exert an inhibitory influence over the spinal reflexes which control the muscular activity responsible for posture and reflex standing. Recent clinical observations reported by Narabayashi (1956), Guiot (1957), and Cooper (1956) that lesions in the globus pallidus produced surgically in the treatment of various diseases result in the reduction of rigidity indicate the possibility that the basal ganglia exert an excitatory as well as an inhibitory influence upon the spinal reflex mechanism responsible for rigidity. However, the physiological explanation of these clinical observations are as yet unknown and anatomical controls are meager. This serves further to emphasize our ignorance in this field.

Automatic associated movements. One thing that characterizes parkinsonism perhaps even more than tremor or rigidity is the loss of automatic associated movements. Commonly this term is regarded as indicating only the swinging of the arms in walking—a type of movement which is abolished by various destructive lesions in the precentral motor cortex, in the cerebellum, as well as in the substantia nigra and globus pallidus in parkinsonism. However, in parkinsonism far more is lost than automatic swinging of the arms. There is a general poverty of movement. The loss of expressional movements of the face results in the familiar masklike face. There is also a generalized loss of movements throughout the body so that the victim is described as being "statuesque." It thus appears that the basal ganglia are responsible for a wide variety of automatic and associated movements.

Abnormal involuntary movements. Lesions of the basal ganglia are commonly associated with various abnormal involuntary movements, the nature of which vary depending upon the part of the basal ganglia which is involved. It is generally agreed that these movements develop because some inhibitory influence is removed allowing some part of the remaining intact neural mechanism concerned with the control of muscular activity to develop increased and abnormal activity. It seems likely that the corticospinal tract is probably the mechanism responsible for

tremor and that some other motor neural mechanism stemming from the precentral motor cortex is responsible for the abnormal movements of choreoathetosis (Bucy, 1949, 1957). Possible inhibitory circuits involving different subcortical nuclei, including the basal ganglia which probably are concerned in the development of these abnormal movements, have been described and discussed (Figs. 7.5, 7.6 and 7.7) (Bucy, 1942). The connections and pathways outlined in these figures exist but whether their destruction is responsible for the appearance of these diseases is hypothetical.

It is known that destruction of the cerebello-dentato-rubro-thalamic system results in intention tremor (Walker and Botterell, 1937). This system ends in the ventrolateral nucleus of the thalamus which in turn sends its efferent fibers to the precentral motor cortex. This system may well exert a controlling influence over the precentral motor cortex which when removed releases the corticospinal tract to the abnormal activity which results in intention tremor (Fig. 7.5).

Destruction of the substantia nigra and globus pallidus is associated with the tremor at rest of parkinsonism. These nuclei are intimately related. The substantia nigra projects onto the globus pallidus directly and *via* the center-median of the thalamus (Fig. 7.4). The globus pallidus projects onto the anterior part of the ventrolateral nucleus of the thalamus which in turn sends its fibers to the precentral motor cortex. Again it is thought that this mechanism may exert control over the corticospinal fibers (Fig. 7.6).

Choreoathetosis is associated with destruction of the caudate nucleus and putamen. These project directly to the globus pallidus, which again sends impulses to the precentral motor cortex *via* the thalamus. It is thought that this mechanism probably exerts control over that part of the precentral motor cortex which sends its efferent impulses to the skeletal musculature over one or more synapses in the various subcortical nuclei. When this controlling influence is removed from the precentral motor cortex choreoathetoid movements may develop (Fig. 7.7).

Conclusions

What is known of the basal ganglia, their fiber connections and their functions, has been briefly summarized here. Much of this is unconfirmed and not a little has been arrived at by inference. The result is very imperfect knowledge regarding

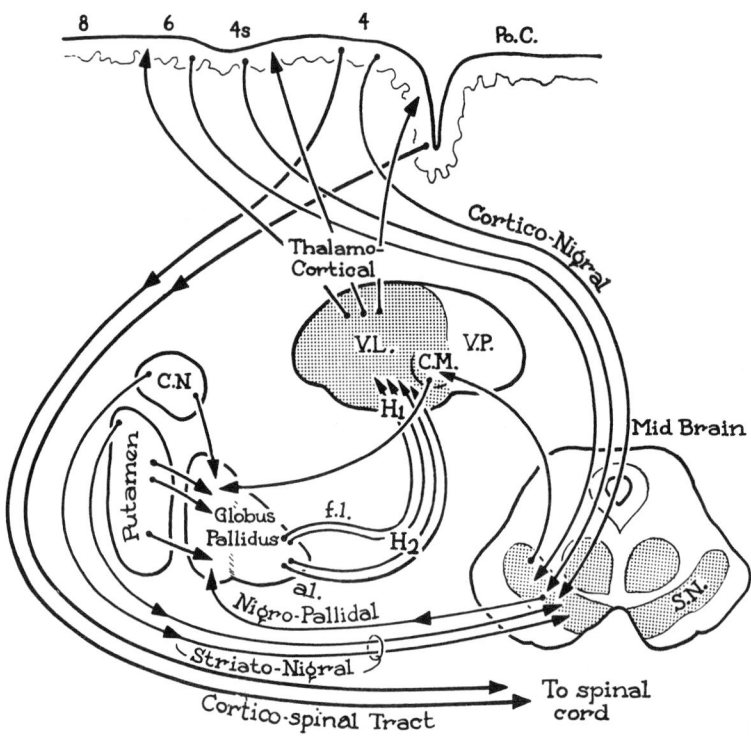

Fig. 7.6. A circular pathway involving the basal ganglia. Lesions of the globus pallidus and substantia nigra in man may be associated with parkinsonian tremor at rest. This diagram shows how impulse from these areas may reach and exert a controlling influence on the precentral motor cortex. The loss of such influence may permit tremor at rest to appear.

this large and obviously important part of the brain. The basal ganglia merit intensive study in man and in animals by various methods. Until better understanding is achieved our knowledge of the central nervous mechanism responsible for the control of muscular activity will continue to be imperfect.

Clinical Manifestations of Disease of the Basal Ganglia

The chief clinical features of disease of the basal ganglia are: (a) muscular rigidity resulting in disturbances of posture and movement, (b) involuntary movements, e.g., tremor, athetosis, chorea, (c) a loss of automatic and associated movements such as those of emotional expression, the swinging of the arms in walking, etc., and (d) absence of a paralysis of voluntary movement, although it may be distinctly impaired by one or all of the other manifestations. The basal ganglia are particularly susceptible to certain toxins (e.g., carbon disulfide), to anoxia, and to certain encephalitic processes. The following are some of the syndromes met with: (a) *Progressive hepatolenticular degeneration*, (b) *parkinsonism—paralysis agitans*, etc., (c) *chorea*, (d) *hemiballismus*, (e) *athetosis*, (f) *torsion spasm*.

Progressive hepatolenticular degeneration (*Wilson's disease*). This was described by Wilson in 1912. It invariably terminates fatally but its duration varies from a few months to several years. The following are its chief features:

1. *Muscular rigidity* is widespread and progressive; it involves face, trunk and limbs. Flexors as well as extensors are affected, but the former more conspicuously than the latter. The hypertonus offers a "lead-pipe-like" resistance to passive movement and results in slowness and difficulty of movement. Eventually, contractures occur and the patient is rendered almost immobile as though carved from stone; he can be lifted or moved *en bloc*. The rigidity of the facial muscles gives a fixed, blank expression. The mouth is sometimes held widely open; the smile or laugh is peculiarly stiff and vacuous. The hypertonus of the muscles of articulation and deglutition leads to dysarthria (p. 182) and dysphagia. The rigidity is temporarily abolished by the injection of novocaine into the muscles.

2. *Involuntary movements*. These consist chiefly

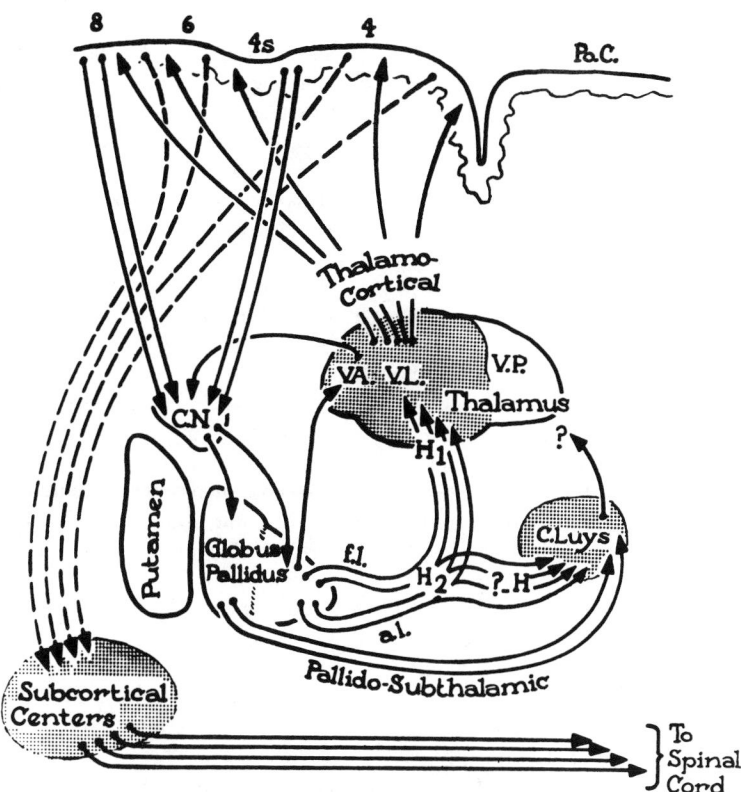

FIG. 7.7. Another circular pathway involving the basal ganglia. Lesions of the caudate nucleus and putamen in man may be associated with choreoathetosis. Such lesions might so distort or disorganize the impulses from the basal ganglia to the precentral motor cortex as to cause the abnormal movements of choreo-athetosis to appear.

of tremor (about 6 oscillations per second) which is increased by excitement or any attempt at voluntary movement; sometimes athetoid movements (p. 170) occur.

3. *The reflexes are normal.* There are no sensory changes and although the muscles often show some weakness and are easily fatigued there is no actual paralysis.

4. *Cirrhosis (multilobular) of the liver* is found at autopsy, but during life there may be no signs of liver disease. In some instances, however, symptoms pointing to the liver precede the nervous manifestations. There is evidence that the changes in the liver and possibly in the brain are associated with disturbances in the metabolism of copper.

5. *Emotionalism.* Involuntary laughing or crying, and some mental deterioration.

6. *Greenish brown pigmentation of the cornea (in Descemet's membrane) occurs in most cases.*

Degeneration of the cells of the putamen and globus pallidus, sometimes with cavitation, is found at autopsy. The caudate nucleus is affected to a much less degree.

THE PARKINSONIAN SYNDROME. The principal features of this syndrome are the following: (a) A *coarse tremor* involving head and limbs. The hand may show "pill-rolling" movements, i.e., rhythmical movements of thumb upon the first two fingers. Alternating movements of flexion and extension at the wrist, or of supination and pronation of the forearm, are frequently present. When the limb is engaged in some voluntary act the movements often temporarily disappear in that limb. The tremor becomes more pronounced during emotional excitement or when the patient is under a nervous strain. It disappears during sleep. The tremor also disappears on the paralyzed side if hemiplegia supervenes. Ablation of the motor area of the cortex, or section of the lateral corticospinal tracts also abolishes it in the related extremities. It therefore seems to be dependent upon an intact pyramidal tract. However, this has been denied by some surgeons who believe they have abolished the tremor by producing lesions in the globus pallidus, the thalamus, or the midbrain. The final solution of the problem must await the accumulation of more accurate anatomical and physiological information. (b) *Muscular rigidity* which leads to slowness and stiffness of movement. The rigidity is different both in its quality and distribution from that characteristic of the decerebrate animal (p. 87) or of the hemiplegic patient. Flexors and extensor muscles are affected about equally, and the resistance of a limb to passive movements has been described as resembling cogwheels moving slowly upon one another, as though groups of muscles gave way in succession to the stretching force. This cogwheel phenomenon is undoubtedly merely a manifestation of the rhythmical innervation of the involved muscles which also gives rise to the tremor. The upper limbs are held in characteristic attitudes of adduction at the shoulders, flexion at the elbows, flexion or slight extension at the wrists, flexion at the metacarpophalangeal joints and slight flexion at the interphalangeal joints. (c) The *gait* is slow and shuffling with short steps, or it may be "festinating" in character, i.e., the patient is bent forward and hastens along with short quick steps as though trying to "catch up to his center of gravity" and prevent his falling. When pushed forward or backward he cannot stop quickly but moves by a series of small rapidly repeated steps in the direction in which he is pushed. *Propulsion* and *retropulsion* are the respective terms applied to these forward and backward movements. There is no true paralysis; the reflexes and sensation are unaffected. (d) One of the most constant manifestations of parkinsonism is the loss of certain automatic and associated movements. As a result the patient does not swing his arms as he walks, the typical facial expressions of various emotions are decreased or absent and the face is said to be masklike. Because the many little movements of the body which characterize normal human activity are absent the patient stands rigidly and without moving, "like a statue."

Parkinsonism appears to be the result of destructive lesions in the globus pallidus or the substantia nigra or both. These lesions may appear as the result of a primary idiopathic degeneration, of toxic processes, of anoxemia, of arteriosclerosis or of encephalitis.

All of the manifestations of parkinsonism are not necessarily present in all cases, or if present they are not of the same intensity. Some patients have the parkinsonian rigidity and lack of automatic and associated movements with little or no tremor. Some have tremor with relatively little rigidity. Some patients, particularly the post-encephalitic group, have associated disturbances of ocular movements known as oculogyric crises, and of vegetative functions such as sialorrhea and excessive oiliness of the skin. Others, particularly those in the arteriosclerotic group, may have exaggerated tendon reflexes, the sign of Babinski and impairment of psychological processes. These disturbances are, of course, due to involvement of other structures and pathways in the internal capsule, the cerebral cortex, the hypothalamus, the midbrain, etc.

Chorea. There are two principal forms of this condition.

1. SYDENHAM'S CHOREA (or St. Vitus's dance) is one of the manifestations of rheumatic fever. Its chief feature is involuntary jerky movements, semipurposeful in character, involving the muscles of the limbs and face. Facial grimacing, an inability to remain quiet, the frequent dropping of objects from the hands, and the inability to maintain sustained muscular contractions characterize the disease.

Sydenham's chorea may be bilateral or unilateral. Death is rare and there is consequently uncertainty concerning its neuropathology. In those few cases where examinations have been made the lesions have been multiple and diffuse, involving both cerebral cortex and subcortical structures.

2. HUNTINGTON'S CHOREA is a rare familial disease which results in severe disability and ultimately terminates fatally. It is transmitted as a dominant characteristic but the onset is usually late in the fourth decade of life. Pathologically one finds severe degeneration and atrophy of the caudate and lenticular nuclei. The small cells of the caudate nucleus and putamen are particularly affected. However, the large cells are not entirely spared and changes are seen in the globus pallidus and cerebral cortex. The disease is characterized by facial grimacing, jerky gesticulating movements of the upper extremities and a lurching, uncertain gait. Speech is dysarthric. The motor disturbances steadily increase until the patient is incapacitated. There is mental deterioration with irritability and occasional homicidal and suicidal tendencies.

3. HEMIBALLISMUS or HEMICHOREA usually results from vascular lesions in the subthalamic nucleus of Luys. It is, therefore, seen most often in older people with cerebral arteriosclerosis. It is characterized by wild flinging movements of the extremities on one side of the body. In some cases the condition subsides spontaneously (Hyland and Forman), in others the violent move-

ments continue unremitting during the patient's every waking moment but subside during sleep. In such cases the patient may injure his extremities and may die of exhaustion. The movements can be abolished by dividing the corticospinal fibers which arise in the precentral gyrus. This can be accomplished at the cortical level, in the cerebral peduncle or in the spinal cord. Pedunculotomy is the simplest of these procedures and should be considered in any case in which the movements show no evidence of subsiding spontaneously and are violent enough to warrant surgical intervention. It has been reported that these movements have been abolished by section of the anterior white column of the spinal cord but this observation needs confirmation. Physiologically it is difficult to understand why section of the corticospinal tract and an anterior cordotomy should both be effective.

ATHETOSIS is a form of abnormal involuntary movements beginning most often in childhood. It is associated with damage to the basal ganglia, particularly the caudate nucleus and the putamen. This damage may result from asphyxia or injury at birth, or from injury or encephalitis subsequently. Pure athetosis consists of slow, writhing, twisting movements of the involved extremities and the face. In many cases there are also quicker, jerky involuntary movements and the condition is then termed *choreoathetosis.* As with most other abnormal involuntary movements these are present during all waking hours and are absent during sleep. They are aggravated by nervous tension and are diminished or abolished by the ingestion of alcohol. In many patients choreoathetoid movements are unilateral and are associated with a hemiparesis on the same side. In some cases with bilateral involvement, or *athetose double*, examination of the brain will reveal congenital changes in the basal ganglia known as *status marmoratus*. Unilateral choreoathetosis can be abolished by removal of the contralateral precentral motor cortex (areas 4 and 6). They can also be diminished by section of the central portion of the contralateral cerebral peduncle which contains the corticospinal fibers from the precentral gyrus. A few cases have been reported in which the movements have been decreased after surgical lesions have been placed in the region of the internal segment of the globus pallidus or the ansa lenticularis. However, these observations lack anatomical confirmation. It appears likely that both corticospinal fibers and multisynaptic neuron chains from the precentral motor cortex which pass downward through subcortical centers to the spinal cord mediate the impulses which are responsible for the abnormal involuntary movements of choreoathetosis.

TORSION SPASM is very rare condition and need only be defined. It consists of abnormal involuntary turning, twisting movements of the neck, trunk, and extremities which distort the body into bizarre postures. Pathological changes in various parts of the basal ganglia have been described.

The Thalamus

This large gray mass is related medially to the third ventricle which lies between the thalami of the two sides. The thalami are joined across the midline by an isthmus, the *massa intermedia*. The posterior limb of the internal capsule lies upon the outer side of the thalamus and separates it from the lentiform nucleus. Above the thalamus is the lateral ventricle, a part of whose floor it forms. In front is the head of the caudate nucleus; the arched *body* of the latter is related to the upper part of the lateral surface of the thalamus. Below the thalamus are the corpus of Luys (subthalamic nucleus) and the forepart of the red nucleus.

There are five main nuclear masses in the thalamus.

A vertical septum of fibers known as the *internal medullary lamina* divides the principal part of the thalamus into: A, a *medial* and B, a *lateral* mass, each of which contains two main nuclear groups. C, In the massa intermedia and the adjacent part of the medial mass are discrete groups of nerve cells known as the *nuclei of the midline*. D, Clusters of nerve cells are present in the internal medullary lamina itself—the *intralaminar nuclei*. E, *Pulvinar.*

A. *Nuclei of the medial mass.* (*1*) *Anterior nuclei.* These form a mass which bulges into the lateral ventricle. They receive fibers from the mammillary bodies (mamillothalamic tract of Vicq d'Azyr) which convey olfactory impulses. They send fibers to the paracentral lobule and the posterior part of the cingular gyrus on the medial aspect of hemisphere. (*2*) *Dorsomedial nuclei*. These consist of a dorsolateral group of small cells, and a medial collection of large cells. The former projects to prefrontal areas of the cerebral cortex. The large-celled portion is connected by both afferent and efferent fibers with the hypothalamus; it also projects to the corpus striatum, and has rich afferent connections with other thalamic nuclei. The dorsomedial nuclei are thought

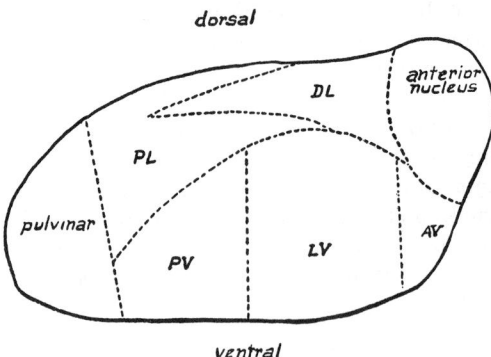

FIG. 7.8. Showing the anterior nucleus and the divisions of the lateral nuclear mass of the thalamus. DL, dorsal lateral nucleus; PL, posterior lateral nucleus; PV, posterior ventral nucleus; LV, lateral nucleus; AV, anterior ventral nucleus. (Courtesy of Dr. Murray Barr.)

to serve as an association center where visceral and crude somatic sensations are synthesized. It is thought to be a conscious center for the cruder (protopathic) sensations, and where sensations are integrated into "feelings", both pleasant and unpleasant.

B. *Nuclei of the lateral mass.* (1) *Ventral group.* This consists of; (a) *Anterior ventral nucleus* which receives fibers from the globus pallidus and projects to different parts of the corpus striatum, but not to the cerebral cortex. This nucleus occupies the most anterior (rostral) extremity of the lateral mass. (b) *Lateral ventral nucleus.* The fibers entering the anterolateral part of this nucleus arises in the globus pallidus, whereas those ending in the posterior and medial part of this nucleus are derived mainly from the dentate nucleus of the contralateral half of the cerebellum (*via* the dentatothalamic and the dentatorubrothalamic tracts). Its efferent fibers pass to area 4, and in much smaller numbers to area 6 of the precentral motor cortex. Thus a pathway is established through which voluntary movements can be brought under the influence of the basal ganglia and the cerebellum. (c) The *posterior ventral nucleus* is the main subcortical center for sensory impulses ascending in the trigeminal, medial and spinal lemnisci (proprioceptive from muscles and joints, light touch, discrimination of two points, pain, heat and cold). It projects to the post central gyrus (somesthetic area), areas 1, 3, 2, 5 and 7. This nucleus also sends fibers to the hypothalamus and corpus striatum. The posterior ventral nucleus is composed of two subsidiary parts: (i) the *posteromedial nucleus*, which receives the trigeminal fibers, and (ii) the *posterolateral nucleus*

which is the thalamic station for the medial and the spinal lemnisci.

(2) *Dorsal group.* This is also called the *lateral nucleus of the thalamus.* It is subdivided into an anterior and a posterior portion, designated, respectively, the *dorsolateral* and *posterolateral nuclei.*

C. *The nuclei of the midline* are, as mentioned above, situated in the massa intermedia, and in the adjacent part of the medial mass forming the upper part of the wall of the third ventricle. They are phylogenetically the oldest of the thalamic nuclei and are a center for the most primitive forms of sensation, e.g., from the viscera and other structures occupying the axial regions of the body. The midline nuclei are connected by many fine myelinated fibers with other subcortical centers, namely, the hypothalamus and midbrain nuclei. They also receive fibers from the corpus striatum. These nuclei have many intrathalamic connections but few if any fibers pass to the cerebral cortex, corpus of Luys (subthalamic nucleus) and the forepart of the red nucleus.

D. *The intralaminar nuclei* are scattered groups of cells within the internal medullary lamina. The connections of these nuclei are imperfectly known, but they are thought to receive both trigeminal fibers and fibers of the medial lemniscus; they project to the globus pallidus and have many connections with neighboring thalamic nuclei. A well defined nucleus in the middle of the thalamus, and usually classed with this group is known as the *central* or *centromedian nucleus.* It is especially well marked in primates, as is possibly an intrathalamic integrating center.

E. *The pulvinar* is the expanded continuation posteriorly of the lateral nuclear mass. It overhangs the superior colliculus. It projects to the cortex, its inferior part to an area comprising part of the temporal lobe, and the anterior part of the occipital lobe. The rest of the pulvinar projects mainly to the parietal and temporal lobes.

The *medial* and *lateral geniculate bodies* are usually included as part of the thalamus or referred to as the *metathalamus*; they are dealt with in chapters 16 and 17.

It will be seen from the foregoing account that the nuclei of the thalamus can be divided upon a functional basis into three categories, namely, (a) those which serve as relay stations of afferent impulses from the periphery to the cortex, (b) those which are connected mainly with other subcortical centers and (c) those whose chief function is associative.

FUNCTIONS

We have seen that the corpus striatum is a part of an old or primitive motor system. The thalamus, on the other hand, is a primitive receptive center wherein sensory impulses give rise to a *crude uncritical form of consciousness*; a consciousness which is greatly elaborated upon, especially in man, by the cerebral cortex (see ch. 8). Sensory localization in the thalamus has been demonstrated by Dusser de Barenne and Sager by means of local strychninization. The injection of a minute quantity of the drug into the thalamus in cats is followed by hyperesthesia and hyperalgesia to cutaneous and deep (muscle, tendon and periosteum) stimuli. The cutaneous hypersensitivity is most pronounced on the contralateral side of the body; increased sensitivity to deep stimuli occurs only on the contralateral side. By this method, and other methods of investigation it has been shown that there is a definite somatotopic organization in the posterior ventral nucleus of the thalamus, which serves the conscious perception of sensory stimuli. The leg is represented most laterally, the face most medially, and the trunk and upper extremity in between.

The thalamus is not, however, entirely sensory in function. In animals possessed of little or no cortex, or in higher mammals (e.g., cat or dog) after decortication, it and the corpus striatum serve for the execution of complex movements of an automatic or reflex nature. Furthermore, the reticular nucleus and the ventromedial portion of the thalamus (including the intralaminar nuclei) form part of the reticular formation of the brain stem and take part in the arousal and alerting reactions produced by that mechanism, as well as other functions referred to on pages 153 and 154.

THALAMIC LESIONS

The effects resulting from a lesion involving the lateral thalamic nuclei will resemble those following an interruption of ascending pathways in the brain stem above their decussation. That is, all types of sensation on the opposite side of the body tend to be lost or grossly affected, or there may be severe pain as a result of destruction of inhibitory mechanisms or possibly of the direct stimulation (irritation) of pain fibers. In addition to the loss or diminution of sensation, lesions of the thalamus are not infrequently associated with spontaneous pain and with marked hypersensitivity which has a very unpleasant quality. These manifestations are part of the thal-

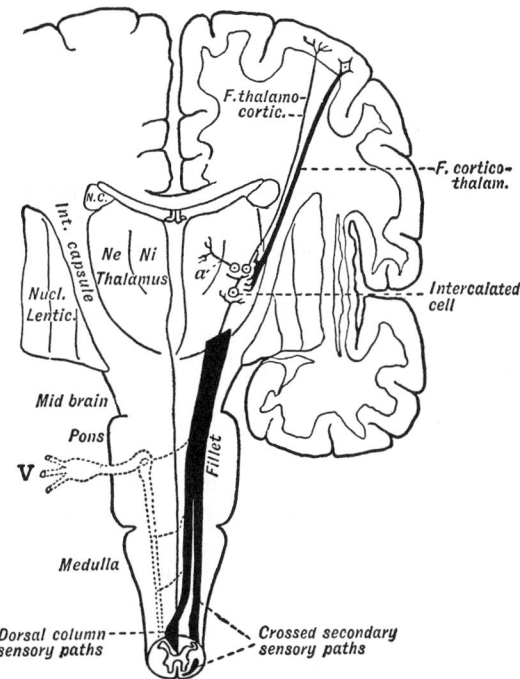

FIG. 7.9. Diagram showing the paths and centers concerned in sensation. All sensory impulses ascend to the lateral part of the thalamus, where regrouping occurs; the cruder sensations (e.g., those of pain and extremes of temperature) are relayed to the medial portion of the thalamus, the remainder (e.g., light touch, discrimination of two points, sense of position and movement, etc.) to the cerebral cortex. The cortico-thalamic fibers, which terminate in the lateral nucleus of the thalamus are also shown. (Modified from Head.)

amic syndrome described below and are not well understood.

THE THALAMIC SYNDROME OF DEJERINE AND ROUSSY. This is a characteristic picture occasionally seen in thalamic disease. The following are its chief features:

(1) Asterognosis and sensory ataxia, due to the impairment of cutaneous and kinesthetic senses. These and the other effects given below are mainly on the contralateral side of the body.

(2) Some loss of tactile and thermal sensations over the body and face. The threshold for these sensations, and for pain, is frequently raised. Sometimes the patient with a thalamic lesion is unable with closed eyes to localize the position of a limb, and must grope in the air in order to find it (*thalamic phantom limb*); or he may have the illusion that the limb is not there at all (*amelognosia*). He also is commonly unable to localize a point which has been stimulated even though he recognizes the stimulus.

(3) Spontaneous pain occurring in paroxysms

and often excruciating. The pain may be so intense as to resist the action of powerful sedatives, e.g., morphine. A painful stimulus is felt much more acutely than is normal (hyperalgesia) and although, as mentioned above, the threshold for pain is often raised, the sensation when once aroused (by increasing the strength of stimulus) is excessively severe. Other stimuli are often associated with an unpleasant sensation. Cold in particular may be most disagreeable but light touch may also be unpleasant. These spontaneous discomforts and unusual reactions to various stimuli are usually referred to as *thalamic over-reaction.*

(4) Lesions in the thalamus are frequently associated with various abnormal involuntary movements. Choreoathetosis and intention tremor are the more common. It is believed that choreoathetosis results from the involvement of the projection system from the basal ganglia to the anterior part of the ventrolateral nucleus of the thalamus and that intention tremor arises when the pathway from the dentate nucleus of the cerebellum and the red nucleus is damaged at its point of termination in the posterior part of the ventrolateral nucleus. This nucleus in turn projects to the precentral motor cortex and it is

thought possible that these abnormal involuntary movements arise because regulating impulses from the thalamus to the motor cortex have been destroyed (Bucy, 1942). Furthermore, such lesions commonly give rise to an abnormal posture of the extended hand known as the *"thalamic hand."* This is characterized by a moderate flexion of the wrist and a hyperextension of the fingers. The same posture of the outstretched hand is also referred to by some as the "athetoid hand."

(5) Hemiparesis and defects in the visual fields which may be seen in some patients exhibiting the thalamic syndrome are not the result of thalamic involvement but are due to damage to the neighboring internal capsule.

The thalamic syndrome may also be associated with disturbances of sensation which are associated with certain emotional reactions. Thus one of Head's patients was so affected by music that he "could not stand the hymns on his affected side," another said that when the choir sang "a horrid feeling came on the affected side and the leg ... started to shake." In another patient pleasant feelings of a psychic nature were referred to the abnormal side. He said "I seem to crave for sympathy on my right side," and "My right hand seems to be more artistic."

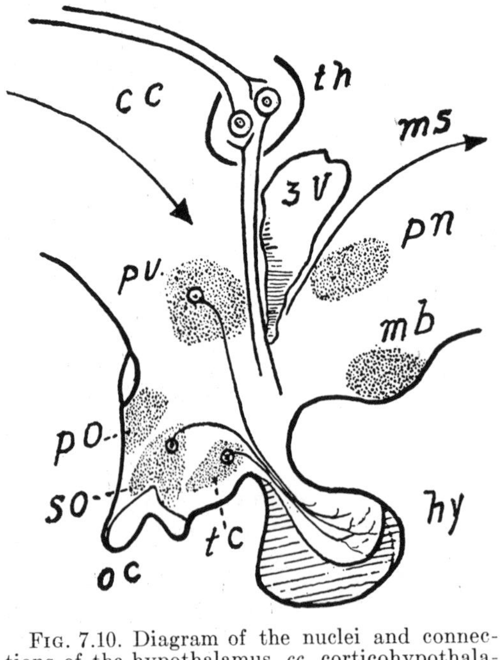

The Hypothalamus

The hypothalamus is the basal part of the diencephalon (interbrain). It forms the floor and lower parts of the walls of the 3rd ventricle (fig. 7.10).

Of the *nuclei of the hypothalamus* the greatest interest from the physiological point of view centers around the following.

The *supraoptic nucleus* lies anteriorly, lateral to the optic chiasma and above the commencement of the corresponding optic tract. The *preoptic nucleus* is situated most anteriorly above and in front of the supraoptic nucleus, and immediately behind the lamina terminalis. The *paraventricular nucleus* is found above the supraoptic nucleus and is in close relationship medially to the wall of the 3rd ventricle. It is richly vascular, and its large vacuolated cells contain numerous granules, possibly the mother substance of a secretory product. The *posterior hypothalamic group of nuclei* lie in the posterior part of the hypothalamus in relation to the wall of the 3rd ventricle, and include the mammillary nuclei. Cells of this group send fibers to the medulla oblongata and the lateral horns of the spinal cord, which constitute the spinal sympathetic center. The *tuber*

Fig. 7.10. Diagram of the nuclei and connections of the hypothalamus. *cc*, corticohypothalamic fiber; *pv*, paraventricular nucl.; *po*, preoptic nucl.; *so*, supraoptic nucl.; *oc*, optic chiasma; *tc*, tuber cinereum; *hy*, hypophysis; *mb*, mammallary body; *pn*, posterior nucl.; *ms*, fiber to midbrain and brain stem; *3V*, third ventricle; *th*, thalamus.

cinereum (*nucleus tuber*) is a small eminence of gray matter situated at the base of the brain between the optic chiasma and the mammillary bodies, i.e., in the midregion of the hypothalamus; from its vicinity grows the pituitary stalk. Two groups of cells can be clearly defined within it; they are known as the *dorsomedial* and *ventromedial hypothalamic nuclei*. The slight swelling caused by these nuclei and covered by the pars tuberalis of the adenohypophysis (ch. 74), is called the "median eminence." The tuber cinereum is a center of the parasympathetic nervous system.

Fiber connections. The hypothalamus receives fibers from the globus pallidus (pallidohypothalamic tract), from the amygdaloid nucleus and through the *medial forebrain bundle*, from the olfactory lobe and the parolfactory area. The medial forebrain bundle sweeps through the hypothalamus and in its course gives off fibers to several of the hypothalamic nuclei. The hypothalamus, especially the supraoptic and paraventricular nuclei, also receives fibers from prefrontal areas and the precentral motor area (6) of the cerebral cortex (ch. 8) both directly and indirectly through the thalamus. There are probably afferent fibers from the spinal cord, doubtless similar to the direct and collateral ascending afferents which go to the reticular formation. It also projects through the anterior and the dorsomedial nuclei of the thalamus to prefrontal areas. The most prominent tract from the hypothalamus to the thalamus is the mammillo-thalamic tract (of Vicq d'Azyr) from the medial mammillary nucleus to the anterior nuclei of the thalamus. Other efferent tracts (sympathetic and parasympathetic) pass backwards in close relation to the ependyma of the third ventricle, and descend in the gray substance of the midbrain (surrounding the cerebral aqueduct), pons, medulla (beneath the floor of the fourth ventricle) and spinal cord (sympathetic).

The various hypothalamic nuclei are in communication with one another through fiber tracts; the best known of these is the paraventricular-supraoptic tract, but others undoubtedly exist.

The supraoptic, and tuberal nuclei, and probably the paraventricular nuclei as well, are linked with the hypophysis by efferent fibers which descend the infundibular stalk (hypothalamo-hypophyseal tract). The majority of these fibers terminate around the pituicytes of the pars nervosa but some can be traced into the pars intermedia.

Thus, there exists a pathway, through the hypothalamus, from the cerebral cortex to the cells (pituicytes) of the neural lobe of the hypophysis.

The Physiology of the Hypothalamic Nuclei

Modern experimental and clinical investigations have revealed the hypothalamus as a region of great physiological importance. Our knowledge of the functions of this part of the cerebrum is still, nevertheless, very incomplete. Much of the evidence is suggestive rather than conclusive and permits only tentative views to be held concerning many of its activities. It is the general opinion, however, that in this part of the diencephalon are contained the mechanisms for the control of certain primitive reactions (visceral and somatic) associated in animals with defense or attack, and in man with emotional states (fear, anger, etc.). This region is also believed to contain centers for the regulation of certain fundamental and vital processes, e.g., fat, carbohydrate and water metabolism, and to exert a governing influence upon the body temperature, the gastric movements, the genital functions and the sleep rhythm (ch. 9), hunger and thirst (ch. 62).

It is now generally conceded that important centers governing the activities of the autonomic nervous system are situated in the hypothalamus. Those cell groups in the anterior part of the hypothalamus and in the tuberal region were at one time believed to constitute a parasympathetic center, whereas the posterior part was thought to be concerned with sympathetic functions. It is now recognized that our knowledge concerning the localization of function in the hypothalamus is still defective.

The pituitary and the nervous structures of the hypothalamus are intimately associated in function; indeed, they should be considered together as constituting a closely integrated neuroglandular mechanism rather than as possessing distinct and independent functions. It will be recalled that the pars nervosa of the pituitary is developed as a downgrowth from the floor of the third ventricle, and that the pituicytes are modified neuroglial cells. On the other hand, the cells of the supraoptic and paraventricular nuclei of the hypothalamus show evidence of possible secretory activity.

A brief summary of the experimental evidence relating to hypothalamic functions will be given in the following paragraphs.

(1) Karplus and Kreidl were the first to furnish evidence of a sympathetic center in the hypothalamus. Upon electrical stimulation of this re-

gion they obtained pupillary dilation, sweating and a rise in blood pressure. Inhibition of intestinal movements also results. Liberation of adrenaline has also been reported to follow stimulation of the hypothalamus. By means of needle electrodes inserted into the region of the lateral nucleus Bronk and his colleagues have recorded impulses from sympathetic efferent nerves during stimulation of the hypothalamus. On the other hand, rhythmical variations in potential were produced in the hypothalamus by the stimulation of certain afferent nerves through which reflex sympathetic responses may be elicited.

(2) Beattie, Brow and Long found that extrasystoles produced in the cat by means of chloroform anesthesia, and which had been shown by Levy to be dependent upon sympathetic impulses (ch. 12), were abolished by a destructive lesion placed in the posterior hypothalamic nuclei or by a section of the brain behind this region. Stimulation of the posterior hypothalamic region, on the other hand, caused extrasystoles to appear in an animal which previously had been free from these cardiac irregularities. Animals subjected to such lesions also showed hyperglycemia and glycosuria. Drowsiness for two or three days following the operation was a noticeable feature in some animals; they also showed a change in behavior, being more docile and "tamer" after the operation (see "sham rage" below). The nervous system of animals examined histologically some time after the lesions in the posterior hypothalamic nuclei had been made showed degenerating fibers which entered the midbrain and descended through the brain stem and cord. Those in the latter situation entered the lateral column of gray matter at different levels down to the third or fourth lumbar segment.

(3) Decerebration by a section through the midbrain causes a profound fall in body temperature. No such loss of temperature control follows the removal of the cerebral cortex and thalamus, provided the hypothalamus is left intact. It is significant that sympathetic effects, e.g., adrenaline liberation, ruffling of feathers or hairs, constriction of vessels and goose flesh, result from exposure to cold. Moreover, Cushing has called attention to the high temperature which frequently follows operations upon tumors in the region of the third ventricle of the brain.

(4) Hess fixed electrodes in the hypothalamus of cats. After the animals had recovered from the operation, a weak electric current passed through the hypothalamus induced a state indistinguishable from normal sleep. More recently Akert, Koella and R. Hess, Jr. were all able to produce sleep in cats by stimulation of the intralaminar thalamic nuclei. Both of these observations are difficult to reconcile with the fact that stimulation of the reticular formation arouses the animal from sleep.

(5) Kabat and associates by means of an electrode fixed in the hypothalamus stimulated this region in the unanesthetized animal. Pupillary dilation, erection of hair, inhibition of gastrointestinal peristalsis, clawing and urination resulted. Stimulation of other parts of the brain produced none of these effects.

(6) Gastric lesions associated with hypothalamic damage, ovulation following stimulation of the hypothalamus, and evidence for hypothalamic control of gastric secretion have all been reported. There is also some evidence of a hypothalamic center for gastric motility.

Quasi-emotional State—"Sham Rage"

It was first demonstrated by Goltz that the reactions which usually accompany displeasure and anger are more readily evoked in an animal deprived of its cerebral cortex (decorticated) than in the normal animal. In Goltz's classical experiment the hemispheres and a large part of the thalamus were removed from a dog. The disposition of the animal was greatly altered by the operation, it being very readily aroused to anger. Barking, growling, baring the teeth or snapping occurred upon the least provocation. Cannon and Britton produced a similar state in cats by removal of the cortex, the decortication being performed by means of a pointed stilet inserted through the orbital cavities. Immediately following recovery from the anesthetic the animals showed the following remarkable phemonena which these observers termed "sham rage"— lashing of the tail, erection of the hairs, protrusion of the claws, dilatation of the pupils, sweating, struggling and biting, greatly increased rate of respiration and a rise in blood pressure. Most of these manifestations will be recognized as being of sympathetic origin. In many instances the picture is a combination of fear and anger. Liberation of adrenaline, as indicated by an increase in the rate of the denervated heart, also occurred. The mildest stimulus such as jarring the table or lightly touching the animal was sufficient to evoke a paroxysm of rage.[1] In his decortication experi-

[1] Pseudoaffective states—displeasure, anger or rage, can be evoked in animals after a section caudal to the hypothalamus, but much less readily

ments Bard found that the posterior and ventral portion of the diencephalon was essentially responsible for the development of "sham rage." The typical quasi-emotional behavior occurred after decortication and section through the hypothalamus at about the middle of the tubercinereum. It also resulted from an operation which removed the basal ganglia and the dorsal half of the diencephalon, i.e., the thalamus, but left the hypothalamus connected with the midbrain. The condition failed to appear if the section separated the caudal part of the hypothalamus.

In view of the excessive display of emotional reactions which can so easily be induced in the cat (or dog) from which the forebrain has been removed, leaving the posterior part of the hypothalamus intact, it was only natural to conclude that the cerebral cortex exerted a regulatory influence over this hypothalamic mechanism. However, Bard and Mountcastle have shown in cats that the restraining influence of higher levels of the cerebrum upon hypothalamic activity is not exerted by the neocortex, but by certain parts of the rhinencephalon (cortex of the pyriform lobe, amygdaloid nucleus and hippocampal formation) and an area of cortex on the medial aspect of the hemisphere lying ventral to the cingular sulcus in front and below the rostrum of the corpus callosum. This latter area of cortex is believed to be a transitional zone between the rhinencephalon and the neocortex. An operation which removed the neocortex alone, leaving the rhinencephalon and the area of transitional cortex uninjured, was performed upon cats whose behavior and temperament had been studied for some time previously. The manifestations of animals prepared in this way were the reverse of those which had been subjected to complete decortication. They showed extraordinary placidity. Responses expressive of of pleasure were predominant and often exaggerated. Procedures, which in a normal animal provoke resentment, anger or even rage, such as, pinching the tail strongly with surgical forceps, tying the animal down on its back, strong electric shocks applied to the skin, etc., evoked no sign of anger or even of resentment. The animals responded to mild nociceptive stimulation by purring or with other expressions of pleasure. An animal which before operation resented handling or petting, became affectionate, purred when stroked and submitted to being tied to the animal board "as though it enjoyed the maneuver."

than after decortication, and they do not constitute the fully integrated response of the animal with hypothalamus intact.

Removal of those parts of the rhinencephalon mentioned above or of the transitional area of cortex, transformed animals deprived of their neocortex, i.e., abnormally placid animals, into ones which, upon the slightest provocation, exhibited all the signs of rage.

It is apparent from these experiments that some part of the rhinencephalon and the transitional area of cortex exerts a restraining influence upon those hypothalamic mechanisms governing the expressions displeasure, resentment and anger in carnivores (e.g., cats and dogs).

Repeatedly attention has been called to the danger in transferring information found to be true for one animal to another species of animal without carefully controlled investigations. Nowhere could this precaution be more appropriate than in connection with the amygdala. Although removal of this nucleus bilaterally renders the dog and cat savage and aggressive, it converts the normally intractable Norway wild rat into a gentle animal; bilateral temporal lobectomy, including removal of both amygdaloid nuclei, converts vicious and aggressive rhesus monkeys into relatively tame animals. There are obviously wide species differences and we cannot conclude that what is true for the hypothalamus or the amygdala or the neocortex of the cat is necessarily true for man unless the fact is established.

Emotion. This is an appropriate place to consider the mental state with its accompanying reactions which is generally referred to as emotion. The word emotion is derived from the Latin meaning a "moving out." But there is an inward as well as an outward component of the emotional state. It can be analyzed into subjective and objective elements—emotional feeling or experience, and certain visceral and somatic manifestations, e.g., pallor, blushing, cardiac acceleration, facial expression, etc.

According to the James-Lange theory, the emotional feeling is not aroused *primarily* in consciousness but is the result of the bodily reactions. Briefly, for example, we are frightened because the heart accelerates, the vessels constrict, the respiration quickens and the skeletal muscles increase their tone, or contract for purposes of defense, or in order that one may run away; the afferent impulses initiated by these various activities impinging upon consciousness arouse the feeling of fear. Sherrington showed, however, that the emotional state of a dog remained unaltered after a high spinal transection and section of the vagus nerves, afferent impulses from the viscera and skeletal muscles being thus largely removed.

The modern view, which was advanced by Cannon and by Dana, proposes that emotional feeling, and the associated bodily reactions are the result of interaction between the cerebral cortex and the diencephalon—hypothalamus and thalamus (anterior nucleus)—visceral and somatic responses being *secondary* to the feeling of rage, delight, grief, etc., rather than the cause, which is dependent upon the cortex, probably of the orbital and cingular gyri and the hippocampus,[2] but the emotional manifestations are initiated in subcortical levels. As we have seen, there is much experimental support for such a view. Also, clinically, outbursts of uncontrollable laughter or crying are sometimes associated with lesions of the diencephalon.

DISORDERS OF THE HYPOTHALAMUS

The effects which may result from lesions (e.g., tumors, encephalitis, etc.) involving the hypothalamic region fall into the following groups: (a) disturbances in fat, in carbohydrate or in water metabolism and (b) disorders of sleep, drowsiness, somnolence and, less commonly, abnormal wakefulness, or reversal of the sleep rhythm,[3] (c) emotional manifestations, laughing, crying, or a state resembling "sham rage" in animals, may result, (d) phenomena attributable to sympathetic or parasympathetic stimulation, (e) disorders of the sexual functions.

Any one of the foregoing groups of effects may dominate the clinical condition to give rise to one or other of the following syndromes: (a) diabetes insipidus, (b) dystrophia adiposogenitalis, (c) the Laurence-Biedl-Moon syndrome, and (d) narcolepsy.

These several conditions, with the exception of the last (d), have been considered in chapter 74.

Narcolepsy. This is the term applied to a disturbance in the sleep mechanism in which sudden attacks of an irresistible desire for sleep occur during the daytime. The duration of the attacks, which resemble normal sleep, is quite brief—from a few seconds to 20 minutes or so. It is only to such sudden and brief naps, and not to persistent drowsiness or to prolonged periods of pathological sleep that the term is applicable. Nocturnal sleep may be normal but it is often disturbed or there may be insomnia. Sleep

may overcome the subject of narcolepsy while he is going about his usual occupation, while walking, in the middle of a conversation, during a meal, driving a car, etc. But commonly they occur at times when anyone would be inclined to sleep. There may be many attacks during the day. A few cases were discovered during the war in soldiers under trial by court-martial for falling asleep on sentry duty. The condition may be a sequel to influenza or to epidemic encephalitis involving the hypothalamus or may result from a tumor or injury in this region. In other instances the condition appears without known cause (idiopathic narcolepsy). Although evidence is not conclusive, it is very likely that in these latter, also, disordered hypothalamic function is responsible, for other features, e.g., obesity, polyuria or impairment of the sexual functions, pointing to an abnormality of this region are frequently present. *Ritalin,* ephedrine sulfate and amphetamine (benzedrine) have been used with benefit in idiopathic narcolepsy. *Cataplexy*[4] is the term given to a condition allied to, and very frequently associated with narcolepsy, in which the patient as a result of some emotion—amusement, anger, fear, embarrassment or surprise—is seized with complete muscular relaxation and weakness. The attack is brief, lasting for a few seconds, or for a minute or two at the most. Consciousness is not lost but the muscles are completely toneless and powerless for the time, and if the attack supervenes while the subject is standing his knees fail him and he sinks to the ground. The deep reflexes are lost. A somewhat similar situation may develop in a normal person who may become "weak with laughter," be "struck all of a heap," or "transfixed" when surprised or shocked. Or his jaw may "drop" when confronted with some unexpected occurrence. Cataplexy is regarded as an exaggeration of this normal tendency, just as narcolepsy is an intensification of the desire of many normal persons to drop into a doze under certain circumstances. Mirth is especially likely to precipitate a cataplectic attack. One victim reported by Adie remarked, "At the scout's camp the boys used to amuse themselves by making me laugh and then running away leaving me helpless on the ground." Though narcolepsy occurs without cataplexy the converse is extremely rare. This association of the two conditions at once suggests a common pathogenesis, but the muscular atonicity characterizing the cataplectic attack cannot be explained upon any physiological basis. An interesting specula-

---

[2] von Bonin speaks of a reverberating circuit—hypothalamus (mammillary body) to anterior thalamic nuclei *via* mammillo-thalamic tract; thence to anterior part of cingular gyrus; thence to cornu Ammonis, and finally back to the mammillary body through the fornix and fimbria.

[3] See Fulton and Bremer.

[4] This should not be confused with catalepsy, an entirely different condition.

tion has been made by Wilson, who compares the attacks to the defense reaction of certain animals whereby they fall into immobility when frightened, and suggests for them a certain biological significance, namely, that they are the relic of a primitive reaction uncovered by disease.

REFERENCES

BAILEY, P. The precentral motor cortex, Ed. 2, p. 227. Edited by P. C. Bucy, Univ. of Ill. Press, Urbana, Ill., 1949.

BARD, P. Am. J. Physiol., 1928, **84**, 490.

BARD, P., Psychol. Rev., 1934, **41**, 309.

BARD, P. AND MOUNTCASTLE, V. B. A. Res. Nerv. & Ment. Dis., 1948, **27**, 362.

BEATTIE, J. Canad. M. A. J., 1932, **26**, 278.

BEATTIE, J., BROW, G. R. AND LONG, C. N. H. Proc. Roy. Soc., London, Ser. B, 1930, **106**, 253.

BRONK, D. W. AND ASSOCIATES. Am. J. Physiol., 1936, **116**, 15.

BUCY, P. C., AND FULTON, J. F. Brain, 1933, **56**, 318.

BUCY, P. C. J. Neuropath. & Exper. Neurol., 1942. **1**, 224.

COOPER, I. S. Clinical results and follow-up studies in a personal series of 300 operations for parkinsonism. St. Barnabas Symposium on Surgical Therapy of Extrapyramidal Disorders, p. 3, 1956.

DUSSER DE BARENNE, J. G. AND SAGER, O. Arch. Neurol. & Phsyciat., 1937 **38**, 913.

FOERSTER, O. Ztschr. ges. Neurol. u. Psychiat., 1921, **73**, 1–169.

GLEES, P. Brain, 1945, **68**, 331.

GUIOT, G. Semaine d. hôp. Paris, 1957, **33**, 3711.

HARMON, P. J. AND CARPENTER, M. B. J. Comp. Neurol., 1950, **93**, 125.

HESS, W. R. Lancet, 1932, **2**, 1199; 1259.

KABAT, H., ANSON, B. J. AND MAGOUN, H. W. Am. J. Physiol., 1935, **113**, 74.

KARPLUS, J. P. AND KREIDL, A. Pflüger's Arch. ges. Physiol., 1911, **143**, 109; 1927, **215**, 667.

METTLER, F. A. J. Neuropath. & Exper. Neurol., 1955, **14**, 115.

NARABAYASHI, H. Arch. Neurol. & Psychiat., 1956, **75**, 36.

POLLOCK, L. J. AND DAVIS, L. Arch. Neurol. & Psychiat., 1930, **23**, 303.

RANSON, S. W. AND RANSON, M. Arch. Neurol. & Psychiat., 1939, **42**, 1059.

RANSON, S. W., RANSON, S. W., JR. AND RANSON, M. Arch. Neurol. & Psychiat., 1941, **46**, 230.

RICHTER, R. J. Neuropath. & Exper. Neurol., 1945, **4**, 324.

RIOCH, D. M. Psychiatry, 1940, **3**, 119.

STERN, K. Brain, 1936, **61**, 284.

SWANSON, H. S. Personal communication.

TOWER, S. S. Brain, 1940, **63**, 36–90.

TRAVIS, A. M. AND WOOLSEY, C. N. Am. J. Phys. Med., 1956, **35**, 273–310.

VERHAART, W. J. C. AND KENNARD, M. A. J. Anat., 1940, **74**, 239.

WALKER, A. E. AND BOTTERELL, E. H. Brain, 1937, **60**, 329–353.

WALKER, A. E. Acta psychiat. et neurol., 1949, **24**, 723.

WALKER, A. E. J. Nerv. & Ment. Dis., 1952, **116**, 766.

WALSHE, F. M. R. Brain, 1924, **47**, 159.

WHITE, J. C. Personal communication.

WOOLSEY, C. N. AND BARD, P. Fed. Proc., 1943, **2**, 55.

Monographs and Reviews

ARIENS KAPPERS, C. U. The evolution of the nervous system in invertebrates, vertebrates and man. Erven F. Bohn, Haarlem, The Netherlands, 1929.

BARD, P. A. Res. Nerv. & Ment. Dis., 1930, **9**, 67.

BARD, P. AND MACHT, M. B. Neurological basis of behaviour, p. 55. Edited by G. E. W. Wolstenholme and C. M. O'Connor. Little, Brown and Co., Boston, 1958.

BRODAL, A. Neurological anatomy in relation to clinical medicine. Oxford Univ. Press, London, 1948.

BUCY, P. C., (Ed.) The precentral motor cortex. Univ. Illinois Press, 1959.

CUSHING, H. W. Papers relating to the pituitary body, hypothalamus and parasympathetic nervous system. Charles C Thomas, Springfield, Ill., 1932.

DANIELS, L. E. Medicine, 1934, **13**, 1.

HEAD, H. Studies in neurology, Vol. II. Frowde, London, 1920.

MAGOUN, H. W. AND RHINES, R. Spasticity: the stretch reflex and extrapyramidal systems. Chas. C Thomas, Springfield, Ill., 1947.

RADEMAKER, G. G. Die Bedeutung der roten Kerne und des übrigen Mittelhirns für Muskeltonus, Körperstellung und Labyrinthreflexe. J. Springer, Berlin, 1926.

WALKER, A. E. The primate thalamus. Chicago Univ. Press, Chicago, 1938.

WILSON, S. A. K. Brain, 1928, **51**, 63.

WILSON, S. A. K. Modern problems in neurology. Arnold, London, 1928.

CHAPTER 8

The Cerebral Cortex and Higher Functions

Minute Structure of the Cortex

The human cerebral cortex (or *pallium*) has a total area of about 220,000 sq. mm.; not more than a third of this lies upon the free surface or crown of the convolutions. The remaining two-thirds of the gray mantle of the cerebrum occupy the walls of the sulci. The total number of nerve cells in the human cerebral cortex has been estimated at around 7×10^9. The number of fibers received from and projected to lower levels of the nervous system is in the neighborhood of 200 million. Added to these are fibers, many times more, which connect cells within the cortex (association fibers). On the basis of cellular structure the major part of the cortical gray matter is divisible into *six layers* or *laminae*. But these layers do not show identical histological appearances throughout the extent of the cortex. Characteristic differences in the depth of the individual layers and in their cellular components are found in the various regions. The six layers from the surface inwards with a general description of their cellular features as given by Economo[1] follows (see fig. 8.1).

I. MOLECULAR (OR PLEXIFORM LAYER). In this, the most superficial layer, the terminal filaments of numerous dendrites from cells of deeper layers, as well as from the axons of Martinotti cells form a dense felted network. Its cells are sparse; they are small (4 to 6μ) and pear-shaped or fusiform.

II. EXTERNAL GRANULAR LAYER consists of large numbers of small round, polygonal or triangular cells closely packed together. Their afferent processes pass into the overlying layer; their axons end mainly in deeper layers, but some enter the white substance of the hemispheres.

III. PYRAMIDAL CELL LAYER. Medium-sized pyramidal cells are contained in the outer part of this layer; pyramidal cells of larger size and more sparsely distributed are present in the deeper part. It is customary, therefore, to subdivide this layer into an outer and an inner portion; Campbell refers to them as separate layers.

IV. INTERNAL GRANULAR LAYER resembles the external granular layer in being composed of

closely packed masses of small stellate cells, but unlike the outer granular layer it is rich in nerve fibers. This layer contains many horizontal fibers which show as a white stripe, or band known as the outer stripe or line of Baillarger, which is especially well marked in the calcarine cortex, but in this situation it is more usually referred to as the line of Vicq d'Azyr or of Gennari.

V. GANGLIONIC LAYER (or internal pyramidal layer) consists of pyramidal cells of graded sizes. This layer is particularly well-developed in the precentral (motor) cortex where giant pyramidal cells (Betz) are conspicuous. It contains, also, cells of Martinotti; these cells are peculiar in that their axons pass *outwards* toward the surface of the cortex and arborize in their own layer, or in overlying layers. Some of these cells can be found in nearly all layers of the cortex. Its deeper strata contain a dense network of fibers which forms the inner line of Baillarger.

VI. FUSIFORM CELL LAYER, in contact with the white matter, is composed of closely packed small spindle-shaped cells with their long diameters perpendicular. Other cells are also present in this layer.

It should be emphasized that the foregoing is no more than a general description of the histological structure of the cortex and that marked regional differences exist. Even the number of layers itself is not a feature common to the entire cortex. In man one-twelfth of the cortical area shows fewer than six layers (typically three); this portion, which is called the allocortex or archipallium comprises the cortex of the olfactory lobe (i.e., the pyriform area and the hippocampal, supracallosal and olfactory gyri, etc.). The six-layered cortex, which in man constitutes the remaining eleven-twelfths, but which in lower mammals is a much smaller fraction of the whole, is called the *isocortex* or *neopallium*.

The greater part of the human laminated cortex shows the cytoarchitectural features described above, and is therefore sometimes referred to as the *homotypical* cortex. In other more restricted areas, the cortex departs from the typical cytological appearance, chiefly in the preponderances of the small granular cells or of the pyramidal elements, and is called *heterotypical*. In areas in

---

[1] For a detailed description, Bucy, or the earlier works of Campbell and of Bolton, should be consulted.

which the internal granular layer is absent or practically so and in which pyramidal cells predominate, the cortex is called *agranular*, and when the small granulelike cells form a prominent internal granular layer with few pyramidal cells, it is called the *granular* cortex. The agranular cortex is thicker than the granular which is particularly thin at the frontal and occipital poles of the hemispheres.

The cortex of the precentral region (areas 4 and 6) is of the agranular type. The granular layers (II and IV) are shallow, being encroached upon by the expansion of the pyramidal layers III and V. In the deep part of layer V of area 4 (the area gigantopyramidalis) are situated the characteristic giant cells of Betz (60 to 80 microns in their greatest diameters) (see below). These cells contribute fibers to the corticospinal tracts (ch. 6). In area 6 in front of area 4 the granular layers are also inconspicuous but the large cells of Betz are absent.

In the cortex of the walls of, and surrounding the calcarine fissure—the *area striata* or *visual area*—the outer and inner granular layers (II and IV) are expanded at the expense of the pyramidal layers (III and V). This very finely *granular* type of cortex, also called from its "dusty" appearance under the microscope the *koniocortex*, is characteristic of sensory areas. It is present, though to a less fully specialized degree than in the visual cortex, in the postcentral gyrus (somesthetic area) and in Heschl's gyrus (auditory cortex, p. 176).

Upon gross examination of a section of the brain two lighter bands can be seen in the cortex against the darker gray matter. These are produced by nerve fibers running parallel to the surface of the convolutions. They are known respectively as the outer (already mentioned) and inner bands of Baillarger. In the visual area the outer band is broad and prominent and is usually referred to in this part of the cortex as the band of Vicq d'Azyr or of Gennari, who had described it previously. The inner band is less dense than the outer, particularly in this area.

The Electrical Activity of the Cortex

Electrical activity in the nervous system is of two types, *evoked* or *spontaneous*. *Evoked* activity is elicited by applying an appropriate stimulus to a sense organ or to the nervous system itself and recording the resultant electrical activity with either a gross electrode or a microelectrode. Examples of such activity are shown in fig. 8.2.

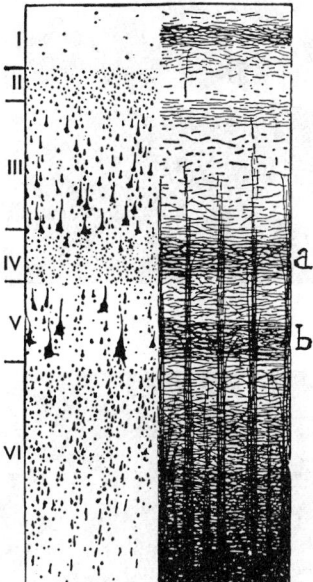

FIG. 8.1. Showing layers of area 4 of human cerebral cortex (agranular); *left*, cell-bodies, Nissl stain; *right*, nerve fibers, Weigert stain; a, outer band of Baillarger; b, inner band of Baillarger. Note the large cells of Betz in the fifth layer. (After Brodmann.)

Spontaneous activity is that electrical activity which is present although the animal is not being stimulated. An example of spontaneous activity is the electroencephalogram, which will be described in more detail later in this chapter. Examples of spontaneous activity are also shown in fig. 8.2. Evoked and spontaneous activity have been subdivided according to whether the activity represents the "spike" like action potential of the neuron recorded with a microelectrode or a sum of the longer lasting post synaptic potentials described in chapter 2.

The action potential of a neuron in the central nervous system may be recorded by one of two methods: extracellular recording or intracellular recording. *Extracellular* recording is accomplished with metal wires which have been electrolytically sharpened to a tip diameter of about 3–5 μ and insulated so that the tip is exposed for only a small distance: glass micropipettes filled with a conducting medium are also used. The electrode must then be carefully inserted into the nervous system with a micromanipulator so as to come close to the neuron without damaging it. The action potential recorded may be derived from the soma or from the axon. It is thought that the action potential of the soma has a longer duration (greater than 1 msec.) than the action potential

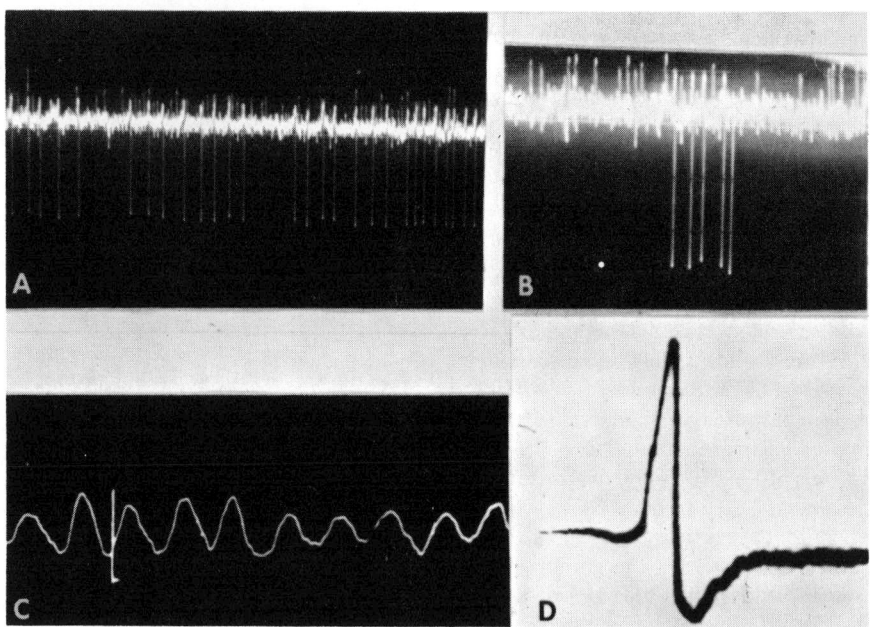

FIG. 8.2. Examples of spontaneous and evoked cortical activity

A. Spontaneous single unit action potentials recorded from cerebellar cortex with a microelectrode. The "spikes" represent the action potentials of a single neuron.

B. Evoked single unit action potentials recorded from primary auditory cortex with a microelectrode. The auditory stimulus (a click) was presented at the point in time represented by the dot. The time delay between stimulus presentation and response represents the latency of the cortical response.

C. Spontaneous slow wave activity recorded from the surface of the scalp with a gross electrode (the electroencephalogram). The subject was awake and relaxed with eyes closed. The waves have a frequency of about 10 per sec.—the alpha rhythm.

D. Evoked slow wave activity recorded from the surface of the primary auditory cortex with a gross electrode. The auditory stimulus was applied at the start of the trace.

of the axon. *Intracellular* recording is accomplished with electrodes made of glass micropipettes in which the tip has been drawn down to a fraction of a micron in diameter. Such electrodes can penetrate a single cell without producing any apparent damage and can record not only the action potential but also the resting potential. Both extracellular and intracellular electrodes can record post synaptic potentials. With an intracellular electrode the post synaptic potentials are derived from the cell penetrated. With an extracellular electrode, be it a microelectrode or a large "gross" electrode, the post synaptic potentials recorded are considered to be largely composed of the sum of the post synaptic potentials of many cells. It is this sum of post synaptic potentials of many cells that yields the electroencephalogram and the slow wave evoked responses recorded from the nervous system in response to stimulation.

Localization of Function in the Cerebral Cortex

Campbell mapped the cortex into 20 areas which could be differentiated on the basis of their cytoarchitectural characters. This number was raised to 47 by Brodmann, and subsequent workers (Vogts) have subdivided these again to make a total of 200.[2] Bailey and von Bonin (1951) in a careful reappraisal of the matter of the subdivision of the cerebral cortex on the basis of cytoarchitectonic studies concluded that most of the divisions of the cortex which had been devised previously were unsupportable. They were able to divide the cerebral cortex into the allocortex of the hippocampal region and the pyriform lobe, the agranular cortex of the precentral region and the anterior limbic area, the koniocortex of the primary sensory areas (the somesthetic areas of the postcentral gyrus, the visual cortex of the calcarine area, and the auditory cortex of Heschl's convolution on the superior surface of the first temporal gyrus), and the eulaminate cortex of most of the remainder of the mantle of the cerebral hemisphere.

Differences, most of them minor, within this broad outline were demonstrable. Thus in the

[2] The microscopical study of the cortex and mapping it into areas according to the cytological characteristics is called *cytoarchitectonics*.

precentral agranular cortex there are two areas—the area gigantopyramidalis (area 4) which lies just in front of the central fissure and contains the large cells of Betz, and the other which Brodmann designated area 6 and which lies immediately in front of area 4 and is devoid of gigantic pyramidal cells. The agranular cortex of the anterior limbic area partakes of some of the characteristics of the allocortex. The koniocortex of the visual area is more complex than that of the somesthetic and auditory areas and there are minor variations in different parts of the eulaminate cortex which need not concern us here. In the following discussion we shall refer to the numerically designated areas described by Brodmann as they are well established in neurological literature and teaching, but his finer subdivisions will not be dwelt upon.

The Frontal Lobe

The Precentral Cortex, Areas 4, 6, 8 and 44

Area 4 is a tapering strip of agranular cortex lying with its wider end at the upper border of the hemisphere, in front of the central fissure (Rolandic), and occupying the posterior part of the precentral convolution. A good part of this area is buried, for it covers the anterior wall of the central fissure. It also turns over the upper border of the hemisphere and extends down the mesial aspect as far as the cingulate sulcus. Area 4 is a center for movement. It gives origin to an important part of the corticospinal tracts, and also projects to the pons (frontopontine tract), corpus striatum, red nucleus, thalamus and the subthalamus. Areas 4 and 6 are also connected by intracortical fibers. The muscles of the various

parts of the body are represented in this area on the mesial and the lateral surfaces, in an order which is, in general, the inverse of that in the body itself, namely, toes, ankle, knee, hip, trunk, shoulder, arm, elbow, wrist, hand, fingers, brow, eyes, face, larynx, jaw and tongue (fig. 8.3). The parts of the face are not inverted. By suitable electrical stimulation of different parts of this area, movements of muscles on the opposite side of the body can be evoked.

The careful studies of Woolsey (on the monkey) suggest that the distal parts of the extremities, i.e., the hands and feet, are represented near the central fissure while the more proximal joints, i.e., shoulders and hips, and the trunk, are represented somewhat more anteriorly. With suitably controlled stimuli discrete movements limited to a small part of the extremity or even to a single muscle may be elicited. Although most of the control of the precentral cortex over the muscular activities of the body are exerted contralaterally, there is also some control over muscles on the same side of the body. This ipsilateral innervation is greater in the proximal joints of the extremities than in the distal parts and is greater in the lower than in the upper extremity. Furthermore, this ipsilateral innervation by the precentral motor cortex is greater in monkeys than in man. Electrical stimulation of the cerebral cortex, although a valuable tool for the study of cortical activity, is a poor substitute for normal physiological activity. The range and extent of movement produced by such stimulation represents but a small fraction of the motor activity which the intact cerebral cortex is able to produce under normal circumstances. A study

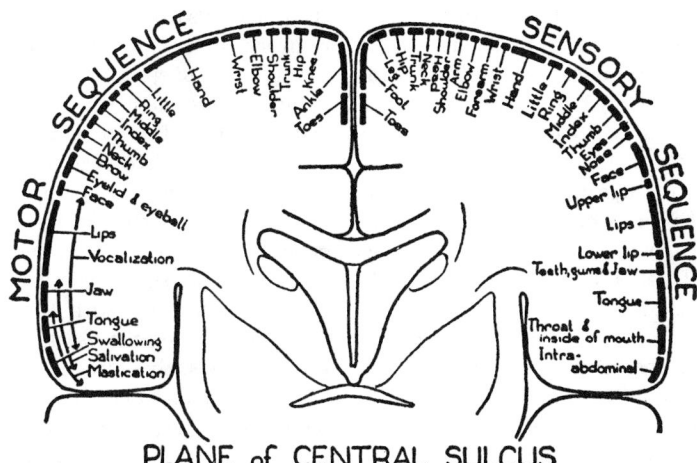

Fig. 8.3. Coronal section through the hemispheres to show the motor and sensory representations in the cerebral cortex. (From Rasmussen and Penfield.)

(Chang et al., 1947) in which movements of single muscles were measured indicates that individual muscles are represented in the cortex. The action of these muscles is presumably then integrated during voluntary movement through intracortical connections. Some controversy with this view still exists since alteration of the parameters of the electrical stimulus will influence the extent of muscles excited as well as the nature of the movement produced. The movements which are induced by electrical stimulation are crude and limited compared with the well co-ordinated, smoothly executed movements of the normal animal. One must never fall into the error of concluding that the results of electrical stimulation are a measure of the extent or nature of the normal activity of the areas stimulated.

Penfield and Welch, and Woolsey and his associates have demonstrated a *supplementary motor area* lying on the medial surface of the hemisphere in both man and monkey. This area lies anteriorly and ventrally to the primary motor area described above. In it the entire body is again represented. The head and upper extremity are represented farther forward and closer to the edge of the hemisphere while the lower extremity is represented more posteriorly and nearer to the corpus callosum. The threshold of this supplementary motor area is somewhat higher than that of the primary motor area which lies immediately anterior to the central fissure. The function of this supplementary area has not yet been well defined.

The corticospinal fibers arise from the precentral gyrus (area 4 in the monkey) and from area 6. Both of these areas also give rise to fibers which descend directly or indirectly to subcortical centers (e.g., basal ganglia, thalamus, reticular formation, pontine nuclei, etc.). Therefore, destructive lesions of area 4 or area 6 are not comparable to an isolated lesion of either the corticospinal or the multisynaptic motor pathways which pass through the subcortical nuclei. Thus a lesion of areas 4 or 6 is not comparable to a section of the corticospinal fibers in the cerebral peduncle or the medullary pyramid; neither will a cortical lesion give rise to a clinical picture typical of destruction of the motor pathways through the basal ganglia, etc.

Destructive lesions of the various parts of the precentral motor cortex have certain important characteristics. If one bilaterally removes the excitable motor cortex (the sigmoid gyrus) from both hemispheres of a dog or cat, or even

if all the cerebral cortex is removed, there is some interference with motor activity, especially with certain stereotyped reactions, such as the hopping and placing reactions, but the animal is not paralyzed. He can still sit, stand, walk or run in a very creditable manner.

If the precentral motor cortex is removed from both hemispheres of a monkey, the loss is somewhat more severe, but over a period of months considerable recovery is seen to the point that, although movements are stiff, visually controlled purposive movement can take place. There is, however, permanent loss of what has been termed by Denny-Brown the "instinctive tactile grasping reaction." This reaction is described as an exploratory palpation which brings an object stimulating light touch into the palm or sole followed by "very facile" grasping. Naturally there has not been an extension of these experimental studies to man, but evidence from patients with lesions resulting from vascular accident, surgery, or head wounds indicates that although the ultimate deficit is clearly greater in man than in monkey, a certain amount of recovery of function is possible. This recovery is due, in part, to a reorganization of remaining intact cortex. Removal of parietal (areas 3, 1, 2, 5, 7) or frontal (areas 9–12) cortex in monkeys who had undergone an earlier ablation of areas 4 and 6 increases the pre-existing motor deficit. After recovery from localized lesions in hand area 4, Glees and Cole (1950) were able to produce hand movements by stimulating an adjacent portion of area 4 which had not previously yielded hand movements. However, the ability of totally decorticate cats to move quite well within a short time after surgery indicates that there may also be a subcortical participation in recovery of function. Evidence from studies of the growth of processes of CNS neurons in tissue culture and also demonstration (Scott and Liu, 1964) of the growth of neuronal processes in the CNS in vivo suggests that the neuronal reorganization implied by recovery of function takes place largely by growth of neuronal processes in the central nervous system. In general, studies show that the extent of recovery of function decreases with age and a higher position on the phylogenetic scale. Recovery increases with post operative care and training and time.

In the cat and dog the *unilateral* removal of the motor cortex, or even the removal of all the cortex from one cerebral hemisphere, causes little motor disturbance. In the monkey there is an initial flaccid paralysis of the contralateral limbs. Within a short time the animal sits, stands, runs and hops about in his cage from one wall to another and back and forth on his trapeze. The extremities contralateral to the hemidecortication are more awkward than the normal ones. In jumping the animal misses the bars of his cage occasionally with the involved digits, and often rests on the backs of the fingers or toes rather than on the palmar and volar surfaces as the normal animal does. So long as his normal extremities are available he seldom uses the involved ones to pick up food, but he can do so in case of necessity. In other words, although the contralateral extremities are not normal, they are far from being paralyzed. Naturally one asks what is the source of the innervation of these extremities. There can be little doubt that it is from the intact ipsilateral cerebral hemisphere, for if it is removed, the animal not only becomes paralyzed in the extremities contralateral to it but in those affected by the original decortication as well. In other words, removal of the cortex from the remaining hemisphere results in a severe paralysis of all four extremities. There are other evidences that the precentral motor cortex is capable of ipsilateral innervation. Homes and May, and later Bucy and Fulton presented definite evidence that ipsilateral movements, particularly in the lower extremity and particularly in the more proximal joints could be produced by electrical stimulation of the precentral motor cortex.

In man the situation is similar but not identical. If the precentral motor cortex is removed from one hemisphere the contralateral extremities are incapacitated but not completely paralyzed. In some cases a slow and rather weak simultaneous flexion of all the digits of the hand can be produced voluntarily. Movements at the shoulder and elbow and at the hip and knee are much fuller and stronger. In the upper extremity the flexor movements tend to be better, whereas in the lower extremity extension at both the hip and knee is more extensive and stronger than flexion. Such movements in the upper extremity are less than in the lower, but this does not account for all of the differences from the standpoint of usefulness. The upper extremity is primarily a prehensile one, designed to bring things to the individual or to pull him to them. Thus a condition in which the fingers, hand and wrist are severely incapacitated with only movements at the elbow and shoulder possible does not result in a useful extremity. On the other hand, the lower extremity is used for standing and walking. It is primarily a supporting pillar. The fact that the toes and foot can not be moved is of relatively little importance while the ability to move the extremity at the knee and hip, especially at the latter, enables the patient with his his precentral motor cortex destroyed or its pathways severed to walk in a very useful fashion, even though he limps and has to circumduct the involved foot with each step. Evidence is not available to prove the source of the innervation which accounts for the remaining muscular activity in the involved extremities in man, but reasoning by analogy from lower animals it would seem most likely that it is largely from the ipsilateral cerebral hemisphere. The few bits of evidence available to us support this view. For instance, in a few human cases in which the upper part of the precentral motor cortex has been destroyed bilaterally by a tumor or by injury, both legs have been paralyzed. If the movement in the lower extremities seen in hemiplegics were produced by the subcortical centers, then such a paraplegia would not be expected as the result of purely cortical lesions. Furthermore, Bates has been able to produce ipsilateral movements by electrical stimulation of the medial surface of the cerebral hemisphere in man.

As noted above there are differences in function between the various parts of the precentral motor cortex. Lesions of area 4 produce more severe motor deficiencies than do lesions of area 6, while lesions of both together produce the most severe deficiency. However, either area 4 or area 6 alone in one hemisphere of the monkey, all other parts of the precentral motor cortices having been removed, is able to produce useful movements in all four extremities. This is evidence of the presence of ipsilateral as well as contralateral motor innervation from both area 4 and area 6, and is also evidence that useful movements can be produced over the multisynaptic neuronal pathways from the precentral motor cortex through the various subcortical centers (the extra-pyramidal pathways) as well as over the corticospinal tract direct from the precentral and postcentral gyrus to the spinal cord. Other evidence in confirmation of this fact is the demonstration that useful voluntary movement is still possible in the monkey after the medullary pyramids have been divided (Tower, 1940) and in man after the central portion of the cerebral peduncle has been cut (Bucy, 1957).

Alteration in only one reflex can be attributed to destruction of the corticospinal tract from the precentral gyrus. If the "foot" area in the uppermost part of area 4 on the medial surface of the hemisphere is destroyed or if the corticospinal fibers to the muscles of the great toe are divided it will become possible to elicit the sign of Babinski. Destruction of other parts of the precentral region or section of other corticospinal fibers, of course, does not have such an effect. Furthermore, this reflex can only appear if the peripheral mechanism is intact. Thus the necessary anterior horn cells, anterior spinal roots, peripheral nerves, and muscles must be present and functioning and the great toe and its joints must be in condition to respond properly if the reflex is to appear.

Lesions of area 6, in contrast with those of area 4, give rise to an awkwardness in the performance of skilled acts, with little loss of strength, spasticity and increase in the tendon reflexes, forced grasping and groping and, in some cases, disturbances in autonomic functions.

Irritative lesions involving area 4 give rise to localized clonic convulsive seizures. The convulsive movement usually begins focally in some part of the body depending upon which part of area 4 is irritated. There may be a localized twitching of the face, or of one or more fingers, or of the foot or of the leg. This convulsive movement may remain localized or it may spread to neighboring parts of the body or even become generalized. This "march" of the convulsive involvement is typical of what is known as a Jacksonian epileptic seizure and is dependent upon a spread of the irritation in the motor cortex. A convulsive seizure produced by irritation of area 6 is characterized by what Foerster termed an adversive seizure. These begin with a turning of the head and eyes and often of the body toward the side opposite the involved cerebral cortex. Bucy and Pribram described a case in which a tumor in the "face" area of the precentral motor cortex was associated with localized convulsions of the contralateral side of the face and with localized sweating of that side of the face and to a lesser extent of the upper extremity. Such paroxysmal outbursts of autonomic activity are far from common but indicate the relationship of this part of the cerebral cortex to vegetative functions.

There is other definite evidence that the precentral motor cortex also exerts some control over various visceral and vascular activities, such as heart rate, vasomotor activities, gastrointestinal motility, perspiration. There is also evidence, at least in the cat, that these activities are also controlled in some measure by the cortex on the mesial surface of the hemisphere, and that of the orbital surface of the frontal lobe.

Destruction of the precentral motor cortex (areas 4 and 6) results in a spastic hemiplegia. However, it is not to be assumed that this condition is identical with the spastic paralysis which results from lesions at lower levels. The spasticity resulting from lesions of the internal capsule is in general greater than that seen with cortical lesions. In all probability this is due at least in part to some destruction in the basal ganglia, which is common with such lesions, as well as the destruction of the fibers descending from the precentral motor cortex. In any event the *pattern* of the increased tone is similar with hemiplegias of both cortical and capsular origin, i.e., the increase in tone in the upper extremity is in the flexor muscles. With severe lesions at the mesencephalic level it is common to see spasticity even greater than is commonly seen with capsular or cortical lesions but the pattern in both the upper and lower extremities is an extensor one. If the lesion is in the spinal cord, one may see either a paralysis with very severe extensor rigidity or a paraplegia in flexion, as has been discussed elsewhere.

Grasping Movements and Tonic Innervation

Involvement of the anterior part of the precentral motor cortex, i.e., of area 6, is not uncommonly associated with a group of phenomena to which various terms have been applied, e.g., "forced grasping and groping", "grasp reflex", "tonic innervation" and so forth. A description of these phenomena follows.

(1) Merely touching the skin between the finger and thumb with a pencil results in slow flexion of the fingers. If the stimulating agent is withdrawn gently without disturbing the position of the patient's fingers no tightening of the grasp results but his hand and arm sometimes move through space (grope) in the direction of the moving object, as if drawn by a magnet.

(2) *Grasp reflex.* When an object is placed in the involved hand of the patient the fingers close slowly and gently around it, but any attempt made by the observer to withdraw the object often results in its being grasped more firmly. Nevertheless, when the patient clenches his empty fist he can relax the fingers again without difficulty.

(3) Any attempt to bend the arm or leg is met by an active resistance exerted by the antagonistic (stretched) muscles; this differs from the resist-

ance offered by the ordinary spastic limb in that there is no sudden giving way with a "clasp-knife effect".

Walshe and Robertson have made a critical study of these phenomena and find that they are separable into two distinct components: (a) the *grasp movement* and (b) *tonic innervation.*

The *gentle* grasp and the groping movements just described (see (1) above) are voluntary and not reflex acts. That is to say, though they are automatic in nature and are taken to indicate deterioration of the psychomotor functions, the patient can prevent their occurrence if asked to do so. They disappear in stupor or in coma. The gentle grasping movement follows tactile stimuli alone or visual and tactile stimuli acting together. The groping movements can be elicited by visual stimuli alone but not by tactile stimuli alone.

Tonic innervation (see (3) above) is a stretch reflex (ch. 5). The *strong* grasp (2) which results when an attempt is made to remove an object from the hand is simply one phase—an incident— of this reflex. It is quite distinct from the gentle grasp movement. It results from the passive stretching of the flexor muscles of the fingers caused by the observer's attempt to extricate the object. The patient cannot relax the grasp and release the grasped object. It occurs in the unconscious patient. The grasp reflex is most pronounced when the patient is on his side and the affected arm uppermost (Fulton).

Richter and Hines produced the "tonic grasp reflex" in adult monkeys by removal of area 6. Excision of the motor areas or the prefrontal areas from both hemispheres did not cause the effect. A similar reflex is present in normal infants, Robinson showing that in these it is sufficiently strong to suspend the body from a bar for 2 minutes. A grasping reflex has also been described for the foot in lesions of area 6; it occurs in the normal infant up to the end of the first year and is said to occur in 50 per cent of Mongolian idiots. It is elicited by stroking the sole.

Area 8 is called the *frontal eye field.* It lies in front of area 6. Stimulation of the cortex here causes a conjugate movement of the eyes to the opposite side, opening and closing of the eyelids, and sometimes dilation of the pupils and lacrymation. No visual hallucinations occur in man, but an epileptiform seizure may be provoked which spreads to the adversive field (area 6).[3]

[3] Stimulation of area 8 in man also causes conjugate deviation of the eyes and turning of the head to the opposite side.

Ablation of area 8 of one side in monkeys or involvement of this area or its projection fibers in man causes the eyes to be turned up toward the side of the lesion, and paralysis of the conjugate eye movement. These effects are temporary. The animal in walking circles toward the side of the lesion. No abnormalities are observed in the pupils or in the movements of the lids. This area receives fibers from the dorsomedial nucleus of the thalamus, through which it is connected with the hypothalamus. It also connects by long association tracts, both afferent and efferent, with the occipital lobe (visual area, 18) and with the tegmentum of the midbrain (probably with the oculomotor nuclei).[4]

Area 44 in the region of the posterior part of the frontal operculum in the *dominant hemisphere* (which is the left in right-handed persons) is the motor area for speech (Broca's area). Stimulation of this area in conscious patients causes their speech to be abruptly arrested.

PREFRONTAL OR ORBITOFRONTAL REGION

The prefrontal region embraces the part of the frontal lobe in front of areas 8 and 44, but it includes the orbital as well as the lateral aspect of the lobe, and for this reason is also known as the orbitofrontal region. It was divided by Brodmann into several different areas (9, 10, 11, 12, 13 and 14) but Bailey and von Bonin do not believe that such subdivision of this area is supportable by a careful study of the cytoarchitecture. These areas were once thought to be inexcitable, and were therefore referred to as "silent" or association areas. But upon stimulation by a suitable electric current having pulses of low frequency, autonomic, respiratory, circulatory, renal, and gastrointestinal responses can be elicited. After bilateral removal of these areas the blood pressure is reduced, gastric secretion suppressed, and gastrointestinal movements increased. In man, suffering from intractable pain is relieved. These areas receive important fibers from the dorsomedial nucleus of the thalamus, which in turn

[4] Unilateral ablation of this area in monkeys is followed by a visual defect in the form of failure to recognize objects in the opposite homonymous halves of the visual fields—*a pseudohemianopia*— results. When area 8 is destroyed on both sides the animal does not react in a normal manner to visual stimuli. It may appear to be blind for it walks into or stumbles over obstructions in its path, and tends to stare straight ahead with an immobile "wooden" expression (see Kennard and Ectors). Yet, an animal will follow an object with its eyes and will seize anything offered to it though failing, apparently, to recognize it or to understand what to do with it.

receives impulses from the hypothalamus. These orbitofrontal areas, especially those of the orbital surface, are also closely associated with emotional feeling.

Area 24, anterior part of the cingular gyrus on the mesial aspect of the hemisphere, is a powerful suppressor area. Various autonomic responses follow stimulation of this area including pupillary dilation, pilo-erection, acceleration of the heart, and a fall in blood pressure. Arrest of respiration in expiration also results.

The prefrontal areas have extensive subcortical and cortical connections (see Fig. 8.4). Areas from 9 to 12 in the monkey receive fibers from the dorsomedial nucleus of the thalamus. Fibers ascending to the orbital areas 11 and 12 from this nucleus have also been demonstrated in man from a study of retrograde degeneration in the nucleus following section of white matter. The anterior nucleus of the thalamus also sends fibers to the prefrontal area (area 23), and both dorsomedial and anterior

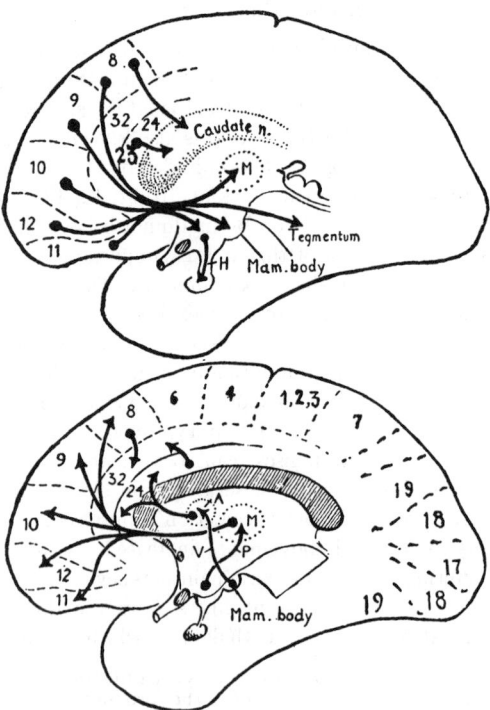

FIG. 8.4. Connections of prefrontal areas. (After Le Gros Clark, with minor additions). *Lower sketch,* right cerebral hemisphere from the medial aspect, showing afferent connections; A, anterior nucleus of the thalamus; M, dorsomedial nucleus of the thalamus; P, periventricular system of fibers ascending from the hypothalamus to the thalamus; v, mammillothalamic tract of Vicq D'Azyr. *Upper sketch,* efferent connections; M, dorsomedial nucleus of the thalamus; H, hypothalamicohypophyseal tract.

thalamic nuclei receive fibers from the hypothalamus. Different zones of the dorsomedial nucleus of the thalamus project differentially to the regions of prefrontal cortex. Pars paralamellaris projects to area 8, pars parvocellularis to area 9, and pars magnocellularis to the orbital region. In addition, prefrontal areas receive fibers either directly or indirectly from the amygdala, septal nuclei and tegmentum.

The projections of the prefrontal region have recently been summarized by Nauta (1964). Nauta describes projections of the prefrontal region to the cingulate gyrus and pre subiculum via the cingulum; via the uncinate bundle to the temporal lobe and, after synapsing here, to the amygdala. There are also projections to the head of the caudate nucleus, putamen, hypothalamus, intralaminar and dorsomedial nuclei of the thalamus, subthalamus, pons and tegmentum. Many of these structures form part of the Papez circuit which is concerned with the mediation of emotional behavior.

Unilateral or bilateral removal of the *prefrontal area* does not cause paralysis either in the monkey or in man. Unilateral removal of the human prefrontal area produces a definite if rather subtle alteration in mental processes. Some loss of initiative and mental alertness are the most outstanding results of the operation. Memory, judgment and intellect often show little or no deterioration. Removal of the prefrontal area of the dominant hemisphere (i.e., the left in right-handed and the right in left-handed persons) is sometimes thought to produce somewhat greater alterations in character or intellect than does a similar operation upon the nondominant side. Even the bilateral excision of prefrontal areas is followed by a surprisingly moderate mental defect, so far as superficial observation and examinations are concerned. However, we must not be misled by such inadequate observations. The fact that the patient following a unilateral or even a bilateral prefrontal lobectomy appears normal, functions as a normal individual during casual associations, or passes the usual psychometric tests with flying colors does not mean that the frontal lobes are without important functions so far as mental activity and behavior are concerned. Halstead has discussed this matter in detail and has developed tests which indicate with amazing accuracy the damage to the frontal lobes. These tests have been elaborated into a battery of very objective tests, the results of which give an impairment index of the functions of the frontal lobes. Damage to other parts of the brain does not give rise to comparable changes in these tests. Subcortical lesions involving the white matter of the frontal lobes do not disturb these functions as do lesions of the frontal cortex. Many of these tests are based upon the ability of the patient to classify and categorize a large number of familiar objects and to recall them once they have been taken from him. In an operation for the eradication of a tumor, Dandy excised the frontal lobes on both sides in front of the motor areas (reported by Brickner). The subject of this extensive extirpation appeared of normal intelligence upon a casual acquaintance. It is reported that for an hour he toured the hospital with two visiting neurologists who failed to notice in him any mental abnormality. A more intimate knowledge of the patient, however, revealed very definite defects of character and mentality. His mental age was about thirteen years; his intelligence quotient eighty. The main features shown by this subject and which may be taken generally as representative of the effects of extensive prefrontal destruction are listed below. They constitute what has been called the *frontal lobe syndrome*.[5]

(1) *Lack of restraint* leading to boasting, self-aggrandizement, hostility, aggressiveness.

(2) *Distractibility* and *restlessness*—difficulty in fixing attention.

(3) *Hypermotility* which appears to be due to the loss especially of area 13.

(4) *Flight of ideas*, puerile fantasies, emotional instability, facetiousness, punning.

(5) *Lack of initiative*, and difficulty in planning any course of action.

(6) *Impairment of memory* for recent events but not for remote events.

(7) *Impairment of moral and social sense*, loss of love for family.

(8) *Failure to realize*, or indifference to, the seriousness of his condition, and a sense of well-being (euphoria).

[5] The classical example of a severe prefrontal injury which resulted in surprisingly little mental defect, is the case of the American, Phineas Gage (1848), who suffered extensive damage of his frontal lobes by an iron tamping bar driven through his head by an explosion. The bar penetrated the left orbit and emerged from the midline of the head just anterior to the coronal suture. He was stunned for only an hour and was able with assistance to walk to a surgeon's office. He lived for 12 years after the accident and showed in general these mental changes. A case has also been reported in which the prefrontal cortex on both sides were absent or degenerated. The condition existed from early childhood yet, at adult age the subject of this defect, after a careful psychologic and psychiatric examination, was reported to be of normal intelligence, though some defect in planning capacity and in the ability "to organize his behavior toward a relatively remote goal" were revealed.

Among some of the other manifestations which may follow a prefrontal defect are: (a) increased appetite, (b) impaired control of the sphincter of the bladder or rectum, (c) disturbances of orientation in time and space, and (d) tremor.

Chimpanzees which have had both prefrontal areas removed show restlessness and are easily distracted, though they remain alert and evince a keen interest in things around them. Fulton and Jacobson reported in 1935 that after this operation chimpanzees failed to show temper tantrums and other neurotic effects of frustration (experimental neurosis). This observation formed the basis for the surgical treatment of certain psychoneuroses in man, first employed by the Portuguese neurologist, Egaz Moniz in 1936. The operation, called frontal lobotomy consists in severing the fibers connecting prefrontal areas with subcortical centers (probably the thalamus and hypothalamus). With the introduction of the various drugs which are capable of reducing nervous tension and rendering the aggressive, agitated patient more tractable the need for this type of operation has been greatly diminished.

The frontal lobes and intelligence. The development of the frontal lobes bears in general a direct relationship to the level of an animal in the phylogenetic scale and to its intelligence. This had led to the belief that this part of the cerebrum is the seat of the intelligence of animals and the "center" or "organ" of the mind of man. Indeed, some early studies suggested that excising the prefrontal lobes or severing their connections did lead to decreased intelligence. These studies, however, were contaminated by the fact that the pathological states which led to the surgery often produced a pre-operative intelligence deficit. World War II provided a source of case material for further study of this problem by supplying a group of traumatic pre-frontal injuries in a previously normal population of men with known pre-injury intelligence test scores on the Army General Classification Test (AGCT). Administration of the AGCT to these men ten years after injury showed no decline in test scores (Weinstein and Teuber, 1957). In spite of difficulties of interpretation due to the unfortunate imprecision of lesions produced by shell fragments and bullets, as well as the current lack of histological confirmation of the extent of the lesion, it seems clear that destruction of the prefrontal region does not produce any notable deficit in intelligence.

Intelligence depends upon a knowledge of the external world received through various chan-

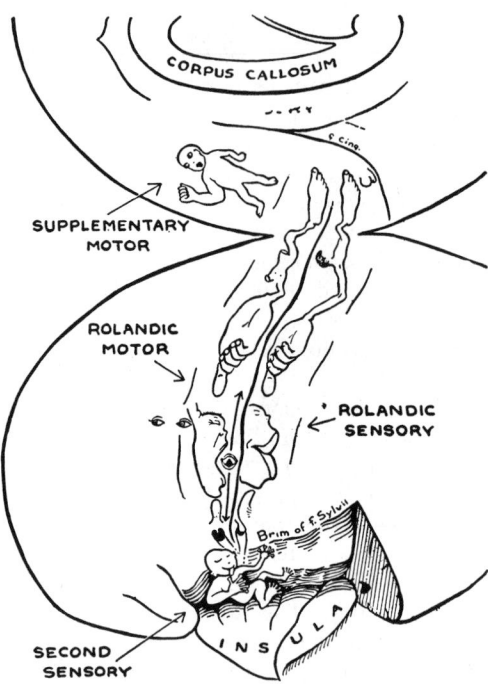

FIG. 8.5. Showing figurines of motor and sensory representation in the cerebral cortex, slightly modified. (From Penfield and Jasper, *Epilepsy and the Functional Anatomy of the Human Brain,* courtesy of Dr. Penfield.)

nels. Visual, auditory, somesthetic perceptions, etc., are received and stored in the occipital, temporal and parietal lobes and perhaps elsewhere as well. Tracts of association fibers in turn link together these several primary areas; sensations of various types are thereby brought into relationship, and synthesized into more complex memories. Thus, as time passes, the fabric of our experience is woven in patterns of greater and greater intricacy.

The progressive increase in size of the frontal lobes through the upper levels of the phylogenetic scale is not as great as that of the parietal lobe, which supports the conclusion derived from extirpation experiments that intelligence, memory, control of behavior, etc. are not solely or even predominantly dependent upon the prefrontal areas.

It is probable that the prefrontal area merely represents a region of relatively high associative or synthetic capabilities. The anatomical connections of this area, as well as the effects upon behavior resulting from its injury, strongly suggest that it is concerned with emotional feeling. After its bilateral removal the cerebrum deprived of the synthesizing faculty of this region is in-

capable of the more elaborate association of those experiences required for the formulation of abstract ideas and more accurate judgment, and for the guidance of conduct in conformity with social customs. Here also are mainly located those mental processes relating to "prediction," forecasting, or to any planned action. A person deprived of these areas would have little ability as a strategist; even a housewife after the loss of these parts of the cortex experiences some difficulty in planning a meal. Nevertheless, synthesis at somewhat lower levels is still possible of achievement through the remaining cerebral tissue. Mental capacity according to this conception is a function of the cerebral cortex as a whole rather than of any particular region.

THE PARIETAL LOBE

The Somesthetic (Somatesthetic) Area

The postcentral gyrus, i.e., the band of cortex lying behind and including the posterior lip and wall of the fissure of Rolando (areas 3, 1 and 2) is sensory in function and is known as the *somesthetic area.* This band of sensory cortex turns over the upper border of the hemisphere, and extends down the mesial surface as far as the cingulate gyrus. As in the case of the primary motor area, the sensory areas of the body are, in a general way, represented mainly in inverted order, from the lowest part of the mesial surface to a corresponding part of the lateral surface (see Fig. 8.5). Thus, the area for the toes is at the lower part of the mesial surface, that for the leg near the upper border of the hemisphere, while the face, mouth and tongue areas are found in the lower part of the lateral surface. The parts of the face, however, are represented in uninverted sequence—brow, eyelids, nose, lips, in this order from above downward (fig. 8.3). Though broadly speaking, sensory representation in the cortex has this regional representation, when the topography of the different parts is examined in greater detail it is found that the order of cortical representation conforms closely to that of the dermatomes, i.e., to the spinal innervation. For example, the cortical sequence for the upper limb (monkey) is postaxial arm, occiput, ear, side of head, neck, shoulder (C2–C6); preaxial arm, forearm, wrist, hand, digits (C7, C8, T1). But it will be seen from figure 8.6 that the dermatomal representation is not in continuous numerical sequence from head to tail. For example, if the sensory band of cortex (which turns over the upper border of the hemisphere) were straightened out, it would appear

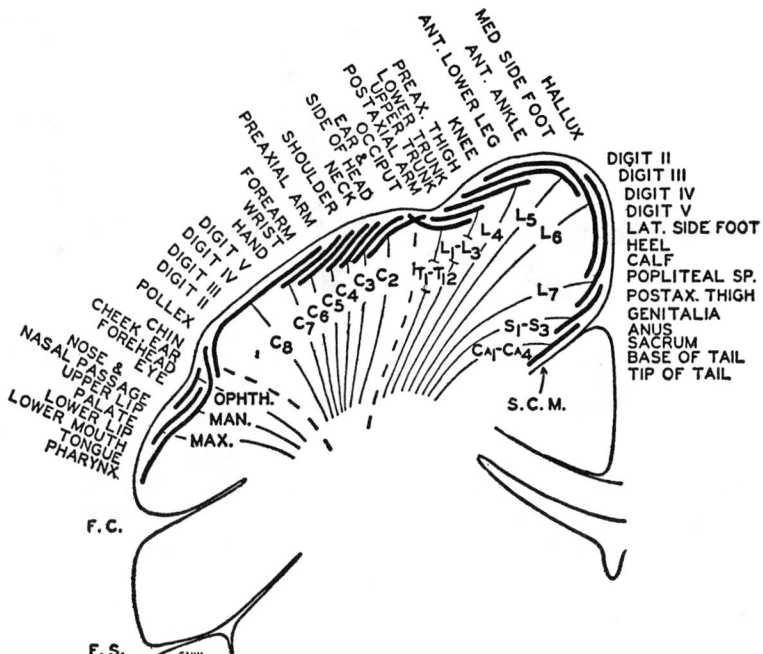

FIG. 8.6. Diagram of a section through the somesthetic area to show cortical representation of the dermatomes. F.S., sylvian fissure; F.C., central fissure; s.c.m., callosomarginal sulcus; MAX., maxillary division of the trigeminal nerve; MAN., mandibular; OPHTH., ophthalmic; C., cervical; T., thoracic; L., lumbar; S., sacral; Ca., caudal. (From Woolsey, Marshall and Bard, Bull. Johns Hopkins Hosp., 70: 399–441, 1942.)

quite clearly that the projection of the dermatomes from the upper thorax to the tail (Thoracic 1 to Caudal 4) was in an order the inverse of that of the spinal segments, whereas, the representations of the head and neck were uninverted, the cervical segments being represented in ascending numerical order from above down, and the ophthalmic division of the 5th nerve following C8. There is no obvious explanation for this arrangement. Excisions of portions of the somesthetic cortex are followed by disturbances of cutaneous and kinesthetic sensations on the opposite side of the body. These subside to a greater or lesser degree with the passage of time.

Cushing, and later, Penfield and his associates have stimulated different parts of the area in conscious patients; sensations on the contralateral half of the body were experienced, their locations bearing a constant relationship to the point stimulated. Dusser de Barenne discovered that the application of a strychnine solution to the postcentral gyrus in monkeys caused sensory effects (paresthesias, hyperesthesis and hyperalgesia) on the opposite side of the body, but also to some extent on the same side.

The sensory area of the cortex is not confined to the postcentral gyrus but extends forward into the precentral gyrus. Penfield and his associates found that 25 per cent of stimulations of the latter area in patients caused a sensation, with or without a motor response. On the other hand, 20 per cent of stimulations of the postcentral gyrus gave a motor response, instead of or accompanied by a sensation. Also ablations of postcentral areas cause motor defects which are not due simply to loss of kinesthetic sense. It appears that the precentral and postcentral areas are knit together by connecting neurons, and are so interrelated functionally as to be called appropriately, taken as a whole, the *sensorimotor area*.

As in the motor area the extent of the sensory representation in the postcentral gyrus is greatest for those parts of the body which are of most importance in acquiring information concerning surrounding objects. Thus, in man and in the monkey, the cortical area for the hand and arm is larger than that for the trunk or leg, while in such animals as the rabbit, cat or pig, the area for the face, lips, snout and vibrissae is much larger than that for the paws. In the pig the representation for the snout takes up a large part of the postcentral gyrus, whereas that for the feet is insignificant. In the Shetland pony the cortical area receiving impulses from the nostril is nearly as

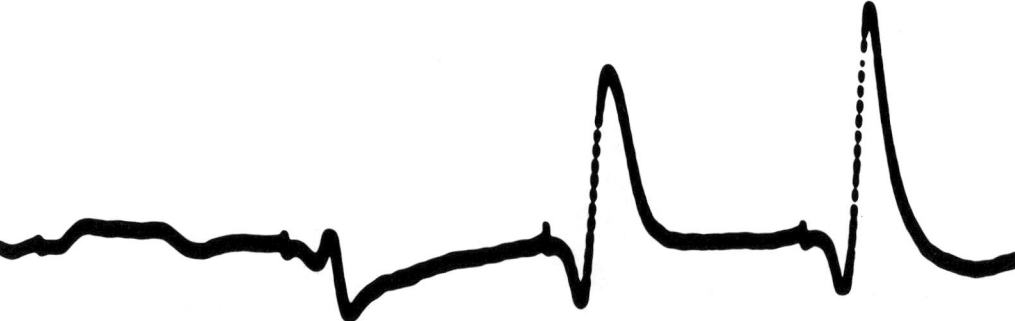

Fig. 8.7. Recruiting response recorded from the cortex. Nonspecific system is stimulated electrically with an electrode in the thalamus. Four stimulus artifacts can be seen, with the response to each successive stimulus showing an increased amplitude. (From Dempsey and Morison, 1942.)

large as that representing the rest of the body surface. The large facial representation in man appears to be an exception for, after infancy, we do not gain information by feeling objects with the lips or by putting them into the mouth. It is looked upon, however, as an inheritance from our animal ancestry.

Somatic sensation as well as the visual and auditory senses have a double representation in the cortex of each hemisphere. This dual somatic representation was first observed by Adrian, in the case of the claws of the cat. The somesthetic area described above and long recognized, is now called the "primary" sensory area, or, as Woolsey has suggested, *somatic area I*. The more recently discovered sensory area is called *somatic area II*. Corresponding terms for the dual visual and auditory areas are employed, namely auditory and visual areas I and II. Somatic area II lies in the upper wall of the Sylvian fissure, that is, below the face area of somatic area I, which is much larger in extent. The order of representation in sensory area II is the inverse of that of sensory area I, the face being above the arm in the upper part of the wall of the fissure and the representation of the foot at the bottom. The significance of the dual cortical representation is unknown.

All somatic sensory impulses ascend in the medial, spinal and trigeminal lemnisci to the thalamus, which is the subcortical destination of crude sensations. Though rather vague sensations described as tingling, numbness, tickling, prickling, or as the movement of a limb, are aroused by stimulation of the postcentral gyrus, and are referred to some part of the body depending upon the area stimulated, pain is never aroused and rarely even discomfort. There does not appear to be an area of the cortex essential for the perception of pain for "no removal of the cortex anywhere prevents pain from being felt" (Penfield).

Impulses for pain reaching the thalamus can arouse this feeling without being transmitted to the cortex. Though, as mentioned earlier, severe intractable pain, usually associated with disease of internal structures is relieved by frontal lobotomy or lobectomy, the perception of pain is not abolished; but the patient ceases to suffer and complain; he no longer worries about it.

The finer sensations of touch and temperature and the sense of position and movement are relayed to the cortex by fibers which ascend through the internal capsule and corona radiata. According to Head, the somesthetic area of the cortex, through the integration of the primary sensations, becomes endowed with three discriminative faculties.[6] These are:

(a) SPATIAL RECOGNITION—the appreciation of relationships in space, e.g., the recognition of position and passive movement of the limb, the discrimination of two points, and the localization of a point which has been touched.

(b) RECOGNITION OF THE RELATIVE INTENSITY of different stimuli, e.g., that one object is warmer or cooler.

(c) RECOGNITION OF SIMILARITY AND DIFFERENCES—appreciation of the shape, relative size and texture of objects, and the estimation of their weights—*stereognosis*.

With a *lesion* involving the cortical somesthetic area, one or the other, but usually all three, of these faculties are disturbed. Spatial recognition shows the greatest disturbance the farther forward the lesion lies in the somesthetic area. Appreciation of intensity is disturbed most by lesions involving the foot of the postcentral gyrus and the

[6] According to the conception of Penfield and Jasper, impulses received in the sensorimotor cortex return to the thalamus and other parts of the centrencephalic system where the highest level of functional integration is situated.

supramarginal and angular gyri. Recognition of similarity and difference is affected most by lesions of the middle of the postcentral gyrus.

If with lesions confined to the cortex, the related nuclei of the thalamus which are concerned with the *primary* sensations, e.g., light touch, temperature, passive movement and position, etc., are intact and the sensations will be appreciated. The patient with such a lesion has difficulty, however, in bringing the necessary discriminative ability to bear upon the sensation in order to judge it, and he is unable to synthesize different sensations into a composite impression which will enable him readily to identify an object. When tested, he is uncertain in his answers, which tend to vary from moment to moment, and it is difficult for the examiner to determine the threshold for a given sensation. For example, though he recognizes that an object is warm, he cannot say whether it is warmer or less warm than another object which he has felt previously or at the same time. He responds to tactile stimuli, but also with inconstancy, and he is often even less consistent in his answers when the strength of the stimulus is increased. He cannot locate the point touched and may respond when not touched (hallucination of touch). The weights of objects placed upon the hand cannot be estimated, and a fabric (e.g., silk or tweed), though felt to be smooth or rough cannot be recognized.

It is not to be assumed that all stimuli of equal intensity are equally perceived by the person stimulated. The perception of a given stimulus is not always the same; the threshold varies. This in part is due to attention or inattention. If a person's attention is concentrated upon one part of his body he will become more acutely aware of stimulation of that part while at the same time he becomes less aware of stimuli received elsewhere. This is common everyday human experience. It also plays an important role in the symptomatology of disease. The patient whose attention is constantly focused upon a diseased or injured part is keenly aware of unpleasant sensations from that area, whereas another patient with a similar disease or injury who is busily engaged with other activities and does not concentrate upon his disease or injury suffers much less discomfort. Likewise, it is a matter of common experience on the part of physicians that some patients have a much lower threshold for pain than others. In general, the patient who is introspective, who concentrates his attention upon himself, his body and its ailments is the one with the lowest threshold for pain and the one who suffers and complains more. What is the physiological explanation for these differences between patients, and from time to time in the same patient. It seems likely that several neural mechanisms are at work here. One of these is the reticular formation in the brain stem. There is ample evidence that it can influence sensory thresholds both peripherally and centrally. Other mechanisms which may be concerned are the corticothalamic, corticobulbar and corticospinal fibers. We have mentioned the projection of thalamic fibers to almost every area of the cerebral cortex. Sensory perception is the primary concern of those from the nucleus ventralis posterior of the thalamus to the postcentral gyrus. It has also been pointed out that there is also an extensive projection system from the cerebral cortex back to the thalamus. In general a given area of the cortex projects back to the same thalamic nucleus as that from which it receives fibers. It seems entirely reasonable that this corticothalamic system is a mechanism for controlling the threshold of the thalamus and thus for regulating sensory attention. There is also a corticobulbar system which extends from the postcentral sensory cortex to the spinal root of the trigeminal nerve, and corticospinal fibers from the postcentral gyrus to the posterior gray horn of the spinal cord in the monkey (Kuypers, 1958). This same investigator also found evidence of a cortical projection from the "leg" areas of both the pre- and postcentral gyri to the nucleus gracilis. Projection from the pericentral cortex to the nucleus cuneatus was also found. Hagbarth and Kerr (1954) have shown that stimulation of the postcentral sensory cortex (in the cat) will depress afferent responses from the spinal dorsal root transmitted over pathways in the spinal cord and the midbrain.

Hypotonia may also be a symptom of lesions of the sensory cortex; it corresponds in distribution to the loss of the sense of position and passive movement.

The cortex at the lower end of the somesthetic area (tongue and face area) appears from the studies of Bornstein to be the *area for taste*. This area lies adjacent to the motor cortex governing the muscles of mastication.[7] It had been generally taught, but on doubtful evidence, that the center for taste lay close to that for smell, namely, in the region of the hippocampal gyrus. It appears from

---

[7] This area probably extends into the upper bank of the Sylvian (lateral) fissure, for the sensation has been aroused in patients by stimulation of the upper bank where it joins the insula (Penfield and Rasmussen).

the results of the stimulation of the human cortex during operations that the taste area extends deeply into the fissure of Sylvius. An electrical stimulus applied to the cortex above the circular sulcus (surrounding the insula), or the surface of the insula itself causes a sensation of taste—a "terrific tight sensation of taste" as one patient expressed it (Penfield).

Motor effects of a generalized type are produced by electrical stimulation of the posterior part of the superior parietal lobule (area 5, parietal adversive field). These are movements of the head and eyes to the opposite side. Stimulation of the angular gyrus causes conjugate deviation of the eyes to the opposite side.

Attacks of Jacksonian epilepsy, due to lesions of the sensory cortex, may be preceded by sensory aurae—comprising pricking sensations, "pins and needles," sensation of cold, etc.

The Temporal Lobe

The primary cortical center for hearing is situated in the transverse gyrus of Heschl lying in the floor of the lateral cerebral (Sylvian) fissure, and an adjoining small area of the superior temporal gyrus. Fibers from the medial geniculate body reach this *auditosensory* area (area 41) via the posterior limb of the internal capsule; they constitute the *auditory radiation*. In the auditosensory area the fundamental auditory sensations—intensity, and pitch—are appreciated. The area is bilaterally represented.

Equilibratory sense is represented in the posterior part of the first temporal convolution. Stimulation of this region in conscious patients causes dizziness or nausea, a sense of swaying, falling, or of rotation.

As in the case of the somesthetic (p. 172) and visual senses, auditory sensations have multiple (Woolsey, 1960) representation in each cerebral hemisphere. Woolsey and Walzl stimulated electrically the different levels of the exposed cochlea in cats and found a point to point projection on to the temporal cortex. In auditory area I, the apical turns of the cochlea were projected posteriorly, the basal turns anteriorly, whereas in AII, which lies adjacent and ventral to AI, the different points of the cochlea showed the reverse distribution, apical turns anterior, basal turns posterior. A large part of the cortex of the superior temporal gyrus lying outside these auditosensory areas is considered to be *audito-psychic* in function. Herein the analysis and interpreta-

tion of auditory sensations, and their integration into more complex perceptions take place.

Fibers descend from the cortex of the temporal lobe to the *medial geniculate* body and *inferior colliculus*; the former is therefore connected with the auditory area by both ascending and descending paths.

It has been taught for many years that fibers descend from the temporal lobe through the internal capsule and the lateral segment of the cerebral peduncle to the pons—the so-called *temporo-pontine* or Türck's bundle. However, in detailed studies of the brains of monkeys following temporal lobectomies neither Rundles and Papez nor Bucy and Klüver were able to demonstrate any such tract. It is possible that these fibers in the lateral part of the cerebral peduncle are parieto-pontine fibers as Mettler suggested. The temporal lobe also receives fibers from the posterior pole of the pulvinar of the thalamus (Bucy and Klüver), and it appears that these terminate in the anterior part of the cortex of the lateral surface of the temporal lobe (Simpson, 1952 and Chow, 1954). There is also a large bundle of fibers (Arnold's) which has an uncertain origin in the anterior part of the temporal lobe and which passes backward to end in the pulvinar of the thalamus. The functions of these connections are unknown.

A LESION OF THE TEMPORAL LOBE may result in:

1. Aphasia. Disturbances of the speech function—understanding, expression, recall of the names of objects, etc.—commonly occur with lesions of the dominant (usually the left) temporal lobe. Frazier and Rowe found aphasic disturbances in 36 per cent of such cases; Kolodny reported 57 per cent. The occurrence of aphasic difficulties will depend upon the location of the lesion. They are unlikely with lesions in the anterior or ventral part of the left temporal lobe and likely with lesions in the postero-superior part near the posterior part of the Sylvian fissure.

2. Auditory disorders may occur with lesions of the temporal lobes. Paroxysmal attacks of tinnitus (buzzing, ringing, etc.) or even of auditory hallucinations may occur. These are often associated with other manifestations of "temporal lobe seizures" or of uncinate attacks or dreamy states. Epileptic attacks induced by various auditory stimuli have also been described. Because of the extensive bilateral representation of both cochleae in both auditory cortices deafness never occurs as the result of a unilateral cortical lesion and is very rare with bilateral ones because involvement of the auditory cortices in both cerebral hemispheres is most uncommon.

3. Disturbances of smell and taste in the form of paroxysmal hallucinations in these sensory fields occur commonly with lesions, especially tumors in the anterior temporal region. These smells and tastes are more often unpleasant. Such attacks are commonly called *uncinate seizures*. Impairment of the sense of smell occurs most often as the result of lesions of the olfactory bulb and tract, rather than from involvement of the so-called rhinencephalon. In fact, the rhinencephalon is much more concerned with the control of emotions and emotional expression and of vegetative functions than it is with the elementary sensations of smell and taste.

4. Dreamy states. Lesions of the anterior part of the temporal lobe are not infrequently associated with peculiar attacks known as dreamy states. In these attacks the patient has a feeling of unreality, a sense of familiarity of his surroundings (*déjà vu*). He may describe these attacks as being similar to a dream. They may be associated with certain activities on the part of the patient over which he appears to have no control and of which he subsequently has no memory. In these attacks he may remove his own clothing, or tear off the clothing of others. He may be destructive or he may merely wander about aimlessly as though looking for something. Because of this combination of psychological disturbance with certain motor activities these have been referred to as *psychomotor seizures*. These seizures may be associated with auditory, olfactory or visual hallucinations. Individuals with temporal lobe seizures not infrequently suffer from generalized convulsions as well.

5. Visual symptoms. Lesions of the temporal lobes, particularly tumors, may be associated with visual hallucinations. Although these hallucinations may take almost any form they commonly are of formed objects,—people, animals, etc. On occasion these may be smaller than normal or the figures may be incomplete. In some cases the hallucinations may be unformed, that is flashes of light. Lesions in the posterior part of the temporal lobe commonly involve the visual radiations which run from the lateral geniculate body to the calcarine cortex, and thus give rise to a defect in the contralateral halves of the visual fields—a homonymous hemianopia. If the hemianopia is incomplete, it is usually the upper contralateral quadrants of the visual fields which are involved.

In monkeys bilateral extirpation of the temporal lobes including both the neocortex and the rhinencephalon on the medial surface of the temporal lobes gives rise to a most interesting group of symptoms (Klüver and Bucy, 1939). (*1*) *Visual agnosia.* These animals seem to have lost the ability to recognize and to detect the meaning of objects on the basis of visual criteria alone. There also seems to be a similar agnosia in the auditory and tactile fields. (*2*) *Oral tendencies.* There is a very strong tendency to examine all objects with the mouth. (*3*) *"Hypermetamorphosis."* There is a marked tendency to take notice of and to attend to every visual stimulus. (*4*) *Tameness.* These animals seem to have lost their sense of fear, and there is a marked diminution in their emotional responses. (*5*) *Hypersexuality.* There is a striking increase in various sexual activities and in their diversity. This change does not occur until several weeks after the operation. Females may show a complete lack of maternal behavior. (*6*) *Changes in dietary habits.* Monkeys do not ordinarily eat meat but after the removal of both temporal lobes they do so without hesitation. There is also an increase in the amount of food consumed. In a few cases some of these symptoms have been observed in human beings following bilateral temporal lobectomy.

Subsequent study has more precisely attributed some of these symptoms to specific structures within the temporal lobe. For example, Schreiner and Kling (1953) have shown that removal of the amygdala and overlying pyriform cortex alone will produce placidity. Green, Clemente and de Groot (1957) have shown that hypersexuality will be seen after lesions of the pyriform cortex overlying the basal amygdalar nucleus. It has been suggested that psychic blindness may be the result of removal of temporal neocortex.

THE OCCIPITAL LOBE

The gray matter forming the walls of, and surrounding the calcarine fissure (on the medial aspect of the occipital lobe) constitutes the primary cortical center for vision—the *visuosensory area.* From the broad stripe of Gennari which can be seen with the naked eye this area is commonly known as the *area striata* or, following the numerical terminology, as area 17. It will be considered in more detail in chapter 16. Its histological features have already been touched upon.

The *second visual area* wherein the visual sensations are interpreted and integrated into more complex perceptions is contiguous to the area striata and lies on the lateral aspect of the occipital lobe (area 18).

Stimulation of the anterior part of the lateral surface of the occipital lobe causes conjugate deviation of the eyes to the opposite side (occipital motor eye field, area 19). In man, visual hallucinations, such as, flashes of light of different colors, or definite images have been evoked by the electrical stimulation of area 18 or 19.

ELECTROPHYSIOLOGICAL STUDIES OF SENSORY FUNCTIONS OF ASSOCIATION CORTEX

Sensory stimuli produce evoked responses at a number of cortical regions other than primary sensory cortex. These regions have been described in the cat (Albe-Fessard and Rougeul, 1958) as the anterior part of the sigmoid gyrus and the suprasylvian gyrus. In the monkey, the corresponding areas have been described (Albe-Fessard et al., 1959) as superior temporal cortex, superior frontal cortex and parietal association cortex (area 5). These responses are particularly evident in the unanaesthetized animal or in animals anaesthetized with chloralose. They are more labile than primary sensory responses, showing wide variations in magnitude of response to repetitions of the same stimulus. When stimuli are repeated, responses in association cortex will fail to appear at every stimulus if the repetition rate is higher than approximately 5 per sec. At times several seconds or minutes may be required for full recovery of response amplitude.

One of the outstanding characteristics of association cortex is the wide range of stimuli that converge on these areas. Within one sensory modality, such as the somatic, stimuli to a wide variety of regions of the receptor surface will produce responses at one recording electrode location on the cortex. Localization seems to be considerably degraded in comparison to the relatively high degree of specificity seen in primary sensory cortex. Stimulation of a variety of sensory modalities will also produce responses at one region. Auditory, somatic, and visual stimuli have typically been employed to produce evoked responses from a single electrode location. In addition to having overlapping fields in association cortex, the responses to stimulation of these sensory modalities have been shown to interact with each other (Berman, 1961; Loe and Coleman, 1965). Studies of the responses of single neurons with microelectrodes (Amassian, 1954) have shown that a single unit in association cortex will respond to stimulation of any of the limbs or to stimulation of other modalities.

Electrophysiological study of the pathway by which sensory impulses reach association cortex have shown that responses remain after ablation of the relevant primary cortical sensory areas (Albe-Fessard and Rougeul, 1958) and after extensive destruction of the mesencephalic reticular formation (Buser et al., 1959). Coagulation of the centrum medianum will, however, abolish the sensory evoked responses in the association cortex ipsilateral to the lesion (Albe-Fessard and Rougeul, 1958). Electrical stimulation of the centrum medianum will also elicit short latency responses in those regions defined above as association cortex. On the basis of such evidence, Albe-Fessard concludes that the sensory input to these cortical areas arrives largely via the centrum medianum.

Experiments in which chronically implanted electrodes were used to record evoked responses in association cortex in unanaesthetized, behaving cats have shown a number of relationships between amplitude of evoked response and various behaviors (Thompson and Shaw, 1965). Response amplitudes recorded at suprasylvian gyrus in response to visual, auditory and somatic stimuli (light flash, click, and forepaw shock) are decreased when the animal is active, relative to amplitudes in the resting state. Novel stimuli in any of these modalities will reduce the magnitude of response evoked by stimulation in any of these modalities. Response amplitude is also decreased when the animal orients toward a stimulus. These results are consistent with the hypothesis that evoked responses in association areas are diminished to the extent that the organism is attending to stimuli in his environment.

THALAMO-CORTICAL PROJECTIONS

The thalamic pathways to the cortex may be placed in two categories: the specific and the non-specific systems. The projection fibers of the *specific* system originate in the sensory relay nuclei (e.g., the geniculates and the ventral posterior group) and the association nuclei (e.g., pulvinar, lateral nucleus) and, in general, project directly to the cortex. Typically these fibers show relatively little lateral spread in the cortex. This is particularly true of fibers originating in the relay nuclei. Consequently, electrical stimulation of restricted regions in these specific thalamic nuclei results in a relatively discretely localized cortical evoked potential. This evoked potential has a latency of 1 to 5 msec. If a specific thalamic nucleus is stimulated repetitively at a rate between 6 and 12 pulses per sec., cortical evoked responses to successive pulses may become larger. These are called augmenting responses and they are limited to the specific sensory cortex.

The *non-specific* thalamic nuclei such as the intralaminar group and nucleus reticularis give rise to a projection system considered to be the rostral portion of the ascending reticular activating system. This non-specific thalamic system is widely distributed over the surface of the cortex, including those cortical areas to which the specific relay nuclei project. Many of these non-specific thalamic nuclei have not been shown to have any direct pathway to the cortex, the conclusion being that these nuclei send fibers to the cortex by an indirect, multisynaptic pathway. The exact nature of this indirect pathway remains to be clarified, but it is currently thought to be via intrathalamic connections to the nucleus reticularis and nucleus ventralis anterior to cortex, and perhaps via the head of the caudate nucleus or a pathway lying close to the head of the caudate. Electrical stimulation of the non-specific nuclei results in a widespread bilateral cortical evoked response. Since the pathway is multisynaptic the latency of this response is relatively long, ranging from 5 to 10 msec. at frontal cortex when stimulating nucleus reticularis to several hundred msec. in posterior regions of the cortex in response to stimulation of nucleus centralis medialis in the intralaminar group. If the intralaminar region or other portions of the non-specific system are stimulated repetitively at a rate between 6 and 12 a second, one obtains a series of successively larger responses which reach a maximum after two to five pulses. These waves are known as the recruiting response (see fig. 8.7). The recruiting response is distinguished from the augmenting response described above by: (1) its origin in the non-specific system, (2) the wide-spread distribution of the responses produced, and (3) a longer latency than that seen for the augmenting response and (4) waveform.

The specific and non-specific systems are not independent, but interact with each other at all levels between the brainstem and cortex. Many physiological and anatomical studies have shown that collateral fibers from the somatic, visual, and auditory specific sensory systems enter the diffuse system in the brain stem and thalamus. Conversely, it has been shown (Nauta and Whitlock, 1954) that fibers pass from the centrum medianum, a nonspecific thalamic nucleus, to terminate in specific thalamic relay nuclei. Electrophysiological studies have shown that stimulation or extirpation of regions of either the specific or nonspecific systems will influence the responses of the other system. For example, recruiting responses recorded from primary visual cortex are increased in amplitude after destruction of the lateral geniculate (Hanberry and Jasper, 1953). This increase in the recruiting response recorded at primary sensory cortex has also been seen after destruction of the other major thalamic sensory relay nuclei. It has also been shown that the responsiveness of sensory cortex to specific afferent stimulation is modified by the activity of the nonspecific projections (fig. 8.8). A possible interpretation of these and many other related studies is that the activity

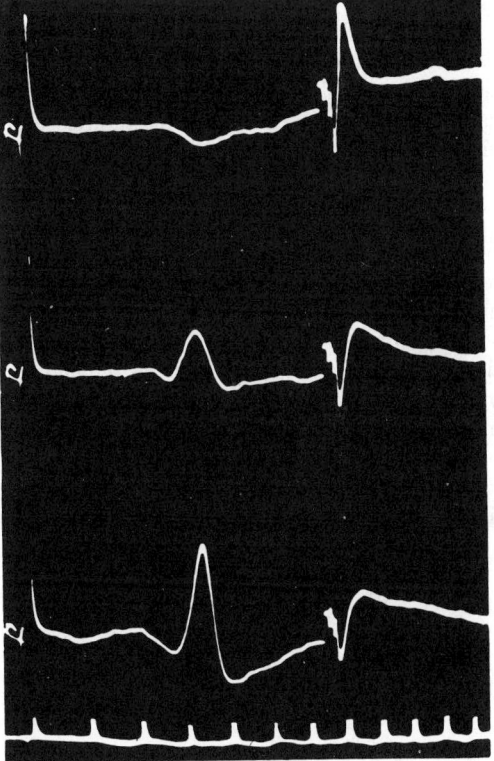

FIG. 8.8. Oscilloscope records of responses of visual cortex to paired shocks applied to nonspecific and specific systems. The initial stimulus, applied to n. ventralis anterior, produces a stimulus artifact at the start of each trace. The cortical response to this stimulus shows variation in amplitude in the three traces. A test shock is delivered to the lateral geniculate 62 msec. later. Note the reciprocal relationship between the variations in the response to stimulation of the nonspecific system and the amplitude of the specific evoked potential. Time line intervals, 10 msec. (From Jasper and Ajmone-Marsan).

of the nonspecific system "sets" the excitability of the cortex.

The Physiology of Speech and Some of Its Disorders

The first stage in the development of speech is the association of certain sounds—(words)—with visual, tactile and other sensations aroused by objects in the external world. These associations are "stored" as memories. After definite meanings have been attached to certain words, pathways between the auditory area of the cortex and the motor area for the muscles of articulation become established, and the child attempts to formulate and pronounce the words which he has heard. This act of verbal expression involves the coordinated movements of a large group of respiratory, laryngeal, lingual, pharyngeal and labial muscles. Later, as the child is taught to read, auditory speech is associated with the visual symbols of speech, and finally, through an association between these and the motor area for the hand, the child learns to express his auditory and visual impressions by the written word.

Aphasia

This term is applied to those disorders of speech resulting from defects in the nervous mechanisms underlying the comprehension and use of symbols (words, numerals) for the formulation, transmission and reception of ideas. General intelligence may be little impaired. Yet aphasia is not a defect in the pronunciation of words as a result of the paralysis of the muscles of articulation. The innervation of the latter—motor area, corticobulbar fibers, cranial nuclei or peripheral nerves—is not necessarily affected. The defects in aphasia involve higher neural levels; they lie in the psychical sphere.

The faculty of speech is based upon a highly complex neural mechanism. In conscious patients electrical stimulation of the cortex of either hemisphere within the lower part of the precentral gyrus (lips, jaw and tongue areas), or in the upper part of the supplementary motor area on the mesial aspect of the hemisphere, causes the emission of a crude vocal sound like the cry of an infant or of an epileptic at the beginning of an attack. The vocal response elicited from the lip, jaw and tongue region never even remotely resembles a spoken word, but that evoked from the supplementary motor area is more complicated. Ablation of one or other of these areas causes only temporary speech defects. If the cortex in the lower part of the precentral gyrus of the dominant hemisphere (left in the great majority of persons) is excised a temporary aphasia results which is probably due to some interference with the blood supply to area 44 (Broca's area). If while the patient is speaking, certain cortical areas are stimulated electrically, speech is arrested; he cannot think of a word or words which he wished to use. There are four such areas situated in the dominant hemisphere: (1) *lower frontal*, area 44; (2) *upper frontal*, motor cortex anterior to the foot area on the mesial aspect of the hemisphere; (3) *parietal*, posterior to the lower part of the postcentral gyrus; (4) *temporal*, posterior part of temporal lobe. Injury to one or other of these areas, with the possible exception of (2), causes persistent aphasia (see fig. 8.9).

Head's Classification of the Aphasias

Head's views, based upon an exhaustive study of patients suffering from gunshot wounds of the cortex, consider speech to be a highly integrated cortical process—a special aspect of intelligence —yet one which can suffer with little lowering of the general intellectual level. The different components of the speech faculty, he decides, cannot be separated from one another by disease. Nor, consequently, can the types of aphasia be classed as "motor" or "sensory," but in any type, deficiencies on both the receptive and the executive side can be demonstrated. Head concluded that cortical representation of speech mechanisms was more diffuse than had been supposed and that strict localization was impossible. Aphasia is a state in which the power to use words and other symbols as instruments of

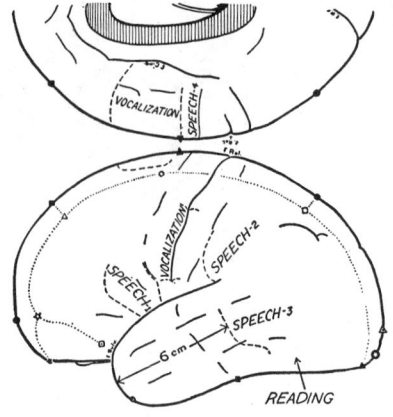

Fig. 8.9. Showing speech areas in the left (dominant) cerebral cortex. (From Penfield and Jasper, *Epilepsy and the Functional Anatomy of the Human Brain*, courtesy of Dr. Penfield.)

thought and expression is affected or, as he expresses it, "aphasia is a defect in symbolic formation and expression." The more complicated or abstract the idea which must be understood or expressed, the greater is the difficulty. Thus an aphasic may be able to name *objects* correctly but fails to find the word for a more *abstract idea*, e.g., color. Shown a black object, for instance, and asked to name its color he fails to do so, yet indicates that he recognizes that it is black by saying "what you do for the dead." An aphasic soldier when shown a red object said, "what the staff wear."

Head, as a result of his investigation of aphasic patients, devised a series of six tests of graded severity. These tests are briefly as follows:

1. Naming and recognition of common objects. Six objects, e.g., a pencil, key, knife, etc. The patient is asked to name each object as it is pointed out to him. Next he is asked to point to each object as its name is called out. He is then given cards upon each of which the name of one of the objects is written. He is asked to indicate the object named.

2. Naming and recognition of colors. This test is carried out in a manner similar to that described for test (1) except that eight strips of differently colored silk are substituted for the six objects.

3. Man, cat and dog test is designed to investigate the powers of reading and writing in their most elementary forms. The printed words "man," "cat" and "dog" are employed. The subject is asked to read these words; to write them from dictation; to copy them or to repeat them after hearing them spoken. Pictures of a man, a cat and a dog are also shown and the patient asked to write or to speak their names.

4. The clock tests. The patient is requested to set the hands of a clock in the same positions as those of a similar one set by the observer. He is then told to set the clock from verbal or printed commands. Again, he is asked to state the time aloud or by writing, of a clock set by the observer.

5. Coin bowl tests. Pennies are placed one in front of each of four bowls. The patient is asked verbally and in writing to place a coin in one or other of the bowls according to their number in the row. He is then asked to give an order himself and to carry it out according to his own words.

6. The hand, eye and ear tests. The patient is requested to repeat the movements of the observer which consist in touching an eye or an ear with one or other hand. When this is done correctly the patient's hand which moves is of course diagonally opposite to the hand of the observer. A much easier form of this test is the imitation of the observers movement as reflected in a mirror.

This simply requires matching without calculation.

The aphasic frequently fails to recognize that when the one hand is brought to his contralateral eye or ear the hand crosses the face. A further part of the test is to ask him to imitate the positions shown in pictorial form upon cards or to carry out the movements from printed and verbal instructions. Finally, he is asked to write down movements made by the observer.

Employing these tests Head divided aphasia into four types, as follows:

1. VERBAL DEFECTS. The outstanding feature is a defect in the utterance of individual words of all kinds. The power to express an idea in words is practically lost. The patient, however is not entirely speechless but can usually utter a few monosyllables, "yes" or "no", etc., or ejaculations and emotional expressions, such as, "damn", "oh dear me". When the disorder is less severe, the words are mispronounced but sentences are correctly constructed. For example, one patient said that he had trouble with "tenical terms" (technical terms) and that he "had *diffulty* in remembering what you do with a skull, *tri-tre-tripine*" (trepan). Another spoke of "*claration* of war by the *Ollies*" (declaration . . . Allies). Another would say "pyramerad" (pyramid), "sissiors" (scissors) and "oboid" (ovoid). Such patients read with difficulty and writing is very defective or impossible. They usually understand printed or oral commands.

2. SYNTACTICAL DEFECTS (agrammatism, jargon dysphasia). The patient is voluble but speaks a jargon in which, though the individual words may be fairly accurately pronounced, they are strung into short phrases or badly constructed sentences without articles, prepositions or conjunctions. The ability to read aloud is impaired, and curiously enough such a patient, though he can write a well constructed letter, may be quite unable to read it coherently. Such a one when asked the contents of a letter which he had just written replied, "I can't; I know, I suppose in time, not now, funny thing, why." In other instances the words themselves are often slurred over, mutilated and may be unrecognizable. Speech sometimes resembles "baby talk". Thus one patient when asked what his right arm felt like replied "Tiffrent from uffer um" (different from other arm). The understanding of ordinary conversation is defective.

3. NOMINAL (NAMING) DEFECTS. In this form of speech disorder the patient has difficulty in finding the right word to express his meaning or

in naming a well known object. He will often employ a descriptive phrase in substitution for the word which he cannot recall. For example, a painter when asked to name a series of colors could not say "violet" but instead explained that "it was made with black, red and a bit of blue." Another when asked to tell the time from a clock which had both hands at 12 replied "That is when you eat." These patients can draw from a model either directly or from memory, after it has been shown and then removed, but are usually unable to draw from imagination. They write a coherent letter with difficulty, usually fail to carry out simple arithmetical exercises and confuse the values of coins.

4. SEMANTIC[8] DEFECTS. A patient suffering from this type experiences little difficulty in articulate speech, can name objects, understands individual words and some sentences, but the general meaning of what he hears escapes him. He often fails to follow his own utterances to an intelligent conclusion, his sentences trailing off as though he had forgotten what he had started out to say. When shown a picture he picks out the details but fails to grasp the meaning which it conveys to others. Such a patient therefore misses the point of a joke whether this is printed, told to him, or is in pictorial form. He fails to comprehend the significance of much that he sees and hears. There is no impairment in the pronunciation of words and, though speech tends to be in short jerky sentences, syntax and intonation are not disturbed.

Head, though he discards the conception that the neural basis of speech consists of strictly localized anatomical "centers" wherein resides *exclusively* one or other of the speech functions—auditory, visual or motor—believes that regions exist in the cortex "where the progress of some mode of action can be reinforced, deviated or inhibited." These regions constitute foci of integration—convergence points for association paths. Destruction of one or other of such foci or "knots" of association paths will depress *as a whole* the psychological processes underlying speech. The speech faculty is disabled; certain faculties are lost, while others are retained. Yet he points out that it is not logical to conclude that the abilities which remain and those which have been abolished constitute essentially separate and distinct functions from which the normal processes of speech have been synthesized, or that they are represented in specific circumscribed areas. To

[8] Semainein = to signify.

make a rather crude comparison—a person who has injured his foot, knee or hip, adjusts his locomotor apparatus as best he can. He hops or limps, yet it cannot be argued that the hopping or the limping motion which he employs is simply one of the component movements employed in the normal act of walking and which the injury has left intact. Nevertheless, the form which the disability assumes is undoubtedly influenced by the site of the injury. The ambulatory abnormality, for example, which results from an injury to the foot is different from that resulting from injury to the knee or hip. So too the nature of the speech disability is influenced by the particular region of the cortex involved. Thus if the lesion is in the neighborhood of the lower part of the precentral and postcentral convolutions of the dominant hemisphere the speech defect tends to be of the *verbal* type. In injury to the temporal lobe the speech defect tends to be of the *syntactical* type. In a lesion in the region of the angular gyrus of the dominant hemisphere the patient has difficulty, particularly, in finding names for things (*nominal defect*); damage to the cortex in the region of the supramarginal gyrus results in a *semantic defect*.

Anarthria or dysarthria is loss or difficulty of speech due to paresis, paralysis or ataxia of the muscles concerned in articulation. There is no impairment of the psychical aspects of speech, i.e., "internal speech" is unaffected; there is no difficulty in the comprehension of spoken or written speech. Other functions, e.g., swallowing, which are dependent upon the same groups of muscles as those used in speech, are also frequently affected. The condition may result from a lesion in the internal capsule or corpus striatum, bulbar nuclei or peripheral fibers, or from disease of the muscles themselves. Since the muscular mechanism of speech is innervated from both sides of the brain unilateral central lesions are not followed by permanent anarthria. A lesion of the cerebellum or of its connections may also cause disordered control of the muscles of articulation.

Apraxia and Agnosia

Apraxia (unable to act) is the inability to perform purposeful movements at will, either at command or in imitation, though the muscles normally engaged in the act are not paralysed. It is allied to aphasia, which might be called apraxia of the speech faculty. Apraxia may be sensory or motor. In the former, the patient does not recognize the significance of an object (visual agnosia), and therefore cannot put it to its proper use; this is simply visual agnosia. When, for example, he is given a pencil he may, upon a request to use it, attempt to clean his teeth with it or smoke it like a pipe. In motor apraxia the patient has no conception, or a very defective one, of the pattern of muscular movement required to perform a purposeful act. For example, apraxia of the tongue is frequently seen in hemiplegic patients. The tongue cannot be protruded upon request, but a moment later the patient may without thought lick his lips. When given an object, and asked to use it, though he recognizes it and knows its use, he cannot form the "motor picture" required to execute the act but manipulates the object in an awkward aimless manner. The defect is not due to disease of the cells of the motor area or of the corticospinal fibers. It is thought to be due to the interruption of association tracts connecting the precentral gyrus with higher psychical regions of the cortex where impressions of the movements of muscles are received, synthesized and stored as kinesthetic memories. This higher ideational area probably lies in the region of the left supramarginal gyrus in right-handed persons. A lesion of this region may cause bilateral apraxia; one confined to the anterior part of the corpus callosum is likely to interrupt fibers passing from the left hemisphere to the right precentral convolution and may cause apraxia of the left side.

Agnosia (not knowing) is a defect of a higher level of consciousness than the mere inability to perceive tactile, visual, auditory or other forms of sensation; it results rather from the failure to interpret sensory impressions which enable an object, sound, symbol, etc., to be recognized and have meaning. A patient suffering from auditory agnosia, for example, cannot appreciate music or the meaning of other sounds. "Word blindness" and "word deafness" are forms of visual and auditory agnosia, respectively. The subject of visual agnosia is unable to name an object, not that he is aphasic in the true sense, but simply because the object is quite strange to him. When shown an object and asked to use it he behaves quite differently from the patient with motor apraxia who recognizes it but is unable to perform the necessary movement.

Astereognosis is a disorder in which though sensations of touch and muscle sense are retained, the patient cannot recognize an object placed in his hand if his eyes are closed. Visual agnosia is seen in lesions of the occipital lobe of the dominant hemisphere, auditory agnosia in injury to the temporal cortex, and astereognosis in lesions of the parietal lobe posterior to the postcentral gyrus.

Agraphia or *dysgraphia*, the inability to write or difficulty in writing, is usually associated with visual agnosia in so far as the recognition of written words is concerned, i.e., word blindness.

Epilepsy

Epilepsy is a disorder arising as the result of an abnormal and severe discharge of nervous energy from some part of the central nervous system, usually the cerebral cortex. Epilepsy may be generalized, involving the entire organism or localized. Generalized seizures are of three types, grand mal, petit mal and psychomotor. In *grand mal* there is an abrupt loss of consciousness and a generalized convulsion. Two stages of the attack or seizure are recognized. In the first or *tonic stage* the muscles contract tonically, the spasms often twisting the facial features and holding the head and limbs in distorted positions. The arms are most commonly flexed and the lower limbs rigidly extended. After a few seconds the tonic spasm gives place to jerking movements, often violent, of the limbs, face and muscles of mastication. This is spoken of as the *clonic stage*. Either during this stage or in the tonic stage the tongue may be bitten. Before the onset of the convulsion a large proportion of epileptics receive a warning in the form of a sensation or hallucination, the character of which varies in individual cases. The warning sensation or *aura*, as it is called, may be auditory, e.g., voices, music, etc., visual, e.g., flashes of light, sparks, etc., olfactory, gustatory, cutaneous, visceral or vasomotor, equilibratory, or anesthetic, i.e., a numbness in some part of the body. Turning of the head and trunk to one side and deviation of the eyes are commonly observed. The patient sometimes utters a cry or scream—the epileptic cry—just before consciousness is lost. After the convulsion the subject remains for a time in a stupor. Sometimes a number of convulsive seizures occur in rapid succession, the patient failing to regain consciousness in the intervals between them. This very serious condition is called *status epilepticus*. Minor seizures known as *petit mal* are characterized by brief periods during which the patient loses contact with his environment. He stares into space. There are no convulsive movements. A third form known as *psychomotor* epilepsy is marked by automatic movements, such as smacking of the lips, chewing, together with a clouded, "dreamy" feeling of unreality, or of having seen or heard before some sight or auditory impression which is actually happening at the moment ("déja vu" or "déja entendu" phenomenon, respectively). Or there may be a confused mental state persisting for a minute or two, or for a longer period. During this time the patient may perform automatic acts of which he is quite unaware and does not remember. Generalized convulsions do not occur nor does the subject fall to the ground during the psychomotor seizure, but patients who have such seizures may also suffer from generalized convulsions. Psychomotor seizures are most commonly due to disturbances in the temporal lobe.

A tumor in the hypothalamic region may cause an outburst of autonomic phenomena.

Localized epilepsy may occur in several different forms. These are often referred to as *Jacksonian epilepsy* because they are indicative of an abnormality in a particular part of the brain. Thus motor Jacksonian seizures are indicative of a disturbance in the precentral motor cortex, hallucinations of taste and smell are indicative of an abnormal nervous discharge from the uncus on the medial surface of the temporal lobe, sensory Jacksonian seizures indicate disease in the parietal region, etc.

Motor Jacksonian seizures commonly begin by a turning of the head and eyes toward the side opposite the lesion in the brain if it is located in the anterior part of the precentral motor cortex, or by a twitching of the foot or leg if it is in the upper part of the precentral region. Such attacks may also begin with a twitching of a finger, or of the hand or the face depending upon the seat of the irritation in the cortex which initiates the attack. These convulsions may remain localized to the part of the body in which they start or they may spread by a steady march to neighboring parts as portions of the cortex lying near to the original focus become involved in the irritative process. The spreading convulsion may cease after extending to all of one extremity or to one side of the body or it may continue until a generalized convulsion has occurred.

Such focal or localized convulsive seizures or seizures with localized onsets may develop as the result of many different kinds of disease processes in the brain. Tumors, abscesses, traumatic scars, vascular abnormalities are among the more common processes found to be responsible for such attacks. It must be noted that not all patients who have such disease processes suffer from epileptic attacks and that even in those patients who do have them the attacks occur at relatively infrequent intervals although the disease process is constantly present. It is thus obvious that some other process, neurological or metabolic, is essential to the development of such seizures. The tumor or scar alone is not enough.

Idiopathic or cryptogenic epilepsy. Epilepsy which cannot be explained by the presence of a demonstrable lesion of the brain is called idiopathic or cryptogenic. Though many theories have been advanced, the cause of this type of the disease remains obscure. There is a tendency today to look upon epilepsy as a symptom, or rather a group of symptoms common to several rather than to a single primary pathological state. Convulsions, whose features are indistinguishable from those of the epileptic seizure, occur in a number of conditions. In animals convulsions may be produced by injections of absinthe or caffeine. Hypocalcemia (ch. 77), hypoglycemia (ch. 67), cerebral edema or anemia and other states may be accompanied by generalized convulsions of an epileptiform character.

With regard to the neural mechanism through which the fits are produced, some authorities have thought that the convulsions are the result of *increased excitability of the cortex* and, therefore, comparable in their mode of production to those of the Jacksonian type, or to those produced by experimental stimulation of the cortex. Others view the convulsions as a *release phenomenon* due to the inhibition of cortical areas which normally exert a controlling influence upon lower motor centers, e.g., weakening of suppressor action. Finally, there is the view of Penfield and his colleagues that the primary disturbance in idiopathic epilepsy has its origin in a subcortical mechanism.

The close correspondence between the convulsive seizure as seen in focal epilepsy or to artificial stimulation of the cortex, and the fits of idiopathic epilepsy appears to support the first alternative as a cause of the generalized seizure known as grand mal. However, the *primary* disturbance responsible for the cortical discharge in idiopathic epilepsy probably lies outside the cortex. Evidence for a subcortical origin of petit mal attacks is provided by electroencephalographic studies. During such an attack, electrical potentials of the wave—spike type (fig. 8.11)—appear synchronously over prefrontal areas as well as from other widely separated cortical areas. This suggests that the cortical discharges are initiated in a common subcortical region (centrencephalic system) connected with extensive areas of the cortex. Jasper and Drooglever-Fortuyn, experimenting with cats produced electrical potentials from wide spread areas of the cortex synchronously in both hemispheres by rhythmical stimulation of a small area (2 mm. in diameter) in the anterior part of the massa intermedia of the thalamus. The cortical potentials were of the wave-spike form characteristic of petit mal.

The nature of the underlying bodily state responsible for the convulsive seizures of idiopathic epilepsy are unknown. There are a number of drugs, e.g., metrazol, which are capable of inducing convulsions, and several others, e.g., phenobarbital and tridione, which are anticonvulsive. Susceptibility to an epileptic seizure is influenced by several physiological and biochemical factors which are given in table 8.1, but they do not bear a specific relationship to the cause of idiopathic epilepsy, but merely affect the tendency to convulsive seizures of any kind.

The view that the actual seizure was initiated by cerebral ischemia resulting from a spasm of the cortical vessels has not been sustained. The blood flow through the brain of epileptics and the oxygen consumption have been found to be no different from that of nonepileptics. In focal epilepsy, however, local ischemia may play a part. Biochemical studies of such epileptogenic areas have not however revealed any important abnormality. The pH of the extracellular fluid shows no change from the normal, or a slight rise.

The induction of a dehydrated state of acidosis (by means of a ketogenic diet) has been employed to reduce the susceptibility of epileptics to seizures but not very effectively, and pitressin combined with an increase in the water intake is used as a test (*water-pitressin test*) in diagnosis. But in only about 30 per cent of epileptics is a seizure precipitated, so a negative result does not exclude epilepsy.

The Electroencephalogram (EEG)

In 1875 Caton first discovered that an electrode placed on the cortex of experimental animals would record spontaneous fluctuations of electrical activity. Although this discovery was widely reported at the time, the EEG did not receive significant attention for over 50 years. It was the work of Berger, reported in 1929, that is usually noted for having stimulated the study of the EEG. Berger reported that changes in electrical potential could be recorded from the head of the human subject by means of electrodes applied to the scalp or needle electrodes placed in contact with the periosteum of the skull. These brain potentials were later studied by Adrian and Matthews. In normal subjects the EEG

FIG. 8.10. Normal electroencephalogram taken from the occipital region. O and C refer, respectively, to open and closed eyes. (After Adrian and Matthews.)

TABLE 8.1

	Conditions Which May Tend To	
	Prevent seizures	Precipitate seizures
Oxygen	Rich supply	Poor supply
Acid-base equilibrium	Acidosis Ingestion of acids or acid-forming salts Breathing CO_2	Alkalosis Hyperpnea— "blowing off" CO_2
Water balance	Dehydration	Edema
Serum calcium	Increase	Decrease (hypocalcemia)
Blood glucose	Normal level	Decrease (hypoglycemia)
Acetylcholine	—	Increase
Cholinesterase	—	Decrease
Body temperature	—	Increase

may be characterized by three frequency bands, the *alpha*, *beta* and *delta* rhythms.[9] The alpha rhythm consists of rhythmical oscillations in electrical potential occurring at the rate of 8 to 10 per second (fig. 8.10). The waves have a voltage of about 50 microvolts on the average. The beta rhythm has a frequency of 15 to 60 per second, and the waves are of lower voltage (5 to 10 microvolts); the frequency of the delta waves is from 1 to 5 per second and the voltage is relatively high (20 to 200 microvolts). No precise cytoarchitectural area can be said to have a characteristic rhythm as was once supposed, but differences are found between rather large areas of the cortex. Thus the alpha rhythm dominates records from the occipital region or from the posterior parts of the parietal and temporal lobes. The sensorimotor region emits waves with a frequency of from 20 to 25 per second; the anterior frontal areas give out waves at the rate of from 8 to 5 per second.

The alpha rhythm occurs in the *inattentive* brain, as in drowsiness or light sleep, narcosis or when the eyes are closed; it is abolished by visual

[9] A faster rhythm (*gamma*) appears in rare instances.

and other types of stimulus or by mental effort (e.g., mathematical calculation). It, therefore diminishes when the eyes are open. This is true even if the subject opens his eyes in the dark and tries to see. It is apparent, therefore, that it is the attention rather than the visual stimulus itself that abolishes the alpha rhythm when the eyes are opened. On the other hand if the visual field is uniform, that is without pattern, or glasses are worn which blur the visual image so that it has no meaning, the rhythm is not abolished. An attempt to discern any detail causes the alpha wave to disappear immediately. A visual field that flickers causes the waves to assume the same rate as that of the flicker within certain definite limits. The delta waves can be recorded very rarely from a normal adult while awake, but appear normally during deep sleep or during the waking hours in early childhood. Generally speaking, their presence in an adult, except during sleep, indicates some pathological process in the brain—tumor, epilepsy, raised intracranial pressure, mental deficiency or depression of consciousness by toxic or other factors. When present they tend to displace the alpha rhythm. Neither the beta nor the delta waves are affected by opening or closing the eyes.

The EEG is affected profoundly by certain general states. *Hypoxia* causes at first a moderate slowing of the rhythm, but as the oxygen lack becomes more severe large delta waves appear; with persistent and severe hypoxia the amplitude of the waves declines and may reach almost the vanishing point. *Hypoglycemia* causes an effect somewhat similar to that of hypoxia; when the blood sugar falls below about 60 mg. per cent, delta waves (1 to 3 per second) are seen, though the alpha rhythm is not abolished entirely. The effects of hypoxia and hypoglycemia enhance one another, their summed effects being much greater than the effect of each alone. Hyperglycemia has little effect upon the cortical potentials. Increase in carbon dioxide tension increases the rate, but reduces the amplitude of the waves. Blowing off of CO_2, as by overbreathing, has the opposite effect.

Abnormalities of the electroencephalogram in brain tumor, especially of so-called silent areas of the brain, and in epilepsy, may be of diagnostic value. In cerebral tumor or brain abscess, as shown by Walter and by Case, the functionally depressed brain tissue surrounding the lesion gives out waves of slow rhythm (delta waves) which, combined with a loss or diminution in the alpha rhythm over the occipital region may be of considerable aid in localization. However, the electroencephalogram may give misleading information as to the location of a brain tumor and a "normal" electroencephalogram in the presence of a brain tumor is not rare.

Epileptic seizures are characterized by pronounced departures from the normal rhythm. In *petit mal* attacks, large slow waves appear about a second before the attack is clinically manifest, and displace the previous rhythm. Each large wave is followed by a sharp spike deflection (fig. 8.11). In the tonic stage of a *grand mal* seizure, waves of relatively high frequency (10 to 30 per second) and of low voltage appear, but as the attack progresses into the clonic phase these fast waves give place to slower and large waves which continue into the stage of stupor following the seizure. Delta waves may be a prominent feature of the electroencephalogram of epileptics between seizures (fig. 8.11). Approximately one-third of

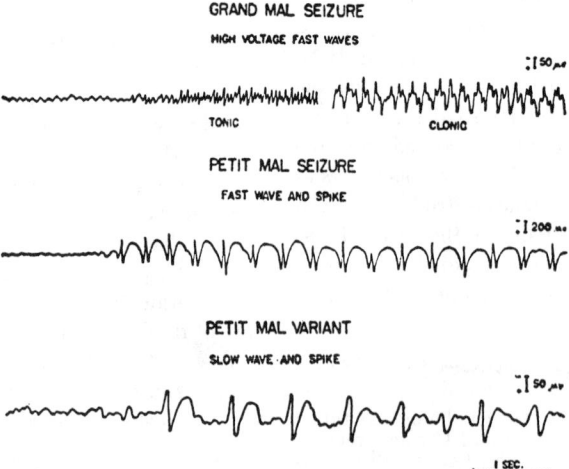

FIG. 8.11. Showing electroencephalograms in epilepsy. (Modified after Gibbs and associates.)

epileptic adults have "normal" electroencephalograms.

Sleep

In normal sleep the pattern of the EEG shows many variations which are to some degree related to the depth of sleep. A number of groups have classified the various EEG patterns seen during the course of a night's sleep and have attempted to correlate these patterns with depth of sleep on the basis of such factors as: reaction time during sleep, intensity of stimulation required for arousal, the order of appearance of the various patterns, and the state of various other physiological variables such as muscle potentials, heart rate, etc. The transition from one EEG pattern to another is not sharp, one pattern fading into the next, which has led to some disagreement over classifications of patterns. For illustrative purposes, however, we may describe one of the more widely utilized classifications, which was basically suggested by Davis et al. Stage A (awake) is characterized by the presence of alpha waves in most individuals which diminish in amplitude and per cent of time present as slight drowsiness appears. In stage B (drowsy) alpha waves further diminish and then vanish with the EEG showing only low voltage fluctuations and infrequent delta waves. Stage C (light sleep) is characterized by 14/sec. spindle bursts superimposed on a low voltage delta wave background. In stage D (medium sleep) delta wave frequency becomes lower with a greater amplitude and the spindle bursts disappear. In stage E (deep sleep) the delta waves become more prominent with higher amplitude and longer duration waves. The major aspects of these changes are illustrated in fig. 8.12.

Within the past decade a major deviation from the above correlation between EEG pattern and depth of sleep has been suggested and/or explored by several groups (Dement and Kleitman, 1957; Jouvet, 1961; Coleman et al, 1959). This stage is characterized by an EEG similar in appearance to that of stage C with, however, a state of consciousness considerably lower than that ascribed to the original stage C. In addition, muscular tension, particularly of the neck muscles, is considerably decreased, thresholds for arousal are raised, and rapid conjugate eye movements are most likely to appear during this state. Awakening of human subjects during this and other states of sleep have shown that the probability of recalling a dream is much greater during these periods of rapid eye movements than during

other states of sleep. There have even been attempts to correlate dream content with the nature of the eye movements, with rapid horizontal eye movements signifying perhaps a dream such as watching a tennis match, and vertical eye movements representing a dream about diving, etc. Since this state of sleep appears to be a deep sleep (on the basis of thresholds, muscular tone, etc.) with an EEG traditionally considered to be characteristic of light sleep, it is referred to as paradoxical sleep. It is also called REM (Rapid Eye Movement) sleep, or rhombencephalic sleep because it appears to be dependent on rhombencephalic structures.

On the basis of the phenomena described above it has been suggested that there may exist two different forms of sleep. One, called slow sleep, would correspond to the events described by Davis et al. which culminate with prominent delta waves. The other form of sleep is paradoxical sleep.

MECHANISMS OF SLEEP

Slow Sleep

An analysis of the mechanisms of sleep is perhaps best started with a description of the classic study by Bremer (1938). Bremer transected the brain stem of cat in the midcollicular region creating what he referred to as a "cerveau isolé preparation." Such a preparation appears to be chronically asleep (in coma). It cannot be effectively aroused; the EEG takes on an appearance characteristic of sleep, the pupils of the eyes are constricted, and the nictitating membrane partially covers the eyes. If instead the transection is at the level between the cord and medulla (encephale isolé) the EEG shows the waking pattern (fig. 8.13). If the encephale isolé preparation is a long term one, the EEG will spontaneously alternate at appropriate intervals between waking and sleep patterns, and the EEG can be changed from a sleep to an awake pattern (defined as EEG activation) by sensory stimuli. Bremer's interpretation of these findings was that the sleep produced by midcollicular transection was the result of the removal of a significant portion of the sensory inflow by the interruption of many ascending pathways. The encephale isolé preparation, on the other hand, left a larger portion of the ascending sensory pathways intact (trigeminal, vestibular, auditory).

Approximately 10 years later Lindsley et al. (1950) further analyzed the basis of the phe-

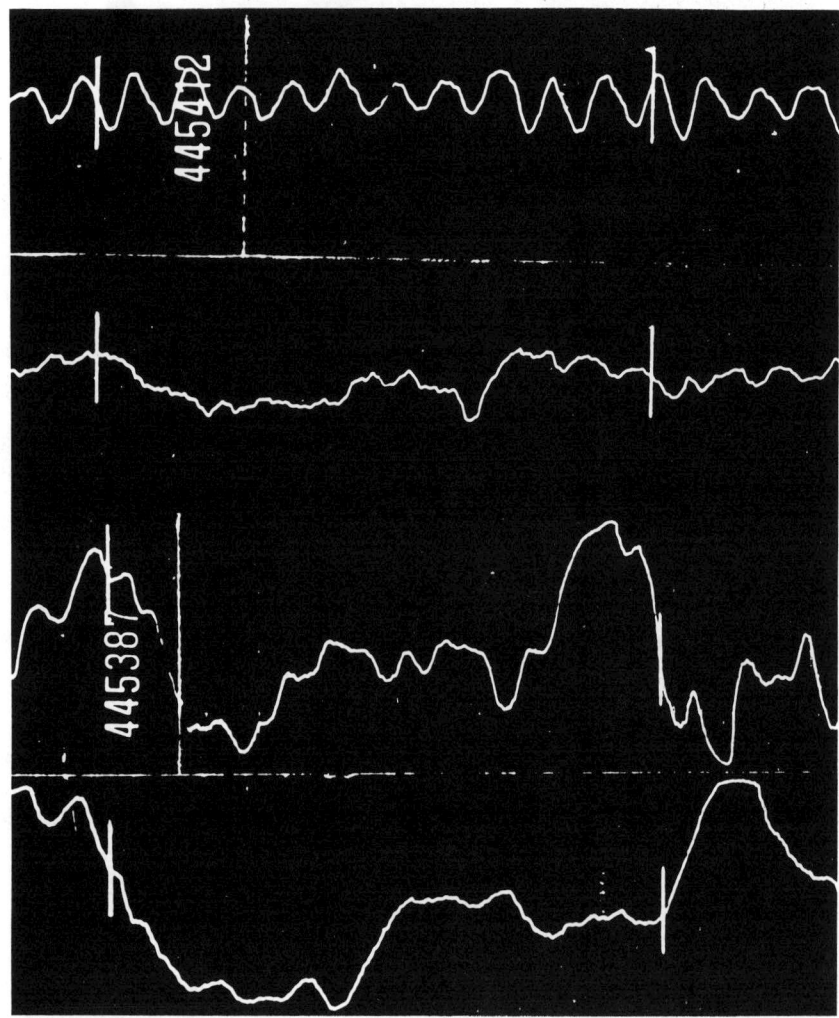

FIG. 8.12. Changes in the electroencephalogram with sleep. The top record represents the relaxed, awake state with eyes closed. Alpha waves are very prominent. Next, the alpha waves have all but disappeared, and the record consists basically of low voltage fluctuations. Next, the low frequency delta waves are becoming prominent, and in the bottom record the delta waves are more prominent, with longer duration waves. (After Coleman).

nomena seen in the cerveau isolé preparation. They made more localized lesions in either the lateral brain stem interrupting the specific afferent (lemniscal) pathways or in the central brain stem in the reticular formation (fig. 8.14). It was found that only the reticular formation lesions caused the permanent somnolence seen in the cerveau isolé preparation, leading to the conclusion that the somnolence of the cerveau isolé resulted from interruption of the ascending reticular system, *not* from interruption of the specific sensory inflow to the cortex. Furthermore, Moruzzi and Magoun (1949) showed that electrical stimulation of the reticular formation could transform a high voltage slow (sleep)

EEG into the low voltage fast EEG characteristic of the awake, alert animal. This change in the EEG is termed activation or desynchronization. The influence of the ascending reticular activating system (ARAS) on cortical activity is transmitted via a pathway from reticular formation to non-specific thalamic nuclei then to cortex. The portions of the reticular formation that are concerned with activation of the cortical EEG are, to some degree, under the control of the cortex. Segundo, Naquet and Buser (1955) have shown that electrical stimulation of certain cortical regions will produce an EEG desynchronization which appears to be identical to the desynchronization shown by Moruzzi and Ma-

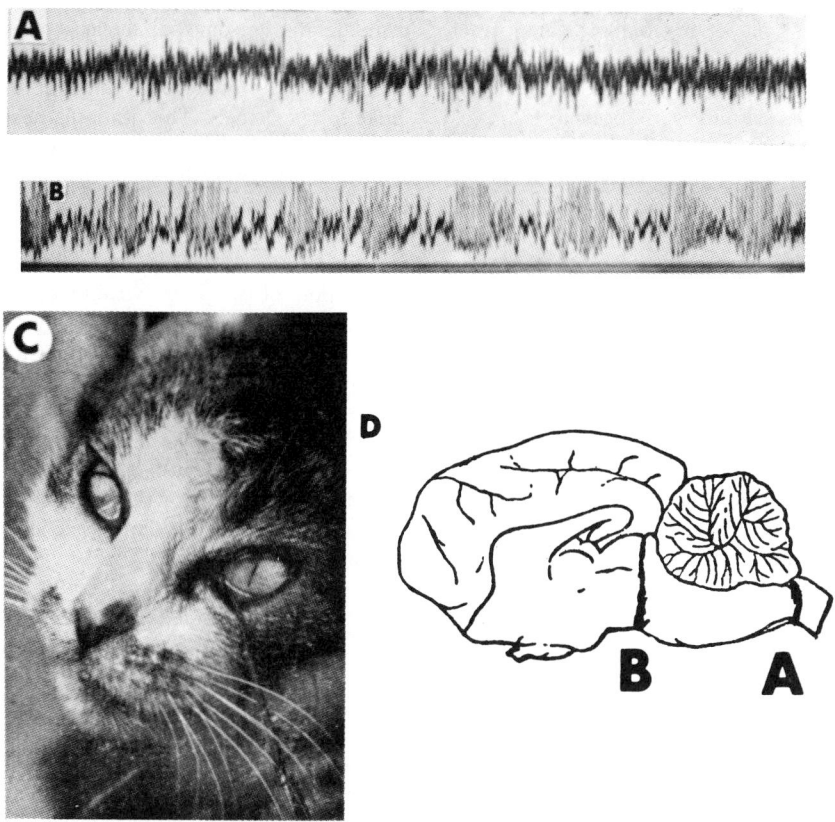

Fig. 8.13. Electrocorticograms from the surface of the cat brain showing waking record (a) of *encephale isolé* following section at bulbospinal juncture (D–A); and sleeping record (B) of *cerveau isolé* following mesencephalic section (D–B). The sleeping appearance of the latter is seen in C. (After Bremer, 1937.)

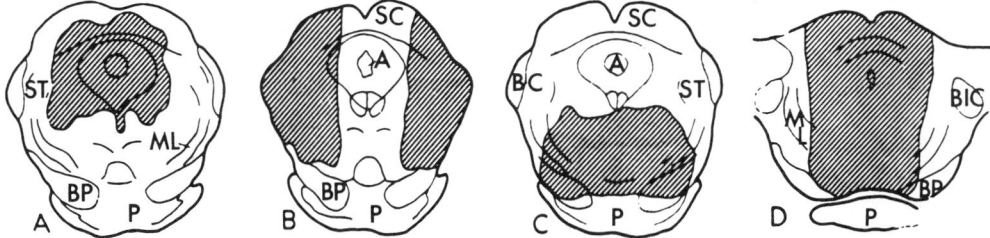

Fig. 8.14. Transverse sections of the brain stem at the collicular level. Cross-hatchings indicate lesions of periaqueductal grey (A), lateral sensory pathways (B), and tegmental reticular formation (C), plus more dorsal structures (D). Only lesions illustrated in C and D gave rise to chronic somnalence. (After Lindsley, Bowden and Magoun.)

goun to result from electrical stimulation of the ARAS. Presumably, this cortical control is affected over a corticofugal pathway to the brain stem reticular formation. The existence of such a pathway has been demonstrated electrophysiologically by French et al. (1955) and by Jasper et al. (1952). Both groups showed that stimulation of wide areas of cerebral cortex would produce evoked potentials in the brain stem reticular formation. Thus we see a system of reciprocal connections in which the cerebral cortex can influence the activity of the ARAS and the ARAS can, in turn, act back on the cortex. The functioning of this system in the control of the sleep-wakefulness cycle appears to be the production of the wakefulness portion of the cycle.

Other regions have also been found to produce wakefulness upon stimulation or somnolence after lesions. Ranson (1939) demonstrated that lesions of the lateral hypothalamus plus mammillary bodies (and/or mammillothalamic tract) produce somnolence in monkeys. Stimulation of these same areas through chronically implanted electrodes causes animals to become alert and active. Subsequent work (Nauta, 1946) suggests that the mammillary bodies may be of greater importance than the lateral hypothalamus in producing these effects.

It becomes appropriate at this point to wonder whether "sleep" areas exist in the brain which act in balance with the wakefulness regions of the reticular system and hypothalamus. In contrast with the somnolence or coma produced by reticular or mammillary body lesions it has been found (Nauta, 1939) that bilateral lesions of the hypothalamic preoptic nucleus produce a continuously wakeful state. Stimulation of this region produces sleep. Nauta has concluded that the pre-optic nucleus constitutes a hypothalamic sleep center. Destruction of both the pre-optic sleep center and the mammillary bodies produces the same degree of somnolence as is produced by lesions of the mammillary bodies alone, leading to the conclusion that the pre-optic sleep center acts by producing an inhibitory effect on the mammillary bodies.

The most important "sleep" region, however, appears to lie in the thalamus. W. R. Hess (1957), in a program of research that began in 1925, has shown that electrical stimulation of the thalamus will produce sleep in conscious, unrestrained animals with chronically implanted electrodes. These results are obtained if the region stimulated is lateral to the ventral half of the massa intermedia.

In comparison to stimulation of hypothalamic sleep regions, thalamic stimulation produces a more highly organized sequence of behavior leading to sleep. Both Hess and Parmeggiani (1964) have described a series of behaviors progressing through yawning and searching for a place to sleep, closing the eyes and then, finally, sleep. Just as the wakefulness system is subject to cortical influences, the thalamic and hypothalamic sleep regions also appear to be under some degree of cortical control. Velasco and Lindsley (1965) have show that ablation of the orbital cortex will abolish thalamically induced recruiting responses and spontaneous spindle bursts, which are seen during some phases of sleep. This suggest that orbital cortex is a vital link in a neuronal circuit responsible for sleep spindles and EEG synchronization. The orbital cortex has reciprocal connections with the intralaminar dorsomedial nucleus of the thalamus (pars magnocellularis), which, as we have already seen, is one of the thalamic regions related to the ARAS. This leads us again to the question of the relationship between the sleep and wakefulness systems, with the indication that the two systems partially occupy some of the same structures. Indeed, several studies have shown that the effects produced by electrical stimulation of sleep or wakefulness regions is strongly dependent on the frequency of stimulation, with low frequency of stimulation able to produce sleep and high frequency stimulation of the same point yielding arousal or EEG desynchronization. This has been demonstrated in both sleep and wakefulness regions. Thus, low frequency stimulation of the wakefulness regions of the brain stem reticular formation has been shown to lead to sleep and high frequency stimulation of Hess' thalamic sleep center will lead to arousal. We need not assume that sleep and wakefulness centers are always the same structures, however, since these electrical stimulation studies show a high degree of sensitivity to electrode location. In addition, results of lesion studies, including those cited above, also show that differential effects (either sleep or wakefulness) are produced by lesions in sleep or wakefulness regions. It seems more reasonable at this time, to assume that the incompletely described complex anatomical and functional relationships among sleep and wakefulness structures allow for a variety of alternate patterns of balance among the subsystems involved. Frequency of stimulation could strongly influence the pattern of balance by differentially activating various neuron populations, depending on differences in requirements for temporal summation.

Paradoxical Sleep

In describing the electroencephalographic correlates of sleep (above), a dissociation between EEG and other signs of sleep was noted. In this state the EEG is indicative of a lighter sleep than is suggested by a variety of other physiological and behavioral measures. The existence of this paradoxical sleep, or REM sleep, has suggested a second type of sleep, characterized by low voltage fast EEG, profound atonia of the somatic musculature and rapid conjugate eye movements. In addition, recordings from deep structures and cortex show a theta (4 to 7 cycles per second) pattern in the hippocampus and intermittent bursts of activity in the lateral geniculate and visual cortex. Jouvet has classified the phenomena of paradoxical sleep into two categories, tonic and phasic. Tonic phenomena include the EEG, hippocampal theta rhythms, and muscular atonia. Phasic phenomena include the rapid eye movements, the bursts of activity in lateral geniculate and striate cortex, and occasional muscle twitches. In a series of studies in which lesions were placed in a variety of regions, Jouvet (1963) has determined that the structures apparently responsible for the phasic components of paradoxical sleep are the rhombencephalic nucleus reticularis pontis candalis and the lateral region of nucleus reticularis pontis oralis. Stimulation of these regions during normal sleep produces paradoxical sleep.

More recently Jouvet has found that bilateral lesions in the region of the locus caeruleus will suppress or abolish the tonic component of paradoxical sleep without affecting the phasic component. Animals in which the tonic component has been abolished by such lesions show considerably increased muscle twitching during phasic paradoxical sleep.

HUMORAL MECHANISMS OF SLEEP AND WAKEFULNESS. Legendre and Pieron (1910) suggested that an unknown substance, which they called hypnotoxin, found in the cerebrospinal fluid (CSF) is involved in producing sleep. They observed that CSF removed from fatigued animals and injected intracisternally into normal, rested animals tended to induce sleep. Schnedorf and Ivy (1939) replicated these experiments with additional controls. Dogs that received CSF from fatigued dogs apparently went into a deep sleep. Control dogs, which received CSF from rested dogs, or injections of their own CSF, however, also showed some depression but to a lesser extent.

The existence of an activating substance has been suggested by Purpura (1956). He connected each femoral artery of a cat to a femoral vein of a second cat and *vice versa* to obtain intermixing of the total blood volume. Stimulation of the medial bulbar reticular formation produced immediate cortical activation in the stimulated cat. After about 60 sec. an activation pattern could be seen in the electrocorticogram of the recipient cat. Unfortunately, Purpura was unable, on the basis of available evidence, to advance an hypothesis concerning the identity of the circulating activator substance.[10]

More recently, Monnier and Hosli (1965) have reported that dialysate from venous blood of sleeping or active donor rabbits will produce sleep or alert behavior, respectively, when injected into the circulation of recipient rabbits.

The more recent studies of paradoxical sleep have suggested humoral mechanisms controlling this form of sleep also. Among the more ingenious studies in this area was one by Jouvet et al. (1964) who devised a method of differentially depriving animals of paradoxical sleep but not slow sleep. Jouvet placed cats on a brick in a shallow pool of water for periods of days. The animals maintained sufficient muscle tone during slow sleep to be able to keep from falling into the water. During paradoxical sleep, muscle tone decreased to the point that the animals fell into the water, waking up. Animals deprived in this fashion of paradoxical sleep seemed to build up a need for paradoxical sleep, for when allowed to sleep normally the percentage of sleeping time devoted to paradoxical sleep was far greater than normal. This build-up of a need for paradoxical sleep is attributed to the accumulation of an unidentified substance during paradoxical sleep deprivation. Related studies in which humans were deprived of paradoxical sleep, by being awakened whenever EEG and eye movement records indicated paradoxical sleep, also show the same build-up of need for paradoxical sleep. This accumulation can be suppressed by monoamine oxidase inhibitors. For example, administration of Nialamide to animals deprived of paradoxical sleep will prevent the subsequent appearance of paradoxical sleep. 5-Hydroxytryptophan will also suppress paradoxical sleep. Gamma-butyrolactone in doses of approximately 50 mg./kg. will produce paradoxical sleep and large doses of Reserpine will differentially produce the phasic phenomena of paradoxical sleep. On the basis of such evidence, Jouvet has suggested that the substance accumulating during paradoxical sleep deprivation may be an amine.

Memory

The exact nature of the changes in the nervous system that constitute the memory trace remains, to a great degree, unknown. There are, however, a number of studies that shed some light on this fascinating problem.

One of the early speculations concerning the

[10] For a brief discussion of neurohumoral reticular mechanisms the reader is referred to the Handbook of Physiology, Sect. I: Neurophysiology, Vol. II, 1960, pp. 1288 ff.

establishment of the memory trace is generally attributed to Müller and Pilzecker (1900). In order to account for the phenomenon of decreased retention of recently learned material when another activity intervenes between initial learning and retention testing, Müller and Pilzecker proposed the existence of a neural perseverative process. This perseverative process was presumed to be easily interfered with by external influences and was also considered necessary to the consolidation of the memory trace for recently learned material. This, then, constituted one of the early suggestions that the establishment of a memory trace took place in two stages; an initial stage in which the memory trace was evanescent and easily disrupted, and a later, more stable state, dependent on the initial process and which would be the "permanent" memory trace.

Until approximately the late 1930's, the only evidence in support of such a proposal was the retrograde amnesia seen in many patients after cerebral trauma. A large number of cases were recorded in which head injuries were followed by loss of memory for events occurring during the period preceding the injury. The advent of electroshock therapy in the late 1930's offered further evidence for the two-stage nature of the establishment of the memory trace. Many people who used or studied electro-convulsive shock (ECS) found that it too produced a differential loss of memory only for events immediately preceding the shock treatment (e.g. Williams, 1950).

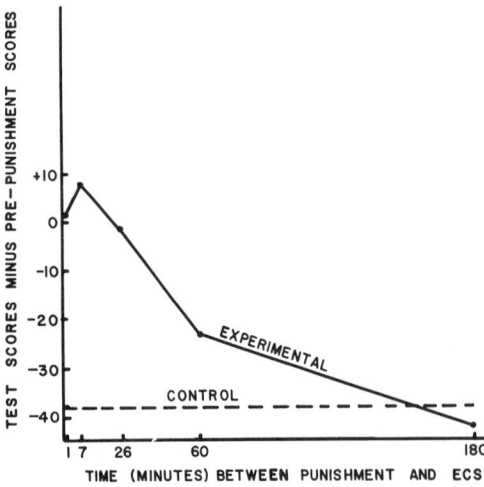

FIG. 8.15. Effect of ECS on retention as a function of time interval between original learning and ECS. A test minus prepunishment score of zero indicates complete forgetting. Control data extended from 1 min. for ease of comparison. (From Heriot and Coleman.)

The time course of the effects of ECS on the memory trace has since been explored in a number of studies. For example, Heriot and Coleman (1962) trained rats to press a lever for a food reward. Then the lever was electrified so that the animals received a shock when the lever was touched. After this, animals avoided the lever. The animals were divided into groups which received an ECS at intervals ranging from 1 to 180 min. after being shocked by the lever. Control animals received no ECS but were shocked through the feet. In later retesting, control animals and animals receiving ECS 180 min. after being shocked by the lever showed a significant decrease in number of lever pressings. Animals receiving ECS within 26 min. after being shocked by the lever, pressed the lever at the same rate as before being shocked by the lever: they apparently did not remember their unpleasant experience with the lever. The results are shown in fig. 8.15 which indicates that the duration of the initial stage of the establishment of the memory trace is between 60 and 180 min. Other studies have shown that this consolidation phase may require from about 15 min. to possibly several months (Gellhorn, 1945), depending on the learning situation and on the procedure used in disrupting the consolidation. Other procedures that have been successfully utilized to disrupt the consolidation phase include hypothermia, insulin coma, Metrazol convulsions, anoxia, some anaesthetic agents, and application of chemicals or electrical stimulation to local regions of the brain. The latter two will be discussed in more detail below.

The exact nature of the initial, or consolidation, phase in the establishment of the memory trace remains unknown, but there is considerable support for the hypothesis that repeated excitation of neurones in a reverberatory or closed circuit maintains the memory until the permanent changes underlying fixation of the memory trace have been completed. This hypothesis has its anatomical roots in the demonstration of local reverberatory circuits by Lorenté de No and the many positive feedback loops known to exist within the brain. The studies of Burns (1958) on the electrical activity of neuronally isolated slabs of cerebral cortex (with blood supply relatively intact) suggest that the maintained neural activity proposed for the initial phase of memory establishment may derive to some degree from the phenomenon of differential repolarization. Once a neuron fires, the different portions of the cell (dendrites, soma, and initial segment of the axon) may repolarize at differential rates. The current flow through the initial segment resulting from the consequent potential differences among regions of the cell may fire the cell again in a repetitive process. Burns has demonstrated that a single train of electrical stimuli can initiate bursts of activity lasting for 30 min. or more in a slab of isolated neural tissue, presumably reflecting activity in reverberatory circuits or differential repolarization or both.

The nature of the long lasting, stable second phase of the memory trace is also not yet established. An early suggestion was that active neurons can attract the growth of processes of other neurons, thereby strengthening synaptic transmission between the neurons (Kappers, 1921). This process is termed neurobiotaxis. Although several studies have demonstrated growth of neural processes in the central nervous system, there is no evidence that such growth is stimulated by learning. There are, however, many indications that intracellular protein synthesis involving ribonucleic acid (RNA) may play a vital role in the long-term memory trace. In order to reconcile the persistence of memory with the high rates of turnover of molecules within neurons shown by radioisotope studies, it seemed logical to consider a substance capable of preserving a structural modification by continually imposing on molecules being formed within neural tissue a structure that could be determined by learning and experience. One of the first to suggest that RNA might be this substance was Hydén (1959). At that time Hydén was able to show that stimulation of the brain tissues of rats and rabbits caused an increase of RNA in the neurons. In later studies Hydén dissected out, and chemically analyzed, single cells from the lateral vestibular nucleus of rats trained to climb and balance on a steel wire inclined at a 45-degree slope, in order to obtain food. He found that significant changes took place in the composition of the nuclear RNA. Of the four amino acids that form RNA—adenine, cytosine, guanine, and uracil—Hydén found an increase in adenine and a fall in cytosine. More recently there have appeared reports of studies which suggest that RNA altered by learning may transfer the memory trace from a trained animal to a naïve animal. One group (Babich et al., 1965) trained one group of rats to press a lever for food in a Skinner box only when a blinking light was on. Another group of rats was trained to press a lever for food only when a click was sounded. RNA was then extracted from the brains (excluding cerebellum, brain stem, olfactory bulbs and prefrontal areas) of these animals and injected intraperitoneally into untrained rats. Some of the untrained rats received RNA from light-trained rats, others received RNA from click-trained rats. The untrained rats were then tested in a Skinner box for number of lever presses, with both click and light flash (at separate times). The click-injected group responded more to click than to light, and the light-injected group responded more to light than to click.

The interpretation of this experiment and other similar studies (Nissen et al., 1965) leave several issues open to question. Of primary importance is the problem of the specificity of the RNA for a particular learned task. It may be that what is transferred is a behavior tendency rather than a specific learned response to a particular stimulus. The experiment of Babich, et al. suggests, but does not prove, specificity. Experiments by Nissen, et al. show that untrained rats receiving intracisternal injection of RNA from rats trained to run down either a lighted or a dark runway responded in a reverse manner; animals injected with light-trained RNA performed better when reinforced for going into a dark runway and animals injected with dark-trained RNA performed better when reinforced for going into a lighted runway. The reason for this reversal is not known, but such a result would certainly not be predicted by the hypothesis that RNA transfers specific memory traces.

Recent attempts to replicate these experiments (e.g., Luttges et al., 1966) have met with failure. The current status of the transfer of specific memory traces by means of RNA injections is, therefore, somewhat dubious.

Other approaches in addition to studies of the transfer of memory by means of RNA injection suggest a role for RNA in memory. Dingman and Sporn (1961) studied the effects of 8-Azaguanine on learning in rats in a water maze. 8-Azaguanine is so similar to the guanine component of RNA that enzymes responsible for RNA synthesis will employ the 8-Azaguanine rather than guanine and proceed to manufacture an RNA quite unlike the usual product. It was first demonstrated that 8-Azaguanine did not affect the ability of rats to swim through a maze learned some time beforehand. In other words, 8-Azaguanine did not affect recall and performance of a well-established memory trace. Ding-man and Sporn next injected rats with 8-Aza-guanine and then tried to teach them to swim a new maze. The injected rats made twice as many errors as a control group, suggesting that the formation of new memory traces is depressed when RNA synthesis is interfered with.

Another study (Flexner et al., 1963) indicates that previously established memory traces are disrupted when animals are given injections which may suppress protein synthesis by neuronal RNA. Mice were trained to run to one arm of a Y-maze. At various times after training, the animals were given local intracerebral injections of puromycin, an antibiotic which inhibits protein synthesis in vivo. The intracerebral injections were administered bilaterally in either the temporal region, the ventricular region, or the frontal region and all combinations of these sites. Studies of the distribution of the dye, fluorescein, showed that in frontal injections the puromycin was probably distributed to the frontal neocortex and pyriform cortex and frontal portions of the corpus striatum. With temporal injection the distribution was to hippocampus and posterior cortex. Ventricular injection showed

TABLE 8.2
Effects of different sites of injection of puromycin on short-term memory (injection one day after learning) and longer-term memory (injection 11 or more days after learning).

T, V, and F refer to temporal, ventricular, and frontal sites of injection. All injections were given bilaterally. (From Flexner et al.).

Site of puromycin injection	Number of mice in which memory was	
	Lost	Retained
Short-term memory		
T + V + F	7	0
T	22	1
V	0	5
F	0	5
F + V	0	2
Long-term memory		
T + V + F	7	0
T	0	7
V	0	3
F	0	3
V+F, V+T, T+F	1	7

a distribution similar to temporal injection but spared the ventral cortex around the caudal rhinal fissure. The results obtained are shown in table 8.2. Short-term memory was lost only with the temporal injections. Loss of longer-term memory required puromycin over basically the entire cortex and possibly the thalamus as well. Various control injections, including puromycin hydrolyzed at the glycosidic bond were without effect on memory. In order to demonstrate that the effect of puromycin in destroying memory is not due to disorganization or incapacitation of the animals, mice were trained to run to one arm of the Y-maze and then 3 weeks later were trained to run to the other arm of the maze. One day after this reversal learning, puromycin was injected at the temporal site. On testing in the Y-maze, the animals reverted to the choice consistent with the older, initial learning, thus demonstrating that they were perfectly capable of performing the learned task.

Although this study does not prove that the effects found are due to inhibition of intraneuronal protein synthesis by RNA, the results are consistent with this hypothesis. Alternative explanations include interference with protein synthesis at some other point or an effect of puromycin unrelated to protein synthesis. Nevertheless, this study is quite useful in clarifying the different anatomical regions concerned with the initial, or consolidation, phase and with the second, stable, phase in the establishment of the memory trace. The results are consistent with the conclusion "that the hippocampal zone is the site of recent memory and, that an extensive part of the neocortex is concerned with longer term memory."

Studies of human patients have also implicated the hippocampus and associated structures in recent memory. Scoville and Milner (1957) and Penfield and Milner (1958) reported loss of recent memory after bilateral extirpations of the hippocampus and hippocampal gyrus. Unilateral excisions of these structures or bilateral excision of the uncus and amygdala alone are without effect on recent memory. These patients retain all old skills and other learned material, but are unable to incorporate new information to the point that they can not learn the way to the bathroom in a new environment.

Lesions that are effective in differentially producing loss of recent memory in man extend beyond the hippocampus itself to include the related structures, the fornix and the mammillary bodies. Williams and Pennybacker (1954), in a survey of 180 patients with verified brain lesions, found that a specific deficit in recent memory was probable when the lesion was in the floor of the third ventricle, involving the mammillary region. There have been isolated reports of loss of recent memory following bilateral surgical sectioning of the fornix.

No studies have delimited any single region of the brain as *the* site of long-term memory. Many studies have shown deficits in the retention of specific tasks after extirpation of localized portions of cortex or subcortical structures without any generalized deficit of long term memory per se. For example, a learned auditory intensity discrimination task is lost after removal of auditory cortex (Raab and Ades, 1946). However, tasks involving other modalities are not lost, and the auditory intensity discrimination can be relearned. It would seem that, although the capacities necessary for performance of the task may have resided in the cortex in the intact animal, sub-cortical centers were capable of providing the requisite capacities for learning the discrimination after the cortical removal. In fact, learning (avoidance conditioning) has been shown to be possible in the totally decorticate dog (Bromiley, 1948).

Other evidence has demonstrated that the long-term memory trace is established in more than one location. Myers (1955) has performed midsaggital surgical transection of the optic chiasma in cats in order to destroy the crossing retinal fibers. If such an animal is taught visual pattern discrimination tasks with a patch covering one eye the visual input is only to the hemisphere ipsilateral to the uncovered eye. Nevertheless, after one-eyed learning these chiasm-sectioned animals are able to perform almost perfectly when tested with only the other eye open, the eye through which the initial learning took place now being covered. This transfer is seen even if the hemisphere in which the initial learning took place is ablated. These results demonstrate that, although the visual inputs provided the animal during learning went directly to only one hemisphere, the memory trace was established in both hemispheres. If the same experiment is conducted in animals with both chiasm section and section of the neocortical commissures (corpus callosum and anterior commissure, the so-called "split brain" preparation) the animals fail to recall through one eye tasks learned with the other eye. Re-learning of the tasks takes as long as initial learning through

first eye. More recent work (Sechzer, 1963) has shown that, using certain learning situations, some interhemispheric transfer can take place even in the "split brain" preparation through the midline crossings remaining at lower levels.

Current evidence, then, indicates that the capacity for long-term memory is widely diffused throughout the nervous system with the memory trace stored in multiple locations in the intact animal.

REFERENCES

ADRIAN, E. D. J. Physiol., 1941, **100**, 159.

ADRIAN, E. D. AND MATTHEWS, B. H. C. Brain, 1934, **57**, 355.

ALBE-FESSARD, D., ROCHA-MIRANDA, C., AND OSWALDO-CRUZ, E. EEG Clin. Neurophysiol., 1959, **11**, 777.

ALBE-FESSARD, D. AND ROUGEUL, A. EEG Clin. Neurophysiol., 1958, **10**, 131.

ALVAREZ, W. C. Physiol. Rev., 1924, **4**, 352.

AMASSIAN, V. J. Neurophysiol., 1954, **17**, 39.

BABICH, F., JACOBSON, A., BUBASH, S., AND JACOBSON, A. Worm Runners Digest, 1965, **7**, 11.

BAILEY, P. AND VON BONIN, G. The isocortex of man. University of Illinois Press, 1951.

BERMAN, A. L. J. Neurophysiol., 1961, **24**, 608.

BORNSTEIN, W. S. Yale J. Biol. & Med., 1940, **12**, 719.

BREMER, F. C. R. Soc. Biol. (Paris), 1935, **118**, 1235.

BREMER, F. Bull. Acad. Roy. Med. Belg., 1937, **2**, 68.

BRICKNER, R. M. Assn. Res. Nerv. & Ment. Dis. Proc., 1934, **13**, 259.

BROMILEY, R. B. J. Comp. Physiol. Psychol., 1948, **41**, 102.

BUCY, P. C. Brain, 1957, **80**, 376.

BUCY, P. C. AND FULTON, J. F. Brain, 1933, **56**, 318.

BUCY, P. C. AND KLÜVER, H. Arch. Neurol. & Psychiat., 1940, **44**, 1142; J. Comp. Neurol., 1955, **103**, 151.

BUCY, P. C. AND PRIBRAM, K. H. Arch. Neurol. & Psychiat., 1943, **50**, 456.

BURNS, B. D. The mammalian cerebral cortex, Arnold, 1958.

BUSER, P., BORENSTEIN, P., AND BRUNER, J. EEG Clin. Neurophysiol., 1959, **11**, 305.

CASE, T. J. J. Nerv. & Ment. Dis., 1938, **87**, 598.

CHANG, H. T., RUCH, T. C., AND WARD, A. A. J. Neurophysiol., 1947, **10**, 39.

CHOW, K. L. J. Comp. Neurol., 1950, **93**, 313.

CLARK, W.E.Le G. Lancet, 1948, **1**, 353.

COLEMAN, P. D., GRAY, F. E., AND WATANABE, K. J. Appl. Physiol., 1959, **14**, 397.

DAVIS, H., DAVIS, P. A., LOOMIS, A. L., HARVEY, E. N., AND HOBART, G. J. Neurophysiol., 1938, **1**, 24.

DEMENT, W. AND KLEITMAN, N. EEG Clin. Neurophysiol., 1957, **9**, 673.

DEMPSEY, E. W. AND MORISON, R. S. Amer. J. Physiol., 1942, **135**, 293.

DEMPSEY, E. W. AND MORISON, R. S. Amer. J. Physiol., 1943, **138**, 283.

DINGMAN, W. AND SPORN, M. B. J. Psychiat. Res., 1961, **1**, 1.

FLEXNER, J. B., FLEXNER, L. B., AND STELLAR, E. Science, 1963, **141**, 57.

FRENCH, J. D., HERNANDEZ-PEON, R., AND LIVINGSTON, R. B. J. Neurophysiol., 1955, **18**, 74.

GELLHORN, E. Proc. Soc. Exp. Biol. Med., 1945, **59**, 155.

GIBBS, F. A., GIBBS, E. L., AND LENNOX, W. G. Brain, 1935, **58**, 44.

GLEES, P. AND COLE, J. J. Neurophysiol., 1950, **13**, 137.

HAGBARTH, K. E. AND KERR, D. I. J. Neurophysiol., 1954, **17**, 295.

HALSTEAD, W. C. Brain and intelligence; a quantitative study of the frontal lobes. Univ. of Chicago Press, 1947.

HANBERRY, J. AND JASPER, H. H. J. Neurophysiol., 1953, **16**, 252.

HERIOT, J. T. AND COLEMAN, P. D. J. Comp. Physiol. Psychol., 1962, **55**, 1082.

HESS, W. R. The functional organization of the diencephalon. Grune and Stratton, 1957.

HOLMES, G. AND MAY, W. P. Brain, 1909, **32**, 1.

HYDÉN, H. in Fourth international congress of biochemistry. (F. BRUCKE (ed.)) Vol. III: Biochemistry of the central nervous system. Pergamon, 1959, pp. 64–89.

JASPER, H. H. AND AJMONE-MARSAN, C. A. Res. Nerv. Ment. Dis. Res. Pubs., 1952, **30**, 493.

JASPER, H. H., AJMONE-MARSAN, C., AND STOLL, J. Arch. Neurol & Psychiat., 1952, **67**, 155.

JOUVET, M. in The nature of sleep. (WOLSTENHOLME, G. E. W. AND O'CONNOR, M. (eds.)) Little, Brown & Co., 1961.

JOUVET, M. The rhombencephalic phase of sleep in: Progress in brain research, vol. 1. Elsevier, 1963.

JOUVET, D., VIAMONT, P., DELORME, J. AND JOUVET, M. C. R. Soc. Biol. (Paris), 1964.

KAPPERS, C. U. A. Brain, 1921, **44**, 125.

KENNARD, M. A. Arch. Neurol. & Psychiat., 1935, **33**, 698.

KENNARD, M. A. AND ECTORS, L. J. Neurophysiol., 1938, **1**, 45.

KUYPERS, H. Science, 1958, **128**, 662.

LEGENDRE, R. AND PIERON, H. C. R. Soc. Biol., (Paris), 1910, **68**, 1077.

LINDSLEY, D. B., BOWDEN, J. W. AND MAGOUN, H. W. Clin. Neurophysiol., 1949, **1**, 475.

LINDSLEY, D. B., SCHREINER, L. H., KNOWLES, W. B., AND MAGOUN, H. W. EEG Clin. Neurophysiol., 1950, **2**, 423.

LOE, P. AND COLEMAN, P. D. Unpublished observations, 1965.

LORENTÉ DE NO, R. J. Neurophysiol., 1938, **1**, 207.

LUTTGES, M., JOHNSON, T., BUCK, C., HOLLAND, J., AND MCGAUGH, J. Science, 1966, **151**, 834.

MONNIER, M. AND HOSLI, L. in Progress in brain Research, vol. 18 (AKERT, K., BALLY, C., AND SCHADE, J. P. (eds.)): Sleep Mechanisms. Elsevier, 1965, p. 118.

MORIZZI, G. AND MAGOUN, H. W. EEG Clin. Neurophysiol., 1949, **1**, 455.

MÜLLER, G. E. AND PILZECKER, A. Z. Psychol. 1900, Suppl. 1.

MYERS, R. E. J. Comp. Physiol. Psychol., 1955, **48**, 470.

NAUTA, W. J. H. J. Neurophysiol., 1946, **9**, 285.

NAUTA, W. J. H. in The frontal granular cortex and behavior, chapt. 19 (WARREN, J. M. AND AKERT, J. (eds.)). McGraw-Hill Book Co., 1964.

NAUTA, W. J. H. AND WHITLOCK, D. G. in *Brain Mechanisms and Behavior*, (DELAFRESNAYE, J. F. ET AL (eds.)) Blackwell, 1954.

NISSEN, T., RØIGAARD-PETERSON, H. AND FJERDINGSTAD, E. Scand. J. Psychol., 1965 (in press).

PARMEGGIANI, P. L. A study on the central representation of sleep behavior: in Progress in brain research, vol. 6, Elsevier, 1964.

PENFIELD, H. W. Arch. Neurol. & Psychiat., 1932, **27**, 30; Ann. Int. Med. 1933, **7**, 303; Assn. Res. Nerv. Ment. Dis. Proc., 1947, **27**, 519, Ibid.; 1950, **30**, 513.

PENFIELD, W. AND BOLDREY, E. Brain, 1937, **60**, 389.

PENFIELD, W. AND JASPER, H. H. Epilepsy and the functional anatomy of the human brain. Little, Brown & Co., 1954.

PENFIELD, W. AND MILNER, B. Arch. Neurol. Psychiat., 1958, **79**, 475.

PENFIELD, W. AND RASMUSSEN, T. Fed. Proc., 1947, **6**, 452.

PENFIELD, W. AND RASMUSSEN, T. The cerebral cortex of man. Macmillan, 1950.

PENFIELD, W. AND WELCH, K. Arch. Neurol. & Psychiat., 1951, **66**, 289.

PURPURA, D. P. Amer. J. Physiol., 1956, **186**, 250.

RAAB, D. AND ADES, H. W. Amer. J. Physiol., 1946, **59**, 59.

RANSON, S. W. Arch. Neurol. & Psychiat., 1939, **41**, 1.

RICHTER, C. P. AND HINES, M. A. Nerv. & Ment. Dis., 1934, **13**, 211.

ROBINSON, L. Nineteenth Century, 1891, **30**, 831; Brit. M. J., 1891, **2**, 1226.

RUNDLES, R. W. AND PAPEZ, J. W. J. Comp. Neurol., 1938, **68**, 267.

SCHNEDORF, G. AND IVY, A. C. Amer. J. Physiol., 1939, **125**, 491.

SCHREINER, L. AND KLING, A. J. Neurophysiol., 1953, **16**, 643.

SCOTT, D. AND LIU, C. N. in Progress in brain research, (SINGER, M. AND SCHADE, J. P. (eds.)) Vol 13: Mechanisms of neural regeneration, Elsevier, 1964.

SCOVILLE, W. AND MILNER, B. J. Neurol. Neurosurg. Psychiat., 1957, **20**, 11.

SECHZER, J. J. Comp. Physiol. Psychol., 1963, **58**, 76.

SEGUNDO, J. P., NAQUET, R., AND BUSER, P. J. Neurophysiol., 1955, **18**, 236.

SIMPSON, D. A. J. Anat., 1952, **86**, 20.

THOMPSON, R. F. AND SHAW, J. A. J. Comp. Physiol. Psychol., 1965, **60**, 329.

TOWER, S. S. Brain, 1940, **63**, 36.

VELASCO, M. AND LINDSLEY, D. B. Science, 1965, **149**, 1375.

WALSHE, F. M. R. AND ROBERTSON, E. G. Brain, 1933, **56**, 40.

WALTER, W. G. Lancet, 1936, **2**, 305.

WEINSTEIN, S. AND TEUBER, H. L. J. Comp. Physiol. Psychol., 1957, **50**, 535.

WILLIAMS, M. J. Neurol. Neurosurg. Psychiat., 1950, **13,** 30.

WILLIAMS, M. AND PENNYBACKER, J. J. Neurol. Neurosurg. Psychiat., 1954, **17,** 115.

WOOLSEY, C. N. in Neural mechanisms of the auditory and vestibular systems. (RASMUSSEN, G. L. AND WINDLE, W. F. (eds.)) Charles C Thomas, 1960.

WOOLSEY, C. N., SETTLAGE, P. H., MEYER, D. R., SENCER, W., HAMUY, T. P., AND TRAVIS, A. M. Assn. Res. Nerv. & Ment. Dis. Proc., 1950, **30,** 238.

Monographs and Reviews

ADRIAN, E. D., BREMER, F., JASPER, H. H., AND DELAFRESNAYE, J. Brain mechanisms and consciousness. Charles C Thomas, 1954.

AKERT, K., BALLY, C., AND SCHADE, J. (eds.). Progress in brain research, vol. 18: Sleep mechanisms. Elsevier, 1965.

AMASSIAN, V. E. Intl. Rev. Neurobiol., 1961, **3,** 67.

VON BONIN, G. Essay on the cerebral cortex, Charles C Thomas, 1950.

BREMER, F. L'Activ. electrique de l'ecorce cerebral. Hermann, 1938.

BUCY, P. C. (ed.). The precentral motor cortex. Univ. of Illinois Press, 1949.

CAJAL, S. Ramon y. Histologie due systeme nerveux de l'homme et des vertebres. 2 vols., A. Maloine, I, 1909, II, 1911.

CAMPBELL, A. W. Histological studies on the localization of cerebral function. Cambridge Univ. Press, 1905.

CRITCHLEY, M. The parietal lobes. Edw. Arnold Co., 1953.

DELAFRESNAYE, J. (ed.) Brain mechanisms and learning. Blackwell, 1961.

DUSSER DE BARENNE, J. B. Assn. Res. Nerv. Ment. Dis. Proc., 1934, **13,** 85.

VON ECONOMO, C. The cytoarchetectonics of the human cerebral cortex. Oxford Univ. Press, 1929.

FIELD, J. F. (ed.) Handbook of physiology. Section 1: Neurophysiology. Amer. Physiol. Soc., 1960.

HEAD, H. Studies in neurology. Oxford Univ. Press, 1920.

HEAD, H. Aphasia and kindred disorders of speech. Cambridge Univ. Press, 1926.

JASPER, H., PROCTOR, L., KNIGHTON, R., NOSHAY, W., AND COSTELLO, R. T. The reticular formation of the brain. Little, Brown, and Co., 1958.

PENFIELD, W. AND RASMUSSEN, T. The cerebral cortex of man. Macmillan, 1950.

SHOLL, D. A. The organization of the cerebral cortex. Methuen, 1956.

WARD, A. A. Intl. Rev. Neurobiol., 1964, **3,** 137.

WOLSTENHOLME, G. E. W. AND O'CONNOR, M. (eds.) The nature of sleep. Little, Brown, and Co., 1961.

CHAPTER 9

Conditioning and Learning

Introduction

One of the important developments in the biological sciences during the last decade has been the growth of interdisciplinary research on the neurophysiological mechanisms involved in behavior. The new field of neurobehavioral research has grown from the correlation of behavioral data with data obtained from anatomy, physiology, pharmacology, and biochemistry, and the field has expanded rapidly. As a result, where once the study of the physiological basis of human and animal behavior was considered the domain of physiological psychologists, today neuroanatomists, neurophysiologists, and neurochemists are frequently engaged in neurobehavioral research. A variety of names have been coined to differentiate this interdisciplinary neurobehavioral field from traditional disciplines, the most common being: neuropsychology, neurobiology, physiological psychology, biological psychology, psychobiology, and psychochemistry (Koch, 1962; Morgan, 1965).

It is evident that progress in this neurobehavioral field will depend upon the reliability, precision, and validity of the experimental techniques of each participating discipline. Since the behavioral data are the universal correlates in this field, a knowledge of behavioral control techniques, as well as of behavioral concepts has become essential for a complete and accurate interpretation of the neurophysiological mechanisms involved in behavior. In neurobehavioral research, behavior may be studied as either the independent or dependent variable. For example, when behavior is the independent variable, the behavior of the organism is manipulated and measurements of resulting anatomical, physiological, or biochemical changes are made. More commonly, behavior is studied as the dependent variable. In this case, manipulations of the physiological capabilities of the organism—that is, anatomical, electrical, or biochemical—are performed and their effects are observed on behavior.

In general, the interpretation of the effects of any of these physiological manipulations on the behavior of an organism must take into account:

(a) the species studied; (b) the nature of the physiological manipulation; and (c) the specific behavioral testing situation. Each of these variables is equally important in the study of the neurophysiological mechanisms of behavior. However, following a brief discussion of the first two classes of variables, this chapter will concentrate on a review of animal behavioral techniques and concepts, with particular emphasis upon behavioral techniques used in the study of learning in animals.

Traditionally, the interest in animal learning has been directed at general principles of learning applicable not only to the species studied but to all species; the assumption being, of course, that the learning of all species depends upon similar mechanisms. Recently, however, behavioral geneticists, comparative psychologists, and ethologists have emphasized that experimental results must be restricted to the species from which they were obtained or else replicated with many species before they are used to provide the basis for general principles of learning (cf. Bitterman, 1965a; Hess, 1962). Similarly, conclusions based on the effects of any physiological manipulation on behavior must necessarily be restricted to the species studied until similar results are observed with other species.

In studies on the effects of various physiological manipulations on behavior, particular emphasis has been placed on the central nervous system, and many studies have shown that different regions of the brain are important for, or essential to, different aspects of behavior. In these "brain localization" studies, the two most common methods for determining brain and behavior relationships have been to study the effect of destroying or stimulating specific brain areas and observing their effects on behavior. Extirpation of brain regions has been accomplished by a variety of surgical techniques (aspiration, electrocoagulation, radio-frequency thermocoagulation, ultrasonic sound, chemical manipulations, etc.). Stimulation, by electrical, and more recently chemical, means through implanted electrodes and catheters in unanesthetized animals has been used to study the function of deep-lying cerebral structures. Of these various techniques to study brain and behavior relationships, electrocoagulation and electrical stimulation have been the most frequently used. However, certain difficulties are inherent in the use of these two techniques to assess the function of a particular part of the nervous system in behavior. For example, both techniques affect fibers that are passing through the area manipulated as well as synaptic processes of neurons within the area; intervening structures may be damaged considerably and adjacent blood vessels may be injured and thus damage tissue remote from the area studied; with electrical stimulation, considerable histological damage may be induced in the brain tissue under study by the presence of the electrodes and the application of the stimulating current (cf. Delgado, 1964). Fortunately, many control studies of the effects on behavior of the implanted electrode *per se* indicate that any damage which is done is of little consequence to the behavior studied.

With electrocoagulation, stimulation of adjacent brain sites may inadvertently occur. For example, the deposit of metallic ions in the brain tissue by the lesioning electrodes (copper, nickel, iron, chromium) may evoke a glial reaction and cause the formation of chronic irritative scar tissue. Thus, electrolytic lesions, particularly in highly vascularized regions may lead to chronic irritative effects on surrounding tissue. Therefore, interpretation of the animal's performance in the behavioral situation following ablation must take into account the fact that the behavior may be due to the stimulating effect on surrounding tissue, rather than to the loss of brain tissue (cf. Reynolds, 1965). In an attempt to minimize the effects on surrounding tissue, radio-frequency and ultrasonic ablation techniques have been used, and these techniques usually result in relatively less damage to surrounding blood vessels and produce a minimum of chronic irritative scar formation.

A technique closely related to the traditional ablation procedures which has recently been used as a tool in brain and behavior research is "spreading depression" (SD). When certain electrical, chemical, or mechanical stimuli are applied directly to the cerebral cortex an initial local depression of the spontaneous electrical activity of the brain gradually spreads across the entire hemisphere. These waves produce dysfunction of the whole hemisphere which may last for several hours. The affected area is,

in a sense, removed temporarily and the effects of the removal may be tested immediately in the treated animals (Bures, 1959). Another variation on the extirpation procedure is the use of the split-brain preparation. In this preparation, the two hemispheres of the cerebrum are isolated by transecting the corpus callosum and, usually, the anterior and hippocampal commissures. In split-brain animals one hemisphere is left intact to prevent incapacitating paralysis, and the effects of cortical lesions on behavior are studied in the other single hemisphere. In perceptual discrimination learning the optic chiasma is also sectioned, so that visual input may be restricted to either the right or left hemisphere. Conversely, instead of the traditional method of studying the effects of removing a critical area, the greater part of the test hemisphere in the split-brain animal can be removed leaving intact only the critical area which is under study (Sperry, 1958).

A fundamental difficulty with any extirpation method, however, is that removal of a structure does not necessarily indicate what the normal function of the structure may have been. Remaining structures of the brain may assume or may already perform the function that was normally performed by the ablated part. Similarly, caution must be exercised in inferring from the behavioral effects of electrical stimulation the normal function of the structures stimulated. Changes in behavior by application of electrical stimulation to a brain site may be due to either excitation of the area or possibly due to dysynchrony or inhibition of electrical activity of the area. Different behavioral responses also may be elicited from the same brain site by varying the time of the electrical stimulation, the frequency and voltage, the length of stimulation, and the environmental situation (cf. Holst & St. Paul, 1962; Miller, 1965). Therefore, before a tentative function may be assumed for a particular region of the brain, a comparison of the effects of both stimulating and destroying the area and observing the effects of these manipulations upon behavior in a variety of behavioral situations is essential. In addition, assuming a function for a particular brain site does not mean that this site controls the behavior in question or that the ability to perform the behavior is localized exclusively in this particular brain region. For example, if a lesion in some part of the brain leads to some behavioral deficit, this result means only that the damaged brain tissue is part of some neural circuit that needs to be intact for the behavior being studied to occur (cf. McCleary & Moore, 1965).

It should be evident by now that the determination of any neurophysiological mechanism involved in behavior is exceedingly complex. The task, however, becomes even more difficult when the behavioral variable being studied is, because of its own complexity, only partially understood. Such is the case in the numerous studies on the age-old problem of the neurophysiological correlates of learning—i.e., the memory trace or engram. A number of psychological theories of learning have been proposed during the last decade but, as yet, no single all-embracing theory of learning has gained general acceptance. As used in psychology, learning refers to the more or less permanent modification of behavior which occurs as a result of practice, experience, or observation. Learning is a concept which has meaning only in terms of the performance of an organism, and performance is the integrated result of many variables besides learning—i.e., motivation, emotion, fatigue, sensory adaptation. Only when these variables, as well as maturational and other physiological variables, are held constant can the change in the organism's performance be attributed to learning *per se*.

Learning has been studied in literally hundreds of different behavioral situations; however, the majority of current animal experimentation is limited to a few standard techniques. These techniques may be classified as being either classical or instrumental conditioning techniques. Classical and instrumental conditioning differ in important procedural details, and there is considerable controversy on whether the principles of learning which underlie them are similar or different (cf. Kimble, 1961). Conditioning in this chapter will refer to the two different training procedures—i.e., classical and instrumental procedures. In classical conditioning, or Pavlovian conditioning, the stimulus to which the subject is to be conditioned is always followed by the unconditioned stimulus (food, shock) no matter what the subject does during the presentation of the conditioned stimulus and the termination of the unconditioned stimulus. In classical conditioning, the subject has no control over receiving, escaping, or avoiding the unconditioned stimulus —the presentation of the unconditioned stimulus is independent of the subject's response. Instrumental conditioning, however, refers to conditioning procedures in which the subject's behavior is

instrumental in obtaining a reward (food, water) or the avoidance or termination of a noxious stimulus. The subject makes a response which may result in a reward or in escaping or avoiding a noxious stimulus. Although the relation among various behavioral conditioning techniques is still the subject of considerable controversy (cf. Bitterman, 1962; Spence, 1956), most classification schemes have been dichotomies which roughly distinguish between these two procedures. For example, the following dichotomies have been proposed: classical conditioning and instrumental conditioning (Hilgard and Marquis, 1940; Kimble, 1961); type S or respondent conditioning and type R or operant conditioning (Skinner, 1938); Type I and Type II conditioning (Konorski and Miller, 1937); and conditioning and problem solving (Mowrer, 1947).

The terms classical and instrumental conditioning will be used in this chapter.[1] Classical conditioning procedures will be described first, followed by a discussion of instrumental conditioning procedures. To illustrate various conditioning techniques and concepts, examples will be drawn from studies on the physiological mechanisms involved in behavior.

Classical Conditioning

DEFINITIONS

It was Pavlov (1927) who, in the course of extensive studies on the physiology of the digestive glands, first began a systematic experimental investigation of conditioning phenomena. Basically, the experimental procedure for classical conditioning involves the repeated pairing of two stimuli: (a) an *unconditioned stimulus* (UCS) which at the beginning of the experiment evokes a regular and measurable response called the unconditioned response (UCR); and (b) a *conditioned stimulus* (CS) which initially is ineffective (neutral) and does not elicit the UCR at the outset of the experiment. Following repeated presentations of the conditioned stimulus and the unconditioned stimulus, a response resembling the unconditioned response may be elicited upon presentation of the conditioned stimulus alone. Such a response is called the *conditioned response* or *reflex* (CR).

[1] For a lucid and detailed discussion of the similarities and differences between classical and instrumental conditioning, as well as the variables which affect learning in general, see Kimble's revision of *Hilgard and Marquis' Conditioning and Learning* (1961).

Classical Conditioning Experiment

In most of the conditioning experiments performed by Pavlov, the secretion of saliva was chosen as the response to be measured. In dogs, the opening of the parotid or submaxillary duct was transplanted to the cheek or chin, respectively. Saliva was collected by means of a funnel sealed over the duct opening. The secretion of saliva into the funnel system was measured in drops. The animal was usually held by a harness in a stand located in a sound-attenuating room with a one-way viewing window. The experimeter and the collecting and recording equipment were in an adjoining room. In the typical Pavlovian experiment a ticking metronome (CS) was presented a few seconds before a small quantity of meat powder was blown into the dog's mouth. The food, of course, elicited a certain amount of salivation (UCR) which was measured. After a certain number of pairings, the sound of the metronome alone (the food being withheld) elicited the secretion of saliva. Pavlov called this response a conditional reflex, meaning that the occurrence of the response to the previously neutral cue was literally conditional upon certain operations, namely, the repeated pairings of the neutral cue (CS) with the unconditioned stimulus. The original Pavlovian procedures of classical salivary conditioning were subsequently modified by Bekhterev (1932). He substituted an electrical shock to the hind legs of dogs in place of food as the UCS and studied withdrawal and respiratory responses evoked by the noxious leg shock. After repeated pairings of the sound of a metronome (CS) with the electric shock (UCS), the CS evoked a conditioned leg flexion.

Unconditioned Stimulus and Response

The actual manner in which the unconditioned stimulus elicits the unconditioned response is usually of no immediate concern as long as the UCS is consistently followed by the desired response (the UCR). This requirement means that the UCS must be a more potent stimulus than other competing stimuli during the conditioning session, and that the subjects must not adapt to the UCS to any great degree. Although it is commonly assumed that the UCS must be a stimulus that elicits its response reflexively without previous training, the only requirement is that the stimulus *reliably* evoke the desired response (the UCR). The unconditioned response (e.g., the amount of saliva secreted or paw with-drawal) is also accompanied by other neural, visceral and neuromuscular effects. Movements of the lips and jaws, snapping, whining or barking, and movement of the limbs are commonly observed during salivary or paw-withdraw conditioning and constitute an integral part of the unconditioned response. The response or responses measured of the numerous UCRs typically elicited by a UCS depends upon the species studied, the degree of instrumentation involved, and the purpose of the experiment. A UCS which elicits a broad spectrum of responses is usually preferred, as conditioning is then easier to obtain. For example, isolated, segmental types of reflexes, such as the abdominal, patellar, plantar, and pupillary reflexes are quite difficult or even impossible to condition (Kimble, 1961; Young, 1965).

Conditioned Stimulus and Response

The conditioned stimulus, instead of initially being neutral, usually evokes some overt, though often not very pronounced reactions upon presentation. These reactions Pavlov named the *orienting, what-is-it,* or *investigatory* reflex, using the particular names equivalently. The orienting reflex (response) is not a single response but, like the UCR, consists of a variety of visceral, somatic, neural, and neuromotor reactions. For example, upon presentation of a novel sound (the CS), a dog may lift its ears, turn its head, shift its weight, etc. Pavlov observed that conditioning proceeds best when the orienting response is of moderate intensity. Much of the Russian work on conditioning has been a systematic investigation of variables which affect the orienting response (cf. Razran, 1961; Sokolov, 1963). In other studies, the response to the conditioned stimulus has been largely ignored or treated as irrelevant and, in these cases, the CS has usually been presented alone many times in order to decrease the strength of the orienting response (adaptation) before pairing the CS and UCS.

It has been mentioned that the conditioned stimulus will, after repeated pairing with the unconditioned stimulus, elicit a response which *resembles* the original unconditioned response. Originally it was assumed that the conditioned response evoked by the conditioned stimulus was the same response elicited by the unconditioned stimulus. Thus the pattern of salivation elicited by meat powder in the mouth was thought to be identical to the salivary response when the metronome was presented alone. It is now known that the conditioned response usually differs markedly from the unconditioned response. The conditioned response typically has a longer latency, occurs less consistently, has less amplitude, and may otherwise differ in form from the unconditioned response. Current views on the relation between the conditioned and unconditioned responses are: (a) that the conditioned response is only a part (fraction) of the unconditioned response; and (b) that the conditioned response is a preparation (anticipatory response) for the occurrence of the unconditioned stimulus (cf. Kimble, 1961).

Measurement of Conditioned Responses

Conditioned responses are observed during conditioning by either omitting the unconditioned stimulus to see whether the response will occur in the presence of the conditioned stimulus alone (test trials) or by noting the occurrence of an anticipatory CR before the presentation of the unconditioned stimulus. In the latter case, the interval between the conditioned and unconditioned stimuli must be of sufficient length to permit the occurrence of a measurable response or the UCR must have a long latency. The acquisition of CRs during conditioning has been assessed according to their frequency, amplitude, and latency. The response measure used depends upon the response being conditioned and the requirements of the experimenter. For example, the most common response measures that have been used are: (a) *frequency of occurrence*, which may be expressed as either the number of subjects exhibiting a conditioned response on a given trial (group comparison), or as the number of trials on which a particular subject gives a conditioned response (individual comparison); (b) *latency*, the time between presentation of the conditioned stimulus and the occurrence of the conditioned response; (c) *rate of responding*, the number of conditioned responses observed in some standard period of time; (d) *amplitude of the conditioned response*, some measure which reflects the magnitude of the conditioned response on the trials when the CR is evoked, e.g.—the amount of saliva secreted per trial; and (e) *trials to criterion*, which may be either the number of pairings between the conditioned stimulus and the unconditioned stimulus before the first measurable CR occurs or before some arbitrary criterion is reached (e.g., a CR must be given at least nine times in a block of ten conditioning trials).

CLASSICAL CONDITIONING PROCEDURES

The apparatus and procedures generally used in classical conditioning experiments have reached a high level of technical sophistication. The onset, duration, and intensity of both the conditioned stimulus and the unconditioned stimulus, as well as the interval between the CS and UCS are accurately and automatically controlled. The conditioned and unconditioned responses are recorded typically by the use of electrical or photographic techniques which permit an accurate determination of the occurrence of the conditioned response as well as its latency and amplitude. Usually, the animal subject is held in a harness or stock in a sound attenuating room and conditioning trials are started only after the animal has been habituated both to the experimental room and to the conditioned stimulus (cf. Prokasy, 1965; Ratner & Denny, 1964).

Different temporal patterns of presentation of the conditioned and unconditioned stimuli have been used in classical conditioning experiments. These temporal spacing procedures include: (a) *simultaneous conditioning*, in which the conditioned stimulus precedes the unconditioned stimulus by a few seconds and usually overlaps in time the unconditioned stimulus, with both stimuli terminating simultaneously;[2] (b) *delayed conditioning*, in which the conditioned stimulus appears before the UCS and lasts *at least* until the onset of the unconditioned stimulus; (c) *trace conditioning*, in which the conditioned stimulus comes on momentarily and terminates before the onset of the unconditioned stimulus; (d) *temporal conditioning*, in which the interval of time between the occurrence of the unconditioned stimulus serves as a conditioned stimulus. For example, if an unconditioned stimulus, such as food, is presented to dogs at regularly spaced intervals of time and then withheld, a conditioned salivary response may occur at approximately the usual interval; and (e) *backward conditioning*, in which the conditioned stimulus follows the onset of the unconditioned stimulus. In general, a comparison of the different conditioning schedules indicates that a delayed conditioned response is more difficult to establish than a simultaneous

---

[2] Strictly speaking, simultaneous conditioning should imply that the CS and UCS come on and go off together; when the CS precedes the UCS by even a few milli-seconds, the procedure should be classified as delayed conditioning. As commonly used, however, simultaneous conditioning refers to procedures where the CS-UCS interval is 5 seconds or less.

one, and a trace conditioned response is still more difficult to establish. Conditioning with a backward conditioning procedure is still a questionable phenomenon.

Besides the different conditioning schedules, there are two other types of temporal variables which affect the acquisition of a conditioned response. These variables are: (a) the time between the conditioned stimulus and the unconditioned stimulus (*CS-UCS interval* or the *interstimulus interval*); and (b) the time between conditioning trials which is commonly called the *intertrial* interval. In general, the optimal CS-UCS interval is approximately ½ second, although recent evidence indicates that the optimal CS-UCS interval is probably response-, species-, and age-dependent (Noble & Adams, 1963; Bitterman, 1965b; Caldwell & Werboff, 1962). In most classical conditioning studies a number of conditioned and unconditioned stimuli pairings are given in a single session. The optimal intertrial interval has been about 90 sec. in the few species that have been studied. In general, longer intertrial intervals do not hinder or facilitate conditioning, but shorter intervals result in slower conditioning (cf. Ratner & Denny, 1964). A constant intertrial interval produces better conditioning than a variable intertrial interval. The constant intertrial interval is, of course, a procedure for producing temporal conditioning. With a constant intertrial interval, the animal may respond to either the time interval cue or the specific conditioned stimulus as the two stimuli are confounded.

Conditioning Controls

Classical conditioning has been defined as the pairing of a conditioned stimulus with an unconditioned stimulus; the conditioned stimulus in time evokes a response (CR) which resembles the UCR. There are examples, however, in which the pairing of the CS and UCS results in phenomena different from conditioning (i.e., where the CS evokes a response which resembles the UCR). In special cases, when the CS and UCS are paired, the unconditioned response may be of smaller magnitude than when the UCS is presented alone. When the CS is removed and the UCS is presented alone the magnitude of the unconditioned response returns immediately to its original level before the pairing began. This implies that the CS, in some unknown manner, actively inhibits the magnitude of the unconditioned response. In other cases, the pairing of the CS and UCS may result in an augmentation of the original response (orienting) to the CS. This process is called *sensitization* or *alpha conditioning*.

Similarly, there are procedures which affect the organism's behavior in the conditioning situation which are not the result of pairing the conditioned and unconditioned stimuli. These modifications are: (a) *adaptation*, where presentations of a noxious unconditioned stimulus alone, before the pairing of the CS and UCS, leads to a decrease in the number of conditioned responses during conditioning; and (b) *pseudoconditioning*, where the presentation of a noxious unconditioned stimulus alone, prior to regular conditioning, sometimes results in conditioned responses on the very first presentation of the conditioned stimulus. This phenomenon is called pseudoconditioning because the response obtained resembles a true conditioned response but does not depend upon the pairing of the CS with the UCS. There is evidence that pseudoconditioning may be a part of all conditioning in which a noxious stimulus is used. Pseudoconditioning probably represents conditioning to the general stimulus situation (i.e., being placed in a harness in a special experimental room and exposed to the sudden onset of a stimulus). As most studies have been concerned with variables which affect conditioning *per se*, pseudoconditioning controls, where the CS and UCS are presented alone and in a random fashion, are run to determine if the occurrence of CRs is due to CS-UCS pairings in the experimental group.

Conditioning Variables

There are many variables which affect an organism's behavior in both classical and instrumental conditioning situations. This means, of course, that whatever the differences between the two procedures, classical and instrumental conditioning have many properties in common. Examples of some of these common basic phenomena will be drawn exclusively from classical salivary conditioning procedures. Similar examples, however, may be found for other classically conditioned responses and for instrumental responses (Kimble, 1961, pp. 81–98). A fairly standard conditioning terminology has developed to describe various experimental operations and the typical results associated with the procedures. As Pavlov (1927) was the first to systematically describe conditioning and the variables which influence the conditioning process, current conditioning terminology retains a flavor of Pavlovian neurophysiological theory.

Basic phenomena associated with the conditioning process are:

a. *Extinction*. Following conditioning, if the conditioned stimulus (tone) is no longer followed by the unconditioned stimulus (food), the conditioned salivary response will steadily decrease and eventually disappear. The reduction in either the number of conditioned responses given or in the amplitude of the conditioned response, when the CS is presented alone, is called *extinction*. The number of conditioned responses made to the conditioned stimulus by the organism during extinction procedures is also used as a measure of the strength of acquisition or learning.

b. *Spontaneous recovery*. Following complete extinction, if the animal is given a rest, and the conditioned stimulus is again presented, the conditioned response may reappear. The return in strength of an extinguished, conditioned response after a lapse of time (rest) with no intervening training is called *spontaneous recovery*.

c. *External inhibition*. If a strong stimulus (e.g., a loud noise) occurs between presentation of the conditioned stimulus and the unconditioned stimulus the animal, which has on earlier trials given a conditioned response, may not respond. This temporary reduction in the strength of a CR during acquisition as a result of the occurrence of an extraneous stimulus is called *external inhibition*. During acquisition, a conditioned response is easily influenced by any change in the conditioning procedure.

d. *Disinhibition*. During extinction of a conditioned salivary response, if an extraneous stimulus is presented after the CS, the conditioned salivary response may increase in amplitude. But, the recurrence of the conditioned response is usually only temporary. This temporary increase in the strength of an extinguished conditioned response as the result of an external stimulus is called *disinhibition*. Since an extinguished conditioned response would reappear without new pairings of the CS and UCS, Pavlov assumed that the conditioned response had been inhibited during extinction. He believed that the new stimulus inhibited the inhibition of the CR, and therefore spoke of *inhibition of inhibition* or *disinhibition* to explain the effects of an extraneous stimulus on the CR during extinction.

e. *Inhibition of delay*. If a conditioned food response is established, and then the duration of the CS is considerably increased, salivary secretions will first begin immediately after an interval corresponding to the original CS termination. As conditioning proceeds, however, with the longer tone interval, the secretion of saliva will be postponed to the end of the lengthened conditioned stimulus. The postponement of the conditioned response to the end of the prolonged trace or delay CS interval is called *inhibition of delay*.

f. *Stimulus generalization*. If a conditioned salivary response is established to a certain tone frequency (e.g. 1000 cps.) it is found that salivary secretion will also be elicited by other frequencies (500, 900, 1200 cps.) not previously paired with the food (UCS). Stimuli having some qualitative or quantitative resemblance to the conditioned stimulus typically elicit upon presentation a conditioned response of considerable intensity. The amplitude of the salivation diminishes with increasing differences between the frequency of the conditioned stimulus and the other tone frequencies. This phenomenon is called *stimulus generalization*.

g. *Generalization of extinction*. If a series of positive conditioned food responses are established to mechanical stimulation of the skin (shoulder, back, thigh, and calf), and responses to one of these points (e.g., the shoulder) are extinguished, on subsequent testing the magnitude of conditioned responses to stimulation of the other points will also be decreased. The effects of extinction thus spread to the adjacent points a phenomenon similar to stimulus generalization, and the process is called *generalization of extinction*.

h. *Discrimination*. When a conditioned salivary response is established with a certain tone frequency (CS), salivary secretion will be obtained with other frequencies similar to the conditioned stimulus (stimulus generalization). Initially the amount of salivary secretion to the nonreinforced test stimuli is significantly less than to the CS. During testing the secretion to the non-reinforced neighboring frequencies (test stimuli) may increase until it reaches the amount of salivary secretion obtained with the CS, but eventually it will begin to decrease and finally cease when the non-reinforced neighboring frequencies are presented. If a subject is reinforced for responding to one stimulus (the CS) and not reinforced for responding to other stimuli, the subject eventually will respond consistently only to the reinforced stimulus and not at all to the non-reinforced ones. This phenomenon is called *discrimination*. It has also been called *differentiation* and *differential inhibition*. If animals are forced to make an extremely difficult discrimination, their discriminative behavior may be disrupted completely (e.g., they may begin struggling, whining, howling, trembling). This behavior was labeled experimental neurosis by Pavlov and has been induced in many animals (e.g., dogs, cats, sheep, pigs, rats). In some instances the condition may be permanent and has served as an animal prototype for psychiatric studies.

i. *Conditioned inhibition.* When a conditioned salivary response is elicited by a tone, the presentation of the tone and another stimulus (combined stimuli) may result in the abolishment of the conditioned salivary response. This special form of discrimination where the conditioned stimulus is paired with a previously indifferent stimulus, and the conditioned stimulus fails to elicit the conditioned response, when paired with the second stimulus, is called *conditioned inhibition.*

j. *Higher-order conditioning.* Under certain conditions, it is possible to use the conditioned stimulus from one phase of an experiment as the unconditioned stimulus for further conditioning. For example, a tone (CS_1) may be paired with food (UCS) to establish a conditioned salivary response (CR_1). After the establishment of the CR_1, a black rectangle (CS_2) may be paired with the tone (CS_1), and following several pairings, a conditioned salivary response (CR_2) may be elicited by the black rectangle. The conditioned responses form a *chain reflex,* and they are called *primary* and *secondary* conditioned stimuli and conditioned responses. Third-order conditioning (*tertiary* conditioned stimuli and responses) is possible to obtain, but usually is found only with defense reflexes such as those in response to shock. Typically the higher-order CRs, when established, are of a longer latency and of smaller magnitude compared to first-order CRs and eventually they disappear. The first-order conditioned response to the original CS undergoes extinction in the absence of the original UCS and as testing proceeds is no longer able to function as a reliable unconditioned stimulus for higher-order responses.

EXTEROCEPTIVE AND INTEROCEPTIVE CONDITIONING

The majority of classical conditioning experiments have used exteroceptive stimuli as the conditioned stimuli—i.e., auditory, visual or somesthetic stimuli. Any environmental change to which the organism is sensitive may serve as a conditioned stimulus providing it does not evoke an intense "orienting response" which interferes with the response to the unconditioned stimulus. Manipulations which make the condi-

tioned stimulus more discriminable or distinctive seem to facilitate conditioning (cf. Kimble, 1961; Ratner & Denny, 1964). External unconditioned stimuli have included practically all stimuli which evoke a reliable and measurable response upon presentation without injury to the organism. The most common exteroceptive unconditioned stimuli have been food, electric shock to various parts of the body, and air-puffs to the eye.

Since the late 1940's Russian physiologists have been doing conditioning experiments in which the conditioned stimulus, the unconditioned stimulus, or both stimuli are applied internally to different organs (interoceptive conditioning). Bykov's *The Cerebral Cortex and Internal Organs,* translated into English, by W. H. Gantt in 1957, describes the findings of many experiments which suggest that various internal organs may be classically conditioned (e.g., kidneys, heart, liver). Interoceptive conditioned and unconditioned stimuli in these studies have been delivered in a variety of ways with special surgical techniques used for animal experimentation. Implanted gastric and trachea fistulas and loops formed in the intestinal wall are favorite means of delivering chemical, electrical, or mechanical stimulation in animals (cf. Bykov, 1957; Razran, 1961). In humans, typical stimuli have been distentions of the intestinal wall by fine-walled rubber balloons swallowed by the subjects and then inflated with air or water. The distentions are recorded and calibrated and are often varied with respect to the rhythm of delivery and rate of onset. The area stimulated is controlled through the use of balloons of different sizes. Balloons filled with water at different temperatures have been frequently used as thermal interoceptive stimuli. Other forms of tactile stimulation used in animal experimentation have been rhythmic scratching of the mucosa, jets of air or water, and direct electrical stimulation. When the lumen of the viscera is small, direct luminal irrigation through inflow-outflow tubes has been commonly used. Irrigation of the viscus also has been used as a common means of administering a variety of chemical stimuli (Razran, 1961).

In classical conditioning studies, the conditioned and unconditioned stimuli may therefore be either exteroceptive or interoceptive. Razran (1961), in a review of Soviet interoceptive conditioning, presents examples of three kinds of interoceptive conditioning: intero-exteroceptive, intero-interoceptive, and extero-interoceptive conditioning. It should be recalled that in classical conditioning studies, the conditioned stimulus always precedes the unconditioned stimulus (except, of course, in backward conditioning procedures). Thus, in intero-exteroceptive conditioning, the CS is interoceptive and the UCS is exteroceptive. In intero-interoceptive conditioning, both the CS and UCS are interoceptive whereas, in extero-interoceptive conditioning, the CS is exteroceptive and the UCS is interoceptive. Finally, when both the CS and UCS are exteroceptive, the conditioning is extero-exteroceptive or, briefly, exteroceptive conditioning.

Examples of the three kinds of interoceptive conditioning are: (a) *intero-exteroceptive conditioning*. A female dog was fistulated in the lower abdomen so that the wall of the uterus could be stimulated with a jet of air for 10 sec. (the CS). An electric shock to the animal's hind paw was used as the exteroceptive UCS and elicited an unconditioned paw-withdrawal response. Following approximately ten pairings of the CS and UCS, the jet of air alone elicited a conditioned paw withdrawal response; (b) *intero-interoceptive conditioning*. Intestinal loops were made in dogs such that rhythmic distentions of the loops (90–100 distentions in one minute at 60–80 mm Hg. pressure) could be used as a CS. The unconditioned stimulus was a 10% mixture of carbon dioxide delivered through an inserted cannula attached to gas chambers which permitted the regulation of the amount and gaseous composition of the air. Initially, the animals were adapted to the experimental apparatus by breathing normal air through the cannula. Conditioning consisted of pairing the rhythmic distentions of the loops with the 10% mixture of carbon dioxide. The UCS elicited rapid breathing as the unconditioned response (hyperpnea). Conditioned hyperpneic responses to the distentions initially appeared after 3 to 6 trials, and became stable after only 5 to 16 trials. The animals were also able to discriminate the conditioned stimulus from another non-reinforced stimulus (distentions at a rate of 15 per minute at 55–60 mm Hg. pressure) in about 6 to 15 trials; (c) *extero-interoceptive conditioning*. In the same hypercapnic preparation 10% carbon dioxide was paired with an exteroceptive conditioned stimulus (tone). The tone elicited a stable, conditioned hypercapnic response faster than when intestinal distentions were used as the CS in intero-interoceptive conditioning. Dogs were also able to discriminate the conditioned stimulus from another tone of a different frequency.

Razran (1961) characterizes interoceptive conditioning as: (a) readily obtainable and largely unconscious; (b) more limited than exteroceptive conditioning in respect to the kind and variety of stimulation but much more recurrent, periodic, and organism-bound than exteroceptive conditioning; and (c) somewhat slower in formation than exteroceptive conditioning but perhaps more difficult to extinguish. The Soviet interest in studying the formation of conditioned responses by stimulation of the viscera is in providing an experimental basis for psychosomatic medicine. Current emphasis is on determining the functional connections of the cerebral cortex with the viscera (corticovisceral conditioning). So far, however, processes which are assumed to occur in the cerebral cortex during the establishment of interoceptive conditioned responses are only inferred.

CLASSICAL CONDITIONING TECHNIQUES

Many different classical conditioning techniques are currently being used to contribute to the growing knowledge of conditioning phenomena. Modern polygraphic instrumentation has made it feasible to simultaneously record various responses of the organism during conditioning. Since different responses show wide variability in the rate of both acquisition and extinction it is not uncommon for autonomic and central nervous system "responses" to be measured concurrently with overt behavioral responses (i.e., defensive paw flexion). Conditioning techniques typically used in neurobehavioral research fall into two main classes—autonomic conditioning techniques and central nervous system techniques. Although autonomic and central nervous system techniques have contributed extensively to fundamental conditioning knowledge, the two techniques also have had rather specific applications. For example, autonomic conditioning procedures have been used in: (a) clinical investigations comparing normal and abnormal psychiatric populations; and (b) experimental-personality studies in which autonomic function is correlated with various psychological variables (i.e., fear, anxiety). Central nervous system techniques have been used extensively in studies on the neurophysiological correlates of learning and memory.

Autonomic Nervous System Techniques

Autonomic conditioning has been the subject of considerable controversy. The term "autonomic" describes a system which is morphologically connected with and functionally controlled

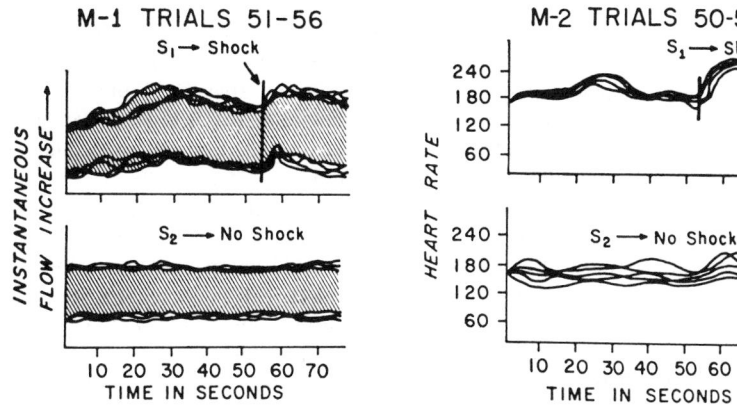

Fig. 9.1. The envelope of five overlapping traces of a conditioned blood flow response (left) and a conditioned heart rate response (right) (S_1, above) and the envelope of five similar traces of a response to a non-reinforced stimulus (S_2, below) (from Smith and Stebbens, 1965).

by the central nervous system and therefore is not really an independent system (Ban, 1964). Many "autonomic" responses which have been conditioned are thus controlled by skeletal muscles, and therefore are subject to "voluntary" as well as autonomic influences. A number of "autonomic" responses have been studied in classical conditioning experiments, e.g., galvanic skin resistance (GSR), salivation, the pupillary response, nictitating membrane movement, eyelid closure, respiration, and heart rate. Each response, however, has certain problems of measurement associated with its conditioning (cf. Ban, 1964; Morgan, 1965; Prokasy, 1965, for reviews). For example, heart rate has been the favorite measure used to study conditioning of the cardiovascular system. Typically the UCS has been an electric shock to the hind paws in animals, although food reinforcement has also been used (Gantt, 1960). Heart rate, of course, is completely under autonomic control; however, it can be affected mechanically by respiratory changes. Respiration is subject to both voluntary and autonomic control. Thus, one of the difficulties in heart rate conditioning is determining whether the conditioned changes are due to primary neural effects or to secondary changes associated with somatic motor activity and respiration. During studies of heart rate conditioning, both increases and decreases in rate have been observed as conditioned responses.

Although an increase in heart rate is usually indicative of an increased cardiac output, the two functions are not perfectly correlated. Heart rate must therefore be considered as an indirect measure of cardiovascular functioning. For example, if stroke volume is sufficiently decreased by the shortened diastolic filling time and not sufficiently compensated for by increased ejection, cardiac output will not increase when heart rate increases. Therefore, conditioned changes in heart rate may serve no significant physiological role in the organism. However, in a recent study with monkeys, plastic flow sections were implanted on the terminal aorta immediately above the iliac bifurcation and blood flow was measured directly during delayed conditioning trials. The onset of a light for 56 sec. was used as a CS and was followed by a brief electrical shock passed between the monkey's neck and buttocks. Conditioned increases in both heart rate and blood flow were observed, and five of the six monkeys tested were able to discriminate between the conditioned light stimulus (S_1) and another light (S_2) (fig. 9.1). Simultaneous recording of respiration and bodily movement showed that the conditioned cardiac responses occurred with either minimal or nonexistent changes in respiration and body movement (Smith & Stebbins, 1965). This study illustrates, of course, that through the use of a conditioning procedure the amount of blood delivered to the tissues supplied by the terminal aorta could be increased by presentation of an external conditioned signal.

The importance of autonomic conditioning is closely related to one of the oldest theoretical controversies in learning theory. The central problem of the controversy is whether responses of the skeletal musculature are necessary for perception and thought. Stated otherwise—must contraction of voluntary muscles occur for conditioning to take place? In attempts to answer this question curare-like drugs have been used to immobilize subjects during conditioning procedures. Early experiments with these drugs indicated that they had a dissociative or amnesic effect on behavior. Recent curare-type drugs (flaxedil, d-tubocurarine), however, appear to result in a complete flaccid skeletal preparation without an amnesic effect on behavior. Recent studies have demonstrated that classical conditioning of heart rate occurs in curarized dogs, and that such conditioning affects subsequent behavior (both autonomic and skeletal) in the normal, undrugged animal (Black, 1965; Black, Carlson, & Solomon, 1962; Solomon & Turner, 1962).

Central Nervous System Techniques

Alterations in brain wave activity during conditioning have been studied extensively with macro-electrodes, and more recently with micro-electrodes, with various regions of the brain implicated in different phases of conditioning. Two major classes of bioelectrical events which have been measured during conditioning are: (a) spontaneous electrical activity of the brain (the electroencephalogram or EEG) which has been observed to vary in frequency, amplitude, and other properties during different phases of conditioning; and (b) electrical activity evoked by a stimulus (e.g., light flash, tone, touch) which may show systematic changes in amplitude and wave shape when the stimulus is paired with an appropriate UCS. The study of alterations in brainwave activity during conditioning has relied on techniques of chronic implantation of recording electrodes into cortical and subcortical areas in animals. Recent advances in modern electronic techniques of data reduction (techniques of averaging, frequency analysis, auto- and cross-correlation, etc.) have made it possible to detect significant patterns of discharge, both for groups of cells and individual cells, during conditioning. (cf. Galambos & Morgan, 1960; Morrell, 1961; John, 1961; Wells, 1963, for reviews).

The prototype of bioelectrical conditioning is the conditioned blocking of the occipital alpha rhythm (8–12 per sec. frequency) which was first observed by Durup and Fessard in 1935. These workers discovered that the click of a camera shutter used to photograph alpha blocking elicited by light sometimes produced attenuation of the alpha activity. Previous testing had shown that the noise of the shutter alone had no effect on the electroencephalogram. Only after the click of the camera shutter was paired with light while photographing the alpha response to light, did a blocking occur when the click was presented alone. Study of this form of "conditioning" then

began in many other laboratories. In a detailed study on alpha conditioning, Jaspar and Shagass (1941) were able to duplicate nearly all the phenomena of classical conditioning (e.g., extinction, discrimination, delayed and trace conditioning).

In addition to blocking the spontaneous activity of the brain, presentation of a novel stimulus through various sensory pathways also evokes brief electrical waves in the brain. The latency, magnitude, and duration of these "evoked" potentials have been studied during conditioning with both macro- and micro-electrode techniques. For example, in a detailed study on cats and monkeys, Galambos and Sheatz (1962) used chronically indwelling electrodes in different brain regions for the study of evoked potentials elicited by clicks and light flashes. A puff of air to the face was used as the unconditioned stimulus. Prior to conditioning trials, the CS was presented many times to habituate the evoked response to the click. When presentation of the CS resulted in no further change in the amplitude of evoked potentials, conditioning trials were started with the click regularly followed by the puff of air (UCS). The evoked potential to the click increased in amplitude following a few pairings of the CS and UCS. Figure 9.2 shows, from top to bottom, the activity evoked: (a) when the naive monkey was first exposed to the clicks; (b) when the animal was habituated to clicks by prolonged exposure to the CS alone; and (c) after the conditioning trials had begun. As can be seen, the conditioned evoked potential was approximately twice as large as the potential when the CS was first presented. Following conditioning the CS was again presented alone (extinction), and the amplitude of the evoked potential returned to the habituated level. Figure 9.3 shows both conditioned and "extinguished" evoked potentials from various brain areas in both monkeys and cats. The amplitude of the evoked potentials could be extinguished and reconditioned again and again (Galambos & Sheatz, 1962).

In recent years, cerebral cortical activity has been studied by the use of microelectrode techniques to monitor single cell discharges during conditioning (Jasper, Ricci, & Doane, 1960; Yoshii & Ogura, 1960; Morrell, 1960; Olds & Olds, 1961; 1965; Kamikawa, McIlwain, & Adey, 1964). These microelectrode studies suggest that changes in single cell discharge rates do occur during conditioning, although there is great variability associated with the response at the microelectrode level of analysis. In the typical experiment, an exteroceptive light flash (the CS) is paired with an appropriate unconditioned stimulus (e.g., shock to paw or sciatic stimulation) and the unconditioned response recorded is either an increase or decrease in the discharge rate of individual neurons. After repeated pairings, the light alone is able to evoke the characteristic discharge rate previously associated only with the unconditioned stimulus. Repeated extinction and reconditioning of single cells has been reported to occur with this procedure (Kamikawa *et al.*, 1964).

The use of recording techniques to correlate electroencephalographic activity with conditioning is beset with many technical difficulties, and as yet no neurophysiological correlate of memory has been found. The variability and complexity of brain wave alterations produced by even momentary excitation presents a major difficulty in the search for neurophysiological correlates of conditioning. The lack of precise information about the genesis of the EEG (the nature and source of brain rhythms) necessarily makes inferences about the changes introduced through conditioning highly speculative. In spite of these difficulties, however, electrophysiological investi-

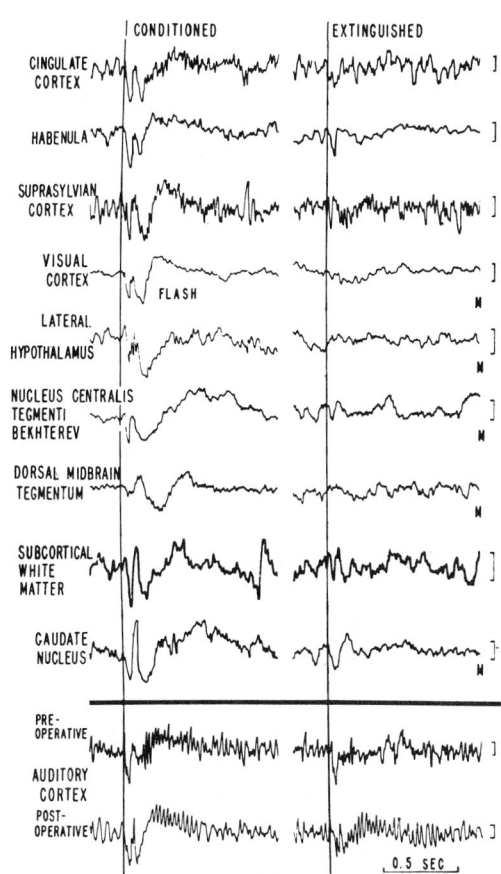

Fig. 9.3. EEG recording from several monkeys (*M*) and cats in extinguished and conditioned states. Stimuli delivered at point indicated by *vertical line*. Calibration 100 μv. (from Galambos and Sheatz, 1962.)

gations of learning are proceeding at a rapid rate in many laboratories (cf. Morrell, 1961).

Another central nervous system technique has been the use of direct brain stimulation as either the conditioned or unconditioned stimulus. As might be expected, interruption of the afferent fibers of an exteroceptive conditioned stimulus prevents the acquisition and the performance of a conditioned response. However, direct electrical stimulation of the spinal cord, cerebellum, and various areas of the cerebral cortex may be substituted for normal exteroceptive stimuli, and serve as conditioned stimuli. For example, instead of pairing an exteroceptive light (the CS) with food (the UCS), electrical stimulation of the occipital region may be paired with the UCS. With this procedure, conditioning takes place in about the same number of trials as when normal exteroceptive signals are used as conditioned stimuli. Even electrical stimulation of non-sensory areas

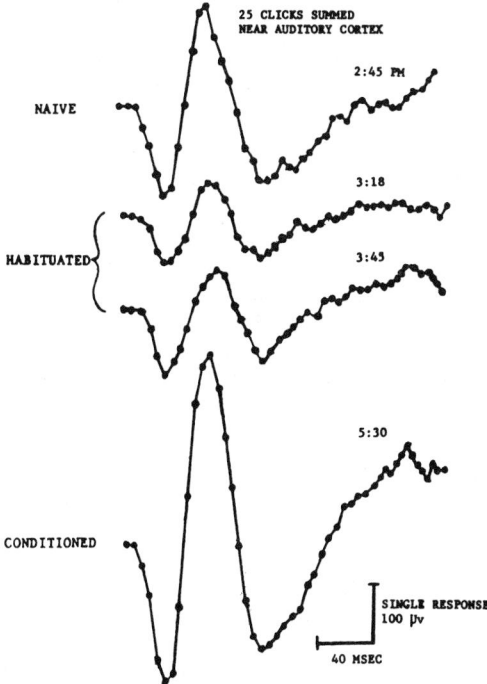

Fig. 9.2. Click-evoked responses averaged by computer. Bipolar recording from cortex of inferior bank of superior temporal gyrus in monkey (from Galambos and Sheatz, 1962).

of the cortex has been used successfully as a conditioned stimulus (Morgan, 1965).

Similarly, the receptive organs and related afferent pathways of unconditioned stimuli are not essential for conditioning. Conditioning has been obtained by substituting electrical stimulation of the cerebellum and of the motor cortex for exteroceptive unconditioned stimuli (Doty & Giurgea, 1961). A long interval between conditioning trials is necessary for successful conditioning when electrical stimulation of the motor cortex is used as the unconditioned stimulus. When an interval of 5 min. is used in dogs, cats, and monkeys, a conditioned response is obtained; with shorter intervals (less than two minutes) the conditioned response disappears (Doty & Guirgea, 1961). It has also been possible to obtain successful conditioning where both the conditioned and unconditioned stimuli are applied to the cortex electrically (Doty, 1961). For successful conditioning in vertebrates excitation must however reach the central nervous system, either by normal afferent pathways or by direct electrical stimulation. Passive flexion of a limb, or direct electrical or chemical stimulation of a muscle or a motor nerve are not effective as unconditioned stimuli. The conditioning of spinal animals is also very difficult to obtain (Kimble, 1961).

Instrumental Conditioning

It has been mentioned that in classical conditioning the conditioned stimulus is always followed by the unconditioned stimulus no matter what response the animal makes during the CS-UCS interval. If, however, the response of the animal can affect the occurrence or duration of the UCS, then the procedure becomes one of instrumental conditioning. Instrumental conditioning refers to procedures where the subject's behavior is instrumental in obtaining a reward, or avoiding or terminating a noxious stimulus. The most common instrumental procedures used in the study of the neurophysiology of behavior may be classified as: (a) escape and avoidance conditioning; (b) operant conditioning; (c) discrimination learning; and (e) problem-solving learning. The same parameters of conditioning (generalization, extinction, etc.) discussed for classical conditioning procedures are also found in instrumental conditioning procedures.

Escape and Avoidance Conditioning

In escape conditioning, the animal can terminate an aversive stimulus by making an appropriate response. In avoidance conditioning, the animal is presented with a conditioned stimulus which is followed by an aversive stimulus (UCS) only if the animal fails to make some arbitrary response, such as lifting its leg (the CR). For example, Bekhterev trained dogs to make a conditioned avoidance response by pairing a bell (CS) with an electrical shock to the leg (UCS). If the animal lifted its leg (CR) during the CS-UCS interval, the animal would not be shocked by the UCS on that trial. In the Russian literature, avoidance conditioning is referred to as defensive conditioning (or Type II) to distinguish it from classical conditioning.

The majority of recent avoidance learning experiments have been with lower animals. The most common responses studied have been paw-withdrawal, jumping, lever pressing, wheel-turning, and shuttling. The shuttle response has been the most frequently used response. In this procedure, the animal is placed in a two-chambered box with the two compartments separated by a hurdle, a swinging door, or a line on the floor. In order to avoid shock, the animal has to learn to respond to a signal (the CS) by shuttling or hurdling from one compartment into the other compartment. In some cases the animal may be only required to run in one direction, for example, from a white into a black compartment. This type of box, with a distinct shock side (white) and a distinct escape side (black) yields faster learning than a uniformly colored shuttle box. It is also easier to train animals to run or jump to escape or avoid a noxious stimulus, than it is to require the animal to turn a wheel or press a panel to avoid the UCS. Running and jumping responses are normally elicited by a noxious stimulus and therefore compete with wheel turning or lever pressing responses during the early stages of training.

The avoidance procedures described so far have been examples of *active* avoidance tasks in which the animal must move or make some other response to avoid the UCS. Other procedures, where the animal must inhibit a previously learned response to avoid an aversive stimulus, are cases of *passive* avoidance. For example, in passive avoidance an animal may be trained to enter a compartment or to insert its head into a tray for food when a CS is presented. After the animal has learned this response, an aversive stimulus is then presented whenever the animal enters the compartment or inserts its head into the tray when the CS is presented. The animal, in order to avoid the shock, must now learn to withhold his approach to food. The behavior of not approaching food is passive avoidance, whereas an animal that must move or make some active response (turning a wheel) is displaying active avoidance. Learning of active and passive avoidance responses seems to depend upon the integrity of different regions of the cingulate gyrus. Cats with anterior cingulate lesions readily learn an active two-way shuttle response but have great difficulty learning a passive avoidance response. Posterior cingulate lesioned cats, however, are able to learn the passive avoidance response, but have difficulty learning the active avoidance response (McCleary, 1961).

Operant Conditioning

Operant conditioning techniques, which provide precise and reliable techniques for controlling behavior, are perhaps the least known behavioral control techniques outside of the field of psychology. The development of operant conditioning procedures is closely associated with the experimental analysis of behavior by B. F. Skinner and his associates (Skinner, 1938; Ferster & Skinner, 1957). In the typical "Skinner box" situation, a hungry rat is placed in a dimly lit box which has a lever with a food tray beneath it. The rat explores the box and occasionally by chance presses its paws upon the lever. The number of presses for some arbitrary time period defines the rat's *preconditioning operant level* of bar pressing. The food magazine is then connected so that when the rat presses the bar a pellet of food falls into the dish. The rat eats, and soon presses the bar again. The delivery of food pellets (the click of the food magazine, the food dropping into the food tray, etc.) reinforces bar pressing. The number of lever presses plotted against time provides a record of the course of operant conditioning (or operant rate). Rate of responding and inter-response time are the typical measures in operant situations, whereas different response measures (latency, number of errors, etc.) are used in other instrumental tasks. When a lever-pressing response is used, many parameters such as the size and position of the lever, the size of the test chamber, the effort of the response and the number of food pellets delivered determine the operant rate. Often, the untrained rat is *shaped* to perform the desired bar pressing response by the procedure of *successive approximations*. For example, food is delivered whenever the hungry rat approaches the bar, then whenever it touches the bar, and finally only after it presses the bar.

In operant conditioning the animal must make a response before the response can be reinforced. Skinner (1938) called this behavior operant be-cause the behavior of the rat operates on the environment. The operant conditioning situation differs from both classical and avoidance conditioning in that: (a) there is no specifiable unconditioned stimulus which elicits the response, and (b) the animal is free to respond at any time in the operant situation, but is usually given discrete trials in avoidance and classical conditioning. Operant techniques have been used in the experimental analysis of the behavior of a wide variety of animals including humans. The objective of operant techniques is to place some arbitrary sample of behavior under experimental control so that behavioral processes may be investigated as a function of a wide variety of conditions.

Reinforcement: Definition and Parameters

The term reinforcement is commonly used when discussing operant conditioning, although the pairing of the conditioned and unconditioned stimulus in classical conditioning is also called reinforcement. A reinforcing stimulus may be operationally defined as a stimulus which increases the probability of occurrence of the response that precedes it. Reinforcing stimuli (reinforcers) may be either positive (e.g., food, water) or aversive (e.g., electric shock). The omission or termination of an aversive stimulus increases the probability of a response occurring (e.g., shuttling, lifting a leg). Other types of reinforcers which have been found to increase the probability of a response in learning situations are: observing or handling new stimuli, turning a light on and off, running in an activity wheel, etc. The quantity and quality of the reinforcement as well as the interval between the response and the presentation of the reinforcement (called delay of reinforcement) are important variables which affect the organism's behavior during learning (cf. Kimble, 1961).

Another important variable is the schedule of reinforcement. Reinforcement may be given on every trial or after every correct response (*continuous reinforcement*) or intermittently, that is, the response is reinforced only part of the time (*partial reinforcement*). The main effect of partial reinforcement is to make it more difficult to extinguish the response once it has been learned. The effect of partial reinforcement is found in both operant situations and discrete trial instrumental tasks. Partial reinforcement in the operant situation may be delivered on either a temporal (interval) schedule or on a response (ratio) schedule. There are four basic schedules of reinforcement, with each schedule generating a particular pattern of operant responding. The four schedules may be described as follows:

a. *Fixed Interval* (FI). Under this schedule, reinforcement is delivered following the first response which occurs after some specified period of time measured from the last reinforcement. For example, if the subject is on a 5-min. fixed interval schedule (FI5), the reinforcement will be scheduled to be available every 5 min. if the animal responds. For FI reinforcement schedules, there is a pause in the bar pressing rate of the animal immediately after a reinforcement, which is then followed by a positively accelerating rate of response near the end of the interval. The pause in operant responding is of greater duration for long fixed intervals than for short ones and may eventually disappear with extended practice.

b. *Variable Interval* (VI). The low probability of response just after a reinforcement on a FI schedule is eliminated by a variable interval schedule. For example, on a variable interval schedule of 5 min. (VI5), reinforcement is administered *on the average* every 5 min. On a VI5, the interval between reinforcements may be as short as a few seconds or as long as several minutes. Since reinforcement under VI schedules occasionally occurs just after the organism has been reinforced the animal continues to respond during this period. The operant rate of animals on VI schedules is remarkably stable and uniform over long periods of time and the VI schedules provide the greatest resistance to extinction.

c. *Fixed Ratio* (FR). Reinforcement, on a FR schedule, is delivered after a certain fixed number of responses by the organism. The FR schedules depend upon the behavior of the animal: he must emit a certain number of responses, for example, ten, before he receives the first reinforcement and ten more responses before he receives the second reinforcement. The FR reinforcement schedules generate very high rates of operant responding providing that the ratio is not too high. Under high FR schedules, the operant rate eventually shows a very low probability immediately after a reinforcement as in the fixed-interval schedules. The effect is marked under high fixed ratios. Pigeons may, under high FR schedules, stop responding for long periods.

d. *Variable Ratio* (VR). To eliminate the pauses in operant rate on a FR reinforcement schedule, reinforcement may be administered by varying the ratios over a considerable range around some mean value. Under a VR schedule, reinforcement occurs after a certain number of responses, with the predetermined number changing from one

reinforcement to another. This is essentially the same procedure used in variable interval schedules except that the average ratio is based on the number of responses emitted by the organism instead of some elapsed time basis. The operant rate produced by a VR schedule is constant and stable over a long period of time and is more powerful in producing a fast operant response rate than is a FR schedule with the same mean number of reinforcements.

Many permutations of these four basic schedules of reinforcement have been studied. Some of these other schedules are: (a) *tandem schedule,* where a single reinforcement is determined by two different schedules operating in succession; (b) *differential rate schedules,* where high or low rates of responding are reinforced; (c) *multiple (mixed) schedules,* where a signal indicates a change from one reinforcement schedule to another, etc. The ongoing bar pressing behavior of rats and the key pecking behavior of pigeons, under different schedules of reinforcement, have been extensively studied by Skinner and his associates (cf. Skinner, 1938; Ferster & Skinner, 1957).

In operant conditioning experiments, the responses of the animal are usually plotted directly on a graph with the number of responses on the ordinate against time on the asbcissa (fig. 9.4, Part A). The recording device used to present a visual record of the subject's rate of response is called a cumulative recorder. The recorder is essentially a kymograph-like device, with a strip of paper driven by a motor at a constant speed, and with a pen riding on the paper. As long as the subject does not respond, the pen draws a line parallel to the direction in which the paper is moving. When the subject responds by pressing the bar the pen is deflected a short distance perpendicular to the direction in which the paper is being driven. The slope of the recording curve is proportional to the subject's response rate. When the curve is flat, it indicates that the subject did not respond at all during that period of time. The faster the animal responds, the steeper the slope of the line. The curve is cumulative in that responses move the pen in only one direction. The pen may be reset to the bottom at any time; however, it automatically resets to the bottom if it reaches the top. By porportionately increasing both the paper speed and the distance the pen travels on each response, the cumulative record can be magnified or reduced without changing the slope. By introducing a brief electrical signal, the pen also may be displaced slightly in an oblique direction to indicate the point where the animal receives a reinforcement.

Although operant conditioning procedures have been used as behavioral control techniques in the study of a wide variety of neurobehavioral problems, they have been closely associated with two specific areas of research. These areas are: (a) psychopharmacological studies on the effects of drugs on behavior, and (b) brain self-stimulation studies, where the animals are trained to press a bar to receive a low voltage electrical brain shock.

Psychopharmacological Investigations

Besides their importance for psychiatric use, drugs have fundamental advantages over surgical procedures in neurobehavioral research: their time of onset, magnitude, and duration are relatively easy to control, and their effects are ordinarily reversible. It is clear from the many studies in psychopharmacology that drug-behavior interactions are dependent upon characteristics of the biochemical events affected, of the subjects employed, of the behavioral patterns observed, and of the conditions under which the behavior patterns are generated (Cole & Gerard, 1959; Uhr & Miller, 1960). Operant conditioning techniques provide a quantitative, continuous record of the behavior of an organism which has proved useful in screening psychopharmacological compounds and for investigating the nature of pharmacological effects. For example, one of the important characteristics of a drug is its time course of action. In order to study temporal relations between a drug and behavior it is necessary to maintain the behavior at a stable level over long periods of time. This, of course, can be accomplished in an operant conditioning situation with the appropriate schedule of reinforcement. The behavioral measure, in addition to being stable in time, should also have a potential wide range of variability from baseline performance in order to provide a sensitive test of the drug action. The response rate in operant conditioning procedures may be either increased or decreased by using multiple schedules of reinforcement in the same experimental situation. Thus, the effects of a drug may be determined on low, medium, and high rates of responding or on any combination of operant patterns.

As many of the psychopharmacological agents are intimately related to emotional behavior, conditioning techniques have been developed to establish a baseline for evaluating the effects of drugs on emotional behavior. For example, a

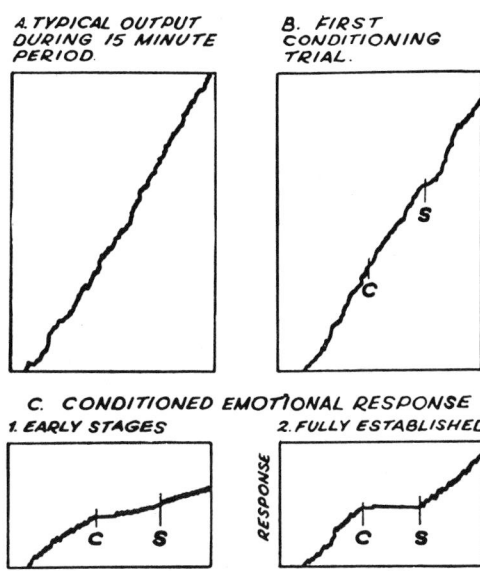

FIG. 9.4. The conditioned emotional response as it appears typically in the cumulative response curve. Clicker introduced at *C*, terminated by shock at *S* after 5 minutes (from Hunt and Brady, 1951).

common clinical and experimental observation is that "emotional" stimuli may disrupt or interfere with an organism's behavior. Experimentally, anticipation of pain will decrease an animal's rate of bar pressing; this effect is called a *conditioned emotional response*. The conditioned emotional response is established by a few pairings of a signal (the CS) with a brief, unavoidable electric shock to the feet (the UCS). This method has many similarities to classical conditioning except that the animal is unrestrained and the CS is typically presented for three to five minutes before it is reinforced at termination with the UCS. Often, this conditioning is superimposed onto a reinforcement schedule by giving emotional conditioning trials during operant responding.

For example, in part A of fig. 9.4 is the cumulative response curve of a rat pressing for water reinforcement on a variable interval schedule. On the first conditioning trial, a clicking noise is introduced at point C on the curve, is continued for 5 min., and is terminated simultaneously with foot shock at point S. It takes only 3 to 6 trials to establish a conditioned emotional response (crouching, immobility, and defecation) to the clicker and this produces a disruption in the ongoing bar pressing. It is important to note that the clicker has a suppressing effect on the bar pressing even though the shocks are paired only with the termination of the clicker, and bar pressing is not intentionally punished with shock.

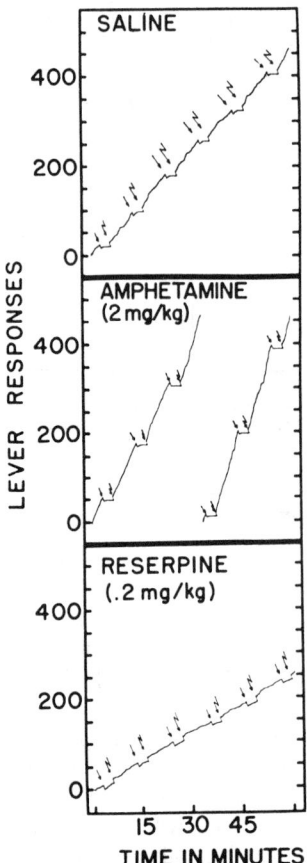

FIG. 9.5. Sample cumulative-response curves showing the effect of amphetamine and reserpine on lever pressing, and on the conditioned emotional response (from Brady, 1956).

Conditioned emotional responses may also be measured in a chamber without any bar (grill box); under these conditions, the clicker reduces or stops completely the exploratory behavior rats normally show in the box.

The conditioned emotional response, in the experimental analysis of emotional behavior, has certain advantages over other types of instrumental procedures (e.g., escape and avoidance conditioning). These advantages, as summarized by Brady (1960), are: (a) the test focuses directly on the conditioned suppression response *per se;* (b) the response can be elicited under a wide range of conditions and in a number of species; (c) the response is remarkably stable; and (d) the technique of using the conditioned emotional response together with lever pressing results in increased sensitivity and ease of quantification. Studying the conditioned emotional response in a Skinner lever pressing situation also makes it possible to determine if the changes in

the conditioned emotional response, produced by drugs or other experimental manipulations, are specific and selective for the suppression effect or represent some general motor disability or a generalized amnesia. For example, fig. 9.5 shows the typical results found in a study on the effects of amphetamine and reserpine on the conditioned emotional response in rats on a variable-interval reinforcement schedule (Brady, 1956). On the cumulative response curve, each solid arrow shows the onset of a clicker with the shock onset indicated by the broken arrow. In order to isolate the operant rate during the three minute interval when the clicker was on, the cumulative record has been displaced downward. In the saline control, shortly after the onset of the clicker, the operant rate falls to zero as indicated by the flat horizontal portions of the record. After the shock is received, the rat begins responding almost immediately and at the normal rate. Injections of the stimulant amphetamine have the effect of increasing the overall rate, as shown in the middle part of fig. 9.5. The onset of the clicker continues to suppress the responding of the animal. Injections of reserpine, however, have the effect of slightly depressing the overall rate and of restoring responding during presentation of the formerly suppressing stimulus. In the lower part of fig. 9.5 the slopes of the displaced segments of the record have the same rate as the overall record itself. The conditioned emotional response, of course, does not exhaust the behavioral testing situations used to evaluate drug behavior interactions. Practically all the instrumental and classical conditioning procedures mentioned or to be mentioned have been, at one time or another, used in psychopharmacological investigations. An important trend in the assessment of various drugs on behavior has been the development of *behavioral profiles,* where different animal species and strains are tested in standardized behavioral situations under the influence of different drugs (Brady & Ross, 1960).[3]

Electrical Self-Stimulation of the Brain

The discovery that low voltage electrical stimulation of various brain loci may be used as positive and negative reinforcement has led to numerous self-stimulation studies. In these studies, stimulating electrodes are chronically inserted into sub-

[3] For a lucid and detailed discussion of the effects of drugs on learning see J. L. McGaugh & L. F. Petrinovich, Effects of Drugs on Learning and Memory. In C. C. Pfeiffer & J. R. Smythies (Eds.) International Review of Neurobiology, Academic Press, New York, 1965, 8, 193.

cortical structures and connected by a light flexible cord to a source of stimulating current. The animal, by pressing a bar or lever, delivers a flow of stimulating current to its own brain. The electrical circuit is constructed so that a fixed duration of stimulating current is delivered for each bar press. Thus, the experimental procedure is the same as other operant techniques, except that instead of receiving a food pellet as reinforcement, the animal receives a slight shock to its brain.

Olds and Milner (1954) were the first to discover that rats, allowed to stimulate their own brains, would maintain high lever pressing rates over long periods of time without any other reward. This interesting and important finding has resulted in extensive experimentation and speculation concerning the variables which influence brain self-stimulation. Some of the variables shown to be critical determinants of this phenomenon are: the specific anatomical locus of the electrode, the intensity of the stimulating current, the schedule of brain reinforcements, and food and water deprivation. For example, rats with electrodes in the lateral hypothalamus will, under continuous reinforcement, press about 10,000 times an hour for brain stimulation but only about 500 times an hour when the electrodes are in the septal or amygdaloid areas. With electrodes in the periventricular system of fibers (dorsal longitudinal fasciculus of Schütz), rats will actively work to prevent or escape the brain stimulation. Stimulation of certain medial hypothalamic areas yields both positive and negative effects. With electrodes in these brain sites animals can be trained to turn on the brain stimulation and then immediately turn it off (cf. Olds, 1962; Olds & Olds, 1965, for reviews). The rewarding effects of intracranial self-stimulation have also been observed in cats, monkeys, and humans (Sheer, 1961). During neurosurgery of humans, stimulation of various brain loci has resulted in verbal reports of feelings of joy and satisfaction and experiences of tickling and fluttering of muscles in the pelvic region which were regarded as pleasurable. The patients, given a key which controlled the delivery of the brain stimulus, would eagerly respond by self-stimulation (cf. Sem-Jacobsen & Torkildsen, 1960).

As with other operant techniques, the most widely used measure of the strength of brain stimulation as a reinforcement has been the rate of responding (pressing a bar). In intracranial self-stimulation tests, at high stimulus intensities, response rate usually declines because of motoric side effects of the stimulation disrupting performance. In a preference test, however, animals may choose the high intensities over lower amplitude stimulation even though the lower intensity results in a higher response rate in the operant situation (Valenstein, 1964). Many other parameters of electrical self-stimulation have yet to be determined. Depending upon the locus of the stimulating electrodes animals may show a strong drive for electrical stimulation during experimental sessions, but bar pressing for this stimulation will extinguish rapidly. In other brain sites, extinction is reported to proceed at the same rate as when food or water is used as the reinforcement (Olds & Olds, 1965). Also, in studies with rats it has been difficult to maintain responding on variable ratio schedules in which the average number of responses required to produce reinforcement is higher than 10:1 (Gallistel, 1964).

DISCRIMINATION LEARNING

Discrimination learning is involved in every learning situation, but has been studied most extensively with instrumental procedures. The general procedure used to establish a discrimination involves the extinction of responses to certain stimuli by withholding reinforcement, while a response to some second stimulus is maintained by the delivery of reinforcement. The discrimination experiment was originally designed to test the sensory capacities of various animals. At present, discrimination behavior is often studied as a learning phenomenon in its own right. The two methods of presenting stimuli in discrimination experiments are: (a) successive presentation of stimuli (contrasts) and (b) simultaneous presentation of stimuli (choice response).

Successive Presentation of Stimuli

In this method, only one of the two stimuli to be discriminated is presented on each trial. Reinforcement follows one stimulus (the positive stimulus) and not the other (the negative stimulus). The subject must learn to respond to the positive stimulus and to suppress his response to the other stimulus. This discrimination technique has been used with both classical and instrumental conditioning procedures. In classical conditioning, for example, successive presentation of stimuli has been used to establish discriminations between different stimuli in the same modality, such as tones of different pitch (see section on discrimination under classical conditioning). In instrumental avoidance conditioning, the animal may learn to lift its hind leg (defensive conditioning) or to shuttle to the other side of the box when the positive stimulus is presented, and not to respond when the negative stimulus is presented. In operant conditioning, the discriminative stimulus which is present when the response is reinforced is called an S^D and the cue presented when a response is nonreinforced is called an S^Δ. In operant conditioning, every response to the S^D does not have to be reinforced—partial reinforcement schedules are quite effective in maintaining the response to the S^D.

Simultaneous Presentation of Stimuli

In the choice methods, two stimuli are presented simultaneously and the animal responds to either one or the other by pushing a lever, opening a door, lifting a cup, etc. If the subject approaches or manipulates the stimulus arbitrarily designated as positive, it receives a reward. If the animal responds to the negative stimulus it will not be rewarded and, in some cases, it may be punished. Simultaneous discrimination learning is usually studied in lower animals in a two-choice discrimination apparatus (a Y- or T-maze) or in a two-key Skinner box. The stimuli are each presented half the time on the left and half the time on the right in a random order to control for any position habits. Successive discrimination learning may also be studied in a two-choice apparatus. In a typical successive procedure, the animal is trained to turn right when one "stimulus" is presented (e.g., two black cards) and to turn left when the other "stimulus" is presented (e.g., two white cards). In simultaneous discrimination, the relationship between the two stimuli may be easier for the subject to notice, and the animal's choice is usually between two responses (pushing one of two doors open) rather than between responding and non-responding (shuttling to the other side or remaining in the same compartment). Of course, when the two-choice discrimination apparatus is used for successive presentation of stimuli the animal has the choice of either responding to the right or to the left door.

The cues the animal uses in learning a discrimination, whether the absolute qualities of the stimuli or some relational cue between stimuli, is still a subject of debate. Many psychologists have considered discrimination learning to be the result of the interaction of two basic processes, those of conditioning (reinforcement) and of extinction (non-reinforcement). As an alternative explanation, some investigators have favored a relational theory of discrimination. Their belief is that discrimination learning involves a comparison between stimuli which are present (simultaneous) or between one stimulus which is present and the neural trace of the succeeding stimulus (successive). The relational theory receives apparent support from studies on a type of transfer problem called *transposition*. In transposition studies, subjects may be trained to discriminate between two gray stimuli with a medium gray as the positive stimulus and a darker gray as the negative stimulus. Under certain circumstances when the animal is tested with a light gray stimulus and the original positive medium gray stimulus, the light gray stimulus is the one chosen. It is as if the animal had learned the relation "lighter" and responds to the stimulus which is lighter. An explanation for the transposition data has been advanced by those theorists who believe the animal is responding to the absolute qualities of the stimuli rather than to the relationship. This explanation is based on the interacting gradients of generalized excitation and inhibition and is able to predict a reversal of transposition—which in fact occurs at some test values (cf. Kimble, 1961).

Types of Discrimination Tasks

Visual, somesthetic, and auditory discriminations have been studied in a variety of instrumental conditioning procedures. The most intensively studied of all types of discrimination has been visual discrimination—particularly form discrimination. Much of the visual discrimination learning of primates has been studied on the Wisconsin General Test Apparatus or in a similar testing situation. Discrimination in non-primates has usually been studied in two-choice discrimination mazes. Typical discrimination tasks used to assess brain function and the ability of monkeys to make discriminations are presented in this section.[4] Discrimination procedures with non-primates are presented under maze learning procedures in the following section.

In the typical discrimination task with primates, two stimulus objects which may differ in either shape, size, or color are placed over two food wells on a test tray. The food well under the correct object is baited with food and the other food well is left empty. The animal must learn to select the correct stimulus and move it aside to pick up the food in the well. The position of the objects on the tray are shifted from one side to

[4] For a detailed discussion of behavioral procedures used with primates see Schrier, Harlow, & Stollnitz (Eds.) *Behavior of Nonhuman Primates.* Volume I (1965).

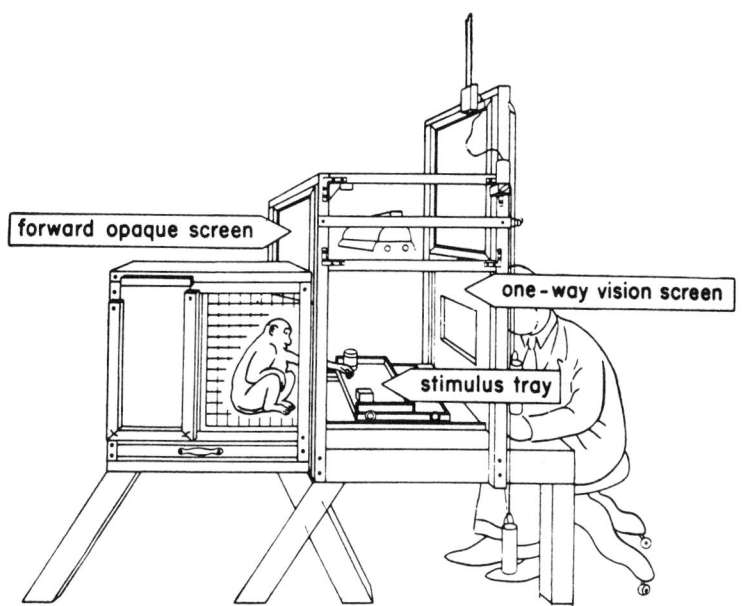

FIG. 9.6. Wisconsin General Test Apparatus (from Harlow, 1959).

the other in either a random or balanced order. Between trials, a screen is lowered in front of the monkey so that the appropriate food well may be baited (fig. 9.6). A more difficult problem than simple object discrimination is the *oddity* problem. In this test, three stimulus objects are presented on the stimulus tray; two of the stimuli are identical and the other stimulus is different in some dimension (shape, size, or color). The animal must learn to select the odd stimulus on each trial to receive food. Usually two different pairs of identical stimuli are used, with only three of the four stimuli presented on any one trial. Adult primates can solve oddity problems, while most sub-primates have considerable difficulty with such problems. Monkeys have been trained to respond to highly complex cues in the oddity task, e.g., to respond to the odd form when the stimuli are presented on a dark background and to the odd color when presented on a light background. Another problem, typically used with primates, is the *matching problem*. In this task, a sample object is set apart from two other objects, one of which is identical to the sample object. The animal is usually permitted to first obtain food from under the sample or standard stimulus object. Then the stimulus tray containing the pair of stimuli is presented to the animal and he must choose the object which is identical to the standard to receive food.

A recent development in visual discrimination learning has been the *learning-set problem* (Har-

low, 1959). The learning-set problem consists of many different problems, each one presented for a limited number of trials; for example, in a two-choice discrimination problem the animal may be presented with a cube and a barrel-shaped stimulus object with the latter stimulus being the positive cue for six trials. Regardless of the animal's performance on the first problem, a new problem employing different stimuli (e.g., a circle and a triangle) is presented on the following six trials. This sequence is followed throughout the testing period with a new problem being presented every seventh trial. The animal must learn that on every new problem, one stimulus object is baited with food and the other object is not. Thus, on the first trial of every new problem, the animal's performance is at a chance level. If the animal has developed a learning set, its choice on the first trial will give it all the information necessary to solve the problem on trials 2–6. For example, if an experienced learning-set monkey, by chance makes a correct response on trial 1, it will continue to respond correctly on trials 2–6. If the animal chooses the incorrect object on trial 1, however, it will immediately shift to the correct object and make no subsequent errors. Occasional errors will occur, but they are relatively infrequent; experienced monkeys typically respond correctly on 95% of the trials after approximately 100 to 200 discrimination problems. Learning sets have been demonstrated in several primate genera, in rats, in cats, and in both normal and mentally defective children. In general, the speed with which learning sets develop is phylogenetically correlated. Learning set formation has been called "interproblem learning" to contrast it with "intraproblem learning" which is limited to learning that occurs during the solution of a single problem (Harlow, 1959).

PROBLEM-SOLVING PROCEDURES

Problem-solving instrumental procedures are probably the most familiar of the animal testing procedures developed by psychologists. Originally, many of the so-called problem-solving tasks were designed to test for symbolic behavior in lower animals. Now, it is generally assumed that the animals learn problem-solving tasks in the same way as other instrumental tasks are learned, except that the discriminative cues are more subtle or complex in the problem-solving tasks. Problem-solving procedures have been classified as learning with complex cues (cf. Ratner & Denny, 1964). In general, the following types of learning tasks may be distinguished.

Maze Learning

The maze provides a learning situation used commonly with small rodents (mice and rats) in which the animal must overcome an obstacle placed between it and a goal box (a place where food is available or a "safe" area). The obstacle may be a path which must be traversed or two doors marked with different stimuli one of which the animal must push open to gain access to the goal box. Mazes may be either simple or complex. The earlier mazes were usually extremely complex with many blind alleys. Now the most common mazes are simple mazes in which the animal is presented with a choice between only two alternatives (the T-maze and the Y-maze). Even when complex mazes are used the animal is usually presented a choice between only two alternatives (turning left or right) at each "choice" point in the maze. Discrimination learning in either a T-maze or a Y-maze is one of the most widely used instrumental learning techniques. The discriminative cue may be either spatial or non-spatial. In a spatial problem, the animal chooses between a pair of stimuli which differ only in their position in space. The animal, for example, may be required to always turn left or choose the left door in order to receive reinforcement. In a non-spatial problem, the two discriminative cues each appear in the two positions in a random order, and reinforcement is correlated with the positive cue. For example, in a red-green visual discrimina-

tion, the green alternative may be reinforced independently of its position. Spatial and non-spatial problems may also be used in complex mazes. For example, at each choice point the animal may be required to always turn left (spatial) or to turn into the lighted alley in a light-dark non-spatial discrimination problem.

In some cases, the animal's own response may be the cue for the correct response at the next choice point. For example, in a *simple-alternation* problem, the animal must alternate left and right turns (LRLR) in a 4-choice maze. Turning left at the first choice point provides the cue for the right turn at the next choice point and so on. Most mammals can readily learn a simple alternation problem as they tend to normally alternate spontaneously in most maze situations. A more difficult problem is the *double-alternation* pattern (LLRR). Rats, typically, fail to learn a double-alternation problem, whereas other mammals (cats, dogs) are capable of learning a LLRR problem but fail to learn a longer sequence. The alternation problems have also been used with primates in the Wisconsin General Test Apparatus. Both spatial and non-spatial problems have been used in which the animals must choose between two food cups. In the spatial simple alternation problem, the food is first under the left cup, then under the right, then under the left, and so on. In the spatial double alternation problem the food is under the cups in a LLRR or a RRLL pattern.

After an animal has learned a simple alternation pattern of LRLR turns, he may be required immediately to learn the opposite pattern of turns (RLRL). This is an example of a *single habit reversal*. The animal may also be required to learn a series of reversals. For example, after learning the first reversal problem (RLRL), the subject is then switched back to the original pattern (LRLR), and after relearning the first pattern is then reversed to the second pattern (RLRL)—and so forth. Spatial habit reversals may be studied in a two-choice situation (left-right positions). The procedure for habit reversal in the non-spatial problem is similar. After the animal has been trained to choose one of two stimuli, either for a fixed number of trials or to some criterion level of correct choice, the positive and negative stimuli are reversed. After the same number of trials as were given in the original problem, or when the original criterion has been reached in the first reversal, the positive and negative stimuli are reversed again and so forth. Animals which show progressive improvement in a habit reversal problem usually have an increase in the number of errors on the first two to three reversals with a progressive decrease in the number of errors made on subsequent reversals.

Another variation in the standard two-choice discrimination task is called *probability learning*. In this procedure instead of reinforcing the responses to one alternative on 100% of the trials (the positive stimulus) and never reinforcing responses to the other alternative (the negative stimulus), responses to one alternative may be reinforced on only 70% of the trials. On the remaining trials (30%), the responses to the other stimulus are reinforced. This reinforcement procedure is an example of a 70:30 probability learning problem. Probability learning may be studied in either a spatial or non-spatial (visual) task. Subjects typically respond in a probability learning situation in one of two ways: (a) they may "maximize", which means they tend to consistently choose the more frequently reinforced stimulus; or (b) they may match, which means that their distribution of choices approximates the distribution of reinforcements. For example, in a 70:30 problem, the subject who maximizes will tend to respond 100% of the time to the 70% alternative and not at all to the 30% alternative, whereas the subject who "matches" will respond approximately 70% of the time to the 70% reinforced cue and 30% of the time to the 30% reinforced cue.

It has been mentioned that the interpretation of the effects of neurophysiological manipulations (i.e., drug, stimulation, ablation) on behavior depends upon the species studied as well as the type of learning procedure used. The results of a series of experiments on habit reversal and probability learning in both spatial and visual two-choice discrimination problems with a variety of animals are summarized in table 9.1 (Bitterman, 1965a). As can be seen, the performance of the various animals depends upon the particular problem used. Notice particularly the performance of the decorticate rats (Gonzales, Roberts & Bitterman, 1964). These animals had approximately 70% of the cortex removed at 15 or 16 days of age and were tested on the problems when they were about 90 days of age. These decorticated rats were able to learn a spatial habit reversal (20 reversals) but were unable to learn a visual habit reversal. In the first 10 reversals on the spatial problem, the decorticate rats made more errors than did the normals, but, as did the normals, they showed progressive improvement. In the last 10 reversals there was no difference be-

TABLE 9.1.

Behavior of a variety of animals in four classes of two choice discrimination problems

Animal	Spatial Problems		Visual Problems	
	Re-versal	Proba-bility	Re-versal	Proba-bility
⌈Monkey	PI	MAX	PI	MAX
⌊Rat	PI	MAX	PI	MAX
Pigeon	PI	MAX	PI	RM
⌈Turtle	PI	MAX	F	RM
Decorticated rat⌋	PI	MAX	F	RM
⌈Fish	F	RM	F	RM
Cockroach	F	RM	—	—
⌊Earthworm	F	—	—	—

Note: PI and MAX indicate progressive improvement (PI) in habit reversal and maximizing in probability learning (MAX). F and RM indicate failure of progressive improvement (F) in habit reversal and random matching (RM) in probability learning. Transitional regions are connected by the stepped line. The brackets group animals which have not yet been differentiated by these problems. (Adapted from M. E. Bitterman, 1965a.)

tween the normals and operates. However, on the visual problem, the decorticate animals' error scores rose sharply and did not show the progressive decrease found with normal rats. In spatial probability learning the performance of the operates was like normals (both groups maximized), but in visual probability learning the operates showed random matching while the normals continued to maximize. It should be apparent from these results that any physiological manipulation which is assumed to affect general learning behavior must be evaluated in the context of a variety of behavioral problems and with a number of animal species.

Delayed Response

The delayed-response problem is one of the most sensitive behavioral tests and has been used in neurobehavioral research to detect the effects of brain lesions, drugs, and radiation. The delayed-response problem is particularly sensitive to damage to the central nervous system, especially the frontal lobes. In this problem, the animal is presented a limited number of choices where food might be placed. The animal is first trained to respond to a particular stimulus in order to obtain food. The animal is then restrained from approaching the food compartments or the stimuli over the food wells until released. The experimenter at the beginning of the trial permits the animal to see where the food is located by turning on a light over the correct food compartment (indirect method) or by directly placing food into a particular food well (direct method). The light is then turned off or a screen is lowered in front of the animal, and following a certain delay, the animal is allowed access to the compartments or food wells. The purpose of the testing procedure is to determine how long the animal can be delayed without "forgetting" where the food has been placed. This task commonly has been used to determine if an area of the brain is involved in immediate memory.

Special Procedures (problem box and detour and reasoning problems)

In the *problem-box*, the animal must learn to release a latch, press a bar, or make some other response to solve the problem. A correct response usually involves a release from confinement as well as access to food or water. In the *detour* or *insight problem*, the path to the goal is not a direct one and the animal may be required to either go around an obstacle by moving away from the goal or make use of tools to solve the problem. *Reasoning problems* are closely related to detour problems. In these tasks, the animal may be taught segments of the correct behavior and the solution to the problem requires the animal to combine the segments in the proper order. These special procedures are not as widely used as they were during the earlier stages of psychological research. Other behavioral control techniques provide more reliable procedures for the control of the discriminative cues in learning situations.

REFERENCES

Ban, T. A. Conditioning and Psychiatry. Aldine Co., Chicago, 1964.

Bekhterev, V. M. General Principles of Human Reflexology. International, New York, 1932.

Bitterman, M. E. Techniques for the study of learning in animals: analysis and classification. Psychol. Bull., 1962, 59, 81.

Bitterman, M. E. Phyletic differences in learning. Amer. Psychologist, 1965, 20, 396 (a).

Bitterman, M. E. The CS-US Interval in Classical and Avoidance Conditioning. In W. F. Prokasy (Ed.) Classical Conditioning: A Symposium. Appleton-Century-Crofts, New York, 1965, (b).

Black, A. H., Carlson, N. J. and Solomon, R. L. Exploratory studies of the conditioning of autonomic responses in curarized dogs. Psychol. Monogr., 1962, 76 (29, Whole No. 548).

Black, A. H. Cardiac Conditioning in Curarized Dogs: The Relationship between Heart Rate and Skeletal Behaviour. In W. F. Prokasy (Ed.) Classical Conditioning: A Symposium. Appleton-Century-Crofts, New York, 1965, 20.

Brady, J. V. Assessment of drug effect on emotional behavior. Science, 1956, 123, 1033.

Brady, J. V. Emotional Behavior. In J. Field (Ed.) Handbook of Physiology, Section 1: Neurophysiology, Vol. 3. American Physiological Society, Washington, D.C., 1960, 1529.

Brady, J. V. and Ross, S. Testing Drug Effects on Controlled Animal and Human Behavior. In L. Uhr and J. E. Miller (Eds.) Drugs and Behavior. John Wiley & Sons, Inc., New York, 1960, 232.

Bures, J. Reversible Decortication and Behavior. In M. A. B. Brazier (Ed.) The Central Nervous System and Behavior. Transactions of the Second Conference. Josiah Macy, Jr., Foundation, New York, 1959, 207.

Bykov, K. M. The Cerebral Cortex and the Internal Organs. Translated and edited by W. H. Gantt. Chemical Publishing Co., New York, 1957.

Caldwell, D. F. and Werboff, J. Classical conditioning in newborn rats. Science, 1962, 136, 1118.

Cole, J. O. and Gerard, R. W. (Eds.). Psychopharmacology: Problems in Evaluation. National Research Council, National Academy of Sciences, Washington, D.C., 1959.

Delgado, J. M. R. Electrodes for Extracellular Recording and Stimulation. In W. L. Nastuk (Ed.) Physical Techniques in Biological Research. Vol. 5, Electrophysiological Methods. Part A. Academic Press, New York, 1964, 5, 89.

Deutsch, J. A. Physiological bases of memory. Ann. Rev. Physiol., 1962, 24, 259.

Doty, R. W. Conditioned Reflexes Formed and Evoked by Brain Stimulation. In D. E. Sheer (Ed.) Electrical Stimulation of the Brain. Univer. Texas Press, Austin, Tex., 1961, 397.

Doty, R. W. and Giurgea, C. Conditioned Reflexes Established by Coupling Electrical Excitation of Two Cortical Areas. In J. Delafresnaye (Ed.) Brain Mechanisms and Behavior. Blackwell Scientific Publications, London, 1961, 133.

Durup, G. and Fessard, A. L'électroencéphalogramme de l'homme: observations psychophysiologiques relatives á l'action des stimuli visuels et auditifs. Ann. Psychol., Paris, 1935, 36, 1.

Ferster, C. B. and Skinner, B. F. Schedules of Reinforcement. Appleton-Century-Crofts, New York, 1957.

Galambos, R. and Morgan C. T. The Neural Basis of Learning. In J. Field (Ed.) Handbook of Physiology. Section I: Neurophysiology Vol. 3. American Physiological Society, Washington, D.C., 1960, 1471.

Galambos, R. and Sheatz, G. C. An electroencephalographic study of classical conditioning. Amer. J. Physiol., 1962, 203, 175.

GALLISTEL, C. R. Electrical self-stimulation and its theoretical implications. Psychol. Bull., 1964, **61**, 23.

GANTT, W. H. Cardiovascular components of the conditioned reflex to pain, food, and other stimuli. Physiol. Rev., 1960, **40**, 266.

GONZALES, R. C., ROBERTS, W. A. AND BITTERMAN, M. E. Learning in adult rats with extensive cortical lesions made in infancy. Amer. J. Psychol., 1964, **77**, 547.

HARLOW, H. F. Learning Set and Error Factor Theory. In S. Koch (Ed.) Psychology: A study of a Science. Vol. 2. General Systematic Formulations, Learning, and Special Processes. McGraw-Hill, New York, 1959, 492.

HESS, E. H. Ethology: An Approach Toward the Complete Analysis of Behavior. In R. Brown, E. Galanter, E. H. Hess and G. Mandler. New Directions in Psychology. I. Holt, Rinehart, & Winston, New York, 1962, 157.

HILGARD, E. R. AND MARQUIS, D. G. Conditioning and Learning. Appleton-Century-Crofts, New York, 1940.

HOLST, E. v. AND ST. PAUL, U. v. Electrically controlled behavior. Sci. Amer., 1962, **206**, 50.

HUNT, H. F. AND BRADY, J. V. Some effects of electroconvulsive shock on a conditioned emotional response ("anxiety"). J. Comp. Physiol. Psychol., 1951, **44**, 88.

JASPER, H. H. AND SHAGASS, C. Conditioning the occipital alpha rhythm in man. J. Exp. Psychol., 1941, **28**, 373.

JASPER, H. H., RICCI, G. AND DOANE, B. Microelectrode analysis of cortical discharge during avoidance conditioning in the monkey. Electroenceph. Clin. Neurophysiol., 1960, Suppl. 13, 137.

JOHN, E. R. Higher nervous functions: brain structures and learning. Ann. Rev. Physiol., 1961, **23**, 451.

KAMIKAWA, K., McILWAIN, J. T. AND ADEY, W. R. Response patterns of thalamic neurons during classical conditioning. Electroenceph. Clin. Neurophysiol., 1964, **17**, 485.

KIMBLE, G. A. Hilgard and Marquis' Conditioning and Learning, 2nd ed. Appleton-Century-Crofts, New York, 1961.

KOCH, S. Psychology: A Study of a Science. Vol. 4. Biologically Oriented Fields: Their Place in Psychology and in Biological Science. McGraw-Hill, Inc., New York, 1962.

KONORSKI, J. AND MILLER, S. On two types of conditioned reflex. J. Gen. Psychol., 1937, **16**, 264.

McCLEARY, R. A. Response specificity in the behavioral effects of limbic system lesions in the cat. J. Comp. Physiol. Psychol., 1961, **54**, 605.

McCLEARY, R. A. AND MOORE, R. Y. Subcortical Mechanisms of Behavior. Basic Books, New York, 1965.

MILLER, N. E. Chemical coding of behavior in the brain. Science, 1965, **148**, 328.

MORGAN, C. T. Physiological Psychology. McGraw-Hill, New York, 1965.

MORRELL, F. Microelectrode and steady potential studies suggesting a dendritic locus of closure. Electroenceph. Clin. Neurophysiology, 1960, Suppl. 13, 65.

MORRELL, F. Electrophysiological contributions to the neural basis of learning. Physiol. Rev., 1961, **41**, 443.

MOWRER, O. H. On the dual nature of learning— a re-interpretation of "conditioning" and "problem-solving." Harv. Educ. Rev., 1947, **17**, 102.

NOBLE, M. AND ADAMS, C. K. Conditioning in pigs as a function of the intervals between CS and US. J. Comp. Physiol. Psychol., 1963, **56**, 215.

OLDS, J. AND MILNER, P. Positive reinforcement produced by electrical stimulation of septal area and other regions of the rat brain. J. Comp. Physiol. Psychol., 1954, **47**, 419.

OLDS, J. Hypothalamic substrates of reward. Physiol. Rev., 1962, **42**, 554.

OLDS, J. AND OLDS, M. Drives, Rewards, and the Brain. In F. Barron, W. C. Dement, W. Edwards, H. Lindman, L. D. Phillips, J. Olds and M. Olds. New Directions in Psychology II. Holt, Rinehart, & Winston, 1965, New York, 327.

PAVLOV, I. P. Conditioned Reflexes. Oxford University Press, London, 1927 (Transl. by G. V. Anrep).

PROKASY, W. F. (Ed.) Classical Conditioning: A Symposium. Appleton-Century-Crofts, New York, 1965.

RATNER, S. C. AND DENNY, M. R. Comparative Psychology: Research in Animal Behavior. Dorsey Press, Homewood, Ill., 1964.

RAZRAN, G. The observable unconscious and the inferable conscious in current soviet psychophysiology: interoceptive conditioning, semantic conditioning, and the orienting reflex. Psychol. Rev., 1961, **68**, 81.

REYNOLDS, R. W. An irritative hypothesis concerning the hypothalamic regulation of food intake. Psychol. Rev., 1965, **72**, 105.

SCHRIER, A. M., HARLOW, H. F. AND STOLLNITZ, F. (Eds.) Behavior of Nonhuman Primates. Volume I, Academic Press, New York, 1965.

SEM-JACOBSEN, C. W. AND TORKILDSEN, A. Depth Recording and Electrical Stimulation in the Human Brain. In E. R. Ramey & D. S. O'Doherty (Eds.) Electrical Studies on the Unanesthetized Brain. Hoeber, New York, 1960, 275.

SHEER, D. E. (Ed.) Electrical Stimulation of the Brain: Subcortical Integrative Systems. University of Texas Press, Houston, Texas, 1957.

SKINNER, B. F. The Behavior of Organisms: An Experimental Analysis. Appleton-Century-Crofts, New York, 1938.

SMITH, O. AND STEBBENS, W. Conditioned blood flow and heart rate in monkeys. J. Comp. Physiol. Psychol., 1965, **59**, 432.

SPENCE, K. W. Behavior Theory and Conditioning. Yale University Press, New Haven, 1956.

SPERRY, R. W. Physiological Plasticity and Brain Circuit Theory. In H. F. Harlow and C. N. Woolsey (Eds.) Biological and Biochemical Bases of Behavior. University of Wisconsin Press, Madison, Wis., 1958, 401.

SOKOLOV, E. N. The orienting reflex. Ann. Rev. Physiol., 1963, **25**, 545.

SOLOMON, R. L. AND TURNER, L. H. Discriminative classical conditioning in dogs paralyzed by curare can later control discriminative avoidance responses in the normal state. Psychol. Rev., 1962, **69,** 202.

UHR, L. AND MILLER, J. E. (Eds.) Drugs and Behavior. John Wiley & Sons, Inc., New York, 1960.

VALENSTEIN, E. S. Problems of measurement and interpretation with reinforcing brain stimulation. Psychol. Rev., 1964, **71,** 415.

WELLS, C. E. Electroencephalographic Correlates of Conditioned Responses. In G. H. Glaser (Ed.) EEG & Behavior. Basic Books, New York, 1963, 60.

YOSHII, N. AND OGURA, N. Studies on the unit discharge of brain-stem formation in the cat. Med. J. Osaka Univ., 1960, **11,** 1.

YOUNG, F. A. Classical Conditioning of Autonomic Functions. In W. F. Prokasy (Ed.) Classical Conditioning: A Symposium. Appleton-Century-Crofts, New York, 1965, 358.

CHAPTER 10

The Cerebellum[1]

General Structure and Divisions

The cerebellum consists of a narrow central body, the *vermis* (or worm) and two lateral masses, the *right* and *left cerebellar hemispheres*. On its upper surface the demarcation between the vermis (*superior vermis*) and the hemispheres is slight. Upon the under surface the hemispheres are separated by a deep depression—the *vallecula;* the floor of the latter is formed by the inferior surface of the vermis. The inferior aspect of the vermis (*inferior vermis*) consists of four subdivisions, these are called (in order from the front backwards) the *nodule, uvula, pyramid* and *tuber*. On either side and continuous with the nodule, is an elongated, somewhat lobulated structure called the *flocculus*. It should be noted that these gross subdivisions of the cerebellum are *not* related to either the developmental or the functional divisions of the cerebellum and are useful only as descriptive terms.

The cerebellar surface is not convoluted like the cerebral cortex but is divided by parallel and curved furrows into numerous laminae or folia (leaves). The total cortical area of the human cerebellum is about 100,000 sq. mm., or less than half that of the cerebral cortex.

Although the division of the cerebellum into the vermis and two hemispheres possesses considerable descriptive value, comparative neurologists (chiefly Bolk, Ingvar, Elliott Smith and Larsell), have suggested other divisions which possess greater significance from a phylogenetic and functional point of view. In Larsell's description the cerebellum is divided into two fundamental or primary parts, (a) the small flocculonodular lobe or vestibular part, and (b) the corpus cerebelli. These two parts are separated by a deep fissure—the *posterolateral fissure*—which is present in all vertebrate brains.

The *flocculonodular lobe* (or archicerebellum) the most ancient part of the cerebellum, comprises the flocculus and the nodule. It is developed from the structures in the region of the vestibular nuclei. The *corpus cerebelli*, which includes the rest of the cerebellum, is separated from the flocculo-

nodular lobe by the *fissura posterolateralis*, and is divided by a well marked fissure—the *fissura prima* of Elliot-Smith—into a small anterior and a large posterior lobe. The *anterior lobe* (or paleocerebellum) consists of three subdivisions, the lingula, lobulus centralis and culmen. The *posterior lobe* (or neocerebellum) includes the lobulus simplex, declive, tuber, pyramid and uvula, together with the associated parts of the hemispheres (lobulus ansiformis and lobulus paramedianus, see below) and the paraflocculus (fig. 10.1). In higher forms a fissure appears in front of the pyramid, known as the *sulcus* or *fissura prepyramidalis*. The part of the posterior lobe between this sulcus behind and the fissura prima in front is sometimes referred to as the middle lobe of Ingvar (fig. 10.1); from the functional view this is a convenient subdivision. The flocculonodular lobe,[2] the anterior lobe, and the lobulus simplex, pyramid, uvala and paraflocculus of the posterior lobe are the phylogenetically old parts of the cerebellum and are referred to as the *archicerebellum* and *paleocerebellum*. The remainder of the cerebellum, i.e., the lateral expansions or hemispheres (ansiform lobules) declive and tuber (superior vermis) are late acquisitions, and constitute the *neocerebellum*; they correspond to most of Ingvar's middle lobe, and appear in phylogenetic development at about the same time as the cerebral cortex and the corticospinal tracts, and the pons. The neocerebellum, cerebral cortex and pons are absent or rudimentary in submammalian forms.

The *paramedian lobule* (or *tonsil*) is a small compact mass lying on either side of the inferior vermis. The ansiform lobule, which constitutes a large proportion of the posterior lobe and forms the expanded lateral mass of the hemisphere, reaches its greatest development in the human brain; its function is concerned with the tonus adjustments and the muscular coordination required in the performance of skilled movements.

INTERNAL STRUCTURE

When sectioned in the sagittal plane each hemisphere of the cerebellum presents a branching core of white matter which from its foliagelike appear-

---

[1] Those interested in a more detailed review of the anatomy of the cerebellum are referred to Larsell, O., "The Cerebellum from Myxinoids to Man", Univ. of Minnesota Press, and for physiology and pathology of the cerebellum to Dow, R. S. and Moruzzi, G., "The Physiology and Pathology of the Cerebellum", Univ. of Minnesota Press, Minneapolis, 1958.

[2] The first appearance of a cerebellum, phylogenetically, is in the primitive fish *Petromyzon* (lamprey), and consists merely of a bridge of nervous tissue formed by an outgrowth from either side of the medulla which fuse in the midline over the fourth ventricle. This is the forerunner of the flocculonodular lobe of higher forms.

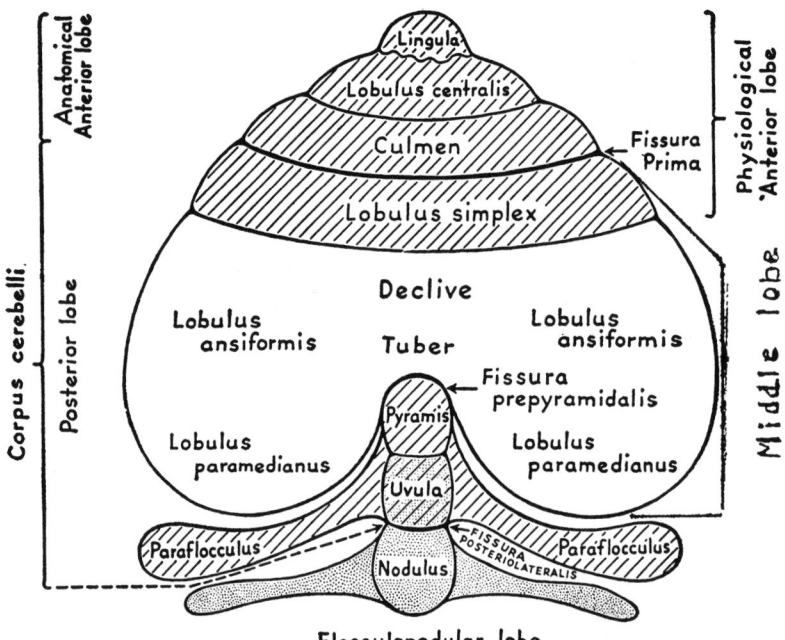

FIG. 10.1. Divisions of the human cerebellum. (After Larsell, modified.) Afferent fiber connections *stippled* vestibular paleocerebellum; *diagonals*, spinal paleocerebellum; *clear*, corticopontocerebellar, neocerebellum.

ance, has been named the *arbor vitae*. The terminal branches of the white matter are covered with a coating of gray substance which constitutes the cerebellar cortex. The leaflike structures so formed are spoken of as folia, and are responsible for the laminated appearance of the cerebellar surface (fig. 10.2). Unlike the cortex of the cerebrum all areas of the cerebellar cortex show a uniform histologic structure.

The Gray Matter

THE CORTEX. Three cell layers are distinguished.

(1) *The molecular (or plexiform) layer* is outermost and consists largely of unmyelinated nerve fibers derived from (a) the white substance, (b) the cells of the two underlying layers, and (c) the cells within this layer itself. The cells of the molecular layer are arranged in a deep and a superficial stratum, their axons synapse with the Purkinje cells, whose dendrites arborize throughout this layer. The cells of the superficial stratum are small, star-shaped and few in number. The deep stratum is composed of larger stellate cells whose axons run transversely in relation to the long axis of the folium and arborize by means of collaterals around the bodies of several Purkinje cells. They are referred to as "*basket*" *cells* (see fig. 10.3).

(2) *The intermediate layer of Purkinje cells.* The

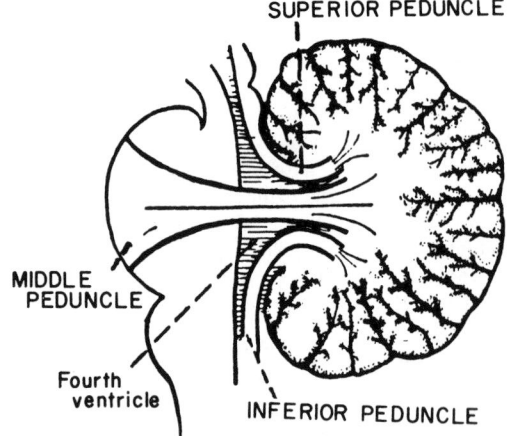

FIG. 10.2. Diagram of the cerebellar peduncles. (Redrawn from Villiger.)

large flask-shaped bodies of these cells, which are peculiar to the cerebellum, form a layer between the molecular and the granular layers. Their dendrites pass outwards through the entire thickness of the molecular layer where they arborize luxuriantly. The axons of the Purkinje cells enter the white substance, and end by synapsing with cells in the cerebellar nuclei.

The Purkinje cells have been referred to as the "final common pathway" of the cerebellar cortex. It is through these cells that the efferent impulses

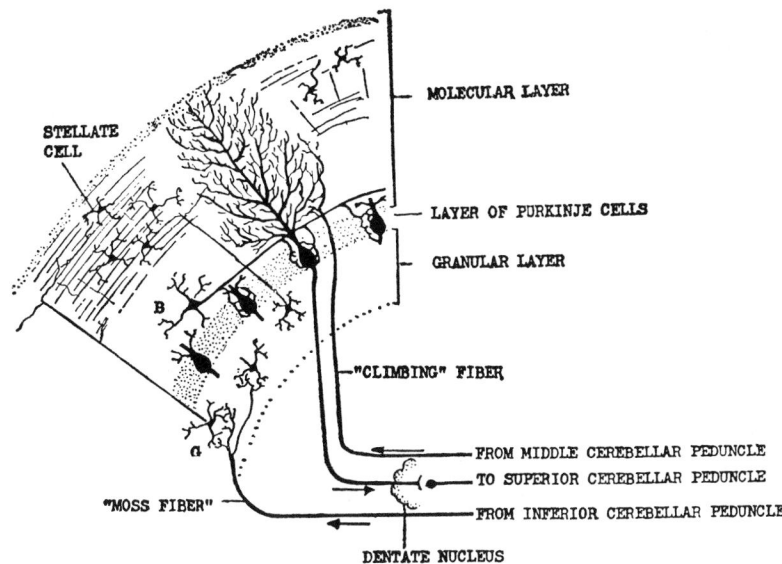

STELLATE CELL

MOLECULAR LAYER

LAYER OF PURKINJE CELLS

GRANULAR LAYER

B

"CLIMBING" FIBER

FROM MIDDLE CEREBELLAR PEDUNCLE
TO SUPERIOR CEREBELLAR PEDUNCLE
FROM INFERIOR CEREBELLAR PEDUNCLE

G

"MOSS FIBER"

DENTATE NUCLEUS

Fig. 10.3. Diagram to show structure of cerebellar cortex. G, granule cell; B, "basket" cell.

of the cerebellum pass to the central nuclei of the cerebellum (dentatus, emboliformis, globosus and fastigii) and thence to other parts of the central nervous system.

(3) *The granular layer*, which rests upon the white matter, is composed of small, round, closely packed cells, and numerous nerve fibers. The cells possess four or five dendrites which end in a tuft of branches close to the cell body and connect with those of neighboring cells. One long process (axon) of each extends into the molecular layer where it connects with the dendrites of a large number of Purkinje cells. Afferent fibers ("mossy fibers,") arriving *via* the inferior cerebellar peduncles make connections with the granule cells.

The Cerebellar Nuclei

The cerebellum contains on either side four separate gray masses. These are: (a) *nucleus fastigii* (nucleus of the roof), (b) *nucleus globosus*, (c) *nucleus emboliformis*, and (d) *nucleus dentatus*. (The nuclei globosus and emboliformis of primates are comparable to the nucleus interpositus of lower mammals.) The first three of these are phylogenetically older than the nucleus dentatus, which is found only in mammals. The fastigial nuclei, which are the most ancient of all, lie near the midline on either side in the roof of the fourth ventricle. They receive fibers from the paleocerebellum (anterior lobe, pyramid, uvula and flocculonodular lobe), and from the vestibular nuclei and eighth nerve through the inferior peduncle;

they also project to the vestibular nuclei. The globose and emboliform nuclei, which are placed more laterally than the roof nuclei receive fibers chiefly from the anterior lobe. The globose nucleus also receives fibers from the flocculonodular lobe. Both nuclei project through the superior peduncles to the large-celled portion of the red nucleus. The more lately acquired dentate nucleus, which is placed most laterally, is a large, crenated mass of gray matter, bent acutely upon itself. It receives fibers from the neocerebellum, chiefly from the Purkinje cells of the ansiform lobule. It projects through the superior cerebellar peduncle to the small-celled portion of the red nucleus (and to some extent also to the large-celled part), and to the ventrolateral group of the thalamic nuclei (fig. 10.4).

The White Matter; Connections of the Cerebellum with Other Parts of the Central Nervous System—Cerebellar Peduncles

The white matter of the hemispheres is composed of: (a) *projection fibers*, i.e., fibers which leave or enter the cerebellum *via* the peduncles, (b) *association fibers*, which connect different regions of the same hemisphere, and (c) *commissural fibers* connecting cortical areas of the two hemispheres.

The flocculonodular lobe, mainly the nodule, is connected by both afferent and efferent fibers (some of which are relayed in the fastigial and globose nuclei) with the vestibular nuclei and the vestibular nerve. The anterior lobes and the ansi-

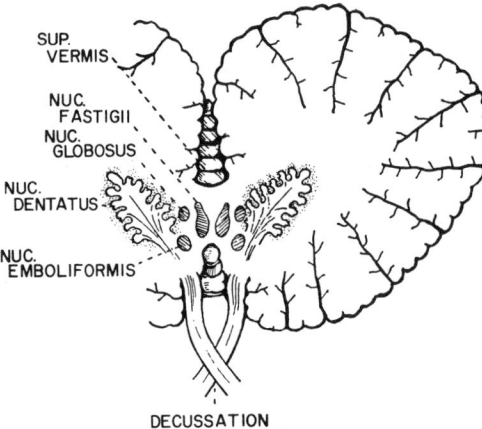

SUP.
VERMIS

NUC.
FASTIGII
NUC.
GLOBOSUS

NUC.
DENTATUS

NUC.
EMBOLIFORMIS

DECUSSATION
SUP.ᴿ PEDUNCLE

Fɪɢ. 10.4. Diagram of a horizontal section through the cerebellum to show the cerebellar nuclei (viewed from in front).

form lobules receive spinocerebellar and ponto-cerebellar fibers, respectively, and project to brain stem and thalamic nuclei. The fibers, afferent and efferent, connecting the cerebellum with extra-cerebellar regions are all carried in three large bundles called the *inferior, middle* and *superior cerebellar peduncles.*

THE INFERIOR PEDUNCLES (RESTIFORM BODIES). Its fibers are predominantly afferent and convey nonsensory impulses from the labyrinth, joints, voluntary muscles and skin (tactile). Its constituent fiber tracts are (figs. 10.2 and 10.5):

A. Afferent (Entering) Fibers

(1) *Dorsal (posterior) spinocerebellar (direct cerebellar) tract.* The fibers of this tract end in the cortex of the anterior and posterior lobes of both sides but mainly of the same side. Some fibers also end in the nodule.

(2) *Dorsal external arcuate fibers* (p. 123) from the nuclei gracilis and cuneatus of the same side, and the *ventral external arcuate fibers* from the corresponding nuclei of the opposite side. These fibers carry impulses aroused by tactile stimuli to the cortex of the paramedian lobule of the posterior lobe and to the lobulus simplex of the anterior lobe.

(3) *Vestibulocerebellar tract* from the vestibular nuclei of the same side, and also directly from the vestibular nerve. They pass to the three cerebellar nuclei (nucleus globosus, nucleus emboliformis and mainly to nuclei fastigii) and are relayed to the cortex of the flocculonodular lobe and of the uvula.

(4) *Olivocerebellar tract* arising in the inferior olive of the opposite side and to some extent in the nucleus of the same side; the fibers of this tract

end in the cortex of those portions of the vermis and hemispheres constituting the posterior lobe.

(5) Fibers of the fifth nerve and possibly of the ninth and tenth nerves which terminate in the pyramid, uvula and paraflocculus.

(6) *Tectocerebellar,* from the colliculi of the midbrain to the cerebellum; the exact course and termination of this tract is unknown.

B. Efferent (Leaving) Fibers

(1) *Fastigiobulbar (or cerebellovestibular) tract.* This is a pathway from the flocculonodular lobe and the roof nucleus to the vestibular nuclei, and the reticular formation of the medulla. Impulses are relayed from the medulla *via* (i) the reticulospinal and the vestibulospinal tracts to the spinal centers, and (ii) the medial longitudinal fasciculus to the nuclei of the ocular nerves and into the anterior ground bundle of the cord.

(2) *Cerebello-olivary tract* to the inferior olives of both sides. The latter may be connected with the spinal centers through the olivospinal tracts (p. 126).

THE MIDDLE PEDUNCLES (BRACHIA PONTIS) are also mainly afferent. Each contains:

(a) fibers which arise from cells of the pontine nuclei and end in the cortex of the posterior cerebellar lobe (declive, tuber, and the ansiform and paramedian lobules) of the opposite side, but also in smaller numbers in the homolateral hemisphere and vermis. These fibers constitute the secondary neurons of the *corticopontine* tracts, particularly the *frontopontine-cerebellar* tracts (b) fibers which pass from the cerebellar nuclei to the hemisphere of the opposite side (see fig. 10.5).

THE SUPERIOR PEDUNCLES (BRACHIA CONJUNC-TIVAE) enter into the formation of the upper part of the roof of the fourth ventricle and plunge into the midbrain just beneath the inferior colliculi. The superior cerebellar peduncle contains both efferent and afferent fibers but is composed predominantly of the former. It is through the superior peduncle that the cerebellum exerts its main influence upon the cerebral cortex and upon voluntary movement.

A. The efferent fibers arise chiefly from the dentate nucleus, but a few are also derived from the nuclei globosus and emboliformis. The Purkinje cells of the cerebellar cortex constitute the primary neurons of these paths. The fibers decussate in the midbrain with those of the opposite side and then divide into an ascending and a descending group.

(1) *The ascending fibers* pass (a) directly to the lateral ventral nucleus of the thalamus where the impulses are relayed to areas 4 and 6 of the cere-

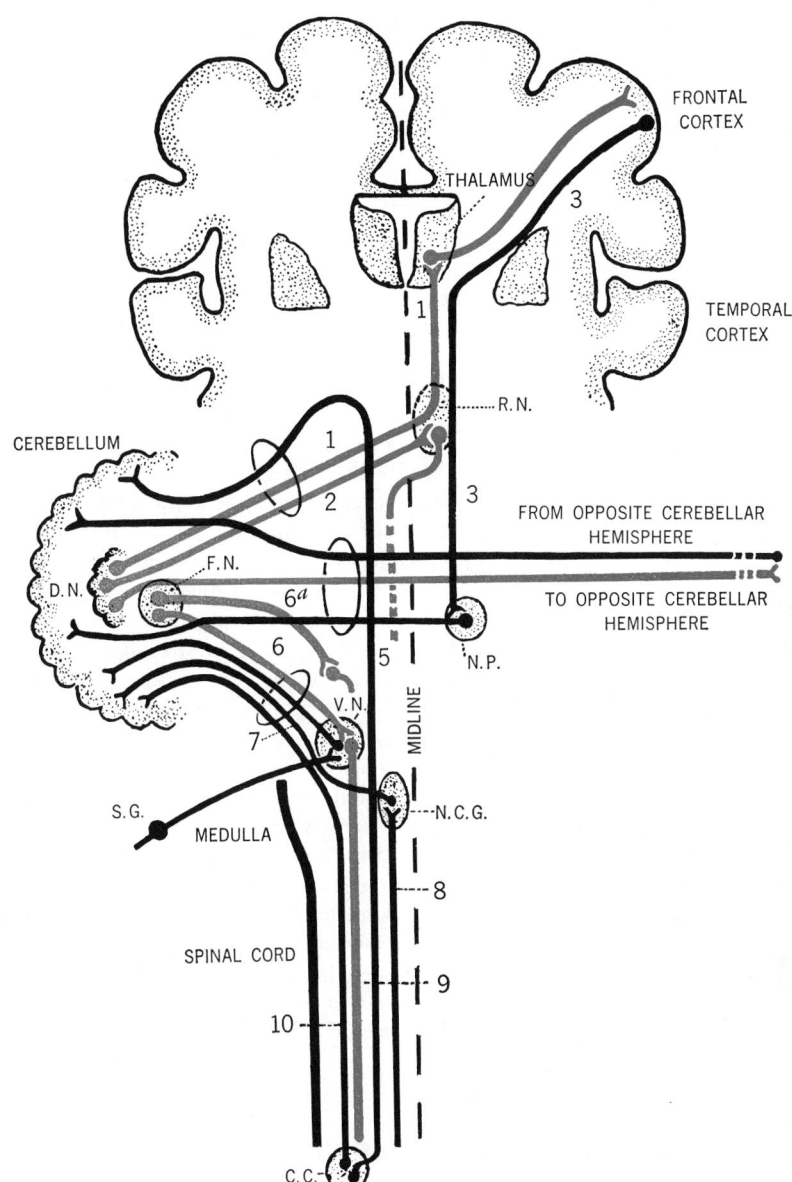

Fɪɢ. 10.5. Diagram of chief cerebellar connections. Afferent fibers, black; efferent fibers, red. R. N., red nucleus; D. N., dentate nucleus; F. N., fastigial nucleus; N. P., pontine nuclei; V. N., vestibular nucleus; N.C.G., nuclei cuneatus and gracilis; S.G., cell of Scarpa's ganglion; C.C., Clarke's column (dorsal nucleus). 1, dentato-rubro-thalamic tract, 1ᵃ dentatothalamic fibers which pass through the red nucleus; 2, cerebellorubral tract; 3, frontopontine tract; 4, rubrospinal tract; 5, ventral (indirect) spinocerebellar tract; 6, fastigiovestibular tract; 6ᵃ, fastigiobulbar tract; 7, external arcuate fibers passing from N.C.G. to cerebelum; 8, fasciculi gracilis and cuneatus; 9, vestibulospinal tract; 10, dorsal (direct) spinocerebellar tract.

bral cortex; (b) from the dentate nucleus to the small-celled nucleus (*n. parvocellularis*) of the red nucleus, and from the globose and emboliform nuclei to the large-celled nucleus (*n. magnocellularis*). The impulses reaching the small-celled nucleus (from dentate nucleus) are relayed *via* the rubrothalamic tract to areas 4 and 6 of the cerebral cortex.

It will be noted that the ascending fibers connect one cerebellar hemisphere with the red nucleus, thalamus and cerebral cortex of the opposite side, but, as a result of the crossing of the rubrospinal and corticospinal and corticobulbar tracts, each cerebellar hemisphere is ultimately connected with the same side of the brain stem and spinal cord.

(*2*) *The descending fibers* terminate around cells of the reticular formation of the pons, medulla and cervical cord.

B. *The afferent fibers* of the superior cerebellar peduncle are:

(1) The ventral (indirect) spinocerebellar tract. This ascends through the spinal cord, the medulla oblongata and pons and, reaching the upper level of the latter turns backwards, arches over the peduncle, enters the anterior medullary velum, and passes within this to the cerebellum. The fibers end in the cortex of the anterior lobe mainly of the same side.

(*2*) *The tectocerebellar tract*, composed of fibers which originate in the superior colliculus. It probably conveys retinal impulses and so constitutes a pathway for visuocerebellar reflexes.

Afferent-efferent (*cerebro-cerebello-cerebral*) *circuit.* This consists of fibers (frontopontine) from areas 4 and 6 of the precentral motor cortex to the pontine nuclei; and from the latter through the opposite middle cerebellar peduncle to the cerebellar cortex. The activity of the cerebellar cortex is finally centered in the Purkinje cells. Their impulses are transmitted to the dentate nucleus; from this nucleus (described on p. 225) *via* the superior peduncle to the brain stem where they cross to the red nucleus of the opposite side; thence to the lateral ventral nucleus of the thalamus, whence they return to areas 4 and 6 of the cerebral cortex. Through these paths a steadying action is exerted upon voluntary movements initiated through the precentral motor cortex.

The fibers reaching the cerebellar cortex *via* the peduncles are of two main types: (a) "*mossy fibers*," which end in mosslike appendages around the cells of the granular layer (fig. 10.3) and (b) *climbing fibers*, which pass outward to the molecular layer; here they give off collaterals resembling the tendrils of a vine which appear to cling to the arborizations of the Purkinje cells. According to Cajal the climbing fibers are derived from the vestibular and pontine nuclei; whereas the direct spinocerebellar and olivocerebellar tracts are constituted of moss fibers. Through their connections with the cells of the granular layer each mossy fiber is connected indirectly with a large number of Purkinje cells, whereas a climbing fiber is in communication with only one or two Purkinje cells.

In the foregoing paragraphs the anatomical connections of the cerebellum have been outlined, as far as they are known at the present time. Over these many pathways a multitude of afferent impulses bring information to the cerebellum. These different types of afferent impulses are distributed variously to the different lobes of the cerebellum.

Thus the vestibular impulses concerned with the position of the body in space pass largely to the flocculonodular lobe, with some going to other parts of the cerebellum.

The impulses from the spinal cord pass over the dorsal and ventral spinocerebellar pathways and the posterior columns (fasciculi gracilis and cuneatus) particularly to the anterior lobe. These bear proprioceptive impulses from muscles, joints and tendons to the cerebellum and in view of this organ's predominant preoccupation with the regulation of reflex muscular activity this is as one would anticipate. But, in addition, impulses of tactile origin arrive in large numbers in both the anterior lobe and in the cortex of the neocerebellum or posterior lobe. Furthermore, there is a strict topographic localization of the termination of these impulses. The "tactile" area of the anterior lobe lies near the midline with each side of the body represented ipsilaterally. The impulses from the lower extremity are received more anteriorly; those from the upper extremity farther back and those from the face most posteriorly. Tactile impulses are received in the neocerebellum on either side of the vermis. Here the face is represented most anteriorly, then the upper extremity and finally the lower extremity, just the reverse of the representation in the anterior lobe. It is doubtless significant that there are both afferent and efferent connections between these same areas of the neocerebellum and the pre- and postcentral gyri of the cerebral cortex. Although there is no evidence that the cerebellum is in any way concerned with the conscious perception of tactile or other external stimuli, such a possibility cannot be excluded. The significance of the arrival of these tactile impulses in the cerebellum and of the connection of the same areas of the cerebellum with the sensory areas (postcentral) of the cerebral cortex are not understood at the present time.

The cerebellum also receives afferent impulses produced by visual and auditory stimuli and is connected with the cortical centers subserving auditory and visual functions. The auditory and visual center of the cerebellum occupies the midline at the junction of the anterior and posterior lobes. This auditory-visual area overlaps the "face" area of the tactile center in the cortex of the anterior lobe. Again the significance of these connections is not fully understood.

As we have indicated above there are many afferent connections from the cerebral cortex to the cerebellum. Those from the precentral motor cortex which are very numerous are easily understood. They are essential for the cerebellum's prominent role in the regulation of movement and they pass predominantly to the neocerebellum. The other connections are with the postcentral gyrus, the auditory cortex in Heschl's gyrus and the visual cortex along the calcarine fissure. It is also interesting and doubtless very significant that the connections between all of these areas of the cerebral and cerebellar cortices are circular ones, i.e., each area of the cerebral cortex projects to a localized area of cerebellar cortex and the latter in turn projects back to the same cerebral area.

In addition to the prominent vestibular connections from the brain stem the cerebellum also has extensive connections with other nuclear structures in the midbrain, pons and bulb. Probably the most important of these, other than the vestibular nuclei, is the reticular formation. This important part of the brain stem has both afferent and efferent connections with all lobes of the cerebellum. There are also extensive connections with the red nucleus, the nuclei of the fifth cranial nerve and with the inferior olive. Through these the cerebellum is able to exert its great influence over the control of muscular tone, postural reflexes, righting reflexes and even over the γ-fibers and the innervation of the intrafusal fibers of the skeletal muscles. It has been demonstrated that the cerebellum is also capable of exerting a controlling influence over various visceral and vasomotor phenomenon as well.

The Experimental Study of the Cerebellum

EFFECTS OF EXCISION OF THE CEREBELLUM AND OF SECTION OF THE PEDUNCLES

The earliest experiments upon the cerebellum were performed by Rolando (1809) and the French neurologist Flourens (1822). The latter removed the cerebellum of pigeons in which he observed, as a result of the ablation, grave disturbances of equilibrium and abnormal postures of the wings, neck and limbs. Luciani, in the later part of the 19th century, carried out cerebellar ablations upon dogs and observed three cardinal effects: (a) muscular weakness or *asthenia*; (b) a reduction in muscle tone, which he called *atonia* (really hypotonia), and (c) unsteadiness of voluntary movement, to which he gave the name *astasia*. These defects which appeared about a month after the operation gave rise to a coarse, jerky *tremor* when an attempt was made to perform any voluntary act. The general terms *ataxia*

or *asynergia* are often used to include all the motor manifestations of cerebellar dysfunction.

Disequilibrium, due to the removal of the vestibular impulses, which is readily demonstrated in monkeys, causes a staggering, reeling, drunkenlike gait. The animal—dog or monkey—stands with limbs spread in order to provide a broad base, sways from side to side with oscillations of the head.

Another characteristic symptom of cerebellar ablation, and which is also seen with lesions of the cerebellum in man, is *dysmetria*—the inability to gauge the strength or duration of the muscular contraction required to execute a certain voluntary act. For example, if the arm reaches for an object it may overshoot the mark (*hypermetria*) or fall short of it (*hypometria*).

The effect of the cerebellum upon muscular tone and muscular reflexes varies with the animal concerned. In the cat and dog the anterior lobe forms a large part of the cerebellum. In these animals excision of the anterior lobe gives rise to a state of increased muscular tone similar to decerebrate rigidity and if decerebrate rigidity has already been produced ablation of this portion of the cerebellum will increase the already existing rigidity. On the other hand stimulation of the anterior lobe of the cerebellum will cause the rigidity characteristic of the decerebrate state to relax. From this evidence it has been concluded that the anterior lobe of the cerebellum is concerned with the inhibition of the stretch reflexes and the postural reflexes of the skeletal musculature. Certainly this is an important part of the function of this part of the cerebellum in these animals, but it has now been shown that stimulation of the cortex of the anterior lobe and of the fastigial nuclei to which it projects can produce *both* inhibition and enhancement of muscular rigidity. It thus appears that the anterior lobe of the cerebellum is an organ for the *regulation* of muscular tone rather than merely an inhibitor of reflex muscular activity. It should be noted, however, that these effects upon muscular tone and muscular reflexes are most marked in the carnivores. They are much less pronounced in subhuman primates and still less so in man. In fact, nothing resembling decerebrate rigidity or enhancement of pre-existing rigidity has ever been reported as the result of a cerebellar lesion in man. In human beings if there is any alteration in muscular tone as the result of a cerebellar lesion it is in the direction of a decrease. The involved extremities tend to become flaccid or hypotonic and tendon reflexes may become pendular.

Unilateral destruction or damage of the cerebellum causes a reduction in tone of the muscles of the same side and a tendency to fall to that side.

Section of the peduncles. Section of all six peduncles causes effects identical with those of complete decerebellation, and division of the three of one side results in effects described for unilateral ablation. In the chimpanzee, *asynergia, hypotonia, easy fatigability*, and a *coarse tremor* appear on the same side as the section. Severance of one superior peduncle causes at first defects somewhat similar although less severe than those following unilateral section of all three peduncles, and is later compensated for through those which have been left intact. Little is known with respect to the disabilities following section of one or both middle peduncles. A lesion interupting the fibers of the inferior peduncles causes, mainly, equilibratory disturbances (due to division of vestibular connections), and ataxia as a result of the interruption of spinocerebellar fibers. Compensation through the intact cerebellum tends to occur later, so that the effects become progressively less severe.

Even after unilateral section of the three peduncles, compensation is brought about after a time through the remaining half of the cerebellum and through the frontal lobes (Botterell and Fulton).

The experiments of Aring and Fulton indicate that the nervous mechanism involved in the production of cerebellar tremor lies in the excitable part of the cerebral cortex (area 4 and the upper part of area 6); removal of these areas after contralateral section of the cerebellar peduncles abolished the tremor. Large parts of the cortex of the cerebellum can be removed with little permanent neurologic deficit, so long as all of the cortex of one hemisphere is not removed. On the other hand damage to the central nuclei or the cerebellar peduncles produces much more severe and lasting disturbances.

STIMULATION OF THE CEREBELLUM

Electrical stimulation of the cerebellum, both of the cortex and of the central nuclei, has supplied relatively little information concerning the functions of this important structure. The results are far less than those produced by stimulation of the precentral motor cortex of the cerebral hemispheres. This is rather surprising in view of the fact that the cerebellum is primarily concerned with muscular activities. In general the responses to stimulation of both the cerebellar cortex and the nuclei are slow and tonic in character. They are also diffuse and complex in contrast with the well localized discrete movements which can be obtained by stimulating the precentral gyrus. It is also common to obtain diphasic responses, i.e., one type of response during stimulation which is followed by an opposite type of response after the stimulation has ceased. Many of the responses concern movements of the eyes toward the same side as that to which the stimulus is applied, or a movement of the eyes to a position in which they gaze forward. If there is a "rebound" response following the termination of stimulation the eyes turn toward the side opposite that on which the stimulus is applied. Such movements of the eyes may or may not be associated with similar movements of the head either to the side or straight ahead. Stimulation may give rise to movements involving the head, extremities, trunk and tail in the long axis of the body producing a concavity of the body on the side stimulated. Stimulation of the cortex of the anterior lobe and of the fastigial and globose nuclei sometimes causes flexion of the ipsilateral limbs and extension of the contralateral ones. It is interesting to note that most responses are obtained by stimulating the anterior lobe and the fastigial and globose nuclei. Stimulation of the posterior lobe or neocerebellum or of the dentate or emboliform nuclei is far less effective. This is surprising in view of the fact that these latter structures are the ones connected with the precentral motor cortex and primarily concerned with the regulation and integration of voluntary muscular activity.

Localization in Cerebellar Cortex

In recent years representation in the cerebellum, afferent and efferent, have been shown to be much more circumscribed than had been supposed. Yet, even so, localization has not been found to be as precisely discrete as in certain regions of the cerebral cortex, e.g., in the motor area. Owing to the double crossing of the pathway for impulses from the cerebellum, as they ascend in the midbrain (dentatorubral tract) and as they descend to the spinal cord (rubrospinal tract), each half of the cerebellum exerts its influence mainly on the musculature of the same side of the body.

Representation in the cerebellar cortex of somatic receptive areas has been studied by Dow, by Snider and his associates, and by Adrian by means of the method of evoked potentials. Adrian recorded the potentials evoked in the cortex of the *anterior lobe* of cats and monkeys by means of a fine wire electrode inserted beneath the surface. Various areas over the limbs and face were stimulated by touch, pressure, joint movement, or stretching of muscles (fig. 10.6).

The representation in the anterior lobe of the different somatic areas is in reverse order. That it to say, the hindlimb area is placed anteriorly to the areas for the forelimbs and face. Thus, stimulation of the hindlimb evoked potentials from the lobulus centralis and an anterior strip of the culmen, stimulation of the forelimb induced responses from the remainder of the culmen, and stimulation of the face (vibrissae in cat) from the lobulus simplex. The spinocerebellar impulses from the tail are probably received by the most anteriorly situated part of the anterior lobe, namely, in the lingula.[3] An even, more precise localization was mapped out within these areas; in the area for the hindlimb, the foot is in front of the knee and the knee in front of the thigh; in the forelimb representation the shoulder is in front of the wrist, with the wrist and hand following in corresponding order.

Potentials were also evoked from the anterior lobe by stimulation (electrical or local application of strychnine) of the motor area of the cerebral cortex, i.e., by causing a discharge over corticopontine and pontocerebellar pathways (fig. 10.7). The anterior part of the precentral motor cortex (area 6) projects to the lateral part of the neocerebellum, where the posterior part (area 4) projects to more medial structures in both the-anterior and posterior lobes. Most of this cerebrocerebellar projection is crossed but some of it is to the ipsilateral cerebellar hemisphere. The projections of area 4 to the cerebellar cortex correspond closely with the termination of tactile impulses. The topographic representation of the face, arm and leg of impulses from the precentral motor cortex followed the same pattern as that for tactile impulses. In the anterior lobe the "leg" area lies most anteriorly and the "face" area most posteriorly. In the posterior lobe the reverse is true. Stimulation of the caudate nucleus will evoke alterations in electrical potentials in the posterior lobe.

Impulses from the auditory and visual systems, from the olfactory bulbs and from the vagi are also conveyed to the cerebellum. Sound, or flashes of light, evoke potentials from an area covering the lobulus simplex, declive and tuber, and extending laterally into the ansiform lobule. The

[3] In the giraffe the lobulus simplex is greatly enlarged, and in monkeys with a prehensile tail the lingula is elongated.

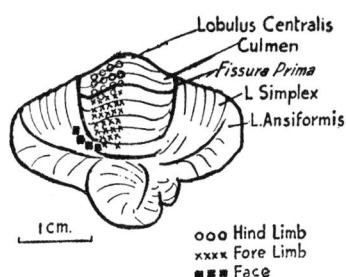

Fig. 10.6. Spinocerebellar receiving areas for hind-limb, fore-limb and face (vibrissae) in the cat, as determined by the method of evoked potentials. (From Adrian.)

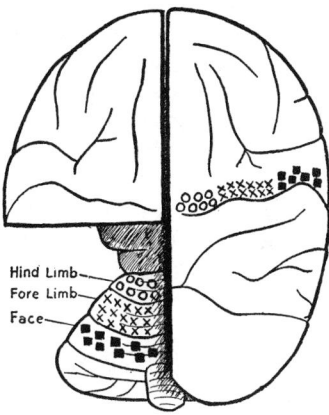

Fig. 10.7. Subdivisions of pontocerebellar receiving area in the monkey, showing their connection with different parts of the motor cortex. (From Adrian.)

visual impulses are relayed to the cerebellum from the superior colliculus, the auditory from the inferior colliculus. The tectocerebellar tracts probably provide the pathways for these impulses. The auditory and visual cortices project to the same areas.

From ablation experiments topographical localization similar in character to that described above for the spinocerebellar and corticopontine-cerebellar systems has been demonstrated for the efferent side. The tail muscles are represented in the lingula, the muscles for the hindlimbs in the lobulus centralis, the forelimb muscles in the culmen, and the cervical and facial muscles in the lobulus simplex. Representation of the limbs in the middle lobe of Ingvar (ansiform lobule, declive and tuber) has not been demonstrated, but from the relatively enormous size of this part of the cerebellum in higher mammals and from the fact that it (ansiform lobule) is the chief receiving station for corticopontocerebellar impulses, it cannot be doubted that it is of paramount importance in volitional movement.

The flocculonodular lobe, through its vestibular connections, is concerned with equilibratory function, severe disturbances of balance resulting from its ablation. Ablation of the nodule in dogs confers complete immunity to motion sickness (Bard and associates. Removal of no other part of the cerebellum or of the cerebral cortex has this protective action (ch. 5). Ablation of the *nodule* and *flocculus* (flocculonodular lobe, p. 223 and 224) in monkeys or of the nodule and part of the uvula (Dow) which causes injury to vestibular paths, is followed by pronounced disturbances of balance. In man a lesion of this part of the vermis is also associated with disturbances of equilibrium. Removal of the *nodule* alone in monkeys is followed by oscillation of the head and neck (and, in some instances of the whole trunk) falling backwards and an unsteady gait with the extremities spread widely apart to provide a broader and thus more certain base.

The functions of the *uvula* are largely obscure; its destruction alone is followed by some transient disturbance of equilibrium. Very little is known of the function of the *pyramid,* although it appears to be concerned in some way with vision or eye movement. Its excision causes no defect of balance. Ablation of the pyramid in the monkey results in an inability to halt its forward progression in time to prevent it from crashing into some obstacle. Faradic stimulation of the pyramid elicits an upward movement of the eyes, and Fulton suggests from this fact and the preceding observation the possibility of the pyramid being concerned in some way with the integration of proprioceptive impulses essential in judging distance.

Summary of Functional Localization

(1) All cerebellar activities, afferent and efferent, are carried out beneath consciousness.

(2) In the anterior lobe are represented in regular order the various receptive and muscular regions of the body. It is concerned mainly with the adjustments of muscle tone and synergic action necessary for posture in subprimate mammals, but appears to be much less important in primates.

(3) The posterior lobe (middle lobe of Ingvar) (neocerebellum) is the chief receptive region for corticopontocerebellar tracts. It is most highly developed in the primates. It is concerned with the integration and regulation of well coordinated muscular activities.

(4) The flocculonodular lobe, the most ancient part of the cerebellum, is intimately connected with the vestibular apparatus both through the vestibular nuclei and directly by fibers from the vestibular nerve, and therefore constitutes an important part of the neural mechanisms underlying equilibratory function.

(5) The functions of the uvula and pyramid are little known, although the latter probably has to do with eye movements and the former, to a minor degree, with equilibrium.

The Manifestations of Cerebellar Disease

The signs of cerebellar disease are much more pronounced in acute lesions, e.g., abscess, hemorrhage or trauma, than in those, e.g., tumor, which develop more gradually. In slowly developing lesions or after the subsidence of acute cerebellar disease a certain degree of compensation for the cerebellar defect always occurs. The majority of the signs of cerebellar disease are the result fundamentally of asynergia of the voluntary muscles.

The more conspicuous signs of a cerebellar lesion are: (1) *Hypotonia of the skeletal muscles.* (2) *Asthenia,* easy fatigability and slowness of movement. (3) *Dysmetria,* which is the inability to adjust the strength of a contraction required to accomplish a given act. For example, when the subject is asked to touch a point with his finger he overshoots the mark, or, less usually, fails to reach it. (4) *Rebound phenomenon.* If the patient is asked to attempt a movement against a resistance which is then suddenly removed, the limb moves forcibly in the direction toward which the effort was made. For example, if the observer holds the wrist of the patient, then asks him to bend the elbow, and while he is making the effort, the forearm is suddenly released, flexion of the arm occurs with an unusual degree of force. This rebound phenomenon can be attributed to the absence of the "braking" action of the antagonistic muscles. (5) *Adiadochokinesis* (a = privative; diadocho = succession, kinesis = movement) is the name given by Babinski to the inability to execute alternating movements rapidly, e.g., pronation and supination of the forearm, or flexion and extension of the fingers. (6) *Deviation of the eyes, and nystagmus.* (7) *Gait* may be staggering, reeling or lurching, often with ataxia of the limbs. The *attitude* of the body may be abnormal, the trunk being flexed toward the side of the lesion and the head rotated with the chin pointing toward the sound side. (8) *Disturbances of speech,* which may be drawling, scanning, sing-song or explosive in character.

The Mechanism of Cerebellar Function

The principle role of the cerebellum is in the control of movement; the main symptoms resulting from cerebellar injury being deficits in motor performance. Injury or ablation of the cerebellum leads to two principle kinds of malfunction: (a) disturbances of posture and postural tone, in which the animal is unable to stand or to balance itself in the standing position (disequilibration) and in which the animal shows overactivity or underactivity of the extensor muscles, (b) disturbances of voluntary movement, in which the animal is unable to walk towards an object without swaying severely or, as in primates, is unable to pick up an object without exhibiting misjudgment of distance and of speed of movement of the limb.

The defect in balance of the body is a complex phenomenon which may result from injury to any part of the cerebellum. The flocculonodular node, however, plays an especially significant role in standing. Removal of this part of the cerebellum causes an inability to stand without disturbing voluntary movement. The inability to stand stems from disruption of the vestibular connections of the cerebellum.

Disturbances in the tone of the limbs are a principle result of total cerebellectomy. In the first few weeks following such an operation in carnivores, opisthotonus and extensor rigidity appear. It is clear from experiments on destruction of the vermis that these symptoms are release phenomena arising from the removal of a tonic (persistent) inhibition by the vermis acting on the fastigial nuclei. The tonic inhibition acts through the motor cortex and the extrapyramidal system. The extensor hypertonus is not a reflex phenomenon since it persists when the forelimbs have been deafferented. The opisthotonus arises from labyrinthine reflexes which have been released by damage to the fastigial nulcei.

In subhuman primates and man, the principle initial postural symptom is hypotonia. Here, a reflex mechanism is at work regulating tone—the γ-efferent system. Hypotonia results from a paralysis of this system that is caused by damage to the anterior lobe. That the γ-afferent system is involved, is suggested by experiments showing that functional ablation of the anterior lobe as by cooling, abolishes the discharge from the muscle spindle. The cerebral cortex is also involved since ablation of the cerebral cortex increases the rigidity of decerebellate animals. The cerebellum can thus act to regulate tone at the level of the motor cortex or the spinal cord. During functional ablations as by cooling, an increased rigidity of the limbs occurs. This implies that the rigidity is caused by impulses acting on the α-motoneurons alone. Thus two types of rigidity may be recognized, α resulting from impulses acting directly on motoneurons and γ in which motor activity results from excitation of the spindles and enhanced reflex discharge. Diminution of extensor tone can result from interference with either system.

CONTROL OF VOLUNTARY MOVEMENT

We have noted that it is possible to produce defects in standing without any effect on voluntary performance so that the two phenomena are presumably governed by different regions of the cerebellum. Disorders of voluntary movement are associated with damage to the lateral and paravermal regions of the corpus cerebelli. The symptoms which develop consist of deficiencies in rate of movement, direction (dysmetria), and strength of individual muscles (asthenia). In addition, a gross tremor of the body and head of an animal appears when the animal makes a deliberate movement. The swaying and disorderly movement of an animal, now termed ataxia, is part of this aberration of movement (Luciani's astasia). Two additional points must be stressed about these symptoms. First, not all motor movements of an animal are affected by cerebellectomy. A dog whose cerebellum has been removed cannot stand or walk after the operation. Nevertheless, it can swim quite well and can remove its fleas with its snout by well-coordinated movements of the head and jaw muscles. Similarly cats can preen themselves after cerebellectomy without any sign of ataxia. Second, the symptoms of cerebellar deficiency tend to disappear with time; the animal is said to compensate. But complete recovery never occurs.

Conspicuous among the disorders of voluntary movement are the misjudgments of distance which occur when the subject attempts to grasp a distant object. It was suggested early that this deficiency resulted from an interference with the reciprocal innervation of muscles (antagonists) involved in a movement. Thus, failure to reach an object would result from excessive movement of an antagonist relative to the agonist. The best evidence indicates that there is no effect on reciprocal innervation in animals in which the cerebellum has been removed. Simultaneous myographic recording from antagonistic muscles of the eye of such rabbits shows that when one

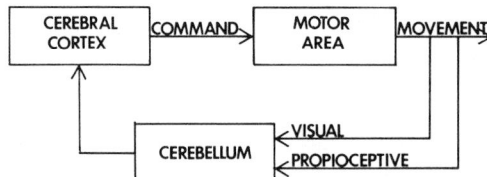

FIG. 10.8. The cerebellar feedback system.

muscle contracts as the result of caloric nystagmus, the other relaxes. The role of reciprocal innervation is also suspect because many skilled muscle movements involve cocontractions of antagonists. Motor skilled performance is quite complicated, involving the excitation of specific muscles at specific intervals. The likelihood is that the interference with skilled movement produced by cerebellar damage arises from an indirect effect on the cerebral cortex. The tremor which accompanies a voluntary movement can be eliminated by decortication; in the primate the removal of the entire premotor cortex removes the tremor. The symptoms of cerebellar deficiency can therefore be attributed to removal of facilitatory influences exerted by the cerebellum on the cerebral cortex.

The deficiencies in motor movement consist of a defect in latency of response (reaction time), the onset and relaxation of muscles, and the strength of the individual contraction. All these effects can also be attributed to a defect in performance of the motoneuron of the cerebral cortex. The cerebellum acts to facilitate the discharge of the motor cortex. Lack of such a tonic influence produced by damage to the cerebellum results in a decrease in the number of pyramidal units discharging and a decrease in strength of the voluntary contraction. The defect in timing, onset and relaxation may also be a result of general decreased facilitation (feedback) from the cerebellar hemispheres.

THE CEREBELLUM AS A FEEDBACK DEVICE

A somewhat more unified view may be given of the function of the cerebellum in the light of modern feedback theory. It is known that a considerable amount of information is sent to the cerebellum by visual, auditory and proprioceptive receptors (Fig. 10.8). The cerebellum, then, receives information about the performance or position and speed of either an individual muscle or of the entire body (as in standing). Corrections can then be made at the cortical or cerebellar level in accordance with what the position should be. It is known that the cerebellum possesses extensive connections to the cerebral cortex

and that it receives information from the cerebral cortex. The elaborate apparatus necessary to feed information back from the internal or external environment of the organism therefore presumably exists. In any such system, interruption of the feedback path may lead to oscillation of the output. This occurs in the cerebellar feedback loop, for damage to the cerebellum does lead to oscillation (tremor) during movement of a limb. The errors in judgment of distance and speed also support the hypothesis that the cerebellum acts to regulate movement.

The cerebral cortex, then, initiates movements; the cerebellum regulates them. This conception is substantiated by experiments showing that cerebellar damage has little effect on the initiation or general execution of a voluntary movement. In an animal with cerebellar damage, motor movements occur in a crudely correct fashion; it is only the smoothness and pattern in time which is disrupted. This suggests that the cerebellum is concerned with regulating the precision of movements. One hypothesis as to how the cerebellum might accomplish this assumes that the cerebellum feeds back information about a movement visually and proprioceptively. The information which is sent to the cerebral cortex determines the exact moment at which the movement of another muscle is to take place as well as the extent of the muscle discharge. For example, the cortex programs a series of movements so that muscles A, B, and C are to fire one after the other. The information obtained by the cerebellum about the position of muscle A enables it to fire B at the exact time for proper execution of the overall pattern of the limb. Cerebellar damage, by preventing information about A from being sent back does not interrupt the program initiated by the cortex but it does prevent the exquisite timing necessary for a skillful movement. Another possible function for the cerebellum in electronic terms, may be to act as a type of "gate" which allows specific information to act at a given time. The program for the sequential movement of the muscles of a limb is sent by the cerebral cortex to the motoneurons of the spinal cord. The time at which a given motoneuron fires is determined by feedback from the cerebellum. The feedback from the cerebellum, by facilitating the motoneuron activity at the proper time, permits it to fire. In this sense then the cerebellum opens the gate to allow the passage of information down the motoneuron. In this system facilitatory feedback (positive) would be used to regulate the exact firing of motoneurons.

Most of the experiments dealing with the influence of the cerebellum on the motor cortex show that the major effect on the cerebral cortex is facilitatory. Stimulation of many regions of the cerebellum increases the excitability of the motor cortex, i.e., the threshold of cortically-induced motor movements can be markedly reduced by stimulating the cerebellar hemispheres. Thus, the feedback from cerebellum to cerebral cortex must be largely positive. Stimulation of the cerebellum, can, under special circumstances, lead to inhibition; as when the motor cortex has been strychninized. If many cells have been activated by this drug, inhibition of cortically induced movements may occur to stimulation of the cerebellum. In other experiments, stimulation of the basal cerebellum of unrestrained, unanesthetized cats leads to behavior with an inhibitory component. Although the type of behavior observed depends greatly on the frequency of stimulation, at the relatively high rates of 60 to 330 per second, a strong inhibition of motor activity may be observed. The animal may collapse and, in the recumbent position, all four limbs may be flaccid. Further work is clearly necessary to clarify the roles of positive and negative feedback in cerebellar function.

REFERENCES

ADRIAN, E. D. Brain, 1943, **66**, 289.

ARING, C. D. AND FULTON, J. F. Arch. Neurol. & Psychiat., 1936, **35**, 439.

BARD, P. AND ASSOCIATES. Fed. Proc., 1947, **6**, 72.

BOTTERELL, E. H. AND FULTON, J. F. J. Comp. Neurol., 1938, **69**, 31.

DOW, R. G. Biol. Rev., 1942, **17**, 179.

DOW, R. G. J. Neurophysiol., 1942, **5**, 121.

HOLMES, G. Brain, 1917, **40**, 461; 1939, **62**, 1.

HOLMES, G., Lancet, 1922, **1**, 1177, 1231; 1922, **2**, 59, 111.

INGVAR, S. Brain, 1923, **46**, 301.

JACKSON, J. HUGHLINGS. Collected Writings, London, 1932, **1**, 8. (Quoted by Holmes, G.)

KELLER, A. D., ROY, R. S. AND CHASE, W. P. Am. J. Physiol., 1937, **118**, 720.

LARSELL, O. Arch. Neurol. & Psychiat., 1937, **38**, 580.

MILLER, F. R. AND BANTING, F. G. Am. J. Physiol., 1922, **59**, 478 (Proc.).

MILLER, F. R. AND BANTING, F. G., Am. Brain, 1922, **45**, 104.

MILLER, F. R. AND LAUGHTON, N. B. Arch. Neurol. & Psychiat, 1928, **19**, 47.

POLLOCK, L. J. AND DAVIS, L. Assoc. Res. Nerv. & Ment. Dis., 1929, **6**, 424.

SNIDER, R. S. Arch. Neurol. & Psychiat., 1950, **64**, 196.

SNIDER, R. S. AND STOWELL, A. J. Neurophysiol., 1944, **7**, 331.

TILNEY, F. AND PIKE, F. H. Arch. Neurol. & Psychiat., 925, **13**, 289.

WALKER, A. E. AND BOTTERELL, E. H. Brain, 1937, **60**, 329.

WEISENBURG, T. H. Cerebellar localization. Assoc. Res. Nerv. & Ment. Dis., 1929, **6**, 497.

Monographs and Reviews

Association for Research in Nervous and Mental Disease. Vol. 6. The cerebellum. The Williams & Wilkins Co., Baltimore, 1929.

BOLK, L. Das Cerebellum der Säugetiere. Haarlem, 1906. Quoted by Miller.

DOW, R. S. AND MORUZZI, G., The physiology and pathology of the cerebellum. University of Minnesota Press, Minneapolis, 1958.

FULTON, J. F. Physiology of the nervous system. Oxford Univ. Press, London, 1938.

FULTON, J. F. Medicine, 1936, 15, 247.

LARSELL, O. The cerebellum from myxinoids to man. University of Minnesota Press, Minneapolis. In Press.

LUCIANI, L. Human physiology. Vol. 3, Macmillan, London, 1915.

MILLER, F. R. The physiology of the cerebellum. Physiol. Rev., 1926, **6**, 124.

RANSON, S. W. The anatomy of the nervous system from the standpoint of development and function. Saunders, Philadelphia, 1921.

SHERRINGTON, C. S. The integrative action of the nervous system. Yale University Press, New Haven, Conn., 1920.

SMITH, G. E. The nervous system. In Cunningham's text-book of anatomy, p. 505, Oxford University Press, London, 1931.

TILNEY, F., RILEY, H. A., POLLOCK, L. J. AND DAVIS, L. Brain, 1927, **50**, 275.

VILLIGER, E. Brain and spinal cord. Lippincott, Philadelphia, 1931.

WILSON, S. A. K. Modern problems in neurology. Arnold, London, 1928.

CHAPTER 11

The Cerebrospinal Fluid

Anatomical Considerations

The interior of the brain contains cavities called ventricles filled with a fluid known as the cerebrospinal fluid. This fluid is formed in all the ventricles and circulates through openings or foramina to bathe the outside of the brain and spinal cord. Three membranes cover the external surface of the brain, an outermost tough layer, the *dura mater;* a middle layer, the *arachnoid* which is a web-like membrane and the innermost membrane, the *pia mater*, which is in intimate contact with the surface of the brain. The cerebrospinal fluid fills the space between the arachnoid and the pia; only an extremely thin film of moisture exists between the dura and arachnoid. The cerebrospinal fluid which is formed in the ventricles passes to the subarachnoid space through the foramina. In certain regions the subarachnoid space is enlarged into cisternae (fig. 11.1). The principal dilations are the cisterna magna below and behind the cerebellum and above the medulla oblongata, the cisterna pontis on the ventral aspect of the pons and the cisterna basalis which contains the circle of Willis.

Site of Formation

Cerebrospinal fluid formation depends upon a highly vascular structure, the choroid plexus, located in the ventricles. The choroid plexuses are tuft-like pouches of pia, capillaries and ependyma (the lining of the ventricles) which project into the ventricles. There is an arterial and venous supply to the plexus and the walls of the pia in this region are very thin and vascular. The double membrane formed of pia and ependymal cells is called the "tela choroidea." Cerebrospinal fluid is secreted into the ventricles from the blood coursing through the capillaries of the tela choroidea. Although the choroid plexus resembles structurally the glomerulus of the kidney, the mechanism by which cerebrospinal fluid is formed is not the same as the formation of urine, since filtration plays a minor role, if any, in the formation of cerebrospinal fluid.

The chief sites of formation of the cerebrospinal fluid are the choroid plexuses in the ventricles but there is probably also some contribution from the ependymal cells lining the ventricles

and spinal cord. The classical experiments are those of Dandy and Blackfan (1914), summarized by Dandy (1919). These workers inserted a cotton plug into the aqueduct of Sylvius which drains the fluid of the third and the lateral ventricles into the fourth ventricle. An accumulation of fluid occurred in the ventricles (hydrocephalus), causing an enormous enlargement of these structures compared to that in a normal dog. This simple experiment demonstrated first, that the cerebrospinal fluid was produced in the ventricles, and second, that the rate of formation (in the ventricles) was much greater than the rate of absorption. To prove that the choroid plexus produced the fluid, they removed this structure from one ventricle only and, at the same time, prevented any influx of fluid from the other ventricle by blocking one foramen of Monro connecting the two cavities. The ventricle in which the choroid plexus had been removed shrank to a slit, whereas the other ventricle was of normal size. Thus, not enough fluid is formed in the plexectomized ventricle to enlarge it.

Circulation

The fluid formed in the lateral ventricles passes through the foramen of Monro to join that produced in the third ventricle and thence through the aqueduct of Sylvius to the fourth ventricle. From the fourth ventricle the fluid passes into the cisternae magna and lateralis through three openings. The central one is the foramen of Magendie and the lateral opening bears the name of Luschka. From the cisternae in the posterior fossa a small amount of the fluid passes downward in the spinal subarachnoid space. Most of the fluid flows upward along the brain stem and then outward and upward over the surface of the cerebral hemispheres. In the subarachnoid spaces additional fluid with a somewhat higher protein content is added, probably by transudation from the various blood vessels.

Absorption

When a readily diffusible dye is introduced into the subarachnoid space its rapid appearance in the blood of the venous sinuses under certain

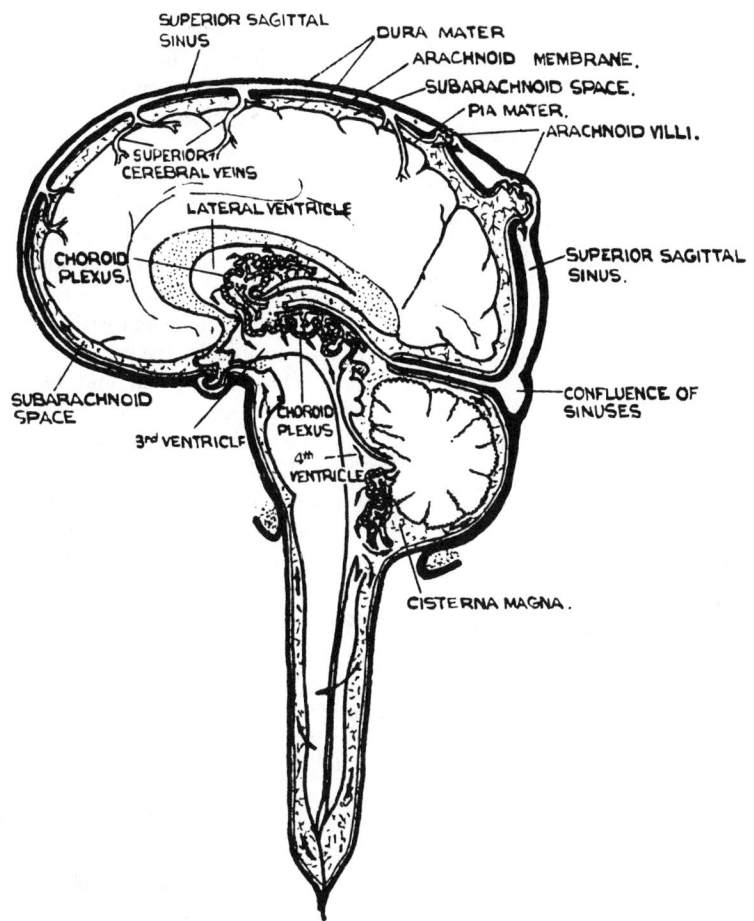

SUPERIOR SAGITTAL SINUS

DURA MATER

ARACHNOID MEMBRANE.

SUBARACHNOID SPACE.

PIA MATER.

ARACHNOID VILLI.

SUPERIOR CEREBRAL VEINS

LATERAL VENTRICLE

CHOROID PLEXUS.

SUPERIOR SAGITTAL SINUS.

SUBARACHNOID SPACE

3ʳᵈ VENTRICLE

CHOROID PLEXUS

4ᵗʰ VENTRICLE

CONFLUENCE OF SINUSES

CISTERNA MAGNA.

FIG. 11.1. Pathways of cerebrospinal flow. (After Rasmussen.)

conditions demonstrates a possible path of absorption of the fluid. When the dye is injected into the cisternae magna and the spinal canal is blocked, the absorption is not significantly lessened. This indicates that the fluid is largely absorbed from the cranial subarachnoid spaces. Key and Retzius believed that the fluid was absorbed through the Pacchionian granulations, but these are absent from the brains of infants and are now regarded as pathological enlargements of a few of the arachnoid villi. By long-continued slow injection of an isotonic solution of a mixture of potassium ferrocyanide and iron ammonium citrate, Weed was able to demonstrate that the particles of Prussian-blue, formed when the tissue was subsequently fixed in acid medium, precipitated in the mesothelial cells of the tips of the arachnoid villi and within the dural sinuses into which these villi project. A relatively slow absorption by way of the perineural spaces into the lymphatic system was also demonstrated. These findings have been confirmed, and it may be accepted that the main absorption of the cerebrospinal fluid is through the arachnoid villi into the great venous sinuses. The pathway postulated by Key and Retzius has therefore been established, but the numerous microscopic arachnoid villi have been substituted for the Pacchionian granulations.

Mechanism of absorption. Since the hydrostatic pressure in the subarachnoid space is always greater than that in the dural sinuses, filtration is apparently adequate to account for the flow of liquid into the venous blood stream. True solutions readily pass through the arachnoid villi, colloids more slowly, the rate depending upon the size of the molecules; particulate matter does not pass. No evidence of any secretory activity of the arachnoid villi has been obtained.

Composition and Method of Formation

Cerebrospinal fluid has the approximate composition of an ultrafiltrate of blood plasma. There are, however, significant differences in the

TABLE 11.1

*Comparisons of amounts of main constituents of blood plasma and cerebrospinal fluid**

	Blood Plasma	Cerebrospinal Fluid
	mg. per 100 cc.	mg. per 100 cc.
Protein	6300–8500	16–38
Amino acids	4.5–9	1.5–3
Creatinine	0.7–2.0	0.45–2.20
Uric acid	2.9–6.9	0.5–2.8
Cholesterol	100–150	0.06–0.22
Urea	20–42	5–39
Sugar	70–120	45–80
Chloride (NaCl)	560–630	720–750
Inorganic phosphate	2–5	1.25–2.0
Bicarbonate (volumes per cent CO_2)	40–60	40–60
Hydrogen ions (pH)	7.35–7.40	7.35–7.40
Sodium	325	335
Potassium	20	12–17
Magnesium	1–3	3–3.6
Calcium	9.0–11.5	4.0–7.0
Lactic acid	10–32	8–27

* Data largely that compiled by Flexner (1934).

ionic concentrations which cannot be explained by the concept that cerebrospinal fluid consists merely of blood plasma minus protein. In table 11.1 the composition of cerebrospinal fluid and blood are compared. The outstanding difference is the lack of protein in cerebrospinal fluid. The proteins present are of the same kind, consisting of albumin and globulin, but the proportions are different. The content of protein in cerebrospinal fluid is highest in samples from the lumbar region; proteins are probably added to the fluid as it moves along the ventricles.

The osmotic pressures of cerebrospinal fluid and plasma are equal but individual ionic concentrations show significant differences. The ratio of the concentration in cerebrospinal fluid to that in blood, (for sodium, potassium and chloride) is 1.03, 0.52, and 1.21 with the ratios for sodium and potassium in opposite directions. It is not possible for such ionic distributions to exist in a system which has been produced as the result of dialysis. A system in which dialysis occurs is governed by the equilibrium known as the Gibbs-Donnan equilibrium. In the general case, such an equilibrium occurs whenever two solutions are separated by a membrane which is permeable to a salt, but in which one solution contains an impermeable anion (or cation). For example, let sodium chloride be present on one side of a membrane and on the other side, sodium chloride plus a protein. The protein cannot pass the membrane. The situation is analogous to that in brain, the ventricles are almost protein free but contain salts; the blood plasma contains salts and protein.

It is a condition of the Gibbs-Donnan equilibrium that the ions which pass the membrane must distribute themselves in accordance with the concentration ratios, (Na)inside/(Na)outside = (Cl)outside/(Cl)inside. The ratio must be constant for all monovalent cations and anions. The rule is violated for the ratio of the concentrations in cerebrospinal blood and blood plasma; the calculated values for a simple dialysate being 0.95 for sodium, 0.96 for potassium and 1.04 for chloride (compare these with the figures given at beginning of the previous paragraph). It appears from this evidence that the ionic composition is certainly not that of a simple dialysate, but that a non-equilibrium distribution exists and energy is required to produce cerebrospinal fluid.

Further evidence that the formation of cerebrospinal fluid requires energy comes from the calculation of the work required to produce a fluid of such composition from blood. The work necessary to produce a liter of cerebrospinal fluid is the work which has to be performed against the concentration differences of all substances in blood and cerebrospinal fluid. The minimum work necessary for any substance is given by the formula 2.3 RT log (concentration) vent/(concentration) plasma times the concentration in plasma. If this work should be negative, the process would not need energy and could occur spontaneously. The work necessary to produce 1 l. of fluid containing the concentration of Na in cerebrospinal fluid (0.142 mequiv.) is 2.3 (2.2)(.142) log 1.03 or +4.2 cal./l. The work required to produce 1 l. of cerebrospinal fluid is calculated by adding the contributions of all the substances listed in table 11.1. The total work required is +13 cal. of which about 11 cal. come from concentrating Na, K, and Cl. It might be thought that the hydrostatic pressure difference between blood and ventricles could account for much of this but the energy available from the hydrostatic pressure difference amounts to only 1 cal./l. Moreover, if the arterial pressure is experimentally altered the production of CSF is unaffected. Therefore, the fluid cannot be an ultrafiltrate or dialysate of blood but energy must be supplied by metabolic process located presumably in the ependymal cells of the tela choroidea. The water production is actually a consequence of the ability of the system to concentrate ions, the water entering together with the ions to compensate for the difference in osmotic pressure.

Such differences in ionic concentrations should be associated with a difference in potential between ventricle and blood, and a potential difference has been detected by a number of workers. The most recent measurements give a value of 5 mv. for the difference in potential, the ventricle being positive to blood. The source of the potential difference is unknown. It probably does not arise at the choroid plexus but at the ependymal cells of the ventricle. The ion responsible is very likely sodium. Energy is also required to pump sodium and potassium against this electrical gradient but the caloric requirement is small compared to the total concentration work amounting to only 2 cal./l.

Additional evidence for the existence of an active transport mechanism comes from the effect of metabolic inhibitors on the rate of secretion of cerebrospinal fluid. Ouabain, a cardiac glycoside which affects sodium transport in many physiological systems, decreases the rate of formation of cerebrospinal fluid. Metabolic poisons which affect the formation of ATP such as dinitrophenol also reduce the rate of formation of fluid. Diamox, an inhibitor of the enzyme carbonic anhydrase, also diminishes the rate of formation. Thus, the evidence from many approaches is convincing that the production of cerebrospinal fluid requires energy from metabolic sources.

The Amount and Pressure of CSF

The amount of cerebrospinal fluid in man averages about 150 ml. The rate of production is difficult to determine in man; early estimates were of the order 0.3 ml./min. or 0.2% per min. Since the rates of inflow and outflow at equilibrium must be the same, the rate of production can be determined from the rate at which materials which are not absorbed in the ventricles leave the cerebrospinal fluid. The rate at which iodinated serum albumin leaves the cerebrospinal fluid has resulted in the estimate of 0.4% per min. Higher values have been obtained from the rates at which radioactive sodium leaves the ventricles—about 0.6% per min. In rabbits, the figure of 0.4% per min. has been found; in dogs, the estimate is 0.2% per min.

The drainage of cerebrospinal fluid depends upon the difference in hydrostatic pressure between the cerebrospinal fluid and the dural sinuses. It is important to understand that the dural venous sinuses collect fluid from the subarachnoid space and from the veins of the brain. The blood of the sinuses then empties into the jugular veins. Thus the pressure in both the ventricles and the cerebral veins is greater than in the dural sinuses and a continuous undirectional flow is made possible. In man the cerebrospinal fluid pressure ranges from 110 to 175 mm saline; the pressure in the dural sinuses is of the order of 20 to 110 mm saline. By injecting tagged proteins into cerebrospinal fluid and analyzing the content of blood, it has been shown that no barrier exists for the passage of large molecules from cerebrospinal fluid into venous blood. A valvular mechanism is present, however, in the arachnoid villi which prevents the return of blood from the dural sinuses into the ventricles. If the difference of pressure between the ventricles and sinuses drops below 20–50 mm saline, the villi, which consist of small tubes in which the flow occurs, collapse, preventing a backflow of fluid.

The cerebrospinal fluid pressure is normally measured by inserting a needle connected to a manometer which will register the average pressure in the ventricles. If the subject is lying down the pressure will be the same in the ventricles and the lumbar region. Since the brain is a closed box, the total fluid content must remain constant in spite of changes in the individual compartments, arterial, venous or ventricular (Monro-Kellie Doctrine). Thus if the arterial system expands, the venous system must diminish in volume so that the total volume remains constant. An increase in arterial pressure normally has little effect on the pressure in the ventricles since the venous system is compressed, relieving the increased pressure in the arterial system. The reverse is not true, however. Changes in venous pressure have a rapid and profound effect on the cerebrospinal fluid pressure. If the external jugular veins are compressed, the pressure in the veins of the brain rises. This increase in venous pressure is communicated immediately to the tissues surrounding the veins since the arteries are not compressible to any extent by the small changes in venous pressure. This forms the basis for a well known clinical test for obstruction in the subarachnoid spaces, the Queckenstedt test. In this procedure the cerebrospinal fluid pressure in the lumbar region is measured. When the jugular veins are compressed in the normal individual the cerebrospinal fluid pressure will rise quickly; when the jugular compression is released, the CSF pressure immediately falls. Obstruction in any part of the path between the jugular compression and the lumbar region will be indicated by slowed responses to compression and release of the jugular veins.

The Blood-Brain and Blood-CSF Barriers

Materials which pass from the blood into the brain enter either from capillaries into the extracellular space of brain, or they pass from the capillaries via the choroid plexus into the cerebrospinal fluid, from which a small amount may pass into the brain tissue. The "milieu interieur" of the neuron is the extracellular space and rapid changes in this ionic environment may be injurious. Thus the passage of materials into the brain is slow compared with other tissues and one speaks of two barriers—the *blood-brain barrier* and the *blood-cerebrospinal fluid barrier*, corresponding to the two routes mentioned above.

If a substance is lipoid-soluble, it will pass more easily from the blood into the cerebrospinal fluid than a less lipoid-soluble material, a characteristic property of biological membranes (cf. ch. 12). Passage of lipoid-soluble materials across the blood-brain barrier is more rapid than across the blood-cerebrospinal fluid barrier. Certain materials, however, are almost completely prevented from passing across the blood-brain barrier. This was demonstrated in early studies by injecting dyes such as trypan blue intravenously and finding that none was taken up by brain. If the dye was injected into the ventricles, however, it stained the brain. When the rate of entrance of sucrose into the brain from blood and ventricles is compared, the rate is found to be much higher from the ventricles. Glucose, the principal substrate of brain metabolism, is especially interesting in that a special unknown factor in the blood is required in order for uptake to occur.

The penetration of the blood-brain barrier by other substances may be quite rapid. The use of heavy water (deuterium) has shown that water reaches equilibrium with all regions of the brain and the cerebrospinal fluid within 20 min. This fact enables the use of relatively impermeable substances such as urea or sucrose to reduce swelling of the brain. Intravenous injection of these materials as hypertonic solutions causes the rapid movement of water from the ventricles to the blood, resulting in a temporarily decreased brain volume.

The nature of the barriers is, as yet, unknown. It has been suggested by several workers that the barrier is caused by the astrocytic glial cells surrounding many capillaries of the brain. These cells, it is believed, either modify the permeability of the capillary membrane, or, by completely covering the capillary, restrict the area available for penetration. Note that for some substances, the concept of a barrier may be misleading. If, for example, the concentration of glutamic acid in blood is raised, the concentration of this material in the brain does not change. Yet, if the penetration of the brain by radioactive glutamic acid is measured, it is found that the radioactive material penetrates quite rapidly. The explanation for this paradox is that there are active transport processes between the blood and brain which prevent any net uptake of glutamic acid. The presence of a barrier would not be detected by the tracer method. Indeed, there is an apparent absence of any barrier. Any excess unlabeled glutamic acid which accumulates in brain is promptly "pumped" back into the blood.

The Extracellular Space of Brain

It has been claimed that the studies which demonstrate the existence of the blood-brain barrier show only that the extracellular space of brain is very small. Thus, if only a small amount of the dye which is injected into the blood to demonstrate the presence of a barrier should get into the extracellular space, the impression would be gained that no penetration was occurring. The amount of brain which consists of extracellular space is a matter of controversy. Electron micrographs of brain tissue show that the cells of the brain are separated by spaces 100–200 Å wide. Calculations based on such spaces give values for the extracellular space which are less than 5% of the brain volume. Other values for the brain space are obtained from the concentration of materials such as inulin and sucrose which are injected into the blood and which do not penetrate the cells of the brain. Values obtained by such 'physiological' methods are higher and are from 10 to 15% of the brain volume. By direct infusion of sucrose into the ventricles, spaces as high as 12% are obtained; whereas by injection into the blood, lower values were obtained—indicating that a blood-barrier to sucrose was present. In view of the possibility of shrinkage in the electron micrographs, the question of the volume of extracellular space remains an open one.

LITERATURE

BAKAY, L. (1951) Studies on the blood-brain barrier with radioactive phosphorus. Arch. Neurol. Psychiat., **66**, 419.

BAKAY, L. (1956) The Blood-brain Barrier with Special Regard to the Use of Radioactive Isotopes. Thomas, Springfield.

BERING, E. A. (1955) Studies on the role of the choroid plexus in Tracer exchanges between blood and cerebrospinal fluid. J. Neurosurg., **12**, 355.

DAVSON, H. (1956) Physiology of the Ocular and Cerebrospinal Fluids. Churchill, London.

DAVSON, H. AND MATCHETT, P. A. (1953) The kinetics of penetration of the blood-aqueous barrier. J. Physiol., **122**, 11.

DE ROBERTS, E. AND GERRCHENFIELD, H. M. (1961) Submicroscopic morphology and function of glial cells. Int. Rev. Neurobiol., **3**, 1.

DANDY, W. E. AND BLACKFAN, K. D. (1914) Internal hydrocephalis. An experimental, clinical and pathological study. Am. J. Dis. Chil., **8**, 482.

EDSTRÖM, R. (1964) Recent developments of the blood-brain barrier concept. Int. Rev. Neurobiol., **7**, 153.

FLEXNER, L. B. (1934) The chemistry and nature of the cerebrospinal fluid. Physiol. Rev., **14**, 161.

MELLEN, J. W. AND WOOLAM, D. H. M. (1962) The Anatomy of the Cerebrospinal Fluid. Oxford Univ. Press, London.

MERRETT, H. H. AND FREMONT-SMITH, F. (1937) The Cerebrospinal Fluid. Saunders, Philadelphia.

MORTENSON, O. A. AND WEED, L. H. (1934) Absorption of isotonic fluids from the subarachnoid space. Amer. J. Physiol., **108**, 458.

RASMUSSEN, A. T. (1952) The Principal Nervous Pathways. (4th Ed.). MacMillan, N.Y.

SWEET, W. H. AND TOCHSLEY, H. B. (1953) Formation, flow and reabsorption of cerebrospinal fluid formation by a carbonic anhydrase inhibitor, Diamox. Proc. Soc. Biol., **84**, 397.

TSCHIRGI, R. D., FROST, R. W. AND TAYLOR, J. L. (1954) Inhibition of cerebrospinal fluid formation by a carbonic anhydrase inhibitor, Diamox. Proc. Soc. Exp. Biol. Med., **87**, 373.

VAN HARREBELD AND SCHADE, J. P. (1960) In: Structure and Function of the Cerebral Cortex (Tower and Schade, ed.). Elsevier, Amsterdam.

WALLACE, G. B. AND BRODIE, B. B. (1940) On the source of the cerebrospinal fluid. The distribution of bromide and iodide throughout the central nervous system. J. Pharmacol. Exptl. Therap., **70**, 418.

WEED, L. H. (1923) The absorption of cerebrospinal fluid into the venous system. Am. J. Anat., **31**, 191.

WOOLAM, D. H. M. AND MELLEN, J. W. (1958) In: Ciba Foundation Symposium on the Cerebrospinal Fluid. Churchill, London.

CHAPTER 12

The Autonomic Nervous System

(Synonyms—involuntary nervous system,
vegetative nervous system)

The autonomic nervous system has been touched upon in many of its aspects in other sections of this book. There remains to be given an account of the structural plan of this system as a whole, a general summary of its functions and of the structures which it innervates. From anatomical, physiological and pharmacological viewpoints the autonomic system falls naturally into two main divisions—the *sympathetic* or *thoracicolumbar outflow* and the *parasympathetic* or *craniosacral outflow* (see fig. 12.1).

The Sympathetic Division

The cells of origin of the sympathetic division are situated in the lateral horns of the spinal cord (intermediolateral cell column) from the 8th cervical or 1st thoracic to the 2nd or 3rd lumbar segments. The axons of these cells leave the cord by the corresponding anterior nerve roots and synapse with nerve cells in one or another of the outlying ganglia. The fibers arising from the spinal cord are medullated and are called *preganglionic*; those arising from cells of the ganglia are nonmedullated, and are called *postganglionic*. Evidence for the existence of a higher center in the posterior region of the hypothalamus has been considered in chapter 7, and in the cerebral cortex in chapter 8.

The ganglion cells are all motor or secretory in function (p. 249). They have no afferent connections from the periphery. However, many afferent fibers from the various viscera and blood vessels pass through the sympathetic nervous system. They have their ganglion cells in the posterior root ganglia as have the somatic afferent fibers.

The ganglia are arranged in three systems or groups: (A) *paravertebral*, (B) *prevertebral* (or *collateral*) and (C) *terminal* (or *peripheral*).

A. The Paravertebral Ganglia and the Gangliated Cord

The paravertebral group lies in close relation to the vertebral bodies and consists, on each side, of a series of some 22 ganglia connected together by intervening fiber tracts to form a nodular cord extending from the base of the skull to the front of the coccyx. This is known as the *sympathetic chain* or the *gangliated cord of the sympathetic nervous system*. It will be described in sections.

The Cervical Part of the Sympathetic Chain

The cervical part of the sympathetic chain possesses three ganglia—the *superior, middle* and *inferior cervical ganglia*. They are relatively large and are believed to result from the fusion of two or more smaller ganglia.

THE SUPERIOR CERVICAL GANGLION, situated below the base of the skull, is the largest of the three. It receives preganglionic fibers from the upper thoracic segments of the spinal cord, and its cells supply fibers (postganglionic) to the vessels, glands and cutaneous muscle of the head. It is probably formed by the fusion of the uppermost three or four cervical ganglia. Its branches are:

(1) THE INTERNAL CAROTID NERVE. This nerve, composed of postganglionic fibers, arises from the upper pole of the superior cervical ganglion and, passing into the cranium with the artery of the same name, forms the internal carotid and cavernous plexuses.

(i) The *internal carotid plexus*, situated on the lateral side of the internal carotid artery sends branches to the following:
(a) The abducent nerve.
(b) The tympanic branch of the glossopharyngeal nerve.
(c) The sphenopalatine ganglion. These fibers pass by way of the deep petrosal nerve and the nerve to the pterygoid canal which is formed by the union of the former nerve with the great superficial petrosal nerve. Orbital branches of the sphenopalatine ganglion convey sympathetic fibers to the lacrymal gland; the soft palate, nasopharynx and pharynx receive fibers through the palatine and pharyngeal branches of the ganglion.
(d) The semilunar (trigeminal) ganglion.
The sympathetic fibers pass through the sphenopalatine and semilunar ganglia without interruption.

(ii) The *cavernous plexus*, situated on the inner side of the internal carotid artery as it lies in the cavernous sinus, sends branches to the following:
(a) The oculomotor, trochlear and abducent nerves and the nasociliary branch of the ophthal-

mic division of the trigeminal nerve. Through the long ciliary nerves (twigs of the nasociliary nerve), sympathetic fibers are conveyed to the dilator pupillae muscle (see also p. 366).

(b) The ciliary ganglion, through which the sympathetic fibers pass without interruption into the short ciliary nerves. These fibers provide an additional pathway for sympathetic impulses to the dilator of the pupil.

(c) The pituitary body (vasomotor).

Through the communicating branches of the cavernous plexus the vessels of the eyeball and nasal mucosa are supplied with constrictor fibers, and the skin of the nose with vasoconstrictor, motor (smooth muscle) and secretory (sweat) fibers. The terminal filaments of the internal carotid and cavernous plexuses are continued as delicate networks over the anterior and middle cerebral arteries to the minute vessels of the pia mater, and along the ophthalmic artery to the structures of the orbit.

(2) Branches to and distributed with the UPPER FOUR CERVICAL NERVES.

(3) Twigs to the JUGULAR GANGLION AND NODOSE GANGLION OF THE VAGUS, to the PETROUS GANGLION OF THE GLOSSOPHARYNGEAL NERVE and to the HYPOGLOSSAL NERVE.

(4) Filaments to the CAROTID SINUS and CAROTID BODY.

(5) Fibers to LARYNGEAL and PHARYNGEAL PLEXUSES.

(6) The SUPERIOR CARDIAC NERVE to the cardiac plexuses.

(7) Branches which ramify in a plexiform manner upon the external carotid artery—the EXTERNAL CAROTID PLEXUS. This plexus is continued over the branches of the external carotid and supplies fibers to the vessels, sweat glands and cutaneous muscles of the face, and to the thyroid gland. Filaments from the plexus investing the facial artery pass to the submaxillary ganglion. The plexus on the middle meningeal artery sends fibers to the otic ganglion; these pass without interruption into the auriculotemporal nerve through which they reach the parotid gland.

THE MIDDLE CERVICAL GANGLION is formed presumably by the coalescence of the 5th and 6th cervical ganglia. Its branches are as follows:

(1) Branches to the *5th and 6th cervical nerves* and thence to the blood vessels, sweat glands and cutaneous muscle within the area of distribution of these nerves.

(2) *The middle cardiac nerve* to cardiac plexuses.

(3) Branches which extend along the inferior thyroid artery to the *thyroid* and *parathyroid glands*.

THE INFERIOR CERVICAL GANGLION probably represents the union of the 7th and 8th cervical ganglia; in the dog and cat, and in most human subjects, it is usually fused with the first thoracic ganglion, and occasionally with the second as well, to form the so-called *stellate ganglion*. It gives off the following branches:

(1) Branches to the *7th and 8th cervical* and the *1st thoracic nerves*, sometimes also to the 6th cervical and the 2nd thoracic.

(2) The *inferior cardiac nerve* to cardiac plexuses.

(3) Branches which form plexuses upon the subclavian artery and its branches. Sympathetic fibers are thus carried into the cranial cavity along the vertebral artery, and over the axillary and commencement of the brachial.

The Thoracic, Lumbar and Sacral Ganglia

The *thoracic ganglia* are 10 or 12 in number on each side. They are evenly spaced, one to each spinal segment. As mentioned above the first thoracic and inferior cervical ganglia are commonly partially or completely fused to form an irregularly shaped mass, called the *stellate ganglion*. There are usually 4 *lumbar* and 4 or 5 *sacral* ganglia.[1] The sacral portions of the two sympathetic trunks converge below and fuse upon the anterior surface of the coccyx to form a terminal swelling—the *coccygeal ganglion* or *ganglion impar*.

B. THE PREVERTEBRAL (OR COLLATERAL) GANGLIA

These lie in the thorax, abdomen and pelvis in relation to the aorta and its branches. The larger of the prevertebral ganglia are: (a) the *celiac (solar or semilunar) ganglion*, lying in relation to the origin of the celiac artery, (b) the *superior mesenteric ganglion*, situated below the origin of the superior mesenteric artery, and (c) the *inferior mesenteric ganglion*, which bears a corresponding relation to the inferior mesenteric artery; this

---

[1] Small accessory ganglia, called *intermediate ganglia*, are found outside the sympathetic chain proper, attached to the rami communicantes close to the spinal nerve roots in the cervicothoracic and lumbar regions. From these ganglia sympathetic postganglionic fibers proceed for distribution by the brachial and lumbar plexuses to the limb vessels. Preganglionic fibers leaving the cord by the anterior roots and entering the intermediate ganglia without passing through the sympathetic chain offer a possible alternative pathway for sympathetic impulses to the limbs. Such fibers would remain intact though the sympathetic chain were excised; their presence would, thus, offer an explanation in some instances for the failure of sympatheticectomy to completely denervate the vessels of the limbs.

ganglion is rarely present in man (see also p. 248).

C. The Terminal Ganglia

These consist of small collections of ganglion cells situated in close relation to the innervated organs, especially those of the pelvis, e.g., the bladder and rectum.

The Outflow of Sympathetic Fibers from the Central Nervous System

It has already been stated that the cells giving rise to the sympathetic fibers (p. 242) are situated in the thoracic and upper lumbar segments of the cord. It is from this limited region (8th C. or 1st T. to 2nd or 3rd L. inclusive) that the

sympathetic (preganglionic) fibers emerge. *This region constitutes the only outlet for sympathetic impulses.* So the term thoracicolumbar outflow simply means the sympathetic division of the autonomic nervous system. The fibers emerge from the spinal cord through the anterior root of the spinal segment in which their cell bodies are placed. In a cross section of the anterior root they appear as fine medullated fibers (2.5μ or less in diameter) intermingled with the larger, medullated, somatic (motor) fibers. They separate almost immediately, however, from the motor fibers of the anterior root—which are concerned with movement of the skeletal musculature—and enter the corresponding ganglion of the sympathetic chain. Thus, the spinal nerves from the 8th cervical or 1st thoracic to the 2nd or 3rd lumbar,

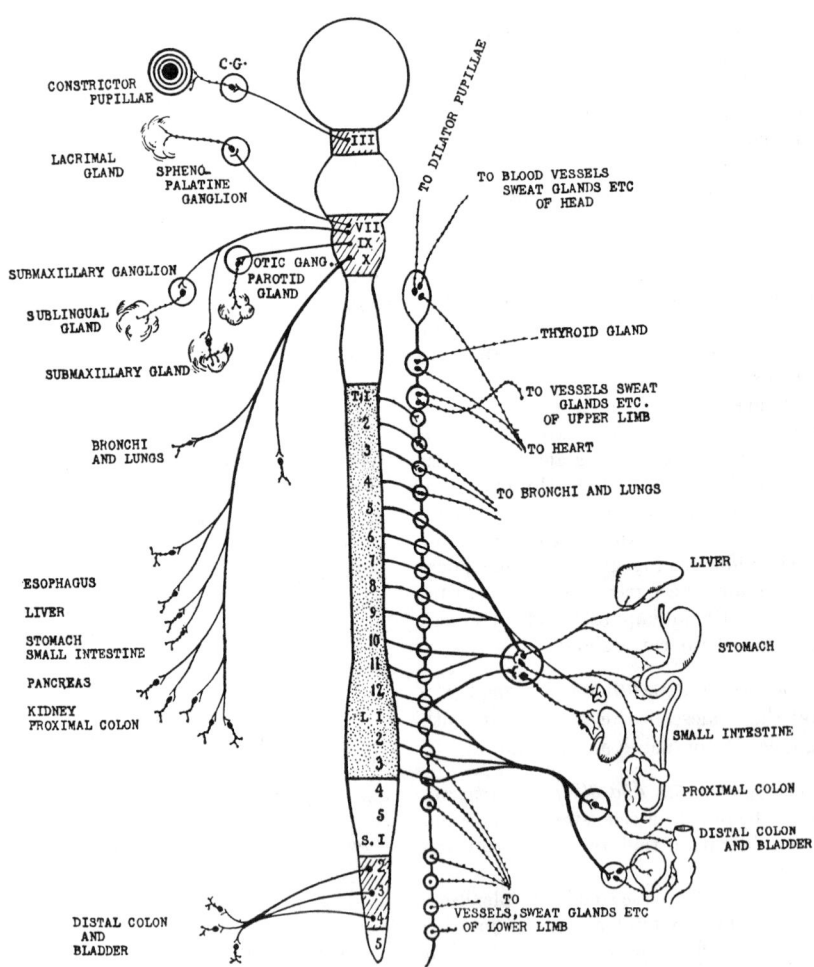

Fig. 12.1. Showing plan of autonomic nervous system from a functional viewpoint. C.G., ciliary ganglion. The celiac, inferior mesenteric and hypogastric ganglia are represented, in this order from above downwards, by the circles in the lower right portion of the diagram.

but not others, are connected each to a paravertebral ganglion by a delicate white strand composed of preganglionic fibers and known as the *white ramus communicans* (plural, *rami communicantes*, fig. 12.2 and fig. 12.1, p. 244). A preganglionic fiber after entering the ganglion may pursue one of three courses: it may (a) form synapses with cells in the ganglion which it first enters, or (b) pass up or down the sympathetic trunk for some distance to terminate in a ganglion at a level higher or lower than that of the segment from which it originated. It may give off collateral branches to ganglion cells along its course. In any event, the preganglionic fibers issuing from a given segment connect with several ganglia (from five to nine). Furthermore, each preganglionic fiber may form a large number of synapses within a given ganglion. Ranson and Billingsley found that in the case of the superior cervical ganglion each fiber communicated with some thirty-two ganglion cells; this accounts for the diffuse nature of the sympathetic discharge. Finally, the preganglionic fiber may (c) traverse the gangliated cord without interruption to find a cell station in either a prevertebral or a terminal ganglion.

PLAN OF DISTRIBUTION OF SYMPATHETIC FIBERS TO THE PERIPHERY

To the Limbs and Trunk

The ganglia of the sympathetic chain are connected with the spinal nerves supplying the limbs and trunk by delicate filaments called *gray rami communicantes*. They are composed of the axons of the ganglion cells in the paravertebral ganglia, and are therefore called *postganglionic*. The gray rami in the thoracic and upper lumbar regions join the spinal nerves close to the points at which the white rami arise. Their constituent fibers are continued in the peripheral nerves for the supply of the blood vessels, sweat glands and smooth muscle of the skin. Whereas, as already mentioned, only a limited number of spinal nerves possess white rami, *every spinal nerve receives a gray ramus*. It therefore follows that sympathetic impulses going to parts supplied by upper cervical, lower lumbar or sacral somatic nerves, must travel considerable distances up or down the sympathetic trunk before reaching an outlet through a gray ramus. The preganglionic fibers to the upper limb arise from the 2nd to the

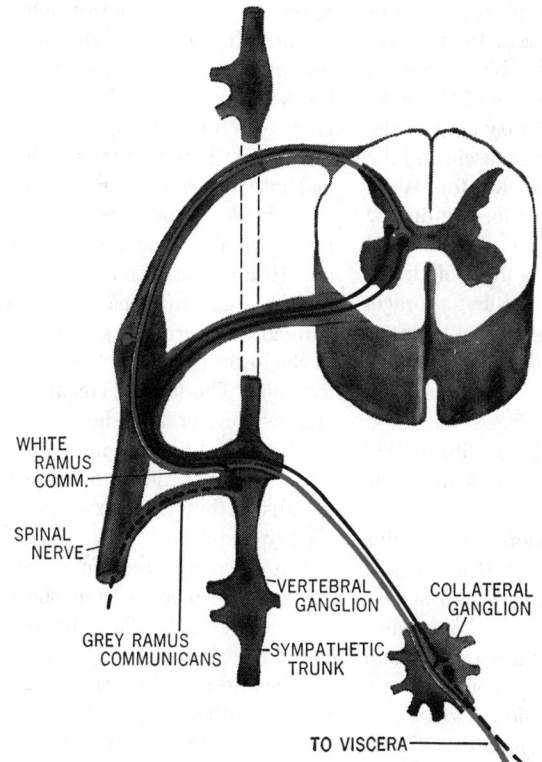

WHITE RAMUS COMM.

SPINAL NERVE

GREY RAMUS COMMUNICANS

VERTEBRAL GANGLION

SYMPATHETIC TRUNK

COLLATERAL GANGLION

TO VISCERA

FIG. 12.2. Diagram showing the connections of sympathetic fibers. Efferent fibers in black; preganglionic, solid lines; postganglionic, interrupted lines. Afferent visceral fiber in red.

7th thoracic spinal segments; most of these fibers are contained in the white rami of the 2nd and 3rd thoracic anterior roots. The postganglionic fibers to the upper limb may arise from the upper 1st to 4th thoracic, and the inferior and middle cervical ganglia (see also ch. 42); those for the lower limb from the lumbar and sacral ganglia. Excision of the inferior cervical or the stellate ganglion when present and the upper three or four thoracic ganglia provides as complete a sympathectomy as it is possible to make of the upper limb, as well as the head and neck. It also will destroy most of the sympathetic nerves to the heart. This operation may fail, however, to remove completely the sympathetic supply to the arm since there may be "intermediate" ganglia which are not removed in such an operation.

To the Head and Neck

Sympathetic impulses to the structures of the neck, face, scalp and intracranial cavity are conveyed from the spinal cord in the white rami of the upper two thoracic nerves. They ascend to connect with cells in the middle and superior cervical ganglia. From the latter postganglionic fibers are distributed through the internal carotid, cavernous and external carotid plexuses as described on page 242. The sympathetic nervous system as well as supplying the blood vessels, sweat glands and pilomotor muscles of the head and neck also innervates the salivary glands, the dilator pupillae muscles, Mueller's muscle and the smooth muscle component of the levator palpebrae superioris. The spinal center for the dilator pupillae is situated (in man) in the 8th cervical or 1st thoracic segment. The preganglionic fibers are found in the white rami of the first thoracic nerve, and are distributed, as already stated through the internal carotid and ciliary nerves.

To the Thoracic Viscera

The sympathetic postganglionic fibers join with the branches from the vagus to form the *cardiac, pulmonary* and *esophageal plexuses.*

The *cardiac plexus* lies in relation to the origins of the aorta and pulmonary artery. It consists of a superficial and a deep portion, and is formed by the interlacement of fibers from the cardiac branches of the vagus (parasympathetic) and sympathetic nerves. The vagus fibers are preganglionic. They terminate around ganglion cells in the walls of the heart. The sympathetic fibers derived from the superior, middle and inferior cardiac nerves are postganglionic, their cell stations lying in the corresponding cervical ganglia (fig. 12.1, p. 244). The preganglionic fibers arise from the upper four or five thoracic segments of the spinal cord.

The *pulmonary plexuses,* anterior and posterior, lie in relation to the corresponding aspects of the root of the lung. They are formed from postganglionic fibers of the sympathetic (T. 2, 3 and 4) and preganglionic fibers of the vagus. The latter connect with ganglion cells in the walls of the bronchi. Herein is situated an intrinsic nervous plexus consisting of these ganglion cells and medullated and nonmedullated fibers.

The *esophageal plexus* embraces the lower half of the esophagus. Vagal and sympathetic fibers (from the upper thoracic ganglia and from the thoracic portion of the great splanchnic nerve) enter into its formation. The vagal fibers end around ganglion cells of the intrinsic plexus of Auerbach in the esophageal wall.

To the Abdominal and Pelvic Viscera

The *greater, lesser and least splanchnic nerves.* These are composed of preganglionic fibers, and may be looked upon as elongated white rami. They connect with cells in the prevertebral (collateral) ganglia. The postganglionic fibers after emerging from the latter join the neighboring plexuses. The *greater splanchnic* nerve arises from the spinal cord from as high as the 4th or 5th thoracic segment, and as low as the 9th or 10th. Its fibers end in the upper part of the celiac ganglion; from here postganglionic fibers are continued into the celiac plexus. The *lesser splanchnic* and the *least* (or *lowest) splanchnic* nerves are much smaller. The former arises from the 9th and 10th or the 10th and 11th thoracic segments and its fibers, after passing without interruption through the vertebral ganglia at these levels, end in the lower portion of the celiac (or aorticorenal) ganglion. The least splanchnic nerve arises from the last one or two thoracic segments and first lumbar segment; it joins the renal plexus (fig. 12.3). Postganglionic fibers arising from small ganglia within the plexus are distributed to the kidney and ureter.

The *lumbar splanchnic nerves* are three or four strands which arise from the second and third lumbar segments. Their fibers pass through the lumbar portion of the sympathetic chain and enter the inferior mesenteric ganglion; here some are relayed, others are continued without interruption and find their cell stations in peripheral ganglia.

THE PLEXUSES OF THE ABDOMEN AND PELVIS. The sympathetic fibers form rich plexuses in rela-

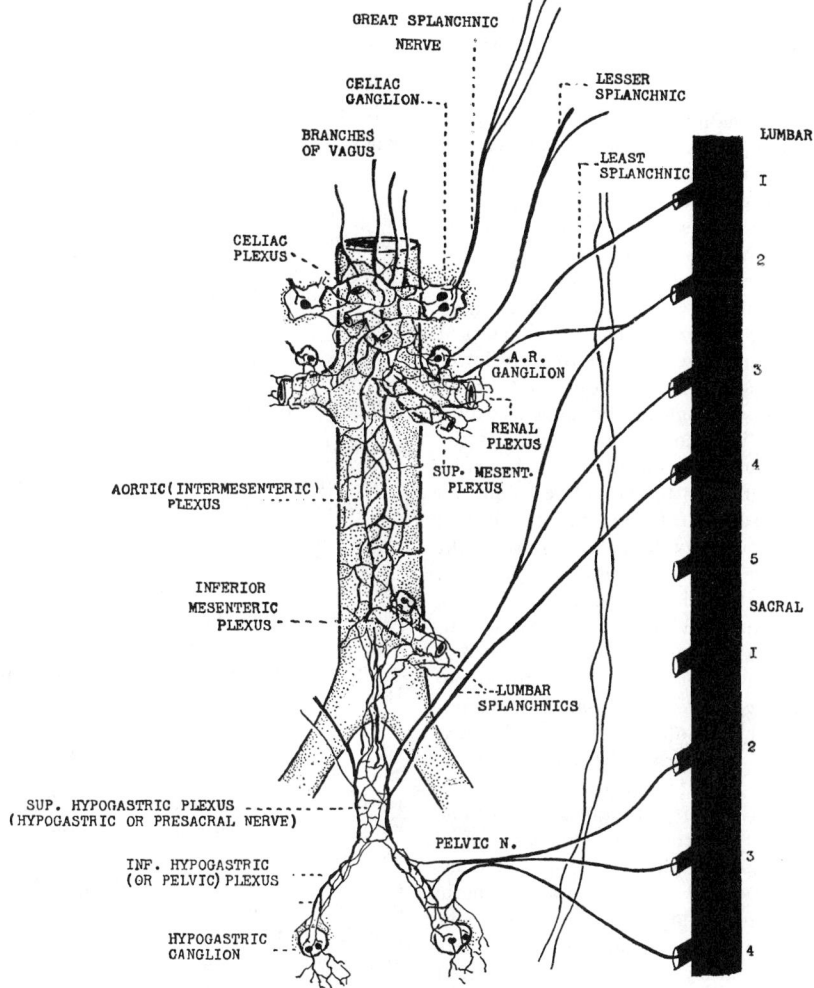

FIG. 12.3. Diagram of the nerve plexuses of the abdomen and pelvis. A.R., aortico-renal.

tion to the aorta and its branches from which filaments pass to the abdominal and pelvic viscera. Parasympathetic fibers also enter into the constitution of these plexuses.

The *celiac* (or *solar*) *plexus* lies upon the abdominal aorta at the origin of the celiac artery. The *celiac ganglia*, right and left, lie embedded within the plexus, which is made up of fibers arising in the ganglion (i.e., postganglionic fibers of the greater and lesser splanchnic nerves) together with preganglionic fibers of the vagus. The lower part of the celiac ganglion is often detached and is then referred to as the *aorticorenal ganglion*. The plexus invests the celiac artery throughout its course and gives rise to several subordinate plexuses—the *hepatic, gastric, splenic, renal* and *adrenal plexuses*—which invest the corresponding arteries and their branches.

The *superior mesenteric plexus* is continuous above with the celiac plexus. It surrounds the superior mesenteric artery, along the branches of which it is prolonged as subsidiary plexuses. The plexus is composed of postganglionic fibers which arise in an aggregation of nerve cells—the *superior mesenteric ganglion*—lying within it, of preganglionic fibers derived from the lumbar segments of the cord, and from the celiac plexus. It and the other plexuses to be described also contain parasympathetic fibers. The superior mesenteric plexus supplies the pancreas, and the small intestine and the large intestines as far as the commencement of the descending colon.

The *aortic* or *intermesenteric plexus* lies upon the aorta between the origins of the superior and inferior mesenteric arteries. It receives fibers from the celiac plexus and from the upper lumbar ganglia. The aortic plexus gives rise secondarily to the *spermatic* and *ovarian* plexuses which supply the testes and ovary with autonomic fibers. It is connected below with the *inferior mesenteric plexus* which invests the artery of the same name. The *inferior mesenteric ganglion*, a collection of ganglion cells lying within the latter plexus, receives the lumbar splanchnics; this ganglion is not present, as a rule, in the human subject (Learmonth) but a number of smaller ganglia are found scattered through the plexus. The plexus is formed of fibers derived from the aortic plexus from the inferior mesenteric ganglion when this is present. From it secondary plexuses arise which invest the branches of the inferior mesenteric artery and carry sympathetic impulses to the descending colon, iliac colon, pelvic colon and rectum.

The *superior hypogastric plexus* is the downward extension of the aortic plexus. It lies over the lower end of the aorta, and in the angle formed by the aortic bifurcation. Though rarely condensed into a single bundle it is sometimes referred to as the *hypogastric nerve* or the *presacral nerve*. It transmits inhibitory impulses to the pelvic colon and via the pelvic plexuses to the rectum, bladder and other pelvic viscera. It divides below into the right and left *pelvic* or *inferior hypogastric plexuses*. These lie one on either side of the rectum and are composed of medullated and non-medullated fibers among which are scattered numerous small ganglia which are sometimes referred to collectively as the *hypogastric ganglion*. Parasympathetic fibers enter the inferior hypogastric plexuses through the pelvic nerve (sacral outflow). The sympathetic fibers contributing to the pelvic plexuses have their ultimate source in the lumbar segments of the cord. They reach the plexuses via the hypogastric plexuses as well as more directly from the sacral part of the sympathetic chain. Through subsidiary plexuses—*hemorrhoidal*, *vesical*, *uterine*, *vaginal* and *prostatic*—fibers (sympathetic and parasympathetic) are conveyed from the pelvic plexuses to the pelvic viscera.

THE PARASYMPATHETIC OR CRANIOSACRAL DIVISION OF THE AUTONOMIC NERVOUS SYSTEM

The cells giving rise to parasympathetic fibers are situated at three different levels of the central nervous system—the *midbrain*, the *medulla oblongata* and the *sacral region of the spinal cord*. The axons of these cells leave the central nervous system to connect with ganglion cells lying within or in close relation to the innervated organ (see fig. 12.1). As in the case of the sympathetic division the axons of the central cells are called *preganglionic*; those of the ganglion cells, *postganglionic*. The former are medullated, the latter nonmedullated. The three levels from which parasympathetic fibers emerge will be referred to as the *tectal* (or *midbrain*), the *bulbar* and the *sacral* outflows, respectively.

A. THE TECTAL OR MIDBRAIN OUTFLOW

The group of cells composing the Edinger-Westphal nucleus of the oculomotor nerve (p. 371), in the floor of the cerebral aqueduct, are believed to give rise to the tectal fibers.

The autonomic fibers are conveyed in the third nerve as far as the ciliary ganglion where they find their cell stations. Postganglionic fibers emerge from the ganglion in the short ciliary nerves, and terminate in the sphincter pupillae and the ciliary muscles (p. 364).

B. THE BULBAR OUTFLOW

These fibers leave the brain in the *facial, glossopharyngeal* and *vagus nerves*.

(1) The parasympathetic fibers (secretory and vasodilator) entering the *facial nerve* arise from the *superior salivatory (salivary) nucleus*, which lies dorsal and lateral to the lower end of the motor nucleus of the facial.[2] These fibers emerge from the brain in the sensory root of the facial nerve (*nervus intermedius*, ch. 6) and travel with the latter to the facial canal of the temporal bone. Here they leave the facial, (i) in its *chorda tympani* branch which later joins the lingual to be conveyed to the floor of the mouth. At this point some of the chorda fibers (secretory and vasodilator in function) separate from the lingual again to enter the *submaxillary (submandibular) ganglion* from where they are relayed; the postganglionic fibers pass to the submaxillary and submandibular glands, and the mucous membrane of the mouth. (ii) In the great superficial petrosal nerve and nerve of the pterygoid canal (Vidian nerve) to the sphenopalatine ganglion. From here postganglionic fibers pass via orbital branches of the ganglion to the lacrymal gland, and to the mucous membrane of the soft palate, nasopharynx and pharynx via the palatine nerves. Vasodilator fibers also leave the facial by the great superficial petrosal nerve, and entering the cranium are conveyed along the middle meningeal artery and its branches.

(2) The parasympathetic fibers (secretory and vasodilator) of the *glossopharyngeal nerve* arise from cells of the *inferior salivatory (salivary) nucleus*. This nucleus lies in the uppermost part of the medulla oblongata immediately below the superior salivatory nucleus, and lateral to the motor nucleus of the glossopharyngeal nerve. The autonomic fibers leave the brain with the latter nerve but separate from it again in its tympanic branch (Jacobson's nerve) which joins a twig from the geniculate ganglion (g. of facial nerve) and

---

[2] This nucleus is actually in the lowest part of the pons.

filaments from the internal carotid plexus to form the *tympanic plexus*. From this plexus emerges the *small superficial petrosal nerve* through which parasympathetic fibers are continued to the otic ganglion. From this ganglion postganglionic fibers are conveyed to the parotid gland via the auriculotemporal nerve. The tympanic plexus itself sends filaments to the mucous membrane of the tympanic cavity, the mastoid air-cells, auditory (Eustachian) tube and the internal ear.

(3) The *vagus nerve* contains the greater proportion of the fibers of the bulbar outflow. They arise from the *dorsal nucleus* of the vagus and are distributed through the latter's numerous branches to the thoracic and abdominal viscera (ch. 6). Unlike those in the other two cranial nerves, the preganglionic fibers of the vagus connect with ganglion cells situated within the innervated organs. Thus the vagal fibers to the heart connect with ganglion cells in the cardiac walls: those to the bronchi with the nerve cells of the intrinsic plexus in the bronchial walls; those to the esophagus, stomach and intestine form synapses with the ganglion cells of the myenteric plexus of Auerbach and the submucous plexus of Meissner. The preganglionic fibers are therefore quite long, the postganglionic very short. The cells of origin of most of the cardiac fibers of the vagus form a discrete group (cardio-inhibitory center) lying alongside the dorsal nucleus of the vagus.

C. The Sacral Outflow

The cells of origin lie in the anterior horns of the 2nd, 3rd and 4th and sometimes the 1st sacral segments of the spinal cord. The preganglionic fibers emerge in the anterior roots of the corresponding sacral nerves. The fibers leave the spinal nerves again and, proceeding peripherally as the *pelvic nerve* (or *nervus erigens*), on each side, enter into the formation of the pelvic plexus. The fibers terminate around ganglion cells lying in close relation to the pelvic organs. They carry motor impulses to the walls of the descending colon, rectum and bladder; inhibitory impulses to the internal anal and vesical sphincters and to the uterus; and dilator impulses to the blood vessels of the bladder, rectum and genitalia.

The Afferent Visceral Nerves

Impulses are transmitted from the viscera by afferent fibers which pass through the various plexuses and reach the central nervous system via the vagus, pelvic, splanchnics and other autonomic nerves.

The *afferent fibers of the sympathetic division* are the peripheral processes of ganglion cells in the posterior spinal root ganglia from the 1st thoracic to the 3rd lumbar segments. *None arise from sympathetic ganglia.* They reach the sympathetic trunk via the white rami communicantes and are distributed to the viscera along with the corresponding efferent fibers (fig. 12.2). Though some of these afferent fibers are nonmedullated, the majority are medullated, and of larger size than the efferent fibers. The ganglion cells of the posterior roots which give origin to the afferent fibers of the sympathetic (or of the pelvic nerve) have not been shown definitely to differ from those giving rise to the ordinary somatic sensory fibers. For this reason the sympathetic system proper is sometimes regarded, though perhaps irrationally, as consisting solely of efferent neurons. The afferent fibers pass to their destinations without interruption in any of the sympathetic ganglia, passing directly to the viscera in the splanchnics or the other visceral nerves. A certain proportion also enter the spinal nerves for distribution to the limbs via the gray rami.

The *afferent fibers of the vagus* are the peripheral processes of cells in the ganglion jugulare and the ganglion nodosum. The central processes of these neurons terminate in the dorsal nucleus of the vagus (ch. 6). Therein connections are made with efferent parasympathetic neurons to complete the reflex arc. The *afferent fibers of the pelvic nerve* arise from cells in the posterior root ganglia of the 2nd, 3rd and 4th sacral nerves. They pass peripherally with the efferent autonomic fibers.

The visceral reflex arc, as pointed out by Gaskell, is formed upon a plan similar to that upon which somatic reflexes are based. The afferent fiber in the latter instance is connected to the anterior horn cell through the intermediary of an intraspinal (internuncial) neuron or a series of such neurons. These are spoken of as connector neurons. In the case of visceral reflexes, the afferent fiber makes contact with a cell in the lateral horn of gray matter. The axon of this cell connects with a ganglion cell of the sympathetic system. This ganglion cell and its postganglionic fiber corresponds to the motor neuron of the somatic reflex arc.

A certain degree of independent reflex activity can be carried out through the intrinsic plexuses, e.g., of the intestine, when these are separated from the central nervous system by division of the main autonomic nerves. It is also true that some independent activity can be carried out through axon reflexes or possibly through some of the more peripherally placed ganglion cells. Other parts of the autonomic system, however, cannot function apart from the central nervous system. The larger ganglia of the parasympathetic or sympathetic, for instance, do not serve as reflex centers. It is clear from the description of the origin and course of the visceral afferent nerves given above that no anatomical basis for such action exists.

The Functions of the Autonomic Nervous System

The autonomic nervous system governs the activities of cardiac and smooth muscle, of the digestive glands and sweat glands, of the adrenal medulla and possibly of certain endocrine organs. It is concerned with those processes which normally are beyond voluntary control and are for the most part beneath consciousness. The term autonomic as applied to this system is not altogether suitable since, as we have seen, it is under the control of centers within the central nervous system, and cannot function as an independent unit.

Through its various activities the autonomic system exercises the important function of maintaining the constancy of the fluid environment of the body's cells; it serves to combat forces, acting either from within or without, which tend to cause variations in this environment. Regulation of the composition of the body fluids and their temperature, quantity and distribution, is effected through the actions of the autonomic nerves upon circulatory, respiratory, excretory and glandular organs. For example, of glandular structures under autonomic influence, the liver, pancreas and adrenal medulla are of especial importance in the regulation of blood sugar; the sweat glands aid in the control of body temperature. The neural lobe of the pituitary is partially under autonomic nervous control. The thyroid gland, adrenal cortex, adenohypophysis and probably also the parathyroid glands, are governed by hormones liberated by the pituitary (ch. 74); though it is not improbable that they may be influenced also by impulses received through autonomic paths. The stability of the internal environment (the *milieu interne* of Claude Bernard) which is so characteristic of the healthy body, is spoken of by Cannon as *homeostasis*. According to Cannon, the essential and particular function of the autonomic system is to bring about the internal adjustments upon which this constant state depends. He therefore refers to the autonomic nerves as the *interofective* system. He speaks of the voluntary system (i.e., the central nervous system and the somatic

nerves) as the *exterofective* system, since through its exteroceptors and effectors a direct relationship is established with the external environment.

The great majority of the effector organs of the autonomic system are innervated by both sympathetic and parasympathetic divisions (see table 12.1), and the effects exerted by the two types of fiber going to a given organ are antagonistic. Thus the heart's action is inhibited by the vagus but augmented by the sympathetic. In the intestine the effects of the two systems are reversed, the parasympathetic (vagus nerve to the small bowel and upper half of the colon, and the pelvic nerve to the lower half of the latter) is augmentative; the sympathetic is inhibitory. The removal of the effects of one set of fibers, as by section, results, as a rule, in the effects of the other set becoming more prominent. This fact indicates that each type of fiber exerts a constant or tonic action and suggests that the two effects are delicately balanced one against the other. Thus, section of the vagus nerves causes an increase in the cardiac rate, and section of the parasympathetic or of the sympathetic fibers to the iris causes, respectively, dilation or constriction of the pupil. (See pupillary reactions, p. 363).

Taken as a whole the actions of the sympathetic division and its ally the medulla of the adrenal gland (sympathoadrenal system, ch. 76) are directed towards strengthening an animal's defenses against the various dangers which beset it, e.g., extremes of temperature, deprivation of water or the attacks of its enemies. It has been shown by Cannon, however, that the sympathetic system is not indispensable; both gangliated cords may be completely removed yet the animal remains in good health provided it is kept in the sheltered environment of the laboratory. Sympathectomized cats if kept warm and carefully tended will live indefinitely. Kittens deprived of their sympathetic trunks grow normally, female cats become pregnant and give birth to young, though the mammary glands do not function normally and the maternal instinct is lacking. Sympathectomized animals are, however, incapable of arduous work, sugar is not mobilized from the liver on demand, an increase of circulating red blood cells does not occur during excitement or exercise, the usual reactions to cold (elevation of the hairs and vasoconstriction) fail, and adrenaline is not liberated in an emergency. They are also less able to withstand oxygen lack or hemorrhage than are normal animals. It is evident that the sympathectomized animal could not fend for itself, and, in the struggle for existence, would soon succumb to the hazards of the environment. The sympathetic ganglionated chain has also been completely removed in man, thus abolishing all connection of the peripheral sympathetic system with the central nervous system, without producing any serious consequences.

Parasympathetic effects, rather than being characterized by a diffuse outburst of activity, as may result from sympathetic stimulation, are more localized in character. It has also been suggested that they are concerned with conservative and restorative processes, and the sympathetic with processes involving the expenditure of energy. Inhibition of the heart, contraction of the pupil for the protection of the eye from intense light and the activities of the digestive tract, through which the energy stores of the body are replenished, are frequently given as examples of acts of conservation presided over by the parasympathetic. These apparent differences in the activities of the two divisions have led some (following Gaskell) to speak of the functions of the sympathetic and parasympathetic divisions as *catabolic* and *anabolic*, respectively. It is an interesting but perhaps a too speculative generalization.

A summary of the actions of the autonomic system upon various structures is given in table 12.1.

Chemical (Humoral) Transmission of Nervous Impulses

Transmission of impulses from neuron to neuron, and from neuron to effector cell is accomplished by the elaboration of chemical substances by the nerves. The classical experiments of Otto Loewi, in 1921, first clearly demonstrated the existence of humoral mediators. Two frog hearts, arranged in standard fashion for recording contractions, were prepared so that the fluid perfusing one heart could come in contact with the second. Upon stimulation of the vagus nerve to the first heart, its rate of contraction was reduced. When the fluid perfusing this heart came in contact with the second it also slowed in rate although its vagus had not been stimulated. Some substance had obviously been released in the first heart which could be carried by the perfusing fluid to the second. Loewi termed this material "*Vagusstuffe*." By the same technique, stimulation of the cardiac accelerator nerve to the first heart increased its rate and also the rate of the second heart when the perfusing fluid reached the latter. This response Loewi attributed to the release of "*Acceleransstuffe*."

By various techniques, described below, "Vagusstuffe" has been shown to be acetylcholine, and "Acceleransstuffe" is identical with or related to epinephrine (adrenaline). In 1933, Sir Henry Dale proposed the terms *cholinergic* and *adrenergic* to describe the nerves which liberated acetylcholine or epinephrine (or related substances). The adjectives are also used to describe agents which cause effects similar to those produced by acetylcholine and epinephrine. Dale has also proposed that cells stimulated by cholinergic or adrenergic nerves be termed cholinoceptive and adrenoceptive respectively.

Acetylcholine is now recognized as the mediator of impulses at all autonomic ganglia, all parasympathetic postganglionic terminations, sympathetic postganglionic endings at sweat glands, and motor nerve endings at skeletal muscle. In these cholinergic nerve fibers acetylcholine is present in an inactive form (probably bound loosely with a protein or a lipoprotein) in morphologically discrete vesicles. Upon stimulation of the nerve the acetylcholine is set free and diffuses from the terminations. These same vesicles contain an enzyme, *cholineacetylase*, which is capable of synthesizing acetylcholine with great rapidity.[3] Which of these two mechanisms is the more important in releasing free acetylcholine remains unsolved.

Free acetylcholine is unstable; it is readily hydrolyzed to choline and acetic acid. This hydrolysis occurs almost instantaneously in the presence of *acetylcholinesterase*, an enzyme present at the termination of cholinergic nerves.[4] The enzyme is one of a group of hydrolytic enzymes, often referred to as cholinesterases, found in the body. Acetylcholinesterase, or *true* or *specific cholinesterase*, has acetylcholine as its preferred or only substrate, and is most effective when the amount of acetylcholine is small. The other (pseudo- or nonspecific) cholinesterases will utilize acetylcholine and other choline and non-choline esters as a substrate and are most effective in the presence of large quantities of acetylcholine.

Cholinesterases may be inhibited by a variety

---

[3] Cholineacetylase is very widely distributed in the nervous tissues, being found in brain, ganglia and peripheral nerves; it is also present in the placenta, but is absent from liver and kidney. For optimal activity this enzyme requires Mg^{++}, K^+ and Ca^{++} ions. The concentration of choline acetylase in nerve fibers declines during their degeneration, but some still remains even after the nerve has ceased to conduct.

[4] Acetylcholinesterase is also present in large amounts in erythrocytes, the chief source of the enzyme for experimental studies.

TABLE 12.1

Organ	Parasympathetic Effects	Origin of Sympathetic Postganglionic Fibers	Sympathetic Effects
Heart (ch. 44):	Inhibition	Superior, middle and inferior cervical ganglia	Acceleration
Vessels:			
Cutaneous (ch. 42 and 46)	Dilation†	Various paravertebral ganglia	Constriction
Muscular (see ch. 42 and 46)	—	Various paravertebral ganglia	Dilation or constriction
Coronary (see ch. 45)	Constriction	Cervical ganglia	Dilation
Salivary glands (ch. 56)	Dilation	Superior cervical ganglion	Constriction
Buccal mucosa	—	Superior cervical ganglion	Dilation
Pulmonary (see ch. 43)	Dilation†		Constriction†
Cerebral (see ch. 46)	—	—	—
Abdominal and pelvic viscera	—	Prevertebral ganglia	Constriction
External genitalia (ch. 78, p. 249)	Dilation	Prevertebral ganglia	Constriction
Eye:			
Iris (ch. 16)	Constriction	Superior cervical ganglion	Dilation
Ciliary muscle (ch. 16)	Contraction	Superior cervical ganglion	Relaxation
Smooth muscle of orbit and upper lid (ch. 16)	—	Superior cervical ganglion	Contraction
Nictitating membrane (cat and dog)	—	Superior cervical ganglion	Retraction
Bronchi:	Constriction	Thoracic ganglia	Dilation
Glands:			
Sweat (ch. 70)	—	Paravertebral ganglia	Secretion
Salivary (ch. 56)	Secretion	Superior cervical ganglia	Secretion
Gastric (ch. 57)	Secretion	Celiac ganglion	Inhibition?
Pancreas (ch. 58)			Secretion of mucus
Acini	Secretion	Celiac ganglion	—
Islets	Secretion	Celiac ganglion	—
Liver	—	Celiac ganglion	Glycogenolysis
Adrenal (ch. 76) medulla	—	No postganglionic fibers	Secretion
Smooth muscle:			
Of skin	—	Paravertebral ganglia	Contraction
Of stomach wall (ch. 62)	Contraction or inhibition	Celiac ganglion	Contraction or inhibition
Of small intestine (ch. 62)	Increased tone and motility	Celiac and superior mesenteric ganglia	Inhibition
Of large intestine (ch. 62)	Increased tone and motility	Inferior mesenteric and hypogastric ganglia	Inhibition
Of bladder wall (ch. 80) (detrusor muscle)	Contraction	Inferior mesenteric and hypogastric ganglia	Inhibition
Of trigone and sphincter	Inhibition	Inferior mesenteric and hypogastric ganglia	Contraction
Of uterus, pregnant	nil	Inferior mesenteric and hypogastric ganglia	Contraction
Of uterus, nonpregnant	nil		Inhibition

* With certain exceptions, e.g., those supplying the sublingual and parotid glands and the sphincter pupillae, the postganglionic fibers of the parasympathetic arise from cells situated in, or in close proximity to, the innervated organ itself.

† These effects are so slight that they are of virtually no functional importance.

of substances. Much of the knowledge about acetylcholine and nerve impulse transmission has been obtained only thrugh the ability of these agents to inhibit acetylcholinesterase. Physostigmine (eserine), an alkaloid extracted from the Calabar bean (*Physostigma venenosum*) was the first substance shown to inhibit these enzymes. Subsequently many synthetic inhibitors have been prepared, among them neostigmine (Prostigmin), di-isopropylfluorophosphate (DFP) and tetraethylpyrophosphate (TEPP). Physostigmine and neostigmine are reversible inhibitors; the enzyme is inactivated only so long as it is in combination with the inhibitor. As the latter is eliminated by the body, the enzyme once more becomes active. DFP and TEPP combine irreversibly with the enzyme, permanently inactivating it. Hence, for cholinesterase activity to be restored new enzyme must be synthesized.

Such minute amounts of the cholinergic mediator are liberated during impulse transmission, and the mediator is so rapidly broken down by acetylcholinesterase, that the identification of the mediator as acetylcholine is still largely indirect. The experimental methods used to identify acetylcholine are, however, sufficiently instructive to consider briefly. First, the effects of nerve stimulation may be compared with those of acetylcholine administration. Second, a modification of Loewi's original experiment, i.e., stimulation of the autonomic nerve to an organ or ganglion and testing the venous blood leaving it, or the fluid perfusing it, for acetylcholine activity on a suitable test preparation. In order to prevent hydrolysis of the acetylcholine after its liberation from the nerve terminals the animal must be given physostigmine or some other inhibitor, or the perfusing fluid must contain it. Five common qualitative tests for the detection of the mediator may be mentioned.

(1) Blood pressure of the cat. Dilation of the arterioles and a fall in blood pressure. The effect should be annulled by atropine. (2) Inhibition of the perfused frog's heart or rabbit's auricle annulled by atropine. (3) Contraction of the voluntary muscle (rectus abdominis) of the frog. (4) Contraction of the muscle in body wall of the eserinized leech. This test is sensitive to 2 μg. (gamma) of acetylcholine per liter. (5) The active substance should be inactivated by alkali or by blood (which contains cholinesterase). Comparison of the response of the test system (i.e., the blood pressure fall in the cat) to the perfusuate with the response to known amounts of acetylcholine makes it possible to quantitatively estimate the amount of acetylcholine actually liberated. Results of such studies coupled with the knowledge that acetylcholine is actually found in cholinergic nerves leaves little doubt that acetylcholine is the mediator.

Summary of Experimental Work Relating to the Role Played by Acetylcholine in the Transmission of Nervous Effects

1. Stimulation of the chorda tympani nerve to salivary glands. Babkin and his associates found that when the chorda of one side was stimulated a substance entered the blood which caused a fall in blood pressure and secretion from the denervated salivary gland of the opposite side. These effects were abolished by atropine. Similar results have been obtained by others. During stimulation of the chorda of a perfused salivary gland, for example, a substance identical in action with acetylcholine was found by Henderson and Roepke in the perfusion fluid.

2. The liberation of acetylcholine from parasympathetic endings in the iris. When a strong light was thrown into one eye, the other eye being shaded, an acetylcholinelike substance was obtained from the aqueous humor of the illuminated eye but not from the darkened eye (Engelhart).

3. Acetylcholine as an intermediary of parasympathetic effects to the alimentary tract and bladder. It has been shown that Ringer's solution in which a beating loop of intestine is immersed is capable of augmenting the activity of another similar loop (Weiland). It has also been found that if the vagus nerve to the intestine is stimulated and a loop then removed and suspended in Ringer's solution, the contractions of this loop are greater than those of a similar one which had not been previously excited in this manner. These experiments suggest that during intestinal activity a substance is liberated by the vagal endings which has an augmenting effect upon the contractions. Evidence for the liberation of acetylcholine by the gastric vagus has been obtained by Dale and Feldberg. A substance identical in action with acetylcholine was detected in the venous blood leaving the resting stomach or in the eserinized fluid perfusing its wall. During vagal stimulation the quantity of the active material was increased fourfold.

An acetylcholinelike substance has also been identified by Henderson and Roepke in the fluid perfusing the bladder during stimulation of its parasympathetic nerves. In the case of the intestine and bladder as in the case of vasodilator nerves, the same discrepancy exists between the action of atropine upon the effects of nerve stimulation and the action of the drug upon the effects of acetylcholine administration. Atropine abolishes the action of acetylcholine when applied artificially to these organs but does not depres the contractions set up by parasympathetic stimulation. Henderson and Roepke conclude from the results of their experiments that, whereas the tone of the intestine and of the bladder is dependent upon the liberation of a choline ester, another mechanism is responsible for the phasic contractions. Atropine, as is well known, depresses the tone of the intestinal and vesical musculatures but exerts no direct effect upon the contractile mechanism.

4. *The liberation of acetylcholine from sympathetic preganglionic fibers.* Feldberg and Gaddum perfused the superior cervical ganglion with eserinized fluid. The inflow cannula was inserted into the common carotid artery, all branches of which had been tied except the one to the ganglion. The fluid was collected from the internal jugular vein, all its tributaries except that from the ganglion having been occluded. During stimulation of the cervical sympathetic trunk below the ganglion the fluid issuing from the vein was found to possess an action identical with that of acetylcholine. When the collected fluid was passed through the ganglion of the opposite side its stimulant action upon this structure was evidenced by a contraction of the nictitating membrane. Fluid collected before or after the period of stimulation showed no such activity.

5. *Acetlycholine liberation during the discharge of adrenaline.* Stimulation of the sympathetic fibers supplying the adrenal medulla causes an acetylcholinelike substance to appear in the blood of the adrenal vein. It has therefore been concluded that acetylcholine acts as a chemical transmitter from the nerve terminals to the medullary cells. It will be recalled that the sympathetic fibers ending in the adrenal are preganglionic, the adrenal cell itself taking the place of the ganglion cell.

6. *Acetylcholine as the transmitter of effects to the sweat glands.* Although the human sweat glands are innervated by the sympathetic, their behavior to drugs is similar to that of structures supplied by the parasympathetic; they are unaffected by adrenaline, stimulated by pilocarpine, and paralyzed by atropine. An experiment by Dale and Feldberg gives an explanation of these discrepancies, or at any rate brings the mechanism of sweat secretion into the general scheme. Excitation of the sympathetic fibers to the foot pads of the cat was followed by sweating and the appearance of acetylcholine in the eserinized fluid perfusing the paw.

Knowledge of the chemistry of the adrenergic mediator has increased dramatically in recent years. Cannon and Bacq, in 1931, demonstrated that stimulation of adrenergic nerves liberated a substance into the circulation which they called "sympathin." Although many of the effects of sympathetic stimulation could be produced by the administration of epinephrine, Cannon and Rosenblueth were unable to demonstrate complete qualitative and quantitative identity between the two types of stimulation. They proposed the "sympathin theory" which is discussed elsewhere (ch. 76). Subsequent work has confirmed their idea that there is more than one type of adrenergic effector.

The confusion arising from much of the original work with the adrenergic mediators was related to the difficulty in separating epinephrine and norepinephrine and correctly identifying these substances. For example, the extracts of the adrenal medulla contain roughly 10% norepinephrine as a contaminant of what was thought to be pure epinephrine. Likewise, the current feeling is that norepinephrine is the only mediator liberated from sympathetic postganglionic nerve endings. While this may not be completely true, norepinephrine is found in high concentration, by current analytical techniques, in all terminations or tissues studied.

The synthesis of the adrenergic mediators from phenylalanine can proceed through a variety of pathways. There are vesicles present in adrenergic nerve terminations which apparently subserve the function of storage of norepinephrine and contain the enzyme *dopamine-β-oxidase* which converts dopamine to norepinephrine. However, most of the norepinephrine present in these vesicles comes from that which was liberated by the nerve ending, the substance diffusing back into the nerve and thence into the vesicles. Stromblad and Nickerson demonstrated that both epinephrine and norepinephrine, exogenously administered, could be stored in the tissues, and that the storage was less in chronic sympathetically denervated tissues, suggesting that the site of storage was in the nerve endings.

There is apparently more than one binding mechanism for catechol amines in nerve endings. *Tyramine*, which produces adrenergic effects by liberating norepinephrine, upon repeated injection soon fails to produce a response. However, at this point, stimulation of the nerve will again produce the response, and, provided there is no interference with synthesis or uptake of the catechol amine, upon repeated stimulation the response will be observed unimpaired.

The concept of the mobility of the adrenergic mediator, out of, and back into the nerve endings is important for an understanding of various drug effects and the duration of the effects of adrenergic nerve stimulation. For, compared to acetylcholine, the adrenergic mediators are inactivated relatively slowly.

Epinephrine was crystalized from adrenal medullary extracts by Abel in 1901. Since then it has been identified in other nervous tissue and found to be secreted at adrenoceptive effector cells. In 1946, Euler reported that adrenergic fibers contained another catecholamine, norephinephrine (levarterenol); the following year Bacq and Fischer found that some adrenergic fibers liberate only epinephrine, others only norepinephrine, and still others both epinephrine and norepinephrine. Isoproterenol (isopropylnorepinephrine) was found by Lockett, in 1956, in pulmonary venous blood following stimulation of the upper thoracic sympathetic chain.

The properties of the first two of these substances, found in the adrenal medulla, are described in chapter 58. The response of the effector cells is the same whether the mediators arrive by way of the circulation or whether they are released by nerve terminal endings on the cells.

At least four possible pathways of epinephrine metabolism have been described. (1) An enzyme, *monoamine oxidase*, is present throughout the body which is capable of oxidatively deaminating primary amines. Epinephrine and norepinephrine are substrates for this enzyme, although the reaction proceeds rather slowly. (2) Conjugation of epinephrine with glucuronic or sulfuric acid at the hydroxyl groups occurs, primarily in the liver and intestines. (3) The phenolic hydroxyl groups of epinephrine are readily oxidized, forming a quinone which in turn forms a cyclic structure *adrenochrome*. (4) Axelrod has demonstrated that the phenolic group in the meta position is methylated by the enzyme O-methyltransferase in the body. There is as yet, however, no evidence that any of these inactivating mechanisms is the one primarily responsible for terminating adrenergic effects. Rather, it seems that the termination of adrenergic effects results from the diffusion of the mediator from the effector site into the nerve termination.

The concept of specific receptors, first proposed by Dale in 1906, aids in understanding the rather complex responses to sympathetic stimulation or epinephrine administration. Noting that epinephrine caused some smooth muscle to contract, while it relaxed others, he proposed that the former had "motor" type receptors while the latter had "inhibitory" type receptors. Ahlquist has divided the adrenergic receptors into two types. Alpha (α) receptors are those associated with vasoconstriction, myocardial ectopic excitation, myometrial contraction, nictitating membrane contraction, intestinal relaxation, iris dilator muscle contraction, pilomotor contraction, and glycogenolysis. Beta (β) receptors are those concerned with vasodilation, cardioacceleration, myocardial augmentation, myometrial relaxation and bronchial relaxation. Furchgott has presented evidence which indicates that with vascular smooth muscle, at least, individual cells may contain both α and β *receptors*.

Norepinephrine appears to stimulate only α-receptors, isoproterenol only β-receptors, and epinephrine is capable of stimulating both. Epinephrine is 2 to 10 times more potent than norepinephrine in stimulating the alpha receptors. Isoproterenol is 2 to 10 times more potent than epinephrine in stimulating the beta receptors and 100 or more times more active than norepinephrine. Therefore, although epinephrine is the more potent agent as a vasoconstrictor, norepinephrine may produce a greater rise in blood pressure for a given dose, since it has no or little effect on vasodilator fibers.

Euler claims that norepinephrine is most commonly found as the mediator in adrenergic nerves. If this is true it readily explains the observed discrepancies between the effects of epinephrine administration and sympathetic nerve stimulation.

From the information now available it is possible to construct the mechanism by which the autonomically innervated effectors are stimulated (fig. 12.4). Impulses leave the central nervous system by way of cholinergic preganglionic fibers which terminate at ganglionic cells. In the sympathetic division these neurons are collected in anatomically discrete bodies. The parasympathetic ganglion cells are rarely discrete, being located usually within the organ innervated. In either case, acetylcholine is liberated from the preganglionic terminals where it is free to act upon the receptor sites of the ganglion cell. This combination of acetylcholine with receptor results in a loss of membrane integrity and the potential difference between the interior and exterior of the cell disappears. The electrical activity associated with this "depolarization" is of sufficient intensity to disrupt the continuity of the adjacent membrane, and the impulse is propagated along the postganglionic fiber. As long as the acetylcholine is bound to the receptor site, the membrane at that point remains deplorized. However, the acetylcholinesterase present at the synapse immediately (less than 1 msec.) destroys the acetylcholine and the polarity of the neuronal membrane is restored. By this mechanism each preganglionic impulse liberates acetylcholine which in turn initiates a postganglionic impulse.

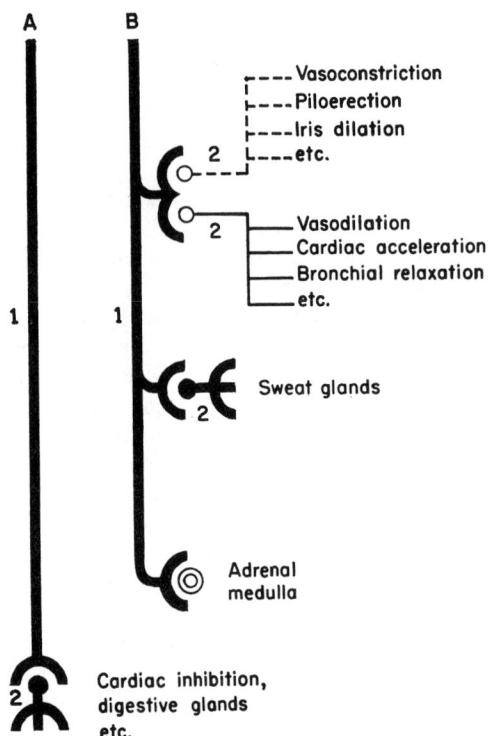

Fig. 12.4. Diagram showing the distribution of cholinergic and adrenergic fibers, A, parasympathetic; B, sympathetic; 1, preganglionic; 2, postganglionic, heavy lines, cholinergic; light lines, adrenergic.

The limiting factor in rate of transmission seems to be the refractory period of the nerve fiber.

Obviously, substances which will prevent access of acetylcholine to the ganglion cell receptors, or which will cause prolonged depolarization of the nerve membrane will block ganglionic synaptic transmission.

The impulse travels down the postganglionic fiber as described and releases a humoral agent at its terminal. If the fiber is parasympathetic or sympathetic to the sweat glands, acetylcholine is the mediator released. This substance then combines with specific receptors on the effector cell to produce the characteristic response of that cell.

If the postganglionic fiber supplies other sympathetically innervated structures, norepinephrine, is liberated from the terminals. In the case of the adrenal medulla, which may be considered to be composed of ganglion cells without axons, epinephrine and norepinephrine are liberated into the blood. The other postganglionic sympathetic neurons liberate the mediator in close proximity to the effector cell.

Drugs Acting on the Autonomic Nervous System

Many agents are capable of eliciting or modifying responses of the autonomic nervous system. A brief survey of the types of drugs used for these effects may help further to understand the function of the autonomic nervous system.

Drugs Acting at the Ganglion

The alkaloid *nicotine* was the first compound found to stimulate postganglionic fibers. The delineation of this effect led to the term "nicotinic" used to describe the effect of acetylcholine on the ganglion cell. In recent years, a number of synthetic compounds have been found to possess ganglion stimulating properties including *carbaminoylcholine, decamethonium* and *tetramethylammonium bromide*. Obviously little therapeutic advantage would be obtained from the stimulation of all postganglionic fibers which would result from the administration of such an agent. However, these substances are useful as experimental tools.

The blockade of ganglionic transmission is a more desirable therapeutic end. Again *nicotine* was the first substance known to cause such an effect. The paradox of the same substance causing two opposing effects is resolved when it is understood that far larger quantities of the drug are necessary to block than to stimulate. The mechanism of action in both cases seems to be that nicotine, like acetylcholine, initiates a response in the postganglionic fibers by depolarizing the nerve membrane. With large amounts of the alkaloid the depolarization is prolonged, preventing repolarization of the neuron, and hence preventing subsequent discharges. Even though acetylcholine is released by the preganglionic termination, it cannot initiate transmission in the postganglionic fiber. The dual nature of the action of nicotine, as well as its effect on skeletal muscle, makes it of little clinical usefulness. Its ganglionic actions are responsible for many of the side effects of the use of tobacco.

Tetraethylammonium chloride (TEA) blocks ganglionic transmission by combining with the acetylcholine receptors of the postganglionic neuron without depolarizing the cell membrane. In this instance the liberated acetylcholine cannot gain access to the receptor site to initiate depolarization. Other ganglionic blocking agents, hexamethonium, pentamethonium, pentolinium (Ansolysen), mecamylamine (Inversine), trimethaphan (Arfonad) and others, produce effects similar to those of TEA. There may be minor differences in mechanisms of action, and they may vary in the duration of their action; however, the qualitative nature of their responses is similar.

The effects of ganglionic blockade can be predicted readily. Depending upon the degree of blockage there will be depression to complete paralysis of autonomic function. This will result in such effects as interference with vision (accomodation and pupillary size), postural hypotension, etc. It must be remembered that the autonomic system is composed of two functional units which frequently antagonize each other to varying extent depending upon the demands made upon the body. No response to the administration of a ganglionic blocker may be observed until some demand is placed upon the autonomic system (e.g., hypotension following change from a recumbent to a standing position). On the other hand, where there is a great deal of autonomic activity (as in hypertension of sympathetic origin) the administration of a drug such as tetraethylammonium may produce a dramatic and immediate response (in this case a decrease in blood pressure). This is not the result of the drug initiating a response but rather of blocking existing physiological activity.

Drugs Acting at Cholinoceptive Effectors

There are relatively few substances which will mimic the effects of acetylcholine liberation at autonomic effectors. The alkaloid *muscarine* from the poisonous mushroom *Amanita muscaria* was the first such substance isolated. From its effect came the adjective *muscarinic* which has been used to describe the actions of acetylcholine at the effector cells. It is now of only toxicological importance. *Acetyl-β-methacholine* (Methacholine, Mecholyl), possesses the actions of acetylcholine. It is destroyed by acetylcholinesterase but not by the nonspecific cholinesterase. When given in sufficiently large amounts its effects are, therefore, somewhat more prolonged than those of acetylcholine. *Carbaminoyl-β-methylcholine* (bethanecol, Urecholine) is similar to methacholine in its actions (at cholinoceptive effector cells) with the exception that it is not destroyed by cholinesterase. Consequently its actions may persist for hours. *Carbaminoylcholine* (Carbachol, Doryl) also stimulates cholinergically innervated effectors. In addition, as mentioned above, it also stimulates ganglionic cells. Like bethanecol, it is not subject to hydrolysis by cholinesterase. *Pilocarpine*, a naturally occurring alkaloid, was at one time an important therapeutic agent that stimulates cholinoceptive effectors directly. Like muscarine, it was of great help in elucidating the dynamics of autonomic function. Despite its long history relatively little is known of its mechanism of action, and its use today is limited chiefly to its local effects upon the eyes.

Many drugs block the stimulation of effector cells by cholinergic agents. The prototype of the group is *atropine*, an alkaloid found in several species of the potato family. The classical source is *Atropa belladonna* (deadly nightshade). A chemical isomer, *scopolamine*, also occurs naturally and has the same effect upon cholinergic transmission. These two agents are essentially interchangeable both quantitatively and qualitatively in their effects upon the autonomic nervous system. Dozens of synthetic compounds, similar to atropine in action, are available. None is as potent (in terms of amount required to produce a given effect) as the natural alkaloids, and they vary one from another in their duration of action and affinity for certain types of effectors. This permits some selectivity in blocking cholinergic responses.

Atropine and its congeners combine reversibly with the receptor site to prevent access of cholinergic substances to the effector cell. As with the ganglionic blockers, acetylcholine is released from their nerve endings, but no response is elicited. The effects produced by atropine are those of interference with parasympathetic function and sweating. Consequently a patient who has received atropine shows exaggerated sympathetic effects, such as tachycardia, decreased intestinal motility, mydirasis, etc. These are not direct responses to atropine but rather the result of blockade of normal physiological antagonism to sympathetic functions.

Drugs Acting at Adrenoceptive Effectors

The effects of epinephrine and norepinephrine have already been discussed (ch. 76). Unlike acetylcholine, these substances are inactivated relatively slowly and hence may be administered exogenously to produce their characteristic responses. However, the administration of a single dose of one of these drugs produces, therapeutically speaking, a transient response. Other drugs are available which produce various adrenergic responses for longer duration.

Ephedrine is an alkaloid from the Asiatic plant *ma huang*. It causes many of the cardiovascular effects of sympathetic stimulation, apparently affecting both alpha and beta receptors for it will increase blood pressure, dilate the pupil, relax the bronchioles, etc. Enough differences exist between the actions of ephedrine and epinephrine to suggest that ephedrine acts directly on the effector cells and indirectly on the nerve terminations to release norepinephrine. It also produces central nervous system excitation, and is at times used to counteract central depression.

Many other adrenergic compounds have been synthesized. Minor chemical variations in some cases cause marked changes in the nature of the response produced. By making appropriate chemical modifications, drugs have been prepared which have primarily only one or two of the actions of epinephrine. The variety of drugs employed and the relationships involved in their actions is prop-

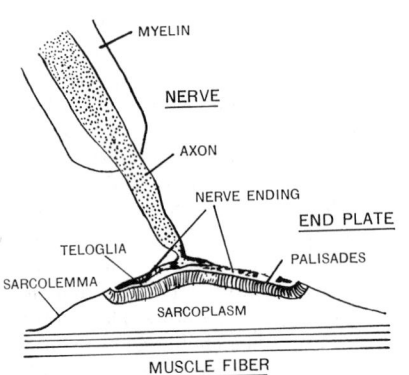

FIG. 12.5. Diagram of the region of the muscle end-plate (from Acheson after Couteaux).

erly the scope of pharmacology and is too extensive a subject for review here.

Certain alkaloids (ergotamine, ergocristine, etc.) found in ergot were found by Dale early in this century to block the pressor effects of epinephrine. In recent years a number of synthetic drugs have been prepared which will block α-receptors selectively. Most widely used of this group are *piperoxan* (Benodaine) *phenoxybenzamine* (Dibenzyline), *phentolamine* (Regitene), and *azapetine* (Ilidar).[5]

More recently drugs capable of blocking β-receptors have been synthesized, including *dichlorisoproterenol* (DCI) and *pronethalol*. To date the clinical usefulness of this type of drug is limited, but they have been useful tools with which to study the sympathetic nervous system.

As with atropinelike drugs, the adrenergic blockers do not of themselves initiate responses, but effects are seen following their administration which are the result of disrupting the balance between the two divisions of the autonomic system or reducing excessive sympathetic activity.

Transmission at the Myoneural Junction

The transmission of impulses at the myoneural junction is accomplished in much the same fashion as synaptic transmission. Acetylcholine, liberated from the nerve ending, reacts with the muscle end-plate to depolarize it and initiate contraction of the actomyosin fibers (fig. 12.5). Acetylcholinesterase immediately inactivates the acetylcholine, the muscle end-plate repolarizes, and the situation is favorable for reception of another nerve impulse and initiation of another muscular contraction.

Evidence that acetylcholine is liberated from

[5] Many other compounds recently introduced into therapeutics produced limited adrenergic blockade which causes "undesirable side effects" at times.

the terminals of motor nerves and serves as a transmitter of impulses to the muscle fibers has been obtained by Dale and his associates.

1. Upon rhythmical stimulation of the hypoglossal nerve of the perfused tongue of the cat, acetylcholine appeared consistently in the venous fluid. Similar results were secured with the perfused leg muscles of the dog during stimulation of the ventral spinal roots after excision of the lumbar sympathetic chain.

2. The sudden injection of a small dose (2 to 10 μg.) of acetylcholine into the artery supplying the gastrocnemius of the cat during circulatory arrest caused a sharp contraction of the muscle. It is annulled by curarine but not by atropine. The direct application of a minute amount (5×10^{-6} μg.) of acetylcholine to the motor end-plate of the muscle fiber causes a short sharp tetanic contraction. Ten times this quantity applied elsewhere to the fiber is ineffective (Buchthal and Lindhard).

3. The intravenous administration of eserine (0.2 to 0.3 mg. per kg.) to a spinal cat caused an increase of 130 per cent in tension of a gastrocnemius twitch provoked by stimulation of the motor nerve. Eserine had no such effect upon the response of denervated muscle to direct stimulation.

Drugs Acting at the Myoneural Junction

Although acetylcholine is the humoral mediator at the junction of motor nerves with skeletal muscle, the other choline esters mentioned above, muscarine and pilocarpine, have no effect at this site. Nicotine is capable of both stimulating and paralyzing the motor end-plate in a manner similar to its action at the ganglia. Neostigmine and *edrophonium* (Tensilon) are capable of potentiating muscular activity, and in larger doses will produce fasciculations as a result of direct stimulation (depolarization) of the motor end-plate. Obviously direct chemical stimulation of muscle fibers is not of therapeutic, but only of toxicologic, importance.

The inhibitors of myoneural conduction are of more importance. The inhibition may be of two types. *d*-Tubo-curarine and its derivatives, as well as the synthetic drugs *gallamine* and *benzoquinonium* paralyze skeletal muscle by blocking access of acetylcholine to the motor endplate. Depolarization cannot occur and contraction cannot be initiated. This blockage is reversible, and to a limited extent paralysis with these agents can be overcome by the administration of a cholinesterase inhibitor (such as physostigmine or neostigmine) which will permit the released acetylcholine to increase to the point that it will "drive the curare molecules from the receptors." *Neostigmine* and *edrophonium*, in addition to their cholinesterase inhibiting action, are direct stimulants to these cholinergic receptors and will reverse curare paralysis directly. A second type of inhibitor, or muscle relaxant, is exemplified by compounds such as *succinylcholine* or *decamethonium*. These agents combine with the receptor site and cause depolarization. Since the compounds are relatively slowly inactivated, the membrane does not repolarize so that impulses cannot be transmitted from the nerve ending, even though acetylcholine is being released. There is no way in which this blockade may be reversed other than permitting the drug to be inactivated. Both succinylcholine and decamethonium are rather promptly inactivated by the tissues.

Myasthenia gravis. This condition, as its name implies, is a condition of profound weakness of the muscles, those of the eyes, face and throat being, as a rule, involved first. Collections of lymphocytes (lymphorrhages) and degenerative changes occur in the muscles. The disease is accompanied by a high degree of creatinuria and a reduction in the excretion of creatinine. The thymus is frequently enlarged, and myasthenia gravis is a frequent accompaniment of thymic tumors. Administered creatine is practically all excreted as such. Death results from involvement of the respiratory muscles. Myasthenia gravis is associated sometimes with thyrotoxicosis in which enlargement of the thymus is also commonly seen.

In 1934 Walker described a dramatic improvement in a case of myasthenia gravis following the administration of eserine; later prostigmine was found to confer even greater benefit. The effect, unfortunately, is transient, lasting for no longer than 3 or 4 hours. Other anticholinesterases like diisopropylfluorophosphate (DFP) have since been employed; the latter agent, though it has a more lasting effect is otherwise inferior to prostigmine or neostigmine. The first drug to be used with benefit was ephedrine, introduced by Edgeworth in 1930, who was herself a victim of the disease.

The muscular weakness is myasthenia gravis is not due to any disease of the central nervous system, nerve trunks, or muscles but, as shown by Harvey and his associates, to some defect at the myoneural junction. With regard to the nature of the junctional disorder, the action of cholinesterases suggests three possibilities, namely (a) deficiency of acetylcholine production, (b) the presence of excessive amounts of cholinesterase, or (c) the production of a substance with a curarelike action. The investigations of Wilson and Stoner point to the last mentioned as the most likely factor. They found no increase in the cholinesterase content of the blood in subjects of the disease, nor any evidence of a failure in acetylcholine synthesis, but the serum of patients suffering from the disease, but not under treatment with prostigmine, caused neuromuscular block in the nerve-muscle preparation of the frog. Serum from patients receiving prostigmine treatment exerted no curarelike action. With the idea that the primary fault originates in the thymus, thymectomy has been resorted to in some instances, with apparently beneficial results.

The Role of Humoral Transmission in the Central Nervous System

There is currently much controversy over the nature of synaptic transmission in the central nervous system. Acetylcholine is involved, but is apparently not the only transmitter. The prevailing concept is that where acetylcholine is involved its mechanism of action is similar to that at the autonomic ganglia. Where acetylcholine is not the transmitter, other substances have been suggested; including levarterenol (or "sympathin"), 5-hydroxytryptamine, histamine and adenosine triphosphate (ATP).

The role of acetylcholine is suggested by the following observations.

1. Feldberg and Vogt found varying concentrations of choline acetylase in different regions of the central nervous system belonging to the same afferent or efferent pathway. They attributed this variation to alternate distribution of cholinergic and noncholinergic neurons. For example, the retina of the dog contains large amounts of choline acetylase, the optic nerve very little, and the lateral geniculate body (where next neuron in the pathway begins) again large amounts.

2. Acetylcholine content of the brain varies with the degree of functional activity. Richter and Crossland have shown that during deep anesthesia the concentration of acetylcholine in rat brains is three times as great as during convulsions. The concentration returned to normal in 10 seconds after cessation of the convulsions.

3. Acetylcholine has been found in the eserinized venous outflow of the isolated cat's brain and in eserinized Ringer's solution which was perfused through the lower end of the spinal cord of the dog. In the latter instance, stimulation of the central end of the divided sciatic nerve increased the concentration of acetylcholine during the period of reflex activity (Bülbring and Burn).

4. Acetylcholine is found in cerebrospinal fluid by a variety of techniques, and it has been observed to transude from the cerebral cortex. This transudation decreases concomitantly with a decrease in electrical activity of the cortex as the depth of anesthesia is increased. Undercutting of the cortex (leading to a "silent cortex") stops the production of acetylcholine (MacIntosh and Oborin).

The evidence for the existence of noncholinergic chemical transmission is more tenuous.

1. Eccles has demonstrated, by intracellular re-

cording, that the electrical activity at synapses can be accounted for only on the basis of a mediator and that this mediator at certain synapses is not acetylcholine.

2. As mentioned, Feldberg and Vogt have demonstrated uneven distribution of acetylcholine in the central nervous system. The cerebellum is notably deficient in both acetylcholine and choline acetylase. Yet extracts of cerebellum injected into the carotid artery have been found to increase electrical activity of the cerebellum. No claim is made that this substance, as yet unidentified, is a mediator, but it seemingly would fulfill the requirements of a central transmitter.

3. 5-Hydroxytryptamine (serotonin) is irregularly distributed in the brain. This agent, as well as drugs which will liberate it and drugs which antagonize its actions peripherally, can elicit pronounced central effects. The objections to its role as a mediator result first from the fact that it is found in those areas also high in acetylcholine concentration, where presumably acetylcholine is functioning as a mediator. Second, drugs which have opposing central effects (such as amphetamine which is a stimulant and reserpine which is a depressant) produce identical quantitative changes in 5-hydroxytryptamine concentrations in the brain.

4. Levarterenol is also irregularly distributed in the brain. Like 5-hydroxytryptamine it is found in highest concentrations in those areas rich in acetylcholine. It has been demonstrated to modify synaptic transmission, but there is little evidence to justify assigning it a primary role in noncholinergic transmission.

No unifying statement may be made of the mechanism of humoral transmission within the central nervous system. That such transmission must exist seems assured. Likewise, it must in part be cholinergic. The identity of other mediators, or what functions are served by the substances found in the brain which are active elsewhere in the body, remains to be elucidated.

REFERENCES

AHLQUIST, R. P. Am. J. Physiol., 1948, 153, 586.

AXELROD, J. Science, 1957, 126, 400.

BABKIN, B. P., ALLEY, A. AND STAVRAKY, G. W. Trans. Roy. Soc. Can., 1932, 26, Sec. V, 89.

BACQ, Z. M. AND FISCHER, P. Arch. internat. physiol., 1947, 55, 73.

BEUTNER, R. AND BARNES, T. C. Science, 1941, 94, 211. Biodynamics, 1942, 4, 47.

BEYER, K. H. AND SHAPIRO, S. H. Am. J. Physiol., 1945, 144, 321.

BEZNÁK, A. B. L. J. Physiol., 1934, 82, 129.

BROCK, L. C., COOMBS, J. S. AND ECCLES, J. C. J. Physiol., 1952, 117, 431.

BRONK, D. W. AND ASSOCIATES. Am. J. Physiol., 1938, 123, 24. J. Neurophysiol., 1939 2, 380.

BUCHTHAL, F. AND LINDHARD, J. J. Physiol., 1937, 90, 82 P.

BULBRING, E. AND BURN, J. H. J. Physiol., 1941, 100.

CANNON, W. B. Lancet, 1930, 1, 1109. CANNON, W. B. AND ASSOCIATES. Am. J. Physiol., 1929, 89, 84. Ibid., 1931, 97, 319, also, MOORE, R. M. A. Res. Nerv. & Ment. Dis., Proc., 1930, 9, 385.

CANNON, W. B. AND BACQ, Z. M. Am. J. Physiol., 1931, 96, 392.

CANNON, W. B. AND ROSENBLUETH, A. Am. J. Physiol., 1933, 104, 557.

CANTONI, G. L. AND LOEWI, O. J. Pharmac., 1944, 81, 67.

CHANG, H. C. AND ASSOCIATES. Chinese J. Physiol., 1938, 13, 153.

CHUTE, A. L., FELDBERG, W. AND SMYTH, D. H. Quart. J. Exper. Physiol., 1940, 30, 65.

COLE, K. S. AND CURTIS, H. J. J. Gen. Physiol., 1940, 24, 551.

CROSSLAND, J. The problem of non-cholinergic transmission in the central nervous system, in Metabolism of the Nervous System, D. Richter, Ed., Pergamon Press, 1957.

DALE, H. H. J. Physiol., 1906, 34, 163. Pharmacol. Rev., 1954, 6, 7. Lancet, 1929, 1, 1179: 1233, 1285. J. Physiol., 1933, 80, 10 P. Brit. M. J., 1934, 2, 1161.

DALE, H. H. AND DUDLEY, H. W. J. Physiol., 1929, 68, 97.

DALE, H. H. AND FELDBERG, W. J. Physiol., 1934, 81, 320. Ibid., 82, 121.

DALE, H. H. AND ASSOCIATES. J. Physiol., 81, 39 P. Ibid., 1936, 86, 353. Ibid., 87, 394. Ibid., p. 42 P.

DU BOIS-REYMOND, E. H. Gesamelte Abhandl. Z. Muskel-u. Nervenphysik. Leipzig, 1877. (Quoted by Dale.)

ECCLES, J. C. Ann. Rev. Physiol., 1948, 10, 93.

EDGEWORTH, H. J. A. M. A., 1930, 94, 1136; 1933, 100, 1401.

ELLIOTT, T. R. J. Physiol., 1904, 31, 20; 1905, 32, 401.

ENGELHART, E. Arch. ges. Physiol., 1931, 227, 220.

ERLANGER, J. J. Neurophysiol., 1939, 2, 370.

EULER, U. S. v. Acta physiol. scandinav., 1946, 12, 73.

EULER, U. S. v. Nor adrenaline. In Metabolism of the Nervous System, D. Richter, Ed., Pergamon Press, 1957.

FELDBERG, W., see under Monographs and Reviews.

FELDBERG, W. AND BROWN, G. L. Ibid., 1935, 84, 12 P. Differential paralysis of the superior cervical ganglion. Ibid., 1936, 86, 10 P. Ibid., p. 290.

FELDBERG, W. AND GADDUM, J. H. J. Physiol., 1934, 81, 305.

FELDBERG, W. AND VARTAINEN, A. J. Physiol., 1934, 83, 103.

FELDBERG, W. AND VOGT, M. J. Physiol., 1948, 107, 372.

FORBES, A. J. Neurophysiol., 1939, 2, 465.

FURCHGOTT, R. F. J. Pharmacol. & Exper. Therap. 1954, 111, 265.

GERARD, R. W. Ann. New York Acad. Sc., 1946, 47, 575.

HARVEY, A. M. AND ASSOCIATES. Bull. Johns Hopkins Hosp., 1941, **69**, 1, 529, 546.

HARVEY, A. M. AND MacINTOSH, F C. J. Physiol., 1938, **97**, 408.

HAWKINS, R. D. AND MENDEL, B. J. Cell. & Comp. Physiol., 1946, **27**, 69.

HENDERSON, V. E. AND ROEPKE, M. H. J. Pharmacol. & Exper. Therap., 1933, **47**, 193. Ibid., 1934, **51**, 97.

HENDERSON, W. R. AND WILSON, W. C. Quart. J. Exper. Physiol., 1936, **26**, 83.

HOET, J. C. J. Physiol., 1925, **60**, x.

LaBROSSE, E. H., AXELROD, J. AND KETY, S. S. Science, 1958, **128**, 573.

LEARMONTH, J. R. Brain, 1931, **54**, 147.

LOCKETT, M. F. Brit. J. Pharmacol., 1954, **9**, 498.

LOCKETT, M. F. J. Physiol., 1956, **133**, 73 P.

LORENTE DE NÓ, R. J. Cell. & Comp. Physiol., 1944, **24**, 85.

MacINTOSH, F. C. AND OBORIN, P. E. Abstr. 15th Int. Physiol. Cong. 1953, 380.

MARNEY, A. AND NACHMANSOHN, D. J. Physiol., 1938, **92**, 37.

NACHMANSOHN, D. Yale J. Biol. & Med., 1940, **12**, 565. Vitamins and Hormones. 1945, **3**, 337. Ann. New York Acad. Sc., 1946, **47**, 392. Rôle of acetylcholine in conduction. Bull. Johns Hopkins Hosp., 1948, **85**, 463. See also under Monographs and Reviews.

QUASTEL, J. H., TENNEBAUM, M. AND WHEATLEY, A. H. M. Biochem. J., 1936, **30**, 1668.

RANSON, S. W. AND BILLINGSLEY, P. R. J. Comp. Neurol. 1918, **29**, 313: 359.

RICHTER, D. AND CROSSLAND, J. Am. J. Physiol., 1949, **159**, 247.

SMITHWICK, R. H. New England J. Med., 1947, **236**, 662.

WILSON, A. AND STONER, H. B. Quart. J. Med., 1944, **13**, 1.

Monographs and Reviews

Association for Research in Nervous and Mental Disease. Vol. 9. The vegetative nervous system. The Williams & Wilkins Company, Baltimore, 1930.

BAYLISS, W. M. The vaso-motor system. Longmans, Green & Company, London, 1923.

BLASCHKO, H. Pharmacol. Rev., 1952, **4**, 415.

BROWN, G. L. Physiol. Rev., 1937, **17**, 486.

BURN, J. H. Physiol. Rev., 1945, **25**, 377.

CANNON, W. B. The wisdom of the body. W. W. Norton & Company, Inc., New York, 1932.

CANNON, W. B. Bodily changes in pain, hunger, fear and rage. Appleton, New York, 1920.

CANNON, W. B. Physiol. Rev., 1929, **9**, 399.

COMROE, J. H. AND ASSOC., Am. J. Med. Sc., 1946, **212**, 641.

DALE, H. H. Bull. Johns Hopkins Hosp., 1933, **53**, 297. Harvey Lectures, 1936-7, Ser. **32**, 229.

ECCLES, J. C. Physiol. Rev., 1937, **17**, 538. Ann. New York Acad. Sc., 1946, 47, 429. Ann. Rev. Physiol., 1948, **10**, 93.

EULER, U. S. v. Pharmacol. Rev., 1954, **6**, 1.

FELDBERG, W. Physiol. Rev., 1945, **25**, 596. Brit. M. Bull., 1949-50, **6**, 1531.

FURCHGOTT, R. F. Pharmacol. Rev., 1955, **7**, 183.

GASK, G. E. AND ROSS, J. P. The surgery of the sympathetic nervous system. The Williams & Wilkins Company, Baltimore, 1934.

GASKELL, W. H. The involuntary nervous system. Longmans, Green & Company, London, 1920.

GASSER, H. S. Physiol. Rev., 1930, **10**, 35.

KUNTZ, A. The autonomic nervous sytem. Lea & Febiger, Philadelphia, 1934.

LANDS, A. M. Pharmacol. Rev., 1949, **1**, 279.

LANGLEY, J. N. The autonomic nervous system. Heffer, Cambridge University Press, 1921.

LOEWI, O. Harvey Lectures, 1932-33, **28**, 218.

LOEWI, O. Proc. Roy. Soc., London. ser. B 1935, **118**, 229.

NACHMANSOHN, D., in The Hormones, PINCUS, G. AND THIMANN, K. V., Eds. Academic Press, 1948.

NACHMANSOHN, D. AND ASSOCIATES. Bull. Johns Hopkins Hosp., 1948, **85**, 463.

PARKER, G. H. Humoral agents in nervous activity. Cambridge University Press, 1932.

RANSON, S. W. Physiol. Rev., 1921, **1**, 477.

RIKER, W. F., JR. Pharmacol. Rev., 1953, **5**, 1.

ROSENBLUETH, A. The transmission of sympathetic nerve impulses. Physiol. Rev., 1937, **17**, 514.

Symposium on Neurohumoral Transmission, Pharmacol. Rev., 1954, **6**, 1.

TAYLOR, D. B. Pharmacol. Rev., 1951, **3**, 412.

TRENDELENBURG, U. Pharmacol. Rev., 1963, **15**, 225.

WELSH AND ASSOCIATES. Fed. Proc., 1948, **7**, 435.

WHITE, J. C. The autonomic nervous system. Macmillan Company, New York, 1935.

WHITTERIDGE, D. J. Neurol. Neurosurg. & Psychiat., 1948, **9**, 134.

ZAIMIS, E. Pharmacology of the autonomic nervous system. Ann. Rev. Pharmacol., 1964, **4**, 365.

II

THE SPECIAL SENSES

CHAPTER 13

The Physiology of Vision

Structure of the Eye

ANATOMICAL OUTLINE OF THE EYE

The human eyeball (bulb or globe of the eye) is approximately spherical, being slightly flattened from above down (see figure 13.1). In the adult it measures about 24 mm. in its anteroposterior and transverse diameters and 23.5 mm. in its vertical diameter. It is compounded of the segments of two spheres, its posterior five-sixths being the large segment of a sphere with a radius of about 8 mm. The center of the anterior curvature of the eyeball is called its *anterior pole* and the corresponding point on the posterior surface the *posterior pole*. A straight line joining the two poles is known as the *optic axis*. The visual axis passes through the cornea a little to the nasal side of its center of curvature and the fovea centralis; the optic and visual axes therefore cross at a point a little behind the center of the lens.[1] The circumference of the eyeball midway between the two poles is termed the *equator*. Any imaginary circle drawn to pass through both poles of the eye is called a *meridian*. The *optic nerve* enters the eyeball a little to the inner side of the posterior pole (see *optic disk*, p. 267). The optic axes are nearly parallel, converging only slightly behind, whereas the optic nerves followed backward converge more sharply to the optic chiasma.

A thin fibrous membrane—the *fascia bulbi* or *capsule of Tenon*—encloses the globe from the entrance of the optic nerve to just behind the circumference of the cornea, where it blends with the outer (sclerotic) coat of the eyeball. The fascia bulbi is pierced a little in front of the equator of the globe by the ocular muscles; it blends with the sheaths of these muscles. Fascial slips (*check ligaments*) pass from the muscle sheaths, especially those of the external and internal recti, to the walls of the orbit and serve, it is believed, to check the movements of the muscles. In the region surrounding the optic nerve entrance the fascia bulbi is pierced by the ciliary vessels and nerves and just behind the equator by the vortex veins. The space between the fascia bulbi and the globe is occupied by a meshwork of fine areolar tissue, the eyeball thus lies in a cushioned socket, separated from the other contents of the orbit.

The exposed part of the eyeball is covered by delicate mucous membrane—the *conjunctiva*—

which is reflected onto the inner surfaces of the eyelids. The conjunctival surfaces are lubricated and kept clean by a film of fluid secreted by the *lacrimal gland* (fig. 13.2). The lacrimal gland is about the size and shape of a shelled almond. It lies under the shelter of the bone forming the upper and outer part of the orbit (i.e., the zygomatic process of the frontal bone). It is of the racemose type, somewhat resembling in structure a serous salivary gland; its secretion—the tears—is delivered through a number of fine ducts into the conjunctival fornix. The secretion is a clear watery, slightly hypertonic fluid having, according to Ridley, the following composition.

	per cent
Water	98.2
Total solids	1.8
Ash	1.05
Total N	0.158
Nonprotein N	0.051
Urea	0.03
Protein (albumin and globulin)	0.669
Sugar	0.65
Chlorides (as NaCl)	0.658
Sodium as Na_2O	0.60
Potassium as K_2O	0.14
Ammonia	0.005

A sample of tears collected from the conjunctival surface contains traces of mucus secreted by the conjunctiva itself. The tears also contain the bacteriolytic enzyme lysozyme (ch. 56).

Several small accessory lacrimal glands are situated in the conjunctival fornices: their secretion suffices for lubrication and cleansing under ordinary circumstances. The main glands are called into play only upon special occasions, e.g., irritation of the conjunctiva, as a result of pain, certain emotional states, such as grief, disappointment, anger, etc., and during the acts of yawning and coughing.

The blinking movements of the lids spread the tears over the conjunctival surfaces; the fluid is directed into the *lacrimal lake*—a small triangular area lying in the angle bounded by the innermost portions of the lids. The center of the lacrimal lake is occupied by a small pink structure, the lacrimal caruncle, composed of modified skin and containing sebaceous glands and a few slender hairs. The tears are drained from the lacrimal lake by two small tubes—the *lacrimal ducts*. The minute orifices of the latter—the *puncta lacrimalia*—may be seen, one on the margin of each lid. The lacrimal

---

[1] The angle formed by the intersection of the optic axis with the visual axis is about 5° and is referred to as the *angle alpha*.

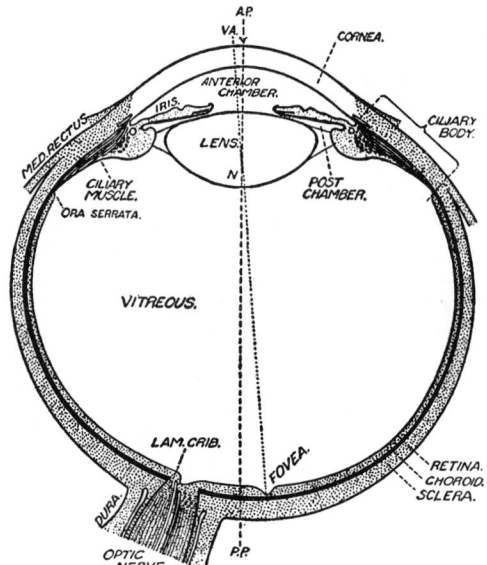

FIG. 13.1. Horizontal section of the right eye. P. P. posterior pole; A. P., anterior pole; V. A., visual axis. (From Wolff, modified from Salzmann.)

ducts lead into the upper part of the *nasolacrimal duct*; this opens into the inferior meatus of the nose; its upper blind end is termed the *lacrimal sac*.

The drainage of tears into the nose does not depend merely upon gravity. Fluid enters and passes along the lacrimal ducts by capillary attraction aided by aspiration caused by contraction of a part of the orbicularis oculi muscle which is inserted into the lacrimal sac (pars lacrimalis muscle). When the lids close, contraction of this muscle causes dilation of the upper part of the sac and compression of its lower portion. Tears are thus aspirated into the sac, and any which have collected in its lower part are forced down the nasolacrimal duct towards its opening into the inferior meatus of the nose. As the lids open, the muscle relaxes. The upper part of the sac then collapses and forces fluid into the lower part which at the same time is released from compression. Thus, the act of blinking exerts a suction-force-pump action in removing the tears from the lacrimal lake and emptying them into the nasal cavity.

The secretory fibers to the lacrimal gland are derived from the parasympathetic. They arise from the superior salivatory nucleus, or, according to some, from a separate group of cells (*lacrimal nucleus*) in close relation to the latter. The fibers leave the brain in the nervus intermedius of Wrisberg, the sensory root of the facial. They pass to the geniculate ganglion which they leave in the great superficial petrosal nerve (see fig. 6.10, p. 130). This nerve joins the deep petrosal nerve to form the nerve of the pterygoid canal (Vidian nerve). The fibers are conveyed in the latter nerve

to the sphenopalatine ganglion and thence into the zygomatic branch of the maxillary nerve. A branch of the zygomatic nerve (zygomaticotemporal) anastomoses with the lacrimal nerve—a branch of the ophthalmic. The lacrimal nerve thus receives the parasympathetic fibers and delivers them to the lacrimal gland; it also carries sensory fibers to the gland.

The sympathetic fibers are derived from the cervical sympathetic; they pass into the carotid plexus and travel in the deep petrosal nerve to the great superficial petrosal nerve. They accompany the parasympathetic fibers to the gland. The sympathetic is probably purely vasomotor in function; it does not appear to furnish secretory fibers to the lacrimal gland.

Lacrimation is induced reflexly by stimulation of nerve endings of the cornea or conjunctiva (ophthalmic division of the fifth nerve). The reflex is annulled by anesthetization of the surface of the eye, by section of the sensory nerves or of the great superficial petrosal nerve, or by blockage of the sphenopalatine ganglion. Emotional lacrimation is not affected by local anesthetization nor by section of the ophthalmic division of the fifth nerve, but is abolished by section of the great superficial petrosal nerve or by blockage of the sphenopalatine ganglion. Defective or complete absence of a lacrimatory response, either psychic or reflex is seen, although very rarely, as a congenital anomaly.

The Tunics of the Eyeball

The wall of the eye is composed of three concentric layers or tunics. (1) An outer or fibrous tunic—the *sclera and cornea*, (2) a middle vascular tunic—the *choroid, ciliary body* and *iris*, and (3) a nervous tunic—the *retina* (see fig. 13.1).

THE OUTER OR FIBROUS TUNIC. The posterior five-sixths of this coat is opaque and is called the *sclera*; it is composed of white fibrous tissue and

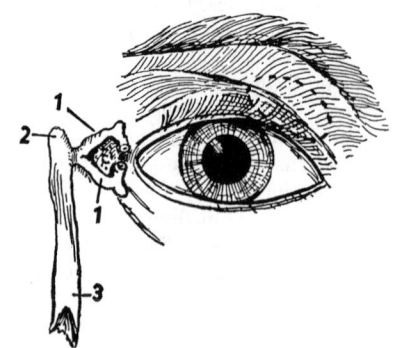

FIG. 13.2. The lacrimal apparatus. 1, Lacrimal ducts; 2, lacrimal sac; 3, nasolacrimal duct. Region marked off by interrupted line indicates the position of the lacrimal gland.

PLATE II

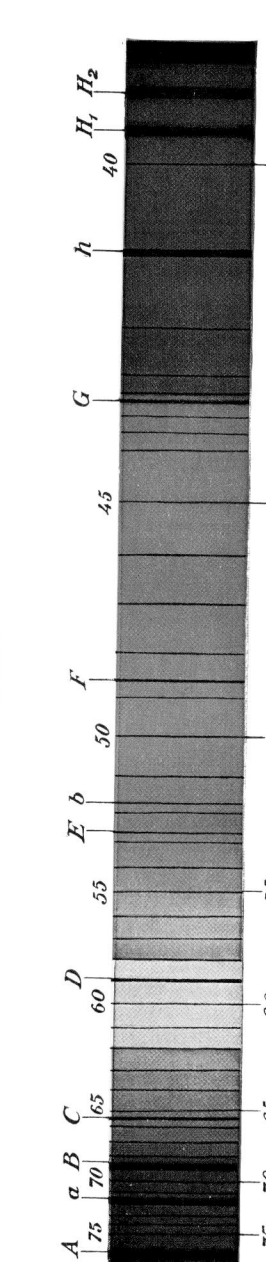

Spectrum as seen by light adapted eye (Photopic vision). (Figures form Duke-Elder *Text-book of Ophthalmology*, by permission of Henry Kimpton, London.)

Spectrum as seen by the dark adapted eye (Scotopic vision).

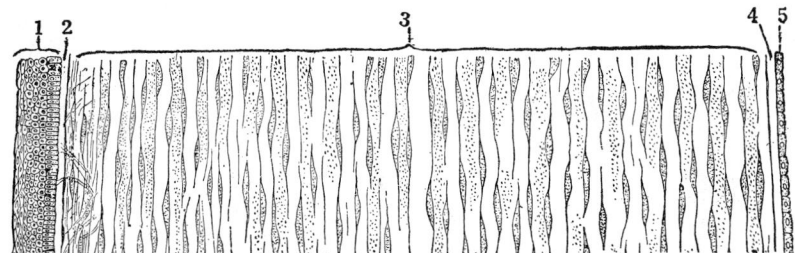

FIG. 13.3. Vertical section of human cornea (lying horizontally); *1*, corneal epithelium; *2*, anterior elastic lamina; *3*, substantia propria; *4*, posterior elastic lamina; *5*, endothelium of the anterior chamber. (After Waldeyer, modified.)

fine elastic fibers. Its anterior one-sixth is perfectly transparent and is called the *cornea*. The sclera appears in front as the so-called "white of the eye." The point where it joins the cornea—the *sclerocorneal junction*—is marked by a faint groove (see p. 354). The sclera where it is pierced by the optic nerve is reduced to a thin membrane containing perforations for the transmission of the retinal vessels and the bundles of nerve fibers. This part of the outer tunic, known as the *lamina cribrosa*, is the weakest part of the wall of the globe and is the first to yield to a persistently high intraocular pressure (see Glaucoma, p. 355), producing the so-called "cupping" of the optic disc. The cornea is convex anteriorly, being the small segment of a sphere having a radius of about 7.7 mm.[2] It is almost circular in circumference, measuring 11 mm. and 12 mm. respectively in its vertical and horizontal meridians. It is from 0.5 mm. to 1 mm. in thickness. The cornea is composed of five layers in the following order (from the front backward); (a) the corneal epithelium, (b) the anterior elastic lamina of Bowman, (c) the substantia propria, (d) the posterior elastic lamina of Descemet, and (e) a layer of endothelial cells (fig. 13.3).

The *corneal epithelium* is continuous with that of the conjunctiva; it consists of several strata of cells of different sizes and shapes. Columnar cells compose the deepest layer; this is overlaid by two or three layers of polyhedral cells. The cells of the superficial three or four layers are of the squamous type. The *substantia propria* is a tough transparent membrane consisting of a number of flattened lamellas composed of bundles of modified connective tissue fibers continuous with those of the sclera and lying in a mucoprotein ground-substance (keratosulfate). The *anterior elastic lamina of Bowman* and the *posterior elastic lamina of Descemet* bound the corresponding aspects of the substantia propria. At the circumference of the cornea the posterior elastic lamina breaks up into fibers which are continued into the pectinate ligament (ch. 15). The cornea is devoid of blood ves-

sels which is an important feature in relation to surgical grafting. The cornea is one of the few tissues which can be successfully grafted from one person to another. It receives nourishment from lymph (derived from vessels at its margin) which percolates through the spaces between its cells. It is supplied around its circumference by a rich plexus of pain fibers. Fine nonmedullated filaments derived from this plexus pass through the posterior elastic lamina and form a second plexus in the substantia propria (stroma plexus). From the stroma plexus, fibers proceed outward through the anterior elastic lamina where they form a subepithelial plexus; nerve filaments can be traced from the latter to the epithelial cells. The pain fibers have a very low threshold being aroused by very mild forms of stimulation. This has led to the general belief that the cornea is devoid of touch receptors and that stimuli which give a sensation of touch when applied to the skin are painful if applied to the cornea. It is claimed, however, that certain weak and innocuous stimulating agents, such as a jet of fluid impinging upon the cornea, arouse a sensation of touch alone.

THE MIDDLE OR VASCULAR LAYER consists from behind forwards of the *choroid, ciliary body* and the *iris*. The choroid is composed of a rich capillary plexus and the numerous small arteries and veins leading to and from it. It is dark brown in color, due to the presence of pigment cells, and forms the middle layer of the posterior five-sixths of the globe; it terminates anteriorly at the level of the ora serrata of the retina. The ciliary body and iris are described elsewhere.

THE NERVOUS TUNIC OR RETINA. The retina proper extends from the margins of the optic papilla (see below) to just behind the ciliary body. At this point it ends abruptly in a dentated border —the *ora serrata* (see figs. 13.1, and 15.29, p. 341). Its thickness diminishes progressively from the optic papilla (where it is about 0.4 mm.) to the dentate border where it is only 0.09 mm.

The *optic disc* is situated about 3 mm. to the nasal side of and a little above the posterior pole of the eyeball; it has a diameter of about 1.5 mm. in man. As viewed in the human eye by means of

---

[2] The peripheral zone is somewhat flattened as compared with the central portion.

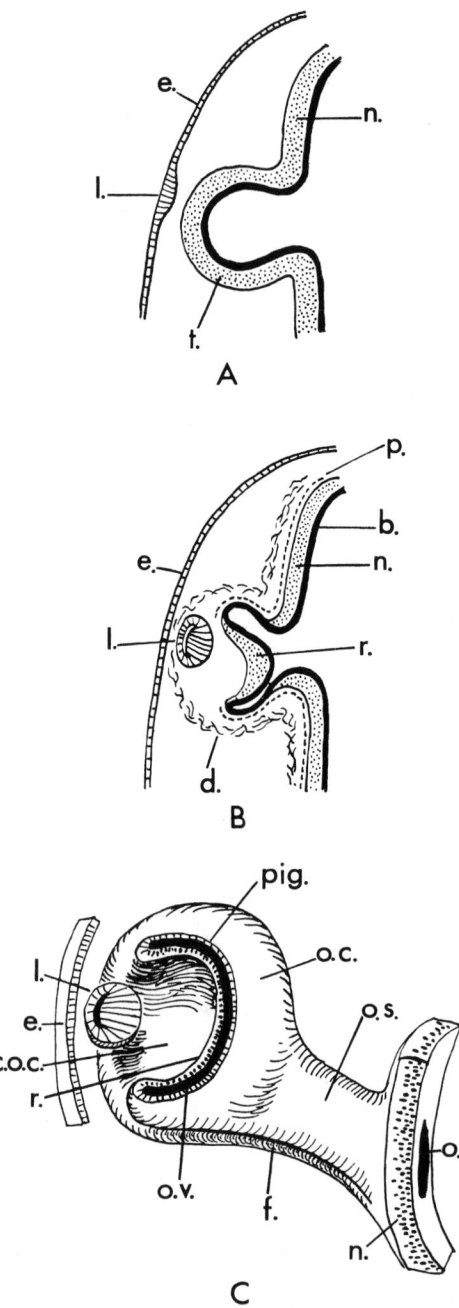

Fig. 13.4. Diagrams of developing eye. (*A*) Sagittal section through left optic vesicle; (*B*) same section at a later stage; (*C*) semisolid diagram to show the method of invagination and the development of the optic stalk.

c.o.c., cavity of optic cup; d, dura mater; e, epidermis; f, fissure; l, lens; n, neural tissue; o.c., optic cup; o.r., optic recess; o.s., optic stalk; o.v., optic vesicle; p, pia mater; pig., pigment epithelium; r, retina.

the ophthalmoscope (p. 335) it appears as a pink circular area fading to a creamy white toward the center. It is pierced near its center by the retinal vessels—*arteria centralis retinae* and its accompanying vein (Pl. III, ch. 15). The circumference of the optic disc is elevated to form the *optic papilla*. The central depressed part is known as the *physiological cup* or the *excavation of the optic nerve*. The vessels climb up the inside of the cup to reach the retina. All layers of the retina except the nerve fiber layer are absent from the optic disc. It is therefore totally insensitive to light and is known as the *blind spot* of the retina (p. 358). The reader is referred to figure 16.3, p. 359, for a demonstration of the blind spot in his own eye.

In order to clarify the relationships of the outer tunics of the eyeball to the retina and to facilitate the description and interpretation of the retina itself, its mode of development will first be outlined.

The rudiment of the eye is first visible in the embryo as a vesicular outgrowth of the neural tube (fig. 13.4). This vesicle grows larger and bulges outward until it meets the epidermis, in which, in some species at least, it is responsible for the induction of a *lens*. At this stage, the walls of the optic vesicle are formed of neuroblastic tissue precisely similar to that of the rest of the neural tube. The vesicle is lined on the inside by cells which are of the same kind as those which, elsewhere in the neural tube, will form the ependyma. To the outside of the neural tissue of the neural tube, neural crest cells will, at a later stage, apply themselves as the pia mater, and blood vessels will ramify among them and form the arachnoid layer. Outside this, the mesenchymal tissues will condense as the dura mater. As the optic vesicle grows out, the same layers are found in it as in the rest of the neural tube, and when the outer pole invaginates and begins to form the optic cup, the lining layer of the vesicle becomes opposed to itself so that the space between the two parts of it (i.e., the cavity of the vesicle) is almost obliterated. The covering layers of the vesicle (i.e., the dura mater which over the vesicle becomes the sclera and cornea, the pia mater and arachnoid, which become the choroid) on the other hand do not follow that part of the vesicle which actually invaginates. The sclera and cornea remain as though surrounding the original sphere and there is a space left in the pia mater and arachnoid which roughly corresponds with the cavity which will form the pupil, and through which the lens (which is now separated from the epidermis and lying within the future cornea) penetrates into the cup, together with the connective tissues for the formation of the vitreous body. The invagination of the optic vesicle is not a symmetrical invagination and the cup is formed partly by the folded sides or margins of the cup growing toward each other until they eventually meet and enclose the arteries which will supply the inner surface of the retina and the vitreous body. The method of this invagination is best understood by reference to Figure 13.4.

In the neural tube, the neural tissue, consisting of neuroblasts and neuroglia, arises by cell multiplication which occurs mostly in or near the ependymal layer. In the optic vesicle, the part of this layer which, after the invagination, forms the outer part of the optic cup, does not give rise to neural tissue but remains as a single layer of cells, which eventually forms the *pigment layer of the retina* and a pigmented covering for the ciliary processes (fig. 13.5). Because of the invagination, this layer is reflected back on itself at the rim of the *iris*, thus lining the posterior surface of the iris with a double layer of pigment epithelium. In this region the outer layer not only forms an epithelium covering the posterior surface of the iris but also gives rise to the *sphincter* and *dilator pupillae muscles.* Continuing towards the retina, this pigment layer (after again covering the ciliary processes, but this time as the colorless columnar epithelium responsible for the secretion of the aqueous humour) reaches the *ora serrata* and the *pars optica retinae.* Here it again gives rise to true neural tissue in a manner which is almost precisely similar to that found in the rest of the nervous system.

Because of the absence of neural tissue on the outside of the optic cup, the ependymal layer (i.e., the pigment layer of the retina) is brought into immediate contact with the pia mater and the arachnoid (which together constitute the choroid coat). Outside the choroid lies the sclera which can thus be seen to correspond to the dura mater. These relationships are set out in figures 13.4 and 13.5.

Thus the retina itself appears as a true part of the central nervous system, and its cells have exactly the same origin as those of other cells of the central nervous system. During the development of the retina there are, in essence, two main waves of cell production. The 'ependymal' and embryonic layer first gives rise to cells which migrate outwards to become the eventual *ganglion cells.* Because of the invagination, 'outwards' now means toward the center of the optic cup. This wave is then followed by a second wave whose cells mainly constitute the layer of *bipolar cells,* and the cells which are left behind in the 'ependymal' layer differentiate to become the sensory layer of the retina, the layer of *rod* and *cone cells.* Thus, basically, the retina

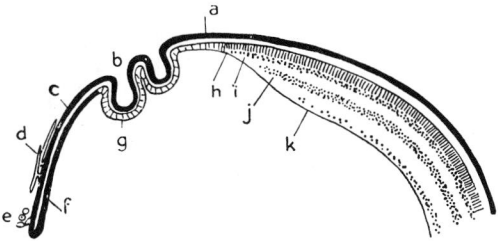

FIG. 13.5. Diagram to show the genetic relationships between the cells of the retina, iris, etc. (*a*) Pigment layer of the retina; (*b*) pigment layer over the ciliary processes; (*c*) anterior pigment layer of the iris; (*d*) dilator pupillae muscle; (*e*) sphincter pupillae muscle; (*f*) posterior pigment layer of the iris; (*g*) columnar epithelium over the ciliary processes; (*h*) rods and cones; (*i*) nuclei of the rods and cones; (*j*) bipolar, horizontal and amacrine cell nuclei; (*k*) ganglion cell nuclei. (From Willmer.)

is built up of three layers of cells, their processes, and the synaptic connections which they make with each other and with the rest of the nervous system; this last connection with the central nervous system is established by nerve fibers growing away from the ganglion cells along the inner surface of the retina to the point known as the *optic disc* (see above) and flowing thence along the fold of neural tissue which encloses the retinal arteries and constitutes the optic stalk and eventually the optic nerve to the brain proper.

Thus a needle pushed into the eye from any point in the posterior half, i.e., behind the ora serrata or rim of the retina, would pass through the following layers (Fig. 13.6).

Sclera: specialized connective tissue.

Choroid: blood vessels mingled with branching and heavily pigmented cells of the pia mater.

Pigment epithelium of the retina: cells arranged as a single layer of hexagonally packed cells, corresponding to the outer fold of ependyma.

(The cavity of the original optic vesicle.)

Rods and cones: these are the processes of rod and cone cells (see pp. 270–275).

External limiting membrane: original 'cuticle' of the neural tube, partly composed of processes of neuroglial cells.

Cell bodies and nuclei of rod and cone cells.

Outer synaptic layer: the connections between rod and cone cells and bipolar cells.

Bipolar cells and their nuclei: this layer also includes the nuclei of *horizontal cells, amacrine cells* and the cells of *Muller's fibers.*

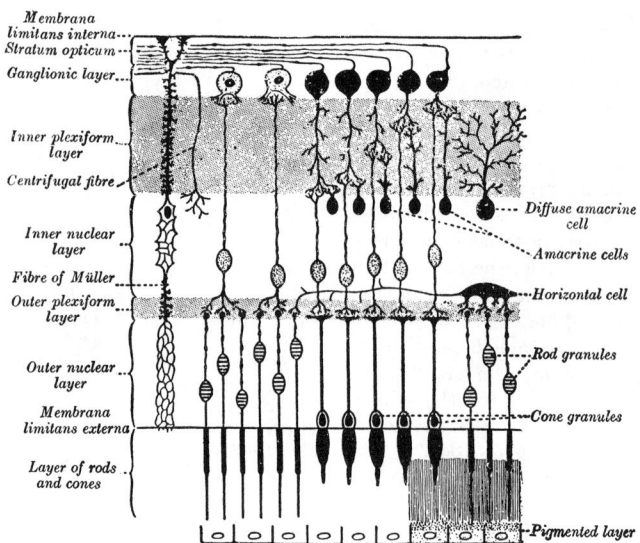

Membrana
limitans interna
Stratum opticum
Ganglionic layer

Inner plexiform
layer
Centrifugal fibre

Inner nuclear
layer

Fibre of Müller
Outer plexiform
layer

Outer nuclear
layer

Membrana
limitans externa

Layer of rods
and cones

Diffuse amacrine
cell
Amacrine cells

Horizontal cell

Rod granules

Cone granules

Pigmented layer

FIG. 13.6. Layers of retina. (After Cajal.)

Inner synaptic layer: the connection between bipolar cells and ganglion cells.

Ganglion cells.

Optic nerve fibers.

Internal limiting membrane: partly composed of the processes or products of the neuroglial cells, the Muller's fibers.

The light which penetrates the eye after passing through the cornea and lens obviously passes through the retina in the reverse order of that just given, i.e., it passes in the direction of the arrow in Figure 13.7. During life, the retina is practically transparent, so that light readily penetrates almost unimpeded to the rods and cones, where some of it is absorbed and initiates the visual processes. In the region of the *fovea*, which is the point on the visual axis at which the most distinct vision occurs, the thickness of the retinal layers is nevertheless reduced by dispersing the bipolar cells and ganglion cells to the sides and so producing a depression in the inner surface of the retina at that point (*fovea* (Latin) means a depression or hearth) and allowing the light to reach the receptors with as little interference as possible (Fig. 13.8).

The light that is not absorbed by the rods and cones is absorbed partly by the pigment layer and partly by the choroid. Only a very small part of the entering light escapes absorption and is reflected back; in this way the pigment layers act like the black paint inside a camera. The absorbing pigment in the epithelium and in the choroid is the inert derivative of tyrosine, *melanin;* there is no evidence that this is a visual pigment in the true sense.

In certain nocturnal animals there may, however, be considerable reflection either from minute fibers or crystals in the cells of the pigment layer, or from special fibers in the choroid coat. These reflecting surfaces (*tapeta*) are the cause of the eyeshine in cats and other animals. The tapetum is essentially a device for making use of whatever light is available at night by allowing it to pass first in one direction and then in the other through the visual pigments in the photoreceptor cells.

The rod and cone cells. In the normal eye, the curved surface of the cornea and the lens cause an image of the outside world to be cast on the layer of the actual rods and cones, that is, the elongated projections of the rod and cone cells which extend beyond the external limiting membrane and each of which is divisible into an outer and inner segment. It is the outer segment which is believed to be the sensitive part. In some animals (e.g., the frog), one class of these structures (the rods) can be seen (if the preparation has been made from an animal previously kept in the dark and only dim red light has been used during the dissection) to contain a reddish pigment called *visual purple* or *rhodopsin.* This pigment is readily bleached by all wave lengths of visible light except those in the far red, e.g., those longer than 650 mμ and so, under the microscope the pink outer segments can be seen to fade rapidly.

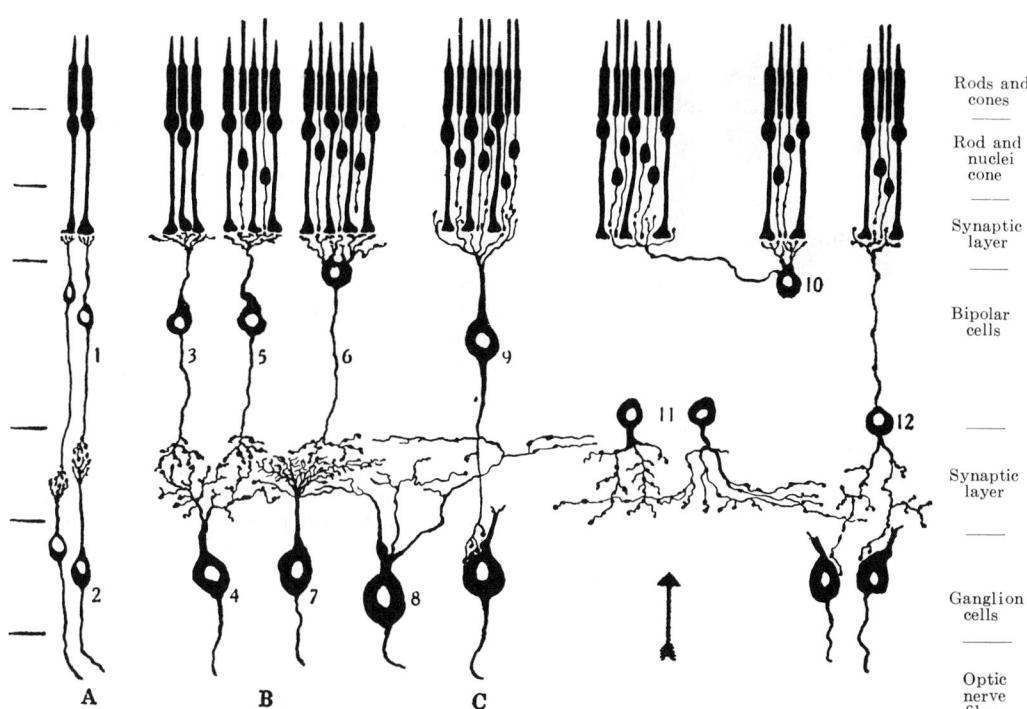

FIG. 13.7. Chief synaptic connections of rods and cones A. Pure cone path, midget bipolar and midget ganglion cells. B. Mainly cone paths, flat and brush bipolar cells. C. Mainly rod path, mop bipolar cells. 1. Midget bipolar cell; 2. Midget ganglion cell; 3. Flat bipolar supplying cones only; 4. Shrub ganglion cell; 5. Flat bipolar cell supplying rods and cones; 6. Brush bipolar supplying rods and cones; 7. Parasol ganglion cells; 8. Garland ganglion cells; 9. Mop bipolar cell; 10. Horizontal cell; 11. Amacrine cells; 12. Centrifugal bipolar cell. (After Polyak.)

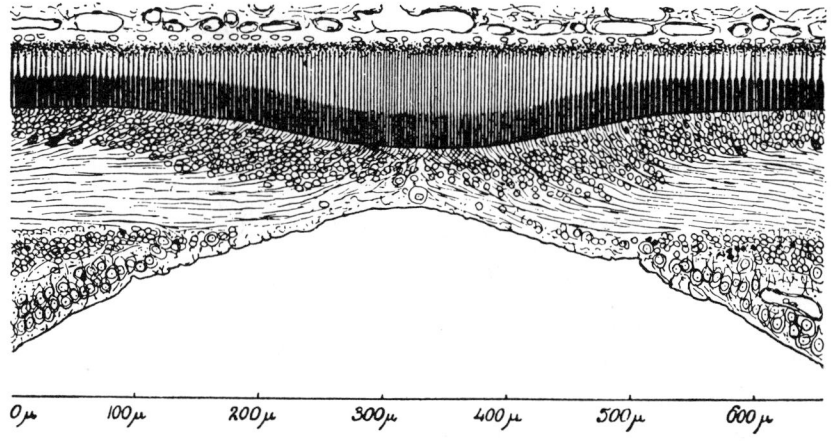

FIG. 13.8. Section through the human fovea. (From Polyak.)

If the eye of a rabbit is excised in darkness or in red light and then exposed to an object clearly defined in light and shade, e.g., a window sash against the sky, an image of the object will be found to have been impressed upon the retina when it is examined in the dark room. The image is caused by the bleaching of the visual purple where the bright parts of the image fell upon the rods. The retina thus behaves like a photographic film; the image so obtained is called an *optogram* (see fig. 13.9).

When a light from a small but intense source is shone obliquely through the sclera into the human eye, shadows of the blood vessels, which

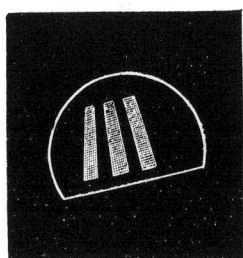

FIG. 13.9. Optogram formed upon the retina of a rabbit by exposing the eye to an object made of a glass plate and strips of black paper. (After Stewart.)

course over the inner surface of the retina, can be seen by the subject, and these shadows (Purkinje's figures) appear to move as the position of the light source is changed. From measurements of the relative movement of the image in relation to that of the light source, it can be shown that the image which is seen must be falling on the outer segments of the rods and cones at a distance of between 0.2 and 0.3 mm. from the retinal vessels (see p. 278 and fig. 13.10). For these and other reasons, the outer segments of the rods and cones are now accepted as the most probable seat of the initial processes which convert radiant energy into something which is capable of being transmitted along the neural mechanisms in the rest of the retina and so to the brain.

The shapes of the outer segments of the rods and cones are extremely variable in different species and often also within the same animal. In man, those of the rods are fairly uniform cylinders (about 24 μ long and 3 μ wide), whereas those of the cones are short (6 μ) and conical in the periphery, but become longer (up to 34 μ), thinner (2 μ) and much more cylindrical toward the center, reaching their extreme limits in this direction in the floor of the foveal depression (fig. 13.10).

In many animals (e.g., perch, frog, guinea pig and rat) evidence from the optical properties, particularly as obtained with the use of the polarizing microscope, and also from electron-microscopy indicates that the outer segments of rods are subdivided into a series of leaflike structures, each composed of a flattened vesicle enclosing a space between a pair of membranes, piled one above the other like a stack of plates and all enclosed within the plasma membrane. The vesicles often have deep incisions into their edges, so that each may be subdivided into several lobes (see Fig. 13.12). The visual purple molecules are oriented with their long axes at right angles to the axis of the rod, in the same plane as these

membranes. The outer segments of cones appear to have a somewhat similar structure but the arrangement of the membranes is somewhat different. The leaflike structures appear to be more simply flattened folds of the plasma membrane. This may indicate that they have a somewhat different origin. The pigment in the cones is not rhodopsin, nor is it known exactly where it is situated in each cone.

It has been suggested, partly on the basis of refractive index differences between the outer segments and their surroundings, that the rods and cones could act as wave guides, but it is probably fair to say that the functional significance of their fine structure is still imperfectly understood, both as to the means of excitation and as to the amplification of the response.

The analysis of their fine structure has abundantly confirmed the older observations based on embryological development that the photosensitive part of the rod process, and with less certainty

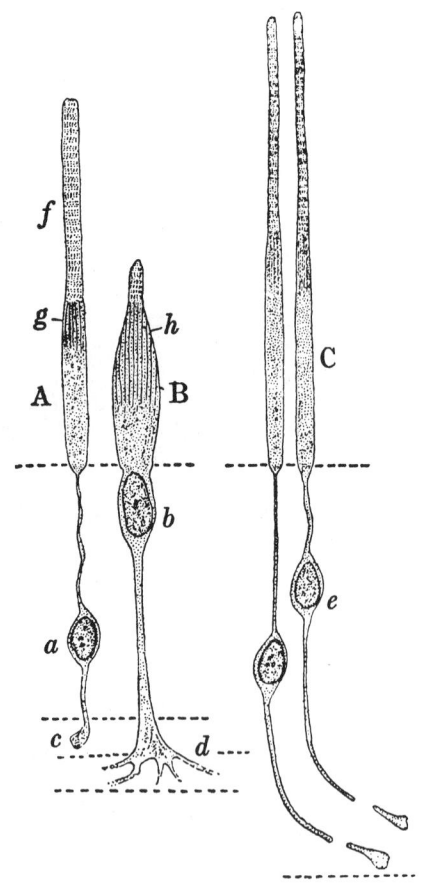

FIG. 13.10. Human rods and cones. (*A*) Rod—*a*, nucleus; *c*, central connection; *g*, ellipsoid; *f*, outer segment. (*B*) Cone—*b*, nucleus; *d*, central pedicle; *h*, ellipsoid. (*C*) Cones in the fovea centralis—*e*, nucleus. (From Cajal.)

of the cone process also, are each derived from a modified flagellum. The inner and outer segments of the rod are connected by a fine fiber which, in transverse section shows a fibrillar structure very similar to that which is characteristic of all flagella though without the two central fibrillae (figs. 13.11 and 13.12). It will be remembered that many of the cells of the neural tube elsewhere, i.e., the ependymal cells, are flagellate, so, from the embryological point of view, it is not surprising to find flagella appearing in a modified form in this 'ependymal' layer of the retina. Just as the ependymal cells often have microvilli as well as flagella or cilia, so the rods and cones may have a palisade of long microvilluslike processes surrounding their outer segments. A somewhat similar juxtaposition of "stereocilia" and kinocilia occurs in the sensory hair-cells of the vestibular and cochlea sense-organs.

The inner segments of rods and cones again show differences, although they are both very rich in mitochondria and metabolic enzymes, e.g., succinic dehydrogenase, lactate dehydrogenase and DPN diaphorase. In many animals, e.g., amphibia, reptiles, birds and monkeys, the cones may have oil globules in the inner segments at their junction with the outer segments. These globules in birds and turtles are sometimes colored with carotenoid pigments of which xanthophyll and astaxanthine are the most usual. Such globules do not occur in human cones but there is evidence that xanthophyll occurs in the cytoplasm of the cones and their centrally directed fibrous processes and gives rise to the yellowish pigmentation which occurs around the fovea for a distance of about 4° in all directions. This area is known as the *yellow spot* or *macula lutea*. The effect of this yellow pigmentation (macular pigment) can be seen, entopically, if a uniform white surface is viewed alternately through a purple (i.e., transmitting blue and red) filter and a neutral grey filter of about the same optical density. The fovea then appears as a reddish spot often surrounded by another reddish ring on a bluish background, and this pattern is always seen at the point in the purple field to which the gaze is directed. The pigment appears to be to some extent orientated with respect to the axis of the cone cell and is probably the agent responsible for the appearance of "blue arcs" or "Haidinger's brushes" sometimes seen when a uniform field of blue polarized light is examined.

Cone cells generally have their nuclei near the external limiting membrane and each has a conspicuous nucleolus. Rod nuclei are smaller, without definite nucleoli, and generally are situated more centrally. The cones tend to make their synaptic connections with bipolar cells in the form of extended 'pedicles,' whereas rods end centrally in knoblike endings (see Fig. 13.10). The electron

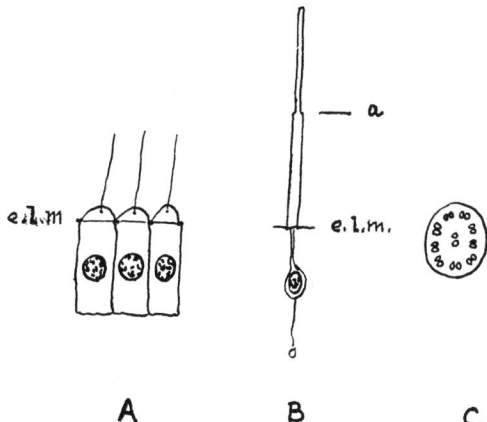

A   **B**   **C**

FIG. 13.11. The origin of rods from flagella. (*A*) The flagellar structure of the rod and cone cells in the developing retina; (*B*) a fully developed rod showing outer and inner segments; (*C*) a transverse section of a flagellum or cilium as seen with the electron microscope, showing the usual arrangement of internal fibers. a, The junction between inner and outer segments (*cf*. Fig. 13.12); e.l.m., external limiting membrane.

microscope shows vesicular invaginations into these endings and the processes of the bipolar cells penetrating into them. The cytoplasm of the knob is also filled with minute closed vesicles, and it has been suggested that these may be concerned with the production of the chemical transmitter, as similar structures in nerve endings elsewhere appear to be.

In man, rods occur all over the retina except for a small area (about 0.44 mm. in diameter and corresponding to a visual field of rather less than 1°) on the visual axis at the center of the fovea. This important area is known as the *fovea centralis*. The receptors present in this area are almost certainly cones, but they are very elongated. Under certain conditions of fixation and staining, two types of inner segment can be distinguished among these cones in the foveal centre, and a third type among the immediately surrounding cones. The functional significance, if any, of these types is at present unknown. Rods are most abundant at about 20° from the foveal center. The distribution of rods and cones is illustrated in figure 13.13, and it will be seen that cones are enormously concentrated around and in the fovea. The intimate pattern of the distribution of rods and cones is often very regular, e.g., in certain areas one cone is surrounded by six rods, and, near the fovea, the cones appear, in histological sections cut transversely to the long axis of the cones, to be arranged in regular rows.

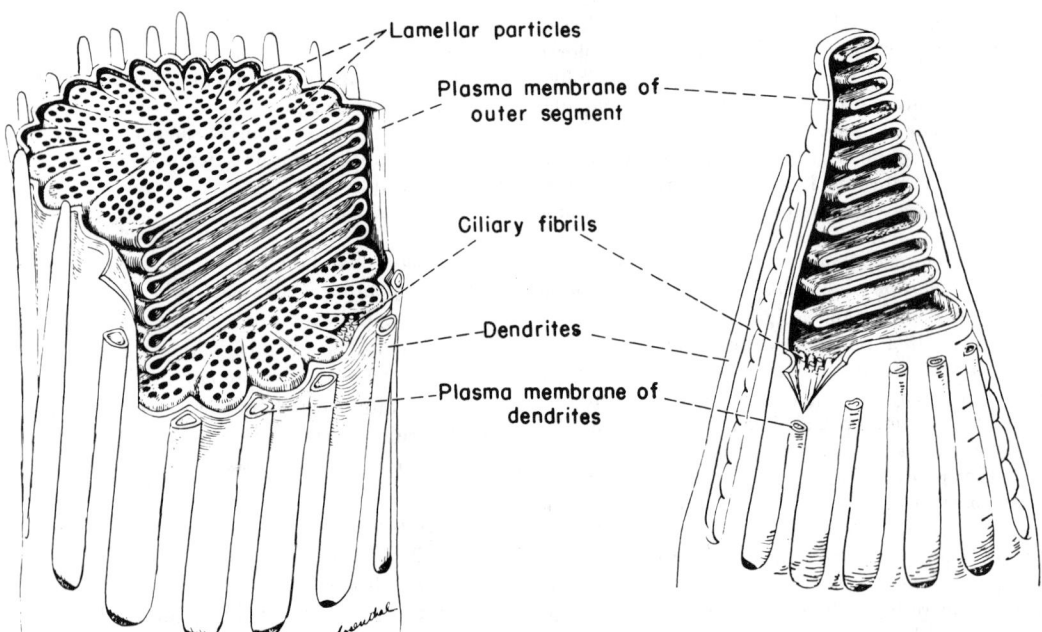

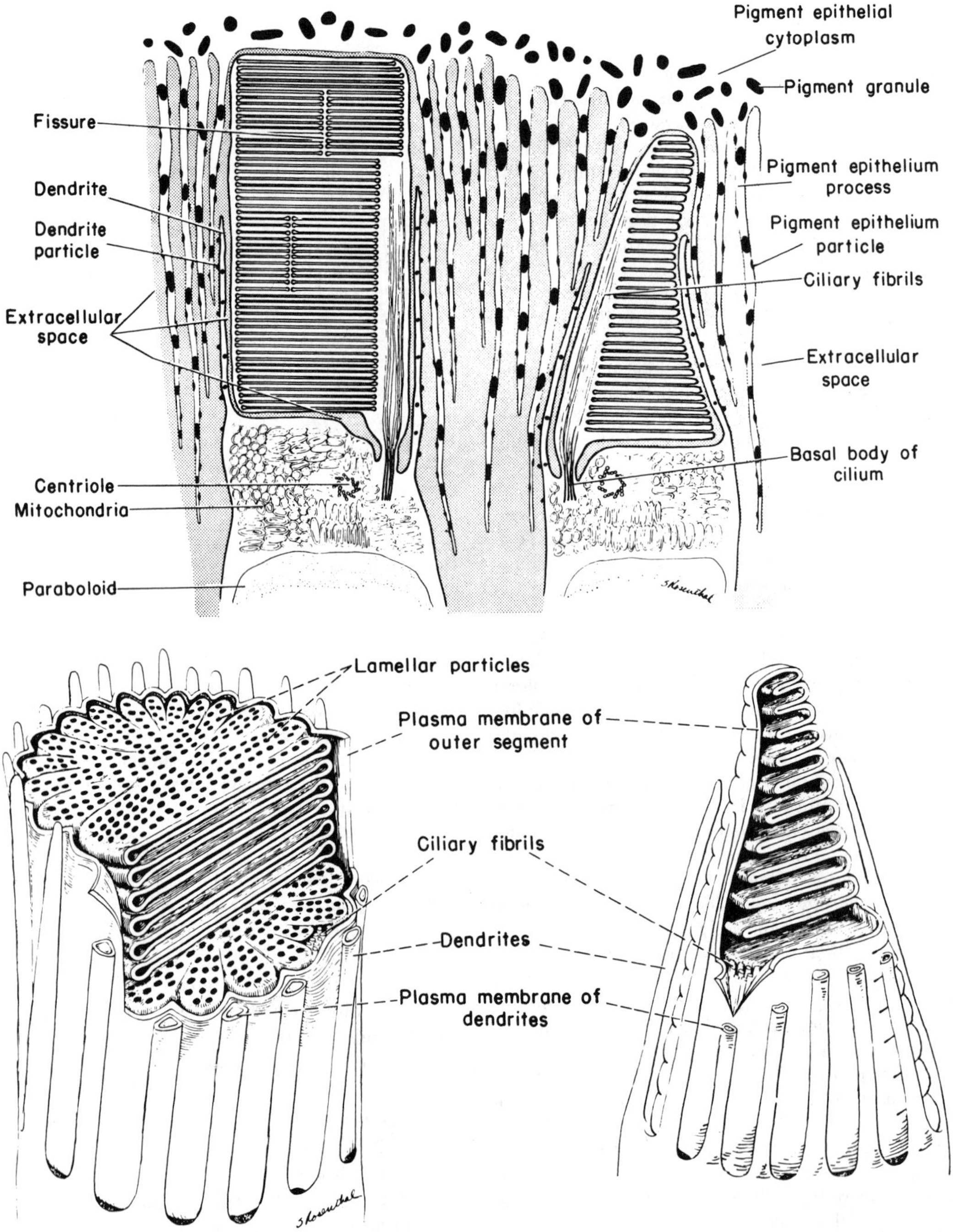

FIG. 13.12. Diagram of the structures at the junction between inner and outer segments of a rod as seen by the electron microscope. OS, outer segment; rs, platelike arrangement of flattened rod sacs; rst, junction of rod sacs with ciliary fibers; cf, ciliary fibers; sm, surface membrane; a, transverse section. CC, cilium connecting the inner and outer segments (*cf*. Fig. 13.11). b.c., transverse section. IS, inner segment; bb, basal body; dp, dense particles; e, transverse section; er, endoplasmic reticulum; mi, mitochondria; mic, mitochondrial cristae. (From de Robertis.)

Diagram to show structural relations between rod and cone outer segments in *Necturus*. In the rod all edges of the double membrane discs involve a differentiated rim structure. The discs are cut into lobules by deep longitudinal fissures; and the disc membranes contain a system of deeply staining micelles in regular array. The stack of doublelayers is completely enclosed within a plasma membrane, continuous with that of the inner segment, and reflected also over the dendrites. In the cones this common plasma membrane is infolded repeatedly on the side opposite from the cilium to form the double layers. The cone double layers lack the special rim structure, fissures, and lamellar micelles.

Diagram to show relationships of rod and cone outer segments to the inner segments and the pigment epithelium.

From the structural point of view there are very good reasons for considering rods and cones to be the processes belonging to two distinct (but closely related) races of cells. It will be seen that experiments on visual performance endorse this

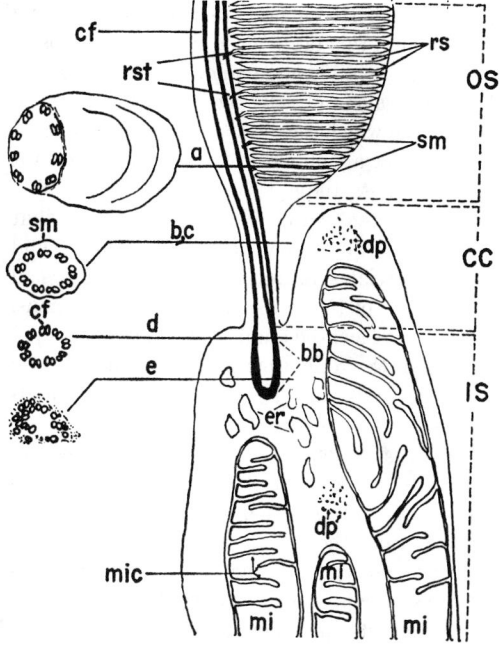

FIG. 13.12—*Continued.*

view. For example Stiles and Crawford have shown that a pencil of light which enters the eye through the center of the pupil causes a more intense sensation than does one of equal physical brightness passing through the pupil nearer its circumference (see Fig. 15.28). This phenomenon is most pronounced at the fovea. The smaller effect caused by the peripheral beam is not due to greater absorption by the ocular media, but to the direction of the beam in relation to the position of the cones, a smaller photochemical change being caused by light passing obliquely across the receptors than by that which traverses their lengths.

This phenomenon is very much more in evidence with the cones than it is with the rods and probably is related to the structural differences between the two types of receptor. Not all the wave lengths of light are affected equally. The blue rays are affected most, then the red end of the spectrum. The directional effect is least with the green rays. There are also slight color differences to be observed between monochromatic rays which have entered the pupil centrally and those entering at the periphery and thus falling obliquely on the receptors.

The outer segments of the rods and cones are often intimately surrounded by the processes of the cells of the pigment epithelium which interdigitate with them across the vanished space of the original lumen of the optic vesicle. This vanished but still potential space may become an actual space as the result of trauma, e.g., detached

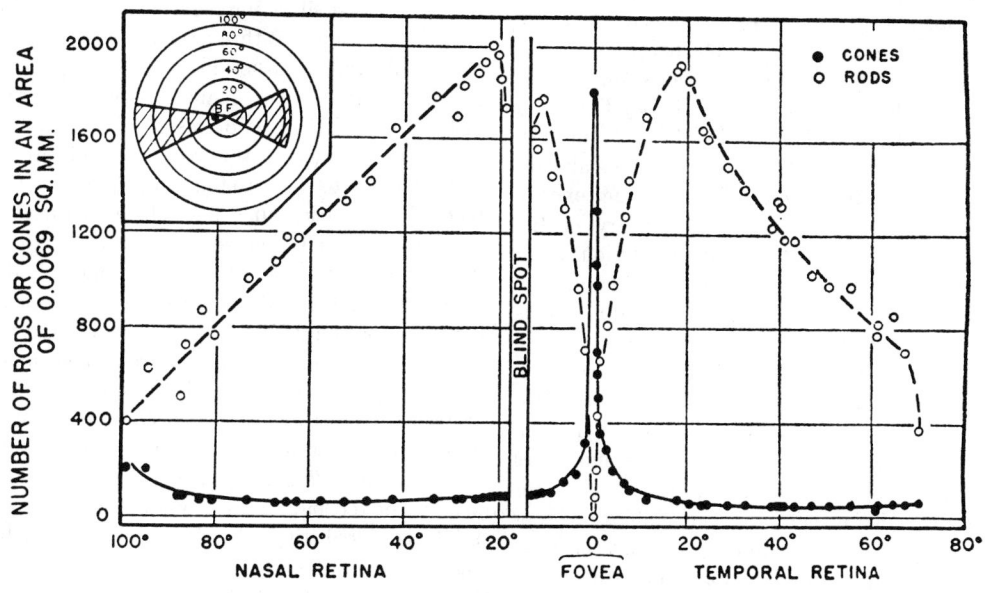

FIG. 13.13. The density of cones and rods on or near the horizontal meridian through a human retina. The inset is a schematic map of the retina showing the fovea (*F*) and the blind spot (*B*). The striped area represents the regions of the retina which were sampled in obtaining the counts plotted here. (From Chapanis after Østerberg.)

retina, or very frequently in histological preparations. In some animals, as for example, the frog,
although not in man, the brown or black melanin
granules in the pigment cells can move up and
down the cell processes in relation to the intensity
of the illumination. In the frog the granules are
caused to extend along the cell processes by the
action of adrenaline, as well as by light, and in
this way these cells contrast with other melanin-
containing cells which generally aggregate their
pigment under the influence of adrenaline. The
pigment epithelium is generally more highly developed in relation to cones than to rods and in
the human eye is most noticeable in the region of
the fovea.

Each rod or cone acts as a separate photosensitive element and, since in each human eye
there are some 120 million rods and 6 million
cones, the visual image cast on this layer is subdivided into some 126 million separate fragments,
rather in the same way as when printing
from photographs the picture is divided into innumerable separate points and the greater the
number of points the better the quality of the
reproduction. Half-tone reproductions obtained
with a very fine screen are clearer and more precise than illustrations in the cheap press where
coarse screens are used. Since a certain quantity
of light has to be absorbed before any photochemical change can be initiated, the photoreceptors have to contain within themselves a certain mass of photosensitive pigment and the
metabolic equipment for its regeneration. Consequently, if they have to be made as thin as possible in order to produce the necessary fine grain
in the picture, they may also have to be correspondingly elongated. Attention has already
been called to this change of form in the cones of
the human eye between the periphery of the
retina and the point of most distinct vision which
lies at the fovea centralis (see fig. 13.10). The
rods show much less change in their dimensions
in different parts of the retina. Probably the
underlying reason for this difference between rods
and cones is related to the roles which the two
types of unit play in vision and these are, in turn,
related to the manner in which rods and cones
are connected with the visual centers. The subdivision of the image into many millions of separate photosensitive stimuli all of about the same
order of magnitude might for some purposes be
ideal and one might expect, at first sight, that
all the information provided in this way would
be relayed to the brain along separate channels.
This, however, is not so. There are only about

one million fibers in each optic nerve of man,
and since there is no evidence for any qualitative difference in types of nerve impulse, only
this number of separate trains of messages can
reach the lateral geniculate body and visual centers. Clearly then there is considerable pooling
and sifting of information as it enters the optic
pathway and this takes place through the cells in
the bipolar layers and ganglion cell layers. Probably these layers of cells code and integrate the
information which the photoreceptors provide and
send on only a summary of the most important
information. A study of the bipolar and ganglion
cells in different parts of the retina shows that
their distribution is by no means uniform and
that it correlates rather closely with the visual
performance of the retina in its different regions.
In the first place, the number of ganglion cells per
sq. mm. in the retinal periphery (about 80° from
the visual axis) is only measured in hundreds
whereas in the central region of the eye, near
the fovea, the density may rise to hundreds of
thousands per sq. mm. Thus the number of receptor cells per ganglion cell progressively diminishes from the periphery towards the center
of the eye, but it never reaches equality, although
it begins to approach it in the fovea. This is
one reason why peripheral vision is blurred and
incomplete as compared with that at the fovea.

Histological studies of the retina, mostly by
means of Golgi silver impregnation methods, indicate that there are three main varieties of bipolar cell, and a rather indefinite grouping of
ganglion cells into two main classes. Again the
distribution of these two classes of cells differs
in different parts of the retina. Golgi preparations have to be carefully interpreted. The
method only picks out a few cells at a time for
impregnation and then apparently coats them
in their entirety. All other cells remain almost
completely untouched. The cellular architecture
can therefore only be surmised from piecing together very fragmentary pictures. The main
types of cell detected by this method are illustrated in figure 13.7 which also shows the shapes
and relative positions of two other types of cell,
the *horizontal cell* and the *amacrine cell*. The *mop
bipolar* (or rod bipolar as it was originally called
by Cajal) is distinguished from the others by
the 'vertical' orientation of its dendrites and by
the fact that it connects with the cell bodies as
well as with the dendrites of the ganglion cells.
It is present over most of the retina but is rare
or absent from among the bipolar cells which

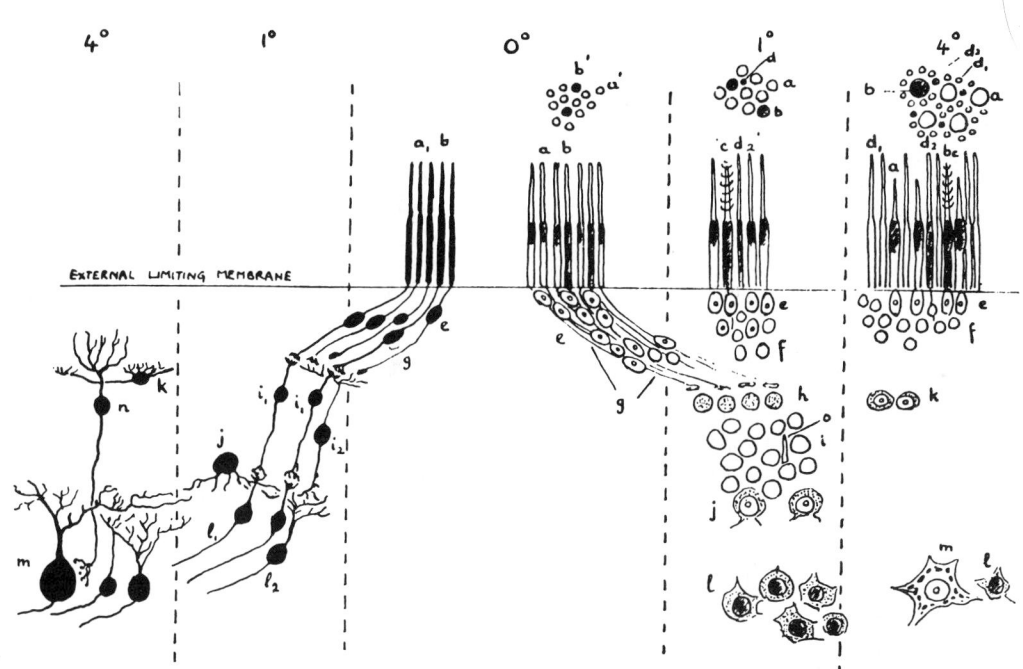

FIG. 13.14. Diagram to illustrate the main features of the foveal center. (On the right) the information obtained by the usual cytological and histological methods; (on the left) information obtained by Golgi methods.

a, light-staining cone; b, dark-staining cone; c, spiral process surrounding some cones; d, rod; d_1, light-staining rods; d_2, dark-staining rod; e, cone nuclei; f, rod nuclei; g, Henlé's fibers; h, midget bipolar cells; i, bipolar cells; i_1, midget; i_2, flat and brush; j, amacrine cells; k, horizontal cells; l, small ganglion cells; l_1, midget; l_2, other types; m, large ganglion cells; n, rod or mop bipolar cells; o, nucleus of cell of Müller's fiber. (From Willmer.)

relay from the foveal region. The *flat* and *brush bipolars*, or the cone bipolars of Cajal, are found in all regions of the retina including the foveal region (fig. 13.14). They are characterized by horizontally distributed dendrites which all end at the level of the internal endings of the cones, i.e., the cone pedicles. In this way they differ from the mop bipolars whose dendrites extend further and enter the little invaginations in the end knobs of the rods, many of which do not reach centrally as far as those of the cones. Centrally, the cone bipolars mostly appear to terminate among the dendrites of the ganglion cells and, distally, they probably make synaptic connections with about a dozen cones. The third class of bipolar cell, the *midget bipolar*, is probably a specialization of the cone bipolar and becomes most numerous in the center of the retina in the region of the fovea. Members of this class have very restricted dendritic branchings and probably make contact with one or two cones only. Similarly at their opposite pole they each connect with one small ganglion cell only. Thus these midget bipolars and *midget ganglion cells* appear to provide private connections from individual cones to neurons in the lateral geniculate body at least. Recent studies with the electron-microscope throw some doubt on the validity of the Golgi method as a means of investigating the branching of the dendrites of these retinal cells. Indeed, it is now suggested that the spread of the dendritic trees of the midget bipolar may be much more extensive than had been previously supposed and the existence of actual one-to-one connections has been called in question. In any case it should be remembered, that although these cells are most numerous near the fovea, they are always mingled with flat and brush bipolars also. There is probably very considerable overlap among the fields covered by the flat and brush bipolars and both probably collect information from cones which may also be transmitting along the "midget pathway." Similarly, there is also likely to be overlapping of the fields of the ganglion cells. Among these ganglion cells there is, in addition to the numerous rather small and histologically featureless cells, a rather distinct class of very large cells, each with a large vesicular nucleus and prominent nucleolus and whose cytoplasm is filled with large Nissl's granules. These cells are readily stained supravitally with methylene blue or neutral red and are evenly distributed all over the retina, but become scarce in, or absent from, the foveal region. These cells possess a very wide arborization of dendrites which may extend over an area with a diameter of more than 1 mm. in the synaptic layer between the bipolar cells and the ganglion cells. The overlap of these cells with the fields of other ganglion cells must therefore be very considerable. Microelectrodes placed near these large cells in the eyes of decerebrate animals (see p. 286) record large spike potentials and, partly for this reason, most of the electrical recording of such spikes which has been possible from the inner surface of the living retina has been localized to these cells. The electrical properties of the small ganglion cells and the bipolar cells still remain somewhat problematical.

Acetylcholinesterase is present in the inner synaptic layer, suggesting that some at least of the cells in the bipolar cell layer transmit by means of acetylcholine. The enzyme is said to be increased by illumination. On the other hand, the outer synaptic layer between the rods and cones and the bipolar cells is histochemically negative in this respect and there is as yet nothing to indicate the nature of the transmitter substances, if any, in that layer. Synaptic vesicles are, however, present.

Horizontal cells are most abundant in eyes with many rods, e.g., in the cat. Their terminals end in the outer synaptic layer but opinions differ on their exact distribution. Presumably they are concerned with the various processes of lateral interaction which go on in the eye. In fish there are some very large cells in the region of the outer synaptic layer which extend laterally in somewhat stellate forms, but how these are related to the horizontal cells of higher vertebrates is not yet clear.

The processes of the amacrine cells end in the inner synaptic layer. In Golgi preparations of the retina of some birds they branch at certain particular levels and spread laterally for long distances within the synaptic layer so that they impart to it a horizontal stratification. This same stratification also appears in sections treated to show acetylcholinesterase and this again is suggestive of acetylcholine transmission in these synapses. Amacrine cells are particularly numerous in retinas in which cones preponderate, e.g., in pigeons, and these retinas are the ones that show conspicuous stratification of acetylcholinesterase in the synaptic layer whereas, for example, the retina of the guinea pig which is very rich in rods, shows an even distribution of cholinesterase in the synaptic layer.

Neither the horizontal cells nor the amacrine cells have any processes running 'vertically' in the retina, i.e., in the direction of the main neural path.

THE OCULAR CIRCULATION. Thirty-three separate arteries enter the eyeball. The *retina* is supplied by the *arteria centralis retinae*, a branch of the ophthalmic artery. The central artery with its companion vein pierces the optic nerve about 1.25 cm. behind the eyeball and, bending sharply, runs forwards in the center of the nerve. Perforating the lamina cribrosa it appears inside the eyeball at the center of the optic disc. It immediately divides into two main branches which redivide to form a vascular network, the finer channels ending in a capillary plexus which extends outwards as far as the inner nuclear layer. The fovea itself is devoid of vessels. The *choroid, iris* and *ciliary body* are supplied by a separate system of vessels derived from the long and short posterior ciliary arteries, branches of the ophthalmic, and from the anterior ciliary arteries which are twigs of the lacrimal branch of the ophthalmic. The two long posterior ciliary arteries pierce the sclera a short distance from the optic nerve and, running forward on either side of the globe between the choroid and the sclera, anastomose with branches of the short posterior ciliary arteries and of the anterior ciliary artery to form a vascular ring (*circulus arteriosus major*) which encircles the periphery of the iris. Branches pass from this vascular circle along converging lines through the tissue of the iris to the pupillary margin; here they join to form a smaller arterial ring (*circulus arteriosus minor*). The short posterior ciliary arteries perforate the sclera around the optic nerve and supply the choroid and ciliary process. The anterior ciliary arteries and their companion veins pierce the globe a little behind the sclerocorneal junction. The blood is returned from the choroid by a system of veins in the outer choroidal layer. From their whorl-like arrangement they are termed the *vortex veins (venae vorticae)*. The smaller and medium sized vessels of this system become confluent to form four trunks which penetrate the sclera and appear on the surface of the globe equidistant from one another just behind its equator. These vessels and the anterior ciliary veins drain into the ophthalmic veins. The central vein of the retina empties into the cavernous sinus either directly or through one of the ophthalmic veins.

In man the pressure in the central artery of the retina is from 70 to 85 mm. Hg systolic and from

40 to 50 mm. diastolic. But owing to the presence of the intraocular fluid and the resistant nature of the sclerotic coat, pulsation of the retinal artery as observed by ophthalmoscopic examination is slight. The pressure in the retinal artery of the intact globe may be determined by the method of Bailliart which consists in observing the vessel with the ophthalmoscope while a measured pressure is made upon the globe. Maximal pulsation is taken as indicating the diastolic level and the disappearance of pulsation as an index of the systolic pressure. There are several fallacies in this or any other indirect method, the results being far from reliable. The pressure in the central vein of the retina is around 25 mm. Hg. A venous pulse is also observed; it is attributed to the transmission of the impulse from the artery through the intraocular fluid to the veins. That is to say, with each expansion of the artery the veins (for a short distance proximal to where they leave the orbit) are compressed and an extra quantity of blood is ejected from the eyeball.

The lens and ciliary body are described in chapter 15, the visual pathway and ocular muscles in chapter 16.

The Photochemistry of Vision

It was suggested as long ago as 1866 by Max Schultze that the retina is a duplex organ, dependent on the activity of its two types of receptor, namely rods and cones. This idea has been abundantly confirmed and it is now generally agreed (for reasons that will appear later) that at ordinary levels of illumination (*photopic conditions*) the activity of the cones predominates, but below an illumination of about 0.01 millilamberts (*scotopic conditions*) the cones cease to contribute; vision then becomes exclusively dependent on rods. This phenomenon obviously simplifies the problem of investigating certain aspects of the visual processes, particularly those which are associated with the action of the rods, since at low light intensities the cones no longer complicate the issue. (See Table 13.1).

In 1922, Hecht and Williams amplified the earlier work of König and Abney, and measured the *absolute scotopic sensitivity* of the human eye to the different wave lengths of the spectrum under more thoroughly standardized conditions than had hitherto been used. Before such measurements are made, the subjects must remain in total darkness for at least an hour (see p. 296) and then the intensity of the light of each wave length, illuminating an area of standard size for a given time, and just causing a sensation of light in 50% of the trials is determined. In order to eliminate the effects of the dilation of the pupil which occurs in darkness, the subject views the test field through an artificial pupil of about 3 mm. diameter.

When the necessary calibrations of the light source, neutral filters, etc., have been made, a curve is plotted to relate the threshold energy in ergs of the light entering the eye to wave length (fig. 13.15). This *scotopic visibility curve* shows that under these conditions the threshold energy is least, i.e., the eye is most sensitive, at a wave length of about 507 mμ. At this wave length the minimal energy entering the eye was found to be between 2.1 and 5.7 $\times$ 10^{-10} ergs as measured at the cornea. On the other hand, the curve indicates that the threshold energy rises enormously beyond about 400 mμ and 650 mμ, at the ends of the visible spectrum.

As already mentioned, the outer segments of the rods of some animals can be seen to contain a reddish pigment which bleaches on exposure to light. The pigment itself can be extracted from excised retinas, including that of man, by the action of bile salts, digitonin or by supersonic disruption of the rods. This visual purple or rhodopsin was first discovered by Boll in 1876 and extracted from the retina by Kühne in 1878. Such solutions are readily bleached by light within the visible range of wave lengths from about 380 mμ to 650 mμ and very much less readily by wave lengths beyond these limits. When the absorption of light by the pigment at different wave lengths is plotted against wave length, a curve is obtained which, when suitably corrected for absorption by breakdown products, etc., is strikingly similar to the visibility curve for the dark-adapted eye, although there are slight differences in shape and in the positions of the maxima.

These observations clearly indicate that vision by the rods is fundamentally a photochemical reaction with visual purple as the photosensitive pigment, a hypothesis which is made even more probable by the fact that vision, up to about 0.03 sec., obeys the Bunsen-Roscoe law formulated for photochemical processes in general, namely, that for the production of a given photochemical effect a constant quantity of energy is required which can be distributed within certain limits by varying either the illumination or its duration. In other words, the product of the illumination (I) and the time of exposure (T) is constant, Energy = kIT.

Nevertheless, if the hypothesis is valid, then various discrepancies between the scotopic visi-

TABLE 13.1

Luminance (Brightness) in millilamberts		
0.0000001	Visual threshold after dark adaptation	
0.000001		
0.00001	White surface lit by moonless night sky	Scotopic (Rod) Vision
0.0001		
0.001		
0.01	White surface lit by moonlit night sky	
0.1	Read newsprint with difficulty	Transition Zone
1		
10	Comfortable reading	
100	Adequate for finest visual task	
1,000	Luminance of white paper in full sunlight	
10,000		
100,000		Photopic (Cone) Vision
1,000,000	Incandescent lamp filament	
10,000,000		
100,000,000	Carbon arc	
1,000,000,000	Sun	
10,000,000,000	A-bomb first 3 milliseconds	Damage to retina

bility curve and absorption spectrum of visual purple must be satisfactorily removed.

In making comparisons between the visual performance and the absorption spectrum of the supposed visual pigment there are several points to be considered. First, it is necessary to take note of the energy distribution of the light source used in each case and of its photochemical efficiency at different wave lengths.

Different sources of light have not the same spectral composition. For example, electric (incandescent tungsten) light is relatively rich in rays from the red end of the spectrum and poor in rays from the blue end; sunlight is much more uniformly distributed throughout the spectrum, whereas "north sky" light is more powerful in the blue region than in the red (Fig. 13.16). Fluorescent tubes generally have, in addition to a fairly uniform background, large peaks of radia-

tion corresponding to the lines of the original mercury arc. It is customary, therefore, to express all visibility and absorption curves in terms of an "equal energy spectrum." This is a purely hypothetical concept. It means simply that the light source must be calibrated in terms of the energy which it emits at different wave lengths so that the sensitivity or absorption can be standardized for each wave length and so made independent of the particular form of illuminant. If, for example, the amounts of light required to reach threshold at, let us say, wave lengths 470 mμ and 550 mμ were determined by either the densities of neutral filters or by the apertures required in rotating sectors in the path of the light, first with incandescent electric light and second with "north sky" daylight the ratios would be entirely different in the two cases. In electric light, far less red would be required than in daylight. When, however, the data are corrected in terms of the actual energy required (as measured by a suitably calibrated photocell) the two sets of figures become comparable. All modern visibility, absorption and threshold measurements starting with those of Hecht and Williams, make not only this correction but also one other similar and necessary correction. The photochemical effects on the pigment depend

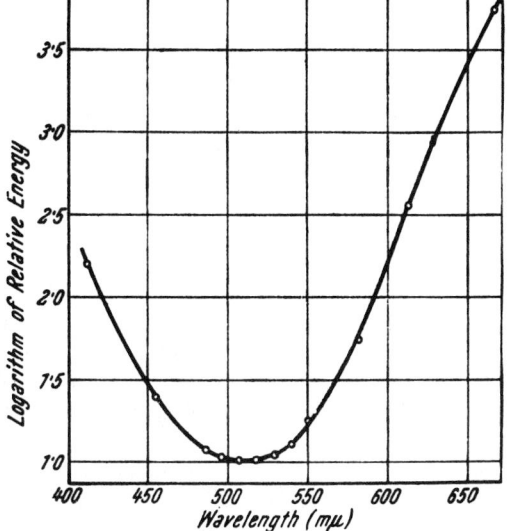

FIG. 13.15. Relation between energy for scotopic vision and wave length. (From Hecht & Williams.)

not so directly on the energy absorbed as on the number of quanta absorbed, so that the energy values at each wave length next have to be converted into quanta. Probably the most accurate scotopic visibility curve so far produced is that of Crawford (1949).

Radiant energy is expressed in *ergs*. The erg is a purely objective or physical unit, being quite independent of visual sensations. The energy is measured by means of a thermopile, bolometer or radiometer. Light is radiated in elementary units called *quanta*. The energy content of a quantum of light is proportional to the frequency of the radiation, ν, and equal to $h\nu$, where h is Planck's *constant of action*, 6.62×10^{-27} erg $\times$ second. The frequency ν is equal to the velocity of light (2.998×10^{10} cm./sec.) c, divided by the wave length λ. The energy content of a quantum of light is, therefore, inversely proportional to the wave length of the radiation. Thus the quantum of green light is 3.84×10^{-12} ergs and it has a greater energy content than one of orange or red. The *meter candle* is a unit which is in part subjective and in part objective. It is a measure of surface illumination, being defined as the light *incident* per second per sq. cm. of a surface placed at right angles to the beams from a standard (international) candle 1 meter distant (a standard candle is made of spermaceti, weighs $\frac{1}{6}$ lb., and burns 120 grains of wax per hour with a flame 45 mm. high). Illumination is measured by means of a photometer. If, for example, the illumination of a lamp is to be

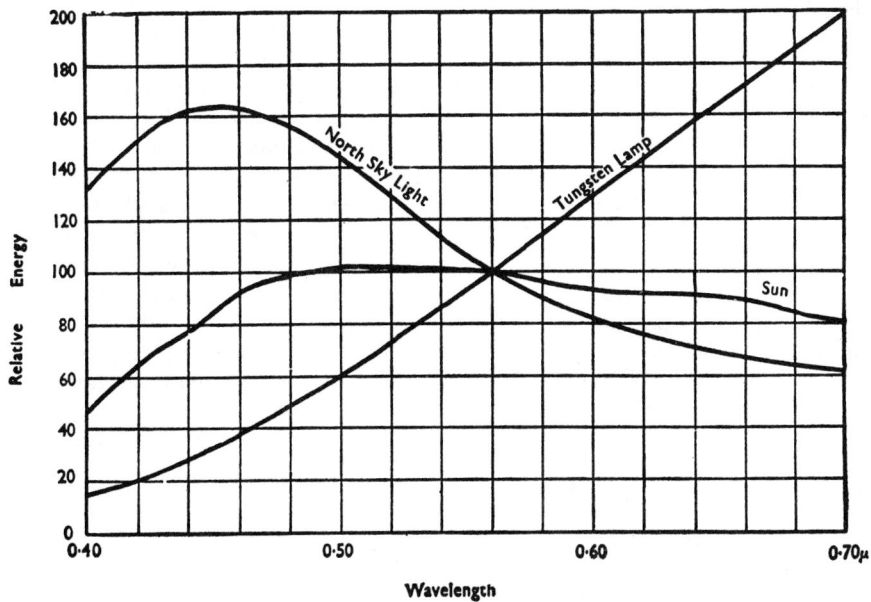

FIG. 13.16. Relative energy distribution curves for light from a gas-filled tungsten lamp, the sun, and average north sky light. (From Wright.)

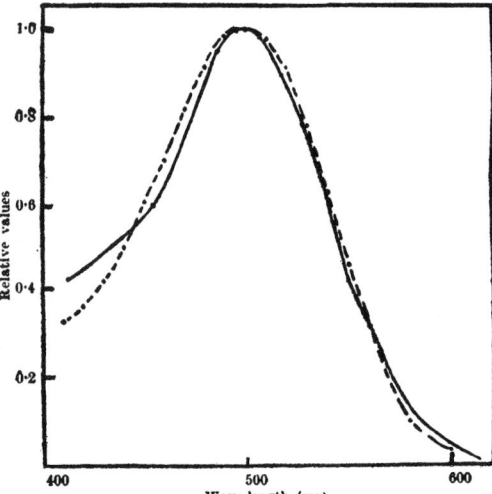

FIG. 13.17. Comparison of the absorption curve of pure visual purple (interrupted line) with the scotopic luminosity curve (continuous line) as obtained with an equal quantum spectrum. (After Ludvigh.)

measured, a photometer is set up at this point, and a standard candle is moved until its light just matches that of the lamp. If the candle's distance in meters is d, then the surface illumination is $1/d^2$. The meter candle is thus a measure of the visual stimulus, not of the sensation itself. The quantity of light *reflected* from a perfectly diffusing surface (e.g., of magnesium oxide) 10,000 meter candles is termed a *lambert;* a millilambert is 1/1000 lambert. The *lumen* is the unit of *emitted* light (*luminous flux*). One lumen is the light emitted in a *unit of solid angle* by a uniform point source of 1 standard candle. A point source is regarded as occupying the center of a sphere; a unit solid angle is the angle subtended at the center of the sphere by an area on its surface equal to the square of the radius. The area of a sphere is $4\pi r^2$, therefore one standard candle emits 4π lumens. The intensity of a light source is expressed in lumens, i.e., the luminous flux emitted in any direction per unit of solid angle.

In recent years the photometric unit system has been revised. The unit of luminous intensity is now called the *candela* which is approximately equal to the obsolete "standard candle." A *full radiator* (black body) at the melting point of platinum emits 60 candelas per square centimeter. The popular unit of illumination is now the *lux* or meter-candle, which is the illumination falling on a surface placed one meter from a point source of one candela. The units of luminance have also altered. The internationally recognized unit of luminance is the *nit* or candela per square meter (*cd*/sq. mm.). The millilambert equals $10/\pi$ or 3.183 *cd*/sq. mm. The *stilb*

is another unit of luminance sometimes used and it is a *cd*/sq. cm.

The unit of retinal illumination is called the *photon*, or, preferably, the *troland*. The amount of light which illuminates the retina depends not only upon the brightness of the object but also upon the size of the pupil. A troland is, therefore, defined as the illumination of the retina by light from a surface having the brightness of one standard candle per square meter, as seen through a pupil having an area of 1 sq. mm.

Such comparisons as those between the scotopic visibility curve and the absorption spectrum of rhodopsin are only legitimate when the data are fully corrected to an equal quantum spectrum. When this is done the two curves become practically coincident over a large part of the spectrum, but still they are not identical (Fig. 13.17). They still diverge somewhat widely and rather inconstantly in the short-wave (blue) part of the spectrum, but this discrepancy can be explained partly on physiological grounds. The amount of light which actually reaches the visual cells of the retina is of course only that which is not absorbed by the ocular structures on its way. It is therefore important to know the absorptive properties of the cornea, aqueous humor, lens, vitreous humor and the neural layers of the retina.

The cornea transmits rays from λ 295 mμ to λ 2,500 mμ, but above 1,800 mμ the transmission is slight. Maximum transmission occurs at around 1,000 mμ and continues high at shorter wave-lengths until the ultraviolet is reached. Absorption then becomes pronounced and is complete at about 295 mμ. The aqueous humor and vitreous body are somewhat less transparent than the cornea. All rays above 2700 mμ are absorbed by the aqueous humor and all above about 1600 mμ by the vitreous. The lens absorbs all rays below 300 mμ, or above 2500 mμ; most of the rays longer than 1300 mμ are absorbed. Maximal transparency is between 400 and 1200 mμ. That is, most of the rays outside this range are absorbed by the lens. Wave lengths between 350 mμ and 400 mμ cause fluorescence in the lens. The phenomenon of fluorescence, in general, is attributed to the transference of the energy of the incident radiations to particles of the substance absorbing them. The particles then act as independent light sources, emitting waves which are, for the most part, longer than the original radiation. Thus, the lens converts the harmful shorter waves to longer ones which are permitted to reach the retina. That wave lengths shorter than those which are transmitted by the lens are capable of stimulating the retina is shown by the fact that the visible spectrum is extended towards the blue end after removal of a lens of normal transparency. The lower limit of transparency of the lens rises with age. This is partly caused by increased pigmentation and partly by more scattering by the lens structures. In the aged it is opaque to rays shorter than about 400 mμ. In the early stages of cataract the lower limit is around 450 mμ.

When the corrections for loss in the optical media are made, the agreement between the two curves becomes very much closer. Not all the light which falls on the rods is absorbed by the rhodopsin. Indeed most of it (80%) passes through the rods to be absorbed by the pigment layers of the retina and the choroid; however, a small fraction is reflected back. When allowances are made for this, it can be stated with some confidence that the maximum sensitivity of the retina is such that only from 2 to 14 quanta of light need to be absorbed by the rods in a given area and within a given time for a sensation of light to be evoked. This means that a stimulated rod must give its signal to the bipolar cell when only a single quantum of light has been absorbed and as the result of the breakdown of a single molecule. Several such discharges must be combined (2 to 14) on to one optic nerve fiber within about 0.1 sec. to cause sufficient impulses for the stimulus to be perceived. The retina has thus achieved almost the highest sensitivity physically possible for the amount of photopigment which it contains. The extraordinary sensitivity of the retina to light may be expressed in simpler terms by saying that light emitted by a standard candle at a distance of nearly a mile would be visible if the air were perfectly transparent. Pirenne has made the interesting calculation that the mechanical energy of a pea falling from a height of 1 inch, if converted to luminous energy would be sufficient to cause a faint visual sensation "to every man that ever lived." The minimum quantity of light energy required to evoke a visual sensation increases progressively towards either end of the spectrum, being several thousand times greater for red and blue than for green light.

In this account of the determination of the absolute threshold at various wave lengths the field of view has been considered as being large and no restrictions have been placed on the part of the retina stimulated. With small fields, and with fixed positions on the retina the results in terms

of threshold may be very different, and will be discussed later. Nevertheless, it is important to emphasize that processes of summation go on extensively in the retina. For example, when the field is small it can be shown that all the light falling within a certain area, the *summation area*, within a given time, the *summation time*, is summed in order to give the response. With very small fields the eye cannot distinguish between an intense point-source and a less intense but larger area of light, provided it falls within the limits of the summation area. Up to a certain size of field (which depends on the wave length of the light used and on the position on the retina) IA is constant, where I is the light intensity and A is the area of the field. This is known as *Riccò's Law*. With larger fields and in the retinal periphery the relationship is much more nearly $I \times \sqrt{A} = K$ and this is known as *Piper's Law*. These are only approximations, and various other formulas have been suggested as describing the relationship in the extra-foveal area more accurately.

From what has already been said about the characteristics of vision as mediated by the rods, it is clear that the essential visual process is the photochemical breakdown of rhodopsin, and reasons will be advanced for the belief that something very similar is the basis for vision by the cones.

Rhodopsin is one of a large class of photosensitive pigments which are formed by combination of a carotenoid derivative with a protein. Such pigments are widely distributed throughout the animal kingdom and indeed almost all the responses of animals (and also of plants) to light which have been investigated have been found to have carotenoid pigments involved in them at some stage.

Rhodopsin, itself, (λ max. 497–500 mμ) is formed from *retinene$_1$* , which is the aldehyde of vitamin A$_1$ and as such is a derivative of β-carotene, the yellow pigment widely distributed in vegetables and fruits, e.g., carrots, tomatoes, oranges etc. (See Fig. 13.18).

When it is acted upon by light, it first breaks down to yellowish substances, which were originally called *transient orange* and *indicator yellow* the latter being so called because its color changes with pH. Eventually it forms the colorless retinene$_1$ and the protein. If retinene is extracted from bleached retinas, it can again be combined with a protein also extracted from rods and unspecifically called *opsin*, and a photosensitive rhodopsin is regenerated if the reaction takes place in the dark. There are several isomers of vitamin A and of retinene and for the regeneration of the photosensitive pigment the 11-cis isomer (neo-retinene b) is required. The all-trans form, in which vitamin A usually occurs, cannot produce the photosensitive pigment and has to be isomerized before it can do so. The breakdown from rhodopsin to retinene appears to be fairly readily reversible, but if the light acts more thoroughly, the retinene changes to vitamin A, i.e., from the aldehyde to the alcohol, and metabolic processes involving the oxidizing systems, e.g., the dehydrogenases, so richly present in the ellipsoids of the inner segments of the rods, are required to reconvert the vitamin to retinene once more. Fig. 13.18 shows some of the main features of the process as it is at present under-

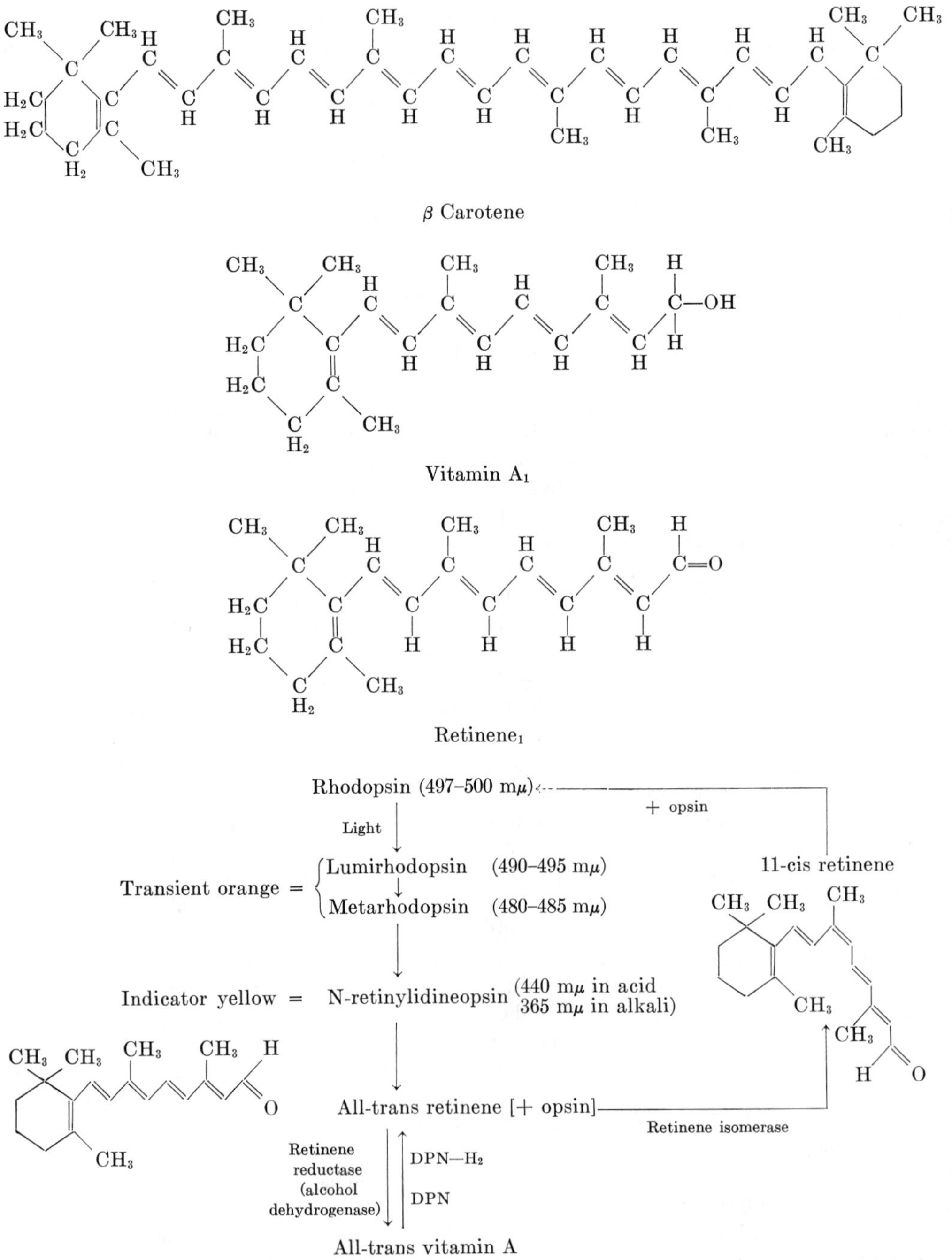

β Carotene

Vitamin A$_1$

Retinene$_1$

FIG. 13.18. Chart showing the main features of the rhodopsin cycle. (After Morton and Pitt.)

stood. The nature of the link with the protein is still under investigation, but an increase in free SH-groups can be detected when rhodopsin yields retinene. There is now thought to be one chromophore group, i.e., one retinene molecule, in each unit of rhodopsin and the molecular weight of the whole has been estimated at about 40,000.

When the retinas of many fresh-water vertebrates are extracted in the dark with digitonin a variant of rhodopsin is found, and, in life, the retinas of these animals appear much more purple than the reddish retinas of most marine and terrestrial vertebrates. This variant, which is named *porphyropsin*, has its maximum sensitivity at about 523 mμ (*cf.* rhodopsin at 500 mμ) and the photosensitivity of the eyes is correspondingly shifted towards the long-wave end of the spectrum. This pigment yields retinene$_2$, differing from retinene$_1$ by the presence of an extra double bond in the ionone ring and yielding vitamin A$_2$ on

thus appears that there are four main classes of visual pigments related to the retinenes.

Pigment	*Composition*	λ *max.*[3]	*Animals*
Rhodopsin	Retinene$_1$ + rod opsin	500 mμ	Frog and mammals
Iodopsin	Retinene$_1$ + cone opsin	560 mμ	Birds
Porphyropsin	Retinene$_2$ + rod opsin	522 mμ	Fresh-water fish
Cyanopsin	Retinene$_2$ + cone opsin	609 mμ	(? turtles)

This is undoubtedly an oversimplification, in the sense that the opsins are not to be considered as single substances, and just as the properties of hemoglobinlike compounds may differ not only with changes in the prosthetic (hæm) group but also with the particular globin, so it appears that

Vitamin A$_2$

further bleaching. The significance of this variation in the structure of the vitamin is still an unsolved problem. It appears to be connected in some way with the ionic content of the animal's environment. Although it may be some advantage to fish living in the deeper waters of the sea to have a pigment that is more sensitive to the blue rays—the only rays which penetrate through any depth of water—it is a little difficult to see that this can apply to the change in the character of the pigment in the eye of the bullfrog when this animal leaves the water and emerges on dry land.

When either of these retinenes, of the correct isomeric form, is mixed in the dark with proteins suitably extracted from eyes in which cones can be seen, histologically, to preponderate, e.g., certain birds, then other photosensitive pigments are obtained whose maxima are located more towards the red end of the spectrum. For example, retinene$_1$ combined with the cone opsin from chicken retinas gives a violet pigment *iodopsin* with maximum sensitivity at about 560 mμ, whereas retinene$_2$ combined with 'opsin' from the eye of the chicken gives *cyanopsin*, with its maximum at about 609 mμ. The difference spectrum of iodopsin corresponds rather closely to the spectral sensitivity of the chicken, and pigments with maxima near 610 mμ also occur in nature, e.g., in turtles where cones again dominate the retina. It

visual pigments may differ not only (as above) in the retinene part of the molecule, but also, more specifically, in the protein part also. Analysis of the retinas of a wide variety of animals suggests the existence of several families of pigments, each based on one of the four main ones indicated, but differing in λ max. by virtue of their different proteins. For example, rhodopsinlike pigments have been obtained with maxima lying between 483 mμ and 510 mμ. It is thus theoretically possible that almost any maximum between about 470 mμ and 620 mμ could be obtained by suitable variations of the molecules in the systems so far revealed. Nor does this rule out other possibilities for visual pigments, because other carotenoids, e.g., xanthophyll, are known to combine with proteins to produce pigments which are photosensitive. Ovoverdin, the blue-green pigment of lobsters and certain marine eggs, is a compound of the carotenoid astaxanthin and a protein and is unstable both to heat and light.

Although there is now no doubt that human rods contain and depend upon rhodopsin, the

---

[3] There are often small differences in the position of λ max. in all these pigments. They are probably dependent on the specific characters of the opsins.

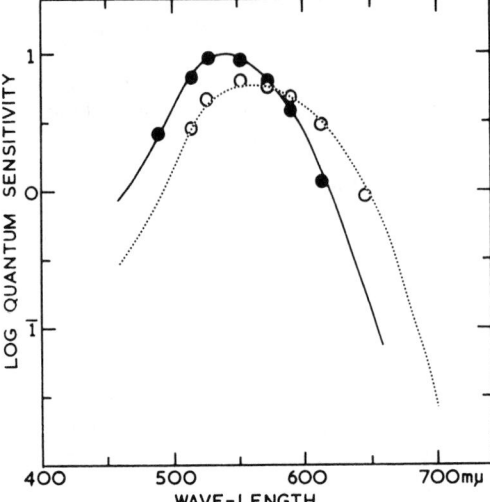

FIG. 13.19a. Pigments in the fovea of the human eye. Black circles show the efficacy of bleaching of chlorolabe by lights of various wave-lengths; white circles show the same for erythrolabe. In the particular form of red-green color blindness known as protanopia, (p. 309) only one pigment (chlorolabe) appears to be present in the fovea. The measurements for chlorolabe were made on protanopes and their spectral sensitivity in the fovea is indicated by the continuous curve. In another form of red-green color blindness (deuteranopia) only erythrolabe is present in the fovea; the white circles and dotted curve refer to such subjects. (Circles from Rushton, curves from Willmer).

visual pigment or pigments in the human cones have not been extracted in the same way, although they must obviously be present in the living eye. Objective evidence as to their nature comes from some recent work of exceptional precision by Rushton, who has made use of the minute amount of light which is reflected back from the foveal region of the eye and which comes from the pigment layer and the choroid and has thus passed twice through the retina (once on its way in and once on its way out). He has found that, after subjecting the eye to a strong light, the test light emerges brighter than before; from this he concludes that the strong light bleaches the cone pigments. By varying the wave-lengths of both the bleaching and test lights, the difference spectra of the pigments can be measured. Red light produced transparency to the red part of the spectrum; green light to the green part. By this technique, which is neither as simple nor unfortunately as accurate as it sounds (because of the incredibly small amounts of pigment present and of the reflected light available), Rushton has demonstrated the probable existence of two cone pigments in the normal eye. These he has christened *chlorolabe* and *erythrolabe* because they ab-

sorb most actively in the green and in the red parts of the spectrum respectively. The relative efficacy of different spectral lights in bleaching erythrolabe and chlorolabe is shown by the circles in figure 13.19a.

Marks, Dobelle and MacNichol have recently gone further and performed the almost incredible feat of measuring difference spectra in individual cones in the freshly excised retinae of monkeys and man, by means of a recording microspectrometer and by feeding the information into a computer. They have found that there are elements with three distinct ranges of spectral sensitivity. One type has a spectral absorption roughly corresponding to that of chlorolabe, another to that of erythrolabe, while a third has a maximum more in the region of 450 mμ. Their curves are shown in figure 13.19b, and somewhat similar results have been claimed by Brown and Wald. If these results, which it must be realised are obtained by pushing a number of procedures up to, or even beyond, their usual limits, can be further substantiated, they become of cardinal importance for theories of colour vision (see p. 301).

Electrical Records from the Eye and Optic Nerve

Electrical records from eyes fall into two main categories. The first includes the *electroretinogram*, which is a more or less generalized electrical response which the eye makes to illumination. It can be picked up from the living intact eye even in man and, like the electrocardiogram and electroencephalogram, has considerable value and importance in diagnosing abnormalities, but is too generalized a response to be easy to interpret in detail. It seems to have its origin primarily in the layer of rods and cones.

The second category includes the records that can be obtained from the eyes of animals by applying microelectrodes to individual cells or nerve fibers. These give much more precise information but cannot be obtained from man. From other animals they can only be obtained after anesthetization or decerebration, and, in any case, under rather unphysiological conditions, but nevertheless they do provide direct evidence as to how some of the neural elements in the retina behave.

RETINAL ACTION CURRENTS; THE ELECTRORETINOGRAM (ERG). When the cornea and the optic nerve or the posterior pole of the darkened eyeball are connected through a galvanometer, a current is set up with the cornea as the positive pole. A steady deflection of the galvanometer re-

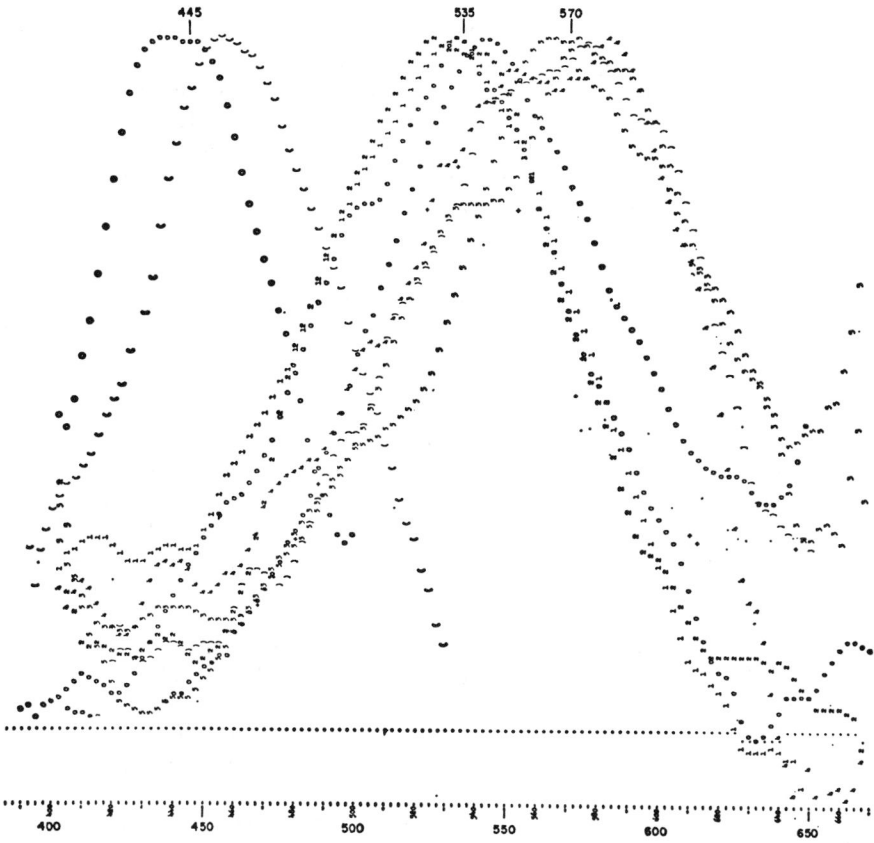

FIG 13.19b. Absorption difference spectra from ten individual primate cones, corrected for bleaching by the measuring beam. Curves recorded from monkey cones (*Macaca nemistrina* and *M. mulata*) are represented by numbers, those from humans by open parentheses. Maximum absorption, 3 to 6 per cent, except the human blue, 0.4 per cent, is decreased by light scattered past the receptor. This figure is a photograph of the original record plotted automatically by a digital computer.

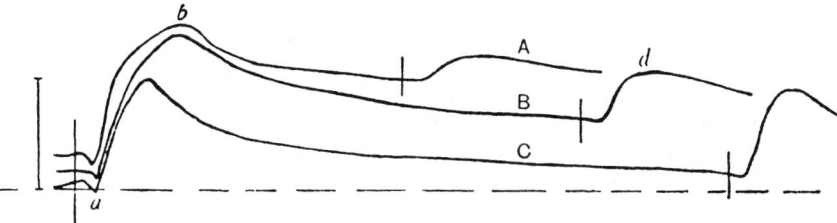

FIG. 13.20. Electroretinograms from the eye of the frog with three different durations of the stimulus. (*A*, 1 sec.; *B*, 1.5 sec.; *C*, 2 sec.) and at two different states of adaptation. In *A* and *B* the frog had been dark-adapted for 4 hr; in *C* it had been adapted to 1800 mc. Strength of stimulus, 1800 mc; calibration 0.673 mv. (From Granit.)

sults. The cause of this resting potential is not clearly understood. When a light is thrown into the eye a series of potential changes is produced which can be recorded as a corresponding sequence of waves. These are the retinal action currents, the record is called an *electroretinogram* (fig. 13.20). A steady current is also set up when the inner and outer surfaces of the eyeball are connected.

Holmgren, the Swedish physiologist, was the first (in 1866) to demonstrate retinal action currents when the eye is stimulated by a beam of light. From then to the beginning of the present century they were studied by a number of investigators, including Dewar and McKendrick, Waller and Gotch. They were recorded with the string galvanometer by Einthoven and Jolly in 1908 and by Piper, by means of the capillary electrometer, in a series of studies from 1908 to 1911. In recent years with the development of more delicate methods of recording the subject has been reinvestigated by Chaffee, Bovie and Hampson, by Hartline, by Granit and his associates, and by numerous others.

In the earlier experiments, records were obtained from the surviving excised eye, and in many instances after removal of the anterior half of the globe, or from preparations in which dissection had caused a considerable degree of trauma. Although it was necessary to place one electrode directly upon the retina in order to prove the retinal origin of the currents, better results can be obtained by leaving the eye *in situ* and placing one electrode, which may take the form of a contact lens, upon the cornea of the illuminated eye and the other (indifferent electrode) upon the eye of the opposite side or upon any moist surface of the body. Typical electroretinograms are obtained in this way. In another method, as used by Hartline and Adrian for man, a cotton-tipped electrode is applied directly to the illuminated eye after anesthetization with a 2% solution of holocaine; the indifferent electrode is placed in the mouth.

The most satisfactory preparation from which to record the electroretinogram is the decerebrate animal, since more perfect immobilization is thus secured, as well as full pupillary dilation. The indifferent electrode is placed upon brain tissue on the proximal side of the decerebration cut, and the other electrode on the cornea. The recording instrument most commonly employed was first the string galvanometer but is now some type of oscillograph, the currents being first suitably amplified.

The latent period of the electroretinogram is shorter than that for any impulses which have ever been picked up directly from the retina. When an electrode is slowly and carefully passed through the retina large potential changes occur at about the level of the external limiting membrane and these are affected by illumination. For these and a variety of other reasons the electroretinogram is thought to originate in the layer of the rods and cones. During embryonic development the ERG first appears when the rod and

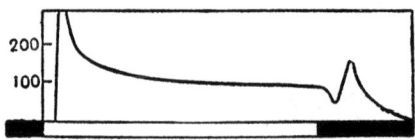

200
100

Fig. 13.21. Curve of frequencies of impulses in optic nerve. Duration of stimulus indicated by space in the base line (several sec.). (After Adrian and Matthews.)

cone layer differentiates and, later in life, damage localized to the rod and cone layer alters or abolishes the ERG. For this reason the electroretinogram is often a rather sensitive clinical sign of degeneration in the receptor layers.

The form of the electroretinogram varies with the state of adaptation of the eye and with the wave length of the light used to produce it (fig. 13.20). The large positive b-wave is probably mostly produced by the rods; it is largest in poor illumination and with blue light. In light-adaptation and with red light the negative a-wave becomes more conspicuous, and an earlier rise occurs in the b-wave often constituting a separate X-wave. This X-wave is absent in cases of total color-blindness and is much reduced in that form of red-green color-blindness which is known as protanopia (see p. 309). This suggests that it is associated with the activity of those cones which are most sensitive to the red end of the spectrum. The ordinary response seems likely to be compounded of two diphasic variations each with an early negative phase followed by a later positive phase. The quicker response is associated with the cone mechanism, which also seems to have the greater negative component.

NERVE IMPULSES IN THE OPTIC NERVE. Action currents in the optic nerve were first investigated by Adrian and Matthews in the optic nerve of the conger eel. This animal was selected because it has a very long optic nerve and few nerve fibers in it, thus facilitating experimentation. The nerve was found to be almost 'quiet' in the dark but when light shone into the eye there was a burst of impulses after a latent period of 0.1 to 0.5 sec. according to the strength of the stimulus. After an initial high frequency of discharge, impulses continued at a decreased frequency for as long as the illumination lasted and then, when the light was turned off, another burst of impulses was recorded (the *off-effect*) (fig. 13.21).

Nerve impulses in the eye of Limulus. Since these early experiments much basic information about the relationship between stimulus and response in a photoreceptor unit has been learned from a study of the eye, not of a vertebrate, but of the king crab (*Limulus polyphemus*), mostly by Hartline and his colleagues. This compound eye is built on very different lines from that of the eye of all vertebrates in that it consists of numerous ommatidia, each comprising a group of 10–20 elongated retinula cells, with which one large central nerve cell is functionally connected, and this cell transmits impulses to the optic ganglion which lies at some distance from the photoreceptors. This eye is therefore somewhat simpler than that of any vertebrate, since the photoreceptors stimulate the central cell directly and impulses can be picked up from that cell or its nerve fiber, whereas in the eyes of vertebrates at least two synapses intervene between the receptor and the first place where impulses can be easily recorded. In the vertebrate eye, potential changes can be recorded in the rod and cone layer and probably even from single cells in it, but the first place where definite nerve impulses appear is in the ganglion-cell layer and the emergent nerve fibers. The evidence as to the nature of the conduction through the bipolar cell layer is somewhat conflicting. Some cells in it appear to produce spikes, but there are also large slow potentials. Limulus is therefore a much more suitable animal than any vertebrate would be in which to investigate the relationship between stimulus and response in a photoreceptor unit. There are, however, reasons to believe that the apparent simplicity of the ommatidium of Limulus may in fact be spurious, for there is some evidence for a feed-back mechanism which regulates the response.

In Limulus the nerve is practically silent in the dark. When a light is shone on the ommatidium there is a short latent period (about 0.1 sec.) and then the frequency of impulses in the neural discharge varies with the intensity of the stimulus and with the state of adaptation of the eye, i.e., on whether the eye has recently been exposed to light (fig. 13.22). The ommatidium, like the receptors in the human eye, can also be stimulated mechanically or electrically and it is interesting to note that the latent period in electrical stimulation is shorter than it is for stimulation by light. Presumably the photochemical changes take time to complete. The amplitude of the impulses, as in other nerve fibers is constant (p. 41) and independent of the strength of the stimulus. As in the eel, the onset of illumination produces a high initial frequency, which rather rapidly dies down to a slower and relatively constant frequency. With short flashes, the impulse frequency varies with the product of the duration of the flash and its intensity, i.e., with the total amount of photochemical change, and thus this system also obeys the Bunsen Roscoe law (fig. 13.23). Within a limited time, therefore, it is possible to record a given frequency of impulses either by using an intense flash of short duration or a longer flash of lower intensity. The summation time, within which this is possible is about 0.2 sec.

The retina of Limulus shows considerable

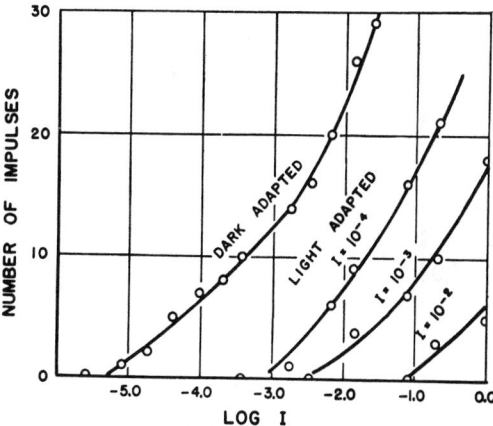

FIG. 13.22. Number of impulses in single nerve fibers in the eye of Limulus in response to test flashes (0.01 sec. duration) of different intensities (abscissae) given when the eye was adapted to darkness or to three different light intensities. (From Hartline and McDonald.)

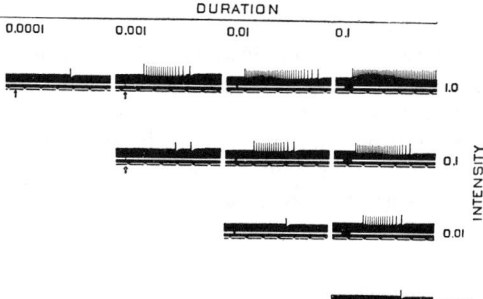

FIG. 13.23. Oscillograph records of impulses from a single optic nerve fiber of Limulus caused by brief flashes of light of varying intensity and duration. Note that the frequency of the impulses is a function of the product of these two variables. When the products are equal, the frequency of the impulses is virtually the same. (After Hartline.)

powers of adaptation and becomes more sensitive, discharging more impulses at a higher frequency for a given stimulus, when it has previously been kept in the dark.

Similarly, when the eye is placed in darkness and the intensity of light which will just produce a single impulse is measured, it is found that the necessary intensity falls rapidly at first and then more slowly and the ommatidium increases its sensitivity continuously and asymptotically for a period of about an hour. This is an important observation in any consideration of the mechanism for the rather similar phenomenon which occurs in the human eye when the subject remains in the dark and where the possibility of the adaptation occurring in the neural mechanism of the retina has to be considered. The relationship

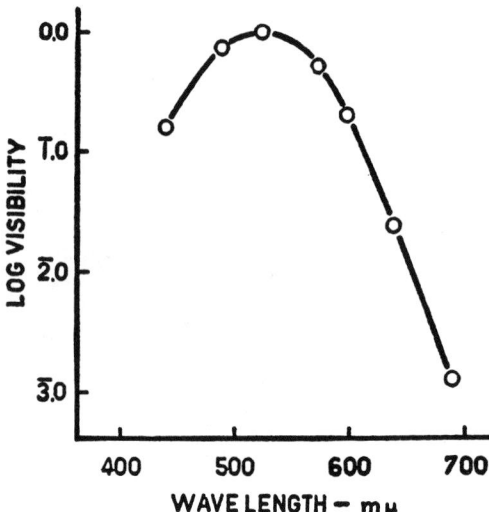

FIG. 13.24. Visibility curve for a single visual cell in the eye of Limulus. (From Graham and Hartline.)

between impulse frequency and strength of the stimulus at different states of adaptation in the ommatidium of Limulus is shown in figure 13.22.

Under constant background conditions, and with a given duration of flash the frequency of impulses in the initial discharge varies more nearly with the logarithm of the intensity of the stimulus than with its intensity directly. This does not apply at very low intensities, near the threshold, nor at very high intensities, but over several $\log_{10}$ units in the middle range of intensities the logarithmic relationship is approximately true. Very much the same remarks apply also to the frequency of the sustained discharge, but the frequencies are then much lower.

If monochromatic light is used, it is found that the frequency of discharge varies with the wave length. By using different intensities of light of different wave lengths it is possible to elicit any given frequency of impulses and when these measurements of intensity are recorded for the different wave lengths it is found that the lowest intensity occurs at about 500 mμ and the curve obtained is almost identical with that obtained by plotting the light intensities necessary to reach threshold in the dark-adapted human eye (fig. 13.24). The probability is therefore very high that the ommatidium in Limulus depends on the same pigment (rhodopsin) and on the same photochemical process as does the human rod. The information obtainable from Limulus is therefore directly relevant to human vision and can be used in trying to analyze the process involved in the much more complex system of the human retina from

which direct information of the same type cannot be obtained.

In Limulus it is clearly impossible for the animal to distinguish between the wave length and the intensity of a light on the basis of the information supplied by the frequency of impulses in a single optic nerve fiber. A given frequency of impulses can arise from stimulation by a low intensity of light to which the ommatidium is very sensitive (e.g., green) or by a high intensity of a light to which it is rather insensitive (e.g., red or violet) and, without further assistance from some other independent source, there can be no means of distinguishing between the two stimuli.

All that has been said so far about Limulus has referred to the stimulation of a single ommatidium. However, if a neighboring ommatidium is stimulated simultaneously, then there is some interaction between the two. They inhibit each other, and the more so the nearer they are together in the eye. Each gives a response which is less than it would give if it were stimulated separately and the impulse-frequencies are almost directly subtractive. The activity of each ommatidium is then the resultant of its own direct excitation and the inhibition exerted upon it by ommatidia simultaneously stimulated in its immediate neighborhood. An interesting example of the effects of this lateral inhibition is seen when three ommatidia more or less in line are investigated. If the first ommatidium (A) is stimulated alone it gives a response (a). When the second ommatidium (B) is simultaneously stimulated the response of the first falls to some value ($a - kb$), where b is the initial response of receptor B and k is a factor depending on the distance between receptors A and B. If now receptor C is stimulated in such a way that it tends to inhibit B but is too far away from A to affect the response of A directly, then the response of A rises owing to the decreased inhibition exerted upon it by B, whose response has fallen from b to ($b - lc$) because of the inhibitory effect of C (c is the original response of C and l is again a constant depending on the distance between B and C). The response of A is then something more like $a - k(b - lc)$, so that the effect of stimulating the third ommatidium is to increase the response from the first.

Since in such systems the interaction is mutual, the relationship is expressed by the pair of simultaneous equations:

$$R_a = E_a - K_{ab} (R_b - R^o{}_b)$$
$$R_b = E_b - K_{ba} (R_a - R^o{}_a)$$

where the subscripts a and b designate the respective receptor units, R is the final response, E is the response of the receptor when stimulated alone and K is the coefficient of the action of the one receptor on the other, which, as stated earlier, is at least partly dependent upon the distance separating the two receptors. R^o is the minimum response required to initiate the inhibition.

These observations on this relatively simple eye are clearly of the utmost importance in showing that the units are not entirely independent of each other and that there is mutual inhibition occurring between them. How this inhibition is brought about is not yet certain. There is a network of fine interlacing fibers at the base of the ommatidia which could be responsible, but it is not known how the impulse frequencies are caused to interfere in this curiously subtractive manner. The interference must occur at a stage when the stimulus has already been converted to something that varies more nearly with the logarithm of the intensity of the stimulus than with the intensity directly. This principle of mutual interference may obviously have important implications not only in relation to the performance of the human eye but also to other sense organs and parts of the central nervous system.

Nerve impulses in the eyes of vertebrates. When the lens and cornea of the eye of a vertebrate (e.g., the decerebrate cat, rabbit or monkey) are removed, microelectrodes can be gently applied to the inner surface of the retina. Provided that Ringer's solution is not used, but only the natural fluids of the eye itself, the isolated eye of the frog may be used in the same way. Under these conditions, single uniform spike-potentials can be obtained, and the majority of these spikes can be localized to the discharges from the large ganglion cells. The frequency and distribution of the impulses that are obtained are very variable and do not always bear any easily discernible relationship to the strength and duration of the stimulus. It seems to be fairly clear that the synaptic connections in the retina itself carry out a large amount of coding and sifting of the information provided by the photoreceptors.

Sometimes, even in complete darkness there may be an almost continuous and not necessarily regular discharge of impulses, and there is some indication from the results of decerebrate preparations in the cat that the better the preparation the more of this resting discharge is obtained. Presumably therefore it is something that is normal to the eye of the cat at least. The application of a stimulus of light may either increase or decrease the resting discharge. At other times, ganglion cells remain silent unless they are stimulated by light falling on the retina in their neighborhood. In this case the response may be very like those recorded in Limulus and correspond reasonably closely with the strength and duration of the stimulus. This type of discharge has been called the *on-discharge* and the fiber has been called an *on-fiber*. Alternatively the cell or fiber may give a rapid discharge of impulses when the light is turned on, then may go silent or at least reduce its frequency of discharge very considerably while the light remains on, and then give another outburst when the light is turned off. This is the *on-off type of discharge.* Thirdly it may sometimes happen that the on-effect is missing altogether and the cell only responds when the light is turned off. Such a unit is called an *off-fiber.*

There is considerable evidence that on-off- and off-effects are the result of inhibitory processes occurring within the retina itself. Nevertheless it has to be remembered that in the eye of the mollusk *Pecten* some nerve fibers yield only off-effects and in this eye the histological structure is such that the opportunity for inhibitory process to occur would appear to be small. It is of course conceivable that the build-up of rhodopsin in darkness could be turned to advantage as a means of exciting a receptor unit in the same way as its breakdown in light has been used.

From a study of the relationship between the wave length of the stimulating light and the character of the response obtained, there is strong evidence that some of these inhibitory effects are caused by interaction between the pathways in the retina activated by rods on the one hand or cones on the other. On-off-units and pure off-units are in general far more frequent in those retinas where there is a good mixture of rods and cones than in the more purely rod-retinas such as that of the guinea pig. However, this interaction between dissimilar units cannot account for the whole phenomenon, because there is, as in Limulus, much evidence for the existence of lateral inhibition when only one class of receptors, in this case rods, are in action. If, for example, a light source is so arranged that it can deliver into the retina just that intensity of monochromatic light at each wave length which would be necessary to stimulate a receptor that was dependent on rhodopsin only to give a standard and constant response, i.e., with intensities corresponding to the ordinates of figure 13.15, then a ganglion cell which gave the same response at all wave lengths would clearly be one which, under the conditions of the experiment, was being activated by receptors dependent on rhodopsin only. If some other class of receptor intervened, e.g., the cones, then the rhodopsin-equated stimulus would no longer give a uniform response from the ganglion cell throughout the spectrum. It is therefore possible to pick out ganglion cells whose response is apparently confined to rhodopsin-activated receptors (rods). Even among these units there may be "on-," "on-off-" and 'off-"elements and, what is even more important, there are some which respond to low light intensities with a pure on-effect, then as the intensity is raised they change to the on-off type and with increasing intensity again become more and more "off," until finally they respond only whenever the light is turned off. If, as seems probable, these effects arise by some sort of lateral inhibition in the retina, then such interaction must occur as the result of the stimulation of one type of receptor only, i.e., the rod, and it would seem to be the direct counterpart of the lateral inhibition discussed in relation to the responses in Limulus.

Further information on the nature of events within the retina itself has been gained by studying the responses of single ganglion cells or optic nerve fibers, mostly in the cat but also in the monkey, not to general illumination of the retina as in the above examples, but to localized stimulation by small points of light (about 0.1 mm. or less in radius). By this means it is possible to investigate directly the area of the retina which feeds its information on to any particular ganglion cell, or in other words to determine in an objective way the *receptive field* of that cell. Histological preparations indicated that such receptive fields might have a diameter of about 1 mm and the electrical records confirm this conjecture. Around the center of the receptive field there may be a plateau of high sensitivity (0.6 mm. in diameter in some peripheral ganglion cells, 0.2 mm. or less in those nearer the center of the eye). This is surrounded by an area with much lower sensitivity. The response in the central area may be an on-effect, an on-off-effect or even an off-effect, which is a point of some interest in relation to the earlier discussion of the nature of these effects. Even more interesting, however, is the fact that stimulation in the periphery of the field, or even of an area outside it, may alter the response from the center. Thus as with larger stimuli, the ganglion cells can be subdivided into on-center, off-center and on-off-center cells and it is again noteworthy that the threshold for evoking the special

on-effect is not necessarily the same as that for evoking the off-effect and, moreover, they are not constantly related to each other in different parts of a receptive field.

If two spots of light, each giving a subliminal stimulus are applied simultaneously to the receptive field of a single ganglion cell the effects are usually additive, indicating that Riccò's law is followed within the receptive field. On the other hand when one of the spots falls outside the receptive field of a ganglion cell that cell may be inhibited. This inhibition from external sources does not usually affect off-center cells but strongly affects on-off center cells, in which case the on- and the off-responses may react differently. In on-off units the inhibitory effects of peripheral stimuli may be produced from within the margins of the receptive field itself. These rather elaborate and complicated results may help to emphasize the complexity of events within the retina. This complexity is all too easily overlooked in attempts to correlate stimulus and response in visual phenomena. Even so it should be remembered that, small as are these stimuli which have been used to explore the receptive fields of ganglion cells, they still cover hundreds of photoreceptors.

By the insertion of microelectrodes into the unopened eye of the decerebrate cat, where incidentally all effects of light are superimposed on a continuous spontaneous discharge of impulses, the effects of changes in the adaptation of the eye on isolated ganglion cells have been studied. It is clear from these results that many ganglion cells receive information from both rods and cones. For example, the wave length of maximum sensitivity of a cell may change with the light intensity, indicating a change-over from the preponderance of one type of receptor to that of another (see Purkinje shift, p. 297). Dark-adaptation curves, i.e., curves relating the intensity of the threshold stimulus to time in the dark, indicate events arising in both cones and rods. If red light (to which the cones are relatively more sensitive than the rods) is used, a simple curve is obtained and the threshold does not sink as far as if green light were used when the curve acquires a knee in it which probably indicates the point at which the rod mechanism begins to determine the threshold rather than the cones (see p. 297). Even in the thoroughly dark-adapted state both on- and off-center units are found, and, in both cases, an increase in the area of receptive field stimulated lowers the threshold, but, in this state, stimulation outside the receptive field no longer exerts inhibitory effects. This change in the effects of stimulation outside the receptive field between the dark-adapted and light-adapted states takes place at lower levels of illumination than that at which the cones are thought to operate, so it is probably a change in retinal organisation rather than the introduction of a different type of receptor. The receptive field becomes smaller in light-adaptation and this effect is probably caused by the increasing effects of lateral inhibition rather than by a decrease in the area of effective synaptic connections made by the ganglion cell. As emphasized already, the lateral inhibition, while it may be partly caused by cones is certainly not entirely dependent on their action.

The extent to which the retina processes the information that it receives is further brought out by the observations of Barlow and Hill on the rabbit, by Maturana and Frenk on the pigeon, and by Hubel and Wiesel on the monkey. These authors have shown that some ganglion cells in the retina respond by trains of impulses when light sweeps across the receptive field, and in rabbits and pigeons the direction of the sweep is important. Some ganglion cells respond to movements of the stimulus in a horizontal direction, others only to vertical movements. Some ganglion cells may not respond at all to a stationary light. Hubel has found that, in the lateral geniculate body of cats, there are rather similar cells. These may respond to a stationary light, but they also respond actively when light falls within their special receptive field in the retina. These cells have on-centres and off-surrounds; they again respond when a small light traverses the receptive field but are not sensitive to the direction of its passage.

Attention has already been called (p. 278) to the presence, in the retinae of certain fish (at a level corresponding to that of the horizontal cells in other animals), of large stellate cells. These cells develop positive potentials when the retina is illuminated by the long-wave end of the spectrum, and negative potentials when illuminated by short waves, an effect which is very suggestive of opposing actions on these cells by two sorts of receptor cells (Svaetichin and MacNichol, 1958).

Such cells have not been observed in the retinae of the higher vertebrates, but De Valois and his colleagues have found cells which behave in a rather similar manner in the middle layers of the lateral geniculate body of monkeys, to which the retinal ganglion cells relay. These cells are activated to give increased numbers of spike potentials when red light falls on the retina and

their spontaneous discharges are reduced by green light on the retina. In the latter case they give an increased discharge when the light goes off. There are also other cells which respond in exactly the opposite sense. In other words, there are among these cells in the lateral geniculate body, cells which give an on-response to red and an off-response to green and other cells which do exactly the reverse. At some intermediate wavelength, depending on the previous stimulation of the unit, the response is zero. Hubel and Wiesel have recorded the presence of a limited number of similar cells among the ganglion cells of the retina of the monkey. In the case of the cells in the lateral geniculate, the minimal effect occurs in the region of 560 mμ while the cells in the retina have their minimum at about 500 mμ. This will be seen to be an observation which may be of some importance in connection with colour vision.

In short, evidence from these studies of the electrical activities of cells in the retina and optic pathway is accumulating to indicate that cells of one group tend to relay on to the cells of the next group in such a way that the latter respond either to the sum of the separate effects or to the difference between them. Moreover, in this process the spacial distribution of the cells concerned is of the utmost importance. Not only may particular regions of the retina be represented in particular parts of the higher centres but, within those centres cells may be grouped with respect to the type of stimulus which excites them. For example, Hubel and Wiesel have shown that in the visual cortex of the cat there are cells which respond only when particular patterns and shapes are projected on to the retina, or when linear stimuli are applied to the retina in particular directions.

The results obtained by such electrical recordings in the retinas of various animals are obviously of the highest importance to the understanding of the physiology of vision. Nevertheless, at this stage, the utmost caution is required in their interpretation; much further experimental analysis with improved methods will be needed before the relationships between receptors, bipolars and ganglion cells are understood. Apart from some of the more complex situations outlined above, the exact meaning to be attached to on-center cells and off-center cells is still obscure, so also is the significance to be attached to stimulation of the dendrites of a ganglion cell as opposed to stimulation of its cell body. When constant currents are passed through the retina it has been found possible to alter a ganglion cell which normally responds only at "on" to one which responds only at "off," and *vice versa*. In the human eye it is interesting to find that such currents can alter the sensitivity to red and green according to their direction.

Finally there exist many ganglion cells in the retina of the cat which apparently contribute nothing in the way of trains of impulses (or at least nothing which has so far been picked up). It is conceivable that they do not exert their effects by means of measurable impulses, but perhaps in the form of slow potentials, electrotonic effects or even chemically. Alternatively, it may be that the correct specific type of stimulus has not been applied to the retina when these cells were under investigation. Any analysis of retinal function based on the responses which have so far been recorded, and on those alone, is likely to be extremely incomplete and probably fallacious. Impulses have not been recorded with certainty from the receptors themselves except possibly in some fish but considerable potentials develop in or near the rod and cone layer during illumination as noted in connection with the electroretinogram. Intracellular recording from what are either large receptors or horizontal cells present in certain fish have recently been made and the results may be of great significance in relation to color vision (see ch. 14).

REFERENCES

ADRIAN, E. D. J. Physiol., 1945, **104**, 84; 1946, **105**, 24.

ADRIAN, E. D. AND MATTHEWS, R. J. Physiol., 1927, **63**, 378; **64**, 279; 1928, **65**, 273.

ARMINGTON, J. C. J. Opt. Soc. Am., 1952, **42**, 393.

BAKER, H. D. AND RUSHTON, W. A. A., J. Physiol. 1965, **176**, 56.

BARLOW, H. B. J. Physiol., 1953, **119**, 58, 69.

BARLOW, H. B., FITZHUGH, R. AND KUFFLER, S. W. J. Physiol., 1957, **137**, 327, 338.

BARLOW, H. B. AND HILL, R. M. Science, 1963, **139**, 412.

BRINDLEY, G. S. J. Physiol., 1956, **134**, 360; 1958, **140**, 247.

BROWN, P. K., GIBBONS, I. R., AND WALD, G. J. Cell Biol., 1963, **19**, 79.

BROWN, P. K. AND WALD, G. Nature, Lond., 1963, **200**, 37; Science, 1964, **144**, 45.

CHAFFEE, E. L., BOVIE, W. T. AND HAMPSON, A. J. Opt. Soc. Am., 1923, **7**, 1.

DE ROBERTIS, E. J. Biophys. Biochem. Cytol., 1956, **2**, 319.

DE VALOIS, R. L. J. Gen. Physiol., 1960, **43**, 115.

DE VALOIS, R. L., JACOBS, G. H., AND JONES, A. E. Optik., 1963, **20**, 87.

CRAWFORD, B. H. Proc. Phys. Soc. (London), 1949, **62B**, 321.

DEWAR, J. AND MCKENDRICK, J. G. Tr. Roy. Soc. Edinburgh, 1873, p. 141.

EINTHOVEN, W. AND JOLLY, W. A. Quart. J. Exper. Physiol., 1908, **1**, 373.

GRAHAM, C. H. AND HARTLINE, H. K. J. Gen. Physiol., 1935, **18**, 917.

HARTLINE, H. K. Am. J. Physiol., 1938, **121**, 400; 1940, **130**, 690, 700.

HARTLINE, H. K. AND GRAHAM, C. H. J. Cell. & Comp. Physiol., 1932, **19**, 277.

HARTLINE, H. K. AND McDONALD, P. R. J. Cell. & Comp. Physiol., 1947, **30**, 225.

HARTLINE, H. K. AND RATLIFF, F. J. Gen. Physiol., 1957, **40**, 357.

HARTLINE, H. K., WAGNER, H. G. AND RATLIFF, F. J. Gen. Physiol., 1956, **39**, 651.

HECHT, S., SHLAER, S. AND PIRENNE, M. H. J. Gen. Physiol., 1942, **25**, 819.

HECHT, S. AND WILLIAMS, R. E. J. Gen. Physiol., 1922, **5**, 1.

HOLMGREN, G. Centralbl. med. Wissensch., 1871, p. 423 (cited by Waller).

HUBBARD, R. AND WALD, G. J. Gen. Physiol., 1952, **36**, 269.

HUBEL, D. H. J. Physiol. 1960, **150**, 91.

HUBEL, D. H. AND WIESEL, T. N. J. Physiol., 1959, **148**, 574; 1960, **154**, 572.

KUFFLER, S. W. J. Neurophysiol., 1953, **16**, 37.

KÜHNE, W. Untersuch. physiol. Inst. Heidelberg, 1883, **2**, 89.

LUDVIGH, E. Arch. Ophth., 1938, **20**, 713.

LYTHGOE, R. J. J. Physiol., 1937, **89**, 331.

MARKS, W. B., DOBELLE, W. H., AND MacNICHOL, E. F. Science, 1964, **143**, 1181.

MATURANA, H. R. AND FRENK, S. Science, 1963, **142**, 977.

ØSTERBERG, G. Acta ophth., 1935, Suppl. 6.

RIDLEY, F. Brit. J. Exper. Path., 1930, **11**, 217.

RUSHTON, W. A. H. Nature, 1949, **164**, 743; 1957, **179**, 571; 1958, **182**, 690.

RUSHTON, W. A. H. AND CAMPBELL, F. W. Nature, 1954, **174**, 1096.

SCHULTZE, M. Arch. mikr. Anat., 1866, **2**, 175.

SJÖSTRAND, F. S. J. Cell. & Comp. Physiol., 1953, **42**, 15, 45.

STILES, W. S. Proc. Roy Soc., London, ser. B., 1937, **123**, 90.

STILES, W. S. AND CRAWFORD, B. H. Proc. Roy. Soc. London, ser. B., 1933, **112**, 428.

SVAETICHIN, G. AND MacNICHOL, E. F. Ann. N.Y. Acad. Sci., 1958, **74**, 385.

WALD, G., BROWN, P. K. AND SMITH, P. H. Science, 1953, **118**, 505.

WALLER, A. D. Quart. J. Exper. Physiol., 1909, **2**, 169.

WILLMER, E. N., J. Physiol., 1949, **110**, 422.

Monographs and Reviews

See Chapter 14

Intensity Discrimination and the Duplicity Theory of Vision; Color Vision; Visual Acuity; Flicker; After Images; Optical Illusions

Intensity Discrimination and the Duplicity Theory of Vision

With this background of more or less objective data concerning the structure of the retina, the distribution of its cells, the nature of its pigments and the electrical records obtainable from retinal structures, it will now be appropriate to examine retinal performance and the so-called psychophysical aspects of vision.

One of the most remarkable features of the human eye is the incredibly wide range of intensities of light over which it is capable of discriminating differences in intensity. This is much the same as saying that the eye performs almost equally well in light of very different absolute intensities. Basically the two main problems of vision are those connected with *intensity discrimination* on the one hand and with *hue discrimination* on the other.

At its most sensitive, the eye can detect light when only a very few quanta are absorbed by the retina and, at the other extreme, it can still detect differences in intensity when the light is more than 10,000,000 times stronger than the minimum required to reach its absolute threshold. It will be noticed that the word intensity has so far been used in this discussion, and not brightness. The reason for this is that brightness is a purely subjective phenomenon and is always more or less relative either to what has gone before or to what is simultaneously presented to the eye. It is well known that when black is placed against white, or *vice versa*, they set one another off; the black looks blacker and the white appears to be a purer white than if either were placed against a gray or colored ground. Gray also appears darker against a white than against a black ground (fig. 14.1). This is known as *simultaneous contrast*. Another example will illustrate a different aspect of the same phenomenon. If one eye, after being kept in darkness, views a field whose *luminance* or luminous intensity is 3 millilamberts while the other eye continues to view a field whose luminance is

15,000 millilamberts the two fields may give the same sensation of brightness, even though one has 5000 times the physical intensity of the other. In other words, the eye as a whole adapts to changes of intensity in much the same way as it was shown in the last chapter that the individual units in the eye of Limulus could adapt. It is largely a consequence of this capacity for adaptation that the eye can work efficiently over such wide ranges of intensity, and this is combined with the fact that there are two distinct mechanisms, the rod and the cone mechanisms, which share the intensity range. Cones predominate at higher intensities whereas the rods begin to take over when the intensity falls below about 0.01 millilamberts. This essential duality of the retinal receptor system was recognized as long ago as 1866 by Max Schultze and the suggestions for the division of labor between the two systems have become collectively known as the *Duplicity Theory of Vision* largely connected with the name of von Kries.

Intensity discrimination. This faculty was first investigated by Bouguer in 1760 and later by Weber (1834) and Fechner (1858). The latter observer found that, when the light intensity is gradually increased, the least change in illumination which can be perceived by the subject occurs in a series of steps. This relationship is expressed in the Weber-Fechner law which is applicable not only to vision but to other senses as well. The law states that the least perceptible difference between a series of stimuli is in each instance a certain constant fraction of the preceding stimulus. For example, let us suppose that for vision the fraction is $1/100$ and the initial illumination is 100 candles. Then, if the light of one more candle is added, the difference in illumination will be recognized; that is, the light of 101 candles is perceived to be greater than that of 100. If there were 1000 candles to start with, 10 more would need to be added before any difference could be noticed. If, therefore, the logarithms of the intensities are plotted (abscissas)

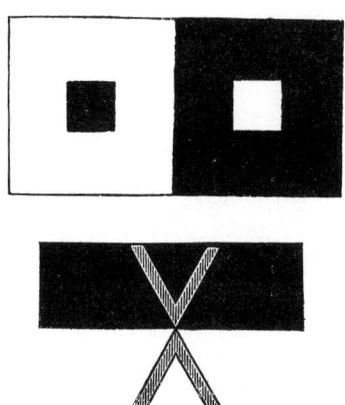

FIG. 14.1. Illustrating contrast (Hering). Observe through tissue paper.

against the least perceptible differences in sensation (ordinates) a straight line should result. The law may be stated in another way, namely, that in order to cause a series of equal increments in sensation the strength of the stimulus must increase in geometrical proportion. Or again, the added intensity (ΔI) necessary to cause a just perceptible difference in sensation (ΔS) bears a constant ratio ($\Delta I/I$) to the preceding intensity (I). Thus, $\Delta S = K (\Delta I/I)$.

When the logarithms of the light intensity are plotted against the just perceptible differences, the curve shown in fig. 14.2 is obtained. The curve is composed of three parts. It is only section A representing the relationship at moderate light intensities that accords even approximately with the Weber-Fechner law. At intensities below and above this limited range marked deviations from the law occur (sections B and C). The whole curve covers a range from the lowest intensity to one of dazzling strength and comprises 572 steps of just perceptible differences. Starting with the very lowest intensities, e.g., 0.0000484 millilamberts (I) the least absolute increment of the stimulus which is effective (ΔI) is very small (König and Brodhun's data), namely, 0.000031 millilamberts, and increases progressively as the intensity rises, so that at an illumination of 147.0 ΔI has a value of 3.803 ml. The fraction $\Delta I/I$, therefore, is not constant, nor does it show a continuous change in one direction, for it diminishes from about $\frac{2}{3}$ at the lowest intensity to about $\frac{1}{65}$ at moderate ranges and then rises again to $\frac{1}{25}$ at the highest intensity. More recent observations indicate that this increase with higher intensities does not occur if the eye is fully adapted to the basic level of intensity (I), the fraction remaining at the lowest value even though the illumination is unpleasantly intense (see Craik). Hecht considers that the low intensity part of the curve (B) represents rod func-

tion and the high intensity portion (C), the activity of the cones. The cones are therefore more sensitive to *differences* in illumination than the rods, although their threshold for light perception (intensity threshold) is higher.

It is interesting to compare these observations with those obtained by Hartline on the eye of Limulus (see p. 288 and fig. 13.22). Impulse frequency, upon which intensity discrimination presumably depends, was there found to be rather closely related to the logarithm of the intensity of the stimulus over quite a wide range of intensity levels. However, the state of adaptation of the eye was also found to be a very important factor in determining the frequency of impulses. Thus, in these psychophysical measurements of intensity-discrimination, the changing state of adaptation of the eye certainly cannot be neglected and probably it is a very large factor in determining the apparent value of $\Delta I/I$ more particularly in the rod part (B) of the curve in figure 14.2.

DARK ADAPTATION

The process of dark adaptation is clearly seen when a subject enters a dark or dimly lighted room after being out in ordinary daylight. In the light, he can see objects clearly and in color. He can read small print and, if tested with a spectroscope, he would find the yellow-green part of the spectrum to be the brightest. On entering a very dimly lighted room his pupils dilate, but at first he can see nothing. After a time, however, the room appears to him to become brighter and he may be able to discern large shapes. His vision will continue to improve for a period of half an hour or more. Nevertheless, if the light intensity is below that which will excite his cone mechanism, the room will only be seen in terms of light and shade and it will be without color; he will not be able to read small print and the spectroscope will show that he now considers the blue-green region of the spectrum to be its brightest

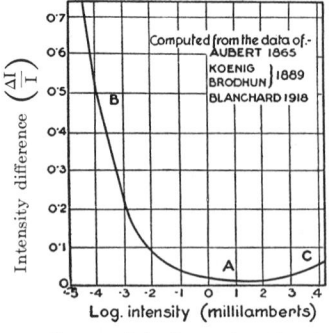

FIG. 14.2. Curve of the intensity discrimination of light. (After Hecht.)

part; he will be completely blind to the red end of the spectrum (see Plate II). This change in the relative sensitivity of the eye to different wavelengths which occurs at the lower ranges of intensity is known as the *Purkinje shift* and accounts for the well known phenomenon that, at twilight in a garden, the red flowers appear black, whereas the blue flowers appear grey or white. In this process of dark adaptation there are four main factors at work in the human eye; (a) dilation of the pupil, (b) change-over from cone to rod vision, (c) adaptation of the actual receptors, probably involving the regeneration of rhodopsin, and (d) reorganization of the neural connections in the retina with a probable reduction in the extent of lateral inhibition.

In other animals, other factors may also enter into the process. For example, in the frog there is retraction of the pigment from between the photoreceptors; in the catfish the rods and the cones interchange their positions so that the inner segments of the rods shorten and the outer segments approach the external limiting membrane, whereas the cones move in the opposite direction toward the pigment layer; in the cat, which can become about eight times more sensitive in the dark than the human being, the reflecting tapetum of the retina adds its effect to the relatively greater size of the pupil.

The process of dark adaptation is usually followed experimentally by presenting the subject, in an otherwise completely dark room, with an illuminated field, often in the form of a Landolt C or other similar test letter, at decreasing light intensities. The Landolt C (see p. 319) is merely an illuminated field in the form of the letter C which can be placed with the opening of the C up, down, or to the right or left, and the subject has to report on the position of the opening. The field is presented in brief flashes at different intensity levels; the threshold is determined by the lowest level at which it is just visible to the subject and at which his diagnoses are more than 50 per cent correct. A curve is then plotted, relating the threshold intensities to the time in the dark. This is known as the *dark adaptation curve*. When a white light is used, a curve with a definite break or "knee" in it is obtained (fig. 14.3). The threshold drops (i.e., the sensitivity rises) very quickly at first and after about five to seven minutes in the dark, it stabilizes for a time. It then drops suddenly again and does not reach a final steady state for about another 30 minutes, at which time the sensitivity will be found to be well over 100 times that achieved at the first plateau and possibly more than 10,000 times that at the start of

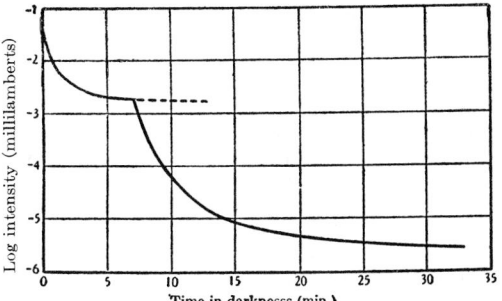

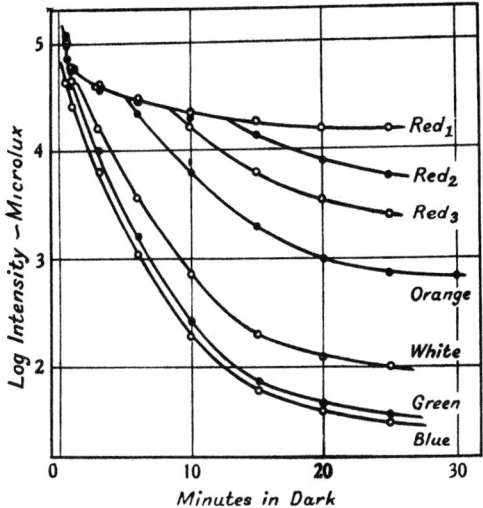

Fig. 14.3. (*Upper*) Dark adaptation curve. The dotted line—continuation of the upper section of the curve—is the cone adaptation curve obtained when a centrally fixated red stimulus is used. The lower part of the curve indicates rod adaptation. Only the upper part of the curve and its extension is obtained in night blindness. (After Rawdon-Smith.) (*Lower*) Dark adaptation curves plotted for different wave-lengths. Only extreme red (Red₁) confines the stimulus to the cones. (From Hecht, after Kohlrausch.)

the observations. In constructing such a curve the effects of the dilation of the pupil are eliminated by using an artificial pupil of about 3 mm. in diameter. Such dark-adaptation curves are purely relative and the absolute values obtained depend upon many factors, such as the area of the test stimulus, the position of the test stimulus on the retina, the duration of exposure of the test stimulus, the wave length of the test stimulus and the physical and mental condition of the subject including the extent and duration of his previous exposure to light.

If, instead of white light, the extreme red end of the spectrum is used, then the second drop in threshold does not occur and the absolute threshold is approached after about 10 minutes. Similarly if white light is used, but only a very small field subtending about 30 minutes is presented and also if a small red point-source is provided to assist the subject to fixate the test field on the central fovea, i.e., to help him to look straight at the test field and not allow his gaze to wander, then a curve precisely similar to that obtained with red light is again found. These two observations are interpreted to mean that vision is confined to the cone mechanism in each case and that the shoulder of the ordinary dark adaptation curve represents the threshold of the cone mechanism and the take-over point for the rods. The extent to which the rod threshold drops below this point, of course, varies with the wave-lengths used, in a manner which is directly related to the spectral sensitivity curve of rhodopsin, and the lowest thresholds are found with blue-green light. It is clear therefore from these curves that both rods and cones have the power to adapt, but the cones adapt much more quickly than the rods and they do not adapt to such low intensities. The absolute thresholds for red and blue stimuli at different positions on the retina are shown in figure 14.4. It will be seen that the threshold for blue (rod threshold) is higher than that for red (cone threshold) in the fovea, but very much lower elsewhere. The threshold for red on the other hand is much more uniform over the retina, but is slightly lower in the fovea than elsewhere. The insensitivity of the foveal center under scotopic conditions, caused by the scarcity of rods and the yellow pigmentation in that area (figs. 14.5 and 14.6), is the reason why it is necessary to look slightly to one side of such a group of stars as the

Pleiades when attempting to determine their number with the naked eye.

When the size of the field is reduced to such an extent that it is commensurate with the size of the receptor units, and spatial summation over an area of the retina is thereby eliminated, the process of adaptation is slower and the ultimate threshold reached is not so very different in the periphery from its value in the fovea, which strongly suggests that the absolute thresholds of rods and cones themselves, as individuals, are not very different, and that quite a large part of the normal dark adaptation process is concerned with the sort of neural reorganization which was discussed in the last chapter (p. 269). The other factor which is important in the process is the accumulation of rhodopsin in the rods, and presumably of the cone pigments in the cones although until recently there was no direct evidence for the latter. At one time it was thought that this regeneration of visual pigment would account for the whole process of adaptation but this now seems unlikely. As the result of measurements of the light reflected back from the fundus of the eye by extremely sensitive methods it is now possible to estimate the amount of rhodopsin actually present in the rods at any given stage of dark adaptation and to be certain that rhodopsin not only accumulates in the dark but also that it is not entirely bleached away under conditions of light adaptation. Similar changes in the amounts of light reflected from the fovea probably also indicate bleaching and regeneration of cone pigments (see p. 286).

It is not at all clear what part, if any, rods play at photopic levels of light intensity. It is a little difficult to believe that they become entirely insensitive to light in the upper ranges of intensity, so long as they contain unbleached rhodopsin. If they do not contribute at all to photopic vision, this must be due either to the breakdown of the mechanism which connects the photochemical process with neural excitation or to some complete inhibition of their effects in the neural mechanism itself. There is indirect evidence, and also evidence from a subject who appeared to be almost devoid of functional cones, that rods continue to give greater and greater response up to a certain level of illumination and then cease to increase their response, i.e. they saturate. It is not, however, clear in what way this constant maximal response contributes to ordinary photopic vision in the normal person.

It is interesting to compare the figures for the thresholds for red and blue stimuli, since these

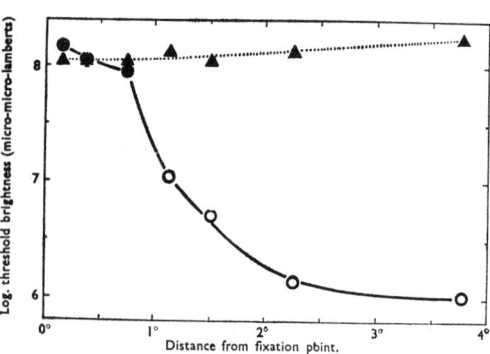

FIG. 14.4. Threshold values for extreme blue (small circles) and extreme red light (triangles) in various parts of the retina near the fovea. The full circles and triangles indicate that the lights give rise to sensations of color, the open circles indicate a colorless sensation. Diameter of test field subtends 10 minutes at the eye. (From Pirenne.)

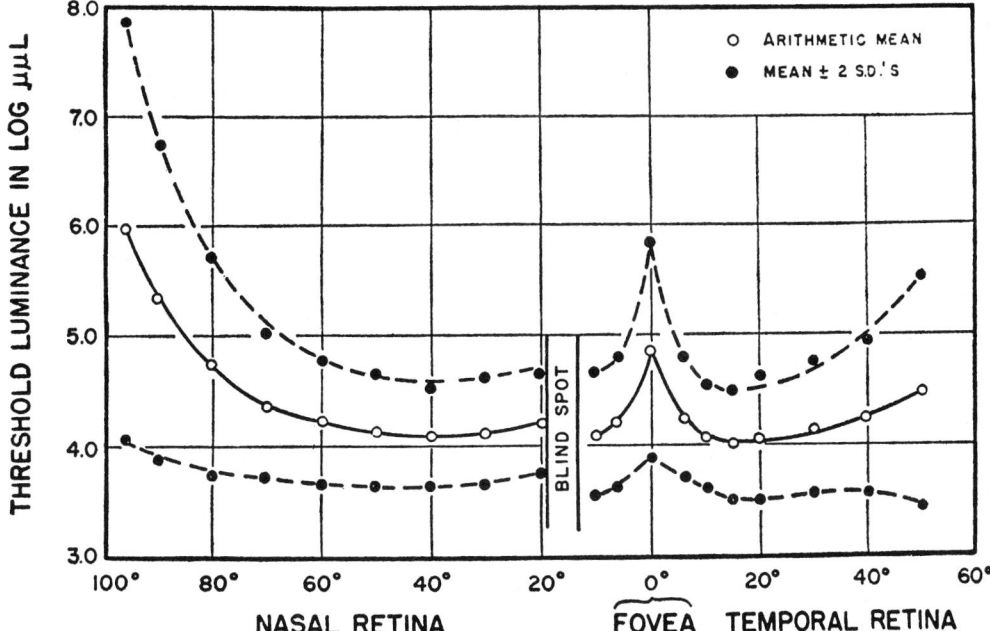

FIG. 14.5. The threshold for white light in different parts of the retina. The solid curve is the average curve for 101 subjects, 95% of whose measurements fall within the broken curves. (From Chapanis, after Sloan.)

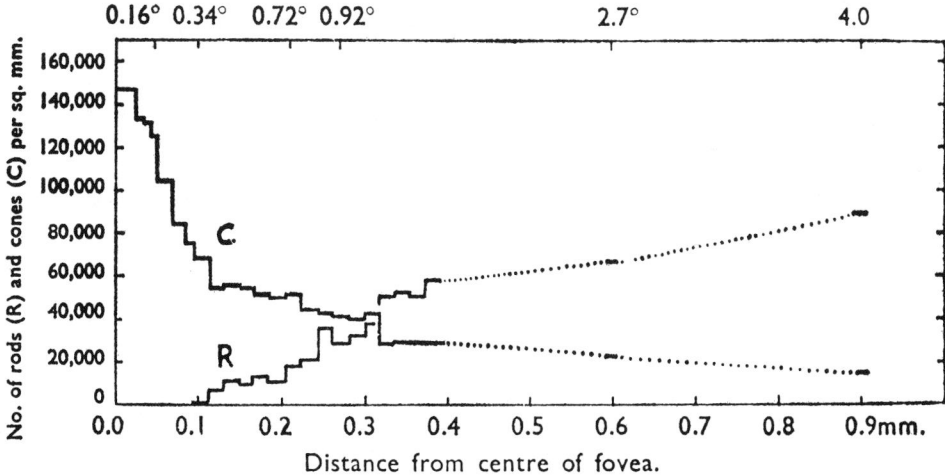

FIG. 14.6. The distribution of rods and cones near the center of the human retina. This figure obtained from histological preparations may be compared with figure 14.4, since blue light stimulates rods at threshold, and red light stimulates cones. (From Pirenne, after Østerberg.)

are undoubtedly determined by the cone and rod mechanisms respectively, in the different parts of the retina. These figures may then be compared with the estimated distribution of the rods and cones themselves in the same areas. The relevant data are set out in figures 14.4 and 14.6. The more rods there are in a given area the lower the threshold for blue becomes. The threshold for red, i.e., of the cones, is not, however, affected so much by the density of the cones per unit area. Thus spatial summation is probably of far more importance in rod vision than in cone vision.

Occasionally, people are found who are described as night blind, meaning that they have very limited powers of dark adaptation (see fig. 14.3) and are unable to see at all when the light intensity falls much below that required for cone vision. In extreme cases of vitamin A deficiency, the threshold of the rods rises and the subject may then become completely night blind. This condition, when severe enough, may involve atrophy of the rods and of the pigment epithelium, and ultimately may involve destruction of the cones also. The eye, however, holds on to its vitamin for longer than most tissues in the body and the deficiency has to be very severe and of long duration before the visual symptoms appear. The congenital and progressive disease, known as retinitis pigmentosa, brings about similar retinal changes with similar effects, but in this case there is also an accumulation of melanin in the damaged tissues. Once again the cones may become involved at a later stage.

Among animals, the type of eye and retina which is found differs according to the way of life of the animal. Nocturnal creatures, e.g., the bat, the rat and the owl, have a preponderance of rods very often associated with a tapetum and a large pupil. Strictly diurnal animals, e.g., the pigeon and the lizard, have retinas with very few or even no rods. These observations are further indications of the essential duality of the retina, but it should be remembered that many animals which have a very heavy preponderance of rods in their retinas are by no means blind by day.

When a person comes out of a dark room into the light, the processes of dark adaptation are all reversed; the pupil constricts, the retina loses its sensitivity and the rhodopsin concentration is lowered, the spectral sensitivity-maximum moves towards the yellow (reversed Purkinje shift) and all this happens very much more quickly than the dark adaptation. After the first few moments of dazzle, the sense of color and the ability to read small print are restored. Moreover, if the adaptation to light is not too prolonged, the return to the darkroom will be followed by a much more rapid dark adaptation than follows a prolonged period of light adaptation.

Photopic Visibility (Sensitivity) Curve

Although the scotopic spectral sensitivity or visibility curve (see fig. 13.15) is a reasonably accurate expression of the sensitivity of the rods to the different parts of the spectrum since it is obtained by determining absolute thresholds, it is much more difficult to obtain any similar expression for the cones. The problem may be approached in one of two ways. Evidence has been presented to show that the very center of the fovea is a part of the retina where cones only are present. A threshold visibility curve for this area therefore should give a good indication of the spectral sensitivity of the cones. Such a curve is plotted in figure 14.7, where it can be compared with the visibility curve for the rods, and some of the reasons for the Purkinje shift become obvious. By the other approach, the sensitivity of the eye to the different parts of the spectrum can be gauged by comparing the intensities of light of different wave-lengths which match a given standard white light in brightness. Since this involves the rather difficult feat of heterochromatic matching, it is inclined to be rather inaccurate, although this difficulty can be overcome to some extent by altering the wave-length of the field to be matched from white to yellow and to the other spectral colors in a stepwise manner so that the color differences between the fields are minimized. For example, instead of matching red with

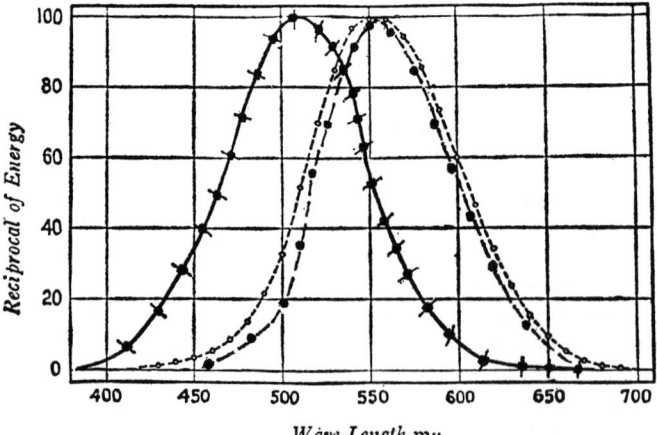

Fig. 14.7. Visibility curves for scotopic and photopic vision. ●——● = scotopic vision; ○-----○ = photopic vision; ●--● = foveal photopic vision. (After Hecht, Thomson and Wright.)

white directly a standard yellow field is first chosen and an orange field first matched against the yellow; the orange is then used as the standard for the red. If the steps in such a matching procedure are made small enough the matches are almost homochromatic but there is then, of course, still the possibility of a cumulative error. The method of flicker photometry (see p. 326) can also be used. In determining the *photopic visibility curve* by the process of matching brightnesses, a field subtending 2° at the eye is traditionally used. Errors or difficulties are introduced with fields that are much larger or much smaller than this.

The photopic visibility curve, although interesting in itself, has not the same objective reality as the scotopic curve. It varies with the size of the matching fields, with the position of the field on the retina, with the brightness level which is used as a standard, and with the direction in which the light impinges upon the receptors. Light falling obliquely on the cones is less efficient than that which traverses their length in an axial direction. Different wave-lengths are affected to different extents. Since there are known to be at least two types of cone (with different pigments in each) in the human eye, the curve must inevitably be composite.

Another and rather inaccurate method of attempting to assess the spectral sensitivity of the cones is to determine the *chromatic threshold*, i.e., the intensity of light at each wave-length which is just sufficient to produce a sensation of color. For most parts of the spectrum, there is a large *achromatic interval*. This means that at some very low intensity the colorless rod threshold is reached, then, as the intensity is raised, the field begins to appear colored, presumably at about the threshold of the cones. The range of intensities between the threshold for light and that for color is known as the achromatic interval. It is very large in the blue region of the spectrum and absent in the red part. In the central fovea there is no achromatic interval in the true sense, although light from the middle of the spectrum tends to appear colorless at threshold levels. Both violet and red are either seen in full saturation or not at all.

Like the electroretinogram, the photopic visibility curve or curves give a general summary of retinal performance but their analysis is beset with difficulties. Consequently, they are only of limited physiological importance, until more is known of the exact meaning to be attached to the sensation of brightness when several types of retinal receptors and pathways may be contributing to it.

Color Vision; The Nature of Color

Before discussing the physiological basis for color vision, it may be desirable to recapitulate some of the main facts about color in general. In the first place, color is entirely a subjective phenomenon, and there can be no such thing as color except for those animals, including man, which have the necessary sensory and analytical apparatus with which to discriminate between the wave-lengths of visible light as well as differences in light-intensity. Lights of different wave-lengths excite the receptor mechanisms in the human eye to different extents, and two colors appear to be identical when they excite the receptor mechanisms in the same way and to equal extents. For example, the sensation of yellow can be evoked either by a narrow spectral band centered around a wave-length of 580 mμ or by a suitable mixture of red (620–700 mμ) and green (500–570 mμ), without any spectral yellow whatsoever. It is almost certainly true that when the receptors are stimulated equally by the lights illuminating two fields, those two fields will match in all respects; however, the reverse is not necessarily true, and certainly not when one field is viewed with one eye and the other with the other eye. A sensation of white is obtained when a suitable mixture of wave-lengths impinges on one eye and an equally colorless sensation of white can simultaneously be obtained in the other eye if it is dark adapted and illuminated by a narrow wave-band at 500 mμ. In the one case, the whole photopic cone mechanism is being activated and, in the other, the scotopic rod mechanism; but the brain produces very much the same sensation in each case.

Each spectral color excites the receptor mechanisms in a characteristic pattern, but quite different patterns of stimulation can be provided when mixtures of spectral wave-bands are used so that there are numerous 'extra-spectral' colors. Similarly when one, or more, of the receptor mechanisms themselves have had their performance modified by such means as adaptation (e.g., to one color), fatigue or even by the action of hormones or drugs, the responses which they can give may be greatly altered. In other words, the number of detectable hues depends upon the number of possible patterns of response from the receptors which can be distinguished by the interpreting neural mechanism. Physiologically, there is no distinction to be drawn between spectral and "extra-spectral" colors. Even so-called spectral colors can produce different sensations under different conditions. For example, when two fields are equally illuminated by wave-length 590 mμ they both appear to be orange yellow, but if one of the fields has its physical intensity reduced to about one half, that field will then appear brown in comparison with the other, but will appear yellow again when the brighter field is turned down in intensity or extinguished. Similarly, if two yellow fields are matched by binocular vision (one field being seen by each eye) and then one eye is adapted to red light, by looking at a bright red light for a few minutes, the yellow field will subsequently appear to be green to that eye. Or, again, if one eye is adapted to red light and then a field illuminated by spectral green (about 530 mμ) is observed by each eye in turn, it will be found to appear as a far more vivid, intense, or "saturated" green to the adapted eye than to the normal eye.

Any color sensation has three main attributes or qualities. They are *hue*, *brightness* and *saturation*.

Hue is the actual color, to be described by "red," "blue," "green," etc.

Brightness or luminosity is the amount of light which is involved. A color can always be described as being lighter, darker or equal in brightness to a given white standard. Alternatively it can always be matched in brightness or be given the same "tone value" as a particular and colorless gray; in other words, its luminosity can be measured by comparison with white standards of known intensity. The relative luminosities or brightnesses of the spectral colors are described by the ordinates of the photopic luminosity curve.

The saturation of a color is very much the same as the "purity" of the color, although this can be misleading. It is perhaps better defined as the extent to which a given color departs from a colorless gray of equal brightness. It can be measured in one of two ways. First, it can be measured in terms of the amount of it which has to be added to a given white light in order to make the white deviate perceptibly in hue from the original white. This can best be done by comparing two adjacent white fields and adding the test color to one, whereas the other may be altered in brightness in order to compensate for any changes in luminosity caused in the first field by adding the test color. The alternative method, which yields similar results, is to proceed in the opposite way, i.e., by adding white to the color until it is noticeably less saturated. Two fields are illuminated with the color to be tested; to one field (A) white light is added until it is detectably different, the luminance of the other field (B) being altered to compensate for the added white. When this first step has been fixed, the field B is desaturated until the two fields again match in all respects. White is then added to field A as before and another step established. The process is repeated until the further addition of white makes no more difference. The number of steps between the original color and white is recorded as the measure of the saturation of that color. The saturation of the spectral colors as determined by these two methods is depicted in figure 14.8. It will be seen that the spectral colors vary greatly in saturation from the intensely saturated violet and red at one extreme to the very unsaturated yellow-green at the other. Mixtures of spectral lights, in general, produce colors which are less saturated than the original separate hues, e.g., mixtures of red and blue-green. Multiple mixtures of many bands, of course, approach white, since white is the sensation evoked by the whole undivided spectrum. Some mixtures of spectral colors can, however, produce very saturated hues, e.g., mixtures of red and blue which produce purples. These observations do not mean that it is impossible for a color to be **more** saturated that the corresponding spectral hue. The eye can certainly be per-

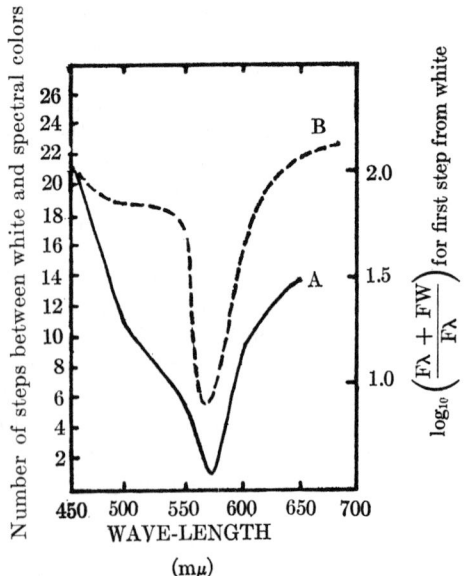

FIG. 14.8. Saturation of spectral colors. (*A*) Log of reciprocal of colorimetric purity of colors which differ from white by one perceptible step. (Ordinates on the right.) F = flux of spectral color, F_w = flux of white light. (*B*) Number of perceptible steps between the spectral colors and white. (Ordinates on the left.) (After Wright.)

suaded into giving sensations of hue which are far more saturated than any spectral color normally appears. This can be done by suitable alterations to the sensitivities of the intrinsic mechanisms of the retina (or visual path), e.g., by adaptation, or by suitable mixtures of stimuli.

The pigments in a paint box are generally fairly saturated colors, although, spectroscopically, they seldom reflect only narrow spectral bands and are usually very "impure." In most cases, as any one who has attempted to paint in water colors knows, when the colors are mixed, they tend to lose their purity and become more grey and less colored. There are however, exceptions to this, since pigment mixtures are "subtractive" in character. For example, when blue and yellow pigments are mixed, the result may be a green which is more saturated than either of the original hues. A yellow pigment tends to be yellow because it absorbs very strongly in the blue part of the spectrum and only reflects green, yellow and red. The green and the red rays combine in their effects on the eye to produce a reinforcement of the pure yellow; this probably accounts for the greater saturation of yellow pigments as compared with spectral yellow. The blue pigment, on the other hand, is blue because it absorbs all the red and yellow part of the spectrum. Therefore, when the two pigments, yellow and blue, are mixed, the only light which is not absorbed by one or other of them, and which therefore continues to be reflected back, is the green light which escapes as a rather narrow spectral band. In contrast to this mixture of pigments which act in a subtractive way, the addition of the right amount of yellow light ($\lambda = 580$ mμ) to blue light ($\lambda = 479$ mμ.) so stimulates the receptor mechanisms that they give almost the same response as they would if stimulated by the whole spectrum and the mixture appears white.

This reconstitution of white light from blue and yellow is an example from the series of *complementary colors*. White can always be reconstituted from three spectral bands, widely spaced through the spectrum, when they are mixed in the right proportions; in addition to this, there are a number of pairs of wave-bands which when mixed in the correct amounts also make white. Such pairs are called complementary colors and a list of specific examples is given in Table 14.1 together with the requisite intensities of each for the match with a standard white. Physiologically, the interpretation usually given for this phenomenon is that these pairs stimulate the receptor mechanisms in the eye in exactly the same manner as

TABLE 14.1

Complementary Colors

Wave-length	Log Energy to Match White
mμ	
700	2.20
492	0.70
650	0.81
492	0.71
600	0.30
489	0.68
580	0.495
479	0.586
570	0.720
450	0.430
568.5	0.77
410	1.398

does white light. Although probably correct, this is not absolutely necessary since there are many different conditions under which the eye yields a colorless or white sensation, e.g., when rods only are functioning (*scotopic white*), when wave-length 574 mμ falls on the very center of the fovea (see p. 312), as well as under ordinary conditions when a white surface is examined (*photopic white*). The complementary colors to the green part of the spectrum (λ 495 mμ to 565 mμ) are not spectral colors, but purples.

The hues produced by the different wave-bands of course change progressively throughout the spectrum, but the rate of change with wavelength is not constant. Yellow changes to orange when the wave-length is changed from 590 mμ to 600 mμ, but there is very little change of hue between 460 mμ and 470 mμ. The spectrum can be divided into a series of steps, over each one of which the hue is effectively constant. These steps (the hue-discrimination steps) are long in some parts and short in others. A curve relating the length (in mμ) of the step to the mean wavelength of the step is called a hue-discrimination curve and is plotted in figure 14.9. It will be seen that hue discrimination is good, i.e., the steps are small, in the yellow and blue-green regions of the spectrum and very poor in the far red, green and violet, where much longer steps occur.

From the physiological point of view, too much accent need not be placed on these characteristics of the spectrum since there is nothing

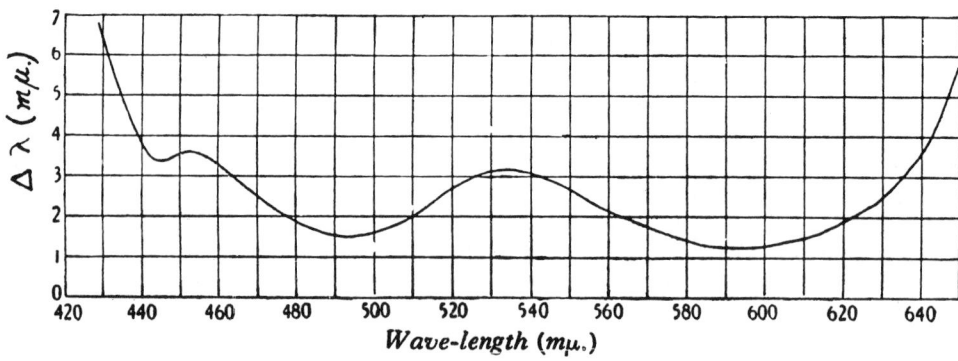

FIG. 14.9. Hue discrimination curve. (From Wright.)

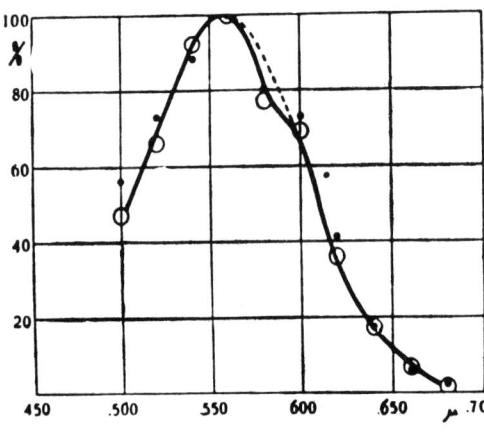

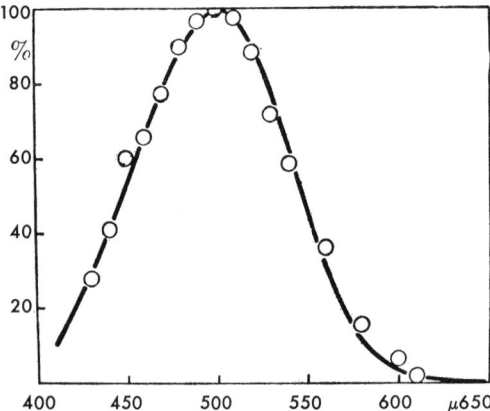

FIG. 14.10. Dominator curves in the retina of vertebrates. (*Upper*) Photopic dominator curve; (*Lower*) scotopic dominator curve. Equal quantum intensity spectrum. Ordinates, sensitivity; abscissas, wave-length. (From Granit.)

physiologically peculiar about spectral colors as distinct from nonspectral purples and browns. Spectral colors are physiologically interesting only in the fact that they can be used as repeatable and defined stimuli, which can be easily mixed and can therefore be used as a starting

point for defining other colors. The basis of color sensation is more profitably sought in the pattern of nerve impulses arising from different receptors in the retina than in the wave-lengths of light which produce them.

This suggests that the first approach to the analysis of color vision should be made by recording, objectively, the impulses which pass up the optic nerve fibers as the result of stimulation of the retina by different wave-lengths. Granit and his coworkers took up this challenge and for a number of years studied the problem by this technique with extremely interesting, but puzzling, results. They found that a great many nerve cells or fibers gave an impulse-frequency versus wave-length curve (the photopic dominator curve) figure 14.10 very similar in shape to the photopic sensitivity curve of many animals, including man. At lower brightness levels some of these fibers showed a Purkinje shift and then yielded a "*scotopic dominator curve.*" By means of selective adaptation to particular wave-lengths and by various other devices, Granit and his colleagues were able to establish that many nerve fibers give responses which are greatly affected by wave-length over quite narrow ranges of the spectrum. Fibers from which this type of information could be extracted were called *modulators* (fig. 14.11) and they are clearly of great importance as indicating the presence in the retina of elements whose responses change rapidly with wave-length and which could therefore participate in hue-discrimination, but how they are to be interpreted is still very much an open question. Modulator curves, on a restricted scale have been obtained from the retinas of both rats and guinea pigs (animals in which rods very heavily preponderate among the receptors to the almost complete exclusion of cones). There are, indeed, so many possible ways in which these modulators could arise in the retina, either directly from receptors or by interaction between cells in different parts of the organization, that further discussion of them at this time is hardly profitable. This becomes even more evident when the numbers of different types of cell in the retina, on the one hand, and the number of different types of information, e.g., concerning brightness, form, contrast and edges, color, saturation, movement etc., on the other, are both considered as part of retinal physiology. The codes used by the retina for transmitting all this information economically constitute a fascinating problem in the theory of communication. Some examples of this have already been given in the preceding chapter (see p. 288 et seq.).

In 1807, Thomas Young emphasized the trichromatic character of color vision and Helmholtz elaborated and developed the so-called trichromatic theory of color vision by his immense researches on the eye during the course of the nineteenth century. All colors, including the 'non-spectral' colors, can be matched by using three primary stimuli, i.e., three wave-bands well separated in the spectrum, e.g., blue, green and red, and mixing them in different proportions. Every color then requires its own unique mixture. There is only one set of intensities of each of those particular primaries which will make the exact match in hue, brightness and saturation. Any color can therefore be expressed by the formula:

$$aC = xB + yG + zR$$

where a is the luminosity of color C and x, y and z are the luminosities of the three primaries chosen, e.g., blue, green and red. If a different set of primaries were used, a similar expression could be written:

$$aC = x_1B' + y_1G' + z_1R'$$

where the symbols have similar meanings with respect to the new primaries.

This formula applies to all colors and it does not matter whether C is a spectral color. If each of the second set of primaries (B', G' and R') is expressed in terms of its "tri-stimulus" values when the first primaries are used, it is clearly possible to convert from one set of primaries to another:

$$x_1B' = pB + qG + rR$$
$$y_1G' = p_1B + q_1G + r_1R$$
$$z_1R' = p_2B + q_2G + r_2R$$

and aC can be expressed as the sum of these three.

When two or more lights are mixed, as in all colorimetrical experiments, the luminosity of the mixture is the sum of the luminosities of the separate stimuli, i.e., if aC_1 is one color and bC_2 is another color, each can be expressed as above in terms of $x_1B + y_1G + z_1R$ and $x_2B + y_2G + z_2R$. Then the new color C_3 can be expressed as

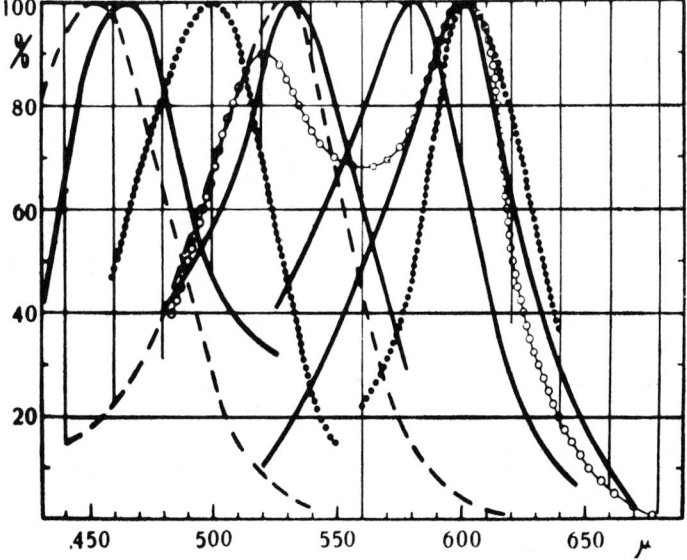

FIG. 14.11. Modulator curves in various animals. Dots = rats; broken lines = guinea pigs; continuous line = frogs; circles = snakes. Equal quantum intensity spectrum. Ordinates, sensitivity; abscissae wave-length. (From Granit.)

$aC_1 + bC_2$ where the luminosity of the new color will be $a + b$:

$$(a + b)C_3$$

$$= (x_1 + x_2)B + (y_1 + y_2)G + (z_1 + z_2)R$$

These two findings, that all colors can be expressed in terms of the luminosities of three primaries and that when colors are mixed by means of spectral lights the luminosities of the components are for all practical purposes additive, are the cardinal features of all color measurement and specification. There are, indeed some minor deviations of the strictly additive law under certain special conditions, e.g., with very small centrally fixated fields and at very high or very low brightness levels, but, in general, the additivity of color mixtures is basic to colorimetry. There are certain colors which can only be matched in saturation by a mixture of three primaries by desaturating the color to be matched on the control side, i.e., by using a negative component of the match. Color mixture, using spectral lights, always tends to give colors which are somewhat less saturated than might be expected. In spite of these minor difficulties the essentially trichromatic character of all color matching is, however, no longer seriously disputed, and it is thought that the trichromacy reflects the existence of three basic mechanisms, if not actually of three different classes of receptors, in the retina.

If the three spectral primaries are so chosen, as they must be, that a particular mixture of them matches white, then the luminosities of the primaries in the match with white can be conveniently regarded as the units of the red, green and blue stimuli, and all other colors can be expressed in terms of these units. If, for example, the spectral colors are matched, one by one, with the use of the three primaries (650 mμ, 530 mμ and 460 mμ), the units of these having first been determined by the match on white, then all the colors can be expressed in terms of these units and a result like that shown in figure 14.12 can be obtained. Each color can be obtained by mixing the three primaries in the proportions indicated by the ordinates in this figure. It will be noticed that, in the blue region of the spectrum, the green stimuli are negative and, in the green region it is the red stimulus that has to be transferred to the matching field. Other units, based on the amounts of red and green necessary to match yellow and the amounts of blue and green necessary to match blue green, are sometimes used as more satisfactory units than the luminosities of each primary in the match on white. *Whiteness* has subjective qualities whereas spectral yellow and blue-green can be determined precisely by specific wave-bands (582.5 and 494 mμ respectively).

If the figures shown in figure 14.12 are converted back to luminosities, i.e., into terms of the absolute amounts of blue, green and red radiations, then the matches on the spectral colors are represented by figure 14.13 in which, owing to the very low luminosity values of the blue stimulus, the figures for the blue primary have been multiplied by 10. The blue stimulus always has a great effect on hue and saturation, but very little effect on

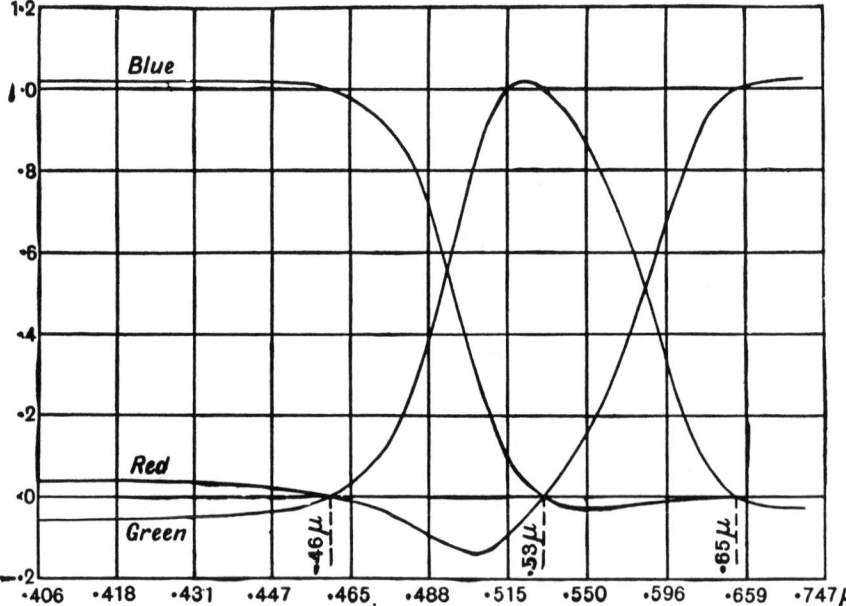

FIG. 14.12. Mean coefficient curves for matches on the spectral colors. Ordinates, coefficients; abscissae, wave-length. (From Wright.)

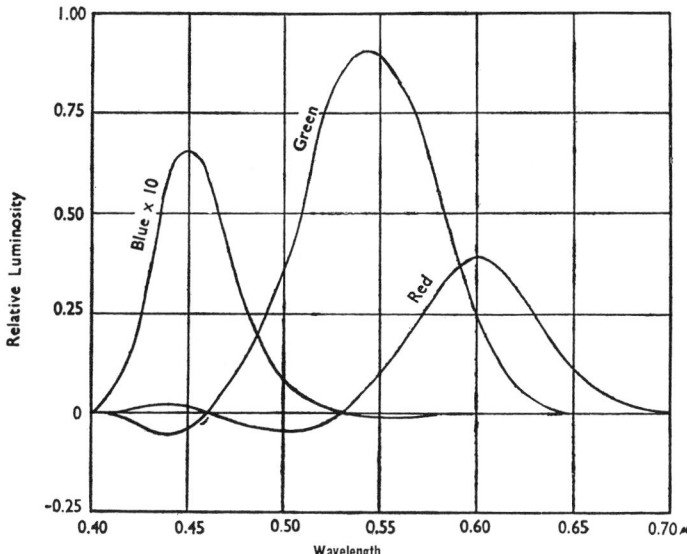

FIG. 14.13. The spectral mixture curves for the equal energy spectrum, in terms of radiations of wave-lengths 650 mμ, 530 mμ and 460 mμ as matching stimuli, the amounts of the stimuli being expressed as luminosity units. (From Wright.)

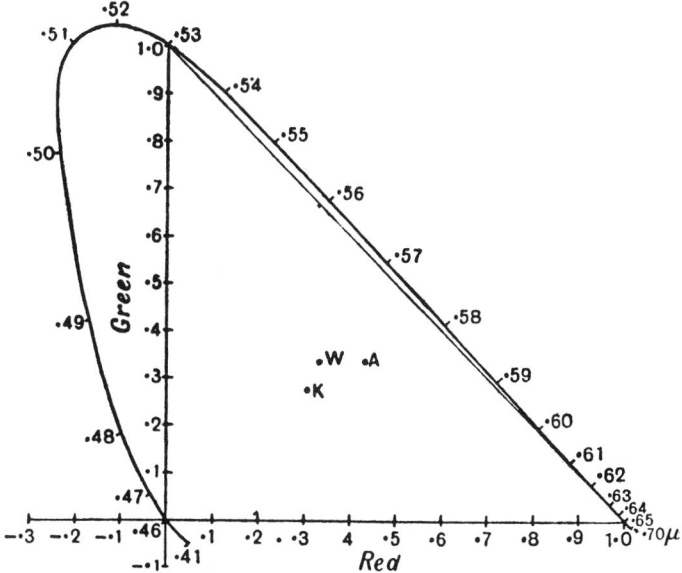

FIG. 14.14. The spectrum locus on a chromaticity chart. The point W is the white point. The coefficient for the blue stimulus can be calculated by subtracting the sum of the red and green coefficients from unity. The primaries used were 650 mμ, 530 mμ and 460 mμ. (From Wright.)

luminosity. Since the coefficients plotted in figure 14.12 are all expressed as fractions of 1 they can be replotted as figure 14.14 where the red and green coefficients (R and G) of the spectral colors are plotted against each other and the blue coefficient (B) can be obtained by difference from 1 (since R + G + B = 1). This figure is of interest because it forms the basis for many standard color charts like the one adopted by the Commission Interna-

tionale d'Eclairage, the so-called C.I.E. chart, upon which any color can be specified by its position on the chart. The white point is represented by the point 0.33, 0.33 and colors increase in saturation from that point towards the spectral locus. On such a chart, the areas occupied by the colors are unfortunately rather irregular in size, most of the chart being occupied by greens, and various modifications have been suggested in order to obtain a more even distribution. The chart is really the modern version of the original color triangle.

From the physiological point of view, the important features in these data on color mixture are that luminosities of colored lights are almost strictly additive, and that if two colors which match in all respects have a third color added to them, the resulting mixture will continue to match in all respects. Similarly, matches made at one brightness level continue to hold over a very wide range of brightness levels, although they may break down at very high brightnesses and also at very low brightnesses where the Purkinje effect and the entry of the scotopic mechanism begin to desaturate colors in the blue and green regions of the spectrum particularly.

The trichromatic coefficients for each color and all the other data on color mixture are of great practical and commercial importance in standardization of colors but they cannot yet be translated into physiological terms. Ideally, a color chart of the form shown in figure 14.14 but recording the response of the three receptor mechanisms, instead of the intensities of the three primary colors used, is how the physiologist would wish to be able to describe colors. But this aim has not yet been achieved, except perhaps to some extent in the restricted form of color vision found in the central fovea, where some approach to it is now possible (see pp. 311, 312).

Color Blindness

As Young realized, when he investigated the color blindness described by Dalton, the chemist, in 1807, information can be obtained on the na-

TABLE 14.2
(After Wright)

Type of Color Defect	Percentage
Anomalous trichromatism	
Protanomaly...............	1.0
Deuteranomaly............	4.6
Tritanomaly...............	0.0001
	———
	5.6
Dichromatism	
Protanopia................	1.2
Deuteranopia.............	1.4
Tritanopia................	0.0001
	———
	2.6
Monochromatism............	0.003
	———
Total.................	8.2

ture of the color mechanisms by a study of the color blind. It will therefore be appropriate to give some account of this before discussing the nature of the color mechanisms themselves.

About 8 per cent of the male population have some degree of color abnormality and about 1 per cent are seriously affected. Only about 0.4 per cent of women are in any way color-abnormal. Most color blindness is inherited and since the gene for it behaves as a sex-linked recessive, it appears most easily in the heterogametic sex, i.e., in the male, and can only be inherited by a son from his mother. Occasionally, color blindness is the result of injury and it may then appear in one eye only. One of the rarer forms of color blindness, tritanopia or blue blindness (see p. 310), is inherited in a different way from the others.

Subjects with abnormal color vision fall into several classes:

MONOCHROMATS. These are totally color blind and see the whole spectrum in shades of grey. Their vision therefore resembles that provided by black and white cinephotography. They fall into two main groups according to their spectral sensitivity and other characters.

Rod monochromats. These behave as if they possessed no cones. Their spectral sensitivity is the same as that of the dark adapted eye. They tend to be photophobic and are dazzled by light, but, interestingly enough, they are certainly not blind in daylight. They may have a "central scotoma" or blind spot where the normal person has his fovea. Such subjects are rare.

Cone monochromats. These are very rare and, as their name implies, they apparently depend on cones, because their spectral sensitivity is not that of rhodopsin, but has its peak near that of the photopic sensitivity curve. Comparatively few subjects have been investigated with sufficient accuracy to be certain, but there are indications of two groups among them, one with maximum sensitivity at about 530–540 mμ and the other with maximum sensitivity at about 560–570 mμ. The former appear to be the more common and, in them, rod vision (i.e., night vision) is apparently normal.

DICHROMATS. All these subjects require only two primary colors with which to match all colors in the spectrum. There are certainly three and perhaps four groups of them. They, and other color-abnormal types, are readily picked out from the normal population by the use of one or more of the standard tests which have been devised for the purpose, such as the Ishihara test, the

Stilling test, Holmgren's wool test, or the 100 hue test of Farnsworth. The Ishihara test is perhaps the one most frequently used as a preliminary screen. It consists of a series of colored plates each composed of a field of colored dots. The dots are so selected and arranged as to constitute patterns visible either to the normal person or to the color blind but seldom to both. For example, a figure composed partly of red and partly of green dots may be lost to the normal observer in a background of other multicolored dots, however it may be quite easily distinguishable for the color blind person who sees no difference between the red and the green dots. Alternatively a red figure on a background of green dots is clearly seen by the normal person but may be invisible to the color blind. The wool test depends upon the inability of the color blind to differentiate between certain pairs of colored wools, and the 100 hue test consists of arranging colored chips in an orderly sequence of hues. From the particular confusions or irregularities in these tests, it is possible to classify the color blind to a limited extent on the tests alone, but further and more searching tests are generally necessary to determine the exact type of defect which is present.

Protanopes. These subjects confuse red with green, and on a 2° field can match these two colors in all respects. They are relatively insensitive to red light and their photopic sensitivity curve is noticeably displaced from the normal curve and has its maximum at about 540 mμ. They see the whole spectrum in terms of blue and yellow (brown?) except for a region near 495 mμ which they match with white. They confuse the colors which lie along the lines in the color chart shown in figure 14.15. Their foveal center apparently is monochromatic and, when their vision is re-

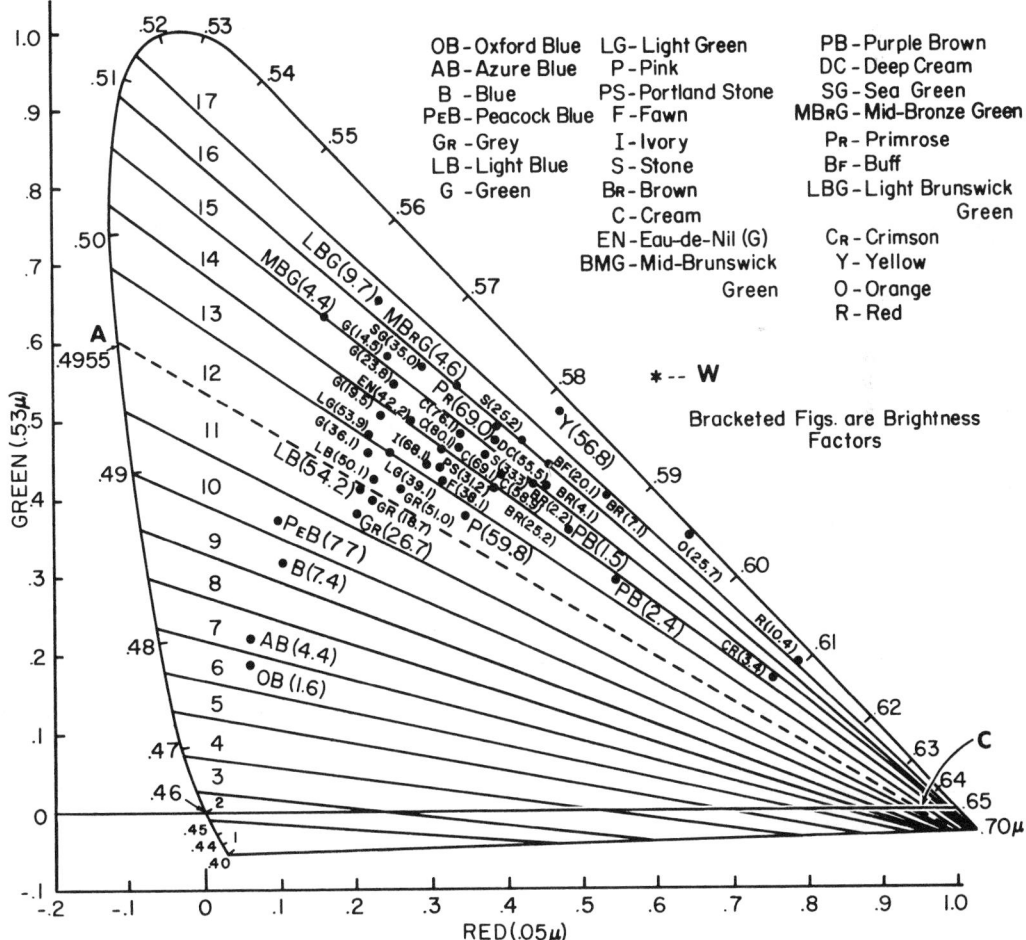

FIG. 14.15. Chromaticity chart similar to that shown in figure 73.14. The lines divide the chart into areas within each of which there is no hue-discrimination and colors are likely to be confused by the protanope. Thus the protanope has 17 color steps in the spectrum. (From Wright, after Pitt.)

stricted to this area, they see all colors as shades of grey.

Deuteranopes. These subjects also confuse red with green, but the particular reds and greens which they confuse are different from those which the protanopes confuse. Unlike the protanopes they can see the whole spectrum to the same limits as the normal person. Their photopic sensitivity curve, which is somewhat variable in position is not always significantly different from that of the normal subject. Like the protanopes they become completely color blind when their vision is restricted to the central fovea, and there is some suggestion that there are two classes of deuteranopes. Again like the protanopes they see the whole spectrum in shades of blue and yellow and they have a neutral point at about 497–500 mμ which they see as white. The colors which they

confuse are those lying on the lines of the color chart in figure 14.16.

Tritanopes. These are very rare and, in some cases at least, the defect is the result of injury or damage. Such subjects see colors with their whole retina in very much the same way as normal subjects see them when their vision is restricted to the foveal center (see pp. 311, 312). The spectrum is divided for them into a blue-green part and an orange-red part by a neutral point at about 574 mμ, which can be matched with white. Colors which they confuse lie along lines radiating from the origin in the color chart (fig. 14.14).

Tetartanopes. A few, rather ill-defined cases of blue-yellow confusion have been included under this heading, but they are not sufficiently standardized or categorized to be of much significance either in elucidating the problems of color vision

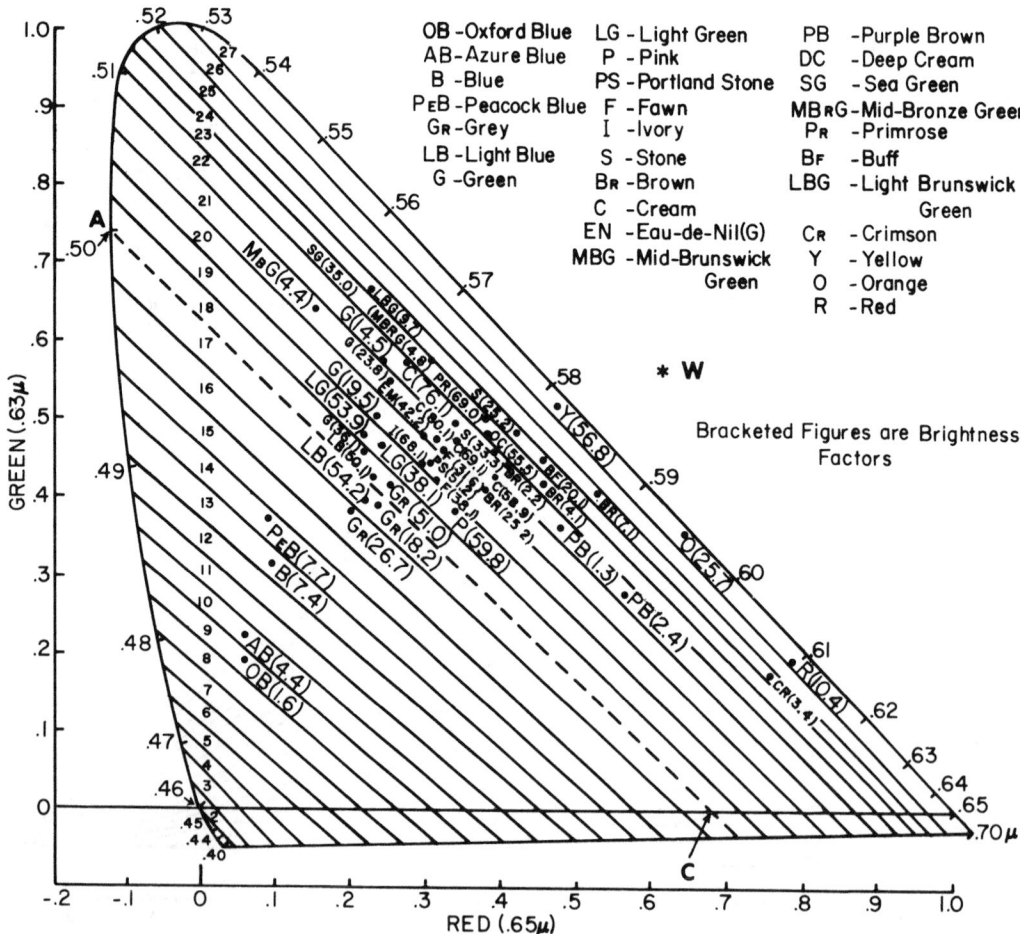

Fig. 14.16. A similar chromaticity chart for the deuteranope, who has 27 steps in his spectrum. In both these cases the steps are based more on differences in saturation than on hue. It is probable that both protanopes and deuteranopes see the spectrum in shades of blue from 400 mμ to the neutral point and in shades of yellow from the neutral point to the red end of the spectrum. The dotted lines represent the real division of the hues. (From Wright, after Pitt.)

or as medical cases. Two neutral points, one at 470 mμ and another at 580 mμ, are reported.

ANOMALOUS TRICHROMATS. If a normal subject examines a yellow field which is subdivided down the middle so that one half is illuminated by a narrow spectral band of yellow (about 585 mμ) and the other by a mixture of red and green, it will be found that, in order to match the yellow, he requires a particular ratio of red to green within rather narrow limits. The instrument is called the Nagel *anomaloscope* and the match is called the Rayleigh match.

There is, however, a large group of people who either make different settings from the normal or who have a much greater tolerance for "incorrect" settings than the normal in what they consider to be satisfactory matches. The subjects who make abnormal Rayleigh matches range form the nearly normal to the frank dichromats who have complete tolerance and so can match the yellow either with pure green or with pure red, provided that the brightnesses of the two fields are adjusted.

Anomalous trichromats require three primary colors with which to match the whole spectrum, but the contributions made by each seem to differ from the normal. Some subjects in this class tend towards the deuteranope (*deuteranomalous*), others towards the protanope (*protanomalous*). It is, however, improbable that there is a complete gradation from the normal to the deuteranopes and the protanopes. These extremes seem to differ qualitatively as well as quantitatively from the normal. Although normal people obviously do not accept, in general, matches which are made by the color-blind, color-blind subjects generally accept matches made by normal people. This, however is not true for anomalous trichromats who sometimes reject matches made by normal subjects.

THE PHYSIOLOGICAL BASIS FOR COLOR VISION

Emphasis has been placed on the fact that at low light intensities, when rods alone are believed to be in action, the eye produces no sensation of color. From the spectral sensitivity curve in the dark adapted state the evidence is very strong that no pigment other than rhodopsin is involved in rod vision. The position is exactly comparable with that in the eye of Limulus where it was shown (p. 288) that there was no possibility for this animal to discriminate between intensity and wave-length, since the same frequency of impulses could result from suitable adjustment of either. The colorless sensation associated with

rod vision and the observations on Limulus make it quite clear that a single set of receptors, containing one pigment only, cannot provide a basis for color vision. Therefore, in any color-sensitive mechanism, there must be at least two (if not more) classes of receptor, each containing a mechanism or pigment for providing it with a specific spectral sensitivity.

In man, as soon as the light intensity is raised to the threshold for the cones, sensations of color arise. This must mean that at least two classes of receptor are then in action. These two classes could theoretically be the rods and the cones, or two or more classes of cones, and the main physiological problem of color vision is to determine the nature of the color receptors.

Attention has already been called to the fact that birds have the photopigment, iodopsin, probably in their cones and that some of them also have oil droplet of different colors in the inner segments of their cones. There is also experimental evidence that these colored droplets alter the spectral sensitivity of the iodopsin of the cones in which they occur sufficiently to provide a basis for color discrimination. Man, however, does not possess such colored droplets in his cones and so must depend upon some other mechanism. Indeed, it seems probable that the problem of providing a mechanism for color vision has been solved more than once in evolution, and probably by several different methods. Color vision occurs sporadically in the animal kingdom, in bees and butterflies, fish, amphibia, some reptiles, some birds and in very few, if any, mammals outside the Primates. In deciding whether an animal has color vision it is necessary to be absolutely certain that apparent discrimination between colors is not really discrimination between shapes, brightnesses etc., or even between smells, or differences of texture.

Apart from some unexplained differences in staining properties and a progressive elongation of those situated nearer the center of the retina, human cones all appear to be histologically the same. Rushton's work on the differential bleaching of the pigments of the fovea certainly indicates the presence of at least two cone pigments (see p. 286), although exactly how these results are to be interpreted is a little uncertain in view of the fact that the field size which was used in these experiments would almost certainly include within it a large number of rods.

The Foveal Center and the Nature of the Color Mechanisms

Since it is known that color vision does not occur in man without the intervention of the cones, and since it is suspected that cones may be entirely responsible for color vision, and since cones occur alone and apparently unmixed with rods in the foveal center, it is logical to examine the performance of this part of the retina to see how much these central cones can achieve on their own. Unfortunately the rod-free area is very small and eye movements are relatively large, so that very small fields (less that 30′ in diameter) have to be used. Rigid fixation also has to be maintained. In spite of these precautions the opportunity for error is large and great will-power has to be exerted by the subject to prevent the eye from moving its point of fixation to other regions in order to gain information. In normal vision constant small eye movements are habitual and really steady fixation is an unnatural form of behavior.

However, when all these conditions are fulfilled, there can be no doubt that although the central fovea is capable of a limited discrimination of color, somewhat surprisingly, it does not have the complete color vision which is characteristic of the retina as a whole. When experiments in matching colors are performed with these small centrally fixated fields, it is found that all the spectral colors can be matched with mixtures of two primaries only, i.e., with mixtures of red and blue. Moreover, certain well defined color con-

fusions occur, such as matching blue with green, pink with orange and so on; spectral yellow becomes indistinguishable from white when seen with the foveal center alone. These are all properties which are to be expected in a system which is based on two types of receptor only, and, what is more, they are identical with the properties of the color vision of the tritanope (see p. 310). Central foveal vision, dependent upon a population of cones only, is therefore a form of dichromatic vision and is probably most easily explained by reference to the curves shown in figure 14.17.

If it is supposed that there are two kinds of receptor in the central fovea, which are functional under the conditions of the color-matching just described, and if it is supposed that their spectral sensitivities are as depicted in figure 14.17, curves P and D, or figure 13.19 for chlorolabe and erythrolabe, then it is clear that each wavelength must evoke a different ratio of responses from the two classes of receptors. Theoretically therefore, this difference could be used to indicate wave-length; and some property of the total response could give information about brightness. Moreover a study of the figure shows that, if suitable intensities of red (stimulating one class of receptor (D) much more than the other) and of blue (stimulating mainly the other class (P)) are mixed together it should be possible to produce almost any desired ratio of responses from the two classes of receptors, including the ratios which are normally produced by the different wave-lengths of the spectrum, and so to match all the spectral colors. Wherever the two curves cross, both classes of receptor might be expected to give the same response, i.e., at this wave-length they would all behave as if they were alike, thus constituting a uniform population, and, just as the rods (which are another uniform population of receptors) give no sensation of color when they are functioning alone in scotopic vision, so it is the spectral wave-length which the central fovea matches with white, and which evokes a sensation of light but no color.

It is evident therefore that the color properties of the central fovea can be adequately described in terms of two types of receptor and two only, whose spectral sensitivities are similar to those depicted in figure 14.17. The normal central fovea thus behaves as if it were partly color blind, dichromatic and tritanopic. Fixation within this area allows all spectral colors between violet and yellow-green to be matched with blue-green and all colors between red and yellow-green to be

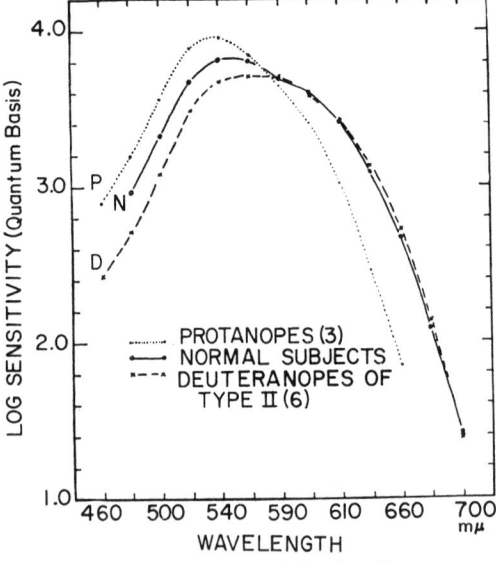

Fig. 14.17. Central foveal luminosity curves. N = Luminosity curve for normal central fovea; P = luminosity curve for the protanope and probable sensitivity curve for one type of receptor in the normal fovea; D = luminosity curve for certain deuteranopes and probable sensitivity curve for the other type of receptor in the normal fovea. (From Willmer.)

matched with orange, provided that the brightness of the matching fields is equalized. If, in the foveal center there is a simpler form of color vision than elsewhere, in fact a two-unit system instead of the full three unit system, its further investigation is likely to be somewhat easier and more immediately rewarding than that of the whole eye. A system with only two variables is always simpler than one with three.

Now it so happens that in certain forms of color blindness (e.g., deuteranopia and protanopia) the subjects are, as indicated above (figs. 15.15 and 15.16) normally unable to distinguish between the two main colors associated with central foveal vision, namely blue-green and orange, provided that the colors are equalized in brightness. As might be expected therefore, such subjects, when they have their vision restricted to the central fovea, are found to be totally color-blind in that area. Once again, the simplest interpretation of this observation is that such subjects have only one type of receptor in the central fovea, or, if they have more than one type of receptor, the information which the two or more types provide is lost before it is used for color discrimination. In other words, either there is only one type of receptor or all types relay on to the same optic nerve fiber. If the first assumption is made, namely that red-green blind subjects have only one type of receptor in the foveal center, then as with rod vision, the spectral sensitivity curve must be a close approximation to the spectral sensitivity of the visual pigment in the receptor. Another very significant fact from the point of view of the subjective interpretation of color is the fact that these color blind subjects who are monochromatic in the foveal center have a sensation of "no color," colorlessness or white, for all wave-lengths, as soon as foveal fixation is obtained. This is not to be confused with another equally important observation that as soon as an image is stabilized on any one part of the retina of a normal person, the color very soon disappears and then the whole image fades away. The time relationships of the two phenomena are quite different. Monochromacy and central fixation are almost simultaneous in the color blind subject who is trained to observe without eye movements. Since it is known that the red-green blind subject can normally receive sensations of color with large fields, probably in shades of blue and yellow, the suggestion is very strong, since color disappears at the foveal center where one type of receptor is working on its own, that color does not depend on the stimulation of one particular form of receptor

alone, but rather on the difference between the responses of two or more classes of receptors.

The curves shown in figure 14.17 are actually the spectral sensitivity curves for the foveal centers of protanopes (P) and deuteranopes (D). The justification for this is that very similar curves are obtained by strongly adapting the fovea of the normal subject first to strong red light and then to strong blue-green light and determining the spectral sensitivity immediately after each type of adaptation. (At the central fovea, since there are no rods, threshold measurements of cone sensitivity can be obtained.) By the first adaptation, the mechanism for the perception of the red end of the spectrum is rendered relatively insensitive and the fovea then becomes dependent upon the "blue-green" mechanism alone at threshold level. This gives the P-curve or something closely approaching it. After the second adaptation, the "blue-green" mechanism is similarly desensitized and the "red" mechanism can be investigated in isolation yielding a close approximation to the D-curve. These facts, all taken together, indicate that in all probability the receptors of the central fovea, or at least those which are active under these conditions, fall into two classes with sensitivities not very different from those depicted in figure 14.17.

Protanopes, who give the P-curve of figure 14.17 also give the *chlorolabe curve* of figure 13.19, and it is therefore extremely probable that, although the agreement is not perfect, these subjects have only one type of receptor and one photo-pigment in their foveal center. In making comparisons between such curves, account must be taken of colored photo-products, macular pigment (see p. 273) and other factors which affect the transmission through the various ocular media. The D-curve, expressing the spectral sensitivity of the monochromatic foveal center of at least some of the deuteranopes, is similarly comparable with the erythrolabe curve. Since differential bleaching with lights from either end of the spectrum which are subjectively equally bright produces the same degree of insensitivity in the central cones of some deuteranopes, at least, quite irrespective of wave-length, these subjects appear to have only one type of cone and the same appears to be true, albeit with somewhat less certainty, of the protanopes.

Although it is too early to be certain, it is probable that the central fovea of the normal person contains two classes of receptors and that these are both cones. Each cone probably contains a single pigment, namely erythrolabe or chlorolabe, and from the shapes of their sensitivity curves the pigments are probably carotenoid-proteins akin to other members of the rhodopsin group. Indeed Brown and Wald have added 11-cis retinene$_1$ to opsins prepared from monkey fovea and have obtained regeneration of pigments which appeared to be the original cone pigments.

Although in some ways it is easier to investigate, this central foveal vision is peculiar and very different from normal color vision, which occurs either when larger fields are being used or when the eye is allowed free movement and the use of other parts of the retina. Under these more normal conditions human color vision is trichromatic, as suggested by Thomas Young, and dependent upon three receptor mechanisms, as emphasized by Helmholtz. Some third factor must therefore intervene to prevent the sorts of confusion which must inevitably occur with any dichromatic system like the one just described for the central fovea.

Although it seems probable that the two classes of receptor in the central fovea are both cones, there is much less certainty about the nature of the third mechanism, whose activities are mostly concerned with the blue end of the spectrum and which therefore is conveniently called the "blue" mechanism. The recent observations of Marks et al. (see pp. 316, 317) strongly support the idea that it also depends on a cone, but the evidence is not by any means conclusive, and, as will be seen, the blue mechanism has many properties which differ greatly from those associated with the known cones.

The effects of this third factor are fourfold. First, three primary colors are required in order to make mixtures which will match each of the colors of the spectrum and all extra-spectral colors. Second, three primary colors are, in general, sufficient. Third, the sorts of confusion found in the dichromatic foveal center no longer occur. Fourth, trichromatic color mixtures are unique, i.e., there is only one combination of the three primaries that are chosen which will make an exact match with any other particular color. There is, however, some suggestion that trichromatic matches may not always be perfect but only within the limits of tolerance. If the brightness level is changed, it sometimes happens that trichromatic matches break down. Matches with four primary colors apparently do not suffer from this defect, probably because they are just that much more precise. The matches are of course still being made by the same trichromatic mechanism. This trichromacy has the important practical applications already discussed (p. 305 et seq.) and allows deductions to be made from color mixture data as to the probable sensitivities of the three basic mechanisms involved.

Attempts have therefore been made to estimate the sensitivity of the three mechanisms responsible for color vision by assuming that the sensation depends upon stimulating the three mechanisms, each of which gives its specific contribution, i.e., blueness, greenness, or redness, in very much the same way as the color mixture itself is made by compounding blue, green and red primaries. In other words, the mixture data for one set of primaries have been converted to another set of primaries, one of which is deemed to be the spectral sensitivity of one of the receptors. How far this is legitimate is somewhat dubious, since color sensations, as determined by the simpler conditions of the central fovea, seem to depend upon the differences between the responses in two receptor systems rather than on the response in only one. Nevertheless, the problem of the nature of the third factor has to be approached by any means that are available.

Stiles has tackled the problem of the sensitivities of the color mechanisms in general by a study of what may be termed increment thresholds. In the description of the dark adaptation curve for the whole eye (p. 296) attention was drawn to the "knee" in the curve and this was related to the dropping out of the cone mechanism at that particular level of illumination, which thus allowed the threshold light-intensity for the cones to be determined.

Stiles has adopted a somewhat similar method for detecting the thresholds for the various cone or photopic mechanisms. If a small test patch of monochromatic light is superimposed momentarily on a uniform background of the same or of a different color (i.e. monochromatic spectral band), a subject can say whether or not he sees the test patch. If then the minimum visible intensity of the test patch is recorded with different intensities of the background field, a curve relating the two intensities can be plotted. As the brightness of the background increases, the brightness of the test patch has to be increased in a corresponding way. The amount of the increase is presumably related to the extent to which the background light alters the sensitivities of the receptors required for the perception of the test light. For example, one might suppose that a dim blue background would have little effect upon the threshold for seeing a red test patch, since the "red mechanism" is unlikely to be stimulated to any great extent by the blue light. When, however, the blue light becomes strong enough, it would begin to affect the receptors concerned with red vision and the threshold for red would then begin to rise. The intensity at which this occurs therefore indicates the threshold of some part of the red receptive mechanism for blue light of the particular wavelength used to illuminate the background. When this is done systematically throughout the spectrum with different wave-lengths in the background, the sensitivity of this part of the red mechanism to all other wave-lengths can be plotted. If the red mechanism depends on two or more receptors or pathways then a further rise in the blue background intensity may produce another break in the regular increment threshold curve for a red test flash at the point where the second mechanism begins to be affected by the blue (or other colored) stimulus.

As a result of a detailed analysis made in this manner, in which numerous wave-lengths have been used both for the test flash and for the background, Stiles has obtained evidence for five separate mechanisms in addition to the rods. The estimated spectral sensitivities of the three main ones (π_1, π_4, π_5) are plotted in figure 14.18. They provide a very important body of concrete information with regard to the color mechanisms in the normal eye. The problem, however, remains as to how these curves should be interpreted and how they can be integrated into the other data on color vision.

Stiles is cautious on this subject and prefers to label the curves π_1 to π_5 and to use the word mechanism rather than receptor, or even pathway. The point that has been determined in each case is the intensity which is required at each wavelength for some process involved in the perception of the test flash to be affected by the conditioning stimulus. On structural and physiological grounds this new process which becomes affected could be: (a) the threshold of a new type of receptor; (b) the threshold of a bipolar cell; (c) the threshold of a ganglion cell; or (d) the threshold at which some inhibitory process came into action. There is nothing as yet to indicate which, if any, of these processes is the effective one in any of the π_1 to π_5 mechanisms. When more information is available, this analysis of increment thresholds will undoubtedly prove of the utmost value. Meanwhile π_1 (blue mechanism) π_4 (green mechanism) and π_5 (red mechanism) agree very well with estimates which have been made of the sensitivity of these color mechanisms from the data obtained by color mixture. π_4 and π_5 are closely similar to the curves obtained from the foveal center and described above. Thus there now seems to be approaching some certainty that the sensitivity of the two mechanisms of the central fovea is very much as has been suggested, and is dependent initially on chlorolabe and erythrolabe activating different cones. In addition to this simple pattern it could be postulated that other retinal nerve cells could also send information about the difference

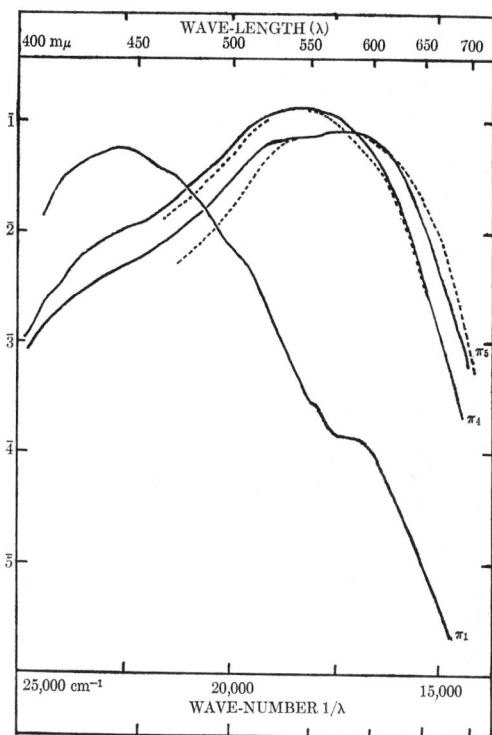

FIG. 14.18. Sensitivity curves for the π_1, π_4 and π_5 mechanisms. The dotted lines represent the P and the D curves from figure 73.17. See text. (After Stiles and Willmer.)

in responses between the receptors and these nerve cells might have very different thresholds from the receptors themselves. Figure 14.19 indicates some such possibilities. Information could pass centrally by the direct paths C and E. It could summate by impinging on a common cell at the next relay (C + E). Alternatively, there could be cells, C − E and E − C, which could be stimulated by one receptor and inhibited by the other. Such cells would then record the difference between the effects of the primary stimulation of the receptors. Only one of the pair would be positively active at any one time, of course, depending upon which receptor was responding more strongly at the time. It will be seen that the cells of this last type would be working in exactly the sort of way required to activate the cells in the lateral geniculate body of the monkey (see pp. 318, 360). The thresholds of these various cells might be very different and very differently affected by adaptation, and so show up by the increment threshold technique which, after all, depends on information supplied to the brain by the optic nerve and not necessarily only on the degree of stimulation of the receptors themselves. This hypothesis should be regarded as only a suggestion as to the manner in which it is now becoming possible to think about retinal physiology; however, since retinal physiology is,

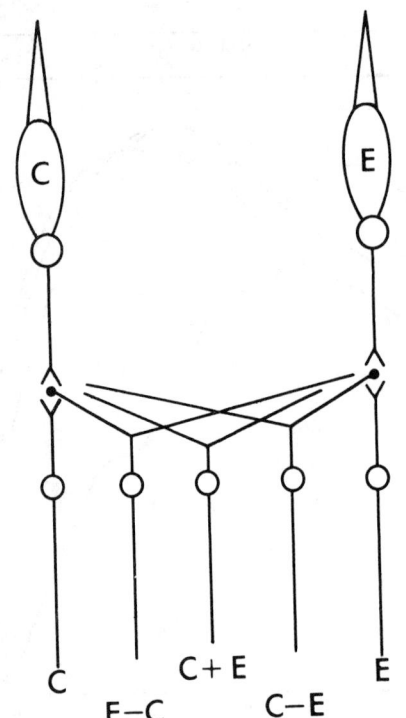

FIG. 14.19. Hypothetical connections of cones at the foveal center.

C and E could be primarily concerned with visual acuity.

C + E could record brightness,

C − E could record blue-greenness,

E − C could record orange-redness,

Note. It is not suggested that these cells are all bipolars. They need not all even be retinal.

in a sense, the physiology of the central nervous system, its implications are far-reaching.

THE BLUE MECHANISM AND π 1. Although some finality appears to be approaching in relation to the identification of the red and green mechanisms, the nature of the blue mechanism remains an unsolved problem. From color-mixture data obtained from both normal and color-blind subjects and from the increment threshold data of Stiles (the π_1 curve) it appears to have its maximum sensitivity at about 450 mμ. In several ways, it appears to differ in kind from the other two mechanisms. Some of these differences are listed below.

1. Blue contributes very little to the luminosity of any color mixture, and the responses from the green and red mechanisms (π_4 and π_5) account for nearly all the luminosity of the spectrum.

2. The blue mechanism does not operate with very small fields, and it may actually be absent from the central fovea.

3. The receptive field of the blue mechanism is about 13′ in diameter, whereas for the red and the green mechanisms it is of the order of 1′.

4. Extrafoveally, a fairly large field has to be

stimulated (or eye movements allowed) in order to allow the mechanism full play.

5. The normal eye can be reduced to a state of monochromatism by sufficient adaptation to violet and blue-green, or to violet and red. When this is done, the eye yields only colorless or very desaturated sensations in response to subsequent test fields over a large part of the spectrum. If, on the other hand, it is reduced to monochromatism by intense stimulation by yellow light (which, incidentally, has very little influence on color sensations in the central fovea, other than raising their threshold) then all wave-lengths from 400–500 mμ subsequently appear as a very saturated violet (which can be matched with 447 mμ). Under these conditions of "violet monochromatism" induced by intense adaptation to yellow light, as distinct from the more usual colorless monochromatisms, intensity discrimination becomes very bad and the visual acuity (see p. 318) becomes very low; black bars on a uniform field have to be separated by more than 7.5′ before they can be resolved, whereas in comparable "red" and "green" monochromatisms visual acuity is little impaired from the normal (bars can be seen as separate entities when only about 1′ apart). This low visual acuity of the blue mechanism is comparable with the low acuity of the rod mechanism, although it is definitely somewhat higher.

6. When the eye is adapted to various colored lights, the effect of the adaptations on subsequent color matches can be recorded and the rate of the recovery of the different mechanisms from the adaptation can be investigated. It is nearly always found that although the red and the green components in the mixture tend to follow similar and rapid recovery curves, the recovery of the blue mechanism is definitely slower and follows a different time course.

7. The estimated spectral sensitivity curve for the blue mechanism (π_1) has an unique kink in it between about 550 mμ and 600 mμ which is not found in other sensitivity curves nor in the absorption spectrum of carotenoid-protein pigments.

8. Tritanopia (blue blindness) is inherited separately from the other forms of color-blindness.

Several features of the blue mechanism suggest that it may be associated in some way with the function of the rods.

1. Neither the blue mechanism nor the rods are present in the foveal center, whereas the blue mechanism, unlike the red and green mechanisms, is in operation almost to the extreme periphery of the eye (see p. 275), or at least as far out as color is recognized at all (fig. 14.20).

2. The blue mechanism is often the first of the color mechanisms to be affected in cases of retinitis pigmentosa. Tritanopia or failure of the blue mechanism often follows any retinal damage or

degeneration which involves the destruction of the rods.

3. When light of any wave-length from 400 to 570 mμ illuminates one half of a divided field (about 4° in diameter) at such a low level of intensity that no sensation of color is aroused, one presumes that only rods are being stimulated. However, the illumination of the other half of the field with light of any wave-length between 570 and 700 mμ, of sufficient intensity to arouse a sensation of color in that half, i.e., to stimulate cones, immediately causes the first half of the field to darken and to appear blue. If the divided field is viewed monocularly, the blue can be matched by a spectral wave-band centered on 464 mμ viewed by the unstimulated eye. The suggestion is very strong that rods are involved in this blue sensation.

4. Twilight vision often has a subjective quality of blueness.

There are, equally, several features which argue against the blue mechanism being dependent upon the rods:

1. The spectral sensitivity of the blue mechanism is not that of rhodopsin; it is more nearly that of indicator yellow, although this is not a photosensitive pigment in the ordinary sense.

2. The color mixture data are incompatible with rhodopsin as one of the primary pigments used for color vision if the curves for the other (π_4 and π_5) mechanisms are valid.

3. The visual acuity in violet monochromatism,

although low, is higher than that with ordinary rod vision.

4. Trichromatic matches made at photopic levels should not break down at scotopic levels if rods are involved in both. In practice such matches do sometimes break down.

5. The direct recording of the spectral sensitivity of 'blue receptors' in the human retina by Marks, Dobelle and MacNichol (see Fig. 13, 19b).

It is clear from these summaries that, if rods are involved in the blue mechanism, they are acting in some rather different way from their more clearly recognized action. Although man has developed from nocturnal ancestors in whose eyes rods undoubtedly preponderated, it is rather extraordinary that his retina should still possess some twenty rods to every cone, if they are of no significance in his apparatus for vision under ordinary daylight conditions, for he has now become such a definitely diurnal animal.

Moreover, there is something very attractive about the "opponent color theories" that have been developed in various forms by Hering, Houstoun, Ladd-Franklin, Gothlin and, more recently, by Hurvich and Jamieson, some of which could well be reconciled with an antagonism between rods and cones. The essence of these theories, all of which vary in detail, is the idea of opposition between blue and yellow, and between red and green. Indeed there are many arguments which can be brought in support of such an interpretation of color vision, particularly if the antagonisms

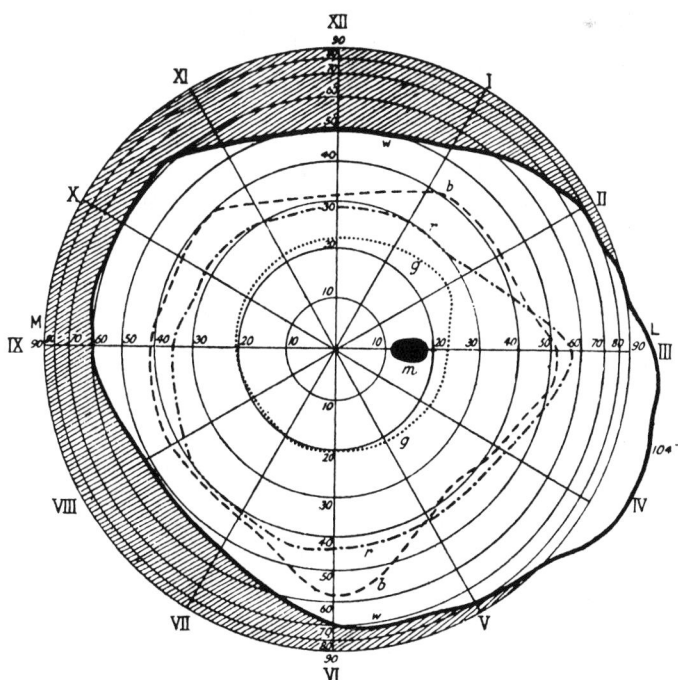

Fig. 14.20. Fields for white, blue, red and green for a normal right eye. (From Hartridge.)

are thought of as not necessarily arising at the receptor level but at some higher level in the neural pathway. On the theoretical side, we have already seen that central foveal color vision is, in general, explicable in these terms. On the observational side, the electrical potentials recorded by Svaetichin and MacNichol in the horizontal cells of fish, by De Valois in the lateral geniculate body of monkeys (see p. 360), and by Hubel and Wiesel in a minority of ganglion cells in the retina of monkeys, all seem to provide evidence for the existence of such antagonisms.

The concept of one neural pathway or mechanism opposing another has much to recommend it as a means of reducing the information entering the central nervous system to manageable proportions and at the same time insuring that the specific qualities of the stimulus are maintained. Redundant information can be eliminated in this manner. For example, and as a pure hypothesis, if both rods and cones are being stimulated, the complete response of the less strongly stimulated together with the excess response from the other provide all the necessary information for recording both luminosity and a limited sensation of hue.

The general hypothesis that the most primitive form of color vision was based on some feature or modification of rod function opposing cone function (or *vice versa*) and giving rise to sensations of blue when the rod function was dominant and to yellow when the cones were in the ascendant is certainly attractive in its simplicity. It also suggests that the red-green blind (protanopes and deuteranopes) who have these two sensations only, may still possess something akin to this more primitive evolutionary condition of the visual system. If some of the cones then acquired a second pigment, just as, among the chromatophores, the xanthophores often acquire a red pigment in addition to their normal xanthophyll and become erythrophores, two groups of cones could then result, and the responses from these two groups could provide the means of subdividing the sensation of yellow into one of blue-green and one of orange-red according to which type of cone gave the greater response. This concept is consistent with the restricted retinal fields over which the red and green sensations are evoked in the normal light-adapted eye, whereas the yellow sensation can be evoked, either by green or red light, as far out in the retinal periphery as any color sensations can be recognized (fig. 14.20). However, in the dark-adapted eye, red is seen, as red, in the extreme periphery; yellow and green then generally appear as white because they excite the dark adapted rods. The physiological interpretation of these color fields is presumably to be sought partly in the distribution of the receptors themselves and partly in the distribution of the various bipolar cells and ganglion cells which integrate and code the information provided by the receptors. Protanopia and deuteranopia may in some cases depend on defective transmitting systems rather than defective receptor systems. Two tentative schemes for retinal function could be summarized as follows (see Diagrams I and II). Both have their difficulties, but they may help to provide some mental picture of present trends in color-vision theory.

The colors named are those seen when the receptor in question dominates over its opponent; e.g. in the fovea, when the chlorolabe dominates over the erythrolabe, the sensation of blue-green tends to appear; when the erythrolabe dominates, the color perceived in some shade of orange or red. Hypothetically one could suggest that the "green-on," "red-off" cell in the lateral geniculate body mediates the blue-green sensation, while the "red-on," "green-off" cell mediates the orange-red sensation. The neutral point of these cells is in the neighborhood of 560 mμ while the neutral point of central foveal vision is about 570 mμ, though both are subject to variation with adaptation. On the same lines, perhaps the "short-wave-on" and "long-wave-off" ganglion cells in the retina, with their neutral point at about 500 mμ are concerned with the blue-yellow dichotomy. Again the neutral point of these cells is in the same region as the neutral points of red-green blind subjects. The fact that one of these cell types is retinal while the other is in the lateral geniculate body could explain some of the qualitative differences between the blue-yellow, and red-green mechanisms. Future research alone can clarify the position.

Visual Acuity

THE RESOLVING POWER OF THE EYE. The acuteness of vision (or visual acuity) is dependent upon several retinal functions, e.g., the sensitivity to light (intensity threshold), the minimum visible (p. 321) and the ability to recognize the separateness of two closely approximated or parallel lines. The threshold of the latter faculty is commonly referred to as the *minimum separable*[1] or the *resolution threshold*. Visual acuity is the basis of the *form sense*, by which is meant the power of determining by sight the shape, form, outline and minute detail of our surroundings. Visual acuity is customarily expressed in terms of the minimum separable or, to be more explicit, as the reciprocal of the angle subtended at the nodal point of the eye—the *visual angle*—by the space between two points situated at the minimum distance apart at which their duality can be recog-

[1] The minimum separable is analogous to two point discrimination in cutaneous sensation.

DIAGRAM I

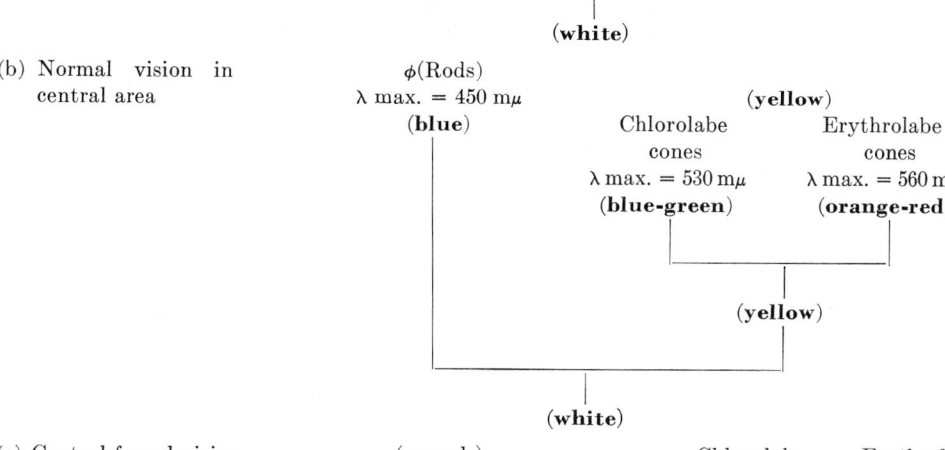

Scotopic vision   Rods, λ max. = 500 mμ   (no cones)
                      (white)

Photopic vision
(a) In primitive eye and   φ(Rods)   Cones
    in retinal periphery   λ max. = 450 mμ   (erythrolabe, chlorolabe
                             (blue)   or a mixture of both)
                                                    λ max. between 530 and
                                                          560 mμ.
                                                        (yellow)

                                  (white)

(b) Normal   vision   in   φ(Rods)   **(yellow)**
    central area   λ max. = 450 mμ   Chlorolabe   Erythrolabe
                             (blue)   cones   cones
                                                   λ max. = 530 mμ   λ max. = 560 mμ
                                                   (blue-green)   **(orange-red)**

                                                             (yellow)

                                  (white)

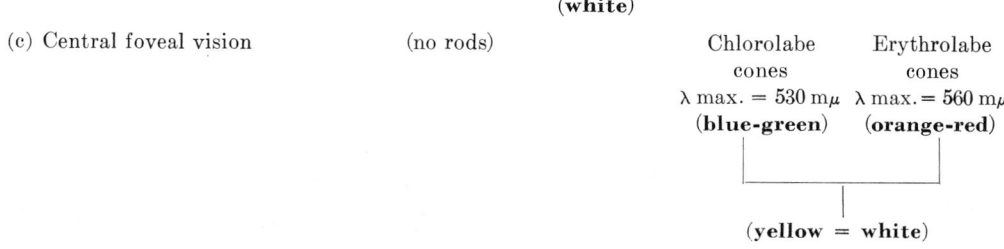

(c) Central foveal vision   (no rods)   Chlorolabe   Erythrolabe
                                                      cones   cones
                                                   λ max. = 530 mμ λ max. = 560 mμ
                                                   (blue-green)   **(orange-red)**

                                                      (yellow = white)

Note: 1. The separation of chlorolabe from erythrolabe cones may have involved only a separation of the neural pathways, the two types of pigment being always present except in the protanopes.

2. φ(Rods) indicates some, as yet undetermined, modification either of the photochemistry of rod vision or in the spectral distribution of the rod response which remains effective under photopic conditions (i.e., which survives inhibition by cones or other similar process).

nized. For example, if the visual angle is 1.321 minute, then the visual acuity is (1/1.321 =) 0.756. The average normal eye can resolve two points when the visual angle is 1 minute (60 seconds). The maximum acuity measured with a Landolt C (see below) is about 2.1. As an object is moved away from the eye its visual angle becomes progressively smaller. Consequently, those details of form and structure which subtend an angle of a minute or more at the nearer point and are therefore visible, gradually become imperceptible with increasing distance. In other words, in order to see an object at a distance as clearly as when it is near the eye, it would need to be increased proportionally in size (see fig. 14.21).

In determining the visual acuity, figures such as the broken circle **C** of Landolt or Snellen's prong, **E**, painted black on a white ground and in graded sizes are employed. The subject is seated at a distance of 6 meters (20 feet) and a figure is placed with the gap of the **C** or the prongs of the **E** turned to the right or left; he is asked to say in which position the figure is directed. The width of the lines composing the figures and the gap in the **C**, or the spaces between the prongs of the **E**, subtend angles of various degrees, depending on the size of the figure, when placed at a distance of 6 meters. The width of the whole figure is five times the thickness of its parts. By

DIAGRAM II

Scotopic vision   Rods λ max. = 500 mμ   (no cones)
                     (white)

Photopic vision
   (a) Retinal periph-   (? max. rods or   "Blue" cones   Chlorolabe and/or erythrolabe
       ery   no rods)   λ max. = 450 mμ   cones
                                  (blue)   λ max. between 530 and 560 mμ
                                                   (yellow)

                                    (white)

   (b) Normal vision   (? max. rods or   "Blue" cones   Chlorolabe   Erythrolabe
       in central area   no rods)   λ max. = 450 mμ   cones   cones
                                 (blue)   λ max. = 530 mμ   λ max. = 560 mμ
                                        (blue-green)   **(orange-red)**

                                                (yellow)

                                   (white)

   (c) Central foveal   (no rods)   (no 'blue' cones)   Chlorolabe   Erythrolabe
       vision   cones   cones
                                       λ max. = 530 mμ   λ max. = 560 mμ
                                       (blue-green)   **(orange-red)**

                                            (yellow = white)

finding the smallest figure whose position can be recognized the visual acuity of the subject (in terms of the visual angle) is ascertained. In testing the visual acuity for the fitting of glasses Snellen's *test type* is most commonly employed. This test is devised upon the basis that two points or lines separated by a space having a visual angle of 1 minute can be resolved by the average normal eye. The test type comprises nine rows of block letters printed in black upon a white card. The rows are arranged in descending order of size from above down. The width of the lines forming the letters of the first row subtends an angle of 1 minute at 60 meters from the eye, whereas that of the letters in the other rows, two to nine, have a visual angle of 1 minute at 36, 24, 18, 12, 9, 6, 5 and 4 meters, respectively. The card is placed in a good light, the patient is seated facing it at a distance of 6 meters and asked to read down as many rows as he can. The visual acuity is expressed as a fraction, the numerator being the distance at which the subject is seated from the card and the denominator the distance at which the letters could be read by the normal eye. Thus, if he reads the seventh row of letters, i.e., those with a visual angle of 1 minute at 6 meters his vision is 6/6

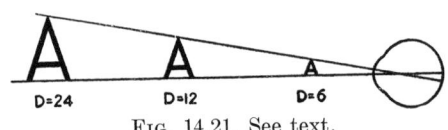

Fig. 14.21. See text.

or normal. If, on the other hand, he can see distinctly only as far as the fourth row, which the normal eye can read at 18 meters, his vision is 6/18; if as far as the third row his vision is 6/24, and so on, for any other row which he is just able to read.

Knowing the distance of the nodal point of the eye from the retina and the visual angle, the size of the retinal image of an object can be calculated (p. 334, 335). With a visual angle of 1 minute the space on the retina separating two point images is 4.4 μ. The diameter of the space occupied by a foveal cone is given by different observers as between 2.5 and 4.0 μ. Even if the higher of these figures is taken, then the image of two dots separated by 4.4 μ would fall upon two cones separated by a single unstimulated cone or by one stimulated differently, i.e., by the image of the interspace (fig. 14.22).

From such calculations it has been argued that the distance between cone centers is the limiting factor in discriminating two points or thin lines, for obviously with an interspace less than a cone width the two dots would fall upon a single cell, and from what is known of the nerve impulse it cannot be admitted that two parts of a visual receptor, upon receiving simultaneously different types of stimulus, can give rise to dissimilar sensations.

Difficulties stand in the way of so simple an explanation. The eyes, even with the most exact fixation, are constantly executing fine movements (subtending as much as 10'), and this means that the retinal image does not stimulate only one group of cones, but must be constantly shifting its position. This theory must also make the assumption that when the angular distance separating two points is about the diameter of a cone the two images must be dodged about with almost incredible precision, so that they come to lie not on adjacent cones (see fig. 14.22) but on two cones separated by an unstimulated cone or by one stimulated differently. Adler concluded from his experiments, in which fixation as exact as possible was secured, that a point image moves over from 2 to 4 cones at least. Furthermore, the size of the image on the retina cannot, owing to the diffusion of light, be calculated with the precision implied by the foregoing calculations (see below). It is true that the smallest visual angle recorded (28″) for the space between two visually discrete objects would give a retinal image of the same order of magnitude as the diameter of a cone—a fact which fits the theory that the latter is the limiting factor. Nevertheless, it is probable that the correlation is little more than a coincidence.

Wilcox and Purdy suggest that the essential factor is the total illumination of the central cone as compared with its fellow on either side. Thus, in figure 14.23 A, cone 2 receives more light than cones 1 and 3. There is no reason then theoretically why the interspace separating two lines could not be narrower than the width of a single cone and still be recognizable. A limit would be reached, however, when the white interspace was reduced to about half the width of a cone; then all three cones must be illuminated equally. It may be asked, what essential difference is there between the minimum visible and the minimum separable (p. 318), that the minimum visual angle should be so much greater in the one instance than in the other? Two parallel black lines upon a white surface are recognized as separate because a third white line is seen between them. Why then, provided it is bright enough can it not be seen, even though reduced to an almost infinitesimal width?

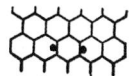

FIG. 14.22. See text

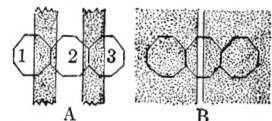

FIG. 14.23. Description in text.

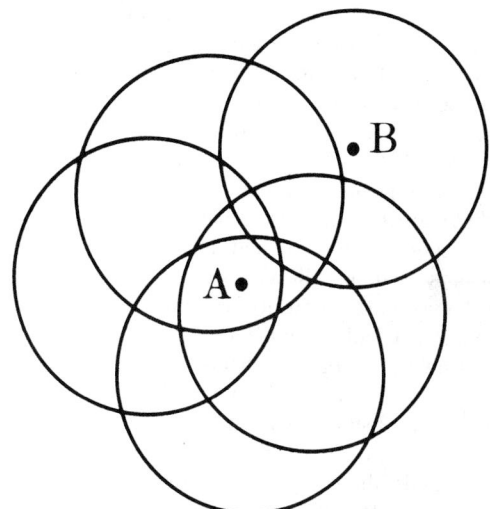

FIG. 14.24. Diagram illustrating the effect of overlapping receptive fields on visual acuity. For explanation see text.

The difference in the two instances appears to be a matter of the background and may be illustrated by fig. 14.23 B. A bright light upon an extensive background illuminates a single row of cones, whereas all cones for a distance on either side are unilluminated. According therefore to the conception of Wilcox and Purdy, no difference exists, in so far as the fundamental retinal process is concerned, between the minimum visible and the minimum separable.

There is one aspect of visual acuity which is probably of far more importance than appears at first sight. It might be supposed that the highest visual acuity would only be obtained if there existed an exactly one to one relationship between each receptor and its optic nerve fiber. It must be remembered, however, that there are, in and around the central fovea, not only midget bipolar cells but numerous flat and brush types also and that these presumably collect information from numerous receptors. Moreover, ganglion cells may again collect information from several of these bipolar cells. The fields of these cells certainly overlap, which incidentally may have considerable advantage in preventing the development of blind spots or scotomas when individual cells degenerate. The situation is diagrammatically represented in figure 14.24 where the circles represent the overlapping fields of five bipolar cells. A study of this figure shows that the field in question must be covered by at least these five fields, and that it can be subdivided into numerous areas in which from one to five of the receptive fields in question may be affected. For example, a receptor situated at point A would affect four out of the five bipolars, but one situated at point B would affect only one. Thus position on the retina is specified by the particular pattern of bipolar cells which are stimulated. Moreover it has been shown that within any one receptive field the center is generally the most sensitive part and that a greater stimulus becomes necessary to elicit a response from the margins of the field; this means that a still greater specificity can be achieved in the pattern of response to stimulation of any particular point in the retina. The point A lies on the margins of fields 1, 2, 4, and 5 and therefore stimulates them all rather weakly, but point B affects field 3 maximally and the other fields not at all. Every point stimulated in the area under discussion thus evokes a particular and specific pattern of responses from the bipolar cells both with respect to the grouping of cells affected and also with respect to the frequency of impulses generated, since these depend on the intensity of the stimulus and the position within the receptive field.

As with other faculties of the eye, no absolute and constant value can be given for the minimum separable. It varies greatly with several factors, viz., (a) the *intensity of illumination* of the test object, (b) the spectral character of the light, (c) the region of the retina stimulated and (d) the size of the pupil.

The resolving power of the eye for two points

increases with the illumination, as illustrated in fig. 14.25. This is a fact difficult to explain. It might be thought that as long as the illumination was above the threshold for a just perceptible sensation, increase in the intensity of the light would be without influence upon the threshold for the minimum separable. Two theories which have been proposed to account for the phenomenon will be mentioned, not because they give any final answer to the problem, but because they bring up some interesting points.

Hartridge proposes a theory based upon the aberrations of the optical system of the eye and the ability of the retina to discriminate between small differences of light intensity (p. 295). The retinal image is not clearly defined but is blurred by diffusion circles or bands, caused by the diffraction of light at the pupillary margin and by colored fringes (chromatic aberration, p. 348). Assuming the pupil to be 3 mm. in diameter and a foveal cone 3.2μ. across, he made the following calculations of the light distribution on the retina caused by a white line separating two dark areas. The illumination of the row of cones corresponding to the center of the line image was taken as 100. The illumination of the next row was 31%, of the next 9%. The diffusion bands thus virtually increase the width of the image of the white line beyond that indicated by calculations from the visual angle, and encroach upon the dark boundaries. The fine movements of the eyes are continually shifting the image and even the slightest movement will cause the line of junction between the outermost diffusion band and the dark area to move from one row of cones to another. A row of cones is therefore stimulated at one instant at a different intensity from that at the next. If the difference in light intensity is greater than 10% it is appreciated, and thus a gap between the two dark areas is detected. Now the threshold for discrimination of differences in light intensity varies with the illumination. Consequently, when the illumination is reduced, the difference between the intensity of the outermost diffusion bands and of the dark areas is not perceived, i.e., the shift of the line of junction from one cone to the next causes no sensation. The difference between the illumination of the inner and outer bands may be still detectable, but the width of the bright line will be reduced. With further reduction in the illumination and the consequent raising of the threshold for intensity discrimination the white image becomes still narrower and finally, when the angular width is about 1″, the dark areas fuse across it.

Hecht's theory postulates a change in the "grain" of the retina as a result of variations in illumination. The retina, according to Hecht, is made up of sensitive elements of different intensity

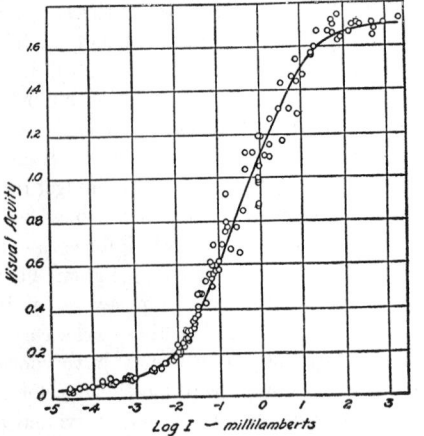

Fig. 14.25. Relation between visual acuity and illumination. (After Hecht.)

thresholds distributed in a statistical manner similar to that of other populations. At low levels of illumination only a proportion of these elements (i.e., rods with the lowest threshold) are excited. The active elements are therefore farther apart and the "grain" of the sensitive surface is relatively coarse. As the light intensity increases, the thresholds of more and more elements are exceeded. More rods function, that is, the number of active elements is increased and the "grain" of the retina is finer. As the illumination rises further, cones, first those with the lowest thresholds and later less sensitive ones, become active. The maximal effect of increasing the illumination upon the resolving power is reached when the entire rod and cone population is responding (see fig. 14.25). Objections to both of the theories just outlined could be cited; several observations indicate that the threshold for the minimum separable is not dependent entirely upon retinal factors but that central processes play an important part.

The influences of such processes as the lateral inhibition already mentioned in sharpening up edges and increasing contrast between illuminated and unilluminated areas must also be important in determining visual acuity at different brightness levels.

Finally, the part played in determining acuity by those ganglion cells which respond to moving edges and to particular directions of movement of the image is another interesting field for investigation.

The resolving power of the eye is greater for monochromatic light than for a mixed light source such as daylight when the two have equal illuminating values. This fact is due to the absence of chromatic aberration in the former instance. Monochromatic yellow light (575 mμ) gives the highest value, next in order come green, red and blue.

Theoretically the resolving power must be limited by half the wave-length of the light and should therefore be higher in the short-wave end of the spectrum. However, the amount of light visible in the short-wave end falls off very rapidly and, as shown on page 315, the visual acuity of the blue mechanism is conspicuously lower than that of either the green or the red mechanisms. For these reasons, the middle region of the spectrum in practice shows the highest acuity. Hartridge has suggested that the visual acuities in white light and in monochromatic lights remain approximately the same, in spite of the fact that there may be blue, green and red-sensitive cones, because the cones of the different types may be grouped together in clusters in a more or less random way and the eye tends to fixate the image on the most appropriate cluster.

Three factors are involved in the effect of pupillary size upon the resolving power of the retina. Increase in diameter allows more light to enter the eye and therefore increases the illumination of the retinal image and raises the visual acuity. Diffraction is also reduced by widening the pupillary aperture which will tend to improve the definition of the image. On the other hand, narrowing the pupil diminishes chromatic aberration. The optimum pupillary size lies between maximum constriction and full dilation, namely, at a diameter of about 3 mm.

With ordinary illuminations the visual acuity is some twenty times greater at the fovea than in any outlying part of the retina. In the dark adapted eye (p. 296) the peripheral retina has a much higher value than the fovea.

The illumination of the field surrounding the test object (the surround) has an important influence upon the resolving power of the eye. A uniform increase in the illumination of the surround up to one-tenth that of the test object progressively increases visual acuity. Raising the illumination of the surround from this point to equality with the test object causes a slight reduction in visual acuity and, when the surround becomes brighter than the test object, there is a decided depression. A very bright but small light source situated in the neighborhood of the test object, e.g., a motor head light, causes a very marked lowering of the visual acuity. The effects caused by such concentrated sources of light are referred to as "glare." If the small light source is not too bright and especially if the surround is dark, little depressing effect upon the acuteness of vision is produced, indeed there may be an improvement due to the accompanying pupillary constriction.

THE DISPLACEMENT THRESHOLD OR THE VERNIER ACUITY. These terms are applied to the visual faculty of recognizing a break in the contour of a border, a variation in width of a line or the lack of alignment of two straight lines placed end to end. This power of the eye is some ten times greater than its ability to resolve two points. A break in a line subtending an angle as small as 5″ or even 1″ can be detected under optimal conditions. It seems quite certain that this visual faculty is not limited by cone diameter, for the break must lie on a single cone, and the lines on both sides of the break on the same row of cones (fig. 14.26). It is probable that the underlying mechanism is different from that governing the

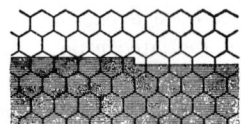

Fig. 14.26. See text. (After Adler.)

threshold for the discrimination of two points. For example, its threshold is only slightly raised by increasing the illumination (p. 322).

Anderson and Weymouth offer an interesting theory to account for the extraordinary accuracy of the vernier acuity. They suggest that the slight but continuous eye movements shift the line image over the retina, causing successive stimulus patterns. The averaging of the successive patterns gives a sense of position which they call *retinal local sign*. The longer the lines the greater are the number of patterns presented to consciousness and, consequently, the more accurate is the averaging process. For details of the view of these authors the reader is referred to their original paper.

The fact that there are cells or groups of cells in the visual cortex (Hubel and Wiesel) and even in the retina itself (Maturana and Frenk) which only respond to particular patterns of image in particular positions on the retina, suggests that the visual mechanism sorts the incoming information in special ways, which are presumably useful and may be unique to the animal. From the records so far obtained it appears that linear patterns of image, either stationary or moving, and related to horizontal and vertical axes, are important in stimulating the cortical cells. Vice versa, the responses from such cortical cells probably contribute in a major way towards the ability of the visual mechanism as a whole to analyse the various features of the images cast upon the retina, and to determine its various forms of acuity.

SOME PRACTICAL CONSIDERATIONS WITH REGARD TO LIGHTING. Besides reducing visual acuity, glare causes discomfort and one instinctively attempts to protect the eyes by closing the lids or raising the hand as a shield; the pupil constricts. A constant source of glare, even of mild degree, results in eye strain. Glare has been classified into three types—veiling, dazzling and blinding. *Veiling glare* is that due to strong light which, being uniformly superimposed upon the retinal image, reduces contrast. The light reflected from a printed page under a bright sky is an example. *Dazzling glare* is due to scattered light in the ocular media which does not form part of the retinal image. Such glare can be produced by a strong light shining into the eye from an angle of about 45°. *Blinding glare* results when one looks directly at a very

bright light. It is due to an actual reduction of retinal sensitivity.

For moderately fine work, such as reading, sewing, typesetting, etc., the illumination of the objects should not be less than from 10 to 20 foot candles. An illumination of 10 foot candles is sufficient for reading ordinary black type on good paper, but higher illumination is necessary if the printing or the paper is of poor quality. The effect of lighting upon the performance of typesetters, mail sorters and others engaged in fine work has been the subject of a number of investigations. Raising the illumination has been found to increase the rapidity and accuracy of the work by from 10 to 16 per cent and to reduce eye strain and general fatigue. The maximum efficiency appears to be reached when the illumination is about 20 foot candles. The lighting should be diffuse, and naked bright light sources which could cause glare eliminated. The central field should receive additional lighting so that its illumination will be from 5 to 10 times that of the surround. The constant use of the eyes in poor lighting leads to ocular strain and fatigue with consequent headache. It may cause increase in pulse rate and even nausea; ultimately serious eye defects, especially in the young, may result. The quality of the light is also an important factor.

THE PERCEPTION OF MOVEMENT. This is the most primitive of the visual functions; in disease it is the last to fail and is the first to return should any improvement in vision occur. The peripheral (extrafoveal) retina is more specially differentiated for the perception of movement than for other purposes. It is a familiar fact that a slight movement is readily detected even if the moving object is not in the direct line of vision, i.e., when its image falls upon the peripheral retina, and the eyes are not fixed upon it. The most sensitive part of the retina is from 10° to 15° from the fovea, but sensitivity diminishes progressively towards the periphery. In the region of maximum sensitivity the angular velocity of a just perceptible movement is from one half to one minute per second, provided that there are stationary objects in the visual field to serve as reference points. When such are absent the angular velocity must be from 10 to 20 times as great in order for the movement to be perceived. On the other hand, if the angular velocity is very great the movement is not perceived; owing to visual persistence a very rapidly moving object appears as a stationary streak. The total distance travelled, i.e., the displacement of the object, as well as the angular velocity is, of course, a factor in movement perception. The minimum displacement is about 17 seconds of arc, under optimal conditions. The sensitivity of the retina to movement is lower in the dark-adapted than in the light adapted eye. Barlow has suggested that the on-off fibers play a large part in the detection of movement.

When the eyes are stationary but the body or head is moved, an *apparent* movement is given to objects in the visual field. To a subject travelling in a train, near objects often appear to move in the opposite direction to the direction of travel, whereas those in the background appear to move with the moving vehicle. Apparent movements of surrounding objects also occur when the eye is displaced slightly by pressure upon it with the finger tip, or as a result of involuntary contraction of the eye muscles. These apparent movements are attributed to the successive stimulation of groups of receptors as the images move over the retina. When the eyes are moved voluntarily from one object to another in the visual field, images must sweep over the retina in a similar fashion, yet there is no apparent movement of stationary objects. An allied phenomenon and one which offers a similar problem to be solved is seen in cutaneous sensation. We are able, for example, to distinguish between the movement of the finger over a stationary object and the movement of an object over a motionless finger. In both instances receptors are stimulated successively. Conversely, the movement of an object is perceived when it is followed by the eyes, although the position of its retinal image does not alter. It is quite evident that the perception of movement is very complex and cannot yet be explained in all its aspects upon physiological grounds. It is suggested that the absence of an apparent movement of stationary objects when the eyes are turned from one part of the visual field to another is to be explained upon the basis of *attention*. The attention exercised by the observer in changing the fixation of his eyes from the one to the other point compensates, it is believed, for the movements of the images over the retina. In other words, the successive stimulation of visual receptors is ignored because the point to which the eyes are to be turned engages the attention at the moment that the eye movement takes place, or even before. The perception of the movement of an object pursued by the eyes must also depend upon cerebral processes.

Apparent movement is also produced by the stimulation of closely approximated retinal areas in rapid succession by a series of images of a stationary object. The two main factors determining this so-called *stroboscopic illusion* of movement are the time interval between the stimuli and the *angular separation* of the successive retinal images. A visual sensation of smooth motion is produced when the angular separation is about 1 degree or less and the intervals between the stimuli about $\frac{1}{10}$ second. At intervals of $\frac{1}{30}$ second or less no sensation of movement is produced. The illusion of motion is also lost if the time intervals are lengthened to $\frac{1}{5}$ second or greater, the impressions then becoming discrete.

Irradiation. Owing to chromatic and spherical aberration the images on the retina are not formed of geometrical points of light, but rather of bright points surrounded by diffusion circles. For this reason, and also probably as a result of the spread of the effect of the stimulus (*irradiation*) to neighboring neural elements of the retina, or even within the visual area in the brain, a bright area on a dark ground appears larger than a dark one of the same size upon a bright ground. In either instance the image of the bright area encroaches upon that of the black area (see fig. 14.1).

INTERMITTENT RETINAL STIMULATION; FLICKER. When the retina is stimulated intermittently by a series of light flashes as may be produced by interrupting a continuous light by a rotating notched disc or by reflecting light from a rotating disc divided into alternate black and white sectors, a characteristic flickering or unpleasant glittering sensation is experienced when the periodic stimulation reaches a certain frequency. This is due to each light stimulus falling upon the retina during the time of the positive after image (p. 327) of its predecessor. The suppression of the after image by the second stimulus causes the first sensation to end more abruptly, and, through contrast, to render the succeeding one more brilliant. Upon further increasing the speed of rotation and, in consequence, the frequency (number per second) of the light stimuli, fusion results and the flicker disappears, to be replaced by a continuous sensation having a brilliance equal to the mean of the two (bright and dark) impressions; the frequency at which this occurs is called the *critical fusion frequency* (C.F.F.). If at the instant of fusion the illumination of the bright patch in millilamberts be designated a, its area designated b, and the total area of the disc, c, then the sensation produced is equal to that which would result from a continuous stimulus having the value $(a \times b)/c$. This is known as the Talbot-Plateau law. It accounts for the well-known fact that a gray sensation of any depth can be matched by throwing black and white images alternately and at a suitable frequency upon the retina. Similarly, at the

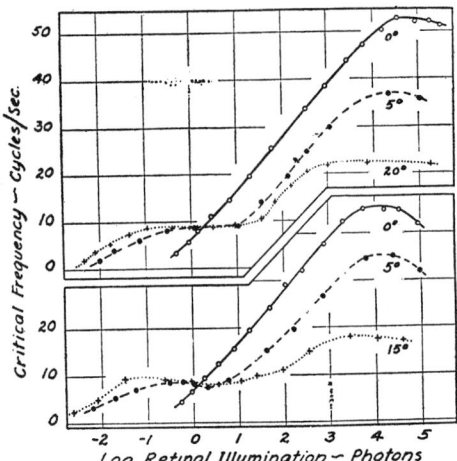

FIG. 14.27. Relation between critical frequency and log *I* for white light with a 2° field in four retinal locations; at the fovea, and at 5°, 15°, and 20° above the fovea. (After Hecht from Hecht and Verrijp.)

critical fusion frequency, white and red images give a sensation of pink; blue and red, a sensation of purple; yellow and green, yellowish green, and so on. These effects are simply explained by *visual persistence*, that is, the sensation evoked by one stimulus has not ceased before the next one is produced, thus a blend of the two sensations in consciousness results. The law holds true only for moderate light intensities.

The value of the C.F.F. is variable, depending upon several conditions the most influential of which is the intensity of the light, the value rising as the intensity increases. That is, a higher rate of stimulation is required for fusion as the intensity of the illumination is increased. The influence of light intensity is embodied in the Ferry (1892)-Porter (1906) law which states that the *critical fusion frequency is directly proportional to the logarithm of the light intensity.* Thus, $n = k \log I + k'$ where n equals flashes per second at the instant of fusion, and I the light intensity; k and k' are constants involving the size of the stimulated area and the sensitivity of the observer's eye.[2]

The Ferry-Porter law is valid, however, only under certain special conditions; it holds over moderate ranges of illumination of the test object when the image is restricted to the fovea. Above and below this middle range the linear relationship

[2] Determination of the critical fusion frequency (C.F.F.) offers an accurate and convenient method for comparing the brightness of differently colored lights. It is especially valuable in this regard because of our natural tendency to confuse the brightness of a color with its hue or saturation.

between the logarithm of the intensity and the critical fusion frequency does not hold. When the value of n is plotted against log I at low and at high intensities the points fall on two straight lines, one at low the other at high intensities. It is believed that these represent respectively rod and cone function, a conception borne out by the results of Hecht and associates and of Lythgoe and Tansley.

Hecht found that with a stimulus restricted to the fovea (cones) the relationship was linear for a middle range of illumination, but above this the curve flattened out, below, it formed a very gentle curve. With the image on extrafoveal regions the data form two intersecting straight lines, one at lower the other at higher intensities, the former presumably represents rod function, the latter peripheral cone function (fig. 14.27).

Lythgoe and Tansley observed that during dark adaptation the C.F.F. falls in both the fovea and the peripheral parts of the retina when the intensity of the test light was high (6.8 foot candles). At low intensities (0.020 foot candles) the C.F.F. also falls at the fovea, but rises in the peripheral retina. Now, as judged by other criteria, only cones are functioning at high intensities whether the fovea or the peripheral retina is being tested, at low intensities only rods. Also, it was found by Lythgoe and Tansley that when red light was used for testing (rods insensitive), and in a case of night blindness (defective rods) a fall in the value of the C.F.F. occurs during dark adaptation. The fall in the value with high illuminations of the test object is due presumably to the cones, and the rise with low illuminations, to the rods. At moderate illuminations of the test object a fall occurs during the first 5 minutes of dark adaptation (due to cones), (see p. 296) followed by a rise (due to rods). The critical frequency due to the rods is highest with dark surrounds; that due to cones is increased by bright surrounds, the maximum being reached when the brightness of the latter and of the test object are equal.

A study of the retinal potentials (ch. 13) during intermittent stimulation shows that when a light flash falls upon the retina during the "off effect" of a preceding stimulus, the *d* wave is interrupted and a pronounced negative dip occurs. This is an exaggerated *a* deflection. The negative deflection is followed by a large positive swing which, if the second stimulus occurs soon after the first, is simply the return of the momentarily interrupted "off effect" of the first. If the interval between the two is greater, the upswing is higher, and is then due to the *b* deflection of the after coming stimulus. Thus, if the light flashes are so timed that each interrupts the "off effect" of its predecessor, a series of regular ripples appears in the electroretinogram which apparently are the cause of the flickering sensation. No negative dip occurs nor do the characteristic ripples appear if a flash falls upon the retina *before* the "off effect" of the preceding one—a continuous sensation should therefore result.

AFTER IMAGES. If the gaze is directed to a bright white light for a moment and the eyes then closed or turned towards a dark surface, an image of the light slowly floats into view, becomes more distinct for a time and then gradually fades. Similarly, if the eyes are stimulated by a colored light or a brightly colored object of any sort, and then darkened, an image of the same color appears. These are called *positive after images*. If, instead of closing the eyes or turning them to a dark surface after looking at a white light, the retinas are stimulated a second time and diffusely by white, e.g., by directing the eyes to a sheet of paper, one then sees a dark image against a white ground. This is called a *negative after image*. If the first stimulus was colored, then this after image is in the complementary color. Negative after images of colored objects are the cause of the phenomenon known as *successive contrast*.

On the basis of Young's theory of color vision, the phenomenon of negative after images is due to adaptation of one or other of the three types of mechanism by the first stimulus. A mechanism which has responded to a given stimulus will not for a time respond as strongly to one of the same type. White light stimulates all three mechanisms. The negative after image which appears upon applying a circumscribed and then a diffuse white stimulus to the retina is, therefore, a dark patch against a white background. When the object looked at is colored and the retina is then stimulated by directing the eyes to a white surface, the image is in the complementary color because those mechanisms which had not been previously stimulated respond more vigorously than the ones stimulated by the colored object. For example, if the object looked at is red, the red mechanism is less excited by a subsequent stimulus of white; those sensitive to green and to violet remain relatively normal and so give a sensation which is the complementary of red, namely, a bluish green.

Positive after images are apparently due to chemicophysical changes in the receptors of the retina caused by and outlasting the stimulus—a form of visual persistence.

Two other features of after images are of some

A   B   C

FIG. 14.28. Optical illusion. The distance from *A* to *B* appears to be greater than that from *B* to *C*; they are the same.

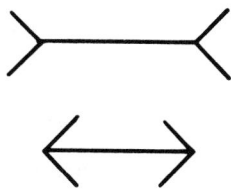

FIG. 14.29. Illusion of size. The horizontal lines are the same length.

FIG. 14.30. Zollner's lines. The long diagonal lines appear to converge; actually, they are parallel.

interest. First, the outlines of the image become progressively blurred, so that they extend beyond the confines of the original image. Second, after images on the fovea have different properties from those on the more peripheral retina.

OPTICAL ILLUSION. The brain may be deceived by imitations of certain effects upon which our visual judgments of the size, shape and distance of objects are based. Visual errors of this nature are called optical illusions or optical deceptions. Some interesting examples are shown in figs. 14.28 to 14.30.

REFERENCES

ADLER, F. H. Arch. Ophth., 1934, 11, 6.

ANDERSON, E. E. AND WEYMOUTH, F. W. Am. J. Physiol., 1923, 64, 561.

ARDEN, G. B. AND WEALE, R. A. J. Physiol., 1954, 125, 417.

BRINDLEY, G. S. J. Physiol., 1953, 122, 332; 1954, 124, 400.

BROWN, P. K. AND WALD, G. Nature. Lond., 1963, 200, 37.

CRAIK, K. J. W. J. Physiol., 1938, 92, 406; Proc. Roy. Soc. London, ser. B., 1940, 128, 232.

DE VALOIS, R. L., JACOBS, G. H., AND JONES, A. E., Optik., 1963, 20, 87.

FLAMANT, F. AND STILES, W. S. J. Physiol., 1948, 107, 187.

HARTRIDGE, H. J. Physiol., 1922, 57, 52; 1946, 105, 5 P.

HECHT, S. AND VERRIJP, C. D. J. Gen. Physiol., 1933, 17, 251.

HUBEL, D. H. AND WIESEL, T. N. J. Physiol., 1959, 148, 574; 1960, 154, 572.

KÖNIG, A. S. B. Akad. Wiss. Berlin, 1894, p. 577.

MATURANA, H. R. AND FRENK, S. Science, 1963, 142, 977.

LYTHGOE, R. J. Med. Res. Council Spec. Rep., 1926, No. 104; 1932, No. 173.

LYTHGOE, R. J. AND TANSLEY, K. Med. Res. Council Spec. Rep., 1929, No. 134.

STILES, W. S. Proc. Roy. Soc. London, ser. B, 1939, **127,** 64.

THOMSON, L. C. AND WRIGHT, W. D. J. Physiol., 1947, **105,** 316.

WEALE, R. A. J. Physiol., 1953, **121, 548.**

WILCOX, W. W. AND PURDY, D. M. Brit. J. Psychol., 1933, **23,** 233.

WILLMER, E. N. AND WRIGHT, W. D. Nature, 1945, **156,** 119.

WRIGHT, W. D. J. Ophth. Soc. Am., 1952, **42,** 509.

Monographs and Reviews

ABNEY, W. DE W. Researches in colour vision and the trichromatic theory. Longmans Green, London, 1913.

BRINDLEY, G. S. Physiology of the retina and visual pathway. Arnold, London, 1959.

CAJAL, RAMON Y. Textura del sistema nervioso del hombre y de los vertebrados. Moya, Madrid, 1904.

DARTNALL, H. J. A. Visual pigments. Methuen, London, 1957.

DAVSON, H. Physiology of the eye. Churchill. London, 1963.

DAVSON, H. The eye. Academic Press. London, 1962.

DETWILER, S. R. Vertebrate photoreceptors. Macmillan, New York, 1943.

DUKE-ELDER, W. S. Text-book of ophthalmology. Kimpton, London, 1932.

GRANIT, R. Sensory mechanisms of the retina. Oxford University Press, London, 1947.

GRANIT, R. Reception and Sensory Perception, Yale University Press, New Haven, Conn., 1955.

HARTLINE, H. K. Neural mechanisms of vision. Harvey Lectures, **37,** 39, 1941–1942.

HECHT, S. Physiol. Rev., 1937, **17, 239.**

HELMHOLTZ, H. VON. Treatise on physiological optics, Ophth. Soc. Am., 1924.

HOUSTOUN, R. A. Vision and colour vision. Longmans, London, 1932.

JUDD, D. B. Docum. Ophth., 1949, **3,** 251.

LE GRANDE, Y. Optique, Physiologique. Vols. 1, 2 and 3, Paris, 1956.

LEGRANDE, Y. Light, colour and vision. Chapman and Hall, Ltd., London, 1957.

MANN, I. C. The development of the human eye. Cambridge University Press, London, 1928.

MORTON, R. A. AND PITT, G. A. J. Fortschr. Chem. org. Naturstoffe, 1957, **14,** 244.

PARSONS, J. H. An introduction to the theory of colour vision. Cambridge University Press, London, 1924.

PIRENNE, M. H. Vision and the eye. Pilot Press, London, 1948.

PIRIE, A. AND VAN HEYNINGEN, R. Biochemistry of the eye, Thomas; Blackwell; Ryerson; 1956.

POLYAK, S. The vertebrate visual system. University of Chicago Press, Chicago, 1957.

POLYAK, S. L. The retina. University of Chicago Press, Chicago, 1941.

ROCHON-DUVIGNEAUD, A. Les yeux et la vision des vertébrés. Masson & Cie, Paris, 1943.

SCHULTZE, M. Arch. mikr. Anat., 1866, **2,** 175.

SMELSER, G. K. The structure of the eye. Academic Press. New York, 1961.

STILES, W. S. Docum. Ophth., 1949, **3,** 138.

WALD, G. The chemical evolution of vision. Harvey Lectures, **41,** 117, 1945–1946.

WALD, G. Docum. Ophth., 1949, **3,** 94.

WALLS, G. L. The vertebrate eye. Cranbrook, 1942.

WALSH, J. W. T. Photometry. Dover, 1964.

WILLMER, E. N. Docum. Ophth., 1955, **9,** 235; J. Theoret. Biol., 1961, **2,** 141.

WOLFF, E. Anatomy of the eye and orbit. Blakiston, Philadelphia, 1933.

WRIGHT, W. D. Researches on normal and defective colour vision. Kimpton, London, 1946.

CHAPTER 15

The Dioptric Mechanisms of the Eye. Cataract.
Optical Defects. Intra-Ocular Fluids

Principles of Reflection and Refraction.
Definitions and Terminology

Light falling upon a surface undergoes *absorption* and *reflection*, and, if the material is transparent, the rays are transmitted through it, either with or without *reflection*.

The proportions of rays falling upon an opaque unpolished surface which undergo absorption and diffuse reflection, respectively, vary with the character of the surface. A large part of the rays striking an unpolished white surface, e.g., a sheet of paper, are reflected but, being thrown off at different angles to the perpendicular, they do not meet at a focus in front of, or, if continued backwards, behind the surface. The light reflected from such a surface is said to be *diffuse*.

The greater proportion of the light striking a polished surface (e.g., a mirror) is reflected, but *the incident and reflected rays are always in the same plane and the angles (angles of incidence and of reflection) which they make with the perpendicular are equal.* This statement is true for any polished surface whatever its shape (fig. 15.1).

Reflected rays from a plane mirror are divergent; if continued backwards they would meet at a point situated at the same distance behind the mirror as the object emitting the light lies in front of it. The eye placed in the path of the reflected rays projects them to this point, where a *full-sized erect image* is formed (fig. 15.2). Since the rays do not actually meet at this point but only appear to do so, the image is called *virtual*.

THE FORMATION OF IMAGES BY SPHERICAL MIRRORS. A spherical mirror is the segment of a sphere; its reflecting surface may be *concave* or *convex*; its *center of curvature* is the center of a sphere of which the reflecting surface forms a part. The middle point of the curved surface is called the *pole* of the mirror, and a line passing through the pole and the center of curvature is termed the *principal axis*. The radius of the mirror is the distance from the pole to the center of curvature. Since the latter may lie on the same side as the source of light (concave mirror) or on the opposite side (convex mirror) the radius may be *positive* or *negative*, respectively.

Rays of light coming from a distant object, i.e., from infinity, are *parallel* (1 and 2, fig. 15.3); if they fall upon a *concave mirror* they are reflected as converging rays and meet in front of the mirror

at a point (F) on the principal axis (p-o). This point (F) is the *principal focus* and the distance from it to the reflecting surface is the *focal length* or *focal distance* of the mirror. It lies in the principal axis, midway between the center of curvature and the surface of the mirror. A *real inverted image* of the object and *smaller* than it, is formed in front of the mirror at the principal focus, that is, in space. The rays from a near object are divergent; the reflected rays are therefore less strongly convergent than when the incident rays are parallel. If the object is at the center of curvature (C) of the mirror then the rays are reflected back to this point. When the object is at *a* between the center of curvature of the mirror and the principal focus, the rays meet beyond the center of curvature at A; when the object is at A the reflected rays meet at *a*. These two points are therefore reciprocally related and are called *conjugate foci*. An object placed between the mirror and its principal focus emits rays which upon reflection are widely divergent and cannot be brought to a focus in front of the mirror. Projected backwards they meet at a point behind the mirror where a *virtual erect* and greatly *enlarged* image is formed.

Parallel rays striking a *convex mirror* are reflected as *divergent* rays which if continued backwards would meet behind the mirror at the principal focus. To the eye they therefore appear to come from this point. Here a *virtual erect image*, smaller than the object, is formed (fig. 15.4).

The position of an image formed by a concave mirror can be found from the construction in figure 15.5. The object AB is situated beyond the center of curvature C. The rays AP and BO parallel to the principal axis MN after reflection meet and cross at the principal focus F. The images of the points A and B, therefore, lie somewhere on the lines PQ and OL. Now, if lines AD and BH be drawn to pass through C, these lines, known as secondary axes, will cut lines PQ and OL at *a* and *b* respectively. Thus, a small inverted real image *ab* is formed. The image is called real because the rays actually pass through *a* and *b*. The construction of an erect virtual image by a convex mirror is shown in figure 15.6. The rays from the object AB diverge after reflection and appear to come from F (dotted lines); the image *ab* is formed at the intersection with the secondary axes AC and BC.

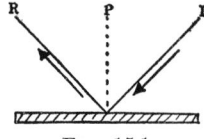

FIG. 15.1

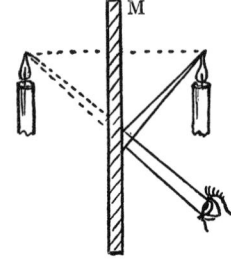

FIG. 15.2

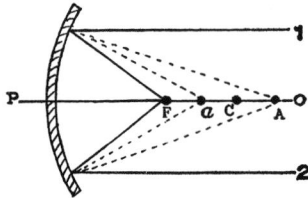

FIG. 15.3

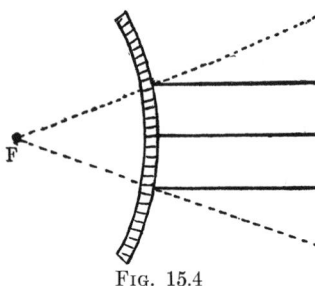

FIG. 15.4

(angle of incidence) to that made by the emergent ray (angle of refraction) is termed the *index of refraction*. The *refractive index* is the index of refraction when the incident rays enter a substance from a vacuum. In practice air is considered to be of the same optical density as a vacuum. The refractive index is expressed as the ratio of the sine of the angle of the incident ray (i) to the sine of the angle of refraction (r), thus, refractive index = sine i/sine r. The refractive index is a measure of refractive power; it is 1.52 for crown glass and 1.66 for flint glass.

Refraction by plane surfaces. Oblique rays striking a medium with plane parallel surfaces, such as a sheet of glass, are refracted to an equal degree upon entering and emerging, but in opposite directions, i.e., towards and away from the perpendicular, respectively. The incident and emergent rays are therefore parallel though not quite in the same straight line (fig. 15.7). A *prism* has its sides inclined towards one another. Since a ray is refracted upon entering at one surface of the prism and again upon emerging at the other, and is bent so as to run more nearly perpendicular to the glass surface in the former instance and away from the perpendicular in the latter; it will be refracted each time towards the base of the prism (fig. 15.8).

Lenses are of two main types, *spherical* whose surfaces are the segments of spheres and *cylindrical*. There are six varieties of the former—*planoconvex, biconvex, planoconcave, biconcave,*

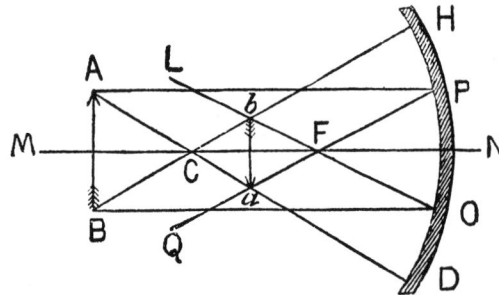

FIG. 15.5. Formation of a real inverted image by a concave mirror.

REFRACTION. Rays of light in passing obliquely from one transparent medium to another of a different optical density (e.g., from air to glass) are bent or refracted. If one medium is surrounded by the other (e.g., glass in air) the ray is refracted twice. In passing from the medium of lower to the one of higher optical density the rays are bent towards the perpendicular; in the transition from the denser to the rarer medium the bend is away from the perpendicular. With any two media the greater the obliquity of the incident rays the greater is the degree of refraction; rays perpendicular to the surface between the two media are not refracted. The ratio of the angle made by the incident ray (i.e., the ray falling upon the surface of the second medium) with the perpendicular

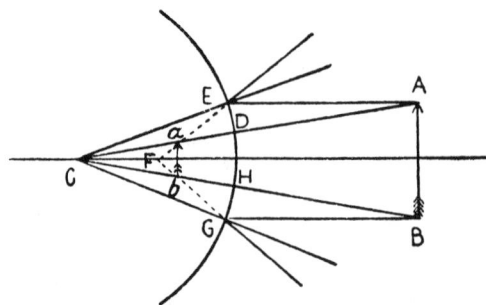

FIG. 15.6. Formation of a virtual erect image by a convex mirror.

convexoconcave and *concavoconvex* (see fig. 15.9). Many modern spectacle lenses are made in the convexoconcave or concavoconvex form in order to reduce distortion of the visual field when the wearer looks through a peripheral portion of the lens. Lenses of these two forms which also include a cylindrical element are described as *toric* lenses.

Convex lenses may be looked upon as a great number of truncated prisms with their bases directed towards the lens center. Concave lenses, on the other hand, are as a number of prisms arranged with their bases towards the periphery (fig. 15.10). It follows then that a symmetrical biconvex lens will bend rays to the same degree at equal distances from its center and bring them to a meeting point or focus, whereas concave lenses will cause divergence of the rays. In either instance the rays are bent towards the bases of the constituent prism.

Refraction by convex lenses. A line passing through the centers of curvature of the lens is termed the *principal axis of the lens.* Any other line intersecting the principal axis within the lens (i.e., a diagonal line) is called a *secondary axis.* The *radius* of curvature of the lens is the radius of a sphere of which the refracting surface forms a part. Rays passing through the principal axis are

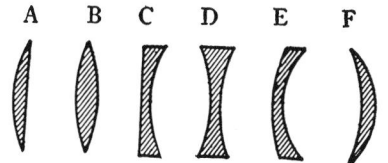

FIG. 15.9. Cross sections of lenses. A, planoconvex; B, biconvex; C, planoconcave; D, biconcave; E, convexoconcave; F, concavoconvex.

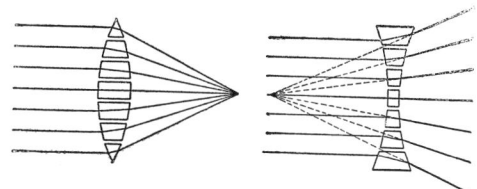

FIG. 15.10. See text.

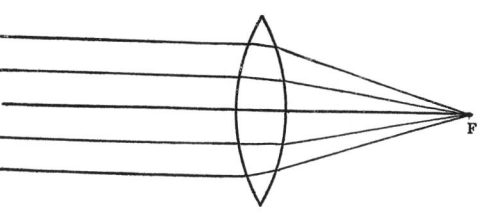

FIG. 15.11. See text.

not refracted, for the incident and the emergent ray strike each surface perpendicularly, and the two surfaces at these points are parallel (see above). Moreover, rays in the secondary axes undergo only very slight refraction, and the incident and emergent rays, through not quite in a continuous line, are parallel, for again the surfaces which they pierce are parallel. The point where the principal axis is intersected by the secondary axes is termed the *optical center* or *nodal point* of the lens. In a biconvex lens with symmetrical surfaces the actual and the optical centers coincide, but in other biconvex lenses the nodal point may be situated nearer to one or other surface.

Light rays from a *distant object*, i.e., from infinity, are parallel (fig. 15.11). The point F where parallel rays meet after refraction is called the *principal focus.* The distance of this point from the lens is called the *focal length* or *focal distance of the lens.* The rays of a light placed at the principal focus traverse the same path but in the opposite direction, and emerge as parallel rays.

A *near object* emits divergent rays. If the source of light (fig. 15.12, B) is on the principal axis a little beyond the principal focus, an image is formed at a distance on the other side of the lens greater than its focal length (at C); when the object is placed in the second position (C) an image is formed at the first (B). These points, therefore,

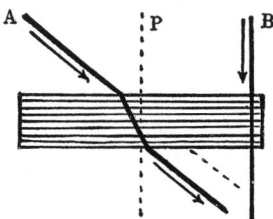

FIG. 15.7. The oblique ray (A) is refracted upon entering and leaving the block of glass. The emergent ray has the same direction as the entering ray but is not in the same line. P represents perpendicular. The ray B which strikes the glass surface perpendicularly is not refracted.

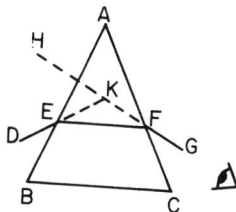

FIG. 15.8. ABC is a prism with the apex at A, the base BC, and the sides AB and AC. The angle of the prism is BAC. A ray of light DEFG is refracted at E and F as in figure [15.7]. The total amount of refraction, that is, the difference in direction between DE and FG, is represented by the angle DKH (the angle of deviation). If the eye is at G, the source of light, D, will appear to be at H. When the ray passing through the prism (EF) is parallel to the base (BC), the ray is said to traverse the prism symmetrically.

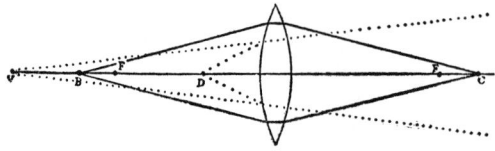

FIG. 15.12. See text.

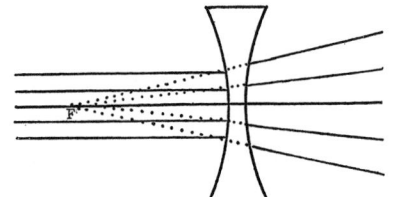

FIG. 15.13. See text.

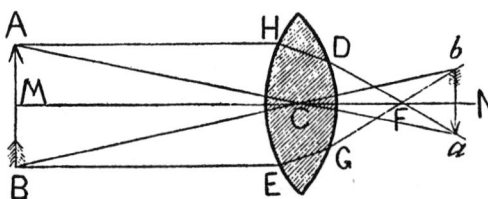

FIG. 15.14. Formation of an inverted image by a biconvex lens.

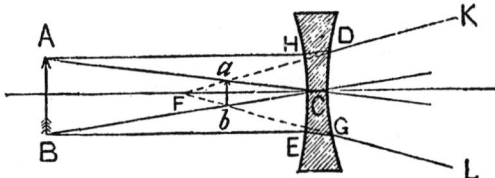

FIG. 15.15. Formation of a virtual erect image by a concave lens.

in respect to an object and its image, are interchangeable and are termed *conjugate foci*. If the object is situated at a distance exactly double the focal length of the lens the conjugate foci are at equal distances on the two sides of the lens. In all these instances a *real inverted image, smaller* than the object, is formed. If the source of light (D) lies between the lens and its principal focus, the rays, after passing through the lens, are widely divergent. To the eye placed in the path of the emergent rays they appear to come from a point (V) at a greater distance behind the lens than the actual. A *virtual, erect* and *enlarged image* is formed.

Light rays in passing through a *biconcave* lens are diverged (fig. 15.13), therefore a *true* image is not formed. The eye in the path of the rays takes no account of refraction, and the rays, in conse-

quence, are projected backwards as straight lines which, meeting at a point on the other side of the lens, from a *virtual erect image, smaller* than the object.

The formation of an image by a biconvex lens is shown in figure 15.14. AB is an object. The rays AH and BE lying parallel to the axis MN meet and cross at the principal focus F. The image of the point A will be at the intersection of the secondary axis AC with AHDF and that of B at the intersection of BC with BEGF. Thus, a small inverted image is formed at *ab*. The formation of an image by a concave lens is shown in figure 15.15. Rays AHDK and BEGL from points A and B of the object AB are diverged in passing through the lens and appear to come from the principal focus F, as shown by dotted lines. The image of A is formed at *a* and of B at *b*, where these lines are intersected by the secondary axes.

Cylindrical lenses (fig. 15.16) have one plane surface, the other may be *convex* (convex cylindrical lens) or *concave* (concave cylindrical lens). A convex cylindrical lens may be regarded as a section of a cylinder sliced down its long axis; its horizontal meridian is convex. Rays transmitted through it at right angles to its vertical axis are converged as they would be by a convex spherical lens. Light traversing its long axis is not refracted, the lens acting in this axis as a plate with parallel sides. A lens of this type may be looked upon as an infinite series of prisms arranged base to base in tiers. In the other type of cylindrical lens the horizontal meridian is concave; rays passing at right angles to the vertical axis are diverged.

The diopter. The converging or the diverging

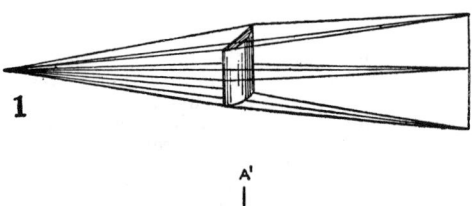

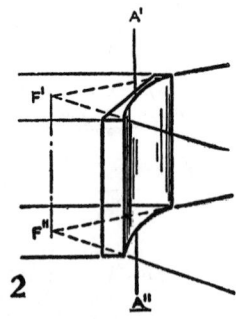

FIG. 15.16. 1, refraction by a convex cylinder. A point of light is brought to a focus as a line after refraction through a cylinder. 2, refraction of light by a concave cylinder. Rays of light striking the cylinder perpendicularly to the axis A'A" are diverged, and appear to be brought to a virtual focal line F'F". (After Duke-Elder.)

power of a lens depends upon the curvature of its surfaces (the greater the degree of curvature, the greater the refracting power) as well as upon the refractive index of the material of which it is composed. The focal length of a lens varies inversely with the refractive power and is therefore a convenient measurement for expressing the strength of a lens. The standard focal length is taken as 1 meter. The refracting power is expressed as the reciprocal of the focal length (given in meters), the unit being the *diopter* (D). Thus, the strength of a lens with a focal length of 1 meter is 1 diopter; of one with a focal length of 2 meters, $\frac{1}{2}$ a diopter; of one having a focal length of $\frac{1}{2}$ a meter, 2 diopters, and so on. The symbols $+$ or $-$ ($+1$ D, $+2$ D, -1 D, -2 D, etc.) are used respectively for a converging and a diverging lens. For example, if a concave lens has a refracting power of -1 D, a small virtual image of a distant object will be focussed 1 meter from the lens and on the same side as the object. A convex lens of a corresponding power ($+1$ D) will bring parallel rays to a true focus 1 meter behind the lens. The power of a cylindrical lens is expressed in a similar fashion.

THE REFRACTING MEDIA OF THE EYE. These are the cornea, the aqueous humor, the crystalline lens and the vitreous body. The refractive indices are given in the following table.

Cornea	1.37
Aqueous humor	1.33
Crystalline lens (whole)	1.42
Vitreous body	1.33

It will be noticed that the refractive indices of the cornea and of the aqueous humor and vitreous are approximately the same; for practical purposes they may be taken as identical and the eye then taken as having two refracting surfaces, (a) the anterior surface of the cornea in contact with air, and (b) the lens surrounded by a common medium in so far as refraction is concerned. The greatest refraction occurs at the corneal surface (42 diopters); of less importance is refraction at the surfaces of the lens (19 diopters with accommodation relaxed and 36 diopters in full accommodation). The whole eye has a refracting power of between approximately 60 and 65 diopters. The value in the table above for the refractive index of the lens is calculated from the refractive power of of the lens as a whole, as though it were a homogenous structure, but such is not the case. On the contrary, the lens consists of an almost spherical *nucleus* with a high refractivity (1.41) surrounded by a zone called the *cortex* of lower optical density (1.38). The surrounding cortex is composed of a series of concave meniscus lens, as shown in figure

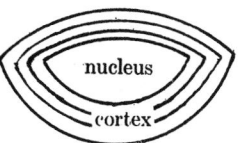

Fig. 15.17. Showing structure of the crystalline lens (diagrammatic).

15.17. The peculiar structure of the lens accounts for the paradox that the mean value of the refractive indices of its parts (1.39) is less than the refracting power of the whole. Several important advantages are derived from this peculiar structure of the crystalline lens; it diminishes spherical aberration (p. 348), tends to prevent the scattering of light within the eye and enhances the power of the lens to alter its converging power during accommodation (p. 340 et seq.).

THE CONSTANTS OF THE EYE. Knowing the curvatures of the refractive surfaces of the eye and the distances between them as well as the refractive indices of the media, the path taken by the rays of light can be determined and the image constructed. The values of the *constants of the eye* are given in the following table.

	mm.
Position of anterior surface of cornea	0
Position of posterior surface of cornea	0.6
Position of anterior surface of lens	3.6
Position of posterior surface of lens	7.2
Position of retina	24.1
Radius of anterior surface of cornea	7.7
Radius of posterior surface of cornea	6.8
Radius of anterior surface of lens (distant vision)	10.0
Radius of posterior surface of lens	6.0

The refractive indices of the media have been given above.

Construction of the image from the foregoing data is a very laborious proceeding. To start with, the image formed by the first refracting surface is constructed; this image now serves as the object for the next refracting surface, the second image in turn is the object of the third surface and so on. The matter is very much simplified, however, by constructing the *diagrammatic* or *schematic* eye by the application of the theorem of Gauss. This states that every optical system composed of spherical surfaces with their centers on the principal axis has three pairs of cardinal points. These are, two *principal points* (H and H', fig. 15.18),

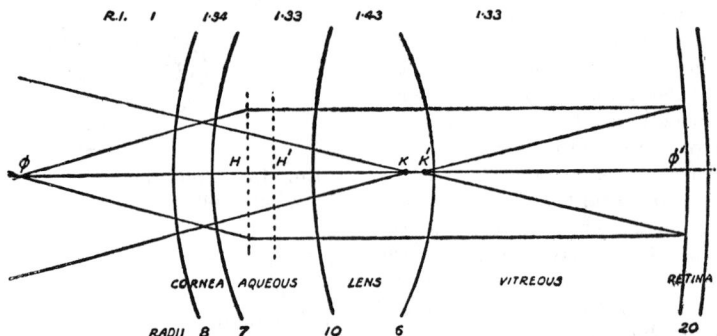

FIG. 15.18. The cardinal points of the eye. ϕ', The anterior focus, 15.7 mm. in front of the cornea. ϕ', The posterior principal focus, 24.13 mm. behind the cornea—that is, upon the retina. H, H', the principal points, in the anterior chamber. KK', the nodal points, in the posterior part of the lens. (After Duke-Elder.)

an *anterior* and a *posterior focal point* (φ and φ') and two *nodal points* (K and K').

The *first and second principal points* lie close together in the anterior chamber 2 mm. behind the cornea. Planes passing through the principal points and perpendicular to the axis are termed the *first* and *second principal planes*; an object in the first principal plane forms an erect *full-sized image* in the second and vice versa. The first and second principal points correspond, therefore, to the conjugate foci of a single lens.

The anterior focal point (φ) is situated 15.7 mm. in front of the cornea. Rays from this point in the axis would, after passing through the system, emerge as parallel rays. Parallel rays entering the system are focussed at φ' which is situated on the retina. φ and φ' therefore correspond to the principal foci of a single lens.

The nodal points (K and K') also lie close together on the axis and near the posterior surface of the lens. They correspond to the optical center of a single lens. Rays passing through the nodal points are not refracted. A ray entering the system and passing through K appears to come from K' and emerges along a line parallel to that along which it entered. The following table for the schematic eye gives the distances of the six cardinal points from the anterior surface of the cornea.

	mm.
Anterior surface of cornea.........	0
First principal point, H...........	1.7
Second principal point, H'........	2.0
First nodal point, K..............	7.0
Second nodal point, K'...........	7.3
Posterior focal point, φ'...........	24.1
Anterior focal point, φ............	15.7

The two nodal points lie so close together that no significant error is entailed if they are taken as one; the same may be said for the principal points. Thus the compound optical system of the eye can be simplified to the so-called *reduced schematic eye* of Listing. This has a single ideally refracting surface situated in the anterior chamber 1.35 mm. behind the cornea and with a radius of 5.7 mm. The nodal point or optical center of the reduced eye lies 7.08 mm., the principal point 2.3 mm. and the posterior focal point 24.13 mm. behind the anterior corneal surface. The anterior focal point is 15.7 mm. in front of the cornea. The distance of the nodal point from the retina, i.e., the focal length of the eye, is (24.13 − 7.08 =) 17.05 mm. The refracting power is therefore (1000/17.05 =) 58.65 diopters.

By means of an X-ray beam, which is not refracted, projected into the eye Goldman and Hagen have measured the length of the globe in the living human subject. The value obtained (23.4 mm.) agrees closely with that of the schematic eye. The value for the total refractive power of the normal human eye, as determined by these observers, is also in close agreement, namely, 59.22 diopters.

THE FORMATION OF THE IMAGE ON THE RETINA. Knowing the foregoing measurements, the paths taken by the light rays can be drawn and a construction of the image upon the retina readily carried out. The formation of the retinal image is illustrated in figure 15.19. The large arrow A–B represents an object emitting divergent rays which are converged and brought to a focus to

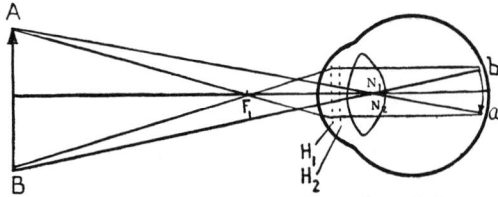

FIG. 15.19. Illustrating the inversion of the retinal image (schematic eye); F_1, first focal point; H_1 and H_2, first and second principal points; N_1 and N_2, first and second nodal points; AB, object; ab, image.

form the image represented by the small arrow a–b. The retinal image, it will be observed, is smaller than the object and inverted. For the sake of simplicity only a few rays are shown, two from a point at either end of the object and one from its center, but of course the surface of an object consists of an infinite number of points, each of which emits divergent rays. One of each pair of rays in the figure (solid line) passes unrefracted through a secondary axis (i.e., through the nodal point N), the ray from the upper part of the object to the lower part of the retina and vice versa. The other ray of each pair undergoes refraction and meets the corresponding unrefracted ray. Similarly, rays from a point on one side of the object will fall upon the retina as a point of light in the opposite part of the image. Thus, it is seen how the image on the retina becomes inverted. Of course we see objects in their true position. Reinversion is a cerebral function developed, probably, through the association of visual sensations with those of touch. If inverting spectacles are placed before the eyes, so as to produce an erect image of the environment on the retina, the visual world appears upside down for some time. But after a period of confusion lasting several weeks the visual environment appears the correct way up. On removing the spectacles only a short period of confusion results.

The idea that the retinal image is inverted was at first difficult to believe. Kepler (1604) inferred from his optical studies that this must be so, but it was Scheiner (1625) who furnished the proof by observing the back of an excised eye from which the sclerotic and choroid coats had been removed. The inverted image of an object was clearly visible upon the translucent retina. The inversion of the retinal image may also be demonstrated during life in persons of blonde complexion because their choroid contains little pigment. The subject is examined in a darkened room, the eye being turned towards a lighted candle placed well to the temporal side. An inverted image of the flame may be seen showing through the inner side of the wall of the globe.

The size of the retinal image is dependent upon the angle *a* N *b*, (fig. 15.19) this—the angle subtended at the nodal point of the eye by an object in the visual field—is called the *visual angle*. The size of the image can be calculated if one knows the distance of the nodal point of the eye from the object and from the retina, and the size of the object. Thus in the figure A B is the object and *a b* its image. The triangle A N B and *a* N *b* being symmetrical, then

$$a\,b : A\,B = b\,N : B\,N$$
$$a\,b = A\,B \times bN/BN$$
$$b\,N = 17.05 \text{ mm.}$$
$$i = 17.05 \times O/d$$

i is the size of the image, O the size of the object and d its distance from the nodal point of the eye (17.05 = distance of retina from nodal point, see p. 1380). An object which subtends one minute of angle at the eye forms an image on the retina of size approximately 4.5 microns. The full moon subtends about $\frac{1}{2}°$, and its image on the retina would therefore be about 0.135 mm. diameter.

THE OPHTHALMOSCOPIC EXAMINATION OF THE EYE. Under ordinary circumstances we cannot see within the eye of another person, because only a limited quantity of light enters his eye through the relatively small pupillary aperture. It is like trying to look through a small window into a darkened room. Furthermore, of the light which enters the eye, a large part is absorbed by the pigment layer of the retina. Even when a light is brought close to the eye under observation, one is unable to see the retina, because the pencil of parallel rays which emerge do not enter the examiner's pupil unless his eye is directly in its path, and when he attempts to bring his eye into the proper position either his head comes between the light and the subject's eye or the light (if between himself and the subject) dazzles his sight.

These difficulties are overcome by means of the ophthalmoscope. This instrument consists of a small mirror with a central perforation through which the observer views the subject's eye. Light furnished by an electric lamp placed above the head of the patient is reflected from the mirror and the pencil of rays emerging from the subject's eye passes through the aperture of the mirror to the examiner's eye.

The invention of the ophthalmoscope is commonly attributed to Helmholtz (1851) but a crude device based upon the same principle was used by Babbage two years previously. The modern ophthalmoscope consists of a small electric tungsten lamp associated switch and battery; an optical system forms a beam of light which may be reflected from a small mirror into the patient's eye. The mirror has a small central aperture to permit the examiner to look through the mirror down the beam of light. Most ophthalmoscopes also have a chain of small lenses ranging from +20 D to −20 D between the aperture and the examiner's eye position, each of which may be brought into position to correct refractive errors both in the patient and in the examiner. The examiner seats himself 1 meter from the subject, adjusts the col-

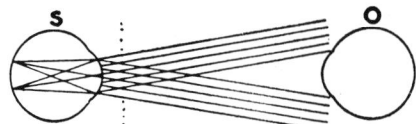

FIG. 15.20. Showing the two extreme pencils of parallel rays arising from the edges of the illuminated area of the fundus in an emmetropic eye. S, subject; O, observer. Vertical dotted line indicates the position in which the extreme ray pencils will enter the observer's eye. (After Duke-Elder.)

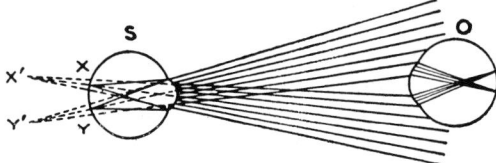

FIG. 15.21. Emergent rays from hypermetropic eye. A virtual erect image is formed at x'y'. (After Duke-Elder.)

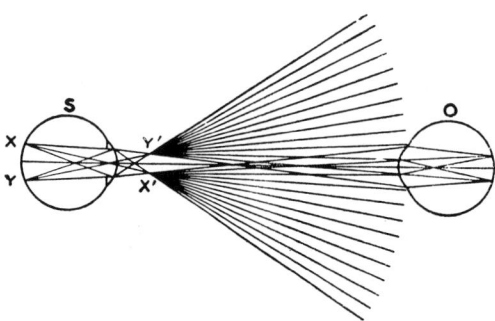

FIG. 15.22. Emergent rays from myopic eye which cross at x'y' and then diverge; a real inverted image is formed at x'y'. (After Duke-Elder.)

limating optical system so that a divergent beam of light enters the subject's eye and looks through the sight hole in the mirror. If the observed eye is emmetropic (i.e., of normal refraction) a uniform red glow—the *red reflex of the fundus*—caused by reflection from the choroid and pigment epithelium is seen lighting up the pupil. No detail, e.g., optic disc or retinal vessels, is visible. This is because the rays emerge from the subject's eye as diverging pencils of *parallel* rays. In order for an image of the subject's fundus to be formed upon the examiner's retina, rays from many pencils must enter his eye simultaneously. At a distance of 1 meter this is impossible, but can be effected if the observer brings his eye quite close to the patient's eye (see fig. 15.20). When the subject's eye is hypermetropic the rays composing the emergent pencils are *divergent*; it is therefore possible at a distance of 1 meter for many pencils to enter the observer's eye. The rays appear to meet behind the subject's eyes where a *virtual erect* image is formed (fig. 15.21).

When the observer moves his head the image moves in the *same* direction. In myopia, the emergent rays *converge*; they meet and cross in front of the eye. Again, diverging rays from several bundles enter the observer's eye and form a *real inverted* image in front of the subject's eye (fig. 15.22); it moves in a direction *opposite* to that of the examiner's head.

After this preliminary examination one or other of two methods of ophthalmoscopy—the indirect or the direct—may be employed. In the *indirect method* a separate biconvex lens with a focal length of 7.5 cm. (about 13 D) is held in front of the eye of the examinee. The observer seats himself 1 meter away and holds the lens in the path of the beam from the mirror and a short distance in front of the eye under observation. The subject turns his eye a little inwards in order to bring the optic disc into view, being directed, for example, to look at the observer's left ear if his left eye is being examined. The rays from the ophthalmoscope are converged upon the hand lens which converges them to the eye. They are more sharply converged by the refracting media and come to a focus in the vitreous. The retina is diffusely illuminated. By moving the hand lens toward or from the patient's eye his retina is brought into focus and the optic disc (Plate III) is clearly seen. The rays reflected from innumerable points of the patient's retina and after refraction emerge from his eye to form an image, the position of which differs according to the refractive state of the eye. The rays emerging from the emmetropic (normal) eye are parallel (fig. 15.23). They are converged by the hand lens and form a real, magnified and inverted image in the air between the hand lens

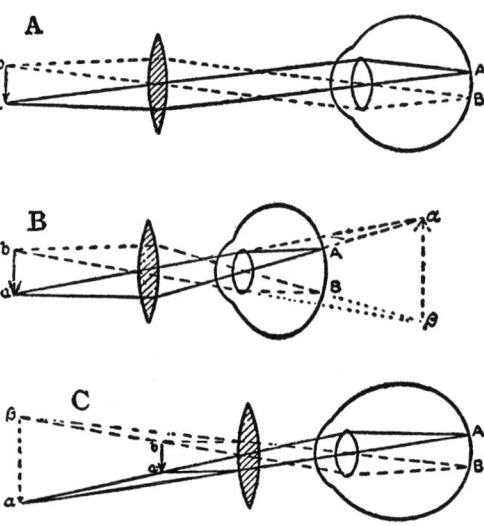

FIG. 15.23. Path of the light from the eye in the indirect method of ophthalmoscopy in emmetropia, hypermetropia and myopia. (After Duke-Elder, *Text Book of Ophthalmology.*)

and the examiner. This is focussed on the examiner's retina. In *hypermetropia* the rays issuing from the patient's eye are divergent, and appear to come from a magnified erect image behind the eye. The hand lens converts this into a small, inverted image in front of its principal focus (fig. 15.23). In *myopia* the emergent rays converge and form a large inverted real image; this is converted by the lens into a smaller image between it and its principal focus.

In the *direct method* a field of smaller area but of higher magnification is seen. The examiner brings the instrument as close as possible to the subject's eye, no hand lens being interposed. He views the subject's fundus with his own right eye, and the subject's left fundus with his left eye. In this position rays from both emergent pencils enter the eye of the observer, and, therefore, except when the observed eye is highly myopic, the details of the fundus can be seen. The image is always erect. The light, after coming to a focus on the retina, emerges from the emmetropic eye as parallel rays which are brought to a focus upon the observer's retina. If, however, the subject's eye is hypermetropic (as described above) the emergent rays will be divergent and can only be focussed by the examiner if he accommodates his eye or interposes a convex lens; if the observed eye is myopic the reflected rays are convergent; the examiner must then use a concave lens in order to focus the image upon his own retina. By the use of a concave or a convex lens which will just bring the image of the fundus into clear focus, and the refractive power of the lens required being known, the refractive error of the patient can be measured.

RETINOSCOPY; SKIASCOPY OR THE SHADOW TEST. This is a reliable objective method for determining the refraction of the eye. It is of special value in children and others for whom the reading of test type is impracticable, and for the detection of malingerers. The method depends upon the fact discovered by Bowman (1859) that the direction of the rays emerging from the eye varies with its state of refraction. Cuignet (1873) elaborated upon this discovery and brought the method into general use in the study of refractive errors. A retinoscope consists of a plane or concave mirror with a central aperture through which the examiner can look and inspect the pupil of the subject. A light source is placed several feet away and the mirror is used to reflect a beam of light into the pupil of the subject. Electric self-luminous versions of the retinoscope are also available. When the rays are reflected from a plane mirror they form a virtual image behind the reflecting surface. Tilting the mirror to one or the other side causes this image to move in the opposite direction. If a concave mirror were used the image, being formed in front of the mirror, would move in the same

direction as the tilt of the mirror. Consequently, when a reflected light is thrown into the eye by means of a plane mirror, owing to a double reversal of the movement taking place (i.e., a movement of the mirror image which now serves as the luminous object in one direction and of the retinal image in the other), a change in the inclination of the mirror causes the illuminated area upon the retina to move in the *same* direction as the tilt. This movement of the illuminated area on the *retina* in relation to the tilt of the mirror is the same whatever the refractive state of the eye. But the rays from the illuminated area on the retina are directed back through the eye and after undergoing refraction emerge through the pupil; the direction of the movement of the illuminated area as it appears to an observer depends upon the direction of the emergent rays, that is, upon the state of refraction of the eye. The eye is examined with the retinoscope at a distance of 1 meter, in a dark room, a mydriatic, e.g., atropine or homatropine is usually employed.

If the subject is *hypermetropic* or *myopic* a pink glow fills his pupil except for a dark semilunar shadow on one side (see fig. 15.24). In the *emmetropic* eye (p. 349) light reflected from the illuminated area on the retina issues from the pupil as diverging pencils of *parallel* rays. The rays meet and cross at the *far point* (punctum remotum), which for the normal eye is at infinity, that is, behind the observer. In a certain position of the mirror one or other of the pencils of rays (see fig. 15.25) enters the observer's eye. The subject's eye appears filled with a pink glare bounded on one side by a very faint shadow; when the mirror is tilted so that the interval between the pencils is in line with the observer's pupil, the subject's pupil is dark. Thus, in emmetropia the subject's pupil is either nearly uniformly bright or entirely dark. A bright area and a pronounced shadow are not seen together. In *myopia* the rays leaving the eye are convergent (fig. 15.22). If the myopia is *greater* than 1 D they meet and cross at the far point which lies somewhere between the subject and the observer. Therefore, when the mirror is tilted, up or down, or to one or other side, the shadow moves *against* it, i.e., in the opposite direction. If the myopia is *less* than 1 D the far point

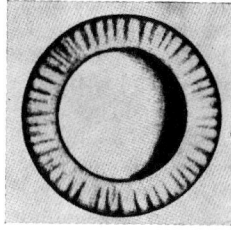

FIG. 15.24. Retinoscopy shadow. (After Duke-Elder.)

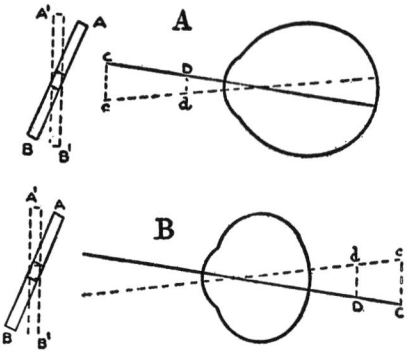

Fig. 15.25. Illustrating the movements of the shadow in retinoscopy. A, in *myopia*. When the mirror is in the position AB, the image is at D in the highly myopic eye, and at C in the less myopic eye. When the mirror is in the position A'B', the respective images are in the positions *d* and *c*. Since D*d* is less than C*c*, the lower the degree of myopia, the larger the excursion and the quicker the movement of the shadow. B, in *hypermetropia*. When the mirror is in the position AB, the image is at D, in the highly hypermetropic eye and at C in the less hypermetropic eye. When the mirror is in the position A'B' the respective images are at *d* and *c*. (After Duke-Elder, *The Practice of Refraction*.)

is behind the observer and, as in emmetropia, only a faint shadow is seen; it moves *with* the mirror. If the myopia is 1 D the far point is at the surface of the observer's eye and the subject's pupil appears, according to the tilt of the mirror, either completely dark or completely bright, that is, without any shadow. In *hypermetropia* the emergent rays are divergent and the far point is virtual; the rays appear to come from a point behind the mirror and therefore do not meet between the subject and observer. The shadow moves *with* the mirror.

In applying these facts to the correction of refractive errors, the movement of the shadow is noted and convex or concave glasses, according to whether the eye is hypermetropic or myopic, respectively, are placed in front of the subject's eye, until the pupil, as in a myopia of 1 D, appears uniformly bright or dark. This state when the shadow disappears is called the *point of reversal*. If the refractive error is even slightly overcorrected a shadow appears which moves in a direction opposite to that of the original movement. Now, when the point of reversal is reached, the far point of the subject's eye is at the surface of the observer's eye, i.e., 1 meter away. The subject therefore, as mentioned above, has still a myopia of 1 diopter. This must be taken into account in calculating the refractive power of the correcting lenses required. If the eye is hypermetropic and, say +4 D brings it to the point of reversal, then a +3 D lens will be sufficient for correction. If the eye is myopic −1 D must be added to the refrac-

tion which was required to bring the eye to the point of reversal.

Papilledema (choked disc, optic neuritis) and optic atrophy. In conditions accompanied by high intracranial pressure, e.g., brain tumor, hydrocephalus and uremia, the optic disc loses its natural translucency and becomes reddened and swollen. The central vein is engorged and tortuous and the venules and capillaries dilated. Small hemorrhages may be seen. The swelling of the disc is due to the transudation of fluid from the engorged vessels and its collection in the anterior layers of the lamina cribrosa and between the nerve fibers. The physiological cup becomes gradually filled up, and may eventually be elevated above the general level of the surrounding retina. The circumference of the disc appears blurred or "woolly." The disc is enlarged and its lateral spread causes the retina to be thrown into folds or ridges. In the older terminology these changes were referred to as choked disc, optic neuritis or papillitis. The condition is now called *papilledema*. The separation and stretching of the nerve fibers, their compression where they penetrate the lamina cribrosa and the overgrowth of glial tissue set up by the presence of the edema fluid leads to nerve atrophy—*secondary optic atrophy*. The disc in this condition is a grayish or dead white, due to the obliteration of capillary vessels by the overgrowth of glial tissue. The optic cup is deepened as a result of the degenerated nerve fibers. The outline of the pale disc is clearly defined against the surrounding retina. The retinal veins are engorged but the arteries are narrower than normal.

It is now widely accepted that mechanical factors, e.g., changes in intracranial or intraocular pressure, are mainly concerned in the production of papilledema. The optic nerve, it will be recalled, is invested by prolongations of the cerebral meninges—the *pia, arachnoid* and *dura*. The spaces between these three layers of the nerve sheath—the *subarachnoid* and *subdural spaces*—are continous, as was first shown by Schwalbe (1870) with the corresponding spaces within the cranium. The dura and arachnoid of the nerve sheath, however, are in close opposition, there being only a potential subdural space in this situation. But the intracranial subarachnoid space is in free communication with the corresponding space of the nerve sheath and the intracranial pressure is transmitted through the cerebrospinal fluid to the intravaginal space right up to the lamina cribrosa. The central vein of the retina with its companion artery makes an almost right angled bend as it leaves the optic nerve and, crossing the intravaginal space, pierces the arachnoid and dura a short distance behind the eyeball (fig. 15.26). Any marked rise in intracranial pressure distends the sheath, for the dura in this situation differs from that within the cranium in being unsupported by bone (Macdonald).

The elevated pressure thus transmitted to the sheath tends to compress the vein in its course across the intravaginal space and to impede the venous return, as well as to block the lymph channels situated in the adventitia of the central vessels. Little or no interference is offered to the blood flow in the artery owing to its more resistant wall and to the higher arterial blood pressure. The venous pressure rises and the intraocular part of the vein and its branches become engorged since they are beyond the influence of the intracranial pressure.

Papilledema is therefore comparable with an edema which may occur in almost any situation as a result of obstruction of the venous and lymphatic channels while the arteries remain pervious.

Atrophic changes in the disc occurring unpreceded by papilledema are referred to as *primary optic atrophy*. The main causes of primary optic atrophy are pressure upon the nerve within the cranium as by a tumor, certain nervous diseases (tabes, general paralysis of the insane and disseminated sclerosis) and toxic substances, e.g., wood alcohol, quinine, lead and salicylic compounds. Since the optic nerve fibers have their cell bodies in the retina (ganglion cell layer) the atrophy of the section between the point of pressure and the retina is in the nature of a retrograde degeneration (p. 28). As already mentioned, the optic nerve fiber is devoid of a neurilemma; regeneration therefore never occurs. In tabes and general paralysis of the insane the atrophy is probably the result of a syphilitic meningitis which affects the nerve secondarily. The toxic substances mentioned exert their action apparently directly upon the ganglion cells of the retina.

BIOMICROSCOPY—THE SLIT LAMP. By means of this instrument an intense narrow beam of light is thrown obliquely into the eye and a small section of the cornea, anterior chamber, iris, lens or anterior part of the vitreous observed stereoscopically through a binocular microscope. The beam passes through an adjustable slit which when narrowed to minimum width concentrates the beam of light upon an area as small as 0.05 mm. in diameter. The illuminated section is in the form of a prism, or more correctly of a parallelepiped. The tissues within this section may be magnified some 25 diameters. Under this method of examination ocular structures which ordinarily appear homogeneous show a definite pattern, and any abnormality is readily recognized by one familiar with the appearance in health. For example, the anterior and posterior epithelial layers of the cornea are seen as bright lines bounding the less luminous substantia propria, and any pathological condition, e.g., erosions, small opacities, keratitis, etc., are easily detected. The laminated structure of the lens is clearly revealed. The central nucleus and

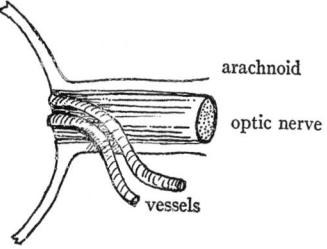

FIG. 15.26. Description in text.

the cortical layers are marked by luminous boundaries; the lens sutures appear as darker lines.

By fitting special contact lenses to the cornea, it is possible to use the slit-lamp to examine under magnification the retina and the angle of the anterior chamber.

ENTOPTIC PHENOMENA. Visual sensations may arise from images of objects situated within the eye itself. The most familiar of these are the *muscae volitantes* (L. *flying flies*) which are seen as faint specks projected some distance in front of the eye. They are due to shadows cast upon the retina by small semi-opaque particles in the vitreous body, such as epithelial cells, small coagula or embryonic rudiments. Particles lying close to the retina are most likely to give rise to these sensations. Lying behind the axis of rotation of the globe such particles cast shadows which move downwards over the retina when the eye is turned upwards but, since the direction of any movement on the retina is reversed in consciousness, they appear to move upwards. This upward movement is followed by a slower downward movement. When any attempt is made to fix one's sight upon the specks they dart away, from which fact their name was derived. These *muscae volitantes* are usually noticed while viewing a bright uniform field, such as the clear blue sky, for then the pupil is small and sharper shadows are cast on the retina. Some of the reports on the sighting of "flying saucers" could be accounted for in this way.

Ordinarily the retinal vessels which, it will be recalled, lie outside the fovea and superficial to the retinal layers, are not perceived. Helmholtz thought that the sensitivity of the retina underlying the vessels was greater than elsewhere, so that the light reaching the retina through them, though reduced in intensity, caused as great an effect as light falling in unshielded regions. When light is thrown into the eye at such an angle (e.g., obliquely through the sclera) that the shadows of the vessels fall upon a retinal region unaccus-

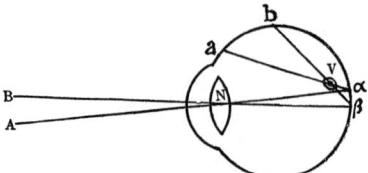

FIG. 15.27. Description in text.

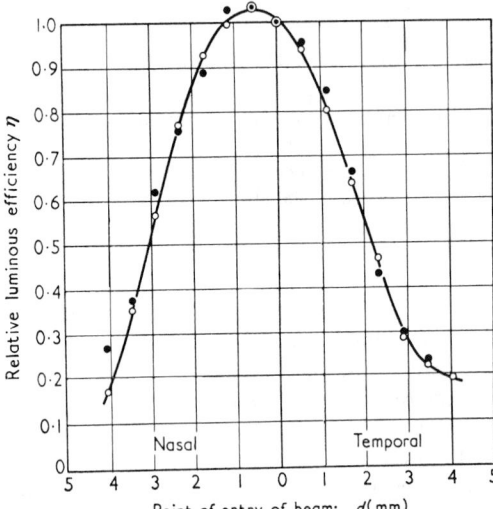

FIG. 15.28. Relative luminous efficiency measured by foveal matching. White light. Horizontal traverse, subject B. H. C. ○ right eye; ● left eye. In this case there is little difference between the the two eyes. (From Stiles and Crawford, 1933)

tomed to receive them, they become visible. If, while his eye is being illuminated in this way in a dark room, the subject looks towards a wall, and the light falling on the sclera is given a slow circular movement, he sees a highly magnified image projected against the uniform surface. The vessels appear as an intricate branching pattern against a bright ground and are known, after their discoverer, as *Purkinje figures*. A method which anyone can employ himself to make the extrafoveal capillaries visible is to look at a uniformly bright surface through a pin-hole in a card held close to the eye while he oscillates the opening quickly (about once per second) from side to side and thereby shifts the shadows from point to point in the retina.

If the oscillation of the pin-hole is stopped, the shadows of the retinal capillaries disappear rapidly from view, only reappearing when the oscillation starts again. It is a fundamental property of the visual system that fine images stabilised in relation to the retina are not perceived. Stabilised images can be produced by special optical means (Riggs, Ratliff, Cornsweet, and Cornsweet, 1953).

Mueller (1855) made use of Purkinje's observation (1811) to prove that the light sensitive elements are the rods and cones. Moving the source of light causes the images to change their positions on the screen. If we measure the distance of this shift (fig. 15.27, A–B) and the distance between the two positions of the light (a–b) then, knowing the distance of the nodal point of the schematic eye (N) from the retina and from the screen, the position of the shadow (α–β) relative to the vessels (v), i.e., the distance α v, can be calculated. This was found to be from 0.17 to 0.36 mm., which is by actual measurement the approximate distance of the vessels in front of the rod and cone layer.

The corpuscles moving in the retinal capillaries can be observed if the eye is directed to a uniformly illuminated surface. The best way to perform this experiment is to look at the sky through a dense blue-violet glass plate. The blood cells then appear projected upon the plate. It is actually possible to calculate the speed of the corpuscles from the distance between their positions at the beginning and end of a given time interval. Vierodt (1873) was the first to make such an estimation. Knowing the distance of the nodal point of the eye from the retina and from the glass screen, the magnification of the travelled distance can be determined.

Other entoptic phenomena which should be briefly mentioned are the colored halos seen around bright lights, especially in dark surroundings. The halos consist of a series of concentric rings of rainbow colors—from blue to red from without in. Actually they are diffraction spectra, due to the structures of the eye acting as diffraction gratings. There are two kinds of halo—*lenticular* and *corneal*. The first is attributed to the radial fibers of the lens and is the larger. The corneal type is believed to be due to the epithelial and endothelial cell layers of the cornea.

The Stiles-Crawford effect. Stiles and Crawford, as mentioned on pp. 275 and 345, discovered in 1933 that the luminous efficiency of a light ray entering the pupil of the human eye and acting on the retina is dependent upon the point in the pupil through which the ray passes. In Fig. 15.28 it can be seen that the relative luminous efficiency of a ray entering about 4 mm. from the pupil center is $\frac{1}{5}$ as efficient in producing a sensation of light as a ray entering near to the pupil center. It was established subsequently that this directional sensitivity is a property of the cones. Rods show this effect to a much smaller extent.

The Accommodation of the Eye

ANATOMICAL SKETCH

Before giving an account of the physiological mechanism of accommodation, the structures concerned, e.g., the ciliary body and the crystalline *lens* will be briefly described.

THE CILIARY BODY. When the interior of the anterior half of the eyeball is exposed by a transection through its equator, a transparent disc—the *crystalline lens*—is seen occupying the center of the bowl-shaped structure (fig. 15.29). On the wall of the globe some distance behind the circumference of the lens lies the dendate border of the retina proper known as the *ora serrata* (p. 267). The ciliary body is a circular zone of tissue extending forwards from the ora serrata to a short distance from the circumference of the lens. It is covered on its inner aspect by the pigment layer of the retina, which we have seen (ch. 13) is continued forwards (as the *pars ciliaris retinae*) from the point of termination of the neural layers. The ciliary body consists of three parts, the orbiculus ciliaris, the ciliary processes and the ciliary muscle. The *orbiculus ciliaris* immediately adjoins the choroid, of which it may be considered the direct continuation. It is a band about 4 mm. broad encircling the eyeball and presents on its inner aspect a number of radially arranged ridges. The *ciliary processes* appear as some seventy triangular elevations on the inner aspect of the ciliary body; they project towards the axis of the eye and form a series of radial fringes (*corona ciliaris*) which completely encircle the equator of the lens, but are separated from it by a very short interval. The great bulk of the ciliary body is composed of the ciliary processes and the ciliary muscle. The fibers of the *ciliary muscle* are arranged in two sets, an outer *meridional* and an inner *circular*. The meridional fibers arise from the scleral spur (p. 354); they run backward to be attached to the ciliary processes and to the orbiculus, and through the latter to the choroid. The circular fibers are fewer; in meridional sections of the globe they appear as a small triangular bundle of cross-sectioned fibers lying behind the angle of the iris (fig. 15.30). As a matter of fact, these fibers are not uniformly circular in direction but take different courses and, interlacing with one another, form a reticulated ring-shaped band (fig. 15.31). Taken as a whole this part of the ciliary muscle constitutes a sphincter (*sphincter muscle of Mueller*) situated in front and to the outer side of the ciliary processes. The fibers composing the margin of the central opening are mainly circular and are attached to a band of elastic tissue situated at the angle of the iris; the outer circumference of the sphincter is connected to elastic fibers which are continuous with similar fibers of the choroid. The muscle is thus anchored by two elastic attachments.

THE CRYSTALLINE LENS is a transparent, biconvex, circular structure about 11 mm. in diameter and between 3.6 and 3.9 mm. thick at the center. It is situated with the center of its anterior surface coinciding with the center of the pupil; the pupil-

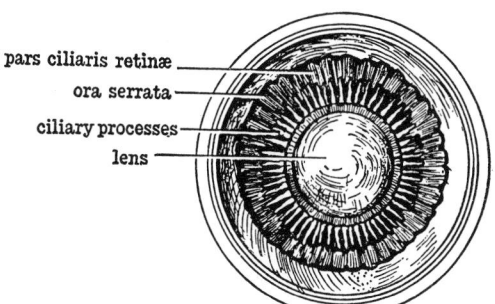

FIG. 15.29. Showing interior of anterior half of the eyeball.

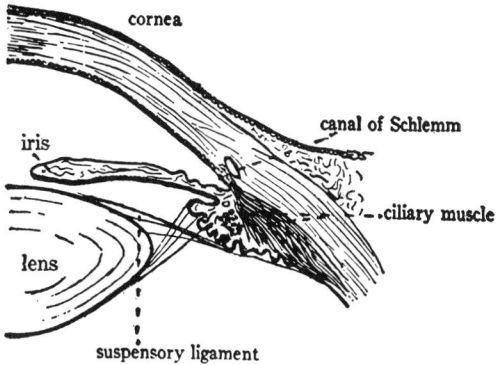

FIG. 15.30. Showing structures in the region of the angle of the iris.

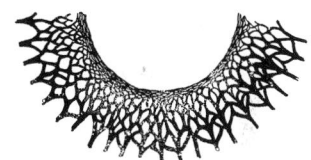

FIG. 15.31. Showing arrangement of circular fibers of the ciliary muscle. (After Fincham.)

lary margin lies in contact with this surface. The center of the anterior surface is termed the *anterior pole* of the lens, the center of its posterior surface, the *posterior pole*. An imaginary line joining the poles is called the *principal axis*. The two surfaces meet at the circumference in a rounded edge termed the *equator*. The posterior surface in the young adult is decidedly more convex than the anterior (see table, p. 333); this difference diminishes somewhat with age. The lens is enclosed in a structureless, highly elastic capsule. The latter is not of uniform thickness, being thinner over the posterior than over the anterior surface, and the part covering the central region of each surface is thinner than the corresponding peripheral parts. The values in ascending order of thicknesses are, center of posterior surface (av. 2.2μ), peripheral part of posterior surface (av. 13.7μ), center of anterior surface (av. 15.7μ), pe-

Posterior surface

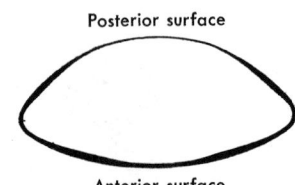

Anterior surface

FIG. 15.32. Showing the regional variations in thickness of the lens capsule. (After Fincham.)

CAPSULE   EPITHELIUM

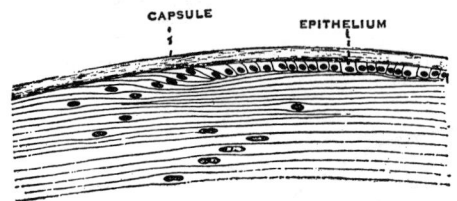

FIG. 15.33. Meridional section of the lens. (From Wolff after Poirier and Becker.)

ripheral part of anterior surface (av. 18.2μ) (see fig. 15.32). A single layer of columnar epithelial cells covers the anterior surface of the lens immediately beneath the homogeneous capsule; the latter is formed as a secretion of these cells. The substance of the lens consists of a series of ribbon-like fibers which arise from the region of the equator and are actually greatly elongated epithelial cells (fig. 15.33). By careful examination of the lens, from the more central part of the anterior surface to the region of the equator the gradual transition of the columnar cells into the attenuated cells of the lens substance can be traced. The fibers proceed from the equator towards the lens center and, abutting against fibers coming from other segments of the periphery, fuse along well-defined lines—the *lens sutures*. These are seen in the adult lens as a series of faint irregular striae radiating from the center to form what is known as the *lens star*. On section, the lens shows a series of concentric laminae with a nucleus of extreme convexity and high refractive index, and a less refractive cortex. The optical advantages of this construction have been pointed out (p. 333). The nucleus is also of much firmer consistency than the cortex which is relatively soft and pliable.

THE MECHANISM OF ACCOMMODATION[1]

The interval between the ciliary processes and the equator of the lens is occupied by a circular membranous band; this is the anterior part of the *zonula ciliaris* (*zonula of Zinn*). The precise origin of the fibers of the zonula is disputed, but they appear to arise as a system of transparent fibers from the anterior part of the hyaloid membrane 1.5 mm. or so in front of the ora serrata. Passing

[1] The mechanism of accommodation is reviewed by M. Alpern in "The Eye," edited by H. Davson, Vol. 4, 1962. Academic Press.

forwards they form a series of bundles which occupy grooves between the ciliary processes, and then bridge the gap, as just mentioned, between the ciliary processes and the lens. Near the lens circumference the zonula splits into an anterior and a posterior lamina; the former is the thicker of the two and blends with the lens capsule a little in front of the equator, and constitutes what is generally known as the *suspensory ligament* of the lens. The space between the two layers of the zonula is called the *canal of Petit*. Slits in the layers of the membrane establish communications between the canal of Petit and the anterior chamber and the region behind the lens (postlenticular space, p. 353).

Light rays from an object at infinity, which is taken as any point more than 20 feet (6 meters) distant, are parallel and are brought to a focus (principal focus) on the retina of the emmetropic eye. Rays from a near object are divergent, but they too are brought to a sharp focus. This adjustment of the dioptrics of the eye whereby it is able to focus the image of both far and near objects is called *accommodation*. That the refracting power of the eye does actually undergo a change when it is turned from a far to a near object or vice versa was shown by Scheiner (1619) by a simple experiment. A card with two pin-holes separated by a distance less than the diameter of the pupil is held before one eye. The eye is focussed upon a needle held in front of the card and perpendicular to a line joining the two holes. The needle appears single; but it appears double if the eye is focussed upon an object placed either beyond it or between it and the eye. The explanation will be evident from fig. 15.34.

There are at least three possible means by which accommodation of the eye could be brought about. The retina might be moved towards or away from the lens, i.e., the eye might be elongated or shortened so that divergent rays in the one instance or parallel rays in the other would be accurately focussed. This mechanism is actually made use of in the mollusc pecten. That it is not the method followed by the human eye was proved by Young (1801). A second possibility is that the distance between the retina and the lens is altered by a movement of the lens; this is the method used in photography, the distance between the film and the lens can be nicely adjusted for the focus of near objects. In the bony fishes accommodation is effected in such a manner.[2]

[2] These fish are myopic when the eye is at rest, i.e., the eye is adjusted for near vision; accommodation for far vision is an active process consisting of contraction of a structure called the campanula which moves the lens backward. In some birds the

PLATE III

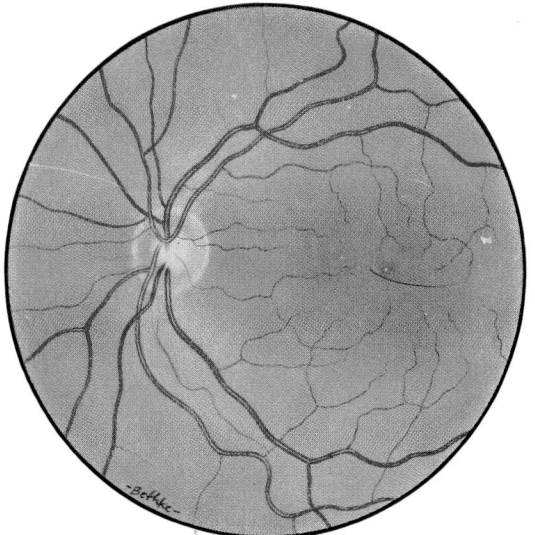

Normal Human Fundus. (From May's *Manual of Diseases of the Eye*, by permission of the author.)

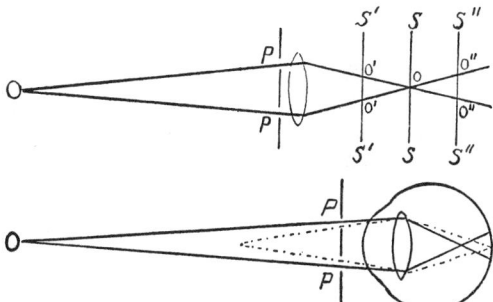

FIG. 15.34. Scheiner's experiment. Upper cut, O, position of needle; PP, pinholes in card; SS, screen with image of needle focussed at o. When the screen is moved forward or backward (S'S' or S"S") the two pencils of light are intercepted before they have reached a focus in the first instance, and after they have met and crossed in the second. Two images are formed at o' and o' or at o" and o". In the case of the eye (lower cut), any difference in its focus must be due to changes in the lens, since the retina is stationary. When the needle is viewed with one eye through the peep holes, and brought into focus one image is seen, but two blurred images appear if the eye is focussed upon a nearer or a more distant object. If when the eye looks at an object near than the needle, and the needle is moved a little nearer to the eye, the two images approach one another; when the needle is moved farther away they become more separated. When the eye is accommodated for far vision, changes in the distance of the needle cause converse movements of the images, becoming farther apart as the needle approaches the eye, and coming closer together as it is moved farther away. The continuous lines represent rays from the needle, the interrupted lines rays from a nearer point in focus.

Variations in the convexity of the crystalline lens and consequently of its converging power is the third possibility (fig. 15.35). This is the method first suggested by Young for the human eye; the conception was later elaborated by Helmholtz. That such is the mechanism adopted by mammals in general is now almost universally accepted. A change in the convexity of the anterior surface of the lens during accommodation is a well-established fact and one which can be demonstrated by the following experiments. A light source is held to the outer side and a little in front of the eye of a subject in a darkened room. Three images (Purkinje-Sanson images, fig. 15.36) within the subject's pupil will be seen by an observer, one bright and

erect reflected from the cornea, another larger, erect and dimmer from the anterior surface (epithelial layer) of the lens which like the cornea, acts as a convex mirror. The third image is inverted, bright and smaller than the other two; it is reflected from the posterior (concave) surface of the lens. The subject is directed to gaze into the distance while the positions of the images are noted; he then looks at a near object when a change in the size and position of the reflection from the anterior surface of the lens will be observed. It becomes smaller and moves towards the corneal image, which, of course, remains stationary, as does also the inverted image from the posterior surface of the lens. The change in size and position of the large erect image must mean that the anterior surface of the lens has become more convex. Now, if one knows the radius of curvature of the cornea, which can be measured by means of an instrument known as an ophthalmometer, then the radius of curvature of the surfaces of the lens and the changes in their curvature during accommodation can be calculated from careful comparative measurements of the sizes of

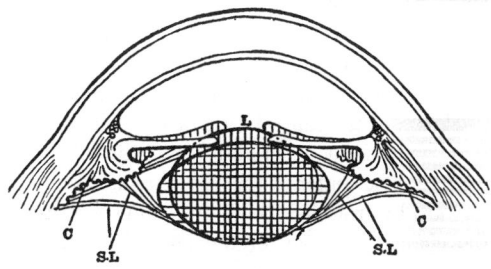

FIG. 15.35. Illustrating the mechanism of accommodation of the eye for near vision. The horizontally shaded lens and the unshaded iris show the position of the parts when at rest; the vertically shaded lens and iris show the position during accommodation for a near point. C. ciliary muscle; S.L., suspensory ligament. (Redrawn from Landolt.)

central part of the anterior surface of the lens moves forwards into the pupillary aperture and as a result of pressure against the rigid margin of the iris becomes highly convex. In other avian species the cornea consists of two lamellae, the posterior being drawn backwards during accommodation for far vision. In others again (owls and hawks) the curvature of the cornea is increased during near vision.

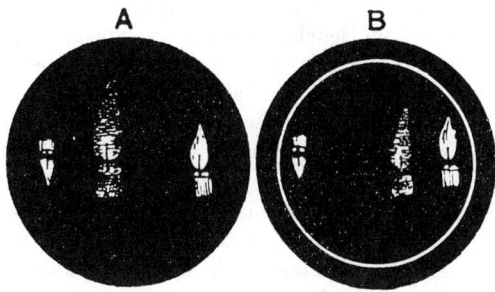

FIG. 15.36. Purkinje-Sanson images. A, during far vision; B, during accommodation for near vision. (Redrawn and modified from Williams.)

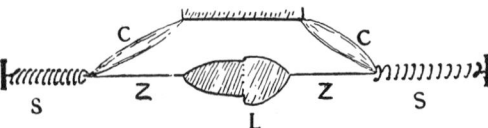

FIG. 15.37. Diagram to illustrate the mechanism of accommodation. C, ciliary muscle, relaxed (left), contracted (right); S, spring representing the elastic choroid; L, lens, left section, for far vision; right for near vision; Z, zonula.

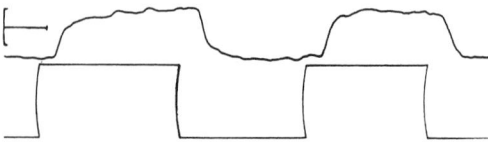

FIG. 15.38. Record of accommodation responses to a 2 D step stimulus and return to zero level of accommodation. Allowance should be made for the arc of the pen. Top line, accommodation (length of horizontal line, 1 sec; height of arc, 1D): upward movement represents far-to-near accommodation. Bottom line, stimulus signal, same scale.

the images from the cornea and lens. The average values for the radius of the anterior surface of the lens in five subjects examined by Fincham were 12.2 mm. for the "resting eye" and 6.8 mm. during accommodation for near vision. The change in curvature of the posterior lens surface was slight (about 0.5 mm.). The average increase in thickness of the central part of the lens was 0.47 mm., while the equatorial diameter diminished by 0.5 mm. The center of the anterior surface moved forward by from 0.3 to 0.4 mm. In general terms the change in shape of the lens during accommodation for near vision can be summed up as follows. The central part of the anterior surface becomes more convex, the posterior surface shows little change. The peripheral region of the anterior surface actually becomes somewhat flatter, this surface taken as a whole therefore assumes a hyperbolic form.

The manner in which the change in shape of the anterior surface of the lens is brought about was explained by Helmholtz as follows. When the eye is accommodated for distant vision the suspensory ligament which, as we have seen, is attached to the lens capsule, is drawn taut as a result of the pull of the elastic structures, e.g., the ciliary body and choroid. The peripherally directed traction exerted upon the lens capsule through the suspensory ligament results in flattening of the curvature of the anterior surface of the lens. Focussing the image of a near object is accomplished by contraction of the ciliary muscle which, by drawing the choroid forward, permits the ciliary processes to

move forward and inward, thus reducing the diameter of the ring (corona ciliaris) which they form. The suspensory ligament and lens capsule are thus relaxed, and the lens, by virtue of its inherent elasticity, assumes a more convex form (figs. 15.35 and 15.37). The excised lens, i.e., one released from the restraint of surrounding structures, is therefore at its maximum convexity. Helmholtz's conception is supported in its main tenets by modern work. The movement inward of the ciliary processes during accommodation for near vision has been observed in the living human eye; and in an eye from which the lens substance had been adsorbed as a result of injury, tightening and slackening of the empty capsule was seen during the corresponding phases of accommodation. Yet the curvature assumed by the anterior surface of the lens is, as mentioned above, *hyperbolic*, whereas one would expect it to assume a spheroid form were the lens substance itself elastic and the change in shape due simply to its recoil when released from restraint.

The details of the mechanism with respect to this point have been elucidated by the work of Fincham. According to this observer, the change in shape of the lens during accommodation is explained by the high degree of elasticity possessed by the lens capsule and by the regional variations in its thickness (p. 341), together with the pliable nature of the cortical part of the lens as compared with the nucleus. When the lens is accommodated for distant vision, its substance is confined under tension within the capsule and, as a consequence, distends the latter to the greatest degree where it is weakest, (i.e., thinnest) namely, on the posterior surface. The convexity of this surface is therefore near its maximum when the eye is adjusted for distant objects and little further change can occur during accommodation for near vision. Upon contraction of the ciliary muscle and the consequent slackening of the suspensory ligament the recoil of the elastic capsule moulds the plastic cortex; the peripheral part of the anterior surface is thus pressed back by the relatively thick capsule but the thinner central part of the latter permits the lens substance, chiefly the highly convex nucleus, to bulge forwards. That is, the anterior surface of the lens becomes somewhat "conoid" (Fincham).

Using photoelectric techniques, it is possible to study the dynamics of accommodation (Campbell and Westheimer, 1960). Fig. 15.38 illustrates the time characteristics of two accommodation responses to step changes of focus of 2 D. The reaction time for near and far accommodation is about 0.37 sec.

THE VISUAL AXES AND PUPILLARY DIAMETER DURING ACCOMMODATION. The complete act of accommodation for a near object comprises, besides an increase in the convexity of the anterior surface of the lens, *convergence of the eyes* and *constriction of the pupil*. The constriction of the pupil which occurs during accommodation serves three purposes. The narrowed aperture of the iris (a) reduces lateral chromatic and spherical aberration, thus increasing visual acuity, (b) diminishes the quantity of light entering the eye and (c) increases the *depth of focus*.

The depth of focus of any lens system is defined as the greatest distance through which an object may be moved and still be sharply focussed. When a clear image is formed by a lens, each point in the object is, as a result of diffraction, a series of small concentric circles of light, rather than a geometrical point. When the distance from the lens is increased the image is formed in front of its previous position (that is, in front of the surface, such as a photographic film or retina); if the distance is reduced, the image is formed behind. In either case the rings of light upon the surface become larger. If they are of such a size as still to remain confined, each to a particle making up the grain of the surface, film or retina, the image is sharp and appears in true focus; if they are large enough to spread to neighboring particles the image of the object is blurred. In the case of the fovea, the "grain" is determined by the cones. The depth of focus of the eye is, therefore, given as the greatest distance through which a point can be moved while its image remains restricted to a single cone. The depth of focus of the eye varies with the diameter of the pupil. The values given in table 15.1 are based on measurements of the sensitivity of the eye to out-of-focus blur and are corrected for the retinal direction effect of Stiles and Crawford. If, for example, the observer has a pupil diameter of 3 mm. a change in the refractive power of the eye of ±0.3 diopter will just be detected, but with a 6 mm. pupil a change of ±0.18 D will be detected. These powers may be translated into distances. Thus, if the observer has a 3 mm. pupil and his eye is focussed on infinity, all objects from infinity down to 3.3 m. will be seen sharply. This near point—the hyperfocal distance—is the reciprocal of half the depth of focus when expressed in diopters. If the eye is focussed on the hyperfocal distance then all objects from infinity to 1.67 m. will be in focus.

TABLE 15.1

Pupil Diameter in mm.	Depth of Focus (D)	Depth of Field, when Focused on:		
		Infinity	Hyperfocal distance	25 cm
1	±0.85	α to 1.18 m.	α to 0.59 m.	31.8 to 20.6 cm.
2	±0.44	α to 2.27 m.	α to 1.13 m.	28.1 to 22.5 cm.
3	±0.30	α to 3.33 m.	α to 1.67 m.	27.0 to 23.3 cm.
4	±0.24	α to 4.17 m.	α to 2.08 m.	26.6 to 23.6 cm.
5	±0.20	α to 5.00 m.	α to 2.50 m.	26.3 to 23.8 cm.
6	±0.18	α to 5.56 m.	α to 2.78 m.	26.2 to 23.9 cm.
7	±0.16	α to 6.25 m.	α to 3.12 m.	26.0 to 24.0 cm.
8	±0.15	α to 6.67 m.	α to 3.33 m.	26.0 to 24.1 cm.

Depth of field of the eye based on the detection of ±0.3 D with a 3 mm. diameter pupil and corrected for the retinal direction effect.

Similarly, it may be calculated that if the eye is in focus for a point 25 cm. away, objects within the range 27 to 23.3 cm. will be perceived sharply. The depth of focus decreases as the distance from the eye is reduced. This tendency is, therefore, counteracted by the constriction of the pupil which occurs as part of the mechanism of accommodation of the eye for near vision.

The range and amplitude of accommodation. The farthest point from the eye at which an object can be seen clearly is called the *far point* or *punctum remotum*. The corresponding point nearest the eye is termed the *near point* or *punctum proximum*. In the emmetropic eye the far point is at infinity, i.e., at a distance of over 20 feet (6 meters) and the near point at from 7 cm. to 40 cm., depending upon age (fig. 15.39). The difference between the far and the near point distances is termed the *range of accommodation*. The difference between the refracting power of the eye when accommodation is completely relaxed for the far point and fully displaced for the near point is called the *amplitude of accommodation*. The far point is conjugate to a point on the retina, i.e., parallel rays entering the eye come to a focus on the retina and rays from the latter upon emerging from the eye are parallel and would meet at infinity. Similarly, in the accommodated eye the near point is conjugate with a point on the retina. The focal length of the eye in each state of accommodation there-

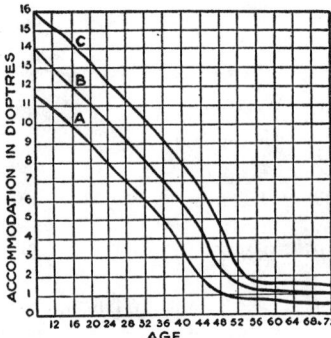

FIG. 15.39. The amplitude of accommoation at different ages. A. The lowest physiological values. B. Average values. C. Maximum values. (After Duane.) The residual accommodation shown after the age of 56 to 60 years is probably due to depth of focus and not to changes in lens shape.

fore corresponds, respectively, to the far and near point distances. It will be recalled that the refractive power is expressed as the reciprocal of the focal distance, the unit being 1 meter and called a diopter. The reciprocal of the far point distance is termed the *static refraction* (designated R) of the eye, and that of the near point distance, the *dynamic refraction* (P). The difference between the two (P−R) gives in diopters the amplitude of accommodation. In the emmetropic eye, since the far point is at infinity, the static refraction is taken as zero. When the near point is at 10 cm. the dynamic refraction is $\dfrac{100 \text{ cm.}}{10 \text{ cm.}} = 10$ D. The amplitude of accommodation in such an emmetropic eye is therefore 10 D.

The amplitude of accommodation diminishes progressively from childhood to about sixty years of age being 16 D at twelve years, 6.5 D at the age of thirty and only about 1 D at sixty. In other words, with advancing years the near point gradually recedes from the eye and at sixty years of age an object must be 1 meter distant in order to be clearly focussed upon the retina (see *presbyopia*). This phenomenon is due mainly to physical changes in the properties of the lens and its capsule (reduced plasticity of the one or diminished elasticity of the other); there may also be a concomitant weakness of the ciliary muscle. It is likely that most or all of the apparent residual accommodation after the age of 60 years is due to the depth of focus of the eye associated with the small pupils found in the elderly.

THE METABOLISM AND COMPOSITION OF THE LENS. The lens, devoid of a blood supply, must obtain all the necessary nutrients for growth and metabolism from the surrounding aqueous and vitreous humors. The aqueous humor is believed to be the main source of supply. The vitreous, aqueous and lens all contain glucose and this appears to supply the

main source of energy, both by aerobic and by anaerobic metabolism. The oxygen tension of the aqueous humor of the rabbit is about 40 to 50 mm. Hg compared with about 72 mm. Hg in arterial blood, but the oxygen has to diffuse over a considerable distance to reach the inner layers of the lens. The rate of metabolism of the lens may be readily determined for it may be removed from the body and maintained in a tissue culture medium containing glucose. In one such experiment Merriam and Kinsey (1950) found that a rabbit lens used about 3.4 mg. of glucose per 24 hours, and that it produced about 2.0 mg. of lactic acid. Rabbit lenses use about 10 to 20 μl. of O_2 per hour and have an R.Q. near to 1. It appears that glucose metabolism in the lens is mainly anaerobic. This anaerobic breakdown of glucose to lactic acid appears to be similar to that found in other tissues, that is, the sequence of reactions in the Embden-Meyerhof scheme. Cytochrome oxidase and flavoproteins have been found in the epithelium of the lens which suggests that this tissue may be responsible for some at least of the small oxygen consumption. The high concentration of glutathione in the lens and of ascorbic acid in the lens and aqueous humor has led to the speculation whether a hydrogen acceptor other than oxygen might be playing a role as both these substances may be reversibly reduced and oxidized, but there is no evidence of their action in lens metabolism. The metabolic function of ascorbic acid remains obscure. Glutathione may be required in the synthesis of the lens proteins and it may be significant that the highest concentration of glutathione is found in the cortex where the new lens fibers are formed.

Four types of protein have been identified in the lens substance, (a) a *euglobin* or *"albuminoid"* (17 per cent) which is water-soluble, and two water-soluble proteins—*pseudoglobulins*, (b) *α-crystalline* (11 per cent) and (c) *β-crystalline* (6 per cent), together with (d) a small quantity of albumin (0.2 per cent). The albuminoid is present mainly in the nucleus, α-crystalline chiefly in the superficial part of the cortex and β-crystalline in the deeper parts. The two crystallines are particularly rich in the sulfur-containing amino-acids cystine and cysteine. The lens proteins as first shown by Uhlenhuth are *organ specific* not species specific, thus differing in their immunological behavior from red cells and blood serum. For example, a solution of lens protein when injected into an animal of the same or of another species causes the production of an antibody—a *precipitin*. This antiserum has then the power to precipitate a solution of lens protein from wherever derived, i.e., from a species other than the one which supplied the antiserum, from the same species or even from the same animal.

The lens substance contains a high concentration of potassium—400 mg. per 100 grams of wet weight—as compared with about 3 mg. per cent in the aqueous and 20 mg. per cent in serum. The concentrations of calcium (5 mg. per cent), sodium chloride (300 mg. per cent) magnesium and silicates are relatively low. The total salt concentration is between 0.7 and 0.8 per cent. Cholesterol and phosphatides amount to about 200 mg. per cent in young lenses, but are from two to four times this value in older specimens. (Consult Pirie and van Heyningen.)

CHANGES IN THE LENS WITH AGE—CATARACT. The loss of plasticity and elasticity of the lens with age as a result of a gradual sclerosis, and the effect such changes have on the mechanism of accommodation are referred to on page 346. Some alterations in lenticular color may accompany the sclerosing process; amber tinting, or even a reddish or brownish discoloration of the lens with consequent filtering of the shorter rays, is of common occurrence.

Cataract is the name given to any partial or complete opacity of the lens. In the commonest variety no ocular or general disease which can be held responsible precedes the development of the opacity, and this, since it appears to be simply a manifestation of age, is termed *senile cataract*. The process leading to the opacity is degenerative in nature, not inflammatory, for the lens is, as just stated, avascular. The opacity commences usually in the deeper part of the cortex and does not, as a rule, involve the nucleus. The lens swells as a result of accumulation of fluid between the fibers, the anterior chamber becoming shallow. So long as the superficial layers of the cortex are clear the cataract is called *immature*. It is said to be *mature* when the opacity has extended to include the superficial layers. The water content of the lens has by this time returned to normal. The mature stage is followed by disintegration of the cortex which becomes softened into a pultaceous mass; this is the stage of hypermaturity; drying and shrinkage of the lens finally result.

The essential change in the cataractous lens is a progressive coagulation of the lens proteins. According to the most generally accepted explanation, such a process is due to the prolonged action of ultraviolet light, and, in some instances, to the thermal effect of infrared rays. The lens as already pointed out, by absorbing a large proportion of the rays below λ 350 mμ and 400 mμ, protects the retina from their injurious effects. Wave lengths below 295 mμ are absorbed by the cornea. The rays absorbed by the lens are not without their effect upon the lens substance itself; it is these which cause the physical change in the lens proteins. Two stages are recognized in the coagulation process: (1) *denaturation of the lens proteins*, con-

sisting presumably of a molecular rearrangement, by light or heat which renders them susceptible to (2) *aggregation (agglutination) of the protein particles* into a flocculent mass—coagulation. This ultimate result occurs only in the presence of certain salts and is enhanced by some organic substances, e.g. dextrose and acetone. The theory that radiant energy is responsible for denaturation of the lens proteins is in accord with many observations. For example, the absorption by the lens of the shorter rays increases with age. The opacity commences in the lower quadrant of the lens which receives the most intense light. In tropical countries, e.g. India and Egypt, cataract is much commoner than in temperate latitudes; it is also less frequent in the latter than in Arctic zones, presumably as a result of the high content in actinic rays of the light reflected from snow and ice. It is also stated that on this continent the incidence of cataract increases from temperate zones to the equator, and that it is also higher in those who work in the fields than in city dwellers. Burge's experiments and the more recent ones of Clarke show convincingly the effect of light upon the development of lenticular opacities. Burge found that whereas exposure of a solution of lens protein to ultraviolet light for 100 hrs. did not cause coagulation, this occurred if $CaCl_2$, $MgCl$, dextrose or acetone were added. Moreover the exposure of the eye of a living fish or frog to short light waves was without effect if the animal had previously been kept in tap water, but definite opacity of the lens followed a few hours exposure, if the fish or frog had been for some days in water containing 0.8 per cent calcium chloride, 0.1 per cent dextrose or 0.1 per cent sodium silicate. Clarke found that heat enhanced the action of the light rays upon solutions of lens proteins, and that opacity could not be produced in the absence of calcium.

The incidence of cataract is much higher in diabetics than in normal persons; it is usually of the ordinary or so-called senile type, but it occurs at an earlier age. The opacity is attributed to the action of dextrose and possibly of acetone bodies in rendering the lens proteins more readily coagulable by light.

Though the factors outlined above appear to be the main ones concerned in the production of the common or senile type of cataract, opinions differ considerably as to the details of the mechanism involved, as well as in regard to the production of other types of lenticular opacity. It is suggested, for example, that the action of ultraviolet rays in inducing denaturation of the lens proteins is due to the reduction of the glutathione and β-crystalline content and the consequent depression of the autoxidative mechanism. Such an effect of ultraviolet radiation has been shown experimentally; it has also been established that the content of the lens in glutathione and in the thermostable pro-

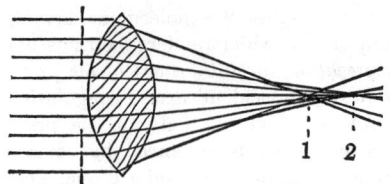

FIG. 15.40. Spherical aberration. Outer rays meet at 1, inner rays at 2.

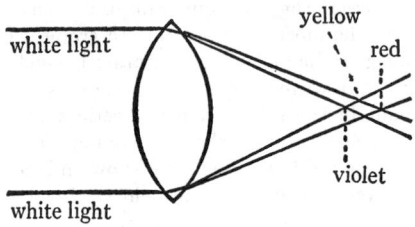

FIG. 15.41. Chromatic aberration.

tein residue diminishes with age. The power of the lens to fluoresce upon exposure to short wave radiations (p. 282) and the disposal of the surplus energy by converting them into long waves, is considered by Burge to be an important factor in ameliorating the effect of light upon the lens; fluorescing bacteria for example are much less readily killed by ultraviolet light than are other types. It is of some considerable interest therefore that the power of the lens to fluoresce diminishes with age.

In glass blowers' cataract, infrared rays would appear to play an important auxiliary rôle. Early cataract has also developed in a few atomic physicists and in some of the Japanese atomic bomb victims. Much research has since been undertaken on the effect on lens metabolism of X-ray and fast neutron radiation. Young animals develop cataract more readily than older animals when irradiated in this way. A latent period of some weeks or months may elapse after the exposure before opacities in the lens appear.

An interesting type of cataract is that following parathyroidectomy; disordered calcium metabolism would appear to be in some way concerned in its production; the calcium content of the lens is increased, whereas that of the blood is reduced. There is no definite evidence, however, to connect ordinary senile cataract with parathyroid deficiency, but there seems little doubt that calcium is concerned in some obscure way with cataract development. A favorite method of producing cataract for experimental study is by the injection of naphthaline; opacities form only if the animal is on a low calcium diet. In rats, lenticular opacity is readily produced by a diet containing a high percentage of lactose or galactose; the former

sugar increases the absorption of calcium, but whether this fact has any bearing upon the development of the cataract is difficult to say; it does not dovetail with other observations in respect to calcium and the development of cataract.

The composition of the cataractous lens shows marked differences from the normal. There is an increase in the insoluble albuminoid and a decrease of the soluble proteins and of glutathione; the oxygen uptake is much reduced. Of the inorganic constituents calcium shows a relatively enormous increase (up to 140 mg. per cent). The concentration of magnesium, sodium and silicates is also raised, whereas that of potassium is greatly reduced.

OPTICAL DEFECTS

SPHERICAL ABERRATION. Rays traversing the peripheral parts of an ordinary convex lens are refracted more strongly and therefore come to a focus nearer the lens than do those transmitted through more central regions. In other words, the outer and inner rays cross in front of the retina and a blurred image is formed (fig. 15.40). This is an inherent defect of convex spherical lenses and is called *spherical aberration*. Spherical aberration is corrected to a certain extent in the crystalline lens, the nucleus having a higher refractive power than the periphery (see p. 333). The iris, since it covers the outer part of the lens and shuts off the peripheral rays, also serves to correct this defect.

The retinal direction effect of Stiles and Crawford (p. 340) also helps to diminish the effects of the peripheral rays at photopic luminances. As the retinal direction effect does not apply to rods, the full pupil area is effective under scotopic conditions. The resulting decrease in image quality is unimportant, for the visual acuity of the retina is poor under scotopic conditions.

CHROMATIC ABERRATION. The colors composing white light are refracted to different degrees according to their wave lengths. The violet rays are refracted most, the refractive power diminishing progressively from the violet to the red end of the spectrum (fig. 15.41). For this reason a series of fringes, colored from violet to red from within outwards, borders the image formed by a simple cheap lens. *Chromatic aberration*, as this defect is called, is corrected in camera and microscope lenses by cementing a biconvex lens of crown glass to a concave one of flint glass. Such a lens is called *achromatic*. The eye is only partially corrected for chromatic aberration. The yellow rays are focussed upon the retina, but the short blue rays being more acutely bent meet in front, while the

longer less strongly refracted red rays come to a
focus behind the retina. Other rays are bent similarly in accordance with their wavelengths. Furthermore, the fovea being on the temporal side of
the optical axis, the blue rays fall upon the retina
nearer to the point (*axial point*) where it is cut by
the optical axis. This, of course, will obtain in
both eyes, and lines projected outwards from the
axial points will meet as shown in figure 15.41.
The blue rays will therefore appear to come from a
point farther away than the point emitting the
red rays; the image formed on the retina by the
shorter blue rays will also be smaller than that
formed by the red rays. These effects of the unequal refraction of the different colors are called,
respectively, *chromatic stereoscopy* and *chromatic
difference of magnification*. In ordinary vision the
colors surrounding the images on the retina are
not perceived.

*Diffraction and the scattering of light within the
eyeball.* Light is diffracted by the pupillary margin
and by the lens fibers and corneal epithelium; as a
result of this and of spherical aberration the retinal image is not made up of points of light but of
diffusion circles (blur circles), i.e., a bright central
disc surrounded by light rings which diminish in
intensity by almost imperceptible gradations towards the periphery. The relative size of the central bright area varies inversely with the diameter
of the pupil and directly with the wave length of
the light. The opposite effects of changes in the
size of the pupil upon this defect and upon chromatic aberration have been pointed out.

None of the ocular media is perfectly homogeneous; owing to their colloidal nature a certain proportion of the light entering the eye is scattered
(Tyndall phenomenon), that is, it is not focussed
upon the retina but is deflected from the course
which it would follow according to the laws of
refraction if the contents of the globe were perfectly transparent. The colloidal particles have a
size of the order of the wave length of light. The
quantity of scattered light is directly proportional
to the square of the size of the particles, and inversely proportional to the fourth power of the
wave length (Rayleigh). Thus the greatest scattering within the eyeball occurs with violet and ultraviolet light and the least with red (see Le
Grand).

PRESBYOPIA (Gr. *presbos*, old; *ōps*, the eye) is
the term given to the gradual reduction in the
amplitude of accommodation which goes hand in
hand with advancing years.

EMMETROPIA AND AMETROPIA. The four optical
defects just described may be regarded as physiological, the first three being inherent to some ex-

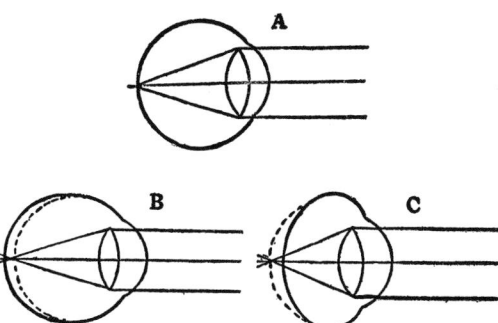

FIG. 15.42. A, emmetropia; B, myopia; C, hypermetropia.

tent in optical systems in general; the fourth is a
natural accompaniment of age. Two other defects
of frequent occurrence are due to incongruity between the length of the eyeball and its refracting
power and must be classed as definite abnormalities.

The refractive state of the normal eye, which
has its far point (p. 345) at infinity, i.e., at a
distance greater than 6 meters (20 feet), is called
emmetropia. Parallel rays entering the emmetropic
eye are brought to a clear focus on the retina
without any effort of accommodation. The static
refraction of such an eye is therefore zero. If the
far point is not at infinity the eye is *ametropic*.
There are two forms of ametropia—myopia and
hypermetropia (fig. 15.42).

In *myopia* (Gr. *myō*, I blink or half close the
eye; *ōps*, the eye) or *short sight*, the eyeball is too
long relatively to its refracting power (fig. 15.42-
B). Obviously, such an eye will bring parallel rays
to a focus in front of the retina, i.e., in the vitreous. After meeting, the rays cross and form a
blurred image or a diffusion circle upon the retina,
just as a camera which is extended too far forms
an indistinct image upon the film. In order to
form a clear image on the retina of the myopic
eye the rays must be, not parallel but divergent;
such as are emitted by a near object. The far point
is therefore at a finite distance, and in extreme
instances may be only a few centimeters from the
eye. Accommodation, of course, is relaxed for the
far point as in the emmetropic eye for, obviously,
increasing the converging power of the lens will
only cause greater blurring of the image. The far
and near points being close together, the range
and the amplitude of accommodation (p. 345)
are reduced. Myopia is corrected by means of
concave (diverging) lenses. If, for example, an
object can be seen clearly no farther away than

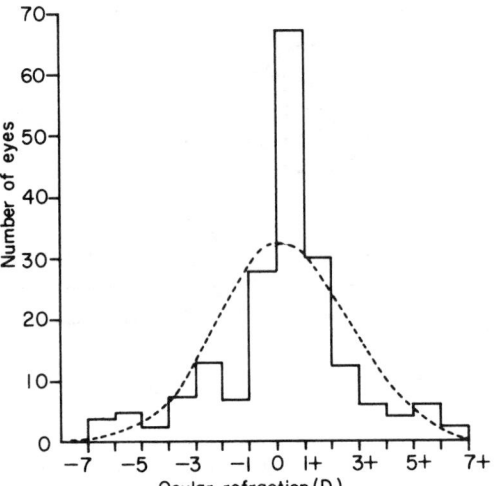

Fig. 15.43. The distribution curve of ocular refraction of 194 eyes. The continuous lines indicate the actual observations and the dotted line indicates the fitted normal curve. As the former is more peaked than the latter it may be concluded that whereas the individual optical components may vary over a wide range in an individual eye these components are usually so correlated that emmetropia results. (After Sorsby, Benjamin, Davey, Sheridan and Tanner.)

1 meter, the myopia is—1 D, i.e., a concave lens of this power is required.

In *hypermetropia* (Gr. *hyper*, above; *metros*, measure; *ōps*, the eye) or *long sight* (fig. 15.42C) the eye is too short for its refracting power. Therefore parallel rays after refraction fall upon the retina before they have come to a focus, and form an image blurred by diffusion circles. The rays as they emerge from the eye are divergent. The far point is *virtual*, i.e., it is behind the eye at the point where the rays would meet if continued backwards through the retina. The hypermetrope must accommodate when he views distant objects in order to focus the parallel rays upon the retina. The range of his accommodation (p. 1391) is the same as that of the emmetrope but the amplitude is greater. Suppose, for example, that the near point is 0.10 meter in front of the eye and the far point is 0.25 meter behind, i.e., negative (-0.25). Then the dynamic refraction is $100/10 = 10$ D, and the static refraction is $-100/-25 = -4$ D; the amplitude of accommodation is therefore 10 D $- (-4$ D$)$, or 10 D $+ 4$ D $= 14$ D. Hypermetropia is corrected by means of a convex lens, the distance of the far point behind the eye giving the measure of the strength of lens required; if this is -0.25 meter then a $+4$ D lens would correct the defect (see p. 337).

Although it is customary to account for myopia and hypermetropia in terms of variations in the axial length of the eye and to assume that the power of the cornea and lens is constant, recent studies suggest that this view is inadequate. If the optical constants of a large number of eyes are measured it is found that the power of the cornea varies from 39 to 47 D and that of the lens from 14 to 25 D. The axial length may range from 22 to 26 mm. Although hypermetropic eyes tend to have a shorter axial length than myopic eyes, it is only in the severe degrees of these defects (over $+$ or -4 D) that the axial length falls outside the normal statistical limits. The refractive errors in a population are so distributed that the three variables, cornea, lens and axial length cannot be distributed in a random fashion, for inspection of figure 15.43 indicates that there is an excess number of emmetropes in the population. A correlation mechanism must be postulated to maintain something like emmetropia during the period of growth of the eye from its newborn length of 16 mm. to that of 24 mm. in the adult state. Most of the growth in length occurs during the first few years of life although myopia often first declares itself at adolescence when the axial length has become stable. Nothing is known about the nature of the process which leads to such a high proportion of emmetropes in the population. Genetic factors are almost certainly involved for refractive errors can often be inherited.

ASTIGMATISM (Gr. *a*, privative; *stigma*, a point). In this condition, as its name implies, rays of light are not brought to sharp points upon the retina, but form short lines. The defect is present in all eyes to a certain degree; when moderate it is therefore physiological. Only when the fault seriously reduces visual acuity is it abnormal. It must be remembered that rays of light pass through all meridians of a lens; in converging to a focus they therefore form a cone of light, not simply a flat pennantlike beam. If all meridians of a lens have the same curvature, then rays in all planes will be refracted to the same degree and come to a focus together. If, on the other hand, the curvatures differ, the rays transmitted through a meridian with the greater curvature will be refracted more strongly and brought to a focus in front of rays passing through other meridians. For example, should the vertical meridian be more curved than the horizontal, then when the rays passing through the vertical meridian are in focus those in the horizontal will form, not a point, but an ellipse, a circle or a line. Thus there are two foci and the distance between two lines—the *focal interval*—is a measure of the degree of the astigmatism (see fig. 15.44). Such inequalities of curvature in the meridians of the cornea or, less commonly, of the crystalline lens, are the cause of what is known as *curvature astigmatism.* The greater curvature may be in either the vertical, horizontal or an oblique meridian. But in physiological astigmatism (which is due most probably to the pressure of the upper lid upon the eyeball during growth) the greater curvature is in the vertical meridian. In pathological types also this meridian has most commonly the greater curvature. When the refractive power though unequal in the various meridians is the same throughout any meridian, and the maximally and minimally curved meridians (*principal meridians*) are at right angles to one another, the astigmatism is called *regular.* In *irregular astigmatism* not only is the refractive power unequal in the different meridians, but it is not uniform throughout a meridian, and the principal meridians are not at right angles to one another. Astigmatism may result from inequalities in the refractive indices between different parts of the lens; this is termed *index astigmatism.* Slight inequalities of this nature in the refractive indices may also contribute to physiological astigmatism. An oblique or other malposition of the lens is sometimes a cause of astigmatism. When the subject of astigmatism looks at a clock face, the straight lines in the vertical numerals XII and VI may be clearly seen, while the horizontal lines in IX and III are blurred, or vice versa. Or, the diagonal numerals may be out of focus while the vertical and horizontal are sharply defined. A chart such as is shown in figure 15.45 is employed to detect the meridian or meridians in which the corneal curvature is abnormal.

Astigmatism is corrected by the use of spectacle lenses convex in the meridian corresponding to that of the cornea (or crystalline lens) having the lesser curvature. Thus if the curvature of the cornea is greater in the vertical meridian, the subject is fitted with a cylindrical lens, which, it will be recalled, refracts in a single plane, having its convexity in the horizontal meridian.

The young emmetrope becomes myopic by 1 to 2 D when viewing a scene in dim lighting, such as twilight. There is evidence that some of this "twilight myopia" is caused by the increased effects of spherical aberration resulting from the dilation of the pupil in dim lighting. However, some of the effect is also due to a small and varia-

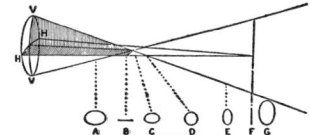

FIG. 15.44. Refraction by an astigmatic lens. VV, the vertical meridian of the refracting body, is more curved than HH, the horizontal meridian. A, B, C, D, E, F, G show different sections of the beam after refraction. At B the vertical rays are brought to a focus; at F the horizontal rays are brought to a focus. From B to F is the focal interval.

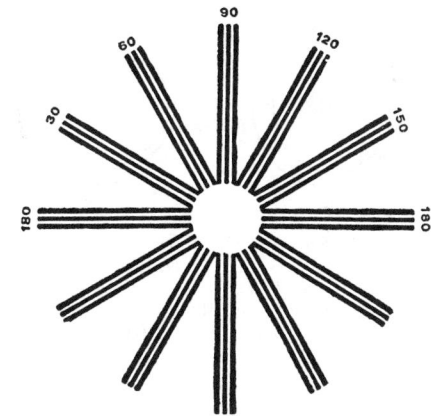

FIG. 15.45. Chart used in testing for astigmatism. One eye being closed the patient is asked to say which of the groups of lines are blackest and most distinct and which are lightest and indistinct.

ble amount of near accommodation of the lens system. Even in bright viewing conditions when the pupils are small and spherical aberration is minimal the emmetrope may become myopic to the extent of 0.25 to 1 D when viewing a scene devoid of visual detail, such as a clear blue sky. This "day myopia" is due to the lens system accommodating for near. It is not known why the accommodation mechanism does not remain focussed at infinity in the absence of a suitable visual stimulus. This condition may cause difficulty in high altitude aircraft and manned spacecraft when pilots are searching for approaching craft against a clear blue sky.

Contact Lenses

The contact lens consists of a thin cuplike shell of glass moulded to fit the cornea and sclera and ground to the required curvature. It is applied directly to the eye and therefore moves with it. Contact lenses are employed for the correction of various types of refractive error, e.g., myopia and

FIG. 15.46. Contact lens.

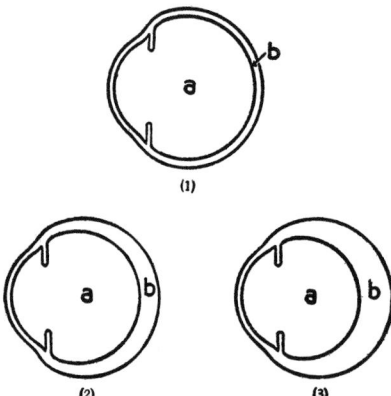

FIG. 15.47. Showing the distribution of volume-pressure in the eye with (1) a collapsed blood pressure, (2) in the normal state, and (3) with raised blood pressure and capillary dilatation. (After Duke-Elder, *The Nature of the Intraocular Fluids*.)

hypermetropia and those due to abnormalities in the form of the cornea (astigmatism or conical cornea) or to absence of the lens (aphakia). Before being applied the concavity of the lens is filled with saline solution and when in position is separated from the cornea only by a thin film of the solution. The refractive indices of the cornea and the saline are approximately the same. The two therefore constitute a single refracting medium moulded as it were by the posterior surface of the glass shell into a normal form. Light rays are refracted at the anterior surface of the cornea in contact with the air and less strongly at the posterior surface, but undergo no further refraction until they reach the crystalline lens (fig. 15.46).

The Intraocular Fluids

THE INTRAOCULAR PRESSURE. The pressure within the chambers of the eye of a living animal is from 15 to 20 mm. Hg and from 8 mm. to 10 mm. Hg in the excised but intact globe; it also falls to the latter level immediately after death or after arrest of the ocular circulation. The difference between these two sets of values, is due to the pressure of the blood in the vessels of the globe. This will be clear from figure 15.47. The vascular bed of the eyeball lies between the relatively resistant sclerotic on the outside and the incompressible intraocular contents on the other. It is evident that blood pumped into the vessels of the

choroid will raise the intraocular pressure above that of a bloodless eye. The intraocular pressure runs closely parallel with that of the blood in the choroidal capillaries. A rise or fall in general arterial pressure therefore may cause a corresponding change in intraocular pressure, though it will be much less in degree. The pulse beat causes a variation in intraocular pressure of from 1 to 2 mm. Hg, and the respiration one of from 3 to 5 mm. Hg. However, since it is the pressure in the capillary bed of the eye rather than that in the larger ocular vessels which is the determining factor and the former pressure can vary as a result of *local* changes in caliber of the minute vessels, the intraocular and arterial pressures do not necessarily change in the same direction. Thus arterial hypertension, in which the capillary pressure is not raised, does not cause a rise in intraocular pressure; amyl nitrite, on the other hand, causes a *fall* in arterial pressure as a result of the peripheral vasodilation, accompanied by a *rise* in intraocular pressure (due to the dilation of the capillaries of the eye and the consequent increase in capillary pressure). The intraocular pressure therefore follows very closely the venous pressure; tying the vortex veins, for example, increases capillary pressure and causes a rise in intraocular pressure of from 50 to 60 mm. Hg. The pressure of 8 or 10 mm. Hg which, as mentioned above, exists within an eye immediately after its circulation has been arrested, may be looked upon as representing the balance struck between the production of intraocular fluid and its removal through the drainage channels.

Other factors which affect the intraocular tension are pressure from without by the action of the eyelids and of the extrinsic muscles of the eye. The effect exerted by the eye muscles in ordinary movements is negligible, but maximally strong convergence of the eyeballs may raise the pressure by from 4 to 10 mm. Hg. Movements of the lids have a greater influence, strong contraction of the orbicularis oculi causing a rise of 50 mm. Hg or more. Exposure of the eye to light causes a fall, and dark adaptation a rise in pressure which is attributed to constriction and dilation, respectively, of the ocular capillaries. Contraction of the ciliary muscle causes no change in the intraocular pressure, nor does the state of the pupil. A change in pressure does not occur therefore upon accommodation of the eye, provided that the associated convergent movement is prevented.

THE VITREOUS BODY. The vitreous body occupies the segment of the globe lying behind the lens and the ciliary processes. In front it presents a saucer-shaped depression—the *hyaloid fossa*—which lodges the posterior convexity of the lens. A narrow space (*postlenticular space*) filled with fluid separates the lens from the concave surface of the vitreous. The *hyaloid canal* (which lodged the hyaloid artery in the embryo) runs from the posterior pole of the lens to the center of the optic disc. The structureless *hyaloid membrane* surrounds the vitreous; anteriorly it is strengthened by radial fibers which have already been referred to as the *zonula ciliaris* (p. 342). In this region it shows a series of grooves which lodge the ciliary processes. The vitreous body is a jellylike material, possessing no obvious structure; but it is claimed that by the use of special fixatives (e.g., a weak solution of chromic acid) a series of superimposed lamellae arranged concentrically around the hyaloid canal and composed of very thin flat cells can be demonstrated. The spaces between the lamellae contain fluid almost identical in composition with the aqueous humor. Though some maintain that the lamellae are fixation artefacts and that the vitreous body is a homogeneous gel, there seems little doubt that a framework does exist. If the vitreous body is examined with the phase contrast microscope a network of fibers of various sizes can be demonstrated and a clear cut hyaline membrane which encloses it. The human vitreous adheres firmly to the retina in the region of the macula and optic disc. Less firm adhesions also occur at the equator and this appears to lend support to the hypothesis that some retinal detachments are caused by traction of the vitreous fiber on the retina. Examination of the vitreous structure with the electron microscope has revealed three types of fibers: (1) fibers without cross striations of diameter 15 to 30 mμ, this type being commonest; (2) fibers showing cross striations of period 61 mμ and diameter 15-30 mμ, (3) fibers showing cross striations similar to collagen (64 mμ) and diameter 50 to 80 mμ.

THE AQUEOUS HUMOR is a clear watery fluid occupying the anterior and posterior chambers of the eye. It has a refractive index of 1.33; it is alkaline in reaction (pH 7.1 to 7.3) and has a specific gravity of from 1002 to 1004. The composition of the aqueous humor closely resembles that of an ultrafiltrate of plasma. The main difference between the composition of plasma and aqueous lines is the very low protein content of the latter (10 to 20 mg., 100 ml. in man). The aqueous contains a lower concentration of glucose and a higher concentration of lactic acid than does plasma. This may be due in part to the metabolism of glucose by the lens and cornea. The ascorbic acid concentration of the aqueous is some 10 to 50 times greater than that in the plasma, and it is thought to be passed into the fluid by the ciliary body. This high concentration may be connected with the metabolism of the avascular tissues such as the cornea, lens and vitreous body. The ascorbic acid content of the aqueous has been shown to fall dramatically in scorbutic guinea pigs but no ocular defects occur in prolonged scurvy in either guinea pigs or man.

The Formation of the Intraocular Fluids

Owing to the importance of the subject to glaucoma, the formation of the intraocular fluids has been investigated most diligently, but the precise mechanism involved has not yet been established. There have been three theories of the process proposed, namely, that it is one of (1) *ultrafiltration*, (2) *dialysis* or (3) *secretion*. None of these theories alone fits all the known facts. The principal process appears to be one of ultrafiltration, and involves those factors, capillary blood pressure and colloid osmotic pressures, which have been described elsewhere in connection with the interchange of water and substances in solution across capillary membranes (chs. 24 and 34). The high capillary pressure required for ultrafiltration into the interior of the eyeball has been shown to exist (owing to the relatively high hydrostatic pressure therein); the mean pressure in the capillaries derived from the retinal artery and the posterior ciliary arteries is 50 mm. Hg which is much higher than that in the capillaries of most other regions. Nevertheless, ultrafiltration is not a complete explanation of the formation of intraocular fluid, for when the concentrations of the constituents of plasma and of the aqueous humor are compared, it is evident that the latter is not simply an ultrafiltrate like the fluid in Bowman's capsule, for example. It is therefore thought that dialysis plays a part, though there are discrepancies here which do not permit the formulation of a theory based upon simple dialysis alone. There is also some evidence that certain substances, e.g., sodium are secreted.

The surface of the ciliary body and the posterior aspect of the iris are believed to constitute the membrane interposed between the aqueous humor and the blood. That diffusion occurs across *both* these surfaces is indicated by the following observations. When the pupillary aperture is occluded either experimentally or as a result of disease, aqueous fluid accumulates behind the iris. On the other hand, fluid is formed after excision of the iris or when it is congenitally absent. In certain fish not possessing a ciliary body and in the congenital absence of the latter in man, normal aqueous humor is present; it has also been found in a cyst of the iris itself.

THE CIRCULATION OF THE INTRAOCULAR FLUIDS.

THE DRAINAGE SYSTEM OF THE EYE. Intraocular fluid is probably reabsorbed to some extent from all parts of the interior of the globe. A small proportion of the dialyzed fluid passes from the posterior chamber through the zonule and down the hyaloid canal to the lymphatics of the optic nerve. However, less than 1 per cent is reabsorbed in this way, or indeed from any region of the eye lying posterior to the iris. The chief exits for the fluid are at the angle of the anterior chamber (*angle of the iris* or *filtration angle*) and from the anterior surface of the iris. It will perhaps be of advantage to the reader if the main structural features of this region are recalled.

On the deep aspect of the sclera at its junction with the cornea and in front of the angle of the anterior chamber lies an annular venous sinus—the *canal of Schlemm* (*sinus venosus sclerae*) (fig. 15.30). The sinus completely surrounds the corneal margin and in meridional sections of the eye appears as a small oval gap or cleft lined by endothelium. The inner or posterior wall of the canal is separated from the anterior chamber by a zone of trabecular tissue formed by the breaking up of the posterior elastic lamina of the cornea and termed the *pectinate ligament*; the intervals between the trabeculae are termed the *spaces of Fontana*. The trabecular tissue of the pectinate ligament is continued around the iridial angle, its fibers terminating in the tissue of the iris. Schlemm's canal is fed by an *afferent arteriole* derived from the ciliary arteries and drained by an *efferent venule* which empties into the episcleral venous plexus (Friedenwald). The spaces of Fontana communicate with the anterior chamber, but there is no *direct* communication between the former and the lumen of Schlemm's canal; the canal cannot be injected, for example, with a colloidal solution introduced into the anterior chamber.

The *scleral spur* is the term applied to a small triangular projection of the sclera on the posterior aspect of the sclerocorneal junction; it lies immediately behind the outer part of the posterior wall of Schlemm's canal and gives attachment to the meridional fibers of the ciliary muscle. Contraction of the muscle, by pulling upon the spur, is said to dilate the canal and thus favor the drainage of fluid from the anterior chamber.

Movement of the intraocular fluid from the posterior to the anterior chamber and from the latter to the filtration angle is brought about largely through intermittent variations in intraocular pressure occasioned by the several factors already discussed (e.g., pulsatile and respiratory variations in blood pressure and actions of the eyelids, etc.). Temperature differences between the superficial and deeper parts of the anterior chamber (*thermal factor*) cause convection currents to be set up which also play an important part in the movement of fluid. At the angle of the iris the fluid percolates into the spaces of Fontana whence it is absorbed across the posterior wall of the canal of Schlemm.

Friedenwald and Pierce have demonstrated a differential absorption between the water, crystalloids and protein constituents of the aqueous. From their experiments which involved the introduction of substances into the anterior chamber, these observers conclude that crystalloids and a small quantity of water are reabsorbed from the anterior surface of the iris, passing by diffusion through the walls of the capillaries. Colloids are removed by the phagocytic action of the surface layer of epithelial cells. A part of the protein is hydrolyzed by the action of enzymes present in the fluid and reabsorbed as amino-acids. Water is absorbed chiefly through the spaces of Fontana and the canal of Schlemm. The rate of passage of fluid through the wall of the canal is governed apparently by hydrostatic and osmotic forces. The pressure of blood in Schlemm's canal (or rather in the small veins leading from it) is stated to be equal to or about 1 mm. higher than that of the fluid in the anterior chamber, but after the absorption of crystalloids one would expect the osmotic pressure of the aqueous to be considerably lower than that of the serum; under such circumstances an uptake of fluid would occur, provided the blood flow through the canal did not fall below a certain level. Slowing of the circulation would tend (as a result of the dilution of serum colloid dilution by the reabsorbed fluid and consequent reduction in osmotic pressure) to reduce the rate of reabsorption, an increase in blood velocity to increase it. Such a relationship was actually observed by Friedenwald and Pierce. Increase in intraocular pressure would quite evidently increase reabsorption, the pressure would thus tend automatically to be restored to its original level.

According to some authorities (Maggiore, Duke-Elder) the canal of Schlemm contains blood only when the ocular venous pressure is inordinately high, being filled under usual circumstances with an aqueous fluid (with an osmotic pressure around that of the fluid in the anterior chamber). Since, as mentioned above, the pressure of blood in the small veins leading from it is higher than the normal intraocular pressure the canal could not serve as a pathway for the continued reabsorption of fluid; it is claimed that reabsorption can occur only if the intraocular pressure rises above the normal level. This conception attributes a safety-valve function to the canal, i.e., it is called into play presumably only in an emergency.

GLAUCOMA OR OCULAR HYPERTENSION. Persistent elevation of the intraocular pressure occurs as an accompaniment of several diseased states of the eye and may then be due to blockage of the drainage channels at the iridial angle or to the excessive production of fluid. The latter effect may result from mechanical irritation of the ciliary processes (e.g., by displacement of the lens) or obstruction of the venous channels with consequent rise in capillary pressure. Ocular hypertension associated with some such obvious disease of the eye is referred to as *secondary glaucoma*. When the intraocular pressure is persistently elevated above 35 mm. or so and no abnormality of the eye exists to account for the hypertension, it is termed *primary glaucoma*. At the outset it may be said that, though primary glaucoma has been the subject of much speculation, its cause remains obscure.

The excessively high intraocular tension causes compression of the vessels and in time serious disturbances in the nutrition of the eye result, namely, optic atrophy, excavation ("cupping") of the disc, blindness and ultimately disintegration of the optical mechanism. Owing to the readjustments which take place in the ocular circulation the hypertension may exist for some time before any of these effects make their appearance. The pressure as it gradually rises first compresses the venous channels but, as a result of the opening up of the arterioles and capillaries, a larger proportion of the arterial pressure is transmitted to the venous side; the compressing force is thus overcome and the circulation maintained. This stage in the progress of the condition is referred to as *compensated glaucoma*. A point will be reached, however, at which the pressure of the intraocular fluids approaches equality with that in the ophthalmic artery; then further compensation becomes impossible and the structural changes just mentioned supervene. The condition is then termed *inflammatory* or *decompensated glaucoma*.

The possible factors which have been suggested in explanation of the elevated pressure will be briefly considered. Mechanical obstruction at the filtration angle due to reduction in the depth of the anterior chamber and the consequent adhesion of the periphery of the iris to the cornea, is frequently present in decompensated cases, but this is secondary and not primarily related to the hypertension. It is not improbable that some abnormality in the nervous control of the vascular bed of the globe is fundamentally responsible. Friedenwald suggests that the reabsorption of water through the mechanism of Schlemm's canal (p.

354) as a result of sclerosis and narrowing of the afferent vessels may be the essential factor concerned. Reduction in the caliber of these vessels would tend, by slowing the blood flow through the canal, to reduce the reabsorption rate. Spasm of the vessels feeding the sinus would have a similar effect. On the other hand, the reduced depth of the anterior chamber in decompensated glaucoma suggests that the increased pressure originates in the posterior chamber of the eye, and the theory has been advanced that swelling of the vitreous is responsible. From the gellike nature of the vitreous body one might expect its water content to vary with changes in its inorganic constituents or in pH. It has been found, however, that the chemical changes necessary to cause any significant increase in volume of the vitreous are far greater than any that could occur in the body. Finally, a vasodilator toxin of the histamine type has been suggested which supposedly, by causing dilation of the intraocular capillaries and an increase in the permeability of their walls, would lead to overproduction of intraocular fluid. The aqueous in decompensated glaucoma has a higher protein, and lower chloride content and osmotic pressure than normal; this fact lends some force to the theory of increased capillary permeability. The abnormal permeability would also, by reducing the effective osmotic difference between the contents of the anterior chamber and the blood, tend to diminish reabsorption. Nevertheless, analysis of the aqueous humor in *compensated* cases shows no significant departure from the normal and therefore lends no support to the idea that a change in capillary permeability is the fundamental factor in the development of glaucoma.

There is no causative relationship between arterial and ocular hypertension.

REFERENCES

BENHAM, G. H., DUKE-ELDER, W. S. AND HODGSON, T. H. J. Physiol., 1928, **92**, 355.

BURGE, W. E. Am. J. Physiol., 1915, **39**, 335.

CAMPBELL, F. W. AND WESTHEIMER, G. J. Physiol., 1960, **151**, 285.

CLARK, J. H. Am. J. Physiol., 1935, **113**, 538.

FINCHAM, E. F. Proc. Optical Conv., Part I, 1926, p. 454.

FRIEDENWALD, J. S. Arch. Path., 1936, **16**, 65.

FRIEDENWALD, J. S. AND PIERCE, H. F. Arch. Ophth., 1937, **17**, 477.

FRIEDENWALD, J. S. AND STIEHLER, R. D. Arch. Ophth., 1935, **14**, 789.

GOLDMAN, H. AND HAGEN, R. Ophthalmologica (Basel), 1942, **104**, 15.

GOLDSCHMIDT, M. München. med. Wchnschr., 1914, **61**, 657.

HARTRIDGE, H. AND HILL, A. V. Proc. Roy. Soc., London, ser. B, 1915, **89**, 58.

HOLMES, G. AND PATON, L. Brain, 1910, **33**, 389.

LUDVIGH, E. Nature, 1938, **141**, 1141.

RIGGS, L. A., RATLIFF, F., CORNSWEET, J. C., and CORNSWEET, T. N. J. Opt. Soc. Amer., 1953, **43**, 465.

STILES, W. S. AND CRAWFORD, B. H. Proc. Roy. Soc. B., 1933, **112**, 428.

Monographs and Reviews

ADAMS, D. R. Proc. Roy. Soc., London, ser. B., 1925, **98**, 244. Brit. J. Ophth., 1925, **9**, 281.

DUKE-ELDER, W. S. Brit. J. Ophth., 1927, Monograph Supp. III. The practice of refraction. Churchill, Lond., 1928.

HELMHOLTZ, H. VON. Treatise on physiological optics. Optic. Soc. Am. 1924.

LE GRAND, Y., Light, colour and vision. Chapman and Hall, London, 1957.

PIRIE, A. AND VAN HEYNINGEN, R., Biochemistry of the eye. Blackwell, Oxford, 1956.

SOUTHALL, J. P. C. Introduction to physiological optics. Oxford University Press, 1937.

CHAPTER 16

The Visual Fields and Pathway. Movements of the
Ocular Muscle. Stereoscopic Vision

THE VISUAL FIELDS. The visual field of one eye is the part of the external world which is seen by that eye at any given moment, i.e., when its gaze is fixed in one direction. It may be likened to a portion of a great hollow sphere—a bowl—upon the interior surface of which the images of the external world are projected. Traquair pictures the visual field as "an island of vision surrounded by a sea of blindness"; carrying the simile further, the surface contour of this imaginary island is described in terms of visual acuity, the highest point corresponding to the fovea, a deep (bottomless) pit to the blind spot and a gradual slope toward the peripheral retina. The visual field of each eye subtends an angle of about 160° in a horizontal and 145° in the vertical meridian. The visual field on each side is divided by a line passing vertically through the fixation point (p. 371) into two unequal parts, an outer or *temporal* and an inner or *nasal*. The latter is smaller owing to the shadow of the nose, its diameter being about 60° whereas the diameter of the temporal part is around 100°. Similarly a line passing horizontally through the point of fixation divides the field into an upper and a lower part, the former being restricted by from 5° to 10° by the upper lid and orbital margin. Rays of light from the outer or temporal half of the visual field fall upon the nasal (inner) half of the retina, those from the inner or nasal half of the visual field fall upon the temporal half of the retina (fig. 16.7, p. 363). Although an image is formed upon each retina the two are fused in consciousness into a single impression (see p. 367). In most animals the visual fields of the two eyes overlap, that is, certain parts of the outside world are seen by both eyes at the same instant—*binocular vision*. In animals with eyes placed laterally in the head overlap of the visual fields must obviously be very small in extent, the visual fields being almost completely separate—*monocular vision*. The extent of overlap of the visual fields of the monkey and of man, whose eyes are placed in the front of the head, is large (120° horizontal diameter) and the monocular field of vision, that is, the field which can be seen by one eye but not by the other, is relatively small (35°) (figs. 16.1

and 16.5). Rays of light entering the eyes from an object in the binocular field of vision fall upon the nasal half of one retina and upon the temporal half of the other. If, however, the object is well to the right or to the left of the line of vision, i.e., in the outer part of either temporal field, the rays then fall upon the nasal half of the peripheral retina of the nearer eye (right or left) but not upon the other retina which is shaded by the nose. So the monocular field of vision consists in man of a crescentic area (35°) at the outer limit of the temporal field of each eye.

When one looks directly at an object the eyes are turned so as to bring an image of the object upon the most sensitive area of each retina, i.e.; upon the nasal and temporal halves, respectively, of the foveae. The horizontal diameter of the entire visual field, that is, of the area of overlap of the two fields plus the monocular fields on each side is about 200°.

We shall see when the arrangement of the fibers conveying visual impulses is considered that fibers arising from the nasal halves of the retinas cross in the chiasma, whereas the temporal fibers remain uncrossed. Thus it is that the occipital cortex of one side receives impulses from the nasal half of the opposite retina and from the temporal half of the retina of the same side, that is, those retinal halves which receive impressions from the opposite halves of the visual fields (fig. 16.7, p. 363). Loss of vision in one half of each eye is called hemianopia. When the blindness affects the right or the left halves of both retinas, i.e., the nasal half of the left retina (temporal half of visual field) and the temporal half of the right (nasal half of the visual field) or vice versa, the hemianopia is said to be *homonymous*—left or right respectively. If the blindness is in the *left* half of one retina and in the *right* half of the other, i.e., in either both temporal retinal halves (nasal halves of visual fields) or in both nasal retinal halves (temporal halves of visual fields) the hemianopia is *crossed* or *heteronymous* and is referred to as *binasal* or *bi-temporal*, respectively. It will be noted that the qualifying terms refer to the affected halves of the *visual fields* and not to the

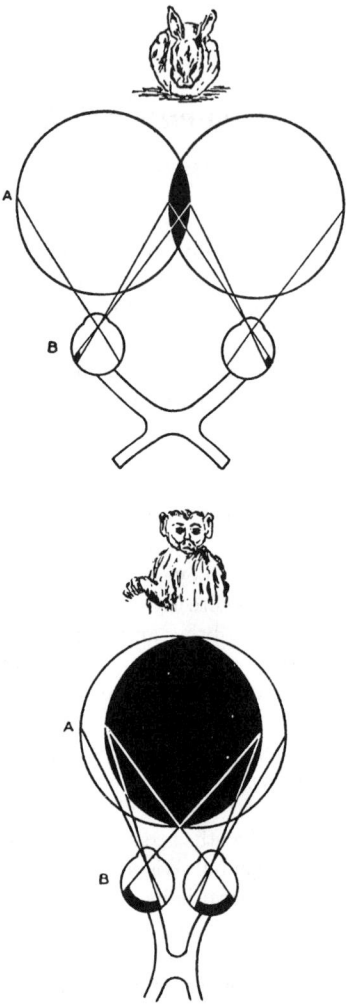

periphery to the fovea can be explored by using a series of test objects of graduated sizes with the perimeter, and determining in different meridians the distance from the fixation point (p. 371) at which each object is just perceptible. The points so determined are marked upon the perimeter chart and lines drawn through each set. Thus a series of boundary lines roughly concentric with the fovea are constructed which indicate the thresholds for the perception of the different test objects. Each is called an *isopter of sensitivity*; they might be compared to the contour lines indicating elevations on a detailed geographical map.

THE BLIND SPOT. The entrance of the optic nerve, since it is devoid of rods and cones, is completely blind. An object whose image falls upon it is therefore invisible (see fig. 16.3). Not even a sensation of blackness results, for when the eye is fixated upon the cross, as described in the legend of the figure, and the book moved until the optic disc is occupied by the circle the latter simply disappears, no sensation whatever being experienced to indicate its existence. Ordinarily this "hole" in the visual field causes no inconvenience because, in any position of the eyes, should one image of an object fall upon the blind spot a sensitive part of the opposite retina receives the other image. Even when one eye is closed, or blind, we are not aware of the blind spot in the seeing eye unless it is specifically demonstrated. Patients, who have had portions of their pe-

FIG. 16.1. Showing monocular (white) and binocular (black) fields of vision. Upper rabbit; lower monkey (or man). (From Parsons, after Brouwer and Zeeman.)

retinal halves. In other instances a quarter only of each visual field is affected, when the term *quadrantic hemianopia* is employed. It may be the upper or the lower quadrants of the nasal or of the temporal fields which are involved, or homonymous quadrants may be affected, i.e., a quadrant in the nasal field of one eye and in the temporal field of the other. The type of hemianopia is further specified by the use of the word "superior" or "inferior" (fig. 16.2). Thus, a superior nasal quadrantic hemianopia is one in which the eyes do not see objects in the upper nasal quadrants of the visual fields (blindness of lower temporal retinal quadrants).

Isopters. The sensitivity of the retina from the

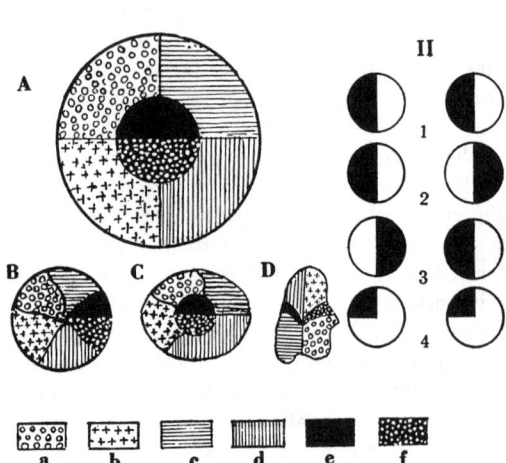

FIG. 16.2. *I*, distribution of visual fibers. *A*, right retina; *B*, optic nerve; *C*, optic chiasma; *D*, opposite lateral geniculate body; *a*, upper nasal quadrant of retina; *b*, lower nasal quadrant; *c*, upper temporal quadrant; *d*, lower temporal quadrant; *e*, upper macular fibers; *f*, lower macular fibers. (Redrawn and modified from Henschen and Brouwer and Zeeman). *II*, Diagram of types of hemianopia, *1*, homonymous; *2*, bitemporal; *3*, binasal; *4*, homonymous superior quadrantic.

ripheral retina destroyed some time previously by localized disease, are often unaware of the presence of the blind areas until they are demonstrated to exist by means of perimetry.

Perimetry is the term applied to the procedure of mapping out the visual fields. The instrument employed is called a *perimeter*. It comprises a metal band or arm, shaped in a large arc of a circle with its concavity directed towards the subject (fig. 16.4). A holder sliding in the arc carries the test object which can be moved centrally or peripherally as required. The arm itself is pivoted at the center enabling it to be rotated to any angle. The subject's head is supported on a chin rest. One eye is covered; the eye under examination is placed at the center of the sphere of which the perimeter arm forms the arc, and made to fix a point straight ahead in the center of the arm. The latter is rotated by degrees through a full circle and at each new position the test object is moved centrally until it is just perceived by the subject. This point and corresponding points at the various positions of the arm are marked upon a perimeter chart and the contour of the visual field outlined through them. The chart (fig. 16.5) is ruled in circles (comparable to latitudes on a geographical map) to indicate degrees from the point of fixation, and in radiating lines ("longitudes" or meridians). The mapping of the blind spot and of the sensitivity of the retina in isopters has been referred to. The reader should consult texts on ophthalmology for a more detailed description of perimetry. A simple but rough method of perimetry (*confrontation method*) which will reveal a major limitation of the visual fields is the following. The observer stands facing the subject and about two feet in front of him. One eye of the patient is covered while the other, which he fixes upon the opposite eye of the examiner, is being tested. The examiner holds his finger midway between himself and the patient but outside the limit of his own visual field and then brings it slowly toward the midline. The observer compares the position at which he first sights his finger with that at which

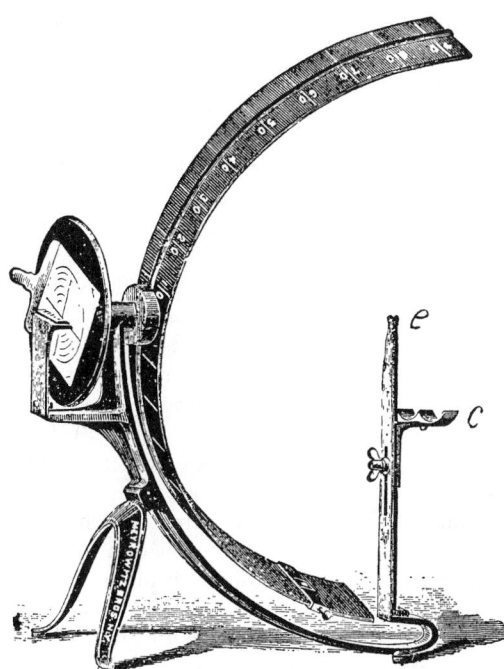

FIG. 16.4. Perimeter; *e*, position of the patient's eye; *c*, chin-rest; further description in the text.

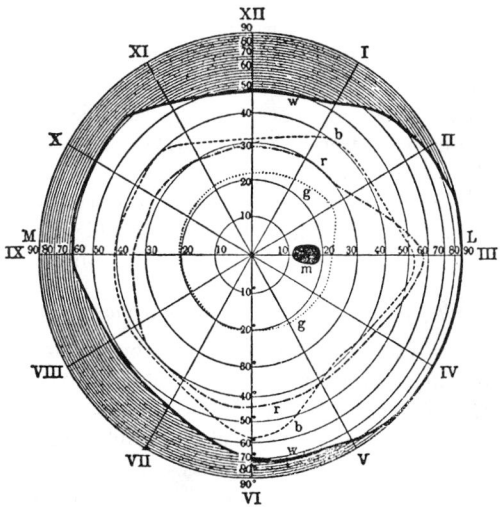

FIG. 16.5. Perimeter chart showing normal visual field of right eye. *M*, blind spot; *g*, *r*, *b* and *w* indicate boundaries of fields for green, red, blue and white, respectively. Meridians indicated by Roman numerals. (After Starling.)

it is first seen by the patient. The procedure is repeated from various directions, above, below and from either side.

The Visual Pathway

The optic nerve. The ganglion cells of the retina (ganglion cell layer) whose central processes con-

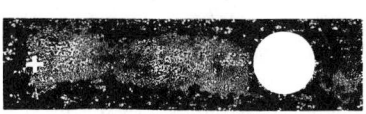 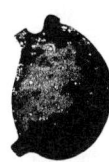

FIG. 16.3. The blind spot. Close the left eye, hold the figure about 6 inches in front of the right eye and look steadily at the cross. Move the book slowly toward the eye until the circle disappears. When this occurs the image of the circle has fallen upon the entrance of the optic nerve from which rods and cones are absent; it is therefore insensitive to light. Figure on the right shows the blind spot projected 6 inches in front of the right eye as mapped out by means of perimetry. (After Helmholtz.)

stitute the optic nerve, are the secondary neurons of the visual pathway (ch. 13). The primary neurons are the bipolar cells of the inner nuclear layer, the peripheral processes of the latter connecting with the visual receptors—the rods and cones. Tertiary neurons complete the pathway from the lateral geniculate body to the visual cortex. The fibers of the ganglion cells as they enter into the formation of the optic nerve are arranged in groups corresponding, in their relative positions, to the quadrants of the peripheral retina from which they arise. That is, fibers from the upper and lower temporal quadrants of the retina are found in the upper lateral and lower lateral regions of the nerve, respectively (fig. 16.3). Those from the nasal quadrants are situated in the inner sections of the nerve, the fibers from the upper quadrant lying above those from the lower. In the distal part of the nerve the macular or foveal fibers are in a lateral position, being wedged between the upper and lower temporal bundles, but again, fibers from the upper half of the fovea lie above those from the lower half.[1]

The optic chiasma. The fibers from the temporal halves of the peripheral retina continue uncrossed into the corresponding optic tracts, while the fibers from the nasal halves cross in the chiasma to the optic tract of the opposite side.[2] In the chiasma the temporal fibers lie in its lateral angle. Those of upper retinal origin lie above those arising from the lower retinal quadrant. In the crossing of the nasal fibers, those from the upper quadrants lie upon the upper aspect, those from the inferior quadrants upon the under aspect of the chiasma; the macular fibers lie in between.

The Optic Tracts and Primary Optic Centers

The visual pathway from the chiasma to the primary optic center consists of compact bundles of fibers—the *optic tract*. In the optic tract, fibers from the upper quadrants of the peripheral retina tend to lie ventro-laterally, those from the lower quadrants ventro-medially. The foveal fibers lie dorso-laterally. The optic tract passes backwards

and outwards between the tuber cinereum and the anterior perforated substance to the cerebral peduncle around which it turns as a flattened band to reach the *lateral (external) geniculate body*. In this, the *primary visual center*, the great majority of the optic fibers make connection. A smaller number are continued to the *superior colliculus* (superior corpus quadrigeminum) but none of these are of foveal origin.

The projection of the retina upon the external geniculate body has been studied by Brouwer and Zeeman in monkeys. These observers produced localized lesions in the retina and examined the geniculate body histologically after time had been allowed for degeneration of the optic fibers. It was found that the retinas were not projected diffusely throughout the primary optic center, but showed localization of their different regions to definite sections. Thus the upper parts of the peripheral retinas, both nasal and temporal, of the two eyes were projected to the medial parts of the geniculate body. The lower parts of the retinas were represented in the lateral part (fig. 16.3, E). Dorsal to these regions and wedged between them was an extensive area wherein the macular fibers terminated. Binocular and monocular types of vision have separate representations. In the monkey the area which receives fibers from only one eye is very small, occupying a small rim on the ventral aspect of the primary center. In the rabbit, on the other hand, the monocular projection occupies almost the entire geniculate body, binocular vision being represented by a narrow area on the medial aspect of the geniculate body.

The cells of the lateral geniculate body with which the visual fibers synapse are disposed in six well defined laminae which have been numbered 1 to 6 from the surface inwards by Le Gros Clark. One set of three (1, 4 and 6) receive crossed fibers, i.e., fibers from the nasal half of the opposite retina. The other set (2, 3 and 5) are cell stations for the uncrossed fibers, i.e., from the temporal half of the retina of the same side.

Our knowledge of the role of the geniculate body is still nebulous. Brindley (1960) reviews the evidence and puts forward the following alternative hypotheses: "1. Its sole function is to transmit visual information from the optic nerves to the visual cortex, but in doing so it usefully either (a) discards that which is unimportant, or (b) compresses it into fewer channels, or (c) changes the code. 2. It is not solely a transmitter of visual information, but receives some afferent supply other than the optic tract. 3. It performs

---

[1] There is some evidence that centrifugal fibers may be present in the optic nerve. Granit has recently succeeded in demonstrating centrifugal effects from the mesencephalic reticular activating system in the cat's retina. These centrifugal signals may adjust the peripheral sensitivity of the retina, although much more work will be required to establish their function. (See Granit.)

[2] The proportion of the fibers which cross in the chiasma varies in different mammalian forms. In the opossum, example $\frac{4}{5}$ cross to the opposite optic tract, whereas in the ferret $\frac{2}{3}$ cross; in the rabbit also the uncrossed fibers are few in number.

no function that would not be equally well performed if the fibres of the optic tract extended, with bifurcations if necessary, to the places that in fact are supplied by the fibres of the geniculocalcarine tract."

The superior colliculi. The superior colliculi are the chief centers for visual reflexes, and constitute as well the highest visual centers in submammalian forms. In the latter they are very prominent structures; in fishes and birds they are as large or larger than the cerebral hemispheres. But in higher animals, they are much reduced in size, and in man, are relatively inconspicuous structures, their visual functions having been taken over by the cerebral cortex. The superior colliculi of mammals receive afferent impulses from (a) the retina through the *optic tracts*, (b) the *occipital cortex* (visual area) and (c) *the spinal cord* via the spinotectal tract. Their efferent connection are with the medulla and the spinal cord through the *tectobulbar* and *tectospinal tracts*.

The reflexes centered in the superior colliculi serve to correlate eye movements with the movements of the head, or with the trunk and limbs. The chief of these visual reflexes are, (a) turning the eyes in order to keep them fixed upon a stationary object when the head is turned in the opposite direction (compensatory reflexes), (b) movement of the head with the eyes so as to keep a moving object in view, and (c) movements of the limbs, neck or trunk as in avoiding a moving object or in fending off a blow threatening the eyes. Closure of the lids to protect the sight occurs simultaneously.

The optic radiation (geniculocalcarine pathway). The visual fibers after leaving the external geniculate body pass through the posterior extremity of the internal capsule, and curving forward and outward into the temporal lobe sweep backward in relation to the outer aspect of the posterior horn of the lateral ventricle to reach the *area striata* (area 17) of the occipital cortex (pp. 177 and fig. 16.6). The optic radiation also contains descending fibers which end in the superior colliculus and the external geniculate body.

The visual cortex. This comprises that part of the cortex referred to above as the area striata,[3] which forms the walls and lips of the calcarine fissure on the mesial aspect of the occipital lobe. The different retinal areas in their projections upon the cortex show definite localization. There is a point to point projection on to the striate

[3] The histology of the striate area is described in ch. 67.

area. The cortical cells, for example, are conceived as receiving individually impulses from single cones to form a pattern corresponding to that of retinal organization.[4] The homonymous halves of the peripheral retinas are represented in the anterior part of the visual area, the upper quadrants in the upper wall and lip, the lower quadrants in the lower wall and lip. In other words, the nasal half of the right retina and the temporal half of the left are projected on to the left occipital cortex—the projection of the upper quadrant in each case lying above that of the lower quadrant. Similarly, the nasal half of the left retina and the temporal half of the right are projected onto the right striate area. The macular representation occupies the posterior part of the striate area reaching backwards to the occipital pole, but it also spreads forwards to overlap the projection area of the peripheral retina (fig. 16.6). As in the case of the peripheral retina, the upper and lower parts of the macula (fovea) are projected to the upper and lower halves, respectively, of this part of the striate area. The cortical projection of the macula is possibly bilateral, i.e., represented in its entirety in both hemispheres, since the retention of macular vision in both eyes after an extensive lesion of an occipital lobe is not infrequent. Indeed sparing of macular vision has been reported after apparently complete ablation of one occipital lobe. It has been supposed by those who believe that the macula is represented bilaterally that fibers pass from the lateral geniculate body of one side through the posterior part of the corpus callosum to join the optic radiation of the opposite hemisphere. In the monkey, however, excision of one occipital lobe is followed by retrograde degeneration of *all* cells of the corresponding lateral geniculate body, which would not be the case if some of its cells sent fibers to the opposite hemisphere. In so far as man is concerned the question is unsettled.

The Effects of Lesions at Different Levels of the Visual Pathway

(1) A destructive lesion of one optic nerve will result in total blindness of the corresponding eye (fig. 16.7). Increased intracranial pressure may cause atrophy of the optic nerves and a gradual

[4] Though the existence of point to point projection of the retina upon the striate area has been definitely established, the cortical representation is not rigidly fixed and circumscribed by anatomical paths, but is capable of considerable functional adaptation and modification under changed conditions (See Hubel and Wiesel.)

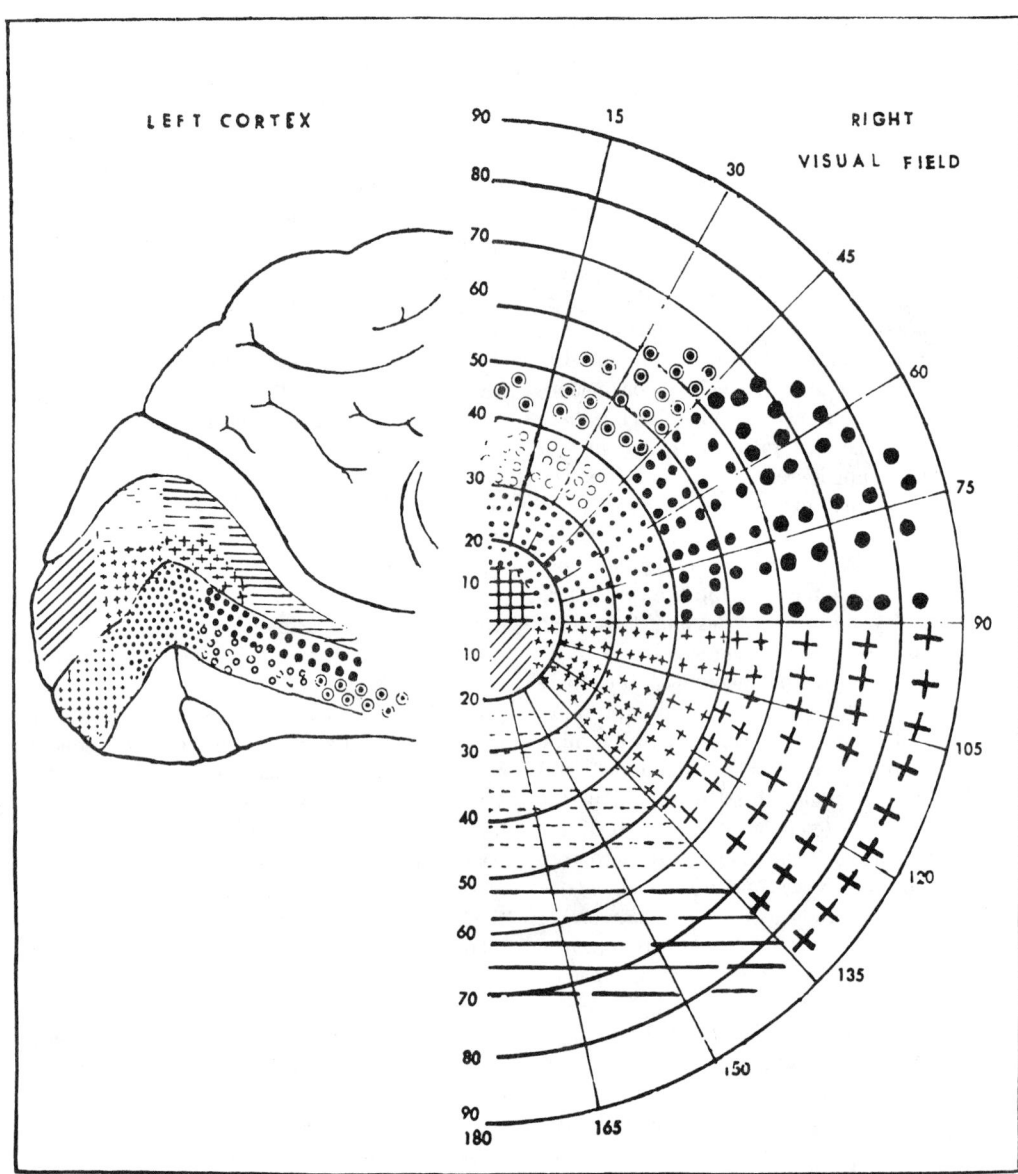

FIG. 16.6. Diagram showing the projection of the retina on the calcarine cortex. Right hand figure is temporal half of right visual field. (From Holmes, redrawn and slightly modified.)

concentric reduction of the visual fields of both eyes.

(2) A lesion involving the chiasma will result in visual defects whose nature will depend upon the fibers destroyed. (a) Pressure upon the uncrossed fibers in the outer angle of the chiasma, as by an aneurysmal dilatation of the internal carotid artery, may produce blindness in the temporal part of the retina of the same side. If these fibers on both sides are affected, the sight in the temporal half of each retina (nasal half of

the visual field) may be lost (*bi-nasal hemianopia*). According to Cushing a dilated third ventricle may, by pressing from above, force the angles of the chiasma against sclerosed internal carotid arteries and so produce a bi-nasal hemianopia. (b) Pituitary tumors, owing to their position, are likely to involve the nasal fibers at the point of their crossing and thus cause *bi-temporal hemianopia*. Since the nasal fibers from the lower retinal quadrants lie ventral to those from the upper, the lower are likely to be involved first in pituitary tumors; *superior temporal quadrantic hemianopia* will result. Lesions (e.g., tumors) pressing from above tend first to cause defects in the lower temporal quadrants of the visual fields. Dilation of the third ventricle or a tumor of the pituitary stalk may produce such an effect.

(3) Lesions of the optic tract, of the primary visual center or of the optic radiation will result in *homonymous hemianopia*. The right halves of the two eyes (left halves of the visual fields) being effected in right-sided lesions and the left halves in left-sided lesions. An abscess or tumor of the temporal lobe may, by involving the optic tract or optic radiation, cause a homonymous hemianopia. When the optic radiation is pressed upon by a temporal lobe lesion the hemianopia is very often incomplete, i.e., quadrantic. The ventral fibers of the radiation are likely to be implicated by a tumor in the lower part of the lobe, and a superior quadrantic hemianopia result. Injury to the dorsal fibers tends to cause a defect confined at first to the lower homonymous quarters of the visual fields.

(4) *Lesions of the occipital cortex.* A lesion involving the area striata of one hemisphere or the optic radiation before their termination therein results in an homonymous hemianopia, right or left, depending upon the side of the brain affected. Quadrantic homonymous hemianopia will result when the lesion is restricted to the upper or lower part of the striate area. Owing to the large cortical area representing the macular region, or perhaps to the fact that the macula is bilaterally represented, extensive unilateral occipital lesions or excision of a large part of this area often leave acute (central) vision intact, the blindness then involving only the peripheral half of each retina. In man, bilateral destruction of the visual cortex causes total blindness.

The Pupil

Pupillary reflexes. Reflex changes in the size of the pupil occur under the following conditions: (a) Constriction or dilation occurs in response to changes in light intensity (*light reflex*). When light is thrown into the normal eye the pupil of that eye constricts promptly; this is the *direct pupillary reaction.* But the pupil of the opposite eye, though shaded, also narrows; this, the *indirect* or *consensual pupillary reaction*, is dependent upon fibers which cross to the pupillary-constrictor center of the opposite side. (b) Constriction occurs as a part of the mechanism of accommodation to

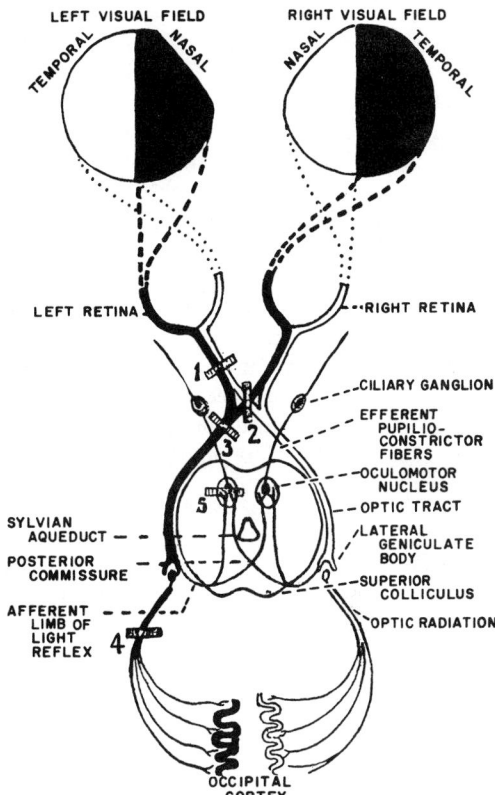

FIG. 16.7. Diagram to show the effects upon vision and pupillary reactions resulting from interruption of retinal impulses at various levels. *1,* Optic nerve; blindness of corresponding eye, direct reaction of this eye and consensual reaction of sound eye lost. Consensual reaction of blind eye and direct reaction of sound eye retained. Near reflex unaffected. *2,* Chiasma; bitemporal hemianopia. Wernicke's pupillary reaction. *3,* Optic tract; homonymous hemianopia (blindness in nasal half of right retina and temporal half of left). Wernicke's pupillary reaction. *4,* Optic radiation; homonymous hemianopia, light and near reflexes retained. *5,* At synapses in the oculomotor nucleus. Light reflex lost, near reflex retained (Argyll-Robertson pupil, see also p. 366). The lesion is usually bilateral (as in tabes, disseminated sclerosis, etc.).

near vision (*pupillary reaction of accommodation*). With it are associated convergence of the eyes and accommodation of the lens. These three reactions are appropriately grouped under the term *near reflex* or *accommodation reflex.* (c) Dilation follows stimulation of the skin of the neck (*ciliospinal reflex*). (d) Irritation of the eyelid or conjunctiva causes dilation followed by constriction of both pupils (oculo-sensory reflex). The afferent fibers of this reflex are contained in the ophthalmic division of the trigeminal nerve. (e) Closure of the eyelid, or an effort made to close the lid while it is forcibly held open causes slight pupillary constriction (lid or orbicularis reflex). (f) Pupillary dilation may occur during certain *emotional states* (e.g., fear), as a result of acute pain or a sudden sound. (e) Finally, stimulation of labyrinthine receptors causes changes in the diameter of the pupil (ch. 5). For example, rapid rotation of the body around its long axis causes dilation of the pupil and large rhythmical changes in its diameter (*hippus*). Even in a constant environment the pupil area is constantly fluctuating by about 10 per cent of its total area. These movements are called *physiological unrest*. These fluctuations are identical in amplitude and phase on both sides and, therefore, must originate central to the iris muscles.

THE IRIS

The iris is the most anterior part of the vascular tunic of the eye. It is a thin contractile disc perforated a little to the nasal side of its center by the pupil. The pupillary margin rests upon the anterior surface of the lens. The space between the lens and the cornea is divided by the iris into a larger *anterior* and smaller *posterior chamber*, the two chambers communication through the pupil. The periphery (root) of the iris is attached to the anterior surface of the ciliary body and is continuous through the pectinate ligament (p. 354) with the posterior elastic lamina of the cornea. The following five layers from before backwards compose the structure of the iris, (a) the anterior epithelium, (b) the anterior limiting membrane, (c) the stroma, (d) the posterior membrane and (e) the posterior epithelium. The *anterior epithelium* consists of a single layer of flat endothelial-like cells. Near the pupillary margin of the iris there are many small pits—the *crypts of Fuchs*—over which the epithelium is absent. The stroma is composed of loose connective tissue. It transmits the vessels and nerves and holds numerous branched cells which in dark eyes contain pigment granules. The iris contains two involuntary muscles—the sphincter pupillae and the dilator pupillae. The *sphincter pupillae* is embedded in the stroma and comprises a band of circular fibers about 1 mm. broad surrounding the pupil. When these fibers contract the pupil is constricted. The *dilator pupillae* constitutes the fourth layer of the iris, i.e., the posterior membrane, mentioned above. It consists of a thin layer of smooth muscle fibers which converge towards the pupillary margin where they blend with the fibers of the sphincter. At the root of the iris the dilator fibers pass into the ciliary body from which they take origin; when they contract they draw upon the pupillary margin and thus dilate the pupil. The *posterior epithelium*

comprises two layers of deeply pigmented cubical cells; it is the continuation anteriorly of the pars ciliaris retinae (p. 341). The arteries of the iris which are loosely coiled form two vascular circles, one near the pupillary margin—the *circulus arteriosus minor*, the other near the root of the iris— the *circulus arteriosus major*. The two circles are connected by vessels which, arising from the larger circle, converge towards the pupillary margin where they form the smaller circle.

Blue or gray eyes owe their appearance to the pigment in the posterior epithelial layer as seen through the unpigmented stroma and other layers of the iris. The pigment cells of the stroma are responsible for the color of dark eyes, the shade varying with the quantity of pigment present. In the white races nearly all newborn babies have light colored irides because pigment does not develop in the stroma until some weeks after birth.

The functions of the iris. The iris has three important functions; (a) it serves as an opaque screen, like the diaphragm or "stop" of a camera, to adjust the quantity of light reaching the retina under different intensities of illumination; (b) it prevents light from passing through the periphery of the lens and thus reduces spherical and lateral chromatic aberration. The image is thus more clearly defined by restricting the transmission of light through the central part of the lens; and (c) when the pupil constricts the depth of focus of the eye is increased (p. 345).

The visual system operates over a very wide range of illumination (10^{12} times). Over this range the pupil area only alters by a factor of 16 times and therefore, the pupil cannot maintain the retinal illumination at a constant level. The pupil light reflex probably adjusts the aperture of the eye so as to obtain the optimum visual acuity at each light level. See Fig. 16.8.

Pupillo-constrictor Pathways

It is generally believed that the receptors of the light reflex are the same as those mediating visual sensations. Alpern and Campbell (1962) have measured the response of the reflex to lights of different wavelengths. They found that a rod luminosity curve could be obtained when the stimulating beam was confined to the blindspot and thus illumination of the retina was entirely with scattered light. Conversely, a photopic cone response occurred when the stimulating light was confined to the fovea, and the rods suppressed with a blue surround. Under normal conditions a mixed rod and cone response occurs with a peak at 535 mμ. These findings confirm that both rod and cone signals can activate the light reflex.

The afferent fibers of the light reflex travel with the visual fibers and with the afferent fibers of the dilator response as far as the lateral geniculate bodies. Here they part company from the latter two sets of fibers. They do not enter the lateral geniculate body, but pass into the brachium of the superior colliculus. They then proceed to a group of cells in the pretectal region—*the pretectal nucleus*—where they make their first synaptic contacts. The impulses are finally conveyed by secondary neurons to the oculomotor nucleus on both sides of the brain, but mostly to that of the opposite side. The superior colliculus itself is not interposed in their path, for Ranson and Magoun did not observe pupillary constriction when this part was stimulated. The partial decussation of the afferent fibers, occurs, Ranson and Magoun believe, in the posterior commissure. An earlier crossing of some fibers occurs also in the optic chiasma. The fibers to the same side pass caudally and ventrally along the side of the central gray matter. Though under ordinary circumstances reduction in the tone of the pupillo-dilator center occurs reciprocally with activation of the pupillo-constrictor center, the light reflex can be carried out through the latter alone. The reflex is therefore retained after section of the cervical sympathetic (which conveys the dilator fibers). Since the afferent fibers mediating the light reflex separate from the visual pathway at the level of the lateral geniculate body, lesions of the optic pathway beyond this point do not interfere with the light reflex.

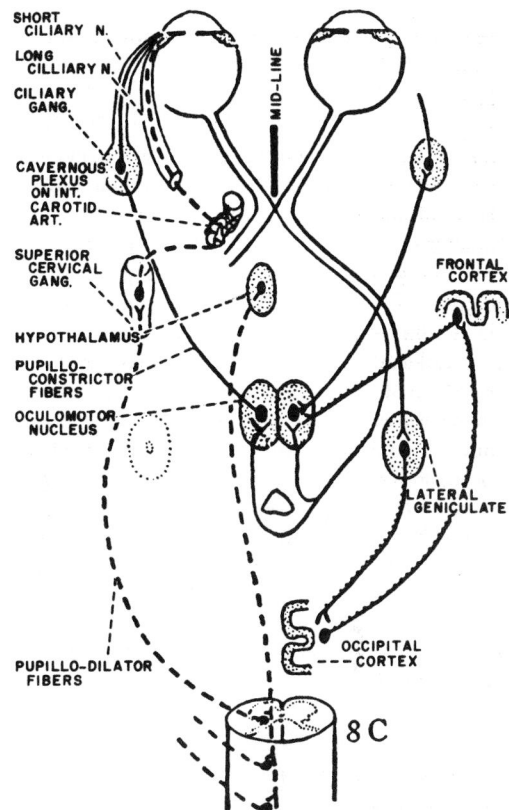

FIG. 16.9. Diagram to illustrate pupillary reflexes. Interrupted lines indicate the dilator reflex, plain lines the constrictor reflex and visual pathway to the level of the lateral geniculate body; hatched lines show path of near reflex from lateral geniculate body to the cortex and nucleus of the third nerve.

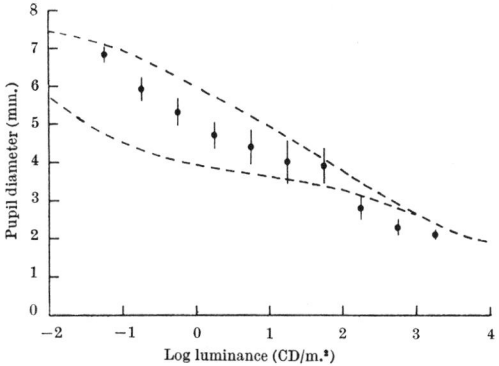

FIG. 16.8. Broken lines indicate natural pupil size as determined by Reeves (upper curve) and Crawford (lower line) at various levels of ambient luminance in adapted subjects. Points represent the pupil size giving the optimum visual acuity at each luminance. Each point is the mean of 4 subjects. Vertical lines indicate the standard error of the mean. (From Campbell and Gregory, Nature, **187**, 1121, 1960).

The *efferent* fibers subserving the light reflex belong to the parasympathetic division of the autonomic nervous system. They originate in the oculomotor nucleus (probably the Edinger-Westphal nucleus) and are conveyed to the iris (sphincter pupillae) via the third nerve, ciliary ganglion and short ciliary nerves (fig. 16.9). The *near reflex* is dependent upon cortical centers. Impulses pass by association fibers from the occipital to the frontal cortex (frontal eye field) and thence via the internal capsule to the nucleus of the third nerve. Constriction of the pupil which accompanies accommodation of the lens is brought about through fibers which probably pass directly to the pretectal region from the occipital cortex adjacent to the visual area. The efferent path from the oculomotor nucleus is the same as that for the light reflex. The afferent pathway is via the visual fibers, i.e., lateral geniculate body and optic radiation, not through the superior colliculus. The reflex is bilateral, i.e., it occurs in both eyes when one is covered and the other directed to a near object.

The Pupillo-dilator Pathway[5]

The dilator muscle of the pupil receives sympathetic fibers which arise from the first and second thoracic segments of the spinal cord, and sometimes from the eighth cervical or the third thoracic. They issue by the white rami and pass via the cervical sympathetic to the superior cervical ganglion. From here postganglionic fibers are conveyed along the internal carotid artery into the cranial cavity. Entering the trunk of the nasociliary branch of the first division of the fifth nerve, they are transmitted to the iris in the long ciliary nerves. Some fibers also pass without interruption through the ciliary ganglion into the short ciliary nerves. These fibers supply in addition the smooth muscle of the orbit which lies in relation to the capsule of Tenon (fascia bulbi) and in the "check ligaments" of the ocular muscles. The smooth muscle forming the deep layer of the levator palpebrae superioris also receives innervation from the sympathetic.

The *afferent* pathway of the pupillo-dilator reflex accompanies the pupillo-constrictor fibers as far as the lateral geniculate body. From here on their course has not been clearly defined, but they presumably descend through the tegmentum of the midbrain, and the reticular formation of the pons, medulla and spinal cord to reach the ciliospinal center.

A higher pupillo-dilator center is situated in the hypothalamus, which, in turn, is probably connected with the cortex of the frontal lobe. It sends fibers through the midbrain which, according to the researches of Beattie, pass ventrally by the posterior commissure to enter the superior colliculus.

The pupillo-dilator reflex involves reciprocal inhibition of pupillo-constrictor tone. This is the paramount factor in the dilator reflex, for after section of the sympathetic pupillary fibers, the pupil dilates in the dark, or in response to a painful stimulus or emotional excitement, in an almost normal fashion. Another factor in the dilation of the pupil by sympathetic stimulation may be the constriction of the vessels of the iris.

When the sympathetic fibers are paralyzed the pupil is narrowed as a result of the unbalanced action of the constrictor fibers, and the dilation

[5] Loewenfeld, I. E. (1958) *Docum. ophthal.*, **12**, 185–448, should be consulted for a comprehensive review and experimental analysis of the mechanisms of reflex dilatation of the pupil.

of the pupil which normally follows the application of a stimulus, such as a scratch or pinch, to the skin of the neck (ciliospinal reflex) fails to occur. The pupil, however, still reacts to light. Drooping of the upper lid (ptosis) will result from paralysis of the smooth muscle of the levator palpebrae superioris and there may be recession of the eyeball (enophthalmos) from paralysis of the unstriped muscle of the orbit.

An investigation of the pupillary reactions may give valuable information concerning the site of a lesion in the brain (see fig. 16.7, p. 363). (a) A lesion destroying one optic nerve, since it interrupts the afferent pathway but leaves the efferent intact, abolishes the direct but not the indirect (consensual) reaction on the blind side. The direct reaction on the sound side is, of course, retained but the indirect is lost. That is to say, a light thrown into the sound eye causes a response in this eye as well as in the blind eye, but a light thrown into the blind eye is without effect upon either eye. The near (accommodation) reflex is not abolished. Blindness due to destruction of both optic nerves results in the loss of the reflexes for light as well as of those for accommodation. (b) Hemianopia due to a lesion of the chiasma, or of the optic tract, results in the loss of both the direct and indirect reactions to light thrown upon the blind half of either retina. Light falling upon the sound halves of the retinas causes the normal response. This is known as *Wernicke's hemianopic pupillary reaction*. However, owing to the difficulty of confining a beam of light to the blind half of the retina it is not an easy matter to demonstrate this reaction. (c) Loss of the light reflex (both direct and indirect reactions) with retention or even exaggeration of the accommodation-convergence reflex is known as the Argyll-Robertson pupil. The pupil is also, as a rule, smaller than normal (myosis) and does not dilate to a painful stimulus nor fully to atropinization; the vestibular reflex is frequently absent as well. The abnormal pupillary responses occur quite apart from any defect of vision. Though usually bilateral the Argyll-Robertson pupil is sometimes confined to one side. It is most commonly seen in syphilitic degeneration of the central nervous system (e.g., tabes), but occurs occasionally in other conditions as well. The site of the lesion responsible for the Argyll-Robertson pupil is not known precisely. Merritt and Moore give evidence for placing it in the region of the posterior commissure where presumably, the neighboring dilator pathway is also interrupted, but the pathway for the accommodation reflex from the cortex to the oculomotor nucleus would be spared. Scala and Spiegel believe from the results of their experiments that the disease involves the synapses between the afferent and efferent neurons of the light reflex, that is, in the oculomotor nucleus itself. But the oculomotor nerve supplies both pupils and a lesion here is difficult to reconcile with the unilateral loss of the light reflex which sometimes occurs. Langworthy and Ortego conclude, after a careful study, that the lesion is peripheral—due to changes in the iris itself involving sympathetic, parasympathetic and sensory nerves as well as the muscle cells of the sphincter. This theory can account for the irregularity of the pupil, and perhaps, if the sympathetic innervation were injured in greater degree than the parasympathetic, for the myosis; but it cannot explain the preservation of the accommodation reflex. (d) Destruction of the oculomotor nucleus or of the efferent pathway abolishes all light and accommodation reactions on the same side. The direct and indirect reactions are retained on the contralateral side. (e) Lesions involving the visual pathway after the separation of the visual and pupillary fibers, e.g. lateral geniculate body, optic radiations or occipital cortex, leave the light reflex unaffected. (f) A bilateral lesion implicating the pathway from the cortex to the center for accommodation in the oculomotor nucleus will cause a loss of the near reflex and leave the light reflexes intact. This is the converse of the Argyll-Robertson pupil, and is sometimes seen in postdiphtheritic paralysis.

The Effects of Drugs upon the Pupil and Ciliary Muscle

Dilation of the pupil is spoken of as *mydriasis*; constriction as *myosis*. Drugs which cause pupillary dilation are therefore called *mydriatics*; those which cause constriction, *myotics*. Paralysis of the ciliary muscles is known as *cycloplegia*; drugs which cause this effect are called *cycloplegics*. Mydriasis is caused by drugs which:

(a) Paralyze the peripheral constrictor (parasympathetic) mechanism, such as atropine, or homatropine. Atropine is also cycloplegic, homatropine much less so.

(b) Stimulate the dilator (sympathetic) mechanism, e.g., adrenaline, cocaine, hydroxy-amphetamine hydrobromide. These drugs have little effect upon accommodation.

Miosis is caused by drugs which:

(a) Stimulate the peripheral constrictor mechanism, e.g., pilocarpine, physostigmine, muscarine. Di-iso-fluorophosphate is a powerful anticholinesterase and produces miosis in small doses. These drugs also causes spasm of the ciliary muscles.

(b) Diminish the inhibition of the constrictor center, e.g., morphine. The action of this drug upon the pupil depends largely upon the intensity of the illumination. It appears, therefore, to exert its effect, mainly, by increasing the sensitivity of the light reflex.

(c) Stimulate the constrictor center, e.g., picrotoxin.

CORRESPONDING RETINAL POINTS

When the gaze is directed to an object, an image is formed by each eye and impulses are conveyed to both sides of the brain, yet perfect fusion of the two images occurs in consciousness and only one image is seen. This characteristic of *binocular vision* is explained upon the theory of *corresponding retinal points*. The corresponding points in the retinas (foveas) which when stimulated simultaneously cause a single visual sensation, lie in the nasal half of one retina and the temporal half of the other. When the eyes are converged, the retinas are turned so that the images fall upon these corresponding parts. If, as a result of unequal action of the ocular muscles, this cannot be brought about, the separate images are not fused in consciousness and an object appears double. This abnormality of vision is known as *diplopia*.

The horopter. When the eyes are fixed upon a point in space, a number of other points can be located by calculation which are projected upon corresponding points of the two retinas (foveas). A line joining such points forms a circle called the *horopter* which passes through the fixation point and the nodal points of the eyes. The horopter will vary of course with the point of fixation of the eyes and does not exist unless the eyes act synergically (see fig. 16.10). Points in the visual field lying outside the horopter do not fall on the

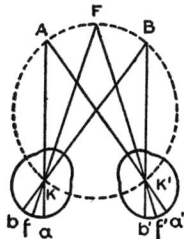

FIG. 16.10. The horopter (Müller). *F* is the fixation point. The images of *A*, *F*, and *B* fall upon the retinae at corresponding points as *aa'*, *ff'*, and *bb'*. The projection of all such corresponding points lies upon the circumference of the dotted circle. It is obvious that there is a different horopter for each position of *F*. (After Duke-Elder, *Text Book of Ophthalmology*.)

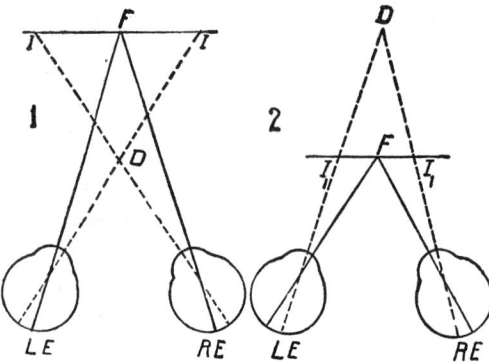

FIG. 16.11. Illustrating the projection of retinal images that fall upon noncorresponding retinal points, i.e., on different sides of the foveae—physiological diplopia. I, heteronymous diplopia (crossed); homonymous (uncrossed) diplopia; D, positions of object in relation to the fixation point. The images, I, I and I_1, I_1 are projected to the plane of the object F upon which the eyes are fixed; LE, left eye; RE, right eye.

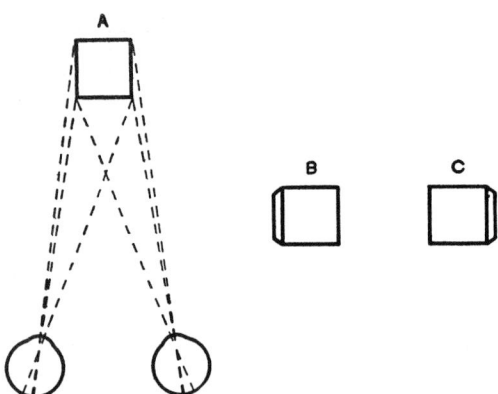

FIG. 16.12. Examples of aspect disparity. *A* is a view, seen from above, of lines of sight when the eyes look at a solid object. Notice that the right eye sees some of the right hand side of the object, while the left eye sees some of the left hand side. *B* is a front view of a cube seen by the left eye with the right eye closed. *C* is a front view seen by the right eye with the left eye closed. When both eyes are open, we see a fusion of *B* and *C*. (After Graham.)

corresponding points in the two retinas (peripheral retinas) and, as a consequence, actually cause a double impression. But this *physiological diplopia* as it is called does not thrust itself upon consciousness; it is suppressed or ignored and therefore does not cause confusion. Yet one can easily demonstrate for oneself that it exists. For example, when the eyes are fixated upon a near object, such as a pencil tip held close to the face, a more distant object may, through a conscious effort, be observed in duplicate. For this reason, it

is also sometimes referred to as *introspective diplopia*.

The double image is always projected to the plane of the object upon which the eyes are fixed, and the doubling of the image is either homonymous (uncrossed) or heteronymous (crossed) depending upon whether the object which produces the double image is beyond the point of fixation or between it and the eyes. That is to say, when the object (D in fig. 16.11) whose images fall on noncorresponding retinal points is closer to the eyes than the object upon which the eyes are fixed, the images, I and I, are projected across the lines of sight, the right hand image being formed by the left eye and the left hand image by the right eye. When the object is beyond the plane of fixation the projection of the images (I_1 and I_1) is homonymous, each being formed by the corresponding eye. The reader may demonstrate these facts for himself. When a pencil is held close to the eyes so as to form a double image while the eyes are focussed upon a more distant object, closing the right eye causes the left hand image to disappear, whereas, if the eyes are focussed upon the pencil and the object giving rise to the double image is more distant, closure of the right eye abolishes the right hand image. Closure of the left eye, of course, produces converse effects.

Depth Perception-Stereoscopic Vision (Gr. Stereos, Solid; Skopeo, I View)

Our visual judgment of solidity, that is, our recognition that the object has depth as well as height and width, is due largely to the fact that vision is normally binocular and corresponding points in the two retinas receive slightly dissimilar images of any given object. If the reader will look at some object in front of him, first closing one eye and then the other, he will find that the view seen by the right eye is slightly different from that seen by the left (fig. 16.12). The right eye is able to see more of the right side of the object, the left eye more of the left side. The two slightly disparate images are fused in the brain, yet the composite image has hidden within it something of each separate one; upon this the stereoscopic effect to a large extent depends.

In order for two dissimilar images to be fused in consciousness, it is not necessary that they fall upon retinal points which correspond exactly; unification of the images results though there is some degree of noncorrespondence. Actually, there is a greater impression of depth when the

A

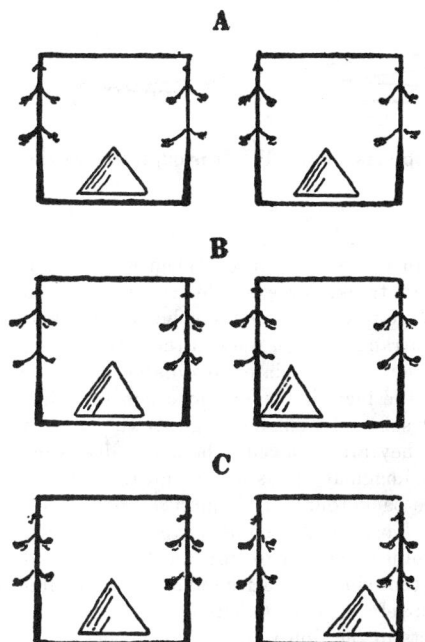

B

C

FIG. 16.13. Diagram of a tent and pine trees to show the impression of depth caused by the fusion of two dissimilar images. If the figures be gazed at steadily at a distance of about 5 inches from the eyes and a card held edgewise from the tip of the nose to the line of letters each horizontal pair of figures can, with a little practice be made to fuse. In *A* the aspect of the two scenes is practiaclly the same and the fused picture appears quite flat. In *B*, the tent in the right hand figure is placed more toward the midline and upon fusion appears to be in front of the pines. In *C*, the disparity of the right hand figure is farther from the midline; the tent is now projected to a point behind the pines.

dissimilar images do not fall on retinal points which fail to correspond perfectly, provided that the discrepancy is not so great as to prevent fusion. In figure 16.13 a scene of a tent and pine trees is represented diagrammatically. When the two scenes are fused the tent is projected closer or farther from the eyes according to its position in the two pictures in lateral relation to the pines. When in one or in both pictures it is moved toward the mid-line it appears to advance in front of the pine trees; when moved laterally it seems to recede. The three dimensional effect is enhanced by increasing the noncorrespondence, as when the tent in one or both pictures is moved, to or away from the mid-line. But if moved too far the noncorrespondence is too great to permit fusion to occur, and the stereoscopic effect is lost.

The instrument known as a stereoscope produces an illusion of solidity by making use of the principle of simultaneous stimulation of the ret-

inas by dissimilar images. A photograph taken with an ordinary camera appears flat because identical images are formed upon the retinas. A stereoscopic photograph, on the other hand, is taken by a camera provided with two lenses which are set, like the eyes, a short distance apart in the horizontal plane. Thus, an illusion of depth is produced. Two slightly dissimilar views are taken which, when looked at through the stereoscope, are projected by means of prisms, one to each eye, so as to fall on corresponding retinal points (fig. 16.14).

The ability to detect a small difference in distance from the eyes of two objects, and so to appreciate depth and solidity, is called *stereoscopic acuity*. It is expressed as the least difference

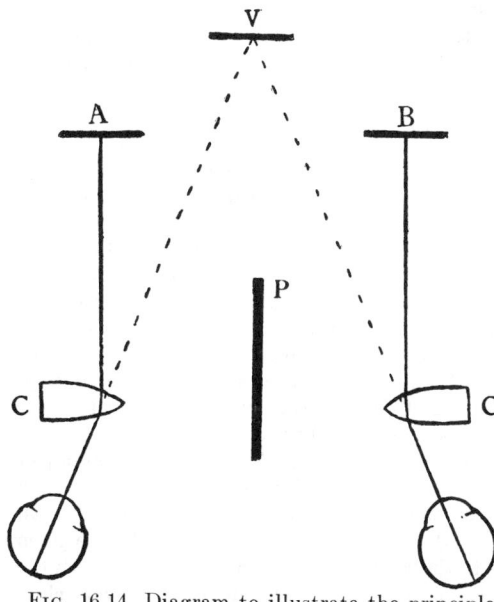

FIG. 16.14. Diagram to illustrate the principle of the stereoscope (Brewster's). *A* and *B* represent photographs of two scenes, slightly dissimilar because they were taken from different positions. *C*, curved prisms; *p*, partition to prevent one eye seeing the picture opposite the other eye; *LE*, left eye; *RE*, right eye. When the two pictures are viewed through the instrument, they are fused perfectly into one of apparently three dimensions, points in the background of which seem to be situated at V.

A similar stereoscopic effect is produced when two scenes are printed each in a different color, e.g., red and blue, and imperfectly superimposed so their outlines overlap. If they are viewed in the ordinary way, they appear as a flat jumbled picture, but if a red glass be held in front of one eye and a blue glass in front of the other, so as to sort out the separate scenes, one to each eye, a clear black and white view is seen in three dimensions. In the modern stereoscopic cinema it is usual to separate the two scenes by using polarized light beams set at right angles to each other, thus allowing color films to be shown stereoscopically.

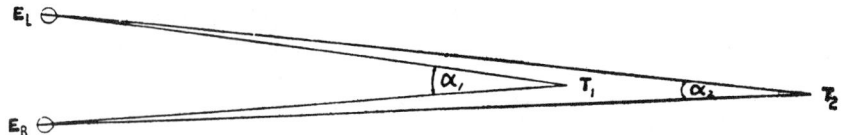

FIG. 16.15. Stereoscopic parallax in the viewing of two objects T_1 and T_2. It is expressed as the difference between the angles α_1 and α_2.

between the angles formed by the lines of sight to two objects when one is just perceived to be farther away than the other (fig. 16.15). The difference in angles is known as *stereoscopic parallax*, and may, in a person with very high visual acuity, be as little as 2 seconds of arc.

Assuming the distance separating the two pupils is 65 mm., this would allow stereoscopic perception up to about 400 yd. under ideal conditions.

Other factors, listed below, do not depend upon binocular vision, but play an important part in depth perception through one eye alone (monocular vision).

(1) *The apparent size of various objects in our field of vision.* We know from experience the approximate dimensions of the objects which we see, but the image which an object casts upon the fovea diminishes as its distance increases (p. 318). For example, a church steeple at a distance casts an image upon the retina no larger, perhaps smaller, then would a pencil held a few inches from the eyes. We know the relative sizes of the two objects, and therefore infer that the steeple must be far away and the pencil near.

(2) *Accommodation of the eye.* Since a near object requires a greater effort of accommodation than does a more distant one for its image to be focussed upon the retina, some clue may possibly be given as to the relative distance of two objects from the eyes. This factor is only important at very close distances.

(3) *The apparent change in color of an object with distance.* The atmosphere is not perfectly transparent or equally so for all wave lengths. Tree-clad hills, which we know to be green, appear bluish in the distance; the colors of many other objects appear to fade with distance, their detail and outline being dimmed by haze. On rare occasions the atmosphere may be particularly clear and then distant hills, etc., will appear to be unnaturally near.

(4) *The blocking out of parts of a distant view by objects between it and the eyes* gives a sensation of depth, for the overlapping of parts of farther objects by nearer ones gives an indication of their relative from the eyes.

(5) *Linear perspective.* Straight lines running into the distance which are actually parallel (or

objects along imaginary straight lines) are convergent in the retinal image. When we look down a railway track, for example, the rails appear to converge towards some point beyond the horizon. This arrangement of lines in the retinal image we have come to associate with distance. It depends upon the fact that points at a constant distance apart subtend a smaller angle at the eye the farther they are removed. The artist draws objects along imaginary lines which run towards a point in the background of his picture.

(6) *Parallax.* When one moves in any direction, near objects appear to move in the opposite direction, those in the background in the same direction as ourselves. This apparent movement of near objects in relation to ones farther away is called parallax.

(7) *The distribution of light and shade over the surface of an object and the shadow which it casts upon its surroundings is* also an important factor in the judgment of distance.

Normally, the images formed by the two eyes are very nearly equal in size, varying by less than one per cent. When they differ in size to a degree which prevents perfect fusion with a consequent impairment of binocular vision the condition is spoken of as *aniseikonia*. Little interference with binocular vision results unless the inequality of the images is more than 4 or 5 per cent.

Ocular Movements

The Innervation of the Ocular Muscles

The nerves supplying the extrinsic muscles of the eye are the third (oculomotor), fourth (trochlear) and the sixth (abducent). The oculomotor nerve supplies all the extrinsic muscles of the eyeball except the superior oblique and the external rectus. It also supplies the striated portion of the levator palpebrae superioris and conveys parasympathetic fibers to the sphincter pupillae (p. 364) and ciliary muscle. The deep smooth muscle component of the elevator of the lid is innervated by the sympathetic.

THE NUCLEUS OF THE THIRD NERVE is situated in the floor of the Sylvian (cerebral) aqueduct and subjacent to the superior colliculus. It is in close relation to the medial longitudinal fasciculus. It is composed of a group of five smaller nuclei (fig. 16.16).

(a) The *central nucleus* (Perlia's nucleus) fuses with its fellow of the opposite side to form a single gray mass in the mid-line. It is probably the center for convergence of the eyes (internal recti). (b) The *caudal central nucleus* lies in line with and behind the former. It also fuses with its fellow of the opposite side. Functionally it is considered a part of the central nucleus and is shown by Brouwer and others as actually continuous with the latter. (c) The *dorsi-lateral nucleus*. It and the next two nuclei are paired. The dorsilateral nucleus is probably the center for upward movements of the eyes (superior rectus and inferior oblique muscles). The *striped* muscle of the levator palpebrae superioris also, it is believed, receives its innervation from this nucleus. (d) The *ventrimedial nucleus*, lying medial, ventral and caudad to the preceding is thought to be concerned with downward movements (inferior rectus). (e) The *Edinger-Westphal* nucleus lies on each side dorsal and lateral to the central nucleus. It is believed to supply fibers to the sphincter pupillae and ciliary muscle.

The axons arising from these cell groups pass for the most part into the nerve of the same side. A few fibers supplying the internal and inferior recti and inferior oblique muscles decussate with those of the opposite side.

The fibers after issuing from the oculomotor nucleus form a well-defined tract (tract of the oculomotor nerve) which runs downwards and forwards through the tegmentum, traversing the red nucleus and medial portion of the substantia nigra. They emerge from the medial aspect of the cerebral peduncle.

THE NUCLEUS OF THE TROCHLEAR NERVE lies in the floor of the cerebral aqueduct adjacent to the posterior end of the ventri-medial nucleus of the oculomotor nerve, and on a level with the inferior colliculus. It supplies the superior oblique, and with the ventri-medial part of the oculomotor nucleus, forms a center for downward movements of the eye. The fibers arising from the trochlear nucleus differ from those of any other cranial nerve in that the great majority decussate with those of the opposite side. After leaving the nucleus the fibers curve dorsally around the central gray mass surrounding the aqueduct to reach the anterior medullary velum in which the decussation occurs. They emerge from the dorsal surface of the anterior medullary velum on one side of its frenulum and immediately behind the inferior colliculus.

THE ABDUCENT NUCLEUS furnishes fibers to the external rectus. It lies in the pons close to the median line and subjacent to the upper part of the floor of the fourth ventricle. Its fibers pass downwards and forwards through the pons to emerge without crossing at the latter's lower border. The fibers of the facial nerve loop around the abducent nucleus (ch. 6).

The nuclei of the three ocular nerves receive

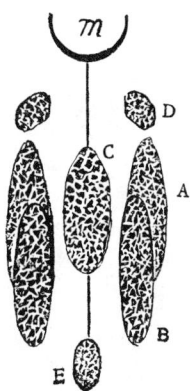

FIG. 16.16. A scheme of the various groups of cells which together constitute the nucleus of the oculomotor nerve. *A*, the dorsilateral nucleus; *B*, the ventrimedial nucleus; *C*, the central nucleus; *D*, the Edinger-Westphal nucleus; *E*, the caudal central nucleus; *m*, the third ventricle. (From Gray, *Anatomy of the Human Body*, after le Gros Clark, redrawn.)

fibers from: (a) the pyramidal tract of the opposite side, (b) the medial longitudinal fasciculus through which the three nuclei are connected with one another, with the vestibular nucleus, with the spinal cord and probably with the facial nucleus. It has been suggested that fibers from the oculomotor nucleus may enter the latter nucleus and be then conveyed in the facial to the orbicularis oculi and the corrugator supercilii, (c) tectobulbar tract which relays to the three nuclei, impulses entering the superior colliculus from the optic tract and the visual cortex.

The eyes are said to be in a *position of rest* or in their *primary position* when their direction is maintained simply by the tone of the ocular muscles, that is, when the gaze is straight ahead and far away and not directed to any particular point in space. The visual axes are then parallel. When the eyes view some definite object they are turned by the contraction of the ocular muscles and converged so that the visual axes meet at the observed object and an image of the object falls upon a corresponding point on each fovea (p. 367). The closer the object to the eye the greater the degree of convergence (p. 345). This movement of the eyes for the acute observation of an object is called *fixation*. The point where the visual axes meet is called the *fixation point* and the lines joining the latter to the fovea, i.e., the visual axes, are sometimes called the *fixation lines*. The widest limits of vision in all directions within which eyes can fixate is called the *field of fixation*. When surveyed by means of the perimeter it is found to be nearly circular with a diameter of

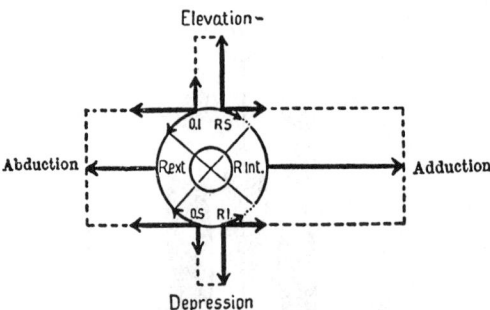

FIG. 16.17. Diagram of right eye from the front to illustrate the actions of the ocular muscles. O.I., inferior oblique; *RS*, superior rectus; *R ext*, external rectus; *R int*, internal rectus; *O.S.*, superior oblique; *RI*, inferior rectus. (From Fuchs after Marquez.)

about 100°. Its boundaries therefore lie well within the limits of the binocular visual field (p. 357).

The eyeball is rotated in its socket (formed by the fascia bulbi) by the ocular muscles around one or other of three *primary axes* which intersect one another at right angles near the center of the globe. One axis is vertical, around it lateral movements (adduction and abduction) take place, i.e., in the horizontal plane. Another runs from before backwards and coincides with the visual axis; movements in the frontal plane (torsion or wheel movements) take place around it. The third is transverse, it is the axis of rotation for upward and downward movements, i.e., movements in the sagittal plane. Though the movements of the eyeball are essentially and for practical purposes rotary in character, a very slight translatory movement may take place as a result of movements of the lids and variations in the width of the palpebral fissure, closure and opening of the lids causing a displacement backward and outward, and forward and inward, respectively. A slight displacement at right angles to the rotary movement also takes place during contractions of the ocular muscles, the eyeball therefore executing what has been described by Berlin as a screw movement. Also for this reason the center of rotation of the eyeball is not an absolutely fixed point but varies slightly. For general purposes, however, it may be taken as the point of intersection of the primary axes. This point is on the visual axis about 13 mm. from the anterior surface of the cornea.

In table 16.1 the actions of the individual ocular muscles are given, but no normal movement is carried out by one of these muscles alone. Thus, when the eye is abducted, the external rectus and the two obliques act in unison to turn the eye

outwards. The depressor and elevator components in the actions of the respective oblique muscles cancel one another. Similarly, adduction is effected by contraction of the internal rectus acting with the superior and inferior recti. Again, the depressor and elevating actions of the latter two muscles neutralize one another. In looking upwards the eye is elevated by the combined action of the superior rectus and the inferior oblique. In looking downwards the inferior rectus and the superior oblique act together, the subsidiary action of the inferior rectus in turning the eye inwards being offset by the opposite action of the superior oblique. This compound action of the ocular muscles makes for smooth and steady movement and rapid fixation of the eyeball. It will be seen from figure 16.17 that the obliques and the superior and inferior recti when contracting individually produce a rotary or wheellike movement, outward (extortion) or inward (intortion). When acting in pairs the rotary actions being in opposite directions antagonize one another so that normally no such movement occurs.

The actions of the eye muscles follow the principle of reciprocal innervation. Thus, when the eye is turned outwards the external rectus and the two obliques contract while their antagonists (inferior, external and superior recti) are inhibited. The two eyes act in unison, both turning in the same direction—*conjugate deviation*—and reciprocal innervation is extended to include muscle groups in the two eyes, thus indicating their control from a single center. Thus, stimulation of the posterior part of the second frontal convolution causes conjugate deviation of the eyes to the opposite side. This involves contraction of the abductors and inhibition of the adductors of one eye and converse actions in the opposite eye (i.e. inhibition of the abductors accompanied by contraction of the adductors). Destruction of the cortical area results in the loss of the conjugate movement without paralysis of the individual muscles. The act of *convergence*, in which both eyes are adducted, is due to the conjoint contraction of the internal recti. The center for this movement is probably in the central nucleus of the oculomotor nerve. A higher center for the movement is also situated in the frontal cortex.

The effects upon the eye movements of paralysis or weakness (paresis) of the ocular muscles. (a) *Limitation of movement* of the eye in the direction of the normal action of the affected muscle. (b) *Paralytic strabismus or squint.* When an effort is made to turn the eyes in the direction of the paralyzed muscle, the affected eye remains stationary or makes a smaller movement than does the sound eye. That is, it deviates in relation to

TABLE 16.1

Muscle		Movement	Innervation	Diplopia due to Ocular Paralysis Position of False Image in Relation to True when Right Eye Affected (Applicable to Left Eye if Right be Changed to Left and Vice Versa)
Rectus	Superior	*Elevation* (10), adduction (Inf. R, Int. R) intortion (SO)	Oculomotor	Above, to left of and tilted away from true image (crossed diplopia)
	Inferior	*Depression* (SO), adduction (Int. R, SO) extortion (SO)	Oculomotor	Below, to left and tilted towards true image (crossed diplopia)
	Internal	*Adduction*	Oculomotor	Level with, parallel to and on the left of true image (crossed diplopia)
	External	*Adduction*	Abducens	Level with, parallel to and on the right of true image
Oblique	Inferior	*Extortion* (IR), elevation (SR), abduction (Ext. R, SO)	Oculomotor	Above, to right of and tilted away from true image
	Superior	*Intortion* (SR), depression (Inf. R), abduction (Ext. R, SO)	Trochlear	Below, to right of and tilted towards true image
Levator palp. sup.		Elevator of eyelid antagonizes the action of the palpebral part of the orbicularis oculi	Oculomotor	

the latter in a direction opposite to that of the normal action of the paralyzed muscle. The visual axes, therefore, do not bear their normal relationship to one another. This is called the *primary deviation*. If a screen is placed in front of the sound eye while an attempt is made to fixate the affected eye upon an object situated towards the side of the paralyzed muscle, the sound eye deviates in the direction of action of the latter. This *secondary deviation*, as it is termed, is greater that the primary deviation of the paralyzed eye. The greater deviation of the sound eye is attributed to the unusual effort exerted in the attempt to fixate the paralyzed eye, an unnecessarily strong motor discharge being transmitted simultaneously to the muscle of the sound eye which normally acts conjointly (conjugate deviation) with the paralyzed muscle.

(c) *Diplopia; false projection of the visual field.* If, as a result of weakness or paralysis of the muscles of one eye, or of an imbalance from whatever cause between the actions of the ocular muscles of the two eyes, the images do not fall upon corresponding retinal points, *diplopia* or *double vision* results. The image seen by the sound eye is called the *true image*, that seen by the affected eye is called the *false image*. The false image lies to one side, above or below the true image, depending upon the ocular muscle which is paralyzed. In the case of the oblique muscles and the superior and inferior recti, the false image lies above or below the true image—a little to one or other side and tilted towards or away from it (see table 16.1). The false image is always

displaced in the direction of the normal action of the paralyzed muscle. Thus, in paralysis of the right external rectus the right eye is not turned outwards when the subject attempts to look at an object towards his right side. The image of the object falls upon the temporal half of the left macula and is therefore projected into the nasal half of the visual field of that eye. But, in the affected eye the image falls upon the nasal half of the retina and is therefore projected into the temporal half of the right visual field. The image seen by the right eye (false image) therefore lies to the right of that seen by the left (true image). When the false image is on the same side of the true image as the affected eye the diplopia is said to be *simple* or *uncrossed;* if it lies on the opposite side of the true image the diplopia is said to be *crossed.*

If strabismus is congenital or of long standing, diplopia is not, as a rule, experienced. This is because though the images do not fall on anatomically symmetrical corresponding points in the two eyes, an area is developed in the peripheral retina of the squinting eye which assumes the function of a fovea. This pseudofovea or false macula, as it has been called, corresponds physiologically to the fovea of the sound eye. Fusion of the two images occurs and stereoscopic vision suffers little if at all. When squint of long standing is corrected surgically to bring the visual axes parallel, diplopia results since the true fovea of the corrected eye does not correspond functionally with fovea of the normal eye.

REFERENCES

ALPERN, M. AND CAMPBELL, F. W., J. Physiol., 1962, **164,** 478.

BEATTIE, J. J. Anat., 1932, **66,** 283.

BIELSCHOWSKY, A. Am. J. Ophth., 1938, **21,** 843.

BROUWER, B. AND ZEEMAN, W. P. C. Brain, 1926, **49,** 1.

CLARK, W. E. LE G. J. Anat., 1941, **75,** 225; Nature, 1947, **160,** 124.

CUSHING, H. Brain, 1921, **44,** 341.

CUSHING, H. AND WALKER, G. B. Arch. Ophth. 1912, **41,** 559.

GRAHAM, C. H. Proc. Fed. Am. Soc. Exper. Biol., 1943, **2,** 115.

HOLMES, G. Proc. Roy. Soc., London. ser. B., 1945, **132,** 348.

HUBEL, D. H. AND WIESEL, T. N. J. Physiol., 1959, **148,** 574; J. Neurophysiol., 1965, **28,** 1041.

RANSON, S. W. AND MAGOUN, H. W. Arch. Neurol. & Psychiat., 1933, **30,** 1193.

MERRITT, H. H. AND MOORE, M. Arch. Neurol. & Psychiat., 1933, **30,** 357.

SCALA, N. P. AND SPIEGEL, E. A. Arch. Ophth., 1936, **15,** 195.

Monographs

BRINDLEY, G. S. Physiology of the retina and visual pathway. Edward Arnold, London, 1960.

DUKE-ELDER, W. S. Textbook of Ophthalmology, 1949, Vol. 4.

GRANIT, R. Receptors and Sensory Perception, Oxford University Press, London, 1955.

TRAQUAIR, H. M. An introduction to clinical perimetry. Kimpton, London, 1931.

The Eye, edited by H. Davson, Vols. 1–4. Academic Press, 1962.

CHAPTER 17

Hearing: Anatomy and Acoustics

The human ear, as the sense organ of hearing, is a highly differentiated and specialized mechanoreceptor, which extracts and transmits to the central nervous system information about the acoustic environment. As a *detector*, the ear is capable of recording almost incredibly minute amounts of mechanical energy in the form of vibrations of the air molecules. As an *analyzer*, it furnishes detailed information about the intensity and frequency spectrum of these air-borne vibrations and thus gives rise to the sensations of loudness, pitch, and timbre. At the same time it provides the faithful, fine-grained record of the temporal pattern of sound stimulation that is essential for the understanding of speech and the appreciation of music. Furthermore, it continuously monitors the speaker's own voice and thus helps him to maintain a standard of speech that he regards as acceptable.

In addition to its obvious value as an alerting or "early warning" mechanism, the ear has a spatial function that is of great importance for survival. Acting together, the two ears serve as a *direction finder*, providing the brain with data for localizing the source of a sound, as well as for deciding whether the sound should be attended to or may safely be ignored.

In the narrow view, the ear, like the other sense organs, may be regarded simply as a *transducer*, having the specialized function of converting the mechanical energy of sound into the form of electrochemical energy that is capable of activating the endings of the auditory nerve. How the ear accomplishes its manifold but closely related tasks has been the subject of philosophical speculation and experimental investigation since the days of Diogenes and Aristotle. Only within the past century, thanks to the refinement of the art of microscopy and to the rise of the sciences of acoustics and electronics, has it become possible to give even a partial and tentative answer to the ancient question, "How do we hear?", to say nothing of the even more difficult question, "How do we listen?"

ANATOMY OF THE EAR

The ear is divided into three parts: the external ear, consisting of the *pinna* and the *external meatus* or *canal*, ending blindly at the tympanic membrane; the *middle ear*, containing the three small auditory ossicles suspended in the air-filled tympanic cavity; and the fluid-filled *inner ear* or *labyrinth*, consisting of (1) the *cochlea*, which contains the *organ of Corti* with the endings of the cochlear division of the auditory nerve, (2) the *vestibule*, which contains the static organs the *utricle* and *saccule*, and (3) the three *semicircular canals* (fig. 17.1).

The *auricle* or *pinna* of the external ear consists of a thin, fibrocartilaginous plate, characteristically folded and ridged and covered with skin. In many animals it can readily be turned to locate the source of a sound or even folded down to exclude unwanted sound. In man the small extrinsic and intrinsic muscles of the auricle are usually functionless. A depression called the *concha* forms the orifice of the *external meatus* or *canal*, which extends inward in a slightly curving course of about 25 mm. to end at the *tympanic* or *drum membrane*. The wall of the outer third of the canal is formed by cartilage, that of the remainder by a tunnel in the temporal bone. The skin which lines the cartilaginous portion has many *ceruminous glands* and laterally directed hairs, which discourage insects from entering the ear. The cerumen, however, can sometimes accumulate in such quantity as to block the canal and impede the passage of sound to the drum membrane.

The skin lining the osseous portion of the canal is thin, closely adherent to the periosteum, and extremely sensitive. It is continued as a delicate lamina, forming the outermost of the three layers, *cuticular*, *fibrous* and *mucous*, of which the tympanic membrane is composed.

The membrane lies obliquely across the end of the canal, sloping downward, forward and medially. It is attached to a bony ring or *annulus* formed by the wall of the canal, and to the handle or *manubrium* of the malleus, which draws the center or *umbo* of the membrane inward by about 2 mm., so that its shape is that of a flattened cone. The diameter along the line of the manubrium is about 9 mm.; the diameter perpendicular to the manubrium is 8.5 mm. The total area of the membrane is approximately 69 sq. mm.

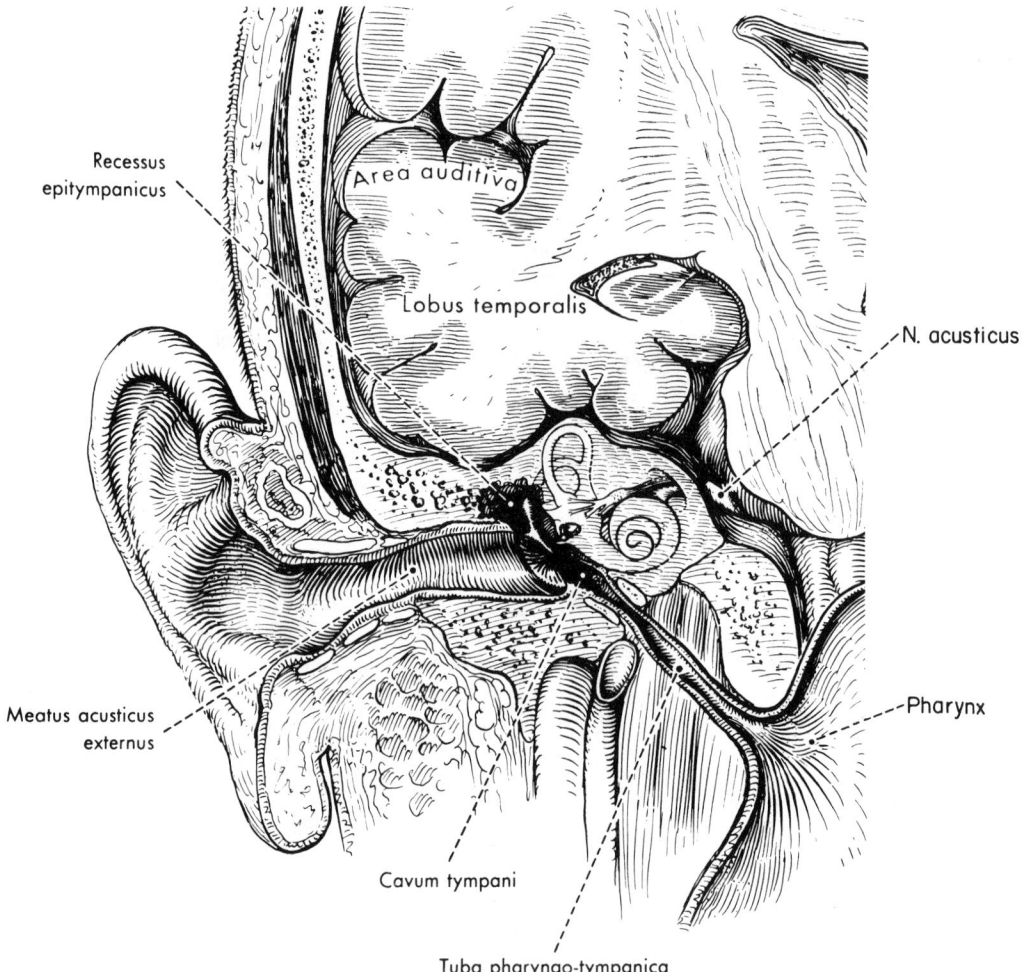

Fig. 17.1. Coronal section through the right side of the head, showing the external, middle, and inner ear. (From a drawing by Biaggio J. Melloni, reproduced by permission of Abbott Laboratories, North Chicago, Illinois.)

When the normal drum membrane is illuminated and viewed through an ear speculum or otoscope, it appears pearl grey, pinkish or yellowish in color. Several landmarks can be seen. The *lateral process of the malleus* projects as a white spot near the upper anterior border of the membrane. Above it, bounded by two faint ridges, the *anterior* and *posterior malleolar folds*, which extend forward and backward, is a small triangular area in which the membrane is thin and slack. This area is called *Shrapnell's membrane* or the *pars flaccida*. The greater part of the membrane is taut and glistening, and is called the *pars tensa*. For convenience in describing the location of lesions in the membrane, it is subdivided into four quadrants by the manubrium of the malleus

and its imaginary projection downward and backward, and by an imaginary line through the umbo at right angles to the manubrium. A brightly reflecting triangular area in the antero-inferior quadrant is called the *cone of light*. In the postero-superior quadrant, the *long crus of the incus* can usually be seen through the drum, just behind and parallel to the handle of the malleus (fig. 17.2).

The appearance of the membrane, its color, translucence, and degree of bulging or retraction, are of invaluable aid in diagnosing disease of the middle ear.

The *middle ear* or *tympanic cavity* is a narrow air-filled chamber in the mastoid portion of the temporal bone. It contains the chain of the miniature bones or *auditory ossicles*, which bear the fanciful descriptive names *malleus* (hammer), *incus* (anvil) and *stapes* (stirrup). The chain extends across the cavity from the drum membrane to the oval window of the cochlea on its inner wall. (fig 17.3).

The malleus, which more nearly resembles a club, has a handle (*manubrium*) attached to the drum membrane and a head (*capitellum*) which extends upward above the upper margin of the drum membrane into the *epitympanic recess*. It bears an articular facet for the body of the incus. The incus, shaped like a premolar tooth with spreading roots (*crura*), lies almost entirely in the epitympanum. It articulates with the head of the malleus by an articular surface on its body. The short crus is attached by a ligament in the *fossa incudis* of the epitympanum, whereas the long crus extends downward and medially parallel to the manubrium of the malleus. Its lower end is bent medially and bears a small knob of bone, the *lenticular process*, which articulates with the head of the stapes.

The stapes, which actually resembles a stirrup, is the smallest of the ossicles. It consists of a *head*, a *neck*, an *anterior* and a *posterior crus*, and a *footplate* which fits into the *oval* or *vestibular window* of the cochlea. According to Bast and Anson, the stapes varies considerably in size and weight from one individual to another. In their series the height varied from 2.50 to 3.78 mm., with an average of 3.26 mm.; the weight varied from 2.050 to 4.350 mg., with an average of 2.860 mg.

Five small ligaments connect the ossicles to the walls of the tympanic cavity. Three of them support the head and processes of the malleus and one supports the short crus of the incus. The

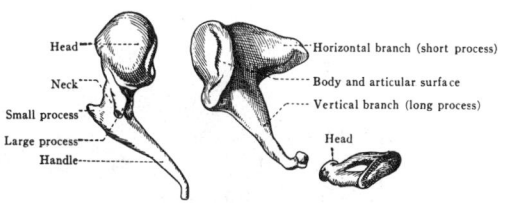

FIG. 17.3A. The three auditory ossicles: A, malleus; B, incus; C, stapes. (From G. Portmann, *Diseases of the Ear, Nose, and Throat*, Williams & Wilkins Company, Baltimore, 1951.)

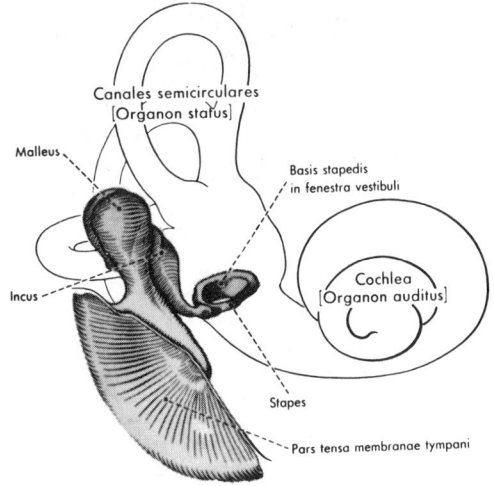

FIG. 17.3B. Position of the tympanic membrane (cut away) and ossicular chain in relation to the bony labyrinth (right side). (From a drawing by Biaggio J. Melloni, reproduced by permission of Abbott Laboratories, North Chicago, Illinois.)

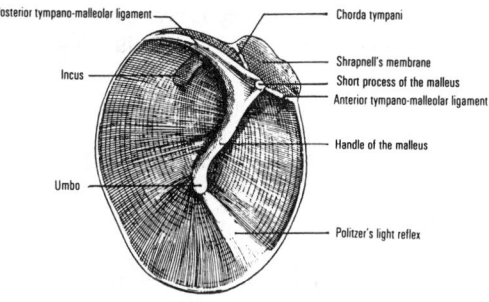

FIG. 17.2. Lateral surface of the right tympanic membrane, indicating the major structures seen with the otoscope. Politzer's light reflex is also referred to as the *cone of light*. Shrapnell's membrane is the *pars flaccida*, the rest of the membrane the *pars tensa*. (From G. Portmann, *Diseases of the Ear, Nose, and Throat*, Williams & Wilkins Company, Baltimore, 1951.)

fifth is the *annular ligament* of the stapes, which surrounds the footplate and connects its margin to the edge of the oval window. Two minute muscles also aid in controlling the movements of the ossicles. The larger, called the *tensor tympani*, issues from a canal parallel to the auditory tube. Its tendon bends laterally over a small ridge of bone which serves as a pulley, and is inserted on the medial surface of the manubrium of the malleus. The smaller, called the *stapedius*, arises in a small, hollow, conical projection on the posterior wall of the tympanic cavity called the *pyramid*. Its tiny tendon is inserted on the posterior aspect of the neck of the stapes. When the tensor tympani, which is supplied by a branch from the mandibular division of the trigeminal nerve, contracts, it pulls the handle of the malleus inward and thus restricts the outward movement of the drum membrane. When the stapedius, supplied by a branch of the facial nerve, contracts, it pulls the neck of the stapes backward, thus tilting the anterior edge of the

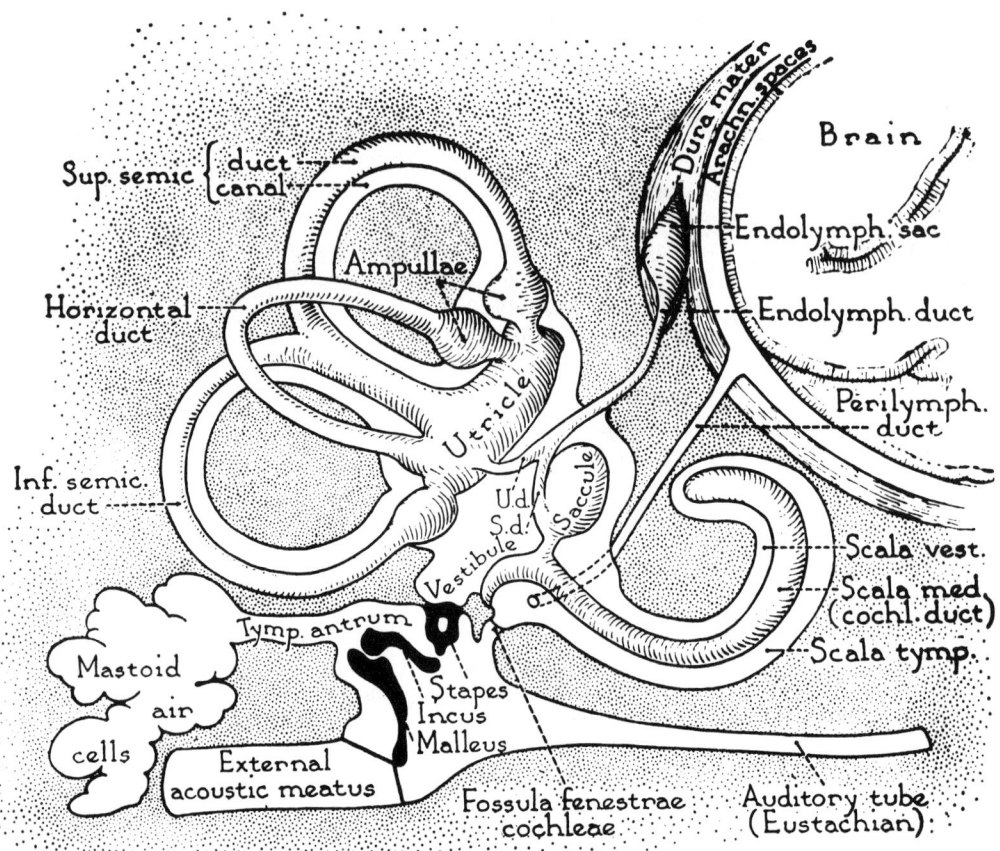

Fig. 17.4. General relations of the membranous, periotic and osseous labyrinths. Diagrammatic· U.d., utricular duct. S.d., saccular duct. (From Bast and Anson, *The Temporal Bone and the Ear*, 1949, Charles C Thomas.)

footplate outward and reducing its inward movement against the fluid in the cochlea. The function of the muscles and ligaments in modifying the movements of the ossicles will be considered in greater detail below.

The inner ear lies within the *periotic labyrinth* which is in turn enclosed by the bony labyrinth in the petrous part of the temporal bone. It is divided into three main parts: the cochlea, the vestibule and the three semicircular canals. Suspended in the periotic labyrinth is an entirely closed system, the *otic* or *membranous labyrinth*, consisting of the *cochlear duct*, the *utricle* and *saccule*, the three *membranous canals* and the various ducts which interconnect them (fig. 17.4). The otic labyrinth is filled by the *otic fluid* or *endolymph*. The spaces of the periotic labyrinth contain a delicate, arachnoid-like tissue. Its interstices are filled with the *periotic fluid* or *perilymph*.

The cochlea, as its name implies, is coiled like the shell of a snail. A section through its axis (fig. 17.5) reveals a central bony pillar, the *modiolus*, the base of which contains the internal auditory meatus with the auditory nerve. The periotic or osseous canal coils about the modiolus for approximately two and one-half turns, tapering in diameter from base to apex. A bony ledge, the *osseous spiral lamina*, projects into the canal, winding about the modiolus like the thread of a screw. It is widest in the basal coil, narrowing toward the apex.

The *basilar membrane* stretches from the tip of the osseous spiral lamina to a tough, dense, fibrous band called the *spiral ligament*, which lines the outer wall of the canal. A second partition, known as *Reissner's membrane*, extends from the upper surface of the osseous lamina obliquely to the upper margin of the spiral ligament. In cross section the membranes enclose a triangular area,

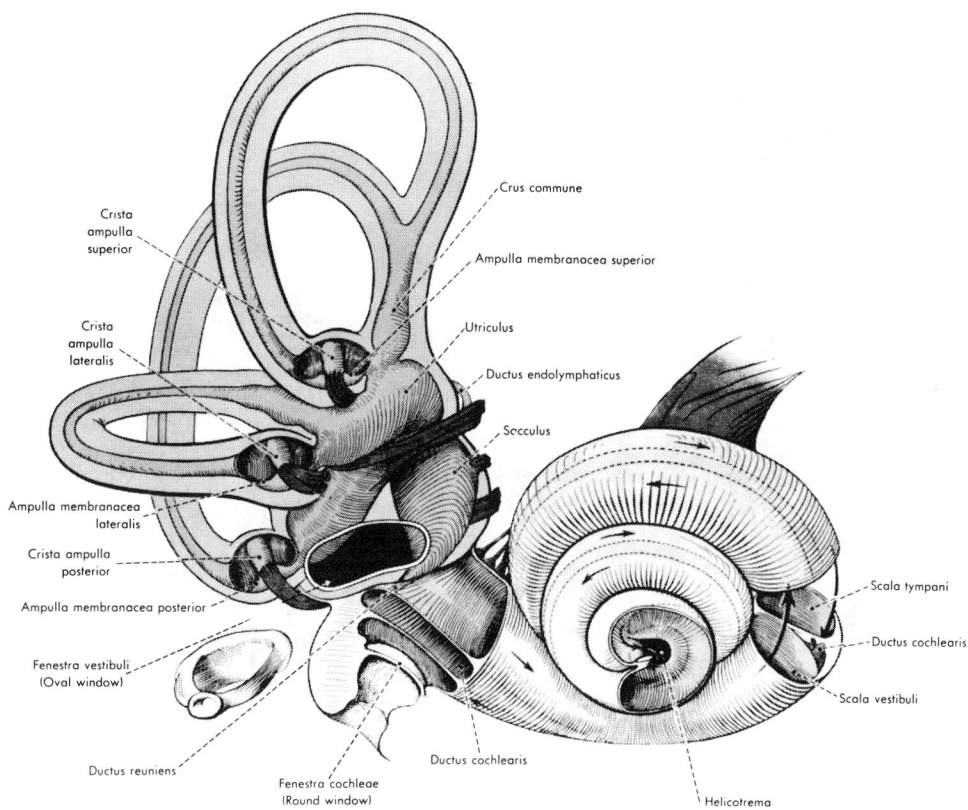

Crus commune

Crista ampulla superior

Ampulla membranacea superior

Crista ampulla lateralis

Utriculus

Ductus endolymphaticus

Sacculus

Ampulla membranacea lateralis

Crista ampulla posterior

Ampulla membranacea posterior

Scala tympani

Ductus cochlearis

Fenestra vestibuli (Oval window)

Scala vestibuli

Ductus reuniens

Fenestra cochleae (Round window)

Ductus cochlearis

Helicotrema

FIG. 17.5A. The right labyrinth opened to show the three scalae of the cochlea and the vestibular end organs. (From a drawing by Biaggio J. Melloni, reproduced by permission of Abbott Laboratories, North Chicago, Illinois.)

the *scala media* or *cochlear duct*. In the conventional description, the *scala vestibuli* lies above the scala media, and the *scala tympani* below it (fig. 17.6).

The scala media or cochlear duct, which is the otic or membranous cochlea, ends blindly, both at the apex of the cochlea and at the basal end. The slender *ductus reuniens* arises near the basal end and connects it with the saccule. The scala vestibuli and scala tympani are in communication at the apex of the cochlea through a narrow opening, the *helicotrema*. At the basal end, the scala vestibuli ends in the vestibule at the oval window, which is closed by the footplate of the stapes. The scala tympani ends at the round window, covered by the thin *round window membrane* (secondary tympanic membrane).

The basilar membrane is a fibrous plate, its radial fibers continuous with those of the spiral ligament. On the tympanic (under) side it is covered by a layer of mesothelial cells constituting the *tympanic lamella*. Their long, fibrous processes form the longitudinal fibers of the membrane. Its

width tapers gradually from 0.250 mm. near the helicotrema to 0.185 mm. near the round window (guinea pig). Von Békésy has observed that when a tiny longitudinal cut is made in the basilar membrane, the edges of the cut do not retract. Therefore, contrary to the opinion long held, the membrane is not under tension.

The cochlear fluids. The *otic fluid* or *endolymph* fills the otic labyrinth, including the cochlear duct, the saccule, the utricle and the three semicircular canals. It is thought to be secreted by the stria vascularis and probably by secretory cells associated with the vestibular neuroepithelia as well. Where it is absorbed is not definitely known. The endolymphatic sac, lying between the dura and the periosteum of the intracranial surface of the petrous bone, has long been considered a probable site. Recent experiments by Kimura have shown that destruction of the sac causes distension (hydrops) of the otic labyrinth in the guinea pig. The endolymph probably has other sites of absorption as well, including perhaps the region of the spiral prominence.

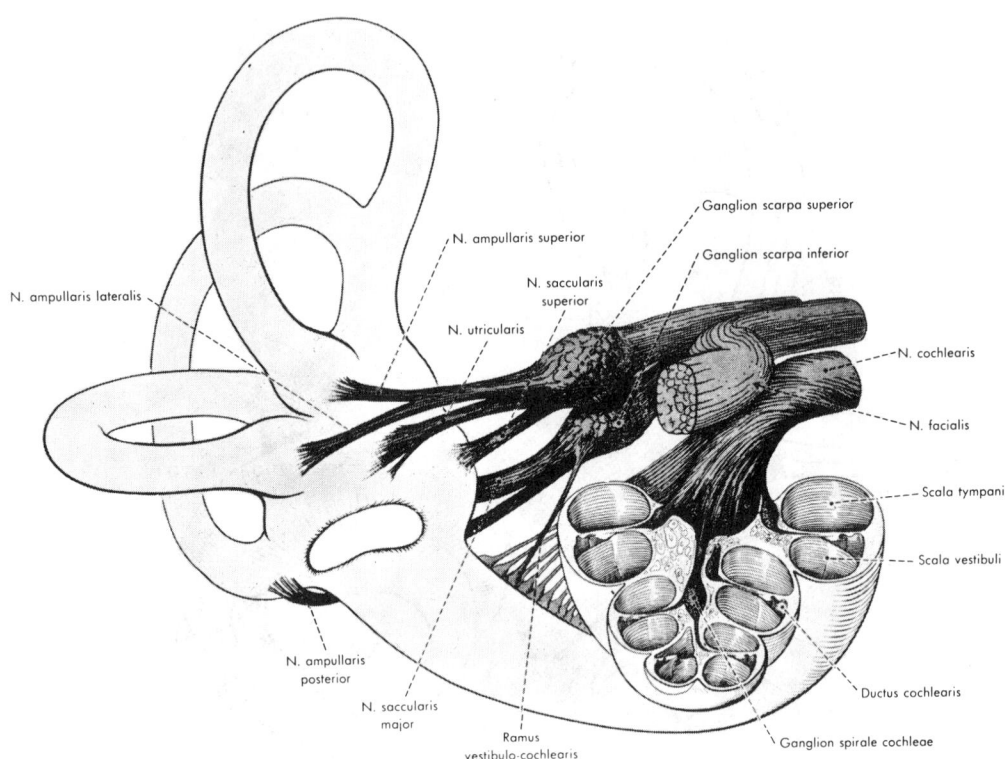

Fig. 17.5B. The right cochlea in mid-modiolar section, with the cochlear and vestibular divisions of the VIIIth nerve. (From a drawing by Biaggio J. Melloni, reproduced by permission of Abbott Laboratories, North Chicago, Illinois.)

The *periotic fluid* or *perilymph* fills the periotic labyrinth, i.e., the scala vestibuli and scala tympani, the vestibule and the periotic semicircular canals. It is in communication with the cerebrospinal fluid in the arachnoid spaces surrounding the brain, by way of the perilymphatic duct, but, this fluid does not represent its only source. Since radioactive sodium (Na^{24}) appears promptly in the perilymph after intravenous injection, it is clear that the perilymph must be an ultrafiltrate of the blood. It is probably filtered from and resorbed into the capillaries of the spiral ligament.

Because the volume of endolymph is so minute, the difficulty of collecting an uncontaminated sample is very great. Nevertheless it has been clearly established that the endolymph has an entirely different ionic composition from perilymph and cerebrospinal fluid. The analyses of Smith, Lowry and Wu have shown that endolymph contains a greater concentration of potassium ions than of sodium and thus resembles intracellular fluid, whereas perilymph, like the cerebrospinal liquor, has a greater concentration of sodium ions than of potassium and thus resembles other interstitial fluids (table 17.1).

The fluid that fills the tunnel of Corti and the Nuel spaces and bathes the hair cells was long assumed to be endolymph, but when the composition of the endolymph became known it was obvious that this could not be the case. The high concentration of potassium ions in the endolymph would make it impossible for the unmyelinated nerve fibers to the hair cells to conduct impulses. The fluid of the organ of Corti must therefore resemble perilymph more closely than it does endolymph. Engström has pointed out, however,

TABLE 17.1

	Spinal Fluid	Perilymph	Endolymph
	m.eq./liter	*m.eq./liter*	*m.eq./liter*
Potassium......	4.2	4.8	144.4
Sodium.........	152.0	150.3	15.8
Chloride.......	122.4	121.5	107.1
	mg. %	*mg. %*	*mg. %*
Protein.........	21.0	50.0	15.0

Mammalian endolymph does not show the high viscosity that has often been attributed to it by analogy with that of the shark, which sets into a jelly after withdrawal.

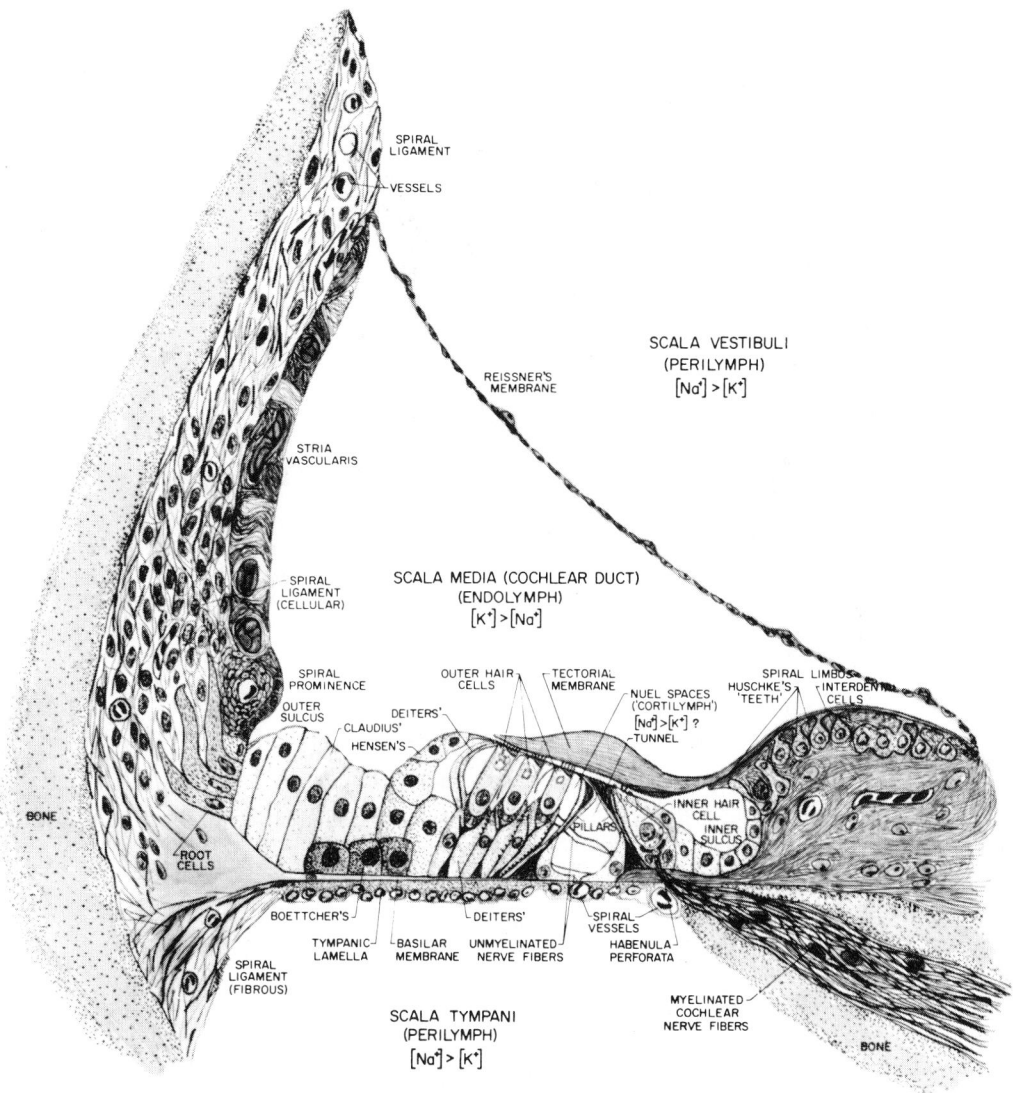

Fig. 17.6. The major cochlear structures, as seen in a transverse section of the cochlear duct from the upper portion of the first coil (guinea pig).

that it need not be identical with perilymph and has suggested that until further information about its composition becomes available it should be regarded as the third fluid of the inner ear, for which he has proposed the name *cortilymph* (fig. 17.6).

Blood supply: The inner ear obtains its blood supply from the *internal auditory artery*, which accompanies the auditory nerve in the internal meatus. The cochlear division of this artery pursues a tortuous course in the modiolus, supplying the nerve fibers and the spiral ganglion, and giving off numerous arterioles which arch across the roof of scala vestibuli to reach the upper margin of the spiral ligament. Here they divide into four groups of capillaries. The first

group supply the upper portion of the spiral ligament, the second form the intra-epithelial capillary network of the stria vascularis, and the third and fourth pass behind the stria to the spiral prominence and the lower portion of the spiral ligament respectively. In the prominence they form the characteristic series of single and paired longitudinal capillaries. These various networks eventually reunite to form collecting venules, which drain into the posterior spiral vein at the bottom of scala tympani (figs. 17.7, 17.8).

Other arterioles from the modiolus enter the osseous spiral lamina, some to be distributed to the spiral limbus, others to form a double set of arcades, the inner and outer *spiral vessels* or

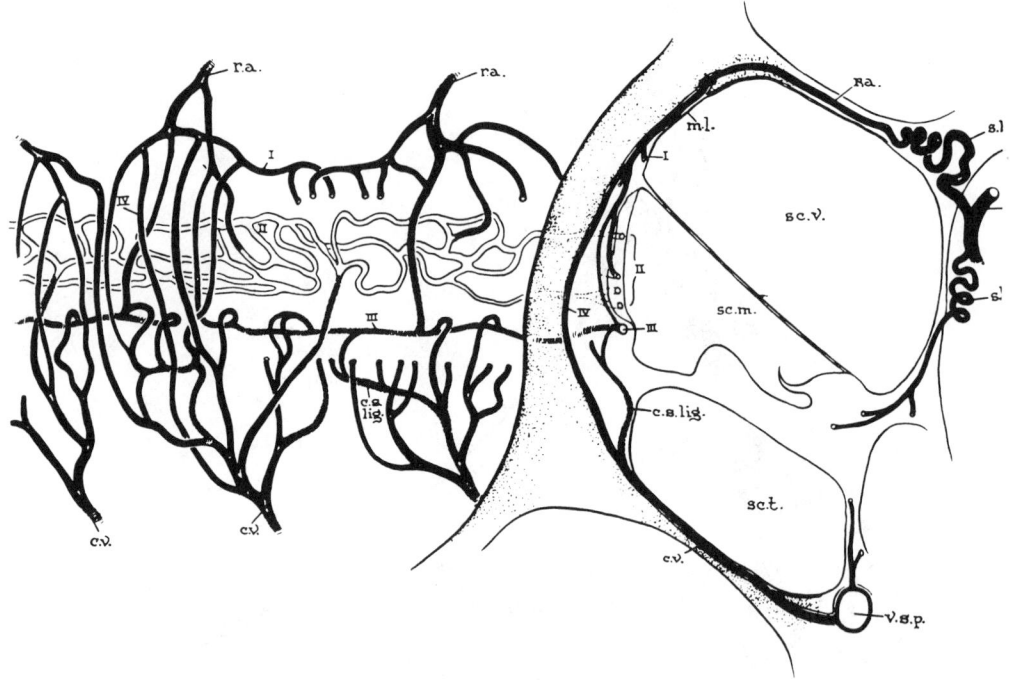

Fig. 17.7. The blood supply of the spiral ligament and stria vascularis in the guinea pig. On the right is a transverse section of the second coil of the cochlea; on the left, a surface view of the spiral ligament and strial vessels. p.b., primary branch; s.b., secondary branch,; r.a., radiating arteriole; m.l., mesothelial layer; I, capillaries of upper spiral ligament; II, intra-epithelial capillaries of stria; III, capillaries of spiral prominence; IV, capillaries passing in spiral ligament behind stria; c.s. lig., crest of spiral ligament; c.v., collecting venule; v.s.p., posterior spiral vein;, sc.v., sc.m., sc.t., scalae vestibuli, media, and tympani. (From Catherine A. Smith, Capillary areas of the cochlea in the guinea pig, Laryngoscope, 1951, **61**, 1073.)

spiral borders, one beneath the lip of the osseous spiral lamina, the other beneath the basilar membrane. These also drain into the posterior spiral vein and ultimately into the internal auditory vein.

Only the neuroepithelium of the organ of Corti receives no direct blood supply. It is entirely dependent upon the oxygen and nutrients brought to it from the capillaries of other areas by way of the endolymph and perilymph. For this purpose the capillaries of the stria vascularis are generally considered to be all-important, but the potential contributions of the spiral vessels beneath the basilar membrane and the capillaries of the spiral ligament should not be disregarded.

The Organ of Corti. The neuroepithelium of the cochlea, known as the *spiral organ of Corti*, rests upon the lip of the osseous spiral lamina and the basilar membrane. It is made up of an orderly arrangement of the actual sensory elements, the *hair cells*, and their various *supporting cells*, and it is covered by a stiff cuticle, the *lamina reticularis*, which looks, from above, like a regularly patterned mosaic. A prominent feature is the *tunnel*

of Corti, formed by the inner and outer *pillar cells* or *rods of Corti*. The flat, expanded bases of the inner pillar cells are close to the lip of the osseous spiral lamina, those of the outer pillars on the basilar membrane. The slender bodies of the inner and outer pillars slope towards each other, and their broader upper ends articulate, at the same time supporting and forming a part of the lamina reticularis. The pillars increase progressively in height from the basal coil to the apex.

On the medial side of the tunnel, i.e., toward the modiolus, a single row of *inner hair cells* is arrayed, closely parallel to the inner pillars. They are surrounded by supporting elements, the *inner border cells* and *phalangeal cells*. On the lateral side of the tunnel are three or more parallel rows of *outer hair cells*. These are supported by the *cells of Deiters*, which actually rest on the basilar membrane and send stiff *phalangeal processes* upwards between the hair cells to form part of the lamina reticularis. The outer hair cells are surrounded by fluid spaces, the *spaces of Nuel*, and the *outer tunnel*, between the last row and the supporting *cells of Hensen*. Beyond the

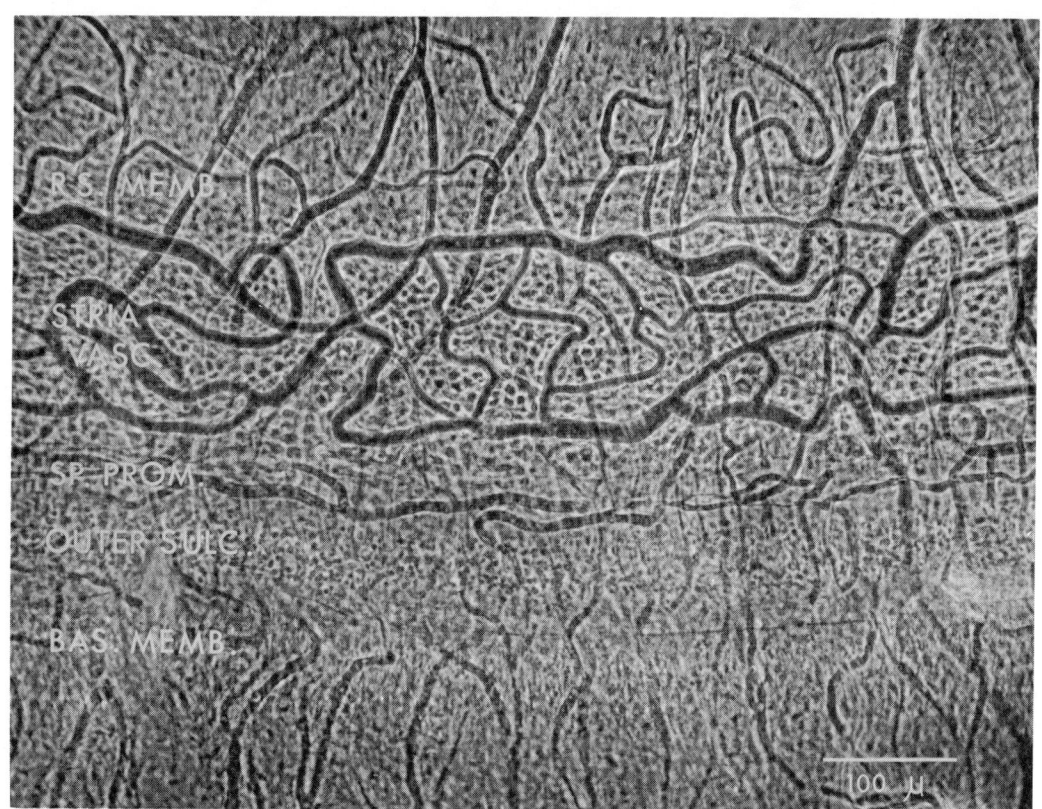

FIG. 17.8. Longitudinal preparation of the spiral ligament, stria vascularis, and spiral prominence in the guinea pig. (Benzidine stain, phase-contrast photomicrograph.)

Hensen cells is a series of cuboidal *cells of Claudius*. They are of simple structure, resembling the *inner sulcus cells* lying medial to the inner hair cells. Under the Claudius cells in the basal turn are the Boettcher cells.

A spiral ridge, the *limbus spiralis*, rests on the osseous spiral lamina medial to the inner sulcus. Fibers of the basilar membrane are anchored in the limbus, and the thin *membrane of Reissner* is attached at its inner margin. To its surface and vestibular lip the *tectorial membrane* is attached. This membrane has a fibrous structure and is reported to contain mucopolysaccharides, like the closely-related cupulae of the semicircular canals and the otolithic membranes of the utricle and saccule. It arches over the inner sulcus and overlies the lamina reticularis, where its under surface is in contact with the tips of the hairs of the hair cells. These hairs do not appear to enter the substance of the tectorial membrane, unlike the much longer hairs of the crista ampullaris, which are enclosed in fine channels in the gelatinous substance of the cupula.

The lateral wall of the cochlear duct is formed by the *outer sulcus cells*, the *spiral prominence*,

the *stria vascularis* and, beyond these, the *spiral ligament*, in which the fibers of the basilar membrane are anchored. The stria, with its pigmented granular cells and its rich vascular supply, is thought to be responsible for the secretion of the cochlear endolymph.

The outer hair cells number about 12,000 according to Retzius, the inner hair cells only 3,500. An outer hair cell has the shape of a test-tube, with a thickened cuticular layer at the upper end, bearing about 120 sensory hairs (stereocilia) ca. 5 μ long, arranged in a regular W-pattern (fig. 17.9). At the base of the W is a small cuticle-free area with a single modified kinocilium, consisting only of the basal body. Beneath the basal body and the cuticular plate are numerous mitochondria, membranes and granules, indicating that this is a region of high metabolic activity. A schematic drawing of the intracellular structures of an outer hair cell is shown in fig. 17.10.

The inner hair cells differ significantly in form from the outer hair cells. They are more rounded, or flask-shaped, and their hairs are fewer and somewhat coarser, being arranged in two or more

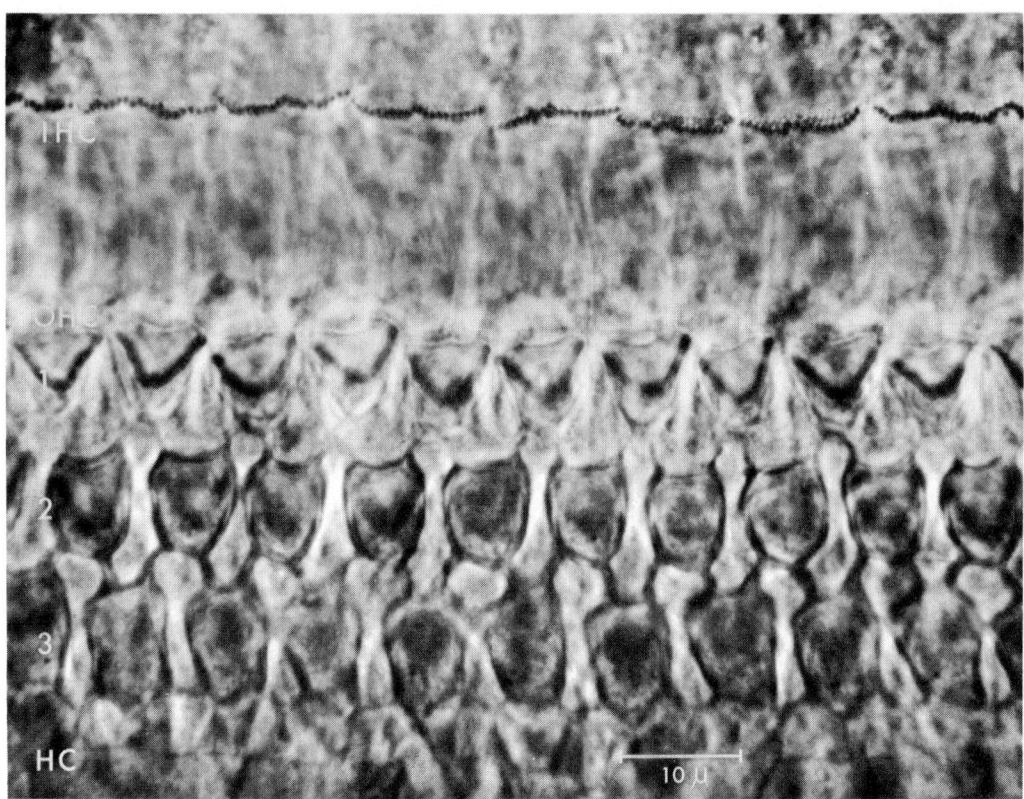

FIG. 17.9. Longitudinal preparation of the organ of Corti in the guinea pig, showing the mosaic pattern of the reticular lamina and the arrangement of the hairs on the inner and outer hair cells. (Osmium tetroxide fixation, phase-contrast photomicrograph.)

uneven rows. Again the basal body of a kinocilium is present in a cuticle-free region on the side of the stereocilia away from the modiolus. The nucleus is larger than that of an outer hair cell, and the intracellular organelles differ in detail, as seen in the drawing in fig. 17.11. These cytological differences suggest important differences in function between the inner and outer hair cells.

Innervation. About the base of each hair cell is a cluster of nerve endings. Two distinct types are recognized: the smaller (type 1) 0.5 to 1.0 μ in diameter, with few vesicles, and the larger (type 2) as much as 5 μ long and 1 to 3 μ in diameter, densely filled with vesicles. The regions of contact between the nerve endings and the hair cell are clearly synaptic in nature. Characteristic presynaptic bars are seen under the plasma membrane of the hair cell where it is in contact with the smaller endings, and postsynaptic membranes in relation to the larger endings. These findings as well as the results of degeneration studies strongly support the sug-

gestion of Engström that the two types of nerve endings serve separate functions, the smaller being afferent and the larger efferent. The larger endings become less numerous toward the apex of the cochlea and eventually disappear from the outer hair cells of the second and third rows.

The "wiring diagram" of the nerve supply to the inner and outer hair cells is obviously far from simple, and it remains largely unknown. It has been said to provide for a diffuse innervation of the outer hair cells and a more specific innervation of the inner hair cells, but recent electron microscopic studies of the region of the *inner spiral bundle* beneath the inner hair cells suggest that this generalization may not be valid. There are many possibilities for neuroneuronal interactions between fibers in this region, and the fibers involved have not yet been sorted out. Other longitudinal bundles of nerve fibers are the *spiral tunnel bundle* beside the inner pillars and the three *outer spiral bundles*, with many cross-connections, parallel to the rows of outer hair cells. In these bundles fibers are said to run for half a turn of the cochlea or more, giving off twigs to innervate many hair cells along the way.

From the inner spiral bundle *afferent* fibers cross the floor of the tunnel between the bases of the pillar cells and come into relation with the Deiters cells, where they form mesaxons and eventually reach the hair cells via the outer spiral bundles. The *efferent* fibers pass from the inner spiral bundle between the bodies of the inner pillars to the tunnel bundle. From the latter, small bundles of fibers, easily seen in celloidin sections of the organ of Corti, cross the middle of the tunnel at irregular intervals to reach the bases of the outer hair cells. In their course through the fluid spaces these fibers are completely bare, without any myelin or neurilemma sheath, whereas the afferent fibers are protected and supported by the bases of the pillar cells and by the Deiters cells. Spoendlin and Gacek have reported that the unmyelinated portions of the afferent fibers within the organ of Corti survive after section of the cochlear nerve at the internal meatus and after complete degeneration of the

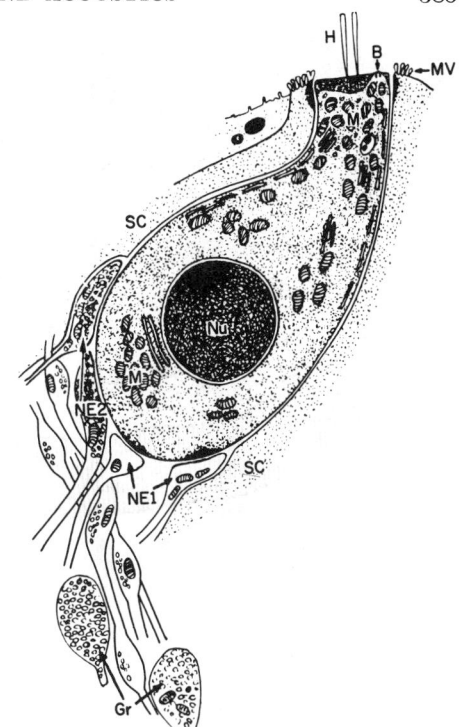

FIG. 17.11. Schematic drawing of an inner hair cell (guinea pig). H, hairs (stereocilia; B, basal body; MV, microvilli on supporting cells, SC; Nu, nucleus; NE₁, afferent nerve ending; NE₂, efferent nerve ending; Gr, granulated enlargements seen in nerve fibers of the inner spiral bundle. (Modified after Engström, Ades, and Hawkins.)

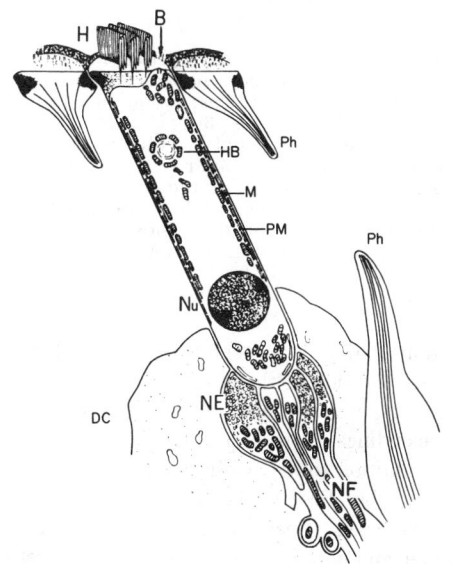

FIG. 17.10. Schematic drawing of an outer hair cell (guinea pig). H, hairs (stereocilia), with rootlets in cuticular plate; B, basal body; HB, Hensen body; M, mitochondrion; PM, parietal membranes; Nu, nucleus; NE, nerve endings, both afferent (small, sparse vesicles); and efferent (larger, with dense vesicles); NF, nerve fibers; DC, Deiters cell; Ph, phalangeal process. Note the groupings of mitochondria: a) beneath the basal body and cuticular plate; b) along the sides of the cell; c) around the Hensen body; and d) below the nucleus. (Slightly modified, from Engström, Ades and Hawkins.)

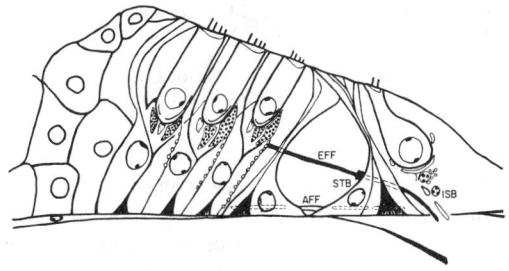

FIG. 17.12. Course of efferent (EFF) and afferent (AFF) fibers within the organ of Corti of the guinea pig (Cf. fig. 17.6). ISB, inner spiral bundle; STB, spiral tunnel bundle. The large, vesiculated endings under the outer hair cells are efferent, the small endings, afferent. (Modified from Spoendlin and Gacek.)

myelinated portions of the fibers as far as the habenula perforata, where the myelin sheath ends. These fibers can also survive destruction of the hair cells but not degeneration of the supporting cells (fig. 17.12).

The bipolar cell bodies of the afferent cochlear neurons are located in the *spiral ganglion*, which

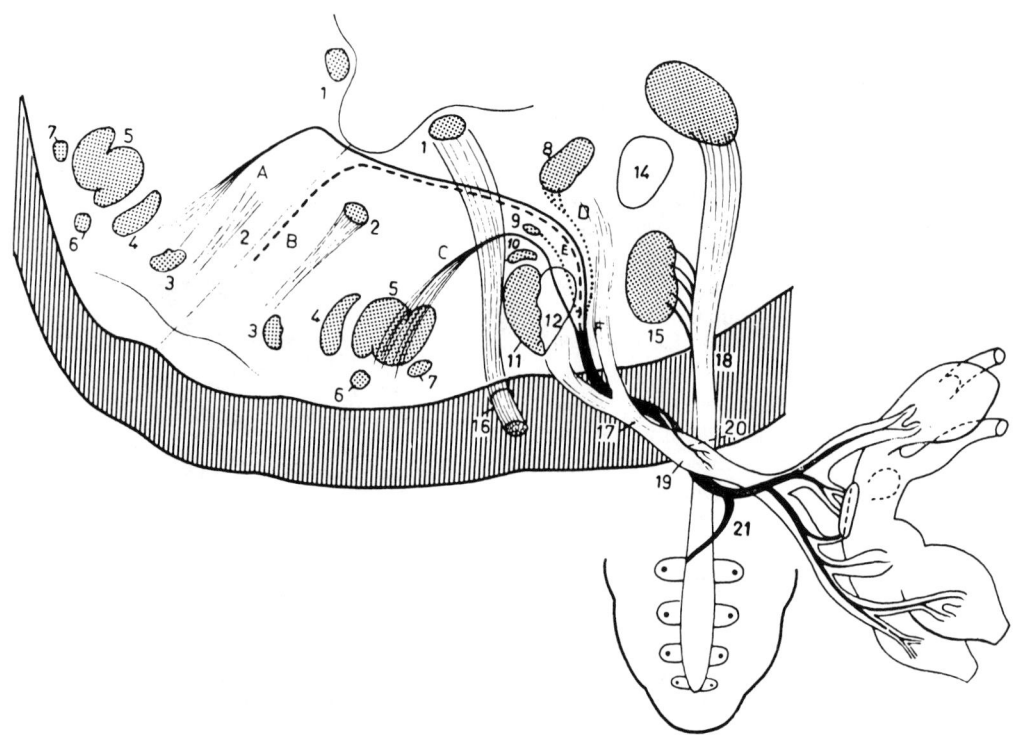

FIG. 17.13. The cochlear and vestibular efferent systems. A, crossed cochlear efferent bundle (Rasmussen); B, uncrossed reticulo-cochlear and -vestibular bundle; C, uncrossed cochlear efferent bundle (Rasmussen); D and E, dorsal and ventral uncrossed vestibular efferent bundles; F, bundle containing all of the efferent cochlear and vestibular fibers. 1, facial genu; 2, abducens; 3, trapezoid nucleus; 4, medial superior olivary nucleus; 5, lateral superior olivary nucleus; 6, medial pre-olivary nucleus; 7, lateral pre-olivary nucleus; 8, lateral vestibular nucleus; 9, interposed vestibular nucleus; 10, inferior vestibular nucleus; 11, nucleus of descending root of trigeminal; 12, descending root of trigeminal; 13, dorsal cochlear nucleus; 14, inferior cerebellar peduncle; 15, ventral cochlear nucleus; 16, facial nerve; 17, vestibular division of N. VIII, with superior and inferior roots; 18, cochlear division of N. VIII; 19, ganglion of Scarpa; 20, efferent fibers to Scarpa's ganglion; 21, vestibulo-cochlear anastomosis of Oort. (From G. Rossi, in L. Candiollo, G. Filogamo, and G. Rossi, *Le basi morfo-funzionali del controllo delle sensazioni acustiche*, Società Italiana di Laringologia Otologia e Rinologia, Torino, 1965.)

is contained in *Rosenthal's canal* in the modiolus. Central to the ganglion the fibers unite to form the cochlear nerve trunk. Fibers from the apical region of the cochlea run a straight course, whereas the others are twisted about them like the strands of a cable.

The efferent fibers to the organ of Corti constitute the *crossed and uncrossed olivo-cochlear bundles of Rasmussen*, which originate in the contralateral accessory superior olive and the ipsilateral main superior olivary nucleus respectively. Their fibers accompany the vestibular nerve as far as Scarpa's ganglion, then join the cochlear nerve via the *vestibulo-cochlear anastomosis of Oort*. In the spiral ganglion they form the *intraganglionic spiral bundle*, from which they pass through the habenula perforata to be distributed to the hair cells of the organ of Corti.

Section of the olivo-cochlear bundles is followed by degeneration of the efferent fibers throughout their entire course and of the large vesiculated nerve endings on the hair cells.

In addition to the crossed and uncrossed olivo-cochlear bundles, Rossi has recently described an uncrossed reticulo-cochlear and -vestibular bundle, and uncrossed dorsal and ventral vestibular efferent bundles. Their relations are summarized in fig. 17.13.

The auditory pathway. Major nuclear masses of the central auditory pathway are located in the medulla oblongata, the midbrain and the thalamic region. The pathway terminates in the cortex of the temporal lobe. At each of these levels an orderly spatial arrangement of the neurons has been found, indicating that the organ of Corti is represented or "unrolled" again

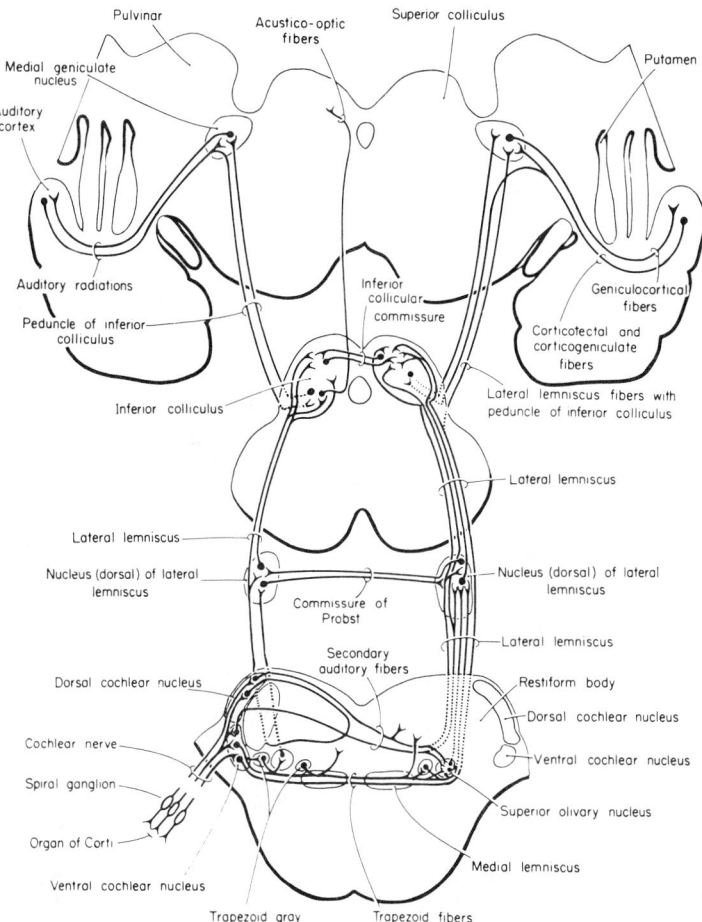

Fig. 17.14. Major central pathways of the auditory system. (By permission from Crosby, Humphrey and Lauer, *Correlative Anatomy of the Nervous System*, The Macmillan Company, New York, 1962.)

and again in the brain. The pathways are both crossed and uncrossed, so that each cochlea is represented in both sides of the brain (fig. 17.14).

The fibers of first-order afferent neurons of the cochlear nerve enter the medulla and immediately divide, sending branches to the *dorsal* and *ventral cochlear nuclei*. Many second-order neurons pass medially from these to the *superior olives* of both sides, forming the *trapezoid body*, whereas others enter the *lateral lemniscus* directly, to terminate at the *nuclei of the lateral lemniscus*. The third-order neurons from the superior olive ascend in the lemniscus to the *inferior colliculus*, whereas those from the nuclei of the lemniscus proceed to the *medial geniculate*. From the geniculate, the auditory radiations pass in the internal capsule to the primary auditory area in the *superior transverse temporal gyrus*, or *gyrus of Heschl* (area 41 of Brodmann). In the

carnivores this area is represented in the *middle ectosylvian gyrus*.

In addition to the direct ascending pathway, there are numerous reflex connections with cranial motor nuclei. A cerebellar auditory center has been found in the *tuber vermis*, which receives fibers from the dorsal cochlear nucleus.

Since a cat with a complete transection at the midbrain level of the classical auditory pathways on both sides can easily be aroused from sleep by sounds, a second auditory route to the cortex has been postulated in the *reticular formation* of the midbrain, the only structure spared by the operation.

Descending pathways from the cortex to the various central auditory nuclei have been described by several authors. Desmedt has analyzed what he calls the *centrifugal extrareticular auditory control system*, which he regards as the main

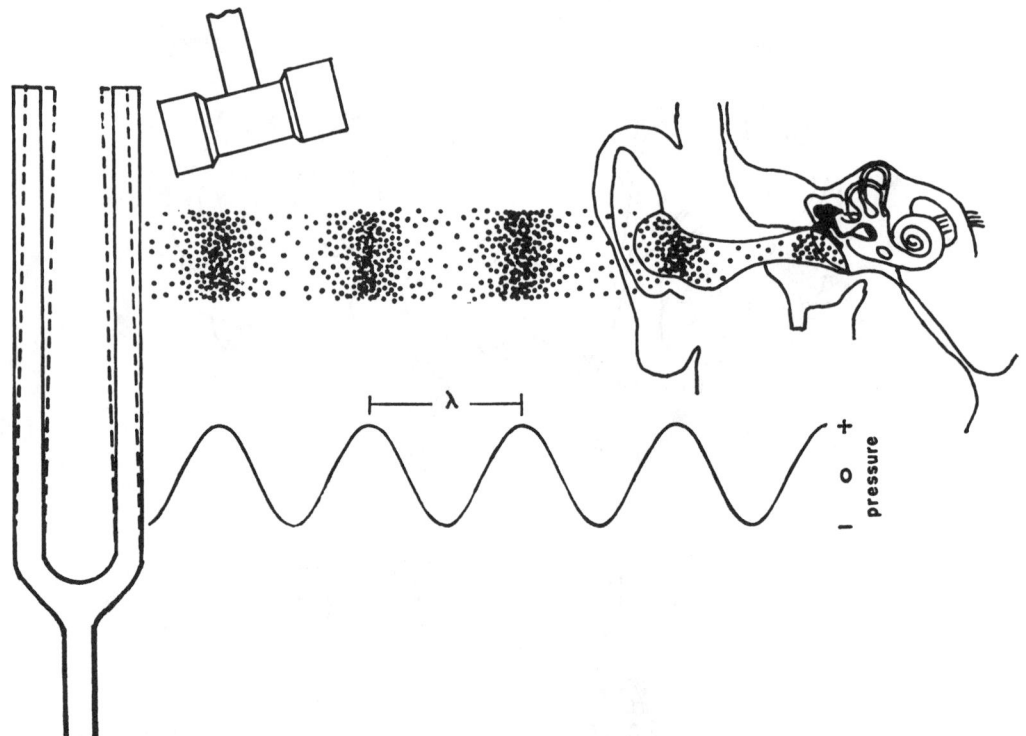

Fig. 17.15. Above, sound waves in air, with regions of compression and rarefaction, produced by a tuning fork. Below, the sinusoidal variation in pressure. λ = 1 wavelength.

channel for the control of the peripheral gating of the acoustic input by the cortex and other higher centers of the brain. It has fibers which terminate on both the cells of origin of the olivo-cochlear bundles and on the neurons of the ventral cochlear nucleus.

The Nature of Sound

Sound may be characterized as a form of wave motion, a transmitted vibratory disturbance in the air or in some other elastic medium like water, wood, steel or bone. Although in this electronic era the sound waves used in the study of hearing usually come from a loudspeaker, an earphone, or some other type of electromechanical transducer, the nature of sound can best be understood by considering one of the simplest sound-producing instruments, the tuning fork. The motion of the fork, like that of all sounding bodies, is determined by three essential physical properties: *inertia, elasticity,* and *resistance.*

When the tuning fork is struck, the kinetic energy of the blow overcomes the *inertia* of the prong and displaces it to one side. The *elasticity,* or *stiffness,* tends to restore the prong to its original position, but the inertia keeps it moving

beyond the position of rest until the elasticity brings it to a stop and causes it to swing back once more. At the end of its swing, the velocity of the fork is zero, and its energy is entirely in the potential form. As it passes through the equilibrium position, its velocity is maximal and its energy is entirely in the kinetic form. These alternating transformations continue until the energy is dissipated, partly in the form of heat due to internal and external frictional *resistance,* partly in the form of sound (fig 17.15).

The rate at which the fork vibrates when struck is called its *natural frequency.* The greater its inertia or *mass* (m), the lower this frequency will be, whereas the greater the stiffness (s), the higher the frequency. If the resistance is assumed to be negligible, this relationship may be expressed by

$$f = \frac{1}{2\pi} \sqrt{\frac{s}{m}}$$

Although the natural frequency is actually reduced somewhat by the effect of resistance, it remains constant as the *amplitude* of vibration decreases continuously until the fork comes to rest.

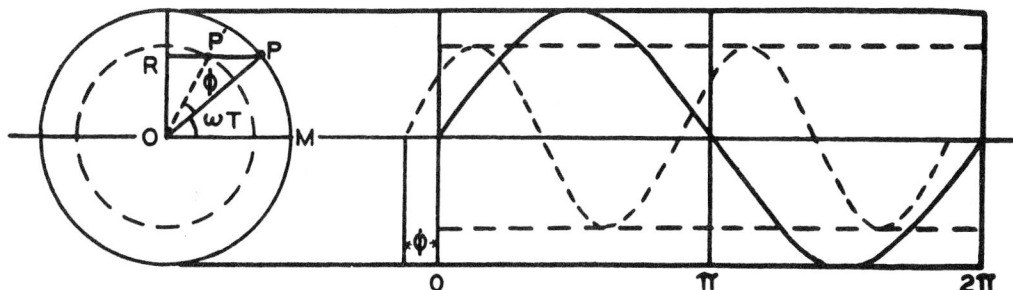

Fig. 17.16. Two sinusoidal waves generated by the projection of circular motions, differing in frequency, amplitude and phase. (Reprinted by permission from Stevens and Davis, *Hearing*, John Wiley and Sons, Inc., 1938.)

As the fork vibrates, it transfers a part of its energy to the molecules of air surrounding the prongs and forces them to vibrate also. Movement of a prong in one direction momentarily pushes the air molecules in its path together, whereas movement in the opposite direction pulls them away from each other. Although these movements of the individual air molecules are exceedingly small, the alternate compressions and rarefactions of the air are transmitted in all directions as waves of air-borne sound.

Like a pendulum swinging through a small arc, the prongs of the tuning fork and the molecules of air execute a form of vibratory motion called *simple harmonic motion*. A body showing this type of motion is said to obey Hooke's law, since the force required to displace the body is proportional to the amount of the displacement. Simple harmonic motion is equivalent to the projection of the motion of a point which moves around a circle at a constant rate, as illustrated in figure 17.16. Here R is the projection of the point P, which moves in a counterclockwise direction around the circle. As P rotates at a constant angular velocity ω (in radians per second), R moves up and down on the vertical axis, executing the same type of motion as the prong of the tuning fork. If we plot the position of R as a function of the angular displacement of P, we have in effect spread out its motion in time. The curve thus generated is called a sinusoid, since the distance OR is proportional to the sine of the angle POM, which is measured by ωt, the product of the angular velocity and the time elapsed since the point P was at M. A writing point attached to a tuning fork vibrating against a revolving smoked drum makes a similar tracing. It may be represented by the equation

$$y = A \sin \omega t$$

where y is the displacement OR, and A is the length of the radius vector OP. The crest, where the angle ωt is $\pi/2$, represents the region of compression, and the trough, where ωt is $3\pi/2$, represents the region of rarefaction of a longitudinal sound-wave. At these points y is at its maximum value A, called the *amplitude* of the wave.

In one revolution of P the sinusoid completes one *cycle*. The number of cycles per second is called the *frequency*, f; its reciprocal, the duration of one cycle, is called the *period*, T. Since there are 2π radians in a circle, the relation of the angular velocity ω to the frequency is given by the equation

$$\omega = 2\pi f$$

A body may execute two forms of harmonic motion at the same time. This motion is represented in figure 17.16 by a second sinusoid of twice the frequency but smaller amplitude. It is also represented by the rotation of point P' about the smaller circle at twice the angular velocity of P. At the instant illustrated, P' leads in *phase* by the angle ϕ. Adding the two curves would give a third curve showing the resultant motion of the body. The addition of other harmonic motions of various amplitudes and phases would give a resultant wave-form of greater and greater *complexity*.

A sound consisting of a single frequency is called a *pure tone*. A tone having 5 per cent of its energy at other frequencies than the lowest or the *fundamental* frequency is said to have "5 per cent distortion," or to be "95 per cent pure." Although the sounds used in measuring hearing often approximate pure tones, those of musical instruments are always more or less complex. They consist of a fundamental frequency or *first harmonic*, and a number of higher harmonics or *partials*, which are simple multiples of the fundamental frequency. The higher harmonics give to the tone of the instrument its characteristic *quality*.

In a sound wave, the individual molecules of air move to and fro in simple harmonic motion for very short distances. Their speed of movement is called the *particle-velocity*. It is zero at the troughs and crests of the waves, and reaches a maximum of a fraction of a millimeter per second as the particle passes its position of rest. The *velocity of propagation* of the sound wave is much greater, varying with the density and elasticity of the medium. In air at 0° C. it is 331 meters per second, increasing somewhat at higher temperatures. In water the velocity is over 1400 meters per second, and in a rigid solid such as ivory, which has physical properties resembling those of the petrous bone, it is 3000 meters per second. The *wavelength* of sound, the distance travelled by sound in one period, is equal to the velocity of sound divided by its frequency. Thus a 1000-cycle tone in air has a wavelength of about 0.33 meter, whereas a 100-cycle tone has a wavelength of 3.3 meters. In water the wavelengths are about four times as great.

When sound in air encounters an obstacle in its path which is small relative to the wavelength, the sound waves are *diffracted* around the obstacle. It is this process of diffraction that enables us to hear around corners. Only if the obstacle is relatively large does it cast a significant "sound shadow." A part of the energy is *reflected*, and in suitable conditions gives rise to an *echo*. The multiple reflections of sound from the walls of a room are called *reverberations*. A third portion of the energy is absorbed and transmitted by the obstacle. The amount of energy transmitted depends upon the relationship of the *specific acoustic resistances* of the medium and the obstacle. These are $R_1 = \sqrt{\rho_1 S_1}$ and $R_2 = \sqrt{\rho_2 S_2}$, where ρ_1 and ρ_2 are the densities of the medium and the obstacle, and S_1 and S_2 are their respective elasticities. If r is used to represent the ratio R_2/R_1, then the fraction of the energy transmitted is expressed by

$$T = \frac{4r}{(r+1)^2}$$

whereas the energy reflected is represented by the remainder $1 - T$. If the specific acoustic resistances are similar, then r approaches 1 and T approaches 1. Most of the energy is transmitted, and very little is reflected. If, on the other hand, the properties of the medium and

the obstacle are very different, then r becomes large and T becomes small, so that the obstacle becomes a sound mirror, and the greater part of the energy is reflected.

A body at rest can be forced to vibrate if it is coupled to another vibrating body, either directly or through the medium of the air. Thus the motion of a tuning fork can be transmitted to a table top by pressing the base of the fork firmly against the table. If a body is forced to vibrate at its natural frequency, the transmitted effect is greatly enhanced, and the body is said to *resonate*. Resonance may be illustrated by singing a brief note while pressing the loud pedal of a piano, so that the dampers are lifted and the strings are allowed to vibrate freely. Those strings with the same natural frequencies as the voice resonate in response, and the note is still heard faintly after the singing has stopped.

Since the ear functions only in response to forced vibration, it is important to examine this phenomenon further. In the example of the tuning fork we have seen that when a body is caused to vibrate by applying a momentary force, it vibrates at its own natural frequency. Because of damping, the amplitude of the vibrations decreases exponentially, and they gradually die out. When a *periodic* force is suddenly applied to a body at rest, it gives a similar *transient* response at its natural frequency. The transient dies out more or less rapidly depending upon the degree of damping, but a *steady-state* response at the frequency of the driving force remains. Since we are not troubled by the persistence of transient responses in our own ears, it is clear that the damping of the ear must be very great.

The response of a vibrating body to an external force is limited by the mechanical impedance of the body. The amplitude of motion is directly proportional to the applied force, and inversely proportional to the mechanical impedance. The mechanical impedance is a complex function made up of three terms: the *mass reactance*, the *elastic reactance*, and the *frictional resistance*, all measured in mechanical ohms. The first two terms are dependent upon the frequency, but the third is not. In mathematical symbols, the expression for mass reactance is

$$X_m = 2\pi f \cdot m$$

where $2\pi f$ is the angular frequency and m is the mass (in grams). The elastic reactance is

$$X_e = \frac{S}{2\pi f},$$

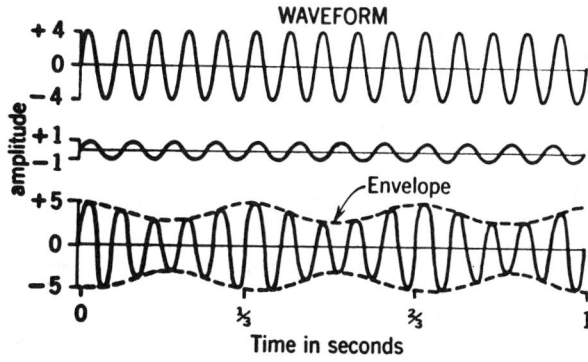 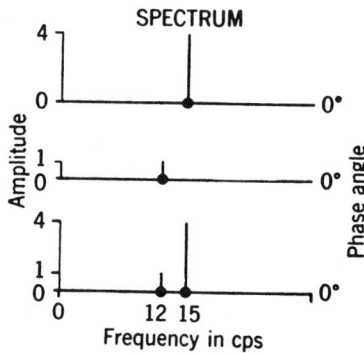

Fig. 17.17. Frequency analysis of a complex wave consisting of two components of different amplitude. (Reprinted with permission from Licklider in *Handbook of Experimental Psychology*, edited by S. S. Stevens, John Wiley and Sons, Inc., 1951.)

where S represents the stiffness in dynes per centimeter. The complete expression for mechanical impedance, Z, is

$$Z = \sqrt{\left(2\pi f m - \frac{S}{2\pi f}\right)^2 + R_m^2}$$

where R_m is the frictional resistance in ohms.

Mechanical impedance is directly analogous to electrical impedance in alternating current circuits, where inductance corresponds to mass, capacitance to the reciprocal of the stiffness (compliance) and the electrical to the frictional resistance. We shall see the importance of the impedance concept when we come to consider the transmission of sound across the middle ear to the cochlea.

The Dimensions of Sound

Waveform and Spectrum

In order to investigate hearing we must be able to measure and specify the sound stimuli that give rise to hearing. Sound waves in air consist in minute variations in pressure above and below the existing atmospheric pressure. If we plot these variations as a function of time for the simple case of a pure tone, we obtain a sinusoidal curve representing the *pressure waveform* for the tone (fig. 17.17). It has two dimensions, *amplitude* and *time*. Frequency is expressed by the number of cycles per second, in this instance 1000 c.p.s. The same information can be presented by plotting amplitude against frequency to show the *spectrum*, which for a pure tone consists of a single component. It is represented in the figure 17.17 by a vertical line, the height of which indicates the maximum amplitude or peak pressure of the tone.

Fourier (1822) discovered that any waveform,

however complex, can be analyzed into a series of simple sinusoids. An example of frequency analysis is given in figure 17.17. On the left, two frequencies of 12 and 15 c.p.s. are shown, with the complex wave produced by combining them. On the right, the spectrum of each indicates the amplitudes and frequencies of the respective components. Figure 17.18 also shows the waveforms of several types of auditory stimuli, with the spectrum of each. The square wave (*B*) has a *line spectrum*, consisting of a fundamental of 1000 c.p.s. and a series of odd-numbered harmonics (3000, 5000, 7000 etc., c.p.s.), of decreasing amplitudes. The train of pulses (*C*) shows both odd and even harmonics, but the amplitudes are smaller. Furthermore, the phase is shifted by 90° because the pulses are not symmetrical about the baseline as the square waves are. The single pulse (*D*) consists of a uniform, continuous spectrum. The amplitude of each component is extremely small, and again the phase is shifted by 90°.

"White" noise (*E*) gets its name from the fact that, like white light, it consists of a random mixture of all frequencies. The spectrum is continuous, with uniform amplitude and random phase. White noise we have always with us, in the thermal agitation or Brownian movement of the air molecules, just below the threshold of hearing. The random movements of electrons in conductors and vacuum tubes also produce white noise, which is audible as the characteristic background "s-h-h-h" from a phonograph or radio.

The spectrum for the short tone of 3000 c.p.s. (*F*) shows that when the tone is turned on and off other frequencies appear above and below 3000 c.p.s. This is always the case when a tone

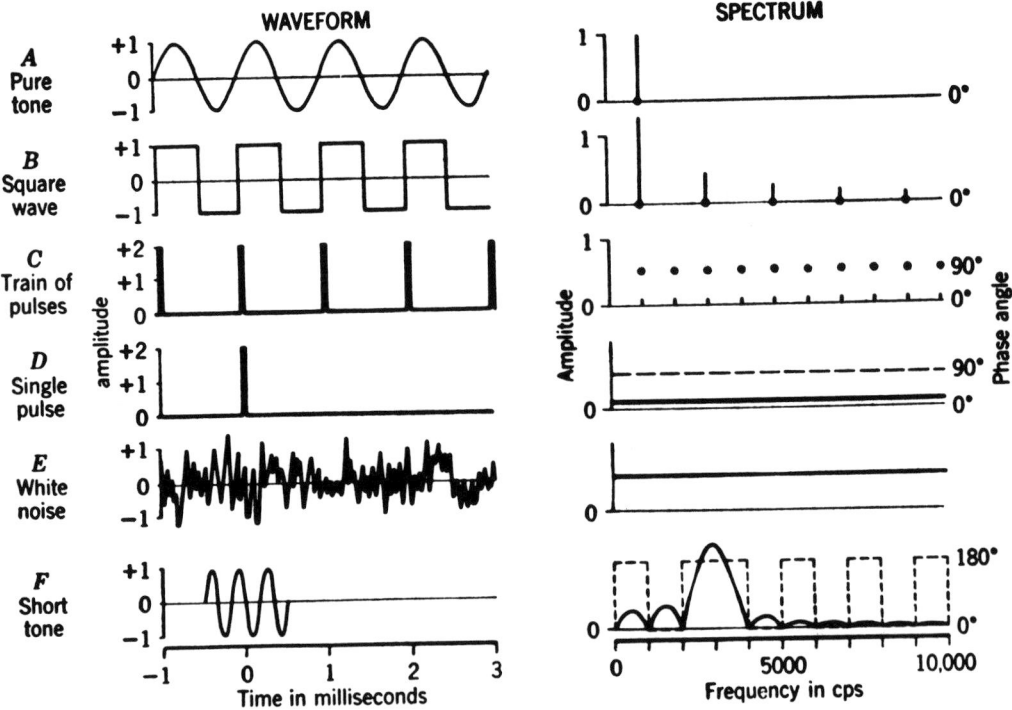

Fig. 17.18. Waveforms and spectra for various types of auditory stimulus. (Reprinted with permission from Licklider in *Handbook of Experimental Psychology*, edited by S. S. Stevens, John Wiley and Sons, Inc., 1951.)

is changed in frequency, amplitude or phase. Only a tone of infinite duration is ideally pure.

The sounds of speech form a constantly changing pattern of complex tones, noise and transients. Although measurements of an average spectrum show that frequencies below 1000 c.p.s. carry most of the energy, it is the transients of higher frequency that provide most of the perceptual clues to the listener.

THE MEASUREMENT OF SOUND INTENSITY

The amplitudes of movement of the air particles in sound waves are exceedingly small, varying from about 10^{-9} cm. for sounds that are barely audible to 10^{-2} cm. for sounds sufficiently intense to injure the inner ear. Although the velocity of the air particles can be determined with great accuracy by noting the force that they exert on a light disk suspended in the path of the sound waves (Rayleigh, 1882), the most convenient measure of sound intensity is the alternating pressure produced by the motion of the particles. This value is readily determined by measuring the electric current generated by a suitably calibrated condenser microphone placed in the sound field. (For measuring the sound

pressure in a confined space such as the external canal, a narrow calibrated probe-tube is attached to the microphone.) Sound pressure can be expressed as the maximum or peak pressure (P_{max}) or as the root-mean-square (rms) pressure which represents an average of all the pressures from moment to moment. For a sine wave, the rms pressure

$$P_{rms} = \frac{P_{max}}{\sqrt{2}} = 0.707 \ P_{max}$$

For noise or speech the peak pressures may vary from one instant to the next over a wide range. The rms values are more stable and are therefore generally used for expressing sound pressures. The pressures of ordinary sounds amount to no more than a fraction of 1 dyne/cm.², in contrast to the atmospheric pressure of about 10^6 dynes/cm.².

We use the term intensity loosely to mean sound pressure, particle velocity or amplitude of movement, sound energy or power. Strictly speaking it should apply only to power or energy. We must now examine some of the relationships among these various quantities. If we know the sound pressure P and the specific acoustic resistance R of the medium, then the particle velocity u, measured in centimeters per second is

$$u = \frac{P}{R}$$

This is clearly analogous to the relationship of electric current to electromotive force and resistance, as expressed by Ohm's law:

$$I = \frac{E}{R}$$

For plane waves, the amplitude of particle movement, or displacement (in centimeters) is

$$d = \frac{P}{2\pi f R}$$

where f is the frequency.

The power J is equal to the pressure times the velocity, or

$$J = P \cdot u = \frac{P^2}{R}.$$

J is measured in ergs per second per cm.^{2} or in microwatts per cm.^{2}, since 10 ergs per second = 1 microwatt. Similarly, the energy is proportional to the square of the sound pressure, just as electric energy and power are proportional to the square of the electromotive force.

The Decibel Notation

In practice, measurements of sound intensity are not expressed as absolute magnitudes. Instead, a given intensity is compared with a standard value by expressing the ratio between the two. Because of the enormous range of intensities involved, it is convenient to express these ratios as logarithms. If one intensity is 10 times as great as another, their ratio is 10 and the logarithm (to the base 10) of the ratio is 1. The two intensities are said to differ by 1 *bel* (named for Dr. Alexander Graham Bell, inventor of the telephone). A more practical unit is one-tenth of a bel, the *decibel* (dB). We may therefore express the number of decibels corresponding to a ratio between two intensities (i.e., powers) as

$$N_{(db)} = 10 \log_{10} \frac{J}{J_o}$$

where J_o is a standard or reference power.

Since power is proportional to the square of the sound pressure, we can also write

$$N_{(db)} = 10 \log_{10} \frac{P^2}{P_o{}^2}$$

$$= 20 \log_{10} \frac{P}{P_o}.$$

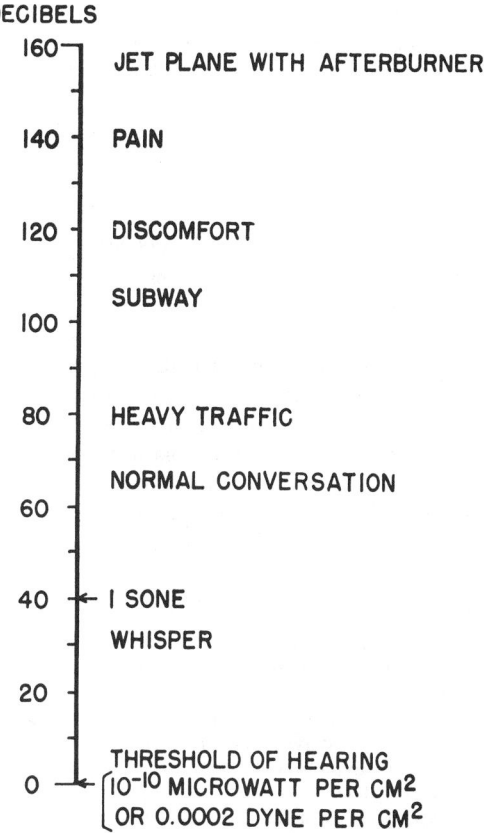

DECIBELS

160 — JET PLANE WITH AFTERBURNER

140 — PAIN

120 — DISCOMFORT

SUBWAY

100 —

80 — HEAVY TRAFFIC

NORMAL CONVERSATION

60 —

40 — I SONE

WHISPER

20 —

THRESHOLD OF HEARING
0 — [10^{-10} MICROWATT PER CM^2
OR 0.0002 DYNE PER CM^2

Fig. 17.19. A decibel scale for sound, showing approximate intensity levels produced by various sources. The *sone* is the unit of loudness; it is defined as the loudness of a 1,000-c.p.s. tone at 40-dB intensity level. (From Stevens, Laryngoscope, **68**, 512, 1958.)

Therefore, if one sound has a pressure 10 times as great as another, they are said to differ by 20 dB. The ratio of the powers is 100, but the difference between them in decibels is still 20 dB. The decibel notation is also used in comparing electric powers, voltages and currents.

Like all logarithmic scales, the decibel scale is particularly convenient because it is compressed. The intensity ratio between sounds that pose an immediate threat to the organ of Corti and those that are just at the threshold of hearing is approximately one hundred million million or 10^{14}:1, yet this vast range is expressed by only 140 dB. Furthermore, if we multiply the power with an amplifier or divide it with an attenuator, we add or subtract decibels. If a sound 60 dB above the reference level is amplified by 20 dB (corresponding to a 100-fold increase in its power) its new intensity is 60 + 20 = 80 dB. We must always remember, however, that the decibel scale has no absolute zero point. When we write *0 dB*, we are simply expressing a power or pressure ratio of 1:1. Therefore the reference level must always be given if decibel readings are used to represent absolute values. Some investigators use a "zero level" of 1 dyne/cm.². The *standard reference level* adopted by the American Standards Association is 10^{-16} watt per cm.². This corresponds to a 0-dB pressure level of 0.000204 dyne/cm.², or 2×10^{-5} N/m^2. (The *Newton*, a unit of force, is equal to 10^5 dynes.) Sound level meters are usually calibrated to measure sound pressure levels in decibels above 0.0002 dyne/cm.². This value approximates the least intensity that can be heard by the normal human ear. A decibel scale showing the approximate intensities of sounds from various sources in relation to the normal threshold of hearing and the unit of loudness, 1 *sone*, is shown in figure 17.19.

REFERENCES

BAST, T. H. AND ANSON, B. J. The temporal bone and the ear. Charles C Thomas, Springfield, Ill., 1949.

VAN BERGEIJK, W. A., PIERCE, J. R., AND DAVID, E. E., JR. Waves and the ear. Anchor Books, Doubleday and Company, Inc., Garden City, N. Y., 1960.

CANDIOLLO, L., FILOGAMO, G., AND ROSSI, G. *Le basi morfo-funzionali del controllo delle sensazioni acustiche.* Società Italiana di Laringologia Otologia e Rinologia, Torino, 1965.

ENGSTRÖM, H. Elektronoptische Histologie des Innenohres. In *Hals-Nasen-Ohren-Heilkunde* (J. Berendes, R. Link, and F. Zöllner, eds.) Band III/Teil 1, 148. Georg Thieme Verlag, Stuttgart, 1965.

ENGSTRÖM, H., ADES, H. W., AND HAWKINS, J. E., JR. Structure and functions of the sensory hairs of the inner ear. J. Acoust. Soc. Am., 1962, 34, 1356.

ENGSTRÖM, H., ADES, H. W., AND HAWKINS, J. E., JR. Cellular patterns, nerve structures, and fluid spaces of the organ of Corti, *in* Contributions to sensory physiology, Vol. 1 (W. D. NEFF, ed.) Academic Press, New York, 1965.

FLOCK, Å, KIMURA, R., LUNDQUIST, P-G., AND WERSÄLL, J. Morphological basis of directional sensitivity of the outer hair cells in the organ of Corti. J. Acoust. Soc. Am., 1962, 34, 1351.

FRIEDMANN, I. Cytology of the ear. Brit. Med. Bull., 1962, 18, 209.

GALAMBOS, R. Neural mechanisms of audition. Physiol. Rev., 1954, 34, 497.

HAWKINS, J. E., JR. Hearing. Ann. Rev. Physiol., 1964, 26, 453.

HAWKINS, J. E., JR. Cytoarchitectural basis of the cochlear transducer. Cold Spring Harbor Symp. Quant. Biol. XXX. Sensory receptors. 1966.

IURATO, S. Submicroscopic structure of the membranous labyrinth. Z. Zellforsch, 1960, 51, 105; 1961, 53, 259; 1962, 56, 40.

IURATO, S. Functional implications of the nature and submicroscopic structure of the tectorial and basilar membranes. J. Acoust. Soc. Am., 1962, 34, 1386.

LICKLIDER, J. C. R. Basic correlates of the auditory stimulus, *in* Handbook of experimental psychology (S. S. STEVENS, ed.) John Wiley & Sons, Inc., New York, 1951.

LORENTE DE NÓ, R. Anatomy of the eighth nerve. The central projection of the nerve endings of the internal ear. Laryngoscope, 1933, 43, 1.

NEUBERT, K. AND WÜSTENFELD, E. Morphologie des akustischen Organs. Handbuch der Zoologie, 1962, 8, 1.

RASMUSSEN, G. L. AND WINDLE, W. F. (eds.) Neural mechanisms of the auditory and vestibular systems. Charles C Thomas, Springfield, Ill., 1960.

RETZIUS, G. Das Gehörorgan der Wirbelthiere, 2 vols., Samson & Wallin, Stockholm, 1881, 1884.

SMITH, C. A. Capillary areas of the membranous labyrinth. Ann. Otol. Rhinol. & Laryngol., 1954, 63, 435.

SMITH, C. A., LOWRY, O. H., AND WU, M-L. The electrolytes of the labyrinthine fluids. Laryngoscope, 1954, 64, 141.

SMITH, C. A. AND SJÖSTRAND, F. J. Structure of the nerve endings on the external hair cells of the guinea pig cochlea as studied by serial sections. J. Ultrastructure Research, 1961, 5, 523.

SPOENDLIN, H. H. AND GACEK, R. R. Electronmicroscopic study of the efferent and afferent innervation of the organ of Corti in the cat. Ann. Otol. Rhinol. & Laryngol., 1963, 72, 660.

STEVENS, S. S., AND DAVIS, H. Hearing: its psychology and physiology. John Wiley & Sons, Inc., New York, 1938.

VINNIKOV, YA. A. AND TITOVA, L. K. The organ of Corti: its histophysiology and histochemistry. Consultants Bureau, New York, 1964.

WEVER, E. G. AND LAWRENCE, M. Physiological acoustics. Princeton University Press, Princeton, N. J., 1954.

CHAPTER 18

Hearing: Biomechanics and Neurophysiology

Sensitivity and Dynamic Range of the Ear

The range of frequencies to which the normal human ear is sensitive is usually said to extend from about 20 to 20,000 c.p.s., covering approximately ten octaves. The upper and lower limits are not sharply defined, but depend to some extent upon the intensity of sound available. For the common laboratory mammals, the upper limit seems to be at least an octave higher. Bats, however, emit and hear frequencies as high as 150,000 c.p.s. when flying in the dark, catching insects and avoiding obstacles in accordance with the patterns of echoes they receive. Porpoises use very high frequencies in a similar type of echo-location or "sonar" system to find their prey in the water.

The threshold of audibility for young adult human subjects with "normal" hearing, as determined at the Bell Telephone Laboratories by Sivian and White, is shown in the lowest curve of figure 18.1. This curve represents the *minimum audible field* pressures which the subjects could hear when placed in a sound field produced by a loudspeaker in an otherwise quiet, non-reverberant environment. The pressure measurements were made by replacing the subject with a condenser microphone in the exact position occupied by the subject's head.

The region of greatest sensitivity lies between 2000 and 3000 c.p.s. This is also the region of the broad resonance peak of the external canal. Here the threshold is 6 to 8 decibels (dB) below 0.0002 dyne/cm.², i.e., 0.0001 dyne/cm² or less.

Above 5000 c.p.s. the threshold curve rises at first slowly, then abruptly; below 2000 c.p.s. the rise is more gradual. At 15,000 c.p.s. and at 100 c.p.s. the threshold intensity is approximately 40 dB higher than at 3000 c.p.s.

The values shown in this curve represent very sensitive ears having almost ideal hearing. According to an extensive survey by the U. S. Public Health Service, only 1 per cent of the population can hear sounds at or below the levels represented by the second curve, whereas half the population can hear the sounds represented by the fifth curve.

As the intensity of a sound is increased above the threshold value, the *loudness* or magnitude of the sensation increases. At about 120 dB (*re* 0.0002 dyne/cm.²) the sound is not only heard but begins to be felt as a vague sensation of discomfort in the ear. This "threshold of feeling" is indicated as the uppermost curve in figure 18.1. Still higher levels cause a tickling or pricking sensation, and may produce definite pain if they exceed 140 dB. These are the levels which readily cause temporary impairment of hearing. The area enclosed by the threshold and the "feeling" curves is sometimes called the *auditory area*. How the ear encompasses the enormous dynamic range that it represents is one of the major questions of auditory research.

Transmission of Sound to the Cochlea

THE EXTERNAL EAR. In many animals the shape and mobility of the external ear give it a directional and sound-gathering function which is of great assistance in localizing the source of a sound. In man this function of the external ear is more or less unimportant, although the shape of the concha does serve to funnel sounds of relatively short wavelength (11 cm. or less, i.e., 3000 c.p.s. and higher) into the canal. Because the canal is a closed tube, it resonates at a wavelength corresponding to four times its own length. Wiener and Ross made probe-tube measurements and found a broad resonance peak in the external canal, centering about 3800 c.p.s., which has a wavelength of 9.2 cm., or four times the average length of the canal. The chief physiological importance of the canal seems to be protective. Not only does it by its depth and shape help to shield the drum membrane from damage by blows or penetrating objects, but it also helps to maintain a favorable environmental temperature and humidity for the membrane.

THE MECHANICAL IMPEDANCE OF THE EAR. Part of the sound energy reaching the drum is reflected back, whereas the rest is absorbed by the drum, setting it in motion. How much energy is reflected and how much is absorbed are functions of the mechanical impedance of the ear. If the drum behaved like a rigid plug, presenting an infinite impedance, all of the energy would be reflected. If,

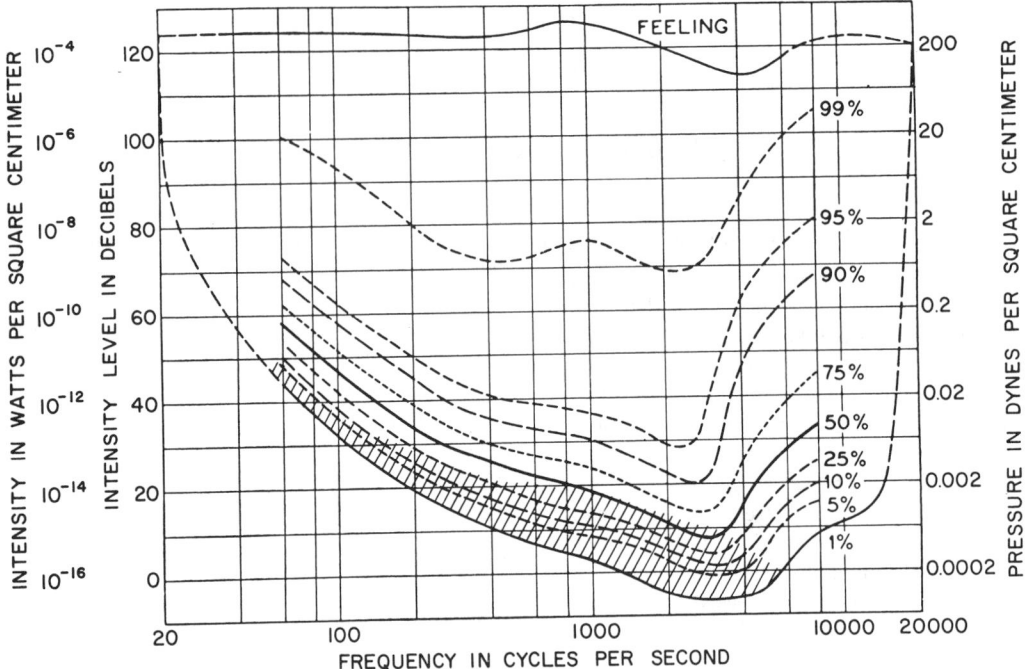

FIG. 18.1. Threshold contours for a typical group of listeners (U. S. Public Health Service Survey). Figures show percentage of group able to hear sounds below the given level. The 1 per cent curve represents ideal normal ears (Sivian and White). Shaded area represents masking by average room noise. (From Fletcher, *Speech and Hearing in Communication*, 2nd edition, 1953, D. Van Nostrand Company, Inc., Princeton, N. J.)

on the other hand, its impedance were precisely matched to that of the air in the external canal, all of the energy would be absorbed and none would be reflected. The impedance is not constant, but varies as a function of the frequency of the sound being transmitted by the ear. At low frequencies it is determined chiefly by the stiffness of the system, at high frequencies by the mass. At intermediate frequencies the frictional resistance alone is the determining factor.

The impedance of the ear is complex, consisting of the summed impedances of: (a) the tympanic membrane, malleus, and incus; (b) the middle ear cavities; and (c) the stapes, cochlea, and round window membrane. Energy leaks occur at the coupling between the eardrum and the malleus, where some energy is absorbed by the flexible drum membrane, and at the incudo-stapedial joint which, unlike the rigid malleo-incudal joint, allows considerable freedom of motion. Zwislocki has analyzed these component impedances experimentally and in terms of an electrical network analog of the ear, from which he has derived the transmission characteristic of the ear shown in fig. 18.2. This curve expresses the ratio between the sound pressure in a free field and the maxi-

mum volume displacement of the basilar membrane. It shows that the impedance of the ear is greatest at low frequencies, declining to a broad minimum between 1000 and 4000 c.p.s. and rising again at the higher frequencies. Comparison with the average threshold curve indicates that the sensitivity of the ear is determined largely by its acoustical properties as expressed in the transmission characteristic. Differences between the two curves are attributed to such factors as increasing temporal summation with increasing frequency (which accounts for an increase in sensitivity of 3 dB/octave) and a supposed reduction in the density of innervation of the organ of Corti toward the apex.

THE TYMPANIC MEMBRANE. Von Békésy has made direct measurements of the amplitude of movements of the drum membrane as small as 10^{-5} mm. For this purpose he used a small capacitative probe, with its fixed plate 2 to 3 mm. in diameter and placed 0.5 mm. from the drum membrane, which itself formed the other plate. A high-frequency voltage of 100,000 c.p.s. was then applied across this condenser. When the drum vibrated, its movements varied the capacity and thus modulated the high-frequency current. By measuring the modulated current he was able to calculate the displacement of the drum membrane.

Using this probe to measure the amplitude of motion of different portions of the drum membrane in response to a constant stimulus, v. Békésy found that, at all frequencies up to 2400 c.p.s., the whole central conical portion of the drum and the handle of the malleus move as a unit about an axis of rotation passing through the anterior and lateral processes. Figure 18.3 shows the contours of equal amplitude of movement for a tone of 2000 c.p.s. The amplitude is greatest near the inferior edge of the membrane. Above 2400 c.p.s. the membrane no longer vibrates as a stiff cone (as in fig. 18.4) but in segments, with the manubrium lagging behind the adjacent portions of the membrane.

THE TRANSFORMER ACTION OF THE MIDDLE EAR. Sound waves do not pass readily from one medium to another of different acoustical resistance, but are largely reflected at the boundary between the two media. Between air with an acoustical resistance of only 41.5 mechanical ohms per sq. cm. and sea water with a resistance of 161,000, the impedance mismatch is obviously very great. Only 0.1 per cent of the energy of sound would be transmitted, representing a loss of 30 dB. A similar loss would occur in the transmission of sound from the air in the external canal to the fluids in the cochlea if the middle ear mechanism did not act as a transformer to match the widely different impedances. This change from a slight pressure exerted over the large area of the drum to a greater pressure exerted over the smaller area of the stapes footplate is accomplished by the acoustical lever system formed by the drum and

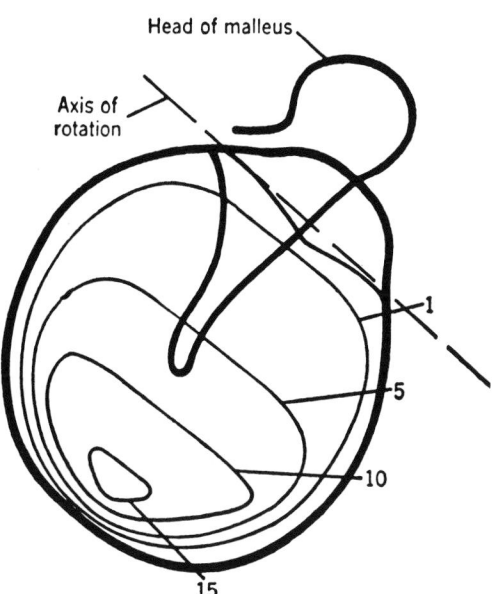

FIG. 18.3. Vibration patterns of the human drum membrane for a 2000-c.p.s. tone. (Reproduced by permission from v. Békésy and Rosenblith in *Handbook of Experimental Psychology*, Ed. by S. S. Stevens, John Wiley and Sons, Inc., New York, 1951.)

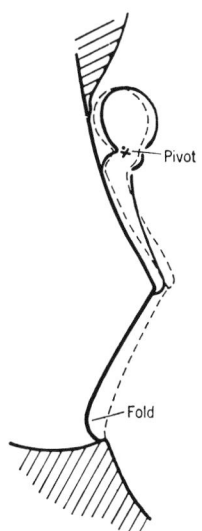

FIG. 18.4. Vibration of the drum membrane as a rigid cone at low frequencies. (Reproduced by permission from v. Békésy and Rosenblith in *Handbook of Experimental Psychology*, Ed. by S. S. Stevens, John Wiley and Sons, Inc., New York, 1951.)

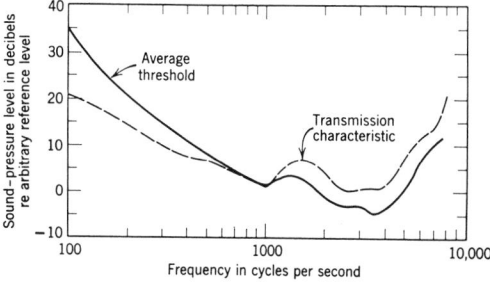

FIG. 18.2. Transmission characteristic of the ear compared with the average threshold of hearing as measured under free-field conditions. (From J. Zwislocki, Analysis of some auditory characteristics, in Handbook of Mathematical Psychology, Vol. III, Ed. by R. D. Luce, R. R. Bush and E. Galanter, John Wiley & Sons, Inc., New York, 1965.)

ossicles. The total area of the drum membrane is about 69 sq. mm. and its effective area is about 43 sq. mm., whereas the area of the footplate is only 3.2 sq. mm. This 13-fold reduction in area

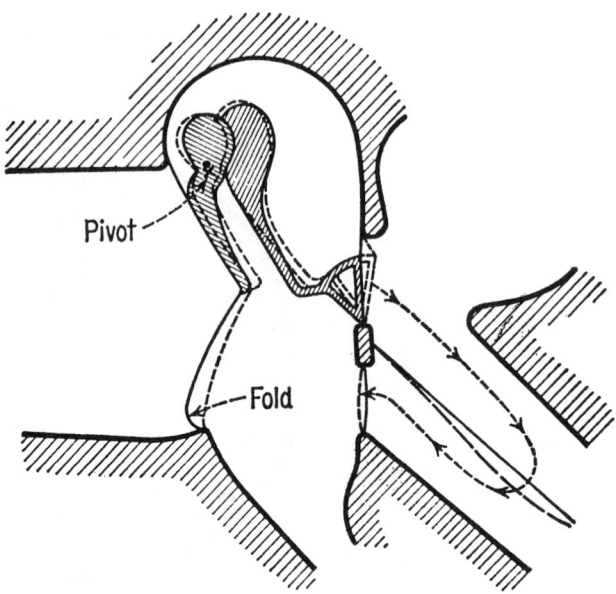

FIG. 18.5. Schematic diagram of movements of the tympanic membrane, the ossicles and the basilar membrane. (Reproduced by permission from H. Davis in *Hearing and Deafness*, Holt, Rinehart and Winston, Inc., 1960.)

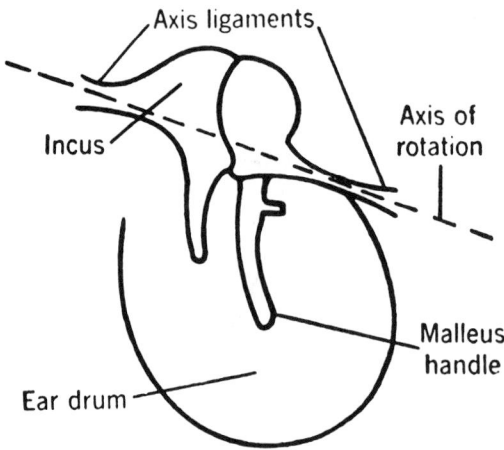

FIG. 18.6. The distribution of the mass of the ossicles about their axis of rotation. (Reproduced by permission from v. Békésy and Rosenblith in *Handbook of Experimental Psychology*, Ed. by S. S. Stevens, John Wiley and Sons, Inc., New York, 1951.)

gives a corresponding increase in pressure at the oval window. Since an additional mechanical advantage of approximately 1.3 is available because the handle of the malleus is longer than the long process of the incus, the pressure exerted by the footplate is approximately 17 times as great as that at the drum membrane.

According to Zwislocki, the middle ear transformer effectively reduces the input impedance of the inner ear from the theoretical value of 5600 cgs units to 193 cgs units. This value is still $4\frac{1}{2}$ times that of air. In the ideal situation, without the energy losses introduced by imperfect coupling, only 40 per cent of the incident sound energy would be reflected from the eardrum, a satisfactorily small figure for any acoustic system.

An additional virtue of the middle ear mechanism is that it provides for selective delivery of sound energy to one cochlear window rather than to both. If both windows were equally exposed to sound, little transfer of energy would occur because it would be opposed by the inertia and incompressibility of the cochlear fluids contained in the unyielding bony capsule. As it is, the fluids offer much less resistance because the round window is free to move outward as the stapes footplate moves inward, and *vice versa* (fig. 18.5).

MECHANICS OF THE OSSICLES. The mass of the malleus and incus is evenly distributed above and below their axis of rotation, as shown in figure 18.6. Since they are suspended by elastic ligaments and closely bound together, they move in and out as a unit. In response to moderate pressures the stapes follows them, so that the whole chain vibrates as a single mass. According to v. Békésy, the footplate of the stapes rocks about its lower, posterior pole, moving like a bell-crank lever rather than a piston (fig. 18.5). When the intensity of a low-frequency tone rises above a critical value, this mode of vibration is said to change, so that the footplate rotates about its long axis. The amplitude of motion is thus reduced, so that less energy is transmitted to the cochlear fluids, and the risk of damage to the organ of Corti is lessened.

The intra-aural muscles provide another means of partial protection against intense sounds of low frequency. When the tensor tympani contracts, it pulls the handle of the malleus and the drum membrane inward. When the stapedius contracts, it pulls the footplate outward from the oval window. The effect of simultaneous contractions is to restrict the motion of the ossicular chain. Wiggers has shown in animal experiments that the transmission of low frequencies to the cochlea is sharply reduced, whereas that for frequencies around 1300 c.p.s. is slightly increased, as if the stiffness of the middle ear mechanism had been increased by the contractions. Higher frequencies are unaffected. The stapedius responds reflexly to sound (the acoustic reflex), much as the eyelid and the sphincter of the iris respond reflexly to light. Just as in the eye, the reflex is consensual, so that a sound stimulus applied to one ear elicits muscle contractions in both ears. The protection offered against intense sounds is only partial at best. According to R. Wersäll, the reflex latency in the decorticate rabbit is 10 msec. for the stapedius and 17 msec. for the tensor tympani. Maximum tension is attained by the two muscles only after 63 and 132 msec., and in this time the ear can suffer severe injury from the initial waves of the noise of an explosion. If, however, the acoustic reflex is activated by pre-exposure to a 1000-c.p.s. tone at about 100 dB SPL, it can give significant protection to an ear exposed to the noise of machine-gun fire (Fletcher and Riopelle).

The high-pass filtering action of the acoustic reflex appears to have another, greater biological value than to provide an imperfect defense against such high levels of man-made noise. By restricting the transmission of the lower frequencies, which carry relatively little information, the reflex reduces their masking effect upon the higher frequencies with their much greater information content, whether for the recognition of danger in the wild or for the understanding of human speech.

The Cochlea

FREQUENCY ANALYSIS. Many attempts have been made to explain the role of the cochlea in the process of hearing, and particularly in the perception of pitch. Some investigators have held that the cochlea performs a frequency analysis of sound, whereas others have reserved that function to the brain. In formulating his *resonance theory* (1863), Helmholtz postulated a series of resonators in the cochlea, each tuned to a different frequency. He first suggested that the rods of Corti with their varying heights might serve as the resonators. Later he proposed the fibers of the basilar membrane, which he compared to the strings of a harp or pianoforte, postulating that the shorter fibers near the oval window respond to higher frequencies and the longer fibers near the apex to lower frequencies. In opposition to the resonance theory Rutherford (1880) put forward his *telephone theory*, ascribing to the cochlea the simpler role of a telephone transmitter. He thought of it as transforming sounds into nerve impulses of the same frequency, which were then analyzed in the central nervous system.

The resonance theory continued to encounter the difficulty that no individual resonators could be identified. Gradually it evolved into the more widely accepted *place theory*, which holds that the entire cochlea is a tuned structure, with different portions of the basilar membrane and organ of Corti responding to sounds of different frequency. The corresponding nerve fibers then report to the brain which portions of the organ of Corti are being stimulated. The telephone theory on the other hand made it necessary to assume that the auditory nerve fibers have the unique property of responding at much higher rates than the theoretical maximum of 1000 impulses per second attributed to other nerve fibers of large diameter. At the same time it left entirely unexplored the question of how the brain might perform a frequency analysis. The implications and shortcomings of those two major theories and of variants put forward by other students of hearing have been reviewed by Wever (1949). He has shown that the two theories, so long thought to be irreconcilably opposed to each other, can be combined in his *resonance-volley theory*, which uses the telephone or volley principle to explain the response of the whole cochlea to low frequencies and the place or resonance principle to explain the cochlear analysis of higher frequencies. Both principles now have a solid basis of experimental fact derived from two types of investigation: (a) the study of the mechanics of the cochlear partition, and (b) the study of the electrical potentials of the organ of Corti.

MECHANICS OF THE COCHLEAR PARTITION. Von Békésy has shown, by painstaking evaluation of

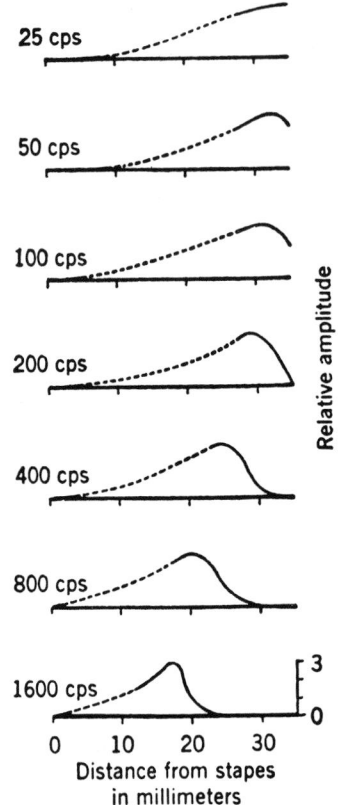

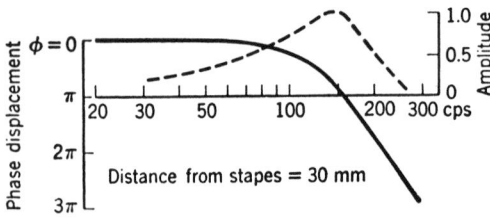

Fig. 18.7. Amplitude of displacement of the cochlear partition at various frequencies. (v. Békésy, J. Acoust. Soc. Am., **21**, 245, 1949.)

Fig. 18.8. The dashed curve represents the amplitude of displacement of a point 30 mm. from the stapes at different frequencies. The solid curve shows the phase lag behind the motion of the stapes. At frequencies over 150 c.p.s., the phase angle is greater than π, indicating that motion is due to travelling waves and not to a simple resonance. (v. Békésy, J. Acoust. Soc. Am., **21**, 245, 1949.)

the physical properties of the various membranes and tissues that make up the cochlear partition, and by direct microscopic observation of their patterns of movement under stroboscopic illumination, that the place principle is correct. The cochlea is indeed a tuned structure which performs a frequency analysis of sound. Part of the tuning is provided by the gradually increasing width of the basilar membrane, from the

basal end of the cochlea to the helicotrema, and part by the gradually increasing mass of the organ of Corti in the same direction. The most important factor is the graded stiffness of the basilar membrane, which is greatest at the stapes and decreases steadily towards the apex. As a result, the stiffness, or "volume elasticity," of the cochlear partition as a whole is said to be about 100 times as great at the stapes as it is at the apex.

The basilar membrane may be thought of as a gelatinous sheet covered by a thin, homogeneous layer of fibers, forming a continuous structure with the organ of Corti. Surprisingly enough, the membrane is not under tension, and therefore does not in any way resemble the strings of a piano as Helmholtz thought. Coupling between adjacent portions is both elastic and frictional, and much of the frictional coupling is furnished by the endolymph and perilymph. As a result of the gradation in stiffness, the resonant frequency of the cochlear partition is highest at the stapes and decreases along its length, but because of the coupling the various portions cannot respond independently as separate tuned resonators.

Observing the movements of the cochlear partition under the microscope, v. Békésy found that each part shows a maximum displacement for a certain frequency of sound. This maximum displacement moves towards the stapes as the frequency is raised (fig. 18.7), and towards the apex as the frequency is lowered. The amplitude of vibration at a given point plotted as a function of frequency resembles a resonance curve, but there is a vital difference. For a simple resonator like a pendulum, the phase angle changes from $\pi/2$ to $-\pi/2$ as the driving frequency is changed, and at the point of resonance the phase angle is zero. When the phase relations of the cochlear partition are measured, it is seen that the basilar membrane, the organ of Corti, the tectorial and Reissner's membranes all move together in phase. However, the phase lag between the movement of the stapes and that of a point on the basilar membrane near the helicotrema increases from 0 to 3π as the frequency is increased (figs. 18.8 and 18.9). Von Békésy has pointed out that this phase shift indicates the presence of travelling waves rather than a simple resonance.

The travelling waves are generated because the stiffest portion of the cochlear partition near the stapes in a sense drives the more flexible portions. Near the stapes the partition vibrates in response to all frequencies. As the waves move along the partition their amplitude gradually increases and

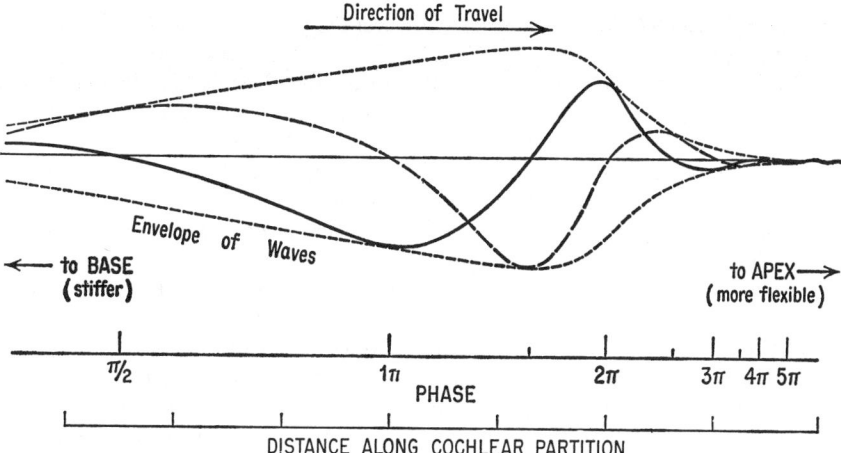

FIG. 18.9. The travelling wave pattern on the basilar membrane, showing the primary and secondary waves and the shortening of the wave length as the travelling wave pattern nears the apex. (Reproduced by permission from H. Davis in *Hearing and Deafness*, Holt, Rinehart and Winston, Inc., 1960.)

reaches a maximum at the point where the natural frequency of the partition is the same as the driving frequency. Beyond this point the amplitude decreases rapidly as the velocity of travel diminishes and the wavelength grows shorter and shorter in the more flexible portions of the membrane. So great is the retardation that a single wave set up by a sudden, brief sound requires about 5 msec. to travel from the stapes to the helicotrema.

The travelling waves are demonstrable in the human cochlea only at frequencies above 150 c.p.s. At lower frequencies the basilar membrane moves more and more as a unit, so that below 50 c.p.s. the entire cochlear partition is moving in phase and the maximum amplitude occurs very close to the helicotrema.

On the basis of his measurements of the physical characteristics of the cochlear partition, v. Békésy constructed models of the cochlea in which the travelling waves could readily be demonstrated. One of the most instructive of these models consisted of a plastic tube cast around a brass tube with a slit. When the tube was filled with fluid and the fluid set in motion by a vibrating piston at one end, travelling waves were set up with broad maxima that shifted with frequency over a two-octave range. The forearm placed lengthwise along the vibrating membrane provided a sensory surface representing the organ of Corti. As the frequency of vibration was changed the maximum could be felt to move along the arm. Although the maximum was quite broad and flat, the sensation of vibration was much more concentrated, so that any frequency shift

could readily be recognized by a shift in the place of stimulation. Even with very brief tones lasting for only two cycles, the "pitch" discrimination was excellent. Some inhibitory process in the cutaneous innervation on either side of the maximum was presumably responsible for "sharpening" the pattern of stimulation. A similar mechanism, which v. Békésy has called "funneling," is thought to act in the organ of Corti to aid in the discrimination of frequency.

The Organ of Corti

THE FINE MOVEMENTS. Although the gross pattern of movement of the cochlear partition permits the cochlea to perform a frequency analysis, it does not account for the actual transfer of energy to the hair cells. This stimulation has been attributed by v. Békésy and Davis to a double transformation, first of the up-and-down movement of the basilar membrane into a rocking motion of the rods of Corti and reticular lamina, and then into a shearing motion between the lamina and the tectorial membrane. According to this view, the shearing motion causes a bending of the hairs, which is considered to be the essential mechanical step in stimulating the hair cells. Engström *et al.* (1962) prefer to regard the hairs (stereocilia) simply as stiff micro-levers, which transmit the vibrations of the tectorial membrane to the cuticular plate and thus to the interior of the hair cell. They suggest that the modified kinocilium represented by the basal body is the essential excitatory structure of the hair cell, in view of the importance of modified kinocilia in many other types of sensory cells. Electron microscopic studies of Flock *et al.* have shown that the hair cells are polarized by the position of the basal body for one direction of movement, viz., away from the modiolus.

The movements of the basilar membrane at the threshold of hearing, as calculated and extrapolated from measurements of the vibrations of the malleus by Wilska and of the stapes by v. Békésy, are almost unbelievably tiny. They are estimated to be of the order of 0.1 Å (10^{-9} cm.) and must therefore be far less than the thickness of the plasma membrane of the hair cells. Contemplation of these subatomic dimensions strongly suggests that it cannot be mechanical displacement as such that excites the hair cells at threshold, but rather some molecular or ionic phenomenon the nature of which is unknown. In these circumstances Vinnikov and Titova's description of the stereocilia as "chemo-sensitive antennae" becomes more appealing and offers a new direction for research on this baffling problem, which has recently been discussed by both Lawrence and Naftalin.

THE ELECTRICAL RESPONSES. Attempting to observe the patterns of impulses in the auditory nerve in response to sound, Wever and Bray (1930) made the surprising discovery that the electrical potentials picked up from the nerve reproduced almost perfectly the frequencies and wave-forms of the sounds reaching the ear. Although this finding seemed at first to support Rutherford's telephone theory, it was soon demonstrated by Davis and Saul that two distinct types of potentials were involved: the cochlear microphonic potential (CM) and the action potentials of the auditory nerve fibers (AP). Although the AP response showed the typical threshold and refractory period, and differed in no way from the action potentials of other nerves, the CM response which preceded it in time had no all-or-none properties, but closely reproduced the wave-form and polarity of the stimulus. More recent studies by von Békésy and by Davis and his collaborators have shown that five different types of electrical potentials can be recorded from the cochlea by means of fine electrodes inserted into the scalae. Two of these are dc resting potentials. The others are responses to sound stimuli.

Cortilymphatic potential. Like other cells, the hair cells and supporting cells of the cochlea presumably have a negative intracellular potential with respect to the fluid that bathes them. When a microelectrode is thrust into the organ of Corti, potentials are recorded which range from -20 to -80 mV. referred to the perilymph. Since this negative potential is found regardless of the position of the electrode so long as it is in Corti's organ, and since no one thus far has shown that it is recorded only from cells and not from the extensive fluid spaces, it seems preferable to refer to it as the *cortilymphatic potential* until more precise information is available about its source.

Endocochlear potential. The endolymph in the cochlear duct shows a remarkable *positive* potential of 80 mV. referred to the perilymph in the vestibular and tympanic scalae. This high positive potential appears to be a unique property of the cochlea, according to the measurements of Davis and his associates. They have found that the potential of the endolymph in the vestibular end organs is only of the order of $+1$ to $+5$ mV. The endocochlear potential depends not upon the ionic composition of the endolymph but upon the metabolic activity of the stria vascularis. It can be recorded from the surface of the stria even when the endolymph has been removed. During asphyxia it decreases, to return to its normal level only when oxygen is readmitted. Injection of azide or cyanide into the scala media abolishes the potential completely. The positive potential can be modified by movements of the basilar membrane. It is increased when the membrane is pushed "downward" towards scala tympani, by inward movement of the stapes, or by injecting fluid into the cochlear duct. Conversely, it is decreased by outward movement of the stapes, causing an "upward" movement of the basilar membrane. Movement of the tectorial membrane with respect to the organ of Corti causes similar changes in the endocochlear potential, suggesting a close relationship between the endocochlear and the cochlear microphonic potentials.

Cochlear microphonic potential. Unlike the dc cortilymphatic and endocochlear potentials, the microphonic potential is an immediate response to acoustic stimulation. For many years it has been known to be associated with the hair cells, and at one time it was thought to be produced by compression and elongation of these cells in much the same way as the piezo-electric potentials are produced in the crystal of a microphone.

Recent studies have focussed attention on the region of the upper ("transducer") end of the hair cells as the site of the mechano-electrical transduction process, but the respective contributions of the tectorial membrane, stereocilia, cuticular plate and basal body to this process remain matters of speculation only. Various authors have suggested that the microphonic action occurs in the tectorial membrane alone as a result of rapid

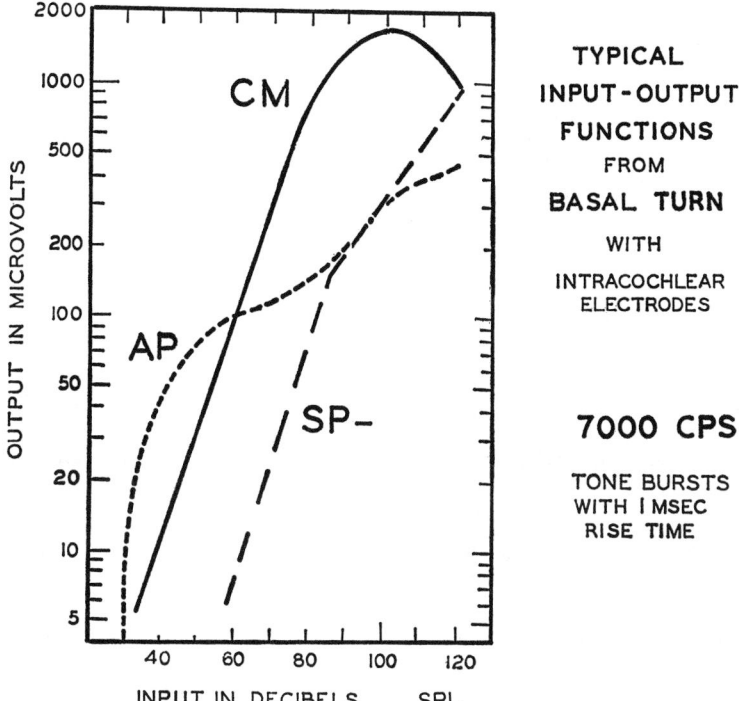

Fig. 18.10. Intensity functions of the cochlear microphonic (CM), action potential (AP) and negative summating potential (SP−), in response to brief tones of 7000 c.p.s., as recorded by intracochlear electrodes from the basal turn in the guinea pig. The voltage of CM is proportional to the sound pressure level up to 80 db SPL, then grows more slowly to a maximum of almost 1 mv. at about 105 db SPL. AP grows rapidly from threshold, then more slowly. The growth of SP− approximately parallels that of CM. (Reproduced by special permission of Dr. Hallowell Davis.)

ion fluxes, but this hypothesis seems to overlook the fact that the hair cells must be present for the microphonic potential to appear. The plasma membrane of the hair cell with its extensions, the parietal lamellae, furnishes abundant surface area for the exchange of ions between the hair cell and the cortilymph, but ion exchanges between the hair cell and the endolymph appear to be possible only through the small cuticle-free area surrounding the basal body.

The cochlear microphonic response may be regarded as a *receptor potential*, having no true threshold or refractory period. It closely reproduces the waveform of the stimulus. Its amplitude is linearly proportional to the displacement of the cochlear partition, and therefore to the sound pressure of the stimulus from moment to moment. As the stimulus intensity is increased, the amplitude of the response grows proportionately (fig. 18.10). At higher levels the response becomes nonlinear, goes through a maximum, and eventually declines. Using intracochlear electrodes to record from individual turns of the guinea pig cochlea, Davis and his collaborators have shown that the basal turn responds to all

frequencies, whereas the third turn responds only to frequencies below 3000 c.p.s. This is further evidence of the broad tuning of the basilar membrane (fig. 18.11).

The microphonic potential is dependent upon an adequate oxygen supply. During anoxia it falls to a very low level, which may persist for some time after death. The precise relationship of the microphonic to the endocochlear potential is not known, in spite of some evidence suggesting that the microphonic may be simply a modulation of the latter by movements of the cochlear partition. Most authors now assume that the microphonic potential is directly concerned in the excitation of the nerve endings. One may still argue, however, that it is merely the electrical sign of the transduction process at the upper pole of the hair cells, and that the actual stimulus to the nerve endings is still to be discovered. In any case the microphonic potential furnishes an excellent means for the experimental study of events in the middle ear, the transmission of sound energy in the cochlea and the effects of toxic agents on the organ of Corti.

Summating potentials. Two dc potential re-

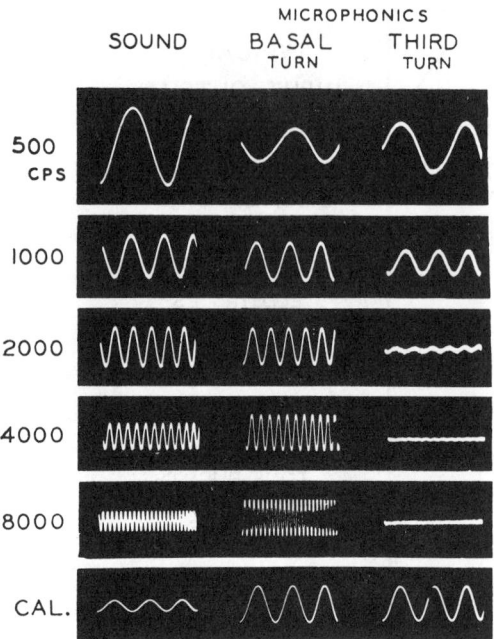

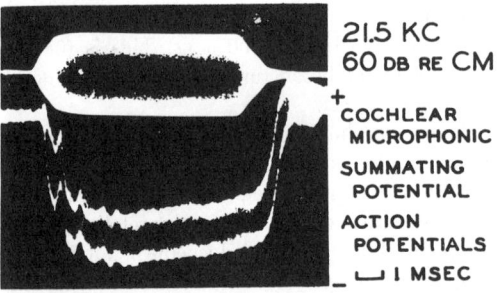

FIG. 18.11. Cochlear microphonic responses reproducing the sinusoidal wave-form of the stimulus, as recorded with intracochlear electrodes in scala vestibuli and scala tympani of the basal and third turns in the guinea pig. The basal turn responds to all frequencies, but the third turn only to frequencies below about 3000 c.p.s. (From Davis, Laryngoscope, **68,** 359, 1958.)

FIG. 18.12. Above: the stimulus, a brief tone of 21,500 c.p.s. Below: the response, including cochlear microphonic, negative summating and action potentials recorded from the round window in the guinea pig. CM is at the frequency of the stimulus; SP is the downward displacement of the baseline, and the action potentials are the peaks and valleys on the descending limb of SP. (From Pestalozza and Davis; Am. J. Physiol., **185,** 595, 1956.)

sponses to acoustic stimulation can be recorded, the positive and negative summating potentials. These potentials reproduce the envelope of a brief burst of tonal stimulation, and are proportional to the root-mean-square value of the stimulus. They appear at levels where the microphonic po-

tential is becoming nonlinear. The positive summating potential, which is more sensitive to oxygen lack, has been thought to originate in the outer hair cells, whereas the more resistant negative potential, which actually increases in amplitude after mild injury to the organ of Corti, has been attributed to the inner hair cells. Their relevance to the process of excitation in the cochlea remains obscure (fig. 18.12).

Action potentials. Although the action potentials can easily be recognized among the mixture of potentials recorded from the round window membrane, special electrode placements or cancellation procedures are required to record them uncontaminated by the microphonic potentials. They show the typical all-or-none behavior of axon-spike potentials of myelinated nerve fibers, having a definite threshold and a refractory period. The response to a click at a moderate intensity level consists of three successive volleys of "spike" potentials, called N_1, N_2 and N_3, representing synchronous, repetitive firing in many fibers. These action potentials are readily "masked" by noise, which stimulates the fibers in random fashion, so that the click finds many of them refractory and therefore unable to contribute to the response (fig. 18.13).

Synchronous volleys of action potentials occur in response to the sound waves of a steady tone of low or middle frequency. Above 1000 c.p.s. fibers may be responding in alternation or in rotation, since the refractory period of about 1 msec. prevents a given fiber from firing with each successive sound wave. At higher frequencies, synchronization of the action potentials decreases, to disappear completely above 4000 c.p.s.

The action potential lags behind the microphonic potential by 0.55 to 1.0 msec. This latency suggests a "synaptic delay" between the hair cells and the nerve endings, but it may also be ascribed to the time required for the conduction of the excitatory process from the upper, transducer end of the hair cell to the lower, transmitter end, and to the conduction time of the nonmedullated fibers within the organ of Corti. Other properties of the action potentials also support the hypothesis of Derbyshire and Davis that a synaptic type of transmission occurs at this point. Their sensitivity to oxygen lack greatly exceeds that of the microphonic response. Furthermore, they can readily be fatigued, and their recovery after masking by a band of noise is not as prompt as it should be if masking reflected only the refractory state of the nerve fibers produced by the noise. As previously described, the junctions between hair cells and afferent nerve fiber endings appear to be synapses, but the type of transmission involved is not known.

The responses of single afferent fibers of the auditory nerve trunk have been studied by Tasaki by means of extremely fine pipette electrodes. Some fibers gave single and others repetitive responses; some had low, others high thresholds. Most of them responded to a wide range of frequencies below a sharp cut-off frequency, above which the fiber would not respond no matter how much the intensity was increased. As the frequency was increased, fibers would stop firing abruptly, and the higher the frequency, the smaller became the number of active fibers. These findings are in full accord with Békésy's description of the behavior of the travelling waves and their sharp decline just above the point of maximum amplitude of vibration of the partition. Unfortunately, they do not bring us much closer to an understanding of how the information from Corti's organ is encoded in the impulses of the auditory nerve fibers.

Role of the efferent system. The physiological role of the efferent system has not yet been defined, but its general effect on afferent impulses is clearly inhibitory. Stimulation of the olivocochlear bundle in the medulla reduces or inhibits the response of the afferent fibers, although at the same time it causes a slight enhancement of the microphonic potentials. Acetyl choline is the probable transmitter for the efferent fibers, since acetyl cholinesterase is present at their endings and disappears after the olivo-cochlear bundles are cut.

Fex has demonstrated activation of single crossed olivo-cochlear fibers by sound applied to the opposite ear. Pfalz has shown that spontaneous firing of single neurons of the ventral cochlear nucleus can be inhibited by sound stimulation of the opposite ear, and that each fiber is inhibited by a definite band of frequencies.

Although the number of efferent fibers in the olivo-cochlear bundle has been estimated to be only about 500, the nerve endings of the efferent type are impressive for their wide distribution as well as for their size. It is reasonable to infer that these endings represent not only the olivo-cochlear fibers but also a local system of fibers within the organ of Corti. Their role would presumably be to sharpen the frequency analysis in the cochlea by producing the selective inhibition that is envisioned in v. Békésy's principle of neural funneling.

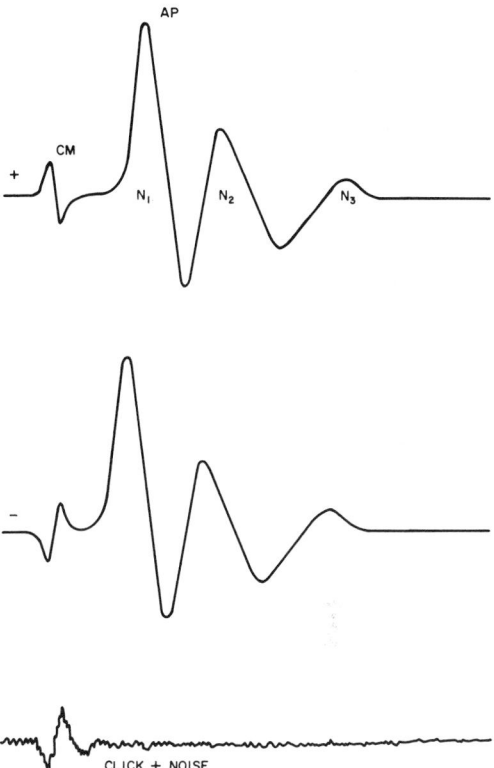

FIG. 18.13. Responses to clicks (approximately 40 dB above threshold) as recorded from the round window of the cochlea in the cat, consisting of cochlear microphonic potential (CM) and action potential of auditory nerve (AP) ,with its three spikes, N_1, N_2, and N_3.

Between A and B the polarity of the stimulus is reversed. As a result, the cochlear microphonic also shows a complete reversal, but the AP shows only a slight shift in latency.

At C, masking by a white noise causes a temporary disappearance of the AP response. CM remains unchanged.

The Central Auditory Pathway

RESPONSES OF MEDULLARY NEURONS. The responses of the second-order neurons of the cochlear nucleus as recorded with microelectrodes closely resemble those of the auditory nerve fibers. Galambos and Davis have observed that each unit responds to a limited range of frequencies, which is narrow at threshold but gradually broadens as the intensity of the stimulating tones is increased. As in the nerve, the high-frequency cut-off is sharp (fig. 18.14). Many of the units show a "spontaneous" rhythmical discharge, which may be inhibited when a tone is sounded. Furthermore, when a unit is responding to a tone,

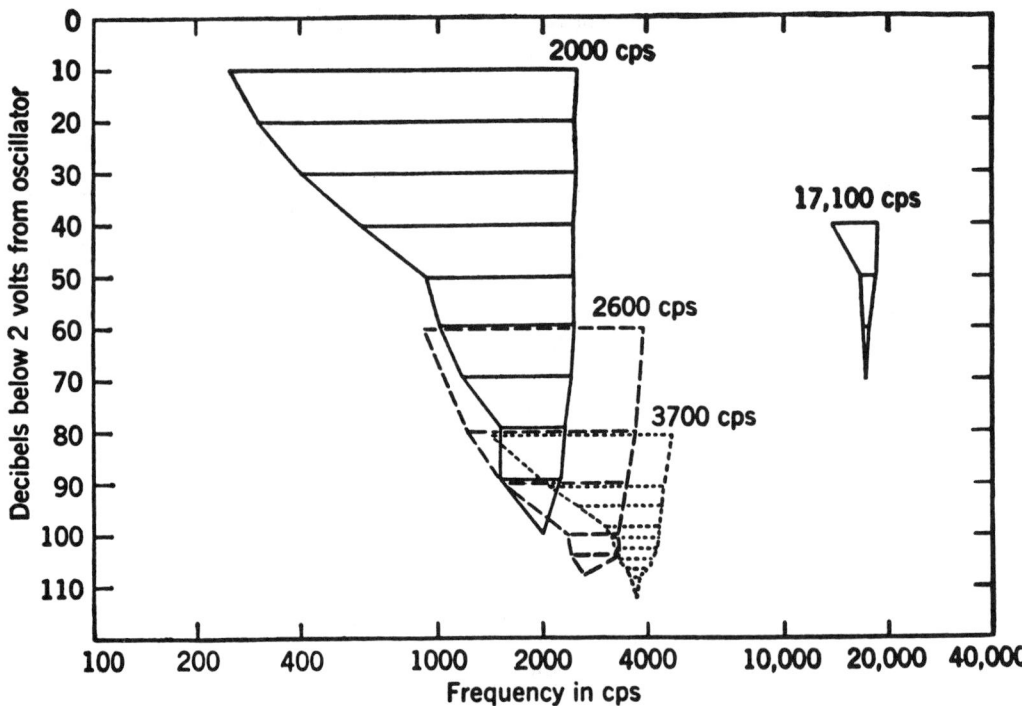

Fig. 18.14. Response areas of four neurons in the cochlear nucleus of the cat. Each neuron has a specific frequency at which a minimal acoustic energy is required to excite it. Each responds also to lower frequencies at higher intensity, but shows a sharp cut-off for higher frequencies, in accordance with the pattern of vibration of the basilar membrane described by v. Békésy. (From Galambos and Davis, J. Neurophysiol., **6,** 1943, 1939.)

presentation of a second tone may inhibit the discharge. The effect of this inhibition is to sharpen the cut-off at the low-frequency end. A tonal stimulus therefore increases the activity in some units and decreases or abolishes activity in others. Galambos suggests that each tonal frequency produces a characteristic pattern of "islands" of active and inactive neurons. In this way the broad tuning of the basilar membrane may be made more precise by a place principle operating at the medullary level, superimposed upon the repeated point-to-point projection of the organ of Corti which has been found in anatomical studies.

RESPONSES OF HIGHER AUDITORY CENTERS. The neurons of the inferior colliculus and medial geniculate body follow in general the patterns of activity seen in the cochlear nucleus. Discharge is increased by certain tones and suppressed by others, and the response areas of individual units are sharply defined. The point-to-point "tonotopic" projection of the cochlea is less firmly established at these levels, but the physiological evidence tends to support it.

The responses of the cortical auditory area have

been most extensively studied in the cat. In this species and in the dog the area is located on the temporo-parietal surface of the hemisphere. It is bounded on three sides by the suprasylvian sulcus and extends ventrally almost to the rhinal fissure. On the basis of anatomical and electrophysiological data, as well as behavioral studies before and after cortical ablations, the six subdivisions shown in figure 18.15 have been delimited. AI receives the major projection of the medial geniculate body (pars principalis), and it is from this area that "onset responses" to clicks and pure tones are most easily recorded in anesthetized animals. According to Tunturi's experiments in the dog, using strychnine to sensitize 1-mm.² areas of the cortex, subdivision AI shows a tonotopic organization. Individual tones activate narrow bands of cortex 8 mm. long, with the lower frequencies represented more caudally and the higher frequencies more rostrally. A weak suprathreshold tone presented to the contralateral ear activates the entire band. The same tone presented to the ipsilateral ear activates only the dorsal portion of the band, but as the intensity is increased more and more of the band is involved. Thus it would appear that pitch alone is represented in the contralateral cortex, but pitch and loudness are both represented in the ipsilateral cortex. A roughly similar tonotopic organization in the cat was revealed by the studies of Woolsey and Walzl, who stimulated nerve fibers at various points in the osseous spiral lamina of the cochlea and recorded the responses from the cortex. On the other hand, single unit studies with microelectrodes have revealed that relatively few cortical units respond selectively to tones, whereas more respond to noise and clicks only. Galambos has recently reported single units which appear to be sensitive to auditory stimuli only when a cat "pays attention" to the sound source—among the few hints that we have as to what neural processes may be involved in listening.

The auditory cortex is not necessary, in the cat at least, for learning responses to tones or for discriminating between tones. It is required, however, for the recognition of simple auditory patterns, such as the difference between two different sequences of three tones each, the first *high-low-high*, and the second *low-high-low*. This type of discriminating depends upon the integrity of the insular (IN) and temporal (TE) areas (Neff).

AUDITORY LOCALIZATION IN THE CORTEX. Both ears are represented about equally in the right and left auditory pathways, thanks to the trapezoid fiber-crossing in the medulla, and to other intercommunications in the midbrain and corpus callosum. A sound applied to either ear alone evokes equal electrical responses in both cortices. On the other hand, when a sound is presented to both ears simultaneously, the responses of the two sides are equal only if the sound is in the median plane. As the source is moved to one side of the head, the response of the contralateral cortex becomes greater, and that of the ipsilateral cortex less (Rosenzweig). In spite of this important cortical correlate, auditory localization persists after bilateral destruction of the auditory areas. Recent studies indicate that localization depends mainly upon a comparison of intensity and phase information from the two ears carried out at the level of the superior olivary nuclei.

Summarizing our still unsatisfactory knowledge of the auditory functions of the central nervous system, we may say that the rather broad frequency analysis performed by the cochlea is sharpened in the cochlear nucleus, where information concerning place of stimulation along the basilar membrane and frequency of stimulation is processed. Although a more or less point-to-

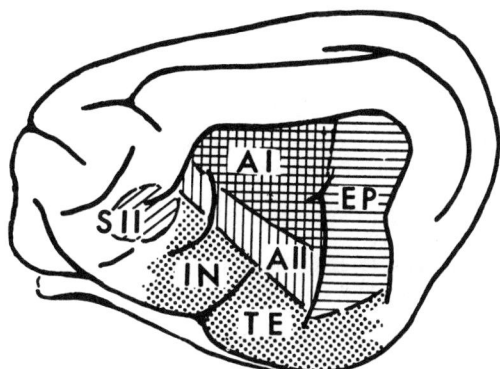

FIG. 18.15. The cortical auditory areas of the cat as described by various authors. AI and AII, first and second auditory areas; EP, posterior ectosylvian area; SII, second somatic area; IN, insular region; TE, temporal area. (Reproduced by permission from H. W. Ades in *Handbook of Physiology*, Section I: Neurophysiology, Vol. 1, American Physiological Society, Inc., 1959.)

point projection of the cochlea at various levels seems to be the rule, the frequency-sensitive units become proportionately fewer and more sharply tuned, whereas more and more units appear which have other functions.

Loudness has long been assumed to be correlated with the rate of discharge in individual fibers of the auditory nerve and with the total number of fibers discharging. At the same time, according to the volley principle, the rate of discharge signals the frequency for low tones. To resolve this apparent conflict, the suggestion has been made that loudness is not a simple function of the total number of impulses per second, and that the inner hair cells, with their higher thresholds, may make a significantly greater contribution to loudness than the more sensitive outer hair cells. How loudness is mediated in the central nervous system is still quite unknown. One possible mechanism is suggested by the studies of Bremer on the *encéphale isolé* in the unanesthetized cat. In this preparation a sustained activation of area AI occurs in response to tones. Raising the intensity of stimulation causes an increase in the frequency of the rhythmical cortical discharge.

Thus far no auditory function has been found to have an exclusively cortical representation in animals except the discrimination of tonal patterns. This fact does not in any way call into question the importance of the auditory cortical areas. Tonal and temporal pattern discrimination is precisely the sort of function that one should expect to find reserved to the cortex as the basis for the interpretation of meaningful acoustic signals.

REFERENCES

ADES, H. W. Central auditory mechanisms, *in* Handbook of physiology, Vol I, Section 1. (eds., J. FIELD, H. W. MAGOUN, AND V. E. HALL). American Physiological Society, Washington, D. C., 1959.

v. BÉKÉSY, G. Experiments in hearing (translated and edited by E. G. WEVER). McGraw-Hill Book Company, Inc., New York, 1960.

v. BÉKÉSY, G., AND ROSENBLITH, W. A. The mechanical properties of the ear, *in* Handbook of experimental psychology (ed., S. S. STEVENS). John Wiley & Sons, Inc., New York, 1951.

DAVIS, H. Excitation of auditory receptors, *in* Handbook of physiology, Vol. I, Section 1. (eds., J. FIELD, H. W. MAGOUN, AND V. E. HALL) American Physiological Society, Washington, D. C., 1959.

DAVIS, H. A model for transducer action in the cochlea. Cold Spring Harbor Symp. Quant. Biol. XXX. Sensory receptors. 1966.

DAVIS, H. AND SILVERMAN, S. R., (eds.). Hearing and deafness. Revised ed., Holt, Rhinehart, and Winston, Inc., 1960.

DESMEDT, J. E. Auditory-evoked potentials from cochlea to cortex as influenced by activation of the olivo-cochlear bundle. J. Acoust. Soc. Am., 1962, **34**, 1478.

ENGSTRÖM, H., ADES, H. W., AND HAWKINS, J. E., JR. Structure and functions of the sensory hairs of the inner ear. J. Acoust. Soc. Am., 1962, **34**, 1356.

ENGSTRÖM, H., ADES, H. W., AND HAWKINS, J. E., JR. Cellular patterns, nerve structures, and fluid spaces of the organ of Corti, *in* Contributions to sensory physiology, Vol. 1. (ed., W. D. NEFF). Academic Press, New York and London, 1965.

FEX, J. Auditory activity in centrifugal and centripetal cochlear fibers in cat: a study of a feedback system. Acta Physiol. Scand., Vol. 55, Suppl. 189, Stockholm, 1962.

FLOCK, Å., KIMURA, R., LUNDQUIST, P-G., AND WERSÄLL, J. Morphological basis of directional sensitivity of the outer hair cells in the organ of Corti. J. Acoust. Soc. Am., 1962, **34**, 1351.

GALAMBOS, R. "Attention" units in the auditory cortex. Science, 1959, **129**, 1279.

GRIFFIN, D. R. Listening in the dark. Yale University Press, New Haven, 1958.

HAWKINS, J. E., JR. Hearing. Ann. Rev. Physiol., 1964, **26**, 453.

HAWKINS, J. E., JR. Cytoarchitectural basis of the cochlear transducer. Cold Spring Harbor Symp. Quant. Biol. XXX. Sensory Receptors. 1966.

HELMHOLTZ, H. L. F. On the sensations of tone as a physiological basis for the theory of music, 4th ed. (1877), translated by A. J. Ellis, 1885. Reprinted, Dover Publications, New York, 1954.

LAWRENCE, M. Hearing. Ann. Rev. Physiol., 1961, **23**, 485.

LAWRENCE, M. Dynamic range of the cochlear transducer. Cold Spring Harbor Symp. Quant. Biol. XXX. Sensory receptors. 1966.

NAFTALIN, L. Some new proposals regarding acoustic transmission and transduction. Cold Spring Harbor Symp. Quant. Biol. XXX. Sensory receptors. 1966.

NEFF, W. D. Neural mechanisms of auditory discrimination, *in* Sensory communication (ed., W. A. ROSENBLITH). M. I. T. Press, Cambridge, Mass., 1961.

ROSENZWEIG, M. R. Auditory localization. Sci. Am., 1961, **205**, 132.

TUNTURI, A. R. Anatomy and physiology of the auditory cortex, *in* Neural mechanisms of the auditory and vestibular systems (eds., G. L. RASMUSSEN, AND W. F. WINDLE). Charles C Thomas, Springfield, Ill., 1960.

VINNIKOV, YA. A. AND TITOVA, L. K. The organ of Corti: its histophysiology and histochemistry. Consultants Bureau, New York, 1964.

WERSÄLL, R. The tympanic muscles and their reflexes. Acta Oto-laryngol., Suppl. 139, Stockholm, 1958.

WERSÄLL, J., FLOCK, Å., AND LUNDQUIST, P-G. Structural basis for directional sensitivity in cochlear and vestibular sensory receptors. Cold Spring Harbor Symp. Quant. Biol. XXX. Sensory receptors. 1966.

WEVER, E. G. Theory of hearing. John Wiley & Sons, Inc., New York, 1949.

WEVER, E. G. AND LAWRENCE, M. Physiological acoustics. Princeton University Press, Princeton, N. J., 1954.

WOOLSEY, C. N. Organization of cortical auditory system, *in* Sensory communication (ed., W. A. ROSENBLITH). M. I. T. Press, Cambridge, Mass., 1961.

ZWISLOCKI, J. Analysis of some auditory characteristics, *in* Handbook of mathematical psychology, Vol. III (eds., R. D. LUCE, R. R. BUSH, AND E. GALANTER) John Wiley & Sons, Inc., New York, 1965.

CHAPTER 19

Hearing: Measurement and Impairment

In the previous chapter the determination of the absolute threshold of hearing was discussed, i.e., the smallest amounts of acoustical energy that the ear can detect when pure tones of various frequencies are presented to it in quiet surroundings. Although the very concept of threshold is controversial, measurements of this type are of prime importance in the evaluation of normal and impaired hearing and are made routinely in clinical practice. The present chapter hardly affords space for a consideration of the principles of classical psychophysics that underlie these procedures. The reader is therefore referred to the textbook by Guilford and to the writings of S. S. Stevens for discussion of the problems of measurement in psychophysics. For an initiation into the theory of signal detectability and its relevance for the assessment of hearing, he should consult the publications of Tanner and Swets.

STANDARD AUDIOMETRY. The basic clinical instrument for the measurement of hearing, the *audiometer*, is an electroacoustic device consisting of an oscillator, an amplifier, an attenuator for controlling intensity, and an earphone. Its frequency range usually extends from 125 to 8000 cps, in discrete steps of an octave or less, and its intensity range covers approximately 100 decibels (dB) in steps of 5 dB. It must be remembered that the "zero-dB" level of the audiometer is not the standard reference level of 0.0002 dyne/cm.^{2}, nor does it refer to the same sound pressure level at all frequencies. Instead it represents the average threshold of hearing for normal young adults, as measured under favorable conditions in the laboratory. The recently adopted International Standard Audiometric Zero Level (ISO 1964) is 6 to 15 dB lower than the previous American Standard (ASA 1951). Differences between the two standards are shown in fig. 19.1, and they should be compared with the still more sensitive Sivian and White curve in fig. 18.1.

Generally the threshold of hearing for an individual frequency is defined as the level at which the subject gives a positive response 50 per cent of the time. If by this criterion he can hear a tone only when its intensity is raised 40 dB above the zero level, he is said to have a

hearing level of 40 dB at that frequency. In practice, deviations of less than 25 dB from the ISO 1964 zero level are not considered significant. A graph showing the audiometric thresholds plotted as a function of frequency is called an *audiogram*. The shape of the audiogram of a patient who is hard of hearing gives the otologist important clues as to the nature of the hearing defect (fig. 19.2).

AUTOMATIC AUDIOMETRY. In conventional audiometry the operator sets the frequency and intensity of the tones presented to the subject, who listens and reports whether he hears them. With the automatic audiometer invented by v. Békésy, the subject sets the intensity himself, and his audiogram is recorded automatically. So long as he hears the tone he presses the button of a handswitch controlling an automatic attenuator which steadily reduces the intensity. When the tone is no longer audible he releases the button, permitting its intensity to rise again until he hears it once more and repeats the cycle. The test is programmed so that the frequency slowly increases from 100 to 10,000 cps. The recording pen, accordingly, moves up and down on the intensity scale, writing the patient's reports of the disappearance and reappearance of the tone, and at the same time moves from left to right on the frequency scale. In this way a complete audiogram can be recorded in a few minutes. The mid-points of the excursions of the pen are generally taken to represent the threshold of hearing. Their amplitude gives an indication of the rate of increase in loudness. As shown below, an abnormally rapid increase in loudness called *recruitment* is characteristic of certain forms of hearing impairment (fig. 19.3).

EDR *and* EER *audiometry.* Two newer forms of audiometry are available for use with very young children or with patients who cannot understand or carry out the instructions for routine hearing tests. In one type of test, the patient is conditioned to expect a mild electric shock whenever he hears a tone. The shock evokes sudden transient change in the electrical resistance of the skin, (the so-called *electrodermal response*, or EDR) and the tone, as the conditioned stimulus, comes to have the same effect.

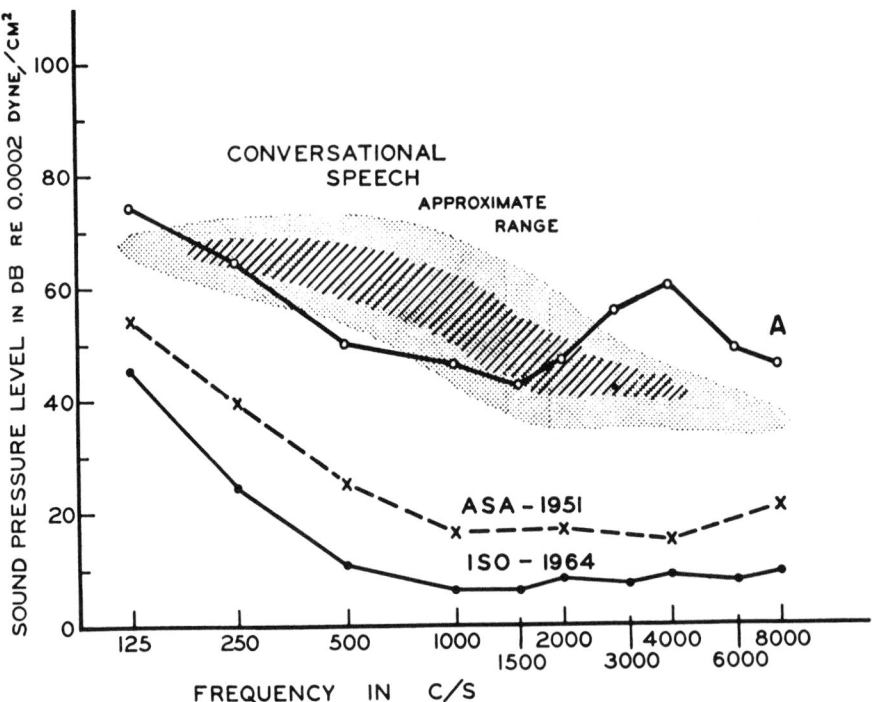

FIG. 19.1. The new International Audiometric Zero (ISO-64) curve compared with the old American Standards Association (ASA 1951) curve. The ISO scale, based on measurements made in many different countries, more closely approximates the thresholds of normal young adults. The shaded area indicates the sound pressures developed in conversational speech. Curve A: thresholds for a hypothetical case of moderate hearing impairment. (From Davis, Trans. Am. Acad. Ophthalmol. and Otolaryng., 1965, **69,** 740.)

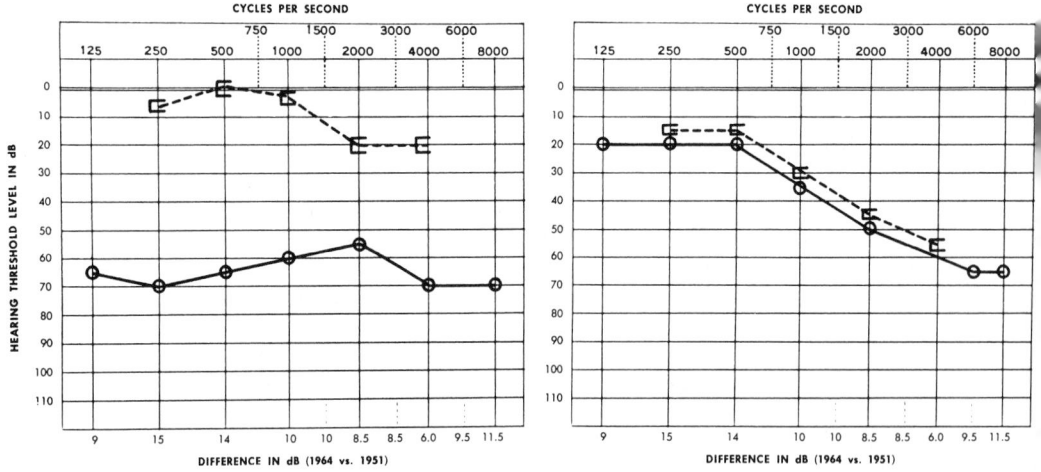

FIG. 19.2. Audiograms illustrating conductive impairment of hearing (left) and sensori-neural impairment (right). Solid curve for air conduction, dashed curve for bone conduction.

By recording the skin resistance and noting whether a change occurs when tones are sounded at various levels, the operator can determine the patient's threshold of hearing. In the EER test, a change in the electroencephalographic pattern in response to sound, the so-called *electroencephalic*

response which occurs in light sleep, is used as an indication that a tone has been heard. Both of these tests require considerable skill on the part of the operator and in the interpretation of the records. For the EER test, averaging of responses by means of a computer lightens the task of

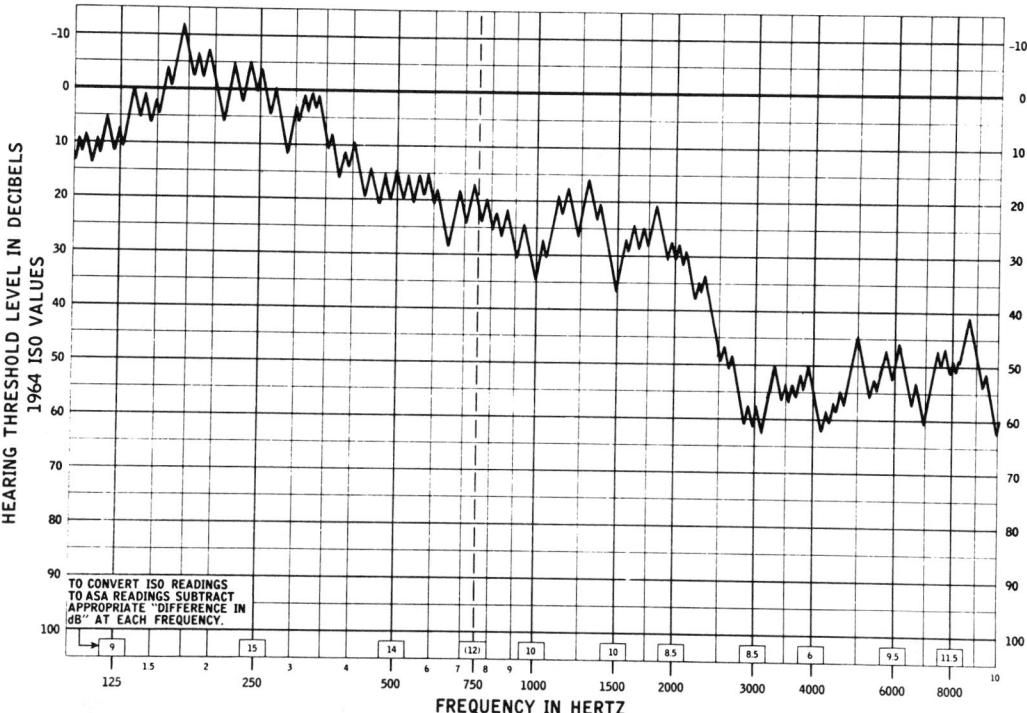

Fig. 19.3 v. Békésy audiogram of middle-aged patient with mild-to-moderate sensori-neural impairment, attributable to cumulative combined effects of quinine ototoxicity, repeated experimental exposures to sound at 120–140 dB SPL, and incipient presbycusis.

judging the thresholds by making it possible to detect responses of small amplitude against a background of other cortical activity.

SPEECH AUDIOMETRY. The frequencies of greatest importance for the understanding of speech are those in the middle of the audiometer range. If the thresholds for 500, 1000 and 2000 cps are significantly elevated, the threshold of hearing for speech is also affected. The average hearing level for these three frequencies usually gives a reasonable approximation of the hearing level for speech.

The hearing level for speech can be measured directly using phonographic or magnetic tape recordings of especially selected test words. These may be familiar words of two syllables equally stressed (spondees), such as *baseball* and *railroad*. Groups of six spondees are presented at successively lower intensity levels (in steps of 4 dB) until the patient can no longer hear them. The intensity at which he can repeat half of the words correctly is taken as his *speech reception threshold* (SRT), and the difference between this value and the average SRT for normal listeners represents his hearing level for speech (fig. 19.4).

Additional information can be obtained by the use of the phonetically balanced (PB) lists of

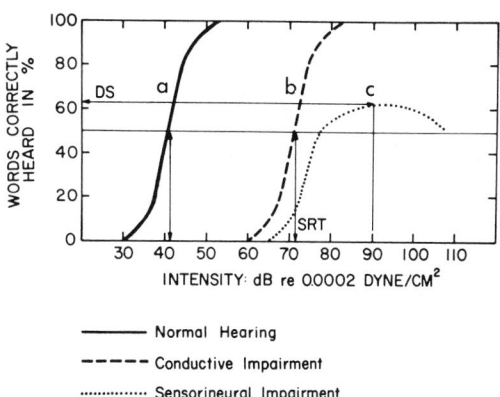

Normal Hearing

––––– Conductive Impairment

·········· Sensorineural Impairment

Fig. 19.4. Speech audiometry. Percentage of words correctly heard plotted as function of intensity level. a, normal hearing; b, conductive impairment; c, sensori-neural impairment. Speech reception threshold (SRT) is given by intensity in dB SPL at which 50 per cent of words are correctly heard (usually spondees). Discrimination score (DS) is given by maximum percentage of monosyllabic words correctly heard.

monosyllabic words. In these lists of 50 words each, the various speech sounds occur with approximately the same frequency as in normal conversational English. Each list is presented at a uniform intensity, and the percentage of words the patient is able to repeat correctly is his

TABLE 19.1

Classes of hearing handicap

ISO—1964

dB	Class	Degree of Handicap	Average Hearing Threshold Level for 500, 1000 and 2000 in the Better Ear*		Ability to Understand Speech
			More than	No more than	
25	A	Not significant		25 dB (ISO)	No significant difficulty with faint speech
	B	Slight handicap	25 dB (ISO)	40 dB	Difficulty only with faint speech
40	C	Mild handicap	40 dB	55 dB	Frequent difficulty with normal speech
55	D	Marked handicap	55 dB	70 dB	Frequent difficulty with loud speech
70	E	Severe handicap	70 dB	90 dB	Can understand only shouted or amplified speech
90	F	Extreme handicap	90 dB		Usually cannot understand even amplified speech

From Davis, Trans. Am. Acad. Ophthalmol. and Otolaryng. 1965, **69,** 740.

discrimination score. His average discrimination score for faint (55 dB), normal (70 dB) and loud (85 dB) conversational speech is a useful measure of his ability to hear in everyday situations. Davis has given it the name *Social Adequacy Index* (SAI). For a person with normal hearing the SAI lies between 94 and 100. A score of 33 is said to represent the lower limit for "socially adequate" hearing. The relation between hearing level and degree of handicap is illustrated in Table 19.1.

BONE CONDUCTION AUDIOMETRY. Sound is normally transmitted to the cochlea in two ways: by *air conduction,* through the external canal and across the middle ear, and by *bone conduction* as a result of vibrations of the skull. Bone conduction furnishes a means of testing the integrity of the cochlear mechanism in patients with damage to the middle ear. Bárány and von Békésy have shown that there are in fact two forms of bone conduction. When a vibrator is placed on the forehead, the skull can move as a rigid body, especially in response to frequencies below 1500 cps. The ossicles, however, are suspended in the middle ear cavity, and do not move with the skull because of their inertia. The cochlea and oval window are set in motion with respect to the stapes, but the result is the same as if the foot-plate of the stapes itself were vibrating. Stimulation of the cochlea by this means is called *inertia bone conduction.* The second form, *compression bone conduction,* occurs at higher frequencies, where the skull no longer moves as a rigid body but vibrates in sections. The vibrations are transmitted directly to the cochlea. As its bony walls vibrate the cochlear fluids are set in motion because the round window membrane moves more freely than the stapes in the oval window, and thus the stimulus is transmitted to the hair cells.

A calibrated bone conduction vibrator is usually furnished with the audiometer. The vibrator is applied to the mastoid process or to the forehead. Since the vibrations are transmitted to both inner ears, it is often necessary to apply a masking noise to the ear not being tested in order to avoid confusion. The diagnostic use of bone conduction audiometry and the classical tuning fork tests are discussed later in this chapter.

PSYCHO-ACOUSTIC MEASUREMENTS

DIFFERENTIAL THRESHOLDS. Discrimination, as in the understanding of speech, means the recognition of differences between sounds in terms of intensity, frequency, pattern, etc. In classical psychophysics considerable weight has been given to the measurement of the *differential threshold*, also called the *difference limen* (DL) or *just noticeable difference* (jnd) for the intensity and frequency of pure tones. Weber's law (1834) states that the increment of a stimulus that is just noticeable is a constant fraction of the intensity of the stimulus itself. In other words, for intensity, the fraction $\Delta I/I$ (or ΔI in dB, which expresses the ratio) must be a constant if Weber's law holds. Actually the law does hold reasonably well over a considerable part of the intensity range, although the actual size of ΔI varies with frequency. For tones near threshold ΔI is relatively large, but it declines rapidly to reach a more or less constant value above a sensation level of 50 dB. (Sensation level, SL, means *decibels above threshold*.) Thus for a 1000-cps tone at 5 dB SL, ΔI is 3 dB, whereas at 50 dB SL, it is only 0.5 dB. For white noise, ΔI is less than 0.5 dB at 20 dB SL, and remains almost constant at least up to 100 dB SL.

For frequencies above 1000 cps at a sensation level of 40 dB or more, the relative DL ($\Delta f/f$) remains almost constant at about 0.003 as the frequency is increased. At 1000 cps the normal listener can detect a change of 3 cps, but at 5000 cps he would fail to notice a change of less than 15 cps.

MASKING. In spite of the ability of the ear to analyze complex tones and separate out individual frequencies, weak sounds may be completely inaudible in the presence of sounds of greater intensity. This familiar phenomenon is called *masking*. White noise is particularly effective in masking other acoustic stimuli.

The degree of masking is measured as the number of decibels by which the intensity of the masked sound must be increased above the quiet threshold to become just audible in the presence of the masking noise. Fletcher has shown that when a tone is masked by noise, the frequencies effective in masking it are those lying in a relatively narrow band centered about the frequency of the masked tone. These frequencies make up the *critical band*. For a tone of 200 cps, the width of the critical band is about 100 cps, for 2000 cps, it is about 300 cps, and for 10,000 cps, it is almost 2400 cps. Beyond these limits, further increase in the width of the band of frequencies in the masking noise does not increase the degree of masking. Although the widths of the critical bands vary as measured in cycles per second, there is evidence that they correspond to equal distances along the basilar membrane, and therefore to equal numbers of hair cells.

The masking of tones by other pure tones has been extensively studied, but it is complicated by the fact that tones close together in frequency interfere with each other and cause fluctuations in loudness, or *beats*, which make the degree of masking difficult to judge. In general, low tones are much more effective in masking high tones than vice versa. This finding is in accord with the patterns of excitation of the basilar membrane described by Békésy, who noted that low tones affect the whole length of the membrane, whereas high tones affect only a limited region near the stapes.

Masking by noise is frequently used in clinical audiometry to "block" the better ear so that it will not respond to loud sounds or to bone-conducted sound used in testing the worse ear and thus give a false result.

LOUDNESS. Loudness is the psychological attribute of sound most closely associated with the physical property of intensity. Being a subjective quantity, loudness cannot be specified directly in terms of physical units, but must be expressed in terms of special psychophysical scales. One of these is the scale of *Loudness Level*, which is based upon judgments of equal loudness. If the experimenter takes a tone of 1000 cps at 40 dB intensity level and asks the subject to adjust the intensity of other frequencies until each is equal in loudness to the 1000-cps tone, he obtains an equal-loudness contour. The loudness level of the 1000-cps tone is said to be 40 *phons*, and all other frequencies on the contour have the same loudness level. We may therefore define the loudness level (in *phons*) of any tone as the intensity level (in dB) of the 1000-cps tone which is equal to it in loudness. A set of equal-loudness contours is shown in fig. 19.5. From the spacing of the curves it is evident that the loudness level of low-frequency tones grows much faster as a function of intensity level than that of medium and high-frequency tones.

A loudness scale can also be based on judgments of loudnesses that are multiples and fractions of a standard loudness. Stevens has set up such a scale, using as a unit the *sone*, which is defined as the loudness of a 1000-cps tone at 40 dB intensity level. A tone that sounds twice as loud has a loudness of 2 sones, whereas one that sounds one-half as loud has a loudness of 0.5 sone. Stevens has shown that the relationship between loudness in sones (S) and sound pressure (p) is a simple power function: $S = kp^{0.6}$. When plotted in the form shown in fig. 19.6, this equation gives a straight line. The plot shows that for each in-

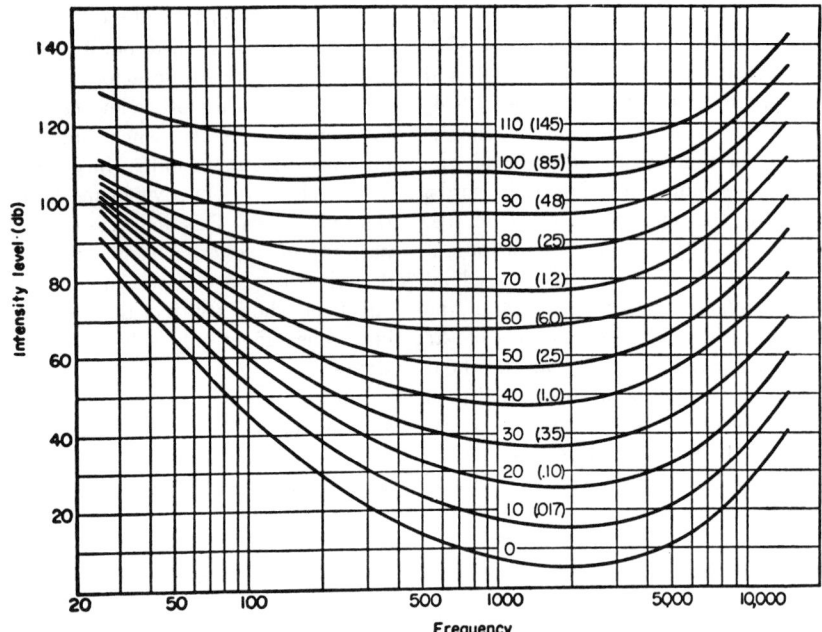

Fig. 19.5. Equal-loudness contours showing the relation between intensity level and frequency for tones at different loudness levels. All of the sounds represented by a given curve sound equally loud. The figures 0 to 110 represent *loudness level in phons*. The 0-phon contour is the normal free-field threshold curve. Figures in parentheses show the *loudness in sones*. (Reprinted with permission from Stevens and Davis, *Hearing*, 1938, John Wiley and Sons, Inc., New York.)

crease of 10 dB in sound pressure level, the loudness is approximately doubled. Note that in fig. 19.5 the corresponding loudness in tones is shown for each of the equal loudness contours.

An abnormally rapid increase in loudness can often be demonstrated in cases of unilateral hearing impairment due to injury to the organ of Corti. If an alternate binaural loudness balance is carried out, it is seen that even though the threshold of the abnormal ear may be much higher than that of the normal, loudness increases so rapidly in the abnormal ear that at higher intensities both ears hear the same loudness when both are stimulated at the same intensity level. This phenomenon is called *recruitment of loudness*. It is of diagnostic importance in distinguishing between lesions in Corti's organ, which usually exhibit recruitment, and those of the auditory nerve, which usually do not (fig. 19.7).

PITCH. Although we most often think of pitch as a function of frequency only, Stevens has shown that pitch can change with intensity. For frequencies below 1000 cps, pitch decreases as intensity is increased, whereas for tones above 3000 cps pitch increases with intensity. For tones in the middle range, slight changes may

occur in either direction, depending upon the intensity level.

Stevens and Volkmann have established a numerical scale of pitch by a fractionation method similar to that used for the scale of loudness. The unit of pitch is called the *mel*. A pitch of 1000 mels is assigned to a 1000-cps tone, a pitch of 500 mels to the tone which sounds one-half as high in pitch, and so on. Pitch intervals 50 mels wide sound to the ear to be equal in subjective extent. It may be noted that there is a close relation between the width in cycles of equal pitch intervals and the width of the critical bands.

The same frequency does not necessarily produce the same sensation of pitch in both ears. In cases where a unilateral partial loss of hearing has occurred as a result of localized damage to the organ of Corti, a tone may sound higher in pitch in the abnormal than in the normal ear. This sensation of false pitch of which the patient is usually unaware, is called *diplacusis*. A small difference in tuning can sometimes be demonstrated even in "normal" ears.

STEREOPHONIC HEARING. Judgment of the direction from which a sound comes is called *directional hearing* and requires the use of both ears. The cues for direction consist in differences

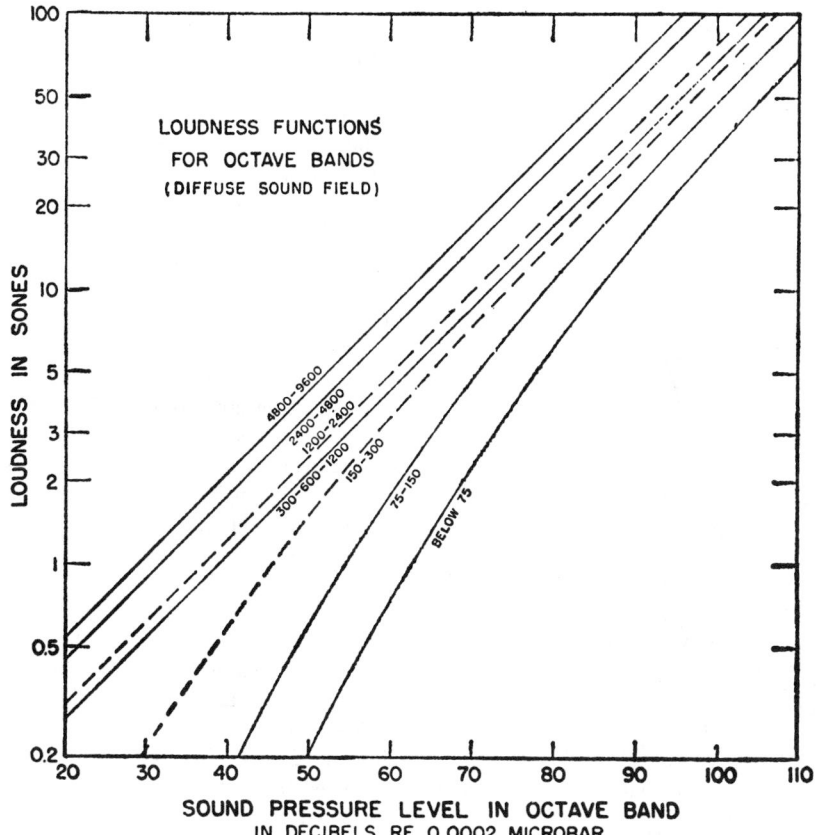

Fig. 19.6. Loudness in sones for octave bands of noise as a function of the sound pressure level in the bands. (By permission from S. S. Stevens, J. Acoust. Soc. Am., **28,** 807–832, 1956.)

in time of arrival or phase of the sound at the two ears, and differences in intensity caused by the sound-shadow of the head. *Auditory localization* implies a judgment of distance as well as direction of the sound source. Measurements of directional hearing and localization are carried out in free-field conditions, usually in an anechoic chamber, and the sound is referred by the subject to a source outside the head.

When sounds are presented to the two ears by means of earphones, the sound source seems to be inside the head. If similar sounds arrive simultaneously and are equally loud in both ears, the sound image is in the median plane of the head, but if the sound in one ear is louder than in the other, or if it leads the other in time of arrival or in phase, the sound image is *lateralized* to that side of the head. To a considerable extent, differences in time of arrival can compensate for differences in intensity, and there is a considerable literature that deals with this "time-intensity trade."

A model of binaural interaction to account for the time-intensity trade has been suggested by van Bergeijk. He assumes that fibers from the cochlear nuclei to the contralateral accessory nucleus are excitatory, whereas those to the ipsilateral nucleus are inhibitory. The degree of excitation and inhibition at each nucleus will depend upon the intensity and time of arrival of sounds at the two ears. Higher centers then make a comparison between the patterns of impulses from the two nuclei. Both neuroanatomical and electrophysiological studies appear to bear out the validity of such a model.

In directional hearing, differences in time or phase are important for frequencies below 1400 cps. The smallest time difference that can be perceived is approximately 13 microseconds, at a frequency of 800 cps. At higher frequencies such differences cannot be recognized, and judgments must be based on intensity differences alone. Small head movements then become very important in making a judgment of direction, since they enable the listener to take advantage of differences in the diffraction pattern at the two

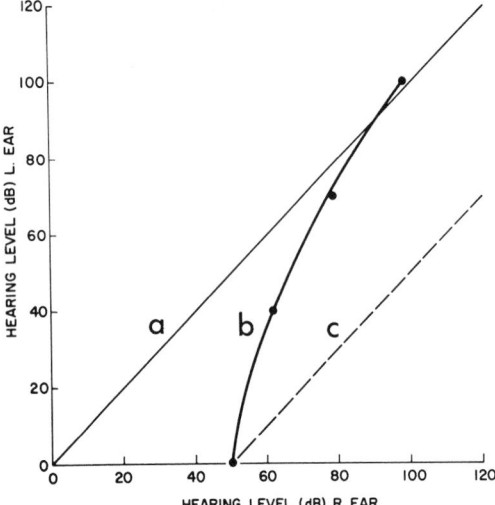

Fig. 19.7. Recruitment of loudness illustrated by binaural loudness matching. Curve a represents ideal loudness matching for two normal ears in which the same intensity produces identical loudness. Curve b represents a right ear with temporary sensori-neural impairment due to exposure to intense sound, matched against the normal left ear. Data points are those for 1000 cps in fig. 19.9. The right ear shows a 50-dB greater hearing threshold level, but the loudness of the 1000-cps tone increases more rapidly with intensity than for the normal left ear, so that at about 90 dB the tone sounds equally loud in both ears. Curve c represents a right ear with a 40-dB conductive impairment in which the rate of loudness increase is the same as that in the normal left ear.

ears as the head is turned slightly from side to side.

TYPES OF HEARING IMPAIRMENT

Any abnormal condition or disease process which interferes with the conduction of sound to the inner ear, with the transduction to nerve impulses in the cochlea, or with their transmission to the appropriate levels of the nervous system can cause an impairment of hearing. The otologist distinguishes between *conductive impairment,* caused by interference with the passage of sound waves through the external and middle ear, and *sensori-neural impairment,* caused by damage to the cochlear mechanism or to the auditory nerve. *Central impairment* involving the auditory pathways of the nervous system, is also recognized. *Conductive* defects take various forms. One of the commonest of these is an accumulation of hard, dry wax in the external canal. Fortunately, it is a condition that can easily be corrected. The tympanic membrane itself may be altered by disease, resulting either in "hardening of the eardrum" with fibrous and calcareous deposits, or in

a perforation. The effect of a perforation upon hearing depends upon its position and size, but it usually involves the low frequencies. Loss of mobility or interruption of the ossicular chain by destruction of an ossicle can occur in chronic otitis media. In such cases the hearing loss may amount to as much as 60 dB.

Otosclerosis is a localized disease of the bony capsule of the labyrinth and a common cause of conductive impairments. It involves destruction of bone in the neighborhood of the windows and replacement by new bone, which may be deposited around the stapes footplate in such a way as to interfere with its motion and ultimately to fix it in the oval window. The increasing stiffness causes a progressive loss of hearing for the low frequencies, usually beginning between puberty and the early thirties. Later the high frequencies may be affected by pathological changes in the cochlea itself.

In recent years, two surgical procedures have been perfected for the restoration of hearing in otosclerosis. One is Lempert's *fenestration* operation, in which a new window is made between the middle ear cavity and the lateral bony semicircular canal. In this way the immobile ossicular chain is bypassed, and sound is once more permitted to reach the inner ear *via* the round window and the new "fenestra ovalis." The second procedure began as a *mobilization of the stapes,* as developed by Rosen. In this operation the ankylosed margins of the footplate are cut through with fine picks or chisels. The operation can be performed under local anesthesia, and the restoration of hearing is sometimes dramatically sudden. A serious problem in the development of both operations has been the tendency of deafness to recur with closure of the fenestra or reankylosis of the footplate. At present fenestration is seldom performed, and stapes mobilization has been largely superseded by *stapedectomy,* in which the entire ossicle is removed. The footplate is usually replaced by a vein graft or pad of fat over the oval window, and the crura by a wire or plastic prosthesis attached to the long process of the incus. This operation has become enormously popular because of the excellent and long-lasting restoration of hearing that can be achieved in appropriate cases of otosclerosis.

Tympanoplasty, the surgical reconstruction of the sound-conducting system, is another example of middle ear surgery. It may be recommended in cases where the middle ear mechanism has been damaged by chronic otitis media. The operation must necessarily take various forms, depending upon the degree of injury found. In some cases a single ossicle between the drum and the oval window, resembling the avian *columella*, is substituted for the defective ossicular chain.

A temporary conductive impairment can occur when the drum membrane is strongly retracted (and its stiffness therefore increased) by a negative pressure in the middle ear. This condition is commonly experienced in aircraft during descents from altitude. When the external pressure exceeds that in the middle ear, the Eustachian tube, the only means by which the two pressures can be equalized, remains tightly closed, and the weak dilator muscle at its pharyngeal orifice, the *tensor veli palatini*, is unable to open it. The drum membrane does not rupture unless the pressure difference amounts to 100 to 500 mm. Hg. Usually the retraction persists for only a short time until the pressure difference is relieved by repeated swallowing, or by making a forced expiration with the nose and mouth closed (Valsalva's maneuver).

When the tube remains closed for any length of time, air trapped in the middle ear is gradually absorbed. If the partial pressure of oxygen in the cavity is reduced below the level of the hydrostatic pressure in the capillary bed, fluid leaves the capillaries and enters the middle ear, which may fill in minutes. Such an accumulation of fluid increases the friction of the system, and thus decreases the transmission of sound.

Sensori-neural impairment. A hearing defect due to interference with the process of excitation in the cochlea or with the transmission of impulses by the auditory nerve may be caused in many ways. In its mildest, reversible form it appears as a *temporary threshold shift* (TTS) after exposure to sound or noise of more than ordinary intensity. If the exposure is very intense or occurs day after day, as in a noisy industrial situation with sustained levels in the neighborhood of 100 dB, it can result in the permanent impairment called permanent threshold shift (PTS). Hearing for the upper frequencies is more affected than for the lower, and a "dip" in the audiogram at 4000 cps is a common finding. The reason for the special vulnerability of this region of the basilar membrane is still obscure.

In the temporary cochlear deafness after exposure to a pure tone, the maximum loss is found about half an octave *above* the frequency of the exposure tone, but never below it. This result fits well with the known shape of the travelling wave. A loss of 40 to 60 dB at one or more frequencies is usually accompanied by a ringing or sizzling *tinnitus* or subjective noise, presumably representing a sustained spontaneous discharge of injured hair cells (fig. 19.8). Recruitment of loudness is present, so that in spite of the elevation of threshold for certain frequencies, the loudness of sounds at higher intensity may be normal (fig. 19.9). Diplacusis, with an upward shift of pitch in the region of the

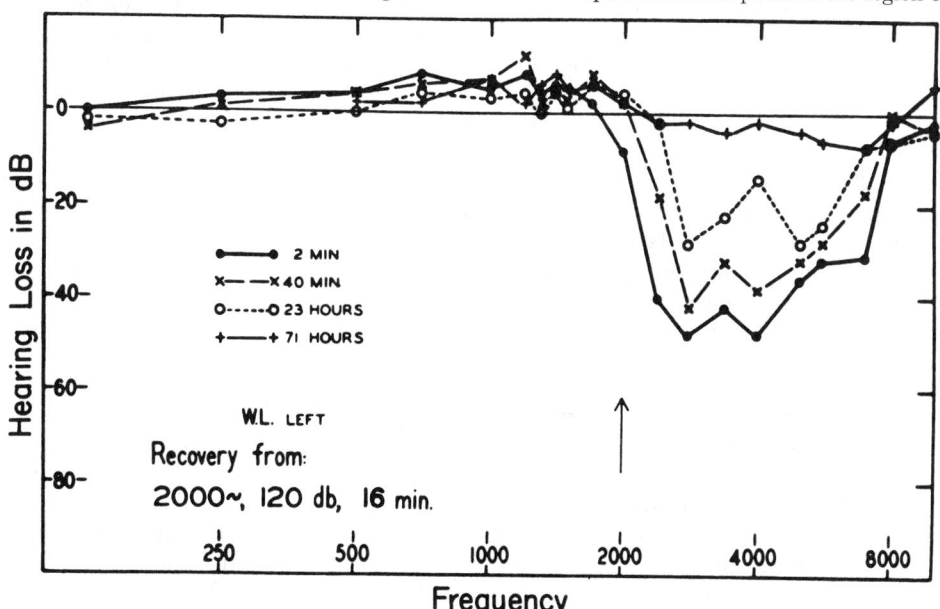

FIG. 19.8. Temporary sensori-neural impairment or threshold shift (TTS) after exposure to a tone of 2000 cps at 120 dB SPL for 16 min., with recovery. The shift, plotted in the form of an audiogram, is greatest for frequencies above that of the exposure tone. (From Davis et al., Acta Oto-laryng. (Stockholm) Suppl. 88, 1950.)

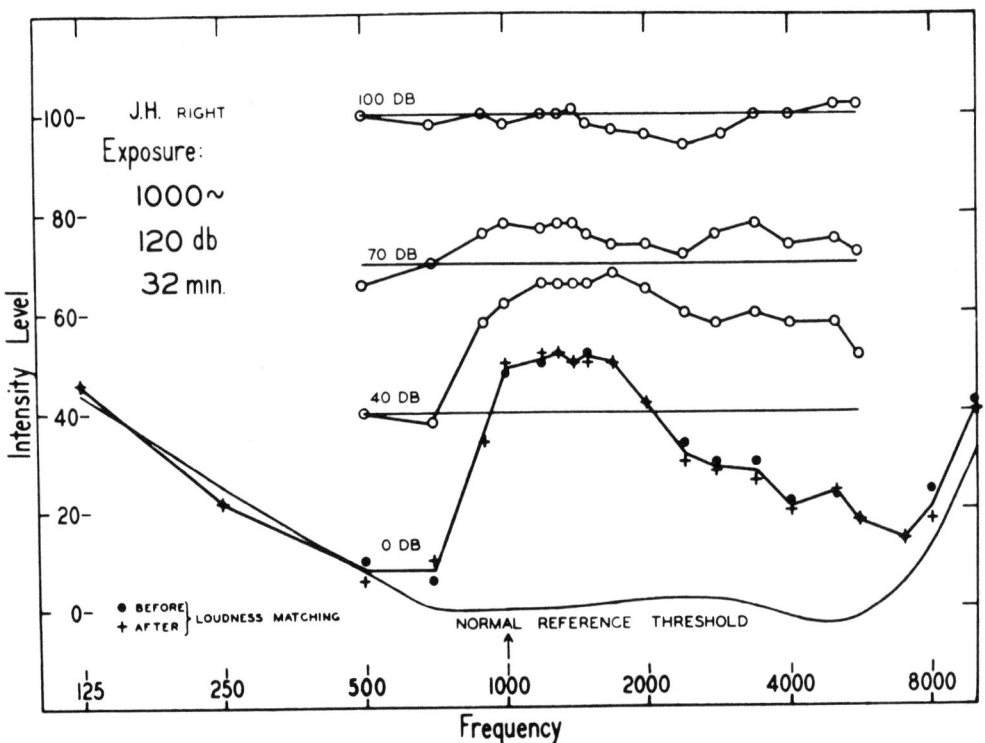

FIG. 19.9. Loudness matching (equal-loudness contours) illustrating recruitment of loudness in a temporary sensori-neural impairment of hearing produced by exposure to 1000 cps at 120 dB SPL for 32 min. There is a marked elevation of the threshold (0 dB) curve, but the curves for 40, 70, and 100 dB loudness levels show progressively less displacement from the ideal normal values (horizontal lines). (From Davis et al., Acta Oto-laryng. (Stockholm) Suppl. 88, 1950.)

hearing loss can usually be demonstrated (fig. 19.10). In animals exposed to intense tones, degenerative changes are found in the hair cells of the organ of Corti. The outer hair cells are more susceptible to such injury than the inner, and the region of damage is usually localized in the basal half of the cochlea.

Sensori-neural hearing impairment can occur at any age. In childhood it can be congenital, or it can be the result of infection, e.g. meningitis or mumps. A form of sensori-neural disorder accompanied by violent attacks of vertigo is *Menière's syndrome*, which occurs most frequently in middle-aged persons. Hearing for the low frequencies is affected, and a roaring tinnitus is often present. The attacks are attributed to an increased hydrostatic pressure of the endolymph (hydrops), causing a bulging of the walls of the cochlear duct which has been demonstrated *post mortem*. The function of the auditory nerve may also be impaired by the pressure of a tumor in the cerebello-pontine angle. Finally, a gradually progressive sensori-neural impairment of hearing occurs with advancing age and is called *presbycusis*.

A new hazard to hearing is found in the antibiotics of the streptomycin group, especially *dihydrostreptomycin*, *kanamycin* and *neomycin*, all of which can cause profound deafness by their ototoxic action. The hearing loss starts with the highest frequencies and may progress even after antibiotic therapy is discontinued. In experimental animals, these antibiotics have been shown to cause degeneration of the hair cells and even complete dissolution and disappearance of Corti's organ. The electrical responses are diminished or absent, especially the cochlear microphonic potential.

Assessment of Hearing Impairments

Bone conduction audiometry plays an important part in the diagnosis of hearing impairments. Because receptor function is affected in sensorineural cases, the bone conduction audiogram shows the same pattern of loss as that for air conduction. In conductive impairments on the other hand, hearing by bone conduction may be perfectly normal, in contrast to the loss shown in the air conduction audiogram. Such an "air-bone gap" is found in otosclerosis. The compari-

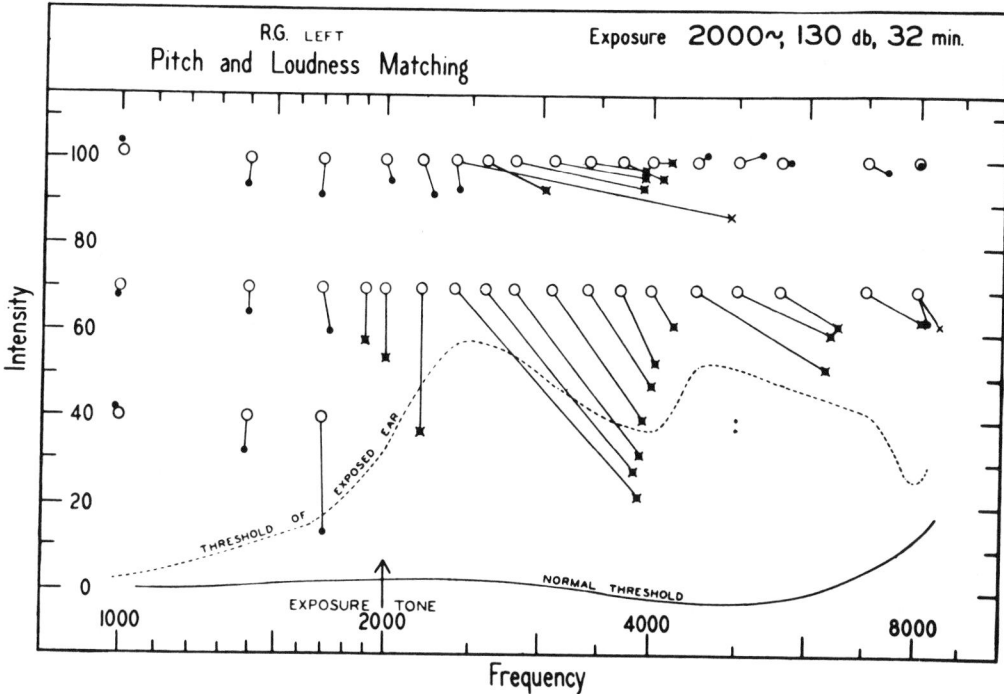

FIG. 19.10. Diplacusis, illustrated by pitch and loudness matching during temporary sensori-neural impairment following exposure to 2000 cps at 130 dB for 32 min. Tones presented at a given intensity level to the exposed left ear are matched for loudness and pitch by adjusting the intensity and frequency to the normal right ear. At the 40-dB level, the exposed ear hears only frequencies below the exposure tone. Tones at the 70-dB level are matched by less intense tones to the normal ear. From 2400 to 3700 cps, all of the tones have approximately the same *higher* pitch for the exposed ear, since they are matched by tones of about 4000 cps to the normal ear. At the 100-dB level, the change in loudness is less because of recruitment, but the upward shift of pitch is still present. (From Davis et al., Acta Oto-laryng. (Stockholm) Suppl. 88, 1950.)

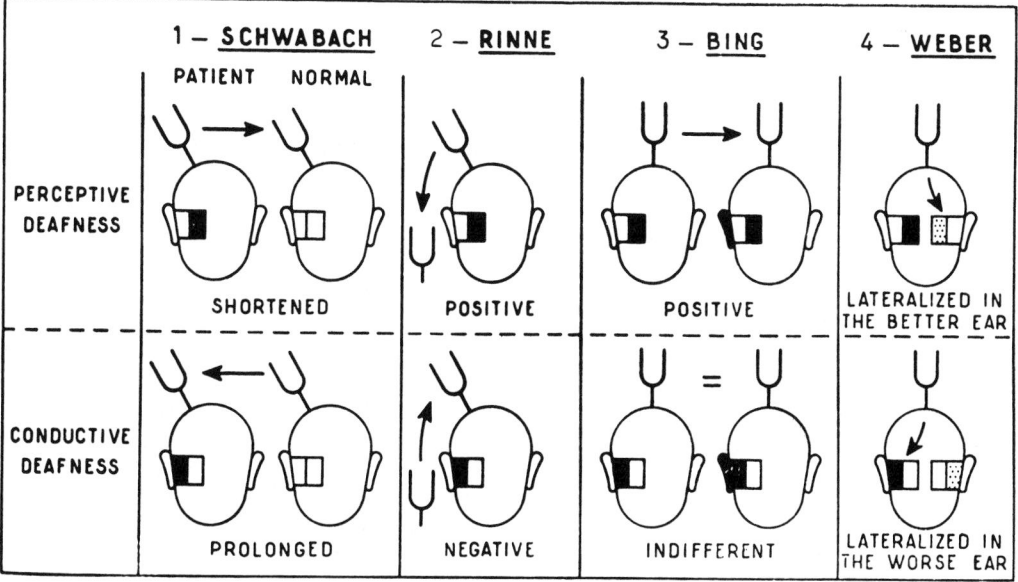

FIG. 19.11. The four classical bone conduction tests with tuning forks. Arrows indicate that the sound is heard for a longer period of time when the fork is moved from one position to the other. Black indicates location of lesion in middle ear or cochlea. (By permission from *The Middle Ear*, by H. G. Kobrak. Copyright 1959. The University of Chicago Press.)

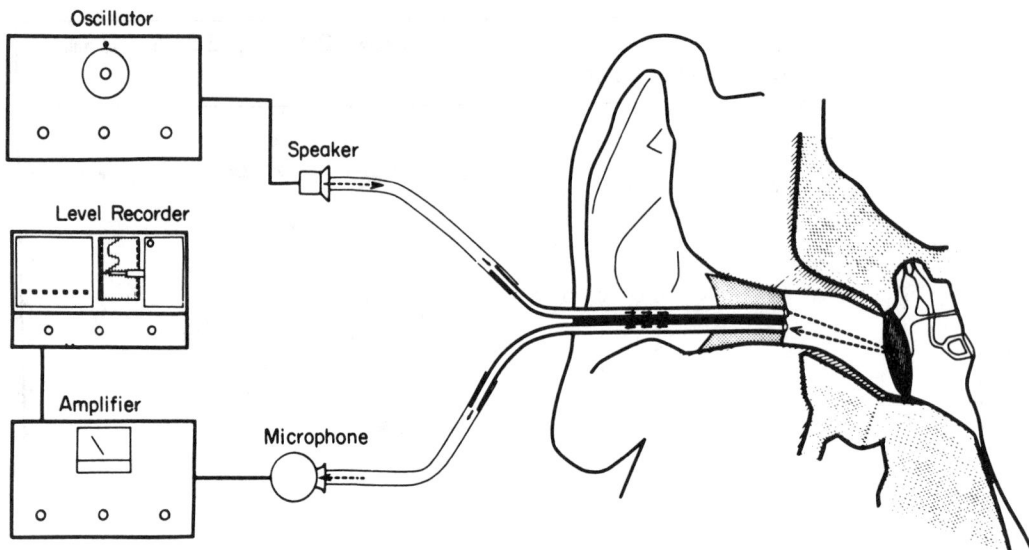

FIG. 19.12. An adaptation of the impedance technique for clinical measurement of intra-aural reflex responses to sound. Part of the sound produced by the speaker is reflected from the drum membrane and recorded via the microphone. When a sudden sound is applied to the opposite ear, it elicits a reflex contraction of the stapedius muscle in the ear under test, changing the impedance of the ossicular chain, and thereby altering the amount of sound reflected from the drum membrane. (After Nordlund and Lidén, in *Nordiska Audiologiska Sällskapets Kurs i Audiologi*, Göteborg, 1962.)

son can also be made in the classical *Rinne*[1] *test* using the tuning fork. The vibrating fork is first placed on the mastoid process. When the patient reports that he can no longer hear its tone by bone conduction, it is removed from the bone and the vibrating prongs are held up to the open ear canal. The normal ear should then hear the fork by air conduction and continue to hear it for about 45 seconds. This "positive" Rinne test is also characteristic of sensori-neural impairment. If the fork is heard longer by bone conduction, the test is negative, and a conductive loss is present (fig. 19.11).

In the *Schwabach test*, the patient's bone conduction hearing is tested against the presumably normal hearing of the examiner. If there is a conductive lesion, the patient will be able to hear the fork longer than the examiner, because the presence of the lesion excludes masking noise. If a neural lesion is present, the patient will hear the fork for a shorter time than the examiner. The bone conduction test made with an audiometer is essentially similar to the Schwabach test.

The *occlusion* or *Bing test* consists in placing the fork on the vertex of the skull and determining the effect of gently occluding the canal on the thresholds for low frequencies. If there is a sensori-neural lesion, sensation at low frequencies

[1] Pronounced to rhyme approximately with *pinna*.

is increased because the bone conducted sound sets up vibrations in the air enclosed in the canal which are transmitted to the cochlea and reinforce the vibrations reaching it directly. If a conductive lesion is present, occlusion of the canal has no effect on the sensation.

In the *Gellé test*, the air pressure in the external canal is increased. If the middle ear structures are mobile, hearing by bone conduction is diminished because the pressure is transmitted to the inner ear. If the stapes is fixed in the oval window, hearing is unaffected.

The *Weber test* is valuable in the diagnosis of otosclerosis and highly reliable in spite of the difficult theoretical problem it has always raised. It consists simply in placing the vibrating fork on the patient's head and asking him to report in which ear he hears it. If one ear has a sensori-neural lesion, the sound will be heard in the opposite, i.e., the *better ear*. If, however, one ear has a fixed stapes, the sound will be heard in the same, i.e., in the *worse ear*. Many hypotheses have been put forward attempting to explain this paradoxical result, but none has been universally accepted. One of the most attractive is that of Langenbeck, who has pointed out that only compression bone conduction can be effective in stimulating the cochlea of an ear with a fixed stapes and has shown how the lateralization of the sound may depend upon a difference in phase between the compression

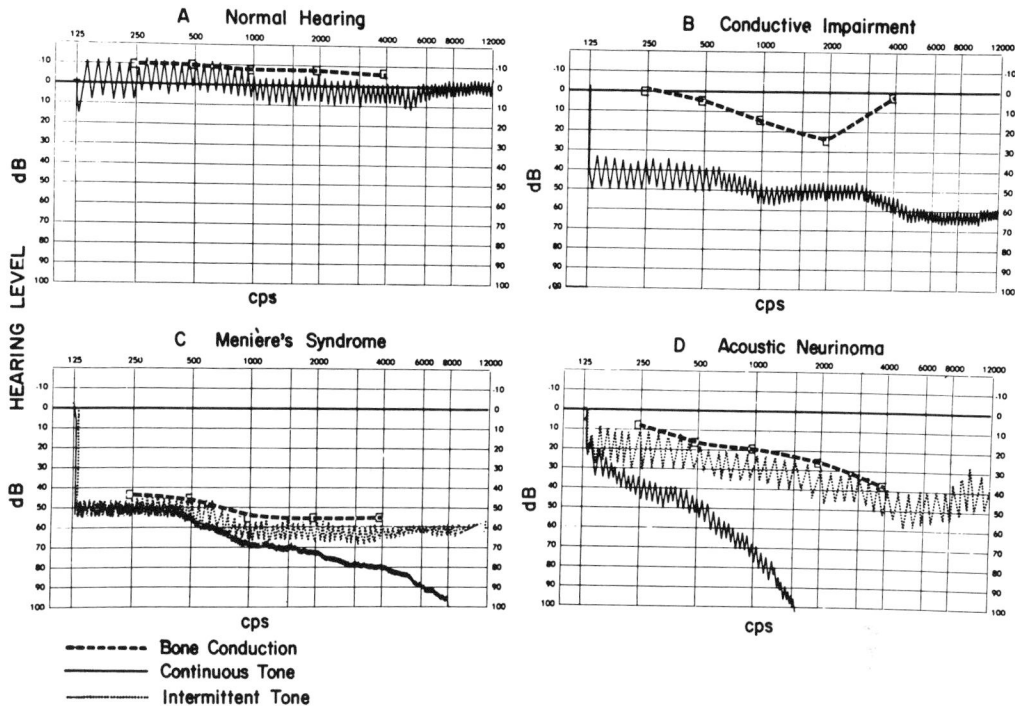

FIG. 19.13. v. Békésy audiograms illustrating various forms of hearing impairment. With conductive impairment there is an "air-bone gap" between the curves for air conduction and for bone conduction. In Menière's syndrome (cochlear impairment), hearing by bone conduction and by air conduction are equally affected. With acoustic neurinoma (neural or retrocochlear impairment) hearing is well maintained when the tone is interrupted, but it fatigues rapidly when a continuous tone is used. (After Nordlund and Lidén, in *Nordiska Audiologiska Sällskapets Kurs i Audiologi*, Göteborg, 1962.)

bone conducted sound reaching that cochlea and the inertia bone conducted sound reaching the other cochlea. Experimental studies in animals tend to support this point of view.

Impedance Measurements. In contrast to all of the subjective audiometric and tuning fork tests, impedance measurements provide an entirely new and promising objective means for evaluating auditory function. Since the complex acoustic impedance at the eardrum depends upon the state of the drum membrane and the ossicular chain, the degree of contraction of the intra-aural muscles, and the pressure differential across the membrane, impedance measurements can be used to reveal pathological changes in the middle ear mechanism and the eustachian tube. Fig. 19.12 shows a simple adaptation of the impedance technique for recording intra-aural reflexes. By appropriate choice of acoustic and tactile stimuli the individual responses of the stapedius and tensor muscles can be elicited to determine whether their reflex arcs, involving motor fibers of the facial and trigeminal nerves respectively, are intact. Even the recruitment phenomenon can be demonstrated objectively by this means.

With cochlear lesions the stapedius reflex can be elicited at the same sound levels as in the normal ear. The decreased difference, in decibels, between hearing threshold and stapedius reflex threshold is a measure of the recruitment. If no recruitment can be demonstrated, either by this test or by loudness balance, a neural or so-called retrocochlear lesion is probably involved.

Despite the wealth of diagnostic tests available to the otologist, the assessment of hearing defects sometimes presents thorny problems, especially when there is a lesion central to the cochlea, or when a non-organic hearing loss is suspected. The form of the Békésy audiogram, and especially a rapid decline in the response to a continuous as compared with an interrupted tone, is often indicative of a lesion beyond Corti's organ (fig. 19.13). In the diagnosis of neural and central lesions it may be helpful to test the patient's ability to localize sounds by means of directional audiometry, and the integrative function of his higher auditory centers by means of special binaural fusion tests employing messages in fractionated, filtered, or distorted speech.

HEARING AIDS. When a hearing handicap is

attributable to a conductive defect, and cochlear function can be shown by bone conduction tests to be satisfactory, surgical intervention for the restoration or improvement of hearing may be indicated. On the other hand, the amplification provided by an electronic hearing aid may be sufficient for the patient's everyday needs. The earphone is usually inserted in the external canal, but for some patients a bone-conduction oscillator placed on the mastoid process may be preferable. In any case it is important to realize that a hearing aid can not be "fitted" to correct for deviations of the audiogram from the normal in the sense that eyeglasses can be fitted to correct for errors of refraction. Adequate but not excessive amplification of sound and good quality of reproduction are the important factors to be considered in the choice of an instrument. Some patients with sensori-neural defects may be helped by wearing a hearing aid, depending upon the severity of the loss and the frequencies involved, but many others obtain no significant benefit.

REFERENCES

BÁRÁNY, E. A contribution to the physiology of bone conduction. Acta oto-laryng. (Stockholm) Suppl. 26, 1938.

VON BÉKÉSY, G. A new audiometer. Acta oto-laryng. (Stockholm) 1947, 35, 411.

VON BÉKÉSY, G. Vibration of the head in a sound field and its role in hearing by bone conduction. J. Acoust. Soc. Am., 1948, 20, 749.

VAN BERGEIJK, W. A. Variation on a theme of Békésy: a model of binaural interaction. J. Acoust. Soc. Am., 1962, 34, 1431.

DAVIS, H. Guide for the classification and evaluation of hearing handicap in relation to the international audiometric zero. Trans. Amer. Acad. Ophthalmol. and Otolaryng., 1965, 69, 740.

DAVIS, H., MORGAN, C. T., HAWKINS, J. E., JR., GALAMBOS, R., AND SMITH, F. W. Temporary deafness following exposure to loud tones and noise. Acta oto-laryng. (Stockholm) Suppl. 88, 1950.

FLETCHER, H. Speech and Hearing in Communication. D. Van Nostrand Company, Inc., Princeton, N. J., 1953.

GLORIG, A. AND DAVIS, H. Age, noise, and hearing loss. Ann. Otol., Rhinol. & Laryngol., 1961, 70, 556.

GRAHAM, A. B., ed. Sensorineural hearing processes and disorders. Little, Brown & Co., Boston, Mass., 1966.

GUILFORD, J. P. Psychometric Methods. McGraw-Hill Book Company, Inc., New York, 1954.

HALLÉN, O., LIDÉN, G., AND NORDLUND, B. Preoperative assessment of hearing loss. Acta oto-laryng. (Stockholm) 1964, 57, 416.

HALLPIKE, C. S. AND CAIRNS, H. Observations on the pathology of Menière's syndrome. J. Laryng. & Otol., 1938, 53, 625.

HAWKINS, J. E., JR. AND STEVENS, S. S. The masking of pure tones and of speech by white noise. J. Acoust. Soc. Am., 1950, 22, 6.

HIRSH, I. J. The measurement of hearing. McGraw-Hill Book Company, Inc., New York, 1952.

JERGER, J. Modern Developments in Audiology. Academic Press, New York and London, 1963.

KOBRAK, H. G. The middle ear. University of Chicago Press, Chicago, Ill., 1959.

MØLLER, AA. Acoustic reflex in man. J. Acoust. Soc. Am., 1962, 34, 1524.

NORDLUND, B. Physical factors in angular localization. Acta oto-laryng. (Stockholm) 1962, 75, 54.

NORDLUND, B. Directional audiometry. Acta oto-laryng. (Stockholm) 1964, 57, 1.

SCHUKNECHT, H. F., ed. Otosclerosis. Little, Brown, & Co., Boston, Mass., 1962.

STEVENS, S. S. Mathematics, measurement, and psychophysics. In Handbook of Experimental Psychology (S. S. Stevens, ed.) John Wiley & Sons., Inc., New York, 1951.

STEVENS, S. S. The surprising simplicity of sensory metrics. Amer. Psychologist, 1962, 17, 29.

STEVENS, S. S. On the validity of the loudness scale. J. Acoust. Soc. Am., 1959, 31, 995.

STEVENS, S. S. AND VOLKMANN, J. The relation of pitch to frequency: a revised scale. Am. J. Psychol., 1940, 53, 329.

SWETS, J. A. Detection theory and psychophysics: a review. Psychometrika, 1961, 26, 49.

SWETS, J. A., TANNER, W. P., JR., AND BIRDSALL, T. G. Decision processes in perception. Psychol. Rev., 1961, 68, 301.

ZWICKER, E., FLOTTORP, G., AND STEVENS, S. S. Critical band width in loudness summation. J. Acoust. Soc. Am., 1957, 29, 548.

ZWISLOCKI, J. Analysis of some auditory characteristics. In Handbook of Mathematical Psychology, Vol. III (R. D. Luce, R. R. Bush, and E. Galanter, eds.) John Wiley & Sons, Inc., New York, 1965.

CHAPTER 20

The Senses of Taste and Smell; Common Chemical Sense

Taste, Gustation

Taste is a chemical sense, that is to say, the receptors (chemoreceptors) for this sense respond adequately to chemical stimuli. In order, therefore, for a substance to arouse a sensation of taste it must be dissolved—either taken in solution or dissolved in the saliva; a solid taken into a perfectly dry mouth is tasteless. For this reason the organs of taste or *taste buds* are present only upon a moist surface, being confined to the mouth region of all air-breathing vertebrates, but may be anywhere upon the body surface of aquatic forms.

THE ORGANS OF TASTE. The taste buds of man are mainly situated on the tongue but a few are also found in the mucous membrane covering the palate, fauces, epiglottis and the larynx in the region of the arytenoid cartilages. Taste buds are more widely distributed in children, and are especially plentiful over the anterior part of the tongue. In the adult they are much fewer at the tip of the tongue and are almost absent from the middle third. In most fishes the skin of the general body surface is plentifully supplied with taste receptors, and in the catfish and certain other species of fish they are contained in the filiform processes known as barbles projecting from the snout and angles of the mouth. In insects (flies, bees) taste receptors are located at the end of the proboscis antennae or upon the tarsal segments of the legs.

The mucosa of the human tongue is studded with large numbers of small elevations—the *lingual papillae*—caused by projections of the lamina propria and called secondary papillae. The papillae are of three main types, filiform, fungiform and vallate. The *filiform papillae* are very minute conical structures covering the anterior two-thirds or so of the dorsal surface of the tongue. They are arranged in rows running roughly parallel with the rows of vallate papillae. The *fungiform papillae* are considerably larger than the preceding type, round in shape and situated mainly at the tip and edges of the tongue. The *vallate papillae* are much larger and become especially prominent posteriorly where from 6 to 12 are arranged conspicuously in the form of a V with its limbs open anteriorly. A vallate papilla consists of a central round elevation with perpendicular sides and surrounded by a sulcus; the taste buds are situated in the mucosa forming the walls of this circular trench. The filiform papillae rarely contains taste buds, but each fungiform papilla usually holds from 8 to 10 embedded in the epithelium covering its free surface.

A section of a taste bud is shown in figure 20.1. It measures about 70 μ long and 50 μ broad, and lies with its long axis perpendicular to the epithelial surface. It consists of groups of *supporting cells (peripheral supporting cells)* shaped somewhat like the sections of a musk melon and arranged side by side to enclose a small oval chamber which opens superficially through a circular gap—the *inner taste pore*—surrounded by the converging ends of the supporting cells. The inner taste pore usually leads into a short canal which opens in turn through the *outer taste pore* upon the surface of the tongue. The cavity of the taste bud is occupied by other supporting cells (*central supporting cells*) in the intervals between which the taste receptors (taste cells) are lodged. The taste cell is spindle-shaped and provided with a fine hairlike process which projects through the inner taste pore into the short canal mentioned above. The taste bud contains a variable number of these sensory cells, usually from 5 to 18. Nerve fibers after losing their medullary sheaths penetrate the bud and arborize upon the surface of the taste cells.

The total number of taste buds varies widely between different species from an estimated 800 in the bat to 35,000 in the ox; there are about 9,000 in man.

The chief nerves of taste are the *chorda tympani* branch of the facial nerve and the *glossopharyngeal nerve* (see fig. 20.2). The former nerve supplies the taste buds over the anterior two-thirds of the tongue, the latter is distributed to the posterior third. The *vagus nerve* innervates the taste buds present on the pharyngeal aspect of the tongue, on the soft palate, epiglottis and the region of the arytenoid cartilages. The *trigeminal nerve* mediates common chemical sense (p. 434) and sensations of touch, temperature and pressure (common sensibility) from the entire buccal mucosa; it does not contain taste fibers. Cushing observed, for example, that removal of the Gasserian (trigeminal) ganglion did not cause any permanent loss of taste. Section of the nerves of taste in animals is followed by degeneration and gradual disappearance of the taste buds. Olmsted has shown in experiments upon the catfish that taste buds reappear upon

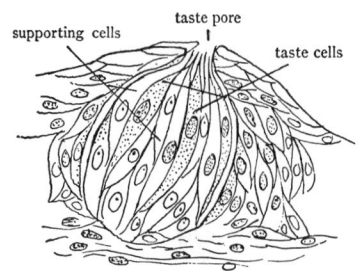

FIG. 20.1. Vertical section through a taste bud

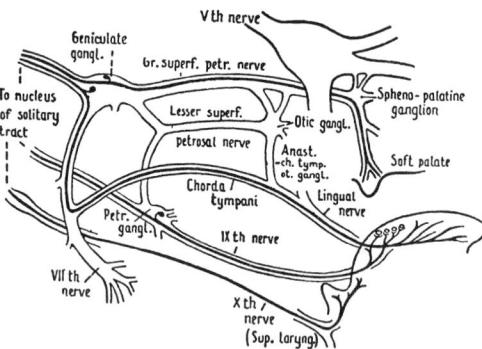

FIG. 20.2. Diagram of the course of the gustatory fibers. (Modified from Brodal, after Rowbotham.)

regeneration of the nerve fibers. The latter evidently exert a formative influence, possibly through the medium of a chemical substance, upon the development of the taste organs.

The central connections of the nerves of taste are described in chapters 5 and 7 (see fig. 20.2).

THE SENSATIONS OF TASTE

There are four *simple, primary* or *fundamental* tasts—*sweet, sour (acid), salty* and *bitter.* Two others are sometimes added, namely, *alkaline* and *metallic.*[1] The various other tastes which we experience are (a) blends of two or more of the primary sensations or (b) combinations of the latter with sensations aroused by the stimulation of the nerves of common sensibility. For example, ginger is recognized not only by its taste (i.e., through impulses from the taste buds), but also by the burning sensation caused by the excitation of the

[1] Opinions differ as to the nature of these two sensations, most investigators contending that the former is a compound sensation, resulting from the excitation of several types of end organs, including those for sweetness and for touch. Similarly, the metallic taste caused by the salts of heavy metals, copper, silver, mercury, etc., is believed to be a complex of sour and sweet. Some maintain indeed that it is due chiefly to the stimulation of olfactory receptors. Stimulation of the tongue by an electric current causes a metallic taste.

ordinary sensory nerves of the mouth and also, we may add, by its odor. Many other substances, such as fats and oils and pungent condiments, are "felt" as well as tasted.

Many of the finer flavors are in reality sensations of smell, and olfaction enters very largely into many of the sensations which we generally class as tastes. For this reason when the nose is held or the nasal passages blocked, as during a common cold, the sense of taste is blunted. It may then be impossible if two bland foods are of the same consistency to distinguish between them; thus an apple and a pear, or a turnip and a potato, taste pretty much alike. On the other hand, certain substances which we think that we detect by smell are actually tasted. The sweetish smell of chloroform is an example; the vapor reaches the taste buds in the inspired air.

The four primary gustatory sensations are not aroused with equal intensity over all parts of the tongue. Apparently there is a functionally distinct type of receptor for each primary taste, and the distribution of each type is not uniform over the lingual mucosa. End organs sensitive to sweet and salty materials are most plentiful at the tip, those responsive to acid are distributed mainly along the margins, whereas those aroused by bitter substances are towards the base of the tongue and in the region of the epiglottis. These facts are recognized generally in practice, for one would no more think of sipping beer than he would of gulping a glass of wine, and a child prefers to lick rather than munch a stick of candy. The taste receptors adapt rather rapidly; for this reason food which we enjoy is moved over the surfaces of the tongue and mouth and brought into contact continually with fresh receptors. Some substances stimulate two types of taste bud. For example, *sodium salicylate, rhamnose* and *parabrom-benzoic-sulfinide,* a substance related to saccharine, give a sweet taste when applied to the tip of the tongue but when swallowed, and thus brought into contact with the vallate papillae, taste bitter. *Ortho-benzyl-benzoate,* on the other hand, gives a bitter followed by a sweet taste. *Magnesium* and *sodium sulfates* are salty-bitter, causing a salty taste at the tip of the tongue and a bitter taste at the base. When the papillae are explored individually with different sapid substances it is found that the filiform type are insensitive. Of the fungiform papillae, some respond to both sweet and salty compounds, others to acid and sweet and others again to bitter and acid. A few respond to all four types of stimulus. These results indicate the existence of functionally distinct types of taste receptors and that different types are present in the same fungiform papilla. Only taste buds responsive to bitter substances are present in the vallate papillae (fig. 20.3).

The sense of taste may be aroused by substances reaching the taste buds in the blood stream. Thus the intravenous injection of histamine causes a metallic taste, glucinum a sweet taste, and in jaundice a bitter taste may be experienced as a result of the high concentrations of biliary constituents in the blood.

Theories of taste perception. The results of experiments in which action potentials were recorded from single nerve fibers when sapid substances were applied to the tongue strongly support the conception of four specific types of taste receptor. Pfaffman identified three types of nerve fiber in the cat: (a) those which responded to acid, (b) those which responded to acid and salt, and (c) those which responded to acid and quinine. Although fibers responsive to sweetness were not found by this investigator, others using an improved method have obtained responses with sucrose. No difference was observed in the character of the impulses which might serve to distinguish the type of stimulus employed. Such a finding is in accord with what we know of other sense organs, namely, that the quality of sensation is determined by the central connections of the nerve fiber, i.e., upon the part of the brain where the impulses, set up in the receptor organ by an adequate stimulus, are delivered.

It is quite evident that stimulation of the different types of receptor in suitable proportions accompanied by the excitation of nongustatory nerves of the lingual and oral mucosa, as well as of the olfactory receptors, could account for the wide range of taste sensations that are experienced.

The mechanism through which the taste receptor is stimulated, and an impulse set up in the nerve fiber is unknown, but a theory has been proposed based upon the inhibition of enzyme systems in the taste cells by the sapid substance. Bourne, for example, found in various mammals a relatively high concentration of alkaline phosphatase in the epithelium overlying the taste buds, and El Baradi and Bourne have demonstrated that a 0.05 per cent cencentration of vanillin strongly inhibits the action of this enzyme. Also a simple esterase is present in the taste buds in fairly high concentration; it is inhibited by quinine but not by salt or sugar.

Discrimination of differences in intensities of stimulation is relatively crude for taste and smell.

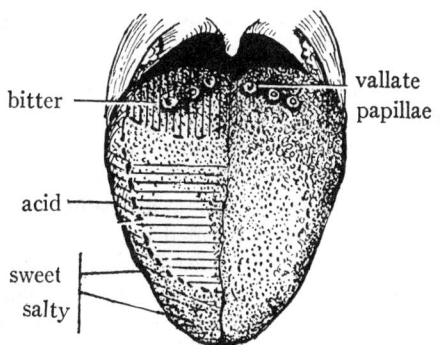

Fig. 20.3. Showing distribution of primary taste sensations on one side of the tongue.

In order for a change to be produced in either of these sensations the intensity of stimulation must alter by about 30 per cent, whereas the eye can detect a change in illumination of 1 per cent and the ear a change in sound intensity of 10 per cent.

TASTE SENSATIONS AND CHEMICAL CONSTITUTION. The *sweet* taste is associated predominantly with organic compounds, especially the *sugars* (e.g., sucrose, maltose, glucose, etc.) certain *polysaccharides*, *glycerol* and other *alcohols*, *aldehydes* and *ketones* of the aliphatic series, and *saccharine*, *dulcine* and *chloroform*. But certain inorganic substances, such as *lead acetate* (sugar of lead) and *alkalis* in high dilution, are also sweet to the taste.

Substances which arouse an acid or a salty taste are always electrolytes, but bitter or sweet substances may be either electrolytes or nonelectrolytes.

Several attempts have been made to relate the sweet taste to chemical constitution. Oertly and Myers, for example, from a study of a large number of sweet organic compounds have proposed the theory that every sweet molecule contains two particular types of radical or an atom upon which the sweet taste depends. One of these they call a *glucophore*, the other an *auxogluc*. A glucophore makes a given compound a potential tastestuff; if it is bound to an auxogluc a sweet compound is produced. Some six glucophores and nine auxoglucs have been identified; four of each are listed in the following table.

Glucophores	Auxoglucs
(1) —CO—CHOH—(H)	(1) H
(2) $CO_2H \cdot CHNH_2$—	(2) CH_3CH_2
(3) $CH_2OH \cdot CHOH$—	(3) CH_2OH
(4) CH_2ONO_2—	(4) CH_2OH CHOH

Thus the hexoses contain the glucophore (1) and the auxogluc (4), glycerol the glucophore (2) and the auxogluc (3), and amino-acetic acid the glucophore (2) and the auxogluc (1).

The *salty* taste is evoked primarily by inorganic compounds, notably the *chlorides* of *sodium, potassium, magnesium, ammonium* and *lithium,* by certain *sulfates, bromides* and *iodides* and by *sodium* and *potassium nitrates.* The saline taste of such compounds is attributed to the anions (Cl, Br, I, SO₄ and NO₃), a conclusion arrived at from a comparison of their tastes when in high dilution with that of an equally weak solution of sodium acetate. For example, a 0.04 molar solution of NaCl, of KCl or of LiCl has a slightly salty taste, whereas sodium acetate in equal or somewhat lower dilution is tasteless or at least is not salty. Similarly sodium bromide, iodide or nitrate loses its saline taste at a much higher dilution than does the acetate. Of the halogens the dilution at which the salty taste is just perceptible is highest for the chloride, next for the bromide and lowest for the iodide ion. The saline taste is not confined to inorganic compounds. Certain organic compounds, such as the *hydrochlorides of monomethylamine* and *diethylamine* also possess this property.

The *sour* taste is produced by acids or acid salts. It is generally agreed that the effective agent is the hydrogen ion. This statement would seem to be contradicted by the fact that solutions of certain organic acids, such as acetic, tartaric, citric, etc., are more acid to the taste than a solution of a mineral acid having a considerably greater hydrogen ion concentration. For example, the acid taste of a solution of acetic acid is about equal to one of HCl in a dilution one third as great. Yet as compared with the latter solution, the solution of HCl, since this acid is highly dissociated, is from four to five times as great. The greater effectiveness of acetic acid for a given H ion concentration is attributed to its greater power of penetrating the tissues, and therefore to its greater effectiveness in raising the hydrogen ion concentration within the taste buds. The *astringent taste* is attributed to acid in very high dilution, that is, to a greatly attenuated sensation of sourness.

The *bitter* taste, like sweetness, is associated chiefly with organic compounds, especially the *alkaloids* (*quinine, strychnine, morphine,* etc.) and certain *glucosides. Picric acid, dexiromannose* and *bile salts* are among the other bitter organic compounds. Of inorganic substances with a bitter taste are *magnesium, ammonium,* and *calcium salts.* The bitterness of these salts is due to the cation. A slight change in the chemical constitu-

tion of a substance often alters its taste from bitter to sweet. Saccharine, for example, is intensely sweet, but some of its derivatives are bitter; dulcin is some 500 times sweeter than cane sugar yet *phenylthiocarbamide,* in which one oxygen atom in the dulcin molecule is replaced by a sulfur atom, is bitter to most persons. Phenylthiocarbamide is peculiar in that to 3 persons out of 10 it is tasteless. The taste deficiency ("taste blindness") in respect to this substance is hereditary, being transmitted as a Mendelian recessive. Many organic compounds having a bitter taste contain NO₂ groups. If the molecule contains two such groups the compound is usually, although not necessarily, bitter; if three are present it is invariably so.

INADEQUATE STIMULI. Of agents other than chemical which are capable of evoking a sensation of taste, by far the most effective is the electrical current. Electrical stimulation by means of the constant current, using a pair of electrodes placed upon the tongue causes, upon breaking the current, a metallic taste which persists for a little time. If one electrode is placed in contact with the surface of the tongue and the other upon some indifferent part of the body, a constant current during its passage causes an acid or alkaline taste, depending upon the direction of the current. If the lingual electrode is the anode an acid taste is experienced, whereas if the cathode is the stimulating electrode the taste is alkaline. Two factors, apparently, are concerned in the production of the acid or alkaline taste, namely, direct electrical stimulation of the taste cells and the production of H and OH ions at the anode and cathode, respectively, as a result of electrolysis of the buccal fluids. That a gustatory response can be produced by direct electrical stimulation is evident from the fact that it is more readily aroused by a rapidly alternating current, which has no appreciable electrolytic action, than by a direct current. Furthermore, when two persons are connected each to a pole of a battery and the circuit completed by bringing the tips of their tongues together, they experience different taste sensations, one acid the other alkaline. Now the two sets of taste buds must be exposed to the action of the same ions, the only condition of the experiment which is different in respect to the taste organs of the two persons is the direction of the current. The electrical taste evoked by a constant current is a rather complex sensation and cannot be described as purely acid or alkaline in quality. It frequently has a bitter metallic component which, as mentioned above, is usually the only taste caused by a single break shock. Very probably

electrolytic products as well as the direct stimulating effect of the current are responsible for
evoking the complex response. The gustatory sensation caused by a single shock is apparently due
purely to direct electrical stimulation, since a
current of such brief duration would not have
any electrolytic action.

Thermal and mechanical types of stimulation
may arouse faint sensations of taste but, as a
rule, are ineffective.

Thresholds of the primary taste sensations. Minimum concentrations of the four main groups of
sapid substances which will evoke the corresponding sensations are given in table 20.1.

AFTER TASTE AND TASTE CONTRASTS. The sense
of taste exhibits phenomena analogous to positive after images and successive and simultaneous
contrast, which have been described for vision
(p. 295). It is a familiar experience that the tastes
of certain substances (e.g., quinine) "cling"
to the tongue. But it is unlikely that the persistent
taste is a true after sensation comparable with an
after image; it is most probably due simply to the
continued action of the stimulating agent which,
having entered the taste pore, is removed with
difficulty by the saliva or even by rinsing the
mouth with water. On the contrary, the metallic
taste which outlasts a single break shock is in all
likelihood an example of the persistence of sensation.

Several observations exemplifying *successive
contrast* can be cited. A sweet taste is enhanced
by a preceding salt or bitter taste and *vice versa.* In
the same way sour and sweet tastes intensify one
another. Even distilled water tastes sweet after
rinsing the mouth with a weak solution of sulfuric
acid, and lemon juice seems much more acid following a sweet stimulus. Other examples which
should probably be placed under the heading of
successive contrast are the sweet taste which is
experienced upon smoking a cigar or cigarette
after washing out the mouth with a weak solution
of copper sulfate, and the bitter taste caused by
smoking if the tongue or buccal mucosa has
been treated with a solution of silver nitrate.
Simultaneous contrast is also demonstrable. For
example, if one border of the tongue is rubbed
with salt the sensitivity of the opposite border
to a sweet stimulus is increased. This contrast
effect must, of course, be of cerebral origin. Salt
and acid also show simultaneous contrast, but
the phenomenon cannot be demonstrated for the
bitter taste.

The effects of drugs upon taste. Certain drugs
have a selective action upon the taste sensations,
abolishing some while leaving others unaffected.

TABLE 20.1

Sensation and substance	Concentraton
Sweet cane sugar........	1 part in 200
dulcin...............	1 part in 100,200
α-antialdoxine	
perillaldehyde.......	1 part in 600,000
Salty, sodium chloride...	1 part in 400
Acid, hydrochloric......	1 part in 15,000
Bitter, quinine...........	1 part in 2,000,000
strychnine............	1 part in 2,500,000

For example, after the application of a decoction
of the leaves of *Gymnema sylvestre* to the tongue,
sweet and bitter substances cannot be tasted,
but saline and acid tastes are retained, and are
only slightly if at all depressed. *Stovaine* acts
similarly to Gymnema but is less effective. *Cocaine*
abolishes all taste as well as common sensibility,

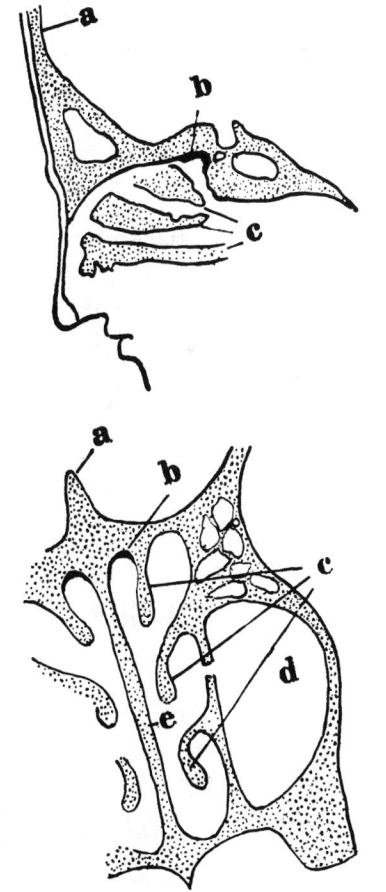

FIG. 20.4. (*Upper*) sagittal section through
skull to show position of olfactory area (*b*); (*a*)
frontal bone; (*c*) nasal conchae. (*Lower*) coronal
section through the nasal cavities; (*a*) crista gal-
lae; (*b*) olfactory area; (*c*) nasal conchae; (*d*)
maxillary sinus; (*e*) nasal septum.

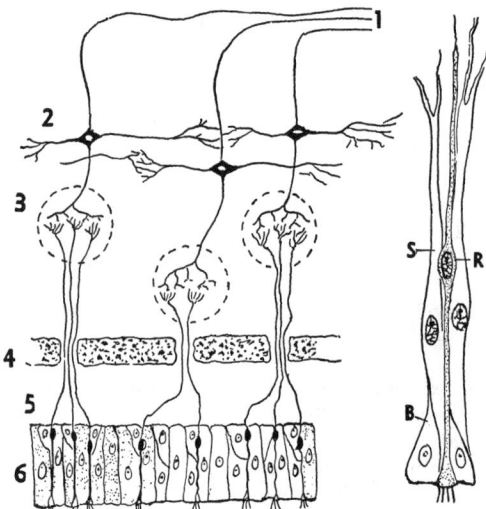

Fig. 20.5. *Left*, diagram showing olfactory epithelium and connections of olfactory nerve fibers. 1, olfactory tract; 2, mitral cells; 3, glomeruli; 4, cribriform plate; 5, olfactory nerves; 6, olfactory epithelium. *Right*, enlarged drawing of cells; B, basal cell; R, olfactory receptory cell; S, supporting cell.

the several sensations disappearing in the following order; pain, bitter, sweet, saline, acid and touch.

Smell, Olfaction

THE OLFACTORY EPITHELIUM. The mucous membrane lining the greater part of the nasal cavity has no true olfactory function. The olfactory receptors are confined to the nasal mucosa over a relatively small region—the *olfactory area*. This area comprises, on each side, the walls of a narrow niche (fig. 20.4) formed by the superior nasal concha, the upper part of the septum and the roof of the nose (cribriform plate of the ethmoid bone). The olfactory epithelium differs both in its gross appearance and histologically from the rest of the nasal mucosa. It is yellowish or brownish yellow in color; its total area, i.e., on both sides of the nose, is about 500 square millimeters.[2]

[2] The *vomeronasal organ* (organ of Jacobson) is a short tubular structure which, although well developed in certain lower vertebrates, is rudimentary in primates. It can be identified in a vestigial form in infants but, although it may persist throughout life, it is commonly absent in the adult. When present it is situated in the lower anterior part of the nasal septum and opens into the cavity of the nose by a minute pore a short distance within the external nares. In the dog and cat it receives both olfactory and trigeminal fibers and contains epithelium similar to that of the olfactory area. The function of the vomeronasal organ is not known with certainty but its general structure and innervation suggest very strongly that it is a subsidiary olfactory sense organ.

The olfactory epithelium is composed of three types of cell (a) supporting cells, (b) basal cells and (c) bipolar nerve cells. The *supporting cells* are of a very high columnar type with large oval nuclei. Superficially, they form a continuous epithelial surface, except for small round gaps between them through which the olfactory vesicles with their tufts of hairs project (see below). Their cytoplasm contains granules of a golden brown pigment to which the color of the olfactory epithelium is due. Proximally, the supporting cell tapers into a long slender process which extends as far as the lamina propria (fig. 20.5). The *basal cells* are squat conical structures which extend for only a short distance above the lamina propria. They are believed to develop into supporting cells, thus serving as a reserve from which the latter when destroyed can be replaced.

The *bipolar nerve cells* are the essential olfactory sense organs. Their two processes arise from opposite poles of the fusiform cell body, the dendrite from its superficial and the axon from its deep aspect. The dendrite is a long straight and relatively stout cylindrical process. It extends to the epithelial surface and projecting through one of the gaps between the supporting cells, expands slightly to form the *olfactory vesicle*. The latter contains from six to eight granules each of which gives rise to a hairlike protoplasmic process. The axon of the bipolar cell proceeds centrally from the deep aspect of the perikaryon and after traversing the lamina propria, joins with the central processes of neighboring cells to form some 20 nerve strands—the *fila olfactoria* or *olfactory nerves*. The latter ascend in grooves in the ethmoid bone and, entering the skull through perforations in the cribriform plate, end within the *olfactory lobe (bulb)* in a tuft of delicate filaments which synapse with dendrites of the *mitral cells* (fig. 20.5). The synapses form conspicuous spherical structures called the *olfactory glomeruli*. The axons of the mitral cells constitute the *olfactory tract*. Most of the fibers of the latter are continued into the *lateral olfactory stria* which conveys the impulses to the cortical center for smell (ch. 8). The olfactory nerves are nonmedullated, but possess a neurilemma. The lamina propria of the olfactory mucous membrane contains glands of the tubuloalveolar type—the *glands of Bowman*. They secrete a serous fluid which bathes the epithelial surface, thus providing a solvent for odorous materials. The fluid is delivered by fine ducts which take a perpendicular course to the surface.

It will at once be recognized from the foregoing description that the end organs of smell differ from those of any other sense in that the cell body of the primary neuron is situated in the peripheral organ itself, and is stimulated directly without the intervention of a specialized receptor cell. No other sensory mechanism possesses both these features. Although the primary neuron of the visual pathway is situated in the retina, the stimulus is received by the rods and cones; pain sensations are subserved by bare nerve endings, the cell bodies of the pain fibers are located in the posterior root ganglia. It is also important to remember that here as nowhere else the nervous system is in direct contact with the external environment. The terminations of the dendrites of the olfactory cells, namely, the olfactory hairs, are covered only by a layer of fluid. Furthermore, the sheaths of the olfactory nerves are continuous with the subarachnoid space. Experimental work indicates that the olfactory nerves constitute one pathway through which the virus of anterior poliomyelitis may reach the central nervous system. Schultz and Gebhardt have shown, for example, that monkeys are protected against the intranasal injection of poliomyelitis virus by a previous section of the olfactory nerves. Intranasal sprays, consisting of solutions of zinc sulfate and other substances have been employed in monkeys with the purpose of blocking these channels. The encouragement derived from the success of these experiments in protecting animals from the disease has led to the trial of similar measures in poliomyelitis epidemics, but unfortunately they do not appear to have any value in reducing the number of cases. It is very difficult, especially in children, to bring the solution into contact with the olfactory epithelium, and this is probably the reason that reliance cannot be placed upon intranasal spraying as a preventive. The recent experiments of C. G. Smith are enlightening. The olfactory areas of rats were treated with a 1 per cent solution of zinc sulfate and examined histologically at periods of from 2 days to 2 months thereafter. In animals so treated, destructive changes amounting even to sloughing of the entire olfactory epithelium were found, and in all cases the bipolar cells showed widespread degeneration. Regeneration of nonsensory cells (supporting and basal) subsequently occurred, but, of course, the nerve cells were not restored. It would appear from these experiments that zinc sulfate solution, if it is to be effective in protecting against the virus of poliomyelitis, must entail permanent loss of the sense of smell.

The Physiology of the Sense of Smell

olfactory sensations. Smell is very closely allied to taste and has been aptly described as "taste at a distance." In many animals the sense of smell is almost incredibly acute, a relatively large part of the brain being given over to it. In the life of such macrosmatic animals the olfactory sense is of paramount importance, warning the animal of the approach of its enemies, guiding it in the quest for food and motivating the sex reflexes. Certain species of moth (e.g., great peacock and banded monk) are credited with a degree of olfactory acuity which seems almost mythical to microsmatic man, the female being able, it is claimed, to attract the male by the odor of its secretions from a distance of a mile or more. The olfactory organs of moths and most other insects are located in the antennae. Even man, in whom smell is a comparatively rudimentary sense, can detect certain substances (e.g., mercaptan and artificial musk) in a dilution of 1 part in several billion parts of air; smell is therefore much more acute than the sense of taste.

The adequate stimulus for the olfactory receptors, as for those of taste, is chemical.[3] An odorous material continuously emits particles of molecular size which reach the olfactory area through the air. Substances which pass readily into the gaseous state, such as turpentine, gasoline, the essential oils, etc., have strong odors, whereas nonvolatile materials, e.g., the heavy metals, are nearly or quite inodorous. Arsenic, which ordinarily is odorless gives off a characteristic smell, however, when heated to a temperature at which it volatilizes, and Elsberg, Brewer and Levy found that the olfactory coefficients (p. 432) of a number of odorous liquids vary directly with their boiling points. The niche at the roof of the nose which is lined by the olfactory epithelium, constitutes a blind pocket, from which the main air currents caused by the ordinary respiratory movements are excluded. Experiments upon the human cadaver have shown that the respired air does not come into direct contact with the olfactory area. A head was bisected in the median plane and the nasal septum replaced by glass. When smoke was forced back and forth through the nose by means of bellows, neither during the artificial inspiratory nor expiratory movement was the current observed to enter the olfactory region. The air flow takes a curved course, the highest point being about the middle of the nose and below the superior concha. The stream reaches a lower level during expiration than in inspiration. In order to excite the olfactory cells the odorous particles must, therefore, be carried upward from the respiratory passages either by diffusion or by eddy currents. In the aforementioned experiment eddy currents were observed both during the inspira-

---

[3] An electric current acts as an inadequate stimulus. When the nose is filled with normal saline and a constant current passed through the solution, an odor which is difficult to describe is experienced upon opening or closing the current.

tory and expiratory movements. In the living subject it is probable that the ascending currents are more pronounced during inspiration; at this time air movements caused by convection are likely to occur, due to the mixing of the cooler ingoing stream with the warmer air within the nose. But, however produced, whether by convection or simply as a result of the mechanical mixing of the inspired air with that within the nasal passages, eddy currents constitute the main factor in the stimulation of the olfactory endings, and a sharp inspiration is the most effective means by which such currents are set up. When, for example, we wish to smell some particular scent more acutely we automatically make a sharp inspiration or "sniff."[4] Diffusion is a relatively slow process and is probably of minor importance in bringing the odorous material to the olfactory endings. Even though the nose is filled with odor laden air we cannot smell while the breath is held. It is during expiration that odorous materials liberated from the food as it is masticated and swallowed enter the nose through the posterior nares and ascend to the olfactory area.

It will be recalled that the olfactory hairs are immersed in a layer of fluid secreted by Bowman's glands. The odorous particles must therefore enter into solution before they can come into contact with and stimulate the sense organs. This fact emphasizes again the similarity between the senses of taste and smell. It is probable that odorous materials before they can act as stimuli must also be dissolved in the substance of the olfactory hairs themselves. These structures, since they are stained best by osmic acid, are believed to be composed largely of lipoid material. One would expect, therefore, that odorous substances must be soluble in oil as well as in water, and that those which are most freely soluble in both media would be the most potent in arousing an olfactory sensation. This supposition is borne out to some extent by experiment. Ethyl and methyl alcohols, for example, which are freely soluble in water but only slightly in oil, have weak odors as compared with butyl alcohol which dissolves very freely in oil and is also soluble in water. *Chlorobenzol, brombenzol, ether, citral* and many other substances with strong odors are soluble in both water and oil. It would appear that high solubility in oil is of more importance for olfactory stimulation than

high water solubility; because, taking two substances, one with a high solubility in oil but sparingly soluble in water, and the other possessing solubilities of a converse kind, the former has the most powerful odor.

Although it is no longer questioned that the olfactory nerves subserve the sense of smell, some of the earlier investigators (e.g., Magendie) contended that olfaction was a function of the trigeminal nerve. The confusion arose from the fact that certain agents, e.g., *ammonia, nitric acid fumes, chlorine, pepper, menthol, peppermint* and many others, cause nasal sensations, usually described as pungent, acrid, irritating or cooling. These are not true olfactory sensations but are due to the stimulation of the trigeminal, which is the nerve mediating chemical sense and common sensibility in the respiratory part of the nasal mucosa. It is often very difficult, however, to dissociate these sensations from smell when the two types of ending are stimulated concurrently. A similar confusion arises, as already mentioned in the case of taste.

Strong reflex effects, e.g., sneezing, lachrymation, respiratory inhibition, vasomotor reactions, etc., result from irritation of the trigeminal endings, whereas reflexes initiated from the olfactory receptors are as a rule mild in character, and in man are concerned mainly with salivary and gastric secretion. In animals olfactory reflexes play their most important role in the reactions of sex and in self preservation—the search for food and protection from enemies. Olfaction is paramount among the senses in its power to awaken a train of associations in consciousness. Everyone is familiar with the strange reminiscent aura of long past events which is aroused by certain familiar scents.

THRESHOLD STIMULI. Among the most effective olfactory stimuli are *artificial musk, mercaptan, butyric acid, iodoform* and *oil of peppermint*. For example, methyl mercaptan (garlic odor) is perceptible to the average person in a concentration of $1/23,000,000,000$ mg. per cu. cm. of air. Assuming that 50 cc. of air is required for arousing an olfactory sensation, this would mean that $1/460,000,000$ mg. of the substance is an effective stimulus. The sense of smell is therefore many thousand times (about 25,000 times in the case of ethyl alcohol) more acute than the sense of taste. The minimum perceptible concentrations of various odorous substances are given in table 20.2.

SENSORY ADAPTATION. The olfactory receptors adapt fairly rapidly. It is a common experience

---

[4] The mechanism of the "sniff" appears to be a compressing together of the septum and the outer wall of the nose at the front of the respiratory passages so as to divert the inspired air to the olfactory area (Ogle).

that a disagreeable odor which when first smelled is almost overpowering soon becomes imperceptible. But although lost for one particular odor the sense of smell is retained for others; the phenomenon therefore is not due to fatigue of the olfactory mechanism (although it is often referred to as such), but is an example of sensory adaptation (p. 59). The rate of adaptation varies for different odors. The receptors becomes insensitive to oil of orange or to oil of lemon after an exposure of from 2.5 to 11 minutes (average 3 minutes), whereas cumarin (0.2 per cent aqueous solution) cannot be smelled longer than from 1.75 to 2.3 minutes, and adaptation for the odor of benzoin is more rapid than for that of rubber.

Olfactory adaptation commences to develop from the moment that the odor is first smelled, the threshold rising gradually until complete insensitivity to that particular odor is reached. Even a previous period of exposure to a given odor raises the minimum concentration at which it is perceived for a considerable length of time afterwards. Elsberg found, for example, that the olfactory coefficients (p. 432) for peppermint, camphor and sassafras were increased to double their normal values if the subject had previously been smelling these substances; and the sensitivity of a person who had been for a time in the operating theater to the odor of ether was below normal several hours later.

CHEMICAL CONSTITUTION IN RELATION TO OLFACTORY STIMULATION. Generally speaking, the olfactory potency of chemical compounds belonging to an homologous series increases progressively from the lowest members of the series to a maximum and then undergoes a gradual reduction in the upper members. The odors of the monatomic alcohols, for example, increase in strength from methyl through ethyl, propyl and butyl to amyl; the relative potencies of methyl and amyl alcohols are as 1 to 10,000. Also, compounds which as a group resemble one another in their chemical and physical properties tend to have odors possessing certain common characteristics. For example, the elements sulfur, selenium and tellurium, which belong to the sixth group in Mendeljeff's periodic table, when combined with hydrogen, methyl or ethyl, etc., have strong disagreeable smells. Similarly members of the seventh group, chlorine, bromine and iodine have kindred odors; the odors of chloroform and iodoform, compounds of the first and third elements respectively, are linked together by that of bromoform in which the fragrance of chloroform and the unpleasant odor of iodoform can be detected. Of chemically allied organic substances, ethyl, propyl and butyl acetates have an acetic odor, whereas amyl acetate has not; nevertheless the smell of the lowest of the series

TABLE 20.2

Substance	Mg. per liter of Air
Ethyl ether....................	5.83
Chloroform...................	3.30
Pyridine......................	0.032
Oil of peppermint............	0.024
Iodoform....................	0.018
Butyric acid.................	0.009
Propyl mercaptan............	0.006
Artificial musk..............	0.00004

(From Allison and Katz.)

is linked with that of the highest through the two intermediate compounds. Thus—

　Ethyl acetate, acetic odor
　Propyl acetate, acetic odor with slight pineapple flavor
　Butyl acetate, slight acetic odor with pineapple flavor
　Amyl acetate, no acetic odor, strong pineapple flavor

Though the foregoing are interesting examples of chemico-olfactory correlation, it is not possible to make anything more than broad generalizations in respect to chemical structure and smell, for compounds which closely resemble one another chemically may have quite different odors and others which show little resemblance in their chemical or physical properties (e.g., hydrocyanic acid and nitrobenzine, garlic and certain arsenical compounds, and artificial and natural musk) may smell very much alike. Many nitrile compounds have an odor resembling bitter almonds or hydrocyanic acid, whereas certain compounds of phosphorus and bismuth, as well as of arsenic, have a garlicky smell. An attempt has been made in the case of aromatic compounds to relate odor to a particular radical on the benzene ring. Hydroxyl, aldehyde, ketone, ester, nitro and nitril grouping—the so-called *osmophoric groups*—have been suggested as determing the character of the odor; it is believed, however, that the latter is dependent not so much upon which particular radical is present as upon the position which any one of them occupies in the benzene ring and the general architecture of the molecule.

A physical property common to many odors is their strong absorption of infrared rays. The significance of this fact, first remarked upon by Faraday, is unknown.

OLFACTOMETRY. The most widely known method of investigating the sense of smell is that of Zwaardemaker. His olfactometer consists of two glass tubes sliding one within the other, as

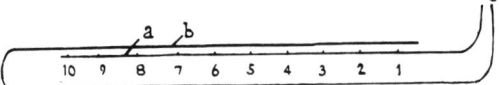

FIG. 20.6. Diagram of Zwaardemaker's olfactometer. See text.

shown in figure 20.6. The inner tube (a) is graduated in sections 0.7 cm. long. The inner surface of the outer tube carries a faintly odorous substance. The curved end (c) of the inner tube is introduced into a nostril, the opposite one being closed; the subject breathes quietly. The outer tube is gradually withdrawn, thus exposing a greater area of its inner surface to the air current and thereby increasing the concentration of the odorous particles in the inspired air. The highest figure visible on the inner graduated tube when the odor is just perceived indicates the subject's threshold for smell in units termed *olfacties*. This method gives at the best only approximate results, chiefly because the volume of inspired air drawn through the tubing varies considerably from subject to subject and in the same person at different times or even during a single period of observation. In the *blast method* of Elsberg and Levy this factor is controlled. Thirty cubic centimeters of an odorous liquid (e.g., benzene citral, oil of orange, oil of turpentine, butyric acid, etc.) are placed in the bottle shown in figure 20.7. The right hand tube is connected to a double nosepiece which fits into the nostrils. By means of a syringe connected to the other tube a measured volume of air is forced from the bottle in one blast at a constant pressure while the subject holds his breath. An equivalent volume of odor-laden air is thus forced into the nose. The volume of the injections is gradually increased in successive blasts until the odor is just perceived and can be

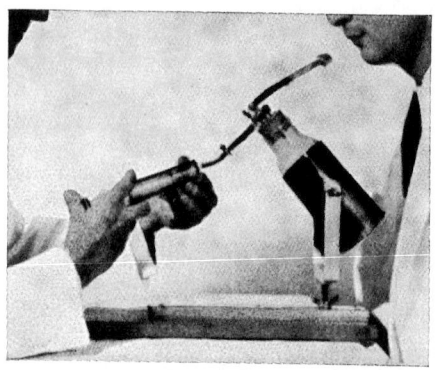

FIG. 20.7. Illustrating the blast method of olfactometry. (After Elsberg and Levy.)

named. The smallest volume necessary for identification is called the *minimum identifiable odor* (MIO) or the *olfactory coefficient*.

This method has been employed by Elsberg as an aid in the localization of tumors in the anterior part of the skull. In this situation a tumor (e.g., of the frontal lobe) is likely, through direct pressure, to involve the olfactory lobe or tract of one or of both sides; or the olfactory nerves may be torn in fractures through the cribiform plate. Unilateral involvement of the olfactory nerves, lobe or tract raises the MIO or completely abolishes the sense of smell on the affected side. A tumor involving both olfactory lobes or tracts will result in lowered acuity of smell or complete anosmia on both sides. Elsberg states that tests for olfactory "fatigue" give valuable localizing aid; the "fatigue" phenomenon is prolonged beyond the normal limits by tumors within the substance of the temporal lobe, but not by those situated extracerebrally (e.g., beneath the frontal lobe). In cases of a generalized increase of intracranial pressure due to other causes the MIO is often lowered.

CLASSIFICATION OF ODORS. The division of odors into categories has proved an extremely difficult problem. There are no basic qualities of olfaction comparable to sweet, salty, sour and bitter tastes. The number of different and distinct smells is legion, and no comprehensive classification upon the basis of chemical constitution or physical properties can be even attempted. The earliest classification of odors was made by the Swedish botanist Linnaeus (1750). The following one proposed by Zwaardemaker, which is little more than an elaboration of that proposed by Linnaeus, consists of nine categories. It has a purely subjective basis and is therefore of little scientific value.

1. *Ethereal odors;* e.g., of fruits, beeswax, ethers.
2. *Aromatic or resinous odors;* e.g., of camphor, bitter almonds, cloves, lavender.
3. *Fragrant or balsamic odors;* e.g., of flowers, extracted or artificial perfumes.
4. *Ambrosial odors;* e.g., of musk, ambergris.
5. *Garlic odors;* e.g., of garlic, onions and of sulfur and selenium compounds.
6. *Burning odors;* e.g., of burning feathers, tobacco, roasted coffee and meats.
7. *Goat odors;* e.g., caproic acid, sweat and ripe cheese.
8. *Repulsive odors;* e.g., of hyoscyamus and several of the family of the deadly nightshade, bedbug.
9. *Nauseating odors;* e.g., of excrement, decaying meat and vegetable matter.

ACTION POTENTIALS FROM THE OLFACTORY PATHWAYS. Gerard and Young have recorded the action currents from the olfactory bulb of the frog. A spontaneous rhythmical discharge occurs in in this part of the isolated brain at the rate of about 4 per second. The discharge is taken as representing true automatic activity of the nerve cells of the bulb itself, for the possibility that it was due to the irritation of traumatized structures seems to have been excluded.

In certain fishes (catfish, carp and tench) the olfactory bulb is connected with the forebrain by a nerve strand (the *olfactory stalk*) which measures about 2 cm. long and is composed of from 500 to 1000 medullated fibers. Adrian and Ludwig studied the action potentials in the olfactory stalk of the catfish during stimulation of the olfactory end organs. The latter are contained in a small sac which opens through a nipple upon the surface of the skin above the mouth. Potential changes of small amplitude pass up the stalk as long as the preparation survives, although nothing but distilled water has been introduced into the sac. This *resting discharge* is of very low frequency. When the sac was irrigated with fluid containing containing small fragments of some odorous material, e.g., putrefying earthworms, a burst of impulses occurred at high frequency after a latent period of from 0.5 to 5 seconds or longer. It was found that the irrigation was more powerfully stimulating if the fluid contained small fragments of the material than if it had been filtered.

THE QUESTION OF OLFACTORY DISCRIMINATION. The great multitude of distinguishable odors brings up a question for which no answer is forthcoming, namely, "What is the mechanism underlying olfactory differentiation?" "How do we detect the difference between two scents such as those of the violet and the rose?" Or, to make the question still more difficult, "How does a dog recognize the smell of his master among the smells of other persons?" Were there a limited number of basic odors, as there are of fundamental tastes, the problem would not be difficult. A theory of color vision can be conceived (ch. 3) based upon the existence of receptors responsive to different wave lengths, and which discharge impulses along specific nerve paths (ch. 14). The resonance-volley theory explains the pitch-discriminating function of the ear (ch. 18), and four functionally distinct types of taste bud, each with its specific nerve fiber, for the perception of the fundamental sensations of taste. But it is not conceivably possible that every one of the immense number of different odors is subserved by a specific type of end organ with its own nerve fiber. Further-

more, new and distinct odors are being created in industry every day.

Theories of the mechanism through which an odorous substance sets up an impulse in an olfactory nerve fiber are of necessity almost wholly speculative. The following catalytic theory of olfaction has been proposed by Kistiakowsky similar to that already described for gustation. He postulates a series of catalytic reactions which may be represented as, $A \to A' \to A''$; $B \to B' \to B''$; $C \to C' \to C''$, etc. Each step is effected by a specific enzyme, and each compound formed A', B', C', etc., stimulates an olfactory receptor and gives rise to a corresponding distinct "basic" odor. Presumably, the odoriferous substance itself inhibits one or more of the enzyme systems. This would lead to differences in the combination of the stimulating compounds, and even a slight change in their relative concentrations could arouse an olfactory sensation. The difficulty here is in defining a basic odor and having to assume an unreasonable number of functionally different receptor cells, for the nerve impulses themselves possess no differentiating characteristics which could serve the brain as cues. But if in addition, areas with different physical or chemical properties were distributed over the olfactory membrane which permitted a selective penetration or adsorption of the odorous substance to or upon the receptors, some sort of pattern of excitation might be established which could be interpreted by the cerebral cortex as a smell of a certain kind; or the different areas might possess specific affinities for certain chemical groups. A mechanism of this nature would not require an immense number of different types of receptor.

From what we know of other senses we can presume that the *intensity* of the olfactory sensation is related to the frequency of the impulses discharged to the olfactory center. This is borne out by the experiments of Adrian and Ludwig just described.

THE EFFECT OF ONE ODOR UPON THE PERCEPTION OF ANOTHER. Strong odors tend to mask weaker ones. If two scents are of about equal strength a blend of the two is smelled or both are identified; but if one is considerably stronger than the other it alone, as a rule, is smelled. On the other hand, certain pairs of odors in appropriate relative concentrations are antagonistic, and when the two are sniffed together both are diminished. Iodoform, for example, is antagonized by balsam of Peru, musk by bitter almonds and ammonia by acetic acid. Other pairs of neutralizing odors are cedarwood and rubber, beeswax and balsam of

Tolu, benzoin and rubber, and camphor and eau de Cologne. Although the neutralizing effect may in some cases be simply chemical or physical in nature, in others there seems to be a true physiological antagonism, for the phenomenon is observed when mixing is avoided by leading the two odors directly one to each nostril.

ANOMALIES OF OLFACTION. Loss of the sense of smell or *anosmia* is not infrequent as a temporary condition, e.g., as a result of inflammation of the nasal mucosa or of the local application of cocaine or adrenaline. Complete and permanent anosmia is rare in otherwise normal persons and is usually due to absence of the olfactory bulb or olfactory nerves, but bilateral or unilateral olfactory deficiencies are frequently associated with lesions in the region of the olfactory lobes. Albinos are said to be anosmic, which suggests that the pigment in the supporting cells of the olfactory epithelium, which possibly serves an essential function, is lacking. Inability to smell certain odors is not uncommon. Some persons, for example, cannot smell hydrocyanic acid; the odor of mignonette, benzoin, methyl alcohol or vanillin cannot be smelled by others. Even such a strong, disagreeable smell as that of a rotten egg or of feces may not be sensed. Partial anosmia for all scents may result from excessive smoking. *Hyperosmia* is not unusual in hysteria, in certain cerebral diseases, in raised intracranial pressure and during the initial stage of the action of cocaine. Olfactory hallucinations may occur in lesions of the temporal lobe (ch. 8). In cerebral tumors, especially of the frontal or temporal lobes, an odorous material introduced into one nostril may be referred to the other. This phenomenon, known as *olfactory alloesthesia*, is analogous to allocheiria mentioned on page 54.

Common Chemical Sense

The general body surface of fish and many other aquatic forms is sensitive to various types of chemical irritant, as are also the moist skins of amphibians. The elicitation of reflex responses from the foot of a pithed frog stimulated by a weak solution of sulfuric acid is a well known laboratory exercise. In man the common chemical sense is restricted to surfaces which are kept constantly moist, namely, the buccal and nasal mu-

cous membranes, the conjunctivae and the mucosa of the anal canal. The common chemical sense of the first three is subserved by the trigeminal nerve, that of the anal canal by the pudendal nerve. It has already been pointed out that the sense organs subserving this sense in the mouth and nose are distinct from the gustatory and olfactory endings, and apparently they are not identical with those subserving pain, for dissociation of chemical and pain sensations can be effected by cocaine, the latter being abolished before the former. Thus, after the application of a 1 per cent solution of the anesthetic to the foot of the frog no response is given to pinching, pricking or scratching, whereas reactions to chemical agents can for a time be elicited.

REFERENCES

ADRIAN, E. D. AND LUDWIG, C. J. Physiol., 1938, **94**, 441.

ALLISON, V. C. AND KATZ, S. H. J. Indust. Chem., 1919, **11**, 336.

EL BARADI, A. F. AND BOURNE, G. Science, 1951, **113**, 660.

BOURNE, G. Nature, 1948, **161**, 445.

CUSHING, H. Bull. Johns Hopkins Hosp., 1903, **14**, 71.

ELSBERG, C. A. AND LEVY, I. Bull. Neurol. Inst. New York, 1935, **4**, 5.

ELSBERG, C. A., BREWER, E. D. AND LEVY, I. Bull. Neurol. Inst. New York, 1935, **4**, 26.

GERARD, R. W. AND YOUNG, J. Z. Proc. Roy. Soc., London, ser. B, 1937, **122**, 343.

KISTIAKOWSKI, G. B. Science, 1950, **112**, 154.

OERTLY, E. AND MYERS, R. G. J. Am. Chem. Soc., 1919, **41**, 855.

OLMSTED, J. M. D. Am. J. Physiol., 1918, **46**, 443; J. Comp. Neurol., 1920, **31**, 465.

PFAFFMANN, C. J. Cell. & Comp. Physiol., 1941, **17**, 243.

READ, E. A. Am. J. Anat., 1908, **8**, 17.

SMITH, C. G. Canad. M. A. J., 1938, **39**, 138.

Monographs and Reviews

CROZIER, W. J. Murchison's handbook of general experimental psychology, p. 987. Clark University Press, 1934.

PARKER, G. H. Smell, taste and allied senses in the vertebrates. Monograph Experimental Biology, Lippincott, Philadelphia, 1922.

III

THE MUSCLE

CHAPTER 21

Muscle Physiology

Basic Properties of Muscle Tissue

The characteristic properties of muscle tissue are development of tension upon stimulation and, provided the load is not too great, shortening against the load, whereby work is done. The development of tension in physiological conditions depends on stimulation of the muscle tissue through the motor nerves. In experimental conditions the reaction can be evolved by electric or chemical stimulation applied directly on the muscle tissue.

Between contractions the muscle tissue appears in a relaxed state characterized by low resistance against stretch. In relaxed as well as in contracted states the muscle is elastic, with great changes in elasticity modulus during transition from a relaxed to a contracted state.

The tension developed by a muscle in the body is graded and adjusted to the load. If contraction is associated with shortening the tension is adjusted to the load and the velocity at which the movement is performed. This graded response is due to variation in the degree of activation of the muscle through the nervous system.

Through nervous control, the activity of different parts of the muscle tissue of the body is coordinated to allow useful movements and postures of the body. The effect of the muscle activity is transferred to the skeleton by means of tendons and the translational movements between various parts of the muscle mass which is associated with movements is facilitated by the interposition of connective tissue, either as thin or thick layers of connective tissue or as compact connective tissue septa. The latter structures are present at places where the translational displacements are most pronounced. The connective tissue divides the muscle mass into muscle individuals.

The activity of muscle tissue depends on a supply of energy through breakdown of primarily carbohydrates. For highest efficiency and sustained activity, this breakdown is oxidative, which implies a constant supply of oxygen through an efficient blood circulation through the muscle tissue. The transport of oxygen through the blood vessels by means of streaming is supplemented by diffusion from the blood capillaries through the muscle tissue. The dense arrangement of narrow capillaries allowing rapid streaming of the blood secures a fairly short mean distance for diffusion of oxygen and the maintaining of a high concentration gradient between the capillary lumen and the oxygen-consuming structures, the mitochondria.

The activation of the contractile apparatus in muscle tissue depends on a transfer of the nerve stimulus from the motor nerve endings to the contractile machinery. Furthermore, the activity of the muscle tissue depends on a precise ionic milieu which is different from that of blood plasma.

The subdivision of muscle tissue into small microscopic units, the muscle fibers, which are delimited by a plasma membrane characterized by selective permeability, facilitates the control of the medium in which the contractile machinery is immersed. The plasma membrane furthermore contributes to the propagation of impulses for activation within the muscle tissue.

Within the muscle fibers, which measure 0.01–0.1 mm. in diameter and which have a length that corresponds to the distance between the tendons at the ends of the muscle, we can distinguish three main components:

(1) The contractile machinery,

(2) The system for propagating the excitation impulses from the plasma membrane to the contractile machinery, including the system responsible for the activation of the latter, and

(3) The system for energy supply.

The Contractile Machinery

Contractility is associated with a change in shape and configuration of macromolecules. At least two different conformational states must be possible corresponding to the relaxed and the contracted states. In muscle tissue the molecules involved are two fibrous proteins, *myosin* and *actin*. Neither protein separately is contractile. Contractility can, however, be demonstrated as a property of acto-myosin, a complex formed under certain conditions when actin and myosin are mixed.

Actin, as well as myosin, appears in minute filamentous structures in the muscle fiber. A third protein, *tropomyosin*, is associated with these structures, but the exact localization and functional significance of tropomyosin is unclear or unknown. These three proteins can be extracted from muscle tissue in neutral salt solutions of high ionic strength. The extracts show a high viscosity reflecting the fibrous nature of the proteins in solution.

Myosin is quantitatively the major protein component in muscle tissue, constituting 34% of the total protein content. It is a highly asymmetric molecule, as indicated by its fairly high intrinsic viscosity (2.0). Its molecular weight has been estimated to be between 400,000 and 500,000 and the length of the molecule to be about 1600 Å. In the electron microscope the molecule appears to consist of a globular region measuring 40 Å in diameter and a rod-shaped tail with a diameter of 15–20 Å.

Myosin can be split by mild action of proteolytic enzymes—for instance, trypsin—into two components, one lighter, light meromyosin (LMM) and one heavier, heavy meromyosin (HMM). The molecular weight of LMM is about 100,000 and that of HMM 230,000–330,000. It is likely that each myosin molecule consists of one LMM and one HMM associated end-to-end.

The myosin, as well as the meromyosins, exhibits the 5.1 Å meridional spacing in wide-angle X-ray diffraction patterns which characterizes the Corey-Pauling α-helix configuration of proteins in a supercoiled state. The helix content of these proteins is high and accounts for their extended filamentous shape. Only the HMM shows a fairly high content of non-helical regions, which presumably accounts for the globular region of the myosin molecule.

Myosin acts as an adenosine triphosphatase, and when adenosine triphosphate (ATP) interacts with myosin it is possible that the terminal phosphate group is transferred to myosin, with the formation of phosphorylated myosin before hydrolysis takes place. Contractility of myosin in the presence of actin and ATP depends on the ATP-ase activity of myosin. The —SH groups of myosin are important for the ATP-ase activity as well as for the formation of the actomyosin complex. The phosphorylation of myosin may result in energization of the myosin molecule as a fundamental step in releasing the molecular reaction responsible for contraction.

Actin constitutes 14% of the total muscle protein. It is a globular protein (G-actin) with a molecular weight of 57,000–70,000, the estimates depending on absence or presence of ions in the medium. The diameter of the actin molecule is about 50 Å.

In the presence of salts, the actin molecules aggregate end-to-end to form long filaments, F-actin. In a test tube such filaments appear to acquire an indefinite length. Each filament consists of two strands of actin molecules helically wound around each other to form a two-stranded rope with a pitch of the helix of each strand about 700 Å. Both strands follow a similar helical path, and the resultant structure repeats after $700/2$ Å $= 350$ Å. There are 13 actin monomers per turn, as determined by the beaded appearance of each strand. The spacing between the monomers is 55 Å.

The polymerization of G-actin to F-actin is reversible in the presence of ATP. F-actin is depolymerized to G-actin if the inorganic ions are removed. G-actin contains ATP, and during polymerization to F-actin inorganic phosphate is split off ATP. The ADP thus formed remains bound to F-actin; ATP appears bound to G-actin.

Actin does not exhibit any α-pattern in the wide-angle X-ray diffraction pattern and the polypeptide chain therefore does not appear to contain portions with the α-helix configuration. The observed X-ray diffraction pattern of actin, a diffuse ring at 4.5 Å, has not yet been interpreted with respect to the polypeptide chain configuration.

Tropomyosin makes up 6–10% of the total muscle protein. It has a molecular weight of 54,000, and the asymmetric molecule has a length somewhat less than 400 Å. The molecules associate end to end to form dimers and polymers. It forms true crystals with 90% water. The crystals show a square lattice structure in the electron micrographs with a lattice spacing of 200 Å. Tropomyosin presumably consists of two α-helical polypeptide chains side by side.

Actomyosin represents a complex formed when actin and myosin are mixed. The complex formation is identified by a sharp rise in the viscosity and a high sedimentation constant reflecting a high molecular weight and high asymmetry of the complex. The molecular weight is either about 470,000 or about 620,000. The high viscosity shows that actomyosin is highly asymmetric in shape, as can be expected from the association of the filamentous F-actin polymer and the asymmetric myosin molecules.

The interaction of myosin with actin is a characteristic property of myosin and is dependent on its ATP-ase activity. At high ionic strength the actomyosin complex is dissociated by ATP, the amount of ATP required corresponding to one mole per unit of myosin monomer. At low salt concentrations, ATP addition produces contraction of actomyosin. This effect can be studied in actomyosin gels, particularly after orienting the molecules in parallel by the preparing of thin actomyosin filaments. The contraction of such artificial filaments is preceded by an increased extensibility before shortening takes place. This possibly indicates a first stage, during which the actomyosin complex is dissociated preceding the stage during which new bonds are formed, resulting in configurational changes of the molecules.

There has been much discussion as to whether the dephosphorylation of ATP by myosin is associated with the contraction or relaxation of the contractile apparatus. According to one view, the contraction is brought about by transfer of phosphate to myosin without dephosphorylation, the latter appearing after contraction in connection with relaxation. According to other workers, contraction is dependent on dephosphorylation of ATP, the energy of this reaction being a prerequisite for contraction, while relaxation can be brought about by ATP without dephosphorylation This latter point of view is supported by A. V. Hill's determinations of heat liberation in contracting muscle showing that energy, as measured by the rise in temperature of the muscle, is released during contraction while no heat is produced during relaxation of an unloaded muscle.

The Structural Arrangement of Myosin, Actin and Tropomyosin in Striated Muscle

The structural organization of striated muscle is characterized by a high degree of order at all organizational levels. The myosin appears in filamentous components with an average length of 1.5 μ and a width of 100–120 Å.

The myosin filaments have a characteristic appearance which reflects the mode of aggregation of the myosin molecules within the filaments. With the exception of a middle section of the filaments, a series of lateral projections extends from the approximately 100–120-Å-thick trunk of the filaments. Similar filaments can be made artificially by allowing myosin in solution to aggregate. Under such conditions the gradual growth of filaments is reflected in the distribution of sizes of reconstituted filaments. The morphol-

FIG. 21.1. Schematic presentation of the likely arrangement of myosin molecules in the myosin filaments.

ogy of the filaments agrees with the assumption that the myosin molecules aggregate with the globular end of the molecules directed toward the ends of the filaments. The middle smooth shaft corresponds to a close packing of the rod-shaped part of the molecules and the series of projections to their globular ends (fig. 21.1).

Such a polar arrangement of the myosin molecules could secure a definite direction of the force developed in connection with a configurational change of the myosin molecules whether these changes are very minute or more extensive.

The smooth shaft of the filaments shows a somewhat thicker segment located exactly in the middle of the filaments, contributing to a dense line, the M band, extending across the middle of the sarcomere.

The actin also appears as filaments in muscle and these filaments show great similarities to the F-actin filaments that are formed *in vitro* by polymerization of G-actin. The axial periodicity is slightly greater (406–411 Å) for the natural than for the artificial filaments (350 Å). It has been suggested that this difference could be accounted for by tropomyosin being present in the natural actin filaments.

The regular arrangement of myosin and actin filaments is reflected in the cross-striated appearance of the muscle when observed in the light microscope and in polarized light. The cross-striations depend on a regular repetition of one structural pattern consisting of 1.5-μ-wide, dense cross-bands separated by less dense segments. The dense cross-bands, referred to as the A bands since they are strongly anisotropic, contain the thick myosin filaments arranged neatly in parallel. Laterally, the filaments are arranged in a hexagonal array, as can be observed in electron micrographs of cross sections. The filaments appear in perfect register due to crossbridges connecting adjacent filaments in the M-band region in the middle of the 1.5-μ-long filaments.

The less dense segments, the I bands, contain the actin filaments that extend in a symmetrical way in two opposite directions from a dense thin line, the Z line, through the I band and part of the A band, where actin and myosin filaments interdigitate. The term I band refers to the weak birefringence of these bands which in early studies was overlooked. The I bands were therefore considered isotropic. The width of the I band varies with the degree of stretch or shortening of the muscle fiber. Since the length of the individual actin filaments is about 1 μ and there are two sets of such filaments extending from the Z line, the total width of the Z line-actin filament complex will be about 2 μ. The Z-line structure contributes toward keeping the actin filaments arranged in register and with a regular spacing. The tropomyosin possibly contributes at least partially to the Z-line structure. It is also possible that tropomyosin is associated with cross-bridges, arranged at regular intervals between the actin filaments.

As repeating unit in this striated structure, we can select the region between two consecutive Z lines, the sarcomere. This unit will consist of one A band and one-half I band at each end of the A band.

At rest-length of the muscle, which here is defined as the maximal length of the muscle *in situ*, the two sets of filaments in most muscle interdigitate with a rather extensive zone of overlap at each end of the A band. In the rabbit psoas muscle the sarcomere length at rest-length

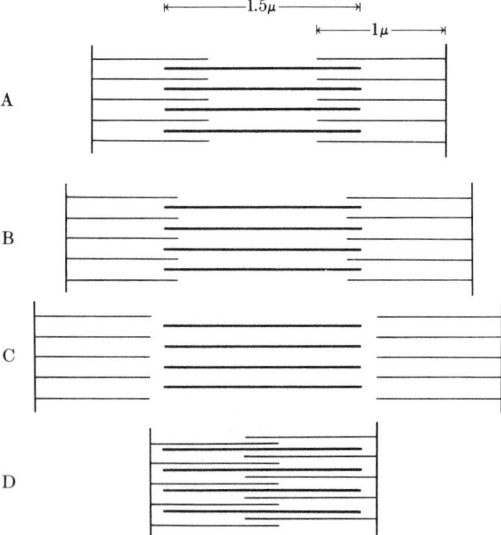

Fig. 21.2. Schematic illustration of the arrangement of thick myosin filaments and thin actin filaments in the sarcomere at various degrees of stretch and shortening. A and B show different degrees of overlap of the two types of filaments. C illustrates the case when the actin filaments have been completely pulled out from the A band with a gap between A band and the actin filaments. In the extensively shortened sarcomere in D a zone of double overlap of actin filaments has developed in the center of the A band.

is about 2.8 μ. If the muscle is stretched, the zone of overlap decreases in width in proportion to the increase in half-width of the I band. The zone in the middle of the A band surrounded by the two zones of overlap, the H zone, also increases in width, this increase corresponding to the decrease in width of both zones of overlap. This means that when a muscle is stretched, the actin filaments are being pulled out of the A band, while the length of both the myosin filaments and the actin filaments remains constant (fig. 21.2). At a sarcomere length of about 3.5 μ, the actin filaments have been pulled out completely, and the two sets of filaments appear now in an end-to-end arrangement. At further stretching, the two sets of filaments become separated by a gap, in which filaments considerably thinner than the actin filaments can be seen extending between the ends of the myosin and the actin filaments.

If a muscle is allowed to shorten, either passively or through an active contraction, and the structure is analyzed after the muscle has acquired a new length, the same relationship between half-width of the I bands, width of zone of overlap and of the H band as described above is observed. At sarcomere length less than 2 μ, that is, less than the sum of the lengths of the two sets of actin filaments in the sarcomere, a dense zone can appear in the middle of the A band which is due to a double overlap of the actin filaments (fig. 21.2D).

When the sarcomere length has decreased to 1.5 μ or less, a dense zone with irregularly arranged filaments, a contraction band, is observed at the Z line. Contraction bands at this sarcomere length involve a rather random arrangement of actin filaments and thin filaments derived from the myosin filaments as a consequence of their splitting up in filamentous subunits.

The myofilaments are arranged in bundles with a diameter of 0.5–1 μ, the *myofibrils*, that can be observed in the light microscope. A large number of myofibrils separated by cytoplasm, *sarcoplasm*, fill the muscle fiber which is delimited by the plasma membrane. The muscle fiber is the smallest metabolically autonomous unit. Each muscle consists of a large number of muscle fibers embedded in a sparse, loose, connective tissue, in which blood vessels and nerve fibers are distributed. The diameter of the muscle fiber presumably is related to the maximal distance of diffusion for oxygen from the blood capillaries to the center of the muscle fiber, which allows efficient oxygen supply to the entire fibers.

Structural Changes Associated with Shortening of the Muscle Fiber during Contraction

When analyzed with interference microscopy, shortening during contraction is characterized by a constant width of the A band within a moderate range of shortening. At extensive shortening, a certain decrease in A-band width has been observed. It must be kept in mind that these observations only allow the conclusion that any shortening of the A band in a range above 0.2 μ (the resolving power of the light microscope) is unlikely, but do not exclude the possibility that shortening below this limit has occurred. Since the A band does not shorten appreciably, the change in length of the muscle fiber is associated with a decrease in width of the I band.

ISOTONIC CONTRACTION

There are, at present, two concepts regarding the structural changes occurring during shortening. One of these concepts is based on electron microscopic studies of fresh as well as glycerinated muscle fibers fixed during contraction; the other is based on a deduction of a mechanism from the electron microscopic appearance of the sarcomeres *after* the muscle has shortened or has been stretched passively.

According to the former concept, the contraction is associated with a splitting up of the compact myosin filaments at their ends into a number of subunits possibly consisting of individual myosin molecules, an interaction of these subunits with the actin filaments resulting in bonds being formed between the subunits and the actin and drastic change of the conformation of the myosin subunits from the originally extended configuration to a compact configuration. This would involve extensive conformational changes in the myosin molecules and would result in a pulling in of the actin filaments toward the center of the A band, since the myosin subunits remain attached to the myosin filaments at the end which is located toward the center of the sarcomere. The splitting up of the end regions of the myosin filaments would be an important first step since it would allow active sites on the myosin molecules to be exposed. In the compact arrangement of the myosin in the thick myosin filaments these sites would be shielded from interaction with actin.

In the case where the two sets of filaments interdigitate over a fairly long distance, for instance at rest length of most muscles, the actin filaments are pulled in toward the center of the A band due to the extensive shortening of the myosin molecules. The regular arrangement of the myosin filaments serves as a guide for the actin filaments so that they can slide in the spaces between these filaments. The observations indicate that, in this case, the actin filaments are not folded to any great extent during shortening. If, however, the shortening is induced in muscle fibers in which the zone of overlap of the two sets of filaments is narrow, the actin filaments can become tangled at the A-I-band boundary to form a contraction-band structure not associated with the Z line.

Since the collapsed myosin subunits are arranged in series along the axis of the myosin filaments, the change in conformation of each subunit does not involve any extensive over-all shortening of the myosin filaments, in agreement with light microscopic observations. The shortening of the myosin filaments that has been observed is of such a magnitude that it would escape detection in the interference microscope.

ISOMETRIC CONTRACTION

At isometric contraction, the shortening of any contractile element is minute, and in this case a moderate configurational change associated with the lateral projections of the myosin filaments can account for the development of tension. This would imply that, during isometric contraction, a large number of subunits in the myosin filaments could interact synchronously to develop tension, the number depending on the degree of overlap. The highest isometric tension has been recorded when the zone of overlap extends the entire length of the myosin filaments over which lateral projections are present. This implies that the development of maximum tension during isometric contraction is related to the condition allowing maximal interaction between myosin and actin. During isotonic contraction, the conditions for interaction between myosin and actin are restricted, since mainly the subunits in the myosin filaments which are located within a limited zone at the ends of the filaments appear to be involved.

According to the other concept of muscle contraction, the "sliding model," there are no extensive configurational changes occurring during contraction. The actin filaments slide along the surfaces of the myosin filaments due to oscillatory, minute movements of the lateral processes of the latter filaments with repeated alternative formation and breaking of bonds between myosin and actin, the bonds being formed in the oscillatory cycle when the processes are in a position close to the Z line, and the bonds broken when the processes have swung to their extreme position in the direction toward the center of the A band.

Mechanical Characteristics of Muscle

THE SINGLE MUSCLE TWITCH

A relaxed, unstimulated muscle is elastic but offers little resistance to stretch. The force needed to stretch the muscle increases, however, as the muscle is being extended. The tension developed in the muscle as a consequence of stretching does not increase linearly but approximately exponentially with the length of the muscle (fig. 21.3).

If the resting muscle is exposed to a small load, which means that the muscle is close to its minimal resting length, its elasticity is "rubber-like." That is, it shortens when warmed and lengthens when cooled. At greater load, meaning greater initial length of the muscle, the elasticity is normal and not "rubber-like."

The elasticity of the resting muscle has been ascribed to properties of the contractile material itself or to the sarcolemma which involves the plasma membrane of the muscle fiber, the "basement membrane" material coating the outer surface of the plasma membrane and connective tissue elements associated with the muscle fiber surface. At least at moderate degrees of stretch it

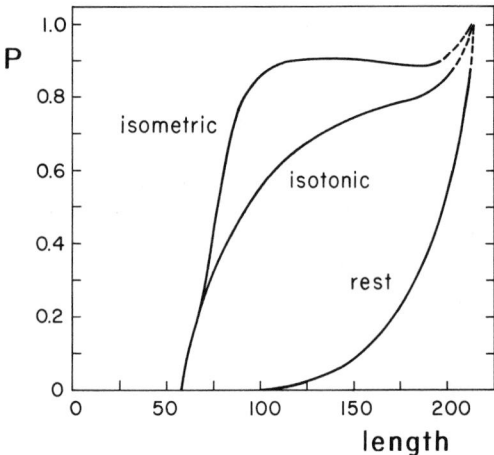

FIG. 21.4. Length-tension diagram of isolated single muscle fiber at rest, during isometric and during isotonic tetanic contraction. (Buchthal, F., Kaiser, E., and Rosenfalck, P., "The reology of the cross striated muscle fiber," Dan. Biol. Medd. **21,** Copenhagen, 1951.)

is unlikely that the sarcolemma would contribute to any essential extent to the elasticity of the muscle.

When a muscle or a single muscle fiber is stimulated by a single stimulus while extended by a moderate load, it develops a tension after a short latency period (2–3 msec. in the frog sartorius muscle). When the tension has reached a value exceeding the stretching force exerted by the load, the muscle shortens rapidly. The development of tension is transient and when the tension decreases the muscle lengthens and returns to its relaxed condition. This simple muscle twitch is therefore characterized by a short period during which tension is being developed, the *contraction* phase, followed by a *relaxation* phase during which the muscle returns to a *resting* condition.

If the load is kept constant during the shortening of the muscle, *isotonic contraction,* and the experiment is repeated applying different loads, there will be a dependence of the amount of shortening as well as of the velocity of shortening on the load. With increasing load, the amount of shortening and the velocity of shortening will decrease, while the latency period will increase. The dependence of shortening on the load means that the maximum tension that the muscle can develop during an isotonic contraction decreases with decreasing length of the muscle. The dependence of maximum tension developed in isotonic contractions at different loads is illustrated in fig. 21.4.

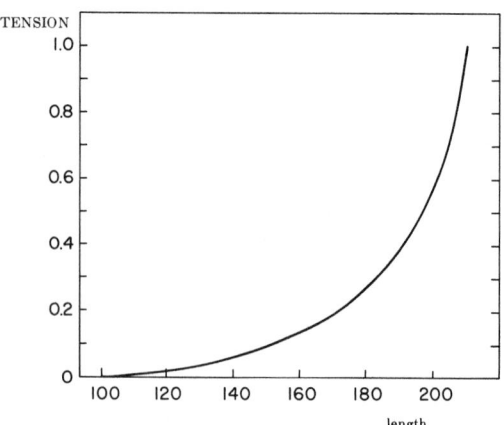

FIG. 21.3. Static length-tension diagram of isolated single muscle fiber at rest. (From Buchthal, F., Kaiser, E., and Rosenfalck, P., "The reology of the cross striated muscle fiber," Dan. Biol. Medd. **21,** 1951, Copenhagen.)

The velocity of shortening is maximal at zero load where the shortening takes place exclusively against internal resistance to deformation of the muscle tissue or the muscle fiber in the single-fiber case. Above a certain limit value for the load, the muscle will not shorten but develops tension at constant length, *isometric contraction.*

If the stimulus is repeated at a certain frequency, the muscle will not relax between each stimulation but will remain in a contracted state, *tetanic contraction.* The tetanic contraction will last as long as the stimulation is repeated or until the muscle is fatigued. The tension developed during a tetanic contraction exceeds that of a single twitch partially because repeated stimulation allows a high degree of synchronization of the activity of the contractile system.

The relationship between the force developed by the muscle and the velocity of shortening is expressed in the Hill equation:

$$(P + a) \ (V + b) = (P_0 + a) \ b$$

where P = force developed by the muscle, V = velocity of shortening, P_0 = maximum isometric tension, a and b are constants with the dimensions force and velocity respectively.

The Series Elastic Element

The lack of synchronization of the activity of the various parts of the muscle is responsible only partially for the gradual increase of tension developed by a muscle when stimulated. If, however, a muscle is rapidly stretched during the early part of the contraction, or even during the latter part of the latency period, it can be demonstrated that it is capable of developing a considerably greater tension than that recorded normally at the same time after stimulation. This observation has been interpreted to reveal the presence in the muscle of an elastic element coupled in series with the contractile elements. The shortening is delayed because the contractile elements must first stretch the series elastic elements before a tension can be recorded externally.

The quick-stretching experiments also show that the contractile machinery is activated already during the latency period and that the activation, the "active state," reaches a maximum very rapidly, whereafter the degree of activation is maintained at a constant level for a short period.

The existence of a series elastic element can be demonstrated in an obvious way by quickly releasing the load on an isometrically contracting muscle and allowing it to shorten to a new equilibrium length. The tension then falls to zero before the tension characteristic for the new length of the muscle has been built up. This instantaneous fall in tension has been ascribed to the undamped series elastic element.

It is likely that the series elastic element resides in the contractile system itself and more specifically in the filamentous structure in which the main muscle proteins are arranged. The Z-line structure has been proposed to be the site of the series elastic element.

The Isometric Contraction

The maximum tension is developed by a muscle during isometric contraction using tetanic stimulation. This tension is also dependent on at what length the muscle is kept during the experiment. The length-tension relationship for isometric contraction (fig. 21.4) shows a maximum tension at a length slightly less than the length of the muscle in the body. It amounts to about 3.5 kg/cm². At this length the actin and myosin filaments overlap to such an extent that there are conditions fulfilled topographically for a maximum interaction between the two sets of filaments. From fig. 21.4 it is obvious that the maximum isometric tension is greater than the maximum tension developed during isotonic contraction.

Latency Relaxation

When a loaded muscle is stimulated, a first mechanical response appears during the latency period in the form of a slight lengthening—the latency relaxation. It begins about 1.0–1.5 msec. after stimulation (frog sartorius) and lasts for about 2 msec. The lengthening for a frog sartorius muscle amounts to about 0.1 μ.

The latency relaxation has been interpreted as the first indication of an interaction between ATP and myosin. This interpretation is supported by the fact that the latency relaxation coincides with a rapid evolution of heat and a transient increase in transparency of the muscle fibers. The latency relaxation is more extensive at longer lengths of the muscle and does not appear at a muscle length about 10% less than that in the body.

The Active State

The active state of the muscle which is generated by the stimulation probably starts at the onset of latency relaxation. It can be determined by a decrease in the extensibility of the muscle.

The intensity of the active state is defined as "the isometric tension which the contractile component can develop" and can be determined at various times after stimulation by determining the maximum load that the muscle can hold after a small quick stretch. When the muscle starts to shorten (about 20 msec. after stimulation for frog muscle), the shortening proceeds at its maximum speed, which indicates that the active state has reached its full intensity. It remains at full intensity over a period of 30–40 msec. at 0° C. and 10 msec at 20° C. for frog sartorius, this period representing the plateau of activity. The active state then declines rather rapidly.

The duration of the active state is greatly affected by temperature, decreasing with increasing temperature with a $Q_{10} = 2.2$. It is also affected by ions and is prolonged by adrenaline, caffeine, nitrate and quinine.

The duration of the active state corresponds roughly to the contraction phase of the single muscle twitch. It can be maintained at a maximum level over prolonged periods of time by repeated stimulation.

HEAT PRODUCTION IN MUSCLE DURING CONTRACTION-RELAXATION CYCLE

Muscle contraction is associated with heat production, a sign of the chemical and physical events associated with contraction. A rise of temperature in the muscle can be measured to within about 10^{-5}° C., and the time-course of heat liberation can be resolved within a few msec. with the thermo-electric method. This technique provides, in fact, the only means to follow the rapid internal physical and chemical changes occurring during and after a contraction.

The heat produced during a single muscle twitch is about 0.003 cal./g. and it appears as (1) an initial very rapid heat production which starts before any shortening has occurred, and (2) heat liberated during shortening in proportion to the amount of shortening of the muscle. If the muscle performs work, additional heat is liberated proportionately to the work done (the Fenn effect). The first heat liberation has been associated with the development of the active state and is referred to as "activation" heat. In a tetanic contraction which is maintained, activation heat is liberated at each stimulus and is then referred to as "maintenance" heat.

The second stage of heat liberation—the "shortening" heat—can be expressed as the amount of heat liberated per centimeter of shortening. It is constant and independent of the extent of shortening, of load and consequently of velocity of shortening, of temperature and of the work done. It therefore appears as a fundamental muscle constant, a, according to Hill's terminology.

If the muscle performs work W during contraction, the total energy E which is liberated in a muscle twitch will consist of (1) activation heat A, (2) shortening heat ax where x is the distance shortened and (3) mechanical work W. That is,

$$E = A + ax + W,$$

in which equation all terms on the right are independent of one another. It means that if the muscle shortens against a load, it provides extra energy exactly equal to the work it has to do without any effects on A and ax.

If the work done is expressed as the weight of the load P times the distance of shortening x, the total energy liberated in connection with shortening will be

$$(P + a)x \tag{1}$$

If the velocity of shortening dx/dt is substituted for the distance x in equation (1) we obtain an expression for the rate of *energy* liberation

$$(P + a)\,\frac{dx}{dt}$$

The rate of energy liberation during the second stage of heat liberation was shown experimentally to be a linear function of the load, increasing with decreasing load and being zero at $P = P_0$, the maximum isometric tetanic tension at rest-length. This relationship can be expressed in the following equation:

$$(P + a)\,\frac{dx}{dt} = b(P_0 - P)$$

where the proportionality factor b has the dimension 1 cm. per sec. Substituting V, the velocity of shortening, for dx/dt, and rearranging this equation, leads to the following relation:

$$(P + a)\,(V + b) = (P_0 + a)b = \text{constant.}$$

This relationship, which is deduced from energy liberation as a function of the work done, is the same as that defining the relation between the speed of shortening V and the force developed by the muscle. The constant b is about one-quarter of the maximum speed of shortening at zero load. The constant a, which has the dimension of a force, occurs in both equations and is about 400

g. wt./cm.² of muscle cross-section. The significance of these simple relationships is unknown.

There is no heat liberated during relaxation, with the exception of the case where a load stretches the muscle. In that case, the liberated heat corresponds to the work done by the muscle during shortening, this work being degraded into heat as the muscle is stretched.

Further heat is liberated during the recovery, "recovery heat," which is associated with the oxidative chemical synthetic processes. The recovery heat is about equal to the total of the initial energy consisting of activation and shortening heat and work. Since about half this initial energy is derived from chemical reactions that are reversed during recovery, it appears that about half the energy associated with the recovery reactions is wasted as heat.

The initial heat liberated during a contraction is the same whether oxygen is present or not. The chemical reactions associated with contraction are therefore non-oxidative. Oxygen is consumed later during the recovery phase.

From a knowledge of the energetics of muscle contraction it is possible to estimate the mechanical efficiency of a muscle, that is, the fraction of the chemical energy liberated during contraction and recovery that is turned into mechanical work. This efficiency is not higher than 20–25%, part of the energy being wasted during contraction and part of it during recovery.

The Activation of the Contractile Mechanism

The activity of the muscle is controlled by the central nervous system through the motor innervation of the muscle fibers. Each motor nerve fiber splits up into a number of branches that make contact with the surface of the individual muscle fibers with several bulb-shaped endings. These endings are arranged in a group, and with a specialized structure of the surface of the muscle fiber they form a motor end plate.

The stimulus conducted along the nerve fiber affects the nerve ending to release acetylcholine, which diffuses across the minute gap separating the nerve ending from the muscle fiber plasma membrane. At the motor end plate, this membrane shows a complex series of invaginations forming minute crypts. At this area of the muscle fiber surface, there is a high concentration of acetylcholine esterase, which will split to acetate and choline the acetylcholine set free during stimulation of the nerve ending. The exact localization of the choline esterase is not known but it is topographically closely related to the plasma membrane of the muscle fiber in the motor end-plate region.

At rest, a potential difference across the muscle plasma membrane of about 90 mV is maintained —the resting potential. The release of acetylcholine affects the permeability of the plasma membrane of the muscle fiber for ions. Due to the difference in concentration of Na ions (high outside) and K ions (high inside), the increased ion permeability gives rise to a sudden influx of Na ions and an efflux of K ions through the plasma membrane. This short-circuits the adjacent parts of the plasma membrane and causes a drop in the membrane potential to the level where the membrane becomes electrically excited, the critical value being about 50 mV. The electrical excitation involves a depolarization of the membrane, which spreads toward the ends of the muscle fiber. The electric response developed as a consequence of the acetylcholine effect on the membrane permeability can be recorded as an action potential showing a potential change across the membrane of about 130 mV with the inside of the membrane becoming about 40 mV *positive*. The resting potential of about 90 mV is therefore not only abolished but the distribution of positive and negative charges is reversed. The conduction of one impulse involves only a minute amount of Na ions (about 4×10^{-12} equiv. per cm.²) entering the muscle fiber and an equivalent leakage of K ions to the extracellular space. Through a recovery mechanism, the nature of which is unknown, the ion concentration difference between the muscle fiber and the extracellular space is maintained through Na extrusion and K uptake.

The esterase activity rapidly abolishes the effect of acetylcholine and secures that this effect is restricted in time. The electric response at the plasma membrane of the muscle fiber will therefore be efficiently controlled by the nerve impulses reaching the motor end-plate. Even without any such impulses there are minute spike potentials developing at the motor end-plate region of the muscle plasma membrane which have been ascribed to a spontaneous setting-free of minute "packages" of acetylcholine. The concentration of acetylcholine that is reached due to this "leakage" is, however, not high enough to produce sufficient permeability changes in the plasma membrane of the muscle fiber to make the potential drop below 50 mV, which is the threshold for the development of a propagated electric response. The minute spike potentials therefore remain localized to the end-plate region.

The impulses conducted along the muscle fiber from the end-plate region account for a spreading of a state of excitation along the fiber. The activation of the contractile elements which are distributed over the whole cross-section of the fiber depends on spreading of the excitatory state from the plasma membrane transversally across the muscle fiber.

The action potential is associated with currents flowing through the interior of the fiber. These currents, however, are not directly responsible for activating the contractile mechanism. It is, furthermore, not possible for any substance liberated at the surface of the muscle fiber in connection with the electric impulse propagation along the plasma membrane to activate the contractile elements by diffusion of the substance through the fiber, because such a mechanism would be too slow. The activation is, furthermore, highly temperature-dependent, which also points against a mechanism involving simple diffusion of an activating substance.

There is good evidence for certain tubular structures in the sarcoplasm, the sarcotubules, being involved in the propagation of impulses inward from the plasma membrane. These tubules measure about 300 Å in diameter and run in a transverse direction through the muscle fiber. They are therefore called the T-system to distinguish them from those tubules (the L-system) with mainly longitudinal orientation. The latter form irregular networks along the myofibrils between the levels at which the tubules of the T-system extend across the muscle fiber. The tubules of the T-system are arranged in a regular fashion extending from the plasma membrane toward the center of the muscle fiber at each A-I-band boundary (at the Z-line in frog muscle). Recent observations provide good evidence that these tubules are in continuity with the plasma membrane. The narrow channel bounded by the tubule wall, therefore, is continuous with the extracellular space. When stimulating a muscle fiber locally by means of a microelectrode in contact with the surface of the fiber, the threshold for a local response is minimal at the level of the I-A-band boundary in muscles where the T-system is located at that level and at the Z-line level in muscles where the T-system is confined to the Z-line level. By applying a minimal strength of stimulation at the proper level, a contraction of half a sarcomere can be provoked.

The nature of the impulse propagation along the T-system is unknown. Structurally, the conditions are fulfilled for an electrotonic spreading along the tubules of the T-system of the electric potential changes associated with the muscle action potential.

The activation of the contractile machinery ultimately depends on the effect of an activating factor or factors. Such factors would release the ATP-ase activity of the contractile machinery, which is inhibited in the resting muscle, and allow a splitting of ATP, which is present at high concentration in the resting muscle. The ATP-ase activity of myosin depends on the presence of small amounts of Ca ions, and it appears likely that the contraction is induced by the setting free of Ca ions that in the relaxed muscle are bound or separated from the contractile structure. The sarcotubular system arranged longitudinally and located between the myofibrils—the L-system—has been shown to concentrate calcium by means of a powerful "calcium pump." The parts of this system that are located closest to the A-I-band boundary are characterized by a high ATP-ase activity which can be related to this calcium pump, the ATP splitting furnishing the energy to drive the pump. High concentrations of calcium also have been demonstrated inside these parts of the tubules of the L-system. It therefore appears likely that the activation of the contractile machinery is due to a release of Ca ions from the L-system, and that the impulse conducted by the T-system affects the permeability of the adjacent parts of the tubules of the L-system, thereby initiating the contraction. The tubules of the T-system are in close apposition to the tubules of the L-system at the A-I-band boundary, the contact relations appearing to be like those at a synapse.

The relaxation of the muscle fiber would be associated with a removal of Ca ions through the calcium pump of the L-system. In addition, a relaxing factor, protein in nature, would inhibit the ATP-ase activity of myosin.

When the sarcotubular system is isolated from muscle homogenates, this relaxing factor can be demonstrated in the supernatant. The sarcotubular system appears in the pellet fragmented into numerous vesicles. These vesicles also show a relaxing effect which is ascribed fully or partially to their ability to remove Ca ions from the medium, the calcium accumulating inside the vesicles.

The Energy-Generating Systems

The energy for the muscle contraction is derived from chemical reactions in the muscle fiber. The main energy source is glycogen, which is present in muscle tissue in a concentration of 0.5 to 1% of the wet weight of the tissue. The energy associated with muscle contraction is (as was pointed out above) made available without any oxygen being consumed, even when oxygen is present. The oxidative (*aerobic*) chemical reactions are therefore not directly associated with muscle contraction but with the recovery processes. The recovery processes involve energy being stored in a form that makes it promptly available to the contractile machinery, thereby securing a quick response of the contractile machinery to a stimulus.

The compound that appears to be ultimately involved in transducing energy to the contractile machinery is adenosine triphosphate (ATP), and the reaction by which energy is utilized is the hydrolytic splitting of the terminal phosphate group from ATP (fig. 21.5).

$$ATP \rightarrow ADP + P_i \text{ (inorganic phosphate)}$$

This reaction involves a liberation of about 7600–7800 calories per mol, which is a large amount of energy released in a single hydrolytic reaction, and it has become customary to refer to the bond between the terminal phosphate group and the neighboring phosphate group as a "high energy bond" and to designate energy-rich phosphate bonds by the symbol $\sim$ ⓟ. The adenosine triphosphate structure, therefore, can be written as follows:

$$A-O-\overset{\overset{\displaystyle O}{\|}}{\underset{\underset{\displaystyle OH}{|}}{P}}-O\sim\overset{\overset{\displaystyle O}{\|}}{\underset{\underset{\displaystyle OH}{|}}{P}}-O\sim\overset{\overset{\displaystyle O}{\|}}{\underset{\underset{\displaystyle OH}{|}}{P}}-OH$$

or

$$A-P\sim ⓟ \sim ⓟ$$

where A = adenosine: adenine + o-ribose. (This formula shows two energy-rich phosphate bonds in the ATP molecule. Only the one associated with the terminal group is directly utilized during muscle contraction.) It should be pointed out, however, that this terminology is misleading, since the energy is not concentrated in a single bond as this symbolization would indicate. The large amount of energy that is liberated at hydrolytic splitting of the terminal phosphate group relates to the change in chemical potential which is associated with the transfer of the phosphate group from ATP to water to form ADP and H_3PO_4, which is a group transfer. The term "group transfer potential" has therefore been proposed as a more correct term than bond

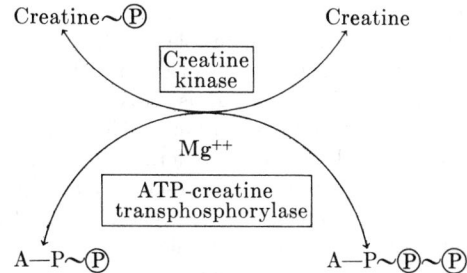

ADENOSINE TRIPHOSPHATE (ATP)

FIG. 21.5

energy. The energy is a property of the ATP molecule as a whole.

The ATP-ase activity of myosin secures that the hydrolysis of ATP will take place at the contractile machinery itself with favorable conditions for energy transfer from ATP to the myosin-actin system.

The restoration involves a phosphorylation of ADP to build up a storage of ATP. In muscle, creatin phosphate (phosphocreatine) represents a second high-energy compound, in which phosphate is bonded to creatine by means of a high-energy bond, C $\sim$ ⓟ. Prompt resynthesis of ATP is possible by phosphate group transfer from creatine phosphate to ADP, the Lohmann reaction, which is catalyzed by *creatine kinase*.

Creatine$\sim$ⓟ   Creatine

| Creatine kinase |

Mg^{++}

| ATP-creatine transphosphorylase |

A—P$\sim$ⓟ   A—P$\sim$ⓟ$\sim$ⓟ

This reaction is reversible, ATP can phosphorylate creatine to creatine phosphate, a reaction which is catalyzed by the enzyme *ATP-creatine transphosphorylase*. The high-energy phosphate group is, in this reaction, transferred from ATP to creatine. ATP, on the other hand, is being formed by oxidative phosphorylation of ADP during the recovery period. In this way a second form of storage of high-energy phosphate as creatine phosphate is built up in the muscle during recovery. The ATP content of resting muscle is about 5×10^{-6} moles per gram muscle tissue. There is four to six times as much creatine phosphate. The ATP and the creatine phosphate represent energy stored in a form that can be utilized rapidly. The recharging of ATP through oxidative phosphorylation is in comparison a slow process. The high-energy phosphate storage in the muscle is sufficient to allow the muscle to contract 50–100 times. The energy reservoirs are then depleted. For maintenance of the muscle contractility, a steady supply of energy is required to recharge ADP.

Since the reactions associated with the contraction, dephosphorylation of ATP, as well as the phosphate transfer from creatine phosphate to ADP, are non-oxidative processes, it becomes obvious that no oxygen is consumed during contraction provided that no recovery metabolism is maintained in parallel. Oxygen is consumed during the recovery phase in connection with oxidative phosphorylation of ADP.

The energy required for the high-energy phosphate bonds of the energy storage molecules ATP and creatine phosphate is supplied by glycolysis and the oxidation of acetate (derived from pyruvic acid) in the citric acid cycle with the associated oxidative phosphorylation by the respiratory chain.

In addition to glycogen, fatty acids and amino acids can furnish fuel for the muscle, and in the resting muscle, glycogen breakdown is not required to maintain the metabolism of the muscle. This metabolism can be maintained by the uptake of carbohydrates and other compounds from the blood capillaries. In the resting muscle, the carbohydrates are responsible for about 60% of the energy requirements of the muscle.

Anaerobically, glycogen is broken down to lactic acid, thereby furnishing 16,300 cal. per gram molecule lactic acid formed, and three moles of ATP per glucose residue of glycogen. It is therefore obvious that a recharging of ADP and creatine can occur in the muscle without access to oxygen. Breakdown of lactic acid, however, depends on the presence of oxygen, and under anaerobic conditions, the lactic acid concentration will increase in the muscle and will diffuse into the blood stream to be transported to the liver.

Glycolysis can be inhibited by iodoacetate poisoning and under those conditions the muscle will contract until the ATP and the creatine phosphate stores have been depleted.

Under aerobic conditions, the end product of glycolysis is pyruvic acid instead of lactic acid, which metabolically represents a blind alley. Pyruvic acid is oxidatively decarboxylated to acetic acid, which as active acetate is bound to coenzyme A, and as acetyl coenzyme A (acetyl CoA) enters the aerobic citric acid cycle of Krebs, leading to a complete oxidation to CO_2 and H_2O. During this degradation, 18 ADP molecules are phosphorylated per molecule of pyruvic acid, which means that 36 ADP molecules are phosphorylated during oxidation of the two pyruvic acid molecules derived from each glucose molecule. Three ADP molecules are phosphorylated during glycolytic conversion to lactic acid of each glucose residue derived from glycogen, which means that a total of 39 moles of ATP are formed per mole glucose residue degraded.

Total oxidation of glucose to CO_2 and H_2O yields 686,000 cal. per mol, but only 56,000 cal. per mole is produced when the glucose degradation does not proceed further than to lactic acid. The efficiency of glycolysis, which represents the efficiency of the energy-generating reactions under anaerobic conditions, can be calculated by assuming that the phosphorylation of three ADP molecules consumes about 24,000 cal. The efficiency will then be 24,000/56,000 × 100, that is, about 43% of the potentially available energy during glycolysis following glycogenolysis. In comparison with the energy released during complete oxidation of glucose—686,000 cal. per mol—the energy stored in the two molecules of ATP will represent 24,000/686,000 × 100, or about 3% of the total energy available as chemical energy in glucose. This shows the low efficiency of anaerobic energy metabolism. In comparison, 36 + 3 ADP molecules are phosphorylated in the aerobic degradation of a glucose equivalent derived from glycogenolysis representing a free energy storage of about 312,000 calories. The efficiency of the oxidative degradation of glucose is therefore 312,000/686,000 × 100, or about 45%, which is in good agreement with the efficiency estimated from measurements of the recovery heat.

Glycogen Metabolism

The first step in the synthesis of glycogen involves phosphorylation of glucose to glucose 6-phosphate, a reaction catalyzed by *glucokinase* and associated with utilization of energy-rich phosphate in the form of ATP.

Glucose + ATP → glucose 6-phosphate + ADP

The product, glucose 6-phosphate, is a relatively energy-poor compound and this reaction therefore means that energy released in dephosphorylation of ATP is being spent. Glucose 6-phosphate is converted to glucose 1-phosphate, a reaction catalyzed by the enzyme *phosphoglucomutase* (fig. 21.6). Glucose 1-phosphate is then activated by reacting with uridine triphosphate UTP to form uridine diphosphate glucose (UDPG). This reaction is catalyzed by *UDPG pyrophosphorylase*. The UDPG units are then connected to one another by bonds across the 1,4 carbon atoms of neighboring molecules. This reaction is catalyzed by the enzyme *glycogen synthetase* (UDPG-glycogen-transglucosylase). The formation of such bonds gives rise to linear chains of glucose residues. At a chain length of 8 to 12 glucose units, the synthesized chain is linked to an existing chain by means of a 1-6 carbon linkage. This reaction is catalyzed by the *"branching enzyme"* (amylo-1,4 1,6 transglucosidase). In this way, a branch point is established, and the glycogen molecule grows to a large, highly-branched structure (fig. 21.7) with a molecular weight that ranges from 250,000 to 10^7.

Glycogenolysis involves degrading of glycogen to α-glucose 1-phosphate, a reaction catalyzed by *glycogen phosphorylase*. The glucose units of the terminal ends of the chains are split off and the activity of the enzyme is confined to the 1–4 links (fig. 21.8). The 1,6 linkage of the branch points is split by *amylo-(1,6)-glucosidase* releasing the glucose unit at the branch point as glucose 1-phosphate.

The glycogen phosphorylase, with a molecular weight of 495,000, consists of four polypeptide chains. The molecule can be split by a muscle enzyme, *phosphorylase phosphatase* (or phosphorylase-rupturing enzyme), by hydrolytic removal of phosphate groups from a serine residue present in each polypeptide chain. This results in a rearrangement of these chains in a dimeric form, which has been reported as inactive in the absence of adenosine-5-monophosphate, AMP. The tetramer, which is active also in the absence of AMP, is distinguished as phosphorylase *a* from the inactive dimer, phosphorylase *b*. The polypeptide chains of phosphorylase *a* and *b* each contain one lysine residue. The amino group of the lysine residue forms the Schiff base of pyridoxal phosphate. Removal of either the pyridoxal phosphate or the phosphate bound to the serine residue inactivates the enzyme. Phosphorylase *b* is found in resting muscle. It is reactivated by conversion to phosphorylase *a* by *phosphorylase b kinase* in the reaction

2 phosphorylase b + 4 ATP →
$$\rightarrow \text{phosphorylase } a + 4 \text{ ADP}$$

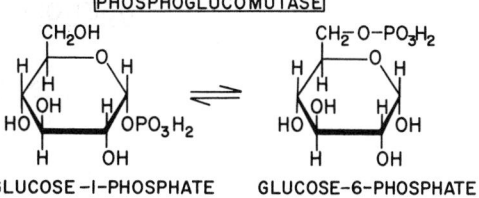

PHOSPHOGLUCOMUTASE

GLUCOSE–I–PHOSPHATE   GLUCOSE-6-PHOSPHATE

Fɪɢ. 21.6

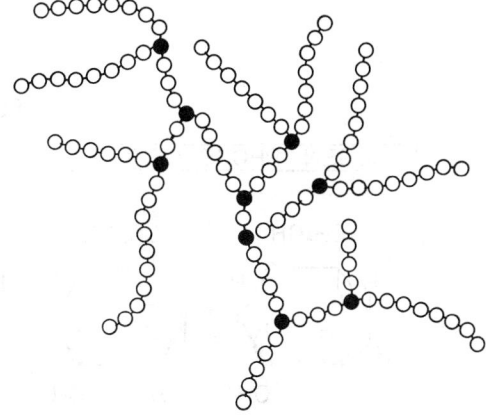

Fɪɢ. 21.7. Part of a branched glycogen molecule with each circle representing one glucose residue.

The phosphorylase kinase also appears in an active and an inactive form, and the inactive form is converted to active enzyme by an enzyme system called adenylcyclase.

The phosphorylase step is rate-limiting in glycogenolysis, and inactivation of the enzyme represents a possible regulating mechanism to turn off glycogenolysis in the resting muscle in favor of glycogenesis and utilization of metabolites entering the muscle fibers from the blood capillaries for maintaining metabolism during resting conditions.

The glucose 1-phosphate is converted to glucose 6-phosphate in a reaction catalyzed by the enzyme *phosphoglucomutase*.

Glucose 1-phosphate $\rightleftharpoons$ glucose 6-phosphate

This reaction requires the presence of glucose 1,6-diphosphate and Mg^{++} The enzyme appears to become esterified during this reaction by a transfer of one of the phosphate groups from glucose-1,6-diphosphate to a serine residue of the enzyme molecule. In the case when the glucose 6-phosphate formation is favored, the phosphate group of the 1-carbon is removed this way.

Enzyme + glucose 1,6 diphosphate $\rightleftharpoons$
$$\rightleftharpoons \text{enzyme-P} + \text{glucose 6-phosphate}$$

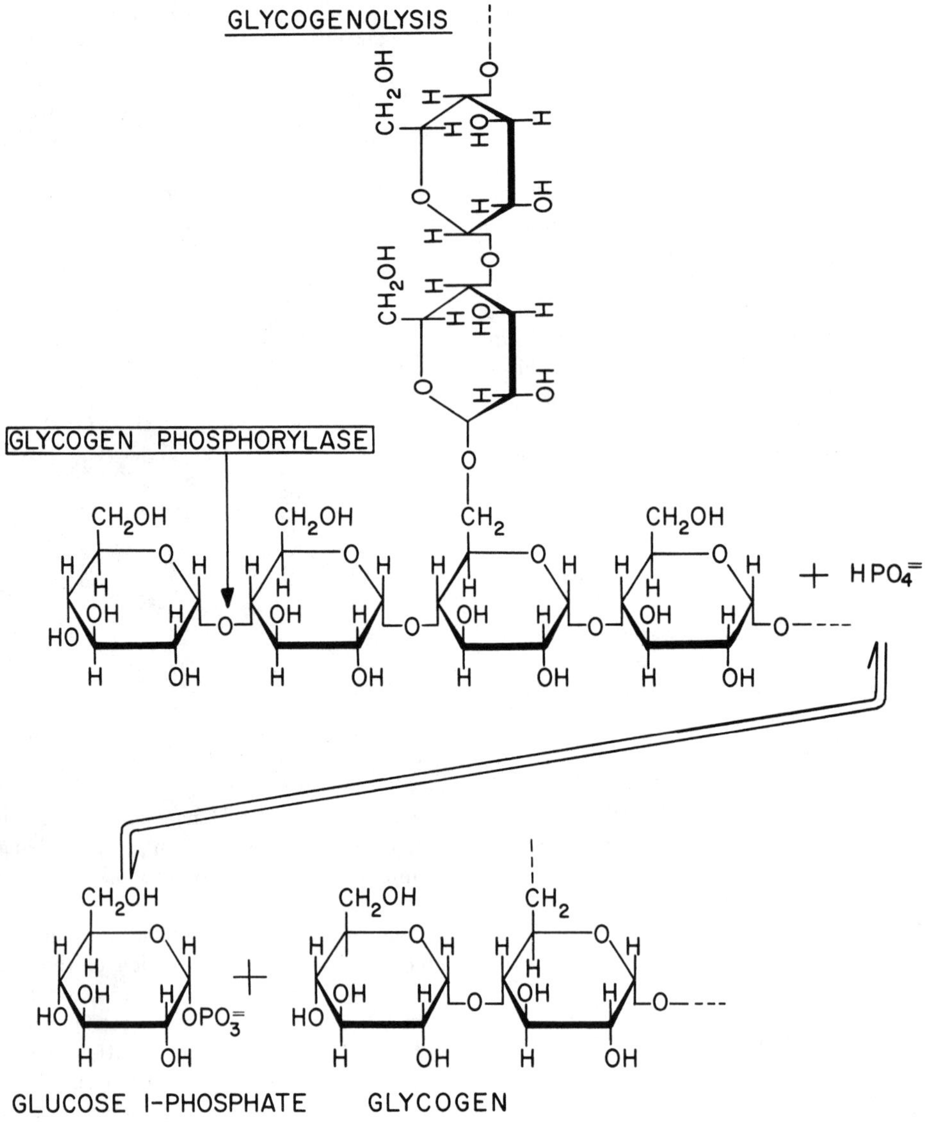

GLYCOGENOLYSIS

FIG. 21.8. Glycogenolysis

The phosphate group of the esterified enzyme then presumably is transferred to the 6-carbon in glucose 1-phosphate to regenerate glucose 1,6-diphosphate.

Enzyme-P + glucose 1-phosphate $\rightleftharpoons$
$\rightleftharpoons$ enzyme + glucose 1,6-diphosphate

The glucose 1,6-diphosphate necessary for this reaction is formed by transfer of a phosphate group from ATP to glucose 1-phosphate in a reaction catalyzed by *phosphoglucokinase*.

Glucose 1-phosphate + ATP $\rightarrow$
$\rightarrow$ glucose 1,6-diphosphate + ADP

Since glucose 1,6-diphosphate is regenerated in the reaction catalyzed by phosphoglucomutase, the energy expense associated with the above reaction is small in relation to the net energy transferred to ATP during oxidation of glucose.

The glucose 6-phosphate enters the main pathway of glycolysis followed by complete oxidation via the citric acid cycle and its associated oxidative phosphorylation system. The following scheme summarizes the pathways of glycogenesis and glycogenolysis.

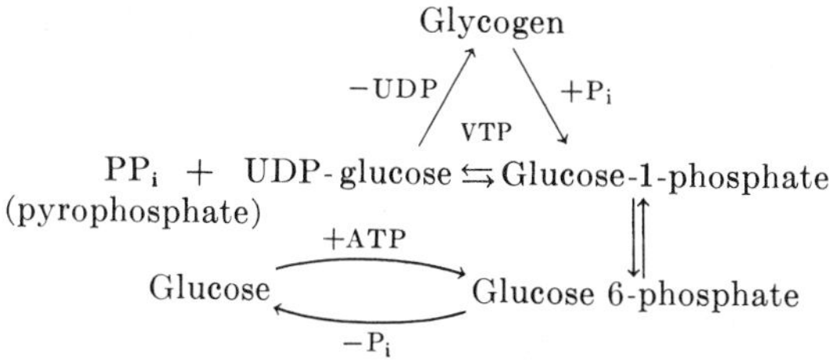

$$\text{Glycogen}$$

$$-\text{UDP} \nearrow \qquad \searrow +\text{P}_i$$
$$\diagup \text{VTP}$$

$$\text{PP}_i \; + \; \text{UDP-glucose} \leftrightarrows \text{Glucose-1-phosphate}$$
(pyrophosphate)

$$+\text{ATP}$$
$$\text{Glucose} \xrightleftharpoons[-\text{P}_i]{} \text{Glucose 6-phosphate}$$

GLYCOLYSIS

Glycolysis involves the degradation of glucose to pyruvic or lactic acid. This breakdown of glucose can occur without access to oxygen, in which case the end product is lactic acid. Two molecules of ADP are phosphorylated to ATP during glycolysis.

$$\text{Glucose} + 2\,\text{ADP} + \text{P}_i \rightleftharpoons 2\ \text{lactic acid} + 2\,\text{ATP}$$

The starting material can either be glucose or the end product of glycogenolysis, glucose 6-phosphate. In the former case, glucose is first converted to glucose 6-phosphate.

The phosphorylation of glucose was described above and involves the dephosphorylation of ATP and spending of the energy liberated in this reaction.

This step is bypassed in glycolysis following glycogenolysis since glucose 6-phosphate is then formed directly from glucose 1-phosphate in a reaction not involving utilization of phosphate-bound energy. The net gain of glycolysis will, therefore, in this case, be three moles of ATP per mole of glucose residue in glycogen.

Glucose 6-phosphate is converted to fructose 6-phosphate in a reaction catalyzed by *phosphohexose isomerase*. A second phosphate group is introduced at the 1-carbon of fructose 6-phosphate to yield fructose 1,6-phosphate. The phosphate group is transferred from ATP and the transfer is catalyzed by the enzyme *phosphofructokinase*. Since one mole of ATP is dephosphorylated per mole fructose 1,6-phosphate formed, this reaction involves expenditure of energy.

In the next step the 6-carbon compound fructose 1,6-diphosphate is split between C-1 and C-4 to yield two three-carbon compounds, dihydroxyacetone phosphate and D-glyceraldehyde 3-phosphate. The enzyme aldolase catalyzes this cleavage.

The two triose-phosphates formed are interconvertible by isomerization, and dihydroxyace-tone phosphate is converted to D-glyceraldehyde 3-phosphate in a reaction catalyzed by *triose phosphate isomerase*.

D-Glyceraldehyde 3-phosphate is then oxidized to 1,3-diphosphoglyceric acid by *phosphoglyceraldehyde dehydrogenase* (triose phosphate dehydrogenase) in the presence of inorganic orthophosphate and DPN$^+$. The enzyme forms a complex with two moles of DPN$^+$ bound to each mole of the enzyme. Sulfhydryl groups in the enzyme molecule are of decisive importance for the activity of the enzyme. The inhibition of glycolysis by iodoacetate is attributed to the fact that this compound reacts with these sulfhydryl groups.

The energy of oxidation involved in the oxidation of the 1,3-diphosphoglyceric aldehyde to a carboxylic acid is retained within the molecule in the form of bond energy, and 1,3-diphosphoglyceric acid, therefore, is an energy-rich phosphate compound.

The bond energy is sufficient for a transfer of a phosphate group from the 1 position of 1,3-diphosphoglyceric acid to ADP. The enzyme *3-phosphoglyceric acid kinase* catalyzes this reaction.

$$1,3 \text{ diphosphoglyceric acid} + \text{ADP} \rightleftharpoons$$
$$\rightleftharpoons 3\text{-phosphoglyceric acid} + \text{ATP}$$

The sum of this reaction and that involving oxidation of glyceraldehyde 3-phosphate is the following:

$$\text{Glyceraldehyde 3-phosphate} + \text{P}_i + \text{DPN} + \text{ADP}$$
$$\rightleftharpoons 3\text{-phosphoglyceric acid} + \text{DPNH} + \text{ATP} + \text{H}^+$$

One molecule of ATP is thus formed for each molecule of 1,3-diphosphoglyceric acid dephosphorylated. The energy now stored in the ATP molecule has been derived from the energy of the exergonic oxidation of D-glyceraldehyde 3-phosphate by transfer to the carboxylic acid and to ADP. This is an example of coupling an energy-releasing oxidation to the high-energy-requiring phosphorylation of ADP with the energy maintained as chemical energy and prevented from dissipating as heat.

The reduced diphosphopyridine nucleotide DPNH can be oxidized after exchange with intramitochondrial DPNH. The oxidation of the intramitochondrial DPNH is coupled to ADP phosphorylation and yields three moles of ATP per mole DPNH (see below).

An exchange reaction between cytoplasmic and intramitochondrial DPNH is required because the permeability of the mitochondrial membrane for DPNH is low. One such reaction involves the reduction in the cytoplasm of dehydroxyacetone phosphate to α-glycerol phosphate by DPNH in a reaction catalyzed by *α-glycerol phosphate dehydrogenase*. The mitochondrial surface membrane is permeable for α-glycerol phosphate which, after entering the mitochondrion, is

oxidation are too high to be satisfied by the mitochondrial system. Lactic acid is therefore formed also under aerobic conditions when the muscle activity exceeds a certain intensity.

The coupling of the reactions leading to restoration of DPN^+ can be summarized in the following way:

$$3\text{-Phosphoglyceraldehyde} \xrightarrow{\textit{Anaerobic}} 1,3\text{-diphosphoglyceric acid}$$
$$DPN^+ \qquad\qquad DPNH + H^+$$
$$\text{lactic acid} \xrightarrow[\textit{Aerobic}]{} \text{pyruvic acid}$$

$$3\text{-Phosphoglyceraldehyde} \longrightarrow 1,3\text{-diphosphoglyceric acid}$$
$$H_2O + DPN^+ \qquad\qquad DPNH + H^+$$
$$\xrightarrow{+1/2\ O_2}$$
$$3\ ATP \qquad\qquad 3\ ADP + 3P_i$$

reoxidized to dihydroxyacetone phosphate while mitochondrial DPN^+ is reduced to DPNH. This reaction is catalyzed by an intramitochondrial *glycerol phosphate dehydrogenase*. The dihydroxyacetone phosphate then diffuses from the mitochondrion to the cytoplasm and can be utilized over again for coupling oxidation of cytoplasmic DPNH to reduction of intramitochondrial DPN^+.

The 3-phosphoglyceric acid is transformed into 2-phosphoglyceric acid over an intermediate step at which 2,3-diphosphoglyceric acid is formed. The reaction is catalyzed by *phosphoglyceromutase*.

2-Phosphoglyceric acid is converted by dehydration to phosphoenol pyruvic acid in the presence of *enolase*. The phosphate group of phosphoenol pyruvic acid is linked to the molecule by a high-energy bond and a group transfer to ADP involving the phosphate group is therefore possible, yielding one molecule ATP, while pyruvic acid is formed. This reaction is catalyzed by *pyruvic acid kinase* in the presence of Mg^{++}.

This is the last reaction during glycolysis that can furnish energy for synthesis of ATP. Under anaerobic conditions, DPNH formed in connection with conversion of 3-phosphoglyceraldehyde to 3-phosphoglyceric acid can be oxidized to DPN^+ in a reaction where pyruvic acid is reduced to lactic acid. The coupling of these two reactions is essential under anaerobic conditions, because DPNH cannot be oxidized by the mitochondrial electron transport system which requires oxygen. The coupling occurs, however, also in the contracting muscle with normal blood supply when the requirements regarding the speed of DPNH

No oxygen, however, is consumed during glycolysis and the presence of oxygen is not required.

The reactions in glycolytic breakdown of glucose are summarized in fig. 21.9.

Glycolysis occurs in the sarcoplasm, and the enzymes involved are part of the easily extracted "soluble proteins" from muscle tissue which constitute about 30% of the total muscle protein.

The citric acid cycle (tricarboxylic cycle or Krebs cycle) represents a cyclic sequence of chemical reactions, by which acetic acid bound to coenzyme A (CoA) as acetyl coenzyme A (Acetyl CoA) is oxidized to CO_2 and H_2O (figs. 21.10 and 21.11). Pyruvic acid derived from glycolysis furnishes one source of acetyl CoA. Pyruvic acid is oxidized in a series of reactions involving several enzymes, and four cofactors which form a complex constituting *pyruvic acid dehydrogenase*. The following overall scheme illustrates the net effect of these reactions.

$$\begin{array}{l} CH_3 \\ | \\ C{=}O + CoA + DPN^+ \rightleftharpoons \\ | \\ COOH \end{array}$$
pyruvic acid

$$\begin{array}{l} CH_3 \\ | \\ \rightleftharpoons C{=}O + CO_2 + DPNH + H^+ \\ | \\ S{-}CoA \end{array}$$
acetyl CoA

The acetyl CoA is an energy-rich compound and can also be formed from fatty acids and certain amino acids. The citric-acid cycle therefore represents a common pathway in the oxidate degradation of carbohydrates, fats and proteins.

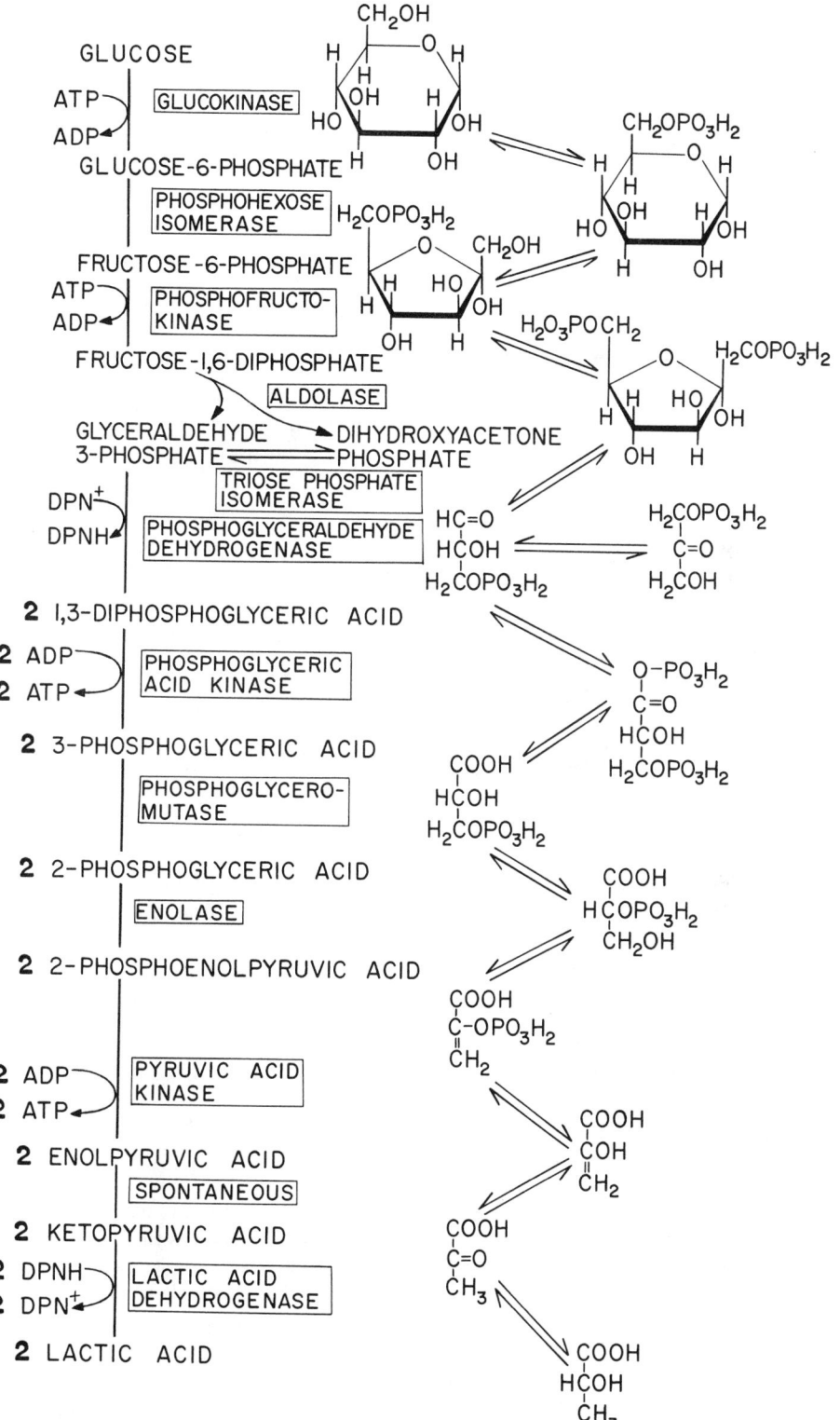

Fig. 21.9. Glycolysis

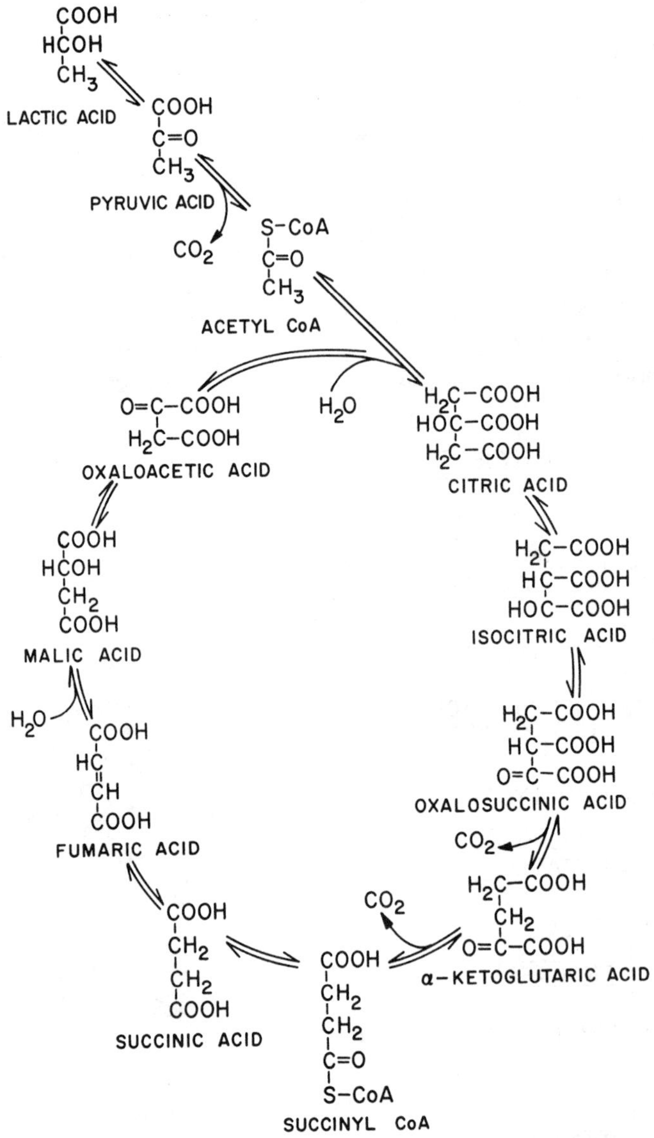

Fig. 21.10. The citric acid cycle

Glucose and fatty-acid metabolism represent, however, the main sources of acetyl CoA.

In the citric-acid cycle, acetyl CoA reacts with the 4-carbon oxaloacetic acid to form the 6-carbon citric acid, a reaction catalyzed by the "*condensing enzyme.*" Citric acid loses one molecule of water and is converted to cis aconitic acid. This then regains a molecule of water to give isocitric acid, which is oxidized to oxalosuccinic acid. Decarboxylation of oxalosuccinic acids yields α-ketoglutaric acid, from which succinic acid is formed by oxidative decarboxylation. Oxalo-acetic acid is then regained by an oxidation yielding fumaric acid, hydration of the fumaric acid to malic acid, and oxidation of malic acid. The oxaloacetic acid is thus regenerated to react with a new molecule of acetyl CoA and the cycle is completed. One molecule of acetyl is oxidized during the cycle, with two molecules of CO_2 and four hydrogen atoms removed. The net exchange during one cycle is shown in the following scheme:

$$CH_3COOH + 2\ O_2 \rightarrow 2\ CO_2 + 2\ H_2O + \text{energy}$$

The energy is derived from the following four

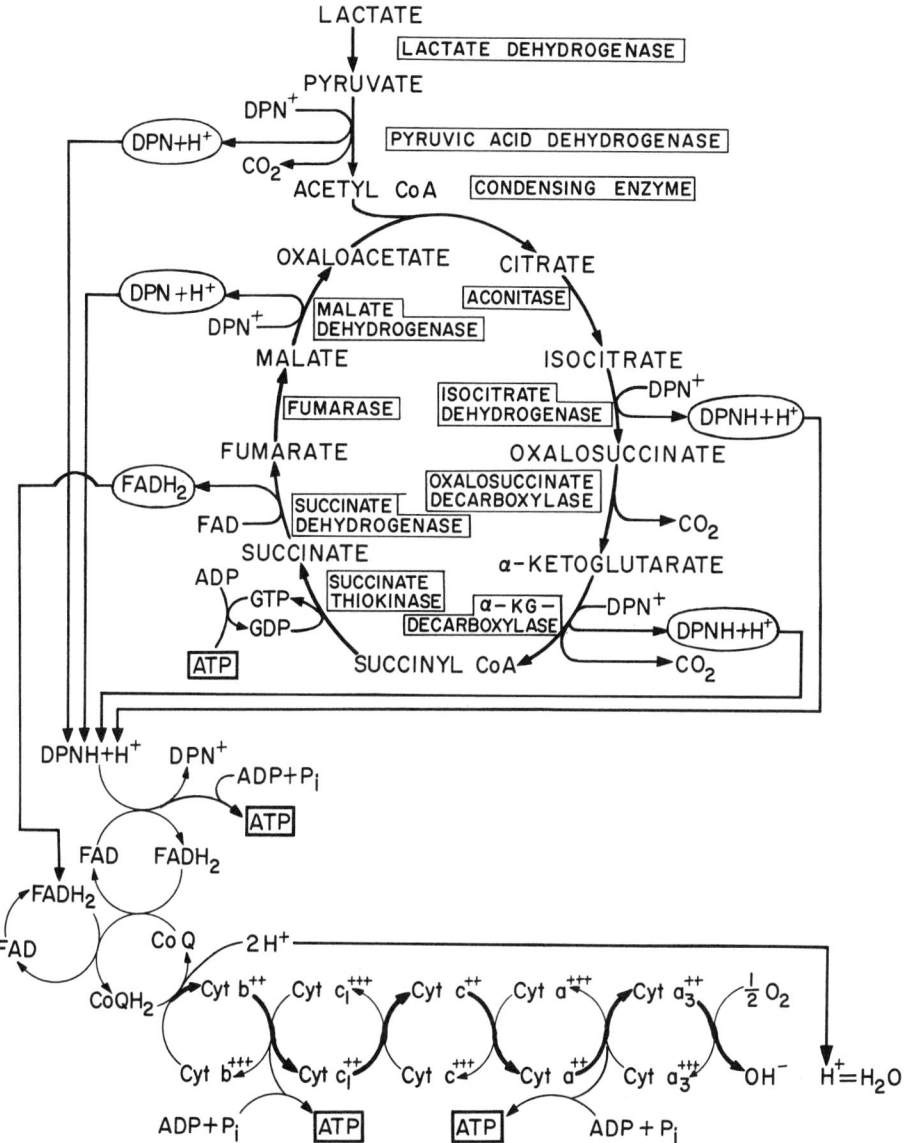

FIG. 21.11. The citric acid cycle and the electron transport chain

dehydrogenations in the cycle, in three of which DPN+ is reduced to DPNH + H+,

$$\text{isocitrate} \rightarrow \alpha\text{-ketoglutarate}$$
$$\alpha\text{-ketoglutarate} \rightarrow \text{succinyl CoA}$$
$$\text{malate} \rightarrow \text{oxaloacetate}$$

At the fourth energy-yielding reaction, the oxidation of succinate to fumarate DPN+ is bypassed and flavoprotein FAD is reduced. In the conversion of succinyl CoA to succinate, guanosine diphosphate (GDP) is phosphorylated to guanosine triphosphate (GTP). The terminal phosphate

group of GTP is transferred to ADP and ATP is formed. This is the fifth energy-yielding reaction associated with the cycle.

Oxidative Phosphorylation (Fig. 21.11)

The reactions in the citric acid cycle are coupled to the respiratory chain, consisting of a sequence of hydrogen and electron carriers.

The electron carriers are iron-containing hemoproteins—cytochromes—which transfer electrons by alternating between reduced and oxidized states, the iron switching between ferrous and ferric forms. An intermediate step involving hydrogen transfer from DPNH to DPNH dehydrogenase (which is a flavoprotein), flavin adenine dinucleotide (FAD), precedes the passage of electrons along the series of cytochromes in the carrier chain. In the flavoprotein the flavin moiety receives the hydrogen. The flavoprotein is oxidized by ubiquinone (coenzyme Q, CoQ), a lipid-soluble quinone acting as a coenzyme. The exact position of ubiquinone in the respiratory chain is not known, but it is frequently considered to be positioned between FAD and cytochrome b, where it then would act as a hydrogen acceptor. In the next step, involving oxidation of ubiquinone, the electron from ionized hydrogen is transferred from ubiquinone to the first cytochrome in the cytochrome series—cytochrome b (Cyt b), and the proton is added to the medium. The electron is now passed along the chain of cytochromes, involving, in addition to cytochrome b, cytochrome c_1 (Cyt c_1), cytochrome c (Cyt c), cytochrome a (Cyt a) and cytochrome oxidase or cytochrome a_3 (Cyt a_3). Only the last member or the last two members of the group, cytochrome a_3 and a, can react directly with oxygen. When oxygen is reduced by cytochrome oxidase, hydroxyl ions are formed that combine with the protons generated at the oxidation of ubiquinone to form water. The net effects of the electron transport along the respiratory chain can be illustrated as follows:

$$CoQH_2 + 2\ Fe^{+++} \rightarrow CoQ + 2\ H^+ + Fe^{++}$$
$$\frac{\tfrac{1}{2}\ O_2 + H_2O + 2\ Fe^{++} \rightarrow 2\ OH^- + 2\ Fe^{+++}}{CoQH_2 + \tfrac{1}{2}\ O_2 \rightarrow CoQ + H_2O}$$

During the electron transfer along the respiratory chain, three ADP molecules are phosphorylated to yield three ATP molecules per atom of oxygen. This is expressed as a P/O ratio of oxidative phosphorylation of 3. The energy for the formation of the high-energy bonds is derived at three points along the respiratory chain, these three points considered to be at the oxidation of DPNH by flavoprotein, the electron transfer to cytochrome c and at the oxidation of cytochrome c by cytochrome oxidase (or of cytochrome a if this cytochrome is considered a link in the chain). The minimum difference in oxidation reduction potential which is required to provide about 8000 cal. for phosphorylation of ADP is 0.18 volt. A difference in potential that is sufficiently large to satisfy this requirement exists at the first point of phosphorylation, and this reaction can therefore proceed in connection with the transfer of a single electron. The potential differences at the two other points are, however, too small to make energy available for ATP synthesis in connection with the passage of a single electron. Two electrons would be required. It is not understood how the energy associated with two consecutive single electron passages can converge to generate one molecule of ATP.

At the fourth energy-yielding reaction in the citric-acid cycle described above, succinic acid is oxidized to fumaric acid by succinic acid dehydrogenase which is a flavoprotein. DPN⁺ is bypassed, which means that the P/O ratio for succinate as substrate is 2 instead of 3. However, one ATP is generated when the terminal phosphate group of GTP is transferred to ATP, which means that also in this step in the citric-acid cycle 3 moles of ATP are formed for each mole of succinic acid oxidized.

The mechanism by which the phosphorylation of ADP is coupled to the electron transport along the respiratory chain is unknown. It has been assumed that the energy is transferred to the $ADP + P_i \rightarrow ATP$ reaction over two intermediate compounds that can transfer the energy in the form of energy-rich bonds to the ATP-generating reaction. If this coupling mechanism is inhibited by drugs, respiration can, under experimental conditions, proceed, indicating that the electron transport system can remain intact when the phosphorylation is uncoupled.

Under physiological conditions, however, respiration and phosphorylation are tightly coupled and the rate-limiting factor for oxidation of foodstuffs is the concentration of ADP and inorganic phosphate. The ADP concentration, on the other hand, is determined by the rate at which ATP is utilized. This represents a self-regulatory mechanism by which the rate of energy generation is adjusted to the requirements of the cell.

Table 21.1 summarizes the energy-yielding and energy-requiring reactions during glucose degradation. In reactions No. 3, 5, and 9, ATP is formed from ADP participating in the reaction. In the other reactions, except No. 10, ATP generation is a consequence of DPNH oxidation in the respiratory system of mitochondria with phosphorylation of ADP coupled to the reaction

$$DPNH + H^+ + \tfrac{1}{2}\ O_2 \rightleftharpoons DPN^+ + H_2O.$$

In reaction No. 10, DPN⁺ is bypassed and hydrogen is transferred to FAD, and ATP is formed in connection with a coupling of FADH₂ oxidation and ADP phosphorylation according to

TABLE 21.1

Energy Yield in Glucose Degradation

Reaction	ATP yield
1. Glucose $+$ ATP $\rightleftharpoons$ glucose 6-phosphate $+$ ADP	-1
2. Fructose 6-phosphate $+$ ATP $\rightleftharpoons$ fructose 1,6-diphosphate $+$ ADP	-1
3. 2 1,3-diphosphoglyceric acid $+$ 2 ADP $\rightleftharpoons$ 2 3-phosphoglyceric acid $+$ 2 ATP	$+2$
4. 2 D-glyceraldehyde 3-phosphate $+$ 2 DPN$^+$ $+$ 2 P$_i$ $\rightleftharpoons$ 2 1,3-diphosphoglyceric acid $+$ 2 DPNH $+$ 2 H$^+$	$+6$
5. 2 Phosphoenolpyruvic acid $+$ 2 ADP $\rightleftharpoons$ 2 pyruvic acid $+$ 2 ATP	$+2$
6. 2 Pyruvic acid $+$ 2 CoA $+$ 2 DPN$^+$ $\rightarrow$ 2 acetyl CoA $+$ 2 CO$_2$ $+$ 2 DPNH $+$ 2 H$^+$	$+6$ CO$_2$
7. 2 Isocitric acid $+$ 2 DPN$^+$ $\rightleftharpoons$ 2 α-ketoglutaric acid $+$ 2 CO$_2$ $+$ 2 DPNH $+$ 2 H$^+$	$+6$ CO$_2$
8. 2 α-ketoglutaric acid $+$ 2 CoA $+$ DPN$^+$ $\rightarrow$ 2 succinyl CoA $+$ 2 DPNH $+$ 2 H$^+$ $+$ 2 CO$_2$	$+6$ CO$_2$
9. 2 Succinyl CoA $+$ 2 GDP $+$ 2 P$_i$ $\rightarrow$ 2 succinic acid $+$ 2 GTP $+$ 2 CoA 2 GTP $+$ 2 ADP $\rightleftharpoons$ 2 GDP $+$ 2 ATP	$+2$
10. 2 Succinic acid $+$ 2 FAD $\rightleftharpoons$ 2 fumaric acid $+$ 2 FADH$_2$	$+4$
11. 2 Malic acid $+$ 2 DPN$^+$ $\rightleftharpoons$ 2 oxalacetic acid $+$ 2 DPNH $+$ 2 H$^+$	$+6$
Total..	$+38$

the following net reaction:

$$FADH_2 + \tfrac{1}{2}\ O_2 \rightleftharpoons FAD + H_2O.$$

In reactions No. 6, 7, and 8, CO$_2$ is formed, one mole for each mole of DPNH formed. In glycolytic degradation of glucose equivalents derived from glycogenolysis reaction No. 1 is not involved and the total number of moles of ATP formed per mole glucose equivalents is, therefore, in this case, 39.

The enzymes of the citric-acid cycle and the components of the respiratory chain are located in the mitochondria (sarcosomes). While the former enzymes can be extracted fairly easily from mitochondria after light homogenization, the components of the respiratory chain can only be released after breaking up the mitochondrial structure. The latter are therefore considered to be bound to the structure of the mitochondria.

The mitochondria are long rod-shaped components with a diameter of 0.1–$0.3\ \mu$. Structurally the mitochondria are characterized (fig. 21.12) by a surface membrane delimiting each mitochondrion and forming a boundary separating the interior of the mitochondrion from the surrounding cytoplasm. In the interior, a system of inner membranes forms plates that are arranged more or less in parallel, and extend perpendicular to the long axis of the mitochondrion, almost across its whole diameter. Sometimes these inner membranes are arranged diagonally or longitudinally. In the muscle mitochondria, the inner membranes are closely arranged and separated by layers of mitochondria matrix that are only a few hundred Ångström units in thickness.

The mitochondrial membranes consist of two presumably identical membrane elements that are in close apposition to form a complex membrane structure. The two membrane elements can easily be separated by uptake of water and they then appear to bound vesicular structures. The whole mitochondrion also can increase its volume considerably by uptake of water, and the maintaining of a normal volume depends on retaining the metabolism of the mitochondrion.

The mitochondria contain 30–40% of lipids, which are mainly located in the membrane structures. The cytochromes and the flavoproteins are associated with lipids and, in addition, the mitochondrial membranes contain lipoproteins of non-enzymatic type—"structural protein."

It is generally accepted that the components of the respiratory chain are arranged in the proper sequence in the membrane elements of the mitochondria and prevented from random motion due to this association. The electron transfer is conceived as being facilitated by the close arrangement of the components of the respiratory chain, which would allow transfer with small changes in orientation of the individual electron carriers. The binding sites for DPNH dehydrogenase and succinic acid dehydrogenase are assumed to face the matrix at the surface of the membrane elements.

The Transmission to the Skeleton of the Force Generated by a Muscle

The force generated by a muscle is transmitted to the skeleton by means of the tendons. The

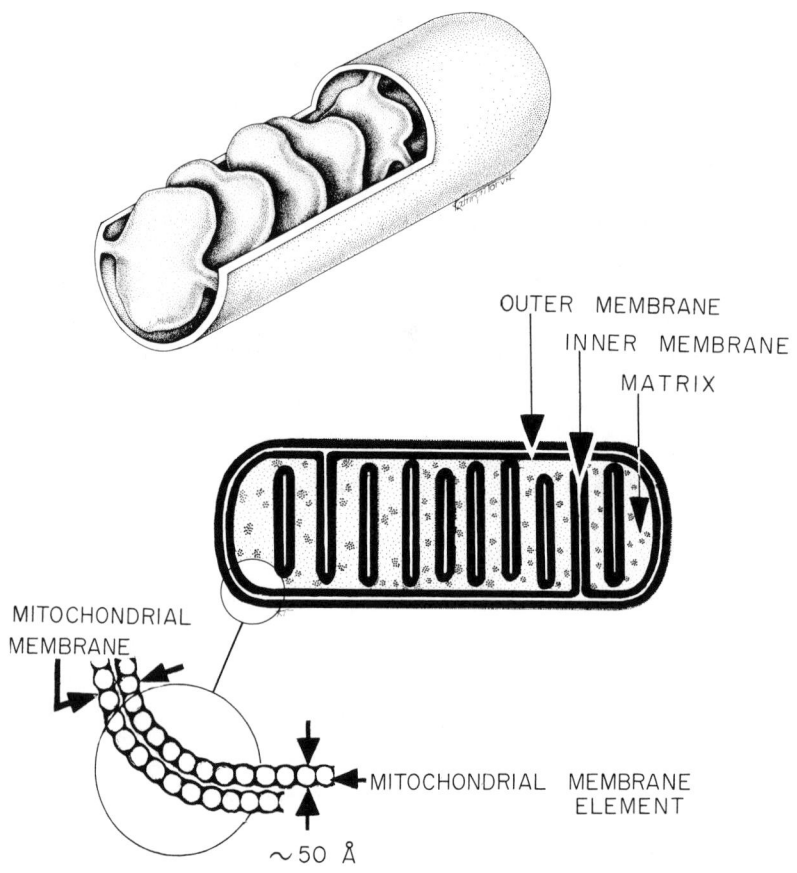

FIG. 21.12. The structure of mitochondria

submicroscopic collagen filaments of the tendons extend along the surface of the individual muscle fibers at the tapering ends of the muscle fibers. The surface area of the muscle fibers is fairly large here due to longitudinal folds of the plasma membrane. The relationship between collagen filaments and the muscle fiber surface is that of a close contact.

The shape of the tendon varies with the shape of the muscle, but there is one feature in common for all tendons—the muscle fibers are oriented at an angle in relation to the main direction of the tendon. When this angle is large, it appears clearly, and such muscles are called pennate muscles. The angle does not exceed 10–20°. This angle is of importance to prevent fraying of the tendon when the diameter of the fibers increases in connection with contraction and shortening.

The tendon forms one or several flat sheets at the region of contact with the muscle, and the muscle fibers can impinge either on only one side of such a sheet or on both sides. Due to the arrangement of the tendon, the length of the

fibers extending between the tendons is usually considerably shorter than the overall length of the muscle. The distance bridged by the muscle fibers is related to the range of shortening utilized under physiological conditions and to the fact that under these conditions the maximal shortening of the individual muscle fibers is kept within a certain limit which is about 30% of the maximal length of the muscle in the body. This is presumably an adjustment to the relationship between the maximal tension developed by a muscle as a function of its length.

In places where a large force is required but where the range of shortening is limited, the muscles are characterized by multipennate structure with the tendons forming several septa arranged in two planes. The efficient cross-section, in this case, is considerably larger than the anatomical cross-section of the muscle. The septa of the tendons in the human deltoid muscle were found to develop gradually during embryologic growth and they were reduced in "old age." It is therefore likely that the gross structure of a muscle is dynamically adjusted to the requirements as is the cross-sectional area.

The cross-sectional area of a muscle increases when the muscle is forced repeatedly to develop maximal or close-to-maximal tension, as in practicing sports that require a forceful action of the muscles. The increase is due to an increase of the cross-sectional area of the individual muscle fibers but not to a formation of new fibers. For continuous growth of the muscle cross-sectional area, the load must be continuously increased during a training period. If the load is kept constant, the growth of the muscle stops when its strength has been adjusted to the load.

Muscles exposed to sustained rhythmic activity over fairly long periods of time at a load below maximum show an increase in the density of the network of blood capillaries extending between the muscle fibers. This appears as an adjustment to the high requirements regarding oxygenation associated with this form of activity. In animals, experiments have shown the effect to be more pronounced in young than in adult animals.

The subdivision of the muscle tissue into individual muscles is, as was pointed out above, determined by mechanical factors, the muscle tissue being split up into individual muscles at places where large relative movements between parts of the muscle mass occur during movement of the body. Such translational movements are most extensive between parts of the muscle tissue that exhibit antagonistic effects, such as flexors and extensors. Such muscles are also frequently separated by extensive connective tissue septa. The individual muscles can therefore be classified with respect to their mechanical effects on the skeleton.

The participation of a certain muscle or portion of a muscle in a particular movement depends on the pattern of impulses from the central nervous system that is transmitted to the muscles of the body. These patterns can involve the activation of mechanically antagonistic muscles or parts of muscles and non-activation of mechanically synergistic muscles. It was found, for instance, by electrymyographic recording, that the ventral and dorsal portions of the human deltoid muscle participate in the abduction of the arm during the whole range of the movement, in spite of the fact that these portions are mechanically antagonistic during part of this movement. On the other hand, these portions are not necessarily activated in adduction—even in a position of the arm in which they are mechanically synergistic.

It is therefore not entirely correct to try to deduce the patterns of muscle activity associated with a particular movement from a knowledge of the mechanical effects of the muscles or from the assumption that only mechanically synergistic muscles or portions of muscles are involved. A direct recording of the muscle activity is required to give precise information regarding the patterns according to which the various muscles are activated in any particular type of movement. This is particularly important when considering movement in ball joints.

The motor unit. Each motor neuron activates a group of muscle fibers through the terminal branches of the axon. When the motor neuron is excited, all muscle fibers innervated by the neuron will be activated, provided the stimulus exceeds a certain threshold value. The single motor neuron and the group of muscle fibers which it innervates represent a motor unit, the smallest part of the muscle that can be made to contract independently. The number of muscle fibers in this unit varies in different muscles, from more than 100 to 20–30, the latter figures applying to the external eye muscles. The size of the unit can be correlated to the precision by which the tension developed by the muscle is graded.

The gradation of the tension developed by a muscle depends on a variation of the number of motor units activated as well as on the frequency at which each unit is stimulated.

REFERENCES

Structure and Function of Muscle, Ed. Bourne, G. H., Academic Press, New York and London, 1960.

HILL, A. V. Muscular Movement in Man. McGraw-Hill Book Co., New York, 1927.

HUXLEY, A. F. Muscle Structure and Theories of Contraction. Progr. biophysics, 1957, **7**, 255.

Electromyography

BASIS OF ELECTROMYOGRAPHY

The structural basis of electromyography is the *motor unit*. In normal skeletal muscles, fibers probably never contract as isolated individuals. Instead, small groups of them contract at almost the same moment, all members of this group being supplied by branches of the axon of one spinal motor neuron, as postulated originally by Sherrington and his students. The spinal motor neuron, its axon, and all the muscle fibers it supplied are called a motor unit (fig. 21.13).

The muscle fibers of a motor unit normally contract sharply upon the arrival of an impulse. Such impulses arrive at frequencies said to range

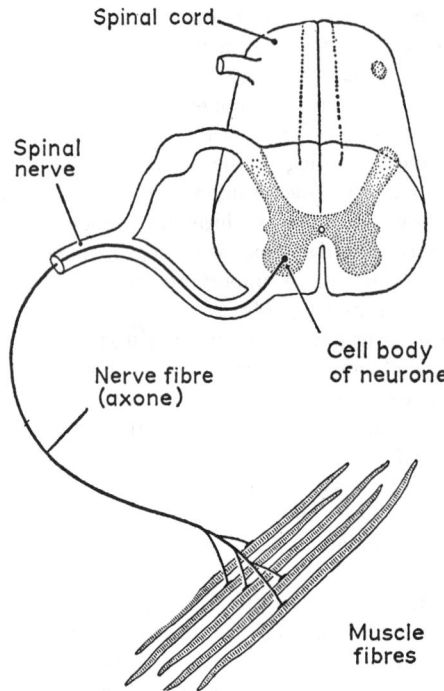

Spinal cord

Spinal nerve

Nerve fibre (axone)

Cell body of neurone

Muscle fibres

FIG. 21.13. Diagram of a motor unit

up to 50 per sec. (Adrian and Bronk). This frequency seems to be the upper physiological limit for axonal propagation of motor neurons in most mammals including man. However, motor units may be deliberately fired at much slower frequencies, even to as low as single isolated contractions at will (Basmajian, '63). Normal human beings can learn easily to provide various frequencies of impulses from their spinal motor neurons, usually below 16 per sec., before impulses appear on neighboring units to confuse the picture. Above the threshold at which this happens—the threshold varying from about 9 to 15 impulses per sec. and often as high as 25 per sec.—there is a further increase in frequencies (Basmajian et al.). Indeed, these might approach the classical figure of 50 per sec.

The number of striated muscle fibers that are served by one axon, i.e., the number in a motor unit, varies widely. Generally, muscles controlling fine movements and adjustments (such as those attached to the ossicles of the ear and of the eyeball, larynx and pharynx) have the smallest number of muscle fibers per motor unit (for details see Basmajian, '62). The muscles that move the eye have less than 10 fibers per unit; the muscles of the middle ear, 10 to 125; the laryngeal muscles 2 to 3; and the pharyngeal muscles have 2 to 6. These are all rather small

and delicate and they control fine or delicate movements. On the other hand, large, coarse-acting muscles have motor units with many muscle fibers, e.g., the human gastrocnemius has 2000 or more.

Even the largest bundles of muscle fibers are quite small, and so a strong contraction of a skeletal muscle requires the contraction of many motor units. Further, there is a complete asynchrony of the motor unit contractions imposed by asynchronous volleys of impulses coming down the many axons. Thus, with motor units contracting and relaxing with twitch-like actions at differing rates, a smooth pull results. (In certain disturbances the contractions become synchronized, resulting in a visible tremor.)

The fibers in a motor unit of the rabbit's sartorius may be scattered and intermingled with fibers of other units (van Harreveld). Thus, the individual muscle bundles seen in routine histology do not correspond to individual motor units as such. In rat muscle, the fibers of a motor unit are widely scattered (Norris and Irwin). In man, a similar condition is probable; Buchthal et al. have found that the spike potentials of each motor unit in biceps brachii are localized to an approximately circular region, with an average diameter of 5 mm. to which the fibers of the unit are confined. However, the potentials can be traced in their spread to over 20 mm. distance. The area of 5 mm. includes many overlapping motor units (Buchthal).

MOTOR UNIT POTENTIAL

During the normal twitch of a muscle fiber, a minute electrical potential is generated, which is dissipated into the surrounding tissues. The duration of the action potential accompanying this twitch is about 1 to 2 msec., or even 4 msec. Since all the muscle fibers of a motor unit do not contract at exactly the same time—some being delayed for several milliseconds—the electrical potential developed by the single twitch of all the fibers in the motor unit is prolonged. The electrical result of the motor-unit twitch, then, is an electrical discharge lasting about 5 to 8 msec. (and often as long as 12 msec.). The majority of these motor-unit potentials have an amplitude of around 0.5 mv. When displayed on a cathode-ray oscilloscope or other display device, the result is a sharp spike that is most often biphasic (fig. 21.14) but it may also have a more complex form, depending on physical and other factors.

Generally, the larger the motor-unit potential

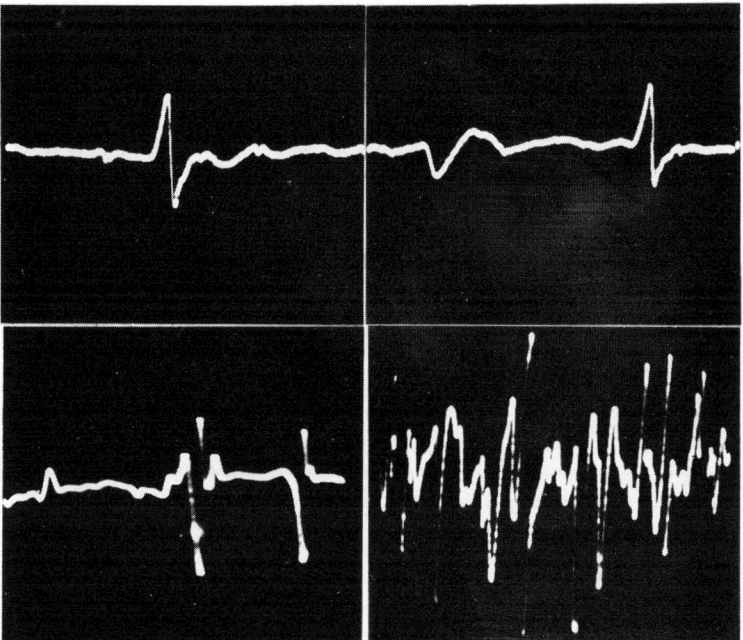

Fig. 21.14. Sample normal electromyograms. The single potential in the upper left corner has a measured amplitude of 0.8 mv and duration of 7 msec.

registered, the larger is the motor unit producing it. However, complicating factors, such as distance of the unit from the electrodes, the types of electrodes and equipment used, etc., enter into the final size of individual motor units recorded. For further details, the reader should consult the papers of Buchthal and of Hakansson.

Petersén and Kugelberg have shown that the electrode type affects the recorded duration and amplitude of the action potentials. They demonstrated characteristic variations, e.g., the smallness of potentials in facial muscles as compared with those in muscles of the extremity. Furthermore, they (and others) have found a slight prolongation with advancing age.

Under normal conditions, the smaller potentials appear first with a slight contraction. As the force is increased, larger and larger potentials are recruited, this being known as the normal pattern of recruitment. It is absent in cases of partial lower motor neuron paralysis; i.e., the small potentials never appear, apparently because only the larger motor units have survived. Using microelectrodes, Norris and Gasteiger have shown that action potentials tend to increase in amplitude with excitation and tension during isometric contractions of normal muscles.

Electromyographic Technique

The types and construction of electrodes used in electromyography vary widely. The two main types of electrodes used for the study of muscle dynamics are surface (or "skin") electrodes and inserted (usually wire or needle) electrodes (described in detail in Basmajian, '62).

Basically, an electromyograph is a high-gain amplifier with a preference or selectivity for frequencies in the range from about 10 to several thousand cps. Hayes suggests that the sharply-peaked spectra of motor-unit potentials derived with surface electrodes make the use of amplifiers with limited frequency-response quite practical. He finds several advantages in rejecting frequencies below 20 cps and above 200 cps. Then, amplifier "noise," general non-muscular "tissue noise" (which he found to be even more disturbing), and movement artifact are largely eliminated without significant loss of motor unit potentials. He suggests an upper limit of 200 cps as satisfactory but admits that a somewhat higher frequency response might be desirable. In general, 1000 cps as the upper limit of the band width is excellent.

REFERENCES

Adrian, E. D. and Bronk, D. W. J. Physiol., 1929, **67**, 119.

Basmajian, J. V. Muscles alive: their functions revealed by electromyography. Williams & Wilkins Co., Baltimore, 1962.

Basmajian, J. V. Science, 1963, 141, 440.

Basmajian, J. V., Baeza, M., and Fabrigar, C. J. New Drugs, 1965, **5**, 78.

BUCHTHAL, F. Am. J. Phys. Med., 1959, **38**, 125.

BUCHTHAL, F., GULD, C., AND ROSENFALCK, P. Acta physiol. scand., 1957, **39**, 83.

ECCLES, J. C. AND SHERRINGTON, C. S. Proc. Roy. Soc., 1930, **106B**, 326.

HAKANSSON, C. H. Acta physiol. scand., 1956, **37**, 14.

HAKANSSON, C. H. Acta physiol. scand., 1957, **39**, 291.

HAYES, K. J. J. Appl. Physiol., 1960, **15**, 749.

NORRIS, F. H., JR. AND GASTEIGER, E. L. E.E.G. & Clin. Neurophysiol., 1955, **7**, 115.

NORRIS, F. H., JR. AND IRWIN, R. L. Am. J. Physiol., 1961, **200**, 944.

PETERSÉN, I. AND KUGELBERG, E. J. Neurol. Neurosurg. & Psychiat., 1949, **12**, 124.

VAN HARREVELD, A. Am. J. Physiol., 1947, **151**, 96.

VAN HARREVELD, A. Arch. néerl. physiol., 1946, **28**, 408.

Gross Organization and Function of Whole Skeletal Muscles

Approximately 434 skeletal muscles, composed of some 250 million muscle fibers, account for 40 to 45% of the human body weight. A muscle is composed of two main elements, the muscle fibers and connective tissue. The muscle fibers are multinucleated giant cells which are cross-striated under the light microscope. A discussion of their light- and electron-microscopic structure will be presented elsewhere in this chapter.

The muscle fibers are enmeshed in collagenous and reticular connective tissue. At the ends of the elongated muscle fibers the connective tissue forms a common bundle of fibers called tendons. The connective tissue surrounding individual muscle fibers is called the endomysium. Groups of muscle fibers, collected into bundles or fascicles, are bound together by a more dense layer of collagenous and elastic fibers called the perimysium. Finally, the collagenous tissue which binds the fascicles into definitive muscles is called the epimysium. The connective tissues of all these three layers are actually in continuity with each other. In addition to the muscle fibers and connective tissue, muscles have a nerve and blood supply. The innervation will be considered briefly in this chapter and in ch. 6, 46. The blood supply is treated in ch. 46.

The arrangement of the muscle fibers in a muscle is variable (see fig. 21.15) and has been classified as follows:

1. Muscle fibers parallel to the long axis of the muscle (e.g., the strap-like sartorius, the pectineus, and the fusiform biceps brachii and flexor carpi radialis).

2. Muscle fibers oblique to the long axis of the muscle. Muscles whose fibers are arranged so that

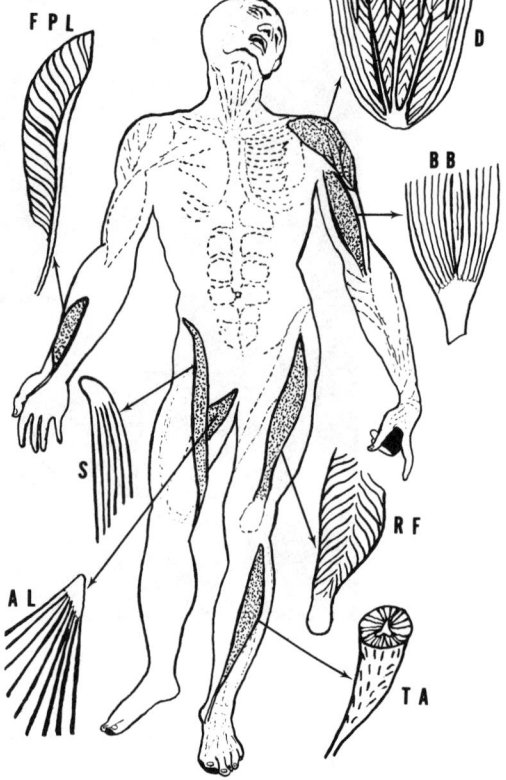

FIG. 21.15. The form and distribution of several varieties of striated skeletal muscle. The pennate, flexor pollicis longus (FPL); multipennate, deltoid (D); fusiform, biceps brachii (BB); bipennate, rectus femoris (RF); circumpennate, tibialis anterior (TA); radial, adductor longus (AL); and strap-like sartorius (S).

The male figure redrawn from the First Muscle Tabula in *Fabrica* by Vesalius.

they insert obliquely into a tendon include several varieties. Because of their resemblance to feathers, with barbs inserted obliquely into the shaft, they are described in these terms: (a) unipennate (e.g., flexor pollicis longus), (b) bipennate (e.g., rectus femoris, (c) circumpennate (e.g., tibialis anterior), and (d) multipennate (e.g., deltoid).

3. Muscle fibers arranged in a radial or triangular shape (e.g., adductor longus, pectoralis minor).

Muscles whose component fibers are in parallel array are able to shorten over greater distances than those muscles whose fibers are organized in the pennate manner. The penniform arrangement of muscle fibers is associated with those muscles which exert great force rapidly over a short distance.

In order for muscles to perform their function

they are attached, for the most part, from one bone across a joint or joints to another bone by *tendons* or flattened sheets of connective tissue called *aponeuroses*. The tendons and aponeuroses are formed of collagen, which is flexible but practically inextensible.

The points of muscular attachment are called the *origin* and the *insertion*. The origin of a muscle is usually the fixed or proximal attachment, while the insertion is the distal attachment to the bone which is moved. There are exceptions and in many cases the terms are used as a matter of convention by anatomists. For a detailed account of origins and insertions and of the action of specific muscles a textbook of anatomy should be consulted.

Muscles are normally activated through their nerve supply to produce tension with shortening (i.e., isotonic contractions) or tension without shortening (i.e., isometric contractions). The force developed by an uncontrolled maximal contraction of a whole muscle is of little practical use in the movements of man and animal. Therefore, the force and movement generated by a whole muscle is fractionated into smaller units which vary in size and in strength. Such a unit is called a motor unit. A *motor unit* is composed of a single nerve fiber together with the muscle fibers which are activated by it. For fine control of movement one or more motor units are employed. As more force is required the number of stimuli carried by each motor unit nerve is increased, along with the recruitment of additional motor units. The grading of muscular activity is the result, therefore, of *asynchronous* firing of the motor units of a whole muscle.

In considering the function of muscles in man, it should be noted that no muscle acts alone even in the simplest movement, i.e., a variety of muscles which are described as *synergists* and *antagonists* are involved in each action. The synergists are muscles which act together to produce a movement which no muscle could produce alone. An example of synergistic function can be seen in the adduction of the hand at the wrist. The flexor carpi ulnaris will both flex and adduct the hand. To produce adduction alone, the *extensor* carpi ulnaris must be brought into action to offset flexion and yet permit adduction of the hand by the *flexor* carpi ulnaris. Antagonists, on the other hand, are muscles with opposed function. For example, the biceps brachii and triceps brachii are mutually antagonistic with respect to movement at the elbow joint. The muscle which produces the movement is termed the *agonist* while the muscle which opposes the movement is termed the *antagonist*. The antagonist is usually reflexly inhibited when the agonist is brought into action. This can be demonstrated as follows. If one holds a weight on the palm of the hand with the elbow flexed perpendicular to the body, the biceps brachii (in this case the agonist) develops tension while the triceps brachii (the antagonist) is flaccid. This action can be reversed, with the triceps contracted and the biceps relaxed when the hand presses down onto a table with the arms flexed. When, however, the arm is extended and the elbow joint is fixed, both the biceps and the triceps are contracted. Muscle reflexes are discussed in detail in ch. 4 and 5.

Not all striated muscles are associated with the movement of skeletal parts at joints or with the fixation or maintenance of joint stability as related to posture. Muscles serve as sphincters when they encircle an orifice (e.g., eyelid, lips, and anus). In a tubular arrangement, striated muscle is found in the upper two-thirds of the esophagus and aids in the swallowing mechanism. The diaphragm is a thin muscular sheet which upon contraction serves to enlarge the thorax and compress the abdomen during inspiration. This action is reversed during expiration when the muscle relaxes. In addition, there are certain cutaneous muscles which have at least one of their attachments to the skin, e.g., the mimetic facial muscles and the panniculus carnosus of the trunk.

It has been recognized for many years that muscles vary in color, not only from species to species but also within the same animal. Striking examples of this are the crimson red pectoralis of the pigeon as contrasted with the stark white chicken pectoralis and the red soleus lying near the white gastrocnemius in the lower limb of animals and man. In birds (falcon, goose, and chicken), it has been shown that the amount of red pigmentation in the pectoralis muscle can be correlated directly with the capacity for sustained flight. Furthermore, it was shown experimentally that it takes fewer stimuli per second to produce a smooth, sustained, maximal contraction (tetanus) in the red muscles than in the white muscles. A generalization derived from many investigations indicates that all slow contracting muscles have red pigmentation, but not all red muscles are slow contracting (e.g., the soleus is a red, slow contracting muscle, while the red masseter is a faster contracting muscle).

In more quantitative terms, whole muscles

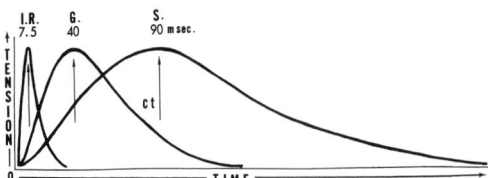

Fig. 21.16. Illustration of the isometric contraction-relaxation (twitch) curves for three mammalian skeletal muscles. The lateral rectus (L.R.), gastrocnemius (G), and soleus (S) represent the extremes (fast and slow) and mid-range in a spectrum of contraction-relaxation times for mammalian muscles. The arrows indicate peak tension development which corresponds to the contraction time for each muscle (lateral rectus, 7.5 msec.; gastrocnemius, 40 msec.; and soleus, 90 msec.).

provide a spectrum of speeds of contraction and relaxation (fig. 21.16). From the diagram it can be seen that the contraction time of an extraocular muscle (7.5 msec. at 37° C.) is 5 times faster than that of the gastrocnemius muscle (40 msec.) and 12 times faster than that of the soleus muscle (90 msec.). The extraocular muscles and the soleus represent the fast and slow extremes in most mammals. It is important to remember that *whole muscles* are not normally activated synchronously to yield the maximal twitch response of the kind recorded in fig. 21.16. Furthermore, the twitch response of isolated whole muscles does not reveal the heterogeneous nature of the tissue either in functional or structural terms.

Correlated Structure and Function of Skeletal Muscle Fibers

Microscopic examination of histologic sections of muscle reveals variability in cross-sectional diameter, internal structure, and certain histochemical responses of the muscle fibers. An examination of the structural-functional components of the gastrocnemius illustrates this heterogeneity vividly. The white gastrocnemius muscle of the cat is in the mid-range of muscle speed (contraction time is about 40 msec. and contraction-relaxation time about 160 msec.). The contraction time of the motor units which comprise the gastrocnemius vary from 17.8 to 129 msec. with a distribution peak between 30 and 40 msec. The peak distribution corresponds to the contraction time for the twitch of the isolated whole muscle. In addition, not all motor units produced a twitch response. However, these motor units *did* develop tension when given multiple (tetanic) stimulation.

In general, large motor units have a higher

threshold, contract more rapidly, and develop a greater degree of tension than the smaller motor units.

Histochemical and electron microscopic studies reveal that the gastrocnemius is composed of three distinct types of muscle fibers. About 50 to 55% of the muscle fibers and 70% of the cross-sectional area is composed of fibers which are large and contain few mitochondria, as demonstrated by histochemical localization of succinic dehydrogenase and adenosinetriphosphatase activity. About 30% of the muscle is composed of smaller dark cells with a greater density of mitochondria. The remaining 14 to 20% is composed of the smallest dark fibers with densely packed mitochondria. The large fibers are the classical white, fast twitch fibers, while the smaller dark fibers are two types of red, slow contracting fibers. The soleus muscle of the cat (but not those of the rabbit and rat) is composed entirely of the same intermediate dark fibers found to comprise 30% of the gastrocnemius. Therefore, these fibers can be classified as slow *twitch* muscle fibers. The smallest dark fibers in the gastrocnemius may be *slow* muscle fibers, judging from the physiological characteristics of some of the motor units.

Although the cat soleus muscle appears to be structurally homogeneous, its motor unit contraction time varies from 50 to 193 msec. The peak distribution of motor units has a contraction time of 80 to 90 msec., which corresponds to the contraction of the twitch of an isolated whole muscle. Approximately 90% of the soleus motor units develop 70% of their maximal tension at low frequency stimulation, i.e., 20 per sec. Some units develop a large fraction of their contractile power at 5 to 10 stimuli per sec. The soleus can maintain tone or tension as required by slow, low frequency firing of its various motor units. Experimental evidence also indicates that there is an overlap in contraction times (from 50 to 129 msec.) between the slower motor units of the gastrocnemius and the faster motor units of the soleus muscle.

Even the fast contracting extraocular muscles from the cat are composed of three morphologically distinct muscle fibers. The isolated muscle produces both twitch-type contraction from single shocks and the slow, graded non-twitch development elicited only by multiple stimulation. The structural and physiological properties of these muscles are, therefore, basically similar to those seen in the slower gastrocnemius.

THE INNERVATION AND SUBMICROSCOPIC ORGANIZATION OF TWITCH AND SLOW MUSCLE FIBERS

The *twitch* muscle fibers can be characterized physiologically by their ability to produce (on nerve stimulation) a propagated action potential and fast shortening or tension development. Within this group many differences exist in color, contractile behavior, rates of conduction and contraction time. The *slow* fibers, however, differ fundamentally from the *twitch* fibers because they do not produce propagated action potentials nor do they demonstrate fast shortening or tension development. Only repeated stimulation results in a significant rise in tension by these *slow* muscle fibers. In addition, the innervation of *slow* muscle fibers is by numerous nerve endings (the en-grappe type), distributed widely over the whole fiber length, whereas the innervation of *twitch* fibers is by a single discrete, localized nerve ending. The numerous areas of nerve contact which *locally* activate the contractile apparatus of the fiber compensate for the inability of a *slow* fiber to produce propagated muscle impulses.

Although the *slow* muscle fiber system is widely found, it has been studied in greatest detail in the frog. In this animal, reflex activation of the *slow* muscle fiber system develops tension in a manner similar to direct multiple (20/sec.) nerve stimulation of most of the small nerve fibers serving an entire muscle. The motor units of the *slow* fiber system may be normally activated, therefore, by a synchronous high frequency discharge from the spinal cord. In the frog, the nerve fibers to the *slow* muscle fibers are small and slow conducting (2–8 m./sec.), while the nerve fibers to the *twitch* fibers are large and fast conducting (8–40 m./sec.). No overlap of innervation between the two muscle groups has been found. The *slow* muscle fibers are reflexly activated even during periods when the *twitch* fibers are at rest. The *slow* fibers can also be activated during *twitch* fiber activity and can maintain over very long periods, by virtue of low frequency stimulation, large tensions originally produced by the *twitch* fibers. A functionally useful synergism has been demonstrated by the *twitch* and *slow* fibers in the frog iliofibularis muscle. First, small nerve stimulation at 30/sec. results in a smooth rise in tension. If a burst of twitch activity is added, via the large nerve system, the final tension developed exceeds that which would have been developed without the twitch activity. Secondly, when stimulation ceases there is a very gradual relaxation of the generated tension. If a burst of twitch activity is initiated during the slow relaxation phase, the residual tension in the *slow* fibers collapses rapidly.

The ultramicroscopic structure of muscle is given in detail elsewhere in this chapter. The discussion here will be concerned only with specific differences and similarities which have been shown in the fine structure of *slow* and *twitch* fibers. In both types of muscle fibers, the myofilaments of the myofibrils are of the same length even though sarcomere lengths may differ. The *slow* fibers have no discrete M lines, the H zones are poorly defined, and the Z lines are thick. Although the myofibrils tend to be large and vaguely defined in cross-section, this cannot be considered as a sole criterion for *slow* fibers.

A striking difference between *twitch* and *slow* fibers is the absence or poor development of the transverse tubular or T-system in the *slow* fiber. This internal tubular network is actually in continuity with the sarcolemma and is a striking cytological feature of *twitch* fibers. The T-system is believed to be the pathway by which the contractile apparatus is activated, although the exact mechanism is uncertain. In those *slow* fibers with a T-system, the small delicate tubules have no specific localization with respect to the sarcolemma or the contractile apparatus. Thus, local contractions are not confined to specific areas of the myofibril. The smallest contractile unit of many *twitch* fibers is that specific *area of the myofibril between two adjacent M lines* or midpoint of the A band, the T-system being located at the Z line. In other *twitch* fibers, the smallest contractile unit is the *half sarcomere*. In this case, the T-system is found at the level of the A band-I band junction (see fig. 21.17).

The motor nerve endings on *slow* muscle fibers, as revealed by electron microscopic studies, are readily distinguishable from those of *twitch* muscle fibers. The specific region of nerve-muscle contact is small compared with that on *twitch* fibers. In addition, there are no junctional folds in the muscle membrane or sarcolemma in the region of the nerve ending. Such junctional folds are a constant feature of the motor end-plate in *twitch* fibers.

DIFFERENTIATION OF FAST AND SLOW TWITCH MUSCLES

The growth and development of muscles with different contraction times has been given some

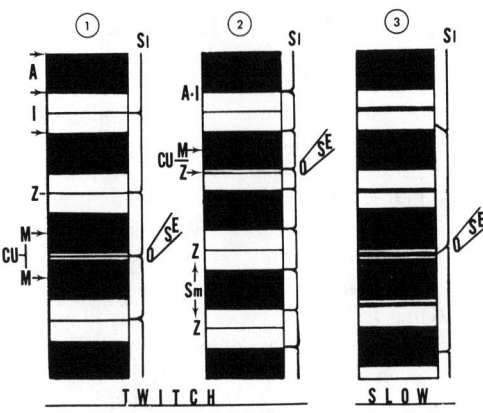

Fig. 21.17. Local excitation of twitch and slow muscle fibers.

The response to local, subthreshold stimulation (SE) delivered to the sarcolemma (Sl) is specific and discrete in twitch fibers. In twitch fiber 1, a localized contraction can be elicited in the region of the Z line. This is the precise localization of the transverse, sarcotubules or T-system in this fiber. The smallest *contractile unit* (CU), therefore, is that area of the myofibril between two adjacent M lines (M). A, A band; I, I band; Z, Z line.

In fiber 2, the local response is found at the level of the A band-I band junction (A.I.). The T-system in this fiber is at the A band-I band junction. The *contractile unit* (CU) is thus a half sarcomere or that area of the myofibril between adjacent Z and M lines. The sarcomere (SM) includes one A band and two half I bands.

Fiber 3 represents a slow muscle fiber. Stimulation of this fiber results in a variable or diffuse response. No portion of the fiber is selectively excitable. The T-system when found in slow fibers has a meandering course.

attention. In general, all muscles in newborn animals are equally slow. It takes about six weeks (in cats) for the fast *twitch* fibers to attain their adult speed. The more slowly contracting muscles, such as the soleus and crureus, pass through a short period during which their contraction times quicken, but this is followed by a progressive slowing until the adult condition appears in about 20 weeks. It can be shown that the differentiation of the slow contraction time can be abolished if the cord is transected or if the lumbosacral spinal cord is isolated from incoming stimuli. In this case, the muscles do not become slow; but after a few weeks the soleus and crureus become almost as fast as normal fast muscles (e.g., gastrocnemius). In adult rabbits, a similar transformation in the soleus will occur if the tendinous insertion of the muscle is cut (tenotomy). Electromyographic studies show that the soleus is normally continuously activated. Upon tenotomy, the continuous activity ceases even with intact motor innervation. It can be concluded that motor impulse activity plays a

fundamental role in determining the speed of contraction in mammalian skeletal muscle, although the exact mechanism is not known.

Following tenotomy, the red, slow contracting soleus is transformed into a white, fast contracting muscle. Not only have the mechanical properties of the soleus been changed, but the red color has disappeared. The red color of muscle is due to myoglobin which is related to the hemoglobin of red blood cells. Myoglobin from skeletal muscles has a molecular weight of 16,700 and contains one heme (iron-porphyrin complex) per molecule. The hemoglobin of the blood is composed of four hemes per molecule and differs also in the protein globin. Myoglobin has a greater affinity for oxygen than does blood hemoglobin, and serves as an oxygen reservoir within the muscle fiber. In addition to its high affinity for oxygen, myoglobin loads and unloads its oxygen with great speed. Myoglobin is probably synthesized within the muscle fiber much as hemoglobin is synthesized within the red blood cell.

Red muscle fibers undergo rhythmic activity and constant adjustments to postural change, and operate during periods of prolonged oxygen stress as demonstrated by the diving mammals. White muscle fibers undergo only short bursts of activity and possess little if any myoglobin. It should be recalled that most muscles, however, are a mixture of both red and white fibers. Nature has devised a mechanism whereby the nervous system employs tonic and phasic contractions which combine to provide an exquisite range of functional activity about which there is still much to learn.

REFERENCES

BULLER, A. J., ECCLES, J. C., AND ECCLES, R. M. Differentiation of fast and slow muscles in the cat hind limb. J. Physiol., 1960, **150,** 399–416.

COOPER, S. AND ECCLES, J. C. The isometric responses of mammalian muscles. J. Physiol., 1930, **69,** 377–385.

GRANT, J. C. B. AND BASMAJIAN, J. V. Grant's method of anatomy, 7th ed. Williams & Wilkins Co., Baltimore, 1965.

HENNEMAN, E. AND OLSON, C. B. Relations between structure and function in the design of skeletal muscles. J. Neurophysiol., 1965, **28,** 581–598.

HESS, A. The sarcoplasmic reticulum, the T-system, and the motor terminals of slow and twitch muscle fibers in the garter snake. J. Cell Biol., 1965, **26,** 467–476.

HESS, A. AND PILAR, G. Slow fibers in the extraocular muscles of the cat. J. Physiol., 1963, **169,** 780–798.

HUXLEY, A. F. AND STRAUB, R. W. Local activation and interfibrillar structures in striated muscle. J. Physiol., 1958, **143**, 40p.

Huxley, A. F. and Taylor, R. E. Local activation of striated muscle fibers. J. Physiol., 1958, **144**, 426–441.

Kuffler, S. W. and Vaughan-Williams, E. M. Properties of the slow skeletal muscle fibers of the frog. J. Physiol., 1953, **121**, 318–340.

Kuffler, S. W. and Vaughan-Williams, E. M. Small-nerve junctional potentials. The distribution of small motor nerves to frog skeletal muscle, and the membrane characteristics of the fibers they innervate. J. Physiol., 1953, **121**, 289–317.

McPhedran, A. M., Wuerker, R. B., and Henneman, E. Properties of motor units in a homogeneous red muscle (soleus) of the cat. J. Neurophysiol., 1965, **28**, 71–84.

Page, S. A comparison of the fine structures of frog slow and twitch muscle fibers. J. Cell Biol., 1965, **26**, 477–497.

Peachey, L. D. and Huxley, A. F. Local activation and structure of slow striated muscle fibers of the frog. Fed. Proc., 1960, **19**, 257.

Romer, A. S., The muscular system, ch. 9, *in* The Vertebrate Body, 3rd ed. Saunders, Philadelphia, Pa. 1962.

Stein, J. M. and Padykula, H. A. Histochemical classification of individual skeletal muscle fibers of the rat. Amer. J. Anat., 1962, **110**, 103–124.

Wuerker, R. B., McPhedran, A. M., and Henneman, E. Properties of motor units in a heterogeneous pale muscle (M. Gastrocnemius) of the cat. J. Neurophysiol., 1965, **28**, 85–99.

Vrbova, G. The effect of motoneurone activity on the speed of contraction of striated muscle. J. Physiol., 1963, **169**, 513–526.

IV

THE BLOOD AND LYMPH

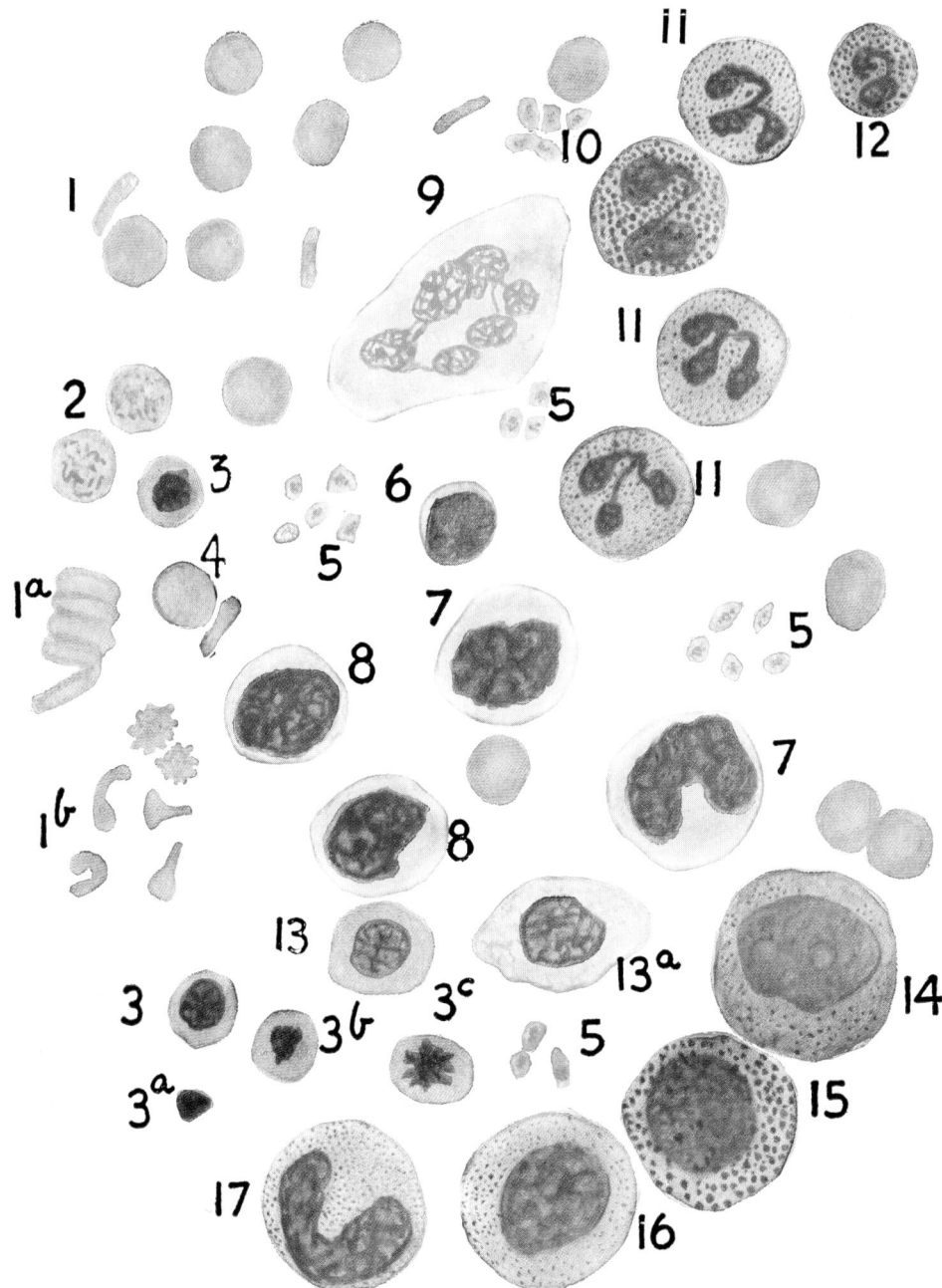

NORMAL BLOOD AND MARROW CELLS

1	Erythrocytes	7	Monocytes
1ᵃ	Erythrocytes in rouleau	8	Large lymphocytes
1ᵇ	Deformed cells (poikilocytes) crenated forms	9	Megakaryocyte
2	Reticulocytes stained with dilute solution of cresyl	10	Eosinophil leucocyte
	blue	11	Neutrophil leucocytes
3	Early normoblasts	12	Basophil leucocyte
3ᵃ	Extruded nucleus	13	Polychromatophil erythroblast
3ᵇ	Late normoblast	13ᵃ	Hemocytoblast
3ᶜ	Normoblast in mitosis	14	Megaloblast
5	Platelets	15	Eosinophil myelocyte
6	Small lymphocyte	16	Neutrophil myelocyte
		17	Neutrophil metamyelocyte

CHAPTER 22

The Physiological Properties, Physical Characters and Composition of the Blood

Outline of the Functions of Blood

In animals whose bodies are composed of many cells (Metazoa) the blood serves those purposes, which for unicellular organisms (Protozoa) are carried out by the fluid medium, the salt or fresh water, which surrounds them and bathes their surfaces. For example, an organism such as the amoeba acquires oxygen by diffusion directly from the environment into the interior of the cell. Similarly the carbon dioxide diffuses outwards. The processes of nutrition and the excretion of the products of the cell's metabolism are accomplished in a manner equally simple. Food is taken in through the cell membrane either in solution or as particulate matter, and waste products pass into the surrounding medium. Other requirements of this organism, such as the maintenance of an optimum temperature and the proper degree of moisture, are dependent on the immediate (internal) environment, the *milieu intérieur* of Claude Bernard.

The elemental needs of each cell in a multicellular individual from the most primitive type to the highest vertebrate are the same as for the unicellular organism; yet in the evolution of the higher forms the cells composing their bodies have become farther and farther removed from immediate contact with the outside world. Myriads of cells have become packed together, and the deeper ones could not possibly satisfy their needs after the direct and simple fashion of the unicellular forms. The more primitive multicellular types overcame the difficulty by the development of canal systems which opened to the exterior and through which the ocean waters flowed freely in and out, bringing oxygen and aliment to the more deeply lying cells and bearing carbon dioxide and other excretory products away. This, the first attempt at a circulation, was an open one. As higher forms evolved the circulation became closed and the waters of the environment no longer flowed and ebbed through the body. No longer could the interchange of the respiratory gases and the absorption of nutriment be carried out in this direct and simple way. Yet the vessels of this closed circulatory system were filled with a fluid which took the place of and fulfilled the duties of the watery environment of the more primitive types. The blood and other body fluids may be looked upon as that environment which has become enclosed within the bodies of the higher forms, and has undergone certain modifications in its composition to meet the requirements of the more specialized cells which it bathes.

The similarity between the composition of sea water and of blood which has been stressed by the researches of Macallum lends support to these views on the evolution of the blood.[1] This brief account will also serve as an introduction to a consideration of the functions of the body fluids, since their duties are to satisfy in the same way as did their prototype, the requirements of the individual cells.

1. Respiratory. The transport of oxygen from the air in the lungs to the tissues, and of carbon dioxide from the tissues to the lungs.

2. Nutritive. The conveyance of food materials, glucose, amino acids and fats from the alimentary canal to the tissues.

3. Excretory. The removal of waste products of metabolism, e.g., urea, uric acid, creatinine, etc.

4. The maintenance of the water content of the tissues. Though the blood itself is contained within vascular channels, a constant interchange of fluid through the vessel walls takes place. This fluid which has left the blood vessels and come into direct contact with the tissue cells is known as the tissue or interstitial fluid. It closely resembles the blood plasma in chemical composition, and is identical with lymph. Through the medium of the transuded fluid the final stage in the transportation of oxygen and food materials to the tissues and the first stage in the journey of CO_2 and waste products from the tissues are made.

5. To regulate body temperature. The body owes its ability to regulate its temperature (ch. 70) largely to the water of the blood and tissue fluids.

---

[1] Sea water of today differs from blood serum in having a total salt concentration of about 3 per cent, a much higher concentration of magnesium and a lower concentration of potassium. But Macallum points out that the sea water of the geological period when the ancestors of mammalian forms adapted themselves to a terrestrial life was probably closely similar in its inorganic composition to blood serum.

Water possesses three qualities which fit it pre-eminently to fulfil this purpose.

a. The specific heat[2] of water is considerably higher than that of any other liquid or solid. On account of this great heat storage power of water, sudden changes of body temperature are avoided and even a cold-blooded animal such as the frog has, due to this purely physical quality, some ability to maintain a relatively constant body temperature against transient fluctuations in environmental temperature. A man of average weight develops 3000 Calories in 24 hours. This amount of heat is capable of raising the temperature of his tissues (which are largely water) only about 32°C. Heat elimination (radiation, etc.) is able to keep pace with heat production and the body temperature varies but slightly within normal limits. But it has been pointed out by L. J. Henderson that if the tissues had the low heat storage capacity (spec. heat) of most substances, an amount of heat equal to 3000 Calories would raise the temperature of the tissues and fluids of the body by from 100° to 150°C.

b. High conductivity. The thermal conductivity of water is greater than that of any other ordinary liquid. The advantage of this in the dissipation of heat from deeply situated regions of the body is obvious.

c. High latent heat of evaporation. More heat is required for the vaporization of water than for that of an equivalent amount of any other liquid. One cubic centimeter of water requires about 0.6 Calories for its vaporization. This figure is 50 per cent higher than that of water's closest competitor. Fluid is being constantly lost from the body through evaporation from the lungs and skin. A large amount of heat is lost in the process.

The physical properties of water which make it ideal as a heat regulating medium are enhanced by other purely *physiological factors*. The mobility of the blood and the readiness with which it may be quickly redistributed in the body, combined with the unique physical properties of the fluid itself, render it highly efficient as a regulator of body temperature. The blood may in a moment be brought from deeper to superficial regions and spread out in fine vessels over a broad area just beneath the skin, thus greatly increasing the radiation of heat. At another instant, in order that heat may be conserved, the fluid may be diverted from the surface areas and collected in the deeper parts of the body—internal organs, muscles, etc.

6. Protective and regulatory. The blood and lymph contain certain substances of a complex nature, (antitoxins, lysins, and antibodies) which are part of the body's defense against injurious agents of various kinds. The circulating fluids are also the vehicle by which the hormones of the different ductless glands are brought into direct contact with the cells of the tissues.

The Composition of Blood

The blood is a highly complex fluid in which solid elements are suspended—the *corpuscles or blood cells.* Its specific gravity varies between individuals from 1.050 to 1.060 and its viscosity from 5 to 6 times that of water. If blood is centrifuged before it has had time to clot, or if clotting is prevented by special means (ch. 33), the solid elements are thrown down and separated from the fluid portion. The latter is called the *plasma* and contains *proteins*, as well as many organic and inorganic substances in solution—nutritive and excretory materials, antibodies and hormones, and other substances of an unknown or imperfectly known chemical constitution. The specific gravity of plasma is normally around 1.027 but varies with the concentration of protein. The cells constitute about 46 per cent by volume of human blood, the plasma 54 per cent. Small variations above or below these values are normally encountered.

The specific gravity of blood or plasma can be measured by a technique devised by Phillips and Van Slyke. This method depends on the fact that a drop of blood or plasma will hang suspended temporarily in a copper sulphate solution if that solution is of the same specific gravity. The technique is a gross one and rarely used.

In the following outline are given the constituents of the blood, grouped upon a physiological basis.

Whole blood:

  A. Cells:

    (1) Red corpuscles or erythrocytes
    (2) White corpuscles or leucocytes
    (3) Platelets or thrombocytes

  B. Plasma:

    (1) *Water*, 91 to 92 per cent
    (2) *Solids*, 7 to 9 per cent

      (a) *Proteins*, 7 per cent. Serum albumin, serum globulins and fibrinogen.[3]

      (b) *Inorganic constituents*, 0.9 per cent. Sodium, calcium, potassium, magnesium, phosphorus, iodine, iron, copper, etc.

      (c) *Organic constituents* (other than (a) and (d)). Nonprotein nitrogenous substances, (urea, uric acid, xanthine, hypoxanthine, creatine and creatinine,

---

[2] The specific heat of a substance is defined as the number of calories required to raise 1 gram of the substance 1°C.

[3] Plasma from which the fibrinogen has been removed through clotting (ch. 33) is spoken of as serum.

TABLE 22.1

Inorganic constituents of plasma, red cells and whole blood, milligrams per 100 cc. average values

	Sodium	Potassium	Calcium	Magnesium	Chlorine	Iodine	Iron	Copper	Phosphate	Sulfate	Total Base cc. N/10 NaOH
Plasma................	340	20	10	2.7	370		0.2				160
Cells.................	20	410	0	6.0	190		100.0				
Whole blood..........	190	220	5.2	4.0	250	0.01	50.0	0.1	3.0	2.0	

The concentrations of these various inorganic constituents are also commonly expressed as milliequivalents (m.eq.) per liter. Thus serum contains 100 mg. of calcium per liter. The molecular weight of Ca is 40.07. So being divalent its milliequivalent is 20.03. The concentration of calcium in serum is therefore $\frac{100}{20.03}$ = 4.9 milliequivalents per liter. Sodium is monovalent and has a molecular weight of 23; serum therefore contains $\frac{3400}{23}$ = 147.8 m.eq. per liter.

ammonia and amino acids) neutral fats, phospholipids, cholesterol, glucose.

(d) *Internal secretions, antibodies and various enzymes, (amylases, proteases, lipases, esterases, etc.)*

Inorganic Constituents

The concentration of the various inorganic materials in the plasma is given in table 22.1.

It will be noted that the plasma is relatively rich in sodium and calcium but poor in potassium and magnesium whereas in the cells conditions are reversed. The cells show a relatively high concentration of potassium and magnesium, but are lacking in calcium and have a low concentration of sodium (human). In the blood of some species sodium is absent or present only in traces. Except for a minute amount of iron in the plasma, this element is confined to the red cells and the greater part of it is attached to the hemoglobin molecule (ch. 27). It has been suggested that the small quantity of nonhemoglobin iron in the erythrocyte is bound loosely with the lecithin of the cell stroma (p. 480); (see also chapter 29).

Phosphorus

Phosphorus exists in blood in four main forms. Most of the phosphorous of the blood is present as organic esters in the red cells. The three major phosphorus fractions in *organic* combination are as follows:

1. Ester phosphorus, e.g., diphosphoglycerate, adenosinetriphosphate, hexose phosphates, glycerophosphate.

2. Lipid phosphorus, e.g., the phosphatieds lecithin, cephalin, sphingomyelin.

3. Nucleic acid phosphorus.

According to Kay the nucleic acid phosphorus in normal human blood is negligible. It is derived from the nuclei of white cells and the reticulum of the reticulocytes. In abnormal blood containing a large number of leucocytes, reticulocytes or nucleated red cells this fraction may however constitute a considerable proportion of the total phosphorus.

The *inorganic phosphorus* (3.8 mg. per 100 cc.) is according to most observers about equally distributed between cells and plasma. The quantity of organic phosphorus in blood is many times greater than the inorganic. In whole blood it amounts to from 35 to 40 mg. per 100 cc. and the greater proportion of this is in the cells. The serum contains about 10 mgm. of total phosphorous per 100 cc. of which 8–9 mgm. is lipid phosphorous.

The inorganic and ester fractions are extracted from blood by the precipitation of the proteins with trichloracetic acid and filtering. The phosphorus contained in the filtrate is spoken of as the acid soluble phosphorus. Upon extraction of blood with alcohol-ether the lipid phosphorus is obtained. The phosphorus of blood is therefore separable into two classes.

(1) *The acid soluble which includes*
    (a) Inorganic phosphorus
    (b) Ester phosphorus
(2) *Alcohol-ether soluble*, i.e., organic phospholipid phosphorus.   lipid phosphorus

The ester, or organic acid-soluble phosphorus is obtained by determing the total acid soluble P and subtracting from it the inorganic phosphorus. Of the ester phosphorus, all of which is intracellular, about one-quarter is hydrolyzable by bone phosphatase (ch. 77). The hydrolyzable portion is mainly adenosinetriphosphate, and the nonhydrolyzable part mainly diphosphoglycerate. Since the nucleic acid phosphorus is negligible in normal blood, the acid soluble + the alcohol-ether soluble phosphorus equals the total phosphorus as determined by wet-ashing.

In the following table is given the distribution of inorganic, ester and lipid phosphorus in normal blood.

Phosphorus in whole blood

Milligrams per 100 cc., average figures

1. Total phosphorus.......................... 40
2. Total acid soluble—90 per cent in cells.... 27
3. Inorganic—in cells and plasma............ 3[4]
4. Ester (2–3)—practically all in cells....... 24
5. Lipid (1–2)—in cells and plasma.......... 13

The phosphorus compounds of the blood and tissues play an important role in maintaining the electrolyte equilibrium within the red cells and in regulating the acid base balance. Diabetic acidosis, for example, and the acidosis induced by the ingestion of ammonium chloride, are accompanied by increased excretion of phosphorus in the urine and a pronounced reduction of the organic acid-soluble phosphorus in the blood cells. Reverse changes occur in alkalosis; the reduction in the chloride of the blood following pyloric obstruction, and the alkalosis caused by overbreathing are associated with a reduction in the urinary excretion of phosphates and a decrease in the inorganic and ester phosphorus of the blood. In renal insufficiency, the inorganic phosphorus in the plasma and cells and the ester phosphorus (diphosphoglycerate) in the cells are greatly increased. The inorganic and ester phosphorus are reduced in rickets but a rapid increase accompanies the healing process. The inorganic phosphorus is diminished after the injection of insulin and in hyperparathyroidism (ch. 77). In anemias associated with high reticulocyte counts in, polycythaemia and in leukemia, the concentration of ester phosphorus in the blood is increased because of the great increase in numbers of cells containing a high concentration of organic phosphorus. The inorganic phosphorus is increased in some forms of tetany.

Organic Constituents (Other than Organic Phosphorus)

Plasma Proteins

The concentration of total protein in the plasma and the proportions of the three fractions —*albumin, globulin* and *fibrinogen*—vary from species to species but under ordinary conditions of health remain relatively constant between individuals of the same species.

Serum proteins can be separated into two heterogeneous fractions—albumin and globulins —by precipitating the globulins with a solution

[4] In infants and young children, the inorganic phosphorus is from 1 to 3 mg. per cent higher than it is in adults.

of 22.2% sodium sulphate. The albumin remains in solution. This is the most commonly used clinical technique for the gross separation of serum proteins. Serum proteins differ from plasma proteins in that the fibrinogen has been removed.

Serum globulin also can be separated by "salting out" into two fractions—*euglobulin* and *pseudoglobulin*. The euglobulin is thrown out of solution by saturation with NaCl, half-saturation with $MgSO_4$, or one-third saturation with $(NH_4)_2SO_4$; it is insoluble in water. The pseudoglobulin is not "salted out" by NaCl but is thrown down by saturation of its solution with $MgSO_4$ or half-saturation with $(NH_4)_2SO_4$. It is soluble in water. These fractions now are of historical interest only. The technique of "salting-out" has been superseded by that of electrophoresis.

The electrophoretic separation of plasma proteins depends in part on the difference in electrical charge of the various proteins, and their consequent different rates of migration in an electrical field. This can take place in a Tiselius apparatus, on paper or cellulose acetate, or through a starch block.

By this technique, the plasma proteins can be separated into albumin, fibrinogen, and α-, β- and γ-globulins. The globulins can be further subdivided into α_1- and α_2- and β_1- and β_2-globulins—and by some investigators into γ_1 and γ_2 globulins. The α, β and γ-globulins have isoelectric points of 5.1, 5.6 and 6.0 pH, respectively. It should be emphasized that these fractions are not homogeneous, and contain proteins with the same mobility but different chemical composition and immunological characteristics.

Cohn's fractionation method can be used to separate various protein fractions utilizing the different solubilities of the proteins and the sensitivity of the solute to variations in ionic strength, in ethanol concentration and in metallic ions.

Ultracentrifugation separates protein fractions on the basis of differences in density. It has been of value in determining the average molecular weight of the proteins.

Immunoelectrophoresis has proven to be a valuable quantitative tool for special investigations, utilizing the patterns formed by precipitation at the site of local antigen-antibody formation.

The electrophoretic fractions of plasma protein are not chemically pure; all contain lipid and carbohydrate material combined probably as prosthetic groups. The albumin fraction also contains bilirubin (ch. 27). Approximately 75 per cent of the carbohydrate and all of the lipid, bound to protein, is found in the α- and β-globulin fractions. The role played by the lipoprotein complexes in atherosclerosis is discussed elsewhere in the book. Many other substances, e.g., calcium, phosphorus, sulfonamide drugs and the dye T-1824 (p. 488) are transported, bound to the albumin fraction (see fig. 22.1).

Fibrinogen has been isolated and prepared in crystalline form. X-ray diffraction studies indicate that its molecule is structurally similar to such fibrous proteins as collagen and myosin (see ch. 71). The molecular weights of the plasma proteins are given on p. 477.

The total plasma protein can be calculated from the specific gravity of the plasma by means of line charts, or by using the formula $P = K (S - A)$, where P is the plasma protein in grams per 100 cc., S the specific gravity and K and A are constants with values of 364 and 1.006, respectively. Thus, if the specific gravity is 1.026, the protein in grams per 100 cc. is $7.28 = 364 (1.026 - 1.006)$.

The values of total protein and of the different fractions in human plasma are given in the following table.

Protein fractions in human plasma

Fractionation by Electrophoresis grams/100 cc.	Fractionation by Salting out with Sodium Sulfate grams/100 cc.
Total protein . 6.03–6.72	Total protein . . . 6.0–8.0
Albumin 3.32–4.04	Albumin 4.3–5.0
Total globulin 2.23–2.39	Total globulin . . 1.1–3.1
α-globulin . . 0.79–0.84	Euglobulin . . . 0.1–0.4
β-globulin . . 0.78–0.81	Pseudoglob-
γ-globulin . . 0.66–0.70	ulin 1.0–2.7
Fibrinogen . . 0.34–0.43	Fibrinogen 0.2–0.3
	Albumin/glob-
	ulin (A/G)
	ratio 1.50

In some animals the globulin is equal to or exceeds the albumin. Of the three fractions fibrinogen is always in lowest concentration and is considerably lower in human plasma than in that of some animals (e.g., 0.58, 0.72, 0.60 gram per 100 cc. in dog, cow and goat respectively) (see fig. 22.1).

PATHOLOGICAL VARIATIONS IN PLASMA PROTEINS. The several protein fractions of plasma may change in value independently of one another, and either with or without alteration in the quantity of total protein. In several pathological states the albumin and globulin fractions may change in opposite directions, i.e., a fall in albumin accompanied by a rise in globulin.

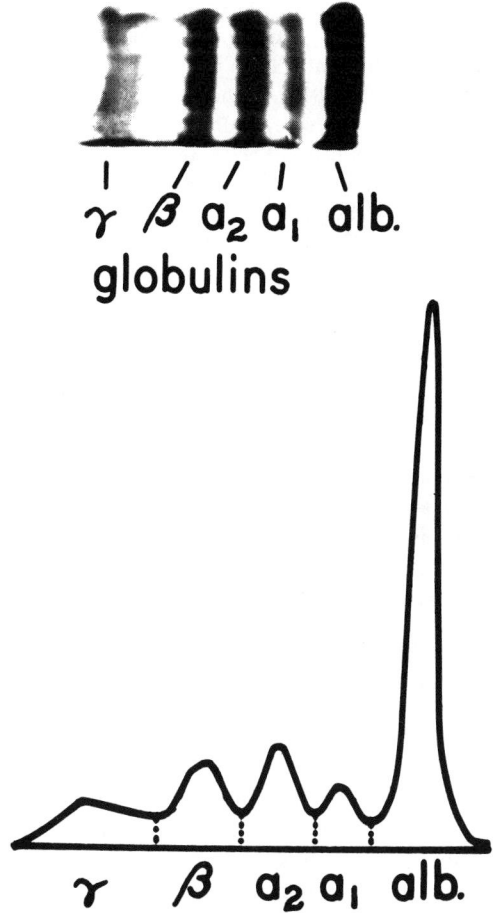

FIG. 22.1. Dyed electrophoretic and corresponding density pattern of human sera.

In *hemorrhage* a loss of all fractions of plasma protein occurs. Their concentrations are diminished as well, since the blood volume is restored initially by the passage of a solution of low protein concentration from the tissue spaces into the blood stream. In extensive *burns*, on the other hand, especially during the first few days, the total plasma protein content is reduced as a result of the leakage of blood and plasma from the denuded surface and into the tissues in the region of the burned area. Since the lost fluid is usually relatively low in its content of protein, the protein concentration of the plasma tends to be elevated.

In any condition associated with a loss of water from the blood (*dehydration, anhydremia,* p. 495), though no change may occur in the absolute amount, i.e., in the total quantity in the blood, the concentrations of all fractions will show an increase. In order to determine whether an *absolute* reduction or increase in one or other of the plasma proteins exists, it would be necessary to measure the total plasma volume (ch. 24) as well as the concentration of the particular fraction.

Reduction of serum albumin occurs in those diseases in which either protein synthesis is impaired or there is chronic protein deficiency. In acute and chronic infections, chronic hepatitis, cirrhosis of the liver and in exudative enteropathies, the serum albumin is lowered. It is low, too, in the nephrotic syndrome and nephritis, in which there is chronic protein loss via the kidney. In the latter two diseases, and in chronic malnutrition with hypoalbuminemia, there may be an associated decrease in plasma volume with an apparent increase in the concentration of plasma globulins. This takes place because of a decrease in plasma oncotic pressure, with loss of plasma fluid into the interstitial tissues.

Physiologically, low plasma albumin is found in pregnancy and the newborn. There is no known condition associated with a consistent increase in plasma albumin.

Plasma fibrinogen is made solely in the liver, but only rarely is decreased in chronic liver disease. Hypofibrinogenemia can occur as a rare congenital disease, or in certain diseases associated with the presence of fibrinolysins, e.g. carcinoma of the prostate. It can occur following pulmonary or cardiac surgery for a similar reason. The most dramatic example of hypofibrinogenemia is seen after certain cases of premature separation of the placenta with release of a thromboplastic agent which precipitates large amounts of fibrinogen, thus depleting the circulating level.

Fibrinogen may be increased in acute infections, malaria, tissue injury, parathyroid hormone overdose, and, physiologically, in pregnancy and menstruation.

The γ-globulin may show an absolute increase in *multiple myeloma, cirrhosis of the liver, subacute yellow atrophy of the liver, acute hepatitis* and *acute nephritis, systemic lupus erythematosis, chronic lymphatic leukemia tuberculosis, scarlet fever* and in *acute* and *chronic infections.* In liver disease the α-globulin is also increased, and in later pregnancy the concentration of β-globulin, which contains a high percentage of lipid, is raised. This fraction serves to bind a considerable proportion of the plasma cholesterol, carotene and phospholipids of the plasma, and is increased in the later months of pregnancy.

ORIGIN. In the *embryo*, the mesenchyme cells, through a process of secretion or by the actual solution of their substance, furnish the fluid (embryonic plasma) which floats the primitive blood cells (ch. 32). The albumin fraction is formed earlier than the other proteins which do not appear in the plasma of the chick embryo until after the 14th day of incubation.

In the *adult*, five possible sources of the plasma proteins have been suggested—namely, disintegrating blood cells (red or white), the general tissue cells, reticuloendothelial cells of spleen, bone marrow, etc., and the liver.

It is now well established that the liver is the site of the production of plasma albumin although there is some evidence that other cells take part in this synthesis as well. This fraction undergoes a pronounced reduction in conditions which depress hepatic function. It is thought that the Kupffer cells are especially concerned in the manufacture. The albumin fraction (but not the globulin) in the plasma of dogs can be reduced and maintained at a subnormal level by intravenous injections of a solution of gum acacia. In these experiments the hepatic cells become swollen and vacuolated. The fall in serum albumin is therefore considered to be due, in part at least, to the failure of the liver to make good the normal "wear and tear" of serum albumin (which amounts to several grams daily), though, possibly, there is also a withdrawal of albumin from the plasma to the liver as a compensatory response to rectify the increase in oncotic pressure caused by the presence of acacia in the circulation.

As mentioned previously, the liver is probably the sole site of fibrinogen production. Severe, extensive acute liver damage, or hepatectomy, produce a decrease in fibrinogen. If the liver recovers from such injury (e.g. by chloroform) the fibrinogen level also returns to normal. Following slight liver injury, or during repair of a hepatic lesion, which might be expected to stimulate the functional activity of the organ, the fibrinogen may be higher than normal.

The globulins can be subdivided, as noted above, into α, β, and γ-globulins. While the exact origin of some of the fractions is still in doubt, it is probable that all the reticuloendothelial cells take part in their production. Using C_{14}-labeled lysine, Miller and his associates perfused intact rat livers and demonstrated that 80 percent of total globulin production takes place in the liver. On the other hand, there is convincing evidence that the lymphocyte-plasma cell axis is the main source of γ-globulin, particularly that fraction concerned with the body's immune mechanism.

There is experimental evidence that the adrenocorticoptrophic hormone of the pituitary through its action on the adrenal cortex affects the manufacture of β- and γ-globulins. Injections of this hormone or of adrenal cortical hormones into rats causes within 24 hours a rise in β-globulin of 30 per cent, and in γ-globulin of from 70 to 80 per cent (White and Dougherty).

FUNCTIONS. 1. Fibrinogen is essential for the *clotting* of the blood (ch. 33).

2. All three proteins serve to maintain the *osmotic pressure* (p. 497) of the blood. The large molecules of the proteins do not pass readily through the normal capillary membrane. The osmotic pressure which they exert amounts to, in man, between 25 and 30 mm. Hg. The pressure which each fraction exerts is inversely related to the size of its molecule and directly related to its concentration in the plasma. The molecular weight of fibrinogen is over 200,000 and its concentration is low; it therefore contributes little toward the total osmotic pressure. Albumin is in the highest concentration and its molecule has the least weight (70,000–75,000). The osmotic pressure of the plasma, therefore, depends largely upon this fraction. The molecular weights of serum globulins vary from 150,000 to 1,000,000 and their total concentration is considerably less than that of albumin. In equivalent concentrations, serum albumin has an osmotic activity 2.4 times that of serum globulin (Keys); it furnishes about 80 per cent of the oncotic pressure of the plasma.

3. *Viscosity.* The proteins give a certain viscosity to the blood which is a factor in the maintenance of the normal blood pressure.

4. They aid in the regulation of the *acid-base balance* of the blood (ch. 34).

5. *Stability of the blood* (see p. 530). The globulin and fibrinogen fractions influence the tendency of the corpuscles to adhere to one another and form rouleaux or clumps.

6. *Trephones.* Carrel has shown that the leukocytes prepare substances from the plasma proteins which are essential for the nourishment of tissue cells grown in cultures. These substances he has termed trephones.

7. *Immune substances* (antibodies) which react with the antigens of several microorganisms, e.g., diphtheria, typhoid and streptococcal infections, and the viruses of mumps, influenza and measles, are associated with the γ-globulin. γ-Globulin, separated from the other fractions, is used as a means of artificially immunizing against measles, infectious hepatitis, rubella and poliomyelitis.[5]

[5] Gamma globulin obtained from any normal person usually contains sufficient immune bodies

Certain other antibodies, the isoagglutinins (anti-A, anti-B, and anti-Rh, ch. 5), are present in the γ- and β-fractions. As might be expected, the globulin fraction of the serum tends to increase during the process of immunization against the infective diseases mentioned above.

8. The α- and β-globulins contain many functionally important substances. Hormones, enzymes, and clotting factors are all part of this protein component.

9. The α_2 and β_1 globulins provide metal-binding proteins (transferrin, ceruloplasmin).

10. They serve as a *reserve of protein* upon which for a time the body draws during fasting or when the protein intake is inadequate.

Plasmapheresis. The importance of the plasma proteins is demonstrated by this procedure which consists in bleeding an animal and returning the red cells suspended in Locke's solution to the body. A state of shock results, followed by death when the total protein is reduced to between 1 and 2 per cent. No ill effects result however if the cells are suspended in serum before they are reintroduced. When depletion of the proteins is not carried to the point where fatal shock ensues, a marked rise in protein concentration occurs within 15 minutes which indicates that during this time a store of preformed protein is drawn upon for the replacement of the protein which has been removed. The regeneration is slower after this, though fairly rapid for the first 24 hours. It becomes progressively slower during succeeding days. The proteins are restored to the normal level in from 2 to 7 days, provided that the diet contains a sufficiency of high quality protein. Plasma proteins themselves have been found to be best for this purpose; the proteins of liver run a close second.

In more chronic plasmapheresis experiments, edema commences when the total protein concentration reaches a value of 5.5 per cent and albumin a concentration of 2.5 per cent.

The Nonprotein Nitrogen (N.P.N.) or Noncoagulable Nitrogen of Blood

By the term nonprotein nitrogen is meant the nitrogen of those substances, e.g., urea, uric acid, creatinine, etc., listed on page 478. They may be extracted from blood or plasma by treating either of these with a reagent, such as trichloracetic acid, which precipitates the proteins, filtering and de-

for protection against measles and infectious hepatitis, but for protection against rubella (German measles), poliomyelitis, whooping cough, chickenpox and mumps, an active immune globulin can be obtained only from subjects convalescent from the particular disease.

TABLE 22.2*

The nitrogen partition in the blood of normal individuals and the distribution of the various nitrogenous constituents between the cells and serum

	Corpuscles			Plasma			Whole Blood		
	Maxi-mum	Mini-mum	Aver-age	Maxi-mum	Mini-mum	Aver-age	Maxi-mum	Mini-mum	Aver-age
	mg. per 100 cc.			*mg. per 100 cc.*			*mg. per 100 cc.*		
(a) Taken from Wu:									
Total nonprotein nitrogen	61	39	49	36	20	29			
Urea N............................	22	12	17	23	13	19			
Amino acid N......................	11	8	10	8	5	6			
Uric acid..........................	4	1	2	5	2	4			
Creatine...........................	8	4	6	0	0	0			
Creatinine.........................	3	1.6	2.5	1.5	1	1.2			
Undetermined N....................			19			2.1			
(b) Taken from Berglund:									
Total nonprotein nitrogen...........	55	38	44	30	18	25	39	28	32
Urea N............................	13	8	10	17	10	12	15	9	12
Amino acid........................	11	7	8	6	4	5	8	6	6
Undetermined N...................	34	18	25	12	2	7	18	10	14

* Reprinted from Peters and Van Slyke, *Quantitative Clinical Chemistry*, vol. I, p. 267. The Williams & Wilkins Company, Baltimore, 1946.

termining the nitrogen in the filtrate. These substances are in part absorbed with, or derived from the food, and in part are the waste products of tissue catabolism. The total N.P.N. of whole blood amounts to from 28 to 40 mg. per 100 cc. It constitutes from 1 to 2 per cent of the total nitrogen of the blood. Its concentration in the cells is nearly double that in the plasma. The proportions of the different constituents are given in table 22.2.

The term undetermined nitrogen embraces the nitrogen of ammonia, purines, and other nonprotein substances of unknown or undefined nature.

Although this determination has persisted as a widely used laboratory test, it is relatively nonspecific. With the advent of the Folin-Wu system of analysis, and the availability of urease, it has been superceded by the measurement of blood urea as an accurate index of renal insufficiency.

PATHOLOGICAL VARIATIONS. The N.P.N. of blood at any given level represents the balance struck between nitrogenous materials formed in the intermediary metabolism of ingested and tissue protein and the excretion of these products in the urine. In renal insufficiency, therefore, the nonprotein nitrogen is elevated, and in certain cases may be ten times the normal. On the other hand, a rise in the N.P.N. occurs in conditions which are associated with excessive tissue catabolism, such as infections, fevers, thyrotoxicosis,

starvation or severe malnutrition. It is also increased following hemorrhage into the stomach or upper intestinal tract. In the later months of pregnancy the N.P.N. is reduced. The reduction has been attributed to the diversion of nitrogen to the growing fetus and the reduction of protein catabolism in the maternal tissues.

The chief conditions associated with an elevation of the N.P.N. of the blood are:

Adrenal insufficiency
Dehydration
Hemorrhage into the gastrointestinal tract
Infectious fevers, lobar pneumonia
Intestinal obstruction
Parathyroid intoxication (in animals)
Peritonitis
Renal insufficiency

Cholesterol

(See also chapters 59 and 68). This sterol is present in serum in the free form and as cholesteryl esters. It is carried in the α- and β-globulins, which contain almost all the lipoproteins. The value for total serum cholesterol exhibits wide ranges in the normal population; it varies from 100 to 250 mg. per cent. The esterified cholesterol is about 72 per cent of the total and this ratio varies within a rather narrow range. Its concentration is increased in several diseases, notably in hypothyroidism and lipid nephrosis and in some cases of atheromatosis. Keys and his associates found that within fairly wide limits (2 to 3 grams cholesterol weekly) the content of the sterol in the diet exerted little effect upon the total serum cholesterol.

REFERENCES

BLOOR, W. R. J. Biol. Chem., 1918, **36,** 49.
CARREL, A. J. A. M. A., 1924, **82,** 255; J. Exper. Med., 1922, **36,** 385.
ELMAN, R. AND HEIFETZ, C. J. J. Exper. Med., 1941, **73,** 417.
KAY, H. D. Brit. J. Exper. Path., 1930, **11,** 148.
KEYS, A. J. Phys. Chem., 1938, **42,** 11.
KEYS, A. AND ASSOCIATES. J. Nutrition, 1956, **59,** 39.
MILLER, L. L. AND ASSOCIATES. J. Exper. Med., 1951, **94,** 431.
MONTGOMERY, D. A. D.; NEILL, D. W., AND DOWDLE, E. G. D., Clin. Sc., 1962, **22,** 141.
PHILLIPS, R. A., VAN SLYKE, D. D. AND ASSOCIATES. Bull. U. S. Army M. Dept., 1943, **71,** 66.
PUTNAM, F. W., Science, 1955, **122,** 275.
SUNDERMAN, F. W., JR. AND SUNDERMAN, F. W. AM. J. Clin. Path., 1957, **27,** 125.

TISELIUS, A. Clin. Chim. Acta., 1958, **3,** 1.
WHITE, A. AND DOUGHERTY, T. F., Endocrinology, 1945, **36,** 207; Proc. Soc. Exper. Biol. & Med., 1944, **56,** 26.

Monographs and Reviews

ALBRITTON, E. C., Ed. Standard values in blood. W. B. Saunders, Philadelphia, 1952.
BIER, M., Ed. Electrophoresis: theory, methods and application. Academic Press, New York, 1959.
FOLIN, O. Physiol. Rev., 1922, **2,** 460.
FREDERICK, J. F. (Ed.) Gel electrophoresis Ann. N. Y. Acad. Sci., 1964, **121,** 305.
GUEST, G. M. AND RAPPAPORT, S. Physiol. Rev., 1941, **21,** 410.
HENDERSON, L. J. Fitness of the environment. Macmillan, New York, 1913.
HOWE, P. E. Physiol. Rev., 1925, **5,** 439.
MACALLUM, A. B. Physiol. Rev., 1926, **6,** 316.
MYERS, V. C. Physiol. Rev., 1924, **4,** 274.
PETERS, J. P. AND VAN SLYKE, D. D. Quantitative clinical chemistry. Vol. I. The Williams & Wilkins Co., Baltimore, 1946.

CHAPTER 23

The Red Cells or Erythrocytes

The Size, Shape and Structure of the Red Cell

Human erythrocytes are disk shaped, non-nucleated elements having a mean diameter of 7.2 μ (6–9 μ: see fig. 23.1) and a thickness of about 2.2 μ (2–2.4 μ) at the thickest part, i.e., near the circumference, and about 1 μ at the center. As a result of osmotic changes[1] and the consequent passage of water into the cell, the diameter increases with a shift in the acid-base balance of the blood toward the acid side. The cell is therefore slightly larger in venous than in arterial blood; its diameter is increased by about 0.5 μ in muscular exercise and reduced by forced breathing. The central portion of the cell is much thinner than its edges, which appear heaped up into a circumferential mound around a central depression. This construction gives it a bicon-cave contour or a roughly dumbbell outline when viewed edgewise (figs. 23.1 and 23.2).[2] The average area of a red cell is 120 μ^2 and the volume 85 μ^3.

There has been in the past a tendency to re-

[1] These are the mean dimensions of the cell measured in dry films. In the fresh state the diameter is larger by about 0.5 μ. There is considerable variation between the diameter of the smallest and largest cells found in a sample of normal blood. The range for dried films is shown in figure 23.2.

[2] Hartridge has pointed out the advantage of this design for the transport of oxygen. Of all geometrical figures the sphere is the one in which its center is equidistant from all points upon its surface. The adoption of this form by the red cell would therefore have ensured the diffusion of oxygen to all parts of its interior at equal rates. But a sphere has the disadvantage of possessing the smallest surface in relation to its mass. A thin disk, on the other hand, presents an almost maximal surface area in relation to its bulk, yet in such a shape all parts on the surface are not equally distant from its center; the ends are further removed than the sides. The shape of the red cell—a thin disk with elevated rounded edges—is a compromise between these two forms. It secures the advantages of equal and rapid diffusion of oxygen to its interior and a relatively large surface area for the absorption of the gas.

The biconcave form also gives the red cell a mechanical advantage, in that the changes in volume which the cell undergoes from time to time can be effected with a minimal amount of tension being placed upon the cell membrane. The membrane covering the concavity of the cell moves freely out or in "like the bottom of an oil-can" as the cell increases or diminishes in volume.

gard the erythrocyte as almost a dead cell, because of its low oxygen consumption, and its lack of a nucleus. However, it should be noted that the erythrocyte carries out certain metabolic processes, and it does have a finite, though low, oxygen consumption. It is therefore better to consider it as a very specialized type of living cell.

The framework, or stroma of the red cell, comprises somewhat less than 5 per cent of the wet weight of the cell. The major constituents of the stroma are lipids and an insoluble protein. The former is mainly made up of cephalin, lecithin and cholesterol; the latter is albuminlike. Almost half of the lipids are bound to the protein, and a lipoprotein complex called elenin has been isolated from the stroma by Calvin and his coworkers. Elenin seems to contain at least the A, B and Rh antigens. (In general, the antigenic nature of the erythrocyte appears to be a property associated with the stroma.) Hemoglobin makes up about 30 to 34 per cent of the wet weight of the cell. This corresponds to an extremely concentrated solution of the proteins, and means that the hemoglobin molecules are packed very tightly into the interior of the erythrocyte (fig. 23.3).

The erythrocyte contains the enzymes of the glycolytic system, catalase, carbonic anhydrase, all of the glutathione of the blood, as well as other enzymes and organic and inorganic salts. Potassium is present in high concentration, relative to sodium.

When a drop of freshly drawn normal blood is placed on a glass slide and examined under the microscope, many of the erythrocytes will be seen to group themselves together with their broad surfaces in contact, like a pile of coins. Groups of cells arranged in this way are called rouleaux (sing., *rouleau*). The normal discoid shape of the erythrocytes is a requisite for rouleaux formation, the property being lost if the cells, as in congenital hemolytic jaundice, assume a more globular form. Rouleaux formation does not occur in the circulation under normal physiological conditions, the moving cells showing little or no tendency to cohere.

"Sludged" blood. In certain abnormal states, e.g., tissue injury and shock, the cells of the cir-

culating blood show a pronounced tendency to stick together and form large clumps or masses which move slowly and cumbersomely through the small vessels—arterioles and capillaries. This "sludged" blood, as it is termed by Knisely who has made an extensive study of the phenomenon, has a deleterious effect upon the general circulation. Normally the blood moves through the minute vessels in stream-lines. The cells remain discrete showing little tendency to cohere. The propulsive force of cardiac systole is transmitted

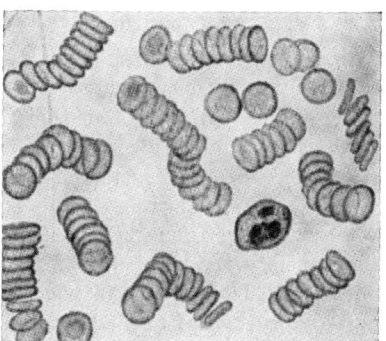

Fig. 23.4. Description in text.

throughout the vascular system with the minimum dissipation of energy. Stream-lining is abolished in sludged blood; a large proportion of the energy is wasted in giving a rolling or rotary motion (angular acceleration) to the massed cells. Sludged blood is thought in some instances to be a factor in thrombosis (ch. 33).

Number

The average number of red cells in man is around 5,000,000 per cu. mm. for males and 4,500,000 for females, but 6,000,000 is not a very unusual figure for a robust young man and 5,500,000 for a healthy young woman.[3] Slight variations in the number of red cells, amounting to about 5 per cent, occur throughout the 24 hours. The count is lowest during sleep, becomes elevated after arising and increases gradually throughout the waking hours. At birth and in infancy the red cells are somewhat more numerous than in later life, but the earlier figures of 7,000,000 and 8,000,000 for the newborn child have not been confirmed by later work. Destruction of a large proportion of the extra cells occurs within the first 10 days, and for a few days the red cell count shows a progressive fall; for some weeks after this the count remains considerably above that of the adult.

The destruction of large numbers of erythrocytes shortly after birth and, as a consequence, the liberation of excessive amounts of hemoglobin into the plasma has been held to be the cause of the physiological jaundice of the newborn, in whom the bilirubin content of the plasma (ch. 59) is from 3 to 5.5 mg. per cent. The infant's red cells are said by some to be more fragile than those of the adult, yet it is questionable, in view

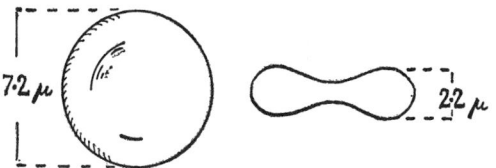

Fig. 23.1. Diagram showing dimensions of the red cell.

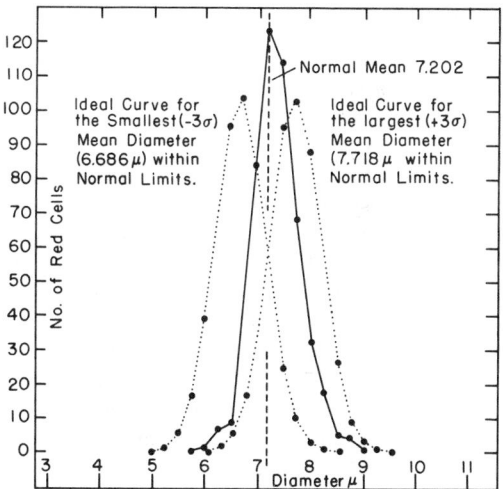

Fig. 23.2. Red cell diameter distribution curve for healthy men (after Price-Jones).

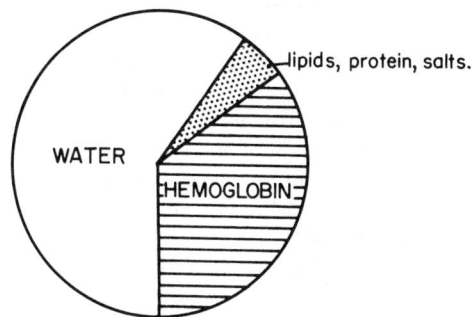

Fig. 23.3. Diagram showing composition of the red cell.

[3] Though very widely accepted, this sex difference has probably been overemphasized. Some workers have found a maximal difference of only 1 per cent in favor of men.

of the revised figures for red cell counts in the newborn, that excessive hemolysis plays a very important part in the production of the jaundice. Furthermore, it has never been demonstrated that the red cells at birth are unduly fragile. Immaturity of the excretory function of the liver probably plays the dominant role.

The total number of red cells in the human body estimated upon the basis of 5,000,000 per cu. mm. is about 33,000,000,000,000 which gives a total red cell area exposed to the plasma of between 3500 and 4000 sq. meters. Eamons has made the interesting observation that in the species which he investigated (cat, rabbit, dog and man) the surface area of the individual corpuscles and the corpuscular count varied in opposite directions, so that the cell area per cu. mm. of blood was nearly the same in all—7.24, 7.55, 7.52 and 7.35 sq. cm. for the four species in the order given above. The quantity of hemoglobin per sq. cm. of red cell area is also about equal in all mammalian species.

Control of Erythropoiesis

While the levels of red blood cells in health and disease are finely regulated, little is known of the exact mechanism by which this control is maintained. Erythropoietic activity is partially regulated by the oxygen content of arterial blood. Anoxia long has been considered to be the stimulus for red cell production. However, since 1950, it has become increasingly apparent that there are hormone-like substances which mediate the effect of hypoxia. There are at least two erythropoietic stimulating factors, (ESF) (*erythropoietin*), which have been chemically characterized as glycoproteins, with the electrophoretic mobility of α-globulins. The kidney is directly

TABLE 23.1

Altitude in Thousands of Feet	Corpuscles in Millions per Cubic Millimeter
0.7	4.5
4.4	5.2
12.0	6.8
15.6	7.8
18.2	8.3

From Barcroft after Hingston. In this table the altitude (in thousands of feet) multiplied by 0.225 gives a figure which approximates the increase in red cell count (in millions per cu. mm.) above that at sea level. In this instance the count at sea level was 4,250,000.

or indirectly responsible for the production of erythropoietin. Its action may be to change undifferentiated stem cells to differentiated pronormoblasts in the bone marrow.

Erythropoietin has been shown to be increased in some hypoplastic anemias, Cooley's anemia, leukemia with anemia, in some cases with secondary polycythemia, and occasionally in polycythemia vera. It has been reported decreased in some patients with chronic renal disease. To date, only minute amounts of purified erythropoietin are available for study.

Certain hormones are known to affect red cell production. Anemia occurs in man with hypothyroidism, adrenal insufficiency and anterior pituitary insufficiency. Polycythemia accompanies adrenal cortical hyperfunction. Experimentally, the influence of hormones of the gonads, thyroid, adrenal cortex and anterior pituitary on erythropoiesis can be confirmed.

PHYSIOLOGICAL VARIATIONS IN THE NUMBER OF RED CELLS

Increase in the number of red cells occurs under the following conditions:

1. HIGH ALTITUDES. It has been known for many years that the inhabitants of mountainous regions, especially where the elevation above the sea is 10,000 feet or more, have constantly a much higher red cell count than persons living at sea level. The natives of some regions in the Peruvian Andes, where the altitude is 14,000 feet or more, have a red cell count 30 per cent above the normal (over 7,000,000 per cu. mm.). Not only the natives, but travellers sojourning even for a short time at these altitudes undergo an almost immediate increase in the number of their red cells. The corpuscular increase is directly proportional to the altitude, as may be seen from table 23.1.

It is perhaps necessary to point out here that an increase or a decrease in the red cell count does not of itself inform one of an increase or decrease in the red cells of the body as a whole. The red cell count gives only an estimate of the *number of cells per unit quantity of blood* (ch. 24). A reduction in the amount of plasma or of the water of the blood, for instance, would cause the *proportion* of red cells in the specimen to be increased. But neither the immediate nor the permanent increase in number of red cells at high altitudes is due simply to a reduction in fluid and a greater concentration of the blood, for estimations of the total volume of blood in the body (see ch. 24) prove that there is an *absolute* increase in the number of circulating cells. How is the *immediate* increase brought about? It is obviously impossible to account for such a rapid rise in the red cell count by a greater production of cells by the bone marrow, and it is at once suggested that large masses of cells are packed away from the general circulation—in a storehouse of some kind—but are quickly mobilized upon demand. When the functions of the spleen are considered (ch. 29) it will be seen that this organ serves as a reservoir for red cells and is responsible for the sudden increase in their number which occurs early in the process of acclimatization to high altitudes.

The *permanent* and great elevation of the red cell count, which is a characteristic feature of the blood of natives and other persons after acclimatization to the rarefied atmosphere, cannot be explained in the same manner, for the number of cells which the spleen can put into circulation is limited. Under these circumstances there is, actually, an increased manufacture of erythrocytes by the blood-forming organ—the bone marrow. Some of the cells which are formed by the over-stimulated marrow are discharged into the general circulation at a somewhat immature stage of their development. They are spoken of as *reticulated cells* or *reticulocytes* since their protoplasm shows a delicate filigree or reticulum which stains supravitally with basic dyes. The ultimate cause of the corpuscular increase (a physiological polycythemia) is undoubtedly the lowered oxygen tension of the atmosphere, and consequently of the blood, since animals placed in an hermetically sealed cabinet and subjected to lowered oxygen tensions exhibit similar blood changes (fig. 23.5).

2. MUSCULAR EXERCISE and certain EMOTIONAL STATES cause a temporary increase in the number of red cells as a result of an outpouring of concentrated blood from the spleen.[4] This may be looked upon as an emergency measure and, like that which initially occurs at high altitudes, is the response of the body to the tissues' call for oxygen.

3. HEIGHTENED ENVIRONMENTAL TEMPERATURE also causes a liberation of red cells from the splenic reservoir.

4. OTHER CONDITIONS which tend to lower the oxygen tension of the arterial blood cause a rise in the number of circulating red cells. As in the response at high altitudes two factors are con-

[4] Though this can be demonstrated in experimental animals, it does not appear to be an important feature in man.

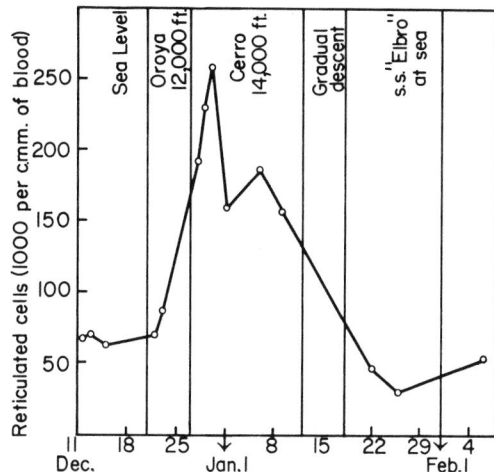

FIG. 23.5. Showing reticulocyte response to altitude (after Barcroft).

cerned, e.g., a discharge of blood from the spleen and other reservoirs, and a greater production of cells by the bone marrow.

Reduction in the number of red cells occurs at high barometric pressures, e.g., when the oxygen tension of the blood is higher than the normal. Animals, for example, living in deep mines have a lower red cell count than those at sea level.

ALTERATIONS IN THE NUMBER OF RED CELLS IN PATHOLOGICAL STATES

Increase in the Number of Red Cells—Polycythemia

Increase in the total number of red cells occurs as a compensatory measure in several pathological conditions and then represents apparently the response of the bone marrow to low oxygen tensions in the arterial blood. A red cell concentration of 7,000,000 or more per cu. mm. of blood is not unusual in the following conditions.

1. EMPHYSEMA (ch. 54) and other chronic diseases which interfere with the oxygenation of the blood in the lungs (anoxia), e.g., tracheal stenosis, pneumothorax, tumor of the lung, pulmonary tuberculosis and pulmonary arteriovenous aneurysm.

2. CONGENITAL HEART DISEASE (ch. 49).

3. AYERZA'S DISEASE, a condition associated with dilation and marked hypertrophy of the right heart, sclerosis of the pulmonary arteries and their branches with consequent obstruction of the blood flow through the lungs. There is extreme cyanosis; emphysema, dyspnea, and attacks of asthma are common accompaniments. The bone marrow is hyperplastic.

4. CHRONIC CARBON MONOXIDE POISONING.

5. Chemicals, e.g., chronic poisoning with arsenic, phosphorus and manganese, gum shellac, and certain aniline dyes.

6. Repeated small hemorrhages, the polycythemia then represents an over-response of the bone marrow to the successive blood losses. This is rare.

Polycythemia vera (synonyms: erythremia, splenomegalic polycythemia, Vasquez-Osler disease). Unlike the preceding types the polycythemia is not secondary to any known pathological condition. This disease is now considered to be one of the myeloproliferative disorders. Although the red cell forming elements of the bone marrow are primarily involved, it is most common to find the myeloid and megakaryocytic tissue hyperplastic as well. The red bone marrow becomes greatly increased in amount, extending into the shafts of the long bones and replacing the fatty marrow. The erythroid hyperplasia takes place at a fairly mature level, and the marrow is packed with normoblasts and erythrocytes. Erythroblasts are absent or scarce. Proliferation of myeloid elements involves myelocytes, metamyelocytes and polymorphonuclear leukocytes, and megakaryocytes may be numerous, with increased platelet production. The number of red cells in the circulating blood may be as high as 14,000,000 per cu. mm. and a count as high as 20,000,000 has been reported. The total white blood cell count is frequently over 25,000 per cu. mm. Due to an absolute increase in polymorphonuclear leukocytes, with an associated "shift to the left" and the appearance of young myeloid forms, platelet counts of over 500,000 per cu mm. are common. The total blood volume is greatly increased. The viscosity of the blood is of course greatly elevated. The concentration of hemoglobin in the individual cells and the chemical and physiological properties of the pigment are normal. The size, shape and general features of the red cells as a rule show nothing unusual and the number of reticulocytes is not greatly increased. Not infrequently, however, the mean corpuscular volume of the red cells is below normal.

The chief features shown by the disease apart from those of the blood itself are cyanosis (ch. 54), dyspnea on exertion, enlargement of the spleen, hemorrhages and a familial tendency. Death may occur from thrombosis of a major blood vessel, e.g. coronary a., cerebral a. or portal vein. The circulation rate (ch. 49) is slowed and the diffusion rates of oxygen and CO_2 (ch. 52) through the pulmonary epithelium are reduced, although during rest the oxygen saturation of the arterial blood is usually normal. The renal blood flow and the filtration fraction (ch. 79) are increased whereas the plasma flow is decreased. The oxygen saturation of the blood is reduced, however, during exercise. Owing to the great increase in hemoglobin concentration the actual *quantity* of oxygen in the blood is greater than normal. If the polycythemia were a compensatory reaction brought about by the lowered rate of diffusion of oxygen through the pulmonary epithelium, one would expect that breathing air with a high pressure of oxygen would be of benefit, but this is not the case. Exposure, in a chamber, to a high oxygen tension for several days does not effect a reduction in the number of red cells. The reduced circulation rate may result in some way from the fact that the blood contains such a large load of oxygen that the tissues can obtain their quota from a smaller quantity of blood than normally. On the other hand, the reduced circulation rate may be due primarily to vasoconstriction in some part of the circulation or to the tremendously increased viscosity of the blood itself. Some believe that narrowing of the caliber of the vessels of the bone marrow and the resulting low oxygen tension produced thereby provide the stimulus for the overproduction of blood cells. Studies of blood lactic acid concentration in polycythemia vera following muscular exercise have been quoted to lend support to the theory that a sluggish blood flow through the tissues is a causative factor. In normal persons and in the secondary types of polycythemia mentioned above, a rise in blood lactate occurs, whereas in polycythemia vera exercise causes a fall. This anomaly could be explained upon the basis of a high resting blood lactate as a result of a slow blood flow and the accumulation of lactic acid in the ischemic tissues. Exercise would then, by causing vasodilation and a freer oxygen supply, in the contracting muscles, tend to reduce the concentration of the metabolite in the blood. That this is the probable explanation is indicated by the observation that vasodilation induced by heat also causes a fall in blood lactate in this disease. However, there are those who feel that the phenomenon is of fundamental significance, and not simply the result of the high erythrocyte concentration, because it is not abolished when the red cell count is brought down to normal by treatment with *phenylhydrazine hydrochloride*, a drug which has been employed in controlling the disease in the past.

Polycythemia can be produced in dogs by the daily administration of cobaltous chloride (8 mg. daily for 2 or 3 weeks) which acts either by producing tissue anoxia or by stimulating erythropoietin production. The high red cell count thus induced is reduced to normal by feeding with whole beef or hog liver or by the daily injection of ascorbic acid. The effect of liver is now felt to be due to the provision of certain amino acids which chelate with cobalt.

The observations of Schafer threw a different light on the pathogenesis of polycythemia vera which it was hoped might show a way to the rational treatment of the disease. In experiments upon dogs he found that excision of the carotid sinus and the aortic nerves caused the development of polycythemia and hypertension in 40 per cent of the animals. Removal of the paravertebral chain of sympathetic ganglia was followed by a gradual return of the erythrocyte count to normal. A similar result followed paravertebral sympathectomy in one patient suffering from polycythemia. The polycythemic response to removal of the influence of the carotid sinus and aortic nerves was felt to be due to constriction of the vessels of the bone marrow, the anoxia caused thereby acting in the usual way to stimulate its hemopoietic function. Unfortunately, this theory has never been proven in humans.

Some investigators have reported an increase in erythropoietin levels in polycythemia, but the reports have been inconsistent.

Treatment of this disorder has consisted of frequent phlebotomies in the past. Radioactive phosphorus (P^{32}) has been used lately with success.

Reduction in the number of red cells below the normal is known as anemia. The causes and varieties of anemia are manifold and will be considered in chapter 29.

An apparent decrease or increase in the number of red cells occurs under certain conditions which upset the water balance of the body. It has already been pointed out that the red cell count gives merely an estimate of the proportion of cells to plasma. There may, for instance, be undue retention of water in the body, and the plasma or its watery constituents may then be increased (hydremia or hemodilution). The blood is diluted, and the number of red cells per unit of blood is reduced, yet there is no absolute decrease in the number of circulating cells. Conversely, a loss of plasma or of merely the water of the blood (anhydremia or hemoconcentration) will increase the red cell count, i.e., the blood becomes more concentrated although the total number of red cells in the body is not altered. Therefore in conditions associated with extreme dehydration of the body the number of red cells per unit of blood is increased.

A practical point to be remembered when counting the red cells or in determining the packed cell volume is that their number may be relatively increased or decreased by purely *local* alterations in blood concentration. Pronounced dilation of the capillaries of the region of skin from which the sample has been taken will cause a local slowing of the blood stream and congestion of the part. The loss of fluid from the vessel into the tissues and the clumping of corpuscles which may result from the greater capillary pressure will give a false estimate of the number of red cells. On the other hand, pressure made upon the part by the examiner in order to hasten the flow of blood from a skin puncture may express fluid from the tissues which will dilute the red cells in the specimen. Moreover, even under ordinary physiological conditions, the concentration of red cells may vary considerably in different parts of the circulation. The proportion of red cells in the capillaries is greater as a rule than in the heart and larger vessels, by around 12 per cent, but in certain states associated with slowing of the peripheral circulation, concentration of red cells in the capillaries may increase the disparity. Trapping of *plasma* in the peripheral vessels may occur in other conditions and will tend to reduce the concentration of cells in the capillary areas below that in the general circulation. These are also important points to bear in mind in estimating the blood volume by the dye method 488.

Estimation of red cells. The concentrations of red (or white) cells may be obtained by counting them directly after suitable dilution beneath the microscope, as in the method of Thoma-Zeiss. The instrument used for this purpose is called a *hemocytometer*. The reader is referred to texts on laboratory methods for details. The relative volumes of red cells and plasma are determined by means of a specially devised centrifuge known as an *hematocrit*. The blood, rendered noncoagulable, is drawn into a graduated capillary tube, placed in a centrifuge and revolved at a speed of 3000 r.p.m. 30 to 60 minutes. At the end of this time the original blood will be found to have separated into a clear colorless column of plasma and a red column —the corpuscles. The lengths of the two columns are read off by means of the graduations on the tube. The normal proportions of plasma and corpuscles in human blood are about 54 (53–56) and 46 (44–47) respectively. That is, the volume of cells (*packed cell volume*) is 46 per cent of the total volume of the specimen of blood. The average volume of the individual erythrocytes is obtained by dividing the packed cell volume by the figure for the red cell count. It is important to use an anticoagulant, such as heparin, that does not cause shrinkage or swelling of the cells.

Variations in Size, Shape and Structure of the Red Cells

Under physiological conditions little change in shape of the red cell occurs, though a few fragmented cells may be found in normal blood. These are, as will be seen later (ch. 29), simply remnants of senile cells which have undergone a natural disintegration in the blood stream. A slight change in volume, about 7.5 per cent occurs, due to osmotic changes incident to the respiratory cycle (ch. 50). The red cells at birth and in early infancy are larger than in adult life. This as well as the higher cell count is responsible for the high packed cell volume (54 per cent) of the infant's blood.

In *disease*, the red cell is subject to many changes in size, shape and structure. The examination of the blood and the identification of the various forms of abnormal cells is an important means employed in diagnosis of the different anemias (ch. 30). Only the more outstanding abnormalities can be touched upon here. The least pronounced departure from the normal blood picture is an increase in the number of *reticulocytes*. These young red cells resemble the ordinary cells in every way except that after supravital staining (alcoholic solution of brilliant cresyl blue added to blood in the fresh state) a fine reticulum of basophilic material can be seen in the cytoplasm. The reticular material is of cytoplasmic origin, probably γ-globulin, and does not represent nuclear remains. A reticulum of similar nature may sometimes be seen in cells in which the nucleus is still intact. In normal human blood the reticulocytes are from 0 to 2 (av. 0.8) per cent of the total red cell count.[5] They are increased after hemorrhage, at high altitudes, by exercise, in acholuric jaundice (p. 544) and in pernicious anemia, especially following specific treatment (p. 544) of the latter condition and during the blood crises. A rise in the reticulocyte count indicates an increased activity of the blood forming tissue—the bone marrow—which as a result of a specific stimulus turns out a larger number of young cells. The maturation of the red cells, that is, the change from reticulocytes to erythrocytes, has been estimated to take from 10 to 24 hours. There is evidence that the thyroid gland liberates a principle which hastens the maturation of reticulocytes.

The next stage in the life of the red cell is represented by the *normoblast*, which appears in the blood in several different types of anemia. This cell, as its name implies, is normal in size and shape, possesses the usual amount of hemoglobin,

[5] These cells are more numerous in rabbit's blood, being from 3 to 3.5 per cent of the total red cell population. The blood of certain other species, also shows a relatively high count.

but contains a nucleus. The bone marrow normally holds large numbers of these immature cells, but in health they do not reach the general circulation. The normoblasts may be subdivided into basophilic, polychromatophilic and eosinophilic cell types. The latter is the form most commonly seen in the peripheral blood. The polychromatophilic normoblast contains a small, sometimes a negligible amount of hemoglobin. Its protoplasm also contains a diffuse or punctate arrangement of basophilic material. Hemoglobin is acidophilic, so these cells may stain with acid as well as with basic dyes. This phenomenon of dual staining, is known as *polychromasia*.

Red cells of various sizes and shapes may be seen in the anemias. Shrinkage of the contents of the red cell with wrinkling of its limiting membrane, as may result from immersing the cells in a hypertonic solution, is termed *crenation*. In pernicious anemia, in particular, the presence of cells of unequal sizes (*anisocytosis*) and of deformed outline (*poikilocytosis*) is common. The poikilocytes may assume the most bizarre forms; mulberry, flask or hammer shapes may appear. Erythrocytes with a globular form (*spherocytes*), or of an eliptoid or crescentic shape (*eliptocytes* and *sickle cells*) are found in certain types of anemia. Pauling, Itano, Singer and Wells have found that in sickle cell anemia the red cells contain an abnormal type of hemoglobin. This is insoluble in the reduced form and forms crystalline "tactoids" within the cell membrane. These distorted, more rigid cells, are destroyed more rapidly than the normal cells. *Macrocytes* and *microcytes* are terms denoting cells of usual structure and without nuclei, but larger and smaller respectively than the normal erythrocyte. In certain conditions, e.g., lead poisoning, fine dots of basophilic material, probably a porphyrin (ch. 27) appear throughout the cell, giving it a stippled appearance. This abnormality is known as *punctate basophilia*. In certain types of anemia rings or twisted strands of basophilic material may be seen near the periphery of the cell. These are derived from the nucleus and are known as *Cabot's rings*. At other times small nuclear fragments—*Howell-Jolly bodies*—are present in the cytoplasm.

REFERENCES

CALVIN, M., EVANS, R. S., BEHRENDT, V. AND CALVIN, G., Proc. Soc. Exper. Biol. & Med., 1946, **61**, 416.

GRANT, W. C. AND ROOT, W. S., Blood, 1955, **10**, 334.

HARTRIDGE, H. J. Physiol., 1920, **53**, lxxxi.

JABOBSON, L. O., GLRNEY, C. W. AND GOLDWASSER, E., Adv. in Int. Med., 1960, **10,** 297.

KNISELY, M. H. AND ASSOCIATES. Arch. Surg. 1945, **51,** 220; Trans. 4th Conf. on Blood Clotting and Allied Problems. J. E. Flynn, Ed., J. Macy Found. 1951.

PAULING, L., ITANO, H. A., SINGER, S. J. AND WELLS, I. C. Science, 1949, **110,** 543.

Monographs and Reviews

BARCROFT, J. Cambridge University Press, London, 1925.

EAMONS, W. F. J. Physiol., 1927, **64,** 215.

GRANICK, S. Blood, 1949, **4,** 404.

HARROP, G. A., JR. Medicine, 1928, **7,** 291.

PRICE-JONES, C. Blood pictures; an introduction to clinical hematology. The Williams & Wilkins Co., Baltimore, 1933.

SCHAFER, P. W. Ann. Surg., 1945, **122,** 1098.

WINTROBE, M. M. Medicine, 1930, **9,** 195.

WOLSTENHOLME, G. E. W. AND O'CONNOR, M., Haemopoiesis, CIBA Foundation Symposium. J. & A. Churchill, Ltd., London, 1960.

CHAPTER 24

Blood Volume: Body Water: Water Balance

Blood volume estimations are of value in many clinical conditions associated with a loss or gain of fluid by the body, or for the purpose of checking the results of corpuscular and hemoglobin estimations. It is also sometimes of interest to know, in experimental investigations and in metabolic studies in man, the *total* amounts of certain blood constituents, e.g., protein, calcium, sodium, etc., as well as their concentrations.

Methods for the Estimation of Blood Volume

DIRECT METHOD

The first attempts to measure the total quantity of blood in the body were made upon animals by Welcker (1854). His method consisted in taking a small measured quantity of the animal's blood and diluting it to 1 in 100 with normal saline.

The animal was then bled, and after the blood had ceased to flow, its vessels were washed out and the muscles minced and extracted with water. Water was then added to the collected fluid— blood and washings—until its color matched precisely the tint of the original diluted blood specimen. The total collected fluid divided by 100 gave the blood volume.

This method was also employed upon decapitated criminals (Bischoff) in order to obtain a value for the blood volume of man; but since its applicability was obviously very limited, indirect methods were later devised.

INDIRECT METHODS

Several methods are available for the determination of the blood volume during life. The carbon monoxide method developed by Grehant and Quinquad for animals and modified by Haldane and Smith for man, has been largely supplanted by the dye method.

The dye method was originally devised by Keith, Rowntree and Geraghty. The degree of dilution in the plasma of a known amount of dye injected into the circulation is employed as the basis of calculation. The color of the stained plasma is compared in a colorimeter with that of a standard dye solution of known concentration.

There are several qualifications required of a dye before it can be considered suitable for blood volume measurements. In the first place, of course, it must be innocuous. It must not diffuse too rapidly from the blood stream; it must color only the plasma, and not be adsorbed by the cells of the blood nor by the walls of the blood vessels. It must not change color itself after entering the blood, nor cause the liberation of pigment from the red cells (hemolysis), and it must be capable of mixing evenly and thoroughly with the plasma. If it lacked these qualifications, the colorimetric readings obviously would be undependable.

The dye most commonly employed is a blue dye, T-1824 (Evans blue). Evans blue has the advantage that the error due to any discoloration of the plasma by hemoglobin (hemolysis) is minimized. This dye is also eliminated very slowly (4.8 per cent per hour) from the circulation. It remains in the circulation because it combines with protein, although this combination apparently is not strong, for the two can be separated by paper electrophoresis.

In making an estimate of blood volume a sample of plasma is obtained before the dye is injected. Then a known amount of the dye is injected intravenously and blood samples are obtained at 10- or 20-, 30-, 40-, and 50-minute intervals after the injection. The concentration of dye in the plasma is measured. Because the dye leaves the circulation to some extent, it is necessary to determine the fall in concentration of the dye with time. By extrapolating back to zero time from the curve of concentrations, the concentration of the dye at zero time can be computed and this is used to calculate the blood volume. Because T-1824 leaves the circulation slowly, in normal persons it is usually possible to obtain a reasonable estimate of the blood volume from a sample taken 10 minutes after the dye has been injected, but under conditions when mixing is slow, the extrapolated values are preferable. From the concentration of dye in the sample and the amount of dye injected, the dye dilution and hence the plasma volume can be computed.

If either lipemia or hemolysis is present, the dilution method with T-1824 is not satisfactory unless a lengthy dye extraction procedure is used.

Also, as we have seen, in many instances the disappearance rate of the dye from plasma must be known if an accurate plasma volume measurement is to be achieved. Another disadvantage is that repeated injections may cause some discoloration of the conjunctivae and skin. Furthermore, because of persistence of the dye in the plasma, repeated determinations become increasingly inaccurate.

Plasma volume may also be estimated by the injection of albumin "tagged" with I^{131}. This is not affected by hemolysis or lipemia, nor does it stain the tissues, but it also has the disadvantage of requiring information concerning its disappearance rate. However, because only minute amounts of radioactivity are used in each test, repeat determinations can be made accurately and in rapid succession. This technique has been adapted for use at the bedside with the advent of improved equipment, and has largely supplanted the use of Evans Blue. Measurements of plasma volumes by the use of T-1824 and by means of I^{131} albumin give similar results. Another procedure has been developed using a dextran fraction which leaves the circulation very slowly. This method has the advantage of requiring only two blood samples, one of which is a control. It is unaffected by lipemai or hemolysis, employs a colorless material and requires no highly specialized equipment for its estimation.

These various procedures give an estimate only of the *plasma* volume. In order to obtain the value for the total blood volume, the proportion of cells to plasma must be determined by means of the hematocrit. If the *packed cell volume* thus obtained is, for example, 45 per cent, the plasma volume is therefore 55 per cent. Thus the total blood volume can be calculated from the plasma volume and the hematocrit reading.

In calculating the blood volume from the plasma volume and the hematocrit reading it is necessarily assumed that the proportion of red cells to plasma is the same throughout all parts of the vascular system, but experimental evidence is strongly against such an assumption. In capillaries the proportion of red cells to plasma may be considerably less or more than in the larger vessels. To eliminate the error of unequal distribution of red cells throughout the circulation, methods have been devised for the estimation of the total circulating red cell volume. These use the dilution of injected red blood cells which have been "tagged" with radioactive iron (Fe^{55}), radioactive chromium (Cr^{51}) or radioactive phosphorus (P^{32}). In the method of Hahn, as modified by

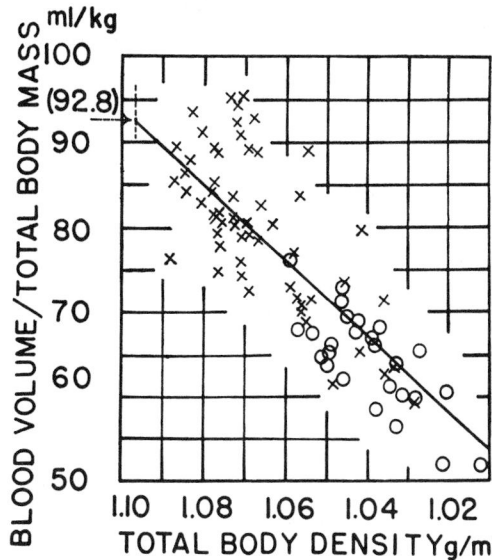

FIG. 24.1. Ratio of measured blood volume to total body mass, plotted against body density ($\times$ 55 men; $\bigcirc$ 26 women). Note that the blood content is 92.8 ml. per kg. in hypothetic body of density 1.097. BV was computed from measured PV and hematocrit with correction of the latter to the over-all cell concentration of the circulating blood.

Gibson and his colleagues radioactive iron (Fe^{55} or Fe^{59}) is incorporated into ferric ammonium citrate, which is injected into a donor belonging to group O (ch. 26). Newly formed cells take up the iron and appear in the circulation in 24 hours, reaching a maximum in 21 days.

From 70 to 100 ml. of the donor's blood (30 to 40 ml. of red cells), having a radioactivity of from 2500 to 3000 counts per minute per ml. (determined by Geiger counter), are injected intravenously or intraarterially into the subject. The quantity of donor's blood injected will depend upon the volume of red cells which the recipient is expected to have, but injections between 70 and 100 ml. cover a range of red cell volumes of from 1500 to 2500 ml.

Between 10 to 20 minutes are allowed to pass after the injection in order for thorough mixing of donor's and recipient's cells to occur. Samples of 15 ml. of recipient's blood are then taken and are followed at 10- and 20-minute intervals by two more samplings. Two milliliters of donor's blood are diluted to 100 ml.; 10 aliquots are then prepared. The recipient's blood samples are centrifuged at 3000 r.p.m. for 30 minutes. Donor and recipient samples are wet-ashed and the iron deposited electrolytically on copper. The radioactive iron in the two samples is determined by means of a Geiger counter; the calculation of the circulating red cell volume is made from the following equation:

$$Vrr = \frac{CD \times VaD}{VaR}$$

where Vrr is the red cell volume, CD the number of milliliters of donor cells injected, VaD the radioactivity of the donor's cells and VaR the radioactivity of the recipient's cells. When Fe^{59} is used, this method can be simplified greatly by eliminating the wet-ashing and electroplating. The whole blood sample (or a dilution thereof) can be counted directly in a well-type scintillation counter.

In order to determine the total blood volume, the plasma volume is measured by the dye method and the result added to the value for the circulating red cell volume.

This method is based on two assumptions—(a) that none of the radioactive iron escapes again after being taken up by the erythrocytes, and (b) that all the labelled cells became mixed with the recipient's cells equally throughout the circulation. Only the principle of the method can be given here; for details the reader is referred to the original papers.

Radioactive iron can be used in tests carried out over a long period of time because it persists in the cells and the blood remains radioactive for much longer than when radioactive chromium or phosphorus are used. The methods employing Cr^{51} and P^{32} are simpler to use than the one just described because the labelling of the red blood cells with these materials can be done *in vitro*. Since it is thus possible to use red blood cells from the individual on whom the test is to be made, the problem of cell compatibility does not arise. Radioactive chromium is the isotope which now is used most frequently for determination of red cell mass. All determinations of blood volume, whatever method is used, are made with the patient recumbent and under basal conditions, some 12 to 14 hours after a meal. The loss of the dye or other material into the tissues at the site of injection must be avoided since this of course will vitiate the results which, since the plasma would be less deeply stained, would be too high. Care must also be exercised to prevent evaporation of fluid from the samples after they have been drawn. Otherwise the concentration of the particular test material in the plasma would be raised and the readings (which would indicate a lower degree of dilution) would be too low.

Normal Values for Plasma and Whole Blood Volumes as Obtained by Different Method

In normal subjects, blood makes up roughly 7 per cent of the body weight, with plasma volume a little over 4 per cent and red cell volume about 3 per cent. The plasma volume of adult males is about 40 ml., the red cell volume about 29 ml., and the whole blood volume in the neighborhood of 70 ml. per kg. of body weight. The blood volume of a man of average weight (70 kg.) is therefore around 5 liters. The blood volume in terms of body weight shows considerable variation from person to person. Changes in body density alter this relationship of blood volume to body weight. The relationship between blood volume and body height shows a similar variability. The most constant relationship is found between a combination of body weight and the cube of body height (fig. 24.1).

Body Water (see also ch. 25)

The blood volume and its variations cannot be considered entirely apart from the fluid content of the body as a whole. Blood volume regulation is largely a question of balance between the fluid within the vessels and in the tissues. When conditions arise which tend to lower or raise the volume of blood, counter forces come into play which restore the normal level. When circulating fluid is lost, the vessels replenish themselves from the extravascular spaces. On the other hand, any tendency for the blood volume to rise is met by a discharge of the excess fluid into the tissues and later from the body in the urine. So, a balance is struck, and in health the blood volume is maintained remarkably constant. For example, after the intravenous injection of a large quantity of saline, the volume of circulating fluid (although raised temporarily) is brought back to normal within 30 minutes or less. On the other hand the loss of whole blood, as by hemorrhage, immediately calls into action processes which may, in a very short time, replenish the blood volume. When an animal is bled to death, at a not too rapid rate, the blood which is withdrawn is found after a few minutes of bleeding to have become diluted—clearly demonstrating the promptness with which fluid (water and salts) has been absorbed into the vessels.

The total volume of the water of the body varies among species but in man has a mean value of approximately 65 per cent (about 10 per cent less for women) of the body weight (it is about 65 per cent in the dog and about 73 per cent for guinea pigs and rabbits). It is difficult to establish proper mean values for body water, because its total volume is related to the mass of the lean tissues of the body rather than to the body weight. In an obese person it is a much lower percentage of the body weight than in one who is lean. The values, therefore, vary widely both between persons and different species of animal in accordance with their fatness or leanness.

The total *volume* of the body water can be determined by injecting into the blood stream a known amount of water containing deuterium or tritium, or antipyrine which becomes uniformly distributed throughout the body fluids (intracellular and extracellular), and then determining its concentration in a sample of serum. Tritium-labelled water may be more conveniently measured than deuterium-labelled water because of the radioactivity of tritium. A further method using N-acetyl-4-aminoantipyrene has also been described.

The water content of various tissues, in average percentages, is given in the following table:

	per cent
Muscle (striated)	75
Skin	70
Connective tissues	60
Adipose tissue	20
Bone (marrow-free)	25–30
Blood:	
Plasma	90
Cells	65
Kidney	80
Liver	70
Nervous tissue:	
Gray matter	85
White matter	70

The *extracellular fluid*, which comprises the blood plasma, the tissue or interstitial fluid, lymph and the fluid in the serous cavities, amounts to about 24 per cent of the body weight; the plasma water constitutes only about 4 per cent of the body weight. The fluid within the cells, the *intracellular fluid* amounts to 41 per cent of the weight of the body, or about two times the extracellular fluid. The skeletal muscles contain about half, the skin about $\frac{1}{5}$ and whole blood only about $\frac{1}{10}$ of the total body water.

In general, the intracellular fluid has a high concentration of potassium and a low concentration of sodium, whereas the extracellular fluids contain relatively large amounts of sodium and small amounts of potassium.[1] In most cells chlo-

[1] In the case of muscle at any rate, this distribution of Na and K between intra- and extracellular

ride is also in low concentration or is absent; the red blood cells and the cells of the gastric glands are notable exceptions. Substances, such as sucrose, mannitol, inulin, thiocyanate and to a large extent chloride, when introduced into the body, become uniformly distributed throughout the extracellular fluids, but do not enter the cells in important amounts and, since they are not metabolized and are not excreted too rapidly, can be employed to estimate the volume of the extracellular fluid in the living animal. When, for example, a known amount of thiocyanate, is injected into the blood stream and sufficient time allowed for equal distribution to occur, the volume of the extracellular water can be calculated from the concentration of the solute in a sample of serum. Radioactive sodium or chloride may also be employed for such determinations, but since these solutes are not excluded from all types of cells they are not as dependable as thiocyanate or sucrose, especially if absolute values are sought. The extracellular fluid is visualized as occupying a space of the determined volume, and according to the solute used in the estimation it is customary to speak of the *thiocyanate space, sucrose space,* etc.

The values for the total body water and the extracellular water being known, the intracellular water is found by subtraction (see table below).

Body water

Body Water	Percentage of Body Weight
A. Extracellular	
In plasma	4
In interstices	15
In hollow viscera, eye, etc	5
B. Intracellular	41

When calculating intracellular water in this way it is well to appreciate that some of the methods for determining extracellular fluid volume, because they measure only the volume of fluid into which the test substances can freely

fluids may be altered in pathological states involving the excessive loss of potassium from the body, e.g., severe and prolonged diarrhea, hyperactivity of the adrenal cortex or the administration of desoxycorticosterone (ch. 76) when muscle potassium is largely replaced by sodium. Increased concentration of K in the serum and other extracellular fluids occurs in adrenal cortical insufficiency, in oliguria or anuria, during tissue breakdown or anoxia, following major surgical operations, and in dehydration.

TABLE 24.1

Concentrations of base in the water of blood plasma and in the water of muscle tissue

(After Gamble, Ross and Tisdall)

	Per 100 cc. Plasma	Per 100 cc. Plasma Water	Per 100 cc. Muscle Tissue	Per 100 cc. Muscle Water
	mg.	cc. 0.1 N	mg.	cc. 0.1 N
Na$^+$.......	330	157.7	80	45.8
K$^+$........	20	5.6	320	108.0
Ca^{++}......	10	5.5	8	5.3
Mg^{++}......	3	2.7	21	23.0
Total...		171.5		182.1

Water of blood plasma is taken as 91 per cent by volume and water of muscle tissue as 76 per cent of weight.

diffuse, exclude a certain amount of fluid outside cells, such as eye humors, cerebrospinal fluid and secretions of glands, whereas these fluids are usually included in the estimation of total body water.

The characteristic distribution of sodium and potassium between blood plasma and tissue fluid is shown in table 24.1. Determinations of the extracellular fluid volume, total tissue water content and sodium space permit one to obtain information regarding shifts of ions or water across cell boundaries. It is probable that changes in electrolyte concentration are primary and that shifts in intracellular water occur secondarily to such changes. The entrance or exit of water thus depends on the balance of ions inside and outside the cell, water passing freely across the cell boundary. The balance of ions inside and outside the cell, with a high potassium concentration inside and a high sodium concentration outside, is best explained by postulating an active process—a sort of "sodium pump"—which excludes, or even extrudes sodium from the cell. The precise way in which sodium is kept out of the cell is not known, but the process requires energy. The immediate energy source is probably adenosine triphosphate or some related compound, and either glycolysis or oxidation may provide the further energy required. The "sodium pump" may become less efficient under circumstances when energy supply is reduced, as, for example, when the blood supply to a tissue is blocked or when there is some metabolic insufficiency. One can think of changes in intracellular water, therefore, as being related to changes in the molar concentrations of intracellular or extracellular electrolytes, and one way

in which an imbalance could be brought about would be through some change in the "sodium pump." Intracellular water under ordinary conditions is a rather fixed quantity, and the fluid of blood is also kept relatively constant. A loss of one-fourth of the body water is usually fatal.

Under physiological conditions the interstitial fluids show the greatest changes. In dehydration the proportion of the total water lost from extracellular and intracellular compartments varies with the manner in which the negative water balance is produced. When, for example, the dehydration is caused by sucrose diuresis, about 85 per cent of the excreted water is derived from extracellular and 15 per cent from intracellular sources. Whereas, in dehydration resulting from water deprivation, the water loss is from 57 to 67 per cent intracellular (Painter and associates).

Hyaluronic acid. Although practically none of the extracellular water is chemically bound, that is to say, substances are dissolved in it readily, and it can be entirely separated from colloidal materials by ultrafiltration, and although free movement and rapid changes of distribution are permitted, its physical state does not appear to be that of a simple solution of electrolytes and protein bathing the cells; it is held in the tissue spaces by a gelating substance. The latter has been identified chemically as a mucopolysaccharide and called *hyaluronic acid.* This substance also enters into the formation of the cement substance binding cells together, and into the production of other gel-like materials, e.g., vitreous body, jelly of the umbilical cord, etc. The physiological significance of this material is dealt with in another place.

Water Balance

In health, except when new tissue is being formed, the body's intake of water obviously must balance the output. When the output exceeds the intake, the body's water content is reduced and the body is then said to be in negative water balance; dehydration results. When, as during growth, convalescence from an acute illness or in pregnancy, new tissue is being formed, or for a time after a subject has been placed upon a reducing diet, the water balance is positive, the intake exceeding the output, i.e., water is retained.

The antidiuretic principle of the hypophysis constitutes part of the mechanism regulating the volume of body water. In dehydrated states, increased amounts of the pituitary hormone are excreted in the urine (ch. 74).

THE WATER INTAKE

Body water is replenished in two main ways, (a) by the ingestion of liquids, semisolid and "solid" food (cooked lean meat, for example, is from 65 to 70 per cent water), and (b) by the water formed in metabolism through the oxidation of the hydrogen of the food, or of the body tissues themselves. Water is absorbed mainly from the small intestine, to a smaller extent from the large intestine, and in small amounts only from the stomach. The following table from Rowntree and Brown compiled from the data of Magnus-Levy gives the quantities of water produced by the metabolism, respectively, of the three main food stuffs and of alcohol.

100 grams of fat   yield 107.1 grams water
100 grams of starch   yield 55.1 grams water
100 grams of protein yield 41.3 grams water
100 grams of alcohol yield 117.4 grams water

Water is also formed in the tissues through the polymerization or synthesis of various compounds, i.e., through a metabolic process the reverse of hydrolysis. An ordinary mixed diet yields as a result of oxidative processes from 300 to 350 grams of water daily, or about 14 grams per 100 Calories. When no food or drink is taken, the body materials themselves are utilized for this purpose, the glycogen, protein and fat supplying important quantities of water. The camel's hump, for instance, which is largely composed of fat, is a reservoir for large amounts of water, and the clothes moth kept in a desiccator and fed upon perfectly dry food lays eggs which are 80 per cent water.

For the adult, the amount of water from all sources and under ordinary circumstances which must be ingested daily is around 2500 cc. or about 1 cc. per Calorie of food intake. This usually means that about 1000 cc. of water as such or in beverages must be drunk in order to maintain the water balance.

The water intake under conditions of average temperature, humidity and diet is summarized in the following table:

	cc.
Solid and semisolid food	1200
Oxidation of food	300
Drinks (water, milk, coffee, beer, etc.)	1000

The volume of body water is held constant through a nicely balanced adjustment between intake and output. The intake is regulated mainly by the sensation of thirst.

Even a slight fall in the total volume of body water arouses thirst. This is caused by the inhibition of salivary secretion and the consequent drying of the oral mucosa, as well as by the rise in the osmotic pressure of the blood. Thirst can be aroused experimentally by the intravenous injection of a hypertonic solution. The subject of thirst is dealt with more fully in chapter 62. In experiments on dogs Robinson and Adolph found that when the animals had ready access to water they drank when they had lost water to the extent of 0.5 per cent of their body weight. The amount of water drunk was just sufficient to replace that which had been lost. It is hard to conceive what signaled the cessation of drinking, for it occurred while the water was still in the stomach, that is before it had been absorbed.

THE WATER OUTPUT

Water is lost from the body in the feces, urine and saliva, and by the evaporation of water from the skin and lungs. The daily loss through these several channels is given in the following table for a man of average size at light occupation in a temperate climate.

	cc.
Skin (at average temperature and humidity)	500
Expired air (at average temperature and humidity)	350
Urine	1500
Feces	150
Total	2500

Under usual conditions of air temperature (23–25°C.), humidity and diet, the heat lost from the lungs and the surface of the body by the evaporation of water amounts to about 24 per cent of the total heat production. The measurement of this *insensible water loss* under standard conditions may therefore be employed as a basis for the determination of the basal metabolism (ch. 63).

The loss in the saliva is negligible under ordinary circumstances but may be considerable in mouth breathing (as a result of evaporation) and in those addicted to the spitting habit.

The water lost through the skin and lungs varies greatly with the temperature and relative humidity of the atmosphere and with the extent of the muscular exercise indulged in. At ordinary temperatures slight secretion by the sweat glands is not perceived since the sweat evaporates as quickly as it is formed. This *insensible perspiration*, as it is called, includes the loss of a greater amount of water by evaporation from the moist tissues beneath the skin; this loss is quite apart from the actual secretion of sweat (ch. 70). The diffusion of water through the skin and evaporation from the surface under ordinary comfortable conditions of room temperature and humidity is around 1 mg. per cm.^{2} of skin surface in a period of 10 minutes. The rate of diffusion is little different for living or dead skin and whether sweat glands are present or absent. The amount of the *insensible perspiration* has the average value given above but may be many times this value; when the air is hot or the body temperature raised. the rate of evaporation of water from the tissues beneath the skin is much more rapid, the secretion of sweat is also likely to be more active, but owing to the higher rate of evaporation a larger quantity of sweat is secreted before it becomes evident. Relative humidity and air movement also influence the rate of evaporation. So, in humid, still atmospheres sweat secretion is more evident though it may be no greater than in a drier atmosphere when evaporation is more rapid. Large quantities of sweat are secreted as a result of muscular exercise or when, as in the tropics, the temperature is high. In hot climates the daily secretion may amount to 3000 cc. daily and in very torrid atmospheres it may be as much as 10 liters. When heavy work is done in a hot environment, sweat may be secreted at the rate of 2 liters per hour. This necessitates the drinking of an equal quantity of fluid in order to maintain the normal water content of the body, since the intake must equal the output.

At ordinary temperatures the inspired air contains negligible quantities of water whereas the expired air is almost saturated with moisture. Any condition which increases the pulmonary ventilation therefore increases the water lost by this route.

The Relation of the Electrolyte Concentration and Tissue Changes to the Volume of Body Water

The isotonicity of the body fluid which depends mainly upon its concentration in sodium and chloride is maintained constant largely by the retention or elimination of water, the kidneys playing the primary role in this regulation. A loss of salt is accompanied by a loss of water and the ingestion of salt is followed by water retention. Thus it is possible to increase the volume of body water in normal persons to the point where edema occurs by the administration of large amounts of sodium bicarbonate and to cause the discharge of nephritic or cardiac edema by the reduction or

withdrawal of sodium from the diet. In the latter instance, only sufficient sodium chloride is available for the production of a more limited amount of isotonic fluid. The fundamental factors controlling the total volume of body water are not clearly understood. The hypothalamus is important in regulating the osmotic pressure of extracellular fluid through its influence on the liberation of antidiuretic hormone by the posterior pituitary gland, and hence its influence on water retention by the kidney (ch. 79). There must be, however, some means of regulating the absolute amount of body water. It is felt that the basic factor in this control is the regulation of sodium excretion by the kidney. Since the transplanted kidney can still regulate body water, this regulation must be finally effected by something carried in the blood. The adrenal cortex undoubtedly is important in this regulation through its influence on the reabsorption of sodium, but other factors must also be involved since even in the absence of the adrenal cortex some regulation of body water can still occur. Part of this regulation is mediated by aldosterone, which stimulates the reabsorption of sodium by the distal convoluted tubules. What starts the chain of events that leads to alterations in renal activity is not clear. Circulatory changes are important. Factors leading to a reduction in circulating blood volume, venous return or cardiac output appear to reduce the excretion of salt and water, whereas factors increasing blood volume or the venous return and cardiac output increase the excretion of salt and water. Whatever the precise initiating factor, it would seem that there must be a mechanism sensitive to changes in the absolute amount of body water as well as one sensitive to changes in the concentration of electrolytes. The details of this mechanism are unknown.

Changes in the diet can bring about changes in the total body water. Protein is laid down in the body with water (about 3 grams of water per gram of solid). During growth or convalescence from wasting diseases, retention of water therefore occurs, i.e., the intake of water, including that derived from solid food, exceeds the output. Fat is laid down with a minimal amount of water (only that in the protein of the connective tissue framework); the deposition of glycogen is accompanied by a small storage of water.[2] Water retention therefore follows a sudden change from

---

[2] Zuntz concluded from his experiments that 3 grams of water were laid down with each gram of carbohydrate, but his results have been questioned and are not now generally accepted.

a high fat to a high protein diet, and to a less degree from a fat diet to one high in carbohydrate. A change from a diet high in carbohydrate or protein to one high in fat is followed by the loss of water.

Reduction of the caloric value of the diet below the energy requirement is accompanied for a time by the retention of water. During the first week or so on a reducing diet the subject's weight may for this reason show little or no change, the fat catabolized being replaced by water. In a prolonged fast after the fat stores have been depleted, protein is also partly replaced by water, the muscles of animals dying of starvation showing a marked reduction in the proportion of protein.

DEHYDRATION

When the output of water exceeds the intake, the body's water content obviously will be reduced. That is, the body is in negative water balance and the condition known as dehydration results.

Causes of Dehydration

Dehydration may result from:

1. Water depletion or primary dehydration. (a) *Simple deprivation of water* from whatever cause: shipwreck, desert travel, dysphagia, extreme weakness, mental patients refusing to drink, etc. Under such circumstances, though there is an effort to conserve the stores of body water, through a reduction in the amount excreted by the kidney, in the sweat and by other routes, some water is always lost though none be drunk. Dehydration occurs more quickly in fever or if the environmental temperature is high.

b. Excessive water loss may result from persistent vomiting (e.g., pyloric or intestinal obstruction) prolonged diarrhea, or the excretion of large quantities of urine or sweat, especially when accompanied by a restricted water and salt intake. In the acute diarrheas of infants, dehydration and loss of weight may occur very rapidly. Such water loss is accompanied by serious derangement of electrolytes.

In water depletion the osmotic concentration of the extracellular fluid rises, water is drawn from the cells, and both extracellular and intracellular compartments shrink. Extreme thirst is experienced.

2. Reduction in the total quantity of electrolytes, salt depletion or secondary dehydration. The electrolytic concentration of the body fluids, both extracellular and intracellular, is maintained constant through the elimination or retention of water. That is, a reduction or increase in the total electrolytes, which comprise chiefly the basic radicles Na (extracellular) and K (intracellular) and the acid radicles HCO_3 and Cl, is accompanied by a corresponding decrease or increase in the volume of body water. The sum of the basic elements and acid elements of course must balance. Loss of Cl can be made good by the retention of H_2CO_3 and a rise in plasma bicarbonate. Excreted base, however, can be replaced only by basic substances supplied in the food. The total concentration of electrolytes in the body fluids is therefore dependent upon the stores of total base. For example, in pyloric or high intestinal obstruction, fluid is secreted in large quantities into the gastrointestinal tract. The fluid may be vomited or may collect and remain in the dilated part of the canal above the obstruction. (The latter occurrence is the rule in the rabbit which cannot vomit.) In either case the secretion of large quantities of gastric juice entails a loss of blood chloride. A similar chloride loss is induced in animals by means of a gastric fistula fashioned by sectioning through the pylorus, stitching the stomach opening to the abdominal wall and allowing the gastric juice to drain to the exterior. In the foregoing instances, the chloride depletion causes at first no ill effects, the normal concentrations in electrolytes of the blood and tissue fluids being maintained for a time by the retention of CO_2, and, as a consequence of this, an increase in bicarbonate. The compensation for the Cl loss leads however to alkalosis which is then countered by an increased excretion of base in the urine. This of course is accompanied by diuresis; marked dehydration results.

On the other hand, the continued loss of pancreatic juice to the exterior causes an immediate depletion of base; plasma bicarbonate is reduced. In the adjustment of the acid-base balance the excess of acid radicles is excreted in the urine; this again entails a loss of water. Similarly, the ingestion of acid-producing salts causes a depletion of base, which is used for the neutralization and excretion of the acid radicles. Such salts therefore act as diuretics and dehydrating agents.

In salt depletion the extracellular fluid is hypotonic; water enters the cells, so that the volume of intracellular fluid is maintained, whereas the extracellular fluid (especially the interstitial) is reduced.

Clinically the failure to ingest sufficient salt or the leaching of salt from the body of a seriously ill patient by glucose infusions is a not uncommon cause of salt depletion.

3. *The injection of hypertonic solutions* into the blood stream. When a strong sugar or salt solution is injected, the temporary rise in the osmotic pressure of the blood causes a flow of fluid from the tissues into the vascular system until equilibrium is re-established. The blood volume is increased, but is soon returned to normal by the loss of the excess material into the tissues and its eventual excretion via the kidney and bowels. A net loss of body water results.

Effects of Dehydration

(a) *Loss of weight* due to the reduction in tissue water as well as to the actual breakdown of body substance which occurs in the effort to furnish water for the maintenance of physiological processes. Fat and carbohydrate stores are first drawn upon for this purpose and later, protein. (b) *Disturbances in acid-base balance,* usually toward the acid side. The diminished quantity of circulating fluid (loss of plasma water, anhydremia) and the consequent depression of oxidative processes in the tissues is held responsible for the excessive production of acid metabolites, e.g., lactic acid. The slowing of the renal circulation also leads to a reduced excretion of urine and the retention of acids (e.g., phosphoric) which under normal circumstances are eliminated. (c) *Rise in the nonprotein nitrogen of the blood.* (d) *Rise in plasma protein concentration* and of chloride though there is no absolute increase. There is an absolute increase in blood sugar, especially when the stage of exhaustion approaches. (e) *Rise in body temperature* as a result of the reduction in circulating fluid (see ch. 70). (f) *Increased pulse rate and reduced cardiac output.* (g) *Thirst.* This occurs in water depletion but not in salt depletion; it will be discussed in chapter 62. Any fall in the water content of the tissues is reflected in the glandular activities especially of the salivary glands. Secretion is suppressed; the mouth and throat become dry. In dehydration thirst is extreme and the mouth parched. (h) *Dryness, wrinkling and looseness of skin* and a pinched expression to the features result from the loss of subcutaneous fat and of water from the deeper layers of the skin. Other manifestations are, reduced intraocular tension and recession of the eyeball and, in infants, depression of the fontanelle. (i) *Exhaustion and collapse.*

WATER INTOXICATION

When an animal is given large quantities of water by stomach tube, especially if urinary secretion is reduced by the administration of pitressin, the tissues become "water-logged," serious symptoms ensue, e.g., depression of temperature, vomiting, convulsions and coma, which shortly end in death. Similar effects also follow in man if large quantities of water are given to a patient with nephritic edema or, if in a subject of diabetes insipidus, pituitrin be administered while the water intake is maintained at the usual level (see ch. 74). The manifestations of water intoxication are believed to be due to the dilution of electrolytes in the body fluids, and the damage caused thereby to the tissue cells.[3]

Adrenalectomy reduces the renal response to water drinking, and thus increases the susceptibility to water intoxication. This susceptibility is reduced by the administration of desoxycorticosterone, of 17-hydroxy-11-dehydrocorticosterone, or of thyroid hormone. A similar protective action is exerted by these principles upon normal animals.

In water intoxication, the protein and chloride of the plasma are diminished and the extracellular water *decreased.* The water retained in the body enters the cells of blood and tissues which become swollen. It is not possible to account for the reduction in plasma chloride by increased renal excretion for both adrenalectomized and normal animals actually excrete less salt than usual; apparently the salt is diverted from extracellular to intracellular fluids.

There is no danger from excess fluid being retained in the body through water drinking, for the sense of thirst and its appeasement nicely control the quantity ingested; but the artificial administration of inordinate amounts of water in the form of glucose solution, especially after surgical operations when there is some tendency toward antidiuresis, may cause serious disturbances in water metabolism. The effects of an excess of body water induced in this way can be corrected readily by the administration of hypertonic saline.

When there has been prolonged ischemic injury of tissues, as occurs following tourniquet application and subsequent release, large amounts of sodium are soaked up by the injured tissues. In ischemic shock in mice, as much as $\frac{1}{4}$ of the total extracellular sodium may be lost into the injured region. The uptake of sodium by the injured cells causes its level in the extracellular

---

[3] Excessive concentration of electrolytes in the tissue fluid with consequent hypertonicity, as occurs in shipwrecked sailors if they drink sea water (which has a concentration in salts about three times that of serum) causes an equally deleterious effect upon the tissue cells. This appears to be the cause of death.

fluids to fall. Normally, the kidney would respond to this reduction in the electrolyte concentration by excreting more water and electrolyte homeostasis would be maintained. But instead, there is renal retention of water and the sodium level of the interstitial fluid and plasma remains low. Infusions with sodium chloride are effective in promoting survival in this condition, but colloid or glucose solutions *not* containing sodium chloride are ineffective.

Factors Governing the Interchange of Fluid between the Tissues and the Vessels

According to Starling's view (which is generally accepted) the physical factors which determine the flow of fluid from the tissues into the blood stream as well as in the reverse direction—from the vessels to tissue spaces—are the *osmotic* and *hydrostatic pressures* of the fluids in the two situations.

OSMOTIC PRESSURE

Osmosis is diffusion through a membrane separating water—or an aqueous solution—to which the membrane is permeable, from another aqueous solution to whose dissolved materials the membrane is impermeable. Such a membrane that permits the passage of water or of some substances in solution, but acts as a barrier to the molecules of certain other substances, is called *semipermeable*.

If an aqueous solution of cane sugar be placed in a vessel and a layer of water poured gently upon its surface, the two liquids will remain separate for a time. Gradually, however, sugar molecules will diffuse upward and intermingle with the water molecules, whereas many of the latter will pass downwards into the sugar solution. The diffusion process, which due to the random movement of the molecules and quite independent of gravity or convection currents, will continue slowly until the concentrations of the two types of molecules become equal throughout all parts of the liquid. If now instead of allowing free diffusion between the two solutions to take place, they be separated by a membrane semipermeable with respect to the sugar molecules, equal and free diffusion cannot occur. Since water molecules can cross the membrane into the sugar solution but sugar molecules cannot pass out, the volume of the solution is bound to rise. The water molecules diffuse in both directions, but their concentrations in pure water being higher than in an aqueous solution a greater number will strike the water side of the membrane and more will pass through into the sugar solution than in the opposite direction; water therefore

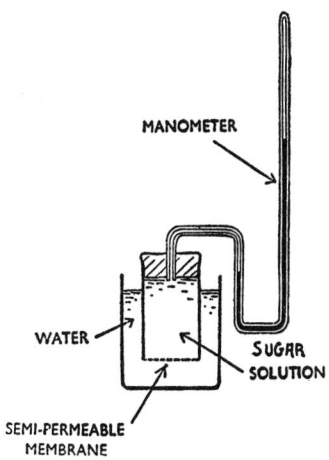

FIG. 24.2. As the pressure rises in the chamber it opposes the inward diffusion of the water molecules.

gradually accumulates on the sugar side of the membrane and dilutes the solution. If the compartment containing the solution of sugar is enclosed by rigid walls and connected with a manometer the pressure that develops can be measured. This pressure since it is caused by osmosis is called the *osmotic pressure*. A manometer (fig. 24.2) designed for the measurement of osmotic pressures is called an *osmometer*. Osmosis when related to the transfer of water across cell boundaries is called *endosmosis* or *exosmosis* according to whether water passes into or out of the cell.

Theoretically, the transference of water through a semipermeable membrane, if unopposed by any other force would proceed indefinitely, although at a progressively slower rate, and cause infinite dilution of the osmotically active substance on the other side. The volume of the solution would continue to increase and the osmotic pressure would not cease to rise until the concentrations of water molecules on the two sides of the membrane were equal. However, owing to the presence of the molecules of the dissolved substance such equalization can never be fully attained. But the rise in pressure itself by opposing diffusion of the water molecules into the solution after a time automatically brings osmosis to a standstill.

Great pressures are capable of being developed by osmotically active substances. A 10 per cent solution of cane sugar, for example, can produce an osmotic pressure of over 6 atmospheres, which is a pressure equivalent to that exerted by a column of fluid between 170 and 200 feet high.

Semipermeable membranes vary greatly with respect to the materials that they will or will not allow to pass. Erythrocytes, for example, are permeable to water but not to hemoglobin and the plasma proteins, and are more permeable to chloride and bicarbonate ions than to potassium and sodium ions. Even the red blood corpuscles of different species vary considerably with respect to their relative permeability to these two cations, but generally speaking blood cells as well as other cells are more pervious to K^+ than to Na^+. The capillary membrane on the other hand permits the passage of all substances of small molecular size dissolved in the plasma and has only a limited permeability to the plasma proteins. The capillary wall of the renal glomerulus lets through very little protein. Artificial membranes such as those made of a precipitate of copper ferrocyanide or of collodion also vary in their permeabilities.

Osmotic pressure measurements give an estimate of the tendency for the diffusion of water to occur across a semipermeable membrane. *The osmotic pressure is a result of the diffusion process, not a cause of it.*

Osmosis is important in many physiological processes in both animal and plant life, e.g., the excretion of urine, the interchange of materials between the interiors of the blood cells or tissue cells and their surroundings, the flow of sap in plants, as well as the regulation of the blood volume. The fluids of the body contain various electrolytes and organic materials in solution. Semipermeable membranes of various types possessing different selective permeabilities, such as the cell wall, the vascular endothelium, the renal epithelium, and the membranes lining the serous cavities and the alimentary tract, are interposed between fluids with different concentrations of osmotically active substances.

Isotonic, hypertonic and *hypotonic* are terms employed to denote the osmotic activity of a solution relatively to that of some other solution. If, for example, two salt solutions of equal strength are separated by a semipermeable membrane neither will develop an osmotic pressure; they are said to be *isotonic*. If the solution on one side of the membrane be stronger, the net amount of water passing to this side will therefore be greater and the solution here is said to be *hypertonic*. The weaker solution from which there is a net transference of water is termed *hypotonic*.

In physiology these terms are used most commonly to indicate the osmotic activity of a solution as compared with that of the body fluids. For example, excised organs or sections of tissue upon which experiments are to be performed are kept moist and viable by a saline solution isotonic with the tissue fluid. Shrinkage of the cells through the loss of water (as would result from the use of a hypertonic solution) or swelling by endosmosis (as would occur if the solution were hypotonic) is thus avoided. Similarly, in order to prevent either shrinkage or swelling of the red blood cells, they must be suspended in a solution, such as plasma, that is isotonic with the fluid in their interiors. See Hemolysis, chapter 28.

HYDROSTATIC PRESSURE

The other important factor in the interchange of fluid between the blood and the general body fluids according to Starling's hypothesis is the hydrostatic pressure within the capillaries, i.e., the blood pressure, and its relation to that of the extravascular fluids.

THE RELATION OF OSMOTIC TO HYDROSTATIC PRESSURE IN THE INTERCHANGE OF FLUID ACROSS THE CAPILLARY MEMBRANE

The walls of the capillaries (generally throughout the body, as already mentioned) permit the free passage of water and substances of small molecular size dissolved in the plasma, e.g., glucose, inorganic salts, urea, etc.

Obviously this must be so, otherwise essential nutritive materials could not reach the tissue cells and waste products could not enter the blood stream to be excreted. But the capillary wall is largely impermeable to the large molecules of the plasma colloids. To this partial impermeability the osmotic activity of the plasma is due. Since the albumin has the smallest molecule of the three plasma proteins, it escapes through the vessel in relatively greater amounts than do the globulin and fibrinogen fractions.

By the use of I^{131} labelled albumin, it has been found that the amount of plasma protein passing through the capillary wall into the interstitial fluid is considerable, amounting to more than the total protein of plasma each day. The rate of return of protein from interstitial fluid is very important in the maintenance of plasma protein levels. The lymphatic system plays a major role in this return (ch. 25).

The manner in which osmotic and hydrostatic pressures act in regulating the interchange of fluids between the tissues and the muscles may now be seen. The blood at the arterial end of a capillary has a pressure, let us say, of 30 mm. Hg (this is an arbitrary figure and will vary according to the activity of the part). This is a force driving the water and the dissolved crystalloids through the capillary membrane. But the hydrostatic pressure of the tissue fluid on the outer side of the membrane offsets, in part, that within. The pressure of fluid in the tissue spaces is difficult to determine but it is considerably less than that in the capillaries. It probably varies considerably in different regions, being low in those containing much loose areolar tissue. But for illustration let it be assumed to be 10 mm. Hg. The hydrostatic pressure, therefore, which is effective in forcing fluid out of the vessel (filtration pressure) is only the difference between the pressure within and that on the outside of the vessel, namely, 20 mm. Hg. But the osmotic pressures of the plasma and tissue fluids must be taken into account. In the plasma it amounts to about 25 mm. Hg. The tissue fluids have a lower protein content and consequently a lower osmotic pressure. The latter amounts to about 15 mm. Hg. Owing to this disparity of 10 mm. Hg between the osmotic pressures of plasma and tissue fluid, there would be a net tranference of water and diffusible substances inwards across the capillary membrane if such transference were unopposed by any other force. But a net hydrostatic pressure of 20 mm. Hg is set against it at the arterial end of the capillary leaving a balance amounting to 10 mm. Hg which serves to filter water, salts, etc., and a little protein out of the plasma. Now as the blood flows rather slowly through the capillary and loses water in this way by filtration, the protein concentration, and consequently its osmotic activity, rises. Coincidently with the progressive rise in osmotic activity the hydrostatic pressure declines, until at the venous end of the capillary there is a balance of net osmotic pressure over net hydrostatic pressure. Water accompanied by freely diffusible materials is therefore absorbed into the circulation. This picture of filtration at the arterial end of the capillary and absorption at the venous end is going on continually at the periphery of the vascular bed. But it is subject to considerable variation, not only in the same capillary from time to time but in different parts of the peripheral circulation at any moment (see fig. 24.3).

As the blood flows through the capillary, as a

result of the passage of water outwards there is a consequent rise in the concentration of protein.

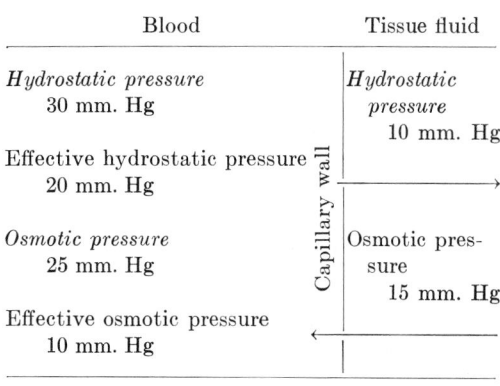

Blood		Tissue fluid
Hydrostatic pressure 30 mm. Hg		*Hydrostatic pressure* 10 mm. Hg
Effective hydrostatic pressure 20 mm. Hg	Capillary wall	
Osmotic pressure 25 mm. Hg		Osmotic pressure 15 mm. Hg
Effective osmotic pressure 10 mm. Hg		

Driving force → 10 mm. Hg (20 − 10)

Metabolic processes in the tissues bring about changes whereby larger molecules are being broken down into smaller ones; other molecules are removed or built up into larger ones. In this way alterations in molecular concentrations and in the diffusibility of the constituents of the tissue fluids with consequent variations in osmotic relationships are occurring ceaselessly. The actual exchange of water across the capillary wall is rapid. Studies with deuterium and tritium-labelled water indicate that in one minute an amount equal to the total plasma water is exchanged.

Under any circumstance in which the blood volume is increased or diminished, either the hydrostatic pressure or the osmotic pressure or both are altered, and it is through such changes that the blood fluid is restored automatically to its previous level. After hemorrhage, for example, the hydrostatic pressure is lowered in the capillary area but the osmotic pressure is unchanged. Fluid will therefore be absorbed from the tissue spaces. Moreover, constriction of the capillaries tends to reduce, dilation to increase the capillary pressure. Therefore, the capillary constriction which follows a severe hemorrhage will slow the filtration rate at the arterial end of the capillary and increase absorption of interstitial fluid at the venous end. Again, when water is drawn from the blood, in consequence of excessive loss of fluid by the kidney, sweat glands or bowels, concentration of the plasma proteins will result. The increased osmotic pressure of the plasma will then hasten the rate of absorption from the tissues. The intravenous injection of large quantities of isotonic saline, on the other hand, will have the twofold effect of diluting the colloids and tem-

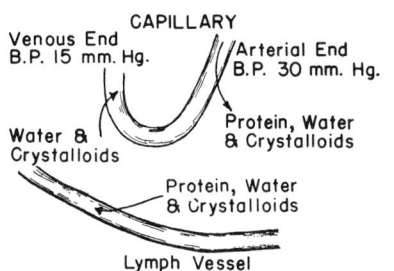

CAPILLARY

Venous End B.P. 15 mm. Hg.

Arterial End B.P. 30 mm. Hg.

Water & Crystalloids

Protein, Water & Crystalloids

Protein, Water & Crystalloids

Lymph Vessel

FIG. 24.3. Illustrating the relation of hydrostatic and osmotic pressures in the regulation of the interchange of fluid between the vessels and the tissue spaces.

porarily increasing the hydrostatic pressure. The excess fluid in consequence is rapidly eliminated from the blood stream into the tissues and later through the kidney and bowels.

Alterations in Blood Volume

Many factors are concerned with the regulation of blood volume, the pressure of blood in the capillaries, the concentrations of poorly diffusible substances on the two sides of the capillary wall, the available capillary surface, the permeability of the capillaries and the total capacity of the vascular bed.

REDUCTION OF THE BLOOD VOLUME

This may result from:

1. A loss of *whole blood* as in hemorrhage.

2. *Reduction in the total number of red cells*, as a result of increased destruction or diminished production (see anemia ch. 30).

3. Loss of *plasma* alone from the vessels as in burns or shock from other causes (ch. 49).

4. *Loss of blood water*. This is called *anhydremia* and is simply a part of a general dehydration and so results from the same causes as the latter.

In the reduction of blood volume resulting from hemorrhage, the concentration of the blood in cells and protein is lowered, since a watery fluid enters the vessels from the surrounding tissues.

When the blood volume is lowered as a result of a loss of plasma, the red cell concentration is increased (hemoconcentration) but the protein of the plasma is little altered.

In anhydremia both the protein concentration of the plasma and the red cell count are raised. The concentration of plasma protein may increase by 50 per cent or more. The viscosity of the blood is therefore raised, and it flows sluggishly from an opened vein. If the anhydremia persists, the red cell count and the protein concentration tend to fall again. Then an estimation of the blood concentration may fail to give a true index of the extent of the blood volume reduction.

Acute exposure to cold causes a moderate loss of water from the blood to the tissues (chiefly skin muscle and probably liver), the total water content of the body remaining unaltered. It is not altogether clear by what means this movement of water is brought about. It is, however, an important factor in the regulation of body temperature (ch. 70). The work of Barbour and others furnishes evidence of a nervous element in the mechanism. Animals in which the cord had been divided in the upper thoracic region when placed in a cold bath did not respond in the normal fashion. Concentration of the blood did not result and the temperature of the body fell to that of the environment. The control is exercised evidently through vasomotor nerves. More *prolonged exposure to cold* (6–12 weeks) increases blood volume in experimental animals.

Posture. The blood volume of the human subject after 30 minutes or so in the erect posture is some 15 per cent less than that in recumbency. A fluid of low protein concentration leaks from the vessels of the lower limbs into the extracapillary tissues, as a result apparently of the increased hydrostatic pressure in the capillaries of these parts. For this reason, a subject must be in the recumbent position in order to obtain an accurate measurement of blood volume.

INCREASE IN BLOOD VOLUME

(1) *High temperatures*. In hydrated subjects, exposure to a high temperature leads to an increase in blood volume. This increase reaches a maximum in about 7 days after which it may return toward normal. The extracellular fluid volume increases also, although initially the greater part of this increase is reflected in the elevated plasma volume. In the first few hours after exposure to heat the changes are slight and inconsistent.

(2) *Muscular exercise*. The effect of a bout of vigorous exercise in man is to decrease the plasma volume. The magnitude of this decrease may be exaggerated when measurements are made by the dye method because of a change in the optical properties of the plasma. However the protein concentration of the plasma, and the red cell count increase. The increase does not seem to be progressive. Some elevation in blood volume may occur with muscular training. This can be demonstrated in dogs, but in men accustomed to hard physical work, the red cell volume in relation to height and weight is only slightly increased over that of sedentary individuals.

(3) *Emotional excitement* in animals and in man causes an increase in blood volume.

(4) *Pregnancy*. In pregnant women, the blood volume though somewhat variable increases on the average by 20 to 30 per cent, though in the last few weeks of pregnancy tends to fall again. There is an increase in plasma volume and in interstitial fluid. Associated with this is a retention of sodium. Restriction or the administration of salt reduces or increases, respectively, the volume of extracellular fluid. The increase in plasma

volume in pregnancy, combined with a lower protein concentration of the plasma is responsible, in part at least, for the edema of the lower limbs which commonly occurs in the pregnant state. Hemoglobin determinations in the last trimester of pregnancy give a falsely low indication of total red cell mass.

(5) *Congestive heart failure.* As a result of the retention of sodium, the extracellular fluid undergoes a pronounced increase.

(6) *The administration of desoxycorticosterone* causes a retention of salt and, as a consequence, a rise in the volume of plasma and interstitial fluid. This depends on the salt load. Aldosterone is much more active than desoxycorticosterone in its effect on sodium retention. It helps to keep in equilibrium the fluid volume and sodium retained, fluid retention varying directly with that of sodium.

Summary of the Pathological States Associated with Alterations in Blood Volume

Reduction

(*a*) *Hemorrhage* (loss of whole blood), (*b*) *burns* (loss of plasma), (*c*) *dehydration* (loss of water), (*d*) *pernicious anemia* (reduction in red cells, with a moderate increase in plasma), (*e*) *certain chronic anemias other than those of the pernicious type.* In these the total volume of red cells is only slightly or moderately reduced and this is to a large extent compensated for by an increase in plasma above the normal standard. The total blood volume is therefore, as a rule, not greatly below normal as calculated upon the basis of weight or of surface area. (*f*) *Obesity.* The blood volume per kilogram of body weight is much reduced but is normal when considered in relation to the body surface. (*g*) *Myxedema* (reduction of both red cells and plasma but mainly of the former).

Increase

(*a*) *Polycythemia vera* (increase mainly of red cells but also of plasma), (*b*) *cirrhosis* of the liver (increase of plasma, (*c*) *leukemia* (increase in white cells and plasma), (*d*) *splenomegaly* with anemia—Banti's disease (increase in plasma), (*e*) *hyperthyroidism* (equal increases both in red cells and plasma), (*f*) congestive heart failure (increase in plasma).

It should be pointed out that the proportions of red cells and plasma may vary from the normal though the total blood volume remains unaltered.

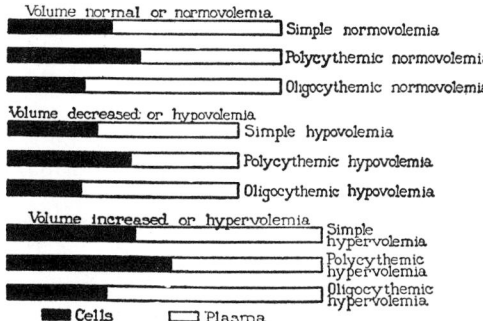

FIG. 24.4. The nine possible combinations of whole blood, plasma and red cell volumes (after Rowntree).

With regard to the blood volume and the proportion of cells to plasma there are therefore nine possible blood states. Rowntree has introduced the following descriptive terminology. A normal blood volume he terms *normovolemia.* If the ratio of cells to plasma is normal as well, he calls the condition *simple normovolemia,* but a decrease or increase in the number of cells in relation to plasma is termed *oligocythemic* or *polycythemic normovolemia* respectively. *Hypovolemia* and *hypervolemia* are corresponding terms for reduced and increased blood volumes; each of these is divisible into simple, polycythemic and oligocythemic forms (see fig. 24.4).

The Effects of Hemorrhage

When more than 30 per cent of the blood volume is lost rapidly, the body is usually unable to repair the loss unaided and, unless transfusion is resorted to, death results. In a healthy man the loss of 30 per cent or less of his blood calls readjusting mechanisms into play which may bring the blood volume back to the normal level within a remarkably short time; 500 cc. or so of blood drawn for transfusion purposes are said to be replaced within an hour or so. The restoration of the blood to its previous concentration in erythrocytes, however, takes about 7 weeks on the average. This time may be shortened considerably by the administration of iron and a diet containing a liberal quantity of high quality protein. Fowler and Barer found in a study of 200 blood donors that, after the removal of 550 cc. of blood, the average fall in hemoglobin was 2.3 grams per 100 cc. Regeneration of hemoglobin occurred at the rate of 0.049 gram per cent for men and 0.040 gram per cent for women per day.

The protective mechanisms which automatically come into action after hemorrhage are several and may be divided into two groups—*immediate* or *early* and *delayed*.

Immediate or Early Effects

If the loss of blood is large, especially if it is of sudden occurrence and from an artery, there is a prompt fall in blood pressure as a result simply of the reduction in circulating fluid. If not too great, the fall in pressure is salutary, since it helps to prevent further bleeding. A moderate loss of blood, 10 per cent of the total amount, produces little or no drop in pressure. This is especially true if the blood is lost gradually and if it comes from a vein, i.e., beyond the peripheral resistance. Under these circumstances compensatory mechanisms easily maintain the pressure of blood at its normal height. Three main compensations relating to the vascular system occur: (a) reduction in the capacity of the vascular bed (b) increased peripheral resistance (c) fluid entry from the tissues. These will be dealt with later.

Clotting of the blood (ch. 33) which occurs within a few minutes serves to close the opening in the blood vessel. The blood tends to clot more rapidly than usual after a severe hemorrhage. The initial drop in pressure, when such occurs, aids the formation of the clot. Stanching of the bleeding is also furthered in the case of an artery by the retraction and contraction of the middle fibromuscular coat of the vessel, as well as by the curling up and crenation of its endothelial lining. Platelets are deposited on the injured surfaces and agglutinate to form a plug or a base of attachment for the clot. Some disintegrate also and liberate a vasoconstrictor substance, serotonin, or 5-hydroxytryptamine which is a material aid in hemostasis (ch. 33). Disintegration of platelets results in the release of substances which are essential for thromboplastin generation and the initiation of clotting. These factors, together with the fall in blood pressure, may be sufficient to stanch the flow of blood from an artery as large even as the popliteal. Clot retraction, which also depends on platelets, leads to the formation of a firmer plug.

In small vessels the opposed endothelial surfaces become sticky and coherent.

Increase in the heart rate. This is almost invariably an accompaniment of a severe hemorrhage and is one of the most valuable signs of concealed, i.e., internal, bleeding; this sign is not seen, as a rule, in moderate blood losses or in slow bleeding. It is brought about through carotid sinus and aortic reflexes (ch. 42 and 53) initiated by the fall in blood pressure. Reduction in blood flow through the vessels of the medulla with the consequent anoxemia of the cardiac centers may be an additional factor. Adrenaline liberation (ch. 76) may possibly play a part. Although the nature of the compensation provided by the increase in heart rate is not clear in view of the reduced venous return, it is possible that the increase in heart rate may lower the central venous pressure and hence improve the pressure gradient in the veins. This would improve venous return over what it would otherwise be.

Release of blood from blood reservoirs into the circulation helps to restore the circulating blood volume. These reservoirs are skin, liver, lungs, spleen and the splanchnic venous vessels. The blood from the spleen is richer in cells than the circulating blood. Its reservoir function in some animals is great, but in man it is not of such importance.

Increased respiration. The anoxia of the chemoreceptors of the carotid and aortic bodies caused by the reduced blood flow is probably responsible for the increased rate and depth of breathing. When the blood loss is more profound, and consequently the oxygen want more urgent, long deeply drawn inspirations, and expirations of a sighing character ensue (air hunger), or periodic breathing of a Cheyne-Stokes type may develop. Gasping respirations precede death.

Reduction in capacity of the vascular bed and redistribution of the blood. When the flow of blood has been stopped or considerably lessened by a complete or partial closure of the wound in the vessel, the blood pressure, if this had fallen, rises again. This is the result mainly of a readjustment of the capacity of the vascular system whereby it is made to conform more nearly to the lessened volume of blood. It is this reduction in the vascular capacity which prevents the initial fall in pressure when the loss of blood is gradual. It is effected by the reflex narrowing of innumerable small vessels (vasoconstriction) in regions such as the skin, mucous membranes, intestine and other parts not immediately essential to life. If the hemorrhage has not been too severe the reduction in the capacity of the vascular bed may result in maintenance of an adequate venous return and consequent maintenance of cardiac output and of arterial blood pressure. If the hemorrhage is somewhat greater, then the venous return and cardiac output may fall, but the blood pressure may be maintained by an increase in peripheral resistance along with a reduction in the capacity of the arterial vessels. If the hemorrhage is still greater, then the arterial blood pressure will fall and may be restored by restoration of blood volume through the entrance of fluid into the blood vessels from the tissues. The vascular response is called into play by the underfilled state of the arteries and large veins feeding the heart (see vascular reflexes, ch. 42).

The vasoconstriction is not confined to the small arteries and arterioles but extends to arteries and veins (Heymans), and vasomotion of metarterioles (ch. 36 and 46) and precapillary sphincters is enhanced. These latter vessels also show increased reactivity to mechanical stimulation and to adrenaline (Zweifach and associates). The level of adrenaline and probably also of noradrenaline in blood is increased following hemorrhage. This probably plays a part in the vasoconstriction. These measures whereby the blood remaining in the vascular system is confined to a smaller space are of the utmost importance; they enable the essential centers in the medulla to be supplied with blood under adequate pressure to sustain their vitality. Also a greater quantity of blood than would otherwise be possible is brought to the heart to supply its muscle, fill its cavities and maintain the circulation. The withdrawal of blood from the less important parts of the body is responsible, however, for some of the characteristic manifestations of hemorrhage: notably the pallor of the skin and mucous membranes, and the coldness of the body surface. The cerebral anemia causes sensations of giddiness or faintness, flashes of light or ringing in the ears (tinnitus). The metabolic changes occurring as a result of hemorrhage or fluid loss are anaerobic in type and in the later stages, at all events, may be a consequence of reduced blood supply to tissues, although it is possible that other factors may be involved in the early changes. The rise in blood pressure at this stage is conducive to fresh bleeding. There is danger at that time of the clot becoming dislodged.

In very severe hemorrhage, the hypernormal phase of capillary reactivity gives place to one of reduced capillary responses as the irreversible stage of hemorrhagic shock supervenes. The minute vessels tend toward dilation and become unresponsive, though the larger vessels still remain constricted.

Delayed Effects

Replacement of the lost fluid. This, it has already been mentioned, commences almost upon the instant that the blood is lost, but takes a variable length of time, depending upon the extent of the blood loss, to become complete. It occurs as a result of the low hydrostatic pressure within the capillaries. Fluid from the tissues moves into the vessels and dilutes the blood. The corpuscular concentration is therefore reduced and since fluid is entering the capillaries directly from the tissues and not by way of lymphatics, less protein is returned with the fluid from the tissues and for a short time after hemorrhage the protein content of the plasma is markedly depressed. Very soon, however, the concentration of protein in the plasma shows a rise again as a result of the mobilization of protein stores probably from the tissue stores. Calvin found, that in dogs 50 per cent of the plasma protein removed by bleeding was restored within 4 hours. The extreme thirst which the subject of acute hemorrhage suffers is the call of the tissues for fluid and indicates that their own fluid stores are being drawn into the underfilled vessels. The administration of water will therefore aid the body in recovering its water balance and replenishing the blood volume.

Replacement of the blood cells finally occurs through the increased activity of the bloodforming organs. This takes several days or weeks, the rapidity of the process depending to a large extent upon the nutrition and recuperative power of the individual and upon the diet as well as the amount of blood lost. While the repair process is in progress reticulocytes are found in increased numbers in the blood.

In summary, following hemorrhage, if the loss of blood is not great, the circulatory effects of a reduction in blood volume may be compensated by vasoconstriction with decrease in the capacity of the vascular system. Thus the venous return, cardiac output and hence arterial blood pressure, may be maintained. If the loss is greater, the venous return and cardiac output may be reduced somewhat, but the arterial blood pressure may still be maintained by increasing the resistance to outflow from the arteries by vasoconstriction, especially of arterioles. If the loss is greater still, then the venous return and cardiac output will be reduced to such a degree that the increase in peripheral resistance may be insufficient to maintain the arterial blood pressure. The vascular compensations are brought about through reflexes initiated by the stimulation of stretch receptors in the blood vessels, principally in the carotid sinus and aortic arch, but possibly also in the great veins and right atrium. Further compensation comes as a consequence of arteriolar constriction and of increased vasomotion in the terminal vascular bed. As a result of arteriolar vasoconstriction, the blood pressure in the terminal vascular bed as a whole is reduced. As a result of increased vasomotion, the hydrostatic pressure in the true capillaries of the terminal vascular bed is reduced. With the fall in hydrostatic pressure in the capillary vessels, fluid entry into the capillaries from the interstitial spaces is increased and the blood volume tends to be restored. Since relatively less fluid reenters the circulation by way of lymphatics, the protein reentry will be less in relation to the fluid and the blood becomes more dilute. Protein is restored relatively quickly thereafter and a still slower restoration of red blood cells occurs

REFERENCES

ALLEN, T. H., PENG, M. T., CHEN, K. P., HUANG, T. F., CHANG, C. AND FANG, H. S. Metabolism, 1956, **5**, 328.

BARBOUR, H. G. AHD HAMILTON, W. F. Am. J. Physiol., 1925, **73**, 315.

BARCROFT, J., KENNEDY, J. A. AND MASON, M. F. J. Physiol., 1939, **95**, 159.

BRODIE, B. B. Methods of Medical Research, Vol. 4. M. B. Visscher, Ed. Year Book Publishers, Chicago, 1952.

BYROM, F. B. Clin. Sc., 1934, **1**, 245 and 273.

CHINARD, F. P. Methods of Medical Research, Vol. 4. M. B. Visscher, Ed. Year Book Publishers, Chicago, 1952.

CRAIG, A. B. AND WATERHOUSE, C. J. Lab. & Clin. Med., 1957, **49**, 165.

CRISPELL, K. R., PORTER, B. AND NIESET, R. T. J. Clin. Invest., 1950, **29**, 513.

CROOKE, A. C. AND MORRIS, C. J. O. J. Physiol., 1942, **101**, 217.

EDER, H. A. Methods of Medical Research, Vol. 4, M. B. Visscher, Ed. Year Book Publishers, Chicago, 1952.

FOWLER, W. M. AND BARER, A. P. J. A. M. A., 1942, **118**, 421.

GAMBLE, J. L., ROSS, G. S. AND TISDALL, F. F. J. Biol. Chem., 1923, **57**, 633.

GAUNT, R. Endocrinology, 1944, **34**, 400.

GIBSON, J. G. AND EVELYN, K. A. J. Clin. Invest., 1938, **17**, 153.

GIBSON, J. G. AND COLLEAGUES. J. Clin. Invest., 1946, **25**, 605, 617.

GRAY, S. J. AND HEDDY, F. J. Clin. Invest., 1953, **32**, 108.

GREGERSEN, M. I., GIBSON, J. J. AND STEAD, E. A. Am. J. Physiol., 1935, **113**, 54.

GREGERSON, M. I. AND STEWART, J. D. Am. J. Physiol., 1939, **125**, 142.

HAHN, P. F. AND ASSOCIATES, J. Exper. Med., 1942, **75**, 221.

HALDANE, J. S. AND SMITH, J. L. J. Physiol., 1900, **25**, 331.

KEITH, N. M., ROWNTREE, L. G. AND GERAGHTY, J. T. Arch. Int. Med., 1915, **16**, 547.

KENNEDY, J. A. AND MILLIKAN, G. A. J. Physiol., 1938, **93**, 276.

MANERY, J. F. Methods of Medical Research, Vol. 4. M. B. Visscher, Ed. Year Book Publishers, Chicago, 1952.

PAINTER, E. E. AND ASSOCIATES. Am. J. Physiol., 1948, **152**, 66.

RAWSON, R. A. Am. J. Physiol., 1942, **138**, 708.

READ, R. C. AND GILBERTSEN, S. Arch. Int. Med., 1957, **100**, 259.

ROBINSON, E. A. AND ADOLPH, E. F. Am. J. Physiol., 1943, **139**, 39.

SCHILLER, R. AND DORFMAN, R. I. Endocrinology, 1943, **33**, 402.

SEMPLE, R. E., THOMSEN, A. E. T., BALL, A. J. AND EXCELL, B. J. Am. J. Physiol., 1956, **187**, 631.

STEVENSON, J. A. F. Recent progress in hormone research., 1949, **4**, 363.

WASSERMAN, K., JOSEPH, J. D. AND MAYERSON, H. S. Am. J. Physiol., 1956, **184**, 175.

WASSERMAN, K. AND MAYERSON, H. S. Am. J. Physiol., 1951, **165**, 15.

WASSERMAN, K. AND MAYERSON, H. S. Am. J. Physiol., 1952, **170**, 1.

ZWEIFACH, B. W. AND ASSOCIATES. Am. J. Anat. 1944, **75**, 239. Am. J. Physiol., 1944, **142**, 80; 1947, **150**, 239. Ann. Surg., 1944, **120**, 232. Surg. Gynec. & Obst., 1945, **80**, 593. Ann. New York Acad. Sc., 1946, **46**, 533, 571. See also CHAMBERS, R. Nature, 1948, **162**, 835.

Monographs and Reviews

ADOLPH, E. F. Physiol. Rev., 1933, **13**, 336.

ADOLPH, E. F. AND ASSOCIATES. Physiology of man in the desert. Interscience Publishers, N. Y., 1947.

ALBERT, S. N. Blood Volume. Charles C. Thomas, Springfield, Ill., 1963.

BARBOUR, H. G. Physiol. Rev., 1921, **1**, 295.

BERSON, S. A. Bull. New York Acad. Med., 1950, **30**, 750.

BROWN, E., HOPPER, J. AND WENNESLAND, R. Ann. Rev. Physiol., 1957, **19**, 231.

BULL, G. M. Lectures on the scientific basis of medicine. Brit. Postgrad. Med. Fed., U. of London. Vol. III, p. 219. The Athlone Press, 1953–1954.

DAVIS, H. A. Blood Volume Dynamics. Charles C. Thomas, Springfield, Ill., 1962.

LANDIS, E. M. Physiol. Rev., 1934, **14**, 404.

LOTSPEICH, W. D. Ann. Rev. Physiol., 1958, **20**, 339.

MANERY, J. F. Physiol. Rev., 1954, **34**, 334.

MARRIOTT, W. M. Physiol. Rev., 1923, **3**, 275.

MILLICAN, R. C. AND ROSENTHAL, S. M. Ann. Rev. Med., 1954, **5**, 285.

PETERS, J. P. Body water. Charles C Thomas, Springfield, Ill., 1935.

PINSON, E. A. Physiol. Rev., 1952, **32**, 123.

ROSENTHAL, S. M. AND MILLICAN, R. C. Pharm. Rev., 1954, **6**, 489.

STARLING, E. H. The fluids of the body. Constable, London, 1909.

CHAPTER 25

The Lymph and Tissue Fluids

Structure of the Lymphatic System

The lymphatic system commences peripherally as a meshwork of delicate vessels (lymph capillaries) which drain the tissue spaces. This is a one-way system, the lymph within it moving toward the great veins. By the confluence of small vessels larger ones are formed which, receiving tributaries along their course, gradually swell in size, and finally form the right lymphatic and thoracic ducts. These pour their lymph into the blood stream by way of the right and left subclavian veins, respectively. The system is a closed one, its vessels possessing complete walls formed of endothelial cells. Small nodes (lymph nodes or glands) are interposed in the course of the larger lymph channels. These vessels, upon reaching the gland, break up into finer channels which, plunging into the node, open into the sinuses of its cortex. After passing through the gland the lymph is collected again on the other side by fine vessels which soon re-form into a few larger trunks. The glands are placed at strategic points along the lymph routes, e.g., the elbow and axilla, knee and groin in the case of the upper and lower limbs, and at points in the abdomen, thorax and neck where several lymph vessels join. Lymph vessels are situated in skin, in subcutaneous tissue, in the fascial planes of muscles, in the linings of the respiratory, gastrointestinal and genitourinary tracts, and in the capsule and septa of the liver. Those in the intestinal villi are known as *lacteals* (fig. 25.1).

In the walls of the abdominal cavity the lymphatics are most abundant on the under surface of the diaphragm, where the greatest lymphatic absorption of colloidal material and minute particles takes place. The respiratory movements hasten absorption from the abdominal cavity, probably by varying rhythmically the intra-abdominal pressure. Absorption also takes place into lymphatics of the omentum. Phagocytes play an important role in absorption through both the diaphragm and omentum. Absorption through the parietal peritoneum is slight and is mainly through the blood capillaries, which absorb only crystalloid solutions. The lymphatic system of the heart consists of intercommunicating plexuses lying beneath the epicardium and endocardium, and within the myocardium. Lymphatics are also present in the areolar tissue underlying the peritoneum and pleurae. They are absent from the central nervous system. In the lung the lymphatics extend no further than the respiratory bronchioles, the alveoli being devoid of lymph capillaries. Because of the poor lymphatic supply to the alveoli, or of its difficulty in penetrating the alveolar wall, protein is not readily absorbed from the interior of alveoli into the lung lymphatics. Water passes readily into the lung capillaries however because of the low pressure within them. The lymphatic system can be considered as taking some part in the regulation of the general circulation although this has not been worked out in detail. For example, if there is an increase in pressure in the pulmonary system there is also a greater pulmonary lymph flow. This fluid can move to a limited extent through lymphatic channels to the systemic circulation. Such a shift would tend to lessen the elevation in pulmonary pressure.

The skin is supplied richly with lymph capillaries. The lymph vessels in the deeper layers of the skin are so abundant, according to McMaster, that the skin cannot be punctured anywhere without tearing them, and since the flow of lymph along these vessels is relatively rapid, foreign material injected into the skin soon reaches the regional lymph nodes. An injection into the skin is, therefore, to a large extent, an injection into the lymphatic system. This is not true for all materials, but protein, so injected, is received by the blood mainly by way of the lymphatics. After destruction of the lymphatics from a region, subcutaneously injected protein does not appear in the blood for a long time and when it is detectable it is only in very small amounts.

The permeability of the lymph capillaries is increased by many agencies, e.g., sunlight, warmth, and by mechanical or chemical stimulation; histamine is particularly effective. Their walls may become so permeable that they can scarcely be considered as channels walled off from the surrounding tissue spaces.

Lymphatic tissue has a great capacity for re-

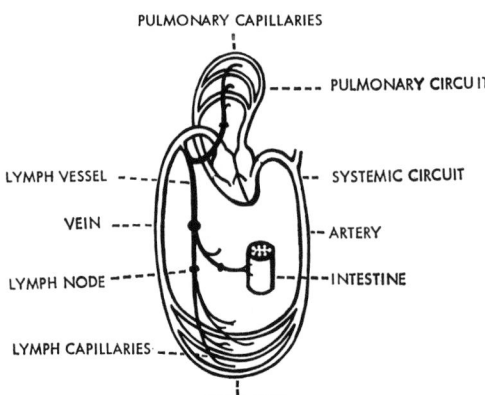

FIG. 25.1. Diagram to indicate the relation of the lymphatic system to the circulatory system.

generation and very active proliferation of lymphatics occurs in an inflamed region.

The Nodes as Defense Barriers

The lymph nodes must be looked upon as important structures for the defense of the blood against the invasion of bacteria or other injurious agents travelling by the lymph paths. When an infection of a part—a finger for instance—lying distal to a gland occurs, the latter becomes inflamed as a result of the localization therein of some of the bacteria or their toxins carried in the lymph. The gland swarms with motile cells (phagocytes) which attack and destroy the invading organisms. In this way a barrier is raised against the passage of deleterious agents, particularly bacteria, into the blood stream. In the case of the limbs at any rate it appears that no material can pass from the tissues to the blood stream *via* the lymph without filtering through the lymph nodes. The effectiveness of the nodes as filters has been clearly demonstrated by Drinker and his associates. The popliteal and iliac lymph nodes of dogs were perfused with solutions containing virulent streptococci (250,000,000 colonies per cc.). After perfusion lasting for over an hour the fluid collected from the thoracic duct was found to be sterile. After the node itself has been attacked by the microorganisms it may then serve as a source from which the blood stream becomes infected. Though highly efficient as filters for bacteria the nodes appear to offer but slight hindrance to the passage of viruses. There is evidence that the lymph nodes contribute towards the body's defense in another way, namely, by the production of antibodies.

Barnes and Trueta have shown that bacteria pass from the tissues to the blood solely by the lymph stream, and that even toxins and venoms of large molecular weight (over 20,000) are not carried into the blood if the lymph vessels have been blocked. These observations in part explain the success which has followed the immobilization of infected parts in plaster; this procedure might be expected to reduce to a minimum the lymph flow from the inflamed region and thus to confine the infective process.

The Composition of Lymph

The lymph of the small peripheral lymph vessels and the fluid of the tissues are closely similar in composition, both resembling the blood plasma. Although this view concerning tissue fluid is based chiefly on evidence from fluid exudates, it is probably true. The protein content of lymph is lower than that of plasma since lymph forms from tissue fluid. Drinker noted that it varied under different conditions from 0.3 to 4.0 per cent in mammals. The higher figure is unusual and, in human leg lymph, concentrations between 0.5 and 0.7 per cent were found.

The total quantity of mobilizable protein in interstitial fluid about equals the entire protein of the plasma. The protein of lymph is derived from this mobilizable mass of tissue fluid protein which varies, of course, with the amount of protein leaking from the capillaries. Differences in the amount of protein and fluid leaving the circulation, and in the amount of fluid reabsorbed by the capillaries as well as differences in the volume flow of lymph, will alter the protein content of the lymph. The amount of protein passing from the plasma into the tissue fluid is related to the surface area of the functioning capillaries and may not necessarily be ascribed to differences in the permeability of the capillaries. Electrophoresis shows the proteins of lymph to be qualitatively identical with the plasma proteins. The protein concentration in thoracic duct lymph, as a rule, is considerably higher than in peripheral lymph, but the lymph flow from the thoracic duct appears to be less than the total flow from several organs or regions. In hepatic lymph, the protein concentration, which is about $\frac{2}{3}$ the concentration in plasma, varies inversely with the lymph flow. This suggests that the rates of exit and reabsorption in liver may be important in producing the relatively high concentration of protein in hepatic lymph. However, labelled albumin exchanges more rapidly between plasma and hepatic lymph than between plasma and intestinal lymph, and still more rapidly than with the lymph of skeletal muscle. Most of the normal components of liver

TABLE 25.1

Chemical composition of peripheral lymph (cervical) and blood plasma from the dog

(From Heim, 1933)

	Protein (Kjeldahl)	Non-protein Nitrogen	Urea	Uric Acid	Creatinine	Sugar	Amino Acids	Chlorides (as NaCl)	Phosphorus		Calcium
									Total	Inorganic	
	per cent	mg. per 100 cc.	mg. per 100 cc.	mg. per 100 cc.	mg. per 100 cc.	mg. per 10 cc.	mg. per 100 cc.	mg. per 100 cc.	mg. per 100 cc.	mg. per 100 cc.	mg. per 100 cc.
Plasma:											
Average..................	6.18	32.6	21.7	Tr.*	1.37	123.0	4.90	678	22.0	5.6	11.70
Range..................	5.54– 7.23	21.1– 46.0	17.9– 28.0		1.22– 1.54	112.0– 143.0		649– 721	18.3– 26.1	4.4– 6.9	10.85– 12.95
Lymph											
Average..................	3.32	34.8	23.5	Tr.*	1.40	132.2	4.84	711	11.8	5.9	9.84
Range..................	1.38– 4.57	19.8– 45.4	19.8– 33.0		1.28– 1.49	107.0– 144.0		690– 730	10.2– 13.7	4.7– 7.3	8.93– 10.84
Number of animals........	16	10	7	3	7	16	1	7	6	3	11

* Tr. = trace.

lymph seem to come chiefly if not entirely from blood plasma, with the exception of glucose which is present in higher concentration in liver lymph than in blood plasma. In anaphylactic or peptone shock, heparin, released from the liver, passes into the blood mainly by way of lymph pathways. Lymph contains prothrombin and clots slowly. It contains large numbers of white cells, mostly lymphocytes, but relatively few red cells. The number of leucocytes varies from 1000 to 20,000 per cu. mm. in thoracic duct lymph of the dog and averages 550 per cu. mm. in peripheral lymph. In peripheral lymph there are from 300 to 13,000 erythrocytes per cu. mm. The lymph flowing from the thoracic duct, since it comes largely from the intestine and liver, will vary in composition in accordance with the digestive processes. Its protein content is, under ordinary circumstances, from 2 to 4.5 per cent. Within 1 or 2 hours after a meal containing much fat the thoracic duct lymph appears milky. The lacteals and the fine lymphatics of the mesentery, being loaded with globules of absorbed fat, are seen as glistening white streaks. The fatty acid of thoracic duct lymph is increased by the ingestion of fat; on a fat-free diet it is about the same as in the fasted animal.

The composition of plasma and peripheral lymph (i.e., lymph in the subcutaneous vessels of the limbs or neck) are compared in table 25.1.

It will be noted that calcium and total phosphorus, which are in part bound with protein, are in lower concentration than in plasma; the other constituents with the exception of protein and amino acids are in higher concentration.

The Formation, Pressure and Flow of Lymph

After what has been said with regard to the forces concerned in the regulation of the fluid interchange between the capillaries and the tissues little need be added in explanation of lymph formation. The two processes are interrelated and similar in nature. Any condition which increases the outpouring of fluid from the capillaries into the tissues will tend to increase the flow of lymph. The lymph capillaries are much more permeable than the blood capillaries, and although the tissue spaces, i.e., the clefts between groups of tissue cells, are separated from the lymphatic system in an anatomical sense, the walls of the latter vessels are so permeable that they offer little impediment to the movement of either protein or crystalloids. It has been stated already that of the fluid which transudes from the blood at the arterial end of the capillary much of the water is reabsorbed at the venous end. The protein, however, passes into the lymph. The lymph capillary is therefore the special channel whereby protein is returned (in a round about way) to the blood. It is also concerned with the absorption of other colloids, or of particulate matter which may be introduced into the tissue spaces. Although in mammals the extravascular circulation of the entire plasma albumin takes place in about 20 hours, in the frog, in which the blood capillaries are more permeable to protein than those of mammals, the entire protein of the plasma passes from the blood and back again to blood *via* the lymph system, some 50 times in 24 hours.

Under ordinary conditions the pressure of the thoracic duct lymph is very low but if the duct is obstructed in the dog, a pressure of 15 cm. of water develops. The *rate of flow* along the human thoracic duct (as measured in cases of duct fistulas) is from 1 to 1.5 cc. per minute. Cain and his associates found an average flow of 0.46 cc. per minute in the thoracic duct, of which more than half, about 0.26 cc., was contributed by the lymph vessels of the liver.

The pressures in the peripheral lymph vessels during rest run from 0 to 6 cm. of water according to different observers using various species of animals. In inflammatory states and during activity the pressure in the larger lymph vessels of the part rises considerably above the resting value. Also when a lymph vessel becomes obstructed, the pressure on the distal side (i.e., toward the finer vessels) of the obstruction increases, the vessel becomes distended on this side and collapsed on the proximal side. The lymph pressures decrease from the periphery toward the more central channels, and are higher on the distal side of a lymph node (mesenteric) than on the proximal side. In the lymph capillaries of the mouse's ear pressures up to 2.7 cm. of water were found by McMaster; the latter figure exceeds that usually found by most observers in the larger lymph trunks of other animals.

Obliteration of the lumen of the finer lymph vessels by a high pressure in the tissues is provided against by the fastening of the walls of the vessels by fibrillae to the surrounding tissue cells. When edema fluid collects and the tissue pressure rises, the fine lymphatics do not collapse, but, on the contrary, their lumens become wider (McMaster).

The mechanism governing the passage of tissue fluid into the lymph vessels is obscure, although the action of the pulse in the blood vessels of the part appears to play a part. McMaster and his associates have demonstrated the importance of a pulsatile flow in the vessels of the perfused rabbit's ear, in the spread of vital dyes through the tissues and in the formation and flow of lymph.

Enlarging the capillary surface by vasodilation, or increasing the number of patent capillaries increases the leakage of protein from the circulation. This happens when infusions of saline or dextran are given. The protein of tissue spaces is returned to the blood by the lymph. If the thoracic duct lymph does not reenter the circulation, the plasma proteins may decrease by 15 to 30 per cent in 3 hours. It seems probable that the exit of protein from blood vessels and the efficiency of its return by lymphatics will be important factors in the regulation of fluid interchange, modifying the balance of forces across the capillary wall.

Functions of the Lymphatic System

1. A primary function of the lymphatic system is to return protein to the blood from the tissue spaces.

2. The lymphatics have a role in the redistribution of fluid in the body, being capable of shifting fluid from one part of the circulatory system to another.

3. The lymphatics remove particulate matter, bacteria etc. from tissues.

4. The lymph flow helps in maintaining tissues. The ligation of lymph vessels in the heart may give rise to myocardial degeneration; in the kidneys it may accelerate the development of hydronephrosis when the ureters are tied; and in the liver it hastens the degenerative changes that follow bile duct ligation.

Conditions Which Increase the Lymph Flow

1. INCREASE IN CAPILLARY PRESSURE AS A RESULT OF VENOUS OBSTRUCTION. Landis and Gibbon found that in man filtration from the capillaries showed a definite increase when the venous pressure rose above 12 or 15 cm. of water. The rate of filtration from the capillaries was directly proportional to the increase in venous pressure (fig. 25.2). At a given venous pressure the filtration rate increased rapidly at first but gradually slowed and finally ceased. This falling off in the filtration rate is ascribed to the rise in extracapillary pressure, due to the fluid accumulation, which opposes the hydrostatic pressure within the capillary. The accumulation of extracellular fluid is therefore greater in regions which are loose in texture and where the skin is readily stretched. In persons with firm, resistant skin, edema, for the same reasons, is later in making its appearance and is less pronounced than in those with loose, flabby skins, as when weight has been lost rapidly.

Increased pressure in the veins of the portal area, as may be produced by obstructing the portal vein or the hepatic veins, causes increased filtration into the tissues of the abdominal viscera and a great increase in the volume of lymph flowing along the thoracic duct.

Increase in arterial pressure, on the other hand, does not increase filtration in animals until the pressure reaches around 300 mm. Hg.

2. INCREASE IN CAPILLARY SURFACE, i.e., increase in the filtering surface. This increases the leakage of protein and fluid. It is due to factors causing distension of the capillary vessels: (a) increase in capillary pressure; (b) increase in the local temperature; (c) infusion of fluid.

3. INCREASED PERMEABILITY OF THE CAPILLARIES. (a) a sufficient rise in temperature may increase capillary permeability.

(b) *Capillary poisons. Peptone* increases the flow of lymph from the thoracic duct probably as a result of its injurious effect upon the abdominal capillaries. The increased flow occurs after removal of the liver so injury to the hepatic vessels is not essential. Other substances which increase lymph flow in this way are extracts of strawberries, crayfish, mussels, leeches, histamine and foreign proteins. To what extent this is due to a change in permeability and to what extent it is a consequence of capillary dilation is not known.

(c) *Reduced oxygen supply* to the tissues (oxygen want), increases lymph flow probably because of dilation of blood vessels but possibly also through damage to the capillary endothelium.

4. HYPERTONIC SOLUTIONS. The intravenous injection of a concentrated solution of glucose, sodium sulphate or sodium chloride causes an increased flow of lymph from the thoracic duct. These substances in concentrated solution, though they permeate the capillary wall, exert an osmotic effect until equilibrium between the extravascular and intravascular fluids is reestablished. Water enters from the tissue spaces, particularly of the muscles and subcutaneous tissues of the limbs, which in consequence show a fall in volume; the brain shrinks. The removal of fluid may actually extend to the fluids within the cells which undergo shrinkage; and general desiccation of the tissues may result. The blood volume for the time is greatly augmented, the excess fluid for the most part being accommodated in the capacious capillary and venous areas of the abdomen. The viscera—liver, kidneys, spleen and intestines—increase in volume, due to the distension of their vascular beds, and a great outpouring of fluid as well as of protein occurs, which swells the volume of lymph in the thoracic duct. In this way these substances produce a redistribution of fluid.

The injection of isotonic saline will also increase the passage of protein and fluid from the capillaries and increase lymph flow. This too is prob-

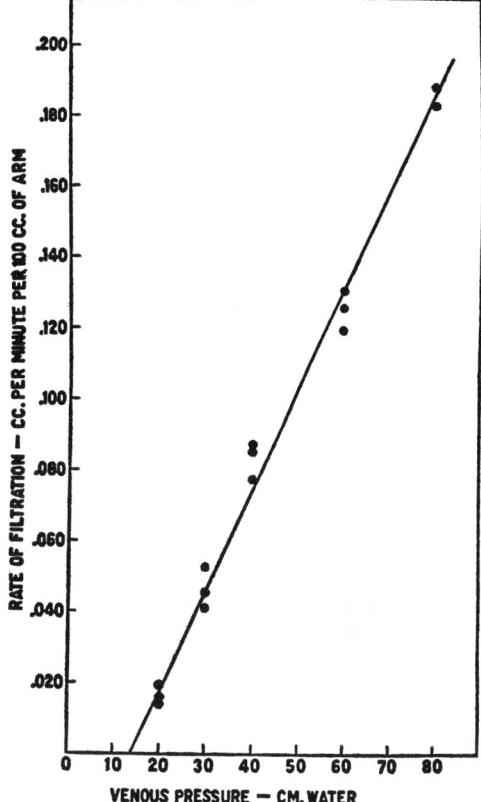

FIG. 25.2. Showing rates of filtration produced during 30 minutes by venous pressures between 20 and 80 cm. water (after Landis and Gibbon).

ably a consequence of the distension of blood vessels. Protein is returned from the tissue fluid by the lymphatics. The concentration of protein in the returning lymph is higher than would be expected if the saline had caused dilution of the lymph. Sometimes the total plasma albumin actually increases. However if the infusion is large, the protein return is not as great as the protein leakage. So with larger infusions (greater than ¾ plasma volume) the protein loss from the blood vessels to the interstitial spaces may be increased.

The effect which hypertonic solutions have upon the movement of tissue fluids had extensive application during the first World War. Sir A. E. Wright introduced the practice of packing wounds with salt crystals or irrigating them with a hypertonic salt solution. This causes an outward flow of lymph and tissue fluid, which results in the mechanical removal of the bacteria and their toxins from the tissues bordering the wound.

5. INCREASED FUNCTIONAL ACTIVITY. When a gland or muscle enters into activity an increase

in lymph flow occurs which starts a little after the commencement of the secretory or contractile response, but is nearly synchronous with the increased metabolism resulting from the activity. The increased flow is ascribed to (a) formation of metabolites which increase the osmotic effect of the tissue fluids and cause more fluid to leave the vessels (b) vasodilation, increased capillary pressure and increased fluid and protein leakage.

During rest the flow along the lymph vessels of the muscles and subcutaneous tissues is slight, and the protein content of the lymph is high. During activity the protein concentrations fall since less transuded water undergoes reabsorption into the blood and more is carried away by the lymph channels. This may occur even though the leakage of protein from the vessels is greater. The contracting muscles exert a pumping effect upon the lymph, driving it along the vessels. The rhythmical movements of the intestinal wall are thought to exert a similar effect in promoting the flow in the fine lymphatics of the submucosa. However, during fat absorption, lymph formation and its movement in the thoracic duct does not seem to be influenced by intestinal motility.

6. MASSAGE AND PASSIVE MOVEMENT act to a certain extent like muscular activity. They augment the blood flow, capillary pressure and capillary surface and so increase lymph formation. The manipulations and movements of the muscles serve to propel the lymph along the lymphatic channels.

Edema (See also pp. 474 and 475)

Edema is the term applied to an excessive accumulation of fluids in the tissue spaces, and is due to a disturbance in the mechanisms of fluid interchange, which have been considered in the preceding pages. Instead of there being a perfect balance struck between the inward and outward flow of fluid through the capillary membrane absorption is exceeded by transudation. The particular factor or factors of the mechanism that are disordered are not always clear, and a satisfactory explanation of all forms of edema cannot be given. But from previous discussions it is evident that the following factors will tend to increase the volume of interstitial fluid: (a) reduction in the protein concentration of plasma. Edema commences when the albumin fraction has fallen to between 2.5 and 3 per cent; (b) a general or a local rise in capillary blood pressure; (c) increased permeability of the capillary membrane; (d) increase in the filtering surface as when the capillaries dilate; (e) obstruction of the lymph channels.

There is a tendency for the accumulation of edema fluid to progress so far and then become stationary provided the conditions producing it remain constant, for as we have seen, when the tissue fluid pressure reaches a critical level its opposition to the force driving fluid from the vessels prevents further transudation. It should be appreciated too that plasma, as a source of edema fluid, has definite limitations and unless the total extracellular fluid is increased, a generalized edema cannot be very severe.

Since edema is only a symptom of some primary condition it may have a variety of causes, according to the particular disease with which it is associated.

1. Cardiac edema. In congestive heart failure there is both an increase in extracellular fluid and salt retention (ch. 46). It is clear that the volume of extracellular fluid can be reduced by restriction of the salt intake or by the administration of diuretics which remove both water and salt. Or it can be discharged by improving cardiac action, as by administering digitalis, lanatoside, or other suitable drug.

2. Mechanical obstruction of veins. When the main veins leading from a part are obstructed by new growth, fibrous tissue, as in cirrhosis of the liver, thrombosis, etc., increased transudation of fluid occurs. This is due in part to the rise in intracapillary pressure and an increase in the filtering surface, but the permeability of the capillary wall may also be increased as a result of the impaired blood supply or, as in the case of new growth, probably by the production of toxic substances as well.

3. Edema due to renal disease. In chronic nephritis edema is not usually pronounced unless the heart is failing; however, in the nephrotic syndrome it is an outstanding feature. In nephrosis a reduction in plasma protein as a consequence of the loss of protein in the urine leads to the passage of an abnormally large volume of fluid from the capillaries throughout the body. This in turn is probably responsible in some way for renal retention of salt and as a consequence of this, retention of water.

4. Inflammatory edema. In this type several factors combine to produce the fluid infiltration of the tissues. Increased capillary pressure occurs, due to dilation of the vessels and local slowing of the blood stream as well as to thrombosis and obstruction of the returning veins. There is an increase in the filtering surface too and the lymphatics for a variable distance from the inflammatory area are obstructed as well.

The capillary walls are also seriously damaged by the bacterial toxin or other injurious agent, so that a fluid with a high protein content escapes from the vessels. The edema is localized to an area of varying extent surrounding the injured site. Certain analgesics, e.g., aspirin, morphine and Demerol, tend to reduce the edema of simple inflammation.

5. Giant edema. This is a localized noninflammatory edema which comes on with great rapidity and involves the loose areolar tissue in such regions as the hands, face, external genitalia or larynx. It occasionally runs in families. Little is known definitely regarding the mode of its production. A histaminelike substance liberated at the site of the edema is apparently the immediate cause. The remote exciting cause is frequently a foreign protein consumed in the diet which apparently gains access to the blood stream in a more or less unchanged state, for the attack often follows a particular food to which the subject is susceptible, and is sometimes accompanied by gastrointestinal disturbances. The effects are therefore of an anaphylactoid nature and constitute one type of allergy. This type, also termed *angioneurotic* edema, is allied to the very localized edemas which constitute the condition known as urticaria and which as suggested by Lewis are caused by the liberation of a histaminelike substance in the skin.

6. Edema caused by malnutrition or toxic substances. Edema may occur in the anemias or in conditions in which the general nutrition of the body suffers. When the diet is deficient in vitamins, or there is too little fat or protein in the diet edema may occur, as in beriberi, scurvy, "war edema" or in the faulty nutrition of infants. In animals edematous conditions have actually been induced by general underfeeding, or by a diet deficient in fat and soluble vitamins, or by one deficient in protein alone. The factors responsible for the increased transudation in these cases are not always clear, but in others there is a marked lowering of plasma protein (more particularly the albumin) which alone is sufficient to account for the edema. In many instances, on the other hand, hypoproteinemia does not occur. In such cases the lack of some essential amino acid may be the determining factor. A simple explanation has been offered by Henschel and his colleagues, namely, that owing to the loss of tissue on the famine diet the extracellular fluids (plasma and interstitial fluid) show an apparent increase, that is, though not showing an absolute increase, they are greater than normal in relation to body weight. Henschel and his colleagues in experiments upon a group of normal young men on a semi-starvation diet found that, although the *absolute* volume of extracellular fluid remained fairly constant at the value

observed before the subjects were put upon the experimental diet, it increased gradually to about 40 per cent above normal when considered in relation to body weight; edema appeared when the relative increase in volume reached from 8 to 10 per cent above normal, which is approximately the same as the increase in volume of interstitial fluid at which other types of edema appear.[1] Increased capillary permeability due to impaired nutrition of the vascular walls was the main cause of the starvation edema in the Netherlands during the last war. In some cases of nutritional edema, excretion of an antidiuretic substance has been reported.

Certain chemical substances such as arsenic, salts of heavy metals, and the toxins of certain infectious diseases, such as diphtheria, acute nephritis, etc., are known to act as capillary poisons and apparently cause edema in this way. An interesting type of toxic edema is that which may be produced in animals by the injection of hematoporphyrin (ch. 27). This substance sensitizes the tissues to ultraviolet rays, and the edema occurs only after exposure. Histamine causes local edema at the point of injection by inducing capillary dilation and increased permeability of the membrane.

7. Edema due to lymphatic obstruction. Obstruction to the outflow of lymph from the tissue spaces may cause pronounced edema, even though the venous channels and the capillary vessels are unaffected. Edema of this nature is readily produced in frogs by compression of the lymph channels alone. It is more difficult to produce edema in this way in higher animals, but if the obstruction is complete edema occurs in them also. Edema of this nature is seen in infections with the filarial parasite which finds its way into the lymph vessels of the limbs and blocks their lumens with the production of the condition known as elephantiasis. The pleural cavities depend for the absorp-

---

[1] When the subcutaneous tissues are involved these appear swollen, and leave the imprint of the thumb when it is pressed into the skin (pitting). Dropsy (hydrops) is an old-fashioned term which is applied to edema as defined above or to a free collection of fluid within one of the body cavities, e.g., the thorax or the abdomen. *Hydrothorax* is also applied to the former of these conditions and *ascites* to the latter. *Anasarca* is a more or less generalized edema involving the subcutaneous tissues.

It is important to remember that the term edema applies to a gross collection of extravascular fluid. The bulk of tissue fluid fluctuates widely in health, and in pathological states may be very considerably increased before the increase is evident clinically. When, for example, a normal person stands for a time the extravascular fluid of the legs increases; and the immersion of a limb in a hot bath hastens the rate at which fluid transudes from the vessels—the limb volume rises as a result, largely, of fluid accumulation in the tissues. Drury and Jones found that edema appeared when the increase in fluid increased the volume of the leg by 8 per cent.

tion of a fluid upon the lymph channels, and accumulations of fluid may occur here as a result of lymphatic obstruction. The edema associated with carcinoma is due chiefly to the filling of the lymphatic channels with cords of cancer cells as well as to venous obstruction caused by the pressure of the growth. The "milk leg" of the puerperium is in part due to lymphatic obstruction. The tissue fluid in these types of edema has a relatively high concentration of protein.

8. *Heat edema.* The effect of heat upon capillary permeability has been mentioned (p. 509). Excessive heat may actually lead to edema in man. It occurs in the tropics and occasionally in so-called temperate zones during an intense heat wave. It is usually dependent in distribution. Increase in blood volume, enlargement of the filtering surface as a result of the opening up of fresh capillaries and the rise in capillary pressure incident to the dilation of capillaries previously patent, are also factors in the production of this type of edema.

REFERENCES

BARNES, J. M. AND TRUETA, J. Lancet, 1941, 1, 623.

CAIN, J. C. AND ASSOCIATES. Surg. Gynec. & Obst., 1947, 85, 559.

BENSON, J. A., LEE, P. R., SCHOLER, J. F., KIM, K. S. AND BOLLMAN, J. L. Am. J. Physiol., 1956, 184, 441.

DRINKER, C. F., FIELD, M. E. AND WARD, H. K. J. Exper. Med., 1934, 59, 393.

DRURY, A. N. AND JONES, N. W. Heart, 1927, 14, 55.

FRIEDMAN, M., BYERS, S. O. AND OMOTO, C. Am. J. Physiol., 1956, 184, 11.

HENSCHEL, A. AND ASSOCIATES. Am. J. Physiol., 1947, 150, 170.

LANDIS, E. M. AND GIBBON, J. H., JR. J. Clin. Invest., 1933 12, 105. (See also, LANDIS AND ASSOCIATES. J. Clin. Invest., 1932, 11, 63, 717.)

McMASTER, P. D. J. Exper. Med., 1937, 65, 373; 1947, 86, 293. Harvey Lectures, 1941–42, Ser. 37, 227.

MARKOWITZ, C. AND MANN, F. C. Am. J. Physiol., 1931, 96, 709.

MERRILL, A. J. J. Clin. Invest., 1946, 25, 389; Proc. 22nd Sc. Assoc., Am. Heart J. 1949, p. 34.

NEWMAN, E. V. Am. J. Med., 1949, 7, 490.

PARSONS, R. J. AND McMASTER, P. D. J. Exper. Med., 1938, 68, 353, 377.

PETERS, J. P. New England J. Med., 1948, 239, 353.

RICHARDS, D. W. Am. J. Med., 1949, 6, 772.

TAYLOR, G. W., KINMONTH, J. B., ROLLINSON, E., ROTBLAT, J. AND FRANCIS, G. E. Brit. M. J., 1957, i, (Jan. 19), 133.

WARREN, J. V. AND STEAD, E. A. Arch. Int. Med., 1944, 73, 138.

WASSERMAN, K. AND MAYERSON, H. S. Am. J. Physiol., 1951, 165, 15.

Monographs and Reviews

CUNNINGHAM, R. S. Physiol. Rev., 1926, 6, 242.

DAVIS, J. O. AND SMITH, J. R. Am. J. Med., 1947, 3, 704.

DENZ, F. A. Quart. J. Med., 1947, 16, 1.

DRINKER, C. K. AND FIELD, M. E. Lymphatics, lymph and tissue fluid. The Williams & Wilkins Co., Baltimore, 1933.

DRINKER, C. K. AND YOFFEY, J. M. The lymphatics, lymph and lymphoid tissue. Harvard University Press, Cambridge, 1941.

LANDIS, E. M. Harvey Lectures, 1936–7, Ser. 32, 70.

McMASTER, P. D. Harvey Lectures, 1941–42, Ser. 37, 227.

SIMONSON, E. Ann. Rev. Physiol., 1958, 20, 123.

STARLING, E. H. The fluids of the body. Constable, London, 1909.

CHAPTER 26

Transfusion; The Blood Groups

When, as a result of blood loss, it is necessary to transfuse fluid in order to maintain adequate oxygen carriage and to maintain the blood volume (ch. 49—Regulation of Circulation Under States of Stress), there are a number of considerations which govern the choice of the transfusion fluid.

Over the years, a large number of different materials have been used—physiological saline, solutions of various compounds of high molecular weight such as isinglass, polyvinylpyrrolidone and dextran, various blood plasma fractions, washed red cells, or whole blood. Substances of small molecular weight tend to maintain the blood volume for only a short time, as the solute molecules rapidly leave the circulation. They are, however, easy to prepare and to sterilize. Solutions of larger molecules tend to remain in the circulation for a longer period of time, but in many cases have given rise to various toxic reactions, and at present the only materials commonly in use are the dextrans, or whole blood and its derivatives. The particular demand of the moment (for fluid, for oxygen carrying capacity, or for particular blood factors which may not be present) governs the choice of the materials.

Whole Blood

In principle, fresh whole human blood is the ideal material for most transfusions. Most of the red cells survive for a period of many weeks and carry out their normal respiratory functions. The plasma components, too, will serve their normal functions in the recipient.

Although transfusion techniques have improved in the past few years so that the procedure is relatively safe and simple, certain precautions must be observed and, economic factors aside, blood should not be transfused indiscriminately, but only when there is a real necessity for it, such as hemorrhage, shock, certain anemias, and defects of coagulation.

The selection of healthy donors is of great importance; and careful screening before donation is necessary to detect conditions such as infectious hepatitis. The blood must be sterile so that no infection will be introduced into the recipient and the transfusion apparatus must be scrupulously clean.

One serious difficulty in connection with blood transfusion is occasioned by the so-called blood groups of the donor and of the recipient. Lack of knowledge of the antigen-antibody reactions which are involved led to a great deal of confusion, error and no doubt loss of life before Landsteiner, at the turn of this century, discovered the ABO blood group system and many of the basic facts regarding the immunological reactions of the erythrocytes.

Blood Groups

The early work of Landsteiner and others showed that blood from different persons could be classified into four groups which we now call A, B, AB, and O. The basis for this classification lies in the antigenic nature of the red cells. In 1927 other blood groups were discovered, namely M and N and P. The discovery of the Rh factor in the late 1930's stimulated renewed interest in the blood groups, and within the past few years many more factors have been found.

The surface of the red cell probably consists of a mosaic of antigenic sites; each antigen is probably represented in many places on the cell membrane. The term "agglutinogen" is sometimes used for these cellular antigens. The surface of the cell in terms of molecular dimensions cannot be smooth but must be very irregular, and a specific topographical pattern is believed to constitute each antigenic site.

Many of the erythrocyte antigens are relatively unimportant except in rare cases, but they can be the cause of transfusion reactions and of hemolytic disease of the newborn (see below). It is therefore wise to restrict the use of transfusions of whole blood or red cells to those persons who are in acute need; transfusions of a "precautionary" nature may assist recovery, but at the price of sensitizing the patient to an erythrocyte antigen.

Blood group antigens are inherited as autosomal dominants. Studies of families show that certain blood group antigens are associated, i.e., they are not inherited independently of each

THE BLOOD AND LYMPH

TABLE 26.1*

System	Antigens
A_1A_2BO	A_1B, H, A_2, A_3, A_x
MNSs	M, N, S, s, M_2, N_2, M^c, Mi^a, Vw, Mu, Hu, M^g, Vr, M_1, Mt^a, Ri^a, St^a
P	P_1, P_2, P^k
Rh	D, C, c, C^w, C^x, E, e, e^s, E^w, G, ce, ce^s, Ce, CE, D^u, C^u, E^u
Lutheran	Lu^a, Lu^b
Kell	K, k, Kp^a, Kp^b, Js^a, Js^b
Lewis	Le^a, Le^b
Duffy	Fy^a, Fy^b
Kidd	Jk^a, Jk^b
Diego	Di^a
I	I, i
Auberger	Au^a
Xg	Xg^a

Very infrequent antigens: Levay, Becker, Ven, Wr^a, Be^a, Rm, By, Sw^a, Good, Bi, Tr^a, Wb

Very frequent antigens: Vel, Yt^a, Ge, Lan, Sm

* Adapted from Table 1 of Race and Sanger, 1962.

other and are then said to belong to the same blood group system. The various antigens within each system are genetically related; the different systems seem to be genetically unrelated. (It should be noted, however, that gene interactions may occur.) Table 26.1 shows most of the human blood group systems and some of the related antigens within each system. Table 26.2 shows the frequency of several antigens in the general American population. The frequency of occurrence of different antigens varies greatly with different ethnic groups—e.g., the D (Rh₀) antigen occurs in approximately 85% of the Caucasian population, but is present in virtually 100% Negro and Oriental populations. A complete discussion of all the systems is beyond the scope of this chapter; the discussion following will refer only to those of greatest clinical importance.

The A-B-O System

Determination of Groups

The presence of antigen A on cells permits them to react with serum containing antibodies called anti-A or α, so that large numbers of the cells stick together (agglutinate). The nature of this reaction is similar to that between any antigen and its antibody. Similarly, cells with

antigen B will react with anti-B or β antibodies. Cells with both A and B antigens are agglutinated by either antibody; cells with neither A nor B antigens (group O cells) are not agglutinated by either antibody. In the plasma of persons with cell group A, anti-B antibodies occur; in the plasma of persons with cell group B, there are anti-A antibodies; group AB blood contains no ABO antibodies, and group O blood contains both anti-A and anti-B antibodies. The relationships are summarized in table 26.3. Obviously, if the serum from a person of group A is mixed with the cells of a person of group B, agglutination will occur. If the same serum is added to group O cells, no agglutination will occur. The antibodies of the ABO system occur naturally in human plasma (or serum) but the mechanism of their production is uncertain. They are called

TABLE 26.2

Occurrence of blood group antigens in the general American population

Blood Group System	Antigen	Positive %	Negative %
ABO	A	48	52
	B	12	88
MNSs	M	78	22
	N	72	28
	S	55	45
	s	89	11
P	P_1	79	21
Rh	C	68	32
	c	81	19
	D	83	17
	E	29	71
	e	98	2
Lutheran	Lu^a	8	92
	Lu^b	99.8	0.2
Kell	K	9	91
	k	99.8	0.2
Lewis	Le^a	22	78
	Le^b	72	28
Duffy	Fy^a	66	34
	Fy^b	83	17
Kidd	Jk^a	75	25
	Jk^b	75	25

TABLE 26.3

Group	Cells Contain Antigens	Serum Contains Antibodies
O	O	anti-A and anti-B
A	A	anti-B
B	B	anti-A
AB	A and B	neither

isoantibodies and they occur in the gamma globulin fraction of the plasma (see below). Other reactions resulting from mixing cells and sera of other blood groups are shown in table 26.4.

By the use of two antisera, one containing anti-A and the other containing anti-B, it is possible to determine to which of the four blood groups any sample of blood belongs. The blood is diluted with physiological saline (0.9% NaCl in water) to give about a 5% suspension of red cells. A drop of this cell suspension is placed on a ceramic tile and mixed with a drop of anti-A serum. Another sample of the cell suspension is mixed with anti-B serum. Agglutination of the cells only by the anti-A serum shows that the cells are of group A. If agglutination occurs with both antisera, the cells are of group AB, and if agglutination does not occur with either antiserum, the cells are of group O.

Agglutination usually occurs quite rapidly, especially if the tile is gently rocked to facilitate mixing of the cells and the antiserum. It is shown by the appearance of clumps of cells that are readily visible to the unaided eye. If there is no agglutination no clumps are formed, although there may be a tendency of the cells to move towards the centre of the drop and to show up as a darker colored region. Microscopically, true agglutinates appear as dense, dark masses. Rouleaux look like rolls of coins and should not be confused with true agglutinates.

Suitable controls with cells of known groups should always be included in every blood grouping test. Failure to agglutinate usually indicates that the appropriate antigen is absent from the cell, but it may mean that the testing serum has lost its potency, through bacterial contamination, heating, or other careless handling. Conversely, agglutination may be seen in the absence of a specific antigen as a result of the production, by bacterial contamination, of enzymes which alter the red cell so that it becomes polyagglutinable or substances which cause nonspecific agglutination of red cells.

Erythrocytes may also be agglutinated by gamma globulins other than the specific isoantibodies that have just been discussed. These so-called autoantibodies usually react with all or practically all human blood samples. Some autoantibodies react best in the cold, but "warm" autoantibodies are also recognized.

In recent years our knowledge of antibodies has expanded greatly and we now know that there are several different kinds of blood group antibodies. The nature of the reactions observed depends to

TABLE 26.4

Red Cells	Serum			
	O	A	B	AB
O	−	−	−	−
A	+	−	+	−
B	+	+	−	−
AB	+	+	+	−

+ = Agglutination.
− = No agglutination.

a considerable extent on the kind of antibody. One kind of antibody causes agglutination of cells suspended in saline whereas another kind (blocking, or "incomplete" antibody) can inhibit agglutination under certain circumstances. Incomplete antibodies are just as specific as the agglutinating antibodies, however, and can be made to cause agglutination under appropriate conditions (when used in media with a high protein concentration, when used with cells that have been treated with certain enzymes, or when used in the antiglobulin test of Coombs, Mourant and Race). Some antibodies cause hemolysis when complement is present.

An important distinction is the size of the antibody molecule. Most antibodies fall into one of two classes. One class consists of globulins with a molecular weight of about 160,000 and by their behavior in an ultra-centrifugal field are classed as 7S globulins. The other class consists of larger molecules with a molecular weight of about 1,000,000 and these are referred to as 19S globulins or macroglobulins. Many (perhaps all) of the 7S globulins can pass the placental barrier and it seems probable that in hemolytic disease of the newborn (see below) it is these smaller antibodies which are responsible.

The presence of antibodies on the cell may be detected by agglutination in appropriate media, or in some cases by hemolysis. A widely used technique involves the use of an anti-human globulin serum (so-called Coombs serum). Antiglobulin serum contains antibodies against human gamma globulin and it will therefore react with the blood group antibodies. After cells have reacted with, and are coated by, an incomplete antibody, no agglutination takes place; the subsequent addition of a potent anti-globulin serum results in agglutination. (The cells must first be washed in saline, to remove any traces of unbound globulin which would neutralize the anti-globulin serum.) The action of the anti-globulin antibody may be visualized as that of a link that binds the blood group antibodies together, and since these in turn are bound to cells, the final result is agglutination of the cells. If addition of anti-globulin serum to a sample of washed red cells causes agglutination, then the cells must have been coated with globulin. Note that this test reveals the presence of *globulin* on the cell surface. When the test is properly conducted, the inference that the globulin is a specific antibody is permissible. This test, called the *direct Coombs test*, is used to detect the presence of antibodies already bound to red blood cells as in hemolytic disease of the newborn or "auto-immune" acquired hemolytic anemia. The presence of a cell antigen may be detected by mixing red cells with antibody known to be specific for a particular antigen and then adding the anti-globulin serum. If the appropriate antigen is present, agglutination results. This test, called the *indirect Coombs test*, may also be used in the reverse fashion, with cells of known antigen content, to identify an antibody present in a sample of serum.

Effects of Incompatible Transfusions

The reactions mentioned above, it should be noted, are those observed when *serum* and *cells* from different persons of the groups indicated are allowed to react *in vitro*. When blood from one person is transfused into another, the conditions under which the reactions take place are modified, and the consequences are somewhat different.

If blood from a person of group A is transfused into a recipient of group B, it can be readily seen that there are two possible ways by which agglutination of red cells may occur. The anti-B antibodies of the donor may agglutinate the B cells of the recipient, and the anti-A antibodies of the recipient may agglutinate the A cells of the donor. In practice, the antibodies of the donor only rarely agglutinate the cells of the recipient, probably because the antibodies in the donor's plasma are well diluted by mixing with the blood of the recipient. On the other hand, antibodies in the recipient's plasma are little diluted by the (relatively) small amount of blood which is usually given in a single transfusion, and they can readily react with the cells of the donor.

Since it is the donor's cells which are most likely to be agglutinated, it might be thought that such a reaction could be avoided by the transfusion of group O blood. Cells of group O cannot be agglutinated by either anti-A or anti-B antibodies, and the antibodies present in the O

blood might not affect the cells of the recipient for reasons mentioned above. The use of the term "universal donor" for group O blood has therefore come into being. Conversely, persons with group AB blood are sometimes called "universal recipients." These terms are misleading, however, and they should be discarded. Some people of group O have high concentrations of anti-A or anti-B antibodies of a kind which is strongly hemolytic, and even after the transfused blood is diluted in the recipient's blood stream, there is sufficient antibody to destroy the recipient's cells. A second very important consideration is that such terminology fails to take into account the existence of other blood groups (see below).

If blood of the wrong (incompatible) ABO blood group is transfused, a hemolytic transfusion reaction usually results. Red cells are destroyed and there may be jaundice with hemoglobinemia and hemoglobinuria. Chills, fever, and shock may occur. Renal insufficiency may ensue, believed by some to be due to a reduced blood flow through the glomeruli.

Subgroups of A

The existence of subgroups of A, called A_1 and A_2, was recognized by von Dungern and Hertzfeld in 1911. Two antigens, A and A_1, are responsible for this difference and the terminology is somewhat confusing. Cells of group A_1 contain both A and A_1 antigens; those of group A_2 contain only A. The use of an anti-serum specific for A_1 permits the distinction to be made. Similarly, group AB may be subdivided into A_1B and A_2B. In Europe, approximately 20% of persons with A blood have the A_2 antigen.

Inheritance of A-B-O Blood Groups

Early workers in the field felt that there were two genes, A and B, that determined the inheritance of the ABO groups, and that group O was produced by a lack of both of these genes. Bernstein later suggested that the four ABO groups were inherited as autosomal characters through three allelic genes A, B, and O. The gene O is now regarded as an amorph, i.e., it has no recognizable specific gene product. It is now thought that there are four alleles A_1, A_2, B, and O and these give rise to ten genotypes with five distinguishable phenotypes (table 26.5).

Other Sources of Blood Group Antigens

The antigens which have just been discussed are typically a part of the red cell membrane, but many other tissues and fluids of the body contain materials which give the serological reactions of the A and B antigens. Although the antigens on red cells have been identified as glycolipids, and those in body fluids as mucopolysaccharides, there is evidence that the antigen sites, which are carbohydrate in nature, are probably chemically identical.

Witebsky, Landsteiner and others have found materials in many body fluids (gastric juice, saliva, etc.) which, when added, for example, to anti-A serum, inhibit the agglutinating power of that serum for A cells. Similarly, many of these materials, when injected, stimulate the production of specific antibodies. Materials from animals, such as extracts of hog gastric mucosa, have been found to contain A and B substances.

The A and B substances present in body fluids have a low nitrogen content (compared with protein) and a high concentration of reducing sugar and hexosamines. Much work has been done in the isolation, purification, and chemical and physical characterization of some of these materials. In all, antigenic specificity lies in the sugar component. For example, group A specificity is associated with α-D-N-acetylgalactosamine, whereas B specificity is associated with α-D-galactose.

Studies on the amounts of blood group substances which can be recovered from body fluids have shown that although ABO antigens are present in the fluids from most individuals, they are sometimes absent. Persons whose saliva, gastric juice, etc. contains appreciable amounts of ABO antigens are classified as *secretors;* the others are *nonsecretors.* The secretion of blood group antigens is genetically determined. It is of interest to note that so-called "secretor status" is related to one of the blood groups. Secretors of ABO do not have the Lewis antigen (Le^a); most nonsecretors have this antigen on their erythrocytes and also in their body fluids.

M, N AND P ANTIGENS

By injecting human red cells into rabbits and neutralizing or removing other antibodies from the rabbit antiserum thereby produced, Landsteiner and Levine were able to demonstrate the existence of a "new" pair of antigens, M and N. By the use of anti-M and anti-N sera, cells may be classified as either M, N, or MN. M and N are poor antigens in man and anti-M and anti-N are rarely found in human sera. At the time of the discovery of the M and N groups, Landsteiner and Levine reported another antigen

TABLE 26.5

Genotypes	Phenotypes
A_1A_1 A_1A_2 A_1O	A_1
A_2A_2 A_2O	A_2
BB BO	B
A_1B A_2B	AB
OO	O

which they designated P, but it is of little clinical importance.

THE RH BLOOD GROUP SYSTEM

Between 1937 and 1940 Landsteiner and Wiener, working with the serum of rabbits and guinea pigs that had been injected with the red cells of a Rhesus monkey, were able to show that the antiserum thus produced agglutinated the red cells of a large proportion of blood samples that were tested. Subsequent work showed that a new human blood antigen called Rh (from Rhesus) was responsible for these reactions. About 85% of Caucasians were found to have this antigen on their cells, i.e., they are Rh-positive. The remaining 15% are Rh-negative. Later work demonstrated the existence of other Rh antigens which are discussed below. The terms "Rh positive" and "Rh negative" as they are now used clinically refer to the presence or absence of the most important of these, the D antigen.

In contrast to the antibodies of the ABO system, which arise without any known antigenic stimulus, antibodies to the Rh antigen are produced, almost always, following exposure to the Rh antigen. Anti-Rh antibodies can be developed only by those who lack the corresponding antigen. Isoimmunization occurs in two ways: First, when a transfusion of Rh positive cells is given to an Rh-negative person. No difficulty is encountered in the first transfusion, but in subsequent transfusions, after the anti-Rh antibody has been developed by the recipient, the same mistake usually leads to destruction of the transfused red cells. Secondly, isoimmunization of an Rh negative mother occurs in a small proportion of pregnancies in which the fetus is positive and subsequently causes hemolytic disease of the newborn.

Hemolytic Disease of the Newborn

In this condition the child may be stillborn or born with evidence of hemolytic anemia. Frequently, signs of hemolysis, such as anemia and jaundice, do not appear until a few days after birth and they may be mild. Damage to brain cells by bilirubin, a degradation product of hemoglobin, results in a condition called kernicterus. It had been thought for many years that hemolytic disease of the newborn (HDN) might be a result of an antigen-antibody reaction, and shortly after the discovery of the Rh antigen it was shown that reactions involving this antigenic factor and the corresponding antibody were indeed the cause of most cases and also of many hitherto unexplained transfusion reactions.

It is now thought that the sequence of events leading to hemolytic disease of the newborn is as follows. An Rh+ fetus is carried by an Rh− mother, the fetus having inherited the Rh+ antigen from the father. In some manner, Rh+ fetal cells enter the maternal circulation and stimulate production of anti-Rh antibodies. Only small quantities of cells are required. There is usually no evidence of HDN in the first pregnancy, but in subsequent pregnancies the antibodies increase in potency and cross the placental barrier into the fetal circulation where they react with the fetal Rh+ cells and lead to their destruction. There is evidence that the incomplete (7S) antibodies are responsible. At least one and often several Rh+ pregnancies may take place before hemolytic disease develops. It should be noted that a transfusion of Rh+ cells to an Rh− woman even years prior to a pregnancy may severely reduce her chances of having a healthy child.

For reasons which are still uncertain the incidence of hemolytic disease of the newborn due to anti-Rh is considerably less than one would expect from the observed frequency of Rh+ children of Rh− mothers. HDN is obviously extremely rare where nearly all of the population is Rh+, e.g., in Orientals, Eskimos, American Indians, and Negroes.

The present treatment of hemolytic disease of the newborn is "exchange transfusion" which consists of slowly removing blood from the affected infant, and at the same time replacing it with Rh− blood. The Rh− cells cannot be destroyed by the anti-Rh antibodies, most of which are removed, along with bilirubin, by the procedure. During the next several weeks, the transfused cells are gradually removed from the circulation to be replaced by the infant's own Rh+ cells.

Attempts to obtain a substance ("hapten") from Rh cells which would neutralize Rh antibodies and could be injected into the maternal circulation in order to reduce the antibody titer have not yet been successful.

In an attempt to reduce the number of stillbirths due to HDN, transfusions of Rh− blood have recently been made into the abdominal cavity of the fetus *in utero*. The cells are absorbed into the fetal circulation. Many successful cases have now been reported.

Hemolytic disease may also result from ABO incompatibility between mother and fetus, but is usually milder than that due to Rh incompatibility. Other antibodies are responsible in rare cases.

Nomenclature

Shortly after the discovery of the Rh antigen a number of related antigens were found. Two systems of nomenclature based on slightly different concepts of the genetics of the Rh antigen are in general used to describe them. In recent years a large number of variants of the Rh antigen have been found, and the terminology has become increasingly complex in order to accommodate the newer variants. A third nomenclature, using numbers, has recently been proposed. The reader is referred to the papers of Wiener and his coworkers for a discussion of the Rh nomenclature, to the papers of Fisher and Race for a discussion of the CDE nomenclature, and to recent publications by Rosenfield et al. for a discussion of the numerical terminology.

Although a complete discussion of all of the Rh variants is beyond the scope of this text, there follows below a brief discussion of some of the more commonly encountered ones. Table 26.6 shows the reactions of the Rh antigens with the more commonly available anti-sera.

According to Fisher and Race, there are at least three sets of antigens: C and c, D and d, E and e. The corresponding antibodies are anti-C, anti-c, anti-D, anti-E, and anti-e. Anti-d has not yet been found. C antigen corresponds to Wiener's rh', D antigen to Rh_0, and E antigen to rh''. The antigen combination CDe corresponds to Wiener's Rh_1. An Rh− type is shown as cde. It should be noted that the use of lower case letters implies not only the absence of one of the Rh antigens, but also the presence of its reciprocal antigen.

Rh variants are indicated by superscripts added to the symbol of the antigen to which they seem to be most closely related, thus C^w or D^u. Originally, an antigen f was postulated, but it is now felt that the so-called anti-f serum reacts with the antigen complex, ce.

D, or Rh_0, is by far the strongest antigen. In European populations most Rh+ cells are CDe, or Rh_1.

Inheritance of the Rh Antigens

According to Fisher and Race, the various Rh antigens are inherited as three closely linked genes. More recently, they have suggested there are three sites within a single "cistron." Since each germ cell carries its own set of Rh genes, the diploid genetic structure of the organism is described by using one set of characters for the genes derived from one parent, and another set for the genes derived from the other parent. Cells will then show a positive test for a given antigen, regardless of whether the antigen is derived from the genetic structure of one or both parents. Thus, if a positive test is shown with anti-C, anti-c, anti-D, anti-e, and a negative test with anti-E sera, the antigenic structure of the cell is shown as CcDee, and this could be derived from the following genotypes: CDe/cde, cDe/Cde, cDe/CDe. The determination of the genetic structure of an individual requires the use of typing sera which will react with only one of the antigens, or a detailed study of the Rh types of siblings and immediate ancestors of the particular individual.

According to Wiener, the Rh antigens are inherited as multiple allelic genes. A gene gives rise to an agglutinogen, that may have two factors represented on it. Thus, using his nomenclature, cells of type Rh_1 could be of different genotypes, viz., Rh_1rh, Rh_1Rh_1, Rh_0Rh'.

Absence of Common Antigens

Certain very rare persons have been encountered in whom some or all of the expected Rh antigens are missing. At first it was thought that there was a chromosome deletion, but most workers now feel that the picture is more complicated. Symbolically, a blood lacking in both the C and E sets of antigens is represented as $-D-$. Several people have now been reported in whom there are no detectable representatives of any of the Rh antigens, i.e., $(- - -)$. This is called an *Rh null*.

TABLE 26.6

Cells		Anti-Serum				
Antigen Combination (Wiener agglutinogen symbol)	Gene Symbol	Anti-C (Anti-Rh')	Anti-D (Anti-Rh$_0$)	Anti-E (Anti-Rh")	Anti-c (Anti-hr')	Anti-e (Anti-hr")
cDe (R_0)	R^0	−	+	−	+	+
Cde (R')	r'	+	−	−	+	+
cdE (R'')	r''	−	−	+	+	−
CDe (R_1)	R^1	+	+	−	−	+
cDE (R_2)	R^2	−	+	+	+	−
CDE (R_z)	R^2	+	+	+	−	−
CdE (R_y)	r^y	+	−	+	−	−
cde (r)	r	−	−	−	+	+
		70	85	30	80	96
		per cent positive in an English population				

Reciprocal Groups

In almost all cases there seems to be a reciprocal relationship between two blood group antigens, i.e., the absence of a certain antigen implies the presence of another (reciprocal). If, for example, there is no C antigen, then the c antigen must be present or, according to Wiener, the absence of rh' implies the presence of hr'. The absence of the E (rh") antigen implies the presence of e (hr"). Anti-c and anti-e sera may be used to demonstrate the existence of the alternative antigens. One might expect that there would be a d (Hr_0) antigen, alternative to the D (Hr) antigen, but its existence has not yet been demonstrated.

Other Blood Groups

Other blood groups include Kell (K) and Cellano (k) (which bear a reciprocal relationship) and Duffy (Fy^a, Fy^b), Diego (Di^a), Lewis (Le^a, Le^b), Lutheran (Lu^a, Lu^b), and Kidd (Jk^a, Jk^b) (table 26.1). Some "private" blood antigens have a very low frequency in the general population and positive reactions occur only in members of a particular family.

Blood Substitutes

The difficulties associated with the transfusion of whole blood have inspired the development of a considerable number of blood substitutes, i.e., solutions which could be administered to provide some of the functions of whole blood. Some of the considerations that bear on the choice of such materials have already been mentioned. Most of the substitutes which have been proposed or which are now in use are solutions of substances of large molecular weight which will remain in the circulation for a relatively long period of time.

The use of plasma or serum alone removes the possibility of agglutination of the donor's cells. Pooling of a large number of samples reduces the strength of any given antibody, and plasma may be conveniently stored for a period of time if it has been taken and processed under sterile conditions. Storage of pooled plasma at 30°C for six months or more destroys the hepatitis virus, and in some countries only plasma which has been so stored may be used. The process of freeze-drying or lyophilization removes the water and leaves the essential constituents in a relatively undenatured state that allows for easy storage for a long period of time. The addition of sterile water reconstitutes the plasma for subsequent use. Certain plasma protein fractions, for example, fibrinogen and albumin, are becoming more widely available and are valuable when it is desired to give only a particular component.

Dextran is a polysaccharide of high molecular weight. Various dextran solutions of different average molecular weight are used for expanding the blood volume. They are not of animal origin and are of low antigenicity and toxicity.

Considerable work, which has met with some success, is being done on methods which will allow the long-term (months to years) storage of frozen red cells. After thawing and removal of certain additives which may be necessary in the preparation, and after suitable reconstitution of the fluid medium, the cells may be reinfused in cases where the patient needs the oxygen-carrying properties of the erythrocyte.

Solutions of Crystalloids

The small molecules of salt or of glucose pass freely through the capillary wall. They exert a negligible osmotic effect; the injected fluid is therefore not retained in the circulation. For this reason such fluids, though capable of raising the blood pressure temporarily, are quite unable to maintain it for any considerable length of time. Indeed, they may do serious harm, for the transfused fluid as it leaks into the tissues carries plasma protein with it. This is particularly likely to occur when saline is used. Transudation of fluid into the tissue of the lung—pulmonary edema—may result. When, on the other hand, dehydration of the tissues and loss of blood water, as shown by the concentration of the plasma proteins or a high hematocrit, are prominent, the subcutaneous or intravenous injection of saline (with or without the addition of glucose) or water by mouth, would appear, from physiological principles, to be rational. In the dehydration resulting from chloride depletion (p. 494) sodium chloride is clearly indicated. A solution of this salt serves not only to supply fluid but to replenish the base, the loss of which is such an important factor in the development of the dehydrated state.

REFERENCES

Boyd, W. C. Fundamentals of Immunology. Interscience Publishers, Inc., New York. 3rd Edition, 1956.

Coombs, R. R. A., Mourant, A. E. and Race, R. R. A new test for the detection of weak and "incomplete" Rh agglutinins. Brit. J. Exp. Path., 1945, 26, 255.

Landsteiner, K. The Specificity of Serological Reactions. Harvard University Press. Revised Edition, 1962.

Liley, A. W. Intrauterine transfusion of foetus in haemolytic disease. Brit. Med. J., 1963, 2, 1107.

Mollison, P. L. Blood Transfusion in Clinical Medicine. Blackwell, Oxford, England. 3rd Edition, 1961.

Race, R. R. and Sanger, R. Blood Groups in Man. Blackwell, Oxford, England. 4th Edition, 1962.

Rege, V. P., Painter, T. J., Watkins, W. M. and Morgan, W. T. J. Three new trisaccharides obtained from human blood group A, B, H and Le^a substances: possible sugar sequences in the carbohydrate chains. Nature, 1963, 200, 532.

Rosenfield, R. E., Allen, F. H. Jr., Swisher, S. N. and Kochwa, S. A review of Rh serology and presentation of a new terminology. Transfusion, 1962, 2, 287.

Strumia, M. M., Crosby, W. H., Gibson, J. G., Greenwalt, T. T. and Krevans, J. R. General principles of blood transfusion. Transfusion, 1963, 4, 303.

Wiener, A. S. Blood Groups and Transfusion. C. C Thomas, Springfield; 3rd Edition, 1943. Blood groups in man and lower primates. Transfusion, 1963, 3, 173.

Wiener, A. S. and Wexler, I. B. Heredity of the Blood Groups. Grune & Stratton, New York, 1st Edition, 1958.

CHAPTER 27

Hemoglobin

(See also Regeneration of Blood, Chapter 29.)

Hemoglobin, the coloring matter of the erythrocytes, makes up about 95% of the dry weight of the cell. The chief function of the red cell is to store this pigment and carry it around the circulation. The hemoglobin in turn functions primarily as a carrier of oxygen, and to a lesser extent is concerned with the transport of carbon dioxide and with the acid-base balance of the body. In the lungs it takes up a comparatively large load of oxygen which it carries to the tissues. One hundred cubic centimeters of water at the temperature of the body and exposed to an oxygen pressure of 100 mm. Hg absorbs a third of a cubic centimeter of the gas. One hundred cubic centimeters of blood, on the other hand, at the same temperature and pressure will take up about 20 cc., i.e. 60 times more. The difference is due to the hemoglobin. The total amount of blood in the human body will hold approximately 1200 cc. of oxygen (200 cc. per liter of blood). This quantity of oxygen is used by the tissues in 5 min. or so during rest and in a fraction of a minute during muscular exertion. In the absence of hemoglobin, the entire carriage of oxygen would have to be performed by the plasma, and in order that this should be able to absorb the necessary amount of gas, it would have to be increased at least 60 times in amount. As pointed out by Barcroft, the circulating fluid, instead of being about 6 l. or $\frac{1}{11}$ of the body weight, would then need to be over 350 l., i.e., more than five times the bulk of the solid tissues.

Human blood contains about 15 gm. (14 to 16 gm.) of hemoglobin per 100 cc. Since the proportion of iron in hemoglobin is 0.334%, the quantity of the metal in 100 cc. of blood is about 50 mg. and in the total blood of the human body about 3 gm. The blood contains a small proportion of iron in addition to that combined with hemoglobin.

The Estimation of Hemoglobin in Blood

Several methods are available for determining the hemoglobin concentration of blood. But whatever the method used, the fundamental information sought is the oxygen capacity of the blood. This may be found directly by means of the Van Slyke apparatus or the apparatus of Barcroft or Warburg. Or, since the hemoglobin molecule contains 0.334% of iron, the hemoglobin grams per 100 cc. can be calculated from an analysis of the blood for its iron content.[1] Thus, if the blood contains 50 mg. of iron per 100 cc., its hemoglobin concentration is $(50/0.334) \times 100 = 15$ gm. (approx.) per 100 cc. Since 1 gm. of hemoglobin can combine with 1.34 cc. of oxygen, the oxygen capacity $= 15 \times 1.34 = 20$ cc. (approx.) per 100 cc.

Various early convenient methods for clinical use were based upon matching a sample of diluted blood with one of a series of permanent color standards, e.g., the *Haldane-Gowers* method in which the hemoglobin is first converted to carboxyhemoglobin, or the *Sahli* method which involves the conversion of hemoglobin in the diluted sample to acid hematin. Modern methods spectrophotometrically measure the absorption of light at certain wavelengths of certain hemoglobin complexes, e.g., cyanmethemoglobin.

Structure and Metabolism

Hemoglobin is a conjugated protein with a molecular weight of about 68,000. It consists of an iron-containing pigment portion combined with a protein, *globin*. The pigments belong to a group of compounds called *porphyrins* which possess the property of being able to combine with metals. *Heme* is the name given to the compound of iron and the particular porphyrin which is found in hemoglobin. The iron-porphyrin-globin complex which constitutes hemoglobin can form a loose compound with oxygen, with the iron in the *ferrous* (Fe^{++}) state. Under certain conditions, it may form a more stable compound with oxygen with the iron in the *ferric* (Fe^{+++}) state.

[1] The estimation of hemoglobin by iron analysis is claimed by King and his associates to be the most reliable method, though even this method is not without error, for a certain small proportion of the iron in blood is not in combination with functioning hemoglobin.

TABLE 27.1

Porphyrin structure

Uroporphyrin I	— acetyl in 1, 3, 5, 7 pro-pionyl in 2, 4, 6, 8
Uroporphyrin III	— acetyl in 1, 3, 5, 8 pro-pionyl in 2, 4, 6, 7
Coproporphyrin I	— methyl in 1, 3, 5, 7 pro- — pionyl in 2, 4, 6, 8
Coproporphyrin III	— methyl in 1, 3, 5, 8 pro- — pionyl in 2, 4, 6, 7
Protoporphyrin IX	— methyl in 1, 3, 5, 8 pro-pionyl in 6, 7 — vinyl in 2, 4

Synthesis of Porphyrins and Heme

The basic nucleus or framework upon which all porphyrins are built consists of four pyrrole rings linked together in a larger ringlike structure called *porphin*. By substitution of the 8 hydrogen atoms about the edge of the porphin structure with various side chains—ethyl, methyl, vinyl, propionyl—the various porphyrins in nature are produced. The positions of some substituents for a few related structures are summarized in table 27.1. The particular compound found in heme is known as *protoporphyrin IX*.

During the last decade a large amount of experimental work has yielded a fairly complete picture of the pathway of porphyrin synthesis. The complex molecule is entirely synthesized by a series of condensations, beginning with glycine and succinate. From these simple structures δ-*aminolevaleric acid* (DAL) is formed, and then 2 molecules of DAL condense to form *porphobilinogen*. The precise mechanisms of the subsequent reactions whereby four molecules of porphobilinogen condense to form proto-porphyrin IX are not yet completely known.

After the protoporphyrin IX has been synthesized it is combined with iron and globin to form the complete hemoglobin molecule. The iron enters the immature red cell and is first associated with the cell stroma. It is then transferred to the site of heme synthesis where it combines with the protoporphyrin under the influence of *heme synthetase*.

The breakdown of heme, when it is released from the red cell in the course of its normal destruction, involves the oxidative splitting of the porphyrin ring to yield biliverdin. By a series of successive reductive processes the variety of substances that constitute the other bile pigments are formed. Biliverdin gives rise to bilirubin. This is normally removed from the blood by the liver, and is secreted into the gall bladder and thence into the intestinal tract. Here further changes in the bilirubin may take place under the influence of the bacterial flora to yield mesobilirubin, stercobilinogen and stercobilin. The latter substance may be readily isolated from feces.

The Structure of Globin

For many years it has been known that a variety of different hemoglobins exist, but the reasons for the differences have only become apparent during the last few years. The pioneering work of Pauling and Itano showed that in sickle-cell anemia the reason for the abnormal hemoglobin found in this condition lay in the structure of the globin molecule. Since that time the amino acid sequence and the precise three-dimensional arrangement of the amino acids have been worked out for a number of hemoglobins.

The hemoglobin molecule consists of four sub-units, and each sub-unit consists of a polypeptide chain and an associated heme molecule. The tortuously coiled polypeptide chains fit together in the complete molecule in such a fashion that the heme portions are more or less at the corners of a tetrahedron, near the surface of the molecule where there can be a ready reaction with the oxygen molecule. The attachment of the heme portion greatly modifies the properties of the globin molecule. The conjugated protein is much more resistant to denaturing agents and to digestive enzymes than the free protein. There are changes in dye-binding capacity, in immunochemical behavior, in ease of crystallization, in dissociability into sub-units and in molecular shape.

It can be easily understood that the differences in the various hemoglobins which are observed can be ascribed to differences in the amino acid sequence of the polypeptide chains, or to different combinations of polypeptide chains. Thus, normal adult hemoglobin has two so-called α-chains, and two so-called β-chains. The differences between the α-chains and β-chains lie in their primary structure. However, adult hemoglobin may be represented symbolically as $\alpha_2\beta_2$. Fetal hemoglobin has two pair of chains of slightly altered primary structure, hence it is shown as $\alpha_2\gamma_2$. Normal adult hemoglobin also has a small portion made of two α chains and two δ chains, so it is shown as $\alpha_2\delta_2$. Two rare, abnormal hemoglobins are hemoglobin H with the structure

β_4, and hemoglobin "Barts" with the structure γ_4.

Modern structural studies have shown a much larger number of different types of hemoglobin than just mentioned, and terminologies may still be revised. It is probably best not to try to present a list of the known types using a terminology which may be superseded, but to indicate the principle that a detailed description of the hemoglobin molecule will be given in terms of its constituent polypeptide chains. A general identification of the hemoglobin will be given by some indication of its origin.

The Combination of Hemoglobin with Gases

Oxygen (see also ch. 50)

Hemoglobin combines with oxygen by virtue of the iron which it contains. The attachment of the iron to the heme and to the protein molecule is very important in giving to the hemoglobin molecule its peculiar property of ready combination or dissociation with the oxygen molecule.

The iron in hemoglobin is in the ferrous (divalent) state. Heme, by itself, readily reacts with oxygen and the iron changes to the ferric (trivalent) state. The combination of the heme with globin, however, brings about a great stabilization of the molecule so this increase in valence does not ordinarily take place, even though there may be a combination with oxygen.

The iron is in a hexacovalent state, with four of the bonds linking it with the planar porphyrin molecule (fig. 27.1). The resulting heme molecules (4 in number) are attached to the surface of the globin molecule by another of the covalent links of the iron atom. The nature of the group in the globin molecule to which the heme is attached is not yet settled, though Wyman, and Coryell and Pauling postulate that it is attached to the imidazole group of a histidine residue. The sixth covalent bond, which sticks out from the plane of the heme, is the point of attachment of the molecular oxygen. The details of the changes which take place in the various bonds upon oxygenation of the hemoglobin molecule are beyond the scope of this book, but it is interesting to note that the postulated linkage of iron with the imidazole group can be shown to provide an explanation for the "Bohr" effect, i.e., the greater acidity of hemoglobin with oxygenation.

Since each hemoglobin molecule contains four iron atoms, it can combine with four molecules of oxygen. The oxygenation of one of the four hemes enhances the oxygen-binding capacity of

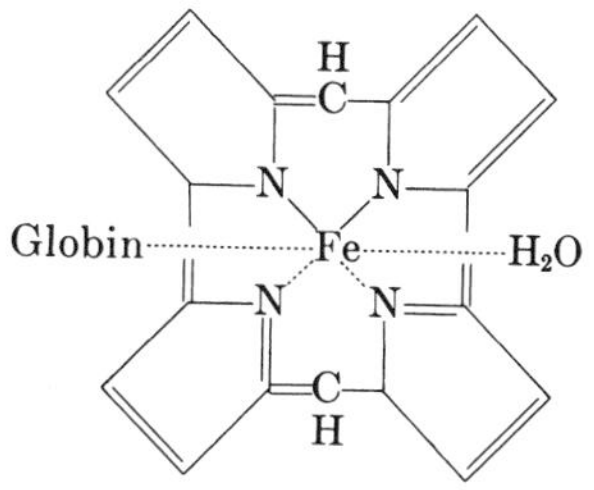

Reduced hemoglobin

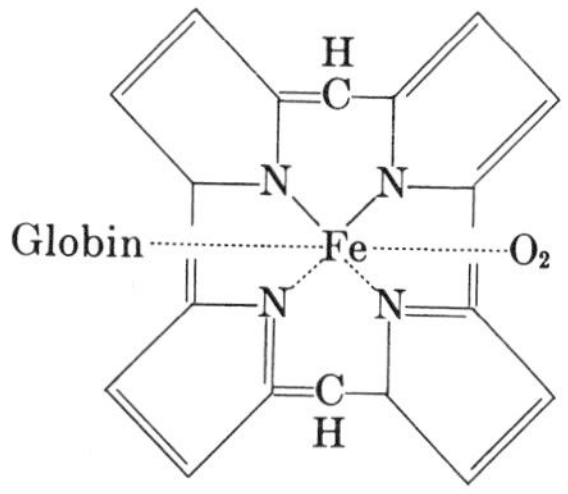

Oxygenated hemoglobin
(oxyhemoglobin)

Fig. 27.1

the now partly oxidized molecule, so that this molecule becomes fully oxygenated in preference to other hemoglobin molecules. This interaction, i.e., the effect of the oxygenation of one heme upon the ease of oxygenation of the other hemes results in a peculiar sigmoid-shaped curve if the percentage of oxyhemoglobin formed from reduced hemoglobin is plotted against oxygen tension. If there were no interaction, such as in the case of the monomeric myoglobin, a similar plot would yield a curve in the form of a rectangular hyperbola.

The increased acidity of oxyhemoglobin (Bohr effect, above) means that the pH of arterial blood is almost the same as that of venous blood; the greater acidity of this oxyhemoglobin compensates for the increase in carbonic acid found in venous blood.

The capacity of the blood for absorbing oxygen is called the *oxygen capacity* and it is proportional to the hemoglobin concentration. The oxygen capacity of 1 gm. of hemoglobin is 1.34 cc., therefore, the oxygen capacity of 100 cc. of normal blood (15 gm. hemoglobin) is 20 cc. (15 × 1.34).

Derivatives of Hemoglobin

Some of the variations of the hemoglobin molecule which may be obtained are described below.

The terms *reduced hemoglobin*, or *ferrohemo-*

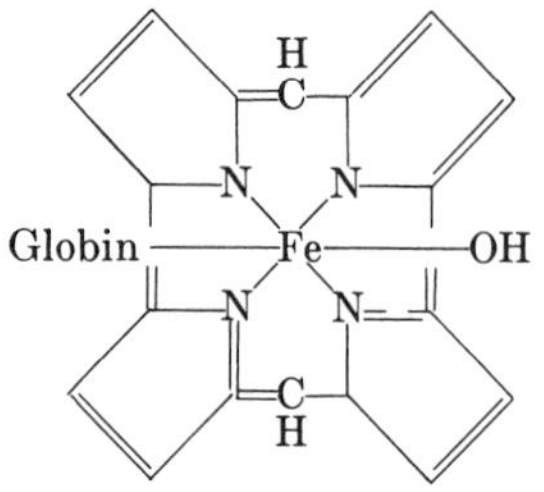

Methemoglobin

FIG. 27.2

TABLE 27.2

Wave lengths (λ) at the points of maximum intensity of absorption bands of hemoglobin and its derivatives as well as some of the other heme compounds

Compound	Number of Bands	Situation of Absorption Bands Wave Lengths in Angstrom Units			
Oxyhemoglobin	2	5769	5448	—	—
Reduced hemoglobin ...	1	5650	—	—	—
Carboxyhemoglobin	2	5709	5350	—	—
Methemoglobin	4	6300	5780	5400	5000
Sulfhemoglobin	3	6180	5780	5400	—
Hemochromogen	2	5585	5275	—	—
	2	5580	5270	—	—
Reduced heme	2	6070	5820	—	—
Cytochrome	4	6046	5665	5502	5210
Protoporphyrin (in acid)	2	6000	5540	—	—
Urobilin	1	4900	—	—	—

globin, are used for the molecule which has given up its oxygen.

Oxygenated hemoglobin, or *oxyhemoglobin*, is applied to the molecule which has oxygen molecules attached.

Methemoglobin, or *ferrihemoglobin* results when, by the action of oxidizing agents, the ferrous iron in the heme is changed to ferric iron. Normal blood contains about 0.1% ferrihemoglobin, but in poisoning by drugs such as nitrites, chlorates, sulfanilamides, etc., the percentage is increased. The larger quantity of the more darkly-colored ferrihemoglobin gives rise to a type of cyanosis to which the term "toxic" is applied. The discoloration of the skin becomes apparent when the ferrihemoglobin amounts to about 3 gm. per 100 cc. of blood. Methylene blue, injected into the blood stream, causes the formation of ferrihemoglobin. (See fig. 27.2.)

A *hemochromogen* of hemoglobin results if the

heme with the ferrous iron is combined with a denatured globin.

Cathemoglobin is a compound of heme containing ferric iron with denatured globin.

The various heme pigments and derivatives of hemoglobin each have a characteristic absorption spectrum, and they may thus be readily identified and measured by appropriate spectrophotometric techniques. The major absorption bands of a few compounds are listed in table 27.2.

CARBON DIOXIDE

Hemoglobin is of considerable importance in the carriage of carbon dioxide. By virtue of the Bohr effect (ch. 50) oxygenation of the hemoglobin molecule causes the release of a proton. This proton in turn reacts with bicarbonate to cause the liberation of CO_2 according to the reaction outlined below.

$$HHb + O_2 \rightarrow HbO_2 + H^+ +$$
$$HCO_3^- \rightarrow$$
$$H_2CO_3 \rightarrow H_2O + CO_2$$

The reactions take place in the directions indicated in the lungs; in the peripheral tissues the reverse reaction takes place and allows more CO_2 to be carried in venous blood. About 60–70% of the total CO_2 transport is accounted for by this mechanism.

A second way in which hemoglobin is important in the transport of carbon dioxide is through the formation of carbamino complexes, similar to the reactions of CO_2 and amines:

$$RNH_2 + CO_2 \rightarrow RNHCOOH$$

Hemoglobin binds more CO_2 as a carbamino compound than does oxyhemoglobin, and thus the shuttle of the hemoglobin between oxyhemoglobin and reduced hemoglobin provides an additional mechanism for the transport of CO_2. About ⅓ of the total CO_2 transport is thus accounted for.

CARBON MONOXIDE

Carbonmonoxyhemoglobin results from the union of carbon monoxide and hemoglobin. The gas unites with hemoglobin in the same proportion as does oxygen. It competes successfully with the latter for hemoglobin and displaces it volume for volume to form carbonmonoxyhemoglobin. Unlike oxygen, however, it forms with hemoglobin a stable compound which can be disrupted only with the greatest difficulty. The much greater avidity (between 200 and 250 times) which hemoglobin shows for CO renders the gas highly dangerous when inhaled in any considerable quantity. *Nitric oxide* gas also has a strong affinity for hemoglobin and forms a stable compound with it. The fumes given off by high explosives during their combustion contain large amounts of nitric oxide and the commonest way in which this poisoning occurs is through persons entering a closed space after an explosion, before the gas has cleared away.

Hydrogen Sulfide

Sulfhemoglobin is formed when ferrohemoglobin is treated with hydrogen sulfide under suitable conditions. It is a green compound, and is formed when blood or hemoglobin undergoes putrefaction.

Except perhaps in extreme cases of intestinal putrefaction hydrogen sulfide is not absorbed in appreciable amounts. But it appears that certain drugs, notably acetanilide and phenacetin sensitize hemoglobin so that it combines more readily with hydrogen sulfide. Small quantities of the gas absorbed from the alimentary canal may then cause sulfhemoglobin to reach a relatively high concentration in the circulation and give a bluish or mauve tint to the skin. This so-called *enterogenous cyanosis* occurs when the abnormal compound amounts to from 3 to 5 gm. per 100 cc. of blood. The presence in the blood of sulfhemoglobin or of methemoglobin is detected by spectroscopic examination (table 27.2).

Other Heme Compounds

Cytochrome

Cytochromes are heme compounds that are widely distributed in the tissues of plants and animals where they play a fundamental role in the oxidation systems of the cells. The different cytochromes take part in a series of coupled oxidation-reduction reactions whereby the oxidation of one of the cytochromes by molecular oxygen ultimately results in the oxidation of a substrate, and energy is thus made available to the organism. The function of hemoglobin, of course, is to deliver oxygen to the cell so that these reactions may take place.

Myoglobin

Myoglobin, the pigment of muscle, resembles hemoglobin in its function. It is the simplest example of a respiratory heme protein, since the molecule consists of but one polypeptide chain and one heme group. It has a molecular weight of about 17,000; the iron content is 0.32%. It acts as an oxygen reservoir within the muscle fibre, since it has a higher oxygen-binding capacity than hemoglobin, and can associate and dissociate much more rapidly than the blood pigment.

Porphyria

A disorder of porphyrin metabolism in which abnormal porphyrins or large quantities of normal porphyrins are formed and excreted is called porphyria.

Congenital porphyria is characterized by sensitivity to light which may result in blistering of the skin upon exposure to sunlight, and excretion of large quantities of uroporphyrin I and III and coproporphyrin III in the urine, which is colored a wine-red. Porphyrins are found in large quantities in certain tissues.

In acute porphyria large amounts of porphobilinogen are excreted in the urine. After exposure to air, this is changed to a porphyrin. This condition is characterized by abdominal, nervous or mental symptoms. There is some suggestion that this may be brought on by chronic ingestion of large amounts of some drugs.

Porphyrinuria refers to the increased excretion of porphyrins in the urine. This may be brought about by disorders of erythrocyte metabolism, or by various hepatic diseases.

REFERENCES

Adair, G. S. Proc. Roy. Soc., London, ser. A, 1925, **108**, 627.

Anson, M. L. and Mirsky, A. E. J. Physiol., 1925, **60**, 50.

Bernhart, F. W. and Skeggs, L. J. Biol. Chem., 1943, **147**, 19.

Granick, S. Blood, 1949, **4**, 404.

Haldane, J. J. Physiol., 1900–01, **25**, 497.

Keilin, D. Proc. Roy. Soc., London, ser. B, 1926, **100**, 129.

King, E. J. and associates. Lancet, 1947, **2**, 789; 1948, **1**, 282, 478; **2**, 563.

Meulengracht, E. and associates. Acta Med. Scandinav., 1938, **96**, 462.

Nomenclature of abnormal hemoglobins—Editorial in Am. J. Clin. Path., 1965, **43**, 166.

Northrop, J. H. and Anson, M. L. J. Gen. Physiol., 1929, **12**, 543.

Sahli, H. Klinische Untersuchungsmethoden, Leipzig and Vienna, 5th ed., 1909, 845.

Monographs and Reviews

Barcroft, J. Physiol. Rev., 1924, **4**, 329; 1925, **5**, 596. The Respiratory Function of the Blood. Part II, Haemoglobin. Cambridge University Press, London, 1928.

BISHOP, C. AND SURGENOR, D. M. The Red Blood Cell. Academic Press, New York, 1964.

CARTWRIGHT, G. E. Diagnostic Laboratory Hematology. Grune & Stratton, New York, 1958.

DRABKIN, D. L. Physiol. Rev., 1951, 31, 345.

FALK, J. E. Porphyrins and Metalloporphyrins. Elsevier Publishing Company, Amsterdam, 1964.

GRAY, C. L. The Bile Pigments. Methuen and Co., London, 1953.

INGRAM, V. M. The Hemoglobins in Genetics and Evolution. Columbia University Press, New York, 1963.

JONXIS, J. H. P. AND DELAFRESNAYE, J. F. Abnormal Haemoglobins, a Symposium. Blackwell, Oxford, 1959.

MASON, V. R., COURVILLE, C. AND ZISKIND, E. Medicine, 1933, 12, 355.

WATSON, C. J. Lancet, 1951, 1, 539.

CHAPTER 28

Hemolysis and Suspension Stability of the Blood

Hemolysis or the Laking of Blood

Under normal circumstances the plasma contains no appreciable quantity of hemoglobin. If normal blood is centrifuged the corpuscles are driven to the bottom of the tube whereas the supernatant plasma is clear but faintly straw-colored. Under certain conditions, however, changes may occur in the red cell which will allow the hemoglobin to escape into the surrounding fluid, which then becomes discolored. This is called *hemolysis* or *laking* and may be carried out in a test tube by means of various agencies both physical and chemical. Certain biological substances such as the toxins of bacteria and snake venoms are intensely hemolytic. On the other hand, substances belonging to the class of immune substances or antibodies, and known specifically as *hemolysins*, are formed in the blood. These have the power to hemolyze foreign red cells. After the action of certain hemolytic agents the dim colorless outline of the red cells—shadow cells or "ghosts"—may be seen; they represent the incompletely destroyed framework or stroma.[1] Some of the means by which hemolysis may be induced will now be considered in greater detail.

Hypotonic solutions

The membranes of plant and animal cells are semipermeable (p. 497). They allow the passage into the cell of water and various substances in solution, but offer a barrier to the entrance or egress of others. The red cell is no exception; it contains substances which cannot pass out, and is surrounded by a fluid (plasma) containing materials which cannot pass in. We have here then a minute and almost perfect osmometer, and indeed much of our knowledge of osmotic phenomena has been gained from the study of the behavior of plant and animal cells when placed in solutions of different concentrations.

[1] When hemolysis is induced by certain reagents, e.g., linoleic acid, but the cell structure remains intact, the addition of electrolytes causes the reappearance of hemoglobin in the cells ("reversed hemolysis"). This phenomenon is due probably to shrinkage of the cells and the concentration of a residue of unliberated pigment and not to the return of hemoglobin to the cell.

In normal blood the plasma and the corpuscles are in osmotic equilibrium, i.e., the fluids separated by the corpuscular membrane are isotonic. If, however, the dissolved substances in the plasma are diluted by the addition of distilled water, a flow of water into the corpuscles occurs. An osmotic pressure is developed within it which the cell membrane is unable to withstand. The cell swells and becomes globular, the membrane stretches and the hemoglobin is liberated.

The process is in reality rather more complicated than this. It is probable that the hemoglobin is not contained within the red cell merely as in a bladder, or even in a number of smaller compartments, but is closely bound in some way to the cell structure. One reason for this belief is that purely mechanical agencies will not liberate the pigment. The cell may be torn into the finest shreds, yet each minute particle still retains its hold upon the hemoglobin. The pigment, however, is soon released when the surrounding fluid is made hypotonic. This suggests that the cell structure consists of semipermeable partitions of almost infinite fineness.

The normal red cell offers a certain resistance to the disintegrating effect of hypotonic solutions. A slight lowering of the osmotic pressure of the surrounding fluid will not produce hemolysis. The normal percentage of salts in human plasma is approximately 0.94. Normal cells may be placed in a 0.6 per cent saline solution without being hemolyzed. The cell increases in volume, but the hemoglobin does not escape. The first trace of hemolysis appears when the saline concentration is about 0.42 per cent and the cell volume increased to about 145 per cent. At 0.35 per cent the cells are fully "laked," i.e., hemolysis is complete; the cell volume is around 165 per cent of normal just before this occurs. The resistance which erythrocytes offer to the hemolytic action of hypotonic solutions is used in this way as an index of the fragility of the red cells.

In performing a fragility test a series of tubes is set up containing solutions of NaCl graded in strength from 0.9 to 0.20 per cent at intervals of 0.05 per cent above and below the range at which hemolysis is expected, and at intervals of 0.025 within that range. A sample of blood is introduced into the saline in each tube, and the one in which hemolysis commences and the one in which the process is complete are noted. A *mechanical fragility test* is sometimes employed, a sample of blood being placed in a flask with glass beads and rapidly rotated. The liberated hemoglobin is then measured. The mechanical fragility is increased in acholuric jaundice, certain other hemolytic anemias and in sickle cell anemia. The degree of hemolysis may be determined by centrifuging the diluted blood sample and estimating colorimetrically the quantity of hemoglobin in the supernatant fluid.

In pernicious anemia the red cells have been found to be actually less fragile than normal whereas in other conditions, e.g., some forms of purpura (p. 590) and acholuric jaundice (ch. 68), their fragility is increased.

Cells that show reduced resistance to hypotonic saline may show a normal resistance to other hemolytic agents, e.g., lysolecithin (p. 529) and *vice versa*. Erythrocytes of spherical form, such as those characteristic of acholuric jaundice, show a lowered osmotic resistance mainly because the cells cannot increase their volume by as great an increment as can normal cells without injury to the cell structure. The resistance to hemolysis by lysolecithin on the other hand is not influenced by the shape of the cells, the hemolytic process being chemical in nature.

The permeability of the membrane of the red cell is quite different from that of the capillary membrane which, as we have seen (ch. 62), allows the passage of all crystalloid substances and to some extent of plasma protein, and is also freely permeable to hemoglobin. The membrane of human erythrocytes, on the other hand, is impermeable under physiological conditions to hemoglobin, the plasma proteins, and to Ca^{++}, K^+ Mg^{++} and organic phosphate ions, but permits the passage of water, H^+, NH_4^+, and of Cl^-, HCO_3^- and $PO^{\equiv}$. Potassium escapes freely from the cells under conditions which injure the cell membrane, the potassium loss is closely related to the escape of hemoglobin, i.e., to hemolysis. The human red cell membrane is not absolutely impermeable to the sodium ion for even under physiological conditions and therefore in the absence of hemolysis minute amounts may pass from the plasma into the erythrocytes.[2] Since the

red cell is impermeable to potassium whereas sodium can cross the membrane, the selective permeability of the latter cannot be explained simply upon the theory that the cell membrane is a sievelike structure whose "pores" are of such a size as to allow the smaller ions, but not the larger ones, to pass. The lipid soluble theory is also unsatisfactory, for the inorganic anions are lipid insoluble. The cell membrane is freely permeable to amino acids, urea and uric acid, so these substances under ordinary circumstances do not enter into the osmotic relationships between cells and plasma. Osmotic changes occur, however, when CO_2 enters the blood and diffuses into the cell.

The exchange of inorganic phosphate across the cell membrane is associated with the enzymatic synthesis and breakdown of organic phosphate esters within the erythrocyte. In the former process inorganic phosphate passes from the serum into the cell and in the reverse direction when organic phosphate compounds are broken down.

Chemical Substances

Ether, chloroform, benzene and alcohol act by dissolving the lipid constituents of the envelope and stroma of the cell. Other substances, e.g., *bile salts, acids and alkalis* and *saponin* cause hemolysis, but the manner in which they act is not altogether clear. Bile salts probably act by combining with the protein constituents, and saponin with the cholesterol. As a result of the chemical changes induced by either of these substances, destruction of the cell stroma—*stromatolysis*—occurs. Acids probably act by penetrating the cell and increasing the osmotic concentration within. Swelling and liberation of the hemoglobin occurs in a manner analogous to that of hypotonic solutions. The stroma is not as a rule destroyed. Alkalis, particularly ammonia, are powerfully hemolytic, as is also ammonium chloride. The NH_3 enters the cell and through the increase in osmotic pressure causes swelling and liberation of the hemoglobin. Stromatolysis accompanies hemolysis by alkali.

Certain chemical poisons such as carbolic acid, nitrobenzene, pyrogallol, ricin, arsenical preparations used in the treatment of syphilis, and many other substances are capable of causing red cell destruction.

Substances of Bacterial Origin or Formed in the Animal Body

1. SPECIFIC HEMOLYSINS. If blood is injected into the veins of an animal of another species, or as already mentioned (ch. 5) into an individual of

---

[2] The results of various investigators in the past have differed rather widely with respect to the permeability of the red cell to the sodium and potassium ions, but the experiments of Kurnick who employed radioactive isotopes of Na and K give strong support to the statement made here.

the same species but whose blood group is incompatible with the blood group to which the injected blood belongs, agglutination of the red cells of the donor occurs, and hemolysis follows as a secondary effect. But if a series of injections of erythrocytes is made over a period of days into the blood of another species the serum of the latter develops a substance which promptly destroys the foreign cells through a *primary* hemolytic effect quite independent of agglutination. This hemolytic reaction, which was first demonstrated by Bordet, is specific, that is to say, it is only the particular species of erythrocyte to which the animal has been sensitized by previous injections that is destroyed by the hemolytic substance. The latter on this account is known as a *specific hemolysin*. It belongs to the class of immune substances or antibodies. Bodies of similar nature cause the destruction of other foreign cells and are known as cytolysins and bacteriolysins. All are part of a general protective mechanism which the body is able to build up against the invasion of foreign cells. When referring to these and other immune reactions the substance which upon entering the body causes their development is referred to as the *antigen* (i.e., the foreign red cells in the case of hemolysins). The antibody itself (e.g., the hemolysin) is heat stable and is spoken of as the *amboceptor*. The latter (which is specific) requires for its action another body which is nonspecific, is present in all sera and is destroyed by heat. It is known as the *complement*. Three factors (antigen, amboceptor and complement) are therefore necessary for the hemolytic or bacteriolytic reaction. After the action of the hemolytic or bacteriolytic amboceptor has been annulled through destruction of the complement by heat, the reaction may be restored by the addition of any serum (i.e., by supplying fresh complement).

When serum which has developed a bacterial antibody is incubated with an emulsion of the particular bacteria which has served as antigen, a reaction occurs which "fixes" or binds the complement. The phenomenon is spoken of as *complement fixation*. These facts were applied by Wassermann to the diagnosis of syphilis, and by subsequent workers as a test for other diseases, e.g., tuberculosis. For example, the previously heated serum of a subject suspected to be suffering from syphilis is incubated with (a) an emulsion of syphilitic liver[3] tubercle or typhoid bacilli respectively (the antigen) together with (b) complement furnished by normal guinea pig's serum. If the suspected serum contains a specific antibody (amboceptor) for the antigen employed, the former will bind the complement to the latter, i.e.,

[3] As a matter of fact syphilitic liver has been found to be unnecessary, since lecithin and other materials for some unexplained reason will serve as antigens.

fixation of complement will occur. The foregoing is an account of a bacteriolytic system. An hemolytic system is employed to render the reaction visible. Washed sheep's corpuscles are added to the former system, together with the previously heated serum of a rabbit which has been sensitized to the latter cells by repeated injections. This serum supplies the hemolytic amboceptor but its complement has been destroyed. If the test is positive no hemolysis of the corpuscles occurs, since the complement (nonspecific) of the patient's serum has been already fixed by the bacteriolytic amboceptor and the hemolysin of the rabbit serum is therefore unable to exert its usual effect.

2. TOXIC SUBSTANCES OF BACTERIAL OR PARASITIC ORIGIN. The toxins of bacteria responsible for many diseases, e.g. streptococcus, staphylococcus, tetanus bacillus and the organism of scarlet fever may cause a destruction of red cells; it may also occur in extensive burns. The more virulent types of other infectious fevers, e.g., smallpox, diphtheria, are also sometimes accompanied by intense hemolysis. When the hemolysis is of moderate degree but occurs over longer periods the hemoglobin is converted into bile pigment. This, if formed in amounts greater than can be disposed of by the liver, undergoes partial retention in the plasma, which together with the solid tissues, especially of the skin and mucous membranes, becomes stained a yellowish tint— hemolytic jaundice (ch. 26). In hemolytic states of long standing an iron-containing derivative of hemoglobin termed *hemosiderin* is frequently deposited in large amounts in the tissues, particularly of the liver and spleen.

3. THE VENOMS OF CERTAIN POISONOUS SNAKES, e.g., the cobra, and the poisons of various stinging insects and spiders cause a destruction of the red cells to a greater or less degree. Snake venom (cobra) has been shown to act indirectly. It contains a principle which has power to remove unsaturated fatty acids from the lecithin molecule. The resulting product which is called *lysolecithin*, is intensely hemolytic. Since lecithin is present both in erythrocytes and plasma and indeed in all cells, the entrance of snake venom into the body causes the production of this intensely hemolytic substance. Kephalin is acted upon by snake venom in a like manner with the production of a lysokephalin which has a similar hemolytic action.

4. HEMOLYSINS FROM NORMAL TISSUES. A nonspecific hemolysin has been extracted by simple means from healthy tissues and identified as cis-vaccinic acid; it probably exists in the free state in the tissues. Other nonspecific hemolysins have been isolated from various tissues after incubation at 37° and extraction with alcohol. These are thought to be present but bound to an inhibitory substance, and may be liberated in active form by disease or injury.

Hemoglobinuria

When the hemolysis reaches such a degree that the hemoglobin cannot be converted into bilirubin as rapidly as it is liberated, as in severe malaria (blackwater fever) *hemoglobinuria* occurs, that is, the pigment is passed in the urine, which is usually turned port wine color or a dark brown or even black, due to the action of the urinary acid in converting the pigment into acid hematin and methemoglobin. The concentration of hemoglobin must, as a rule, reach a level of about 0.13 gram per 100 cc. of blood before it appears in the urine. It should be remembered that hemoglobin once it has escaped from the erythrocytes is functionless. Not only is it unable to be retained within the capillaries on account of the relatively small size of its molecule but the environment of the plasma is unsuitable for its action.

The hemolysis in *blackwater fever* is not due to the destruction of erythrocytes by the malarial parasite, nor does the parasite affect the hemopoietic tissue in such a way that it produces cells which are unduly fragile. The cells are apparently not defective, but the work of Macgraith and his associates may provide an explanation of the high degree of hemolysis in this disease. They found that normal human tissues contain a hemolysin which is inhibited in its action by normal serum but not by the serum of a patient suffering from blackwater fever. It is suggested, therefore, that there is no special hemolytic agent in the blood in blackwater fever but rather an absence of a normal inhibitory substance.

Paroxysmal (cold) hemoglobinuria. This form of hemoglobinuria occurs most usually upon exposure to cold. There may be fever, headache, abdominal pain, vomiting and transient jaundice. It is sometimes associated with Raynaud's phenomenon, in which condition spasmodic constrictions of the small vessels of the peripheral parts of the body occur, particularly after exposure to cold. The occasional association of the two conditions has suggested to some that they have a common cause, but direct evidence for this is lacking. It is an interesting observation that the blood of a subject of paroxysmal hemoglobinuria if cooled (to 5°C). outside the body and subsequently warmed undergoes hemolysis (Donath phenomenon). There is apparently no defect, however, of the subject's corpuscles; they seem to be no less resistant than normal to hypotonic saline; the serum, on the other hand, has the power to hemolyze the cells of a normal person. The great majority of subjects are syphilitic. The hemoglobin, it seems, is liberated from the erythrocytes by the action of an endogenous hemolysin which in the presence of complement becomes fixed to the red cells when the blood is chilled (cold phase). The presence of some thermolabile component of complement is required when the blood is again brought to ordinary body temperature (warm phase) to bring about hemolysis (see Siebens and associates). The phenomenon is quite distinct from cold auto-agglutination.

March hemoglobinuria. Hemolysis may occur and hemoglobin appear in the urine even in healthy persons after strenuous muscular effort. In certain persons this tendency is exaggerated and hemoglobinuria may follow relatively mild muscular exercise. It is seen not infrequently in soldiers after long marches. The free pigment in the blood and urine of such cases is oxyhemoglobin, not myoglobin as might be expected. The fragility of the red cells is not increased and neither hemolysins nor autoagglutinins which might account for the hemolysis have been discovered.

In the third type of paroxysmal hemoglobinuria —the *nocturnal hemoglobinuria of Marchiafava*— hemoglobin or hemosiderin (pp. 529 and 542) is passed almost continuously in the urine, but in greatest amounts at night. It is accompanied by a severe hemolytic anemia. The cause of the hemolysis is believed to be a peculiar susceptibility of the red cells to acid metabolites, their greater destruction at night being attributed to the accumulation of carbon dioxide during sleep. The abnormal cells are hemolyzed when incubated in serum made slightly acid (Ham), or in any normal serum, but normal cells are not destroyed by the patient's serum. The fault in the patient's cells is thought to be some abnormality of the stroma protein.

The Suspension Stability of the Blood
Erythrocyte Sedimentation Rate (E.S.R.)

The blood is a suspension of cells in a viscous fluid, the plasma. It is only the constant movement of the fluid that keeps the cells evenly distributed throughout. When the circulation comes to rest the cells at once commence to sink. Under ordinary circumstances the sedimentation of the cells in a sample of blood can progress to only a negligible extent, for it is soon circumvented by the clotting process which fixes them in a jellylike matrix. If for any reason, the blood is delayed from clotting, sedimentation may continue until an upper layer of clear plasma becomes separated from the cells which have descended through the fluid. When clotting then ensues the blood consists of two strata, a thin yellowish or buff-colored layer of clotted plasma laid upon a much deeper red stratum of cells. When blood had clotted in this way the upper layer was known to the older physiologists as the "buffy coat." Ancient and medieval physicians carried out crude observations of the quantity of clear fluid which separated from blood upon standing as a means of diagnosis. In conformity with their humoral theories of disease, they believed it to be the "phlegm" which had separated from the other humors.

Biernaki (1891) was the first in modern times to draw attention to the increase in the rate of sedimentation of the blood in various pathological states. The subject has been studied in more recent times by Fahraeus and the *erythrocyte sedimentation rate* (E.S.R.) has come to be recognized as a useful diagnostic procedure. The sedimentation rate is measured by the depth in millimeters of clear plasma which is formed at the top of a vertical column of blood at the end of one hour. For the determination of the E.S.R. either Westegren's or Wintrobe's method is usually employed. In Westegren's method, the blood for examination (about 1.5 ml.) is diluted 4 parts to 1 of a 3.8 per cent solution of sodium citrate.[4] It is then drawn into a graduated glass tube about 300 mm. long, and having a bore of 2.45 mm.[5] The upper end of the tube which is fixed in a strictly perpendicular position is left open, whereas the lower end is closed, usually by a removable rubber cap held in position by a spring.

The determinations should be made at a temperature of 20°C.

The sedimentation rates expressed as the height of supernatant plasma, in mm. per hour for normal blood of men, women and infants, are given in the following table.

	mm. per hour
Men	1–3
Women	4–7
Newborn children	0.5

In normal pregnancy and in certain pathological states, the sinking rate of the red cells is found to be very markedly increased; in other words, the suspension stability of the blood is reduced. The average figure during pregnancy is about 35 mm. per hour. The rate is also increased during menstruation. The pathological states which show the most noteworthy increase in the rate are septicemia, 100 mm. per hour, and pulmonary tuber-

---

[4] This is isotonic with plasma and has the same specific gravity.

[5] Since the concentration of the blood in red cells influences the sinking rate, Walton recommends that their number be standardized to 5,000,000 per cu. mm. by the addition or removal of plasma if the subject's blood is below or above this level. In Wintrobe's method his hematocrit tube is employed, the packed cell volume (p. 18) being determined if desired after measuring the E.S.R. In the final calculation of the latter, a factor is used to correct for any existing anemia.

culosis, 65 mm. Anemia (sickle cell anemia and acholuric jaundice excepted), malignant tumors, inflammatory conditions of the female pelvic organs and many other conditions increase the rate moderately above the normal. *Reduction* in the sedimentation rate is rare; it occurs in allergic states, in peptone shock and in sickle cell anemia and acholuric jaundice.

The physical changes in the blood which might cause this unusually rapid rate of red cell settling are of considerable interest and were investigated thoroughly by Fahraeus. In considering the sedimentation rate of particles suspended in a fluid when they are of a size comparable with that of the red cells, four factors must be taken into account. These as applied to blood are:

1. Specific gravity of the plasma as compared with that of the corpuscles. Corpuscles of high specfic gravity would sink more quickly in normal plasma, and normal corpuscles more quickly in a plasma with a low specific gravity. In neither corpuscles nor plasma was any significant change of this nature found to explain an increase in the E.S.R.

2. Lowered viscosity of the plasma is another factor which could cause an increase in rate of sinking, but no such change could be detected.

3. Increased size of the corpuscles would increase their mass disproportionately to their surface and in consequence enhance their rate of sinking, but no significant alteration in size was found.

4. Clumping together of cells of normal size would have the same effect as an increase in size of the individual cells for just as lumps of clay sink rapidly in water, whereas clay in the form of fine particles remains suspended almost indefinitely, so aggregation of the corpuscles would cause their more rapid sedimentation.

This last factor is the chief cause of the lowered stability of the blood suspension in the pathological conditions cited above. The roughness and granular appearance of the blood, due to the corpuscular aggregation is evident to the naked eye when the blood is spread in a film upon a slide (fig. 28.1). Normal blood, in marked contrast, forms a smooth homogeneous film. Under the microscope the crowding together of the cells in large masses is quite obvious. An increase in the fibrinogen and euglobulin fractions of the plasma is held responsible for the effect. Dextran increases the sedimentation rate and is used to produce more rapid separation of plasma and formed elements. These substances act upon the corpuscles in some unknown way to make them adhere to one another and form clumps of agglutinated

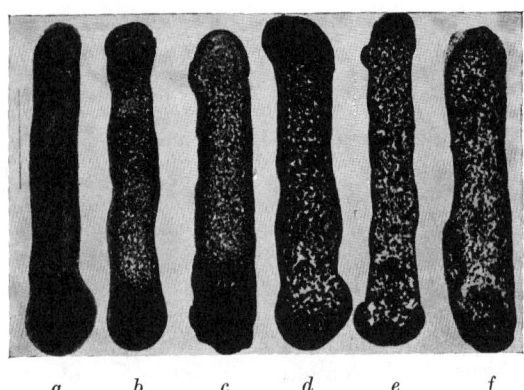

FIG. 28.1. Showing the naked-eye appearances of specimens of blood spread upon glass slides. The specimens, left to right, are from (a) healthy man, (b) healthy woman, (c) healthy pregnant woman, (d) man, appendicitis, (e) man, pneumonia, (f) sepsis. Note the especially granular appearance of specimens e and f (after Fahraeus).

TABLE 28.1

Showing the sedimentation rates of corpuscles from the same sample of blood suspended in different protein fractions of plasma (from Zozaya)

Protein Fraction	E.S.R.
Fibrinogen	41–61 mm.
Euglobulin	42–64 mm.
Pseudoglobulin	5–12 mm.
Albumin	3– 6 mm.

cells.[6] It is probable that it is the relative proportions of the fibrinogen, globulin and albumin fractions of the plasma rather than their absolute concentrations which are of importance in determining the E.S.R. Thus a fall in the albumin concentration alone may have as great an accelerating effect as a rise in the other fractions. That the character of the plasma and not that of the cells is the principal determining factor is shown by the fact that if erythrocytes from blood with a high sedimentation rate (e.g., of pregnancy) are suspended in the plasma of blood having a low rate of sedimentation (e.g., of newborn) they settle at the slower rate, and conversely, erythrocytes with a normal sedimentation rate in their own plasma settle rapidly in plasma from blood with a high E.S.R. See table 28.1.

Though the protein constitution of the plasma is usually the most important single factor affecting the sedimentation rate, several other factors exert an influence, e.g., (a) the *shape* of the erythrocytes, any tendency toward a spherical form by reducing the proclivity of the cells to cling

[6] The red cells of normal blood show an incipient tendency to cling together in chains—the so-called *rouleaux formation* (pseudoagglutination).

together (rouleaux formation) will retard sedimentation; (b) *temperature*, a rise in temperature above 20°C., as a rule, accelerates the E.S.R., a fall retards it; (c) the *lecithin-cholesterol ratio* of the plasma, the rate is retarded by an increase in the lecithin concentration and accelerated by cholesterol; (d) *red cell concentration*, a high erythrocyte count retards the E.S.R., a low count accelerates it.

The nonspecificity of the test is evident; nevertheless determinations of the sedimentation rate are of considerable value, especially, (a) in gauging the degree of activity of tuberculous processes; (b) as an aid in the differential diagnosis of certain gynecological lesions. Benign tumors of the pelvic organs cause no change in rate whereas, as already mentioned, malignant growths, inflammatory states, and pregnancy cause a pronounced rise; (c) as an index of the extent and intensity in pyogenic infections, and (d) in estimating the activity of the inflammatory process in rheumatic fever.

REFERENCES

BIERNAKI, E. Ztschr. Physiol. Chem., 1894, **19,** 179.
KURNICK, N. B. J. Biol. Chem., 1941, **140,** 581.
MACGRAITH, B. H. AND ASSOCIATES. Lancet, 1941, **2,** 530.
SIEBENS, A. A. AND ASSOCIATES. Blood, 1948, **3,** 1367.
WALTON, Z. C. R. Quart. J. Med., 1935, **2,** 79.
Monographs and Reviews
FAHRAEUS, R. Acta med. scandinav., 1921, **55,** 3. Physiol. Rev., 1929, **9,** 241.
GILLYGAN, D. R. AND BLUMGART, H. L. Medicine, 1941, **20,** 341.
PONDER, E. The erythrocyte and the action of simple haemolysins. Oliver, Edinburgh, 1924.
YUILE, C. L. Physiol. Rev., 1942, **22,** 19.

CHAPTER 29

The Spleen; The Life of the Red Cell; The Regeneration of Blood; Iron Metabolism

The Structure of the Spleen

The spleen is an important part of the reticuloendothelial system. Its structure is such that blood is brought into intimate contact with phagocytic cells. Dotted throughout the spleen, like islands, and surrounded by the pulp are lighter areas of lymphoid tissue. These are the Malpighian corpuscles. The Malpighian corpuscle (fig. 29.1) is pierced by a small artery. It is analogous to similar areas in lymph nodes, and serves the same function, namely the manufacture of lymphocytes. Blood enters the substance of the spleen by fine arterial vessels which pass through the Malpighian corpuscles and out into the splenic pulp. Here two different descriptions of its circulation have been given. Briefly, one of these indicates that the vessels open into and flood the splenic pulp, from which it passes back into the venous sinuses through numerous perforations in their walls. According to this view, the circulation through the splenic pulp is an open one. Others contend that the blood vessels are continuous throughout the splenic pulp and lead into the splenic sinuses. According to this view, the circulation through the splenic pulp is closed, the blood cells passing into the pulp or out from the pulp through openings in the vessel walls.[1]

The Functions of the Spleen

The spleen has several important functions. The first three of these below are common to all parts of the reticuloendothelial system: (a) It has a part in the final disposal of red blood cells; (b) it phagocytoses bacteria and other particulate matter; (c) it produces antibodies; (d) it manufactures lymphocytes; (e) it has actions, possibly hormonal in nature, which influence the length of life of the erythrocytes and exert some influence on hematopoiesis; (f) it influences the number of platelets and leukocytes; (g) it has an important

[1] Weiss contends that the walls of the splenic sinusoids are made up of reticuloendothelial cells in flattened form. Some of these cells may become round and form "core" tissue, whereas others remain flat in the walls of the sinusoids.

reservoir function in many animals, though little in man.

1. The role played by the spleen in the destruction of the blood cells. In the pulp of the spleen are to be found relatively enormous mononuclear ameboid cells which have the power to engulf foreign particles of various sorts. They are known as *macrophages* and at times may be seen with fragments of erythrocytes or even whole corpuscles within their cytoplasm. These cells belong to the reticuloendothelial system (ch. 32). In certain conditions in which a great destruction of red cells is a feature, immense numbers of these phagocytic cells may be seen loaded with erythrocyte fragments of various sizes. Sometimes merely a dustlike residue (*hemoconia*) containing hemoglobin is all that remains of the blood cell. The disposal of abnormal or senescent erythrocytes by the spleen may not be a phagocytic process entirely.

Attempts to demonstrate the red cell disposal function of the spleen by comparative estimates of the corpuscular contents of the arterial (ingoing) and venous (outgoing) bloods have not, on the whole, been very successful. But Mann and his associates have been able, by spectroscopic examination of the arterial and venous bloods, to show a definite excess of bilirubin (iron-free pigment) in the blood of the splenic vein over that of the splenic artery. The bilirubin in the venous blood of other organs was no greater in amount than that in the arterial blood. In diseases with marked red cell destruction, the spleen becomes impregnated with iron and with an iron-containing pigment, *hemosiderin*, derived from the hemoglobin of the disintegrated cells. Similar deposits occur in the liver and to a less extent in other reticulo-endothelial tissues.

Although evidence derived from microscopical studies and from bilirubin estimations shows undoubtedly that red cell disintegration occurs in the spleen, it is believed that only fragmented, dead, or effete and senile erythrocytes or those which are abnormal are disposed of in this way. The organ is believed not to attack healthy circu-

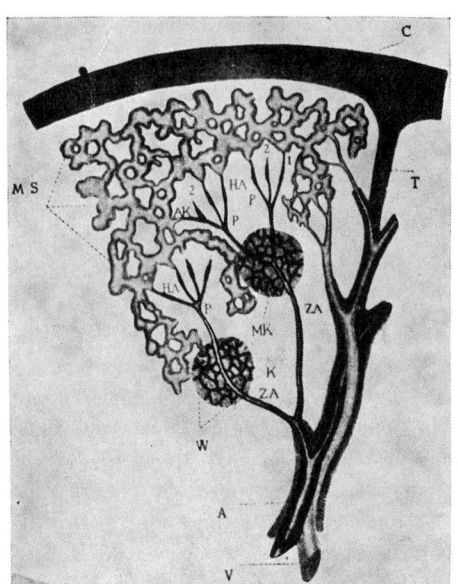

FIG. 29.1. Diagram of the human spleen. (A) artery and vein (V) in a trabecula (T) of the capsule (C); ZA, central artery of the corpuscle of Malpighi (MK); P, small arteries; HA, arteries with a sheath; AK, arterial capillaries which terminate in the sinuses (*1*) or in the meshes of the reticulum (*2*); MS, venous sinuses; W, white pulp (from Cajal after Szymonowicz).

lating cells. The reticuloendothelial cells of the spleen, in common with those elsewhere, conserve the iron from hemoglobin.

2. Other phagocytic activity. The phagocytic activity of the reticuloendothelial cells of the spleen, which has been considered in relation to the removal of red blood cells, is also important in the defense against infection, bacteria or other particulate matter being taken up by these cells. After splenectomy, animals become more susceptible to certain parasitic and bacterial infections; there is some evidence of a similar increased susceptibility in children who have undergone splenectomy. Although the spleen may hold only a small percentage of any particulate matter injected intravenously, nevertheless it also can be stimulated to form more reticuloendothelial cells and discharge them into the circulation. The phagocytic activity of the spleen, in common with other parts of the reticuloendothelial system, is is influenced by various hormones. It can be strongly stimulated by estrogenic materials such as diethyl stilbestrol and estradial benzoate, and its phagocytic activity is greatly depressed by cortisone.

3. Antibody production. This function of the spleen resides in the splenic macrophages. They rapidly ingest bacteria or larger parasites. When

paralyzed by the injection of colloidal particles, the immune response of an animal so treated is markedly reduced. Splenectomy can abolish the immune reaction of animals to certain toxins. The macrophages of the germinal centers destroy lymphocytes, releasing their γ-globulin. It is also believed that the macrophages of the spleen are stimulated during the immune response to produce the precursors of lymphocytes and plasma cells, the antibody forming cells of the body.

4. Lymphocyte production. The spleen contains much lymphoid tissue particularly in the Malpighian follicles and manufactures lymphocytes.

5. The hemopoietic function of the spleen in the embryo. In the embryo, the spleen in common with the bone marrow and liver is active in the production of erythrocytes and granulocytes as well as of lymphocytes. But erythropoiesis and granulopoiesis in the spleen normally cease at birth. Yet, many observations point to the spleen as exerting an influence upon erythrocyte production as well as destruction in the adult.

6. Suggested influences of the spleen on the structure and number of the blood cells. Although, as mentioned before, the spleen destroys abnormal cells (e.g., the spherocytes of chronic congenital hemolytic anemia, the erythrocytes in sickle cell anemia) it does not normally destroy erythrocytes until after they have served their purpose. Splenectomy affects all three formed elements of the peripheral blood.

The primary change in the red cells is a morphologic one. Anemia may occur, but is transient. Nucleated red cells, Howell-Jolly bodies, siderocytes and diffuse basophilia are all common. The percentage of reticulocytes is increased. The surface area of the red cells is increased, while the cell volume remains normal, thus producing the so-called "thin macrocyte." Some of these cells are apparent as target cells. Red cell osmotic fragility is decreased, but red cell life span is normal.

Both leukocytes and platelets increase, beginning during the first week after splenectomy. The white cells reach their peak during the first week, but the maximal peak of thrombocytosis may not be achieved for three weeks. Splenectomized patients have been studied many years after operation. At that time, the only consistent abnormalities found in the peripheral blood were the morphological changes previously described in the red cells, and a mild eosinophilia.

It has been suggested that the effects of removal of the spleen on white cells and platelets are due to a normal inhibitory action of the spleen either upon the production of these cells or upon their release into the circulation. There is no good evidence that the spleen normally participates directly in the *destruction* of either of these cell types.

7. Reservoir function of spleen. Animal experiments in dogs, cats, and a number of other mammals have shown that the spleen has a large reservoir capacity. The splenic blood was found to be richer in red cells so that with splenic contraction, in the cat, there might be expelled into the circulation an amount of blood equal to one-sixth of the blood volume and red cells equal to one-fourth of the body's total supply. In these animals, splenic contraction occurs with exercise, anoxia, hemorrhage, when the pressure in the carotid sinus is reduced, and when splanchnic nerves are stimulated or adrenaline injected. Although the reservoir function in animals may be of great importance, in man, under normal conditions, it is slight. The total volume of the spleen in man is not great and, at best, only a relatively small volume of blood could be released into the general circulation from it.

However, the sequestration of red blood cells in the spleen probably is an important step in their destruction. Crosby has coined two words to describe part of this process—"culling" and "pitting." "Culling" describes the ability of the spleen to remove certain cells from the circulating blood which do not meet minimum requirements, e.g., spherocytes. "Pitting" on the other hand is used to describe the alteration of certain cells in their passage through the spleen. The most commonly cited example is the removal of granules from siderocytes.

8. Other effects. A curious and unexplained action of the spleen has been discovered by Cullumbine and Simpson, who found that toxic doses of the antithyroid compound, thio-thymine (2-thio-5-methyl-uracil) causes the death of normal rabbits from pulmonary edema, but not of splenectomized animals. Moreover, if a splenectomized animal is injected with an aqueous-acid extract of hog or beef spleen, its susceptibility to the action of the drug in causing pulmonary edema is restored. Splenic extracts alone produce no such effect.

HYPERSPLENISM. Hypersplenism is a poorly understood phrase, used to describe a condition in which there is an excess of one of the normal functions of the spleen affecting the blood cells. It is frequently a complication of splenomegaly. One or more of such blood states as thrombocytopenia, leucopenia, and anemia may be present.

Various causal factors have been suggested: (a) antibody production (b) excessive phagocytosis (c) excessive production of an agent suppressing marrow activity.

IRRADIATION AND THE SPLEEN. Animals can be protected from usually lethal, although not massive, doses of irradiation of the general body surface by shielding the spleen with lead, or by the intravenous injection of ground up spleen or bone marrow. In the latter instance the protective effect is obtained with that part of the material containing the cell nuclei. It has been suggested that relatively undifferentiated cells in the material injected or discharged by the shielded structures protect, in some way, the hematopoietic tissue exposed to the irradiation, or restore it if it has been injured, as it is thought that the cells, although injured; still retain their potentiality to divide and mature.

Enlargement of the Spleen

Enlargement of the spleen is associated with a large number of pathological states; only a few will be mentioned.

In *idiopathic thrombocytopenic purpura* the spleen may be enlarged and its removal is frequently followed by a rise in the platelet count and amelioration of the symptoms. Also, substances such as antiplatelet serum or diphtheria toxin, which when injected cause platelet destruction, are rendered much less effective if the spleen has been removed. Splenectomy brings about a cure in *congenital hemolytic jaundice* (acholuric jaundice). The spleen may be considerably enlarged in *pernicious anemia* but splenectomy exerts no effect upon the course of the disease. In *splenic anemia* (congestive splenomegaly, Banti's disease), the spleen is tremendously enlarged and the liver is cirrhotic. There are portal hypertension and repeated hemorrhages. Splenectomy has been practiced in this disease with variable success. Relief of the portal hypertension and splenic congestion by anastomosis of the portal vein to the inferior vena cava is advocated by Whipple. Splenic enlargement is a feature of many other abnormal conditions, such as malaria, Hodgkin's disease, leukemia, etc., but in these, benefit does not follow its removal. The organ is also enlarged sometimes enormously in *polycythemia*, but splenectomy fails to cure the condition, and indeed is attended by grave risks to life (Moynihan).

Gaucher's disease is an interesting although rare condition which, commencing usually in childhood, is associated with a colossal enlargement of the spleen. The enlargement is due to hypertrophy and hyperplasia of reticuloendothelial elements. Masses of very large vesicular cells (Gaucher's cells) filled with a cerebroside called *kerasin* are seen in the lymphoid tissue and venous sinuses of the spleen. Hyperplasia of reticuloendothelial elements also occurs in other locations, e.g., bone marrow and liver. The disease is due to a disorder of lipid metabolism. Splenectomy is the only effective treatment in those cases complicated by thrombocytopenia. *Niemann-Pick's disease* is a somewhat similar condition affecting the reticulo-endothelial system and lipid metabolism. Characteristic cells, known from their appearance as "foam cells," are present in large numbers; they are loaded with sphingomyelin. Accumulations of this phospholipid are found also in the liver and brain. Subjects of this and the preceding disease are usually children of the Jewish race. *Von Jaksch's disease* occurs in infants and is characterized by splenomegaly, anemia and an increase in the number of white blood cells. Great enlargement of the spleen also occurs in *glycogen storage (von Gierke's) disease*. The chief characteristics are hypoglycemia, with ketosis, a slight rise only in the blood sugar after an injection of adrenaline (ch. 76), and extensive deposits of glycogen, particularly in the liver and spleen associated usually with a deficiency in glucose-6-phosphatase.

From its position in the portal circulation the spleen is also very susceptible to enlargement, either as a result of mechanical obstruction to the veins or to high venous pressure resulting from cardiac or hepatic disease.

The Life of the Red Cell

From the amount of bile pigment which is excreted daily by the liver the conclusion must be drawn that a very large amount of hemoglobin (since this is the sole or at least the main source of bile pigment) is liberated from disintegrated red cells in 24 hours.

Despite extensive investigation, there is no satisfactory explanation of the way in which final destruction of the red blood cells is achieved. There are three possible ways in which erythrocytes normally might be destroyed in the body: (a) by the macrophages of the spleen, (b) by the action of a hemolytic substance in the blood, (c) through simple wear and tear and disintegration in the blood stream. There is no evidence that hemolysis occurs to any significant extent in normal blood and the phagocytic cells of the normal spleen seem quite inadequate to account for the wholesale destruction of cells which evidently must be going on continually in the body. The work of Rous indicates that the erythrocytes to a very large extent undergo disintegration in the blood stream as a result of the stresses and strains to which they are incessantly subjected during their passage through the vessels. When it is

considered how delicate is the structure of the red cell and to what violent treatment it is exposed during its lifetime, this wastage is not surprising. The cells are flung from the heart into the arteries at high velocity. In their voyage around the circulation they are exposed to jostlings and innumerable collisions with one another and with the arterial walls. At times they are forced through channels which are too narrow to permit their passage without marked distortions of their shape; or they may be caught in a fork at the branching of a vessel and become "saddlebagged" over it. Their membranes are almost continually undergoing alterations in tension as a result of osmotic changes. At last, becoming older, they are unable to withstand these abuses and undergo fragmentation. Fragments of different shapes and varying in size from that of a half or a quarter of the whole cell, to mere dustlike remnants containing hemoglobin (hemoconia) may be found in the circulating blood, in the spleen and to a limited extent occasionally in other tissues.

From determinations of bile pigment excretion it has been estimated that in health about 3,000,000 cells are destroyed in this way every second—and of course the same number must be formed afresh by the blood-forming tissue. In the normal adult between 5.6 and 6.7 gm. of hemoglobin are removed and replaced daily. The number of red cells and hemoglobin concentration in the circulation at any moment represents the balance struck between blood wastage and blood formation by the bone marrow.

Many attempts have been made to determine the life span of the erythrocyte. Several methods have been employed, e.g., stimulation of the discharge of reticulocytes from the marrow and determining the time of their maturation, measuring the bile pigment excretion. A commonly employed method is some form of the *selective or differential agglutination technique*, introduced in 1918 by Ashby. This method consists in transfusing compatible red cells and later examining the recipient's blood from time to time for the presence of the foreign corpuscles, which are counted in a hemocytometer. The foreign cells are distinguished from the transfused person's own cells by means of the serum of another belonging to a group with which the recipient's cells, but not the foreign cells, are incompatible.[2] That is,

[2] Thus if corpuscles of Group O are transfused into a person belonging to Group AB then, when the recipient's blood is mixed outside the body with Group B (anti-A) or Group A (anti-B) serum,

the recipient's cells are agglutinated but not the foreign (donor's) cells. A plot of the number of surviving cells against time gives a straight line which meets the time axis at a point indicating the life span. To obtain accurate results it is necessary to agglutinate the recipient's cells completely; potent agglutinating sera must therefore be used.

Using this method, it has been found that the life of the average red cell is about 120 days.

Landsteiner, Levine and James have employed the M and N groups in a similar way, injecting M cells into an N recipient, or vice versa, and using anti-M or anti-N serum to agglutinate the *transfused* cells, leaving the recipient's cells unagglutinated.

A more recent method is that which employs the isotope of nitrogen (N^{15}) to tag the red cell in the bone marrow. This is done by feeding glycine into which the isotope has been incorporated; this amino acid is utilized in the synthesis of protoporphyrin. It is necessary to the method that the isotope should not leave the cell and be utilized again for the manufacture of hemoglobin, but should persist throughout the life of the cell. Unfortunately, there is some evidence that such loss of this isotopic tag does occur. Furthermore, since the uptake time is long, and occurs *in vivo*, the tagged cells are not all of the same age and hence with this procedure it is difficult to obtain a precise determination of the survival time. The life span of the red cell as determined in man by this method is 127 days. Whipple and Hawkins, by determinations of the bile pigment excretion, obtained a figure in dogs, of 120 days.

Survival of cells tagged with radioactive iron or radioactive chromium may also be followed. The radioactive chromium technique is the one most commonly used at the present time. Tagging takes place *in vitro*, the tagged cells are injected, and their rate of disappearance from the peripheral blood is followed by means of serial samples. Either the patient's own cells, or those of a suitable donor may be used. This technique has the great clinical advantage that external scanning over organs such as liver and spleen may be carried out at the same time, to detect the sites of deposition of the labeled red cells. Once tagged with radioactive chromium (Cr^{51}) the red cells retain this label until death or loss from the body. The tag is neither lost significantly nor re-utilized. The values obtained for the life span

are similar to those obtained by differential agglutination procedures.

Using differential agglutination, Mollison reported that normal erythrocytes infused into patients with hereditary spherocytosis survived normally, but erythrocytes from such patients had a short survival time in normal recipients. Ashby has found that in pernicious anemia the average life of transfused cells was 110 days; in aplastic anemia, 41 days; in malignant disease, 52 days, whereas in transfusions given postoperatively to ordinary surgical cases, uncomplicated by severe anemia or malignancy, the survival time of the transfused cells averaged 124 days. The latter survival time depends in large part on the age of the stored blood used in transfusion, and the technique used for storage.

The Regeneration of Blood

The red blood cells are formed in the red bone marrow (ch. 32). Anoxia, no matter how produced, is a fundamental factor in stimulating erythrocyte production. This stimulating effect seems to be a consequence of an increase in the blood level of a hematopoietic factor of extramedullary origin which results from the anoxia. Anoxia is important also in bringing about the release of iron from its stores.

THE MATERIALS NECESSARY FOR ERYTHROCYTE FORMATION

1. The red cell stroma. It is doubtful whether the materials required for the construction of the framework of the cell, e.g., nucleoprotein, globulin, lecithin and cholesterol are ever lacking. The body possesses large supplies of these materials and an ordinary diet contains them in adequate amounts. In certain anemias, however, e.g., pernicious anemia and Cooley's anemia, the failure of the body to assemble and utilize these materials for the manufacture of cell stroma is a fundamental causative factor.

2. Hemoglobin is added to the red cell only after the cell's development has progressed to a certain stage (ch. 32). Synthesis is believed to take place in the nucleus of the cells in the bone marrow. The complete history of hemoglobin in the body has yet to be written, but it is now established that the body can synthesize pyrrol groups from simpler and readily available compounds, possibly, as suggested by Hans Fischer, from acetoacetic acid; glycine,[3] proline, oxyproline and tryptophane

---

[3] The most convincing evidence that this amino acid is a precursor of pyrrol has been obtained by

have been proposed by others as possible building stones. Given the pyrrol group, synthesis of protoporphyrin is readily effected (ch. 27). An interesting experiment in this connection is described by Whipple and his associates. When hemoglobin was given intravenously to anemic dogs, the animals' hemoglobin was increased by an amount equal to that injected. At the same time the excretion of bile pigment was increased by a corresponding amount. This paradoxical result is interpreted in the following way. The pyrrol of the injected hemoglobin is excreted as bilirubin, whereas the globin part of the molecule is utilized for the production of new hemoglobin, the pyrrol groups of which must therefore be derived from some other source—food or body tissue—and synthesized to protoporphyrin. It has already been pointed out that heme (porphyrin + iron) is a universal material and is present in the great majority of foodstuffs. So here, it might be supposed, was a source of an almost unlimited supply of the necessary pigment element. Yet heme cannot be split by the digestive secretions and it has been generally agreed that iron so combined cannot be utilized for hemoglobin synthesis. Recent experiments, using isotopically labelled hemoglobin, have shown that heme iron can be absorbed from the gastro-intestinal tract and incorporated into body iron. Globin, of course, is required to complete the hemoglobin molecule. Whipple and his associates have found that this protein is well utilized for hemoglobin synthesis, yielding from 30 to 40 grams of blood pigment for each 100 grams fed to anemic dogs. Hemoglobin or globin, or a digest of the latter when given intravenously to anemic animals forms hemoglobin almost gram for gram. They found that, as compared with the porphyrin part of the molecule, globin was of much greater importance for hemoglobin regeneration; this protein apparently is a limiting factor in hemoglobin synthesis. Upon a diet low in protein but adequate in iron, hemoglobin regeneration was minimal. The amino acids necessary for the construction of hemoglobin are present in milk, meat, and other sources of first class protein. Globin can also be synthesized to a limited extent apparently from endogenous sources. This function is probably situated in the liver. Certain amino acids, especially proline and threonine, were found to increase hemoglobin regeneration after hemorrhage, which suggests that they are used for the synthesis of globin. Histidine which constitutes 8 per cent of the globin molecule is, contrary to expectation, less effective. It seems likely, that coproporphyrin is a precursor of protoporphyrin and thus constitutes a step in hemoglobin synthesis. The evidence for this is that: (a) in pernicious anemia the protoporphyrin of the erythrocytes is closely correlated with the reticulocyte percentage, and (b) when the disease is in relapse the protoporphyrin is very low and coproporphyrin cannot be demonstrated, but after treatment with vitamin B_{12} the coproporphyrin increases rapidly and in advance of the protoporphyrin.

Whipple, Hooper and Robscheit carried out a series of experiments upon animals made anemic through repeated bleedings, and tested their power to regenerate hemoglobin when fed upon various diets. Meats were found to be the most potent for this purpose. Carbohydrates in the form of bread and sugar were found to be ineffective. In fact they had actually a definitely depressing effect upon the hemoglobin repair process, for animals regenerated their blood more rapidly when starved than when fed upon a bread and sugar diet. In explanation of this fact Whipple suggested that the starved animal drew upon its tissues to supply the basic elements for hemoglobin synthesis, whereas carbohydrate food on account of its well known protein-sparing effect prevented the tissues from being utilized in this way. Infection or very severe liver damage markedly depresses hemoglobin regeneration in anemic dogs. The depressing effect upon regeneration of hemoglobin which is seen in the Eck fistula animals is apparently due to interference with liver function (defective protein synthesis) and to the reduction in iron absorption.

These workers found that, of all protein foods, liver was by far the most effective for blood regeneration. Next in order came kidney and chicken gizzard. Milk had little regenerating effect. Table 29.1 shows the comparative values of the various articles of diet. A bread mixture consisting of potato and wheat flour, bran, sugar and the necessary salts and vitamins was used as the basal diet. This was practically inert so far as the regeneration of hemoglobin was concerned. The article to be tested was added to this basal diet.

The animals (dogs) were rendered anemic by three or four successive bleedings until the hemoglobin had been reduced to 30 per cent of the nor-

Shemin and Rittenberg who fed glycine to rats and to men, after incorporating isotopic nitrogen into its molecule, and found it in the newly formed protoporphyrin.

mal. The item of food to be tested was then added to the basal diet and the animal bled from time to time in order to maintain the hemoglobin at the original level of 30 per cent. The amount of blood removed expressed in grams of hemoglobin gave a direct measure of the amount of pigment regenerated in a given time.

Iron Metabolism

Being an essential constituent of the hemoglobin molecule, this mineral must be available in adequate amounts in order that normal blood regeneration shall occur. Iron provides the keystone for hemoglobin construction; unless it is supplied in appropriate amounts the maturation of the red cells is retarded, and the numbers discharged from the bone marrow into the general circulation reduced.

ABSORPTION, STORAGE AND EXCRETION OF IRON

Iron is absorbed to some extent throughout the entire intestinal tract, but in by far the greatest amount from the upper part of the small intestine. The absorption is by way of the blood. There is no evidence for a significant uptake by lymphatics. After absorption the element is stored in the intestinal mucosa, the liver and to a less extent in the spleen and kidney. Liver iron is readily increased by iron feeding or injection. Under ordinary circumstances only minute quantities of iron are detectable in the plasma, the normal amount being about 0.1 mg./100 ml., although the iron-binding capacity of plasma is about three times this value. The great proportion of the iron of the blood is present in the red cells. A smaller quantity is present in the muscle (myoglobin, cytochrome, etc.); the remainer is stored in liver, kidney, and various other tissues as *ferritin* and *hemosiderin*. Whole blood contains from 45 to 50 mg. per cent and the total quantity in the adult human body is between 4 and 5 grams. See table 29.2. Iron is present in the blood mainly as (a) plasma iron, and (b) iron combined with hemoglobin, which accounts for from 92 to 98 per cent of the total. There is very little excretion of iron by the bowel or kidney under ordinary conditions. The daily loss in adults is about 1 mg. The view of McCance and Widdowson that normally the iron stores of the body are regulated not by excretion but through the *control of absorption* is now generally accepted. Iron is, therefore, very largely a "one way" element. That which is absorbed is held by the body with great avidity and the iron liberated from hemoglobin is used again for the

TABLE 29.1

Hemoglobin production influenced by diet

Diet, Grams Daily	Hemoglobulin Production (Two-Week Feeding Period)
	grams
Bread 400	3
Milk 450, bread 400	3
Cream 100, bread 400	10
Butter 100, bread 350	15
Asparagus 200, bread 300	9
Spinach 200, bread 300	15
Raspberries 200, bread 300	5
Raisins 200, bread 300	25
Apricots 200, bread 300	48
Eggs 150, bread 300	45
Whole fish 250, bread 300	13
Beef muscle 250, bread 300	17
Pig muscle 250, bread 300	30
Chicken gizzard 250, bread 200	80
Kidney 250, bread 300	70
Chicken liver 250, bread 300	80
Beef liver 300, bread 300	80
Beef liver 450	95

TABLE 29.2

The distribution of iron in the body of a dog weighing 20 kilograms (Hahn)

	mg.	per cent total body iron
Blood hemoglobin iron	900	57
Muscle hemoglobin iron	110	7
Total hemoglobin iron	1010	64
Parenchyma iron (muscle and other tissues)	240	16
Available visceral storage (liver, spleen and marrow)	225	15
Available iron of other tissues (estimated)	75±	5±
Total iron	1550	100

manufacture of new hemoglobin, the pigment part of the molecule alone being excreted in the bile.

Several factors influence iron absorption. It will be affected by the acidity of the intestine and motility of the gut and by the presence of reducing agents such as ascorbic acid. The level of phosphate also has an important effect, its presence decreasing absorption and its absence increasing it. Indeed a low level of phosphate in the diet accompanied by a high intake of iron may lead to a very high absorption of iron. Interference with the external pancreatic secretion by duct ligation or ethionine damage also enhances iron absorption. Inorganic iron seems to be more readily absorbed than the iron found in various foods. The iron in milk, cereal and meat is absorbed relatively well. When given with phytic acid the absorption or iron is poor. It is now known that the truly organic iron of foods, namely that combined in heme, is only minimally available since it is not released by peptic or tryptic digestion, whereas the inorganic iron which may represent 50 per cent or more of the total iron of the food is available. About 5 to 10% of the food iron is absorbed. Severe infection reduces iron absorption very markedly, sometimes to only one-tenth of the normal.

In iron deficiency anemia the absorption of iron is enhanced. This seems to be related to a reduction in the hemoglobin levels and an increase in hematopoietic activity rather than to the state of the iron stores, though this point is still somewhat controversial.

A conception of the mechanism whereby the iron absorption occurs has been offered by Granick and his associates. Their results with radioactive iron indicate that ferrous iron passes from the intestinal lumen into the mucosal cells, and is here oxidized to the ferric form (FeOH). The ferric iron, as ferric hydroxide phosphate, combines with a protein known as *apoferritin* (mol. wt. around 460,000) the iron-phosphorus-protein complex *ferritin* being formed. Ferritin is thus a conjugated protein containing about 23 per cent of iron. The iron-phosphorus portion has the approximate formula $[(FeOOH) \cdot (FeOPO_3H_2)]$.

At the vascular surface of the mucosal cell the iron of ferritin is reduced to the ferrous form; the conversion is facilitated by vitamin C. Immediately upon entering the blood stream it is oxidized and combined with the B_1-iron-binding globulin, named *transferrin* or siderophilin, of the plasma; in this complex form iron is carried. At the periphery of the circulation ferric ions diffuse across the capillary wall into the tissue fluids but iron enters the cells in the ferrous form. Probably under some circumstances, especially when the oxygen supply to the tissues is low, ferrous iron passes directly into the plasma without going through the ferritin stage.

It was believed originally by Granick that saturation of the apoferritin of the mucosal cell acted as a form of block against further absorption of iron. It is now believed that iron passes directly through the mucosal cell under ordinary circumstances. When excessive amounts of iron are presented to the cell, more or less saturation of apoferritin occurs, as a form of temporary storage of iron. When there is a scarcity of iron in the intestinal lumen the iron thus stored in the epithelial cells is released into the circulation. Thus the ferritin mechanism tends to stabilize the level of plasma iron. However, the so-called mucosal block is by no means perfect, for iron, if in high concentration in the intestinal contents, continues to be absorbed into the plasma. But the homeostasis of plasma iron is not dependent altogether upon the ferritin mechanism, for even while iron is passing in considerable amounts into the blood, its concentration in the plasma shows little or no rise. This is because it is taken up for the manufacture of hemoglobin by the red bone marrow, and when this has been satisfied, by the reticuloendothelial and parenchymal cells of other tissues where it is stored, especially in the liver and spleen, or utilized in the formation of muscle hemoglobin, respiratory enzymes and other complexes. These compounds, and to a much greater extent, the hemoglobin of effete erythrocytes is continually yielding iron to the plasma. The endogenous iron amounts to about 24 mg. daily, and, except for the very small amount that is excreted in the urine, feces and bile, is available for re-use. The level of plasma iron represents the balance struck at any moment between the iron from such sources, together with that absorbed from the intestine, and the iron taken up by the bone marrow and other tissues. Excretion plays a negligible part in the stabilization of the plasma level of iron. Ordinarily, the greater part of the iron of the body is in the form of ferritin. Ferritin is an iron-protein complex present in all body tissues, invisible by light microscopy; but it has a characteristic structure by electron microscopy.

Hemosiderin is a heterogeneous substance composed in part of ferritin aggregates. It is the visible form of storage iron, and is found in the reticuloendothelial cells. Generally speaking when iron storage increases, the proportion deposited in the tissues as hemosiderin also increases.

An adequate supply of pyridoxin is essential for the normal absorption of iron from the intestine.

The main features of iron metabolism are summarized in the following scheme.

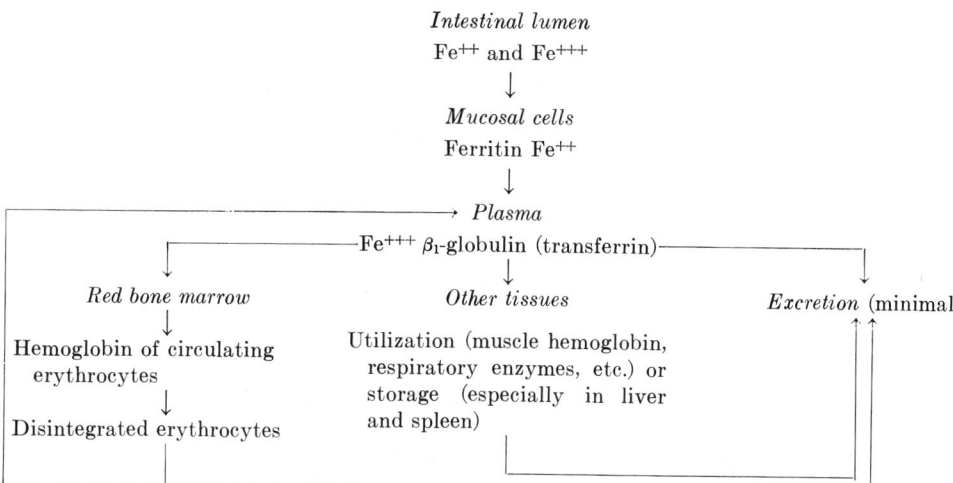

Besides its well known function as an essential element in the hemoglobin molecule, and as a constituent of other respiratory pigments, iron appears to play a role in the nutrition of epithelial surfaces. Abnormal nail growth, glossitis, fissures around the corners of the mouth and localized thickening of the mucous lining of the esophagus leading to dysphagia occur in anemias due to iron deficiency, and are cured by iron administration.

It has been calculated by Moore that the adult male loses 0.5 to 1.5 mg. of iron per day. This loss is increased by about 0.5 to 1 mg. per day in the adult female before the menopause, and during pregnancy the iron requirements of the female are further increased by 1 to 2 mg. per day. Children require 1.0 to 1.3 mg. per day to build up their iron stores during growth. Since, normally, about 10 per cent of the dietary iron is absorbed, it will be evident that the daily requirement for the adult male, i.e., the amount required to replace the small amounts lost in the excreta and in discarded cells from the skin and gastrointestinal tract, is approximately 12 to 15 mg. It will also be clear that for growing children and for women before the menopause or during pregnancy, the requirement for iron will be very considerably increased. While the figures are confusing, it has been estimated that the average North American diet contains only 12–15 mg. of available iron a day. The possible consequences during periods of increased iron demand are obvious.

Iron is sometimes given parenterally but it should be remembered that plasma has a limited iron-binding capacity and that the free metal exerts a toxic effect. If this iron-binding capacity is not exceeded, injected ionized iron will combine with the metal-combining protein as does the iron absorbed from the gut. Injected colloidal iron will be taken up by reticuloendothelial cells and will be dealt with much like the iron from hemoglobin breakdown.

The Significance of Copper, Manganese and Cobalt

Copper is believed to act as a catalyst in some stage of hemoglobin synthesis. It does not itself enter into the structure of the hemoglobin molecule. Waddell, Elvehjem, Steenbock and Hart found that in young rats rendered anemic by being placed upon a diet of whole cow's milk, iron alone failed to promote hemoglobin regeneration.[4] When the iron was supplemented by a very small quantity of copper, blood regeneration was induced. *Manganese* exerts a similar though less pronounced supplementary effect. The liver is the main storehouse for copper and minute amounts (0.1 to 0.5 mg.) are present normally in blood.

Though anemia due to copper deficiency is unknown in man, a severe and even fatal anemia due to the lack of this metal may occur in farm animals, e.g., the "falling sickness" of South African cattle.

Cobalt has a powerfully stimulating effect upon red cell production and in repeated doses may induce polycythemia in many species. When rats were injected with cobaltous chloride their plasma rather quickly showed a high titer of a factor

[4] Some experimenters have obtained a certain degree of hemoglobin regeneration with iron alone, although the rate of regeneration was much increased by the addition of copper.

stimulating erythropoiesis. Cobalt is also an essential dietary constituent in animals for the synthesis of hemoglobin. Experimental animals kept upon a diet adequate in all respects for normal erythropoiesis, except for the absence of cobalt, develop a severe anemia. Cattle and sheep grazing upon land lacking in this mineral become anemic and fail to respond to iron therapy, but are cured dramatically by the administration of traces of cobalt. Cobalt is a constituent of vitamin B_{12}. No evidence has been secured that cobalt is essential for erythropoiesis in man.

Hemochromatosis

This is a disturbance in iron metabolism in which extensive deposits of a colloid iron-containing pigment called *hemosiderin* are found in the cells of the liver, spleen and other tissues. Hemosiderin contains up to 55 per cent of iron, but its exact chemical composition is unknown. It is made up in part of aggregates of ferritin. The total iron content of the body is greatly increased; it may be 10 times the normal amount. A second yellow pigment known as *hemofuscin* is also sometimes present in the connective and muscular tissues. Other features of the condition are *bronzing of the skin, cirrhosis of the liver, sclerosis of the pancreas* with diabetes (bronzed diabetes), and sometimes testicular atrophy. The clinical syndrome may appear after repeated transfusions (see below).

Hemochromatosis has been attributed to a high iron content of the diet combined with a deficiency of some essential constituent although its exact cause is unknown. A condition resembling hemochromatosis has been reported in Negroes of certain South African tribes who subsist mainly upon a diet of maize and ingest excessive amounts of iron derived from the pots in which the food is cooked. In rats and dogs on a somewhat similar diet, a high absorption of iron was obtained. The low phosphate level of the diet was thought to be a major factor. It is probable that other factors are involved however in hemochromatosis. A patient suffering from hemochromatosis absorbs 20 per cent of a dose of ferrous iron given orally, or more than 10 times the amount absorbed by a normal person. Yet the quantity found in the blood is less than that present in the blood of a normal person receiving such a dose. Sheldon believed that hemochromatosis was an inherited, inborn error of metabolism. This may be true of some cases.

Hemosiderosis is the term applied to the deposit of hemosiderin in the tissues which occurs as a result of the excessive breakdown of red cells in malaria and hemolytic types of anemia. It may be looked upon simply as an exaggeration of the normal process of iron deposition. It also occurs after multiple transfusions.

REFERENCES

Ashby, W. J. Exper. Med. 1919, **29**, 267. Blood, 1948, **3**, 486.

Ask-Upmark, E. Acta Soc. Med. Suecanae, Stockholm. 1935, **61**, 197.

Balfour, W. M. and associates. J. Exper. Med., 1942, **76**, 15.

Cullumbine, H. and Simpson, M. Nature, 1947, **159**, 782.

Elvehjem, C. A., Hart, E. B. and Sherman, W. C. J. Biol. Chem., 1933, **103**, 61.

Erslev, A. J. Blood, 1955, **10**, 954.

Granick, S. Science, 1946, **103**, 107; Chem. Rev., 1946, **38**, 379.

Granick, S. and Michaelis, L. J. Biol. Chem., 1943, **147**, 91; Bull. New York Acad. Med., 1949, **25**, 403; Physiol. Rev. 1951, **31**, 489.

Gray, C. H. and Neuberger, A. Biochem. J., 1949, **44**, xlvii.

Grindlay, J. H. and associates. Am. J. Physiol., 1939, **127**, 119.

Hahn, P. F. Fed. Proc., 1948, **7**, 493.

Ham, T. H. Arch. Int. Med., 1939, **69**, 1271.

Hawkins, W. B. and Whipple, G. H. Am. J. Physiol., 1938, **122**, 418.

Hill, R. Proc. Roy. Soc., London, ser. B, 1930, **107**, 205.

Hughes, J. H. and Latner, A. L. J. Physiol., 1936, **86**, 388.

Krumbhaar, E. B. Am. J. M. Sc., 1932, **184**, 215.

Landsteiner, K., Levine, P. and James, M. L. Proc. Soc. Exper. Biol. & Med., 1928, **25**, 672. (See also Wiener, A. S. J. A. M. A., 1934, **102**, 1779.)

McCance, R. A. and Widdowson, E. M. Lancet, 1937, **2**, 680.

Nicol, T., Bilbey, D. L. J. and Ware, C. C. Nature, 1958, **182**, 534.

Shemin, D. and Rittenberg, D. J. Biol. Chem., 1946, **166**, 621.

Singer, K., Miller, E. B. and Dameshek, W. Am. J. M. Sc., 1941, **202**, 171.

Waddell, J., Steenbock, H., Elvehjem, C. A. and Hart, E. B. J. Biol. Chem., 1929, **83**, 243, 251.

Whipple, A. O. Ann. Surg., 1945, **122**, 449.

Whipple, G. H., Hooper, C. W. and Robscheit, F. S. Am. J. Physiol., 1920, **53**, 151, 167.

Whipple, G. H. and associates. Am. J. Physiol., 1936, **115**, 651. J. Exper. Med., 1937, **66**, 565; 1938, **67**, 89; 1939, **69**, 315. Proc. Soc. Exper. Biol. & Med., 1937, **36**, 629.

Monographs and Reviews

Barcroft, J. Lancet, 1925, **1**, 319.

Barcroft, J. Features in the architecture of physiological function. Cambridge University Press, London, 1934.

Harris, J. W. The Red Cell. Harvard University Press. Cambridge, Mass. 1963.

Bothwell, T. H. and Finch, C. A. Iron Metabolism. Little, Brown and Co. Boston. 1962.

BERLIN, N. I., WALDMANN, T. A. AND WEISSMAN, S. M. Physiol. Rev., 1959, **39**, 577.

BOND, V. P. AND CRONKITE, E. P. Ann. Rev. Physiol., 1957, **19**, 299.

CALLENDER, S. T., MALLETT, B. J. AND SMITH, M. D. Brit. J. Haemat., 1957, **3**, 186.

CROSBY, W. H. Blood, 1959, **14**, 399.

HAHN, P. F. Medicine, 1937, **16**, 249.

JOSEPHS, H. W. Blood, 1958, **13**, 1.

LE ROY, G. V. M. Clin. North America, 1953, **37**, 181.

MOLLISON, P. L. The life-span of red blood cells. Lectures on the scientific basis of Medicine, University of London. The Athlone Press, 1954.

MOORE, C. V. Am. J. Clin. Nutrition, 1955, **3**, 3.

PERLA, D. AND MARMORSTON, J. The spleen and resistance. The Williams & Wilkins Co., Baltimore, 1935.

ROBSCHEIT-ROBBINS, F. S. Physiol. Rev., 1929, **9**, 666.

ROUS, P. Physiol. Rev., 1923, **3**, 75.

SHELDON, J. H. Haemochromatosis. Oxford University Press, London, 1935.

CHAPTER 30

The Anemias

Classification

We have seen that in health the population of red cells and the concentration of hemoglobin in the blood are kept at normal levels by a nice balance between the new formation and the wastage of erythrocytes. Anemia results when the balance is tipped one way or the other, i.e., by a defect of blood formation or an increase in blood wastage. Basically, it is a condition in which the hemoglobin level of the blood is reduced below the normal limits. The anemias may be classified broadly into (A) *those associated with blood loss or increased blood destruction* and (B) *those caused by defective blood formation.*

A. ANEMIAS CAUSED BY BLOOD LOSS OR INCREASED BLOOD DESTRUCTION

I. *Posthemorrhagic anemias*
   Hemorrhage
   a. *Acute*
   b. *Chronic*, as a result, for example of peptic ulcer, uterine bleeding, ankylostomiasis (hookworm disease), purpura, etc.

II. *Hemolytic anemias*
   Red cell destruction, as a result of:
   (i) *Intracorpuscular defects:*
      (a) *Abnormal structure of the red cells* which renders them more susceptible to phagocytosis in the spleen or to disintegration in the circulation. These defects may be congenital or acquired, e.g., hereditary spherocytosis or elliptocytosis, the hemoglobinopathies, thalassemia (Cooley's anemia, Mediterranean anemia), congenital non-spherocytic hemolytic anemia, paroxysmal nocturnal hemoglobinuria.
   (ii) *Extracorpuscular causes:*
      (a) *Infectious agents,* e.g. malaria, *Cl. Welchii* septicemia, viruses, non-protozoal parasites (Bartonella).
      (b) *Chemical agents,* which may be dose-dependent, or due to hypersensitivity, e.g., phenacetin, lead, coal-tar derivatives, sulfonamides, quinine, etc.

(c) *Physical agents,* e.g. heat.
(d) *Vegetable and animal poisons* such as fava bean, snake venoms and other endogenous agents.
(e) *Iso-agglutinins.* Anti-Rh, and occasionally Anti-A and Anti-B agglutinins, causing hemolytic disease of the newborn. In adults, in transfusion reactions.
(f) *Paroxysmal cold hemoglobinuria.*
(g) *Symptomatic hemolytic anemias* as seen in association with chronic lymphatic leukemia, Hodgkin's disease, sarcoidosis, collagen disorders, malignancies, etc.
(h) *Idiopathic acquired hemolytic anemias.*

In the hemolytic group the increased blood destruction is manifested by a rise in the concentration of bile pigment in the plasma which gives an indirect van den Bergh reaction, a greater excretion of bile pigment and porphyrin in the urine and feces, and the deposit of an iron-containing pigment in the liver and other tissues. There is frequently jaundice of a slight or moderate grade.

Sickle cell anemia is one of the hemoglobinopathies and is caused by blood destruction as a result of a congenital anomaly of the red cells. In this type, which occurs almost exclusively in Negroes, elongated crescent or sickle shaped birefringent erythrocytes some 15 μ or so in length are a characteristic feature. Such cells are found in the blood of a high percentage of Negroes (8 to 9 per cent) though only relatively few, 1 in 40, of these develop anemia. There is also a proportion of Negroes and also a few whites whose red cells become sickle shaped under certain adverse conditions, especially as a result of reduction in the oxygen tension of the blood. This is spoken of as the *sickle cell trait* and is due to a single sickle cell allelomorphic gene (sickle cell anemia being caused by the presence of two genes). It has been shown by electrophoretic studies that the hemoglobin (the globin rather than the heme) of the erythrocytes in sickle cell anemia, in those showing sickle cells but no anemia, or those in which sickling can be induced, differs in its amino acid content from normal hemoglobin. The abnormal hemoglobin constitutes 100 per cent of the blood pigment in sickle cell anemia, up to 60 per cent when

PLATE I

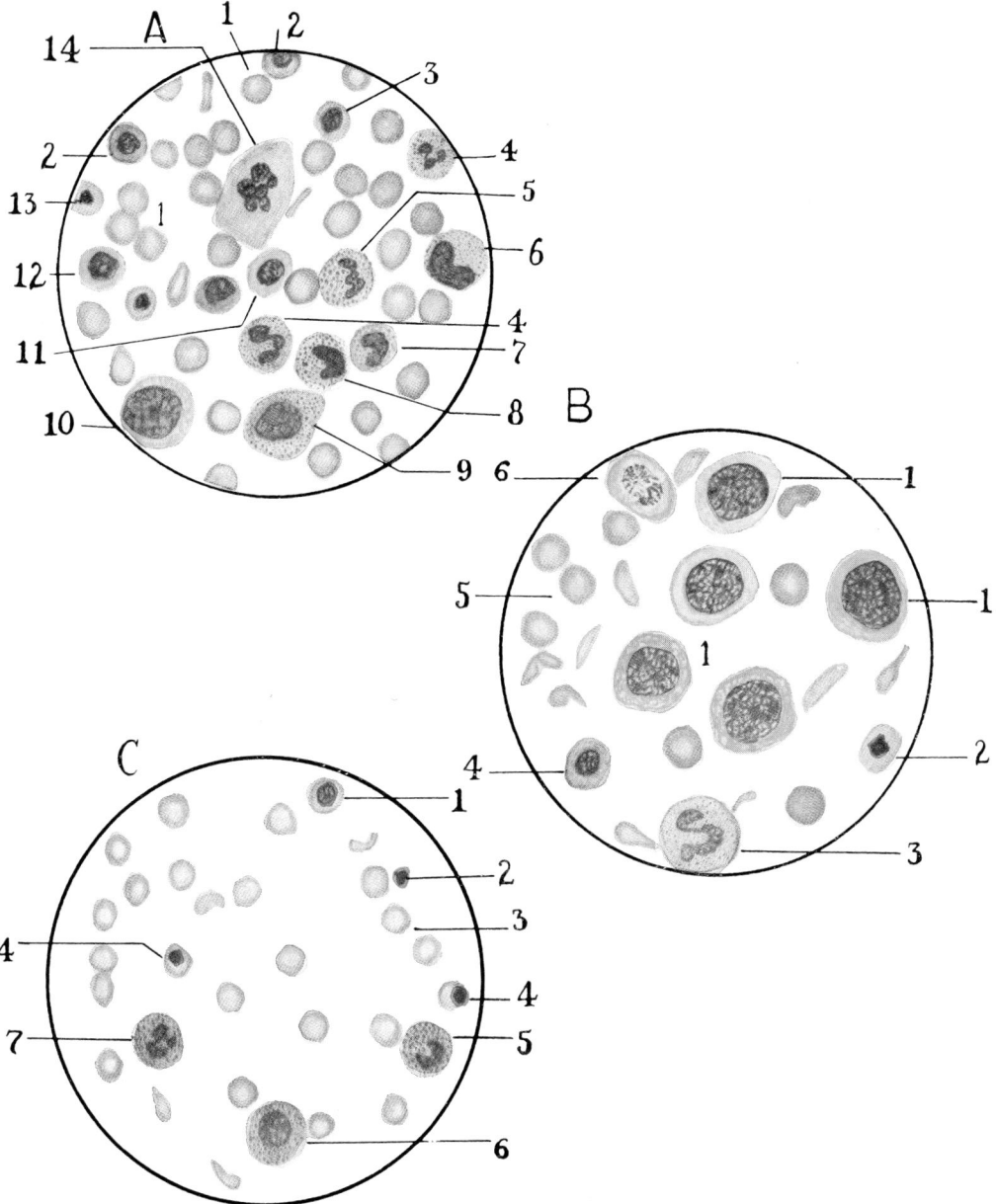

Samples of bone marrow obtained by sternal puncture

A. Normal

1. Erythrocytes
2. Erythroblasts
3. Early normoblast
4. Neutrophil leucocyte
5. Eosinophil leucocyte
6. Neutrophil metamyelocyte
7. Basophil metamyelocyte
8. Eosinophil metamyelocyte
9. Neutrophil myelocyte
10. Myeloblast
11. Hemocytoblast
12. Lymphocyte
13. Late normoblast
14. Megakaryocyte

B. In pernicious anemia

1. Megaloblasts
2. Late normoblast
3. Giant neutrophil leucocyte
4. Erythroblast
5. Erythrocytes (macrocytes)
6. Megaloblast in mitosis

C. In microcytic anemia due to iron deficiency

1. Early normoblast
2. Erythrocytes (microcytes)
3. Extruded nucleus from normoblast
4. Late normoblasts
5. Eosinophil leucocyte
6. Myelocyte
7. Neutrophil leucocyte

sickle cells are present but there is no anemia, and less than 40 per cent in those in whom sickling can be induced by a low oxygen tension.

The other inherited hemoglobinopathies may also be accompanied by anemia. The basic abnormality in all is the inheritance of a globin structure which differs from that of adult hemoglobin. Such alteration in structure produces certain physico-chemical changes in the hemoglobin produced, which in turn are manifested in a corpuscular defect which can lead to increased red cell destruction and anemia (Ch. 32).

Chronic congenital hemolytic jaundice. Synonyms, *acholuric jaundice, spherocytic anemia, hereditary spherocytosis, chronic familial jaundice, hemolytic splenomegaly.* The chief features of this form of anemia are *jaundice* and a high incidence of pigment gall stones, *spheroid erythrocytes* (i.e., the diameter of the cells is reduced but their thickness is increased, their volume being approximately normal), *reticulocytosis* which may go up to 60 per cent or more of the total red cell population, increased osmotic *fragility* of the cells and *enlargement of the spleen.* Splenectomy is usually followed by the disappearance of jaundice, a return of the red cell count to normal, and a marked reduction in the reticulocytosis and correction of the anemia, though the spherocytosis usually persists. The cause of the hemolysis is unknown though it is probably due to the reaction of the macrophages of the spleen to the defective cells. Trapping of spherocytes has been demonstrated in the spleen. As produced by the bone marrow the cells are normal, but become progressively more spherocytic in the circulation. Some believe that an endogenous hemolytic agent is responsible, a view which receives support from the experiments of Dameshek and Schwartz in which a hemolytic serum produced by the injection of guinea pig's cells into rabbits was employed to produce anemia. The injection of this anti-guinea pig hemolytic serum into guinea pigs caused a profound drop in the red cell count and the appearance of cells with spheroid shape, increased fragility and a reticulocytosis. These observers suggest that the greater fragility of the red cells is simply a function of their globular shape and that spherocytosis is a reaction of the bone marrow to excessive destruction of red cells caused by a circulating hemolysin. This theory is no longer given much credence. More recently it has been shown that there are changes in the metabolism of the erythrocyte, there being a defect in glycolysis which may be a result of deficient phosphorylation. The administration of glucose diminishes the hemolysis in this condition. Radioactive techniques, using radioactive phosphorous (P^{32}) as a tracer, have confirmed the presence of a basic intracellular defect in phosphorylation. Other metabolic abnormalities have been shown to involve the phospholipid component of the red cell membrane.

It is possible to differentiate between hemolysis of corpuscular and extracorpuscular origin by means of radioactive tracer methods. If the cells of the former type of anemia are transfused into a normal recipient they still have a reduced life span, while normal cells transfused into the patient have a normal life span. In an anemia of extracorpuscular origin, however, the reverse is true. Normal cells show a shortened life span in the abnormal milieu, while the patient's cells survive normally in a normal milieu.

Lederer's anemia is an acute hemolytic anemia. The leukocytes are increased in number and phagocytosis of red cells may be a pronounced feature. In Thalassemia major, or Cooley's anemia, there is microcytosis and some of the red cells show concentric rings like a target (*"target cells"*). The disease is congenital, being inherited as a Mendelian dominant. In the "major" form of the disease there may be also splenomegaly and bony changes. It is now known that the fundamental abnormality is a defect in the formation of hemoglobin. This disease exists in many clinical forms, depending on the degree of change (and the inter-relationship) of various hemoglobins involved. Basically, there is suppression of adult hemoglobin production, with varying amounts of hemoglobin A_2, and F present.

B. Anemias Due to Defective Blood Formation

I. Nutritional anemias

a. *Iron deficiency*—hypochromic, microcytic anemias. The deficiency may be due either to the excessive loss of iron from the body as in chronic hemorrhage or to an inadequate quantity of this element in the diet. The former is the usual cause in adult males, but in infants and adolescents, and in pregnancy or other conditions where the iron requirement is increased, the latter may be a factor. Under some circumstances too, a failure in the absorption of iron may be a cause of the intractability of anemia to iron administration by mouth.

b. *Protein deficiency,* although in itself a rare cause of anemia, may be a contributory factor.

c. *Lack of folic acid.* The macrocytic anemias of sprue and pregnancy are usually classed with the nutritional anemias.

d. In man, lack of vitamin C is a possible factor also and in animals, deficiency of certain other vitamins, pyriboxin, riboflavin, nicotinic and pantothenic acids.

II. *Lack of or failure in the absorption or in the utilization of the specific antianemic factor* (*cyanocobalamin, vitamin B$_{12}$*)—Addisonian pernicious anemia and certain related hyperchromic macrocytic anemias with a megaloblastic type of bone marrow. The anemia associated with infestation with *diphyllobothrium latum* belongs in this category. It is caused by competition of the parasite for vitamin B$_{12}$ with a subsequent relative deficiency.

III. *Macrocytic anemias (hypo- or hyperchromic) with normoblastic bone marrow.*

IV. *Anemias due to interference with marrow function, either by depression or replacement.*

a. *Toxic agents.* These either induce aplasia or depress marrow function. Among such agents are quinacrine, gold salts, benzol, arsphenamine, radium, X-rays, and sometimes bacterial and syphilitic toxins. The red marrow is greatly reduced in amount, being replaced by fatty tissue. Blood formation is profoundly depressed.

b. *Infections*—the anemia accompanying infection is usually a mild, normocytic, normochromic type. As a rule, hemolysis is not a factor. The exact defect is not clear but there is a decreased production of hemoglobin associated with decreased absorption of iron, decreased β, metalcombining globulin of plasma and a decreased plasma iron level.

c. *Primary bone marrow failure* (idiopathic aplastic anemia) in which depression or complete suppression of marrow function may occur without a known cause.

d. *Renal disease.*

e. *Malignancy.*

f. *Replacement of marrow tissue by fibrous tissue* (myelofibrosis), tumor, or bone (myelosclerosis).

The cause of *splenic anemia* (Banti's) is unknown; it is therefore difficult to fit this type into any of the preceding categories. According to some there is increased blood destruction, but important factors appear to be depressed marrow function and the loss of blood resulting from repeated gastrointestinal hemorrhages.

Blood indices. The following indices calculated from the hemoglobin concentration, red cell count and packed cell volume of a specimen of blood are employed to express the characters of the individual cells in the different types of anemia.

The *color index.* This is a numerical (although purely relative) expression of the hemoglobin content of the individual red cells. It is obtained by dividing the hemoglobin value in grams per 100 cc. by the red cell count, both values being expressed as percentages of the normal. (The normal weight of hemoglobin per 100 cc. is taken as 14.5 grams (15.6 grams in some areas) and the red cell count as 5,000,000.) Thus, if the hemoglobin is 60 per cent of normal and the red cell count 50 per cent, then 60/50 = 1.2 color index. But if the hemoglobin percentage is reduced to a greater degree than the red cell percentage the index will be less than unity. That is, each red cell contains less than its normal quota of hemoglobin. On the other hand, the hemoglobin concentration of the blood may be greatly reduced but if the reduction runs parallel with the reduction in red cell percentage the index will have the normal value of 1.0.

Mean corpuscular volume (M.C.V.). This expresses the volume of the individual red cell in μ^3 (1 ml. = $10^{12}\ \mu^3$). The mean corpuscular volume in μ^3 is obtained by dividing the volume of packed cells expressed in ml. per liter by the red cell count in millions per cu. mm. (e.g., $\frac{450}{5} = 90$)

Anemias may be classified according to the M.C.V. as macrocytic (over 96), normocytic (86 to 96), and microcytic (under 86).

Mean corpuscular hemoglobin (M.C.H.) is the hemoglobin per red cell expressed in $\mu\mu g$ (10^{-12} g.). This may be obtained by dividing the hemoglobin in grams per liter by the red blood cell count in millions per mm.^{3} (e.g., $\frac{150}{5} = 30\ \mu\mu g$.). The mean corpuscular hemoglobin may vary with the concentration of hemoglobin within the cell and with the volume of the cell.

Mean corpuscular hemoglobin concentration (M.C.H.C.) is the hemoglobin in grams per 100 ml. of blood divided by the packed cell volume per 100 ml., expressed as a percentage

$$(\text{e.g., } \frac{15}{45} \times 100 = 33 \text{ per cent}).$$

This value is never greater than normal but may be normal (above 30 per cent, normochromic) or less than normal (below 30 per cent, hypochromic).

Attempts have been made to estimate the *total erythropoietic activity* of bone marrow from the erythroid-myeloid ratio, plasma iron turnover and fecal urobilinogen, and the effective *erythropoiesis* (i.e., the proportion of cells produced by the bone marrow that are delivered into the circulation), by means of erythrocyte count, and by the uptake of radioactive iron by the red cells. It has been found that the effective erythropoiesis can be increased three times in acute anemia, and six times in chronic anemia.

Hypochromic Microcytic Anemias—Iron Deficiency

In this group the essential defect is one of hemoglobin formation. The hemoglobin percentage of the blood is reduced to a greater extent than the number of red cells. These, indeed, may show only a slight reduction. The color index and M.C.H. are considerably below the normal, which means that each red cell has received less than its normal quota of pigment. The erythrocytes are also smaller than normal, so the M.C.V. is also low. The low M.C.H. is in part the result of the smaller size of the red cell but also of a reduced concentration of pigment throughout the red cell's substance. Some of the corpuscles are so pale that they resemble "ghosts" or only the peripheral zone of the cell is colored (anisochromasia) (see figs 30.1 and 30.2).

Iron deficiency is the cause of almost all the anemias belonging to this class. The deficiency may result from increased iron requirements coupled with either a relative or absolute inadequacy of iron in the diet or from defective absorption of the metal from the food but the usual cause, in adult males, is blood loss.

Hypochromic anemia occurs most frequently in women of childbearing age in whom the dietary intake of iron is insufficient to meet their needs. The anemia is aggravated by the losses of iron incident to menstruation or repeated pregnancies. Davidson has recently emphasized the need for larger amounts of iron during this period in women. In the previous chapter, iron loss and iron requirements have been discussed.

Anemia of Infants

The fetus accumulates a store of iron in the liver in the later months of gestation. This serves as a reserve that is drawn upon for the manufacture of hemoglobin in infancy. The high red cell concentration (p. 11) with which the infant comes into the world also contributes to the iron reserves. In the normal infant the iron stores are sufficient for the manufacture of hemoglobin for the first six months or so. Growth, however, makes heavy demands upon the iron supplies and after the first half year it is necessary to provide a diet which will contain adequate amounts of iron in order to guard against the development of hypochromic anemia. Milk, it will be recalled, is very poor in both iron and copper. The iron content of milk is doubled by the pasteurization process and tripled in the drying or evaporation processes. The development of anemia in milk-fed rats has been mentioned and the anemia of

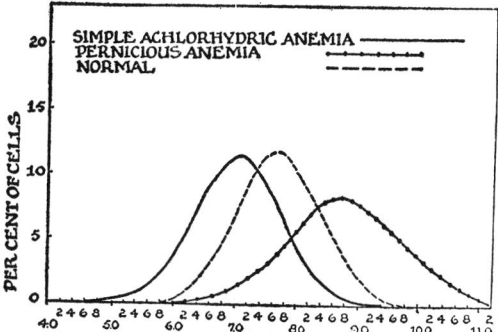

FIG. 30.1. Red cell diameter distribution curves in simple achlorhydric anemia and in pernicious anemia compared with the normal (after Haden; see also fig. 30.2).

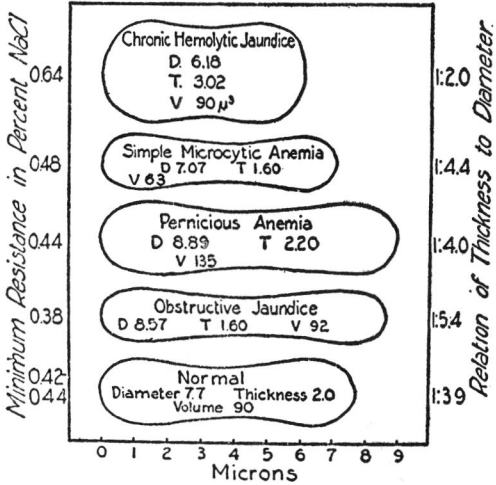

FIG. 30.2. Red cell diameter, thickness and volume in various clinical conditions compared with the normal (after Haden). *D*, diameter; *T*, thickness; *V*, volume.

sucklings is a problem in the breeding of farm animals. If the iron stores are deficient at birth as in premature infants or as a result of maternal anemia, anemia may occur in the very young infant.

The hypochromic anemias respond in a spectacular fashion to the administration of inorganic iron (e.g., ferrous sulphate, ferrous carbonate, etc.) The administration of copper is never necessary since this occurs in sufficient quantity in the diet and as an impurity in iron preparations.

Pernicious Anemia (Addison's Anemia) and Related Macrocytic Anemias

Pernicious anemia is due to a defect in the formation of the red blood cells.

Chief features of the blood picture are:

1. Great reduction in the number of red cells and consequently in the hemoglobin percentage. The blood count in a very severe case may be less than 10 per cent of the normal.

2. The red cells are reduced in number below the normal to a greater extent than is the hemoglobin percentage. The M.C.V. and M.C.H. are therefore *raised* above normal. The high M.C.H. is due to the greater size of the cells. The M.C.H.C. is normal.

3. Large cells—the average diameter of the cells is increased to between 8 and 9 μ. These large cells are called *macrocytes*. The average volume of the individual red cells (figs. 30.1 and 30.2) is about 135 μ^3 (normal about 90 μ^3). *Normoblasts* and earlier forms may be present in the circulation. A characteristic large nucleated cell containing basophilic material in its cytoplasm and little or no hemoglobin is a feature of the bone marrow picture. This cell, known as the *megaloblast*, differs chemically and morphologically from any normal cell of the erythrocyte series found either in bone marrow or blood. The reticulocytes are not usually greatly elevated, and average about 2 per cent.

4. The total *number of leukocytes is reduced* but the lymphocytes are relatively increased due to neutropenia. Those neutrophils present show a marked shift to the right with hypersegmented nuclei.

5. Great variation in the size of the cells— *anisocytosis*, the cells varying from those smaller than normal to the large cells mentioned above. *Poikilocytes* are markedly increased.

6. Increase in iron and bilirubin of the plasma; increased excretion of pigment (urobilin)—indirect van den Bergh. The increase in plasma iron is due to its decreased utilization for the formation of red cells. The increased plasma bilirubin is the result of increased red cell breakdown.

7. Blood volume reduced mainly as a result of the red cell diminution, the plasma volume being around the normal level.

8. Fragility of the red cells is usually normal to osmotic changes.

OTHER FEATURES:

1. The red bone marrow is hyperplastic. It extends into the shafts of the bones displacing the yellow marrow and even the bony walls may be eroded. Upon microscopical examination the marrow shows megaloblasts and other immature forms in large numbers (see ch. 32).

2. Achlorhydria almost always exists.

3. Sore, shiny tongue, *glossitis*, atrophy of lingual papillae.

4. Chronic *combined degeneration of the spinal cord.*

5. There is an atrophy of the mucosa of the fundus and body of the stomach.

6. Urobilin appears in the urine in severe cases; and in all those in which plasma bilirubin is increased urobilinogen is in excess in the feces. In health from 1/140 to 1/340 of the total amount of hemoglobin in the blood is excreted daily as urobilinogen. In pernicious anemia 1/10 of the total hemoglobin may be excreted as urobilinogen. Hemosiderin deposits (p. 11) occur.

7. The disease shows remissions and relapses. During the remissions, the blood picture approaches the normal and the percentage of reticulocytes increases—*reticulocyte crises.* During the relapses, the characteristic hematological features of the condition are exaggerated.

The essential factor in the production of pernicious anemia is not increased blood destruction, but rather a defect in blood formation. Increased blood destruction undoubtedly occurs as evidenced by the rise in plasma bilirubin, but it is a secondary effect. Radioactive chromium studies have shown a red cell rate of destruction three times normal. The abnormal erythrocytes may stimulate the phagocytic activities of the reticuloendothelial cells in the spleen, liver and elsewhere. Since the fragility of the red cells is normal rather than increased it would not appear that they disintegrate more readily in the blood stream. The discovery of an antianemic principle in liver and subsequent researches arising from the employment of this principle in the treatment of pernicious anemia have shed a flood of light upon the nature of the disease.

LIVER, LIVER EXTRACT, GASTRIC TISSUE AND THE ANTIANEMIC FACTOR

In 1926 Minot and Murphy, inspired by the laboratory finding of Whipple and his associates, namely, that liver was the most effective article of diet for the treatment of anemia in dogs, tried the effect of adding liver to the diet of pernicious anemia patients. The spectacular success which followed this treatment is well known and today lightly cooked liver (from $\frac{1}{2}$ to 1 pound per day) but preferably an extract of liver, or the essential principle, vitamin B_{12}, is recognized as a specific for the disease. Kidney tissue was shown to have a similar though less pronounced curative effect. The hematopoietic substance present in the liver and in nonprotein extracts of liver tissue and which is effective in the treatment of pernicious

anemia is known as vitamin B_{12}, or cyanocobalamin and formerly as the antianemic or hematinic principle. The action of vitamin B_{12} is
many times more potent given parenterally than
when given orally. It may be mentioned here that
Wilkinson found that the antianemic principle
was present in normal human liver and in the
livers of pernicious anemia patients who had received specific treatment, but was absent from
the livers of untreated subjects of the disease.

The Chemical Identification of the Antianemic Factor, B_{12}

In 1948 Rickes and his associates and Smith reported the isolation of red, needle-shaped crystals
of a substance which was many times more potent
than the most purified extracts of liver in the
treatment of pernicious anemia, causing a reticulocyte response in pernicious anemia patients in
a parenteral dose of 1 μg., or even less. The red
crystalline material, now generally referred to as
vitamin B_{12}, has since been shown to be a cobalt
complex, and is apparently the antianemic factor
in pure or nearly pure form. It also contains phosphorus and nitrogen, but no sulfur; its molecular
weight is around 1350 and its formula is
$C_{63}H_{90}O_{14}N_{14}PCo$. Its chemical designation is cyanocobalamin.

Several analogues of this compound have been
obtained from bacterial cultures, from the gastrointestinal contents of animals and from feces,
sewage, etc.

It may be mentioned that the cobalt ion by itself elicits no hemopoietic response in pernicious
anemia.

Besides its importance in hemopoiesis and its
action in promoting the growth of certain bacteria, vitamin B_{12} is a growth factor for higher
animals, including man. It also has an influence
upon the metabolism of certain sulfur containing
amino acids (e.g., conversion of homocystine to
methionine). According to Niewig, vitamin B_{12} is
essential for the synthesis of ribonucleic acid, a
constituent of the nuclei of all cells; this would
account for the neurological defects in pernicious
anemia, and for the abnormalities of certain epithelial surfaces, such as that of the tongue (in the
production of glossitis), as well as for the failure
in erythrocyte maturation.

Vitamin B_{12} is by far the most potent hemopoietic principle known, being several thousand
times more potent weight by weight than folic

acid. B_{12} is also effective in arresting the course of
the neurological lesions of pernicious anemia.

The Production of the Antianemic Principle, Intrinsic and Extrinsic Factors

As already mentioned, irreversible gastric
atrophy occurs and achlorhydria is virtually an
invariable accompaniment of pernicious anemia.
The significance of this fact was demonstrated in
1929 by Castle who found that the gastric contents of a normal person during the digestion of
meat were curative when fed to a subject of pernicious anemia. Later Castle and his associates
showed that pure gastric juice obtained from a
normal person by the administration of histamine
when incubated with beef steak produced the
curative material. The active principle was not
produced when beef was incubated with gastric
juice of a patient with pernicious anemia. The
production of the anti-anemic principle is not due
to the action of hydrochloric acid, pepsin, rennin
or lipase but to the presence of an enzymelike
but unidentified substance which acts at a pH of
7 (the optimal pH for the action of pepsin is 1.6).
Before this, Sturgis and Isaacs found that gastric
tissue contained the material necessary for the
formation of the antianemic factor, it being, like
liver itself, effective in the treatment of pernicious anemia. Desiccated defatted hog stomach is,
therefore, also employed as an alternative to liver
or liver extract for oral administration. The gastric factor is less stable than the liver principle,
being destroyed by temperatures above 45°C. or
by digestion with pepsin or trypsin. In the hog,
the gastric factor is produced by the mucosa of
the pyloric and cardiac regions of the stomach
and the commencement of the duodenum, i.e.,
regions which secrete an alkaline juice (pyloric,
cardiac and Brunner's glands). In the human subject the factor, according to Fox and Castle, is
formed in the fundus and body of the stomach;
none is found in the pyloric region nor in the duodenal secretions. Radioautographic studies with
labelled B_{12} indicate the chief cells at the base of
the gastric glands as the source of intrinsic factor.

Two factors, therefore, were recognized as being
essential for normal erythropoiesis: one in the
food, especially in such items of diet as are rich in
the vitamin B complex; it was called the *extrinsic*
factor and for years eluded the keenest research,
but was finally identified as vitamin B_{12}; the
other factor is secreted in the gastric juice and is
known as the *intrinsic* factor.

A characteristic lesion is found in pernicious anemia which readily explains the achlorhydria, and the lack of the intrinsic factor. The fundus and body of the stomach show atrophy of the mucosa and extreme thinning of all coats. The gastric glands are almost completely destroyed; the muscular coat is atrophic. The pyloric region, which does not produce the intrinsic factor, is normal. One would be led to expect that total gastrectomy in man would be followed by pernicious anemia. If the survival time following total gastrectomy is sufficient to permit exhaustion of the vitamin B_{12} stores an anemia of the pernicious type develops.

The Extrinsic Factor; the Action of the Intrinsic Factor

The extrinsic factor (vitamin B_{12}) is present in liver, beef, rice polishings, yeast, and other substances rich in the vitamin B complex. It is also found in the intestinal contents of normal persons, as well as in the feces of patients with pernicious anemia. There is, therefore, no reason to believe that a dietary deficiency of this factor is the cause of the disease. The basic defect in pernicious anemia is the failure of the gastric mucosa to produce, at least in effective amounts, the intrinsic factor. It is now believed that this factor is essential for the adequate *absorption* of vitamin B_{12}. This may involve some combination with the vitamin or it may influence some specific process in the gut wall involved in the absorption of the vitamin. When the intrinsic factor is given, to a patient with pernicious anemia, the excessive fecal excretion of vitamin B_{12} labelled with radioactive cobalt is reduced. There is also the possibility that the intrinsic factor by binding vitamin B_{12} keeps it from being taken up by the intestinal bacteria, thus ensuring that it will be available for absorption. In the absence of the intrinsic factor there is "starvation in the midst of plenty" in so far as the extrinsic factor is con-

cerned. For this reason B_{12} is effective given parenterally in pernicious anemia in a fraction of the dose that is required by mouth. However, if B_{12} is administered with normal gastric juice the size of the effective oral dose is much reduced.

With the advent of radioisotopic tracer techniques it became possible to label vitamin B_{12} with radioactive cobalt (Co^{58}). Schilling devised a test in which a small dose (0.1 to 1.0 μg) of labelled B_{12} is given by mouth. This is followed in two hours by a "flushing dose" of 1000 μg non-radioactive B_{12} intramuscularly. Normally, over 10% of the radioactivity appears in the urine in the next 24 hours. In patients with pernicious anemia, less than 3% appears in the urine. In subjects with a macrocytic anemia not due to intrinsic factor deficiency, the values usually lie between these levels. The oral administration of intrinsic factor with the radioactive B_{12} restores the test results to normal in pernicious anemia and after total gastrectomy but not in the other macrocytic anemias.

In concluding this section the following remarks of Castle may be quoted:

"The disease would not develop if the patient could effect daily the transfer of a millionth of a gram of vitamin B_{12} the distance of a small portion of a millimeter across the intestinal mucosa and into the blood stream. This he cannot do, principally as a result of failure of his stomach to secrete into its lumen some essential but still unknown substance. Yet the patient may each day absorb without much difficulty the products of the digestion of many grams of carbohydrate, fat and protein from foods that in addition may contain consequential amounts of vitamin B_{12} in terms of his trivial need."

Other Megaloblastic Anemias

Though pernicious anemia is the most common type of anemia showing a megaloblastic bone marrow, there are other forms with closely similar marrow and blood pictures (table 30.1). Such megaloblastic anemias occur in *tropical sprue, pregnancy, carcinoma of the stomach, gastrointestinal surgery* which short circuits the region of the small intestine from which B_{12} is absorbed, and *infestation with the tapeworm, Diphyllobothrium latum.* The anemia of sprue, in which the absorption of fat is defective, is due possibly to the interference with the absorption of vitamin B_{12} other than through a lack of the intrinsic factor, though in certain cases the latter is absent even though there is not achlorhydria. In the megaloblastic anemia of pregnancy the

TABLE 30.1

Classification of Megaloblastic Anemias

A. Pernicious anemia.

B. Sprue, idiopathic steatorrhea, intestinal stricture or resection, gastro-colic fistula, celiac disease.

C. "Tropical" nutritional macrocytic anemia; refractory megaloblastic or "achrestic" anemea.

D. Following total gastrectomy; occasional cases of carcinoma of stomach.

E. Macrocytic anemia of pregnancy.

F. Megaloblastic anemia of infancy.

G. Diphyllobothrium latum infestation.

H. Antimetabolites and some drugs.

marrow and blood pictures are similar to those of pernicious anemia, but there is as a rule not true achlorhydria, nor degenerative changes in the spinal cord; recovery follows childbirth or after treatment with folic acid. Also, many cases of this disease, like that described by Wills as occurring in the tropics, and called *tropical nutritional (or macrocytic) anemia*, are unresponsive to the administration of vitamin B_{12}, but respond readily to crude liver extracts or to folic acid.[1] In carcinoma of the stomach there is achlorhydria and the anemia may be indistinguishable in every way from pernicious anemia, even to the neurological symptoms; it is probably produced in the same manner—lack of the intrinsic factor. In the anemia caused by *Diphyllobothrium latum*, there is no lack of the intrinsic factor, but the worm interferes in some way with the utilization of the vitamin. Possibly this is caused by the parasite producing a principle that inhibits the specific action of the intrinsic factor, or by its absorbing or utilizing the vitamin in its own metabolism. The investigations of von Bonsdorff indicate that the parasite must be situated high up in the small intestine in order to cause anemia. Finally, a rare type of megaloblastic anemia which fails to respond to the hematinic principle was described originally by Wilkinson and Israels. It is not due to the lack of the erythrocyte maturation factor (B_{12}), but to failure of the latter to be utilized by the bone marrow. It was, therefore, named *achrestic anemia*.

The Response to Liver or Gastric Tissue

The antianemic principle acts upon the bone marrow, restoring the blood-forming processes to normal. It is believed that megaloblastosis is not the result of a simple arrest of the maturation of red blood cells, but that the megaloblasts result from a prolonged resting phase between stages of mitoses. This prolongation is a consequence of the inability of B_{12} deficient cells to synthesize the extra DNA required for mitosis. Such impaired synthesis is felt to be due in part to decreased methylation of uracil to thymine—a reaction in which B_{12} acts as a catalyst. The associated build-up of RNA in the cytoplasm of these cells is considered a result of the impaired synthesis of DNA, part of which is derived from the cytoplasmic RNA.

[1] Tropical nutritional anemia occurs most frequently and severely in pregnant women. An anemia with similar characters, which is resistant to treatment with purified preparations of liver, but is amenable to crude liver extracts or folic acid can be produced in monkeys.

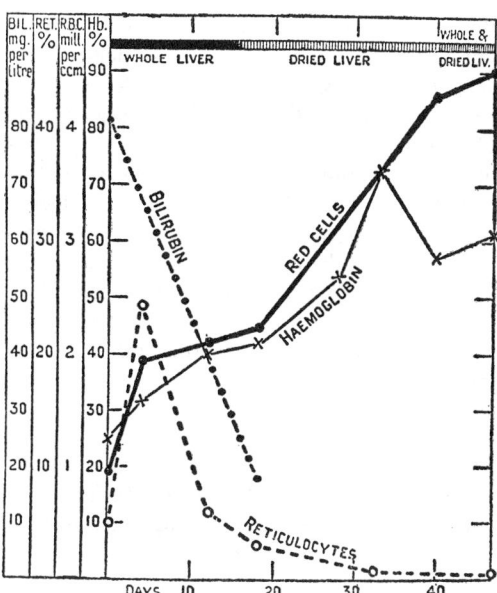

Fig. 30.3. Showing effect of specific liver therapy upon the reticulocytes, erythrocytes, hemoglobin and plasma bilirubin (after Dyke).

The direct local effect of B_{12} upon erythropoiesis has been demonstrated in man; when the vitamin is injected into megaloblastic bone marrow, the abnormal erythropoiesis is corrected locally before a general effect occurs (i.e., on the marrow in other situations).

The first detectable effect of specific treatment in pernicious anemia is a rise in the reticulocytes (fig. 30.3). In untreated cases of pernicious anemia these constitute 2 per cent or less of the red cells. Within 2 to 5 days after vitamin B_{12}, a potent liver extract, or a preparation of gastric tissue has been administered, large numbers of reticulocytes appear. The increase reaches its maximum about the fifth day, when the percentage is from 10 to 40 per cent. From then on the reticulocyte population declines, and there is an increased number of mature erythrocytes. The lower the red cell count before treatment, the greater is the reticulocyte response to specific therapy.

The rise in the hemoglobin concentration of the blood lags behind the multiplication of the red cells. If the stimulus to erythropoiesis is intense, or total body iron stores are subnormal, the hemoglobin cannot be manufactured in sufficient quantities to furnish each cell with its quota of pigment and the color index and M.C.H. fall well below the normal value.

With the improvement in the blood picture the general symptoms of the disease abate, but the secretion of acid gastric juice is rarely if ever restored. Specific treatment therefore does not remove the primary cause of the disease, but must be persisted in for the rest of the patient's life. The maintenance dose is, of course, much less than that required originally for the restoration of the normal blood picture. The neurological symptoms may improve if vitamin B₁₂ is given early, and in a dosage considerably greater than that required for maintaining the normal blood picture. The degenerative changes in the cord are due to the lack of the hematinic principle, and are not simply secondary to and caused by the anemia.

Pteroylglutamic Acid. Synonyms: Folic Acid, Vitamin B$_c$,[4], Liver *Lactobacillus casei* Factor, Norite-eluate Factor, Vitamin M, Wills Factor, Factor U

In 1941 Mitchell and his associates obtained a substance with acidic properties from the green leaves of various plants, e.g., spinach, peas, clover, etc., and gave it the appropriate name of *folic acid*. What has since proved to be the same principle had previously, from microbiological studies, been found in concentrates of liver and yeast (*norite-eluate factor*). It stimulates the growth of certain microorganisms, e.g., *Lactobacillus casei, Streptococcus faecalis* R (or *S. lactis* R), and is essential for the existence of certain protozoa and insects. It is, therefore, also known as the *liver L. casei factor*, but is now more commonly referred to by its chemical name *pteroylglutamic acid* (PGA). It is made up of a pteridyl ring joined through para-aminobenzoic acid to a molecule of glutamic acid. Para-aminobenzoic (PAB) acid appears to be a precursor from which pteroylglutamic acid is synthesized in nature. The chemical structure of pteroylglutamic acid is shown below.

Of fundamental importance in the physiology of pteroylglutamic acid is its indispensability for the synthesis of desoxyribonucleic acid, a constituent of the nuclei of all cells (ch. 66). Certain

analogues of folic acid, such as, *aminopterin* (4-aminopteroylglutamic acid, or 4-aminofolic acid), *amethopterin* (4-amino-10-methyl pteroylglutamic acid) *aminoan-fol*) (4-aminopteroylaspartic acid) antagonize this action of the vitamin. Pteroylglutamic acid is synthesized in the intestine of some mammals, especially of the rat, and the analogues are useful in producing folic acid deficiency for experimental purposes. They have also been used in the treatment of acute leukemia, especially in children; the number of leukemic cells is reduced, and temporary remissions of the disease induced. A permanent cure does not, however, result, and the administration of the compounds is attended by certain toxic symptoms, e.g., stomatitis, diarrhea, alopecia and deafness.

THE HEMOPOIETIC ACTION OF PTEROYLGLUTAMIC ACID

Several observations had pointed to the existence in liver, or in crude liver preparations, of a principle effective in certain macrocytic anemias which failed to respond to highly purified liver extracts. There also appeared reports of a beneficial action of preparations of brewer's yeast, which does not contain vitamin B₁₂, in macrocytic anemias and in the nutritional anemia of monkeys. Suspecting that the unknown hemopoietic substance in crude preparations of liver was "folic acid," Spies and his associates administered it to pernicious anemia patients with remarkable hematological success. Pteroylglutamic acid is also effective in other anemias characterized by a megaloblastic bone marrow, e.g., the anemias of sprue and pregnancy, but fails in the treatment of macrocytic and other types of anemia with a normoblastic or macroblastic bone marrow. It relieves the nutritional leukopenia of monkeys and stimulates the production of granulocytes, and is therefore of value in the treatment of agranulocytosis. *It has no effect whatever in arresting the progress of the neurological lesions (chronic combined degeneration of the cord) in pernicious anemia.* Indeed, the neurological signs

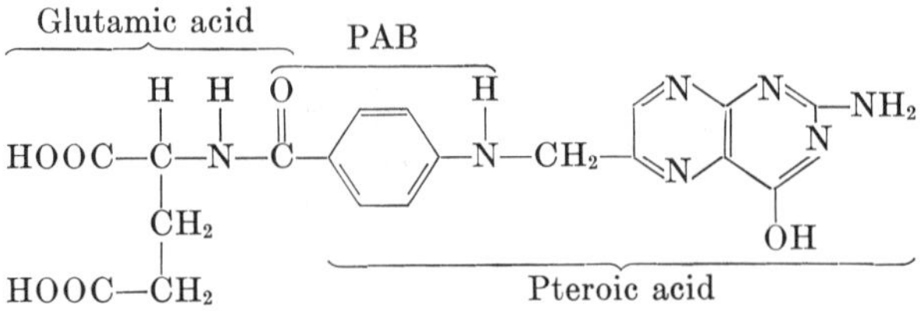

FIG. 30.4. Pteroylglutamic acid: N-[4-{[(2-amino-4-hydroxy-6-pteridyl) methyl] amino}-benzoyl] glutamic acid.

appear to be aggravated by its administration. Its action in restoring the bone marrow to normal is identical with that of the vitamin B_{12}.

Pteroylglutamic acid was synthesized by Angier and associates in 1945. The synthetic compound is as therapeutically effective as the natural principle.

The chief sources of "folic acid" are liver, kidney and green vegetables; its concentration in plant foods appears to run parallel with their chlorophyll content.

The Possible Relationship of the Anti-anemic Factor of Liver and Pteroylglutamic Acid

The chemistry and actions of "folic acid" and of the antianemic factor of liver show that they are separate and distinct principles. Moreover, it soon became evident that the concentration of "folic acid" in highly purified and potent liver extracts is equivalent to only a small fraction of the amount required to elicit a reticulocyte response in pernicious anemia. Again, as mentioned above, pteroylglutamic acid is wholly ineffective in arresting the cord changes of pernicious anemia. The nonidentity of the two principles was finally settled by the isolation of crystalline B_{12}. Both vitamin B_{12} and folic acid seem to be essential in the synthesis of nucleoproteins. It is thought that folic acid is necessary for DNA formation, but that vitamin B_{12} is essential for both DNA and RNA synthesis. Since both DNA and RNA are necessary for the maintenance of the structure and function of neurons, this may explain why B_{12} is effective in improving the neurological condition in pernicious anemia, and folic acid is not. The exact details of the mechanisms of action of these substances, and their interrelationship, are unknown.

"Citrovorum factor"; "folinic acid"; leucovorum. A derivative of pteroylglutamic acid which promoted the growth of the microorganism, *Leuconostoc citrovorum*, was isolated in 1948 by Sauberlich and Baumann from liver extracts and yeast. This substance which is now known as the *"citrovorum factor"* has an action similar to that of pteroylglutamic acid in pernicious anemia and other megaloblastic anemias; it also annuls the toxic effects of such folic acid antagonists as aminopterin and amethopterin. Substances with the same action, and apparently identical with the "citrovorum factor" have been prepared artificially, and named *"folinic acid"* (Shive and associates), and *leucovorum* (Jukes and associates).

Other antianemic agents. The pyrimidine base *thymine* (5-methyluracil) and *xanthopterin* (uropterin) give a hematopoietic response, but one which is much inferior to that of pteroylglutamic acid. An amount of thymine several thousand times the weight of an effective dose of pteroylglutamic acid is required to produce a reticulocyte response in pernicious anemia (Spies and associates).

Macrocytic (Hypochromic or Hyperchromic) Anemias with Normoblastic Bone Marrow

Macrocytic anemias showing a resemblance to Addisonian anemia, in so far as the blood picture is concerned, occur in various diseases, e.g., carcinoma (other than gastric), syphilis, cirrhosis of the liver, etc. But the bone marrow is of the normoblastic type. Since they are not due to deficiency of the antianemic principle, they do not respond to the administration of liver extract or of gastric tissue. Nor do they respond to the administration of "folic acid."

Idiopathic Aplastic Anemia

This is a comparatively rare type of anemia in which there is a rapidly progressive reduction in all the blood cells—erythrocytes, leukocytes and platelets. There is little or no evidence of blood regeneration, reticulocytes are very scarce and nucleated forms are usually absent. The red cell count may reach an extraordinarily low figure—213,000 per cu. mm. in a case reported by Ehrlich. Granulocytes and platelets may entirely disappear. The marrow is hypoplastic or aplastic; there is a great reduction in its cellular elements and almost complete absence of hemopoietic activity. The lymphocytopenia which also occurs, but is less marked than the reduction in granulocytes, suggests that the entire hemopoietic system is affected. The causes of the bone marrow hypoplasia have been mentioned.

A number of cases have been reported (Thompson, Richter and Edsall; Anderson) in which the typical blood picture of aplastic anemia was associated with a normal or even a hyperplastic marrow. In these, to which the term "pseudoaplastic anemia" might be applied, there would appear to be some interference with the maturation and delivery of the cells into the blood stream rather than to absolute suppression of marrow function.

Conclusions

It is only upon pernicious anemia or macrocytic anemias of the pernicious anemia type with a megaloblastic bone marrow that vitamin B_{12} or "folic acid" therapy has any specific effect. Other macrocytic types (with a normoblastic type of marrow), the microcytic anemias and aplastic anemia fail to respond to the administration of liver extract, gastric tissue or pteroylglutamic acid. It has been mentioned that certain megaloblastic anemias (e.g., that of pregnancy) are resistant to the action of vitamin B_{12} but respond to folic acid. In posthemorrhagic anemia and certain other secondary anemias *whole liver* is of value, not from any specific action but simply because it furnishes iron and protein of high quality.

REFERENCES

ANGIER, R. B. AND ASSOCIATES. Science, 1946, **103**, 667.

VON BONSDORFF, B. Blood, 1948, **3**, 91.

CASTLE, W. B. AND ASSOCIATES. Am. J. M. Sc., 1929, **178**, 764. New England J. Med., 1948, **239**, 911; 1953, **249**, 603.

DAMESHEK, W. AND SCHWARTZ, S. O. Am. J. M. Sc., 1938, **196**, 769.

ERSLEV, A. J. Blood, 1955, **10**, 954.

FOX, H. J. AND CASTLE, W. B. Am. J. M. Sc., 1942, **203**, 18.

GIBLETT, E. R., COLEMAN, D. H., PIRZIO-BIROLI, G., DONOHUE, D. M., MOTULSKY, A. G. AND FINCH, C. A., Blood, 1956, 11, 29.

HORRIGAN, D.. JARROLD. T. AND VILTER, R. W. J. CLIN. INVEST., 1951, **30**, 31.

JACOBSON, B. M. AND SUBBAROW, Y., J. Clin. Invest., 1937, **16**, 573.

JUKES, T. H. Fed. Proc., 1953, **12**, 633; B-vitamins for blood formation, Am. Lecture Series, Charles C Thomas, Springfield, Ill., 1952.

KARRER, P. Schweiz. med. Wchnschr., 1941, **71**, 343.

LOUTIT, J. F. AND MOLLISON, P. L. J. Path. Bact., 1946, **58**, 711.

MINOT, G. R. AND MURPHY, W. P. J. A. M. A., 1926, **87**, 470; 1927, **89**, 759.

MITCHELL, H. K., SNELL, E. E. AND WILLIAMS, R. J. J. Am. Chem. Soc., 1944, **66**, 267.

MULLER, G. L. Am. J. Physiol., 1927, **82**, 269.

NIEWEG, H. O., CITED BY CASTLE, W. B., New England J. Med., 1953, **249**, 603.

PFIFFNER, J. J. AND ASSOCIATES. Science, 1945, **102**, 228. J. Biol. Chem., 1945, **157**, 413.

REISSNER, E. H. Blood, 1958, **13**, 313.

RICKES, E. L. AND COLLEAGUES. Science, 1948, **107**, 396, 398; **108**, 134.

SAUBERLICH, H. E. AND BAUMANN, G. A. J. Biol. Chem., 1948, **176**, 165.

SHIVE, W. AND ASSOCIATES. J. Am. Chem. Soc., 1950, **72**, 2818.

SMITH, E. L. Nature, 1948, **161**, 638.

SPIES, T. D. AND ASSOCIATES. South. M. J. 1945, **38**, 590; Blood, 1946, **1**, 271; Lancet, 1948, **2**, 519.

STURGIS, C. C. AND ISAACS, R. J. A. M. A., 1929, **93**, 747.

SUÁREZ, R. AND ASSOCIATES. J. Lab. & Clin. Med., 1946, **31**, 2384.

THOMPSON, W. P., RICHTER, M. N. AND EDSALL, K. S. Am. J. M. Sc., 1934, **187**, 77.

WILKINSON, J. F. AND ISRAELS, M. C. G. Brit. M. J., 1935, **1**, 139.

Monographs and Reviews

CASTLE, W. B. Harvey Lectures, 1934–1935, **30**, 37.

CASTLE, W. B. New England J. Med., 1953, **249**, 603.

DAVIDSON, L. S. P. AND LEITCH, I. Nutrition Abstr. & Rev., 1934, **3**, 1.

HEATH, C. W. AND PATEK, A. J. Medicine, 1937, **16**, 267.

JACOBS, M. H. Ann. Rev. Physiol., 1958, **20**, 405.

JOSEPHS, H. W. Medicine, 1936, **15**, 307.

JUKES, T. H. AND STOKSTAD, E. L. R. Physiol. Rev., 1948, **28**, 51.

MOORE, C. V. Am. J. Clin. Nutrition, 1955, **3**, 3.

PINEY, A. AND WYARD, S. Clinical atlas of blood diseases. J. and A. Churchill, Ltd., London, 1932.

SPIES, T. D. Experiences with folic acid. Year Book Publishers, Inc., Chicago, 1947.

VAUGHN, J. M. The anaemias. Oxford University Press, London, 1934.

WELCH, A. Fed. Proc., 1947, **6**, 471.

WINTROBE, M. M. Medicine, 1930, **9**, 195.

WINTROBE, M. M. Clinical hematology. Lea and Febiger, Philadelphia, 1961.

WINTROBE, M. M. AND BEEBE, R. T. Medicine, 1933, **12**, 187.

CHAPTER 31

The White Blood Corpuscles or Leukocytes—The Platelets

Classification and Morphology

The white blood cell differs from the erythrocyte in that it contains no hemoglobin and has a nucleus. The majority of the white cells are also considerably larger than the erythrocytes, measuring from 8 to 15 μ in diameter, the size depending upon the particular variety. They are much less numerous than the red cells; in the adult they number from 5000 to 9000 per cu. mm. of blood. In infancy they are twice as numerous and throughout childhood the count is higher than in the adult. When a film of adult blood is examined under the microscope the white cells appear very sparsely scattered here and there among the crowds of colored corpuscles which outnumber them more than 600 to 1.

On the basis of morphological differences the white corpuscles are divided first into two main groups: (I) *Cells with a single nucleus* and *a clear nongranular cytoplasm*—the lymphocytes and the monocytes; (II) *cells having a lobed or incompletely partitioned nucleus*, and a *cytoplasm containing fine chromophil granules*—the granulocytes. Each of these two main classes is divided further into subgroups on a basis of differences in structure or staining properties.[1]

I. The Nongranular Leukocytes— Agranulocytes

These are of three varieties: (1) *Small lymphocyte*, (2) *large lymphocyte*, (3) *monocyte*. Although these forms show no granules in the protoplasm under the ordinary methods of staining, granulation may be demonstrated after staining with azure blue. The lymphocytes contain a few coarse azurophil granules; those of the monocytes are fine and very numerous.

1. SMALL LYMPHOCYTES. These are slightly larger than the red cells—7–10 μ in diameter. The nucleus is relatively large, slightly indented and stains more deeply with basic dyes than the

[1] The term leukocyte is employed by most authors to denote all the white cells, and this from the simple meaning of the word seems logical. Some, however, confine the term to the granulocytes. The first of these usages will be followed in this text.

surrounding narrow rim of cytoplasm which separates it from the boundary of the cell. The small lymphocytes originate in lymphoid tissue and are found in large numbers in the lymph nodes and spleen. They constitute in the adult from 20 to 25 per cent of the total number of white cells in blood and are the commonest cells found in lymph. In childhood lymphoid tissue is much more abundant than in adult life and the lymphocytes are more numerous. They amount to from 50 per cent or more of the leukocytes in early childhood and to about 35 per cent at the age of 10 years.

2. LARGE LYMPHOCYTES. These resemble the preceding in general appearance but are considerably larger, being 10–14 μ in diameter. The cytoplasm is more abundant, and the nucleus is oval or kidney shaped. These cells are found in insignificant numbers in adult blood but are more plentiful in the blood of young children. They are largely confined under physiological conditions to the lymphoid tissue, but even here they are greatly outnumbered by the small lymphocytes. They are considered to be a younger form of the small lymphocyte.

3. MONOCYTES are from 10 to 18 μ in diameter. They possess a relatively larger amount of cytoplasm. The nucleus has a deep indentation on one side, which gives it a kidney or saddlebag shape, although some cells have a round or oval nucleus. On the supposition that this cell represented a stage in the development of the polymorphonuclear leukocyte, it was called the "transitional leukocyte" by Ehrlich. For some years, this view was discarded, and it was felt that these cells arose from lymphocytes as postulated by Maximow. Recently, however, a growing body of evidence supports Ehrlich's original thesis, and monocytes are now believed to be intimately related to the polymorphonuclear leukocytes. It has been mentioned that the monocyte contains, like the lymphocytes, azurophil granules in the cytoplasm. The monocytes are actively motile and phagocytic, and are considered by most observers to be derived from fixed histiocytes. Such an origin would class them as circulating elements of the reticuloendothelial system. They constitute from 5 to 7 per cent of the white cells.

II. The Granulocytes

These are divided into three groups according to the staining reactions of their granules. One type—the *eosinophilic*—stains with acid dyes, e.g., eosin; another—the *basophilic*—stains with basic dyes, e.g., methylene blue; and the third type—the *neutrophilic*—with neutral dyes, i.e., mixtures of acid and basic dyes. These staining reactions apply to human leukocytes, but such distinctions cannot always be made in other animal species. The nucleus of an adult granulocyte is composed of two or more lobes connected together by strands of chromatin.

1. Eosinophils are not numerous; they amount to no more than 2 to 4 per cent of the total white cell count. The granules which are oval and much coarser than those in the other two varieties are stained a bright red with eosin. The cell is also slightly larger and the nucleus usually bilobed. In certain pathological conditions which will be mentioned later they may form a much larger percentage of the leukocyte population.

2. Basophils are present to the extent of only 0.15 per cent or less. Their granules are large and coarse and stain deeply with methylene blue. They completely fill the cytoplasm and frequently obscure the nucleus. Their significance is not known. They have been considered in the past to be degenerated neutrophils, but there appears to be little doubt that they are a distinct type and like the other granulocytes are a product of the bone marrow. Support is lent to the latter view by the fact that they are increased in conditions associated with excessive marrow activity,

e.g., chronic myelocytic leukemia and polycythemia vera. They are also increased in chronic inflammation of the accessory nasal sinuses. Similar, larger cells are found in the tissues where they are known as mast cells.

3. Neutrophils are by far the most numerous, constituting from 65 to 70 per cent or more of the total number of white cells. Their granules are fine and are stained a violet tint with neutral dyes. As will be seen presently the neutrophils are actively ameboid in character, i.e., they are capable of locomotion and ingest foreign particulate matter. They are 10 to 14 μ in diameter. Their nuclei show a variable number of lobes depending upon the age of the cell.

The Arneth Count or Index

It was pointed out by Arneth that the number of lobes in any neutrophil depends upon the cell's age, the older cells having the larger number.[2] A five-lobed nucleus for instance indicates a stage in the life of a cell just preceding its final dissolution; an unlobed but deeply indented nucleus, a very young cell. Five stages in the life history of the polymorphonuclear leukocyte are therefore distinguished corresponding to the number of lobed developed in the nucleus. A count of the nuclear lobes in the cells of a blood film will give the proportion of cells of different relative ages. In figure 31.1, stage I shows a nucleus with a single lobe. Constriction of the nucleus can be seen but the nuclear substance is continuous from one part to the other. In stage II the nucleus is partitioned into two parts which are connected only by chromatin threads. In the next stage 3 lobes are seen and so on to the last or senile stage in which the nucleus has five or more lobes. The cells of this stage are large, edematous and nonmotile; their granules stain poorly or not at all. In some conditions, e.g., acute septic infections and pernicious anemia, enormous neutrophils (up to 20 μ) with a great number of nuclei are seen. These are known as *macropolycytes*.

The Arneth index is determined by counting the number of nuclear lobes in each of 100 neutrophils. The cells in the different stages are expressed as percentages of the total. The count under the ordinary conditions of health is as follows:

	Percentages of leukocytes
Stage I	5
Stage II	30
Stage III	45
Stage IV	18
Stage V	2

[2] The extent of the previous activity of the cell, rather than its age, may be the important factor determining the number of nuclear lobes.

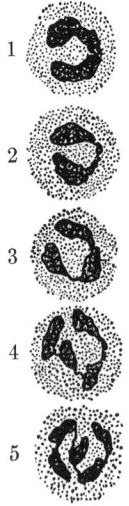

Fig. 31.1. Arneth stages.

In certain diseases the youngest cells (stage I) are much more numerous and may constitute 50 per cent of the total. There may be an entire absence of cells in the later stages (IV and V). An increase in the percentage of cells of the earlier stages is spoken of as a "shift to the left." It is seen in conditions which stimulate the bone marrow to a greater production of white cells, e.g., pyogenic infections. It is also seen in tuberculosis and after exposure to the X-rays and after the injection of thyroid extract. In children a shift to the left occurs much more readily than in adults. In pernicious anemia the percentages of the older cells increase—"shift to the right"—and in some cases, as mentioned above, macropolycytes appear. Except in the case of the senile nonmotile cells a relationship between the phagocytic activity of a particular cell and its age has not been demonstrated.

The Schilling index employs a simpler classification of the neutrophils but includes marrow elements. Four stages are recognized (see table 31.1) (a) the myelocyte which shows a single spherical nucleus; (b) young metamyelocyte with a slight indentation of the nucleus; (c) older metamyelocytes with the process of lobulation definitely indicated; this is known as the band cell of Schilling or "Staff" cell and corresponds to the first stage of Arneth; (d) older neutrophils, i.e., the other stages of Arneth. Stages (a) and (b) are not found normally in the blood. They appear when a pronounced "shift to the left" occurs (see ch. 32).

The nonmotile cells of the last or fifth stage of Arneth appear, periodically in increased numbers—in "showers"—in the blood stream. They are replaced by young cells from the marrow. Like the red cell the dying neutrophils disintegrate in the circulation or are disposed of by the macrophages of the spleen or the tissues. The life span of the neutrophils has been variously estimated. By some it is believed to be no more than about 3 days and by others no more than a few hours. Ponder used the injection of thyroid extract to produce a shift to the left then followed the return of the Arneth count to normal to measure the white cell life span. He estimated it to be 21 days.

With the advent of radioactive tracer techniques, it has been possible to obtain a more precise measurement of white cell intravascular "life-span." Cell protein may be labelled with (S^{35}) L-cystine, or cell deoxyribonucleic acid with C^{14}-adenine or radioactive phosphorus. The latter, as diisopropylfluorophosphate (DFP^{32}) is the more commonly used isotope.

Using DFP^{32} it has been possible to demonstrate

TABLE 31.1

Showing Schilling index and differential count of mature cells; figures indicate percentages

Neutrophils				Eosinophils	Basophils	Lymphocytes	Monocytes
Myelocytes	Juvenile metamyelocytes	Older metamyelocytes	Nucleus lobular				
0	0–1	3–5	55–70	2–4	0–1	20–25	5–7

TABLE 31.2

Sizes of granulocytic pools

Cells per Kg. Body Weight					
Mi	Ma	S	MGP	CGP	T
2.6×10^9	6.3×10^9	2.5×10^9	30.7×10^7 ± 11.8	34.6×10^7 ± 15.6	?

at least five cellular compartments, with interchange between them (table 31.2). The intravascular lifetime of the leukocyte is a relatively short period of time, amounting to about 9 hours. At least half of the granulocytes in the blood are in the marginated granulocyte pool (MGP) as opposed to the circulating granulocyte pool (CGP). Some of the changes in leukocyte count which are discussed below are due to release of cells from the marginated into the circulating granulocyte pool.

In the mitotic pool, division and maturation occur simultaneously. The cells pass into the maturation pool and thence into the storage pool, which they probably leave in a random way. Transit time from the mitotic pool to the tissues has been estimated at from 6½ to 11 days. Once a granulocyte has passed into the tissues it does not return to the intravascular pool. Loss of granulocytes from the blood occurs in random fashion into the tissues, as well as by the process of senescence with subsequent removal by the reticulo-endothelial system.

The Functions of the Leukocytes

The neutrophilic polymorphonuclear leuko- as well as the monocytes and other reticuloendothelial elements constitute probably the most important elements which the body possesses for its defense against invading microorganisms. Their power to attack bacteria depends upon their motility and a proclivity for the ingestion of solid

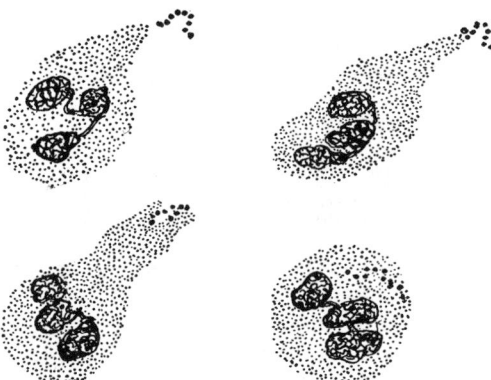

FIG. 31.2 Drawing of a neutrophil at half-minute intervals to show motility and phagocytosis of bacteria.

particles. The latter action, which was first demonstrated by Metchnikoff, is termed *phagocytosis* (phago—I eat). These two varieties of white blood cell are free lances among the body cells; they wander from place to place through the tissues and practically no part of the body is barred to them. They insinuate a process (*pseudopodium*), improvised at the moment from their cell protoplasm, through one of the joints in the endothelium of the capillary wall. Then by causing the semifluid substance of the cell body to stream into the protoplasmic projection, they pass out of the blood vessels "at will." By this action of *diapedesis*,[3] as it is called, myriads of white corpuscles may pass out of the vessels in a remarkably short time. Reaching a point where the bacteria have entered the body they surround the threatened area and proceed to destroy the invaders. If, for instance, an actively inflamed region should be examined under the microscope, masses of neutrophils would be seen, and many of these would be observed to hold bacteria imprisoned within their bodies. As many as 15 or 20 microorganisms may be seen at times within a single cell. It has been shown that the bacteria are ingested alive and remain so for a time within the leukocyte (fig. 31.2).

When a tissue such as the mesentery or web of a frog, in which the capillaries are clearly visible, is examined in the living state a short time after a culture of bacteria has been injected into it, the small vessels leading to the site of inoculation are found swarming with neutrophils. In the surrounding tissues the ameboid cells are seen moving some-

[3] The term diapedesis, literally a "leaping through," is sometimes applied to the passage of red cells through an unbroken capillary wall, but the term is scarcely appropriate for a passive process of this nature.

what ponderously hither and thither to engulf the offending bacteria. When the latter are intensely virulent in nature this normal leukocyte reaction may be seriously depressed. The monocytes, though much less numerous, also join in the general attack and show their phagocytic propensities to a marked degree. After the first flooding of the tissues with neutrophils and monocytes, numbers of the latter come to rest and together with other reticuloendothelial elements of the tissues undergo transformation to fixed tissue macrophages. They aid in isolating the infected area from the neighboring healthy tissues. Until this is accomplished the danger of the infection becoming more widespread always exists. In their struggle against bacteria, equipped as these are with powerful toxins, many of the white cells are killed. These collect within the center of the inflamed area together with exuded plasma, liquefied tissue cells and a few red cells that have escaped through the injured walls of the capillaries. This material constitutes pus, and the so-called pus cells are dead leukocytes. The circumscribing wall and its semifluid contents constitute an abscess. By the action of the phagocytes, aided by a protein-digesting ferment (protease) which they elaborate, the overlying structures whether connective tissue, mucosa or skin are in part removed piecemeal. In this way a communication with the exterior is effected and the contents of the cavity are discharged.

Not only bacteria but practically any foreign material, whether a rose thorn or a catgut suture, is attacked and removed if possible, or loosened by the neutrophils aided by the monocytes and other phagocytic cells of the tissues. The removal of dead tissue or of blood clot or the separation of necrotic from living structures is accomplished in the same way. Devitalized bone, although not removed in its entirety, unless it is of very small size, is nevertheless eroded and separated from the living tissue by the leukocytes. The disappearance of effete organs such as the tail and gills of the metamorphosing tadpole or the creeping muscles of insect larvae, as these develop to the mature form, is effected by similar phagocytic cells. The application of heat to a part also attracts leukocytes in large numbers to the capillaries from which they immediately commence to migrate.

The activity of the leukocytes is best studied by the method of Sandison and Clarke, in which a transparent chamber is inserted into the tissues, e.g., the rabbit's ear. After a time fine vessels grow into the chamber through openings in its sides which may be examined under the microscope. Another very simple method is that of *supravital staining*. A thin film of a non-toxic (supravital) dye, e.g., neutral red, azure, or brilliant cresyl blue, is laid upon a glass slide and allowed to dry; a film of blood is laid over this and covered with an ordinary cover glass which is then sealed with vaseline around the edges. The preparation is kept warm and examined under the microscope, the cells remaining alive and active. The neutrophils seen in such preparations are not uniformly spherical as in fixed smears, but are continually changing their shape. Pseudopodia are in constant movement and the granules can be seen streaming through the cytoplasm with each movement of the cell. The rate of progression of the neutrophil is from 30 to 35 μ per minute at body temperature (fig. 31.2).

Of the functions of the other varieties of granulocytes—the *eosinophils* and *basophils*—little is known. The eosinophils are not markedly motile and only slightly phagocytic. They may play an important role in detoxification, and in the disintegration and removal of protein.

Basophils, like connective tissue mast cells, are found in great numbers during the healing phase of acute inflammation or in chronic inflammation. Like mast cells, their metachromatic granules contain heparin, hyaluronic acid, and 5-hydroxytryptamine. They probably function in part to produce local anticoagulation in inflammation, and are intimately concerned with the deposition of ground substance.

The *lymphocytes*—although, generally speaking, they are not phagocytic—appear to exert such an action upon certain pathogenic microorganisms, notably, pneumococci types III and IV. A great migration of lymphocytes characterizes certain chronic types of inflammation.

An important function of the lymphocytes is the manufacture of serum globulin, both β- and γ-fractions having been found in extracts of lymphocytes. Immune substances (antibodies) are recognized as being associated with the γ-globulin fraction, so it was presumed that the lymphocytes occupied a key position in defense reactions of an immunological nature. The investigations of White and Dougherty have gone a long way to substantiate this idea. The lymphocytes and serum of mice which had been immunized to sheep erythrocytes contained an antibody which lysed these cells, but none was found in the lymphocytes or serum of nonimmunized mice. Furthermore, extracts of the lymphocytes of the immunized animals contained antibody in a concentration from six to eight times higher than that found in the serum. Antihemolysins to staphylococcus toxin have also been demonstrated in the lymphocytes of mice immunized to this toxin. The production of antibodies in the lymph nodes was first demonstrated by McMaster and Hudach in

1935, and Ehrich found that a threefold increase in output of lymphocytes from the nodes accompanied the antibody production.

McMaster demonstrated agglutinins in lymph nodes draining the area of intradermal injection of antigen in mice before the appearance of circulating antibody. Harris also showed that the highest concentration of antibodies occurred in the lymph nodes draining the site of a previous antigen injection. Nevertheless, it should be pointed out that lymphocytes are not the sole source of antibody. There is considerable evidence to prove that plasma cells are actively involved in antibody production.

The manner in which the lymphocytes add globulin to the plasma appears to be by a process of cytoplasmic budding and ultimate dissolution in the lymphoid tissues and blood stream. Budding can be observed within a Sandison-Clarke chamber inserted into the tissues.

The supply of globulin to the blood is apparently under the control of the pituitary gland through the action of its adrenocorticotrophic hormone upon the adrenal cortex. The pituitary-adrenal influence was demonstrated by White and Dougherty in the following way. Rabbits were immunized to sheep corpuscles and, after the specific antibody had appeared in the circulation, were left untreated for a period of three months, when all antibody had disappeared. They were then divided into four groups. One group was injected with the original antigen; no significant rise in antibody concentration of the blood of these animals occurred. Of the remaining three groups, one was injected with steroid fractions of the adrenal cortex, another with the adrenocorticotrophic hormone of the pituitary (ACTH) and the third with an aqueous extract of adrenal cortex. The steroid hormones caused an increase in antibody concentration, nearly as great as that caused originally by immunization—a maximal dissolution of lymphocytes in the lymphoid tissues and a scarcity of lymphocytes in the circulation. The response to the pituitary principle was also pronounced, although not as great as that given by the steroids, whereas the aqueous extract caused a relatively small reaction. The adrenal cortical fractions which exert this effect are those with an oxygen atom in the 11 position (see chapter 76). Corticosterone and 11-dehydro-17-hydroxycorticosterone are therefore effective in this respect but not desoxycorticosterone.

It has also been found that injections of adrenal cortical hormone, or of the pituitary principle, increase the bulk of lymphoid tissue as a result of edema, the edema fluid containing larger numbers of lymphocytes undergoing dissolution. Later, after the edema has subsided, the tissue shrinks until its weight is less than before the injections. Adrenalectomy is followed by an increase in the mass of lymphoid tissue.

The reduction in lymphocytes in response to adrenal cortical hormones and ACTH is of moderate degree. The eosinophils show a much more pronounced reduction in number following the administration of these principles. The eosinopenia occurs so consistently and is so delicate that it is employed as a means of assaying the potency of cortisone and ACTH. Adrenaline also causes eosinopenia, perhaps by stimulating ACTH production. Adrenalectomized animals show a lymphocytosis, and overgrowth of lymphoid tissue is not an uncommon feature of adrenal insufficiency (Addison's disease) in man.

The Fate of the Lymphocytes

This has been a puzzling question for a number of years, for it has long been known that immense numbers of these cells disappear from the circulation daily. According to one estimate, the entire population of lymphocytes in the circulation of the dog are replaced twice each day (Drinker and Yoffey); replacement five times daily is given for the cat (Sanders and associates). Some have thought that lymphocytes were transformed into other types of cell, others that they returned to the lymph nodes and were destroyed in the germinal centers. But the most widely accepted explanation of the wastage of lymphocytes has been that they are shed from the mucosa of the gastrointestinal tract, and no doubt large numbers are discharged from the body in this way. Nevertheless, little effect is exerted upon the disappearance of lymphocytes in rabbits by the removal of the entire gastrointestinal tract and the injection of some 300,000,000 leukocytes into such a preparation does not cause a rise in the leukocyte count. It appears now from the work of the authors mentioned above that the large daily turnover of these cells is to a great extent at least the result of their dissolution in the lymphoid tissues and blood; thus globulin is supplied to the plasma.

DNA labelling with isotopes has demonstrated a life span of 100–200 days for the greater number of lymphocytes. Some 20% however, have an apparent life span of 3–4 days. This anomaly may in part be explained by recirculation of lymphocytes. As well, the two morphological types of lymphocytes may have widely divergent life spans.

Variations in the Number of Leukocytes in the Blood Stream

Leukocytosis

In the event of some damage to the tissues which calls forth a leukocytic response, not only is there a migration of leukocytes from the blood to the site of injury, and a shift of cells from the marginated to the circulating granulocyte pool, but also a discharge of these cells from the marrow and an increase of their total number in the general circulation. Instead of the normal count of 7000 or 8000 per cubic millimeter the colorless cells may number from 20,000 to 30,000 within a short time. *Leukocytosis* is the term used to designate an increase in the total number of white cells. All varieties of the white cells do not necessarily share in the increase. In one instance it may be the neutrophils, in another the lymphocytes or the eosinophils that are increased, and it is the presence in abnormal numbers of one or other of these which then gives the high total leukocyte count. It is of great diagnostic value to know which type of cell is responsible for the leukocytosis, and in order to determine this a so-called *differential count* of the cells is made. That is, the numbers of the different types in a stained smear of blood are counted and their percentages of the total count determined. However, changes in the proportions of the different white cell types may occur although their total number is normal. Such alterations can be revealed only by a differential count. The following example is given in illustration; the lymphocytes and monocytes are relatively increased; the neutrophils and eosinophils reduced. In such instances, it is important to calculate the absolute number of each cell type. If this is done, it will become apparent that the abnormality is an absolute decrease in neutrophils, and that the lymphocytes and monocytes are actually normal in number.

Total white cells per cu. mm......	7500
Lymphocytes, per cent.........	35
Monocytes, per cent..........	8
Neutrophils, per cent.........	56
Eosinophils, per cent.........	0.7

Very commonly an increase in the neutrophils is entirely responsible for the leukocytosis. On this account the latter term is used frequently but somewhat loosely to imply an increase in the count caused by the neutrophilic elements alone. *Neutrophilia* is a more precise term that has come into use for the latter condition. *Lymphocytosis, monocytosis* and *eosinophilia* are the respective terms employed to designate increase in the other elements.

Acute infections by the pus-forming organisms —staphylococcus, streptococcus, etc., are the most potent causes of a neutrophilic increase. On this account the examination of the white cells furnishes a valuable diagnostic sign for the detection of hidden inflammatory conditions, e.g., appendicitis, empyema, etc. A neutrophilic leukocytosis occurs also in pneumonia, whooping cough, scarlet fever and some other infectious fevers. The nuclear count shows an increase in the young stages at the expense of the older (ch. 32).

Neutrophilia also occurs with intoxications such as those associated with metabolic disorders; e.g. uremia, diabetic acidosis, gout, or those accompanying poisoning with chemicals or drugs; e.g. lead, mercury, digitalis, phenacetin, etc. It may accompany poisoning by insect venoms, or follow the injection of foreign proteins.

Neutrophilic leukocytosis will follow acute blood loss within the hour. It is of greatest degree when the hemorrhage has occurred into one of the body cavities e.g. ruptured tubal pregnancy. Post-operatively, neutrophilia is seen within 12–24 hours, probably as a result of tissue injury. The same mechanism probably accounts for the leukocytosis which follows myocardial infarction. Malignant neoplasms frequently are associated with a neutrophilia, as are acute hemolytic episodes.

Pteroylglutamic ("folic") acid is a dietary constituent required by many species for the production of granulocytes by the bone marrow, and for the maintenance of the normal population in the circulation. Absence of this vitamin from the diet of monkeys and chicks is followed by a profound leukopenia.

Chemotaxis; Chemical Factors in Inflammation

Chemotaxis is the term applied to the unknown "force" which draws the white cells from the blood stream, to the point of injury in the tissues. This property of responding by a locomotory movement to chemical substances is not peculiar to leukocytes, but is possessed by many types of free-living, unicellular organisms. Chemotaxis may be positive (i.e., attractive) or negative (repellant)

and, although the former is most commonly observed in leukocytic behavior, certain chemicals produce the opposite effect.

It was formerly thought that the chemical properties of the bacterial toxin were responsible for this effect, but it has since been shown that nucleic acid and its derivatives guanine, adenine, adenosine, etc. or some other principle supplied by the tissues (see below) are the specific stimulants. Injections of these substances cause a rapid rise in the leukocyte count. Toxins or other injurious agents act probably indirectly by liberating nucleic acid from the tissue cells as well as from injured leukocytes themselves. It has been suggested that the actual force which attracts the cells from the vessels to the tissue focus may have changes in surface tension of the blood cell membrane as its basis, for during the early stages of the inflammatory reaction the leukocytes in the small vessels near the injured site appear "sticky." They collect and cling to the walls of the vessels and are thus separated from the red cells which occupy the axis of the stream. An artificial cell model may be used to illustrate the surface tension theory. When a small globule of mercury is placed in a weak solution of nitric acid, the globule moves rapidly toward a crystal of potassium dichromate dropped near it upon the surface of the solution, as a result of a chemical reaction leading to surface tension effects; or if the mercury is placed in a dilute dichromate solution, it will move away from a drop of nitric acid in its vicinity (negative chemotaxis). Experiments, however, upon unicellular organisms such as the amoeba, to which the white cell bears a strong resemblance, have failed to show that the spontaneous movements are surface tension phenomena. It must be admitted that the problem of chemotaxis remains unsolved. Phagocytosis does not necessarily depend upon chemotaxis but may occur quite apart from it, as when chemically inert material, e.g., particles of carbon or silica are engulfed by leukocytes coming into contact with them at random. On the other hand, a positive chemotactic effect may not be followed by phagocytosis; for neutrophils may be attracted by some dead or foreign material and more toward it with the apparent "intention" of devouring it, but not do so.

Menkin has obtained a nitrogenous, crystalline principle from inflammatory exudates which increases capillary permeability, allowing the free escape of plasma protein, and induces the migration of leukocytes through the capillary wall. This substance, named *leukotaxine*, appears to be a simple polypeptide and is related neither to histamine nor to nucleic acid. It has also been found by others in the succus entericus of the rabbit. It seems to be the factor responsible for the swarm of leukocytes which in infective and inflammatory states are attracted from the circulation into the tissues of the affected part. Four other substances have been recovered by Menken from inflammatory exudates; these are called *the leukocytosis-promoting factor* (L.P.F.), *necrosin*, *pyrexin* and the *leukopenic factor*. These findings have not yet been fully confirmed by other investigators. However, Menken's theory of their mechanism of action allows an orderly approach to the basic mechanisms behind the inflammatory response, and merits a detailed description.

The *leukocytosis-promoting factor* causes the discharge of immature leukocytes from the bone marrow and hyperplasia of granulocytes and megakaryocytes within the latter. It is a pseudoglobulin, or closely associated with this fraction of the exudate, and is presumably responsible for for the leukocytosis which is so often a feature of the blood in infective states. Although increased manufacture of granulocytes is induced by L.P.F., the rapid increase in leukocytes suggests that preformed cells are discharged into the circulation, and there is evidence that in the early stages of leukocytosis capillary sinuses of the marrow, harboring masses of leukocytes, are suddenly opened up and their cellular contents discharged. This suggests a vasomotor reaction, which is substantiated by the fact that even saline (1 cc.) injected intravenously into a rabbit causes about 300,000,000 mature neutrophils to enter the general blood stream within 1 hour.

Necrosin, which is associated with the euglobulin fraction of inflammatory exudates, is the substance which causes tissue injury, lymphatic obstruction and necrosis in inflammation. This temporary lymphatic blockage, according to Menken, is salutary since it tends to limit the spread of the infection. Injection of this substance intravenously into animals causes widespread injury, e.g., hemorrhages into the gastrointestinal tract, focal necrosis of the liver and leukocytic infiltration of the kidneys. Necrosin is thermolabile and nonpyrogenic.

Pyrexin is a thermostable fraction also associated with the euglobulin. It appears to be a glycoprotein. It induces fever.

The *leukopenic factor* causes leukopenia as a result of the trapping of leukocytes in the lungs, spleen and liver. This factor causes nausea and vomiting when injected intravenously. It is closely associated with pyrexin and, although it can be separated by incomplete hydrolysis from the pyrogenic factor, it has not been shown with certainty that the two factors are separate and distinct.

Inasmuch as the leukocytes, especially the neutrophils, are essential elements in the defensive mechanisms of the body against infective microorganisms, their attraction to an infected part must be looked upon as a physiological and salutary response. It should, therefore, not be discouraged in any way by agents, e.g., many antiseptics, which, although themselves inimical to bacterial growth, defeat their own purpose by destroying the leucocytes, or reducing their activity. Such agents may even act to repel the neutrophils from the injured region. Sulfanilamide, on the contrary, is claimed to actually stimulate leukocyte activity either directly or by rendering the invading microorganisms less resistant, or more "appetizing," to the phagocytes. Some interesting observations have been made by Mallery and McCutcheon on the movements of leukocytes in attack, which give a meaning to the well worn phrase "lowered resistance." The neutrophils in samples of blood from patients acutely ill and from those convalescent from various diseases were observed, and their rates of approach to a minute clump of bacteria measured and compared with the rates of approach of the observer's cells under identical conditions. In the acutely ill patients the rate of approach was 9.7 μ per minute, as compared with the normal of 16.1 μ per minute. No significant difference was observed between the phagocytes of the convalescent patients and those of the observer.

Physiological leukocytoses. It had formerly been taught that an increase in the neutrophils occurred during digestion—*digestive leukocytosis*—but it seems that this was a misconception. These cells show spontaneous rhythmical variations in their numbers, the total white cell count reaching its maximum of about 7000 to 8000 in the afternoon, and its minimum, 5000 to 6000, in the early morning. These variations occur quite independently of meals. Leukocytosis also occurs during pregnancy, parturition and menstruation, in muscular exercise and after adrenalin administration, or in states such as fear, pain, anoxia, etc., which cause the liberation of adrenaline from the adrenal gland. In infants and young children the leukocyte count is considerably higher than in adults; the count is also less constant in infancy, varying without apparent cause by 2000 or more per cu. mm. Many of these so-called "physiological" leukocytoses are the result of deviation of cells from the marginated to the circulating pool of intravascular granulocytes, rather than to their release from storage. For example, adrenalin, which was formerly believed to act by causing release of cells from the spleen, is equally effective in a splenectomized patient or animal. Its prime site of action now appears to be the reduction of the ratio of marginated to circulating granulocytes, producing a peripheral leukocytosis.

Eosinophilia, or increase in the number of circulating eosinophils, occurs in several conditions, notably allergic states, e.g., asthma and anaphylactic shock, and in infections by various animal parasites, e.g., *hookworm (ankylostoma duodenal) disease*, in which the eosinophils may be 30 per cent of the total white cell count, and *trichinosis*. In the latter infection there is a general leukocytosis, with the eosinophils running as high as 50 per cent of the total. Infections with hydatids, ascaris and other worms also cause eosinophilia to a greater or lesser degree. The significance of this association of eosinophilia with parasitic infection is unknown. These white cells are also increased in Leoffler's disease and in a number of skin diseases; the tissues in the neighborhood of the cutaneous lesions may be infiltrated with eosinophils. Certain collagen disorders, and occasionally Hodgkin's disease, may be accompanied by eosinophilia. During the acute stage of pyogenic infections the eosinophils are usually reduced in number (eosinopenia); in the convalescent stage they are, as a rule, increased. The eosinopenia caused by ACTH and by adrenaline has been mentioned.

Lymphocytosis. The neutrophils are not stimulated by tuberculous, malarial, or syphilitic infection. In the active stage of such conditions either an absolute or relative increase in the number or circulating lymphocytes is the rule. In other chronic inflammatory states and in infections with the colon or diphtheria bacillus also, it is the lymphocytes rather than the neutrophils that are increased in number. They indicate in general an inflammatory condition that is undergoing repair, is being held in check, or at the most is making slow progress. Lymphocytosis, therefore occurs as an aftermath of acute infections. The neutrophils on the other hand represent the "shock troops" and their presence indicates that a more active campaign is being waged. In young children a relative lymphocytosis is the rule.

Monocytosis. An increase in the monocytes is seen much less frequently than that of the other leukocytic types. Apart from monocytic leukemia and glandular fever (see below), the chief conditions in which they appear in greater numbers than normal are tuberculosis, malaria, syphilis, brucellosis and bacterial endocarditis. According to Cunningham, a decline in the lymphocyte count with an increase in the monocytes in pulmonary

tuberculosis is an indication that the tuberculosis process is being arrested.

As well as the leukocytosis which occurs in physiological states and in response to stimuli such as infection, there is a phenomenon known as a leukemoid reaction. This reaction is so named because it resembles leukemia, either quantitatively or qualitatively. Counts as high as 250,000 have been reported although the usual range is up to 100,000. Myeloid, lymphocytic or monocytic cells may be involved, and immature forms may appear in the peripheral blood. Special stains of the white cells may be used to differentiate this reaction from leukemia, e.g. alkaline phosphatase stain. A leukemoid response may occur with infection, (pneumonia, tuberculosis), intoxication, (eclampsia, mercury poisoning) or in malignancy.

Pathological Increases in the Leukocyte Population; Leukemia, Glandular Fever

The leukocytic increases discussed in the foregoing sections, even those associated with abnormal states, are moderate in degree, and are due to reactions which in themselves are of a "purposeful" character and on the whole physiological. But in the *leukemias* we find an altogether uncontrolled and often relatively enormous increase (up to 1,000,000 per cu. mm.) in the number of leukocytes, and a distorted mode of white cell production with the appearance of immature forms in the circulation.

The exact cause of leukemia is still unknown. The disease can occur spontaneously in some animals, and extensive investigation of this phenomenon has been carried out in fowl and in mice.

Fowl leukosis occurs spontaneously, is very common, and appears in a number of forms, both leukemic and visceral or "aleukemic." It can be transmitted by the transfusion of leukemic cells, or of a cell-free filtrate after passage through a Birkefield filter. Two agents have been identified, both viruses. Both agents require a cellular host for in vitro multiplication, and apparently confer neoplastic properties on these cells in the process.

Murine leukemia has undergone intensive study in the past few years. Undoubtedly genetic factors play a prominent role. It is possible to produce an inbred strain of mice in which 80–90% of the animals spontaneously develop leukemia at 6–9 months of age. Age itself is an important factor in the susceptibility of mice to the transmission of leukemia. Exogenous factors, such as exposure to X-irradiation and state of nutrition also affect the success of transfer of this disease from one animal to another.

The thymus appears to enhance the susceptibility of mice to the spontaneous development of leukemia. Removal of the thymus in newborn mice reduces its incidence sharply. The bone marrow, on the other hand, exerts a protective influence on the x-ray induction of lymphoid tumors in mice.

The incidence of the disease in mice is greater in females than in males, which has suggested an influence of the sex hormones, and the administration of estrogen or androgen has been found to increase or reduce, respectively, the susceptibility of these animals to the experimental transmission of the disease. 11-Dehydro-17-hydroxycorticosterone for a time reduces the number of leukocytes in the leukemia of mice and causes the shrinkage of lymphosarcomatous tissue; little lasting effect upon the course of the disease has been observed. Adrenalectomy has a pronounced effect in increasing the susceptibility of mice to the experimental disease.

Recent evidence from Gross and others has confirmed the possibility that murine leukemia, too, is transmitted by a virus. The transfer of a cell-free filtrate from a high incident strain (AK) to a low incident strain (CSH) produced leukemia if inoculation took place before the mice were 16 hours old. A leukemic agent with the characteristics of a virus has been isolated from the ova and tissues of high incidence strains.

In man, the evidence for the viral origin of leukemia is less convincing. Although attempts have been made to transmit human leukemia to animals and to man, none have been successful. Viral particles have been reported in the lymph nodes of patients with acute leukemia, and in the leukemic cells of a few patients. Other investigators have reported a leukemogenic agent in the cell-free filtrates of human leukemic brain when injected into mice.

There has been a body of evidence accumulated to suggest that ionizing radiation may play an important role in the pathogenesis of leukemia in man. Following the atomic bombing of Nagasaki and Hiroshima, 92 cases of leukemia were reported in Japanese exposed to high doses of radiation. A high incidence of leukemia has been reported in patients receiving X-ray therapy for ankylosing spondylitis. There is now sufficient data to support the statement that the incidence of leukemia is linear with the dose for single, high dose exposures.

Some years ago, Miller and Turner, and Wearn and colleagues found that the urine of patients with leukemia contains principles which stimulate leukopoiesis in guinea pigs and produce a blood picture resembling human leukemia. These two substances were named myelokentric and lymphokentric acid. The former stimulates myelopoiesis and the latter stimulates lymphopoiesis while inhibiting myelopoiesis. However, there is no proof that these substances are important in the pathogenesis of leukemia.

The leukemias are usually classified on the basis of the cell type—lymphoid or myeloid (e.g., granulocytic)—involved in the malignant hyperplasia. Thus, *lymphatic* (*lymphoblastic* or *lymphocytic*) *leukemia* and *myeloid* (*myelocytic* or *myeloblastic*) *leukemia*, respectively, are usual designations. Either of these may be classed as *acute* or *chronic*. This latter division is based not so much upon the clinical course of the disease as upon the degree of immaturity of the cells in the blood and bone marrow. The acute form, as compared with the chronic, is characterized by cells in the earliest stage of development. In *acute myeloid* (*myeloblastic*) *leukemia* the type-cell is the *myeloblast*. The myeloblast is an entirely abnormal cell and not simply an immature leukocyte, as seen normally in the bone marrow. It is a large cell about 20 μ in diameter with a single round or oval nucleus which nearly fills the cell. The chromatin is distributed evenly throughout the nucleus with little condensation into masses. The nucleus contains from four to five nucleoli. The cytoplasm is strongly basophilic, shows no granulation and is thin and irregular at the cell boundary. In suitable preparations a slow snail-like movement of these cells can be demonstrated by slow cinematography. Undifferentiated myelocytes are also found in the blood. In the chronic form of *myeloid leukemia* (*myelocytic leukemia*) myeloblasts are infrequent and the myelocytes more plentiful.

In *acute lymphatic* (*lymphoblastic*) leukemia, the characteristic cell is the *lymphoblast*. This cell closely resembles, but can be distinguished from the myeloblast by the coarser chromatin structure in its nucleus, by possessing only one or two nucleoli, and by showing a characteristic movement described by Wintrobe as "stately" and apparently purposeful. In the chronic form of *lymphatic* (*lymphocytic*) *leukemia*, the leukocytosis is due to small lymphocytes, which make up over 90 per cent of the total number of white cells, and may be 250,000 per cu. mm. Few immature cells are seen.

Leukemias in which the type cell is the monocyte, basophil, or even the megakaryocyte also occur rarely.

The somewhat redundant or contradictory terms *leukemic leukemia, subleukemic leukemia* and *aleukemic leukemia* are used, respectively, to designate the abundance, scarcity or absence of leukocytes in the blood. The first mentioned term is applied to those leukemias in which the blood picture is dominated by leukocytes. In subacute leukemia, the white cell count is normal or near the normal and only an odd immature form can be found, and in the aleukemic type few or no abnormal cells are present; the total count is not increased and may be subnormal. But this is only a phase of the disease, a rise in the leukocyte count eventually occurs, the leukemia being usually of the lymphatic type. Even when the peripheral blood is normal in these patients, the bone marrow contains large numbers of immature cells.

In the treatment of the leukemias, the destructive action of the X-rays upon lymphoid tissue and bone marrow is widely employed. The life of sufferers from the chronic form is thereby prolonged, but neither X-ray nor any other agent is of any avail in the acute forms. Internal radiation with radioactive phosphorus (P^{32}) is also used in the chronic form and acts like X-rays, but has a more selective action. Within recent years several chemical agents have been advocated for the treatment of chronic leukemias, e.g., *myleran*, in the chronic myeloid type, *nitrogen mustards*, chlorambucil and steroids in the lymphatic type, and 4-amino-methyl-pteroyl-glutamic acid (aminopterin) or other folic acid antagonists, and 6-mercaptopurine (purinethol), a purine antagonist, in the acute forms.

In *Hodgkin's disease*, which is allied to the leukemias, there is general enlargement of the lymphoid tissue and usually a moderate leukocytosis (15,000 to 25,000 per cu. mm.), in which neutrophils predominate and lymphocytes are reduced.

The monocytes and lymphocytes are increased, in the condition originally named *glandular fever* by Pfeiffer (1889) and *infectious mononucleosis* by Sprunt and Evans (1920). There is enlargement of the cervical lymph glands, spleen, and liver, and a leukocytosis, usually not exceeding 20,000, of which the mononuclear leukocytes (monocytes and lymphocytes) constitute from 60 to 90 per cent or more. Certain well documented

changes occur in the lymphocytes which are the hallmark of this disease. A characteristic serological feature is the usual, although not invariable, finding of a high titer of agglutinins against sheep corpuscles (heterophil antibodies), as first shown by Paul and Brunnell. It is said to occur in 80% of cases if repeated tests for its presence are performed.

LEUKOPENIA

Leukopenia means a reduction in the number of circulating leukocytes. It is seen in certain diseases, notably typhoid fever, and may be induced experimentally by injections of the toxin of the typhoid bacillus—or emulsions of the dead organisms, and also by the injection of Menken's leukopenic factor (p. 562); the action of the adrenal cortical hormones and ACTH in producing a reduction in lymphocytes (*lymphopenia*) has been mentioned (p. 560). Leukopenia is also a feature of "folic acid" deficiency in some species, e.g., monkey and chick. In some cases in which the white cells are reduced in number in the blood, the reduction is due to their attraction to some solid organ such as the lung or spleen. This has been shown by taking blood counts from various regions. In other words leukopenia may be due to a redistribution of leukocytes in the body, rather than to an actual reduction in their number. A temporary fall in the leukocyte count may precede a leukocytosis. Certain poisons, e.g., benzol, cause leukopenia by depressing the activity of the bone marrow.

Granulocytopenia, agranulocytosis, etc. Granulocytopenia is the term applied to an abnormally low leukocyte count due to the reduction in granulocytes. The lymphocytes and monocytes are but slightly reduced or not at all, so that their relative proportion of the total count is increased. One or both of these types of agranular cells sometimes show an *absolute* increase. There may be complete absence of granulocytes when the term *agranulocytosis* is applicable. In most instances the absence of granulocytes is associated with a severe septic or necrotic condition of the throat. This condition, called *agranulocytic angina*, is fatal in the great majority of cases. In some patients, the cause of the agranulocytosis is unknown but the fault is one of the bone marrow. In many, however, it is induced by a toxic agent. The marrow shows, most frequently, an almost complete suppression of granulocyte formation but is normal so far as erythropoiesis is concerned. Occasionally, the marrow contains large numbers of myeloid cells which fail to be released into the circulation. In animals reduction in the granulocytes is readily

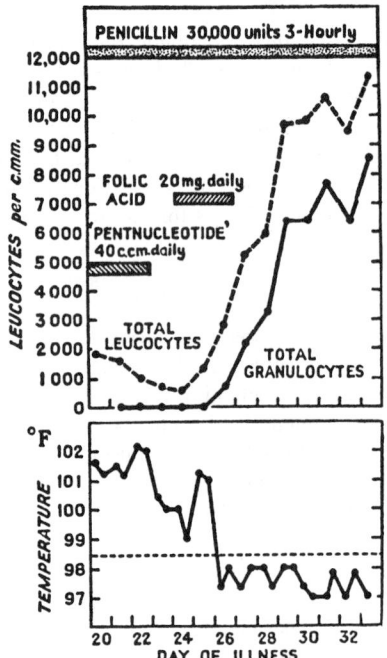

FIG. 31.3. Showing the effect of folic acid upon the granulocytes, in agranulocytosis. (After Black and Stanbury, slightly modified.)

induced by the administration of benzol, which acts specifically to depress marrow activity, and there is a belief that in some cases agranulocytosis is induced by certain benzol derivatives employed for their antipyretic or analgesic properties. The arsenobenzenes, dinitrophenol and, rarely, sulfanilamide and sulfathiazole have been incriminated. Amidopyrine was the first drug shown to exert this effect but other drugs, e.g., sulfonamides, arsenicals, certain derivatives of quinine, and chloramphenicol sometimes cause the disease. In the treatment of these conditions, pentose nucleotide has been employed with the object of stimulating the granulopoietic functions of the marrow; but pteroylglutamic acid ("folic acid") appears to be the most promising agent yet discovered for the treatment of some granulocytopenias (fig. 31.3). Testosterone and steroids can also be of value.

In some cases of agranulocytosis in which the bone marrow shows an increase in the number of primitive cells of the granulocyte series (myelocytes and myeloblasts), cells of these stages appear in the circulation. The maturation of granulocytes is apparently arrested at an early stage (ch. 32). From the analogy between this fault in granulopoiesis and the erythropoietic abnormality seen in pernicious anemia, the condition has been termed *pernicious leukopenia*, or the *maturation type* of the disease.

The Blood Platelets (Thrombocytes)

These are commonly stated to be simply fragments of protoplasm (i.e., non-nucleated) derived from the cytoplasm of the megakaryocytes. Their colorless cytoplasm contains two types of granule. Those of one type are arranged centrally in clumps or chains and stain supravitally with neutral red or azure blue. Those of the other type are discrete, stain supravitally with Janus green and are scattered throughout the body of the cell. The platelets have an average diameter about a third that of a red cell, namely, 2.5 μ, and number from 200,000 to 400,000 per cu. mm. The most usual figure found in health is around 250,000 per cu. mm. These blood elements vary considerably in shape. Their best known function is concerned with the mechanism of blood clotting (ch. 33). The disintegration of the platelets is said to occur more readily in blood drawn during the digestion of a meal of meat.

Variations in the number of platelets occur in the following conditions. They are *increased* after a meal of meat, after hemorrhage, and in certain allergic conditions, in myeloid leukemia and polycythemia rubra vera and in convalescence from infections.

They are *diminished* in purpura hemorrhagica, aplastic anemia, pernicious anemia, in anaphylaxis and in the acute stage of septic infections and as a result of irradiation.

The number of platelets per cubic millimeter may be determined by diluting a sample of blood with a fluid composed of sodium citrate 3.8 per cent, formalin 0.2 per cent and brilliant cresyl blue 0.1 per cent, and counting immediately. The proportion of platelets to red cells (normally about 1 to 20) is determined. If the number of red cells per cubic millimeter is known then the corresponding number of platelets is readily calculated. More commonly now a count of the platelets is made after diluting the blood with a solution which destroys the red cells. Probably the most accurate method is that described by Brecher and Cronkite who used ammonium oxalate as a diluting fluid and phase contrast microscopy for counting.

Besides their well known role in the coagulation of blood (ch. 33) the platelets probably serve other functions. They have a pronounced tendency to agglutinate into masses and to form deposits upon any roughened surface or foreign material. Particles of India ink or microorganisms injected into the body become surrounded by a mass of agglutinated platelets. They may therefore aid in the body's defense against infective agents. It is probable also that they serve to seal leaks in the capillaries by adhering to small defects which may occur from time to time in the delicate endothelial wall. They constitute the first defense against the loss of blood from larger vessels. Collecting around the margins of the vascular wound they help to close it, or at any rate, serve to fasten the clot, which subsequently forms, to the vascular wall; through their action in inducing retraction and consolidation of the clot, they narrow the opening in the vessel and form a firm plug within its lumen. They liberate substances essential for normal thromboplastin production and a vasoconstrictor principle which is identical with a substance extractable from serum (serotonin or 5-OH-tryptamine). Platelets possess substances which exert complex antigenic effects. They contain some materials which appear to be identical with the ABO blood antigens and others which are distinct and seemingly specific. According to Harrington antibodies for platelet antigens may be naturally-occurring or immune, complete or incomplete, agglutinins or lysins. Platelets prepared by differential centrifugation are relatively free from the other formed elements of the blood. These preparations may be effective in improving vascular tone and preventing loss of blood in severe thrombocytopenia. The length of life of the platelets has been estimated at from 8 to 11 days, using a technique which labels the platelets with radioactive phosphorus (P^{32}).

REFERENCES

BLACK, O. A. K. AND STANBURY, S. W. Lancet, 1947, 1, 827.

BRECHER, G. AND CRONKITE, E. P. J. Appl. Physiol., 1950, 3, 365.

CLARK, E. R. Physiol. Rev., 1938, 18, 229.

COHN, Z. A. The Macrophage, in "The Inflammatory Reaction"; Zweifach, Grant & McCluskey, eds. Academic Press, 1965.

EHRICH, W. E. Ann. New York Acad. Sc., 1946, 46, 823.

FAGRAEUS, A. Acta Haemat., 1958, 20, 1.

GROSS, L. Cancer Res., 1958, 18, 371.

GROSS, L. Acta Haemat., 1960, 23, 259.

HARRIS, T. N., GRIMM, E., MERTENS, E. AND EHRICH, W. E. J. Exper. Med., 1954, 100, 269.

HEINLE, R. W. AND COLLEAGUES. Ann. Int. Med., 1942, 17, 902; Proc. Soc. Exper. Biol. & Med., 1945, 58, 5.

HEYSSEL, R. Blood, 1960, 15, 313.

KLEIN, E., ARNOLD, P., EARL, R. T. AND WAKE, E. New England J. Med., 1956, 254, 1132.

LEEKMAN, C. H. W. AND COHEN, J. A. Nature, 1955, 175, 552.

MALLERY, O. T. AND McCUTCHEON, M. Am. J. M. Sc., 1940, 200, 394.

McMASTER, P. D. AND HUDACH, S. S. J. Exper. Med., 1935, 61, 783.

MENKIN, V. Am. J. Path., 1943, 19, 1021. Ann. New York Acad. Sc., 1946, 46, 789. Arch. Path., 1946, 41, 376. Lancet, 1947, 1, 660.

MILLER, F. R. AND TURNER, D. L. M. Clin. North America, 1944, 28, 1376.

PONDER, E. AND FLINN, Z. M. Quart. J. Exper. Physiol., 1926, 16, 207, 277, 241.

SANDERS, A. G. AND ASSOCIATES, Brit. J. Exper. Path., 1940, 21, 254.

SPRUNT, T. P. AND EVANS, F. A. Bull. Johns Hopkins Hosp., 1920, 31, 410.

TULLIS, J. L. Blood, 1952, 7, 891.

VAUGHAN, J. Blood, 1953 8, 1.

WHITE, A. AND DOUGHERTY, T. F. Proc. Soc. Exper. Biol. & Med., 1944, 56, 26; Ann. New York Acad. Sc., 1946, 46, 859.

Monographs and Reviews

BERNSTEIN, A. Medicine, 1940, 19, 85.

BIERMAN, H. R. (ed.) Leukopoiesis in Health and Disease, Ann. N. Y. Acad. Sc. 1964, 113, 511.

DRINKER, C. K. AND YOFFEY, J. M. Lymphatics, Lymph and Lymphoid Tissue. Harvard University Press, Cambridge, 1941.

KIRSCHBAUM, A. Yale J. Biol. Med., 1944–45, 17, 163.

McCUTCHEON, M. Physiol. Rev., 1946, 26, 319.

MENKIN, V. The Physiol. Rev., 1938, 18, 366.

SPECTOR ET AL. J. Path. & Bact., 1965, 90, 181.

TOCANTINS, L. M. Medicine, 1938, 17, 155.

VOLKMAN AND GOWANS. Brit. J. Exp. Path., 1965, 56, 50.

WINTROBE, M. M. Clinical Hematology, Ed. 3. Lea and Febiger, Philadelphia, 1951.

WHITE, A. Influence of Endocrine Secretions on Structure and Function of Lymphoid Tissue. Harvey Lecture, 1947–1948, 43, 43.

CHAPTER 32

Origin of the Cells of the Blood

Blood formation is a body function necessary for life. Events of the last twenty years have served to emphasize the truth of this statement. For example, ionizing radiation has become an increasing part of our environment and exposure to excessive amounts of ionizing radiation leads to death because of cessation of blood production. This is important to the physician, not only because of dangers from exposure in war or industrial accident, but also because ionizing radiation is frequently used in the treatment of cancer. As a treatment, its usefulness is limited by the ability of the blood-forming organs to repair damage to their capacity of producing new cells. In addition, many of the drugs currently used in medical practice are known to damage hemopoietic organs and such damage may lead to the death of the patient.

The physician is interested not only in ensuring that nothing prevents his patient from receiving a continuing supply of blood cells but he also desires to observe the way in which the hemopoietic system responds to various disease states or environmental changes. For example, the presence of an increased number of polymorphonuclear leukocytes in the peripheral blood may indicate bacterial infection, or a rise in the number of eosinophils may indicate that a patient is reacting to a foreign antigen. The physician, therefore, as well as the physiologist, is concerned with the origin of the blood cells and the mechanisms by which their orderly delivery from their sites of manufacture to the peripheral blood is achieved. These problems are considered in the present chapter. It is assumed that the reader is familiar with the names and morphology of the mature cells of the blood and of their immediate, histologically-identified precursors.

The Anatomical Sites of the Formation of the Blood Cells

There are five distinct classes of formed elements in the peripheral blood—erythrocytes, granulocytes, platelets, lymphoid cells and monocytes. Of these, the first three classes, that is erythrocytes, granulocytes and platelets, are formed in the marrow of the bones. In man, marrow function is usually limited to the skull, the vertebral columns, the pelvis, the sternum and the proximal ends of the long bones. However, under conditions of increased demand, blood formation may also occur in the shafts of the long bones and even in extramedullary sites. The lymphoid cells are formed in lymphatic tissue, which is spread widely throughout the body. Prominent collections of lymphatic tissue are found in the mediastinum, the mesentery, along the roots of the great vessels, in the tonsils and Peyer's Patches along the intestine, in the axillae and inguinal regions. Lymphatic follicles are present in the spleen and also foci of lymphatic tissue are present in the bone marrow. The anatomical source of the monocytes has not been well established but it appears probable that these originate in many areas of the body including lymphatic tissue, spleen and marrow. From this anatomical consideration, it is evident that there are two separate sources for blood cells, the bone marrow and the lymphatic tissues. It is perhaps not surprising, therefore, to find that the function and control of the cells from each space are quite different. Indeed, it is important to consider the erythrocytes, granulocytes and platelets together as a group and the lymphoid and monocytic cells as a separate group. Both groups are, of course, mixed together in the peripheral blood, but they vary in number independently of each other, and respond quite differently both to injury and disease. At the cellular level the origin of erythrocytes, granulocytes and platelets also appears to be distinct from the origin of lymphoid cells and monocytes. This subject will be discussed in a later section.

The Hemopoietic System as a Cell Renewal System

The cells of peripheral blood have finite life spans. For erythrocytes, the life span has been measured with some accuracy and is known to be about 120 days. For the nucleated cells of the blood precise information is not available but it is probable that granular leukocytes exist for between three and seven days while lymphoid cells may survive for as long as three months. Regardless of the extent of these life-spans, the existence of the mature cells of the blood is limited in time. Therefore, the maintenance of normal numbers of peripheral circulating blood corpuscles depends on the constant production of these cells by progenitor cells in the hemopoietic organs. Leblond and Walker have suggested the term "cell renewal system" as a general way of describing all of those body systems in which the elements are continuously replaced.

Since mammalian cells are produced by the process of cell division, the renewal of blood cells must depend upon cell division occurring in the blood-forming organs. The cellular basis for this cell renewal will be the subject of the next section.

The Concept of Stem Cells

The mature blood cells contain molecules or structures which permit them to perform specific functions. For example, red cells contain hemoglobin, a specific protein adapted for the transport of oxygen. These functional cells are the descendants of progenitor cells within hemopoietic spaces which do not contain functional molecules or structures similar to hemoglobin. The process by which cells change and develop the capacity to carry out specific functions is called differentiation and this process is of great importance in the production of the cells of the blood.

The second important difference between mature cells in the blood and their progenitors in hemopoietic spaces is that the mature cells are incapable of cell division while the progenitor cells must be able to divide a large number of times. Thus, the process of blood formation consists of two important cellular activities, cell proliferation and cell differentiation. By the first, new cells are formed, and by the second, cells acquire specific structures needed for their function.

From the foregoing it may be seen that as the process of cell differentiation proceeds, the capacity for cellular proliferation decreases. The system, therefore, contains cells of two contrasting types. On the one hand, the most primitive progenitors have extensive capacity for proliferation and are able to give rise to a large number of differentiated descendants. On the other hand, these differentiated descendants have the capacity to fulfil specific functions but have lost the ability to renew their own numbers. Between these two extremes are found the great majority

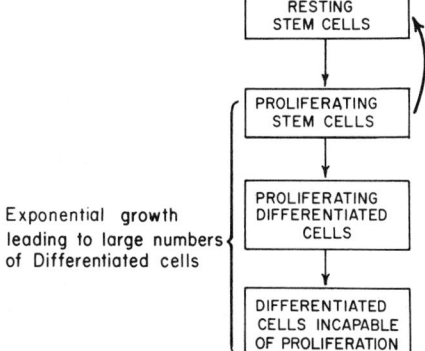

MODEL OF THE ORIGIN OF BLOOD CELLS

Fig. 32.1. This is a schematic diagram of the relationship between stem cells and their differentiated descendants. Each box represents a population of cells. At the top of the figure is a population of stem cells resting either in the G_0 state or in state of prolonged cell cycle. Members of this population may pass into a different physiological state, characterized by rapid proliferation. Cells derived from this proliferation may either retain stem cell properties and return to the resting compartment, or may differentiate. Many of the cells in the differentiated compartment can divide several times, but finally a state is reached in which cell division is no longer possible. Cells in the proliferating compartments are growing exponentially, so that the differentiated cells greatly outnumber the stem cells.

of the nucleated cells present in hemopoietic tissues. These are cells which have started on the course of differentiation, contain some of the features which will finally mark them as functional elements and are capable of a limited number of cell divisions. It is these cells which the clinical hematologist recognizes in smears obtained from bone marrow, and it is upon their characteristics that most of his clinical diagnoses are made (fig. 32.1).

The progenitor cells with extensive proliferative capacity and ability to give rise to differentiated descendants are often called "stem" cells because they are the source of so many progeny. However, these stem cells are difficult to recognize morphologically for the following reasons. First, stem cells are a very small minority of the cells of hemopoietic tissues; since they have extensive capacity for proliferation, they are greatly outnumbered by their differentiated descendants. It has been estimated that in the mouse, only one in about every thousand cells of the bone marrow is a stem cell. Because they occur so infrequently, their recognition is very difficult. Secondly, since stem cells are not yet differentiated, they do not contain specific cytological features by which they might be recognized. These difficulties in identifying stem cells as physical entities have made it very difficult to study them. The student, therefore, will not be surprised to find that they are the subject of considerable controversy.

THE STEM-CELL CONTROVERSY

The controversy about stem cells has centered around their capacity to give rise to one or more classes of differentiated descendants. Some workers have held that members of a single homogeneous class of stem cells have capacity for differentiation along many different pathways, giving rise to all of the cells found in the peripheral blood. This view has been termed "monophyletic," in contrast with the "polyphyletic" view of those who believe that each differentiated cell-type is maintained by the activity of a specific class of stem cell with capacity for differentiation only along a single line. The controversy between these views was most active throughout that period of develop-ment in hematology when morphological techniques dominated the field. However, unproductive controversy may be avoided and a better understanding of the physiology of blood formation may be obtained if the definition of "stem cell" is based on functional rather than morphological characteristics (fig. 32.2).

THE FUNCTIONAL CHARACTERISTICS OF STEM CELLS

The functional tests for the recognition of stem cells depend on the properties of these cells. Two properties have been described in the foregoing sections; they are capacity for extensive proliferation and capacity to give rise to differentiated descendants. Stem cells require two additional properties if they are to fulfil their function in blood formation. They must be capable of self renewal; that is, not all of the descendants of stem cells must start on an inevitable process of differentiation with its concomitant loss of proliferative capacity. If this were to occur, marrow function would eventually cease. Instead, some of the descendants of stem

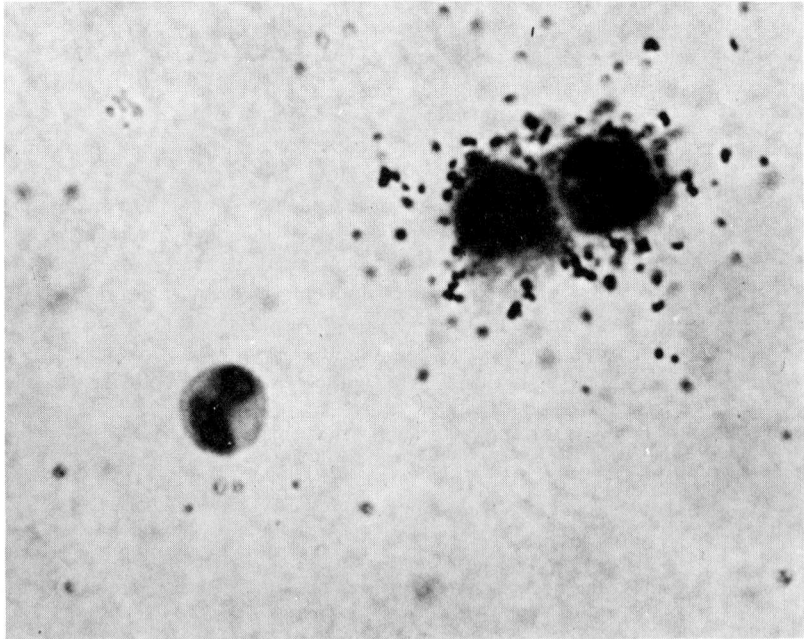

FIG. 32.2. This photomicrograph represents the results of a functional test for members of the erythropoietic series of cells. The cells shown are from a suspension of mouse bone marrow cells incubated for 2 hr. in the presence of radioactive iron. During this incubation erythroid cells that synthesized iron-containing hemoglobin took up radio-isotope. After incubation, the cells were deposited on a filter, fixed, dried and dipped in photographic emulsion. After a period of time, the emulsion was developed, and grains resulting from exposure of the emulsion by radioactivity are seen. The presence of grains serves to identify the two iron-incorporating cells of the erythroid series at the top of the picture, while there are no grains associated with the granulocytic cell at the lower left hand corner. (Picture courtesy of Dr. J. H. Fowler.)

cells must retain the properties of stem cells in order to maintain the integrity of the system. The fourth property of stem cells is that they must be able to respond to normal control mechanisms. This property is required, since, under physiological conditions, proliferation and differentiation proceed in an orderly fashion. In functional terms, therefore, stem cells may be defined as cells which have the four characters described above. Classes of stem cells may be separated on the basis of the degree to which the members of each class have stem cell properties.

TRANSPLANTATION STUDIES OF HEMOPOIETIC STEM CELLS

Normal hemopoietic cells may be transplanted successfully into animals whose own blood-forming capacity has been destroyed by large doses of ionizing radiation. In these hosts, the transplanted cells proliferate and differentiate, providing the recipient animals with the functional cells necessary for their survival from radiation damage. By the use of marrow transplantation in mice, Till and McCulloch have been able to obtain populations of hemopoietic cells, each derived from a single cell. By analyzing such clonal populations it is possible to examine the properties of the cells of origin, and in this way to determine the extent to which such cells may be considered hemopoietic stem cells. The technique used to obtain clones is as follows: Heavily irradiated animals are injected with marrow cells derived from healthy donor mice. After nine to fourteen days, the recipient animals are killed, and their spleens are found to contain discrete nodules, which, on histological examination, prove to be colonies of proliferating and differentiating hemopoietic cells (fig. 32.3).

Becker and colleagues obtained evidence that spleen colonies are clones by the use of the following experimental technique. Recognizable and unique chromosomal abnormalities (markers) were induced by irradiation in some of the cells used to initiate the growth of colonies. When the colonies had developed, their dividing cells were examined for markers In any colony where a particular marker was present, this same marker was found in all of the dividing cells of that colony. This provided excellent evidence that all of the cells of such a colony were derived from a single progenitor possessing this marker. Enough colonies with markers were found to establish

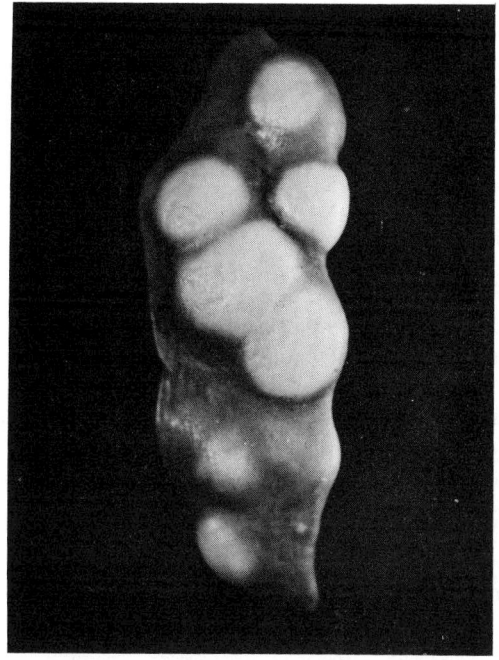

FIG. 32.3. This is a photograph of a spleen taken from a heavily irradiated mouse 10 days after the injection of 8×10^4 normal bone marrow cells. Many discrete colonies are seen, which are clones of proliferating and differentiating hemopoietic cells. The spleen is fixed in Bouin's solution.

the probability that all or almost all spleen colonies are clones.

Analysis of clonal populations obtained by the spleen colony technique provides evidence that the cells from which the colonies grow are indeed stem cells. First, after ten days growth, spleen colonies contain more than a million cells, indicating their origin from cells with extensive proliferative capacity. Second, spleen colonies have been shown to contain cells themselves capable of colony-formation, indicating that self-renewal has occurred. Third, many spleen colonies contain recognizable erythroblasts, granulocytes and megakaryocytes, showing that the original cells could differentiate along these three lines. Finally, the colony-forming efficiency of cells from marrow and spleen of normal mice remains relatively constant during adult life, indicating that cells capable of colony formation respond to homeostatic control mechanisms. Thus cells with colony-forming potential have the four properties of stem cells, and it appears justifiable to refer to them as hemopoietic colony-forming stem cells, and consider them as one class, though not the only class, of marrow stem cells.

Chromosomal Evidence for a Common Stem Cell for Erythropoiesis, Granulocytopoiesis and Platelet Formation

The evidence given in the preceding sections shows that hemopoietic colony-forming stem cells have capacity to differentiate along erythrocytic, granulocytic and megakaryocytic lines. Evidence for stem cells in man with similar capacity for differentiation has been obtained from the study of the malignant disease, chronic myelogenous leukemia. In this condition there is a great increase in bone marrow cell proliferation with the production of large numbers of granulocytic cells at various stages of development. Recently, techniques have been devised which permit detailed study of the chromosomes of mammalian cells; Nowell and Hungerford applied these techniques to the cells of patients with chronic myelogenous leukemia and found a specific abnormal chromosome in almost all these leukemic cells. The abnormal chromosome is usually called the Philadelphia chromosome, after the City in which it was first recognized (fig. 32.4). Whang and his colleagues have combined chromosomal analysis with other functional tests, and found that the Philadelphia chromosome is present not only in the cells of the granulocytic series but also in the progenitors of erythrocytes, and certain large polypoid cells, almost certainly megakaryocytes. Since these relatively differentiated progenitors of red cells and platelets have only limited proliferative capacity, it was concluded that they are the partially-differentiated descendants of leukemic progenitors. Since the Philadelphia chromosome, a specific marker, is found in granulocytic, erythrocytic and megakaryocytic cells, but not in other dividing cells of the body, a single progenitor must possess the capacity to differentiate

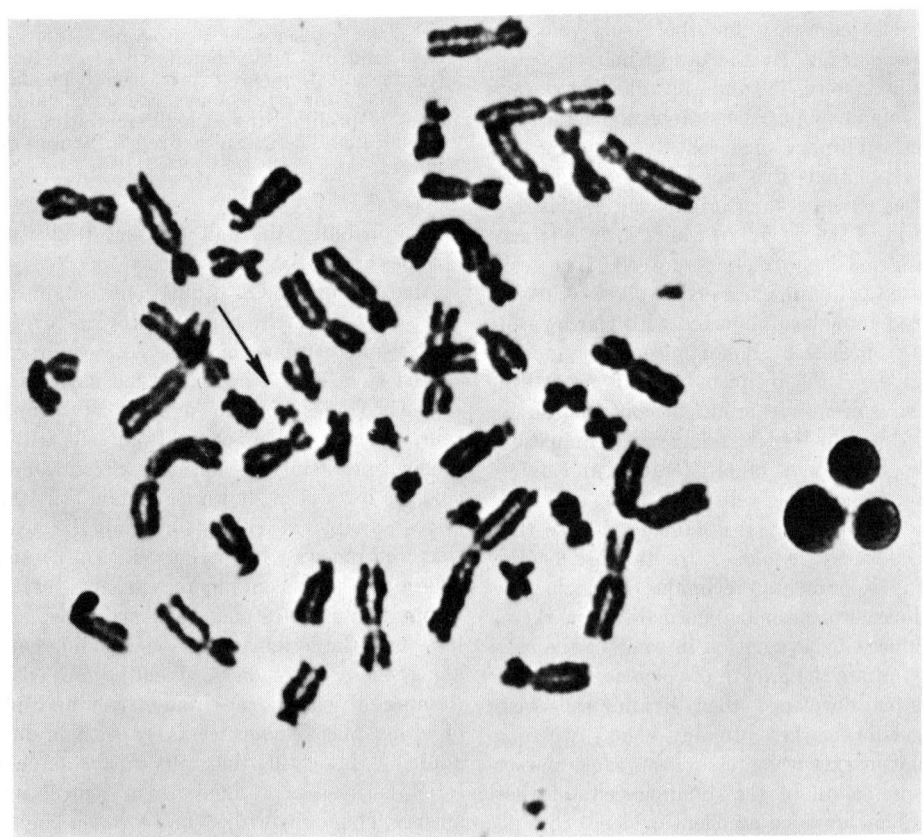

Fig. 32.4. This is a photograph of a chromosome preparation from a patient with chronic myelogenous leukemia. The arrow points to the Philadelphia chromosome. (Picture courtesy of Dr. D. E. Bergsagel.)

in these three different directions. The existence of a pluripotent leukemic cell is strong evidence that there also exists a normal human stem cell with capacity for differentiation towards erythocytic, granulocytic and megakaryocytic pathways.

An Example of the Clinical Significance of Stem Cell Potential

The evidence obtained from studies of spleen colonies and from the cells of patients with chronic myelogenous leukemia provide strong support for the view that adult hemopoietic tissue contains a class of stem cells capable of differentiating along erythrocytic, granulocytic and megakaryocytic lines. The question arises: do cells of this class have potential for proliferation along other lines? For example, do lymphoid cells derive from them? The student of medicine may ask whether or not this question is important. Indeed, the student might suggest that the matter is trivial, for, as all individuals are derived from single cells at the time of conception, all blood cells must at some stage have a common ancestor. Consideration of modern clinical problems soon supplies reasons why physicians would find it most helpful to know the full potential for differentiation of various classes of stem cells. An example may serve to illustrate the point. Consider a patient who comes to hospital with severe anemia and deficiency of both granulocytes and platelets. Investigations show that he has marrow aplasia because he is unusually sensitive to the toxic effects of the antibiotic chloramphenicol. The patient is in danger of dying because he lacks the class of stem cell which differentiates along erythrocytic, granulocytic and megakaryocytic lines. His doctor knows that these cells can be replaced by transplantation provided immunity mechanisms which normally reject foreign transplants are suppressed. If hemopoietic stem cells which the patient lacks normally also produce cells with immunological function, the physician may hope to transplant normal marrow which will supply his patient with the mature cells he needs until his own marrow can recover. However, if a separate class of stem cell differentiates to produce cells with immunological competence, these may not have been damaged by the drug and the transplantation treatment will fail. Many other clinical conditions would be more readily understood if information about stem cell potential in man were available.

Relationship of the Stem Cells Responsible for Erythrocytic, Granulocytic and Megakaryocytic Differentiation to Lymphopoiesis

The controversy about the potential for differentiation of hemopoietic stem cells has been, in part, resolved by the functional studies described above, which show that members of a single class of cells may include erythrocytes, granulocytes and platelets among their progeny. It remains to be determined whether or not these same stem cells also possess the capacity to give rise to lymphoid cells or cells with immunological functions. Evidence which favors the view that a common stem cell may exist for all of these functions has been presented by Barnes and his colleagues. They examined the chromosomes of cells from various organs of mice surviving large doses of radiation. Members of clones could be identified in such animals because they contained the same, radiation-induced, chromosomal abnormality. Cells of a single clone were identified in both marrow and lymphatic tissue. This finding, however, need not be interpreted as proof that the cells giving rise to such cytologically identified clones can differentiate along lymphoid as well as myeloid lines. The cells prepared for chromosome analysis in this study could not be identified as members of specific differentiated classes; since cell migration is common following irradiation, the presence of cells within a certain anatomical site does not establish their relationship to the differentiated cells usually found in that site. Findings which suggest that lymphoid cells have an independent stem have been obtained by studies of patients with chronic myelogenous leukemia, and from work using spleen colonies. These results will be summarized next.

When normal human lymphoid cells are exposed in tissue culture to a bean extract called phytohemagglutinin, these cells will divide, and their chromosomes may be studied. Therefore one may ask whether lymphoid cells in patients with chronic granulocytic leukemia contain the Philadelphia chromosome which serves as a marker of the granulocytic, erythrocytic and megakaryocytic cells of such patients. Whang and colleagues examined the blood of myeloid leukemia patients when it had been cleared of leukemic cells by treatment. The remaining lymphoid cells did not contain the Philadelphia chromosome, although the chromosome marker was still found in the great majority of the cells of bone marrow. This finding would indicate that the lymphatic cells are derived from a different source than the granulocytic, erythroid and megakaryocytic cells which contain the chromosomal marker. Attempts have also been made to demonstrate the presence of cells of the lymphoid series within spleen colonies. When mice in which spleen colonies are developing are exposed to antigen, antibody-producing cells are distributed randomly in the spleen and are found as commonly in areas devoid of colonies as in areas where colonies are present.

These latter findings suggest, but do not prove, that lymphoid cells are derived from one or more different classes of stem cells not related to those which give rise to erythrocytic, granulocytic and megakaryocytic cells. Earlier in this chapter it was pointed out that certain of the cells of the peripheral blood were derived from bone marrow while others were derived from lymphatic tissue. It now becomes evident that this separation may also be valid at the cellular level. *The erythrocytic, granulocytic and megakaryocytic cells which are derived from bone marrow all appear to share a common stem cell, while the lymphoid elements derived from lymphatic tissue are probably descended from a different class of progenitor.*

The Cell Cycle and the Regulation of Hemopoiesis

A population of stem cells provides an efficient mechanism for varying the number of differentiated cells delivered to the periphery. If a single cell with great potential for proliferation and differentiation realizes that potential, a large number of mature cells will result. Thus, regulation may be achieved by any mechanism which determines the rate at which the potential of members of a stem cell pool is realized. Further, any population of mature cells may be regulated independently if it is derived from a class of stem cell able either to maintain, or to realize, the potential of its members in response to appropriate stimuli.

The potential for proliferation of stem cells depends on the process of cell division. In this process, cells halve their content of Deoxyribonucleic Acid (DNA) at the time of mitosis, dividing it among two daughter cells. Thereafter, before another division can occur, each cell must synthesize exactly enough to DNA to provide for two new daughters. The period of time between successive mitoses (the generation time) is known

to consist of a series of phases, which are defined in relation to mitosis and to the synthesis of DNA. This series of phases is termed the cell cycle. After

CELL CYCLE OF MAMMALIAN CELLS

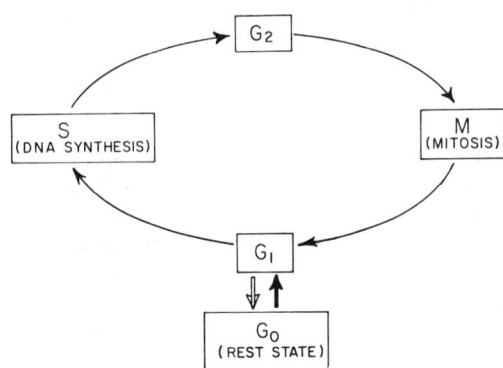

Fig. 32.5. A diagrammatic representation of the various phases of the cell cycle.

each mitosis there is a time period in which DNA is not synthesized. This period is called G_1, and it is followed by a period, the S phase, in which the DNA content of the cell is exactly doubled. Then there is a further period, G_2, before the cell again enters mitosis. Lajtha has suggested that hemopoietic cells may have the capacity to exist in a separate physiological state, not identical with any of the stages of the cell cycle. This state has been termed G_0, and it is suggested that cells may enter G_0 after mitosis and before the synthesis of DNA; in this state a population of cells could accumulate, ready, under suitable conditions, to enter again into the cell cycle (fig. 32.5). It should be noted, however, that techniques which measure the time parameters of the cell cycle do not permit a distinction to be made between cells in a very long G_1 phase and cells in a G_0 phase.

Recently experimental evidence has been obtained which supports the view that hemopoietic colony-forming stem cells can alter the time parameters of their cell-cycle in response to varying host demands for differentiated cells. The experiments depended on the use of radioactive tritiated thymidine (H^3TdR); thymidine is a specific precursor of DNA, and cells in the DNA-synthetic (S) phase of the cell cycle can be recognized by their incorporation of the radioactive label. Radioautographic techniques usually employed to detect the presence of tritiated thymidine in cells cannot be applied to hemopoietic colony-forming cells since these cells have not been identified morphologically. Instead the presence of H^3TdR was detected because those cells which incorporated the isotope were deprived of capacity to form colonies by its radiation. Using this technique, it has been shown that the great majority of hemopoietic stem cells in mouse marrow and spleen are not in a DNA synthetic state; however, when these cells are transplanted into a mouse depleted of blood cells by radiation, the transplanted stem cells changed their state so that the great majority were found to be proceeding through the cell cycle. It appears probable, therefore, that some stem cells can respond to their environment by changes in the time parameters of the cell-cycle. Thus, hemopoietic colony-forming stem cells may remain in a state which is either a prolonged G_1 or G_0, thereby maintaining their potential, or, in response to suitable stimuli, may enter a state of rapid cell cycle, thereby realizing their potential for extensive proliferation and differentiation. It remains to be demonstrated whether this mechanism is a general one applicable to other classes of stem cells.

Specific Control of Erythropoiesis

In previous sections evidence has been presented which indicates that members of a relatively homogeneous class of hemopoietic stem cells have the capacity for differentiating to produce granulocytes, erythrocytes and platelets. Moreover, control mechanisms appear to act on the production of blood cells rather than on their destruction, and stem cells with great proliferative capacity are important sites of action for such control mechanisms. These considerations suggest that the various descendants of a single class of stem cell should behave in a similar way. Clinical experience provides examples of conditions in which this prediction is indeed fulfilled. Thus, in pernicious anemia, a specific lack of vitamin B12 affects the proliferation of erythrocytic, granulocytic and megakaryocytic elements, while leaving the production of lymphoid elements intact. However, it is much commoner to observe erythrocytes, granulocytes and platelets responding to stimuli independently of each other. For example, bacterial infection usually induces a rapid and large increase in the polymorphonuclear leukocytes of the peripheral blood without any change in red cells. Another example is provided by the situation following bleeding, in which though red cell production continues until the lost erythrocytes are replaced, the granulocytes respond, with different kinetics to the trauma of hemorrhage. Thus additional mechanisms must exist for the specific control of the proliferation and differentiation of each class of the descendants of hemopoietic stem cells. Perhaps the best understood of these are the mechanisms which govern the production of erythrocytes in response to increased demand.

The most potent known stimulus to erythrocyte production is hypoxia. Persons living at high altitudes have unusually high levels of circulating erythrocytes, and patients who, because of disease of heart or lungs, have blood undersaturated with oxygen, frequently develop erythrocytosis. However, oxygen lack does not appear to act directly on marrow tissue to cause increased red cell production. Rather hypoxia results in the secretion of a specific hormone, *erythropoietin*, and it is this hormone that is responsible for increased red cell production.

Erythropoietin is obtained from the serum of animals made highly anemic by some agent such as phenylhydrazine or ionizing radiation. Extensive purification of the hormone has been obtained, and while exact characterization has not been achieved, it appears probable that erythropoietin is a glycoprotein. In animals, it appears that the principal source of erythropoietin production is the kidney, although some of the hormone is also probably produced elsewhere in the body. However, from the point of view of this chapter, the importance of erythropoietin is to be found in the work that has been done on its mechanism of action.

Gurney and his colleagues have shown that the effects of the administration of erythropoietin may be observed most clearly and conveniently in mice rendered polycythemic by transfusion. In such animals erythropoiesis is suppressed. Their circulating blood contains no reticulocytes and their hemopoietic organs are devoid of erythropoietic activity. When such animals receive an injection of erythropoietin, there is, after a latent period of from two to three days, a rise of reticulocytes in the peripheral blood (fig. 32.6). In histological studies of spleen and marrow of erythropoietin-stimulated mice a wave of erythropoiesis is observed; approximately one day after injection of the hormone early erythroblasts appear and on each successive day an orderly sequence of more mature forms is seen (fig. 32.7). If large doses of erythropoietin are given, the time sequence is not changed but rather the extent of response is increased. These results have been interpreted to mean that the hormone acts on relatively undifferentiated erythroid precursors, at a stage prior to the erythroblasts, causing them to proliferate and differentiate to produce mature descendants. The primitive cells which respond to erythropoietin possess at least some of the properties of stem cells. For example, in the polycythemic mouse,

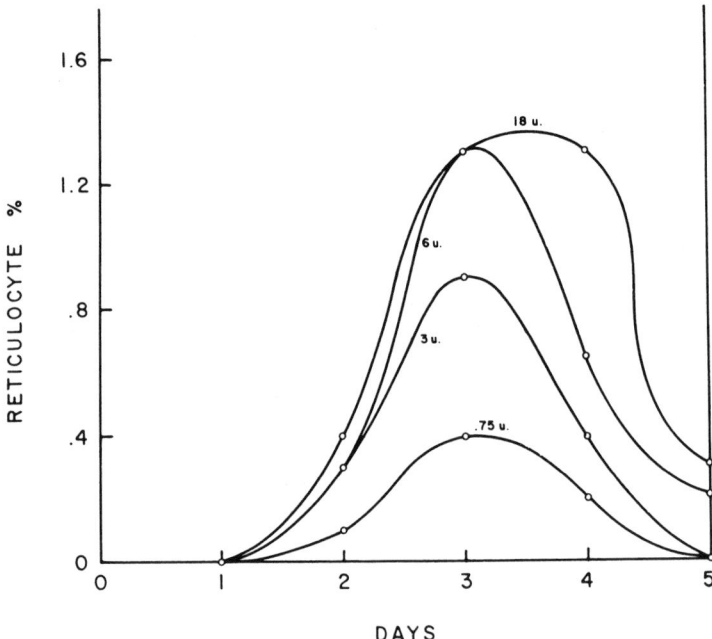

FIG. 32.6. A graph showing the reticulocyte response of polycythemic mice to single doses of erythropoietin of different concentrations. The percentage of reticulocytes in the peripheral blood is shown on the vertical axis, and time after administration of erythropoietin is shown on the horizontal axis. The dose of erythropoietin used is shown for each curve. (From: Studies on erythropoiesis. XVI. Response to a single dose of erythropoietin in polycythemic mouse. E. Filmanowicz and C. W. Gurney, J. Lab. Clin. Med., 57: 65–72, 1961, by permission of the authors and publishers.)

they must exist in a resting state, prepared to proliferate when erythropoietin is administered; thus they have the capacity to respond to a demand from the environment. Further, the character of their response indicates that these cells possess a capacity for both proliferation and differentiation. Indeed, the response of polycythemic mice to administered erythropoietin is used by Gurney, Lajtha, Schooley and others as an assay procedure for progenitor cells of the erythropoietic series. It is appropriate to refer to the cells whose activity is detected by this assay procedure as *erythropoietin-sensitive stem cells.*

Relationship between Erythropoietin-Sensitive Stem Cells and Colony-Forming Stem Cells

The relationship between erythropoietin-sensitive stem cells and colony-forming stem cells is a controversial one. The controversy concerns the two functional methods of detecting primitive cells, that is, whether responsiveness to erythropoietin and capacity to form spleen colonies, are measuring the same kind of primitive cell or whether each test detects a different class of cell. Attempts to demonstrate a direct effect of erythropoietin on the capacity of marrow cell suspensions to form spleen colonies have been

failures. Further, when the test of erythropoietin-responsiveness and the test of colony formation are both applied at various times during the recovery of animals from irradiation, each test yields a different picture of recovery kinetics.

These findings indicate that at least a functional separation exists between erythropoietin-sensitive stem cells and colony-forming stem cells. However, both classes have the capacity to give rise to erythrocytic descendants, and therefore a relationship may be presumed to exist between them; it would seem likely that one of the two classes represents a more primitive cell type than the other. Two features of colony-forming stem cells suggest that these are more primitive than erythropoietin-sensitive stem cells. First, colony-forming cells have been shown to have potential for between forty and sixty divisions, while the proliferative potential of erythropoietin-sensitive cells may be more limited. Second, colony-forming stem cells have capacity to differentiate along granulocytic and megakaryocytic lines, while the differentiation of erythropoietin-sensitive stem cells appears to be limited to the erythrocytic pathway. From this point of view, colony-forming stem cells may be considered as progenitors of erythropoietin-sensitive stem cells. The transition between colony-forming stem cells and erythropoietin-sensitive cells involves, presumably, a loss of potential for both proliferation and differentiation. However, erythropoietin-sensitive cells retain sufficient stem cell properties to serve as the site of action of control mechanism. They acquire, as a result of this postulated step in differentiation, capacity to respond specifically to erythropoietin by the production of erythrocytic descendants. Thus, the retention of some stem cell properties by the erythropoietin-sensitive descendants of colony-forming cells provides a mechanism by which erythropoiesis may be regulated independently from the regulation of the other types of differentiated descendants of colony-forming stem cells.

Specific Control of Granulopoiesis and Platelet Production

The demonstration of the hormone erythropoietin and its specific effect on erythropoiesis has led to an extensive search for similar hormones affecting granulopoiesis and the production of platelets. While a number of investigators have reported increased numbers of circulating granulocytes following the injection of various materials, there is no conclusive evidence for a "granulopoietin." Similarly, there is no conclusive evidence for a specific hormone controlling the production of platelets, although Schulman and his colleagues have reported a patient with severe thrombocytopenia who responded to transfusion with plasma by a striking increase in platelet production from marrow megakaryocytes.

One of the difficulties that has been encountered by those searching for stimulators of granulopoiesis has been the response of the system to a number of non-specific agents and particularly to endotoxins produced by bacteria. However, bacterial endotoxin has proved a useful tool for the study of granulopoiesis. Following the injection of this material into animals there is a very rapid increase in granulocytes in the peripheral blood. The increase occurs within a matter of hours, too rapidly to be a result of cell proliferation. It has been shown rather, that granulocytes emerging into the periphery as a result of endotoxin administration come from a storage pool which exists in the marrow spaces and probably in other areas. Thus very many more granulocytes exist as mature elements within the bone marrow than are present in the peripheral blood, and the mechanism by which a rapid granulocytosis is achieved in response to infec-

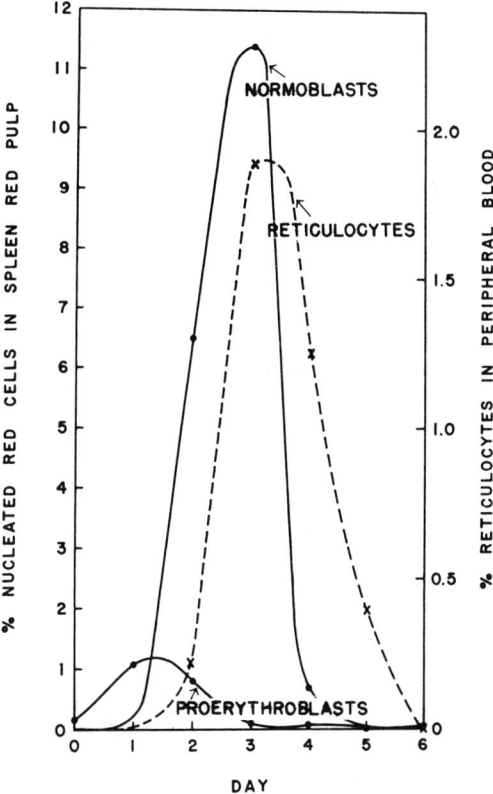

DAY

FIG. 32.7. A graph depicting the cellular events following administration of a single dose of erythropoietin to polycythemic mice. In the red pulp of the spleen (left vertical axis) immature red cell precursors are seen at one day, and more differentiated erythroid precursors reach a maximum number at 3 days. Reticulocytes appear in the peripheral blood on the second day and reach a maximum between the third and fourth day (right vertical axis). (From: Studies on erythropoiesis. XVI. Response to a single dose of erythropoietin in polycythemic mouse. E. Filmanowicz and C. W. Gurney, J. Lab. Clin. Med., **57:** 65–72, 1961, by permission of the authors and publishers.)

tion probably depends on the release of these cells from the marrow pool.

This pool, of course, depends on the proliferative activity of primitive precursors. However, probably only from four to six divisions separate the most primitive recognizable myeloblasts from mature polymorphonuclear leukocytes. Thus, hemopoietic colony forming cells with capacity to give rise to cells of the granulocytic colony are probably very much more undifferentiated than the earliest recognizable myeloblasts.

Summary of Control Mechanisms Affecting Hemopoietic Stem Cells

From the physiological studies outlined in this chapter three broad principles emerge concerning the origin of blood cells and the control of their production. (1) Continuing production of blood cells depends on the presence of stem cells with great proliferative capacity. (2) Stem cells respond to control mechanisms by altering the time parameters of their cell cycle. Thus stem cells may, on the one hand, retain potential for proliferation by maintaining a long generation time or resting in the G_o state, or, on the other hand, they may realize their potential for production of descendants by entering a cycle of rapid multiplication. (3) The regulation of the production of mature cells depends on interaction between stem cells and their environment. One mechanism by which this interaction is accomplished is through the hormone erythropoietin. However, this hormone appears to be very specific for erythropoiesis; analogous hormones for granulopoiesis and platelet production have not been isolated. It may be, therefore, that additional mechanisms by which stem cells relate to their environment may be uncovered.

Control of Lymphopoiesis

In previous sections it was suggested that lymphoid cells are derived from a different source than that of the erythrocytes, granulocytes and platelets. However, the lymphoid cells have always been puzzling to hematologists; morphologically they are relatively featureless, consisting of a compact nucleus, which, by electron microscopy, can usually be demonstrated to include a nucleolus, and varying amounts of clear blue cytoplasm (fig. 32.8). Electron micrographic study of this cytoplasm has shown it to contain a golgi apparatus, a few mitochondria and ribosomes, and a very poorly developed endoplasmic reticulum. Studies of lymphoid cells with the electron microscope have failed to demonstrate the presence of structures which might be fairly easily related to specific functions.

The lack of specific functional characteristics of lymphoid cells has made it extremely difficult

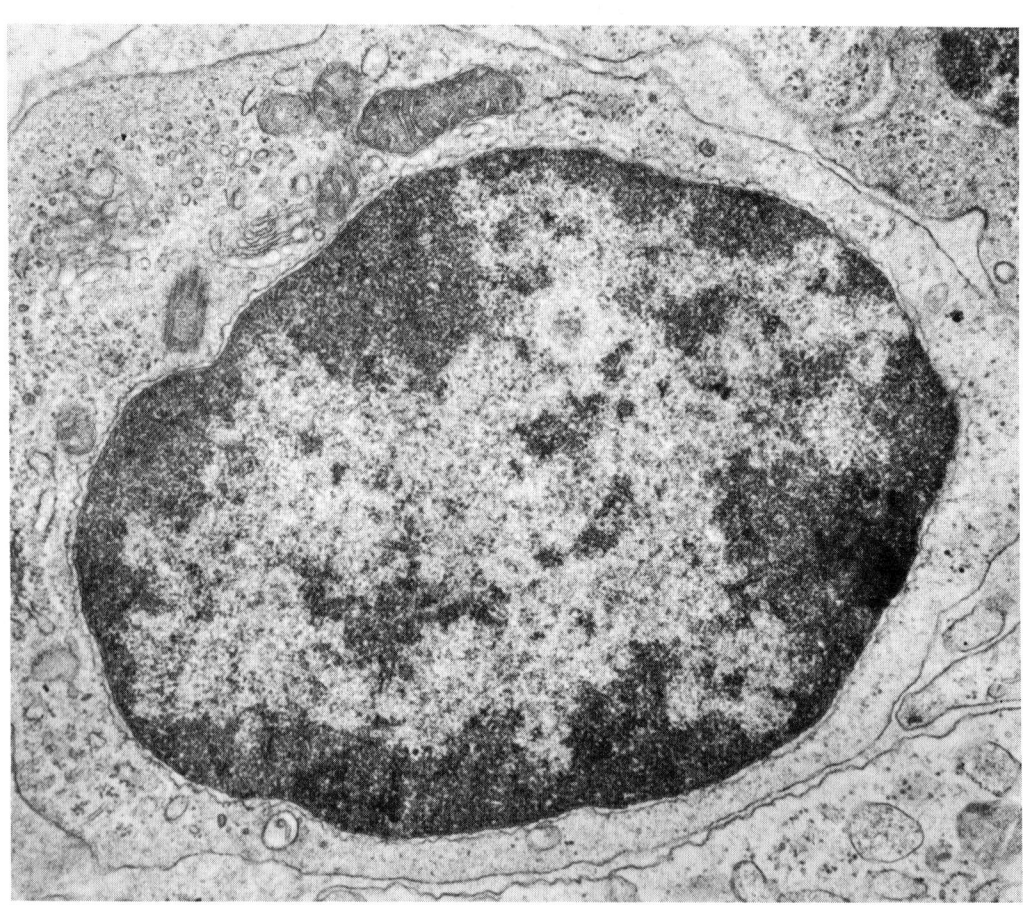

Fig. 32.8. This is an electron micrograph of a human lymphoid cell obtained by marrow aspiration. The cytoplasm is scanty and the endoplasmic reticulum is poorly developed. Magnification 27,000 ×. (Picture courtesy of Dr. A. F. Howatson. Preparation by Miss M. Nagai.)

to trace their origin, and information comparable to that presented for hemopoietic stem cells and their descendants is not available. It seems moreover, that cells sharing a common, relatively featureless, morphology may possess very different functional capabilities. Indeed, it has been suggested that small round cells with the morphology of lymphoid cells may be stem cells with great proliferative capacity or alternatively that they may undergo a simple transformation without proliferation into large cells participating in immunological response. It is because of this possible heterogeneity of function that throughout this chapter these cells have been referred to as lymphoid cells rather than by the more usual term, lymphocyte. The latter term would imply a relatively homogeneous population while the evidence would suggest that the cells are indeed homogeneous only in morphological characteristics.

Lymphoid Cells and Plasma Cells as Participants in the Immunological Response

The function that is most clearly related to lymphoid tissue is capacity to give rise to an immunological response. A brief account will be given of some of the features of the cellular events that underlie immunological responsiveness.

Two different forms of immunological response are usually recognized. The first is characterized by the appearance in the peripheral blood of a specific antibody capable of combining with the antigen used to elicit the response. Circulating antibody consists of globulin molecules and it appears certain that these molecules are the product of plasma cells. Electron micrographic examination of plasma cells shows that their cytoplasm contains a very well organized endoplasmic reticulum to which are attached many ribosomes (fig. 32.9). Thus, plasma cells have a well developed apparatus for protein synthesis. In addition, Coons and his colleagues developed techniques of immunofluorescent staining and by their use have shown antibody molecules associated with plasma cells.

The second type of immunological response which is recognized does not appear to involve the production of circulating antibody. Rather, cells with lymphoid characteristics, which develop as part of an immunological reaction, make direct contact with the antigenic material leading to its destruction or rejection. This type of reaction is found when foreign tissue grafts are rejected, and is often referred to as cell-mediated immunity because the direct intervention of cells appears to be required.

The two types of immunological reaction described above differ in the final step by which the foreign material is rejected by the body. Nonetheless, in both instances, populations of cells capable of a specific immunologic function must be developed. Indeed, the cells involved are probably closely related. Gowans has presented experimental evidence that lymphoid cells obtained from the thoracic duct can develop the morphological characteristics of plasma cells following injection into new hosts. This morphological change may result from immunological stimulation of the lymphoid cells by antigens of the recipients. Thus the origin of cells responsible for the production of circulating antibody and cells responsible for cell-mediated immunity may be similar.

Proliferation and Differentiation of Cells in the Immune Response

Cells that have acquired immunological competence may be generated either by direct transformation from pre-existing cells or through the mechanism of cellular proliferation. Histological studies of tissues during immunological responses reveal that the number of cells within lymphoid spaces greatly increases following antigenic stimulation. More recently, direct techniques for detecting cells producing specific antibody molecules have been developed and these techniques have indicated that extensive cellular proliferation occurs during immunological response. It appears, then, that the cells which mediate immune responses are developed by the process of cell proliferation. In addition, capacity to manufacture antibody or make direct destructive contact with antigen represents a new function possessed by progeny cells and not by their progenitors. Therefore, development of plasma cells or lymphoid elements in an immune response depends on the process of differentiation. In response to antigenic stimulation progenitor cells proliferate and differentiate, giving rise to functionally competent descendants. On this basis, such progenitor cells may be considered to have stem cell properties, and in this sense, the processes by which cells responsible for immunological reaction are generated are similar to those used for the production of erythrocytes, granulocytes and platelets. It is not surprising that the

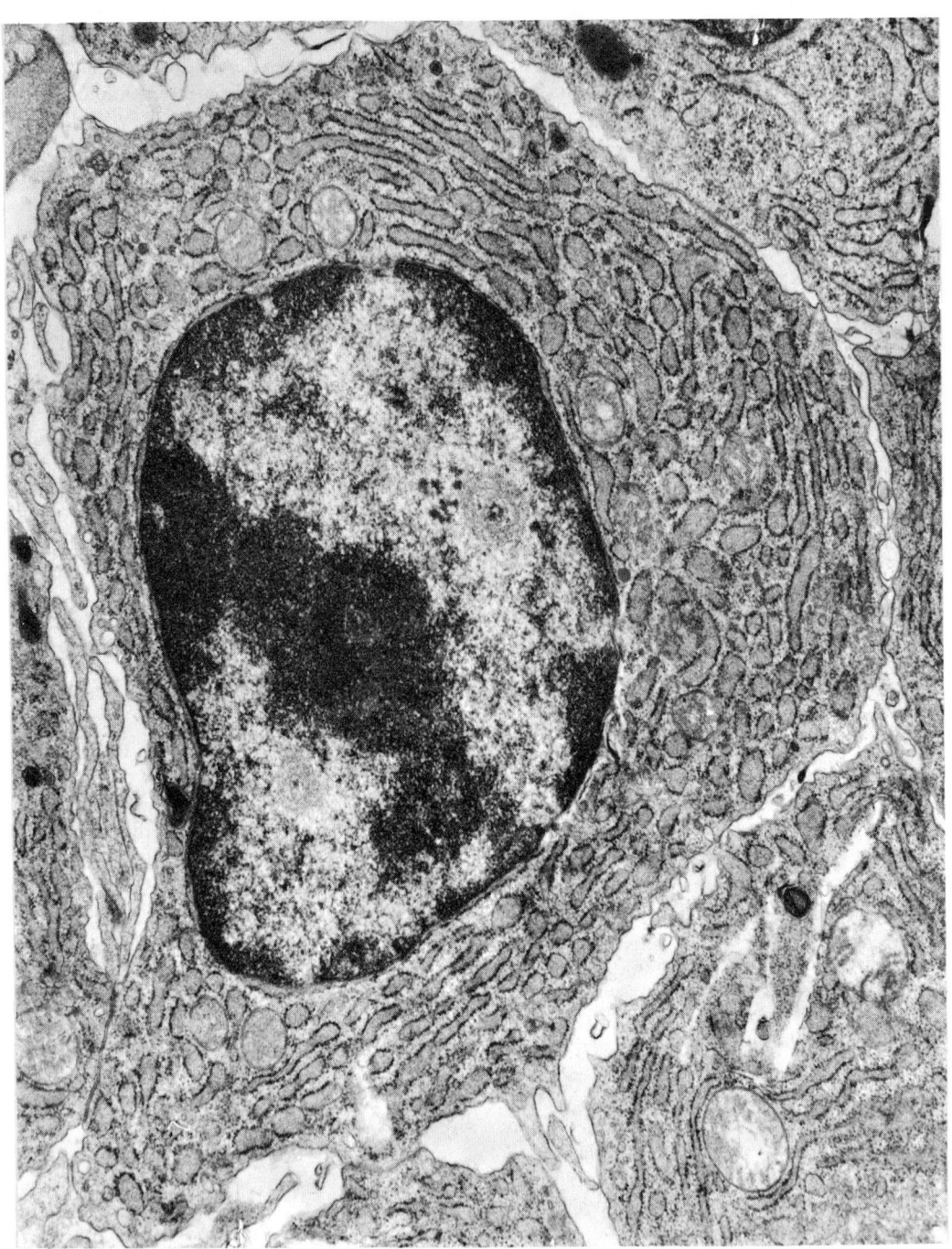

FIG. 32.9. This is an electronmicrograph of a human plasma cell obtained by marrow aspiration. The cytoplasm contains a well developed endoplasmic reticulum, to which are attached ribosomes. Magnification 24,000 ×. (Picture courtesy of Dr. A. F. Howatson. Preparation by Miss M. Nagai.)

questions which were asked about the production of the descendants of hemopoietic stem cells are also relevant to the production of lymphoid and plasma cells. These questions are: (1) can pro-genitor cells be identified? (2) what is their potential for proliferation and differentiation, and (3) how is this potential controlled? Firm answers to these questions are not available but the questions themselves form the basis of two contrasting views about the cellular events involved in antibody synthesis.

THEORIES OF THE CELLULAR BASIS OF THE IMMUNE RESPONSE

One view of the cellular basis of immune responses has been termed the *instructive theory* of antibody formation. According to this theory progenitor cells of the immune response have very extensive capacity for cellular differentiation. A single progenitor cell is envisioned as having the capacity to react with a large variety of different antigenic substances, and the specificity of the response of the descendants of such a cell results from the characteristics of the antigen itself. This view is called instructive because it postulates the antigen as providing cells with information or instruction which directs differentiation.

An essential feature of the instructive theory is that all antigenic substances are able to carry information that can direct cellular activities, and particularly the production of specific proteins. Modern biochemical information about protein synthesis would indicate that information directing the primary structure of proteins is carried by nucleic acid. The fact that nucleic acids are poor antigens, and many excellent antigens are not nucleic acids, has been cited as an objection to the instructive theory of antibody synthesis; this objection has been fortified by the recently reported observations that the specificity of antibody molecules resides, at least to some extent, in their primary structure. However, the control of protein synthesis as part of the differentiation of mammalian cells is not well understood, and it remains possible that an antigen might influence this control in such a way as to direct the transcription and translation of information from nucleic acid to protein; this form of direction of protein synthesis by antigen, if it were to result in the production of specific antibody molecules, would be compatible with the instructive theory.

A second theory of antibody production is the *clonal selection theory* of Burnet. This theory envisions the development, during cell replication, of a population of progenitor cells of the immune response heterogeneous in respect to their capacity to respond to various antigens. The process by which this heterogeneity arises might be considered to be one of somatic mutation, which would affect the cellular genomes. Such heterogeneity would develop without the intervention of specific antigen. When antigen is introduced into the environment of such cells, their proliferation is stimulated and a clone of cells develops; as a further consequence of the presence of antigen, the cells of this clone realize their capacity for the production of specific antibody directed against that antigen.

A choice might be made between these two views of antibody production if clones of cells with immunological competence were available. The instructive theory predicts that such a clone, developing in response to more than one antigen, should contain cells producing antibodies with more than one specificity. The clonal selection theory predicts that the antibody produced by each clone should have only a limited specificity. Unfortunately methods for obtaining clones of antibody-forming cells are not available. In their absence, workers have concentrated on the question of whether or not a single cell can produce antibody against more than one antigen. The great majority of antibody-producing cells derived from an animal stimulated by two antigens have been found by Attardi and by Nossal and their colleagues to make antibody against only one antigen. However, some cells are found which produce two different kinds of antibody. The progenitor of a single cell producing two different antibodies must have had the capacity to respond to two antigens. This finding of cells producing more than one antibody is evidence, therefore, against the simplest form of the clonal selection theory of antibody formation. One must conclude that neither of the theories described above can at the present time adequately explain the phenomenon of immunity. It seems likely that resolution of the problem must await the development of better techniques for measuring the potential of the stem cells of the immunological system.

IMMUNOLOGICAL UNRESPONSIVENESS

The most important controlling influence on cell proliferation in the immune system appears to be the presence of antigen. However the progenitor cells of the immune response appear to be able to respond to the same antigen in two quite different ways. The usual response is the one described above, that is, proliferation and differentiation with the production of mature cells with immunological capabilities. A second type of response is also possible; in this, not only is an immunological reaction unobserved, but the animal is rendered incapable, at least for a period of time, of responding to antigen in the usual way. In the adult, this response, first studied by Felton, is termed *immunological paralysis* and is achieved only under special circumstances and by the use of very large doses of antigen. However, in immature animals such a response has been observed following administration of many different kinds of antigen including homologous cells and foreign proteins. Under these conditions the response, first observed experimentally by Billingham, Brent and Medawar, is termed *actively acquired immunological tolerance*.

The phenomenon of immunological tolerance may most readily be described in terms of an experiment using inbred mice. Strains of mice are available which have been maintained over many generations by brother to sister mating. Members of these strains are genetically and antigenically identical; for example, mice of a given strain will accept tissue grafts from other mice of the same strain while rejecting tissue grafts from mice of a different strain. If cells from inbred mice are injected into newborn mice of a different strain, the injected animals, when adult, will regularly accept skin grafts from animals of the strain from which the cells were originally obtained. The tolerance to these skin grafts is specific because the recipient animal will reject grafts obtained from mice of a third, unrelated, strain. Immunological tolerance constitutes a specific feature of the cellular system of the animals, since transplantation of immunologically competent cells from a non-tolerant mouse into a tolerant mouse of the same strain results in the abolition of tolerance, and rejection of grafted skin. Thus, under these conditions, antigen has acted as a powerful control of the immunological response but the control has been in the direction of prevention rather than promotion of an immunological response. The phenomenon of immunological tolerance is particularly interesting because it may provide the explanation for how individuals usually fail to produce antibodies aginst the large number of antigens present within their own bodies. These antigens were present when the individual was immature and for this reason tolerance was developed towards them. Although many theories for the mechanism and cellular basis of tolerance have been proposed, none of these have been supported by substantial experimental evidence.

The Role of the Thymus in Lymphopoiesis

Recently it has become apparent that the thymus plays an important role in the development of the lymphoid system. Miller and his collaborators have shown that when the thymus is removed from mice very shortly after they are born, many display a characteristic lesion as they grow and develop. First, the thymectomized animals fail to thrive; they grow poorly and never achieve a body size comparable with that of their litter-mates. Second, the lymphatic organs of the thymectomized animals are found to be atrophic; lymph nodes are small or nonexistent and the lymphatic follicles of the spleen fail to develop. Lymphoid cells are reduced in the peripheral blood. Third, the thymectomized animals fail to show a normal immunological

response. They will frequently accept and retain skin grafts from unrelated mice and are often unable to respond to antigen with the production of circulating antibody. Thymectomized animals, as a result of these changes, have a shortened life span and appear unhealthy. In contrast to these dramatic effects of neonatal thymectomy, when the thymus is removed from adult animals, they recover well from the operation and appear to suffer from no deleterious affects. It is apparent, therefore, that the thymus plays a role in the normal development of the lymphoid system and that this role is completed soon after the animal is born. If the thymus is removed before its function is fulfilled, lymphatic areas remain atrophic. As a consequence the animal is immunologically handicapped. The failure to grow and thrive exhibited by these animals may well result from this immunological incompetence, since stunted growth is not observed in animals thymectomized at birth but kept in a germ-free environment.

Two possible mechanisms have been suggested to explain the effect of neonatal thymectomy. First, it was postulated that the thymus provides a suitable environment in which relatively undifferentiated cells can differentiate along lymphoid lines. Following this differentiation, these cells might leave the thymus and populate lymphatic areas such as the spleen and lymph nodes. There they might retain sufficient proliferative capacity to maintain lymphatic populations and the intervention of the thymus would not again be necessary in adult life. Support for this view has been obtained by Harris and Ford using mouse cells which could be recognized in mitosis by the presence of a morphologically distinct chromosome. In this way it has been possible to observe that cells found in thymus tissue migrate to peripheral lymphatic areas.

A second hypothesis is that the thymus secretes a diffusable substance—a hormone—which is required for the differentiation of cells along lymphoid lines. Evidence for the existence of the thymic hormone derives from experiments by Osoba and Miller and by Levey and his colleagues. Fragments of thymus were placed in chambers sealed with membranes having a pore size too small to permit the passage of cells but large enough to allow free passage to large molecules. Thymus fragments in such chambers were implanted in the peritoneal cavities of mice thymectomized at birth. In spite of the fact that cells were not able to pass from the thymus, immunological function was restored in the mice in which the chambers had been implanted, indicating that thymic function may be mediated by a diffusable substance or hormone. A thymic hormone has not, however, been isolated or characterized.

Conclusions and Projections

The use of physiological methods for the study of blood formation has cast new light on the nature of the stem cells from which mature blood cells are derived. These methods have permitted the development of a functional definition of stem cells based on their properties. These properties are capacity for proliferation, for differentiation, and for self renewal and an ability to respond to normal control mechanisms. Classes of stem cells may be characterized in terms of the extent to which they can be shown to possess these properties.

In the past, intense controversy has centered about the second of the stem cell properties, that is, capacity for differentiation; the controversial question has been: How many kinds of differentiated cells can derive from a single cell? This controversy has been resolved in part by the demonstration that normal hemopoietic tissue contains a class of cell capable of differentiating along erythrocytic, granulocytic and megakaryocytic lines. However, when the importance of the other stem cell properties is realized, new problems become apparent. For example, stem cell properties may be considered in quantitative terms. Thus, the property of proliferative capacity may be expressed as the number of possible generations included in the potential of a class of stem cells.

Evidence has been presented for the existence of a class of stem cell with relatively limited proliferative capacity, able to differentiate in only one direction, but fully capable of responding to control mechanisms. These are the erythropoietin-sensitive stem cells of the erythrocytic series. It remains to be shown whether other classes of cells with limited stem cell properties also exist.

Functional tests for the study of stem cells of the lymphatic series are largely undeveloped. These stem cells have not been identified by clonal methods and in the absence of such methods the relationship of the cellular basis of lymphopoiesis to the stem cells of erythropoiesis, granulopoiesis and platelet formation has not been established. However, lymphoid cells or cells with immune capacity have not been identified with certainty among the progeny of the latter class of stem cell, and on this negative evidence it is suggested that the lymphatic system may contain one or more classes of independent stem cells.

The final property of stem cells, capacity to respond to control mechanisms, remains relatively unexplored. Evidence exists that the response may be achieved by varying the time parameters of the cell cycle, and in one specific case, erythropoiesis, control appears to be mediated through the action of a hormone. A hormone derived from the thymus may also be important in lymphopoiesis. Evidence of hormonal control of other kinds of blood cells has been extensively sought, but to date the results of such searches are either inconclusive or negative. Moreover, it is this property, response to control which is of greatest interest to the physician. For example, if immunity mechanisms could be controlled, the transplantation of cells and tissues might become feasible in man. Perhaps of more importance, if normal control mechanisms were understood, the breakdown of these mechanisms in disease might be prevented or corrected. Leukemia is an outstanding example of a disease in which control mechanisms are at fault, for in this condition, the proliferation of malignant hemopoietic cells continues uninhibited by the forces which limit the growth of normal cells. If such normal control mechanisms were understood in detail, the lesion in leukemic cells might be identified. This information might be expected to provide the clue needed to develop prevention or control of this fatal disease.

REFERENCES

ARCHER, O. AND PIERCE, J. C. Fed. Proc., 1961, **20**, 26.

ATTARDI, G., COHN, M., HORIBATA, K. AND LENNOX, E. S. Bact. Rev., 1959, **23**, 213.

BARNES, D. W., FORD, C. E., GRAY, S. M. AND LOUTIT, J. F. Progs. Nucl. Energy (Biol.), 1959, **2**, 1.

BECKER, A. J., McCULLOCH, E. A. AND TILL, J. E. Nature, 1963, **197**, 452.

BECKER, A. J., McCULLOCH, E. A., SIMINOVITCH, L. AND TILL, J. E. Blood, 1965, **26**, 296.

BILLINGHAM, R. E., BRENT, L. AND MEDAWAR, P. B. Phil. Trans. of Roy. Soc. of London B., 239, **56**, 357.

COONS, A. H., LEDUC, E. H. AND CONNOLLY, J. M. J. Exp. Med., 1955, **102**, 49.

FELTON, L. D. J. Immunol., 1949, **61**, 107.

FILMANOWICZ, E. AND GURNEY, C. W. J. Lab. Clin. Med., 1961, **57**, 68.

GOWANS, J. L. Ann. N.Y. Acad. Sci., 1962, **99**, 3.

GURNEY, C. W., LAJTHA, L. G. AND OLIVER, R. Brit. J. Haemat., 1962, **8**, 461.

Gurney, C. W., Wackman, N. and Filmanowicz, F. Blood, 1961, **17,** 531.

Harris, J. W. and Ford, C. E. Nature, 1964, **201,** 884.

Haurowitz, Felix. Ann. New York Acad. Sc., 1965, **124,** 50.

Lajtha, L. G., Oliver, R. and Gurney, C. W. Brit. J. Haemat., 1962, **8,** 442.

Levey, R. H. Trainin, N. and Law, L. W. J. Natl. Cancer Inst., 1963, **31,** 199.

Makela, O. and Nossal, G. J. V. J. Immunol., 1961, **87,** 447, 457.

Miller, J. F. A. P. Lancet, 1961, **2,** 748.

Nossal, G. J. V. Ann. New York Acad. Sci., 1965, **124,** 37.

Nowell, P. C. and Hungerford, D. A. J. Natl. Cancer Inst., 1960, **25,** 85.

Osoba, D. and Miller, J. F. A. P. Nature, 1964, **199,** 653.

Osoba, D. and Miller, J. F. A. P. J. Exptl. Med., 1964, **119,** 177.

Schooley, J. C. Blood, 1965, **25,** 795.

Schulman, I., Pierce, M., Lukens, A. and Currimbhoy, Z. Blood, 1960, **16,** 943.

Till, J. E. and McCulloch, E. A. Radiat. Res., 1961, **14,** 213.

Till, J. E., McCulloch, E. A. and Siminovitch, L. Proc. Nat. Acad. Sci. U.S., 1964, **51,** 29.

Whang, J., Frei III, E., Tjio, J. H., Carbone, P. P. and Brecher, G. Blood, 1963, **22,** 664.

Monographs and Reviews

Brecher, G. and Stohlman, F., Jr. Humoral Factors in Erythropoiesis in Progress in Hematology, (L. M. Tocantins, ed.) Vol. 2. p. 110, Grune and Stratton, New York, 1959.

Burnet, F. M. The Clonal Selection Theory of Acquired Immunity. Vanderbilt University Press, Nashville, Tenn., 1959.

Ciba Foundation Symposium on Cellular Aspects of Immunity. (Wolstenholme, G. E. W. and O'Connor, M., eds.) J. and A. Churchill Ltd., London, 1960.

Ciba Foundation Symposium on Haemopoiesis. (Wolstenholme, G. E. W. and O'Connor, M. eds.) J. and A. Churchill, London, 1960.

Cronkite, E. P. Fed. Proc., 1964, **23,** 649.

Jacobson, L. O. and Doyle, M., eds. Erythropoiesis. Grune and Stratton, New York and London, 1962.

Stohlman, F., Jr., Ed., The Kinetics of Cellular Proliferation. Grune and Stratton, New York, 1959.

Leblond, C. P. and Walker, B. E. Physiol. Rev., 1956, **36,** 255.

Patt, H. M. and Quastler, H. Radiation effects on cell renewal and related systems. Physiol. Rev., 1963, **43,** 357.

CHAPTER 33

The Coagulation (Clotting) of Blood

General Description of Clot Formation

If blood is collected into a test tube at the end of a few minutes it will have lost its fluidity and set into a jelly. If it were possible to magnify this clot many times and to look within it, one would see a mesh of very delicate fibrils among which were entangled, as in a net, the red and white cells and many fragmented platelets. The fibrils can be readily revealed when a thin section of the clot is examined under the high power of the microscope. They are composed of fibrin which is formed by the alteration and polymerization of the fibrinogen molecules. If the clot is allowed to stand for an hour or so, it will be found to have shrunk, and in shrinking to have expressed from its interstices a clear faint straw-coloured fluid. This is the *serum*.

In this retraction of the clot or *syneresis*, as it is termed, the platelets play an essential role. They attach themselves to the fibrin threads which then contract, and drawing the fibrin compactly together, squeeze out the fluid (serum). Clots formed in blood deficient in platelets are soft and friable and easily loosened from the injured vessel. The importance of these small particles of protoplasm in hemostasis will be dealt with later.

The Clotting Mechanism

No field of physiology is more complex or has been so confused by contradictory results, differences of interpretation and diversity of opinion as that of blood coagulation. Blood coagulation is essentially a series of enzymatic reactions involving a number of plasma proteins. Many of these are present only in traces. Within an intact healthy circulatory system these enzymes, for the most part, are in an inactive form. However, when blood is shed or placed in contact with a "wettable surface," such as glass, a series of autocatalytic enzymatic reactions is initiated. In a frantic effort to understand the order in which the numerous factors enter into the process of coagulation, the results of an enormous number of "mixing" experiments have been reported. This has resulted in a confusion not only of terminology, but also between what is a separate enzyme entity and what is merely a resultant

activity. To make some order out of chaos an international system of numbering has been introduced for the identification of those factors which have been accepted by a majority of authorities in the field. In table 33.1, the international number system and the synonyms most commonly used for the accepted coagulation factors are shown. No numbers have been suggested for the physiological anticoagulants.

Recently Macfarlane has suggested that the clotting mechanism is a sequence of proenzyme-enzyme transformations, in which each enzyme activates the next until the final substrate, fibrinogen, is involved. He claims that coagulation is an example of a biochemical amplifier system, where a relatively small initial activation can, through the autocatalytic activation of a succession of enzymes, bring about a large total reaction.

This is indeed an intriguing hypothesis but cannot as yet be substantiated by fact. Since the clotting process can be stopped at various points in its progress, it is useful (both to understand its mechanism and as an aid in clinical diagnosis) to treat blood coagulation as though it took place in a series of stages.

Development of Thromboplastin Activity

By the end of the nineteenth century it was established that extracts of tissues free of blood accelerated the clotting of whole blood or plasma but had no effect on solutions of fibrinogen. According to the hypothesis put forward at that time, this tissue extract (called thromboplastin), in conjunction with calcium, acted by converting prothrombin to its active form thrombin. During the early nineteen-forties it was shown, particularly by the work of Macfarlane and his colleagues on viper venom, that thromboplastin required both lipid and protein constituents for full activity. Also, at about the same time, work in a number of laboratories indicated that factors other than thromboplastin were involved in the normal conversion of prothrombin to thrombin. It was believed, however, that blood contained no thromboplastin activity itself. This factor was considered to be available only from tissues.

With the introduction of silicone, a new phase

TABLE 33.1

Synonymous terms for clotting factors

International Committee Nomenclature	Synonymous and Descriptive Terms
Factor I	Fibrinogen
Factor II	Prothrombin
Factor III	Thromboplastin
Factor IV	Calcium
Factor V	AC-Globulin, proaccelerin, labile factor
Factor VII	Proconvertin, SPCA
Factor VIII	Antihemophilic factor
Factor IX	Plasma Thromboplastin Component (PTC), Christmas factor
Factor X	Stuart-Prower factor
Factor XI	Plasma Thromboplastin Antecedant (PTA)
Factor XII	Hageman factor, contact factor
Factor XIII	Fibrin stabilizing factor, Fibrinase

in the study of blood clotting began. With proper solutions of silicone, test tubes, syringes and needles can be covered with a smooth "non-wettable" surface. This makes it possible to withdraw blood and prepare plasma for study without causing changes due to surface action. Using siliconed glassware it is possible to show that blood contains all the factors for thromboplastin generation; it requires only a change in surface contact to trigger the mechanism. Thus there are two sources of thromboplastin activity, one from tissue extracts sometimes called the extrinsic source, and the other from the interactions of a number of trace plasma proteins, calcium ions and platelets called the intrinsic source.

While there is agreement on the various factors involved in this reaction there is, as yet, no unanimity of opinion regarding the order in which the various factors enter into the reaction.

The factors that are involved in the formation of intrinsic, or plasma, thromboplastic activity are illustrated in fig. 33.1 A. It is now generally accepted that Factor XII when activated by surface contact initiates the reaction. Then, in the presence of calcium ions, other trace proteins, Factors XI, IX and VIII (possibly in this order) are in turn activated. Factor VIII (antihemophilic factor) is present in normal fresh plasma but is absent or inactive in normal serum and it rapidly disappears from stored blood. It is not readily adsorbed on the usual prothrombin-adsorbing reagents such as aluminum hydroxide or tricalcium phosphate. It is relatively stable in plasma stored at −20°C. Factor IX (Christmas factor) is present in both plasma and serum and

is readily adsorbed on prothrombin-adsorbing agents. It is present in stored blood. Deficiencies in Factor VIII or Factor IX result in a bleeding condition known as hemophilia. This is an hereditary condition linked with a defect of the X chromosome. Factor XI (plasma thromboplastin anticedent) has some of the characteristics of both Factor VIII and IX. It is not readily adsorbed on prothrombin-adsorbing reagents but is stable and is found in serum. Bleeding defects due to lack of Factor XI activity are quite rare. In addition to these, and possibly other as yet unidentified proteins, a phospholipid is required for development of optimum thromboplastin activity. During normal coagulation this is supplied through platelet breakdown. In *in vitro* coagulation studies the platelet phospholipid moiety can be replaced by phospholipid from brain tissue or soya bean.

There are a number of ways in which the for-

Stage I: Formation of Plasma Thromboplastin

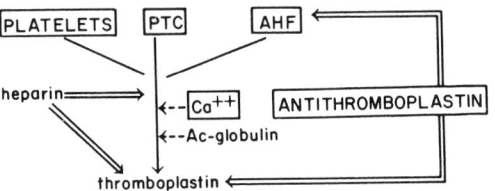

Stage II: Formation of Thrombin

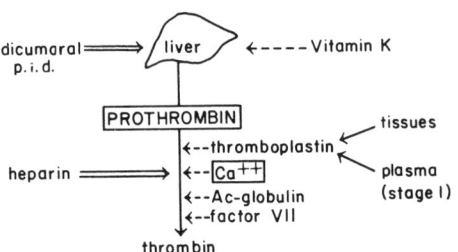

Stage III: Change of Fibrinogen to Fibrin

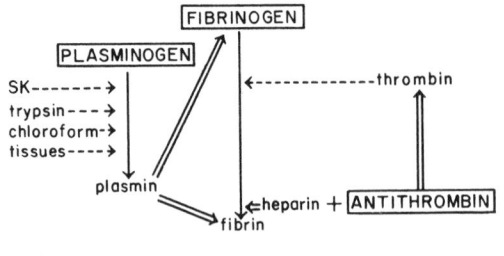

gives rise to ⟶ acts on ---⟶

inhibits or destroys ⟹ present in blood ▭

FIG. 33.1

mation of thromboplastin activity can be delayed or prevented. According to the work of Tocantins and Carroll a thromboplastin inhibitor is present in normal plasma. They have isolated this material from both normal and hemophilic plasma. It appears both to delay the development of thromboplastin activity and inhibit its action. Agents such as citrate, oxalate or ethylene-diamine-tetra-acetic-acid (EDTA) by binding calcium ions will completely inhibit the development of thromboplastin activity. Heparin, which is not present in normal blood in measurable amounts, is probably of no importance in preventing normal blood coagulation. However, when added as a therapeutic agent, it acts at a number of sites along the chain of reaction. There is good evidence that its initial action is to prevent the development of thromboplastin activity. It probably does this by combining with the reactive sites on the trace proteins and by preventing platelet disintegration and release of phospholipids. Heparin is a mucopolysaccharide and for therapeutic use is normally prepared from beef lung or beef and hog intestinal mucosa. A number of synthetic mucopolysaccharides have been prepared but have not as yet proven satisfactory for clinical use.

Activation of Prothrombin

Recent studies have favored the hypothesis that both the thromboplastin formed from the interaction of plasma proteins and the thromboplastin in tissue extracts need an additional factor for full activity. This is Factor X (Stuart-Prower Factor). In addition to Factor X, tissue thromboplastin requires Factor VII (convertin). The exact order in which these proteins enter into the reaction is not yet established, but most recent experimental results of Macfarlane and his colleagues would support the order suggested in Fig. 33.1 B. Calcium ions are also required for prothrombin conversion and Factor V (AC-globulin) increases the rate of the conversion. It is known that heparin when added to a physiological system will inhibit the conversion of prothrombin, but much, if not all, of this inhibitory activity may be through the action on thromboplastin. In common with most other plasma proteins, prothrombin, Factor X and Factor VII are formed in the liver. The ability of the liver to maintain normal blood levels of these protein fractions, however, depends on the presence in the liver of sufficient amounts of vitamin K. Dicumarol, and other similarly acting drugs, antagonize vitamin K and depress the rate of production of prothrombin, Factor VII and Factor X.

Conversion of Fibrinogen to Fibrin

Once thrombin is formed it acts enzymatically to convert the soluble fibrinogen into insoluble fibrin. It has been established that thrombin is a proteolytic enzyme having the same sequence of amino acids at its active site as digestive enzymes such as pepsin and trypsin. Most proteolytic enzymes break down fibrinogen completely, but thrombin splits off only a few terminal peptides. Two of these known as fibrin peptides A and B are the result of selective action of thrombin at terminal glycine-arginine bonds. The splitting off of the peptides causes a change in charge at the ending of the molecules of fibrinogen and allows them to polymerize end to end in long insoluble strands. When purified fibrinogen is clotted by purified thrombin the clot is found to be soluble in urea. But the clot formed in plasma is not soluble in urea. A factor has been isolated from human and animal plasma which will render the clot formed from purified fibrinogen insoluble in urea. This factor has been named fibrin stabilizing Factor or Factor XIII. This factor greatly facilitates the healing of wounds. It has been found missing from the blood in some subjects. Many authorities in the field of coagulation adhere to the view that fibrin is being continually formed and destroyed and that the integrity of the endothelium depends on the presence of a physiological mechanism for the constant removal of fibrin. Such a mechanism does indeed exist. It depends on the presence in blood of an inactive proteolytic precursor called plasminogen, which has been identified as a β-globulin with a molecular weight in the region of 150,000. During clotting or purification of fibrinogen it is associated closely with the fibrinogen molecule. It is extremely difficult to prepare fibrinogen free of plasminogen and a normal clot usually contains sufficient amounts of plasminogen to insure clot dissolution if circumstances permit its activation. Plasminogen activators are of two different types. Activators from tissues and urine act directly on both human and bovine plasminogen. Activators such as streptokinase (prepared from streptococcal cultures) and lysokinases from tissues and blood must act first on a globulin fraction called proactivator. This proactivator is present in large amounts in human plasma, but is virtually absent from the blood of cattle and other animal species. There is usually an excess of plasmin inhibitor in normal blood. However, when large amounts of plasminogen are activated (this can occur during surgery, childbirth or prostatic cancer), fibrinogen as well as fibrin is destroyed by the enzyme and serious hemorrhage can result. Small increases in the fibrinolytic activity of plasma have been reported following exercise, anoxia or the injection of adrenalin or serotonin. On the other hand, high levels of lipoproteins tend to inhibit fibrinolysis.

It has been known for decades that normal plasma can neutralize large amounts of thrombin. Morawitz proposed the name antithrombin for this activity in plasma. The neutralization of thrombin in plasma, however, is a complex action and is not due to a single effect. Thrombin can be neutralized without being destroyed. Break-down products of fibrin digestion can do this by blocking the thrombin-fibrinogen reaction. Heparin in combination with a plasma factor (heparin-cofactor) acts in a somewhat similar manner. There is, however, an enzyme in plasma (true plasma antithrombin) which destroys thrombin. This has been shown to be an alpha globulin. Relatively large quantities of this are present in normal plasma. In fact the amount of antithrombin available far exceeds the amount of thrombin formed during coagulation.

Antithrombin, however, is slow in action compared to thrombin, and during *in vitro* coagulation where thrombin is formed rapidly and in excess of requirements, has virtually no effect on blood coagulation. However, in an *in vivo* system where thrombin will form slowly, antithrombin can play an important role. Experiments in which thrombin has been perfused into the circulation slowly, give evidence as to its ability to function in this regard. A great deal more needs to be learned about this relatively abundant naturally-occurring anticoagulant if the best physiological approach to anticoagulant therapy is to be achieved.

Test Employed in the Investigation of Defects in the Clotting Mechanism

COAGULATION TIME

This is the time taken for blood to clot after it is withdrawn from the body. Decreased coagulability of the blood is manifested by lengthening of the coagulation time and vice versa. A number of methods have been developed to measure the precise moment in which clotting occurs. The clotting time of normal blood will depend upon the size of the tube, the number of tubes employed, the temperature at which the blood is kept during the test, and the amount of tilting and agitation of the tube. It is important to do the clotting test in exactly the same manner each time. If the method is standardized serial determinations of the clotting time will provide useful information.

A modification of the Lee-White method for whole blood clotting time is widely used. One ml. quantities of blood drawn by clean venipuncture are placed in each of three small test tubes (11 mm internal diameter) placed in a water bath. A stop watch is started at the time of venipuncture. After 3 min. the first tube is tilted at 15 sec. intervals. When the blood clots in this tube, the next tube is tilted until clotted and then the third tube is treated similarly. The clotting time is taken as the time of clotting of the blood in the third tube. The coagulation time by this method varies between 9 and 11 min. for normal individuals. By using three tubes, variations in clotting time due to variation in rate and degree of tilting (surface effect) are reduced.

In small children venipuncture may be difficult and the clotting time can be measured on capillary blood. With a sharp lancet a drop of blood is obtained from the finger, ear lobe or heel and allowed to run into a capillary tube. The ends of the tube are sealed with plasticine and then the tube is immersed in a water bath at 37°C. At 15 sec. intervals small fragments of the tube are broken off and the end point is taken when a string of clot is observed. The normal coagulation time by this method is between 3 and 5 min.; it is shorter than clotting time by the Lee-White method because of the relatively greater surface area of glass in contact with the blood.

Prothrombin time. In the one-stage method developed by Quick, excess of tissue thromboplastin and optimal calcium is added to citrated or oxalated plasma. The tubes are placed in a water bath at 37°C. and the time for clotting to occur is recorded. A standard value for the day is determined using a sample of normal plasma. This standard time will vary between 14 and 16 sec. A dilution curve may be prepared with normal plasma diluted with adsorbed plasma (prothrombin free) to relate clotting times to prothrombin concentration in percent of standard. This is done in an attempt to reduce the variability caused by the tissue thromboplastin, the activity of which differs from day to day. It is doubtful, however, whether the dilution curve is worth the effort in the practical management of patients taking oral anticoagulants.

Clot retraction time. In this test 2-3 ml. of venous blood are placed in a test tube kept at 37°C. in a water bath. After clotting has occurred the clot is freed from the sides of the tube by means of a wooden applicator stick. Normally in a couple of hours the clot contracts to a firm mass expressing serum from its interstices. Clot retraction is normal in hemophilia but abnormal in thrombocytopenia.

The bleeding time. Bleeding time is determined by nicking the skin with a pointed scalpel blade, the ear lobe being a convenient site. Drops of blood are wiped away every few seconds with filter paper. The end point is taken as the moment when bleeding ceases. The normal bleeding time is about $2\frac{1}{2}$ minutes. The ability to seal the wound depends on the platelets and on the state of the small blood vessels. The bleeding time in hemophilia. This at first seems to be a paradox until it is realized that the platelets and blood vessels are normal in this condition. In hemophilic patients manipulation of the small wound later causes renewal of bleeding which may be extremely troublesome to control. It is believed this is due to failure of an effective clot to back up the platelet plug.

Thromboplastin generation test. This test resembles the one-stage prothrombin time but instead of saline extracts from acetone treated brain as a source of thromboplastin activity, plasma components and platelets are first incubated together to produce plasma thromboplastic activity. Normal thromboplastic activity requires factor VIII and Factor IX from plasma, cephalin obtained from platelets, and calcium. The generation mixture is kept at 37°C. and at minute intervals thromboplastic activity is tested by adding samples to a substrate of normal platelet poor citrated plasma and calcium. The time of clotting of the substrate reflects the thromboplastic activity of the generation mixture. In the test 0.2 ml. quantities of normal alumina plasma, diluted 1 to 5 (Factor VIII), normal serum diluted 1 to 10 (Factor IX) cephalin or platelets and M/40 calcium chloride solution are placed in a test tube. At intervals of 1 min. 0.1 ml. of the mixture is withdrawn into a Pasteur pipette and discharged simultaneously with 0.1 ml. of M/40 calcium chloride solution into a tube containing 0.1 ml. of normal platelet poor citrated plasma. A convenient substitute for platelets is cephalin prepared from brain or soya bean. The clotting times of the substrate samples may be plotted on a curve showing normal thromboplastin generation. Having prepared a normal thromboplastin generation curve, aluminium plasma or serum from a test subject may be substituted for one of the normal components and the resulting curve compared with the normal. If the subject lacks a component necessary for thromboplastin generation, decreased thromboplastic activity will be detected.

Partial thromboplastin time. This test is widely used and has the advantage of being a one-stage test and is simpler to perform than the thrombo-plastin generation test. It resembles the Quick one-stage prothrombin time as well. Instead of acetone treated brain being added to plasma, cephalin is used in this test. If normal amounts of Factors VIII and IX are present in the plasma, a short clotting time will be observed. If one of these factors is lacking, the time will be prolonged. Since the early stages of clotting are influenced by surface contact it is customary to add kaolin to the plasma while doing the test to provide maximum activation of contact factors. The test may be used for both the diagnosis and control of treatment of hemophilia.

Hemorrhagic Diseases

HEMOPHILIA. In this condition the coagulation time (but not the bleeding time) is usually prolonged. In some cases the blood may not clot for several hours. Fatal hemorrhage may follow a minor wound or a simple operation such as a tooth extraction. It is important to realize, however, that certain hemophiliacs have a clotting time which is normal or only slightly prolonged. In these patients it is necessary to confirm the diagnosis with the thromboplastin generation tests or partial thromboplastin time. Hemophilia is transmitted as a sex linked recessive character. Females carrying the abnormal X-chromosome transmit the disease to half their sons while half their daughters will be carriers. A hemophilic father will have normal sons but carrier daughters. If a hemophilic man marries a hemophilic carrier, it is possible to have a female hemophilic. This occurrence is very rare. The disease is also found in domestic animals and in several centers colonies of hemophilic dogs are maintained for experimental purposes. Even hemophilic patients with normal or slightly prolonged clotting times may bleed to death following procedures such as tonsillectomy or tooth extraction. There is, therefore, really no such thing as mild hemophilia. Since the disease carries an increased mortality it would eventually disappear were it not for fresh mutations appearing. Approximately 30% of patients with the disease do not have a previous family history.

Two distinct types of hemophilia may be recognized by laboratory testing. Certain patients lack Factor VIII while others lack Factor IX. From the practical standpoint it is important to distinguish between the two types of hemophilia. Factor VIII deficient patients require fresh blood or plasma since this activity disappears rapidly on storage. Both human and animal Factor VIII concentrates are now available. By their use lives have been saved and major surgery has been possible. In Factor IX deficiency it is not necessary to use fresh plasma since the factor is more stable on storage. Satisfactory concentrates of Factor IX are not generally available.

AFIBRINOGENEMIA. The lack of fibrinogen may be either inherited or acquired. It is formed in the liver and in the end stages of serious liver disease, the level in the blood may fall. It may also temporarily disappear due to destruction by fibrinolysins. This may occur following surgery on prostatic cancer, presumably due to release of fibrinolytic enzymes into the blood stream. It also may occur in abruptio placentae when sudden and abrupt separation of the placenta may also result in release of fibrinolytic and thromboplastic material in the blood stream causing rapid destruction of fibrinogen with bleeding.

PURPURA. There are three lines of defence against bleeding. When a blood vessel is injured platelets adhere to the injured area and form sticky plugs. The coagulation process results in fibrin threads which cover the platelet deposit and form a thrombus. The blood vessel wall itself has contractile properties that enable the flow of blood to be shut off or diverted. Purpura is hemorrhage into the skin and mucous membranes. It may be due to an abnormality of the platelets or the blood vessels. Thrombocytopenic purpura may be either idiopathic or secondary to a toxic agent. The former variety frequently responds very well to splenectomy. The mechanism of vascular purpura is not well understood and the diagnosis is made very often by excluding other causes. Damage to the blood vessel wall may occur in scurvy, in uremia and in severe infections. An important type of vascular purpura is due to hypersensitivity or allergy.

HYPOPROTHROMBINEMIA. Depression of the prothrombin level in the blood (hypoprothrombinemia) may be found in severe liver damage and in conditions where there is malabsorption of Vitamin K, such as obstructive jaundice and steatorrhea. Hemorrhagic disease of the newborn results from lack of Vitamin K in the mother. It may be prevented by giving the mother Vitamin K before the baby is born. Administration of coumarin drugs results in lowering of the prothrombin level of the plasma and clotting factors —VII and X.

Intravascular Clotting—Thrombosis

Coagulation of blood within vessels may be brought about experimentally by the injection of thrombin or thromboplastin into the blood stream. There is an immediate reduction in the number of platelets and the level of fibrinogen. After a short time the platelet count returns to normal suggesting that the platelets were not destroyed but were merely sequestered somewhere in the vascular system. Return of the fibrinogen level takes longer and is not complete for 24 hours indicating that fibrinogen was destroyed and was replaced by newly formed fibrinogen. Injury to the vessel wall results in a deposition of platelets from the flowing blood at the site of injury. The platelets stick to the injured area and also to each other forming a platelet plug. On top of the platelet nidus fibrin threads are formed which enmesh red and white blood cells. This is known as a thrombus and it is important to distinguish this from a simple blood clot formed in a stagnant pool of blood. A thrombus may either partially or completely plug the lumen of a vessel. The head of a thrombus at its point of attachment consists mainly of platelets and fibrin. The tail of the thrombus frequently lies within the lumen of a vessel and consists of fibrin and red cells.

A thrombus or a portion of it may break free and be carried away in the blood stream lodging in some remote area. The portion of the thrombus that travels is known as an embolus. Emboli from the leg veins lodge in the lung, producing an area of consolidation in the lung known as a pulmonary infarct. If an embolus originates in the left side of the heart it will be carried to a peripheral artery for example a cerebral artery giving rise to a cerebral infarct.

CAUSES OF THROMBOSIS IN MAN

The causes of thrombosis in man may be considered under the following headings:

Injury to a blood vessel. For many years it has been known that the segment of vein containing blood may be tied off and removed from the body. The blood within the segment will remain fluid for many hours. On the other hand, injury to a blood vessel by trauma, or the application of an irritating substance leads to thrombosis, but the basic mechanism underlying its development remains obscure. It is possible that a damaged endothelial lining causes the release or activation of substances that initiate the clotting process.

Deposition of platelets. Aschoff some years ago made an experimental study of postoperative thrombosis. He described the deposition of the platelets and compared them with sand which is kept in suspension in a rapid stream. Just as sand is deposited in a ribbed pattern upon the seashore or at a river's mouth where the current is slowed, so platelets are deposited in a thrombus forming characteristic ridges. The identification of platelet strands or ridges enables the pathologist to distinguish a thrombus from a postmortem clot. *In vitro* the addition of adenosine diphosphate (ADP) to a platelet suspension causes rapid clumping of the platelets. It is possible that damaged endothelium releases substances similar to ADP which alter the platelet membrane causing them to adhere to each other and to the endothelium. Cinematograph studies by Fulton of the hamster cheek-pouch have shown platelets adhering to an injured area in a blood vessel. The platelet mass may completely obstruct the vessel. Occasionally it is seen to break away forming a small embolus. When this happens another plug of platelets forms at the site of injury.

Slowing of the blood stream. After major surgery or childbirth there is an increased risk of developing thrombosis and embolism. This may be due to the flow of the blood in the veins becoming sluggish resulting in platelet deposition and clotting. Early ambulation after surgery and childbirth has been accompanied by a lowered incidence of thrombosis.

Changes in the blood. After operation and childbirth both the number of platelets and the level of fibrinogen are increased. Many investigators have carried out tests of clotting factors in an attempt to demonstrate a pre-thrombotic state. All such studies have been inconclusive and while some workers have reported changes these have not been confirmed by other investigators. An important factor leading to thrombosis is probably an alteration in platelet stickiness, associated with alterations in the endothelium and slowing of blood flow.

SUMMARY

The first event in the development of a thrombus is probably an alteration in the endothelial lining. Platelets adhere to this area and to each other forming a white thrombus. The growth of the thrombus occurs by the deposition of further platelets and the formation of fibrin, which enmeshes red and white cells. The accumulation is favoured by a sluggish blood flow. The clot that has been formed may remain fixed and either completely or partially occlude the blood vessel. The tail of the thrombus may lie free in the flowing stream of blood. The thrombus may grow by the fresh deposition of platelets and fibrin.

The thrombus may have a precarious hold on the lining of the vessel and break loose from its point of attachment; or a piece of the tail may become detached. When this occurs an embolus is carried in the blood stream to lodge in a distant part. Once the thrombotic process is recognized in leg veins, treatment consists of moderately active exercise, e.g., walking to increase venous return from the part and to lessen the chance of a clot forming in stagnant blood. Secondly, anti-coagulant therapy with heparin or dicumarol may be given with the hope of lessening the buildup of a thrombus by fresh clot. Anti-coagulant therapy might be expected as well to allow the natural fibrinolytic process to proceed without hindrance.

The Means used to Prevent or Retard Coagulation—Anticoagulants

Cold. Since the clotting mechanism consists of a series of chemical and enzymatic reactions, it is to be expected that coagulation will be retarded by lowering the temperature. Keeping blood at a temperature of from 5 to 10°C. postpones coagulation but does not absolutely prevent its occurrence. Cold, e.g., ice, etc., applied to the surface of the body as a means of arresting hemorrhage has, however, no effect in retarding the coagulation process. Actually a hemostatic action is exerted in such instances as a result of the vasoconstriction reflexly induced.

Avoidance of contact of the blood with foreign materials or injured tissues. Drawing the blood directly from an artery or vein (in order to prevent contact with the tissues—a source of thromboplastin), and collecting it into a receptical whose walls have been made smooth and *unwettable* by a coating of paraffin, or preferably of *silicone*, will slow greatly the coagulation process. Silicone is the most effective substance known for this purpose; it acts like the vascular endothelium in inhibiting the break down of platelets (Jaques and associates) and the formation of thromboplastin activity. Plasma, after collection in silicone-lined apparatus and centrifuged at high speed in order to remove the platelets as completely as possible, will remain fluid for three or four days even at room temperature. The importance of a smooth surface in maintaining the fluidity of blood is also shown clearly in the classical experiment of the "living test tube." If a section of the jugular vein of an animal, e.g., the horse, be isolated between ligatures and carefully removed with its contained blood, this will not clot for a long period, not until changes occur in the lining of the vessel wall and the necessary thromboplastin is thereby provided.

Decalcification. The addition of oxalate (sodium,

potassium or ammonium) or a fluoride to blood to the extent of 0.1% or more, completely destroys its power to clot spontaneously. In the former instance the calcium is precipitated as calcium oxalate. Oxalated blood recovers its ability to clot if shaken with chloroform, but the fibrin which forms redissolves after the blood has stood for a time. Fluoride does not precipitate the calcium but forms a weakly dissociated calcium compound. Sodium citrate also prevents coagulation. In this instance a double salt—calcium sodium citrate— is formed which again is only slightly dissociated.

Neutral salts. Magnesium sulfate solution in a strength of 27% mixed in the proportion of one to four of blood postpones coagulation for some time, but does not prevent it indefinitely. Sodium sulphate in half saturated solution added to an equal quantity of blood has a similar effect, as has also a 10% solution of sodium chloride in the same proportion. The manner in which these substances act is not clear. They do not decalcify the blood.

ANTICOAGULANTS USED THERAPEUTICALLY

At the present time there are two types of anticoagulants used for therapeutic purposes. The anticoagulant heparin which has an immediate direct action on the coagulation system, and a group of drugs, represented by dicumarol, which have an indirect effect on the coagulation system through their action on the liver.

Heparin is a natural occurring sulphonated polysaccharide with strong anticoagulant action. It can be prepared from bovine lung and porcine and bovine intestinal mucosa. It requires a plasma fraction for its antithrombic activity but can inhibit at a number of points during the coagulation process (fig. 33.1). Heparin must be given parenterally since it is not absorbed from the alimentary tract. It is rapidly inactivated and removed from the circulation and the difficulty is to maintain a therapeutic level in the blood while avoiding the danger from bleeding. Prolonged action can be obtained by intramuscular injections of concentrated solutions of heparin. Heparin readily combines with basic peptides and proteins and can be inactivated by protamine.

Dicumarol (4-hydroxycoumarin), which was originally extracted from spoiled sweet clover, lowers the level of prothrombin and associated coagulant factors by acting as an antagonist to vitamin K. There are now a large number of analogues of dicumarol and phenol-indane-dione compounds which are more potent than dicumarol but act similarly. The effect of these drugs can be prevented or overcome by the administration of vitamin K. These drugs have no effect on coagulation when added directly to blood.

The whole problem of anticoagulant therapy is undergoing a great deal of study and there are many physicians who question the therapeutic value of anticoagulants. This problem, however, is beyond the scope of this chapter.

SUBSTANCES WHICH HASTEN THE CLOTTING PROCESS (HEMOSTATICS)

It has been widely accepted that adrenaline hastens coagulation, but such an effect has not been proved. The effects of thrombin and thromboplastin have been discussed. Tissue extracts especially those of lung and thymus which are rich in thromboplastin are powerfully coagulant, as are also the venoms of some species of snakes. The coagulant property of such venoms depends upon their containing a proteolytic enzyme which converts prothrombin to thrombin; the conversion occurs in the absence of ionized calcium.

Thrombin sprayed upon the bleeding surface in conjunction with fibrinogen to form a covering film or foam of fibrin, is an effective means of arresting bleeding, especially from numerous small vessels. Among other hemostatic agents used to hasten the clotting process are sodium alginate, derived from seaweed, and a gauze made of oxidized cellulose, which swells when soaked with blood. When sodium alginate comes into contact with the blood and serum of the wound, it is converted to calcium alginate, which "clots" to form a tenacious layer.

Relation of Blood Fat to Clotting

In recent years evidence that an increase in the level of plasma lipids causes an increase in the development of atherosclerosis and thrombosis has increased. The assumption that there is a relationship between blood clotting and thrombosis has led to numerous studies on the role of lipid in blood coagulation.

The results of tests carried out on whole blood have been controversial. Waldren, Beidelman and Duncan found a shortening of the clotting time in siliconed tubes following a fat meal. Manning and Walford in similar experiments failed to find any significant change. Mirskey and Nossel found their results varied depending on the type of meal ingested and were not directly related to the fat content. Poole found that when plasma was freed from chylomicra by high speed centrifugation its clotting time was increased. The clotting time of such plasma could be returned to normal by the addition of a washed suspension of chylomicra. Robinson and Poole showed that the active fraction of chylomicra was phosphatidyl ethanolamine and that the clotting time of high-spun plasma could be greatly decreased by adding phosphatidyl ethanolamine to it. It is generally agreed that the phosphatides play an important part in the reactions which result in the formation of a clot. As for the neutral fats, results are inconclusive. The variability in results may be a consequence of the type of fatty acid being adsorbed. There is some indication that saturated fats are more active in decreasing clotting time than are the unsaturated. Finally, it has been shown by numerous workers that an increase in neutral fat and phospholipids in blood results in an increased inhibition of the fibrinolytic system. This will result in a decrease in the rate of removal of fibrin. Fibrin deposits may accumulate and thrombus formation be enhanced.

REFERENCES

BEST, C. H., COWMAN, C., AND MACLEAN, D. L. J. Physiol., 1938, **92**, 20.

BIGGS, R. AND DOUGLAS, A. S. J. Clin. Path., 1953, **6**, 23.

BORN, G. V. R. AND CROSS, M. J. J. Physiol., 1964, **170**, 397.

CHARLES, A. F. AND SCOTT, D. A. J. Biol. Chem., 1933, **102**, 425, 437; Biochem. J., 1936, **30**, 1927.

DUGUID, J. P. J. Path. Bact., 1946, **53**, 207.

FANTL, P. AND NANCE, M. Nature, 1946, **158**, 708.

GAARDER, A., JONSEN, J., LALAND, S., HELLEM, A. AND OWREN, P. A. Nature, 1961, **192**, 531.

HEDENIUS, P. Lancet, 1937, **ii**, 1186.

HOWELL, W. H. AND HOLT, E. Am. J. Physiol., 1918, **47**, 328.

DE JONG, B. La Coacervation. Herman, Paris, 1936.

JORPES, E. Naturwissenschaften, 1935, **23**, 196.

LAKI, K. Scientific American, 1962, **206**, 60.

LINK, K. P. AND ASSOCIATES. J. Biol. Chem., 1941, **138**, 21; 1943, **147**, 463. Harvey Lectures 1943–44, **39**, 162. Fed. Proc., 1944, **4**, 176.

LUTZ, B. R. AND FULTON, G. P. Anat. Res., 1954, **120**, 293.

MACFARLANE, R. G. Nature, 1964, **202**, 498.

MACFARLANE, R. G., BIGGS, ROSEMARY, ASH, B. J., AND DENISON, K. W. E. Brit. J. Haemat., 1964, **10**, 530.

MACMILLAN, R. L. AND BROWN, K. W. G. J. Lab. Clin. Med., 1959, **44**, 378.

MANNING, P. R. AND WALFORD, R. L. Am. J. M. Sc., 1954, **228**, 652.

MARGOLIS, J. AND BRUCE, SALLY. Brit. J. Haemat., 1964, **10**, 513.

MCLEAN, J. Am. J. Physiol., 1916, **41**, 250.

MOMMAERTZ, W. F. H. M. J. Gen. Physiol., 1946, **29**, 103, 113.

MONKHOUSE, F. C. Am. J. Clin. Nutrition, 1960, **8**, 1.

MONKHOUSE, F. C. AND CLARKE, D. W. Can. J. Biochem. Physiol., 1957, **35**, 373.

MOOLTON, S. E. AND ASSOCIATES. Arch. Int. Med., 1949, **84**, 667.

OWREN, P. A. Thesis, Oslo, 1947. Lancet, 1947, **i**, 446.

PINNINGER, J. L. AND PRUNTY, F. T. G. Brit. J. Exper. Path., 1946, **27**, 200.

POOLE, J. C. F. Brit. M. Bull., 1958, **14**, 253.

POOLE, J. C. F. Brit. J. Haemat., 1955, **1**, 229.

QUICK, A. J. Am. J. Clin. Path., 1940, **10**, 222; 1945, **15**, 560; Proc. Soc. Exper. Biol. & Med., 1946, **62**, 249; Lancet, 1947, **ii**, 379, 772; Am. J. Physiol., 1947, **151**, 63.

RODERICK, L. M. J. Vet. M. A., 1929, **74**, 314.

SCHOFIELD, F. W. Canad. Vet. Rec. 1922, **3**, 74; Am. Vet. M. A., 1924, **64**, 553.

SEEGERS, W. H. AND ASSOCIATES. Blood, 1946, **1**, 156; Nature, 1958, **182**, 1031.

SHERRY, S., FLETCHER, A. P., AND ALKJAERSIG, N. Physiol. Rev., 1959, **39**, 343.

TOCANTINS, L. M. Am. J. Physiol., 1936, **114**, 709; Am. J. Clin. Path., 1936, **6**, 160; Blood, 1946, **1**, 156.

WALDRON, J. M., BIEDELMAN, B., AND DUNCAN, G. G. Gastroenterology, 1951, **17**, 360.

WATERS, E. T., MARKOWITZ, J., AND JAQUES, L. B. Science, 1938, **87**, 582.

WILANDER, O. Skandinav. Arch. Physiol., 1938, **81**, (Supp. 15), 89.

WRIGHT, H. P. J. Path. & Bact., 1942, **54**, 461.

YUDKIN, J. Lancet, 1964, **ii**, 4.

Monographs and Reviews

BIGGS, R. AND MACFARLANE, R. G. Human Blood Coagulation and Its Disorders. 3rd ed. Blackwell Scientific Publications, Oxford, 1962.

HOWELL, W. H. Harvey Lectures, 1916–17, **12**, 272.

JORPES, J. E. Heparin, Ed. 2. Oxford University Press, London, 1949.

MACFARLANE, R. G. Physiol. Rev., 1956, **36**, 502.

MACMILLAN, R. L. AND MUSTARD, J. F. Anticoagulants and Fibrinolysins. MacMillan Co. of Canada, Toronto, 1961.

MANN, F. D. Ann. Rev. Physiol., 1957, **19**, 205.

QUICK, A. J. Hemorrhagic Diseases. Lea and Febiger, Philadelphia, 1957.

SEEGERS, W. H. Advances Enzymol., 1955, **16**, 23.

WRIGHT, I. S., KOLLER, F. AND BECK, E. Heparin and Thromboplastin with a Survey on Von Willebrand's Disease. Thrombosis et Diathesis Hemorrhagica. Supp. 2, Vol. IX, 1963.

WRIGHT, I. S., KOLLER, F., AND STREULI, F. Thrombolitic Activity and Related Phenomena. Thrombosis et Diathesis Hemorrhagica. Supp. 1, Vol. VI, 1961.

CHAPTER 34

The Regulation of the Hydrogen Ion Concentration
of the Body Fluids

Of all the many characteristics of the body fluids which must be continuously and fairly precisely controlled if the body cells and tissues are to function in a normal way, none is more important than their "reaction"—their degree of acidity or alkalinity. This reaction is determined by, and can be expressed most accurately and clearly in terms of, the concentration of hydrogen ions which these fluids contain and which are present to a greater or less degree in all aqueous solutions. In health, the concentration of hydrogen ions in these fluids is very low, and it is kept constant at a level which is somewhat less than half that present in pure neutral water. Therefore, the "reaction" of these fluids is very faintly on the alkaline side of neutrality. This relative constancy of hydrogen ion concentration in the body fluids is maintained by the activities of numerous homeostatic mechanisms which neutralize, depress, or excrete hydrogen ions at a rate, and in amounts, which are just sufficient to keep their concentration within the normal range —in spite of the continuous production of widely varying amounts of new hydrogen ions every day in the course of normal metabolism.

In many disease states events occur which tend very strongly to increase or decrease the hydrogen ion concentration of the body fluids to levels which are abnormally high or abnormally low and thus to alter seriously the "reaction" of these fluids. These changes are minimized and controlled as much as possible by the homeostatic mechanisms mentioned above and only when these mechanisms are seriously impaired or are overwhelmed do the deviations from normal become so great that they are no longer compatible with life.

The regulation of the "reaction" of the body fluids, then, can be looked upon most simply as the regulation of their hydrogen ion concentration. Instead of "acid-base balance" or "acid-base regulation" or even "neutrality regulation" we can therefore speak of "hydrogen ion balance" or better still, perhaps, of "hydrogen ion homeostasis."

Physicochemical Principles

IONS AND IONIZATION

When certain chemical substances, belonging generally to one of the classes of acids, alkalis, or salts, are dissolved in water, a proportion of their molecules—the proportion varies widely with different substances—is dissociated or "ionized" into their constituent ions. An ion is an atom or group of atoms which has acquired an electric charge because of the loss or gain of one of its negatively charged orbiting electrons and it is referred to as a cation or an anion, respectively, according to whether the charge it carries is a positive or a negative one. Cations are positively charged and are denoted by a plus sign. Anions carry a negative charge and are denoted by a minus sign. In any given substance or solution the number of positively charged cations must always be the same as the number of negatively charged anions. This is the law of electroneutrality.

Such ionizable substances are called *electrolytes*. They are so called because a solution in which one or more of them is dissolved is able to transmit an electric current. When the current is applied the ions migrate in the electric field and carry a charge of electricity to the electrode of opposite charge, the anions going to the positive electrode or anode, the cations going to the negatively charged cathode. The ability of such a solution to conduct an electric current will therefore be a measure of the degree of ionization of the dissolved electrolyte because the conductance will be determined by the concentration of ions in the solution (i.e., by the concentration of the particular electrolyte and by the degree to which this electrolyte is dissociated into its individual ions). Aqueous solutions of substances which, when dissolved in water are highly ionized, are good conductors of electricity, whereas solutions of other substances such as cane sugar, which undergoes little or no dissociation, are not much better conductors than pure water. Most of the inorganic salts are highly ionized and their solutions make excellent conductors of electricity. X-ray studies of sodium chloride crystals, for example, show that the salt crystals are not made up of molecules of NaCl but rather that they are composed entirely of sodium ions (Na$^+$) and chloride ions (Cl$^-$) arranged in a perfectly orderly fashion in what is called a space or ionic lattice. When the crystals are dissolved in water the ions of this lattice are distributed homogeneously throughout the water molecules. Sodium chloride then is 100% dissociated or ionized when present in water in any concentration. Most other salts are also completely or almost completely dissociated into their constituent ions when they are dissolved in dilute aqueous solutions.

The Nature and Origin of Hydrogen Ions

As its name implies, hydrogen ion is derived from hydrogen, the first element in the periodic table. An atom of hydrogen is made up of two primary particles, a positively charged nucleus, the proton, and a negatively charged orbiting electron. When the proton is separated from its electron it becomes the positively charged and highly active hydrogen ion, H$^+$.

A large number of compounds, including many of biological importance and generally known as acids, have one or more hydrogen atoms so situated in their molecular structure that when they are dissolved in water a proportion of their protons can escape to form H$^+$. These hydrogen ions immediately interact with the water molecules to form hydronium ions, leaving their electrons with their negative charge attached to the remaining part of the molecule which now becomes an anion. Using as an example a hypothetical acid HA this reaction may be depicted as:

$$HA + H_2O \leftrightharpoons H_3O^+ + A^- \quad (1)$$

undissoci- water hydronium anion
ated acid   ion

This is a reversible reaction which proceeds simultaneously in both directions, a condition indicated by the use of the double oppositely directed arrows in the equation.

To be chemically correct, therefore, the term hydronium ion or the symbol H$_3$O$^+$ should be used to designate the cation resulting from the ionic dissociation of an acid in water. For ease of presentation, however, in the remainder of this chapter the ordinary term hydrogen ion and the more familiar symbol H$^+$ will generally be used in their stead, it being understood that this is a shorthand device and that by either of these is meant the hydrated hydrogen ion, hydronium ion or H$_3$O$^+$.

The hydronium ion or, more simply, the hydrogen ion is a very powerful chemical agitator and when it is present in a solution in any significant concentration it stimulates a high degree of reactivity and instability among its atomic and molecular neighbours. It therefore plays a very important part in many of the biochemical and metabolic reactions going on in the living organism.

Acids and Bases. The Brønsted-Lowry Concept

From ancient times the characteristic properties of certain substances have caused them to be known as acids or alkalis. An acid substance, such as vinegar, was one which was sour to the taste, and it turned the colour of the blue vegetable dye, litmus, to red; an alkali, such as potash, was bitter or brackish to the taste, was "soapy" to the touch, it turned red litmus blue again and it was able to neutralize of "*kill*" the acid properties of an acid and in so doing to produce a "salt." In 1887 the Swedish chemist Arrhenius proposed that the characteristic properties of acids were due to the properties of hydrogen ions which were produced by ionization of the acid when it was dissolved in water, and that the basic properties of alkalis were due to the presence of hydroxyl ions similarly produced by ionization of an alkali in aqueous solutions. An acid, therefore, was a substance which, when dissolved in water, produced an excess of hydrogen ions, a base was one which gave rise to an excess of hydroxyl ions. This was, and still is, a reasonably true concept, particularly for biological reactions but, since it applies to aqueous solutions only, its application to the broader fields of chemistry is somewhat limited.

In the more recent past it has not infrequently been the custom among clinicians, physiologists and even biochemists to equate the terms "acid" and "base" with anions and cations respectively. Thus the term "acid" has been used to mean any anion such as chloride ion (Cl$^-$), sulphate ion (SO$_4^=$) or phosphate ion (H$_2$PO$_4^-$), whereas the term "base" has been used to mean any cation such as sodium ion (Na$^+$), potassium ion (K$^+$), ammonium ion (NH$_4^+$) and so on. The total "base" of the plasma, for example, has frequently been defined as the sum of the concentrations (in mEq./l.) of all the cations present in it. According to this terminology, H$^+$ would be a "base!"

TABLE 34.1

Some conjugate acid-base pairs

	Conjugate Acid			Conjugate Base	
	$HCl \rightleftharpoons H^+$	$+$	Cl^-		
	$CH_3COOH \rightleftharpoons H^+$	$+$	CH_3COO^-		
Increasing strength of Acid	$H_2CO_3 \rightleftharpoons H^+$	$+$	HCO_3^-		Increasing strength of Base
	$H_2PO_4^- \rightleftharpoons H^+$	$+$	$HPO_4^=$		
	$H\,Pr \rightleftharpoons H^+$	$+$	Pr^-		
	$NH_4^+ \rightleftharpoons H^+$	$+$	NH_3		
	$H_2O \rightleftharpoons H^+$	$+$	OH^-		

Such usage is completely at variance with the language of most other branches of present-day chemistry and its only justification is historic rather than scientific. This misuse of the terms "acid" and "base" has led to many difficulties and misunderstandings and, most important, it neglects to do justice to the central role played by the H^+ ion in acid-base relationships.

A more generally applicable and now widely accepted definition of acids and bases is that proposed independently in 1923 by J. N. Brønsted in Copenhagen and by J. M. Lowry in Cambridge and known as the *Brønsted-Lowry* or *proton* theory of acids and bases. According to this concept an acid is any molecule or ion which can donate a proton to any other substance, whereas a base is any molecule or ion which can accept a proton. In other words, then, an acid is a proton donor, a base is a proton acceptor.

Consider for example the ionization of an acid, depicted, as is usually done, in a simplified form of eq. (1)

$$HA \rightleftharpoons H^+ + A^- \qquad (2)$$

As this reaction proceeds in the forward direction the molecules of HA yield H^+ ions and the anions A^-. HA is therefore an acid. In the backward direction the anion A^- accepts a H^+ to form undissociated HA, and A^- is therefore a base. HA is known as a conjugate acid, A^- is a conjugate base and the two together are known as a conjugate acid-base pair.

According to the Brønsted-Lowry concept, the more readily an acid gives up its protons the stronger it is as an acid and the weaker is its conjugate base. A "strong" acid such as hydrochloric acid donates its protons very readily and its conjugate base Cl^- is correspondingly a very weak base. A "weak" acid, on the other hand, is one which has only a slight tendency to donate its protons and its conjugate base is correspondingly strong. A "strong" base such as NH_3 is one which

has a strong tendency to attract and to hold protons.

Table 34.1 gives a short list of some common conjugate acid-base pairs. The acids are arranged in ascending order of strength and the strength of their conjugate bases is therefore tabulated in the opposite direction. Of the bases listed in the table, Cl^- ion has an almost negligible ability to bind protons. The other bases, however, are relatively strong and they can therefore function effectively in buffer systems as proton acceptors. When present in a solution, they accept and tightly bind H^+ ions and in this way they prevent to a great extent the increase in H^+ ion concentration that would otherwise occur when new H^+ ions are added.

It is to be noted that, in the Brønsted-Lowry definition, acids and bases are not synonymous with anions and cations. An acid, or proton donor, for example, may be an electrically neutral molecule such as HCl, a negatively charged anion (e.g. $H_2PO_4^-$), or even, as in the case of the ammonium ion NH_4^+, a positively charged cation. Similarly, a base or proton acceptor, may be a negatively charged anion such as HCO_3^-, or a neutral molecule such as NH_3. Substances such as Na^+ and K^+ are neither acids nor bases because they can neither donate nor accept protons.

Amphoteric substances. Depending upon the conditions, many substances may, at one time, act as acids or, at other times, as bases. The ion $H_2PO_4^-$, for example, in the presence of a stronger acid, can accept a proton to form H_3PO_4 and under these conditions it is acting as a base. In the presence of a stronger base, $H_2PO_4^-$ can donate a proton yielding H^+ and $HPO_4^=$ and it is here, therefore, acting as an acid. Amino acids and proteins are also able to function as proton donors or as proton acceptors. These and other substances which behave similarly are said to be *amphoteric* or *amphiprotic* in nature.

Ionization of "Weak" Acids. Ionization Constants. "Strong" and "Weak" Acids

When similar volumes of 0.1 M acetic acid and 0.1 M hydrochloric acid are titrated to neutrality with an 0.1 M sodium hydroxide solution it is found that the same amount of the alkali is required for the titration of each of the acid solutions. From this it might be assumed that the two acids are equally "strong." But it is known that at similar concentrations the "acid" properties of hydrochloric acid are very much greater than those of acetic acid. The former, for example, has a much sharper taste, it inverts cane sugar more rapidly, it reacts more vigorously with an active metal such as zinc, it has a more destructive effect upon animal tissues and it will displace acetic acid from its salts.

The difference in the acid properties of the two acids when they are dissolved in water at the same molar concentration is due to the difference in the concentration of the hydrogen ions in the two solutions. Hydrochloric acid, in dilute aqueous solution, is 100% ionized and therefore an 0.1 M solution of HCl is also an 0.1 M solution of hydrogen ions. Hydrochloric acid then is said to be a "strong" acid. Acetic acid, on the other hand, at the same molar concentration, is only 1.3% ionized at 25° C. and therefore an 0.1 M solution of acetic acid is only an 0.0013 M solution of hydrogen ions, the rest of the acid molecules being present in the undissociated state. In dilute solutions of acetic acid, then, the hydrogen ion concentration is only about 1% of that which is present in an HCl solution of the same concentration, and acetic acid is said to be a "weak" acid.

All acids owe their acid properties to the hydrogen ions which are present in their solutions, and the relative "acidity" of different acids is determined not by the molar concentration of the acid but rather by the concentration of hydrogen ions present in equimolar solutions. This in turn will depend upon the extent to which the acid molecules are ionized. In the case of the weak or partially ionized acids this comparison of acid "strength" can be quantitatively expressed in the form of an *ionization* or *dissociation* constant.

When acetic acid is added to water a reversible reaction occurs, in which a proportion of the acid molecules become dissociated, giving rise to a quantity of hydrogen ions and acetate ions. This reaction may be expressed by the chemical equation:

$$CH_3COOH \rightleftharpoons H^+ + CH_3COO^- \qquad (3)$$

Acetic acid	Acetate ions
Conjugate acid	Conjugate base
or	or
Proton donor	Proton acceptor

As indicated, this reaction is one which goes in both directions and not only are acetic acid molecules being dissociated into hydrogen and acetate ions but, at the same time, hydrogen ions and acetate ions are recombining to form molecules of the undissociated acid.

The velocity (V_1) at which this reaction proceeds to the right at any one instant, is, in accordance with the Law of Mass Action, proportionally related to the concentration of the reacting substance or:

$$V_1 = k_1[CH_3COOH] \qquad (4)$$

(Enclosure of the chemical symbols in squared brackets indicates that quantities are being expressed in molar concentrations). Similarly the reverse reaction proceeds from right to left at a velocity V_2, which is also proportional to the concentration of the reacting substances, i.e.

$$V_2 = k_2[CH_3COO^-][H^+] \qquad (5)$$

As V_1 declines and V_2 increases, the two velocities approach each other very quickly and become identical. In this way an equilibrium is reached, at which new undissociated molecules of acetic acid are being formed as rapidly as others are being dissociated. Consequently at this point:

$$V_1 = V_2 = k_1[CH_3COOH]$$
$$= k_2[H^+][CH_3COO^-] \qquad (6)$$

or by rearrangement:

$$\frac{k_1}{k_2} = \frac{[H^+][CH_3COO^-]}{[CH_3COOH]} = K_A \qquad (7)$$

in which K_A is a new constant expressing the relationship of k_1/k_2 at the equilibrium state.

For any partially ionized or weak acid then one can write:

$$\frac{[H^+][A^-]}{[HA]} = K'_A \qquad (8)$$

in which the new constant K'_A indicates that a particular value for K is valid only over a narrow range of special conditions for a particular acid-base or proton donor-proton acceptor system. Conventionally arranged in this way K'_A becomes the *apparent ionization constant*.[1]

Acids containing more than one ionizable hydrogen are known as polybasic acids. They dissociate in stages and there is a dissociation constant, designated by the appropriate number, for each stage. Phosphoric acid is a good example.

$$H_3PO_4 \rightleftharpoons H^+ + H_2PO_4^- \qquad K_1 = 1.1 \times 10^{-2}$$

$$H_2PO_4^- \rightleftharpoons H^+ + HPO_4^= \qquad K_2 = 1.6 \times 10^{-7}$$

$$HPO_4^= \rightleftharpoons H^+ + PO_4^\equiv \qquad K_3 = 3.6 \times 10^{-13}$$

Because of the difficulties associated with the use of such very small and awkward numbers as

[1] For a much more complete consideration of these relationships the student should consult W. Mansfield Clark's "Topics in physical chemistry" (1952).

1.6×10^{-7} as an example (the K_2 of H_3PO_4), the ionization constant is often expressed (as is also the H^+ concentration, (p. 599) in the less cumbersome form of its negative logarithm and in this form it is called the "pK", i.e. $pK = -\log K$.

Taking the K_2 of phosphoric acid (1.6×10^{-7}) as an example:

$$pK_2 = -\log K_2 = -\log (1.6 \times 10^{-7})$$
$$= -(\log 1.6 + \log 10^{-7})$$
$$= -(0.204 + (-7))$$
$$= -0.204 + 7.0 = 6.8$$

$$\therefore pK_2 \text{ of } H_3PO_4 = 6.80.$$

The ionization constants and the pK's of a number of acids are given in table 34.2.

Equation (8) can be rearranged to give a direct expression of the hydrogen ion concentration:

$$[H^+] = K'_A \frac{[HA]}{[A^-]}$$

or

$$[H^+] = K'_A \frac{[\text{Proton donor}]}{[\text{Proton acceptor}]} \quad (9)$$

The hydrogen ion concentration of an aqueous acid solution is therefore expressly related to the ionization constant K'_A and to the pK'_A of the acid. The higher the K'_A and the lower the pK'_A for a given acid, the higher will be the $[H^+]$ for a particular molar concentration and the "stronger" the acid.

The Ionization of Water K_w

Water is an extremely poor electrolyte but even the most highly purified water that can be prepared has a definite and measurable specific electrical conductivity. Therefore, water itself must be slightly ionized and this can be considered to result from the following reaction:

$$H_2O + H_2O \rightleftharpoons H_3O^+ + OH^- \quad (10)$$

or more simply:

$$H_2O \rightleftharpoons H^+ + OH^- \quad (11)$$

In accordance with the Law of Mass Action, equation (11) may be written:

$$\frac{[H^+][OH^-]}{[H_2O]} = K \quad (12)$$

In this equation, the molar concentration of water in water $[(997 \text{ g./l.})/(18.0 \text{ g./M}) = 55.4 \text{ M/l.}]$ can be considered as being constant and it can therefore be neglected. Equation (12) then

may be written as:

$$[H^+][OH^-] = K_{H_2O} = K_w \quad (13)$$

This constant K_w is called the *dissociation constant, ionization constant, or ionic product of water*, and it is of the greatest importance in the consideration of all acid-base relationships.

Extremely careful conductivity measurements indicate that at 24° C. pure water has a hydrogen ion concentration of 1/10,000,000 g./l. This may be written as 0.000,000,1 or as $1/10^7$ or as 1×10^{-7} g. H^+ ion/l.; and as 1 g. H^+ ion = 1 mole H^+ ion, the concentration of H^+ ion in pure water is 1×10^{-7} moles/l.

As the concentration of hydrogen ions and of hydroxyl ions in pure water must always be the same as each other, eq. (13) becomes (at 24° C.):

$$[H^+][OH^-] = (1 \times 10^{-7}) \times (1 \times 10^{-7})$$
$$= 1 \times 10^{-14} \quad (14)$$
$$= K_w$$

and *in all aqueous solutions, regardless of the concentration of H^+ or of OH^-, the product of $[H^+]$ and $[OH^-]$ must always be 1×10^{-14} moles per liter.*

As is true of all other ionizable substances, the ionization of the water molecule is influenced by temperature, and as the temperature rises the degree of dissociation increases and vice versa. Therefore, measurement of hydrogen ion concentrations must always be carried out at known and controlled temperatures.

Equation (14) means, of course, that not only is the product of the concentrations of the hydrogen ions and the hydroxyl ions always the same (at any given temperature), but it also means that if the $[H^+]$ is increased the $[OH^-]$ must correspondingly be decreased. Whereas if the $[H^+]$ is decreased, the $[OH^-]$ must be correspondingly increased to keep K_w constant at 1×10^{-14}. All that is required, therefore, to indicate the concentrations of both H^+ and OH^- ions in any solution is an expression which denotes the concentration of either one. By convention the concentration of H^+ ion has been chosen to express the "reaction" of the solution. If the concentration of H^+ ions in a solution is greater than it is in pure water, i.e., $>1 \times 10^{-7}$ M/l., the reaction is acid; if less than this value, the reaction is alkaline; if precisely the same, the reaction is neutral.

The pH Scale

The concentration of hydrogen ions in a 1.0 M solution of a completely ionized strong acid will be about 1.0 g. ion, 1.0 M or 1×10^0 M/l. As the ionic product $[H^+][OH^-]$ (or K_w) is always approximately 1×10^{-14} at ordinary temperatures in any dilute solution, it follows that in this 1.0 M acid solution the hydroxyl ion concentration must be about 1×10^{-14} M/l., i.e. $(1 \times 10^0) \times (1 \times 10^{-14}) = 1 \times 10^{-14}$. On the other hand in a 1.0 M solution of a fully ionized strong alkali the hydroxyl ion concentration will be about 1.0 g. ion, or 17 g. or 1×10^0 M/l. and in it the $[H^+]$ will be decreased to about 1×10^{-14} M/l. in agreement with the dissociation constant of water K_w, i.e. $(1 \times 10^{-14}) \times (1 \times 10^0) = 1 \times 10^{-14}$. In ordinary dilute aqueous solutions, then, the hydrogen ion concentration can vary tremendously from 1.0 to 0.000,000,000,000,01 M/l. The numerical expression of values which differ so widely can be very unwieldy and inconvenient and they are often difficult to comprehend.

For this reason the "pH" scale in which the whole gamut of hydrogen ion concentrations is expressed by simple numbers ranging only from 0 to 14 (a method first proposed by Sørensen in 1909), has been almost universally adopted for the quantitative way of indicating the concentrations of hydrogen ions present in a solution. The "pH" of a solution is determined electrometrically by a special instrument known as a "pH meter" and the observed value is quantitatively related to the hydrogen ion concentration by the equation:

$$pH = \log \frac{1}{[H^+]} = -\log[H^+] \qquad (15)$$

and *the symbol pH can be defined as the negative common logarithm of the hydrogen ion concentration.*

Although eq. (15) is the one most commonly used in physiology texts to express this relationship, modern electrolyte theory has made it clear that the observed pH is not, in fact, a precise measure of the actual hydrogen ion concentration. The observed values are more closely related, but in a very complex fashion, to hydrogen ion "activity" but this, too, is a relationship which is not absolute and never can be so (Bates, 1964). For this reason the modern pH scale has been given an arbitrary and conventional meaning which is established by calibration with one or more standards, such as those put out by the National Bureau of Standards in Washington, whose assigned pHs are thermodynamically and otherwise acceptable to the theoretical chemist. Although these observations about the exact relationship of pH to absolute hydrogen ion con-

centrations and activities should be kept in mind, no serious difficulties will arise, as far as the present discussion is concerned, if the symbol $[H^+]$ in equation (15) continues to be used in its usual sense perhaps with the added concept, in the biological field at any rate, that it corresponds to the "effective" concentration of hydrogen ions.

It has already been pointed out that the hydrogen ion concentration of pure water is 1×10^{-7} M/l. In this case, by definition,

$$pH = -\log[H^+] = -(-7) = 7.0.$$

Similarly in an 0.01 M solution of a completely ionized strong acid the $[H^+]$ will be $1/100 = 1/10^2 = 1 \times 10^{-2}$ M and this will be represented by a pH of 2.0; or in an 0.00046 M (or in other words in a 4.6×10^{-4} M) solution of HCl, the pH of the solution can be calculated as follows:

$$pH = -\log [H^+]$$
$$= -\log (4.6 \times 10^{-4})$$
$$= -(\log 4.6 + \log 10^{-4})$$
$$= -(\log 4.6 + (-4))$$
$$= -(0.6628^* - 4)$$
$$pH = -0.66 + 4.0 = 3.34.$$

On the other hand, in a solution in which the pH is 4.8 the hydrogen ion concentration can be calculated as follows:

By definition: $-\log [H^+] = pH$
In the above solution then:

$$pH = -\log [H^+] = 4.8; \quad or \quad \log [H^+] = -4.8$$

$\therefore [H^+] = 10^{-4.8} = 10^{+0.2} \times 10^{-5} = 1.58 \times 10^{-5}$ M/l (From antilogarithm tables 1.585 is the antilog of $10^{+0.2}$)

NANOMOLS

Although the pH method of expressing hydrogen ion concentrations has certain virtues, it also suffers from a number of disadvantages, and these have been emphasized in recent years by Huckabee (1961), Campbell (1962) and others. For example, as the H^+ ion concentrations increase, the pH values decrease, and vice versa; for every decrease in 0.3 pH, the $[H^+]$ is doubled, and for every increase of 1.0 pH, the $[H^+]$ falls to one-tenth of its former value.

Again the magnitude of the difference in H^+ concentration represented by a given difference in the pH value varies greatly with the position

* From log tables, 0.6628 is the log of 4.6.

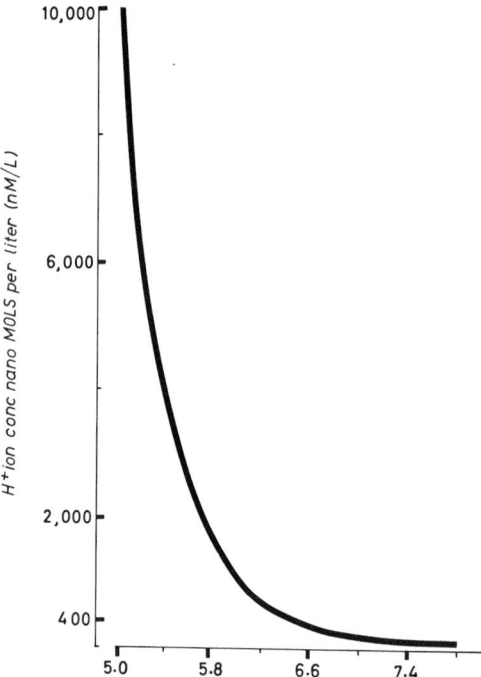

FIG. 34.1. Relationship between pH values and concentrations of hydrogen ions expressed as nanomols per liter (nM/l.)

of the latter in the pH scale. The actual difference in [H$^+$] between pH 7.4 and 7.7 for example is 0.2×10^{-7} M/l., whereas between pH 5.6 and 5.9 (where the difference in pH is the same) the difference in [H$^+$] is 12.8×10^{-7} M/l. or almost 65 times as great and so on. The pH scale, therefore, is neither directly or linearly related to the hydrogen ion concentration. On the contrary, the relationship is inverse and curvilinear in a logarithmic way. This is most easily perceived by inspection of a diagram such as that presented in fig. 34.1, in which the relationship between pH and [H$^+$] is graphically presented.

The concentrations of all the other electrolytes in the body fluids are expressed in terms which are related to the number of their chemical equivalents, or of their gram mols (or gram ions) per liter, and there would not seem to be any logical reason for not expressing the concentrations of H$^+$ in the same way. The use of the term "milliequivalent" (mEq.) or "millimol" (mM) allows the small concentrations of these other electrolytes in the body fluids to be more easily expressed and comprehended than when "mols" or "equivalents" are used. It is simpler for example, to say that the concentration of potassium in a given serum is 4.2 mEq./l. than to say that it is 0.0042 equivalents per liter.

The concentrations of H$^+$ in most of the body fluids is much smaller than the concentrations of the other electrolytes, and a smaller unit than the millimol therefore is necessary to express them easily. At the neutral point the [H$^+$] is 1×10^{-7} or 100×10^{-9} M/l. Thus if we use 1×10^{-9} M as the unit and call it a "nanomol" (a micromillimol), the [H$^+$] in pure water, expressed in terms of this unit, is 100 nanomols per liter or 100 nM/l. Similarly, in the circulating blood, in which the normal reaction expressed in pH units varies from 7.36 to 7.44, the normal range of H$^+$ concentration is 44 to 36 nM/l. with an average of 40 nM/l. The conversion of pH values (in terms of which the H$^+$ concentration is always determined) to nM/l. is done simply by the use of the equation

$$nM/l. = 10^{(9.00-pH)} \qquad (16)$$

e.g. if the pH of a given sample of blood as determined by a pH meter is found to be 7.36, then

$$[H^+] = 10^{(9.00-7.36)} = 10^{1.64} = 43.7* \ (44) \ nM/l.$$

Within the limits of pH 7.28 and 7.45, as pointed out recently by Kassirer and Bleich (1965), each 0.01 decrease in pH below the normal 7.40 means an increase of [H$^+$] of approximately 1.0 nM/l. above the normal average of 40 nM/l., whereas each 0.01 increase in pH above 7.40 means a decrease in [H$^+$] of about 1.0 nM/l. Thus pH 7.40 means a [pH$^+$] of 40 nM/l. whereas pH 7.28 means 52 (actual 52.5) nM/l., and pH 7.46 means 34 (actual 34.7) nM/l. Beyond these limits the logarithmic character of the pH:[H$^+$] relationship causes the [H$^+$] calculated in this simple way, to deviate by more than 1.0 nM/l. from the true values. Remembering however, that a difference of 0.3 pH means doubling or halving the [H$^+$], one can quickly calculate that, if at pH 7.4 the [H$^+$] is 40 nM/l., then at pH 7.1 it must be 80 nM/l., at 6.8 it must be 160 nM/l., and at 7.7 it must be only 20 nM/l.

In table 34.3 the hydrogen ion concentration of body fluids is expressed in terms of the pH scale and also as nanomols per liter. These latter values emphasize clearly that, although the normal range of [H$^+$] of the blood is small, the body, in disease, can at times tolerate levels of [H$^+$] which may be as great as 3–4 times, or as low as ½–⅓ the normal average. The values in table 34.3 emphasize the great ability of the kidneys not only to vary their output of H$^+$, but also to excrete relatively large amounts of H$^+$ ion when the need to do so arises—as it does in states of severe acidosis.

(* 43.7 is the antilog of 1.64).

BUFFERS

When mixtures of weak or poorly ionized acids, and their almost completely ionized soluble salts, are present in a solution, they are able to prevent, or to minimize greatly, the changes in pH which would otherwise be caused by the addition of strong acids or alkalis. For this reason they are called "buffer mixtures" or "buffer systems." Acetic acid and sodium acetate, carbonic acid and sodium bicarbonate, sodium dihydrogen phosphate and disodium hydrogen phosphate are examples of such buffer pairs. For example, if 1.0 ml. of 0.1 M HCl were added to 99 ml. pure water, the pH of the water would be decreased from 7.0 to 3.0, representing an increase in [H+] from 100 nM/l. to 1,000,000 nM/l, an increase of 10,000 times. On the other hand, if the same amount of 0.1 M HCl is added to 99 ml. of a buffer mixture containing equal parts of 0.1 M acetic acid and 0.1 M sodium acetate and having a pH of 4.73, the pH will be depressed by about only 0.02 unit, representing a change in [H+] from 18,600 to 19,500 nM/l., an increase of only 900 nM/l., or only about 0.1% of the increase which the same amount of acid would produce when added to pure water. Similarly, the addition of 1.0 ml. of a solution of a strong alkali such as 0.1 N NaOH to the same buffer mixture will increase the pH, not from 7.0 to 11.0 as it would in pure water, but only from pH 4.73 to about pH 4.75, a change in reaction which is almost negligible.

This "buffering" action of the above buffer mixture can be explained simply by stating that, when a fully ionized strong acid such as HCl is added to such a mixture of sodium acetate and acetic acid, practically all the protons of the HCl are immediately accepted by the acetate ion of the sodium acetate. This forms molecules of almost completely undissociated acetic acid, and at the same time the Cl⁻ ions of the HCl are balanced by an equal number of Na⁺ ions from the sodium acetate to form neutral sodium chloride. As acetic acid is only very slightly ionized, the new acetic acid molecules add only a small number of protons to the mixture and the [H+] is raised by only a slight degree. In other words a strong, fully ionized, acid is replaced by a very weak, poorly ionized one. Similarly, when a fully ionized strong alkali (such as sodium hydroxide) is added to the mixture, the acetic acid of the buffer yields protons to unite with the very powerful base OH⁻ of the NaOH to form neutral water, and the Na⁺ unites with acetate ion to form sodium acetate. The decrease in

[H+] which occurs will, therefore, correspond only to that produced by the decrease in the concentration of the poorly ionized acetic acid. In other words, a buffer mixture is able, within the pH range of its usefulness, to absorb protons whenever the concentration of H+ ions tends to increase, or to liberate protons whenever the [H+] tends to decrease. In this way a buffer mixture acts to keep the [H+] constant, or to resist significant change in this respect in either direction.

Solutions of buffers are used in experiments when, for any reason, it is desired to maintain the fluid medium at a constant hydrogen ion concentration—as for example in studies of enzyme action. Buffer mixtures of various kinds also play an important part in keeping the hydrogen ion concentration of the body fluids within the normal range, in spite of the many metabolic and other activities which tend to change it in one direction or another.

The Henderson-Hasselbalch Equation

The properties of individual buffer systems (including their pH, their range of effectiveness, and their total capacity), are related to the ionization constant of the acid concerned, to the molar proportions of acid to base in the mixture, and to the absolute molar concentrations of its constituents. These relationships are best expressed by the Henderson-Hasselbalch equation.

In the discussion of the ionization of weak acids it was seen that, by a rearrangement of the mass action equation, the hydrogen ion concentration of a weak acid dissolved by itself in water could be expressed as:

$$[H^+] = K'_A \frac{[HA]}{[A^-]} = K'_A \frac{[\text{conjugate acid}]}{[\text{conjugate base}]}$$
$$= K'_A \frac{[\text{proton donor}]}{[\text{proton acceptor}]} \qquad (17)$$

in which K'_A is the dissociation or ionization constant of the acid in question. That is to say, the [H+] of a solution of a weak acid is proportional to the *ratio* of the concentration of the undissociated conjugate acid or proton donor HA, to the concentration of the conjugate base[2] or proton acceptor A⁻.

This equation also holds, except when the ratio of salt to acid is very high or very low, for mixtures of weak acids and their highly ionized salts such as those which make up the buffer systems mentioned above. In these buffer mixtures practi-

---

[2] Used in the Brønsted-Lowry sense.

TABLE 34.2

Ionization constants of some acids at 25°C

(Constants for polybasic acids are indicated by K_1, K_2, K_3; pK_1, pK_2, pK_3)

Acid		K_A		pK_A
Acetic		1.86×10^{-5}		4.73
Acetoacetic		1.6×10^{-4}		3.8
Benzoic		6.6×10^{-5}		4.18
Boric		6.4×10^{-10}		9.19
Carbonic	K_1	7.9×10^{-7}	pK_1	6.1
	K_2	6.0×10^{-11}	pK_2	10.4
Citric	K_1	8.0×10^{-4}	pK_1	3.1
	K_2	2.0×10^{-5}	pK_2	4.7
	K_3	4.0×10^{-7}	pK_3	6.4
Formic		2.0×10^{-4}		3.7
Glucose-1-phos-				
phoric	K_1	7.9×10^{-2}	pK_1	1.1
	K_2	7.4×10^{-7}	pK_2	6.13
Glucose-6-phos-				
phoric	K_1	1.15×10^{-1}	pK_1	0.94
	K_2	7.76×10^{-7}	pK_2	6.11
β-Hydroxy-butyric		3.98×10^{-5}		4.4
Lactic		1.38×10^{-4}		3.86
Phosphoric	K_1	1.10×10^{-2}	pK_1	1.96
	K_2	1.6×10^{-7}	pK_2	6.8
	K_3	3.6×10^{-13}	pK_3	12.4
Sulphuric	K_2	1.2×10^{-2}	pK_2	1.92

cally all the conjugate base A^- present can be assumed to come from the completely dissociated salt. The molar concentration of the base A^-, therefore, will correspond closely to the molar concentration of the salt. The ionization of the weak acid, low to begin with, will be further depressed by the common ion effect and practically all the acid will be present in the unionized form. Therefore, the $[H^+]$ of the mixture will be considerably lower than that of the acid by itself. Equation 17 can then be written as:

$$[H^+] = K'_A \frac{[acid]}{[salt]} \tag{18}$$

and this means that the hydrogen ion concentration of a mixture of a weak acid and one of its salts—or in other words, of a buffer solution—is proportional to the ratio of the molar concentrations of acid to salt in the mixture.

When this equation is written in the form of negative logarithms and "base" is substituted for "salt" it becomes:

$$-\log[H^+] = -\log K'_A - \log \frac{[acid]}{[base]} \tag{19}$$

and when the conventional pH and pK are used

in place of $-\log [H^+]$ and $-\log K'_A$, and when $-\log$ acid/base is replaced by its equivalent $+\log$ base/acid, the equation becomes:

$$pH = pK'_A + \log \frac{[base]}{[acid]} \tag{20}$$

This is the well known Henderson-Hasselbalch equation.

If the pK'_A of the acid, and the molar concentrations of the acid and its salt are known, one may directly calculate the pH of a buffer solution by the use of this equation. For example, in a buffer solution containing 100 ml. of 0.10 M acetic acid and 200 ml. of 0.10 M sodium acetate, and made up to a final volume of 1 l., the pH (knowing that the pK_A' of acetic acid is 4.73) (table 34.2) will be:

$$pH = pK'_A + \log \frac{[base]}{[acid]}$$

$$pH = 4.73 + \log \frac{0.02}{0.01} \tag{21}$$

$$= 4.73 + \log 2.0$$

$$= 4.73 + 0.30 = 5.03$$

Again if a buffer mixture contains equal parts of 0.1 M acetic acid and 0.1 M sodium acetate (the final concentration of each being 0.05 M):

TABLE 34.3

Range of reaction of some body fluids

Fluid	pH	Hydrogen Ion Conc. Nanomols per l.
Pure water	7.0	100
Blood		
Normal mean	7.40	40
Normal range	7.36–7.44	44–36
Very severe acidosis	6.8	160
Very severe alkalosis	7.8	16
C.S.F. normal range	7.36–7.44	44–36
Pure gastric juice, normal	1.0	100,000,000
Urine		
Normal average, about	6.0	1000
Maximum acidity	4.5	31600
Maximum alkalinity	8.0	10
Intracellular fluid (muscle) (DMO)*	6.8	160

* Determined indirectly by the distribution of 5,5-Dimethyl-2,4 oxazolidinedione (Waddell and Butler 1959).

$$pH = pK'_A + \log \frac{[base]}{[acid]}$$

$$pH = 4.73 + \log \frac{0.05}{0.05} \qquad (22)$$

$$= 4.73 + \log 1.0$$

$$= 4.73 + 0 = 4.73$$

From eq. (22) it is seen that when the molecular ratio of base (salt) to acid in the mixture is unity, the pH of the solution will be the same as the pK'_A of the buffer acid. This fact is used experimentally to determine the pK'_A of weak acids. A solution of a weak acid exactly half neutralized by a strong alkali will contain equimolar concentrations of salt and acid and the pH of the mixture determined at that point will be the pK' of the acid being titrated.

When the pH values of different buffer mixtures, containing various base/acid ratios, are determined experimentally or by the use of equation (20), and are plotted against the base/acid ratios (fig. 34.2), typical sigmoid curves are obtained. These curves show that the change in pH produced by the addition of acid or base to these buffer mixtures will be the least, and the effectiveness of the buffer will be the greatest, when the base/acid ratios are not far from unity, and that a buffer mixture will therefore function best at pH values which are within 1.0 pH unit on either side of the pK' value of its acid component. On the other hand, it is also obvious from these curves that the ability of the buffer mixture to resist change in its pH on the addition of acid or base becomes increasingly less towards either end of the sigmoid curve.

The curve for the $[HCO_3^-]/[H_2CO_3]$ system deserves special mention because of its physiological importance and because the acid portion of the buffer pair—carbonic acid—is formed by the reaction between the gas carbon dioxide and water, i.e.:

$$CO_2 + H_2O \rightleftarrows H_2CO_3 \rightleftarrows H^+ + HCO_3^- \quad (23)$$

The equilibrium of this reaction is far to the left, and in blood plasma the concentration of *dissolved* CO_2 is about 1000 times that of the carbonic acid. If more CO_2 is dissolved in the solution, however, more carbonic acid and more H^+ will also be present; and if CO_2 is removed, the concentrations of carbonic acid and of H^+ will be decreased. In a sense then, carbonic acid is volatile, for its concentration in any solution will be determined by the amount of the dissolved volatile CO_2 present with which the carbonic acid is always in equilibrium. In turn, the amount of dissolved CO_2, in mM/l., is related by the factor α to the partial pressure of the CO_2 (pCO_2), in

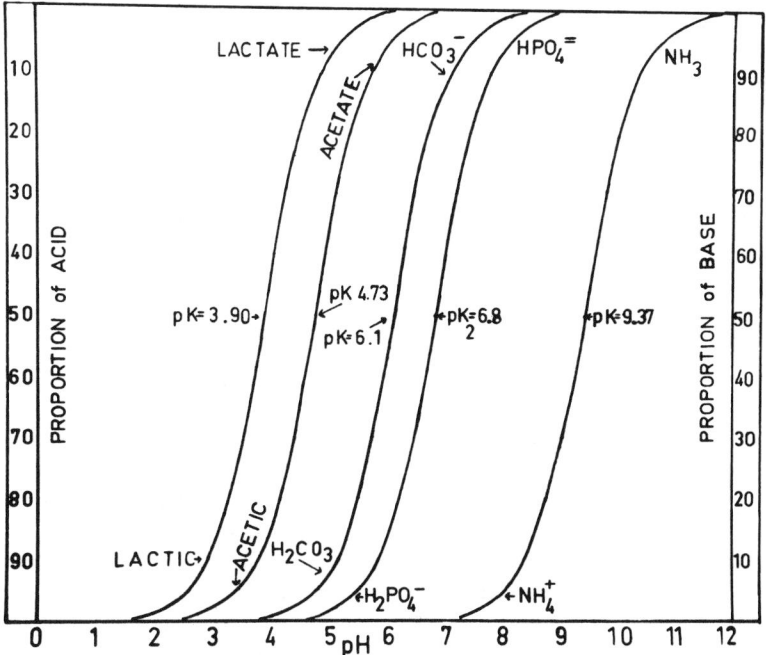

Fig. 34.2. Calculated titration curves for several buffer systems showing the relation between [Base]/[Acid] ratios and pH.

mm. Hg, in the gaseous phase with which the solution is in equilibrium (Henry's Law). The value for factor α varies with the temperature and the nature of the solution, and for blood plasma and carbon dioxide at 38° C., α is 0.0301, i.e.:

$$pCO_2 \text{ (in mm. Hg)} \times 0.0301 \tag{24}$$
$$= \text{dissolved } CO_2 \text{ (in mM/l.)*}$$

It is obvious that the bicarbonate buffer curve (fig. 34.2) is one which could be produced only in a closed system in which it is possible to vary the CO_2 tension. The curve also illustrates that within the possible range of pH in the living individual (pH 6.8–7.8), the chemical efficiency of the bicarbonate/carbonic acid buffer mixture—that is, its ability to resist pH change following the addition of acid or base—is very low. Nevertheless, this buffer system is an excellent one to help regulate the hydrogen ion concentration in living organisms because of the ease with which the pCO_2 in the body fluids (and therefore the concentrations therein of dissolved CO_2 and H_2CO_3) can be varied by respiration so that the $[HCO_3^-]/[H_2CO_3]$ ratio (and therefore the pH) of the extracellular fluids is kept relatively constant under a wide variety of circumstances. The great usefulness of this buffer system will be discussed later on in this chapter after the mechanisms which carry CO_2 in the blood and regulate the plasma CO_2 tension have been more fully considered.

Proteins as Buffers

Among the various buffer systems in living individuals, the proteins occupy a prominent

* Although the denominator of the bicarbonate buffer pair $[HCO_3^-]/[H_2CO_3]$ is usually written as H_2CO_3, in fact, it is made up almost entirely of dissolved CO_2 which is in equilibrium with a very small amount of carbonic acid (eq. 23). The pK' (6.1) of the so-called "carbonic acid," as it is used in the Henderson-Hasselbalch equation (eq. 20), has, however, been determined by calculation using this equation, after measuring the pH and the "total CO_2" (see below) of blood and plasma equilibrated with CO_2 at 38° C, and at accurately known CO_2 tensions. The "acid" of which the pK' has been determined is therefore:

$$0.0301 \times pCO_2 \text{ (mm. Hg)} \rightleftharpoons$$
$$\text{dissolved } CO_2 \rightleftharpoons H_2CO_3 \tag{25}$$

To simplify expression, however, and to prevent confusion between "dissolved CO_2" and "total CO_2," the term "carbonic acid" and the chemical symbol "H_2CO_3" will generally be used in the remainder of this chapter to designate the acid denominator of the bicarbonate buffer pair, remembering that both of these are simply abbreviated ways of stating the more cumbersome expression (25) which is given above.

place because they are able at one time to act as proton donors and at another to act as proton acceptors. In other words, depending upon the conditions, they may function either as acids or as bases and they are therefore said to be *amphoteric*. The reason for this kind of behaviour is that the amino acids making up the protein molecule contain both basic —NH_2 groups and acidic —COOH groups.

The dual nature of these substances may be illustrated by the behaviour of glycine, the simplest of the amino acids. The ordinary structural formula for glycine may be written as $NH_2 \cdot CH_2 \cdot COOH$, in which the carboxyl group —COOH is the acidic group or proton donor, and the —NH_2 group is the basic group or proton acceptor. However, it has been shown both in the solid state and in solution, that such amino acids exist almost completely as "hybrid" ions or "zwitterions" and these can be considered to be the result of the transfer of a proton from the carboxyl group to the amino group thus:

$$NH_2 \cdot CH_2 \cdot COOH \rightleftharpoons NH_3^+ \cdot CH_2 \cdot COO^- \tag{26}$$
$$\text{glycine} \qquad \text{zwitterion of glycine}$$

In this way one part of the glycine molecule acquires a positive charge and the other a negative one, but the molecule as a whole remains electrically neutral.

When H^+ ions (protons) are added to the amino acid in solution they are accepted by the —COO^- portion of the zwitterion to form an undissociated —COOH group and a positively charged glycine cation:

$$NH_3^+ \cdot CH_2 \cdot COO^- + H^+ \rightleftharpoons$$
$$NH_3^+ \cdot CH_2 \cdot COOH \tag{27}$$

On the other hand, when a base such as OH^- is added to the amino acid solution, the NH_3^+ portion donates a proton which unites with the hydroxyl group to form water and a negatively charged glycine anion results:

$$NH_3^+ \cdot CH_2 \cdot COO^- + OH^- \rightleftharpoons$$
$$NH_2 \cdot CH_2 \cdot COO^- + H_2O \tag{28}$$

Thus glycine and other amino acids can function as buffer systems, donating or accepting protons when necessary and in this way diminishing the changes in pH which would otherwise be caused by the addition of acids or bases.

The numerous amino and carboxyl groups which are united with one another in proteins to form the peptide bonds do not take part in this buffering action. Other basic and acidic groups, however, are present and free in the molecule—

such as the ε-NH₂ group of lysine, the guanidine group of arginine, the imidazol group of histidine, the free carboxyl groups of the dicarboxylic acids, the phenolic hydroxyl group of tyrosine and the sulfhydryl group of cystein, which do allow proteins to act as zwitterions and to function as potent buffer mechanisms.

This buffer potential of protein molecules is graphically represented in fig. 34.3 (adapted from Davenport, 1958).

Conditions in a Multibuffer System

No matter how many different buffer systems are present in a given solution, the pH of the mixture is, of course, the same throughout. The different buffer mixtures must, therefore, all be in equilibrium with one another and in each case the ratio of base to acid will be determined by the pH's and by the pK's of the acids concerned. In the plasma and interstitial fluids, for example, the equilibrium can be represented as follows:

$$pH = pK_{A_1} + \log \frac{[HCO_3^-]}{[H_2CO_3]} =$$

$$pK_{A_2} + \log \frac{[HPO_4^=]}{[H_2PO_4^-]} = pK_{A_3} + \log \frac{[Pr^-]}{[HPr]} \quad (29)$$

If the [H⁺] tends to become altered, all the buffer systems simultaneously take part in resisting the change, and any shift in the ratio of base to acid in one will take place in all the others. As a corollary, the quantitative determination of the base/acid ratio of the bicarbonate buffer system, which can be done easily, will allow not only the pH of the mixture to be calculated, but it will also be representative of the changes in the base/acid ratios of all the others as well. Although not necessarily the same as that of the plasma, the pH of the intracellular fluid buffers will also be in equilibrium with those of the extracellular fluids, and the control of the intracellular pH will, therefore, be largely dependent upon the regulation of the H⁺ ion concentration of the extracellular fluids.

Mechanisms and Reactions Concerned with the Regulation of the Hydrogen Ion Concentration of the Body Fluids

HYDROGEN ION BALANCE

The normal concentration of H⁺ ions in the extracellular body fluids, ranging as it does from 44 to 36 nM/l., and represented by a pH variation from 7.36 to 7.44, is the result of a continuously maintained dynamic equilibrium between the intake and production and the suppression and excretion of hydrogen ions.

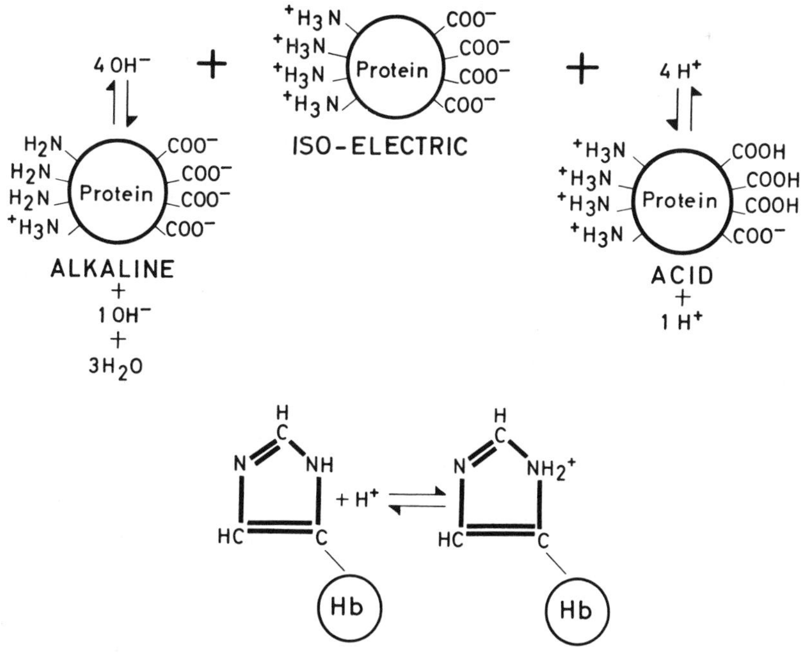

FIG. 34.3. Schematic representation of the buffering of acids and bases by plasma proteins and by the imidazole groups of hemoglobin histidine. (Adapted from Davenport, H. W.: The ABC of acid-base chemistry, 4th ed., University of Chicago Press, Chicago, Ill. 1958.)

A. Sources of Hydrogen Ion

Although a small amount of hydrogen ions may be taken in with the food or as medication, most of them arise from the numerous metabolic activities which are going on unceasingly in the living individual. The major sources of new hydrogen ions include:

1. *Oxidation of carbon compounds to produce carbon dioxide.* Carbon dioxide is the ultimate end product of the oxidation of carbon compounds, and in an average adult at rest, about 200 ml. (almost 10 mM) of this gas is produced in the tissues, transported by the blood, and eliminated by the lungs per minute, or about 10,000–14,000 mM per day. The rate of its formation depends upon the rate of metabolism and during severe exercise it may be increased to ten or more times this amount. Carbon dioxide is soluble in water and the actual concentration of CO_2 in the tissue fluids at any one time is determined by the partial pressure of the gas in these fluids. This in turn is regulated by the respiratory system, which normally keeps the pCO_2 in the pulmonary alveoli and in the arterial blood at about 36–44 mm. Hg. At this partial pressure the concentration of CO_2 in the plasma is 1.1–1.3 mM/l. and this is always in equilibrium with a small amount of hydrated carbon dioxide or carbonic acid:

$$CO_2 + H_2O \rightleftharpoons H_2CO_3 \rightleftharpoons H^+ + HCO_3^- \quad (30)$$

Although the actual amount of carbonic acid present in a solution of carbon dioxide is very small, and although carbonic acid is a weak acid ($pK_1' = 6.1$) solutions of carbon dioxide in pure water have a much higher concentration of hydrogen ions than do the body fluids; and even though the CO_2 is normally excreted by the lungs as rapidly as it is formed, the continuous addition of this acid-producing gas to the blood at the periphery, and its loss from the blood in the lungs, requires the activities of efficient mechanisms to prevent serious changes in blood pH from being caused by these two events. These mechanisms will be discussed below. They are efficient, as is shown by the fact that the pH of venous blood differs from that of arterial blood by only a few one-hundredths of a pH unit. Any condition which prevents the lungs from excreting carbon dioxide as rapidly as it is formed, or causes them to excrete more than is being produced, will of course result in a change in the CO_2 and carbonic acid concentrations of the body fluids and this, if not counterbalanced, may cause significant changes in blood pH.

2. *Conversion of neutral food stuffs to organic acids.* A great variety of moderately strong organic acids are produced during the normal intermediary metabolism of neutral carbohydrates, fats and proteins, and equivalent amounts of H^+ ions are temporarily released into the body fluids. Most of these intermediary acids are oxidized to CO_2 and H_2O or otherwise metabolized and in this way are eliminated as rapidly as they are formed. As long as this occurs their hydrogen ions disappear again, and no effect is produced on the overall hydrogen ion balance. At times, however, because of excessive metabolic activity, or because of the presence of certain diseases or for some other reason, these intermediary organic acids may be produced in greater quantities than can be metabolized or excreted, and when this occurs there will be a greater or less accumulation of H^+ ions and a fall in the pH of the body fluids.

3. *Oxidation of the sulfur in organic compounds.* The oxidation of the sulfur-containing amino acids methionine and cysteine will yield equivalent amounts of hydrogen ion and sulfate ion. This can be illustrated by the equation (greatly simplified):

$$2C_5H_{11}N_1O_2S + 15O_2 =$$
methionine

$$\underbrace{4H^+ + 2SO_4}_{\substack{\text{sulfuric} \\ \text{acid}}} + (NH_2)_2CO + 7H_2O + 9CO_2$$
$$\text{urea}$$

That H^+ are produced in this way is shown by the finding that the administration of a methionine load to an individual is followed by an increase in the renal excretion of H^+, which parallels very closely the excretion of sulfate ions (Relman, 1964).

4. *Formation of inorganic phosphate.* The hydrolysis of phosphoesters and the breakdown of phosphoproteins, nucleoproteins and phosphatides in foods, result in the formation of inorganic phosphates and the liberation of corresponding amounts of H^+ (Relman, 1964). This can be illustrated by the following equation:

$$R-O-\underset{\underset{OH}{|}}{\overset{\overset{O}{|}}{P}}-OH + H_2O =$$
ortho
mono ester

$$R \cdot OH + \frac{0.8HPO_4^- \; (4)}{0.2H_2PO_4 \; (1)} + 1.8H^+$$
(Ratio at pH 7.4)

In normal persons, on the usual protein intake, the last three of the above processes produce only about 50–90 mM H^+ per day, but as the acids from which these are derived are nonvolatile or "fixed" they cannot be excreted by the lungs and their elimination must, therefore, be brought about by the action of the kidneys. The production of H^+, particularly by the last two mechanisms, will be increased by any acceleration of protein breakdown and especially by the elevated rate of endogenous protein destruction which follows a severe tissue injury or other cause of increased catabolism. When these injuries are accompanied, as they often are, by shock and by severe renal failure from acute tubular necrosis, the increased production of these strong acids, coupled with the impaired renal ability to excrete them, may lead rapidly to a serious accumulation of H^+ ions, and to a sharp and dangerous fall in the pH of the body fluids.

5. *Medication.* Medication with ammonium salts or with mineral or organic acids, such as mandelic acid, may occasionally add significantly to the load of H^+ ions that must be handled by the body. Ingestion of ammonium salts is equivalent, as far as supplying H^+ ion is concerned, to the ingestion of the corresponding amount of the free acid, since each ammonium ion taken in is converted in the liver to urea with the liberation of a proton:

$$2NH_4Cl \quad + CO_2 =$$
ammonium
chloride

$$\underbrace{2H^+ + 2Cl^- } + H_2O + (NH_2)_2CO$$
hydrochloric   urea
acid

B. Excretion and Fixation of H^+ Ions

The addition of new H^+ to the body, whether from intake or metabolism, is balanced by the action of chemical or physiological mechanisms which normally remove them as rapidly as they are formed so that the $[H^+]$ of the body fluids remains reasonably constant. These mechanisms include:

1. *Dilution.* Hydrogen ions formed in excess at any one site—as for example in an exercising muscle—are rapidly distributed by the circulation throughout the whole of the extracellular fluid. Although not a regulatory mechanism in the usual sense, the dilution brought about in this way will help to minimize the local increase of H^+ concentration which would otherwise occur.

2. *Buffer systems.* A variety of buffer systems are present in the extracellular and cellular fluids of the blood and tissues. These function in the manner already described (p. 604), as the first line of defense in preventing alterations in $[H^+]$ from being produced by the addition of acids or bases, and to help keep the H^+ concentration of these fluids within the normal range. These buffer systems are:

a. *In the blood plasma.* (i) *The bicarbonate/carbonic acid buffer system.* Quantitatively the

most important buffer in the plasma is the one made up of sodium bicarbonate and carbonic acid. The normal ratio of the two components of this buffer system in the plasma is:

$$\frac{[HCO_3^-]}{0.0301 \times pCO_2 \text{ (43 mm. Hg)}} =$$

$$\frac{[HCO_3^-]}{[H_2CO_3]} = \frac{26 \text{ mM/l.}}{1.3 \text{ mM/l.}} = \frac{20}{1} \tag{31}$$

As the pK_A' of carbonic acid is 6.1, it can be calculated from the Henderson-Hasselbalch equation that as long as this *ratio* of bicarbonate and carbonic acid is maintained, the pH will be 7.4:

$$pH = pK' + \log \frac{[base]}{[acid]} = \tag{32}$$

$$6.10 + \log 20 = 6.10 + 1.30 = 7.40$$

The very great importance of this buffer system in the control of the extracellular pH and its association with the respiratory regulation of carbon dioxide excretion will be discussed below.

(ii) *The phosphate buffer system.* This consists of the mixture of the alkaline and acid phosphates of sodium:

$$\frac{Na_2HPO_4}{NaH_2PO_4}$$

In this buffer pair the acid phosphate may be regarded as a weak acid (pK_{A2}' for phosphoric acid is 6.8) and the alkaline phosphate as the fully ionized salt of the buffer pair. The normal ratio of base to acid in this case at the pH of normal blood is 4/1.

$$pH = pK_{A2}' + \log \frac{[base]}{[acid]} = \tag{33}$$

$$6.8 + \log \frac{4}{1} = 6.8 + 0.60 = 7.4$$

(iii) *Plasma proteins.* As discussed previously, the plasma proteins act as buffers and, at the pH of the blood, they behave as a mixture of poorly dissociated weak acids and their almost completely ionized sodium salts:

$$\frac{Na^+ \text{ proteinate}^-}{H \text{ proteinate}}$$

b. *In the red blood cells.* Important buffer systems, distinct and separate from those of the plasma, are also present and active within the red blood cells and these are:

(i) $\dfrac{Potassium\ oxyhemoglobinate}{H\ oxyhemoglobin}$ $\dfrac{K^+\ HbO_2^-}{HHbO_2}$

(ii) Potassium hemoglobinate   K⁺ Hb⁻

    H hemoglobin   HHb

(iii) *Intracellular organic phosphate complexes* such
as adenosine diphosphate, creatine phosphate, etc.

Within the red blood cells the oxygen-carrying protein, hemoglobin, acts as a buffer to H^+ ions much in the same way as do the plasma proteins (p. 604) but in this case the buffering is done mainly by the imidazole groups of the histidine in the Hb molecule (fig. 34.3). Both the oxygenated and the reduced Hb systems are depicted above, because oxidation of Hb to HbO_2 causes it to become a stronger acid, that is, to donate more H^+ ions, whereas the reduction of HbO_2 to Hb causes it to become less acid and to become more effective as an acceptor of H^+ ions. The formation of the more acid oxyhemoglobin in the alveoli by the oxidation of reduced hemoglobin will, therefore, compensate in part for the loss of H^+ ions and for the decrease in H^+ concentration at this site resulting from the excretion of CO_2. In the same way the reduction of arterial HbO_2 to Hb in the peripheral circulation, where oxygen is given up, enables the hemoglobin molecule to accept and to fix more of the extra hydrogen ions added to the blood by the addition of carbon dioxide from the tissue cells. Because oxyhemoglobin has a somewhat greater ability than plasma proteins to bind H^+ and because about four times as much red cell hemoglobin as of plasma proteins is present in a given volume of whole blood (150 g. to 40 g./l.), the protein buffering capacity of whole blood is about six times that of a similar volume of plasma.

c. *In the extracellular fluids and tissue cells.* Only a portion of the total buffer capacity of the body resides in the buffers of the blood plasma and red blood cells. The interstitial fluids have a bicarbonate and phosphate buffer concentration similar to that of the circulating plasma, and these play their part in all buffer reactions. In addition to these buffer systems, however, it has been shown by Pitts and his co-workers (1963) and by others, that somewhat more than 50% of the hydrogen ions, infused as strong acid intravenously into nephrectomized animals, are transferred into tissue cells in exchange for sodium and potassium ions. These exchange reactions occur across all tissue cell membranes and make available in this way the large quantities of cellular protein and organic phosphate complexes for the buffering of extracellular hydrogen ions. The superficial surfaces of the bones may also play a role in these reactions. Similar ionic exchanges in the reverse direction allow the cellular constituents to take part in the buffering of extracellular base whenever this becomes necessary.

All the buffer systems in the blood plasma and extracellular fluids, in the red blood cells and in the cells of the various tissues are of course in dynamic equilibrium with one another and take part in all the buffer reactions.

3. *The handling, transport and excretion of carbon dioxide.* This subject is fully covered in chapter 50 "Uptake and Delivery of Respiratory Gases" so that there is no need here to do more than to review it quickly in relation to H^+ regulation.

The large amounts of potentially acid-producing carbon dioxide, continuously being released from all the body tissues by cellular metabolism, are handled without seriously disturbing the $[H^+]$ of the body fluids in a manner which may be briefly described as follows:

a. *The role of the plasma in the transport of CO_2.* The metabolically produced carbon dioxide is transferred as dissolved CO_2, under a partial pressure of from 45–60 mm. Hg, from the tissue interstitial fluids to the blood coming from the arterial system as it passes through the tissue capillaries and where, at the same time, some of the red cell oxyhemoglobin is being converted to the reduced form as a part of its oxygen is given up to the tissues. A portion of this CO_2 unites with the proteins of the blood plasma to form carbamino compounds:

$$-RNH_2 + CO_2 \rightleftharpoons -R \cdot NH \cdot COO^- + H^+ \quad (34)$$
free protein   carbamino group
amino group

but the amount handled in this way, however, is very small because the plasma proteins have only a few NH_2 groups which are capable of uniting with CO_2 in this manner. Some of the CO_2 remains dissolved as such in the plasma. A small portion of this becomes hydrated and gives rise to H^+ ions by the familiar reaction:

$$CO_2 + H_2O \rightleftharpoons H_2CO_3 \rightleftharpoons H^+ + HCO_3^- \quad (35)$$

Although the equilibrium point of this reaction is far to the left, the reaction is pushed slightly to the right by the new CO_2 added from the tissues and this results in the liberation of a small amount of new hydrogen ions. These, as well as those liberated by the formation of the plasma protein carbamino compounds (eq. (34)) are buffered by the phosphate and protein buffers of the plasma, with the result that the $[H^+]$ of the plasma is increased by only a slight degree due to the addition of the new carbon dioxide.

b. *The role of the red blood cells in the transport of carbon dioxide.* Most of the CO_2 which is added to the capillary blood from the tissues diffuses quickly into the red cells. Here a portion of it combines with hemoglobin to form carbamino compounds as in eq. (34) and the degree to which this occurs is considerably enhanced by the reduction of some of the oxyhemoglobin to the reduced form which is going on at the same time. The greater part of the CO_2 entering the red cells, however, is very quickly changed into carbonic acid by the high intracellular concentration of carbonic anhydrase, an enzyme which specifically accelerates the rate of the reaction between CO_2 and water (eq. (35)) in both directions by more than 1000 times (Roughton, 1935). The marked increase in $[H^+]$ caused by this reaction is buffered mainly by the imidazole groups of the hemoglobin buffer system (see fig. 34.3):

$$K^+Hb + H^+HCO_3^- \rightleftharpoons K^+HCO_3^- + H\ Hb \quad (36)$$

The buffering of these H^+ ions is also made more effective by the simultaneous reduction at this site of HbO_2 to the less acid Hb and, for every mM of Hb formed, an additional 0.7 mM H^+ can be buffered by this protein. Thus it is seen that the ability of the blood to handle CO_2 both as carbamino compounds and as carbonic acid is much increased by the change of hemoglobin to its reduced form, an event which takes place where the CO_2 is added and where this increased ability is most needed.

As the bicarbonate ion concentration inside the red cells is increased by the above reaction, it tends to exceed the concentration of this ion in the plasma fluid with which it is always in equilibrium. Consequently a portion of the red cell bicarbonate ion diffuses through the cell membrane into the plasma in exchange for an equimolar amount of Cl^- which passes in the opposite direction. This is the phenomenon known as the *chloride shift*. The exchange of one negative ion for another which occurs here is necessary for the preservation of electrical neutrality because the positively charged K^+ ion associated with the intracellular bicarbonate does not readily pass through the red cell wall. The addition of bicarbonate ion to the plasma produced in this way helps to keep the $[HCO_3^-]/[H_2CO_3]$ ratio in the plasma at a constant level and it also enables the blood plasma to transport a considerable portion of the CO_2 produced by cellular metabolism from the tissues to lungs in the form of bicarbonate ion, without causing more than a slight increase in the $[H^+]$ of this fluid.

c. *Excretion of CO_2 by the lungs.* When the venous blood, with its CO_2 tension elevated to 46 or more mm. Hg, reaches the lungs it comes into intimate contact with an alveolar pCO_2 which is normally kept at a constant level of about 40 mm. Hg by the activities of the respiratory system. Because of this difference in CO_2 tension, carbon dioxide now rapidly diffuses from the blood in the pulmonary capillaries into the alveolar spaces (and thence with each exhalation into the expired air) in amounts just sufficient to reduce the pCO_2 in the pulmonary capillary blood to that in the pulmonary alveoli. All the carbon dioxide which

was picked up by the blood in the peripheral tissues, and transported mainly as bicarbonate ions and carbamino compounds, is now released for excretion into the alveolar spaces by reactions which are exactly the reverse of those which took place in the periphery and need not again be described. At the time that the pCO_2 in the plasma is being decreased by diffusion into the alveoli, the plasma bicarbonate concentration is also being lowered by the diffusion of some of it, again in exchange for Cl^- ions, back into the red cells. Here it is quickly broken down into CO_2 and water by the action of the now more acid oxyhemoglobin and the red cell carbonic anhydrase. The CO_2 thus released diffuses rapidly first into the plasma and thence into the alveoli to be excreted to the outside air in the usual way. During this period the plasma and red cell buffer systems are acting now to minimize the effect of the *loss* of large quantities of carbon dioxide on the blood hydrogen ion concentration. This is done very efficiently and is greatly helped by the increased acidity of the oxyhemoglobin being newly formed in the lung capillaries.

d. *The integrated role of the respiratory system and the bicarbonate/carbonic acid buffer system in the regulation of hydrogen ion concentration.* The ultimate regulation of the pH level of the arterial blood is carried out by the respiratory system, which, by controlling the minute volume of respired air, is able to vary the amount of CO_2 excreted to the outside air in such a way that the $[HCO_3^-]/[H_2CO_3]$ ratio in the plasma is kept relatively close to the normal value of 20/1 no matter how much or how little carbon dioxide is being produced and at this ratio, as has already been emphasized, the pH will be 7.40. If the quantity of CO_2 being removed from the blood by respiration is not sufficient to keep up with that being added by metabolism, the pCO_2 and the carbonic acid content of the arterial plasma leaving the lungs and passing through the respiratory center will be slightly higher than normal. The $[HCO_3^-]/[H_2CO_3]$ ratio and the pH of this blood will be slightly depressed and the $[H^+]$ will be slightly elevated. As a consequence the respiratory center, being very sensitive to changes in the pH and pCO_2 of the blood passing through it, will normally be stimulated to increase the degree of pulmonary ventilation. More CO_2 will be exhaled and removed from the venous blood and this will continue until the $[HCO_3^-]/[H_2CO_3]$ ratio and the pH of the blood leaving the lungs are restored to normal again. On the other hand if too much CO_2 is being lost by respiration this ratio will be increased, and the pH of the arterial blood will be slightly elevated. This change in the pH of the blood passing through the respiratory center will cause the pulmonary ventilation to be decreased. Less CO_2 will be excreted and more will be retained in the arterial blood until the ratio and pH return once more to the normal values.

The above discussion of the handling of carbon dioxide emphasizes the very important role played by the respiratory system, and its very sensitive feedback controls, in the normal regulation of the [H+] of the body fluids; it also enables us to understand more readily the great ability of the bicarbonate system, in spite of being such a poor buffer from the chemical point of view, to prevent the serious changes in [H+] which would otherwise be produced in many pathological conditions. Consider for example the situation in which an overproduction of the relatively strong organic acid acetoacetic acid (pK = 3.8) is occurring in a patient with uncontrolled diabetes. As soon as this strong acid is formed its hydrogen ions will be bound by buffer bases, including bicarbonate ion from plasma sodium bicarbonate, to form weak undissociated acids, including potentially volatile carbonic acid. If 4 mM of acetoacetic acid (HAc) were neutralized by bicarbonate in a *closed stationary system* having a volume of 1 l. and containing bicarbonate ion and carbonic acid in the concentrations usually present in blood plasma, the immediate reaction could be expressed as follows:

$$\frac{26 \text{ mM NaHCO}_3}{1.3 \text{ mM H}_2\text{CO}_3} \frac{(20)}{(1)} + 4 \text{ mM HAc} = \qquad (37)$$
$$\frac{22 \text{ mM NaHCO}_3}{5.3 \text{ mM H}_2\text{CO}_3} \frac{(4)}{(1)} + 4 \text{ mM NaAc}$$

In such a *closed system* the pCO_2 and the concentration of carbonic acid would be quadrupled by the reaction between 4mM of the strong acid and 4 mM of NaHCO$_3$. The [HCO$_3^-$]/[H$_2$CO$_3$] ratio would be lowered from the normal

$$\frac{26}{1.3} \frac{(20)}{(1)} \text{ to } \frac{22}{5.3} \frac{(4)}{(1)}$$

and the pH would therefore be reduced to 6.70 (calculated from the Henderson-Hasselbalch equation (eq. 32). In the individual with a functioning respiratory apparatus, however, the system is *not a closed but is an open one*, and moreover it is open to a gaseous phase (in the alveolar spaces) in which the pCO_2 is regulated by pulmonary ventilation so as to keep the plasma [HCO$_3^-$]/[H$_2$CO$_3$] ratio at close to 20/1 and the pH therefore at 7.40. As rapidly as the extra H$_2$CO$_3$ is produced by the buffering of the acetoacetic acid in the above reaction, it is transported to the lungs where the increased ventilation, stimulated by the slight fall in the pH of the blood flowing through the respiratory center, causes it to be excreted rapidly to the open air in amounts almost sufficient to keep the ratio and the pH at normal values.

It will be noticed from the above equation that for each 1 mM of strong acid neutralized, 1 mM

HCO$_3^-$ is lost and the capacity of the buffer system to handle more acid is thereby reduced to this extent. In serious acidosis this reduction of plasma bicarbonate may continue as more acid is added and, as a result, the bicarbonate concentration may be depressed to levels as low as $\frac{1}{4}$ or even $\frac{1}{10}$ the normal. At the same time the ventilation is accelerated, sometimes to the very noticeable and labored degree known as Kussmaul's breathing, removing not only the CO$_2$ which has been set free from bicarbonate ion but additional amounts as well, thereby decreasing the pCO_2 in the alveoli and plasma to values below the normal levels and low enough, in many cases, to keep the [HCO$_3^-$]/[H$_2$CO$_3$] ratio, and therefore the plasma pH, close to normal. If the pH of the plasma is in fact kept within the normal range by the loss of extra CO$_2$ in the face of a decrease in bicarbonate concentration the situation is said to be fully compensated. Usually, however the respiratory compensation is only partial and, particularly in severe cases, the pH will be slightly or even markedly below the normal range. The fall in the pH level occurring under these circumstances is very much less, however, than it would have been if the respiratory system had not been able to "blow off" CO$_2$ in amounts sufficient to maintain the [HCO$_3^-$]/[H$_2$CO$_3$] ratio close to its usual normal level of 20/1.

Similarly, when the plasma bicarbonate ion concentration is increased and the [H+] diminished, as for example by the ingestion of base such as bicarbonate ion in the form of NaHCO$_3$, or by the loss to the outside by the vomiting of highly acid gastric juice, the resulting increases in the [HCO$_3^-$]/[H$_2$CO$_3$] ratio and in the arterial plasma pH, tend, by their effect on the respiratory center, to slow down ventilation. The excretion of CO$_2$ will thus be diminished, the plasma pCO_2 and [H$_2$CO$_3$] elevated, and the plasma [HCO$_3^-$]/[H$_2$CO$_3$] ratio and pH will be at least partly restored to their normal values. The effect of an elevated pH on the respiratory center may however be only slightly evident because the slowing of respiration will also cause a lowering of oxygen tension in the blood and this will stimulate the respiratory center in the opposite direction.

It is not to be inferred from the above that the plasma bicarbonate buffer system and its regulation by the respiratory apparatus are alone responsible for the buffering of all the changes in [H+] which may be produced by the addition or loss of acids or bases to the body fluids. However as has been pointed out in a previous section, all the buffer systems of the body are in equilibrium with one another and the effect of the respiratory control on the bicarbonate system is transmitted to all the others.

4. Metabolic events such as the oxidation or utilization of certain organic acids. Most of the organic acids, except uric acid, produced during the breakdown of normal food stuffs, appear only momentarily as intermediary products of metabolism and, as they usually disappear as quickly as they are formed, they normally have little effect on the hydrogen ion regulation. Occasionally, however, as for example during severe exercise, lactic acid may be produced in amounts larger than can quickly be metabolized and, in spite of a large increase in respiration and the "blowing off" of large amounts of CO_2, the pH of the blood may be lowered appreciably below the normal range. The subsequent disappearance of the lactic acid, resulting from its oxidation or conversion to glycogen, removes the extra protons associated with its accumulation, replenishes the depleted store of HCO_3^- ions and restores the pH back to normal. Similarly the low levels of blood pH and of plasma bicarbonate which are present in severe diabetic acidosis are at least partially restored to normal when the excess acetoacetic acid present in the blood is destroyed following adequate treatment with insulin and glucose.

5. *Renal mechanisms in the regulation of hydrogen ion concentration.* A very important part in the control of the [H$^+$] of the body fluids and in the regulation of the overall H$^+$ ion balance is also played by the kidneys. This particular activity of the kidneys, along with the many other aspects of renal function, is fully discussed in ch. 79 and little therefore needs to be said about it here. In brief the kidneys are able, mainly through the activities of the cells lining the tubular lumina, to excrete widely varying quantities of H$^+$, both as titratable acid and as ammonium ions (NH_4^+), into the urine or to eliminate excessive quantities of base whenever either of these actions is necessary for the purpose of maintaining a normal level and balance of hydrogen ions. The tubular cells also help to maintain the concentration of bicarbonate ions in the blood and other extracellular fluids at the normal level of 24–28 mM/l. by varying the extent to which bicarbonate ion in the glomerular filtrate is reabsorbed back into the blood again or is passed on to the bladder urine to be excreted to the outside. Also, when the normal store of bicarbonate ion in the body is depleted, as it may be by the addition of more nonvolatile acid than can normally be handled, the kidney tubules, in association with their excretion of H$^+$ ions, form large quantities of new bicarbonate ions, which, when added to the blood, help at least partially to restore the concentration of this ion towards its normal level. The decrease in plasma HCO_3^- concentration resulting from diabetic acidosis, for example, would be much more severe and would occur much more rapidly than it does, if it were not for the ability of the renal tubules not only to excrete appreciable quantities of hydrogen ions but also, at the same time, to make new bicar-

bonate ions to take the place of those which have been used up in the neutralization of the excess acid.

Disturbances in the Regulation of H$^+$ Ion Concentrations in the Blood

ACIDOSIS AND ALKALOSIS: DEFINITIONS

In the healthy person, as has already been stated, the H$^+$ concentration of the blood and extracellular fluids is maintained, by a number of regulating mechanisms, at a level which is slightly lower than that of strict neutrality. That is to say the blood is normally faintly alkaline in reaction and the pH rarely varies more than 0.04 pH units on either side of the average pH 7.40. It has also been shown that this regulation is closely related to the regulation of the ratio existing between the concentrations of bicarbonate ion and of the carbonic acid in the blood plasma and that the concentrations of both these components and their relative amounts are closely controlled by the correlated activities of the renal mechanisms and the respiratory apparatus. The renal mechanisms so function that they endeavour to maintain the bicarbonate ion concentration in the blood at the normal level of 24–28 mM/l., and the respiratory activities attempt to control the output of carbon dioxide in such a way that, regardless of the actual concentration of bicarbonate ion, the ratio between the bicarbonate ion and the carbonic acid in the blood is at all times kept close to 20 to 1. As long as these controlling mechanisms continue to function properly, and as long as the loads they have to bear are within their capabilities, both these objectives will be achieved, and not only will the pH be kept within the normal range but so will the capacity of the body to deal with added demands upon the regulatory mechanisms be kept at full effectiveness.

In a large number of pathological conditions the clinical and metabolic disturbances associated with, or caused by, the illness, subject the mechanisms responsible for the control of the pH of the body fluids to a considerable strain. In other conditions too, the functional ability of these mechanisms to meet this strain is decreased either by disease or for other reasons, sometimes to a point where even a normal load cannot be properly handled. In all such cases the ability of the body to resist changes in the pH of its fluids may at times be overcome and if this occurs the [H$^+$] of the body fluids will, depending upon the nature of the underlying primary cause, be either increased or decreased to levels which are more or less beyond the normal range.

Two major departures from the normal in this respect are obviously possible.

1. The blood and extracellular fluids may become more acid (or, if preferred, less alkaline) than normal. Here the pH is depressed to a greater or less degree below pH 7.36 and the hydrogen ion concentration will be correspondingly higher than 44 nM/l. This is the state of *acidosis*[4] and in the most severe cases the pH may fall as low as pH 6.9 or even pH 6.8.

2. The blood and extracellular fluids may on the other hand become more alkaline (or less acid) than normal. Here the pH is elevated, again to a greater or less degree, above pH 7.44 and the hydrogen ion concentration is less than 36 nM/l. This is the state of *alkalosis*[4] and in the most severe cases the pH of the blood may be as high as pH 7.8.

The mathematical relationship between the pH of the plasma and the concentration of bicarbonate ion and carbonic acid is defined by the Henderson-Hasselbalch equation, which for this system can, when everything is normal, be written:

$$pH = pK'_A(H_2CO_3) + \log \frac{[HCO_3^-]}{[H_2CO_3]} =$$

$$6.1 + \log \frac{26 \text{ mM}}{1.3 \text{ mM}} \left(\frac{(20)}{(1)} \right) = 6.1 + 1.3 = 7.4.$$

(38)

This equation makes it evident that the determining factor fixing the pH of the blood is the $[HCO_3^-]/[H_2CO_3]$ ratio. When this ratio is decreased the pH of the blood is lowered and a

[4] Some will disagree with using the terms "acidosis" and "alkalosis" in the sense in which they are employed in this chapter and would prefer, perhaps, to use the terms "acidemia" and "alkalemia" (or "basosis") in their place. "Acidosis" and "alkalosis" have long been used by clinicians and they are consistent with the initial direction of the change taken by the H[+] concentration in response to the primary clinical disturbance. It does not seem valid to define these terms, as some have done, solely on the basis of the concentration of plasma "bicarbonate," "total CO₂," or "total buffer base," because the determination of any one of these by itself gives no indication at all of the $[HCO_3^-]/[H_2CO_3]$ ratio and it is this *ratio* rather than the absolute amounts of either (or of the sum of both) that determines whether the plasma is more acid or more alkaline than normal. For further discussions of these and of other words used in the terminology acid base disturbances, see Creese et al. (1962) and also the proceedings of the "Conference on Current Conception of Acid Base Measurements," New York Academy of Sciences, November, 1964 (Ann. N. Y. Acad. Sci., 133: in press, 1965).

state of acidosis is present; and when it is increased the pH is elevated and an alkalosis has developed. It also shows that the ratio may be decreased or increased by changes either in the concentration of the carbonic acid (the denominator) or of the bicarbonate ion (the numerator) component of this buffer fraction. pH changes in the blood caused primarily by alterations in carbonic acid levels are, as a general rule, brought about by alterations in respiratory function and can, therefore, be referred to as being "gaseous" or "respiratory." On the other hand, pH changes which are primarily due to alterations in the bicarbonate ion concentrations are usually associated with metabolic disturbances and therefore can be called either "metabolic" or "non-respiratory."

With these observations in mind the possible primary abnormalities in hydrogen ion regulation may be listed as in table 34.4.

Compensatory reactions. Whenever any clinical or other disturbance threatens to alter the [H[+]] of the body fluids in one direction or another the mechanisms responsible for the maintenance of the normal state come into action to minimize the effect of the addition or loss of excess acid or base. The buffer systems of the blood and other extracellular fluids, and indeed, of the whole body, play their part in resisting alterations in pH and they serve as the first line of defence against the initial onslaught.

Because of its great sensitivity and rapid response to slight changes in the blood pH, the respiratory system also plays an important part in restricting the magnitude of pH changes. By altering the rate of excretion of CO_2, the $[HCO_3^-]/[H_2CO_3]$ ratio and the plasma pH are kept as close to normal as possible. When, as in metabolic acidosis, the HCO_3^- ion concentration has been reduced, the pCO_2 (and carbonic acid) content of the plasma will, by hyperventilation, also be decreased. When the bicarbonate ion concentration is increased, as in metabolic alkalosis, the pCO_2 will, by hypoventilation, also be elevated. The renal mechanisms also have an indispensable role in this regulating activity. Through the activities of the renal tubular cells, the kidneys are able to excrete or to retain large quantities of acids or bases when it is necessary to prevent these from accumulating or decreasing in the body fluids, and the tubules can also manufacture new bicarbonate ions when these are required. When disturbances in H[+] concentration are due primarily to respiratory abnormalities which cannot

TABLE 34.4

Illustrative examples of possible primary abnormalities in hydrogen
ion regulation (if uncorrected or uncompensated)

Clinical Condition	Biochemical Abnormality	Plasma $\frac{[HCO_3^-]}{[H_2CO_3]}$ ratios		
		mM/l.	Numerical	pH
Normal	None $[HCO_3^-]$ molar conc. $[H_2CO_3]$ and ratio normal	26 mM/1.3 mM	20/1	7.4
Acidosis I. "Gaseous" or "Respiratory" acidosis	*Primary CO_2 excess* $[H_2CO_3]$ increased $\frac{[HCO_3^-]}{[H_2CO_3]}$ reduced *pH decreased*	26 mM/2.6 mM	10/1	7.1
II. "Metabolic" or "non-Respiratory" acidosis	*Primary bicarbonate deficiency* $[HCO_3^-]$ decreased $\frac{[HCO_3^-]}{[H_2CO_3]}$ decreased *pH decreased*	13 mM/1.3 mM	10/1	7.1
Alkalosis I. "Gaseous" or "respiratory" alkalosis	*Primary CO_2 deficiency* $[H_2CO_3]$ decreased $\frac{[HCO_3^-]}{[H_2CO_3]}$ increased *pH increased*	26 mM/0.65 mM	40/1	7.7
II. "Metabolic" or "non-Respiratory" alkalosis	*Primary bicarbonate excess* $[HCO_3^-]$ increased $\frac{[HCO_3^-]}{[H_2CO_3]}$ increased *pH increased*	52 mM/1.3 mM	40/1	7.7

be relieved, the major correction or compensation is accomplished by the renal mechanisms. In the presence of respiratory acidosis, for example, in which the plasma pCO_2 and H_2CO_3 content is high, the kidneys retain and manufacture new bicarbonate ions which, when added to the blood, elevate the plasma bicarbonate ion concentration above the normal. In this way the $[HCO_3^-]/[H_2CO_3]$ ratio, which would otherwise be decreased because of the elevation of the pCO_2, is at least partially prevented from falling as low as it would otherwise do. For this reason the bicarbonate concentration (and the total CO_2 content) may be considerably higher than normal in the plasma of patients who have a CO_2 retention acidosis. On the other hand, when a primary respiratory alkalosis is present and the plasma CO_2 concentration has been lowered by excessive overventilation, the kidneys, in an attempt to keep the $[HCO_3^-]/[H_2CO_3]$ ratio normal, excrete an alkaline urine containing considerable quantities of bicarbonate ion. Therefore, in respiratory alkalosis the plasma bicarbonate and the total CO_2 content may be definitely reduced. These renal compensatory activities take place relatively slowly, however, and an appreciable length of time is necessary before the full effect of their actions become apparent. For this reason, marked compensatory alterations in bicarbonate concentrations in the respiratory disturbances will usually be seen only in chronic cases.

Because all the buffer systems are in equilibrium with one another the effect of the respiratory and renal mechanisms on the ratio of base to acid in the bicarbonate system is transmitted to all the other buffer and regulatory mechanisms.

TABLE 34.5

Illustrative examples of possible results of complete or partial compensation on $\dfrac{[HCO_3^-]}{[H_2CO_3]}$ *ratios* $\Big($ *normal* $\dfrac{26 \text{ mM}}{1.3 \text{ mM}}$ *or* $\Big(\dfrac{20}{1}\Big)\Big)$, *and pH (normal = 7.40) in the four major types of Acid Base Disturbances.*

	Ratios								
	If uncompensated (unlikely)			If fully compensated (unlikely)			If partially compensated (usual)		
	mMolar	Numerical	pH	mMolar	Numerical	pH	mMolar	Numerical	pH
A. *Acidosis*									
I. Respiratory (Denominator increased)	26 mM/2.6 mM	10/1	7.1	52 mM/2.6 mM	20/1	7.4	46 mM/2.6 mM	17.7/1	7.35
II. Metabolic (Numerator decreased)	13 mM/1.3 mM	10/1	7.1	13 mM/0.65 mM	20/1	7.4	13 mM/0.8 mM	16.2/1	7.31
B. *Alkalosis*									
I. Respiratory (Denominator decreased)	26 mM/0.8 mM	32.5/1	7.61	16 mM/0.8 mM	20/1	7.4	22 mM/0.8 mM	27.5/1	7.54
II. Metabolic (Numerator increased)	39 mM/1.3 mM	30/1	7.58	39 mM/1.95 mM	20/1	7.4	39 mM/1.5 mM	26/1	7.52

For this reason, too, the chemical analyses of the components of the bicarbonate system, which now can be easily and accurately carried out by modern methods, will reflect the condition of all the others.

Although the various activities briefly described above are reasonably successful in preventing large and dangerous changes in H$^+$ concentrations the compensation is rarely complete. In most cases of acidosis, other than in those of mild degree, the pH of the blood will be displaced to a greater or less degree below the lower range of normal. Similarly, in most cases of alkalosis the pH will be elevated to levels which are more or less above the upper limit of the normal range (table 34.5).

The four major types of acid base disturbances may be briefly described as follows:

1. *Respiratory acidosis. Primary carbon dioxide excess. Carbon dioxide retention. Hypercapnia.* In emphysema, pulmonary fibrosis, acute pulmonary edema, pneumothorax and in other pulmonary diseases; in conditions such as abdominal distention, gross obesity, bulbar poliomyelitis, opiate poisoning and in situations in which the air being breathed already has an elevated CO$_2$ content, the ability of the lungs to excrete even normal amounts of carbon dioxide may be grossly impaired. As a result the pCO$_2$ and [H$_2$CO$_3$] of the body fluids may become markedly elevated. The [HCO$_3^-$]/[H$_2$CO$_3$] ratio and the pH of these fluids will consequently be depressed below the normal values because of increase in the denominator of the buffer pair and a state of *respiratory acidosis* will be produced. The extent to which these changes do occur will be minimized by the following reactions:

a. Whenever CO$_2$ tends to accumulate, the respiratory center, if not depressed, will stimulate an increased degree of ventilation if this is possible, and the excess CO$_2$ will be excreted. Often, however, as in conditions such as those mentioned above, the respiratory mechanisms are not able, for one reason or another, to respond to a sufficient degree to the stimulus and the pCO$_2$ remains elevated. The respiratory center soon loses its sensitivity to increased CO$_2$ tensions and a chronic state of carbon dioxide retention is established. In severe cases the CO$_2$ accumulation may continue to elevate the CO$_2$ concentration in the body fluids and a CO$_2$ narcosis may eventually develop. Mechanical aids to respiration may be necessary to control the accumulation and to prevent the onset of this dangerous complication.

b. The buffering actions of the various body

buffer systems, including those inside the tissue cells, help to limit the extent of the [H$^+$] increase associated with the accumulation of the excess carbonic acid and at the same time they cause the HCO$_3^-$ concentration in the plasma and other extracellular fluids to be increased to some degree.

c. The kidneys increase the excretion of hydrogen ions and, by almost completely reabsorbing the bicarbonate ions from the glomerular filtrate and making new bicarbonate ions which are added to the circulation, the renal tubular cells increase the bicarbonate ion content of the body fluids so that the lowered [HCO$_3^-$]/[H$_2$CO$_3$] ratio and the depressed pH are raised towards more normal values.

In the acute cases of severe respiratory acidosis there may be insufficient time for the renal mechanisms to compensate for the increased CO$_2$ retention and the pH may, therefore, be quickly reduced to dangerously low levels. In the more chronic cases, the plasma bicarbonate concentration may be elevated to levels high enough to return the pH of the blood close to the normal range. Although the pH in the blood of these patients may be almost normal or at most, only slightly depressed, the total plasma CO$_2$ content and plasma bicarbonate will be much increased. Overly enthusiastic ventilation by mechanical means could, by removing some of the excess CO$_2$, readily convert the disturbance in such a patient into one of respiratory alkalosis.

2. *Metabolic acidosis. Non-respiratory acidosis. Primary bicarbonate deficiency.* The addition of excess amounts of non-volatile or "fixed" acids to the body fluids will produce a greater or less degree of *metabolic acidosis.* These acids may have their origin from medication (e.g. ammonium salts), from overproduction (acetoacetic acid in uncontrolled diabetes mellitus, lactic acid in severe hypoxia, formic acid in methanol poisoning), or from inadequate renal excretion of acids produced in normal metabolism as in patients with chronic nephritis or renal tubular acidosis. The hydrogen ions of these fixed acids are taken up by bicarbonate ions and other extracellular and intracellular proton acceptors, but by this action the concentration of bicarbonate ion and other available buffer bases may be considerably reduced. A similar reduction in the concentration of bicarbonate ion will be produced by the actual loss from the body of this ion by diarrhea or drainage from a biliary, pancreatic or intestinal fistula. By any of these means the [HCO$_3^-$]/[H$_2$CO$_3$] ratio is decreased because of a decrease in the numerator of the buffer pair and the pH of the body fluids is correspondingly lowered. These changes are "compensated" in part by an increased pulmonary ventilation, which, by "blowing off" CO$_2$, decreases the carbonic acid concentration of the body fluids and thus, by lowering the denominator, helps to elevate the depressed [HCO$_3^-$]/[H$_2$CO$_3$] ratio and the pH of these fluids towards more normal values. The kidneys also play their part for not only do the renal tubular cells increase their hydrogen ion excretion in the form of ammonium salts and titratable acid but they also aid in the restoration of the lowered plasma bicarbonate ion by almost completely reabsorbing this ion from the glomerular filtrate, and by forming new bicarbonate ion which is added to the circulating blood.

3. *Respiratory alkalosis—primary CO$_2$ deficiency.* Excessive hyperventilation, due, not to an elevated pCO$_2$ or increased hydrogen ion concentration, but to voluntary effort, hysteria, anoxic anoxemia, central nervous system disease, or to toxic stimulation of the respiratory center (as in salicylate poisoning), will cause an excessive excretion of carbon dioxide from the body, a decrease in the CO$_2$ tension and carbonic acid content of the body fluids and, because of the decrease in the denominator, an elevation of the [HCO$_3^-$]/[H$_2$CO$_3$] ratio to levels higher than the normal 20 to 1. The pH of the body fluids will be elevated and a respiratory alkalosis established. In compensation, the decrease in [H$^+$] of the body fluids will be partly buffered by protons derived from the buffer systems of the extracellular and cellular compartments. The renal tubules conserve H$^+$ by ceasing to excrete ammonium ions and titratable acid. Reabsorption of bicarbonate ion from the glomerular filtrate is sharply diminished and considerable amounts of bicarbonate ion are excreted in the urine. The plasma [HCO$_3^-$]/[H$_2$CO$_3$] ratio and pH are thus lowered towards normal by decreasing the numerator and at the expense of some of the extracellular bicarbonate. In respiratory alkalosis the plasma bicarbonate concentration may be decreased to below the normal range.

4. *Metabolic alkalosis: primary bicarbonate excess. Non-respiratory alkalosis.* This type of alkalosis can result from the ingestion of excessive amounts of sodium bicarbonate (or of salts such as sodium citrate or sodium lactate which are transformed by metabolic oxidation into sodium bicarbonate) for therapeutic reasons, or it may be caused by the loss of H$^+$ ion from the body by the vomiting of hydrochloric acid containing gastric juice. In each of these cases the plasma

TABLE 34.6

*Biochemical abnormalities of the blood plasma
in the four principal types of H^+
ion disturbances*

	pH	pCO$_2$*	HCO$_3^-$	$\dfrac{[HCO_3^-]}{[H_2CO_3]}$
		mm. Hg	*mM/l.*	*Numerical ratio*
Normal	7.4	43	26	*20/1*
Respiratory acidosis	↓	↑	↑	↓
Respiratory alkalosis	↑	↓	↓	↑
Metabolic acidosis	↓	↓	↓	↓
Metabolic alkalosis	↑	↑	↑	↑

*mm. Hg. [H$_2$CO$_3$] = 0.0301 × pCO$_2$ at 38° C.

bicarbonate concentration, the [HCO$_3^-$]/[H$_2$CO$_3$] ratio, and the plasma pH all become elevated and a *metabolic alkalosis results*. The increased amount of base is buffered by protons from extracellular and intracellular buffers. The elevated pH depresses the respiratory centre and a compensating retention of CO$_2$ by the lungs may occur to some degree but the simultaneous decrease in oxygen intake, caused by the decreased ventilation, prevents this type of compensation from being very effective. Hydrogen ions are conserved by the kidney and some of the elevated plasma bicarbonate is excreted into the urine. In the presence of the depressed H$^+$ concentration, in the tubular fluid reabsorption of sodium by the distal renal tubules is accomplished by exchange for secreted K$^+$ instead of H$^+$ and this may lead to an increased K loss in the urine and to a depletion of body potassium. If not replaced from exogenous sources, the loss of potassium from the extracellular fluids is partly replaced by potassium liberated from tissue cells in exchange for extracellular H$^+$ and Na$^+$. This transfer of H$^+$ from the extracellular fluid to the cells brought about in this way, accentuates the extracellular alkalosis and tends at the same time to cause an intracellular acidosis. Similarly, in other cases of potassium depletion, no matter how produced, the loss of H$^+$ from the extracellular fluid to the cells in exchange for a part of the cellular K decreases the [H$^+$] of the extracellular fluids and causes the development of an extracellular alkalosis. Also, in the potassium depleted individual, the low potassium content of the distal renal tubular cells causes the Na$^+$ reabsorption occurring at this site to take place mainly in exchange for secreted H$^+$ instead of K$^+$. In such cases the urine may be acid (paradoxical aciduria) in spite of the extracellular alkalosis, and the loss of H$^+$

produced in this way may tend to aggravate the alkalotic state. In these cases too, it may be possible to relieve the alkalosis only by supplying the missing potassium.

INVESTIGATION AND ASSESSMENT OF DISTURBANCE IN H$^+$ REGULATION

The direction of the deviations from normal shown by the more important biochemical characteristics of the blood in each of the four major types of acid-base disturbance are set forth in table 34.6. As the data in this table show, a depressed pH would be found in both the respiratory and metabolic type of acidosis, a lowered pCO$_2$ could indicate the presence of either a respiratory alkalosis or a metabolic acidosis, and an elevated plasma bicarbonate concentration could be a characteristic of either a respiratory acidosis or a metabolic alkalosis. Although, in most cases, the nature of the responsible clinical disturbance would suggest the type of acid-base abnormality present, it is obvious that it is not possible to be certain of the exact diagnosis on the basis of the determination of any single biochemical characteristic of the blood plasma, such as the pH or the bicarbonate ion concentration, by itself alone. A complete interpretation of the situation in any given patient will require accurate information about each of the three responsible variables: the pH, the pCO$_2$ (H$_2$CO$_3$ = 0.0301 × pCO$_2$), and the bicarbonate ion concentration of the arterial plasma. Only when the values of all three are known will it be possible to understand accurately the true nature of the disturbance.

An inspection of the Henderson-Hasselbalch equation:

$$pH = pK'_A + \log \frac{[base]}{[acid]}$$

indicates that if the pK$'_A$ of the acid is known and if any two of the other three unknowns (pH, concentration of base, concentration of acid) can be measured, the third unknown can then be calculated. With the development of modern measuring devices it is now possible to measure all three with great accuracy provided the necessary care is taken to collect the blood in such a way that its contents are not disturbed, and to carry out the measurements under the exact conditions of temperature, and O$_2$ and CO$_2$ tension which actually exist in the blood.

Collection of Blood

To obtain the most accurate results, heparinized arterial blood or arterialized capillary blood should be used for the determination of pH, pCO_2 and total plasma carbon dioxide content. Arterial blood can be collected by puncture of the femoral or brachial artery, using a plastic syringe in which the dead spaces in both the syringe and needle are occupied by 0.15 ml. or so of 1% ammonium heparinate. After the blood has been removed a drop of mercury may be introduced into the syringe to aid in mixing and the tip of the syringe is sealed with a tightly fitting plastic or rubber cap. Analyses should be done as soon as possible to avoid pH changes which may be caused by loss of CO_2 or by glycolysis. These changes are minimized but not completely prevented by immersion of the charged syringe in ice water or by storing it at 3° C. After mixing by gentle rotation, samples of whole blood for pH measurements and other determinations can be transferred directly to the apparatus from the syringe tip with minimal exposure to air. The syringe and its contents can be centrifuged, tip end up in a special holder and the plasma then can be sampled directly by an anerobic technique for determination of the total CO_2 content and other constituents. Arterialized capillary blood can be collected from a freely flowing lancet stab of the warmed ear lobe, finger tip or heel (in babies), directly into special capillary tubes coated on the inside with a small amount of dry heparin, and containing a small steel wire which permits mixing by the use of a magnet. After complete filling, the capillary ends are sealed with wax. The analyses are carried out as soon as possible by one or other of the special techniques such as the one developed by Astrup (1961) for use with micro samples.

In many cases venous blood obtained from the patient in the fasting and resting state and collected into a heparinized syringe from an arm vein without the use of a tourniquet will be reasonably satisfactory for most clinical purposes. Blood collected directly into commercially available heparinized vacuum tubes is also suitable for these determinations—provided the tubes are completely filled with blood and no space is left into which the blood gases may move.

Determination of Total CO₂ Content

The term "total plasma CO_2 content" means all of the carbon dioxide that can be liberated from blood plasma obtained from arterial blood collected and handled anerobically as described above, when it is acidified and shaken in a vacuum. It represents, therefore, the sum of the carbon dioxide dissolved as such in the plasma, including the small amount present as carbonic acid, plus all the CO_2 derived from the action of the liberating acid on the plasma bicarbonate. It can be conveniently determined by the Van Slyke macro- or Natelson micro-manometric techniques with great precision and it must be determined in one of these ways if it is to be used in the calculation of the pCO_2 and bicarbonate concentration, both of which may be necessary in the careful investigation of a respiratory problem. In many cases, however, such as in following a patient with diabetic acidosis under therapy or a patient vomiting from pyloric obstruction, or in the investigation of other types of acid-base disturbances in which the physician wishes to know only the extent to which the plasma bicarbonate has been lowered or elevated, the determination of the total CO_2 content of carefully taken venous plasma in the Technicon or other type of automatic analyser will give answers which are sufficiently accurate for most purposes. In many routine hospital laboratories, the determination of the "total plasma CO_2" in this way has displaced the older "CO_2-combining power" test because of a number of fundamental and inherent objections to the way in which the latter is carried out.

Determination of pH

The pH is generally determined on whole blood obtained without loss of CO_2 as described above. Any one of the excellent pH meters, equipped with a temperature controlled container for the blood, a sensitive glass electrode, and having a scale reading directly to 0.01 pH, now commercially available may be used. The determination should be carried out with the temperature of the blood controlled at 38° C., and the pH meter must be repeatedly checked and adjusted using accurately standardized reference buffer solutions.

Determination of the pCO₂

The pCO_2 can be measured directly, as for example, by bubble equilibration techniques, by rebreathing procedures, or by the use of special pCO_2 electrodes. It can also be determined, as it is in the Astrup technique, on the basis of the fact that the relationship between log pCO_2 and pH is practically a straight line. Exact measurement of the pH of the sample as collected, and then again after equilibration with accurately known high and low CO_2 tensions, will therefore permit the pCO_2 of the blood, as collected, to be read directly from a graph. The pCO_2 may also be calculated from the results of the determinations of the pH and the total CO_2 (see above) of the specimen. This calculation is based on the Henderson-Hasselbalch equation which, for the bicarbonate-carbonic acid buffer system, may be written:

$$pH = 6.1 + \log \frac{[HCO_3^-]}{0.0301 \times pCO_2}$$

Because the total CO_2 of the plasma as it is actually determined includes the CO_2 from both the HCO_3^- ion and the dissolved CO_2, this equation may be written:

$$pH = 6.1 + \log \frac{[\text{Total } CO_2] - (0.0301 \times pCO_2)}{(0.0301 \times pCO_2)}$$

If, for example, the pH of a sample of blood has been found to be 7.31, and the total CO_2 content, on being measured, was 13.0 mM/l. the equation becomes:

$$7.31 = 6.1 + \log \frac{(13.0) - (0.0301 \times pCO_2)}{(0.0301 \times pCO_2)}$$

or:

$$7.31 - 6.10 = 1.21 = \log \frac{(13.0) - (0.0301 \times pCO_2)}{(0.0301 \times pCO_2)}$$

or:

$$\text{Antilog } 1.21 = \frac{(13.0) - (0.0301 \times pCO_2)}{(0.0301 \times pCO_2)}$$

From log tables antilog $1.21 = 16.22$

$$\therefore 16.22 = \frac{(13.0) - (0.0301 \times pCO_2)}{(0.0301 \times pCO_2)}$$

or:

$$(0.488 \times pCO_2) + (0.0301 \times pCO_2) = 13.0$$

$$pCO_2 = \frac{13.0}{0.518} = 25.1 \text{ mm. Hg}$$

and $\therefore$ the sum of [dissolved CO_2] +

$$[H_2CO_3] = 25.1 \times 0.0301 = 0.75 \text{ mM/l.}$$

Determination of Plasma Bicarbonate Ion Concentration

The plasma bicarbonate ion concentration also cannot be determined directly but it is readily

obtained by subtracting the [dissolved CO_2] + [H_2CO_3] from the total plasma CO_2. In the example given above the bicarbonate ion concentration is obviously:

$$13.0 - 0.75 = 12.25 \text{ mM/l.}$$

The Henderson-Hasselbalch equation, using the above example with all the unknowns determined, then becomes:

$$7.31 = 6.1 + \log \frac{12.25}{0.75} =$$

$$6.1 + \log \frac{16.3}{1} = 6.1 + 1.21 = 7.31.$$

The McLean Nomogram

In actual practice a nomogram, such as that developed by McLean (fig. 34.4), is generally used to obtain the pCO_2 and bicarbonate concentration instead of the rather complicated method of calculation, requiring the use of log tables, which is given above. With the use of this nomogram the accurate determination of any two of the above variables (such as the pH and the total CO_2 content) allows the remainder of the necessary information to be quickly obtained simply by the use of a ruler.

DIAGNOSIS OF NATURE AND SEVERITY OF ACID-BASE DISTURBANCES

On the basis of the clinical history, physical and laboratory findings, and with the help of the determined or derived values of the blood pH and pCO_2 and the total plasma CO_2 content, it should be possible to come to a reasonable conclusion about the type and severity of most acid-base disturbances. The pH determination will usually indicate whether one is dealing with an acidosis or alkalosis, the pH plus the pCO_2 values will indicate whether the abnormality is a "respiratory" or "metabolic" one and the plasma "total CO_2 content" will give a reasonable estimate of the degree to which the plasma bicarbonate has been depleted or increased. In most cases of obvious metabolic acidosis or alkalosis the determination of the "total CO_2" will give all the information necessary to determine the severity of the disturbance and to follow the effectiveness of treatment. On the other hand, in respiratory problems it may be necessary to have the results of all three determinations if a reliable diagnosis is to be made.

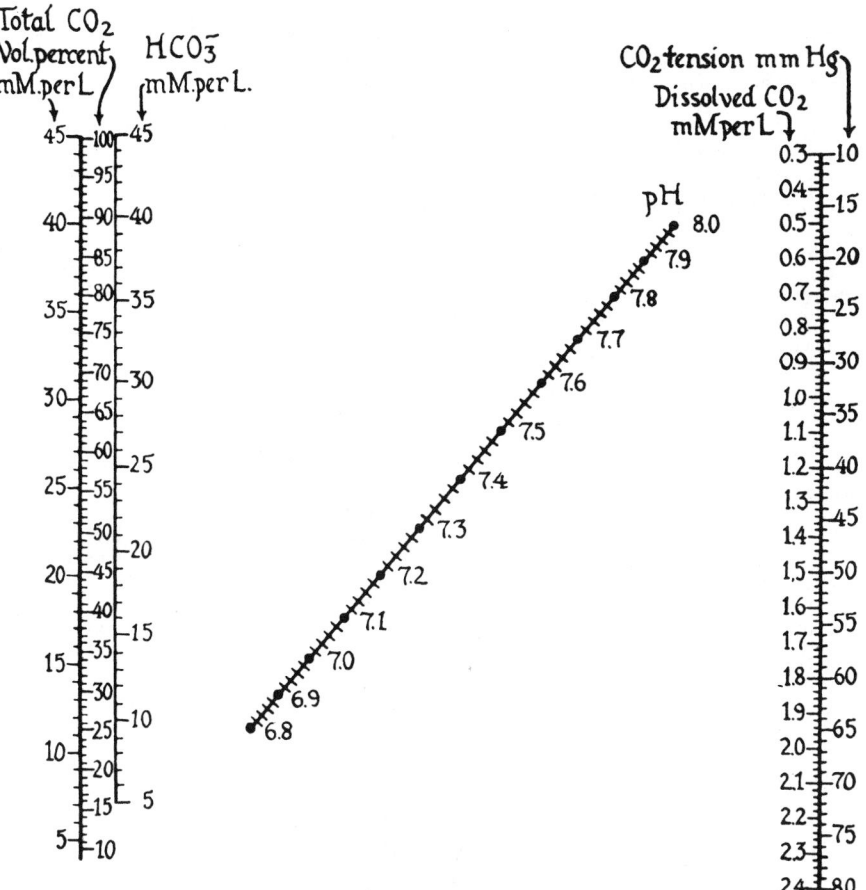

Fig. 34.4. Nomogram for graphic deter mination of serum or plasma values by the Henderson Hasselbalch equation. A straight line through given points on any two scales cuts the other two scales at points indicating simultaneously occurring values. (From F. C. McLean "Application of the law of chemical equilibrium (law of mass action) to biological problems." Physiol. Rev., 1938, 18, 495 (with permission).)

"Mixed" Acid-Base Disturbances

Although the four different major types of acid-base disturbances described above have been dealt with as distinct and separate entities, it must be remembered that "mixed" types are not uncommon and that a primary abnormality of one kind may readily be superimposed upon one of a different variety. A patient with respiratory acidosis from pulmonary emphysema may, for example, develop a metabolic acidosis from uncontrolled diabetes or a potassium depletion metabolic alkalosis from the large doses of steroids which may be used in the treatment of an attack of status asthmaticus; or a patient with a metabolic disturbance may develop an acid-base upsetting abnormality of respiration. The likelihood that such a "mixed" picture is present will frequently be obvious or be suggested by the history and physical examination. The biochemical upset,

however, may be quite complicated, since, depending upon the nature of the disturbances, some of the effects of one may either be partially cancelled out or greatly augmented by those of the other. In these "mixed" conditions, it is particularly necessary to know not only the "total CO_2 content" but also the pH and pCO_2 of the blood as well. In addition, the concentrations of sodium, potassium and other constituents of the blood should also be determined if a full and correct assessment of the actual acid-base status of the individual is to be made.

REFERENCES

Ad Hoc Committee, New York Academy of Sciences, Statement on Acid-Base Terminology, Conference on Current Concepts of Acid-Base Measurements Nov. 1964. Ann. Int. Med. 1965, 63, 885.

Astrup, Poul. A new approach to acid-base metabolism. Clin. Chem., 1961, 7, 1.

BLUMENTALS, AUSMA S. (Editor) Symposium on Acid-Base Balance (13 separate papers on various aspects of acid-base balance) A.M.A. Arch. Intern. Med., 1965, 116, 647.

BRØNSTED, J. N. Einige Bemerkungen über den Begriff der Säuren und Basen. Rec. Trav. Chim. Pays-Bas, 1923, 42, 718.

CAMPBELL, E. J. MORAN. R I pH. Lancet, 1962, 1, 681.

CHRISTENSEN, H. N. General concept of neutrality regulation. Amer. J. Surg., 1962, 103, 286.

CREESE, R., NEIL, M. W., LEDINGHAM, J. M. AND VERE, D. W. The terminology of acid-base regulation. Lancet, 1962, 1, 419.

ELKINTON, J. RUSSELL. Hydrogen ion turnover in health and in renal disease. Ann. Intern. Med., 1962, 57, 660.

FRAZER, S. C. AND STEWART, C. P. Acidosis and alkalosis: a modern view. J. Clin. Path., 1959, 12, 195.

HASSLEBALCH, K. A. Die Berechnung der Wasserstoffzahl des Blutes aus der freien und gebundenen Kohlensäure desselben, und die Sauerstoffbindung des Blutes als Funktion der Wasserstoffzahl. Biochem. Z., 1916, 78, 112.

HENDERSON, L. J. The theory of neutrality regulation in the animal organism. Amer. J. Physiol., 1908, 21, 427.

HUCKABEE, W. E. Henderson vs. Hasslebalch. Clin. Research, 1961, 9, 116.

KASSIRER, J. P. AND BLEICH, H. L. Rapid estimation of plasma carbon dioxide tension from pH and total carbon dioxide. New. Eng. J. Med., 1965, 272, 1067.

KAUFMAN, H. E. AND ROSEN, S. W. Clinical acid-base regulation—the Brønsted schema. Surg. Gynec. Obstet., 1956, 103, 101.

LEMANN, J. JR. AND RELMAN, A. S. The relation of sulfur metabolism to acid-base balance and electrolyte excretion: The effects of d-l-methionine in normal man. J. Clin. Invest., 1959, 38, 2215.

LENNON, E. J., LEMANN J., JR. AND RELMAN, A. S. The effects of phosphoproteins on acid balance in normal subjects. J. Clin. Invest., 1962, 41, 637.

LOWRY, T. M. Uniqueness of hydrogen. Chem. & Indust., 1923, 42, 43.

McLEAN, F. C. Application of the law of chemical equilibrium (Law of Mass Action) to biological problems. Physiol. Rev., 1938, 18, 495.

RELMAN, A. S. Renal acidosis and renal excretion of acid in health and disease. Advances Intern. Med., 1964, 12, 295.

ROUGHTON, F. J. W. Recent work on carbon dioxide transport in the blood. Physiol. Rev., 1935, 15, 241.

SWAN, R. C. AND PITTS, R. F. Neutralization of infused acid by nephrectomized dogs. J. Clin. Invest., 1955, 34, 205.

WADDELL, W. J. AND BUTLER, T. C. Calculation of Intracellular pH from the distribution of 5,5-dimethyl-2,4-oxazolidinedione (DMO). Application to skeletal muscle of the dog. J. Clin. Invest., 1959, 38, 720.

WINTERS, ROBERT W. Terminology of acid-base disorders. Ann. Int. Med., 1965, 63, 873.

Monographs and Reviews

BATES, ROGER G. Determination of pH. Theory and Practice. John Wiley & Sons, Inc., New York, 1964.

CHRISTENSEN, H. N. Body Fluids and Their Neutrality. New York, Oxford University Press, 1963.

CLARK, W. MANSFIELD, Topics in Physical Chemistry. Williams and Wilkins, Baltimore, 2nd Ed. 1952.

DAVENPORT, HORACE W. The ABC of Acid-Base Chemistry. University of Chicago Press, Chicago, 4th Ed. 1958.

PITTS, ROBERT F. Physiology of the Kidneys and Body Fluids. Year Book Medical Publishers Inc., Chicago, 1963.

SIGGAARD-ANDERSEN, OLE. The Acid-Base Status of the Blood. Munksgaard, Copenhagen, 2nd Ed. 1964.

V

CIRCULATION

CHAPTER 35

Basic Properties of the Heart

The important characteristics of the heart include excitability, rhythmicity, conductivity, contractility, and distensibility.

Excitation of Cardiac Muscle

The ability of a tissue to respond to a stimulus is spoken of as excitability or irritability. In the case of muscle, the response is the development of a potential difference and shortening of its fibers. The motion of the heart is controlled by these changes of the potential difference between the inside and the outside of individual myocardial fibers. For many years the monophasic action potential of the heart recorded with one electrode on injured or depolarized and supposedly inactive tissue, and the other electrode on active or normal tissue has been employed to show or to reveal the time course of depolarization and repolarization of the myocardial muscle membrane. Measurement of this action potential has been employed to correlate changes in the state of the membrane with observed variations in excitability and with the simultaneous cardiac electrogram or myogram. Use of the monophasic action potential, however, has numerous drawbacks and, at best, can serve only as a record of the average time course of the membrane potential change in many cells.

The studies of Weidmann, 1949, and Woodbury, 1951, showed that the potential difference across a limited area of muscle membrane of a single heart fiber could be faithfully recorded in the beating heart by use of an intracellular micro electrode of the type developed by Ling and Gerard, 1949. Glass tubes of about 1 mm. external diameter are drawn out to an extremely small tip of about 0.2 μ. When these are filled with concentrated potassium solution and inserted through the fiber membrane into the sarcoplasm, they can be used to measure the potential difference between the outside and inside of a single fiber in the beating heart. By cutting off the tip of the glass capillary electrode and suspending it on a wire, the electrode is free to move up and down. Thus artefacts from heart movements are minimized and recordings from human hearts during cardiac surgery have been made. Human atrial and ventricular muscles, excised from patients undergoing open-heart surgery, were also studied *in vitro*. Where studied simultaneously, the transmembrane potentials from fibers in the intact heart are qualitatively and quantitatively similar to those recorded from single fibers of isolated preparations of either atria or ventricles. Information thus obtained concerning the state of polarization of the muscle membrane serves as a much better basis for correlation with studies of excitability and refractoriness than the less direct and more variable measurements obtained with surface electrode techniques (fig. 35.1).

TRANSMEMBRANE POTENTIALS OF VENTRICLE AND ATRIUM. Figure 35.2a shows the potential changes that are observed when a capillary microelectrode is inserted into a single fiber of a rhythmically beating ventricle. When both the microelectrode and the indifferent electrode are outside the cell, there is no potential difference. When, however, the tip of the microelectrode penetrates the membrane of a single myocardial fiber, a sudden potential of 80 to 90 mv. is recorded with the inside of the fiber negative to the indifferent electrode. This resting potential difference across the muscle membrane remains at the same value as long as the tissue is quiescent. Following stimulation, however, there is an extremely rapid phase of depolarization (1 to 2 msec.) and change in the membrane potential so that the intracellular microelectrode momentarily becomes positive with respect to the indifferent electrode. Therefore, at the peak of the action potential, the membrane is not only depolarized but actually exhibits a reversal of polarity or exhibits overshooting amounting to 15 to 30 mv., and lasting 6 to 15 msec. Immediately after this reversal there is a plateau of about 100 msec. and then a moderately rapid repolarization of the membrane for 100 to 150 msec., as the resting potential is restored. On pulling back the electrode, the potential jumps back to the zero level. It is believed that use of an intracellular microelectrode gives a true picture of the time course of depolarization and repolarization in a single cardiac muscle fiber and provides an accurate measurement of the size of transmembrane potentials.

Transmembrane potentials recorded from the atria and auricles in the open chest dog (or from

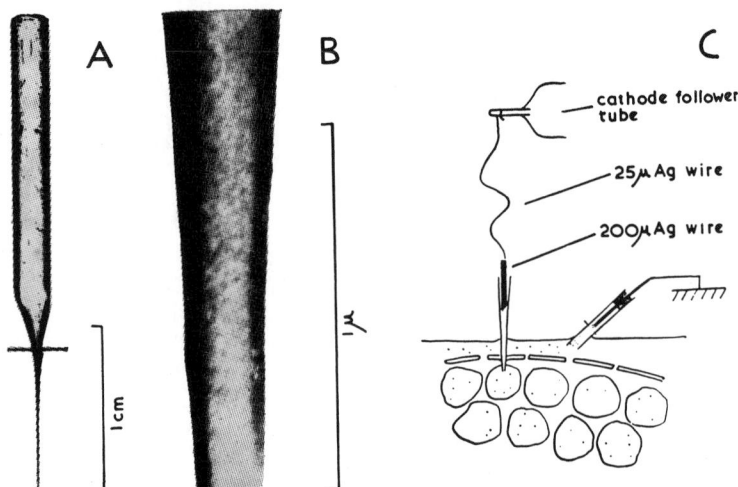

Fig. 35.1. Microelectrodes used for determining transmembrane potential in single myocardial fiber as modified by Alexander and Nastuk from Ling and Gerard.

single fibers of isolated preparations) are not significantly different from those of the ventricles except that following depolarization, the atrial records show an immediate slow phase of repolarization without an intervening plateau such as occurs in ventricular muscle (fig. 35.2b).

The temporal relationship between the action potential of a single fiber and the local ventricular electrogram of the intact and *in situ* heart is shown in figure 35.2a. The upstroke of the action potential coincides with the R wave of the electrogram, the plateau with the R-T segment, and the phase of repolarization with the T wave. Although the mechanism is unexplained, the temporal relation between the electrical and mechanical activity is very close (fig. 35.2e). Contraction starts a few milliseconds after depolarization, and tension reaches a peak when the membrane undergoes repolarization. The state of contraction is maintained as long as the fiber is depolarized, and relaxation sets in as soon as the resting potential is re-established. Under some conditions it has been possible to obtain dissociation between mechanical and electrical events, i.e., electrical activity is obtainable when there is no longer a recorded mechanical response.

The transmembrane potential and mechanical response of cardiac muscle are very sensitive to certain inorganic ions. Changes in concentration of potassium, calcium, and to a lesser extent sodium, have a profound effect on the excitability and contractile response of the mammalian myocardium. Magnesium has little action in the presence of normal calcium concentration, but when the latter concentration is decreased both mag-

nesium and strontium have a marked effect on membrane potential. It is possible that changes in myocardial function which are encountered in man in disease states can be explained on the basis of the known effects of these ions on the membranes of cardiac muscle fibers.

TRANSMEMBRANE POTENTIALS OF SPECIALIZED TISSUES. Of the 3 specialized tissues in the mammalian heart, i.e., the sinal atrial node, the atrial ventricular (A-V) node, and the ventricular conducting system (Purkinje fibers), only the latter has been studied extensively by microelectrode techniques. Figure 35.2c illustrates the electrical peculiarities of Purkinje fibers in the dog heart. In contrast to the constant diastolic membrane potential in auricular and ventricular muscle, there is in the ventricular conducting system a slow depolarization throughout diastole when local electrical activity is induced by a distant pacemaker. When pacemaker activity originates in the local area there is, in addition, a slow upward curvature in late diastole which continues until a level of instability is reached and a more rapid depolarization, the action potential, spontaneously begins (fig. 35.2d). This peculiarity was first described by Bozler. The assumption is made that normal pacemaker activity in the sino-atrial, A-V nodal tissue, and in undifferentiated ventricular muscle of the mammalian heart is similar to the above when they act as pacemakers, but as yet this has been shown to be true for these areas only in the frog and turtle heart.

As to be expected, the electrical properties of the pacemaker region change with factors that alter heart rate. Vagus stimulation, acetylcholine

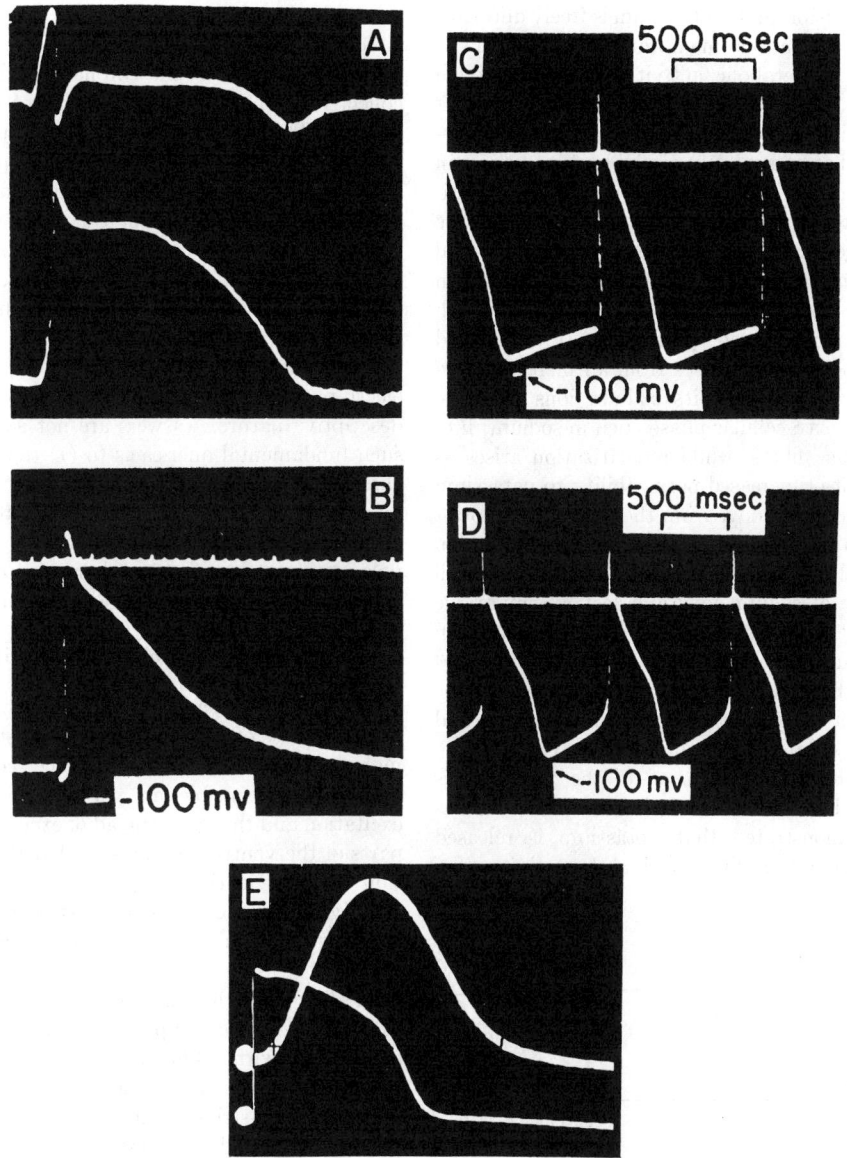

FIG. 35.2*A*. Transmembrane action potential of a single ventricular fiber (*lower curve*) and simultaneous ventriculogram of the intact heart *in situ*. The upstroke of the action potential coincides with the R wave of the electrogram, the plateau with the R-T segment, and the phase or repolarization with the T wave. (After Brooks and associates.) *B*, Normal transmembrane potential recorded from a single fiber of the intact auricle. (After Brooks and associates.) *C*, Transmembrane action potential of a single Purkinje fiber in a nonpacemaker activity. Note slow loss of resting potential during diastole. (After Brooks and associates.) *D*, Spontaneous activity recorded from Purkinje fiber in a pacemaker area. Note slow depolarization during diastole and then abrupt onset of spontaneous depolarization. (After Brooks and associates.) *E*, Temporal relation between action potential and mechanical contraction recorded from a papillary muscle. (After Dudel and Trautwein.)

and hypothermia lower heart rate by decreasing the rate of diastolic repolarization and thus lengthening the time taken to reach a critical level at which an action potential is initiated, whereas sympathetic stimulation and epinephrine injection, by inducing a faster rate of depolarization with an earlier firing, accelerate heart rate.

MECHANISM OF TRANSMEMBRANE POTENTIAL. What causes the resting potential and what causes this potential difference to change during myocardial contraction and relaxation is not known. There is no doubt that the state of membrane permeability is the basis for excitability. About all that is known is that at rest potassium is not diffusible and that sodium is freely diffusible through the muscle membrane, and that this is caused by metabolic activity. Largely through the work of Hodgkins and associates (carried out on the giant nerve fibers of the squid), ion movements that may be responsible for change in membrane potential have been partially identified. Extension of their work by others to cardiac tissue demonstrated that the resting potential across the myocardial membrane depends upon the concentration gradient of potassium to which the membrane is not permeable. It is believed that depolarization arises from an increased permeability which permits sodium ions to move from the extracellular phase (rich in sodium) into the cardiac fibers, while repolarization arises as the result of increased permeability to potassium ions which now move from the cell (rich in potassium) to the outside. Thus, following each action potential the inside of the fiber has gained a small quantity of sodium ions and lost a comparable quantity of potassium ions. In order to maintain ionic equilibrium, the shifts have to be reversed during the period of diastole. The ions must be "pumped" against electrochemical gradients and this necessitates metabolic energy.

Experimental verification of the preceding is difficult but for the turtle heart at least, it has been demonstrated that potassium is released from the myocardium during its activity (fig. 35.3). To study this, K^{42} was injected into the peritoneum of a living turtle. A few hours later, the heart was cut out and the coronary circulation perfused with radio inactive Ringer's solution. Samples of the coronary outflow were collected at short intervals and counted for the isotope. The results show a large increase in K^{42} outflow associated with each period of activity, that is, with each systole, and when corrections are made for the travel time between the release of the potassium in the muscle fibers and the arrival at the venous outflow, then the extra K^{42} release occurs some time during the Q-T interval of the ECG.

From what has been said, our knowledge of the electrophysiology of the heart is obviously of a descriptive nature. Answers are not available to such fundamental queries as to (1) the nature of change in selective permeability and in transmembrane passage of ions in the presence of altered permeability, (2) the linkage between depolarization and mechanical shortening of muscle, and between metabolism and active ion transport.

Rhythmicity and Conductivity

To produce efficient pumping of blood, the complex mass of myocardial fibers must contract more or less simultaneously. The conducting system is responsible for periodic initiation of excitation and the rapid spread of excitation to all parts of the ventricular walls so that the conduction is sufficiently simultaneous to produce effective pumping. This is a stereotyped and repetitive sequence of events during each cardiac cycle.

Cardiac tissue in addition to nerve fiber and ganglion cell is made up of 3 types of syncytial muscle each with a different embryological origin: specialized nodal tissue, Purkinje fibers, and ordinary cross-striated cardiac muscle. The first two are concerned with initiation and conduction of impulses through the myocardium, the last with muscle contraction. The specialized tissue consists of the sino-atrial (S-A) node, the atrioventricular (A-V) node, the A-V bundle, its bundle branches, and the Purkinje system (fig. 35.4). This specialized tissue ends by a gradual end-to-end transition into ordinary heart muscle. While it is generally considered probable that these peculiar specialized cells are the agents which conduct the stimulus to the ventricles, absolute proof that the sympathetic fibers which accompany the bundle and its branches have nothing to do with conduction is yet to be produced. Procedures involving cutting, crushing, ligation or injection must, of necessity, damage

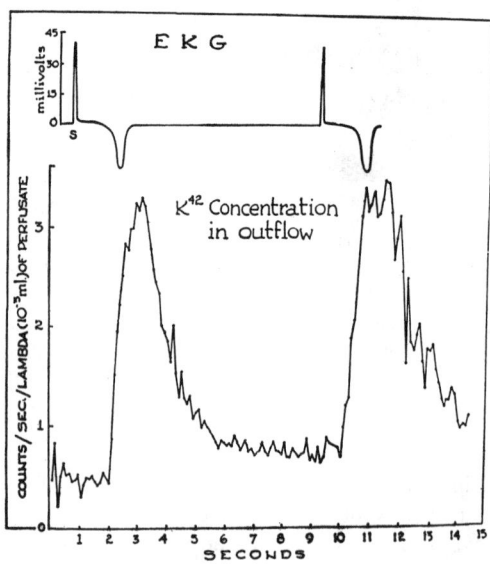

FIG. 35. 3. K^{42} effluogram of a turtle ventricle. (From Wilde and associates.)

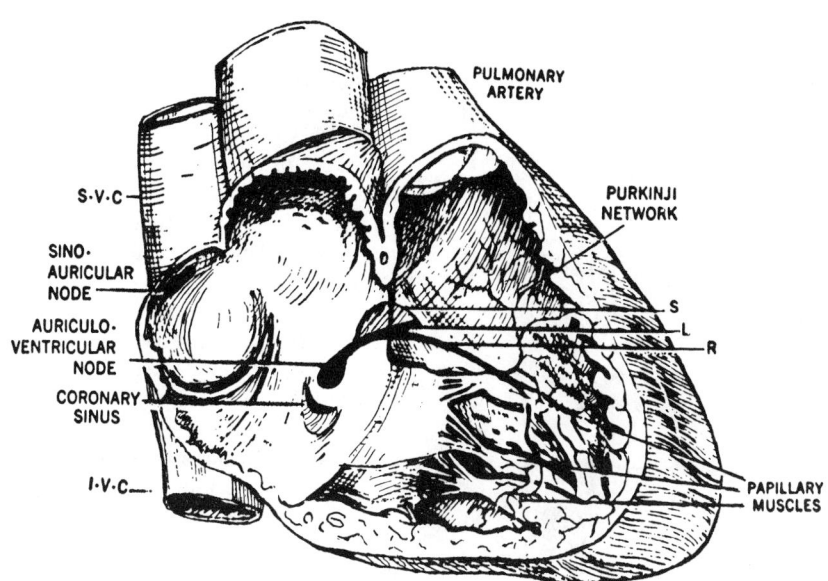

FIG. 35.4. Showing the specialized tissue of the mammalian heart. *S.V.C.*, superior vena cava; *I.V.C.*, inferior vena cava; *S*, membranous part of interventricular septum; *L*, left branch of bundle; *R*, right branch of bundle.

both these characteristic cells and the nerve cells also because of their intimate admixture.

The time of arrival of excitation in various regions of the mammalian heart has been determined in different ways: for the epicardial surface from the deflection obtained by placing one electrode directly on different areas of the epicardium and a second electrode on a distant part of the body, or from paired contiguous electrodes; for the nodal and specialized conducting tissue from the deflection obtained with intracellular electrodes; for the ventricle proper from deflections obtained with multiple intramural electrodes.

IMPULSE INITIATION. Keith and Flack, 1907, suggested that the S-A node embedded in the right atrial wall near the entrance of the superior vena cava is the focus in the mammalian heart from which each heart beat normally starts. Evidence of such origin is that (1) its excision or inactivation causes cessation or slowing of the atrial or ventricular contractions, (2) temperature change of the node but not of the surrounding tissue changes heart rate, (3) the node becomes electrically active before any other region of the heart. This cannot be regarded as positive proof of origin from the S-A node but rather from this general region which includes other types of cells including ganglion cells.

Although spontaneous and repetitive depolarization arises normally only in this region, there are other areas in which electrical activity can arise under some circumstances and initiate cardiac contraction. When the S-A node is destroyed or inactivated, the A-V node becomes the sight of impulse formation and develops spontaneous depolarization. In turn, in the presence of inactivation of the A-V node, the ventricles develop a slow rhythm. Since both ventricles receive the excitation through natural pathways and contract in a coordinated way, the rhythmical center is the A-V bundle. If both bundle branches are cut, impulse initiation arises in the ventricular muscle. The natural rate of automaticity of these areas is of a descending order of magnitude, the S-A node being 70 to 80 per min., atria 60 per min., A-V node 40 to 60 per min., and ventricles 20 to 40 per minute. It is obvious that normally, the atria, A-V node, and ventricular tissue cannot set the heart rate because the S-A node repolarizes and automatically discharges more rapidly than any of these tissues. Hence, an impulse from the S-A node will always depolarize these tissues before either could initiate a rhythm. On occasion, however, an ectopic focus in the atrium or ventricular muscle can assume a rhythm faster than that of the S-A node, and hence, it becomes the pacemaker.

There is suggestive evidence that the rhythmicity of the various cardiac pacemaker tissues is affected by the catecholamine stores of the heart. Isolated atria from animals previously treated with reserpine (which depletes cardiac

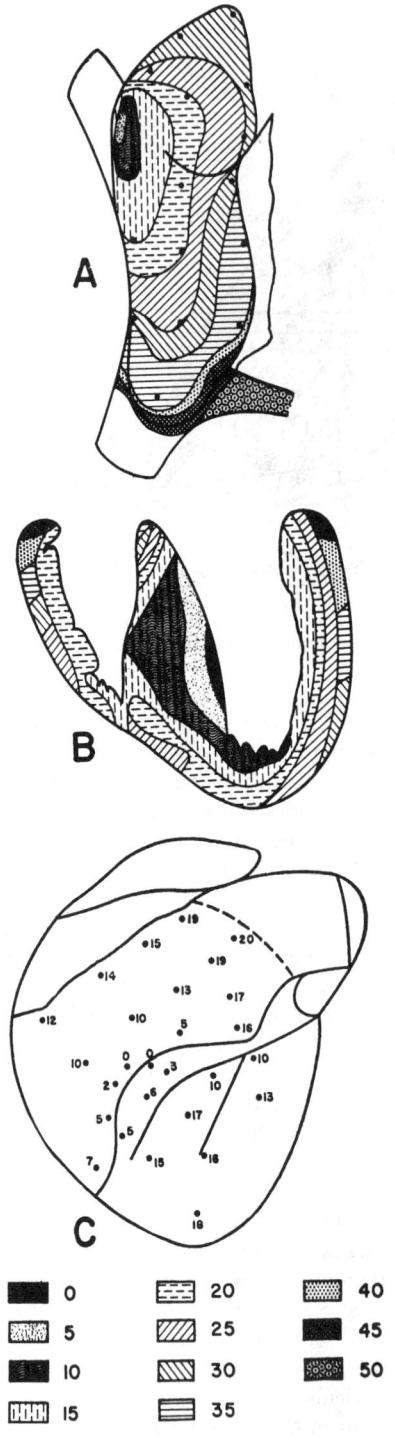

norepinephrine) exhibit a slower rate of contractions than atria of control animals. In dogs with surgically created atrio-ventricular block, reserpine slows the rate of both the atria and the ventricles, the latter to a greater extent than the former. Infusion of norepinephrine tends to restore the control rate.

PATHWAYS OF CONDUCTION. Following each spontaneous depolarization in the region of the S-A node, near the mouth of the superior vena cava, the activation process is transmitted radially throughout the muscle of both atria at about 1 meter per sec., and reaches the outermost portions of the atria in about 50 msec. (fig. 35.5*a*). No specialized tissue appears to be present although the transmission is thought to follow at least partially, certain direct muscular fasciculi; thus, the impulse reaches the A-V node in advance of its arrival at the wall of the left atrium. The plan of activation of human atria has not been directly studied.

As the depolarization approaches the interatrial septum, it reaches a mass of specialized tissue, the A-V node, which is located near the posterior margin of the interatrial septum near the entrance of the coronary sinus into the right atrium. Complete dissociation of the auricles and ventricles follows cutting, tying, or crushing of an A-V node or bundle, thus creating what is called complete heart block. Delay of the impulse for from 80 to 120 msec., normally occurs at the A-V node, for the activation process travels slowly (0.2 meters per sec.) through this tissue. Although the cause is unknown, this delay is helpful for it permits completion of atrial contraction and emptying during diastole of the ventricles. The aggregate potential by these few fibers is too small to be recorded except locally. After leaving the A-V node, the wave of excitation passes rapidly (4 to 5 meters per sec.) by the common A-V bundle, its branches, and by the Purkinje network of subendocardial fibers to spread throughout the endocardial surfaces of both ventricles. The exact course by which the wave of excitation is distributed throughout the ventricular musculature from the endocardial surface is not definitely established except that it penetrates the ventricular wall from endocardial to the epicardial surface. Present evidence indicates that

FIG. 35.5*A*. Spread of activation through right auricle of dog. Auricle viewed from right side showing superior and inferior venae cavae, coronary sinus and atrial appendage. Time of activation in milliseconds following activation of the S-A node. (From Puech.) *B*, Frontal plane section showing spread of activation through the ventricular septum and ventricular walls of the canine heart. Lower left part of septum is activated first at time zero. Time of activation of other portions in milliseconds. (From Sodi-Pallares.) *C*, Spread of excitation on the ventral surface of the dog heart. Region near the interventricular sulcus on the right ventricle excited first. Time of activation of other portions of epicardial surface in milliseconds. (After Harris.)

such spread of excitation is not by anatomical muscle bundles but by the specialized tissue. By some this is believed to be not merely a subendocardial layer but a profuse myocardial network ramifying in many muscle planes and extending deeply into the myocardium. This would cause almost simultaneous activation of much of the ventricular muscle mass. At all events, the intraventricular septal surface is excited first, the papillary muscles next, but conduction is so fast that the inner surfaces of both ventricles are excited almost simultaneously, the whole of the endocardium being activated in about 50 msec. (fig. 35.5*b*). Excitation of the ventricular muscle is much slower (0.4 meters per sec.) and proceeds first through the septum and then through the lateral walls of the ventricles from endocardial to epicardial surfaces. This is entirely different from the spread of excitation in the atrial muscle which is radial. Muscle activation occurs first in the subendocardial layers of the midportion of the left ventricular septum to spread inward; this is quickly followed by inward activation from the right endocardial surface of the septum. Within 10 to 20 msec. after first activation of the septum, deflections are recorded on the anterior surface of the left ventricle along the interventricular groove near the apex. Within 25 to 30 msec., all the right ventricular surface is activated. Regions of the lateral wall of the left ventricle are excited slightly later (at 25 to 35 msec.) since the wall is much thicker. Finally, at 40 to 45 msec., the epicardial surface over the pulmonary conus region of the right ventricle and the base of the left ventricle and septum respond. In general, excitation of the epicardial surface occurs 1 to 20 msec. later than its endocardial counterpart. Many investigations with more refined techniques have confirmed the original findings of Lewis that the maximum difference in time of excitation of different regions of the ventricular surfaces is also quite small, being of the order of 10 to 20 msec., and that surface excitation of the ventricles proceeds from point to point as it does in the atria (fig. 35.5*c*). In the human, the patterns of activation have not been detailed but are believed to be similar to those in the dog heart. However, the time for activation might be twice as long because of the much thicker myocardium.

EFFECT OF CARDIAC NERVES ON RHYTHMICITY AND CONDUCTIVITY. The inherent automaticity and conduction properties of the heart can be altered antagonistically through the action of the sympathetic and vagus nerves to the myocardium. The parasympathetic fibers from the right vagus terminate mainly near the S-A node but some fibers spread throughout the atria. Most left vagal fiber endings supply the A-V node and the A-V bundle. Many endings are spread throughout the atrial muscle but they have not been demonstrated in the ventricles.

Stimulation of vagal fibers to the heart presumably results in the secretion of acetylcholine at the vagal endings in the heart causing slowing of the heart through S-A nodal depression (chronotropic effect), decrease in the rate of the depolarization wave through the atria and through the A-V bundle, and an increase in the refractory period of the A-V bundle. Very often, as to be expected from its anatomical distribution, stimulation of the right vagus affects mainly the heart rate and atrial contractility: left vagal stimulation may result mainly in a partial functional heart block at the A-V node. Very strong stimulation of either one or both vagi generally completely stops the rhythmical contraction of the S-A node or completely blocks transmission of impulses through the A-V node and bundle so that impulses are no longer transmitted to the ventricles. Ventricular beats in the open chest dog can be stopped in this manner for at least a minute although the usual effect is for a few seconds only. The ventricles then establish their own slow rhythm. Vagal stimulation in the turtle or frog heart can arrest the ventricles for 2 to 4 hours.

The sympathetic fibers to the heart are derived from the cervical and upper thoracic ganglia. The cardiac fibers supply the S-A node, A-V node, atrial muscle, and unlike the parasympathetics, the ventricular muscle as well. Norepinephrin, secreted at the sympathetic nerve endings causes effects almost exactly opposite to those of acetylcholine. Stimulation of cardiac nerve fibers isolated from the stellate ganglia releases norepinephrine, increases the rate of rhythm of the S-A node, increases the rate of conduction through all parts of the heart, and increases the refractory period of the A-V bundle, Purkinje system, and muscle fibers. Maximal sympathetic stimulation can, at times, almost triple heart rate. Epinephrine has essentially the same effects. Thus, sympathin release or stellate stimulation increases the over-all heart rate.

Contractility and Distensibility

CONTRACTILE PROCESS. The chambers of the heart are surrounded by walls made up of bundles and sheets of myocardial fibers. The fibers form a syncytium which gives protoplasmic continuity between adjoining fibers and throughout an entire mass of cardiac muscle (fig. 35.6). In spite of

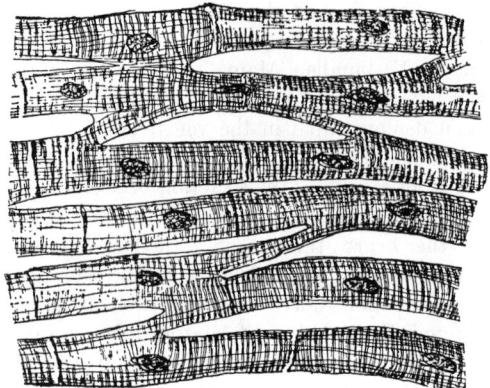

Fig. 35. 6. Cardiac muscle fibers.

the apparent protoplasmic continuity, the electrical resistance between two cardiac cells is high (about 25 megaohms) which is twice as large as the resistance within a single cell. This suggests that the cardiac cells are electrically isolated from one another by high resistance membranes.

The major organized parts of the fibers are the myofibrils, the sarcosomes or cytochondria, and the sarcoplasm. The fibrils are the fundamental contractile units of the heart. The nature of the contraction and relaxation of muscle is on a theoretical basis and beyond the present scope. It is, however, generally believed that the contractile elements in cardiac, also skeletal and smooth muscle fibers, are formed from myosin, a protein of rather short molecular rods, and actin, a long continuous protein thread, both of which are dissociated in resting muscle and neither of which will contract independently. Excitation passing along the muscle results in the formation of actomyosin which is unstable in its extended or resting state and which now dissipates energy either by shortening or increased tension. Actomyosin is thus changed to its energy poor state and may accomplish work if it shortens.

In terms of metabolism, the fibrils are the structures which, with the purpose of generating mechanical work utilize the metabolic agent which supplies chemical energy to be transformed into work. In the past, the assumption has been made, based on indirect evidence, that the immediate source of energy or the metabolic agent in contracting muscle is the enzymatic hydrolysis of adenosine triphosphate or creatine phosphate. Direct measurements, however, show no such breakdown in a single muscle twitch and even a tetanic contraction can take place without significant decomposition of these compounds. Inorganic phosphorus is, however, liberated during the contraction from an unidentified precursor in just sufficient amounts to supply the required energy but whether this source is the phosphate bond energy of an unidentified compound such as another nucleotide has not been determined. At all events, regeneration of such a substance is the task of metabolism. Glycolysis as a source of such energy is carried out in the sarcoplasm but in a heart which cannot accumulate a large oxygen debt, this is scarce. Respiration is a function of the sarcosomes and, presumably, such regenerative processes are carried in the sarcosomes which are abundant in the heart. However, very little is known regarding the mechanism of reloading and muscle relaxation.

While there are some differences among the actomyosin complexes in skeletal, smooth and cardiac muscle, the contractile mechanisms appear to be closely related. In functional characteristics, however, the myocardium resembles visceral smooth muscle more than skeletal muscle from the standpoint of autogenic excitation and inherent rhythmicity, and intercellular transmission of excitation and nervous control. Both have rapid depolarization and tend to remain depolarized for a period about equal to the duration of contraction; both are not directly innervated by motor nerves, but waves of excitation originate in the muscle fibers and are conducted through the contiguous cells (although smooth muscle is not strictly speaking a syncytium); both are controlled by the autonomic nervous system by way of release of hormonal substances.

PREPARATIONS AND METHODS. In the earlier investigations of the physical properties of the myocardium, the hearts of the frog and tortoise were used. Later, with the development of better technics in methodology, the isolated hearts or heart-lungs of warm-blooded animals such as the cat and dog were used. Subsequently, studies were made on the heart *in situ* in the open and closed-chest anesthetized dog, in the unanesthetized dog, and more recently studies of the heart of the dog and of man *in situ* in which, by means of a heart-lung oxygenator system, the systemic circulation is maintained while only the coronary flow to the heart muscle is maintained, i.e., the left ventricle is empty and the right ventricle is a conduit for coronary venous return. These studies have been very fruitful and have revealed some of the fundamental characteristics of the myocardial process.

In estimating the myocardial or contractile response in these preparations, measurements of interest are the contractile force (contractility) and the distensibility (extensibility) of the myocardium. The term "contractility" although very useful is rather difficult to define. For purposes of consideration, increase in contractility signifies that the mechanical response during contraction is faster (steeper gradient), higher (greater amplitude), generally shorter in time, and that the muscle has a more abrupt and rapid relaxation. Similarly, a decrease in distensibility (extensibility) occurs if the resistance to stretch (muscle tension) increases in a muscle strip or the pressure within a ventricular cavity at rest rises. Such comparisons should be made at the same resting muscle fiber length or size of ventricular cavity.

Such measurements are comparatively easy in isolated strips of myocardium but they are difficult in the whole heart especially within the body. Both are measured in the beating, exposed, empty, or full heart by stretching all or a small portion of the ventricular mass and then determining by use of a strain gauge arch or by direct measurement the isometric tension developed at different muscle lengths during rest and during stimulation. Distensibility as well as contractility is also estimated in the beating heart by measuring the intraventricular pressure, stroke volume, and stroke work responses to changes of ventricular volume (used as a guage of myocardial fiber length). The ventricular volume in systole and diastole is determined directly by a mechanical plethysmograph or by a dye dilution technique. An index of directional change in ventricular cross-section is obtained by a sonar technique, by change in resistance of a mercury filled rubber tube wrapped around the ventricle, by an intraventricular diameter gauge, and by surface calipers, or by electromagnetic plethysmography (see ch. 39).

FACTORS AFFECTING THE CONTRACTILE RESPONSE. The impulse from the sinoatrial node over the cardiac syncytium constitutes the natural stimulus. Its intensity exceeds the threshold of response by 4 to 5 times. Quiescent heart muscle responds to all types of stimuli—mechanical, thermal, electrical, and chemical.

A. Intensity of stimulation. The existence but usually not the magnitude of the contractile response depends upon the intensity of the stimulus. When a quiescent ventricle is excited directly by properly widely spaced electric shocks of increasing intensity, all stimuli above threshold result in contractions of the same amplitude. This was called the "all or nothing response" by Bowditch (1871). It is due to the spread of the excitatory process to all parts of the cardiac syncytium.

A single skeletal muscle fiber responds in the same way but an entire skeletal muscle gives an increasing response with increasing effective stimuli because more and more of the fibers which are insulated from each other now respond.

Although this reaction in cardiac muscle means that the response is not related to stimulus strength, it does not follow that contractile force cannot change with repetitive stimulation. As in a single skeletal muscle fiber with altered condition of the muscle, a minimal effective stimulus at one time may at another be subminimal should the excitability of the muscle be reduced. On the other hand, should the excitability increase, a subminimal stimulus may become effective and the size of the response may vary with the same stimulus if the conditions of the muscle are altered. This is illustrated by the fact that enhancement of contraction with the same intensity of stimulation can be observed to follow increased cardiac work (such as is produced by increasing the resistance to ventricular ejection) without change in frequency of the heart beat, and increased frequency of stimulation from slow to fast rates (fig. 35.7a). This is called Treppe or staircase. If the stimulus is too close to the previous contraction, the mechanical response becomes small or may disappear. Thus, by some unknown mechanism each preceding contraction alters the internal condition of the muscle to change its responsiveness.

B. Spacing of stimuli. The existence and actual magnitude of the contractile response is dependent upon the time of the stimulus relative to the previous contraction (fig. 35.8). In the beating heart, stimuli are generally not effective during the period of contraction since the muscle remains depolarized throughout the period of contraction, and since the muscle must be repolarized in order to induce a new state of contraction. This period is called the absolute refractory period.

During early relaxation, excitability increases progressively but only stimuli still stronger than normal are effective. This is called the relative refractory period. On occasion this refractory period is followed by a subsequent phase in which a subnormal stimulus gives a contraction (super normal period).

This prolonged period of refractoriness normally present in heart muscle prevents the passage of a second impulse over the heart until the preceding contraction is over, and thus allows the ventricles to relax and fill with blood before another contraction can occur and also permits the maximum development of tension by the myocardium. By contrast, the refractory period of skeletal muscle is very brief since in skeletal muscle the duration of depolarization lasts only 1/300 of a second. Therefore, a rapid series of stimuli timed to fall just after this short refractory period will produce a rapid series of shortenings of skeletal muscle which fuse into an apparently maximal contraction (tetanus) which is maintained as long as stimulation continues or until fatigue occurs.

It is obvious that an effective stimulus not coming from the sinoatrial node can affect the cardiac rhythm. A long pause follows the contraction caused by the artificial stimulus (fig. 35.9). The artificially induced contraction is called an extrasystole or premature contraction.

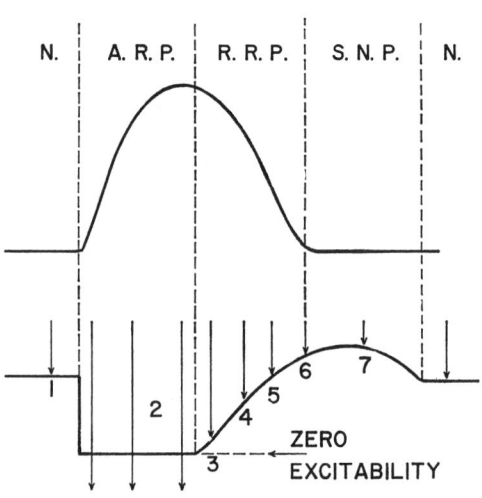

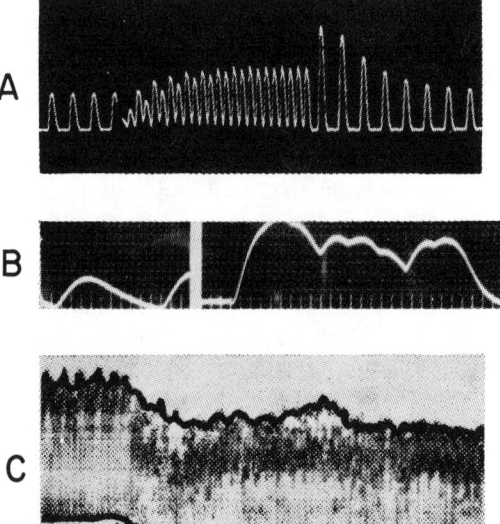

Fig. 35.7*A*. Staircase phenomena due to change in frequency of stimulation. Pressure change in right ventricle during isometric contraction. Perfused heart. S-A node crushed. Frequency of stimulation of left auricle: 1.5, 4, and 1.5 per sec. pressure scale: mm.Hg. (After Rosenblueth 1959*a*.) *B*, Summation of contraction in isolated papillary muscle of cat heart. Temperature 24° C. *Left*, single contraction from single stimulus; *right*, incomplete tetanus from repetitive stimulation. Frequency of stimulation 200 per sec. (After DiPalma.) *C*, Response of left ventricular "diameter" of a dog running on a treadmill at 5 per cent grade. Recorded with very slow camera. A ventricular "diameter" was determined continuously by a sonar technic. Top of record represents diastolic diameter; bottom of record, systolic diameter; difference is stroke volume change in diameter. *Left*, dog is at standing rest. *Arrow*, onset of exercise. Note that during exercise diastolic diameter decreases and stroke volume diameter does not increase. (After Rushmer 1959.)

Fig. 35.8. Diagram illustrating excitability cycle of heart muscle during contraction and relaxation. *Upper curve*, isometric; *middle curve*, excitability changes: *1*, control excitability at rest; *2*, zero excitability during contraction; *3 to 6*, recovery of excitability during relaxation; *6 to 7*, supernormal excitability. Length of arrows indicates relative intensity of shocks required to obtain mechanical response. *Bottom curve*, resulting effects on amplitude of contraction. (After Wiggers.)

The long interval following the extrasystole is termed the compensatory pause since its duration is such that when the next normal beat is resumed, it occurs at precisely the same time as it would have appeared had no premature contraction been provoked. The occurrence of the long pause is explained as follows. The normal impulses pass from the auricle to the ventricle in a perpetual stream and in orderly sequence. When the ventricular muscle is stimulated artificially during diastole, and an extra contraction induced, the normal impulse when it arrives from the auricle at the usual time finds the ventricle already in the contracted state and, in consequence, refractory. The impulse is therefore ineffective. Not until the arrival of the next normal impulse is the muscle in a condition to respond. This accounts for the fact that the time elapsing between the normal beats preceding and following, respectively, the premature contraction, is equal to the length of two normal cardiac cycles. In other words, the heart after the interruption in its rhythm again "gets into step."

The long refractory periods of the cardiac muscle serve to preserve the cardiac rhythm. The absolute refractory phase makes the summation of contractions and the production of tetanus impossible. The relative refractory period tends to discourage the occurrence of a second contraction before sufficient time has elapsed to allow the complete relaxation of the muscle from a preceding contraction. When a premature contraction does occur, its refractory period serves to restore the normal rhythm.

The problem of identification of the boundaries of the refractory period is an old one, and the boundaries are not always in accord with the previous considerations. The absolute refractory period may be altered by various agencies. It is shortened by a rise in temperature and by rapid heart action. It is prolonged by the action of certain drugs. Vagal stimulation shortens the refractory period of the atrial muscle but has no effect upon that of the ventricular muscle. This refractory period does not necessarily last throughout the contraction period but the muscle may respond by a contraction in early diastole to a stimulus applied at the very end of systole. Presumably this arises from the fact that in any muscle mass composed of so many fibers, a considerable number have repolarized and are responding by contraction to the stimulus while a great majority of the fibers are still in the depolarized state. In addition, when very strong ventricular stimuli up to 30 ma., and of 10 to 15 msec. duration are used in the open chest dog, there is in some hearts practically no absolute refractory period. It is also possible to show summation and tetanic response in isolated cardiac muscle of the rat under normal condition and of the frog and cat under unusual conditions of temperature and drugs. For example, papillary muscle maintained at a temperature of 26° C., or less, exhibits summation and tetanus similar to that seen in skeletal muscle (fig. 35.7*b*).

In recent years it became possible to study the various phases of the refractory period in man. Ventricles of patients with complete atrio-ventricular block can now be artificially stimulated by means of an implanted pacemaker, delivering rhythmic electrical impulses. In some of the patients treated in this manner normal atrioventricular conduction may intermittently return, allowing stimuli from the sino-atrial node to reach and depolarize the ventricles. Under these circumstances the ventricles are subject to impulses from two different pacemakers: the artificial one and the sino-atrial node, each

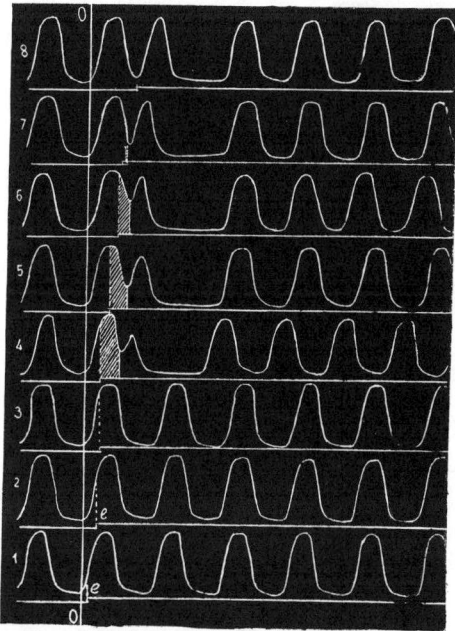

Fig. 35.9 Myograms of frog's ventricle showing effect of excitation by break induction shocks at various moments of the cardiac cycle. The line 0 indicates in all tracings the commencement of the beats during which the shocks were sent in. It will be noted that in 1, 2 and 3, the heart is refractory to the stimulus. The signal (the break in the horizontal line) indicates the moment at which the stimulus was applied. The latent period (hatched area) does not alter as this figure shows. See text. The extrasystoles increase in height from 4 to 8, each being followed by a compensatory pause. (After Marey.)

functioning at a different rate. Analysis of the electrocardiograms of such patients shows that pacemaker impulses delivered immediately following ventricular depolarization fail to elicit a ventricular response, corresponding to the absolute refractory period. This is followed by a phase during which the pacemaker discharges result in delayed and deformed QRS complexes, representing the relative refractory period. After complete recovery ventricular response is immediate. The supernormal phase can be demonstrated by pacemaker stimuli of subthreshold intensity which produce depolarization only when they fall within that period.

C. The effect of stretch. When an isolated ventricular strip is moderately stretched, its tension rises progressively, and upon electrical stimulation the amplitude and duration of its contraction increase (fig. 35.11). This relationship between length and contractile response which is firmly established for the amphibian and mammalian heart has been demonstrated in various ways. Muscle tension rises progressively as the

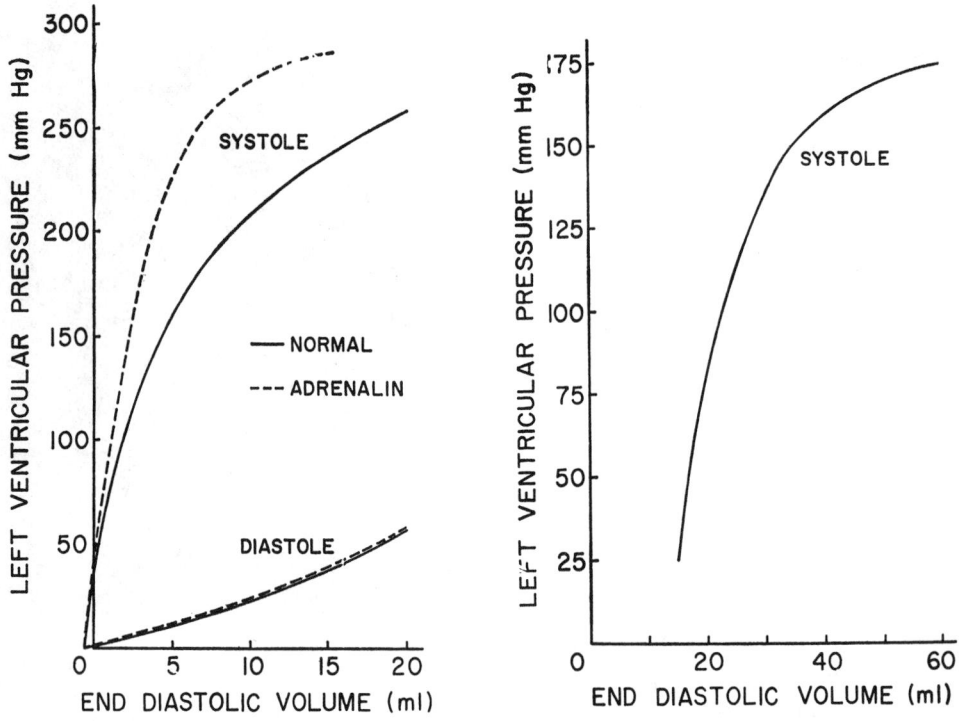

Fig. 35.10 (*Right*). Effect of plethora and hemorrhage on the relationship between left ventricular end diastolic volume and left ventricular systolic pressure in the anesthetized dog. Estimate of trend based on data from experiments. (After Holt.) (*Left*) Pressure volume curves of the left ventricle in the open chest dog under isometric conditions. Broken line curves, relation of ventricular end diastolic and systolic pressure, respectively, to ventricular end diastolic volume under normal conditions. Solid line curves, relationship of ventricular end diastolic pressure and systolic pressure, respectively, to ventricular end diastolic volume following administration of epinephrine (35γ) intravenously. To obtain the curves, the pulmonary venous return to the left ventricle was occluded and the ventricle emptied of blood by manual compression. The aorta was then occluded and successively known volumes of blood were injected into the ventricular cavity and the ventricular pressures recorded. Note that ventricular distensibility with epinephrine is increased during systole but is unchanged during diastole. (After Ulrich and Kramer.)

whole mass of an isolated heart with perfused coronary arteries and contracting isometrically is stretched. Intraventricular pressure rises as the intraventricular volume (index of fiber length) is increased (1) by vagal stimulation owing to the resultant slower heart rate and increased diastolic stretch and filling, (2) as the return of blood to the heart is augmented by infusion in the isolated heart, heart-lung, open and closed chest anesthetized dog, or (3) as the exit of blood from a ventricle is temporarily blocked in the isometrically contracting heart in the open chest dog (fig. 35.10).

Despite the preceding, in any one ventricle the relation of the contractile response to muscle length at any one length is not constant but can be made to vary, or varies spontaneously under many conditions including the normal state, i.e., ventricular volume at rest can vary without corresponding changes in diastolic pressure

(change in distensibility), while the pressure or output of the ventricle during systole can vary without change in diastolic volume (change in contractility). As illustrated in figure 35.10 left, epinephrine causes no change in resting distensibility whereas it increases distensibility during systole. These active changes in distensibility and contractility can be brought about under many conditions and are generally caused by nervous and humeral influences. Thus, the heart is not a passive servant of the peripheral circulation; it does not merely pass on what it receives but is capable of changing its performance at the same diastolic size, thereby initiating circulatory modifications irrespective of primary changes in filling of the heart by venous return and in the arterial resistance to flow.

Some of the cardiac nerve fibers are quite potent in this respect. Vagal stimulation leads to depression of vigor of atrial contraction (inotropic

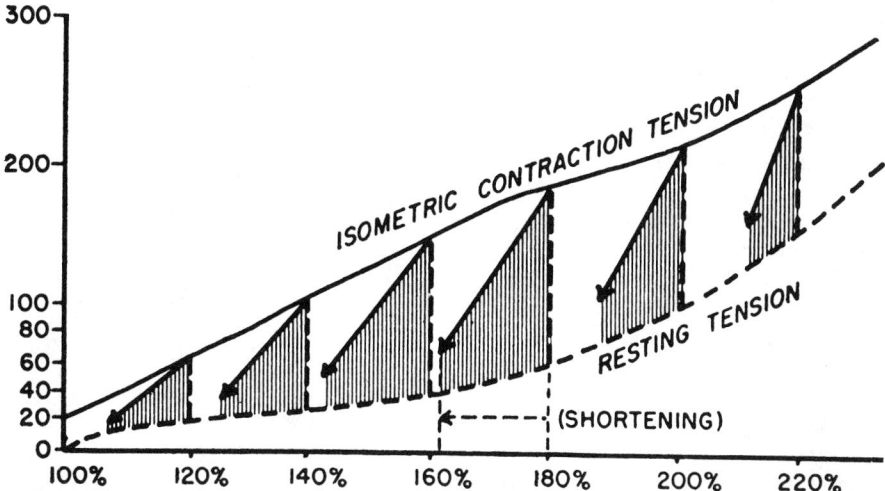

FIG. 35.11. Tension developed by stretched isolated muscle strip during rest and isometric contraction. (After Rushmer, 1955.)

effect). Histologically, however, vagal fibers have not been demonstrated to reach the ventricles and if cholinergic substances are released in the atria, they are presumably destroyed before they reach the ventricles. Left ventricular contractility, as measured by the strain gauge arch in open chest dogs, is depressed on stimulation of the cardiac vagal nerves, but when slowing of the heart rate is avoided through electrical pacing, vagal stimulation has no apparent effect on contractility. Despite this, attention is called to experiments in which continuous stimulation of vagus nerves in the neck of the open chest dog resulted in a decreased stroke volume and stroke work of the left ventricle, for the same left atrial pressure and in the presence of a constant (but high) heart rate. This suggests a depressor action of the vagi on the ventricles.

The effect of sympathetic fibers on the myocardium has been observed by stimulating electrically the stellate ganglia directly or indirectly through activation of the carotid sinus receptors. Such stimulation increases the force of both atria and ventricles, and shortens the period of contraction much more than can be accounted for by an increase in heart rate. When the heart rate and the mean atrial pressure are maintained constant in the closed chest dog, reduction of the activity of the cardiac sympathetic nerves is accompanied by a reduction of the cardiac output. With selective stimulation, when all known connections to the peripheral vascular bed have been previously cut, only the positive inotropic effect can be demonstrated in which the arterial blood pressure and cardiac output rise greatly

through augmented force of contraction. Stimulation of stellate fibers to the heart, epinephrine injection or treadmill exericse in unanesthetized dogs reduce ventricular volume while maintaining or increasing stroke volume; they also give more rapid myocardial relaxation or increased distensibility during diastole thus facilitating diastolic filling, while during ventricular systole the myocardium contracts more rapidly, ventricular pressure rises more rapidly and blood ejection is more complete (fig. 35.7c). In human subjects undergoing cardiac surgery for the correction of congenital heart lesions, the contractile force of the right ventricle, as measured by the strain gauge arch, is increased by the administration of norepinephrine and epinephrine. Finally, if in the open chest dog the perfusion pressure in the carotid sinus is decreased, the circulatory response to such baroreceptor stimulation is dominantly an increased heart action; the effector portion of this reflex appears to be sympathetic fibers from the stellates to the heart, since, following their section these effects disappear and cannot again be induced.

D. Other determinants. In addition, myocardial hypoxia (within limits), an increase in muscle temperature, an increase in the calcium content of the blood, all increase the contractile force. Conversely, deletion of functional cardiac muscle blocks, by crushing, burning or coronary occlusion, decrease in temperature, addition of acetylcholine, hypercapnea, increased concentration of inorganic ions in the blood such as potassium and magnesium will decrease the excitability or the contractile force of the myocardium. Temporary functional deletion of contractions also occurs when two opposing impulses from different directions block each other out. Smaller responses also occur when different fractions of heart muscle are excited more slowly than others. This happens with beats from ectopic foci or with abnormal impulse distribution as in bundle branch block.

E. Isometric versus isotonic contraction. The tension or contractile force developed by a contracting ventricle is different in the isometric and isotonic states (fig. 35.11). When a muscle first contracts isometrically and then is allowed to shorten abruptly, the tension produced falls abruptly because a portion of the energy of contraction is used to overcome the high resistance from viscosity of the myocardium. This situation is comparable to that during systolic ejection since blood cannot be ejected from a ventricle without shortening of its fibers. In general, the contractile energy lost in overcoming myocardial viscosity and in creating tension between muscle layers is less at large diastolic volumes. Similarly, a relaxed myocardium responds to a rapid stretch by an immediate increase in tension which progressively diminishes as the muscle remains stretched. This has its counterpart in the intact heart in which, if inflow is rapid, the ventricular myocardium exerts tension to resist rapid elongation, thus stopping filling in early diastole while a slow inflow would prolong the period of diastolic filling.

During late diastole the tension developed between ventricular muscle layers is minimal. The myocardial layers of the two ventricles which are oriented in different directions contract in different directions and shorten by different amounts during systole. Since these layers are firmly fixed to each other, some of the tension from the shortening myocardial fibers will be used to stretch the connections. This is wasted energy which opposes ventricular ejection. During ventricular relaxation, however, this stored energy is released and is helpful in early diastolic filling. Here also, the greater the systolic and diastolic volumes, the less the contractile energy lost in creating tension between muscle layers.

According to the law of LaPlace ($T = P. R.$), the tension (T) developed in the ventricular wall is related to the pressure developed within the cavity and to the radius of the cavity. For the active ventricle, this indicates that the greater the ventricular size, the greater the wall tension needed to maintain a given intraventricular pressure.

REFERENCES

ALEXANDER, J. T. AND NASTUK, W. L. An instrument for the production of microelectrodes used in electrophysiological studies. Rev. Sci. Instr., 1953, 24, 528.

ANZOLA, J. AND RUSHMER, R. F. Cardiac responses to sympathetic stimulation. Circulation Res., 1956, 4, 302.

BOWDITCH, H. P. Ueber die Eigentöumlichkeiten der Reizbarkeir, welche die Muskelfasern des Herzens zeigen. Berichte d. Konigl. Sachs d. Ges. d. Wissen, Bd. 1871. 23, 652.

BOZLER, E. The initiation of impulses in cardiac muscle. Am. J. Physiol., 1943, 138, 273.

BRADY, A. J. AND WOODBURY, J. W. The sodium-potassium hypothesis as the basis of electrical activity in the frog ventricle. J. Physiol., 1960, 154: 385.

BURN, J. H. AND RAND, M. J. Action of nicotine on the heart. Brit. Med. J., 1958, 1: 137.

CORABOEUF, E. AND WEIDMANN, S. Potentials d'action du muscle cardiaque obtenus a l'aide de microelectrodes intracellulaires. Presense d'une inversion de potential. Compt. rend. Soc. Biol., 1949, 143, 1360.

DiPALMA, J. R. AND MASCATELLO, A. V. Excitability and refractory period of isolated heart muscle of the cat. Am. J. Physiol., 1951, 164, 589.

DRAPER, M. H. AND WEIDMANN, S. Cardiac resting and action potentials recorded with an intracellular electrode. J. Physiol., 1951, 115, 74.

DUDEL, J. AND TRAUTWEIN, W. Das Aktionspotential under Mechanogramm des Herzmuskels Unter den Einfluss der Dehnung. Cardiologia, 1954, 25, 344.

ECKSTEIN, J. W. AND HORSLEY, A. W. The effects of reduced cardiac sympathetic tone on myocardial function. J. Clin. Invest., 1961, 40: 555.

FLECKENSTEIN, A., JANKE, J., DAVIES, R. E., AND KREBS, H. A. Contraction of muscle without fission of adenosine triphosphate or creatine phosphate. Nature, 1954, 174, 1081.

GOLDBERG, L. I., BLOODWELL, R. D., BRAUNWALD, E. AND MORROW, A. G. The direct effects of norepinephrine, epinephrine, and methoxamine on myocardial contractile force in man. Circulation, 1960, 22: 1125.

HAJDU, S. Mechanism of staircase and contracture in ventricular muscle. Am. J. Physiol., 1953, 174, 371.

HARRIS, A. S. The spread of excitation in turtle, dog, cat and monkey ventricles. Am. J. Physiol., 1941, 134, 319.

HILL, A. V., WEBER, H. H., ASTBURY, W. T., DUBUISSON, M., BAILEY, K., PRYOR, M. G. M., LUNDSGAARD, E., NEEDHAM, D., ELLIOTT, A., BARBER, R., MacARTHUR, I., AND EDSALL, J. T. A discussion on muscular contraction and relaxation; their physical and chemical basis. Proc. Roy. Soc., London. Ser. B, 1950, 137, 40.

HOFFMAN, B. F. AND SUCKLING, E. E. Cardiac cellular potentials: effect of vagal stimulation and acetylcholine. Am. J. Physiol., 1953, 173, 312.

HOFFMAN, B. F., deCARVALHO, A. P., MELLO, W. C., AND CRANEFIELD, P. F. Electrical activity of single fibers of the atrioventricular node. Circulation Res., 1959, 7, 11.

HOLT, J. P. Effect of plethora and hemorrhage on left ventricular volume and pressure. Circulation Res., 1957, 5, 273.

HUTTER, O. F. AND TRAUTWEIN, W. Vagal and sympathetic effects on the pacemaker fibers in the sinus venosus of the heart. J. Gen. Physiol., 1956, 39, 715.

KEITH, A. AND FLACK, M. The form and nature of muscular connection between primary divisions of the vertebrate heart. J. Anat. & Phys., 1907, 41, 172.

LEWIS, T., MEAKINS, J., AND WHITE, P. D. The excitatory process in the dog's heart. I. The auricles. Phil. Trans. Roy. Soc., London, Ser. B, 1914, 205, 375.

LEWIS, T. AND ROTHSCHILD, M. A. The excitatory process in the dog's heart. II. The ventricles. Phil. Trans. Roy. Soc., London, Ser. B, 1915, 206, 181.

LINENTHAL, A. J. AND ZOLL, P. M. Quantitative studies of ventricular refractory and supernormal periods in man. Trans. Ass. Amer. Physicians, 1962, 75: 285.

LING, G. AND GERARD, R. W. The normal membrane potential of frog sartorius fibers. J. Cell. & Comp. Physiol., 1949, 34, 383.

MOMMAERTS, W. F. H. M. The proteins of muscle and their participation in the process of contraction. Am. J. Phys. Med., 1955, 34, 11.

MOMMAERTS, W. F. H. M. Investigation of the presumed breakdown of ATP and phosphocreatine during a single muscle twitch. Am. J. Physiol. 1955, 182, 585.

MONROE, R. G., FRENCH, G. AND WHITTENBERGER, J. L. Effects of hypocapnia and hypercapnia on myocardial contractility. Am. J. Physiol., 1960, 199: 1121.

PUECH, P., ESCLAVISSAT, M., SODI-PALLARES, D., AND CISNEROS, F. Normal auricular activation in the dog's heart. Am. Heart J., 1954, 47, 174.

REEVES, T. J. AND HEFNER, L. L. The effect of vagal stimulation on ventricular contractility. Trans. Ass. Amer. Physicians, 1961, 74: 260.

ROBB, J. S. AND ROBB, R. C. The normal heart. Am. Heart J., 1942, 23, 455.

ROBB, J. S. AND KAYLOR, C. T. A study of specialized heart tissue at various stages of development of the human fetal heart. Am. J. Med., 1948, 5, 324.

ROBERTS, J. AND MODELL, W. Pharmacological evidence for the importance of catecholamines in cardiac rhythmicity. Circulation Res., 1961, 9: 171.

ROSENBLUETH, A., ALANIS, J., RUBIO, R., AND LOPEZ, E. The two staircase phenomena. Arch. Intern. physiol. et biochem., 1959a, 67, 374.

ROSENBLUETH, A., ALANIS, J., LOPEZ, E., AND RUBIO, R. The adaptation of ventricular muscle to different circulatory conditions. Arch. Intern. physiol. et biochem., 1959, 67, 358.

ROSENBLUETH, A., ALANIS, J., AND RUBIO, R. Some properties of the mammalian ventricular

muscle. Arch Intern. physiol. et biochem., 1959, 67, 276.

RUSHMER, R. Constancy of stroke volume in ventricular responses to exertion. Am. J. Physiol., 1959, 196, 745.

SARNOFF, S. J., BROCKMAN, S. K., GILMORE, J. P., LINDEN, R. J. AND MITCHELL, J. H. Regulation of ventricular contraction. Influence of cardiac sympathetic and vagal nerve stimulation on atrial and ventricular dynamics. Circulation Res., 1960, 8: 1108.

SCHER, A. M. Direct recording from the A-V conducting system of dog and monkey. Science, 1955, 121, 398.

SCHER, A. M., RODRIGUEZ, M. I., LUKANE, J., AND YOUNG, A. C. The mechanism of atrioventricular conduction. Circulation Res., 1959, 7, 54.

SCHER, A. M., YOUNG, A. C., MALMGREN, A. L., AND PATON, R. R. Spread of electrical activity through the wall of the ventricle. Circulation Res., 1953, 1, 539.

SCHER, A. M., YOUNG, A. C., MALMGREN, A. L., AND ERICKSON, R. V. Activation of the interventricular septum. Circulation, 1955, 3, 56.

SHIPLEY, R. E. AND GREGG, D. E. The cardiac response to stimulation of stellate ganglia and cardiac nerves. Am. J. Physiol., 1945, 143, 396.

SPERELAKIS, N. Additional evidence for high-resistance intercalated discs in myocardium. Circulation Res., 1963, 12: 676.

SPERELAKIS, N., HOSHIKO, T. AND BERNE, R. M. Nonsyncytial nature of cardiac muscle: membrane resistance of single cells. Amer. J. Physiol., 1960, 198: 531.

TRAUTWEIN, W., KASSEBAUM, D. G., NELSON, R. M. AND HECHT, H. H. Electrophysiological study of human heart muscle. Circulation Res., 1962, 10: 306.

ULLRICH, K. J., RIECKER, G., AND KRAMER, K. Das Druckvolumdiagramm des Warmbluterherzens, Isometrische Gleichgewichtskurven. Pflugers Arch. Bd., 1954, 259, 481.

WANG, H. H., BLUMENTHAL, M. R. AND WANG, S. C. Effect of efferent vagal stimulation on coronary sinus outflow and cardiac work in the anesthetized dog. Circulation Res., 1960, 8: 271.

WHITEHORN, W. V. Summation and tetanus in cardiac muscle. Efforts of temperature, epinephrine and digitoxin. Proc. Soc. Exper. Biol. & Med., 1954, 85, 268.

WIGGERS, C. J. AND WEGRIA, R. Ventricular fibrillation due to single localized induction and condenser shocks applied during the vulnerable phase of ventricular systole. Am. J. Physiol., 1940, 128, 500.

WOODBURY, J. W. AND BRADY, A. J. Intracellular recording from moving tissues with a flexibly mounted ultramicroelectrode. Science, 1956, 123, 100.

WOODBURY, L. A., HECHT, H. H., AND CHRISTOPHERSON, A. R. Membrane resting and action potentials of single cardiac muscle fibers of the frog ventricle. Am. J. Physiol., 1951, 164, 307.

WOODS, R. H. Applications of a physical theorem

to membranes in the human body in a state of tension. J. Anat. & Physiol., 1892, **26,** 362.

Monographs and Reviews

BROOKS, C. McC., HOFFMAN, B. F., SUCKLING, E. E., AND ORIAS, O. Excitability of the heart. Grune & Stratton, Inc., New York, 1955.

CRANEFIELD, P. F. AND HOFFMAN, B. F. Electro-physiology of single cardiac cells. Physiol. Rev., 1958, **38,** 41.

HODGKIN, A. L. AND HUXLEY, A. F. Movement of sodium and potassium ions during nervous activity. Vol. 13, p. 176. Cold Spring Harbor Symposia on Quantitative Biology, Long Island Biological Association, 1952.

HOFFMAN, B. F., AND CRANEFIELD, P. F. Electro-physiology of the heart. McGraw-Hill Book Co., New York, 1960.

HUTTER, O. F. Mode of action of autonomic transmitters on the heart. Brit. M. Bull., 1957, **13,** 176.

KRAMER, K. Druckvolumdiagramm der Ventrikel und dynamische Faktoren der Herztätigkeit im intaken Kreislauf. Herzinsuffizienz und Digitaliswirkungen. Bad Oeynhausener Gespraeche III, 1958.

LAPLACE, P. S. Mechanique celeste, Vol. 10, 1841.

LEWIS, T. The mechanism and graphic registration of the heart beat. Ed. 3. Shaw and Sons, London, 1925.

LUNDIN, G. Mechanical properties of cardiac muscle. Acta physiol. scandinav., 1944, **7,** Suppl., 20.

MITCHELL, F. A. G. Cardiovascular innervation. E. & S. Livingstone, Ltd., Edinburgh and London, 1956.

MOMMAERTS, W. F. H. M. The actomysin system and its participation in organized enzyme reactions. Henry Ford Hospital International Symposium on Enzymes. Academic Press, Inc., 1956.

RUSHMER, R. F. Cardiac diagnosis. A physiological approach. W. B. Saunders Company, Philadelphia and London, 1955.

SODI-PALLARES, D. AND CALDER, R. M. New bases of electrocardiography. C. V. Mosby Company, 1956.

STARLING, E. H. The linacre lecture on the law of the heart. Cambridge University Press, London, and Longmans, Green & Company, Inc., New York, 1918.

SZENT-GYORGI, A. Chemical physiology of contraction in body and heart muscle. Academic Press, Inc., New York, 1953.

WEIDMANN, S. Elektrophysiologie der Herzmuskelfaser. Sammlung Innere Medizin und ihre Grenzgebiete, Hubr, Bern, Switzerland, 1956.

WEIDMANN, S. Electrical events underlying the cardiac contraction. Proc. of Harvey Tercen. Congress, May 1958, Circulation, 1958, 100.

WEIDMANN, S. Transport of ions across cardiac membranes. Metabolic aspects of transport across cell membranes, edited by Q. R. MURPHY. University of Wisconsin Press, 1957.

WHITELOCK, O. V. The electrophysiology of the heart. Ann. New York Acad. Sc., 1957, **65,** 653.

WIGGERS, C. J. Physiology in health and disease, Ed. 5. 1949.

WILDE, W. S. The pulsatile nature of the release of potassium from heart muscle during the systole. Ann. New York Acad. Sc., 1957, **65,** 693.

CHAPTER 36

Functional Characteristics of the Systemic and Pulmonary Circulation

The hemodynamic characteristics of the systemic and pulmonary circulations have profound effects on the function of the heart. The principal function of the heart is to convert or change chemical energy into mechanical energy or work so that blood is moved through the cardiovascular system. The external work performed by the heart is measured by the quantity of blood ejected and the pressure developed during each ventricular contraction. The magnitude of both factors is determined by conditions in the circulatory bed which is served by the right and left ventricles. In turn, the amount of external work or useful work performed by the ventricle balances precisely the frictional loss of energy as the blood flows through the vascular circuit.

Figure 36.1 illustrates diagrammatically some of the primary characteristics of (1) the systemic circulatory system of man beginning at the aorta, extending to the venae cavae and emptying into the right atrium, and (2) the lesser circulatory system or the pulmonary circulation consisting of the right ventricle, the pulmonary venules, the veins and the left atrium. The ventricles pump the blood from the terminal reservoirs of the collecting systems, i.e., the atria into the distributing systems under an initial pressure sufficient to insure a continuous capillary flow as well as a return of the blood to the heart.

The Systemic Circulation

Volume Flow

The anatomical complexity of the circulation may obscure some basic facts which should be stressed. The volume flow of blood through any part of the circulation must equal that flowing through any other part, i.e., the flow through all the arteries equals that through all the capillaries, all the arterioles, all the veins, the right ventricle, etc. There may be regional shifts of flow so that some arteries or capillaries carry more or less flow than in other arteries or capillaries, or there may be a small difference in the blood volumes put out by the two ventricles, but the former does not affect the relative total flow through

the capillaries and arteries while the latter can only exist momentarily for a few heart beats, else the organism dies.

DIAMETER AND CROSS-SECTIONAL AREA. If the left ventricle is regarded as a cylinder, then its diameter might be 6 cm. The diameter and cross-sectional area of the ascending aorta approximate 2.5 cm. and 4.5 cm.^{2}, respectively. The large branches of the aorta have a total cross-sectional area which is approximately the same as that of the parent vessel, but the total cross-sectional area of all arteries is much greater. In the periphery, as the vessels become very narrow and short their total cross-section becomes very large because of the large number of vessels involved. The total cross-section of the arterioles with an individual diameter of .016 mm. and length of the order of .015 mm., might be 400 cm.^{2}, whereas the cross-section of the capillaries might be 4500 cm.^{2} (based on an estimated capillary diameter of .008 mm., length 0.05 cm., and about 3,000 million capillaries). This is about 700 times that of the aorta. The figure for the number of capillaries is probably quite low since the capillary bed does not inject very well and there is every reason to believe that not all capillaries are open or shut at the same time, i.e., their state of patency varies with different physiological conditions. The cross-sectional area of the venules is also high, approximating that of the capillaries but with their confluence into veins and then into the venae cavae, their total diameter and cross-section progressively diminish so that the diameter and cross-section of the latter are about two and four times, respectively, those for the corresponding aorta and arteries.

BLOOD CONTENT. An important function of various parts of the circulation is the dynamic storage of blood. Its importance lies in the fact that it is this blood which is mobilized in time of stress to fulfill the needs of the body. The blood content of the various portions of the systemic circulatory tree bears no relation to its cross-sectional area (fig. 36.1). Quantitation of the blood volume existing during life in different parts of the vascular system is fraught with great

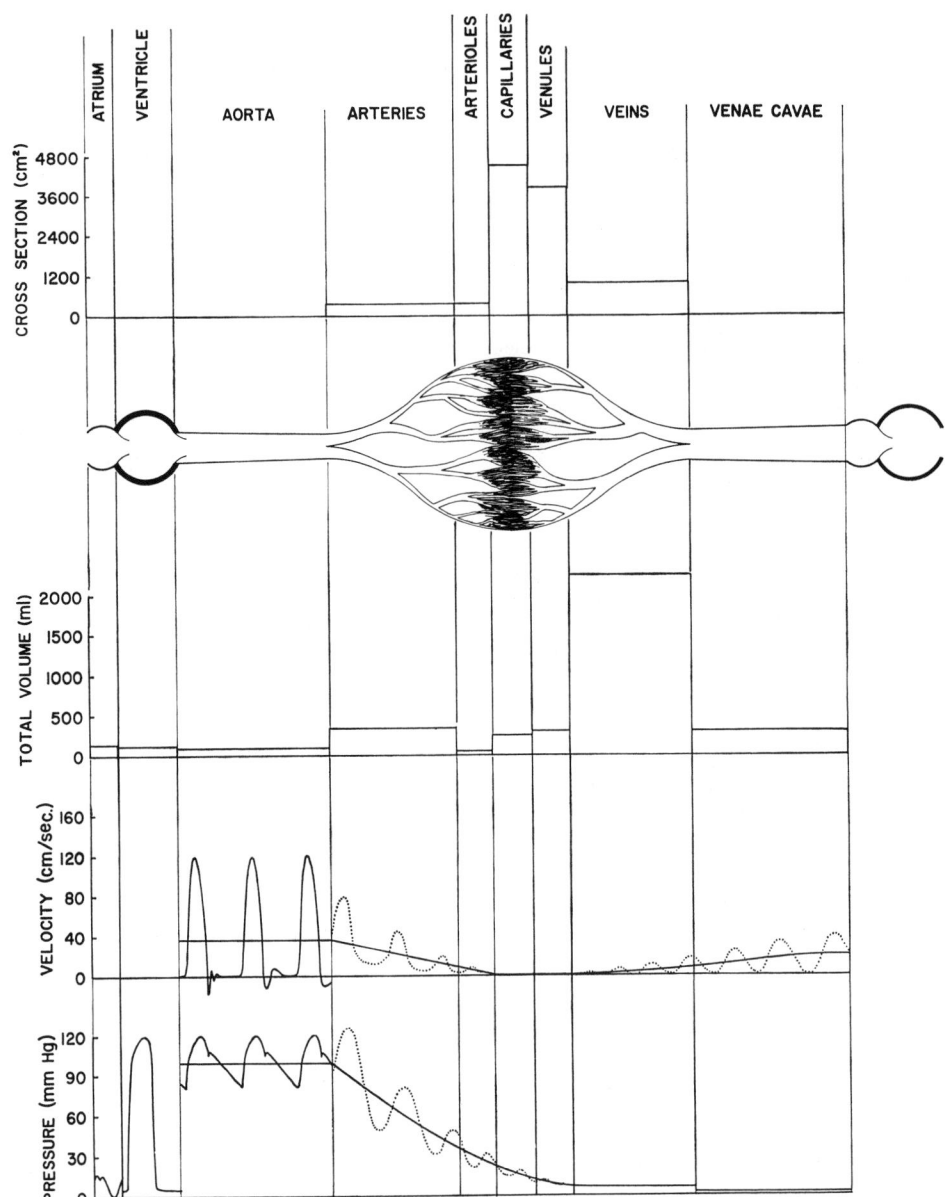

Fig. 36.1*A*. Schematic representation of the cross-sectional area, blood distribution, velocity and pressure in different regions of the systemic and pulmonary circulations. Dotted waves of pressure and velocity indicate estimated trends only.

difficulty, and the values obtained are only approximate. They are, however, helpful in orienting our thinking. The aorta contains about 100 cc., or 2 per cent of the blood volume of 5500 cc. The arteries contain about 8 per cent of the blood volume; the arterioles about 1 per cent. The capillaries probably contain from 75 to 250 cc., or about 5 per cent of the blood volume. Since the capillaries are about one-half a millimeter long, the blood remains in the capillaries not more than 1 to 2 seconds. This figure for blood

content of the capillaries is obviously quite variable since not all capillaries are patent at one time.

Thus, the blood content of the arterial or high pressure system is quite small being about 800 cc., or 15 per cent of the total volume. The systemic venous system accommodates the major portion (at least 50 per cent or about 3200 cc.) of the blood volume; the four heart cavities (600 cc. or 12 per cent); the pulmonary circuit 1000 cc. or 18 per cent. Thus, the low pressure system or,

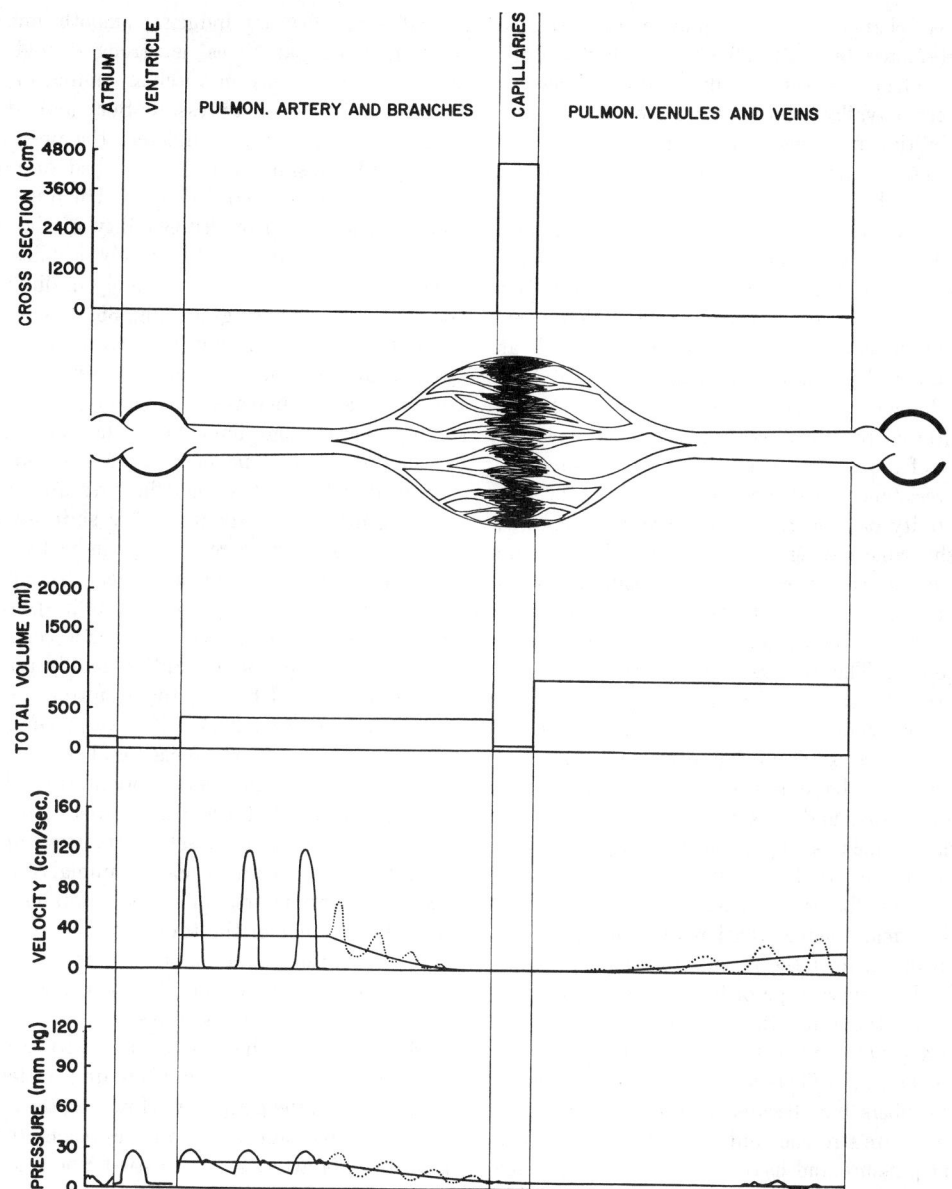

FIG. 36.1*B*. See figure 36.1*A*.

as it is sometimes called, the extra-arterial system which is made up of the systemic venous and pulmonary circuit up to the left ventricle, contains about 80 to 85 per cent of the blood volume.

The blood content of different areas is not constant but is continuously changing and is available for redistribution to other vascular areas where it may be needed. The volume in any one compartment depends not only upon the basic anatomical size of the bed but upon dynamic changes induced by passive and active changes in capacity and content, i.e., distensibility. Although

obviously very important, it is very difficult to make comparisons of distensibilities of different anatomical compartments of the vascular system. Such comparisons would be based upon plots (preferably *in vivo*) showing the relations of percentage increase in volume $(dv)/(dV)$ of the vascular compartment to the increase in intravessel pressure (dp). Experimental data pertaining to distensibility of vessels containing much smooth muscle or which have an active response such as arterioles (resistance vessels), veins, or cardiac chambers, present a rather confusing picture since passive changes in their lumina is normally counteracted by "active" changes of the wall. This balance is very easily changed. Despite this, from available information the different distensibilities are suggested in figure 36.1 by the thickness of the lines. The distensibility of the capillaries has not been documented.

A. *Basic control.* Such storage can be on a long term basis (blood reservoir) and/or it can change rapidly during a cardiac cycle (compression chamber). Both are dependent on the blood content of the cardiac cavities and of the vessels at zero internal pressure and on their distensibility, i.e., change of diameter and length with change of internal pressure; in turn, the basic distensibility of the cavities is governed by the myocardial resistance to stretch. For example, the distensibility of a heart cavity actively changes if, for the same resting size or volume, the pressure within the cavity is altered. As pointed out in chapter 35, the distensibility of the ventricles can be grossly altered by nervous, humoral, and other influences. The distensibility of the vessels is governed by their content of elastic and collagen tissue and smooth muscle (fig. 36.2). All varieties of blood vessels except the arterioles, capillaries and venules have a prominent component of elastic tissue, and in some vessels such as the aorta, as much as 40 per cent by weight is elastic tissue. The elastic fibers with their great range of extensibility before their elastic limit is reached, produce maintenance tension without energy expenditure against the normal blood pressure. In the wall of every type of blood vessel except the capillary, there are white collagenous fibers in a matrix penetrating between the other elements. The collagenous fibers act in a similar way to the elastic fibers but, because of the architecture of the wall, are stretched only at higher than normal blood pressure and have a protective supporting role (fig. 36.2). If, however, the vessels reacted in a purely passive way based on their content of collagen and elastic fibers, their internal pressure would be determined only by the volume of contained blood and, at any constant mean pressure the mean volume of blood within them would also not change. However, many types of vessel contain much smooth muscle which does not contribute significantly to the elastic tension of the wall. Its function is to produce active tension under vasomotor stimulation or local action of various chemicals (vasodilator and vasoconstrictor substances and oxygen lack) and so change the size of the lumen. Such vascular tone adjustment is seen in most vascular areas. It counter-

acts distensibility by inducing smooth muscle reaction which, at times, is strong enough to induce a net decrease in vascular lumina in the presence of an elevated pressure. Such activation will, of course, change completely the pressure-volume relationship in a vascular bed or area.

B. *Aorta and its arterial branches.* The pressure-volume relationship or distensibility of the isolated aorta has been exhaustively studied *in vitro.* The distensibility varies widely in different aortae in the same age group (fig. 36.3). There is no statistically significant correlation between age and absolute distensibility. However, aortic size or capacity increases considerably with age so that the average diameter of the aorta may exceed that of the sum of its branches and the contained volume at a diastolic pressure of 80 mm. Hg may almost double. This shift toward larger volumes with increasing age indicates that the enlarged aorta does not now need to expand as much to accomodate the same systolic ejection. The distensibility of an isolated aortic segment studied *in vivo* and *in vitro* differs mildly during its inflation and deflation, the resulting curves forming a loop (fig. 36.4). This is presumably because of hysteresis of the elastic fibers.

Although such studies aid in orientation, there is no guarantee that the characteristics of the aorta or, indeed, any vessel postmortem apply to conditions in the intact normal animal or man. Since the systemic arterial system contains only about 10 per cent of the total blood in the systemic circulation, even if smooth muscle contraction reduced its volume by 25 per cent (or 125 cc.), its function as a reservoir would be small. Actually, during systole and cardiac ejection, much of the pressure and flow are transferred immediately to the periphery. However, the aorta and some of its immediate branches belong to the elastic type of arteries, i.e., elastic tissue is abundant and muscle fibers are relatively scarce. Because of their large distensibility, the walls of these large central arteries act as compression chambers which serve to buffer the more peripheral branches from too sudden an increase in pressure and flow. The volume of blood suddenly injected into the aorta by the powerful ventricular action is only partly moved forward; a considerable portion is stored locally by the successive expansion of the large vessels. Although earlier work indicated that there is no radial expansion of the aorta beyond the arch, later work using cinematographic films at 1500 frames per second showed dilation of the thoracic aorta during systole of 15 to 20 per cent of its diastolic

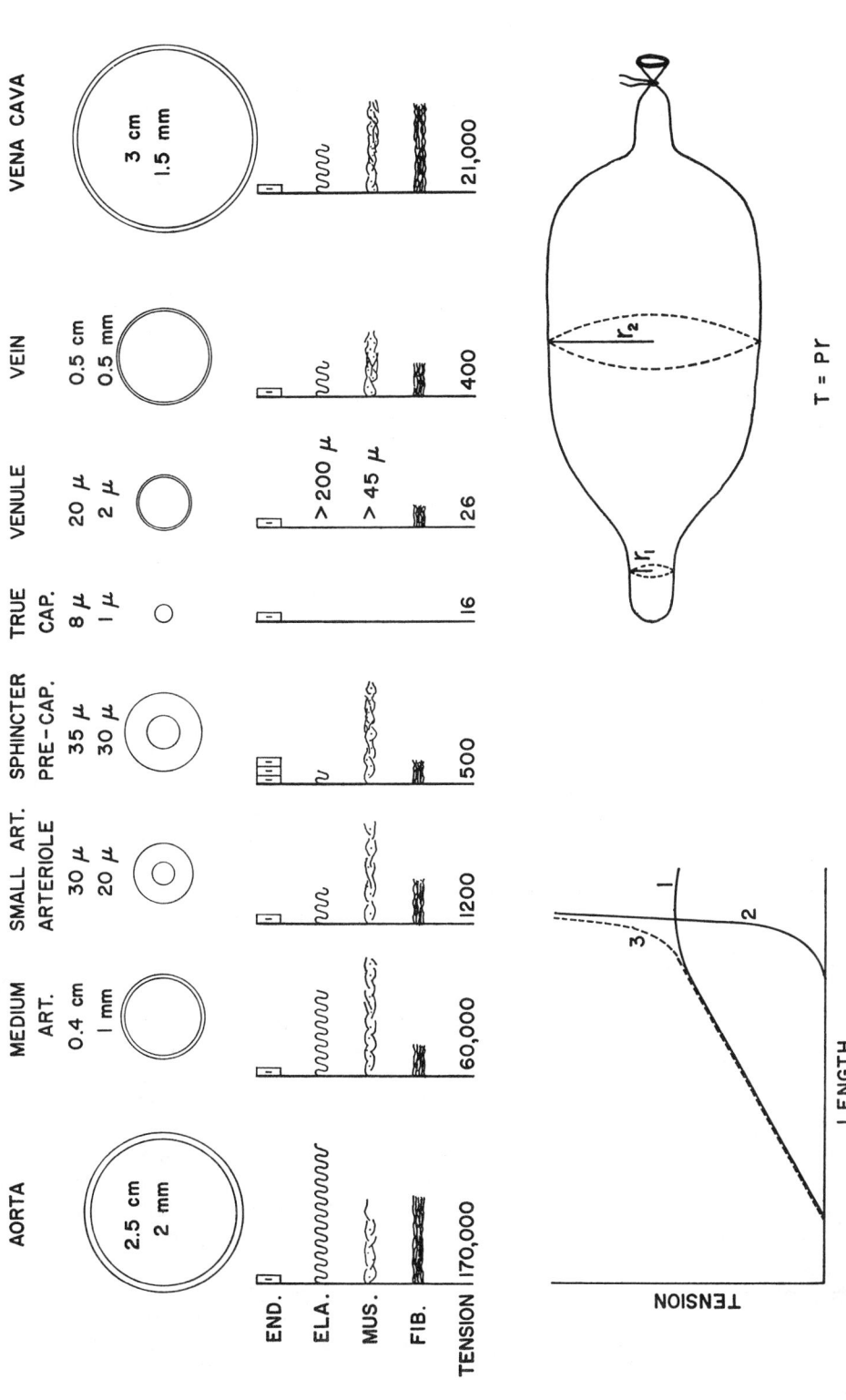

Fig. 36.2. Illustrated are the lumen diameters, wall thickness, relative amounts of different tissues and wall tensions in the various blood vessels. *Lower left;* tension-length diagrams of elastic (1) and collagen fibers (2) presented alone and in combination (3). *Lower right;* balloon demonstrating pressure-tension relation. The pressure (P) within the balloon is equally transmitted to all parts of the contained air (Pascal's law), and the tension (T) in the balloon varies with the radius (r) in that portion. La Place's Law. (Modified after Burton, Physiol. Rev., 1954, 34, 619; and Wolf, Science, 1952, 115, 243.)

diameter which corresponds to a 30 to 40 per cent increase in volume per unit length of the artery; radial enlargement of the more distal aorta was somewhat less. Thus, it is estimated that up to one-half of the pressure and flow discharged during systole is stored here and that this moves forward during diastole through the elastic recoil of the arterial walls. This enables a portion of the blood to run off into the capillaries during diastole and not during systole.

Whether active changes in aortic distensibility normally occur is only incompletely investigated. Simultaneous measurements have been made of phasic aortic blood pressure by an appropriate pressure manometer and of changing aortic circumference during a cardiac cycle. In the open-chest dog or man the latter is obtained by noting the movement of a pair of recording mechanical calipers placed around the aorta; in the unanesthetized dog, aortic circumference is detected by measuring the changing resistance in a mercury filled rubber tube wrapped around it. In the

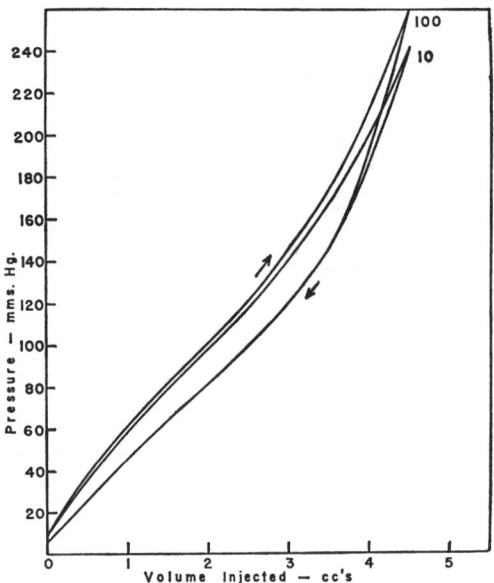

Fig. 36.4. Pressure volume diagrams obtained from an isolated segment of thoracic aorta by injections and withdrawals (arrows) at rate of 10 and 100 cc. of blood per minute. (Alexander, Circulation Res., 1954, **2**, 140.)

open-chest dog, when the arterial blood pressure is elevated to a high level by mechanical constriction of the aorta, the size of the aorta during diastole initially increases but then decreases in the presence of an elevated internal pressure, and at the same time, its distensibility increases, i.e., the pulse pressure becomes larger. A large intra-arterial injection of adrenaline constricts an aortic segment being perfused *in vivo* so that it may contain less than half the volume of the normal aorta in the low pressure range, while in the high pressure range the volumes are almost equal, i.e., the constricted aorta now has a much greater distensibility than the normal aorta. These changes are presumably related to active changes in the smooth muscle which is abundant in these vessel walls. However, these experiments must be interpreted cautiously, for preliminary measurements in intact unanesthetized dogs have shown an intimate relation between the aortic pressure and aortic circumference Thus, the actual amount of and the significance of active alteration of aortic size under changing physiological states is not known.

The more peripheral arteries such as the carotid, brachial, and femoral and their branches, are predominantly muscular types of arteries containing circularly arranged smooth muscle fibers in large numbers which, by their shorten-

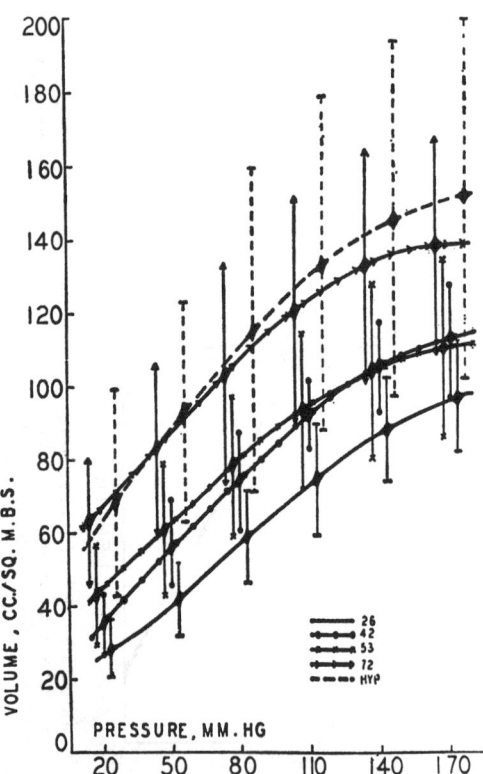

Fig. 36.3. Influence of age on the volume-pressure relations of human aortas. Each curve represents the average values for a given age group. Vertical lines represent standard deviations. (Remington and associates, Am. J. Physiol., 1948, **153**, 298.)

ing, can reduce the lumen of these vessels considerably. Such a set-up obviously permits adaptation or adjustment of this distributing system to accommodate changing volumes of circulating blood. This is initiated by heat, cold, trauma, and many other physiological events. In the latter instance, pressure-volume curves done *in situ* on small (1.2 mm. or less internal diameter) and very muscular arterial segments of the intestine showed that with elevation of the aortic distending pressure, directly or through an increased portal venous pressure, the segment diameter may actually decrease. Since intra-arterial procaine did not block the response and since the vessel constriction was abolished after ischemia, papaverine or cyanide, an active response of the arterial smooth muscle wall (and probably of myogenic origin) is suggested which is caused by the elevated wall tension.

It can also be demonstrated that the femoral artery dilates in response to contraction of the peripheral muscles. This persists with local nerve section, occurs only on the stimulated (active muscle) side, and is abolished by local procaine or cutting of the artery distal to the point of measurement of femoral artery volume. Therefore, the response is by way of a conducting system in the arterial wall. The velocity of such peripheral conduction is 10 cm. per sec., and therefore, the conducting elements are probably the smooth muscle of the media of the vessel wall.

C. Arterioles. The arterioles contain the smallest blood volume of the cardiovascular system, but the pressure and flow in the circulatory system are more sensitive to minute changes in blood content of the arterioles than to that of any other part of the circulatory system. The arterioles are the final or end branches of the distributing system and operate as stopcocks which control the run-off of blood from the arterial system into the capillaries. The caliber of these vessels is controlled by the state of contraction of their circularly disposed and strongly developed smooth muscle fibers. The latter are regulated by local metabolic processes and by blood borne substances. They are also supplied with vasomotor fibers which are controlled by centers in the spinal cord and medulla. Their distensibility other than through myogenic change has not been determined.

D. Capillaries. The blood content of the capillaries (75 to 300 cc.) is also very small. It is probably the most important blood volume since not only is all gas and nutrient exchange effected through its walls, but the number of patent capillaries and the size of their lumina is exceedingly variable. The arteries even as far as the commencement of the true capillaries are impervious. It has been calculated by Krogh that the total filtering surface by the capillary endothelium in the adult human body amounts to about 6300 m.^{2} (68,000 ft.^{2}). The summed areas of the capillary walls in all regions could be imagined, therefore, as constituting an endothelial membrane over 12 miles long and a foot wide, yet so thin that when tightly rolled, it would form a cylinder of about the thickness of a lead pencil.

The capillary wall proper is composed of a single layer of endothelial cells and is about the most tenuous structure conceivable (fig. 36.5). It does not exceed half a micron in thickness. The endothelial cells which are flat are joined at their fringes by a so-called "intercellular cement" which fills in between adjacent cells. The cellular area makes up more than 99 per cent of the total area across which exchange takes place, the small nonliving zone (cement) less than 1 per cent. The cement substance which binds the endothelial cells at their edges is being continuously washed away and renewed again by the endothelial cells. Its basic structure is a porous network of a complex cement substance, presumably a calcium proteinate. At one time it was thought to be hyaluronic acid, but this idea is no longer held. Superimposed on this network, either by electrical, chemical or surface tension forces, is a large adsorbed molecular component of protein which lines the inner surface and plugs most of the large pores in the cement, considerably reducing the perviousness of the structure. The capillary endothelial tube is enclosed and supported by a delicate sheath or membrane of fine fibrils derived from or closely related to the surrounding connective tissue. The intervening space between capillary and this membrane contains a freely moving fluid. Surrounding this in the interstitial spaces is the so-called tissue fluid which is of a gel-like consistency.

It is still debatable whether the bulk of ex-

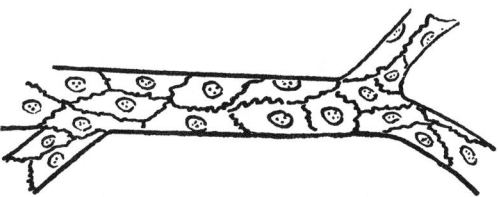

Fig. 36.5. Section of capillary wall stained with silver nitrate to demonstrate the intercellular cement. Nuclei of the cells stained with hematoxylin.

change occurs across the entire surface area or is restricted for most molecules to the pervious intercellular cement. Ions and small molecules diffuse across the capillary wall at such an incredibly fast rate (at least 100 per cent exchange within 1 minute) that it has been suggested that the whole capillary wall is permeable to these substances. The penetration, however, of capillary walls by water and dissolved substances appears to take place solely by processes which require no energy transformation by the capillary endothelial cells. From this has arisen a general belief that the capillary walls, or specifically the intercellular cement, is pierced with numerous ultramicroscopic openings or pores with an average diameter of about 30 Å which are generally too small to allow the passage of plasma protein molecules, but are of sufficient size and number to account for the observed rates of passage of water and nonprotein constituents of the plasma. Considerable evidence has been adduced that lipid soluble molecules, such as oxygen and carbon dioxide, can penetrate rapidly the plasma membranes of the capillary endothelial cells and are not restricted to the aqueous intercellular spaces. Finally, the evidence is fairly clear that

penetration of large molecular aggregates and formed elements, such as the red and white cells, occurs through the intercellular portion of the wall.

Although the preceding generalization is probably true, one must not lose sight of the fact that capillary permeability is by no means uniform throughout the body. For example, skeletal muscle capillaries are about one hundredfold less permeable to water than the glomerular capillaries. Using as a gauge of permeability the protein concentration of the lymph draining different regions, it is found that liver lymph may contain 7 per cent protein (plasma has 6 per cent); lymph from lungs, heart, kidney and intestines, 3 to 4 per cent protein; skin, 1 per cent protein.

The functional anatomy of the capillaries has been worked out for some cold-blooded animals, for the rat and dog mesentery through microscopic observations of the *in vivo* vessels, and for the myocardium by both anatomical and microscopic observations (fig. 36.6). Briefly, blood flows generally from the arterioles directly into a metarteriole, and then into capillaries. The metarterioles lead directly into channels which are main thoroughfares from the capillary bed to the venules. The true capillaries concerned with interchange between blood and tissues are inter-anastomosing side branches of the main channels through the bed. At the ostia of each capillary is a small pre capillary sphincter of smooth muscle which is controlled by nerves presumably from the sympathetic nervous system, in the same manner that these nerves control the arterioles and metarterioles. In the body, the metarterioles and their precapillary sphincters undergo periodic contractions at intervals of 15 seconds to 3 minutes. When the tissue is in a resting state, the constrictor phase of this rhythm predominates and the precapillary sphincters may be completely closed. When the tissue becomes active, the dilator phase of the metarterioles predominates and the precapillary sphincters are open. Thus, in skeletal muscle, it is believed that the increase in blood flow with exercise comes in large measure from this opening up of large numbers of additional capillaries. It is believed that the factors that affect the degree of constriction and relaxation of the metarterioles and the precapillary sphincters during vasomotion are the same factors that affect arteriolar diameters. These are the nervous and hormonal stimuli and local conditions in the tissues. Thus, sympathetic stimuli and epinephrine in the blood intensify the constrictor phase of vasomotion in most areas

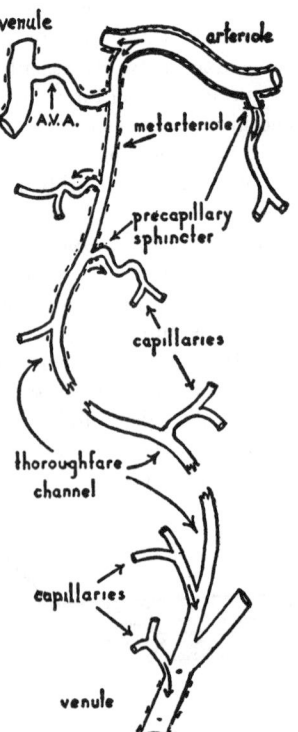

Fig. 36.6. Diagram of a functional unit of the capillary bed; A.V.A., metarteriolar-venural anastomosis. (Chambers and Zweifach.)

of the body in the same manner that these two constrict the arterioles. On the other hand, vasodilator substances decrease the vasoconstrictor phase. The significance and value of this arrangement generally to capillary beds and to over-all circulatory dynamics remains to be established.

Although controversy has raged for many years, at present it is believed that change in capillary diameter is on a purely passive basis, i.e., by change in intracapillary pressure or in extravascular tissue pressure; supposedly, the active changes in capacity previously described by many workers is probably due to the activation of smooth muscle whose presence was unsuspected at that time in the metarterioles and A-V capillaries.

E. Veins. Since the systemic veins contain such a large proportion of total blood volume, they must function as blood reservoirs. The responses by which they may counteract distending forces and thus prevent excessive pooling of blood have been of great interest and have been documented in animals and human experiments. As the venules merge to form larger veins, they acquire a layer of connective tissue and then distinct muscle fibers. These vessels have a larger blood content than the corresponding arteries. Their walls are also much thinner and contain less elastic tissue but have a rather well-developed muscular coat. When the volume of blood in a normally partially collapsed vein is augmented, the intravascular pressure barely increases until the vein becomes round and has a certain degree of fullness. The volume increase up to this point is similar to the filling of a collapsible tube without distending the walls. True distension now occurs when further volume increments lead to an elevation of intravascular pressure (fig. 36.7). Veins excised or within the organism have a very low distensibility when the increase in volume is rather rapid. With prolonged elevation of intravenous pressure, there is a delayed compliance or passive yielding of the venous walls which is attributed to the visco-elastic properties of the smooth musculature. Thus, although initially the low distensibility of veins may prevent blood pooling, the delayed compliance favors it. It is estimated that the ability of the venous system to take up blood is at least 100 times that of the whole circulatory system. Thus, if 1000 cc. ol blood is transfused in a human, about 990 cc. wilf reside in the extra-arterial or low pressure system, and 10 cc. in the arterial system. The pressure in the whole circulation might rise by 5 mm. Hg.

The diameter of these venous capacitance ves-

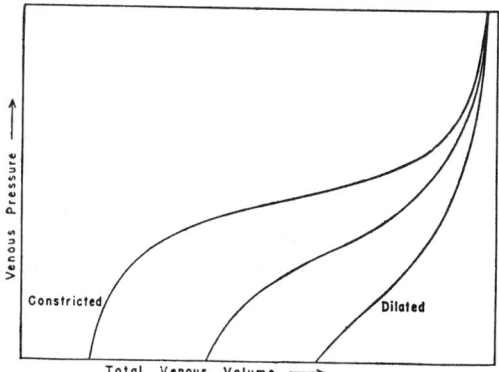

FIG. 36.7. Venous distensibility patterns with different degrees of vasomotor tone. (Alexander, Circulation Res., 1954, **2**, 405.)

sels may be changed either passively by external forces (gravity, respiration or pressure breathing) or actively by contraction or relaxation of their walls. There is considerable evidence to indicate that the venous system (including the pulmonary system) behaves somewhat like an elastic bag. For example, change in posture has no particular effect on their state of contraction; when human subjects are bled or transfused with about 500 cc. of blood, the pressures in the central veins, the pulmonary artery, and left atrium rise and fall in parallel as the blood volume is changed by bleeding or transfusion (fig. 36.8).

While this leads to the conclusion that the venous system operates in a passive manner, it must also be emphasized that this may be true only if the induced changes in central blood volume are moderate or gradual and not in the nature of emergency reactions. It is easy to demonstrate that a fixed pressure-volume relationship need not apply to the veins and venules for they are the most sensitive of all vessels to all types of mechanical, chemical and temperature impacts. For example, the trauma attendant to dissection or to needle insertion may completely close a medium sized vein. In addition, they are supplied with vasomotor nerves through the action of which the distensibility and capacity of the venous system can be actively and greatly changed. This provides a means by which the volume of the venous system can change within wide limits without significant corresponding changes in venous pressure. Such innervation has been demonstrated for the vena cava and veins of the hind limb and mesentery in animals. Active contraction or relaxation of the venous smooth muscle (venoconstriction or dilation) can be elicited by activation of local stretch receptors in the venous

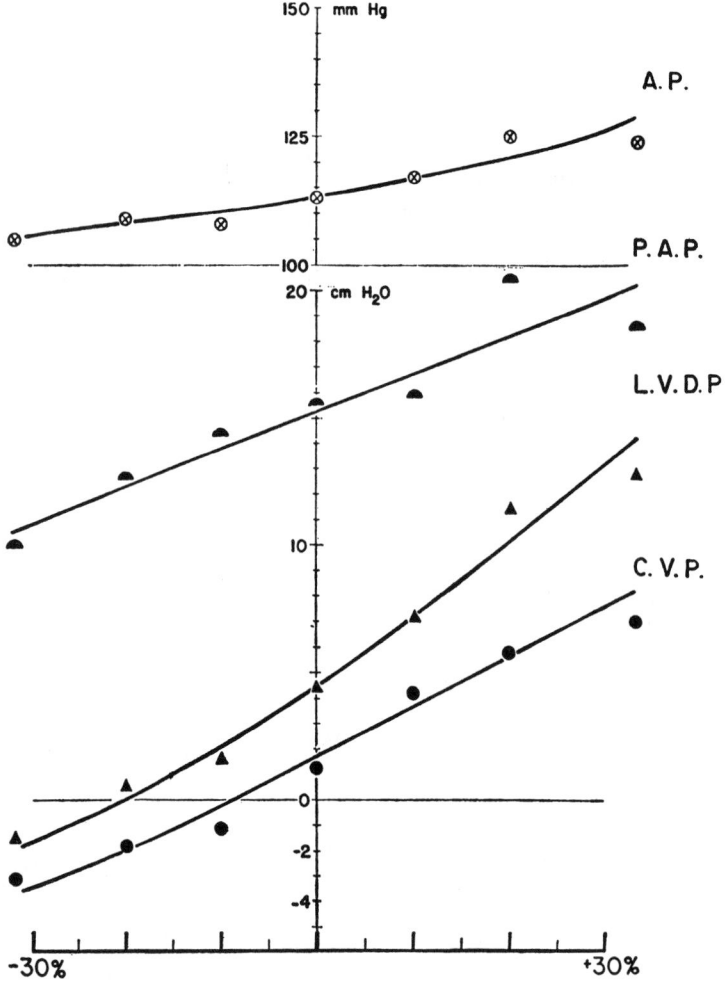

Fig. 36.8. Effects of changing total blood volume (by transfusion (+) or bleeding (−)) upon aortic (A.P.), pulmonary artery (P.A.P.), left ventricular diastolic (L.V.D.P.) and central venous pressures (C.V.P.). (Gauer and associates, Circulation Res., 1956, 4, 79.)

walls, and reflexly by activation of the baroreceptors (stretch receptors) in other veins and in the aorta and carotid arteries, by hypoxic stimulation of the carotid chemoreceptors, and by direct local action of adrenergic or cholinergic substances (fig. 36.7). The reflex venoconstriction produced by carotid artery occlusion in dogs can be abolished by the administration of reserpine or guanethidine, suggesting that these reflexes are mediated through the sympathetic nervous system. Reflex venomotor activity has also been measured in normal subjects by means of pressures developed within isolated segments of superficial veins. An arm superficial vein segment without tributaries is temporarily isolated by applying pressure at the segment ends so that the volume is held constant and vein contraction can

be reflected by an increase in pressure which is recorded continuously by an indwelling needle connected to a pressure manometer. Changing from the supine to the erect posture results in venoconstriction, as indicated by an increase of the venous pressure within the isolated segment; on resuming the supine position venodilatation occurs. Reduction of the circulating blood volume by means of phlebotomy also produces an increase of the venous tone. Strong contractions are caused by the Valsalva maneuver, cold, exercise and hyperventilation. Persons with postural hypotension or with absent circulatory reflexes (as in tabes dorsalis) show little or no segment or central venous response to these stimuli, indicating impaired reflex venomotor activity. Although the entire venous bed may be regarded as a large variable blood depot, the central systemic veins constitute the most important part of this depot for supplying the right heart. It is estimated from observations in dogs that the pressure-volume curve of the venae cavae in the intact living dog can be varied by 15 to 20 times and with only a small effect on venous pressure. This means that translocation of large volumes of blood to the pulmonary and systemic arterial circuit is easily effected.

Velocity Changes

A. In different vessels (fig. 36.1). Just as the cross-sectional area varies greatly in different parts of the cardiovascular system, so does the velocity of blood flow. Since the velocity of flow is inversely proportional to the cross-sectional area of the vessel through which it flows, velocity will be maximal in regions of the circulation with the smallest total cross-sectional area. Hence, the blood velocity in the aorta is the most rapid of that in any part of the body, but even here the average velocity of about 40 cm. per. sec., is low. In the capillaries, it is least, at about 0.07 cm. per sec. This slow rate of passage in the peripheral capillaries, of course, provides time for the exchange of materials across the capillary membranes or walls. After passing into the veins, the blood again accelerates as the cross-sectional area progressively decreases. However, since the caliber of the veins is larger than that of the corresponding arteries, the velocity of venous blood flow never becomes equal to that of the arterial blood and generally equals about ¼ of that in the arteries. For example, the flow of blood along the two venae cavae which together have a cross-sectional area some 4 times as great as that of the aorta, is only about 8 to 10 cm. per sec. under resting conditions.

Although the average blood velocity is low, the peak velocity of blood flow may be high since this changes greatly from moment to moment during each heart beat in the systemic arterial system. In the ascending aorta near the aortic valves, the peak velocity during systole may be 120 cm. per

sec.; during most of diastole, the velocity may approximate zero. Further down the thoracic aorta and in the abdominal aorta, the small back flow present in the ascending aorta at time of closure of aortic valves is greatly accentuated and extended, while forward flow during diastole is increased. In the major aortic branches these violent fluctuations of velocity, although somewhat damped, are largely retained. However, except for the coronary, femoral, and axillary arteries, backflow disappears, and the flow curve is often patterned after its corresponding pressure pulse. At the capillary level, these fluctuations in velocity are pretty well removed so that a smooth rate of flow is attained. In the venules and as the veins become larger, fluctuations or variations in the velocity of flow again reappear. In the venae cavae near the right atrium, blood velocity may become much greater during ventricular systole than during its diastole, indicating that contraction of the myocardium itself draws blood towards the heart. During inspiration, the whole flow curve in the venae cavae is greatly elevated.

B. Across a blood vessel. Finally, the velocity of flow will vary in different portions of the cross-sectional area of a blood vessel, especially in the larger vessels (fig. 36.9). In the larger vessels there is a cylindrical layer of blood which adheres to the vessel wall and wets it. Inside this motionless layer is another cylindrical fluid layer which flows and rubs against it, and inside this there is another flowing faster, and so on, until the central axial core of blood is reached which has the maximum velocity. In arterioles and vessels of quite narrow caliber, red cells are concentrated pretty much in the axial part of the blood stream so that plasma flows along the walls. As a result, the red cells move faster than plasma by a significant amount, and hence, the hematocrit in capillaries is somewhat less than that of the larger vessels. The effect of this is, of course, to change the distribution of the velocity in the various parts of a cross-section of such a vessel.

The flow of blood is laminar or streamlined in

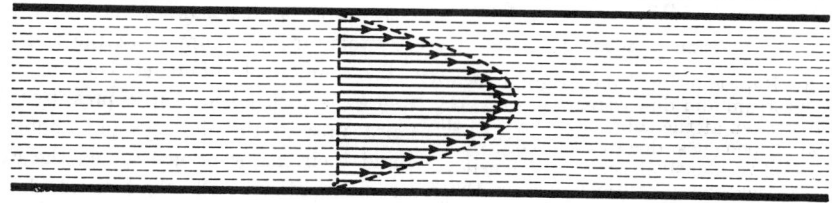

Fig. 36.9. Schematic representation of the variable velocity of blood flow in vessels. Flow is fastest in the central axial stream and progressively decreases to zero at the vessel wall.

most portions of the circulatory tree. When the velocity of flow is increased above some critical level, turbulence develops. The formula RVD/v = a critical constant for turbulence (Reynolds number) expresses the conditions producing turbulence in fluid flowing through tubes of constant diameter in which, v is viscosity, D is density, V is mean velocity, R is tube radius. This indicates that turbulence occurs when low viscosity fluid flows through tubes of large diameter at quite high velocity. If this formula applies to the cardiovascular system, the big variable is the blood velocity since the blood viscosity and vessel diameter do not change greatly. Blood flows rapidly through the biggest arterial channels and with the highest velocities at the roots of the aorta and of the pulmonary artery. It is debatable whether the critical level for turbulence is normally exceeded at these points during the rapid ejection phase of ventricular systole.

Pressure Changes

A. Kinetic and potential energy, lateral and end pressure. Of the energy developed by the left ventricle, more than 98 per cent is normally in the form of potential energy, 1 per cent or less as kinetic energy. When the left ventricle pumps

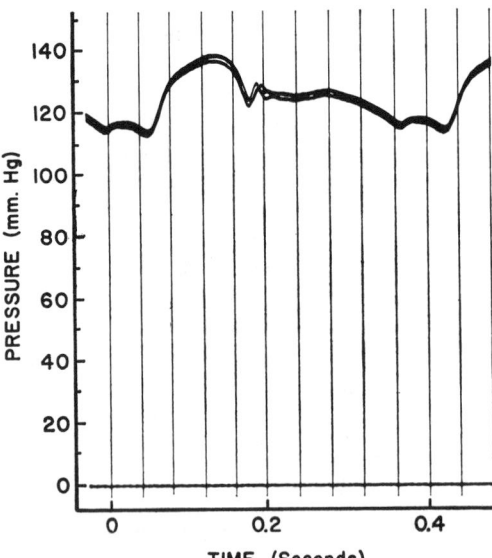

Fig. 36.10. Reproduction from original record of lateral, upstream and downstream phasic pressure patterns taken at the subclavian level in the aorta of a large open chest dog by means of 3 strain gauges adjusted to identical zeros and sensitivities. The patterns and pressure values of the 3 curves are almost identical at systolic pressure 139 mm.Hg; diastolic pressure 115 mm.Hg; heart rate 150 minute.

out blood, it increases the radius and length of the aorta and its large branches to store potential energy as tension in the arterial walls. Because of the motion (velocity) of the blood during ejection, a certain amount of kinetic energy is also transferred to the blood. During exercise with a very large cardiac output or in the presence of aortic stenosis, as much as 10 to 50 per cent of the energy expended by the heart is used for increasing blood velocity. Ultimately, however, most of the potential energy is changed to kinetic energy to produce flow through vascular elements, and then is finally dissipated as heat through friction. The kinetic energy of flow can have a real effect on intravascular pressure. This can be demonstrated by inserting into the flowing bloodstream small catheters or cannulas connected to pressure manometers (fig. 36.10). With the catheter opening pointing upstream, end pressure or potential energy is measured; with the opening at right angles to direction of flow, *lateral* pressure or the pressure actually pressing on the vessel is measured. In the vessels of humans, end pressure and lateral pressure are almost equal except in the aorta and its immediate branches in which the kinetic energy is sufficiently high from prevailing blood velocity to cause the lateral pressure to be significantly lower, i.e., lateral pressure is inversely proportional to the blood velocity (Bernouilli effect). At rest, the average aortic lateral pressure is about 1 mm. less than the end pressure; with exercise, the difference might be 15 mm. Hg. If one is recording phasic aortic pressure throughout the cardiac cycle, then with exercise the lateral pressure might be 40 mm. Hg less than the end pressure during the period of rapid blood ejection (first third of systole). Ultimately, most of the potential energy is converted into kinetic energy in producing flow. In this exchange no energy is lost. However, as blood progresses from the aorta to the atrium, the intravascular pressure decreases to very low values. This permanent loss of energy or pressure arises from fluid friction developed within the vessels with gradual change of energy into heat.

B. In different vessels. (fig. 36.1). Pressure in the aortic arch reaches a maximum during midsystole, and a minimum at the end of diastole. The numerical difference between these pressures is called the "pulse pressure." Similarly, pressures in the thoracic and abdominal aorta and their major branches, i.e., the carotid, the radial, and especially the femoral, show that the values for the systolic pressure increase and those for diastolic pressure decrease, i.e., pulse pressure increases. In still smaller arteries, the pulse pressure progressively diminishes, systolic pressure falling more than diastolic. However, this does not represent a frictional loss of energy but merely a replacement or shift in the temporal relations of pressure during a cardiac cycle, since the mean pressure, for example, in the femoral arteries is the same as that in the aorta.

As the arteries divide and subdivide, the caliber of the individual vessels diminishes and the pressure gradients become correspondingly steeper, particularly in the arterioles and capillaries. Not only is the pressure gradient steeper, but the oscillations of pressure during a cardiac cycle are reduced to a minimum at the time the arterioles are reached. At the arterioles there is a pronounced decrease in pressure gradient, a second abrupt decrease in the capillaries with almost no residual pressure fluctuations. A more gradual pressure decline occurs in the venules and veins until a negative pressure is actually reached in the central veins owing to the effect of the subatmospheric pressure within the thorax.

FUNCTIONAL CHARACTERISTICS OF THE PULMONARY CIRCULATION. In many respects the pulmonary vascular bed (pulmonary artery through pulmonary veins) is similar to the systemic circuit but certain differences deserve emphasis. The pulmonary circulation is a low resistance circuit, arterioles being essentially absent; the pulmonary vessels supply only one type of tissue (alveoli) so vasomotor requirements are low; pulmonary blood volume is less than that in the systemic circuit; extravascular conditions (within the thoracic cage) are fairly uniform (fig. 36.1).

The main pulmonary artery and its branches are structurally similar and of about the same or slightly larger diameter than the aorta, but their walls are one-third the thickness and their branches are much shorter and of very small capacity. Small arteries in both systems have thick muscular walls. Arteries less than 0.1 mm. in diameter are endothelial tubes without muscle. There are no vessels corresponding to arterioles, i.e., no small bore high resistance vessels. The capillaries are somewhat larger, appear to take off very densely from the above endothelial tubes, and have multiple anastomoses. There are numerous A-V shunts. The pulmonary veins are short and contain less blood than the systemic veins.

The pulmonary artery and pulmonary bed in general are many times more distensible than the systemic portion of the arterial circuit and probably represent the most distensible part of the

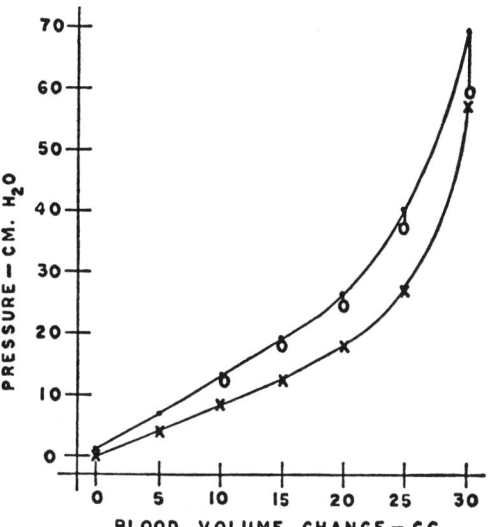

FIG. 36.11. Pressure volume relationship of the pulmonary vascular bed. Injections and withdrawals made at 10-second intervals. Dots: pressures immediately after end of each injection. Circles: pressures 5 seconds after end of each injection. Crosses: pressures immediately after each withdrawal. (Sarnoff and associates, Am. J. Physiol., 1952, **171**, 238.)

low pressure system. Simultaneous pressure and diameter measurements of the main pulmonary artery in living, thoracotomized dogs show a linear relationship over relatively wide ranges of pressure up to 50 cm water. The pressure and diameter pulse contours are almost identical, indicating minimal inertance and viscous resistance of the vessel wall. *In vivo* pressure-volume curves of the entire pulmonary vascular bed and of the pulmonary veins (and left atrium) have pretty much the shape of venous pressure volume curves in the relaxed state (fig. 36.11). The blood volume of the pulmonary system is only 800 to 1200 cc., of which 75 to 100 cc. is in the capillaries, and the rest is in the major arteries and veins. Since the pulmonary vessels are a low pressure distensible system, a minute increase in outflow pressure at the left ventricle, or an increase in pressure at the right ventricle results in a sizeable accumulation of blood in the lungs. With change in posture in man, it is estimated that as much as 400 cc. goes into and out of the lungs. Thus, the blood volume of the pulmonary vascular bed (about 25 to 30 per cent of circulatory blood volume) has an important reservoir function and is about the most important depot for supplying the left heart.

There is some evidence that the distensibility of the pulmonary vessels can be altered. This is based on the findings that the pulmonary vessels contain a considerable amount of smooth muscle; in the living dog, norepinephrine infusion decreases the ratio of pulmonary artery radius to pulmonary artery pressure, indicating a stiffening of the vessel wall; plastic casts of two sides of a lung are very different if one side is perfused with adrenaline up to the moment of plastic injection (this especially affects vessels less than 25 μ in diameter); stimulation of the carotid body chemoreceptors decreases pulmonary vascular resistance; extreme hypoxia (4 per cent oxygen) in one lung causes vessel constriction in that lung; intrapulmonary artery injection of acetylcholine decreases the pulmonary hypertension caused by breathing a low oxygen mixture. It is obvious, however, that the functions of dilation and constriction have been demonstrated under rather extreme conditions. There is thus no strong evidence that the distensibility characteristics (pressure-volume) of the pulmonary circulation can be significantly altered under normal conditions and, hence, it is believed to be mainly a passive vehicle for blood flow. Present experimental evidence (fig. 36.8) supports the view that the pulmonary circulation together with the systemic veins or capacitance vessels form a functional unit or reservoir in which passive and/or active changes in the capacitance system regulate the store of blood in the pulmonary reservoir where it is handled passively.

Since the stroke volume and mean velocity of flow are almost identical in the aorta and pulmonary artery, the kinetic energies of the two bloods are the same, but because the potential energy imparted to the blood by the right ventricle is much less, the kinetic factor is a greater proportion of the energy output of the right ventricle. Phasic variations in blood flow velocity are possibly even more marked in the pulmonary artery than in the aorta. In contrast to the systemic circulation, a markedly pulsatile flow is retained in the pulmonary capillary bed during rest and after exercise. During systole, blood is accelerated in the right ventricle and pulmonary artery by contraction of the right ventricle. The blood gains kinetic energy or energy of motion. As blood distends the arterial tree, the latter acquires potential energy (elastic and hydrostatic). At the same time, energy is partially dissipated by resistance to systolic flow in the small vessels. During diastole the potential energy in the arterial tree is partly lost in hysteresis, and the remainder is dissipated in elastic recoil as blood flows through the resistance of the small vessels. By the end of diastole, the pressures in the vascular bed are almost equilibrated and capillary flow practically ceases.

The resistance to blood flow in the pulmonary circulation is about one-thirteenth that of the systemic circulation. This is because there are no high resistance arterioles, the pulmonary capillaries are large and very numerous; the pulmonary vessels are so easily distended passively, and large portions of the pulmonary bed are only partially used normally. The pressure pulsation in the pulmonary artery of 22/8 (mean 13 mm. Hg) is fairly well maintained in the capillary bed and pulmonary veins since the capillary flow is so pulsatile during a cardiac cycle. However, the capillary pressure has not been directly measured. Phasic pressures taken indirectly through a catheter passed through the pulmonary artery until it is "wedged" in its small branches have been assumed to represent "capillary" or left atrial pressures since the blood obtained through the catheter is well-oxygenated. However, what such recorded phasic pressure curves represent has never been clearly defined. The pressure gradient through the pulmonary bed is quite small. Its highest pressure (pulmonary artery 13 mm. Hg mean) drops to about 7 mm. Hg in the left ventricle at the end of diastole and at the site of outflow from the pulmonary circuit. This pressure gradient of about 6 to 7 mm. Hg causes to flow through the pulmonary circuit the same volume of blood as flows through the systemic system with a pressure gradient of about 90 mm. Hg.

INTERRELATION BETWEEN CALIBER OF VESSELS, INTRAVESSEL PRESSURE AND WALL TENSION. The law of LaPlace is that the tension (T) in the wall of a cylinder is directly proportional to the product of the intracylinder pressure (P) and the radius of the tube (R), i.e., ($T = P \times R$). This has been graphically portrayed using a rubber balloon (fig. 36.2). With partial inflation, the upper part of the balloon expands largely, the distal portion only slightly. Internal pressure is the same throughout, but the greatly expanded portion of the balloon with the large radius has a high tension as evidenced by its resistance to indentation, while in the slightly distended area the walls are soft and easily deformed. Burton has pointed out the application of this law to the ventricular cavities and the vascular system and has calculated the wall tension in the various vessels. In the aorta with a radius of 1.2 cm., it takes the highest wall tension of 170,000 dynes per cm. length to support the transmural pressure of 100 mm. Hg, while in the capillaries with a radius of 4 μ, it takes the lowest tension, only

16 dynes, to support a blood pressure of 30 mm. Hg. In the same capillaries in the legs while standing, the pressure can be 100 mm. Hg. Thus, it takes only about $\frac{1}{10,000}$ as much wall strength in the capillaries as in the aorta to support the same range of internal blood pressure.

As has already been pointed out, the tension in a vessel wall that resists the prevailing internal pressure is supplied by the elastic tissue at normal pressures and by the collagenous fibers at higher pressures. A second important function of the elastic tissue is to make possible a graded constriction or dilation under vasomotor change induced by active wall tension change via smooth muscle. When, however, elastic tissue is absent or in very small amounts, vessels can only be completely closed or open when under vasomotor tone. Intermediate diameters would not be possible. This may explain why tissues deficient in elastic tissue but with smooth muscle, such as A-V shunts and precapillary sphincters, are always either widely open or closed. Thus, with the combination of elastic tension and active tension, grading of degree of vessel constriction is possible but only over a limited range. If the pressure in a vessel is reduced far enough, its wall will eventually reach its unstretched length and the elastic tissue is not functioning. At pressure lower than this, in spite of elastic tissue there will be no elastic tension to provide the automatic adjustment needed for stability, the vessel will become unstable and close. Such "critical closing" pressures have been experimentally demonstrated in many vascular beds and may under certain circumstances approximate a prevailing blood pressure of 100 mm. Hg.

INTERRELATION BETWEEN PRESSURE, FLOW AND RESISTANCE. Hemodynamics is the study of the forces which cause, alter, and regulate the flow of blood through the body. The central problem in hemodynamics is, "What is the relation between the rate of flow of blood in the vascular bed and the pressure which drives it?" Knowledge and understanding of the factors that determine the shape of the curves of flow and pressure is essential to proper interpretation of the changes in blood flow and blood pressure in normal or pathological physiology.

A simple association of pressure and flow can obviously serve as an index of total peripheral resistance (TPR) to flow in the cardiovascular system

$$\frac{\text{(aortic pressure}}{\text{(aortic flow}} \text{ or } \frac{\text{pulmonary artery pressure)}}{\text{pulmonary artery flow)}}$$

or to local resistance in single bed or organ, for example:

$$\frac{\text{(renal artery pressure)}}{\text{(renal artery flow)}}.$$

Such measurements and calculations have been used extensively in recent years in clinical and experimental investigation and, especially in the aorta, to separate the resistance changes due to central or cardiac factors from those due to peripheral factors. The architecture of the whole circulatory distributing system is such that the organs are supplied through many parallel shunts. In this the total peripheral resistance (TPR) is

$$\frac{1}{\text{TPR}} = \frac{1}{\text{r1}} \text{ plus } \frac{1}{\text{r2}} \text{ plus } \frac{1}{\text{r3}} \cdots \frac{1}{\text{r}^n},$$

but since the aorta supplies all the regions with pressure and flow, TPR can be calculated as mean aortic pressure divided by cardiac output. A little reflection will indicate, however, that the resistance to flow can arise from active changes in the smooth muscle of the particular vascular bed in question, or it could be related to passive changes in the geometry of the same vascular bed due to internal and external variations of the pressure. The above approach does not permit separation and quantitation of active and passive changes in vessel size which is essential to the proper understanding of pressure and flow relations. In a modified form, some physical laws derived from hydrodynamics have application to the flow of blood, and they will be considered next.

A. Poiseuille's Law. Generally stated, the volume (F) of blood flowing through a circulating system increases with the perfusing pressure (P) and decreases with the resistance (R) to flow as indicated by the equation $F = P/R$. This is Poiseuille's experimental law which is expressed in more detail as:

$$F = (P_1 - P_2) \cdot \frac{(\pi r^4)}{(8L)} \frac{(1)}{(v)}$$

in which F is flow per unit of time; P_1 is pressure at an upstream point in the tube; P_2 is the pressure at a downstream point in the tube; π is 3.1416; r is the tube radius; L is tube length; v is fluid viscosity. Poiseuille's experiments were based upon measurements of stream-lined flow (nonturbulent) in nondistensible tubes with Newtonian fluids at constant temperature. This means that flow is augmented by an increase in any factor in the numerator and decreased by any factor in the denominator. Thus, flow would decrease by one-half if tube length is doubled or if blood became twice as viscous. Blood is caused to flow from one point to another in a tube by the difference of pressure between such points. This means that doubling the pressure gradient ($P_1 - P_2$) along the tube will double the flow. Change of radius is much more effective in changing flow for doubling the radius will increase flow 16 times.

The resistance to flow, defined as the ratio of the driving force to the flow, is obtained by a rearrangement of the above formula in which:

$$R = \frac{P}{F} = \frac{(8L)}{\pi r^4} \frac{(v)}{(1)}.$$

Resistance to flow is made up of two distinct factors. These are the viscosity (v) or inner friction of the fluid and the geometry of the tube

$$\frac{(8L)}{(\pi r^4)}$$

which is made up of the radius and length. In his system, the resistance was constant since both the viscosity and the geometry of the tube were unchanged and did not change with rate of flow or pressure. A plot of flow versus pressure gave a straight line through the origin, and one of resistance versus pressure a horizontal straight line (fig. 36.12).

B. Application of Poiseuille's law to the circulation. The applicability of this law *in toto* to the circulation depends upon whether resistance is independent of pressure and flow. In the circulatory system peripheral resistance is a measure of the totality of all factors affecting blood flow. These include change (decrease) in apparent blood viscosity (which is known to occur with increase in perfusion pressure, occasioned by the movement of the red cells to form a central axial rod) the existence of stream-lined versus turbulent flow, the length of vessels and the cross-sectional areas of the blood vessels. The latter is determined by the extravascular pressure provided by surrounding tissue; by mechanical dilation with rising perfusion pressure; by opening of new capillaries and vessels with change in metabolism and with rising perfusion pressure, and by active changes in the state of contraction of the muscular walls through vasomotor nerves, humoral substances and metabolic products.

The flow-pressure curves obtained with blood in vascular beds are quite different from those obtained in the artificial system used in Poiseuille's experiments. The chief differences are: the curves do not pass through the origin, and flow is insignificant until a critical level of pressure is attained (called by Burton the critical closing pressure). The curves for dilated vessels are almost linear but with increasing tone the curves become sigmoid and then convex to the flow axis. At sufficiently high pressures, the curves tend to become straight lines pointing toward the origin. The resistance is almost constant at high pressure but rises as the pressure is reduced to reach very high values near the critical closing pressure. Such deviations could arise if (1) the geometric factor of Poiseuille's law is not constant but varies with the distensibility of the blood vessels and (2) blood has anomalous viscosity so that the viscosity factor of Poiseuille's equation varies with the rate of flow and, hence, the driving pressure. While experimental evaluation is difficult, it does appear that vessel distensibility is the major factor responsible for the deviation of *in vivo* pressure-flow curves from Poiseuille's law. This in turn is related to the active tension or contraction of smooth muscle in the vessel walls and to the combined effects of elastic and collagenous fibers in the architecture of the vessels.

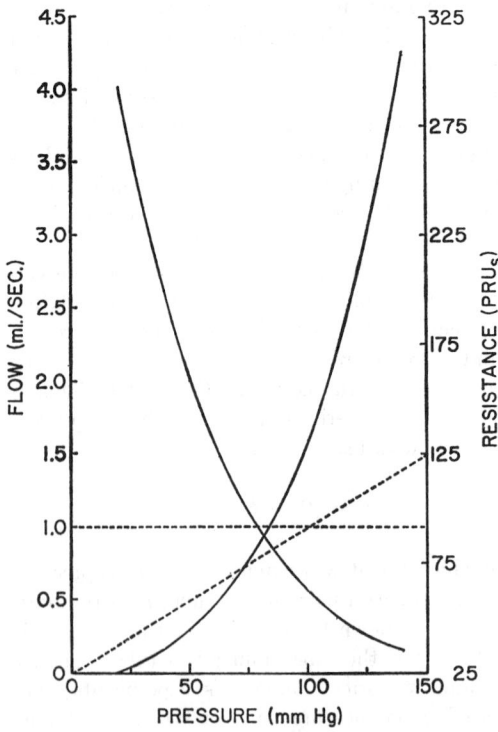

Fig. 36.12. The relationships of flow, pressure and resistance in nondistensible tubes using Newtonian fluids (*dotted lines*) at constant temperature (Poiseuille's law) and blood in vessels (*solid lines*). See text for details.

Apparently anomalous viscosity is a minor factor in large (non-capillary) blood vessels. While the viscosity of moving blood does change, i.e., with increased flow rates there is an axial accumulation of red cells, any change of viscosity from such accumulation of red cells is complete at very low flow levels and, throughout most of the physiological range of flow, viscosity does not change appreciably with flow. This is borne out by the experimental observations that flow-pressure curves using fluid of normal viscosity, such as plasma, are essentially similar to those obtained when blood is used but, when blood is used in rigid, nondistensible tubes, the flow-pressure curves are almost linear within the physiological range.

C. Use of peripheral vascular resistance as an index of vasomotor activity. In view of the multiplicity of factors which affect peripheral resistance in the cardiovascular system, it remains to be seen to what extent changes of peripheral resistance may be used to interpret vasomotor activity. Still, in studies of peripheral circulation reactions, it is desirable to measure the peripheral resistance. This represents the ratio of transmural pressure to the rate of flow through the organ or region being studied. Vascular tone or vasomotor action represents the active contraction of the muscular walls of the blood vessels and is influenced physiologically by vasomotor nerve impulses, humoral substances and metabolic products. The fact that changes in intravascular lumen occur with altered intraluminal pressure on a purely physical basis, points up the difficulty in establishing to what extent alteration of peripheral resistance may be used to interpret vasomotor activity.

The interpretation of changes in peripheral resistance in the presence of an alteration of vasomotor activity associated with a rise or fall of blood pressure or blood flow is difficult. In this instance, changes in vasomotor activity cannot be deduced unless it is possible to know in some way what portion of the change in peripheral resistance would have resulted from the observed alterations of pressure or flow alone. It is obvious that as long as either arterial pressure or the blood flow remain constant while the other is changing, or if pressure and flow change in opposite directions, the fluctuations of peripheral resistance correctly indicate the direction and, roughly, the magnitude of alteration of vasomotor activity. A fairly satisfactory and practical way of estimating change in vascular tonus due to vasomotor activity when pressure and flow change in the same direction, is to determine during a control period, the pressure-flow relationship over the range of flows anticipated during the experimental period and thereafter to compare these with the pressure-flow ratios during the experimental period. Their difference would be caused by a vasomotive change. Possibly the most useful approach is to calculate resistance values from directly measured levels of pressure and flow while either the pressure or flow is controlled by a pump. This type of measurement has been made in the conscious dog and man.

REFERENCES

ALEXANDER, R. S. The influence of constrictor drugs on the distensibility of the splanchnic venous system, analyzed on the basis of an aortic model. Circulation Res., 1954, **2**, 141.

ALEXANDER, R. S. The participation of the venomotor system in pressor reflexes. Circulation Res., 1954, **2**, 405.

ALEXANDER, R. S., EDWARDS, W. S., AND ANKENEY, J. L. The distensibility characteristics of the portal vascular bed. Circulation Res., 1953, **1**, 271.

BAYLISS, W. M. On the local reactions of the arterial wall to changes of internal pressure. J. Physiol., 1902, **28**, 220.

BRAUNWALD, E., FISHMAN, A. P., AND COURNAND, A. Estimation of volume of a circulatory model by the Hamilton and Bradley methods at varying flow volume ratios. J. Appl. Physiol., 1958, **12**, 445.

BRAUNWALD, E., ROSS, J., JR., KAHLER, R. L., GAFFNEY, T. E., GOLDBLATT, A. AND MASON, D. T. Reflex control of the systemic venous bed. Effects on venous tone of vasoactive drugs, and of baroreceptor and chemoreceptor stimulation. Circulation Res., 1963, **12**, 539.

BURCH, G. E. AND ROMNEY, R. B. Functional anatomy and "throttle valve" action of pulmonary veins. Am. Heart J. 1954, **47**, 58.

BURTON, A. C. Improvement in construction of apparatus for demonstrating turbulence. J. Appl. Physiol., 1954, **6**, 719.

BURTON, A. C. On the physical equilibrium of small blood vessels. Am. J. Physiol., 1951, **164**, 319.

BURTON, A. C. AND ROACH, M. R. The reason for the shape of the distensibility curves of arteries. Canad. J. Biochem. &. Physiol., 1957, **35**, 681.

COULTER, N. A., JR. AND PAPPENHEIMER, J. R. Development of turbulence in flowing blood. Am. J. Physiol., 1949, **159**, 401.

DALY, I. DEB. AND DALY, M. DEB. The effects of stimulation of the carotid body chemoreceptors on pulmonary vascular resistance in the dog. J. Physiol., 1957, **137**, 436.

DUBOIS, A. B., AND MARSHALL, R. Measurements of pulmonary capillary blood flow and gas exchange throughout the respiratory cycle in man. J. Clin. Invest., 1957, **36**, 1566.

FOLKOW, B. AND LOFVING, B. The distensibility of the systemic resistance vessels. Acta physiol. scandinav., 1956, **38**, 37.

FOLKOW, B. Intravascular pressure as a factor regulating the tone of the small vessels. Acta physiol. scandinav., 1949a, **17,** 289.

GAUER, O. H., HENRY, J. P., AND SIEKER, H. O. Changes in central venous pressure after moderate hemorrhage and transfusion in man. Circulation Res., 1956, **4,** 79.

GREEN, H. D., LEWIS, R. N., NICKERSON, N. D. AND HELLER, A. L. Blood flow, peripheral resistance and vascular tonus, with observations on relationship between blood flow and cutaneous temperature. Am. J. Physiol., 1944, **140,** 518.

GREENFIELD, J. C. AND PATEL, D. J. Relation between pressure and diameter in the ascending aorta of man. Circulation Res., 1962, **10,** 778.

HALLOCK, P. AND BENSON, I. C. Studies on the elastic properties of human isolated aorta. J. Clin. Invest., 1937, **16,** 595.

HAYNES, R. H., AND BURTON, A. C. Role of non-Newtonian behaviour of blood in hemodynamics. Am. J. Physiol., 1959, **197,** 943.

HENRY, J. P., GAUER, O. H., AND SIEKER, H. O. The effect of moderate changes in blood volume on left and right atrial pressures. Circulation Res., 1956, **4,** 91.

HILTON, S. M. A peripheral arterial conducting mechanism underlying dilatation of the femoral artery and concerned in functional vasodilatation in skeletal muscle. J. Physiol., 1959, **149,** 93.

JOHNSON, P. C. Myogenic nature of increase in the intestinal vascular resistance with venous pressure elevation. Circulation Res., 1959, **7,** 992.

LOFVING, B. AND MELLANDER, S. Some aspects of the basal tone of the blood vessels. Acta physiol. scandinav., 1956, **37,** 134.

McDONALD, D. A. The occurrence of turbulent flow in the rabbit aorta. J. Physiol., 1952, **118,** 340.

McDONALD, D. A. Lateral pulsatile expansion of arteries. J. Physiol., 1953, **119,** 28P.

PAGE, E. B., HICKHAM, J. B., SIEKER, H. O., McIntosh, H. D., AND PRYOR, W. W. Reflex venomotor activity in normal persons and in patients with postural hypotension. Circulation, 1955, **11,** 262.

PAPPENHEIMER, J. R., RENKIN, E. M., AND BARRERO, L. M. Filtration, diffusion and molecular sieving through peripheral capillary membranes. A contribution to the pore theory of capillary permeability. Am. J. Physiol., 1951, **167,** 13.

PATEL, D. J. AND BURTON, H. C. Active constriction of small pulmonary arteries in rabbit. Circulation Res., 1957, **5,** 620.

PATEL, D. J., SCHILDER, D. P. AND MALLOS, A. J. Mechanical properties and dimensions of the major pulmonary arteries. J. Appl. Physiol., 1960, **15,** 92.

PETERSEN, L. H. Participation of the veins in active regulation of circulation. Fed. Proc., 1951, **10,** 104.

POISEUILLE, J. L. M. Recherches sur les causes du mouvement du sang dans les veines. J. Physiol. et pathol., 1830, **10,** 277.

PROVENZA, D. V., AND SCHERLIS, S. Demonstration of muscle sphincters as a capillary component in the human heart. Circulation, 1959, **20,** 35.

REMINGTON, J. W., NOBACK, C. R., HAMILTON, W. F., AND GOLD, J. J. Volume elasticity characteristics of the human aorta and prediction of the stroke volume from the pressure pulse. Am. J. Physiol., 1948, **153,** 298.

RENKIN, E. M. Capillary permeability to lipid-soluble molecules. Am. J. Physiol., 1952, **168,** 538.

REYNOLDS, S. R. M. Nondilation of arteries with pulsating blood flow. Science, 1952, **115,** 485.

REYNOLDS, O. An experimental investigation of the circumstances which determine whether the motion of water shall be direct or sinuous, and the laws of resistance in parallel channels. Phil. Trans. 1883, **174,** 935.

RUSHMER, R. F. Pressure-circumference relations in the aorta. Am. J. Physiol., 1955, **183,** 545.

SALZMAN, E. W. Reflex peripheral venoconstriction induced by carotid occlusion. Circulation Res., 1957, **5,** 149.

SARNOFF, S. J. AND BERGLUND, E. Pressure-volume characteristics and stress. Relaxation in the pulmonary vascular bed of the dog. Am. J. Physiol., 1952, **171,** 238.

SHARPEY-SHAFER, E. P. Venous tone. Brit. Med. J., 1961, **2,** 5267.

SHIPLEY, R. E., GREGG, D. E., AND SCHROEDER, E. F. An experimental study of flow patterns in various peripheral arteries. Am. J. Physiol., 1943, **138,** 718.

SPENCER, M. F., JOHNSTON, F. R., AND DENNISON, A. B. Dynamics of the normal aorta: "Inertiance" and "compliance" of the arterial system which transforms the cardiac ejection pulse. Circulation Res., 1958, **6,** 491.

WHITTAKER, S. R. F. AND WINTON, F. R. The apparent viscosity of blood flowing in the isolated hind limb of the dog, and its variation with corpuscular concentration. J. Physiol., 1933, **78,** 339.

WIGGERS, C. J. Active changes in size and distensibility of the aorta during acute hypertension. Am. J. Physiol., 1938, **124,** 603.

WILENS, S. L. The postmortem elasticity of the adult human aorta. Its relation to age and to the distribution of intimal atheromas. Am. J. Physiol., 1937, **13,** 811.

WOODS, R. H. A few applications of a physical theorem to membranes in the human body in a state of tension. J. Anat. & Physiol. 1892, **26,** 362.

WOLF, A. V. Demonstration concerning pressure-tension relations in various organs. Science, 1952, **115,** 243.

Monographs and Reviews

BEST, C. H. AND TAYLOR, N. B. The physiological basis of medical practice. Ed. 6. The Williams & Wilkins Company, Baltimore, Maryland, 1955.

BURTON, A. C. Relation of structure to function of the tissues of the wall of blood vessels. Phys. Rev., 1954, **34,** 619.

CHAMBERS, R. AND ZWEIFACH, B. W. Intercellular

cement and capillary permeability. Physiol. Rev., 1947, **27**, 436.

DANIELLI, J. F., AND STOCK, A. The structure and permeability of blood capillaries. Biol. Rev., 1944, **19**, 81.

FRANKLIN, K. J. A monograph on veins. Charles C Thomas, Publishers, Springfield, Illinois, 1937.

GAUER, O. H. AND HENRY, J. P. Beitrag zur Homeostase des extraarteriellen Kreislaufs. Klin. Wchnschr., 1956, **34**, 356.

HADDY, F. J. Vasomotion in systemic arteries, small vessels and veins detected by direct resistance measurements. Minnesota Med., 1958, **41**, 162.

KROGH, A. Anatomy and physiology of the capillaries. Yale University Press, New Haven, 1929.

LANDIS, E. M. Capillary pressure and capillary permeability. Physiol. Rev., 1934, **14**, 404.

PAPPENHEIMER, J. R. Passage of molecules through capillary walls. Physiol. Rev., 1953, **33**, 387.

RAPPAPORT, E. AND DEXTER, L. Pulmonary "Capillary" Pressure. Methods in Med. Research, 1958, **7**, 85.

SJOSTRAND, T. Volume and distribution of blood and their significance in regulating circulation. Physiol. Rev., 1953, **33**, 202.

SJOSTRAND, T. Distribution of blood and regulation of the blood volume. Klin. Wchnschr., 1959, **34**, 561.

WEARN, J. Myocardial Capillaries. Harvey Lectures, 1939–40, **35**, 243.

WEZLER, K. AND SINN, W. Das stromungsgesetz des Blutkreislaufes. Editio Cantor K G./Aulendorf, Wurtt, 1953.

ZWEIFACH, B. W. Structural make-up of the capillary wall. Ann. New York Acad. Sc., 1955, **61**, 670.

CHAPTER 37

Electrocardiography

Electrocardiography may be defined as that branch of physiology which is concerned with the recording and analysis of the electrical activity of the heart. The electrocardiograph is an instrument which receives the electrical impulses as they vary during the heart cycle and transforms them into a graphic record called the electrocardiogram. Records obtained from muscle strips are called electrograms.

Instrumentation

The first electrocardiogram was obtained in 1887 by Waller who employed a capillary electrometer. Einthoven became the real father of electrocardiography when he described the string galvanometer in 1903. This instrument became the standard apparatus for the recording of electrocardiograms until it was largely supplanted by the vacuum tube, amplifier-driven oscillograph in the 1930's. This type of instrument was later modified by increasing the amplification sufficiently to drive a mechanical lever arm so that directly written records might be obtained either with an ink writer or a hot stylus applied to specially waxed paper. Recently transistorized modifications of the vacuum tube type of oscillographic instrument have come on the market. Common to all these instruments is the property of faithfully inscribing the variations of the cardiac voltages on an accurate time scale abscissa.

The cathode ray oscilloscope has been employed for specialized research in electrocardiography and recently it has been adapted by means of the sweep circuit to give a constant visual display of the electrocardiographic pattern which can be monitored during surgery or other critical clinical conditions.

Depolarization and Repolarization of Cell Aggregates

The electrocardiogram which is recorded from body surface electrodes is the result of a vast number of systematically propagated electrical events taking place in the individual muscle cell fibers of the heart. We have seen that the individual myocardial fiber is depolarized and repolarized with large voltage fluctuations across the cell membrane, but with only small potential differences being recorded outside the cell. How then does the transmembrane action potential relate to the electrocardiogram recorded from the surface of the heart or from the surface of the body?

It must be remembered first that the depolarization of a portion of a fiber initiates a flow of current from the polarized zone to the depolarized zone. This flow of current propagates the wave of depolarization until the entire tissue is depolarized. Since the heart is functionally a syncytium of muscle fibers, if one portion of the muscle becomes depolarized it will initiate a wave of activation that will eventually depolarize the entire heart. That such is indeed the case is shown by the fact that extra systoles may be produced by touching the epicardium of the exposed heart at surgery or by touching the endocardial surface with a cardiac catheter during diagnostic studies. The localized point of depolarization initiated by the mechanical stimulus is propagated to the entire heart muscle.

The Isolated Muscle Strip

The relationship between the surface electrocardiogram and the spread of depolarization through the muscle is illuminated by experiments on isolated strips of heart muscle. Figure 37.1 illustrates the sequence of events when a wave of activation sweeps over a strip of myocardium with electrodes applied directly to its surface. On the resting polarized muscle there is no difference of potential since all parts of the surface are equally positive in charge. Hence the galvanometer records only a straight line at zero potential. When the strip is stimulated at the region of the negative electrode to the left of the drawing, this zone becomes depolarized and is electrically neutral. The other end of the strip is now positive with respect to the depolarized zone, and the galvanometer records a positive deflection. As the wave of activation approaches the positive electrode more and more positivity is recorded until the muscle strip is completely depolarized whereupon there is no longer a

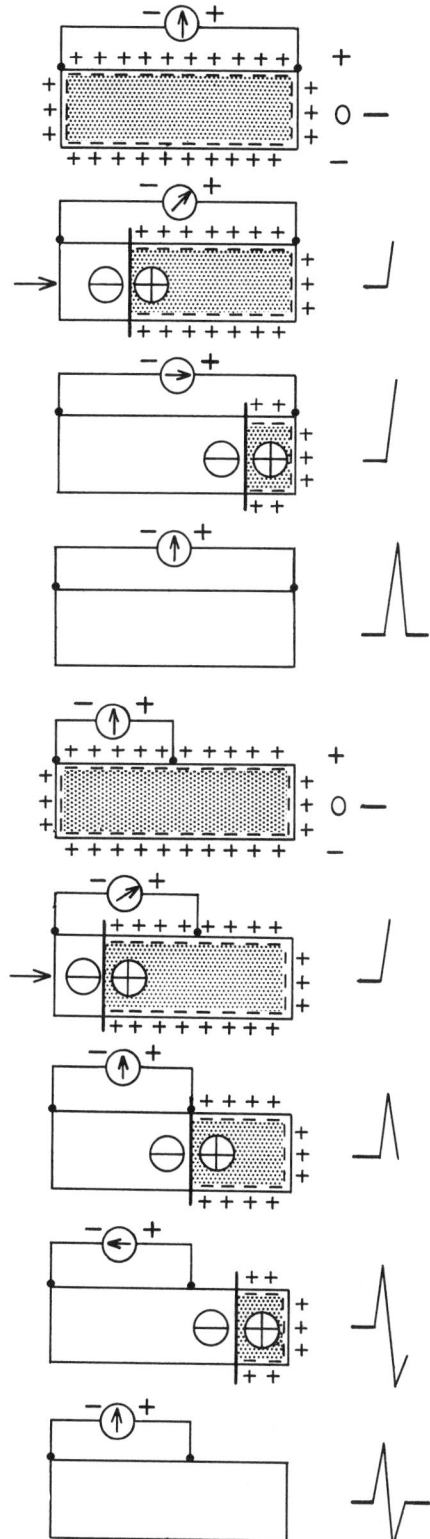

FIG. 37.1. Depolarization of a strip of myocardium with electrodes in direct contact with tissue. During the resting stage no difference of potential

potential difference, and the recording drops abruptly to the zero line.

When the positive electrode is placed in the middle of the strip and the stimulus is applied to the region of the negative electrode, positivity is recorded until the wave of activation passes beneath the positive electrode whereupon the recording drops abruptly to a negative potential which returns to the zero line when the strip becomes completely depolarized. In a series of simple but beautifully conceived experiments, Craib was able to show that this phenomena could best be accounted for in terms of the migration of a dipole across the length of the muscle strip.

A dipole may be conceived of as two points of opposite electrical charge separated by a very small distance. If these points are connected by a wire it is understood by convention that current will flow along the wire from the positive pole to the negative pole. (In point of fact the electrons actually flow from the negative to the positive pole.) If the dipole is immersed in a volume conductor such as a pool of weak saline solution, then a three dimensional field will be set up with the lines of current flow distributed in a pattern as illustrated in figure 37.2. Isopotential lines are arranged at right angles to the lines of current flow. Thus, all points which lie on the plane perpendicular to the center of the axis connecting the two points of the dipole are at zero potential. The human electrocardiogram may be analyzed in terms of the body surface potentials generated by a series of dipoles within the heart and distributed throughout the body which behaves as a volume conductor.

This concept may be clarified by reference to an isolated heart muscle strip immersed in a volume conductor as shown in figure 37.3. In the resting state the strip is polarized with innumerable dipoles distributed about the surface of the strip, positive charges on the outside and negative charges on the inside. Since the positive charges facing the electrode are exactly balanced

---

is recorded. When stimulated at *arrow*, depolarization begins, and stimulated end becomes negative relative to opposite end. Positivity is recorded from positive electrode until activation is completed whereupon no more difference in potential exists and recording drops to zero. With positive electrode in middle of strip, positivity is recorded until the activation wave arrives under the electrode. Since the plane that divides a dipole is at zero potential, the recording drops immediately to zero. As soon as the dipole passes the electrode, maximum negativity is recorded and it gradually lessens until the return to zero when activation is completed.

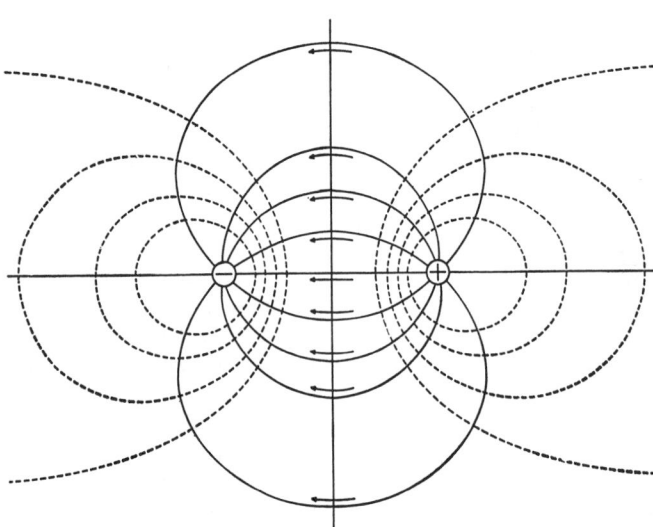

FIG. 37.2. Electrical field of a dipole in a volume conductor. Solid lines are current flow. Dotted lines are isopotential lines. (From Fulton, J. F. A textbook of physiology. Ed. 16. W. B. Saunders Co., Philadelphia, 1951.)

by the positive charges facing away from the electrode, there is no difference of potential, and no deflection is registered on the galvanometer or on the electrographic tracing.

When a stimulus is applied to the end of the strip facing away from the electrode, depolarization begins at that point. The dipoles at the point of stimulus are obliterated by a flow of current across the stimulated membrane, the electrical resistance of which has dropped precipitously. The stimulated area then loses all surface charges and this area is now electrically negative with reference to the remainder of the strip which is still positively charged. Thus, the plane that divides the depolarized from the polarized portion may be considered as an interface separating the positive and negative poles of a dipole, and the propagation of the wave of depolarization down the muscle strip may be thought of as the sweep of a dipole across the length of the muscle strip. As the dipole approaches the electrode increasingly larger voltages are recorded as the electrode intersects isopotential lines of higher voltage. Maximum potential is reached when the dipole arrives at the end of the strip nearest the electrode. When the entire strip becomes depolarized, it suddenly becomes electrically inert and the galvanometer and electrogram immediately fall to the zero level.

Figure 37.4 illustrates the electrograms which are inscribed when the positive electrode is placed at the stimulated end of the strip or at the midpoint.

REPOLARIZATION

The process of repolarization is of relatively long duration in contrast to the rapid spike of depolarization, as demonstrated by the monophasic action potential recorded from single fibers with the micropuncture technique. Since the resting transmembrane potential is fully restored after each beat, the total electrical charge of repolarization must be equal and opposite to the discharge of depolarization. If it were presumed that repolarization followed the same pathway across the muscle strip as the wave of depolarization, then one would expect that the repolarization wave should be inscribed by the recording oscillograph as a slow deflection opposite in direction to the depolarization spike but encompassing the same area. While this is indeed the case in the isolated muscle strip electrogram, it is not the case in the normal human electrocardiogram in which the depolarization and repolarization deflections usually have the same direction, and the areas of the two are rarely if ever the same. The reasons for the paradoxical orientation of repolarization in the human electrocardiogram will be discussed in a subsequent section.

Since repolarization is of long duration, different phases of it are proceeding simultaneously in various portions of the muscle strip and indeed throughout the heart (fig. 37.3). Repolarization, therefore, cannot be analyzed as a sequence of propagated electrical events and cannot be viewed as a wave front sweeping across the

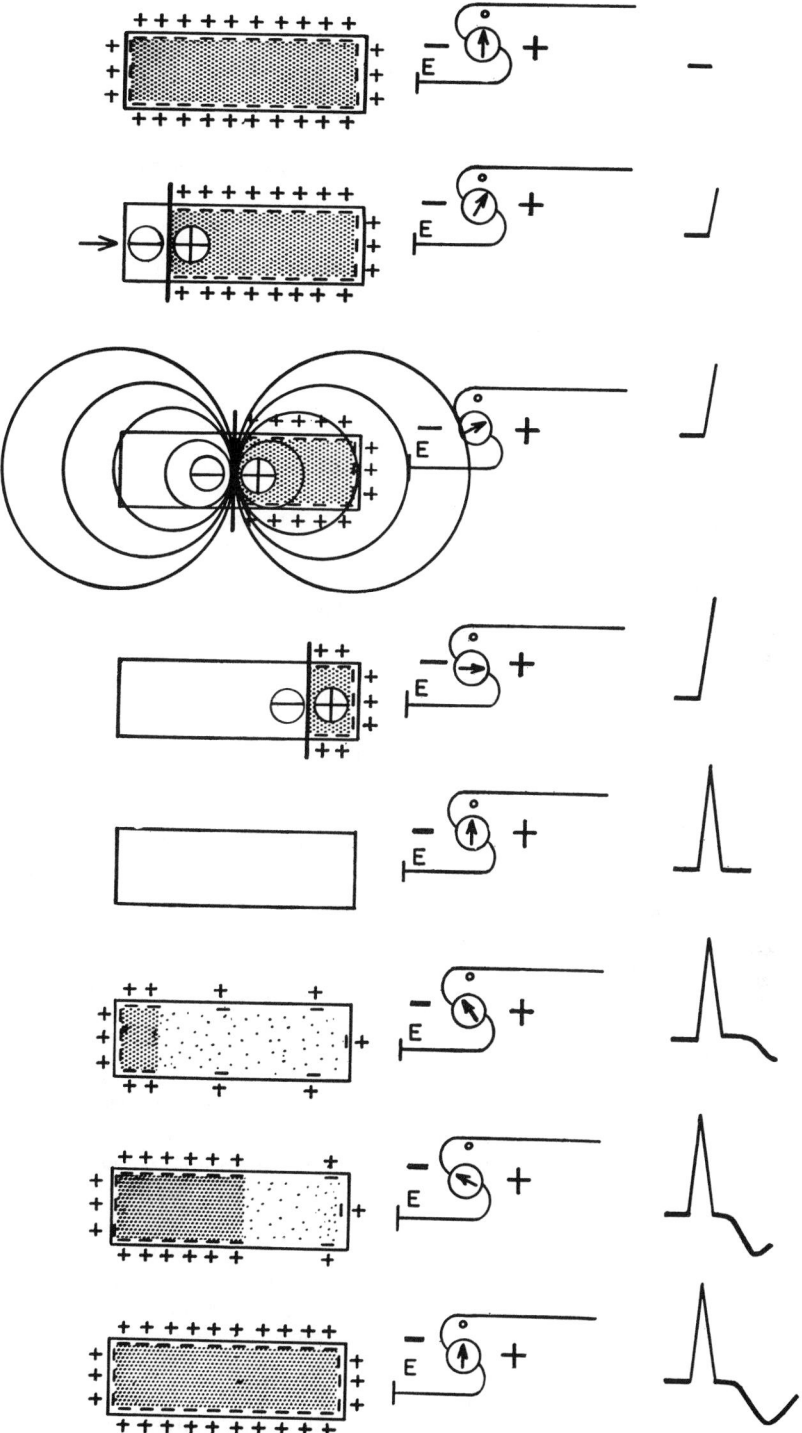

Fig. 37.3. Depolarization and repolarization of a strip of myocardium immersed in a volume conductor. Electrode E connected to positive pole of recording galvanometer which is paired with a distant electrode at near zero potential. The advancing dipole at the border between activated and inactivated muscle produces an electrical field which moves toward the electrode. The electrode is intersected by isopotential lines of increasing force until all difference of potential is extinguished by completion of depolarization. Recovery occurs in all parts of the muscle simultaneously but is completed at the stimulated end first thus producing relative negativity at the side facing the electrode and giving rise to a negative repolarization wave.

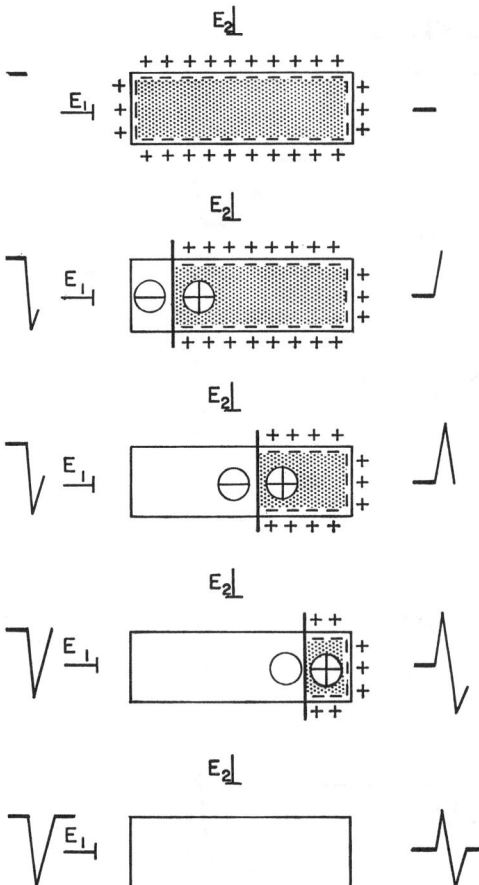

FIG. 37.4. Form of complexes inscribed from electrodes placed at positions E_1 and E_2 during depolarization of a strip of myocardium suspended in a volume conductor. Each electrode paired with a distant indifferent electrode. Tracings on the left side are related to E_1 while tracings on the right relate to E_2 electrode.

muscle. Changes in temperature, chemical environment, and pharmacological agents may produce marked alterations of the repolarization wave without noticeably affecting the depolarization spike.

CURRENT OF INJURY

When a portion of myocardium becomes injured, whether it be mechanically, chemically or thermally, the cell membranes in the injured area become more permeable to sodium ions which leads to a lessening of the ionic concentration gradients of sodium and potassium across the cell membranes and thus to a reduction of the charge density in the resting polarized state. This reduction of positivity in the injured area produces a gradient of charge from the uninjured to the injured zone. A current flows from the area of high positivity to the area of low positivity; this current is called the current of injury. It flows during the resting polarized state.

Figure 37.5 shows how the injury current affects the depolarization and repolarization waves of the electrogram of the isolated muscle strip. Prior to injury the polarized muscle strip gives rise to no potential difference and the electrogram tracing is at zero. Upon injury of a portion of the strip near the electrode, the baseline shifts in a negative direction since the charge density at the injured area is less than that over the remainder of the strip. The injured area is thus electrically negative to the noninjured area. When the strip is stimulated from the noninjured side the dipole of the depolarization wave sweeps toward the electrode producing a positive deflection. The tracing shows an increasing positive spike until the entire strip has become depolarized whereupon the electrogram deflection falls to the original zero potential, which is well above the negatively displaced baseline of the depolarization spike. Repolarization then begins at the zero potential line giving the appearance of elevation of the repolarization wave.

If the electrode is placed on the opposite side of the strip, then the injury potential displaces the baseline upward from the zero line. The depolarization spike is negative, and its termination at zero falls below the point of origin. This gives the appearance of depression of the repolarization wave. Thus, the injury potential produces elevation of the origin of the repolarization wave when the electrode faces the injured zone and depression of the origin of the depolarization wave when the electrode faces the noninjured zone.

Another form of injury potential may become apparent when the injured zone fails to completely depolarize. As the dipole of the depolarization advances toward the electrode, increasing positivity is inscribed until the activation wave arrives at the border of the injured zone where it is blocked. At this point, the injured zone maintains its weakly polarized state, but the noninjured zone has become depolarized making it electrically negative to the injured zone. The persistence of the dipole at the completion of activation maintains positivity at the electrode until the repolarization process in the uninjured zone slowly returns the tracing to the isoelectric line. The resulting complex representing a fusion of depolarization and repolarization waves has been called the monophasic injury wave (fig. 37.5B).

A third explanation for the injury potential

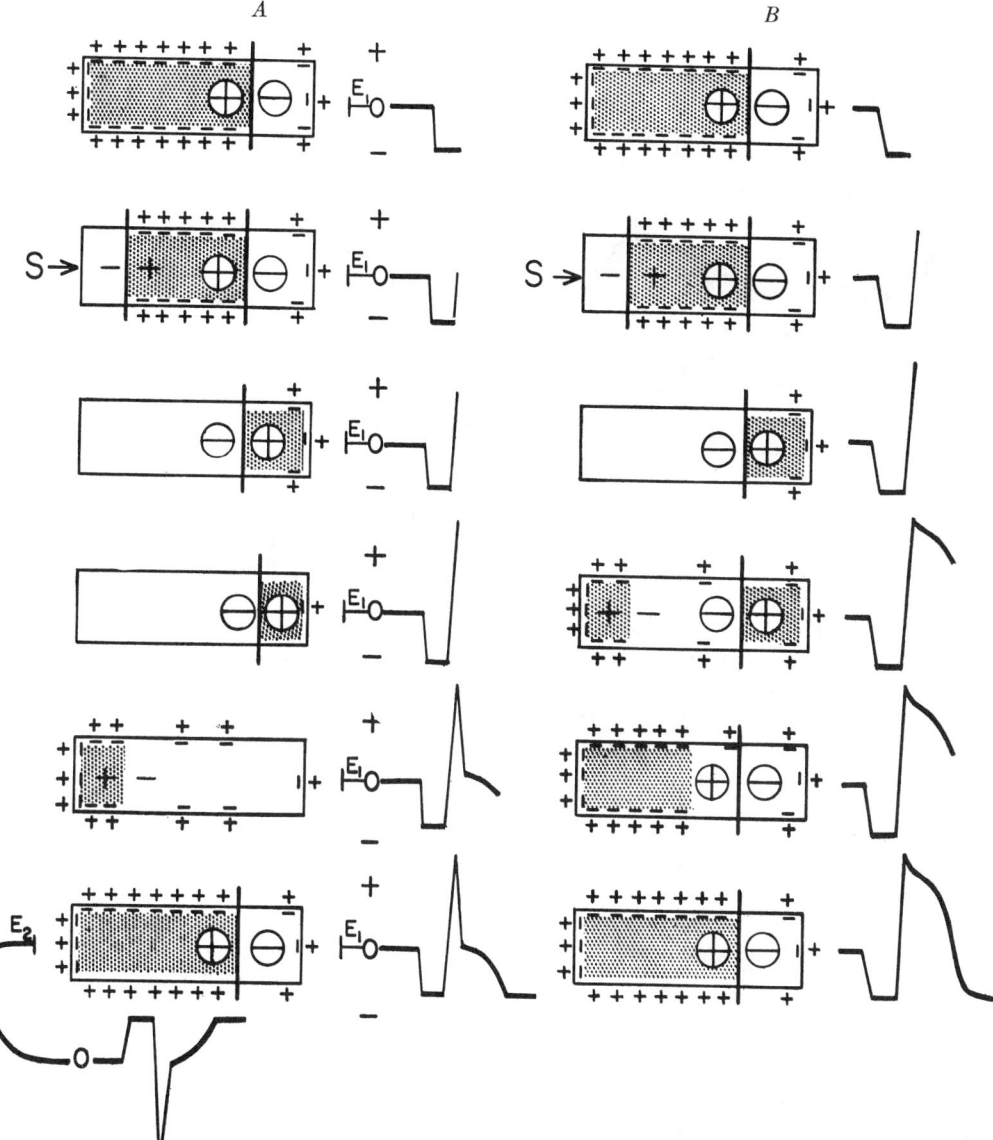

Fig. 37.5. Sequence of electrical changes in myocardial strip which has been injured at end near electrode E_1. When portion of strip becomes injured, there is leakage of ions and reduction of surface charge density making injured zone less positive than noninjured zone. A dipole is thus produced at border of injured zone with negative pole facing the electrode during the resting phase. The baseline is, therefore, displaced downward to negative position. Following stimululation, the dipole of depolarization sweeps toward electrode, producing positive force which neutralizes effect of injury dipole. In 5A, the injured zone becomes depolarized and injury dipole is abolished. Upon completion of depolarization, recording falls to original zero position. As repolarization is completed from left to right, the injury dipole is re-established and tracing returns to negatively displaced baseline, giving appearance of elevation of onset of repolarization deflection. If electrode is on opposite side of strip, baseline is displaced upward, and onset of repolarization appears to be displaced downward. 5B shows the sequence when injured zone fails to depolarize. The impulse is blocked at the boundary of the injured zone which remains polarized and, therefore, during systole presents a dipole with its positive pole facing the electrode holding the recording in a positive position until repolarization returns the tracing to the negative baseline. This phenomenon is called the monophasic injury wave.

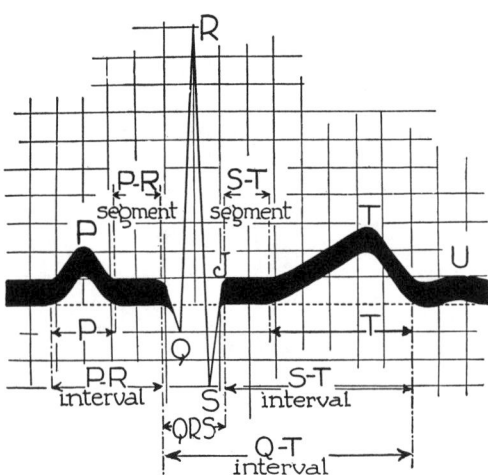

FIG. 37.6. A single electrocardiographic complex giving nomenclature of the deflections and the intervals. (Burch and Winsor.)

is that the injured tissue repolarizes more rapidly than normal and therefore has a positive charge in relation to the surrounding normal tissue during an early part of the recovery period. An electrode near the injured zone faces relative positivity during this part of the recovery period and thus records elevation of the origin of the repolarization wave.

The Mammalian Electrocardiogram

Nomenclature

The mammalian electrocardiogram contains three major components during each cardiac cycle (fig. 37.6). According to the nomenclature devised by Einthoven, the component produced by atrial activation is called the P wave, the one produced by ventricular activation is the QRS complex, and the component produced by ventricular recovery is the T wave. The P wave is separated from the QRS complex by an isoelectric interval called the PR segment. Individual deflections in the QRS complex are labelled as follows: if the initial deflection is negative (downward from the baseline) it is a Q wave, the first positive (upward) deflection is an R wave, and a negative deflection following the R is an S wave. Subsequent positive and negative deflections in this complex are labelled R′ and S′, respectively. The interval between QRS and T is the ST segment. The junction between the end of the QRS complex and the ST segment is called the ST junction or J point. A small after-potential called the U wave is sometimes seen following the T. The duration of the components and intervals

vary with species and age. The intervals also vary inversely with heart rate. In the normal adult human the P wave is 0.07 to 0.12 seconds in duration, the PR interval measured from the beginning of the P wave to the beginning of the QRS complex is 0.12 to 0.20 seconds, the QRS complex is 0.05 to 0.10 seconds, and the QT interval measured from the beginning of the QRS complex to the end of the T wave is 0.26 to 0.45 seconds at normal heart rates.

The Distribution of Electrical Forces in the Body

In accordance with dipole theory, the wave front of activation is considered to be a polarized surface with positive charges on its leading side and negative charges on the trailing side. The axis joining each pair of positive and negative charges is perpendicular to the polarized surface, and the density of charges is considered to be a constant. Atrial and ventricular activation are schematically described by the development of polarized surfaces which spread across the myocardium and are extinguished when they reach a margin of the myocardial syncytium or an area of activated muscle. Laws governing the distribution of electricity in a volume conductor define the electrical field produced in the body by such polarized surfaces.

When viewed from a sufficiently distant point P, a polarized surface can be represented by a single central resultant dipole with its axis perpendicular to a plane intercepting the boundary of the surface, and its charge proportional to the area of this plane (fig. 37.7A). The electrical potential (V_p) at a distant point in a large volume conductor containing a dipole with charges close together is proportional to $M \cdot \cos \theta / R^2$, where M is the electrical force of the dipole (determined by the quantity and distance between charges), R is the distance from P to the center of the dipole, and θ is the angle between the dipole axis and the line from P to the dipole center. A positive potential is recorded at P when it faces the positive side of the polarized surface. The direct relationship between V_p and $\cos \theta$ indicates that potential at P is maximal when the dipole axis is parallel to R and zero when it is perpendicular to R. V_p is also proportional to the solid angle at P which is subtended by the boundary of the polarized surface (fig. 37.7B). This solid angle is equal to the area cut on a unit sphere by lines drawn from its center at P to all points on the boundary of the polarized surface. When two or more polarized surfaces subtend solid angles at P, the resultant V_p is proportional to the sum of the solid angles, with due regard for their sign.

The electrical potential at any point in the body or on its surface can theoretically be predicted in terms of the solid angles subtended by polarized surfaces developed in the heart during activation, and this has been done in a qualitative fashion. However, it is impossible to reverse the procedure and derive information about the size and orientation of the individual polarized surfaces from a knowledge of the resultant solid angle. It has been more practical to analyze tracings recorded at a distance from the heart in terms of resultant vectors which indicate the magnitude and mean direction of electrical forces developed during the cardiac cycle without any implications about the polarized surfaces responsible for them. When viewed from a distance, the total electrical forces of the heart at any instant can be considered as a single dipole that is described by a vector oriented in the direction of the dipole axis with magnitude proportional to the dipole moment. This vector represents the sum of many individual vectors each of which describes a single dipole at a polarized surface.

Vector Analysis and Electro-cardiographic Leads

A vector quantity is represented geometrically by an arrow with its direction and length related to the direction and magnitude of the quantity it describes. It can be shown that electrical potential (V_p) at a point P in a volume conductor is proportional to the geometric projection of an arrow representing a dipole vector onto a line (the lead axis or lead line) drawn from P to a point of zero potential at the center of the dipole. V_p is proportional to $E \cdot \cos \theta$ when E is the magnitude of the dipole vector and θ is the angle between the vector and the lead line (fig. 37.7C). An electrocardiograph will record this potential if one electrode is placed at P and the second electrode is placed at a point of zero potential. However, when two electrodes are placed on the body surface, the tracing recorded represents only the difference between potentials of the same order of magnitude at each electrode and does not give any specific information about the potentials at either point.

Einthoven described a method for vector analysis of such tracings recorded from pairs of electrodes on the body surface at a distance from the heart. He assumed as a first approximation that electrical forces of the heart originate in a relatively small area at the center of a homogeneous volume conductor, and that the regions where each arm and the legs join the trunk are points equidistant from each other. The extremities behave as linear conductors connected to the trunk so that an electrode placed anywhere on an extremity is equivalent to one at its junction with the trunk. Electrodes placed on each arm and a leg are then considered to be located at the apices of an equilateral triangle with the heart at its center, and differences in potential recorded between these points represent the projection of vector forces originating from a dipole at the center of the triangle onto lead lines drawn between its apices. Potential differences between the extremities are customarily recorded in three standard limb leads obtained by connecting two of the limb electrodes at a time to the electrocardiographic instrument in the manner illustrated in figure 37.8. The polarity of the electrode connections is such that a positive charge facing the left shoulder will produce a positive deflection (upward from the base line) in lead I, and a positive charge facing the foot will produce positive deflections in both leads II and III. Einthoven deliberately arranged the polarity of lead II in a manner inconsistent with the other two leads so that ventricular activation would produce positive deflections in all three leads of most normal records. Differences in potential are recorded in the three limb leads according to the following relationship: I = VL − VR, II = VF − VR, III = VF − VL, where VR, VL, VF represent potentials at the right arm, left arm and left leg respectively. Since the three leads form a closed circuit the algebraic sum of their potential differences at any instant is zero. Because of the reversed polarity of lead II, this relationship (Einthoven's law) is actually: I − II + III = 0, or I + III = II. The validity of this equation does not depend on any assumptions relating to the electrical homogeneity and geometry of the volume conductor or location of the heart.

It is possible to derive the potentials at each extremity from these bipolar leads if Einthoven's hypotheses are correct. That is, if the location of the extremity electrodes is equivalent to the apices of an equilateral triangle on the surface of a homogeneous volume conductor with a point source of electrical potential in the center, then VR + VL + VF = 0, and it can be demonstrated algebraically that VR = −(I + II)/3, VL = (I − III)/3, and VF = (II + III)/3. However, if Einthoven's hypotheses are correct it is also pos-

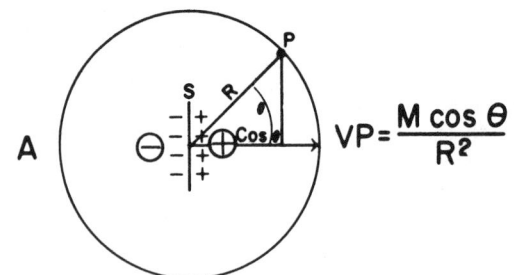

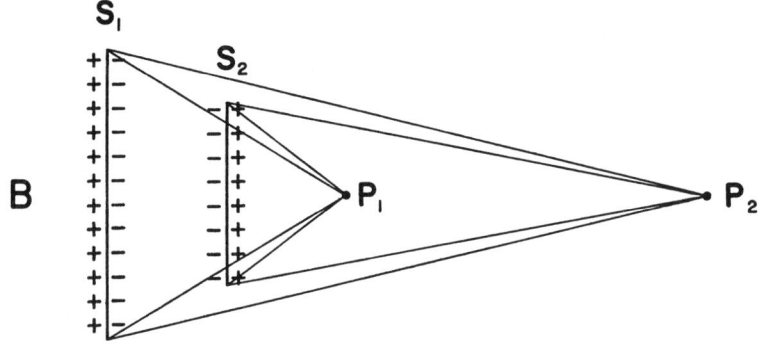

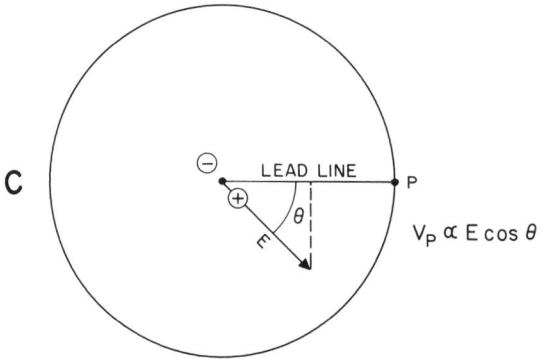

Fig. 37.7A. Calculation of positive potential (V) at point P when polarized surface S is considered as a single dipole. *Arrow* indicates axis of dipole. If P is located on a unit sphere, then R = 1. As P moves away from the dipole axis, its potential diminishes as cos ⊖ diminishes from 1 toward zero. The numerical value of cos ⊖ is given by the distance on the axis from the center of the circle to the perpendicular dropped from P. M = dipole moment. *B.* Illustration of solid angle principle. Two charged surfaces S_1 and S_2 have similar charge density but different areas, and opposite orientation of charge. At point P_1 the net potential is positive because S_2 subtends a larger solid angle than S_1. At point P_2 the net potential is negative because S_1 subtends the larger solid angle. *C.* Determination of voltage at point P when strength of dipole is represented by vector E. Voltage is proportional to E cos ⊖, and is found by drawing perpendicular from the lead line to the terminus of vector. Voltage at P is determined by the distance measured along lead line from center of dipole to the perpendicular.

sible to obtain an indifferent electrode of zero potential from a network connecting the three extremities, and then one may determine the potentials at any point in the body with an exploring electrode. Wilson demonstrated that the potential (VT) at a central terminal connecting the three extremities through equal resistances is equal to the mean of the potentials at the extremities, and so VT = (VR + VL + VF)/3 = 0 in this special situation. Differences between resistances at the three skin-electrode interfaces which would affect VT are minimized by a high input resistance in the circuits of modern electrocardiographic instruments. Although Einthoven's hypotheses are only a first approximation of actual conditions, several studies suggest that changes in VT are so small during the cardiac cycle that they can usually be disregarded for most clinical purposes, and the central terminal is considered to have a constant or "zero" potential. Tracings which record differences in potential between an exploring electrode and the central terminal are called "V" leads and are often described as "unipolar leads" to indicate that they essentially represent changes in potential at the site of the exploring electrode. The exploring electrode in V leads is always attached to the positive pole of the electrocardiograph so that when a positive charge faces the exploring electrode a positive (upward) deflection is recorded. Since the central terminal is considered to have a zero potential, the lead lines of the V leads extend

from the exploring electrode to the center of the exploring electrode to the zero point at the center of the dipole, and projections of vector forces on these lines can be analyzed as described previously.

Clinical electrocardiograms usually include six V chest leads recorded with the exploring electrode at the positions indicated in figure 37.9. The normal precordial lead V_1 displays a small R wave due to the initial activation of the septum from left to right. The small R is followed by a deep S wave due to activation of the free wall of the left ventricle which produces electrical forces directed to the left and away from this electrode. Leads V_5 and V_6 are more or less the inverse of V_1. They usually show a small Q wave followed by a large R wave. In the intermediate leads progressing from V_2 to V_5 there is increasing R wave amplitude and decreasing S amplitude. Usually at V_3 there is approximately equal R and S amplitude. This is referred to as the transition complex. Occasionally the transition complex may be recorded as far to the right as the V_2 position or as far to the left as V_5.

Goldberger suggested that the potential at an extremity could be obtained simply by disconnecting one extremity electrode from the central terminal and recording the difference in potential between it and the remaining two electrodes. Such tracings have the same configuration and $1\frac{1}{2}$ times the amplitude of a V lead recorded with an exploring electrode on the same extremity. The Goldberger arrangement for recording "augmented unipolar" extremity leads (named aVR, aVL, and aVF) is incorporated into the lead selector switch of modern electrocardiograph instruments.

Knowledge about the pathway of activation of the mammalian heart (Ch. 35) and the geometry of lead lines as developed from the Einthoven hypotheses can be used schematically to describe the effects of cardiac activation on the extremity leads. Ventricular activation can be described by a series of instantaneous vectors, each of which is the resultant of dipoles representing the polarized surfaces present at that instant. It is usual to consider only three or four such instantaneous resultant vectors (fig. 37.10): 1) Initial activation of the septum is represented by a small vector directed to the right and forward. 2) Simultaneous activation of the lower septum, free wall of the right ventricle and anterior left ventricle is represented by a resultant vector directed to the left, forward, and downward. 3) Continuation of the activation process

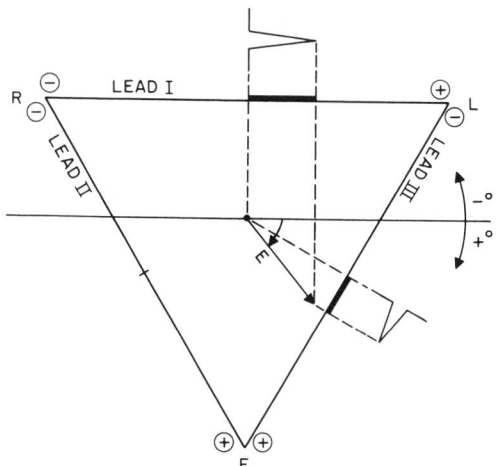

Fig. 37.8. Einthoven triangle, R = right arm, L = left arm, F = foot. Mean electrical axis is derived from lead I and lead III QRS complexes by drawing perpendiculars from the lead lines at points determined by amplitude of QRS. Intersection of perpendiculars determines the mean electrical axis, E.

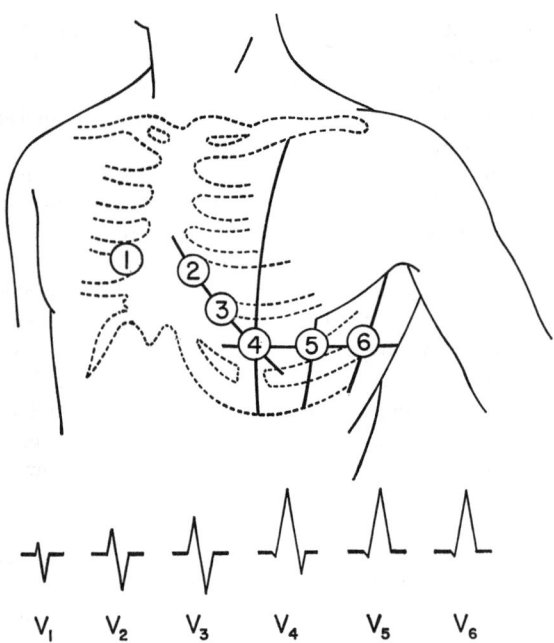

V_1 V_2 V_3 V_4 V_5 V_6

Fig. 37.9. Positions of the chest electrodes for 6 standard precordial leads. V_1, 4th intercostal space to right of sternum. V_2, 4th intercostal space at left of sternum. V_4, 5th interspace at midclavicular line. V_3, midway between V_2 and V_4. V_5, anterior axillary line, same level as V_4. V_6, mid axillary line, same level as V_4 and V_5. Below are shown general form of QRS in normal precordial leads. V_3 represents transition from predominant negativity on the right to predominant positivity on left. (Lipman, B. S. and Massie, E. Clinical Scalar Electrocardiography. Ed. 4. Year Book Publishers, Chicago, 1959.)

in the postero-lateral left ventricular wall after its completion in most regions of the right ventricle is next represented by a large vector directed to the left and backward. 4) Terminal activation of the postero-basal left ventricle and upper septum is represented by a small vector directed backward and upward.

The interval between these instantaneous vectors is 0.01 to 0.015 seconds in the dog heart and approximately twice as long in the human heart. One can roughly predict the configuration of tracings in various leads by projecting these hypothetical vectors onto the appropriate lead line, or conversely one may derive the instantaneous vectors from the recorded tracings. For example, potentials recorded at the same instant in two standard limb leads are measured and plotted in arbitrary units along the appropriate lead lines of an equilateral triangle, starting from the zero point at the center of each bipolar lead line and extending toward the end with the proper polarity. Perpendiculars dropped from the ends of these two linear plots will meet at points which define the origin and terminus of the instantaneous mean vector responsible for that particular deflection (fig. 37.8). Derivation of a series of instantaneous vectors in this manner is a la-

borious process and requires special equipment to record two leads simultaneously. A single vector depicting the mean direction of the total electrical forces developed during ventricular activation can be derived by plotting the algebraic sum of positive and negative deflections in QRS complexes from each of two leads on the appropriate lead lines and dropping perpendiculars as described above. The similarity between this derived vector, called the "mean electrical axis", and the true mean cardiac vector depends on the validity of the Einthoven hypotheses. The electrical axis is described according to a system of polar coordinates with 0° at the right hand end of a horizontal line; positive values are below and negative values above this line (fig. 37.8). In normal humans, the electrical axis commonly falls between 0° and +90°; displacement in a clockwise direction beyond +90° is called right axis deviation, and displacement in a counter-clockwise direction beyond 0° is called left axis deviation. The electrical axis is influenced by the position of the heart, changes in the functioning myocardial mass or the pathway of activation, and changes in the conducting medium surrounding the heart. A change in the direction of the long axis of the heart produces a shift in electrical axis in the same direction. The electrical axis will shift toward an area of hypertrophied myocardium and away from an area of infarcted myocardium. Since the electrical axis is determined from potentials recorded at the body surface, it will also be influenced by changes in the conducting medium, such as the introduction of air or fluid into the pleural space. The electrical axis determined from the limb leads represents the projection of spatial vectorial forces onto a frontal plane defined by the Einthoven triangle; an additional lead having a lead line in an anteroposterior direction is required to estimate the spatial orientation of these forces.

The problem of whether the direction of electrical forces originating from a dipole in the heart can be accurately determined from limb lead tracings has been investigated by placing an artificial dipole generator in or near the human heart. The frontal plane projection of the dipole axis was determined with fair accuracy from the limb lead potentials. However, recent studies with a dipole generator in torso models indicate that the eccentric position of the heart in the body significantly distorts its electrical field. When the dipole generator was placed in the heart region of the torso model a smaller electrical potential was recorded at the right shoulder than at the left shoulder or pubic region, so the right shoulder must be more "distant" from the heart in an electrical sense than the other apices of the Einthoven triangle. The irregular contour of the body surface and differences in tissue conductivity may also cause distortion of the electrical field.

The validity of the assumption that the electrical forces of the heart at any instant can be considered to originate from a single resultant dipole depends on the distance from the heart at which the potentials are recorded. At a very distant electrode the solid angles subtended by polarized surfaces in various regions of the heart will not be significantly influenced by the relatively small differences in their distance from the electrode, and dipoles representing each surface may be considered to originate at a single common point. On the other hand, when the electrode is close to the heart, the solid angle subtended by an adjacent region of myocardium will be much larger than that subtended by a more distant region of similar area, and so dipoles from various regions cannot be considered to originate at a single point. Instantaneous forces of ventricular activation may be described by a single resultant dipole vector when they are recorded from an electrode

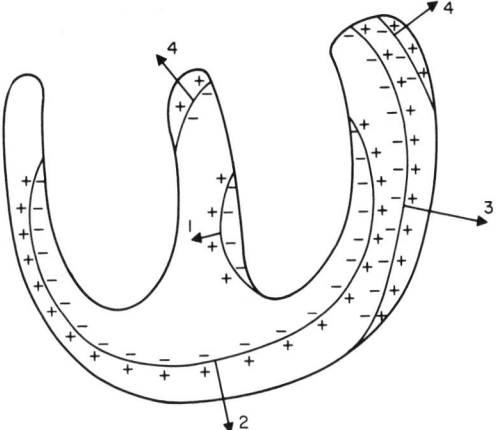

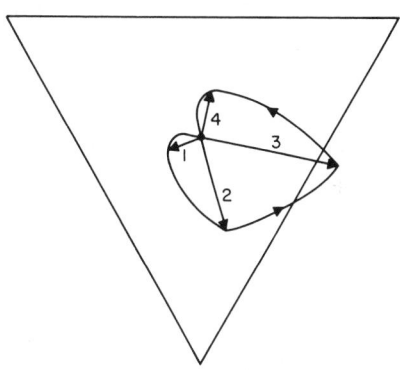

Fig. 37.10. The four major dipole vectors generated during ventricular activation giving rise to the deflections of the QRS complex. By Einthoven's hypothesis these vectors may all be considered as originating from a single point at the center of an equilateral triangle. When the termini of all resultant instantaneous vectors are connected, a loop is described. The loop is the vectorcardiogram.

more distant than 2 heart diameters from the cardiac surface.

Recent studies suggest that potentials recorded from exploring electrodes on the chest wall also represent to a major degree electrical forces from single resultant dipole vectors. When Wilson introduced the use of V chest leads, he pointed out the similarity of the tracings to those recorded with direct epicardial leads. He re-emphasized the concept of Lewis that the large rapid deflection in a direct epicardial lead (the intrinsic deflection) represented the activation of myocardium directly under the electrode, and suggested by analogy that the rapid downstroke recorded in chest leads (the "intrinsicoid" deflection) also represented local activation of myocardium closest to the electrode and could be used to time the arrival of the activation process in that area. However, it appears likely from recent studies that the rapid downstroke in chest leads represents a change in direction of the instantaneous resultant cardiac vector rather than local activation of adjacent myocardium.

Although the process of ventricular activation has been schematically represented by four instantaneous resultant vectors, it is described more adequately by a great number of such instantaneous vectors distributed at short intervals throughout the cardiac cycle. A line joining the termini of all the instantaneous resultant vectors will form a loop representing the sequential change in amplitude and direction of the resultant electrical forces throughout the cardiac cycle (fig. 37.10). Such a loop can be derived by graphic or electronic integration of potentials from two simultaneously recorded leads. When a loop is obtained by electronic integration on an oscilloscope, it is called a vectorcardiogram. The spatial orientation of the loop can be derived by using three leads with mutually perpendicular lead lines to obtain projections of the loop onto three planes. The hope that most information about the electrical forces of the heart could thus be derived from three mutually perpendicular leads stimulated several investigators to devise leads that are approximately orthogonal in an electrical sense. The recently proposed orthogonal lead systems employ networks of electrodes and resistors to minimize the distorting influences of cardiac eccentricity and body configuration. It is not feasible to evaluate the relative merits of these newer lead systems at the present time.

The Recovery Process and the Ventricular Gradient

The recovery process, which is simply a reversal of changes that occur during activation, is characterized by deflections of much longer duration and lower amplitude than the activation process. Atrial recovery produces a prolonged deflection (T_p or T_a wave) which continues through the PR interval and into or beyond the QRS complex, but it is generally of such low amplitude that it is clearly defined only in tracings where P waves are widely separated from the QRS complexes, as in heart block. The T_p is opposite in direction to the P wave in tracings obtained from strips of atrial muscle and also from the intact heart, which indicates that the recovery process follows the same sequence of activation since the two processes have opposite electrical signs. Ventricular recovery occurs during inscription of the ST segment and T wave. The ST segment corresponds to the plateau and the T wave corresponds to the rapid final phase of repolarization recorded from single myocardial fibers. The electrocardiogram generally shows little or no deflection from the base line during inscription of the ST segment when large areas of myocardium are undergoing recovery simultaneously. The T wave occurs when recovery is complete in some areas but is continuing in other regions. The T wave recorded from muscle strips is opposite in direction to the QRS, as expected when recovery occurs in the same sequence as activation, but this is not true in direct leads on the surface of the intact ventricle where the T wave is in the same direction as the major deflection of the QRS. This indicates that the sequence for completion of recovery in the intact ventricle is opposite in direction to the activation process, and therefore occurs later at endocardium than at epicardium.

It has not been possible to map the sequence for completion of the recovery process in different regions of the heart by methods used to study the activation process because there are no rapid "intrinsic" deflections that can be correlated with changes in localized areas. However, vector analysis has been used to study both the instantaneous and mean resultant forces of the recovery process. The instantaneous forces during ventricular recovery produce a loop in the vectorcardiogram which is oriented in the same general direction as the loop inscribed during activation. The relationship between the orientation of the electrical forces during activation and recovery has been expressed in vector terms by Wilson, Ashman and Beyer, and others. These investigators determined the net area enclosed by QRS deflections and that enclosed by ST and T deflections in the limb leads, and used these areas (which represent the product of time and voltage) to plot mean vectors called Â QRS and Â T respectively. The resultant of these two vectors is called the ventricular gradient Ĝ. If Â T was equal in amplitude and opposite in direction to Â QRS, as expected on a theoretical basis from electrograms of muscle strips, their resultant or ventricular gradient would be zero. The degree to which the actual Â T deviates from the theoretical one is expressed by the vector Ĝ. The gradient is thus a reflection of the difference between the sequence of activation and recovery. The normal ventricular gradient is explained on the basis of a delay in recovery of the subendocardial region due to local differences in some metabolic or mechanical factors which influence the recovery process. QRS amplitude and duration may change due to a difference in the activation pathway, as occurs with a premature ventricular beat or bundle branch block, without effecting the metabolic or mechanical factors which determine the normal ventricular gradient. Changes in amplitude or duration of the QRS are then accompanied by equivalent changes of the T wave in the opposite direction and $\hat{G}$ may remain unchanged. Such T wave changes are called secondary, in contrast to primary T wave changes due to factors which specifically influence the recovery process and are therefore accompanied by changes in the gradient. Primary T wave changes may occur after exercise or eating, with decreases in coronary perfusion due to atherosclerosis, or in a variety of other physiological and pathological situations. Calculation of changes in ventricular gradients should theoretically allow one to differentiate between primary and secondary T wave changes, but this has not proven very useful in clinical electrocardiography because of the wide range of normal gradients and the fact that both physiological and pathological factors can cause either primary or secondary T wave changes.

Abnormalities of the Electrocardiogram

Left Ventricular Hypertrophy

Enlargement of the left ventricle commonly gives rise to four deviations from the normal electrocardiogram, not all of which need be present to establish the diagnosis (fig. 37.11). These deviations are: (1) increased voltage in the leads exploring the left ventricle, (2) increased duration of the QRS complexes, (3) rotation of the mean electrical axis toward the left and posteriorly, and (4) secondary ST and T wave abnormalities in the left ventricular leads.

The increased voltage is seen primarily as increased negativity in the right precordial leads V_1 and V_2, and increased positivity in the left precordial leads, V_5 and V_6. The reasons for this increased voltage are not entirely clear. It may be that the hypertrophied myocardial cells have a greater charge density, or that closer proximity of the enlarged ventricle to the chest wall causes higher voltage by subtending a larger solid angle. It has been postulated that the increased thickness of the hypertrophied left ventricle permits the activation of this area to continue unopposed after activation of the right ventricle is completed. Increased positivity is inscribed in a leftward and posterior direction as the left ventricular free wall completes its prolonged activation.

Sokolow has shown that if the absolute sum of the positivity in V_5 and the negativity in V_1 is 3.5 mv. or more there is a strong statistical likelihood of left ventricular hypertrophy. These values, however, may be seen in normal young adults particularly if there is a thin chest wall.

The increased duration of the QRS appears to be due to the longer time necessary for the wave of activation to spread from endocardium to epicardium through the thickened ventricular wall. In many cases of left ventricular hypertrophy the onset of the intrinsicoid deflection is delayed over the left precordial leads beyond 0.05 seconds, and the total duration of QRS may be 0.10 or 0.11 seconds.

Since the thickest portion of the free wall of the left ventricle lying just beneath the atrioventricular groove faces the region of the left shoulder and is the last part of the left ventricle to be depolarized, it is not surprising that hypertrophy of the ventricular wall directs more and more voltage toward the left posterior shoulder region. In the limb leads, the mean electrical axis lies in the 0 to $-90°$ quadrant (left axis deviation). The posterior displacement is seen in the horizontal plane vectorcardiogram, and it may be apparent in the precordial leads by a shift of the transition zone to the left.

When left ventricular hypertrophy becomes severe, the QRS changes are usually accompanied by ST and T wave abnormalities which may vary from flattening of the T waves in the left precordial leads to depression of the ST segment with downward slanting of ST and deep T wave inversion in these leads.

The exact mechanism by which these ST-T changes are produced is not understood. Some believe that they are secondary to the increased area of the QRS. Others believe that they may be primary changes perhaps due to relative ischemia of the subendocardial layers of the hypertrophied ventricular wall.

Right Ventricular Hypertrophy

The right ventricle is thin-walled and lies in an almost direct anterior anatomical position. Normally the voltages generated by this ventricle are greatly overbalanced by the voltages coming from the much greater mass of the left ventricle. The right ventricle may undergo a great deal of hypertrophy before its muscle mass begins to approach the mass of the left ventricle. In the lesser stages of hypertrophy of the right ventricle the electrocardiographic changes are the result of rotation of the heart on its long axis in

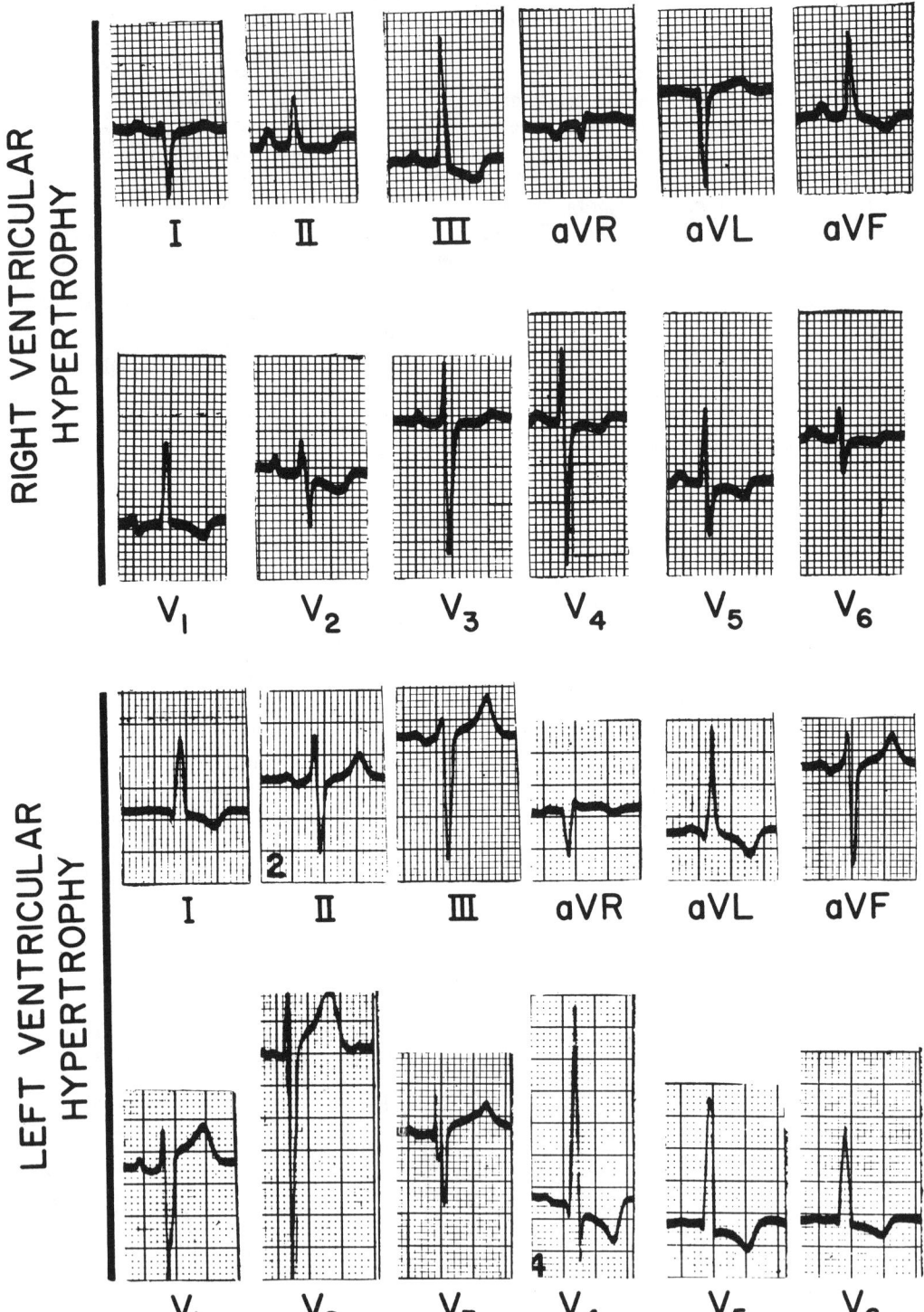

RIGHT VENTRICULAR HYPERTROPHY

I   II   III   aVR   aVL   aVF

V$_1$ V$_2$ V$_3$ V$_4$ V$_5$ V$_6$

LEFT VENTRICULAR HYPERTROPHY

I   II   III   aVR   aVL   aVF

V$_1$ V$_2$ V$_3$ V$_4$ V$_5$ V$_6$

FIG. 37.11. Electrocardiogram patterns of right and left ventricular hypertrophy.

a clockwise direction when viewed from the apex. The enlarging right ventricle, restricted anteriorly by the sternum, pushes the left ventricle around toward the left and downward toward the diaphragm. The electrical forces are still dominated by left ventricular voltages which may be somewhat smaller than normal since they are opposed by larger right ventricular voltages. The net effect is to direct the major left ventricular voltages posteriorly and inferiorly toward the foot, producing a vertical electrical axis in the frontal plane as visualized in the limb leads. In the precordial leads there is a delay in transition with an S wave persisting through V_5 and perhaps V_6. These changes are due primarily to rotation of the heart by the enlarging right ventricle. They are likely to be seen in chronic cor pulmonale due to pulmonary disease and in mitral valvular disease.

In severe pulmonic valvular stenosis, in severe pulmonary hypertension, and in advanced stages of mitral valve disease there may be sufficient right ventricular hypertrophy to exceed the muscle mass of the left ventricle. In this situation the major voltages are generated in the right ventricle, and the major electrical forces are directed anteriorly and to the right.

In the frontal plane, the limb leads show right axis deviation with a mean electrical axis usually greater than $+105°$. The precordial leads show predominant positivity in V_1 with R usually far exceeding S in amplitude. The transition toward the left discloses a progressively diminishing R wave and an increasing S wave. This is opposite to the normal QRS precordial transition.

ST and T wave changes similar to those seen in left ventricular hypertrophy may occur in right ventricular hypertrophy. These changes are seen in leads with maximal positivity; that is, in V_1, V_2, and in II, III, and aVF. Their pathogenesis is just as uncertain in right ventricular hypertrophy as it is in left ventricular hypertrophy.

Right Bundle Branch Block

Although Lewis and his associates carried out experiments in which one or the other of the major conducting bundles was interrupted and changes in the electrocardiogram were observed, it was the work of Wilson and his associates that firmly established the nature of bundle branch block. The concepts described here stem from their beautiful and precise experiments.

It will be recalled that in the normal sequence of activation the left side of the septum starts to depolarize slightly before the right side, the free wall of the right ventricle is depolarized simultaneously with the left ventricle, and the greater thickness of the left ventricle produces much larger voltages than those from the right ventricle. Thus, the only rightward directed voltages seen in the normal electrocardiogram are those generated initially from the left side of the septum and in some instances a small late voltage from a late activation of the pulmonary conus.

When the right conducting bundle is blocked either by cutting it experimentally or by some pathological process, the activation of the right ventricular free wall is greatly delayed (fig. 37.12). The first portion of the QRS complex up to about 0.04 seconds is inscribed in a normal manner as it records the activation of the septum from left to right and the free wall of the left ventricle. When the left ventricle has become completely depolarized, there still remains a considerable portion of the right ventricular free wall which has not been depolarized. The impulse may spread slowly in a tangential direction through the free wall of the right ventricle rather than being transmitted almost instantaneously to all parts of the endocardium by Purkinje fibers and spreading from endocardium to epicardium. This slow late right ventricular activation wave, now unopposed by left ventricular forces and not having the high proportion of internal cancellation characteristic of normal transmission, produces a large voltage directed anteriorly and to the right which appears late and prolongs the QRS to a duration of 0.12 seconds or more.

This late right ventricular voltage is inscribed in the electrocardiogram as a late slurred R wave in V_1 and aVR, and a late slurred S wave in V_5, V_6, and aVL.

Left Bundle Branch Block

Interruption of the left conducting bundle causes delay in activation of the left ventricle. The first portion of the heart to be activated is now the right side of the septum by way of the right bundle branch. The septum is thus activated from right to left, producing a large voltage directed leftward. This large leftward voltage is opposed to a small degree by a rightward voltage from the almost simultaneous activation of the free wall of the right ventricle, but because of the greater muscle mass of the septum the net initial voltage is directed toward the left. The effect on the electrocardiogram is to produce initial positivity in leads I, V_5 and V_6. The normal septal Q wave is thus abolished in these leads.

The wave of activation is transmitted through

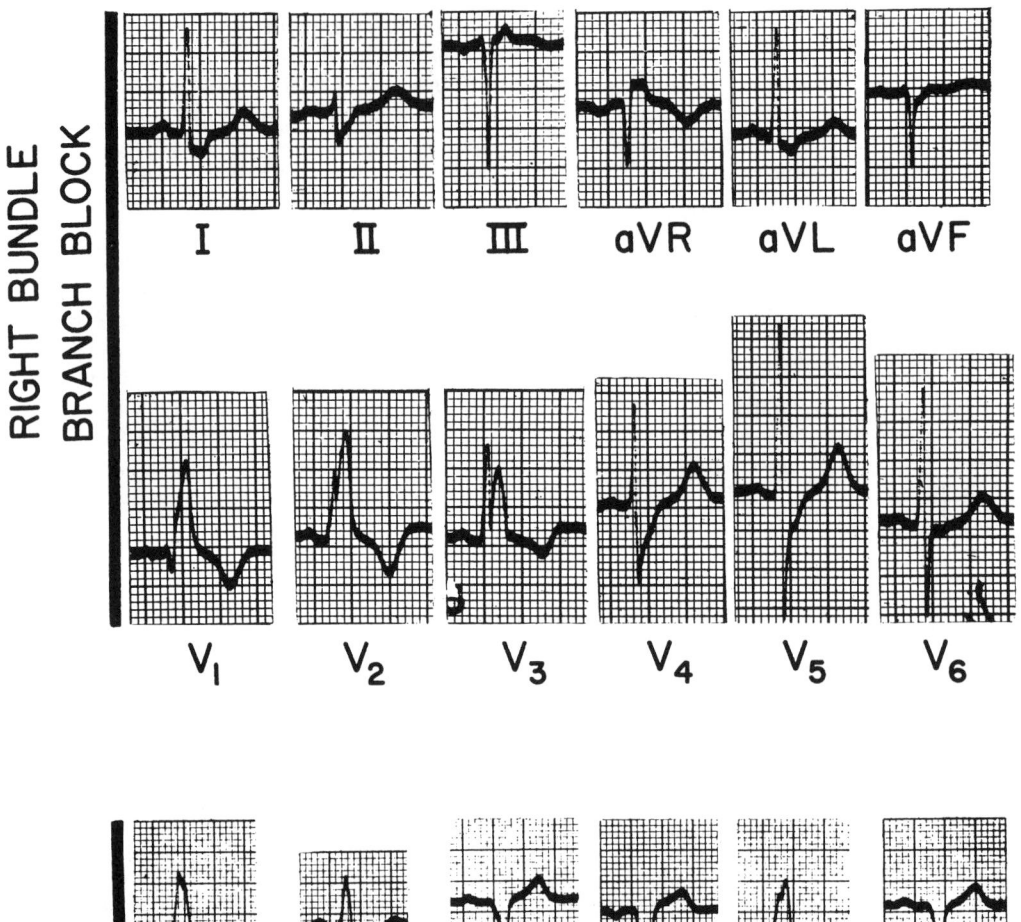

FIG. 37.12. Patterns of right and left bundle branch block.

the septum to the free wall of the left ventricle through which it passes slowly in a tangential direction from apex to base. It is probable that there is also some transmission from the anterior and posterior septum circumferentially so as to envelope the free wall in the activation wave. The slow activation of the left ventricle continues to produce leftward directed voltages which are

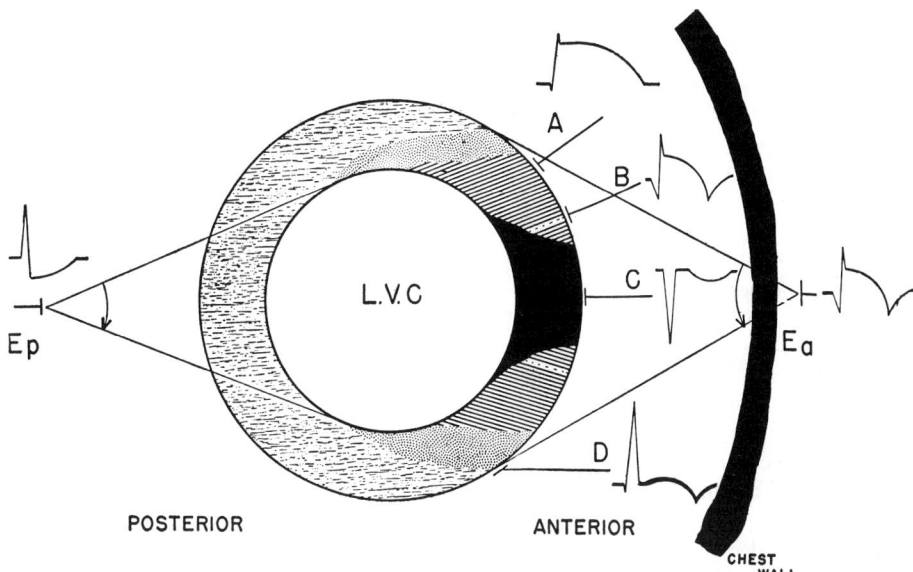

Fig. 37.13. Schematic diagram of direct epicardial leads taken over an area of myocardial infarction and over adjacent zones of injury and ischemia. Also shown is a chest lead facing the infarct, and a lead from the opposite side of the heart. At C cavity negativity is reflected in the epicardial lead over the necrotic zone. At A is recorded a monophasic injury wave over the injured zone. At B the complex reflects a combination of necrosis and injury. At D there is only T wave inversion of the ischemic type over the ischemic zone. At E_A over the chest the complex combines features of all three zones, and on the opposite side of the heart there are reciprocal changes of increased positivity of the R wave and depression of ST. (From Barker.)

inscribed in the electrocardiogram as broad notched or slurred R waves in the left precordial leads V_5 and V_6. Duration of the QRS complex is 0.12 seconds or greater. In general the ST and T waves are opposite in direction to the QRS complexes. If the concept of the ventricular gradient is valid, this divergence in direction of QRS and T may be considered secondary to the increased area of the QRS. The large increase in the magnitude of the QRS vector would necessitate a reversal in direction of the T vector in order to preserve the magnitude and direction of the ventricular gradient. Whether or not the ST and T abnormalities of left bundle branch block are adequately explained by the ventricular gradient concept, one would expect to see abnormalities in the repolarization waves simply because the pathway of depolarization is so drastically altered.

Myocardial Ischemia, Injury and Necrosis

In animal experiments epicardial leads applied directly to the surface of the heart have been used to study the electrocardiographic changes associated with impairment of the coronary blood flow (fig. 37.13). When a coronary artery is gradually compressed, the first change seen in tracings from the area of myocardium supplied by that vessel is a deep and symmetrical inversion of the T wave. This symmetrical form of T wave inversion is referred to as T wave inversion of the ischemic type. It is believed to be due to delay in recovery at the epicardial region so that there is reversal of the normal order of repolarization.

The ischemic T wave inversion is rapidly reversible if adequate circulation is restored to the myocardium. When the blood supply to the myocardium is more drastically impaired by sudden ligation of a coronary artery, the direct epicardial tracing shows the rapid onset of elevation of the ST segment. This elevation may be almost as high as the QRS complex and may yield a wave form closely resembling the transmembrane action potential obtained with micropuncture of a single myocardial fiber. The ST elevation is believed to be due to a strong current of injury causing marked depression of the resting isopotential line. The ST displacement may be accompanied by ischemic changes in the T waves. This injury pattern is also rapidly reversible upon restoration of adequate blood flow.

When a coronary artery is permanently ligated, a portion of the myocardium becomes infarcted. The presence of electrically inert necrotic myocardium results in alterations of the QRS complexes of the direct epicardial lead. If the infarction is completely transmural from epicardium to endocardium this mass of tissue contributes no potential of its own, but simply conducts to the surface the potentials which are to be found in the underlying cavity. The depolarization wave in this case is a purely negative QS complex identical to that found in the left ventricular cavity. The repolarization phases contain elements of injury and ischemia patterns derived from adjacent viable portions of the myocardium.

Exploration of the adjacent areas of myocardium about a zone of necrosis discloses a zone of injury surrounding the necrotic areas (fig. 37.13). Complexes recorded from the injury zone are characterized by marked elevation of the ST segment without significant change in the morphology of the early portion of the QRS. The injury zone is surrounded by a zone in which the T waves show inversion of the ischemic type. This is called the ischemic zone. Beyond it lies normal muscle disclosing normal QRS-T complexes.

Electrocardiograms made from the surface of the body include potentials from the entire heart, and therefore, the precise localization of zones of necrosis, injury and ischemia cannot be derived from the clinical electrocardiogram. When infarction is present, all of the phenomena observed in the three zones will be reflected in the appropriate electrocardiographic lead. Even a precordial lead adjacent to a large area of infarction is influenced by electrical events in other parts of the heart and is likely to record elements from all three of the zones of necrosis, injury and ischemia.

Thus the classical pattern of myocardial infarction consists of a deep wide Q wave, ST segment elevation, and T wave inversion. Muscle necrosis cannot be identified with certainty from the electrocardiogram without the appearance of a pathological Q wave which indicates a removal of electrically active myocardium. ST and T wave changes of injury and ischemia may occur when myocardium becomes temporarily or even chronically hypoxic but not sufficiently so to produce muscle death. On the other hand, there may be myocardial necrosis in areas completely surrounded by viable tissue or in subendocardial zones such that the general pathway of activation might not be markedly altered. In such intramural or subendocardial infarctions abnormal Q waves may not appear even though injury and ischemic ST and T changes may be present. In such cases the presence of muscle necrosis

cannot be proven by the electrocardiogram Evidence of its presence might, however, be obtained by other clinical means.

LOCALIZATION OF MYOCARDIAL INFARCTION

The general anatomical localization of areas of cardiac infarction may often be made from the standard nine or twelve lead electrocardiogram. Each lead constitutes, so to speak, an electrical view of the heart from a different point in space (fig. 37.14). In accord with both solid angle and dipole analyses, positive electrodes record maximum positivity when the wave front of ventricular activation is advancing directly toward the electrode. Thus, the early positivity in V_1 derives from the left to right activation wave across the septum. V_2 and V_3 derive their positive deflections mainly from the anterior left ventricle near the septum. Positivity in V_4 is derived mainly from activation of the anterior free wall of the left ventricle, and in V_5 and V_6 from the lateral free wall of the left ventricle. Positivity in leads aVF and III is derived from the posterodiaphragmatic wall of the left ventricle, and in aVL from the lateral wall of the left ventricle. In general then, a positive electrode records maximal positive forces from the area of myocardium toward which it faces.

Infarction of myocardium abolishes positive forces in those leads which face the infarcted area. Loss of positive forces advancing toward the electrode leaves unopposed forces moving away from the electrode. The result is the appearance of Q waves in leads facing the infarcted areas of myocardium. ST and T wave changes due to injury and ischemia of adjacent viable tissue are also reflected in these leads but may in addition be present in leads which do not show alterations in the QRS.

The appearance of the infarction pattern in leads V_1, V_2 and V_3 indicates anteroseptal infarction, in V_3 and V_4, anterior infarction, in V_5 and V_6 lateral infarction, in aVF and III posterior or diaphragmatic infarction, in aVL high lateral infarction. The infarction pattern may be present in various combinations of leads, such as aVF and V_6 (posterolateral location) or V_4, V_5 and V_6 (anterolateral location). Sometimes the appearance of right bundle branch block associated with the anteroseptal infarction pattern gives evidence of extensive involvement of the septum.

Left bundle branch block in most instances completely obscures the pattern of myocardial infarction because of the gross alteration of the

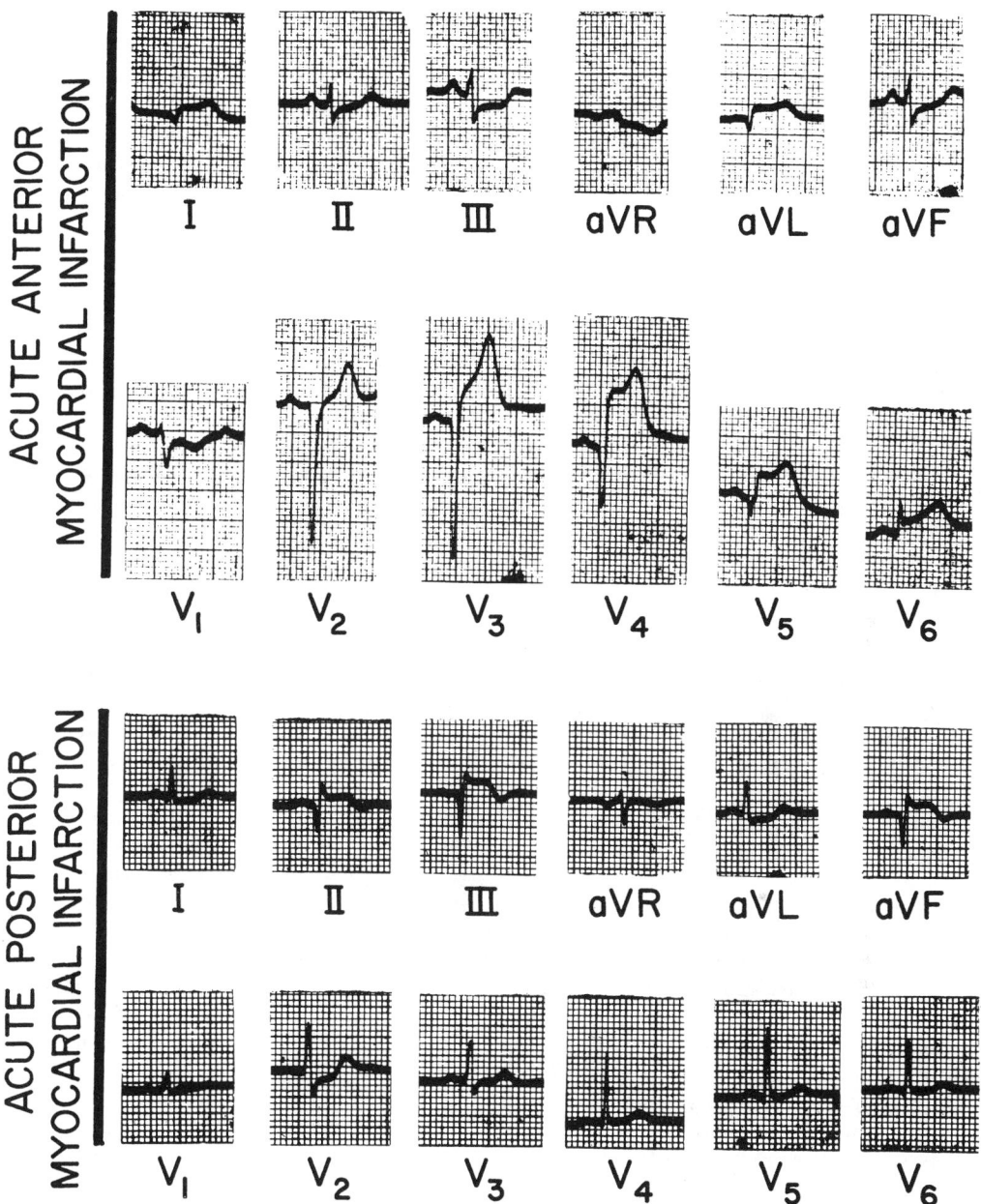

Fig. 37.14. Patterns of acute anterior and posterior myocardial infarcts.

pathway of activation, particularly because the reversal of the direction of depolarization of the septum produces initial positivity in the left ventricular cavity and thus prevents the appearance of Q waves over an area of infarction of the left ventricular free wall. Only when there is extensive destruction of the lower septum and apical portions of the left ventricle does a Q wave appear in the left precordial leads in the presence of left bundle branch block.

LOCATION OF MYOCARDIAL INJURY

Well known clinical conditions illustrate the electrocardiographic effects of temporary injury to subepicardial and subendocardial heart muscle. When subepicardial myocardium is injured, whether by disease such as pericarditis or by the intentional instillation of irritating substances into the pericardial sac, elevation of ST segments appears in all leads except those which explore primarily the heart cavities (aVR and V_1). In

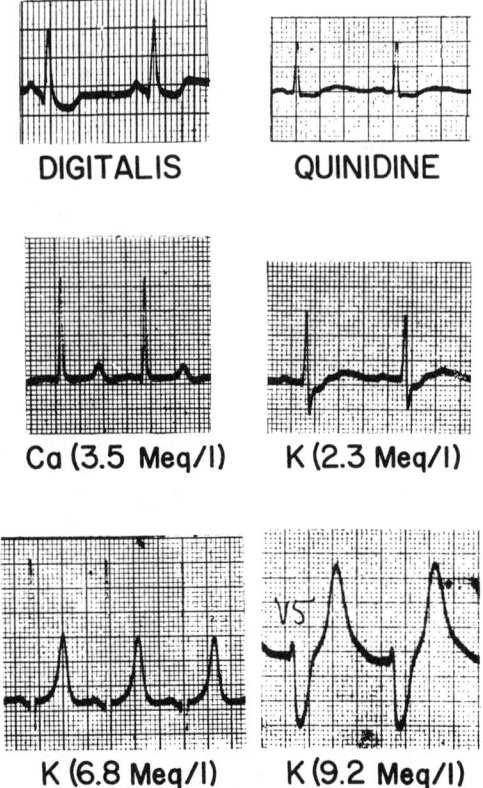

FIG. 37.15. Patterns of digitalis and quinidine effect, low serum calcium, low serum potassium and high serum potassium.

other words, leads taken from electrodes facing the injured surface display positive ST segment displacement. On the other hand, when there is subendocardial injury such as may occur in coronary insufficiency during an attack of angina pectoris, there is ST segment depression in many of the leads exploring the free wall of the left ventricle. In this case, injury to the side of the myocardial wall facing away from the electrode produces negative ST segment displacement. The principle is borne out by the observation that a localized infarction on one side of the heart leading to elevation of ST segments in leads taken from that side will produce ST depression in leads recorded from the opposite side of the heart. In acute posterior infarction with Q waves and ST elevation in leads III and a VF there will often be ST depression in leads V_2 and V_3. The ST depressions in the anterior leads are said to be reciprocal to the elevations in the posterior leads.

DRUGS AND ELECTROLYTES

Digitalis produces a characteristic alteration of the ST and T complex which might sometimes be mistaken for an injury effect (fig. 37.15). The change consists of a shortening of the QT interval and a sagging of the ST segment. The sagging ST has a "scooped-out" or "cuplike" concavity that is easily recognized. This electrocardiographic sign of digitalis effect is not related to the adequacy of the dose of the medication nor to drug intoxication.

Quinidine and procaine amide have similar effects on the electrocardiogram. They cause depression of the ST segment, a decrease in amplitude or diphasic configuration of the T wave, and an increase in amplitude of the U wave. The QT interval may be prolonged, or may appear prolonged because the U wave is superimposed on the descending limb of the T wave producing a broad T-U complex which may have a notched or undulating appearance. As the dose is increased slowing of conduction through the ventricle is produced with resulting widening of the QRS complexes. Normal complexes of 0.06 to 0.08-second duration may be prolonged to 0.12 to 0.14 second by increasing quinidine or procaine amide doses. Upon finding such prolongation most clinicians would elect to stop the drug or reduce its dose for fear of stopping all conduction and precipitating ventricular standstill.

Among electrolyte ions, calcium and potassium have the most significant effects on the ECG. Hypocalcemia causes prolongation of the QT interval due to prolongation of the ST segment without distortion of the T wave. The long flat ST segment is followed by a T wave of normal amplitude and duration. Micropuncture studies of transmembrane action potentials have shown that the long ST segment is due to prolongation of the plateau phase of the recovery process. The later phases continue at their usual rates.

Elevation of the serum calcium has the opposite effect of shortening the ST segment by shortening the plateau phase of the monophasic action potential. The T wave itself appears undisturbed.

Reduction of serum potassium appears to have two effects; one on the ST-T complex and one on the U wave. When the potassium level in the serum falls to about 3 m.eq. per liter, the ST begins to sag and the T wave becomes lower while the U wave becomes more prominent. The T and U seem to merge into a single wave separated only by a slight indentation or dimple on the crest. This gives a false impression of a markedly prolonged QT. With very low levels of potassium the ST segment becomes depressed below the base line and the U wave exceeds the T in height. This gives the appearance of a stepwise ascent of the ST-T complex. This pattern is usually seen with serum potassium of 2.5 m.eq. per liter or less.

Elevation of serum potassium leads first to an increasing amplitude of the T wave in leads where the T is normally upright. The tall T waves have a tentlike appearance with similar slopes on the upward and downward limbs. With higher levels of serum K (8 m.eq. per liter approximately) the PR interval becomes prolonged and the QRS begins to widen out as conduction becomes impaired. At about 9 m.eq. per liter, the P wave disappears entirely and the QRS takes on a bizarre shape merging with the tall T wave to produce a distorted sine wavelike pattern which usually heralds terminal ventricular fibrillation or standstill.

REFERENCES

ABILDSKOV, J. A. The atrial complex of the electrocardiogram. Am. Heart J., 1959, 57, 930.

BARBATO, E., PILEGGI, F., DEBES, A. C., FUJIOKA, T., MAGALHARE, M. S., TRANCHESI, J., SAN JUAN, E., AND DECOURT, L. V. Study of the sequence of ventricular activation and the QRS complex of the normal human heart using direct epicardial leads. Am. Heart J., 1958, 55, 867.

BAYLEY, R. H. AND LADUE, J. S. Electrocardiographic changes of impending infarction, and the ischemia-injury pattern produced in the dog by total and subtotal occlusion of a coronary artery. Am. Heart J., 1944, 28, 54.

BECKER, R. A., SCHER, A. M. AND ERICKSON, R. V. Ventricular excitation in experimental left bundle branch block. Am. Heart J., 1958, 55, 547.

CRAIB, W. H. A study of the electrical field surrounding active heart muscle. Heart, 1927, 14, 71.

EINTHOVEN, W., FAHR, G. AND DEWAART, A. On the direction and manifest size of the variations of potential in the human heart and on the influence of the position of the heart on the form of the electrocardiogram. Translation by Hoff, H. E. and Sekelj., Am. Heart J., 1950, 40, 163.

ERICKSON, R. V., SCHER, A. M. AND BECKER, R. A. Ventricular excitation in experimental bundle branch block. Circulation Res., 1957, 5, 5.

FISCHMANN, E. J. AND ELLIOTT, B. J. Experimental comparison of "parallel grid leads" with simple bipolar, and the SVEC-III, Frank and McFee-Parungao systems. I. Sagittal leads. Am. Heart J., 1964, 67, 792.

HORAN, L. G., FLOWERS, N. C. AND BRADY, D. K. Principal factor wave forms of the thoracic QRS complex. Circulation Res., 1964, 15, 131.

MACLEOD, A. G. The electrogram of cardiac muscle: an analysis which explains the regression of T deflection. Am. Heart J., 1938, 15, 165.

MACLEOD, A. G. The electrogram of cardiac muscle. II. The lengths of the stages of activity. Am. Heart J., 1938, 15, 402.

MANN, H. A. A method of analyzing the electrocardiogram. Arch. Int. Med., 1920, 25, 283.

PENALOZA, D., GAMBOA, R. AND SIME, F. Experimental right bundle branch block in the normal human heart. Am. J. Cardiology, 1961, 8, 767.

PRINZMETAL, M., TOYOSHIMA, H., EKMEKCI, A., MIZUNO, Y. AND NAGAYA, T. Myocardial ischemia. Nature of ischemic electrocardiographic patterns in the mammalian ventricles as determined by intracellular electrographic and metabolic changes. Am. J. Cardiology, 1961, 8, 493.

REYNOLDS, E. W., VANDERARK, C. R. AND JOHNSTON, F. D. Effect of acute myocardial infarction on electrical recovery and transmural temperature gradient in left ventricular wall of dogs. Circulation Res., 1960, 8, 731.

SAMSON, W. E. AND SCHER, A. M. Mechanism of S-T segment alteration during acute myocardial injury. Circulation Res., 1960, 8, 780.

SIMONSON, E., SCHMITT, O. H., DAHL, J., FRY, D. L. AND BALKEN, E. E. The theoretical and experimental bases of the frontal plane ventricular gradient and its spatial counterpart. Am. Heart J., 1954, 47, 122.

SOKOLOW, M. AND LYON, T. P. The ventricular complex in left ventricular hypertrophy as obtained by unipolar precordial and limb leads. Am. Heart J., 1949, 37, 161.

SOYEN, J. J., SHELDON, W. F., PEIRCE, G., KATCHER, A. H. AND KUO, P. T. Electrocardiogram, myocardial oxygen and contraction in scar and collaterally supplied muscle after experimental coronary ligation. Circulation Res., 1962, 11, 994.

SURAWICZ, B. Electrolytes and the electrocardiogram. Am. J. Cardiology, 1963, 12, 656.

TACCARDI, B. Distribution of heart potentials on the thoracic surface of normal human subjects. Circulation Res., 1963, 12, 341.

WALLER, A. D. Demonstration on man of the electromotive changes accompanying the heart's beat. J. Physiol., 1887, 8, 229.

WILSON, F. N., JOHNSTON, F. D., MACLEOD, A. G. AND BARKER, P. S. Electrocardiograms that represent the potential variations of a single electrode. Am. Heart J., 1934, 9, 447.

WILSON, F. N., JOHNSTON, F. D., ROSENBAUM, F. F., ERLANGER, H., KASSMAN, C. E., HECHT, H. H., COTRIUN, N., MENEGES DE OLIVLIRA, R., SCARSI, R. AND BARBES, P. S. The precordial electrocardiogram. Am. Heart J., 1944, 27, 19.

WILSON, F. N., MACLEOD, A. G. AND BARKER, P. S. The distribution of the action currents produced by heart muscle and other excitable tissues immersed in extensive conducting media. J. Gen. Physiol., 1933, 16, 425.

Monographs and Reviews

ABILDSKOV, J. A. (Guest Editor) Symposium on the present status of electrocardiography. Am. J. Cardiology, 1964, 14, 285.

BARKER, J. M. The unipolar electrocardiogram, A

clinical interpretation. Appleton-Century-Crofts, Inc., New York, 1952.

BAYLEY, R. H. Electrocardiographic Analysis, Volume I. Biophysical Principles of Electrocardiography. Paul B. Hoeber, Inc., New York, 1958.

BURCH, G. E. AND WINSOR, T. A primer of electrocardiography. Ed. 4. Lea and Febiger, Philadelphia, 1960.

LEPESCHKIN, E. Modern Electrocardiography. The Williams & Wilkins Company, Baltimore, 1951.

LEWIS, T. The Mechanism and Graphic Registration of the Heart Beat. Ed. 3. Shaw and Sons, London, 1925.

PIPBERGER, H. V. Current status and persistent problems of electrode placement and lead systems for vectorcardiography and electrocardiography. Progress in Cardiovas. Dis., 1959, 2, 248.

POZZI, L. Basic Principles in Vector Electrocardiography. Charles C Thomas, Springfield, Illinois, 1961.

SCHER, A. M. Excitation of the heart. Handbook of Physiology, Section 2: Circulation, Volume I, edited by W. F. HAMILTON, American Physiological Society, Washington, D.C., 1962.

SIMONSON, E. Differentiation between Normal and Abnormal in Electrocardiography. The C. V. Mosby Company, St. Louis, 1961.

SODI-PALLARES, D. AND CALDER, R. M. New Bases of Electrocardiography. The C. V. Mosby Company, St. Louis, 1956.

WHITELOCK, O. V. (Editor) The Electrophysiology of the Heart. Ann. New York Acad. Sc., 1957, 65, 653.

WILSON, F. N. Selected papers of, edited by F. D. Johnston and E. Lepeschkin. Heart Station, University Hospital, Ann Arbor, Michigan, 1954.

WILSON, F. N., ROSENBAUM, F. F. AND JOHNSTON, F. D. Interpretation of the ventricular complex of the electrocardiogram. Advances in Internal Medicine. Vol. II, Interscience Publishers, Inc., New York, 1947.

CHAPTER 38

Disorders of the Heart and their Investigation by Graphic Methods

The following is a convenient classification of cardiac irregularities:

A. *Affections of rhythm due to impaired conduction through the A-V node and the bundle of His.*
   I. Delayed conduction
   II. Missed beats, partial heart block
   III. Complete heart block
B. *Wolff-Parkinson-White syndrome*
C. *Affections due to abnormal impulse formation*
   I. Extrasystoles
     (1) Ventricular
     (2) Nodal
     (3) Auricular
   II. Paroxysmal tachycardia
     Auricular, nodal and ventricular
   III. Auricular flutter
   IV. Auricular fibrillation
   V. Ventricular fibrillation
D. *Alternation of the heart*
E. *Affections due to vagal influences*
   I. Sinus arrhythmia
   II. Phasic irregularity
   III. Sinus bradycardia
   IV. Sino-auricular block
   V. Auriculoventricular block

A. Affections of Rhythm Resulting from Impaired Conduction

I. In the A-V Node or Stem of the Bundle
Auriculoventricular Block

In animals, conduction from auricle to ventricle can be depressed or blocked by crushing, cutting, or the application of cold to the A-V bundle. This strategic point in the pathway of the excitation wave is also attacked by disease, and conduction through it may be depressed or completely abolished. Depression of conduction through the node or bundle varies in degree. Three stages are recognized.

(1) Delayed Conduction

In this stage conduction is merely slowed; every impulse reaches the ventricle. The intervals between the auricular and ventricular systoles (A_s-V_s intervals) are lengthened beyond the normal maximum of 0.2 second and may have a duration of 0.5 second, though, as a rule, they are considerably shorter than this. The condition can be recognized only by means of the electrocardiograph or a venous pulse tracing. Lengthening of the P-R interval in the former tracing, or of the *a-c* interval in the latter, beyond 0.2 second is taken to indicate delayed conduction (fig. 38.1).

(2) Missed Beats—Partial Heart Block

When impaired conduction reaches a certain degree, impulses from time to time fail to reach the ventricle, and a beat is missed. The auricular beats are perfectly regular, and in this way the condition differs from sino-auricular block (p. 695). A ventricular beat may be missed only occasionally and at irregular intervals. The P-R interval of the electrocardiogram, or the *a-c* interval of the venous pulse, may generally, though not invariably, be seen to lengthen progressively for several heart cycles preceding the dropped beat. The periods of delayed conduction preceding the missed beat are called, after their discoverer, the Wenckebach periods. The interval of the cycle succeeding the missed beat is shortened again to near the normal length. In a further stage of the condition the beats are dropped more frequently and may be spaced at either regular or irregular intervals in the tracing. When the grade of block is still more advanced, impulses fail to penetrate the bundle after every second auricular beat; or three, or even four auricular contractions may occur before an impulse reaches the ventricle, i.e., the ventricle responds only to every third or fourth auricular beat. So, an auriculoventricular rhythm becomes established in which the two chambers beat in the ratio of 2:1, 3:1, or 4:1.

(3) Complete Heart Block

When the A-V node or bundle offers an absolute barrier to the passage of the impulse, the dissociation of the rhythms of the upper and lower chambers is complete (fig. 38.2). The auricles beat at their own rate of about 70 per minute and the ventricle at its inherent rate of

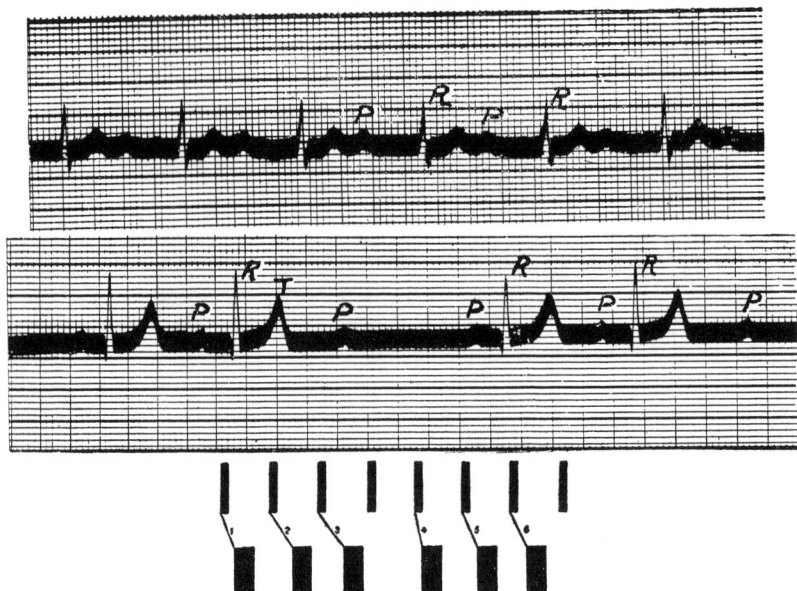

FIG. 38.1. Upper tracing, delayed conduction, lead I. Lower tracing, incomplete heart block, lead I (missed beats). (Kindness of Dr. John Hepburn.) The diagram below (after Lewis) represents incomplete heartblock. The thin rectangles, A, represent contractions of the auricle, the thicker ones, V, contractions of the ventricle. The obliquely directed lines represent conduction over the A-V bundle; the slower the conduction rate the more oblique the line. The gaps in the lower rectangles indicate missed beats of the ventricle. It will be noted that delay in conduction increases progressively in successive cycles until a beat is missed. Heavy vertical lines = ⅕ sec.

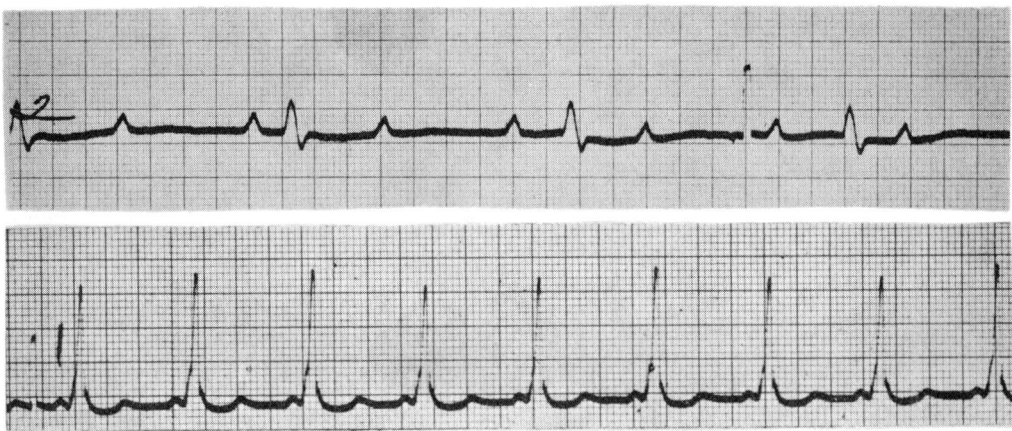

FIG. 38.2. Above—Complete heart block, auricular rate 75, ventricular rate 36, lead 2. Below—Wolff-Parkinson-White syndrome, lead 1, P-R interval .09 seconds, QRS interval .11 seconds.

about 35. The impulses that drive the ventricles are believed to arise only in the A-V node, bundle or His, right or left bundle branches or in the Purkinje fibers. Hoffman has shown through extensive investigation of the transmembrane action potentials of many areas of the heart that only the specialized conducting tissues have the property of automaticity that would permit their cells to take over pacemaking function. The property of automaticity is characterized by the ability of the cell to undergo gradual spontaneous diastolic depolarization to the threshold level of potential at which an action potential spike is initiated. Ventricular myocardial cells do not have this property. The speed with which a particular region of the heart can develop and discharge impulses apparently determines its ability to dominate other regions. It has been mentioned that when a region of higher rhythmicity is destroyed or isolated the region next in order of rhythmical power assumes the role of pacemaker (ch. 35). When, for instance, the S-A node is destroyed or isolated the A-V node assumes control, and when this or the upper part of the bundle is separated from the tract of tissue below, the lower lying portion takes over the government of the ventricular rate.

Partial and complete heart block are accompanied by changes in the rhythm of the arterial pulse. When beats are missed occasionally the pulse intermits either at regular or irregular intervals. In the more fully developed conditions marked slowing (bradycardia) of the pulse occurs. Visible pulsations in the veins at the root of the neck may occur when the auricle contracts against a closed tricuspid valve producing a giant A wave in the jugular pulse. A certain proportion of the venous pulsations may be seen to be unassociated with an arterial pulse. Sometimes a sound may be heard over the heart at the time of the isolated venous pulsation since the auricular contraction is unusually forceful and the sound vibrations thus set up are not smothered by the first heart sound which, in the normally beating heart, follows so closely upon auricular systole.

The venous pulse tracing and electrocardiogram show characteristic features. The *a* and P waves of the respective records occur at the usual times, but the ventricular complex (*c* and *v* in the venous curve and QRS and T in the electrocardiogram) is absent, a gap appearing in the tracing each time a beat of the ventricle is missed. In incomplete heart block, as one would expect, a relationship between a ventricular complex and a preceding auricular wave can always be made out, whereas in complete block there is no relationship. In the venous pulse, for example, the *a* and *c* waves may occur simultaneously, and produce a large *a + c* wave. Or the *a* and *v* waves may coincide. Corresponding effects are produced upon the electrocardiogram.

Temporary heart block may result from excessive doses of digitalis, strophanthus, quinidine, etc., which exert a specific effect in depressing auriculoventricular conduction. Heart block may be a sequel or an accompaniment of several acute infectious maladies, e.g., diphtheria, rheumatic fever, etc. It is produced in animals by asphyxia and its commonest cause in adults is ischemic heart disease. Increased vagal tone is sometimes responsible for delayed conduction over the A-V bundle. Partial heart block is not uncommonly seen in the course of rheumatic fever and is then, in many instances, of vagal origin, being temporarily abolished by atropine. *Persistent* heart block due to increased vagal tone and abolished by atropine occasionally occurs. Some cases are congenital.

Stokes-Adams syndrome. This condition was first described by Adams (1827) and later by Stokes (1842). Its features are a slow pulse and syncopal attacks or convulsive seizures, usually epileptiform in character due to sudden temporary cessation of the heart's pumping action. It is probable that the underlying morbid state upon which the syndrome depends is not identical in all instances (see also carotid sinus, ch. 42). In the majority, however, the slowed cardiac action is the result of the heart block, and the cerebral symptoms result from temporary periods of cardiac standstill or ventricular fibrillation. Occasionally seizures may result from sudden slowing of the pulse such as that which occurs when the heart rhythm shifts back and forth between normal rhythm and complete heart block. Such episodes have been documented repeatedly in human electrocardiograms. In recent years it has become possible to initiate emergency treatment of Stokes-Adams seizures by delivering timed AC electric shocks to the heart through the chest wall by means of an external artificial pacemaker. For long-term treatment of the slow heart rate of complete heart block and for the prevention of Stokes-Adams attacks small, transistorized, totally implantable DC pacemakers have become available. Small wire electrodes are sutured directly to the myocardium and these are connected by insulated wires to the miniaturized pulse generator and battery power supply which is implanted in the tissues beneath the skin of the abdominal wall. Isoproterenol has proven to be the most potent pharmacological agent for treatment of this condition.

B. Wolff-Parkinson-White (WPW) Syndrome

In this rare congenital anomaly the P-R interval of the electrocardiogram is shortened and the QRS complex prolonged. The P-R interval is 0.12 second or less and the QRS complex extended to over 0.10 sec. (fig. 38.2). The shortened P-R interval may be due, in some cases, to an accessory conducting strand between auricle and ventricle. Butterworth and Poindexter fashioned an extra electrical conduction pathway in the dog's heart, which, when stimulated, produced an electrocardiogram similar to that characteristic of the syndrome. Wood and Wolferth, in the histological examination of the heart of a patient which had shown this syndrome, also found three accessory pathways from the right auricle to the ventricle.

On the other hand, cases of the WPW syndrome occur in which no anatomical anomaly in the conducting system can be demonstrated, and even when such exists there is no conclusive evidence that it is the cause of the accelerated auriculoventricular conduction. Prinzmetal and his colleagues have produced typical WPW complexes

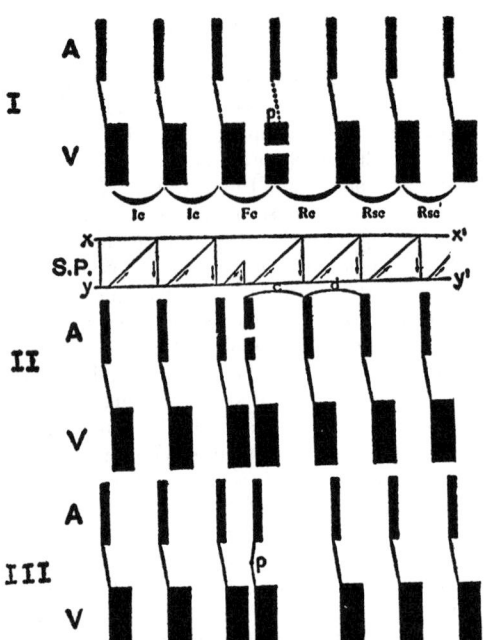

FIG. 38.3. (After Lewis). I. A diagram illustrating disturbance of the heart's mechanism when a systole is caused by exciting the ventricle during diastole. Ic, initial cycle, Fc, forced or extrasystolic cycle; Rc, returning cycle; and Rsc, restored cycles. p is the premature or forced beat. Note that the auricular rhythm remains undisturbed. The forced and returning cycles are together equal in length to two initial cycles. II. A diagram illustrating the events when a premature contraction is excited from the pacemaker. Stimulus production in the tissue which originates the heart rhythm is indicated by the line S.P.; the impulse is supposed to discharge when it reaches the line xx' and to fall at each contraction of the heart to the level yy'. c and d are equal in length. III. A diagram illustrating a premature beat arising in the A-V node.

in dogs by applying a noninterrupted direct current of subthreshold strength to the A-V node; but such complexes could not be induced after severance of the A-V bundle—an indication that the impulses traverse the normal A-V connections. These investigators carried out a large number of similar experiments in which the movements of the heart were recorded by high speed cinematography, and the records analyzed after slowing down to half speed. They conclude from their observations that the accelerated conduction of the WPW syndrome is due to shortening of the delay of the impulse at the A-V node to a fraction of the normal which amounts to about 0.12 seconds.

These experiments have thrown considerable doubt upon the anatomical explanation of the WPW syndrome. Prinzmetal and his colleagues

consider it to have a physiological rather than an anatomical basis.

The prolongation of the QRS complex is attributed to early activation of a portion of myocardium followed by normal activation of the remaining muscle. The significance of this unusual mechanism lies in the fact that persons who display this electrocardiographic pattern are particularly prone to have frequent bouts of paroxysmal rapid heart action of one type or another.

C. Disturbances of Rhythm Due to Abnormal Impulse Formation

I. Extrasystoles or Premature Contractions

An extrasystole can be induced experimentally by stimulating the cardiac muscle at any time except during its phase of absolute refractoriness. Extrasystoles occur in the human heart as a result of some abnormal process of impulse formation. Though extrasystoles may be associated with organic heart disease they more frequently occur in its absence; they may then be of reflex origin initiated from the abdominal viscera or be due to some form of intoxication, e.g., digitalis, cyclopropane anesthesia, hyperthyroidism, excessive smoking, excessive coffee or alcohol ingestion, stimulant drugs such as amphetamine, nervous tension, anxiety or exhaustion. Beattie, Brow, and Long produced extrasystoles in cats by stimulation of the hypothalamus (ch. 7), and their occurrence in man following brain lesions has been reported by Lucke and by Korth, which indicates that in some instances they are of central origin. The auricle or the ventricle may be the site of origin of the premature contraction, or the extra impulse may arise in the A-V node (see diagrams, fig. 38.3).

(1) Ventricular Extrasystoles

The premature contraction occurs after the normal ventricular beat has ceased and the muscle has recovered from its absolute refractory state. It is not preceded by an auricular contraction, and is not dependent upon an impulse received from the upper chamber (fig. 38.4). Since the impulses arise in one or the other bundle branches or in the Purkinje fibers, the electrocardiographic patterns of ventricular premature beats resemble those of right or left bundle branch block. They are broad and bizarre not resembling the normal complexes. The premature contraction is followed by a long pause. This is usually of just sufficient duration to cause the succeeding normal ventricular beat to occur at the instant that it would have occurred had there been no premature contraction. The cause of this *compensatory pause* has been explained elsewhere. Briefly, it is due to the normal impulse reaching the ventricle when the muscle is still refractory as a result of the premature beat. The interval between the normal beat and the one following the premature contraction is therefore equal in length to two normal cardiac cycles (fig. 38.3, I). Sometimes, however, when the extrasystole occurs early in diastole and the heart rate is slow, there may be no compensatory pause. The auricular impulse then reaches the ventricular muscle after it has recovered from the refractory state resulting from the premature beat; the auricular impulse therefore brings about a response at, or (as a result of some lengthening of the As-Vs interval following the premature beat) slightly after the usual time. The normal ventricular systoles are then all equally or nearly equally spaced and the extra contractions are interposed here and there between them. That is, the time interval from the normal beat preceding the extra contraction to that following it is of normal length or but slightly lengthened. Premature beats of this nature are called *interpolated extrasystoles* (fig. 38.4).[1]

(2) Auricular Extrasystoles

The premature contraction arises in the auricle at some point outside the S-A node. The abnormal impulse reaches the ventricle along the usual paths evoking a ventricular contraction and giving rise to an electrocardiographic complex similar to the normal ones. If the auricular beat is so premature that sufficient time has not elapsed to permit complete recovery of the ventricular muscle from its refractory state, then the impulse may be conducted aberrantly through the ventricle giving rise to a weak contraction and to an electrocardiographic complex having a different pattern from the normal beats. The premature auricular beat prevents the occurrence of the next normal auricular impulse and the pause of the auricle which follows the abnormal auricular contraction is usually precisely equal to a normal interval. This fact has been explained upon the assumption that, normally, impulse formation in the S-A node is the result of the

---

[1] It should be noted that except in the case of interpolated beats there is not an extra or additional beat, as the term extrasystole seems to imply. The premature beat, in effect, displaces the normal beat.

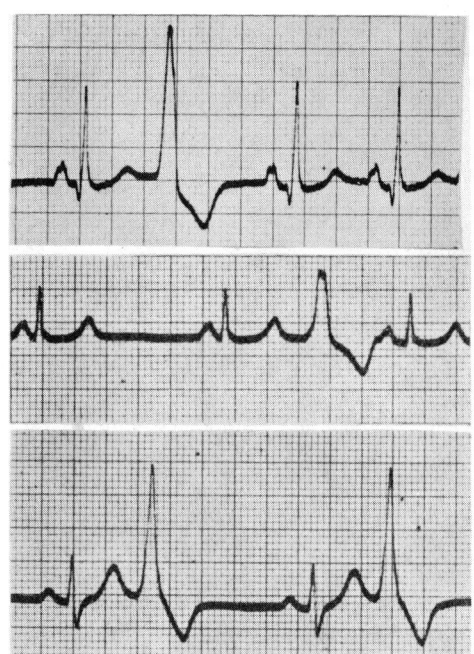

FIG. 38.4. Top—Ventricular extra-systole with compensatory pause. Middle—Interpolated ventricular extrasystole. Bottom—Coupled ventricular extrasystoles (bigeminal rhythm).

liberation of energy which has been built up during the previous quiescent period. Upon the occurrence of the abnormal impulse this store of energy, accumulated for the normal impulse, is discharged and a definite time interval must elapse before it is again built up to the required level (see fig. 38.3, II). Sometimes, however, the interval following the premature contraction is slightly lengthened, suggesting that the rate at which the S-A node builds up its store of energy is lowered. In any event, there is rarely a long (compensatory) pause following the beat of the *ventricle*, the interval between the two normal beats, i.e., from the beat preceding to the one succeeding the premature contraction, being nearly always shorter than two normal cycles. In other words, the normal auricular impulse following the premature auricular contraction upon reaching the ventricle does not "miss-fire", as in the case of ventricular extrasystole, but calls forth a response from the ventricle.

(3) Nodal Extrasystoles

Extrasystoles occur sometimes as a result of impulse formation in the A-V node or supraventricular part (stem) of the bundle. On account of its central position between the two chambers, impulses arising in the A-V node pass upward and

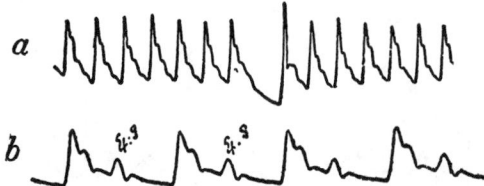

FIG. 38.5. (After Price.) *a*, intermission of the pulse; *b*, pulsus bigeminus, due to a single extrasystole with its succeeding compensatory pause occurring regularly after each normal beat. *Ex.S.*, extrasystole.

downward to cause simultaneous or nearly simultaneous responses from auricle and ventricle. Sometimes the ventricular contraction may actually occur first, in which case it is suggested that the impulse has arisen in the stem of the bundle and so has its course to the ventricular muscle considerably shortened. The extra cycle is usually, though not invariably, followed by a compensatory pause (fig. 38.3, III).

In rare instances extrasystoles arise as a result of abnormal impulses initiated in the sino-auricular node—*sinus extrasystoles*. Except for the interposition of the extra beat the rhythm of auricles and ventricles is but little disturbed. The interval following the extra beat is normal in length or slightly shortened.

The Effects of Extrasystoles upon the Characters of the Electrocardiogram and of the Arterial Pulse

THE ELECTROCARDIOGRAM. In *ventricular extrasystoles* the electrocardiogram shows irregularity in the spacing of the ventricular complexes. The following characteristics are found:

(1) The intervals between the R wave caused by the premature beat and the corresponding waves of the normal beats preceding and following it, respectively, are altered in length. The interval between the last normal R wave and the premature R wave is short, while the interval following this to the next normal R wave is prolonged—compensatory pause. The time elapsing between the two normal R waves is usually equal to the length of two normal cycles.

(2) The premature R wave is not preceded by a P wave. Since the premature ventricular contraction occurs unrelated to auricular systole it frequently happens that a normal contraction of the auricle occurs about the same time as the ventricular extrasystole. P and R waves then become fused. At other times the P wave follows closely upon the premature R wave.

(3) The P waves are equally spaced and some

appear which are not succeeded by a ventricular complex (refractory period of the ventricular muscle). In the case of the *interpolated* type of extrasystole, however, each P wave is followed by an R wave, and no long pause is seen.

(4) Ventricular extrasystoles also show abnormalities of the QRS complex which distinguish them from premature contractions of auricular or nodal origin. An impulse arising in the heart below the point where the bundle forks will activate one ventricle slightly in advance of the other. It is to be expected then that the QRS deflections of the electrocardiogram will be a record of unbalanced electrical effects. This is actually the case (fig. 38.4). In other words, if the extrasystole arises in the left ventricle its record will be deformed much in the same manner as that already described (p. 673) for right bundle branch block. If the premature beat arises in the right ventricle the electrocardiogram will show the features of a left branch defect.

In *auricular extrasystoles* the electrocardiogram shows disturbances in the timing of both the auricular and the ventricular complexes, but, as already mentioned (p. 685), a normal or only a slightly lengthened pause follows the extra beat. The P waves are unequally spaced but each is followed by a ventricular complex. The abnormal auricular wave may coincide with and be buried in the QRS complex of the preceding normal cycle.

The records of *extrasystoles arising in the A-V node* or supraventricular part of the bundle are variable according to the timing of the auricular and ventricular contractions. When the auricles and ventricles are excited simultaneously, the P and R waves become fused. When the two chambers are not activated simultaneously, the P precedes the R wave by a short interval, or the order of the waves may be reversed (R-P interval).

THE ARTERIAL PULSE. It has been demonstrated that several long-recognized irregularities of the pulse are the result of extrasystoles. For example, in the irregularity known as *intermittent pulse* there appear from time to time relatively long intervals during which no beat is felt in the radial (fig. 38.5*a*). The intervals are most pronounced when a premature contraction of the ventricle which is too weak to open the semilunar valves occurs. This most commonly happens when the heart muscle receives the abnormal impulse during the earlier part of its relative refractory phase. The premature beat may be detected by hearing a faint first heart sound which is not succeeded by a second sound. No pulse is produced in the radial at the time, nevertheless the extrasystole may be followed by a compensatory pause, and graphic records show as a rule that the gap in the radial tracing is just equal to two normal cycles. That is, a beat is dropped completely from the arterial record. The detection of an extra contraction of the ventricle, however, enables the irregularity to be distinguished from the missed beats of partial heart block (p. 191) which may give an arterial tracing with similar characters.

If ventricular extrasystoles which fail to open the semilunar valves are repeated after each normal beat, the long intervals separating the latter will cause pronounced slowing of the pulse rate. The pauses between the arterial pulses are doubled in length and the pulse frequency as a consequence is reduced to half the normal. Bradycardia produced in this way and sometimes termed *false heart block* is distinguished from true heart block by a study of the venous pulse or the electrocardiogram which reveals the extra ventricular complexes; or the faint sounds of the extra contractions may be heard upon auscultation.

When the extrasystoles are forceful enough to open the semilunar valves, and occur regularly one after each normal systole, paired pulse beats, each couple being followed by a long pause, are felt in the radial (fig. 38.5b). This type of pulse irregularity, which is sometimes seen following overdosage with digitalis, is called the *bigeminal pulse* (*pulus bigeminus*).

II. PAROXYSMAL TACHYCARDIA

This may be defined as a condition in which the rate of the heart is greatly accelerated for a longer or shorter period without obvious cause. The rate varies in different cases from 140 to 250 per minute. The onset of the paroxysm is sudden and the increased rate is maintained for a variable length of time with perfect regularity, successive cycles usually not varying in length by more than a hundredth of a second. The paroxysm lasts for only a few beats in some instances, in others it persists for a few minutes, hours or even days, though attacks of more than ten days' duration are very rare (Lewis). The attack ceases as abruptly as it commenced, the heart resuming its normal rate almost instantly.

The paroxysm, it is believed, consists of a series of rapidly recurring extrasystoles which completely submerge the physiological rhythm. The site of origin of the extrasystoles, as in the case of single premature beats, may be in the *auricle*, the *A-V node or stem of the bundle*, or in the *ventricle*

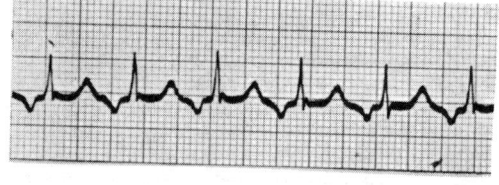

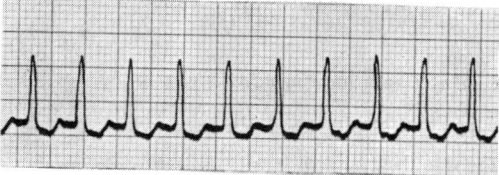

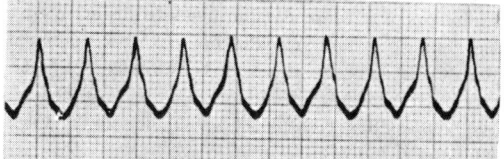

FIG. 38.6. Top—Nodal tachycardia at a rate of 120, lead 2. Note inverted P waves. Middle—Auricular tachycardia at a rate of 200, lead 3. Bottom—Ventricular tachycardia at a rate of 200, lead 2.

(fig. 38.6). The auricular type is the most common; each auricular impulse spreads to the ventricle and causes a contraction whose features as indicated by the electrocardiogram are normal. The P wave is frequently inverted.

When the impulses arise in the A-V node or supraventricular part of the bundle, the P-R intervals of the electrocardiogram are shortened. Inversion of the P waves is common. Or, the contractions of the two chambers may be simultaneous, the P waves being then buried in the ventricular (QRS) complexes. Again, the contraction of the ventricle may occur before that of the auricle; it then sometimes happens that a progressive lengthening of the intervals between the R and P waves (R-P interval) of the electrocardiogram is seen; ultimately an auricular beat is missed. This is termed *reversed heart block*. In other instances, as the R-P intervals reach a certain length, a contraction of the ventricle occurs prematurely, and is not followed by a contraction of the auricle. It is thought that the ventricular contraction is caused by the same impulse that caused the preceding auricular beat. That is, the impulse arising in the node first excites the auricle, then re-enters the junctional tissue, which has now recovered from its refractory phase, and passes downwards to the ventricle. This is spoken of as *reciprocal rhythm*.

When the impulses arise in the ventricle the QRS complexes have the characteristics of those caused by ventricular extrasystoles (p. 684). The

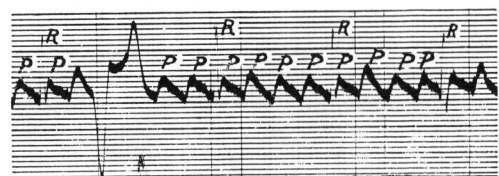

FIG. 38.7. Pure flutter with a ventricular extra-systole. (Kindness of Dr. John Hepburn.)

auricular rhythm is usually undisturbed, but occasionally it is abnormal, for when a series of rapidly recurring contractions arises in the ventricle, the impulses may pass along the bundle in a retrograde fashion and activate the auricle to the exclusion of the normal impulse. In other words, the ventricle then sets the pace, and the auricle follows. In such instances the P waves are inverted and succeed the QRS deflections, or are buried in the ventricular complexes as in the nodal type mentioned above.

III. Auricular Flutter

There are two forms of this disorder, *pure* and *impure flutter*. In both types the auricle beats at the phenomenally rapid rate of from 250 to 400 beats per minute, but in pure flutter the rhythm is regular, in impure flutter it is irregular. Flutter differs from paroxysmal tachycardia in the following particulars.

(a) The auricular rate of beating is usually much greater than that seen in paroxysmal tachycardia.

(b) The disorder is of much longer duration, persisting unchanged for months or years, though it is sometimes transient.

(c) The ventricle fails as a rule to follow the rate of the auricle; a state of relative heart block becomes established as a result of the comparatively long refractory phase of the functional tissue.

(d) It is produced by the passage of the impulse over one or more circular pathways—*circus movement* (p. 689).

Auricular flutter may become converted to auricular fibrillation.

In pure flutter the rhythm is remarkably regular (fig. 38.7). The lengths of the auricular cycles vary no more than a few thousandths of a second over comparatively long periods. In impure flutter this constancy of cycle length is not seen and varying degrees of irregularity occur. In flutter the auricular walls do not completely relax. That is, though the proportion of active to inactive fibers varies during the rapid beating, at no one time are all the fibers in the relaxed state. In the electrocardiogram, therefore, the level of the tracing between the P waves lies for the most part above the isopotential line, only touching the latter for an instant. The level of the tracing is continually changing and the electrical changes of the auricle are carried over to alter the form of the ventricular complex. On the other hand, the fibers are never all contracted at the same time, so that auricular systole as well as diastole is incomplete.

The ventricle rarely keeps pace with the racing auricle, the refractory phase of the conducting tissue being longer as compared with that of the auricular muscle. As a consequence, a state of relative heart blocks develops and an auriculoventricular rhythm of 2 to 1, or less frequently, of 3 to 1 or 4 to 1, becomes established. Sometimes there is variable block with 2 to 1, 3 to 1, 4 to 1, and occasionally even greater intervals occurring in the same strip of record. Should the ventricle respond to each beat of the auricle, as occasionally happens, serious circulatory disturbances follow; ventricular diastole is so shortened that the ventricle receives a greatly reduced load of blood. The output of the heart may be so reduced as a result that loss of consciousness resulting in death may follow.

IV. Auricular Fibrillation

The auricular muscle is the seat of incomplete contractions which recur at a frequency of from 400 to 600 per minute. So incomplete are the contractions and so rapidly are they produced that the individual beats are scarcely distinguishable from one another. The auricular cavity is never emptied of blood and its wall is a quivering sheet of muscle. Auricular fibrillation is the most common of all the serious cardiac irregularities, being associated, according to Lewis, in 60 to 70 per cent of all cases of cardiac failure in hospital practice. It is most frequently seen in mitral stenosis and in thyrotoxicosis (ch. 75), but sometimes occurs in the absence of myocardial disease.

Only a proportion of the auricular impulses pass through the A-V bundle and activate the ventricle. The relatively long refractory period of the conducting tissue shields the ventricle from the high rate of the auricular beating. The arterial pulse, nevertheless, is usually considerably faster than the normal (100 to 150) though it may be normal or even slowed. Those impulses which reach the ventricle do so in a somewhat haphazard manner, and indeed one of the most characteristic features of fibrillation of the auricles is absolute irregularity in the rate and force of the ventricular beats. These features are expressed in the

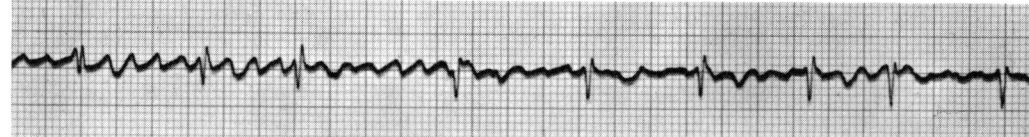

FIG. 38.8. Auricular fibrillation, lead V_1.

terms *"delirium cordis"*, *"complete irregularity of the pulse"* or *"perpetual arrhythmia"*, which were applied to the condition before its true nature was recognized. A proportion of the heart beats are frequently so weak that they fail to cause pulse in the radial. The apex beat is therefore much more rapid than the pulse. The former, for example, may be 150 and the latter only 60 or 70. The difference is called the *pulse deficit*. With treatment and improvement in the condition of the cardiac muscle, the pulse rate therefore may increase.

The venous pulse in auricular fibrillation is of the ventricular form; *a* waves are absent, being represented by a series of rapid vibratory waves (*f* waves). Similarly in the electrocardiogram, small rapid undulations replace the *P* waves (fig. 38.8).

THE UNDERLYING PROCESSES CONCERNED IN THE PRODUCTION OF FLUTTER AND FIBRILLATION OF THE AURICLES.[1] *The circus movement theory versus the theory of numerous separate points of excitation.* The observation that fibrillation could be induced in animals by electrical stimulation has led to a much clearer understanding of auricular fibrillation and flutter in man. Lewis, employing faradization as the method of inducing fibrillation, studied the subject intensively and, applying the results of the fundamental work of Mayer, of Mines and of Garrey conceived that the excitation wave followed a circular pathway through the auricular muscle—the so-called *circus movement*. That is to say, the wave starting at one place took a devious course through the cardiac musculature, returned to the point from which it started and re-entered the path which it had previously traversed. Mayer induced a circus movement in the umbrella of the jellyfish (Medusa) by creating a local block and applying a stimulus to one side of the blocked region (fig. 38.9, I,*A*). The contraction wave which resulted was forced as a result of the block to take a unidirectional course, and after completing the circuit of the disk of tissue returned to the region of the block, which by this time had disappeared. If the tissue from which the wave had been initiated was again excitable, i.e., had passed from the refractory state, the wave circled the ring a second time, then a third time, and so on repeatedly. When, on the other hand, the disk was stimulated in the absence of a block,

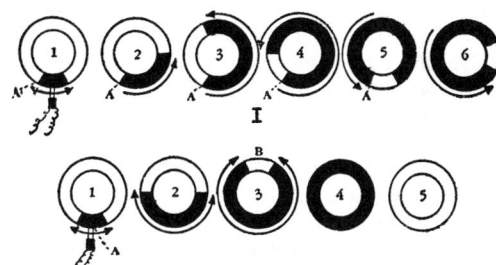

FIG. 38.9. (Modified from Lewis.) Black = contraction wave. Description in text.

a contraction wave set out in both directions and the two waves meeting, after having completed half the circumference of the strip, were suppressed at B (fig. 38.9, II). That is, further progress of the waves was arrested, for each came to a region of tissue which, being occupied by the other wave, was refractory.

Mines and Garrey linked up Mayer's observations upon Medusa with the fibrillation of cardiac muscle. Mines showed that a similar circular motion of the contraction wave could be induced in the cold-blooded heart. Muscular rings cut from the auricles of large rays were employed. Garrey thought that he had refuted the prevailing belief at that time, namely, that fibrillation of the auricle was due to the initiation of impulses from multiple foci throughout the auricular muscle—as proposed originally by McWilliam. Garrey found that if he cut a small piece from the fibrillating auricle, the severed tissue at once ceased to fibrillate, an event which he contended could not occur if numerous points of excitation existed; but such would naturally result if the impulses travelled over a circular pathway from which other parts of the auricle were excited. He induced a circulating contraction wave in large annular strips cut from turtles' ventricles.

Evidence was obtained by Lewis which seemed to show that the impulses in the fibrillating auricle travelled in the natural rings of muscle encircling the openings of the vena cavae.

The theory of circus movement has been very widely though not universally accepted. Brams and Katz contended that if a circus movement is responsible for flutter and fibrillation more than one circulating wave must exist. They base this conclusion upon the observation that if after experimental flutter or fibrillation has been established, the auricles (or in the case of ventricular fibrillation, the ventricles) are separated from one another by crushing between them the rapid beating persists with little change in each of the separated parts. Scherf, as a result of his failure to abolish auricular fibrillation by clamping or ligaturing the auricular muscle in the path of the supposedly circulating waves, was one of the first (1928) to throw doubt upon the existence of a circus movement. A little later Andrus and Carter concluded, from their experimental results in which fibrillation was induced by a single induction shock applied to the auricular appendix, that the waves did not originate and travel in a ring of muscle.

Evidence against the circus movement theory has been secured by Prinzmetal and his associates. They induced auricular fibrillation by the application of aconitine to the auricles of dogs and observed the auricle by means of high speed cinematography. They saw no indication of a circus movement. Two types of activity were observed; (a) contractions and relaxations of microscopic or minute segments of muscle, which they term the *"M" activity*; and (b) stronger contractions and relaxations of macroscopic or larger muscle segments which appear upon the background of the innumerable "M" contractions. This type of movement they have designated the *"L" activity*. Both types of activity are heterorhythmic and utterly chaotic, and apparently arise from numerous discrete ectopic foci.

Moe has proposed a variant of the circus movement theory in which he suggests that fibrillation is maintained by the irregular wandering of numerous wavelets generated by the fractionation of a wave front passing through tissue in a state of inhomogeneity with respect to excitability and conduction velocity. He has devised a most ingenious computer model of atrial fibrillation which supports his theory.

The Actions of the Cardiac Glycosides, such as Digitalis, and of Quinidine upon Fibrillation and Flutter, and in Heart Failure

DIGITALIS belongs to a class of drugs known as the *cardiac glycosides*, which also includes strophanthin, ouabain (G-strophanthin from *S. gratus*), and squill. Digitalis in therapeutic dosage exerts a threefold effect upon the action of the heart. (a) It increases the force of the ventricular contraction both of the failing (hypodynamic) heart, and of the normal myocardium as shown for the isolated papillary muscle of the cat by Cattell and Gold. This is the drug's most valuable property. Ouabain and strophanthin have a similar action. (b) It depresses A-V conduction, and (c) it stimulates the vagus, a reflex effect through the carotid sinus and the vagus center (Heymans and associates).

These last two effects cause slowing of the ventricle in fibrillation and flutter, but exert no significant effect upon the rapid auricular rate of sinus tachycardia. The depression of A-V conduction shields the ventricle from the fibrillating auricle; the weaker impulses fail to reach the ventricle, the pulse therefore becoming slower and more regular. In therapeutic dosage the drug has little or no effect upon the rate of the heart if the auricular rate is normal. In overdosage the drug may cause complete blockage of impulse conduction in the A-V bundle. It used to be thought that digitalis was of value only in fibrillation or flutter, but it has been shown conclusively within the last two decades that it strengthens the ventricular beat, and is of the utmost value in cardiac failure whether or not either of these arrhythmias are present. The digitalis glycosides have been shown to be useful in converting superventricular tachycardias back to normal sinus rhythm. This is probably mediated largely through the vagus effect but it is not at all clear why vagus tone should affect ectopic auricular foci.

Certain effects of the cardiac glycosides upon the metabolism of the myocardium have been demonstrated which help to explain their beneficial action upon the cardiac contraction. (a) They increase the oxygen consumption of the heart. (b) They increase the utilization of glucose and of lactic acid. (c) They cause a partial restoration of the adenosinetriphosphate and phosphocreatine contents of the failing myocardium in which these energy-rich phosphate-bond metabolites are depleted. In overdosage these drugs themselves cause depletion to the extent of 50 per cent or more of these materials.

The action of digitalis and other cardiac glycosides appears to be mainly in improving the utilization of chemical energy by the myocardium, rather than by increasing the total amount of energy liberated, though the latter probably also occurs.

The cardiac glycosides exert no beneficial effects upon myocardial insufficiency due to anoxia, in thyrotoxicosis, or in vitamin B₁ deficiency. The reason for this is unknown.

QUINIDINE (an isomer of quinine) also exerts a threefold action in fibrillation. (1) It depresses or abolishes vagal tone and so lengthens the refractory period of the auricular muscle and decreases the transmission rate. This action upon the vagus is therefore opposite to that of digitalis. (2) It acts directly upon the auricular and ventricular muscle, lengthening the refractory period (by from 50 to 100 per cent) and slowing the transmission rate. (3) It depresses conduction in the junctional tissues—a direct action. The abolition of the fibrillation of the auricle and the restoration of the normal rhythm was believed, on the basis of the circus movement theory, to be due to the lengthening of the refractory period of the auricular muscle, and as a consequence, to closure of the gap of excitable tissue between the crest and tail of the wave (see fig. 38.9). In other words "the head catches up to the tail" (Osler). But however fibrillation is produced, we know at any rate that quinidine restores the normal auricular rate and thus acts upon this arrhythmia in a manner different from that of digitalis. In the restoration of the normal auricular rhythm by quinidine fibrillation is frequently converted first to flutter.

The different effects of quinidine upon the heart interact in a complicated manner. For example, its action upon the ventricular rate will be the resultant of the following three effects.

(1) Rapid auricular beating tends automatically to depress conduction through the A-V connections. Therefore when the rate of the auricle is reduced by the drug, A-V conduction is increased.

(2) The reduction in vagal tone also increases A-V conduction.

(3) The direct effect of the drug upon A-V conduction, as stated above, is one of depression.

As a matter of fact (1) and (2) frequently overbalance the last effect (3) and some increase in the ventricular rate results.

Quinidine in overdosage produces severe toxic effects among which are auriculoventricular block, extrasystoles, paroxysmal tachycardia, and even death as a result of ventricular fibrillation. The return of the normal auricular contractions under quinidine treatment is sometimes, though rarely, followed by the dislocation of an intra-auricular thrombus and death from embolism. Complete standstill of the heart has also been reported as a result of the paralysis by the drug of the sino-auricular and auriculoventricular nodes and other tissues capable of impulse initiation. Procaine amide has an action closely akin to quinidine. It appears to be less effective on the auricular arrhythmias than quinidine but being less toxic than quinidine it may be given intravenously. It is most useful in converting ventricular tachycardia back to normal rhythm by intravenous administration. It is also used orally in suppressing frequent ventricular premature beats.

Direct Current Cardioconversion

In the years between 1962 and 1964 the method of direct current cardioconversion devised by Lown came into wide clinical usage for the conversion of superventricular arrhythmias as well as ventricular tachycardia back to normal rhythm as the apparatus for carrying out this procedure became commercially available. The apparatus is designed to deliver a capacitor discharge shock of 100 to 400 watt seconds through the chest wall via electrodes 4 inches in diameter. The shock is timed to fire at the peak of the R wave when conversion of atrial fibrillation, flutter or tachycardia is being carried out, so that the ventricle will be completely refractory when the current hits the heart. The atria are depolarized completely, ectopic foci are extinguished and the opportunity for the sinus node to resume pacemaker function is made available.

Lown has had approximately 95% success in converting superventricular arrhythmias to normal sinus rhythm. Maintenance of the sinus rhythm often requires quinidine therapy and even with maximal tolerable doses of this drug, relapse into the arrhythmia may occur, particularly if serious heart disease is present.

The cardioconversion apparatus is also effective in abolishing ventricular tachycardia and ventricular fibrillation by administering direct current shock to the heart through the intact chest wall.

V. Ventricular Fibrillation

The ventricular muscle may pass into a state of rapid, tremulous and ineffectual contractions closely similar in nature to the condition just described as occurring in the auricle. In animals, ventricular fibrillation may be initiated by direct electrical stimulation of the ventricular muscle, as was first shown by Ludwig in 1850. Mechanical stimulation of the ventricle, especially by pricking the tissue in the A-V groove, ligation of a coronary artery (Porter) or certain chemicals and drugs in excess, e.g., digitalis or calcium chloride, may induce fibrillation. Levy found that chloroform anesthesia renders the hearts of experimental animals (cats) highly susceptible to fibrillation. A mere touch of a finger or instrument, the stimulation of a sensory nerve, section of the vagi or their paralysis by atropine, may set the ventricle fibrillating. The heart behaves as though sensitized by the anesthetic and ready at the least provocation to fibrillate. Adrenaline was found to greatly enhance the effect of chloroform—a fact which indicates the danger of adrenaline administration while a subject is under the effect of this anesthetic. Fibrillation may also ensue spontaneously under chloroform, and Levy found that the condition is more likely to supervene when the animal is passing from deep to light anesthesia. Cyclopropane, like chloroform, has the effect of sensitizing the heart to the action of adrenaline in inducing ventricular tachycardia and fibrillation, but these cardiac irregularities are rarely seen under ether anesthesia. Quinidine reduces the susceptibility to fibrillation during cyclopropane anesthesia.

The effects of ventricular fibrillation upon the circulation are incomparably more serious than those of the corresponding auricular condition.

This is evident when the importance of the two musculatures in the dynamics of the circulation are compared (p. 736). In fibrillation of the lower chamber the propulsive force of its contraction is practically abolished and the circulation comes to an end; death follows within a few minutes.

Since continuous electrocardiographic monitoring with the oscilloscope during surgery and other serious illness has become common practice, many cases of ventricular fibrillation have been observed. It may occur suddenly or it may be ushered in gradually. Ventricular extrasystoles may appear, become more frequent until there is coupling, tripling, and then short runs of ventricular tachycardia. Longer paroxysms of rapid beating follow. Finally as the tachycardia becomes more rapid it merges into fibrillation.

When fibrillation is induced suddenly as by electric shock its development may be somewhat different. According to Wiggers and his associates, only the first contraction is a true premature beat; those which follow are caused by re-entry of the excitation wave. These investigators, who induced ventricular fibrillation in dogs by the application of single strong induction shock to the ventricle late in systole, recognize four stages in the development of fibrillation. In the *first* or *undulatory stage*, which lasts for only a second or two, the contractions are rapidly repeated but do not follow the same course over the surface of the ventricle; the electrocardiographic deflections show considerable variability in form. In the *second* stage of *convulsive incoordination*, which lasts for from 15 to 40 seconds, the contractions are more frequent and involve smaller areas of the ventricular muscle. The contractions of different areas of the muscle are out of phase so that the ventricle appears to be pulled about convulsively. The *third* stage of *tremulous incoordination* lasts for 2 or 3 minutes, the surface of the muscle is broken up into independently contracting areas of ever-decreasing size which are out of phase with one another. Thus, a tremulous appearance is given to the ventricles. The *final* stage of *atonic fibrillation* develops when the developing anoxia of the cardiac muscle causes weakening of its contractile force. This stage appears usually within from 2 to 5 minutes following the first stage and is marked by weak contractions or wavelets which travel only a short distance over the ventricular surface. It ends in complete cessation of all activity.

Ventricular fibrillation in man may result from:

a) Electric shocks—electrocution, lightning stroke.
b) Chloroform or cyclopropane anesthesia.
c) Coronary occlusion and other causes of severe anoxia.
d) Trauma to heart or chest wall.
e) Ventricular paroxysmal tachycardia, in which fibrillation may be a terminal event.
f) Toxic doses of digitalis or quinidine.
g) Manipulation of the heart during cardiac surgery.
h) Various diseases during the death agony.

The fundamental factor or factors leading to fibrillation of the ventricles have been the subject of research by several investigators. Kebar and Hooker have found microscopical tissue changes in the dog's heart, in which fibrillation was induced by electric shock. There also occurred an increase in potassium in the outflowing fluid perfused through the heart. They attribute the fibrillation to a leakage of potassium from the cells and an unbalance of the potassium ion. The addition of potassium to the perfusion fluid brings the fibrillation immediately to an end and restores the normal beat. According to Nahum and Hoff, the essential condition for the onset of fibrillation is the establishment of a block or blocks of the conducting system in a heart whose automaticity is simultaneously stimulated; either factor alone is ineffective. They found that the rapid injection of a concentrated solution of KCl throws the ventricles immediately into fibrillation. This does not occur if the injection is made slowly, for then automaticity instead of being stimulated is depressed; block of the conducting system occurs, but fibrillation does not ensue. Thus, they believe that the two essential elements in the production of ventricular fibrillation are intraventricular block and automaticity of the ventricles. Ventricular fibrillation, though usually fatal is not invariably so, for rare instances have been reported in which the ventricles after fibrillating for a brief period resumed their normal rate and recovery occurred. Two methods, chemical and electrical, have been used in attempts to restore the normal rhythm to the fibrillating ventricles. Hooker has shown the efficacy of an excess of potassium in stopping fibrillation and of calcium in restoring the normal beat in the hearts of dogs subjected to electric shock. A 0.5 per cent solution of KCl is injected under pressure into the carotid toward the heart, so that it reaches the coronary system. This stops the heart. When a 0.023 solution of $CaCl_2$ is then introduced by the same route, the normal cardiac rhythm, in a successful experiment, is restored. Hooker and his associates showed that defibrillation of the dog's heart can be accomplished and the normal beat restored if a countershock, consisting of an alternating current of about one ampere, is passed through the heart.

The basic knowledge of countershock defibrillation acquired through animal experimentation has been applied countless times for the saving of human life. The first reports originated from operating room incidents where the exposed heart could be defibrillated by application of the electrodes directly to the epicardium. Direct hand pumping massage of the heart was used to sustain circulation until the defibrillating apparatus could be brought to bear. Subsequently numerous reports of emergency thoracotomies with open chest massage and defibrillation both in and outside of hospitals appeared. Some of these cases were saved, but a distressing number of unsuccessful terminal thoracotomies were carried out.

A great advance was made in 1960 when Kouwenhoven, Jude and Knickerbocker reported the method of closed-chest cardiac massage in which circulation is maintained by rhythmic compression of the fibrillating heart through the intact chest wall by strong intermittent manual pressure over the sternum. Life can be sustained for periods of time up to an hour or more until external defibrillation can be achieved either by AC or DC countershock through the intact chest.

Many reports in both medical and lay press have recounted dramatic stories of lives saved by closed-chest cardiac massage followed by external defibrillation. It has become the obligation of all medical and many paramedical personnel to learn the technique of external cardiac masage so that they might be prepared to deal with this most urgent of all medical emergencies, ventricular fibrillation. It has been well established that unless circulation can be restored in less than 4 minutes, irreparable cerebral damage will have occurred, and even though heart action might be restored, a decerebrate patient will be the result.

D. Alternation of the Heart. Pulsus Alternans

This is a condition in which every second wave in a pulse tracing is of relatively small amplitude. This peculiarity of the arterial pulse is due to alternate variations in the strength of the ventricular systoles, and to a smaller quantity of blood being ejected into the aorta during the weaker beat. Figure 38.10 shows a typical sphygmogram of this condition. There is as a rule little or no difference in the lengths of the intervals between pulse beats. When a slight difference does exist, the interval succeeding the strong beat is then longer than that following the weak beat. It will be remembered that in the bigeminal pulse, which might in some instances be confused with alternation, there is inequality in cycle lengths, but the longer interval follows the *weak* (premature) beat. Furthermore, in alternation the ventricular rhythm does not share, or does so very rarely, in any irregularity of the pulse intervals which may occur in the arterial tracing. The electrocardiogram, for instance, shows no discrepancies in the length of

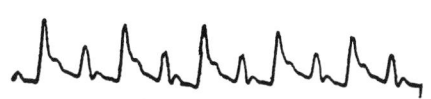

FIG. 38.10. Radial tracing showing pulsus alternans. (After Mackenzie.)

the intervals between the R waves. The slight variations in the pulse intervals are attributed by Lewis to a slower rate of transmission of the weaker pulses to the periphery. The appearance of alternation in the electrocardiogram (e.g., alternate variations in the height of the R wave) is rare. When this so-called *electrical alternation* does occur the larger deflections sometimes correspond to the weaker pulse beats. But, it will be recalled in this connection that the deflections of the electrocardiogram are determined by the balance of the electrical forces developed during the cardiac contraction rather than upon their total value. Electrical alternation bears no relation to the strength of the heart beat.

Sometimes it is not possible to detect pulsus alternans by palpation of the pulse, the variations in strength of the pulse beat being too slight to be perceptible, but it is clearly revealed in the sphygmogram (fig. 38.10). It may also be detected by means of a blood pressure armlet. The pressure in the armlet is raised gradually, when it is found that at a certain level the weaker beats are suppressed, but the stronger beats get through. The pulse at the wrist is then precisely half the ordinary rate. The pressure during the weaker beats may be as much as 25 mm. Hg below that during the stronger, but usually the pressure difference is not more than 5 or 10 mm. Persistent alternation of the heart when the pulse is slow or of normal frequency is usually indicative of grave disease of the myocardium. Alternation sometimes also occurs at rapid rates of beating, e.g., auricular fibrillation, paroxysmal tachycardia etc., but it is then of less serious significance.

THEORY OF ALTERNATION. Three major theories regarding the mechanism of pulsus alternans have been proposed. One of these advanced by Wenckebach suggested that variations in the venous return influencing the magnitude of ventricular filling were primarily responsible, with the weak beat originating from a smaller diastolic volume. Straub believed that incomplete metabolic re-

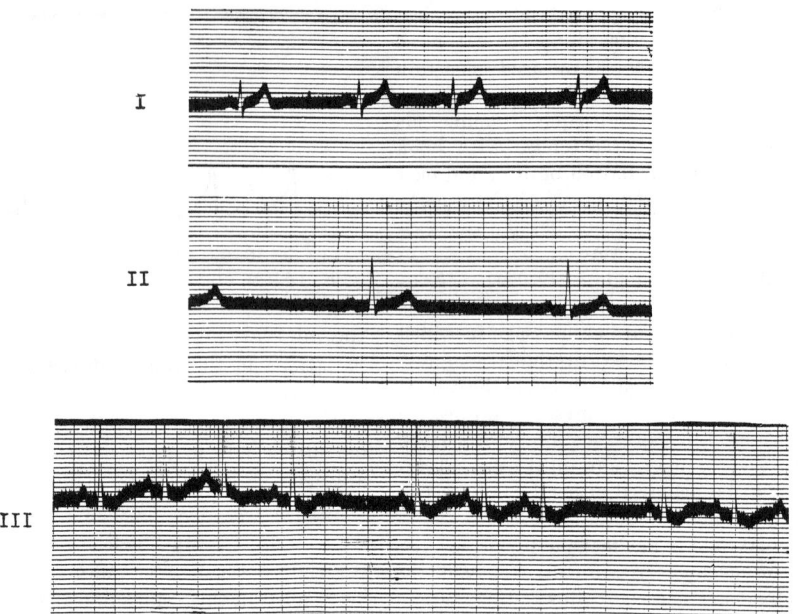

I

II

III

FIG. 38.11. *I*, sinus arrhythmia; *II*, sinus bradycardia; *III*, sino-auricular block. (Kindness of Dr John Hepburn.)

covery from the strong beat resulted in insufficient energy for the succeeding beat. Another view, first proposed by Hering, states that in the depressed state of the myocardium of the hypodynamic heart the recovery of a certain proportion of the muscle fibers is delayed so that they remain refractory when the next beat arrives and hence fail to contract with the rest of the heart on the succeeding beat. By the time the following beat arrives, all fibers have recovered and a strong beat ensues.

Mitchell, Sarnoff and Sonnenblick have recently presented experimental evidence which they believe helps to reconcile the three previously held views and more precisely defines the mechanism of pulsus alternans. From their experiments on dogs and from a close perusal of the available data in the literature they conclude that the basic fact common to all observations is that the weak beat is initiated from a shorter end-diastolic fiber length than is the strong beat, no matter what the end-diastolic pressure might be. The short end-diastolic fiber length may result from too short a time for diastolic filling of the ventricle or for complete relaxation of the ventricle. If the ventricle is not completely relaxed, then its compliance will be low and the end-diastolic pressure will be high. If the ventricle is incompletely filled when relaxation is complete the compliance will be high and the end-diastolic pressure will be low. In either case, the fiber length will be short and a weak low-output beat will ensue.

Clinical observations that pulsus alternans may be observed in patients with normal hearts at fast pulse rates or in patients with failing hearts at normal pulse rates is in accord with the theory of short fiber length due to insufficient diastolic filling time, for the diastolic time is compromised in the normal heart only at fast pulse rates, while in the failing heart the prolonged ejection time encroaches on the diastolic period of the heart cycle. Furthermore, it has been shown that shortening the ejection period of the failing heart by administration of inotropic agents and thereby lengthening the diastolic filling period effectively abolishes pulsus alternans.

E. Irregularities Due to Variations in Vagal Tone

I. Sinus Arrhythmia (fig. 38.11, I)

This is a condition in which rhythmical variations in the rate of the whole heart occur synchronously with respiration. It is due to alterations in the strength of the vagal influence upon the pacemaker (S-A node) as a result of the respiratory excursions, the heart rate increasing toward the end of inspiration and slowing toward the end of expiration. It is a youthful irregularity, being very common in children, and may be considered a physiological phenomenon. That it is entirely of vagal origin is shown by the fact that it is abolished by atropine. It also disappears when the heart rate increases as a result of exercise, fever, etc., but is enhanced by deep breathing.

II. Phasic Irregularity

In this disorder periodic slowing of the heart occurs for a few seconds quite independently of the respirations. It also is a vagal effect since it is abolished by atropine. The manner of its production is unknown. It occurs in convalescence from acute fevers, and sometimes during the administration of digitalis.

III. Sinus Bradycardia (fig. 38.11, II)

This is a persistent slowing of the whole heart due to increased vagal tone influencing the sino-auricular node. The rate may be as slow as 40 per minute. Bradycardia of this nature occurs in apparently healthy persons, many of whom are athletes.

IV. Sino-auricular Block (fig. 38.11, III)

The entire heart (auricles and ventricles) misses a beat at regular or irregular intervals. The condition thus differs from A-V block in which only the ventricle misses (p. 681). A complete set of waves is therefore dropped from the venous or electrocardiographic tracing, and the arterial pulse intermits. Since the condition is temporarily abolished by atropine and may be induced by stimulation of the vagus, it is probable that the missed beats are due to the action of the nerve upon the S-A node. Sino-auricular block sometimes results from digitalis administration.

V. Auriculoventricular Block

Defective conduction between auricle and ventricle due to heightened vagal tone is occasionally seen; it is abolished by atropine.

REFERENCES

Barker, P. S., Macleod, A. G., and Alexander, J. Am. Heart J., 1930, **5**, 720.

Beck, C. L., Pritchard, W. H., and Feil, H. S. J. A. M. A., 1947, **135**, 985.

Brams, W. A. and Katz, L. N. Am. Heart J., 1931, **7**, 249.

Butterworth, J. S. and Poindexter, C. A. Arch. Int. Med., 1942, **69**, 437.

Cattell, McK. and Gold, H. Arch. Int. Med., 1940, **65**, 263. J. Pharmacol. & Exper. Therap., 1938, **62**, 116.

Garrey, E. W. Am. J. Physiol., 1914, **33**, 397.

Heymans, C., Bouckaert, J. J., and Regniers, P. Compt. rend. Soc. Biol., 1932, **110**, 572.

Hoffman, B. F. and Cranefield, P. F. Am. J. Med., 1964., **37**, 670.

Hooker, D. R. Am. J. Physiol., 1929, **91**, 305; Ibid., 1930, **92**, 639; Ibid., 1932, **99**, 279. Ibid.,

Hooker, D. R., Kouwenhoven, W. B., and Langworthy, O. R. Am. J. Physiol., 1933, **103**, 444.

Katz, L. N., Mendlowitz, M., and Kaplan, H. A. Am. Heart J., 1938, **16**, 149.

Kehar, N. D. and Hooker, D. R. Am. J. Physiol., 1935, **112**, 301.

Kouwenhoven, W. B., Jude, J. R. and Knicker-Bocker, G. G. J.A.M.A. 1960, **173**, 1064.

Levy, A. G. Heart, 1913, **4**, 319; Ibid., 1914, **5**, 299; Ibid., 1919, **7**, 105, Brit. Med. J., 1914, **2**, 502.

McWilliam, J. A. J. Physiol., 1887, **8**, 296; Proc. Roy Soc., 1918, **B90**, 302.

Mayer, A. G. Papers from Tortugas Laboratory, Carnegie Inst., Washington, 1908, **1**, 115.

Mines, G. R. J. Physiol., 1913, **46**, 349; Trans. Roy. Soc. Can., Sec. IV, 1914, **8**, 43.

Mitchell, J. H., Sarnoff, S. J. and Sonnenblick, E. H. J.C.I., 1963, **42**, 55.

Moe, G. K., Rheinboldt, W. C. and Abildskov, J. A. Am. Heart J., 1964, **67**, 200.

Nahum, L. H. and Hoff, E. H. J. Pharmacol. & Exper. Therap., 1939, **65**, 322.

Prinzmetal, M., Corday, E., Brill, I. C., Oblath, R. W., and Kruger, H. E. The auricular arrhythmias. Charles C Thomas, Springfield, Illinois, 1952.

Prinzmetal, M., Corday, E., Brill, I. C., Sellers, A. L., Oblath, R. W., Flieg, W. A., and Kruger, H. E. Circulation, 1950, **1**, 241.

Prinzmetal, M., Oblath, R. W., Corday, E., Brill, I. C., Kruger, H. E., Smith, L. A. Fields, J., and Kennamer, R. J. A. M. A., 1951, **146**, 1275.

Roberts, G. H., Crawford, J. H., and Abramson, D. I.: Am. Heart J., 1932, **7**, 505; J. Clin. Invest., 1935, **14**, 867.

Weirich, W. L., Paneth, M., Gott, V. L., and Lillehei, C. W.: Circulation Res., 1958, **6**, 410.

Wiggers, C. J., Bell, J. R., Paine, M., Shaw, H. D. B., Theisen, H., and Maltby, A.: Am. J. Physiol., 1930, **92**, 223; Am. Heart J., **20**, 399, 413 (1940).

Wilson, F. N., Macleod, A. G., and Barker, P. S. Am. Heart J., 1931, **6**, 637.

Wood, F. C. and Wolferth, C. C. Am. Heart J., 1943, **25**, 454.

Monographs and Reviews

Garrey, W. E. Auricular fibrillation. Physiol. Rev., 1924, **4**, 215.

Glenn, W. W. L. and Whipple, H. E., (Eds.) Cardiac Pacemakers. Ann. N. Y. Acad. Sci., 1964, **111**, 813.

Hecht, H. and Sandberg, A. A. The mechanism of auricular fibrillation and flutter. Circulation, 1953, **7**, 594.

Lewis, T. Clinical disorders of the heart beat. Paul B. Hoeber, Inc., New York, 1916.

Lewis, T. The mechanism and graphic registration of the heart beat. Shaw, London, 1920.

Lewis, T. Clinical science. Shaw, London, 1934.

Lown, B. Modern Concepts of Cardiovascualr Disease, 1964, **33**, 863.

Mackenzie, J. Diseases of the heart. Frowde, London, 1913.

Pardee, H. E. B. Clinical aspects of the electrocardiogram. Ed. 4. Paul B. Hoeber, Inc., New York, 1941.

Roth, I. R. Cardiac arrhythmias, clinical features and mechanism of the irregular heart. Paul B. Hoeber, Inc., New York, 1928.

Wollenberger, A. Cardiac energy metabolism. Pharmacol. Rev., 1949, **1**, 311.

Wilius, F. A. Clinical electrocardiograms. Their interpretation and significance. W. B. Saunders Company. Philadelphia and London, 1929.

CHAPTER 39

Estimation of Volume of Blood Flow, Velocity of Blood Flow, Volume of Organs, Cavities and Regions. Circulation Time

Our knowledge of the modus operandi of the circulation has progressed no faster than advancement of methodology that has given answers to certain problems.

Volume Flow of Blood

The most important measurement in the circulation is that of the volume flow of blood through the aorta or through any vital region or organ. The blood flow is most sensitive to a change in dilation in a vascular bed. If the blood pressure is doubled, the blood flow might also double but doubling the mean bore of a vascular bed might increase the blood flow by 16 times. In the past, advancement of flow methodology has been slow and limited in large measure to devices applicable under highly abnormal conditions. In use, the animals have been exposed to so much insult by anesthesia, surgery and trauma that the measurements do not necessarily have resemblance to normal values, i.e., the relative importance of factors regulating flow can be quite different than in the normal state. Recently, progress has been much more rapid because of the development of methods applicable to the normal circulation in the unanesthetized resting and active states.

VISUALIZATION (HUMAN OR ANIMAL). Direct microscopic *in vivo* visualization of the components of the microcirculation (terminal arteries, arterioles, capillaries, venules, and very small veins) offers a means for studying qualitatively the peripheral circulation and control of blood flow in various regions. When capillaries, arterioles or any of the above vessels are observed to decrease in diameter, they are assumed to have constricted and thus to decrease flow. However, interpretation is always difficult for the apparent change in flow could arise from decrease in perfusion pressure, enlargement of other already patent vessels, opening of other drainage vessels, or increase in pressure in the surrounding tissue. Despite this, such observations have contributed greatly to our knowledge of the circulation. Direct microscopic and high speed photography have been used in the frog skin, bat wing, rat mesoappendix, dog omentum, lungs of the open-chest dog, transparent viewing chamber of the rabbit's ear, bulbar conjunctiva and skin of humans, and pial vessels of the brain through a transparent viewing chamber. Change in small terminal arteries (and possibly arterioles) has been visualized in the coronary circulation of the heart of the closed-chest dog and in humans with cinéphotography following injection of contrast medium directly into the coronary arteries. Progress using the latter approach has been very rapid in the last few years so that gross encroachment by an atheromatous process on the coronary arterial lumen can be detected. Future comparable advancement might permit detection of early small lesions and study of factors which affect their growth.

VENOUS DRAINAGE. One of the oldest, simplest and most satisfactory means of determining blood flow is to collect and measure the outflow from a cannulated vein draining a particular organ. The rate of flow can be read from a graduate; or from the change in weight of a collecting container on a scale. Venous outflow can also be measured by causing the blood to enter the bottom of a closed chamber and with a bellows in the chamber recording the increase in pressure or volume of displaced air as the fluid level rises, or by recording in an open chamber the changing height of a float riding on top of the fluid. For very low rates of flow, drop recorders are used in which each drop shorts a pair of contacts in an electrical system or interrupts a photocell light beam. In all cases, the blood is generally returned to the circulation by some form of atraumatic pump that does not cause significant hemolysis of the red cells. Such a collection of venous drainage has its modern counterpart, considered in more detail in the next section, in which total venous drainage in perfusion systems applied to humans and animals is collected and metered before its return to the body. Venous drainage avoids the interference with nervous control of blood vessels which occurs when metering blood flow on the arterial side. It has the disadvantage of generally measuring only a portion of the arterial inflow since most organs have multiple venous drainage channels.

PERFUSION SYSTEMS FOR USE WITH ISOLATED ORGANS (WITHIN OR WITHOUT THE BODY), WITH REGIONS OF THE BODY, AND WITH THE WHOLE BODY. For many investigations and certain surgical procedures, it is desirable to have controled perfusion of an organ, body region, or the whole body at constant flow rates and/or at constant perfusion pressures, which are the same or different from the prevailing aortic pressure. Over the years a large number of such systems have been devised. Because of their practical use to the surgeon, the development of pumps or pump-oxygenator systems for maintaining blood flow at a constant rate or constant pressure has been rapid. Such pump systems have been used to perfuse isolated organs and to perfuse, in the unanesthetized as well as the anesthetized animal, the vessels of an extremity, the brain, liver, kidney, and the coronary vessels of the heart. Such mechanical pumps serve also as temporary replacement for the left ventricle, right ventricle, and the whole heart, i.e., the whole body including the coronary arteries is perfused with a pump. The minimal criteria that must be satisfied in such artificial systems are: the blood must be maintained at a constant temperature, preferably near body temperature; the blood must be suitably oxygenated; the pH of blood should be maintained at approximately a normal level; the blood flow rate should be adjusted to that which normally exists without a pump; excessive trauma to the red cells must be avoided. To minimize hemolysis, valves to direct the flow are generally avoided, and blood is moved through rubber or plastic tubing by multiple fingers or by a continuous roller over the tubing.

The use of such systems for bypass of the right heart, left heart and whole heart is shown in principle in figure 39.1*A*, *B*, and *C*.

For the right heart bypass, the systemic venous return is prevented from entering the right atrium and right ventricle by special fenestrated catheters passed through the right appendage and tied in the superior and inferior venae cavae. The collected blood flows by gravity into a reservoir from which it is pumped through the pulmonary artery. The coronary venous drainage which under this arrangement continues to enter the right atrium and fill the right ventricle, can by an appropriate catheter be made to drain into the same venous reservoir, thus insuring collection of total systemic venous flow. This type of bypass: (1) permits measurement of coronary venous flow and coronary A-V oxygen difference and, therefore, presumably gives an index of total

coronary flow and myocardial oxygen usage; (2) permits hemodynamic studies on the left or right heart separately; (3) permits operative procedures on the right heart in the presence of a dry field.

For the left heart bypass, the pulmonary venous return is prevented from entering the left ventricle by a clamp between the left ventricle and left atrium. The blood is drained by gravity into a reservoir from which it is pumped into the aorta. Since the left ventricle is now mechanical with a constant output, this arrangement: (1) permits study of those factors which regulate the vascular volume and the systemic venous return, especially the state of the venous system and activity of the right ventricle (this can be determined from observation of the height of blood in the reservoir); (2) permits operative procedures on the left heart with a dry field.

For total heart bypass, the systemic venous return is prevented from emptying into the right ventricle and is drained by gravity into a reservoir from which it is pumped through some form of oxygenator to a second reservoir. A second pump (set at the same flow rate) moves the blood into the aorta. To obviate filling up of the left ventricle from bronchial flow drainage into the pulmonary veins and left atrium, a catheter is inserted into the left atrium. Initially, the blood was oxygenated by passing it through a donor human or animal in which the lungs oxygenated the blood; later, the blood was passed through autogenous lungs. With present technical development of artificial blood oxygenators, this is not necessary and, after priming with blood, an artificial pump-oxygenator system can support the circulatory system for some time.

Various expedients have been used to perfuse an organ or region (fig. 39.1*D*). (1) The simplest arrangement is to connect the peripheral end of the artery (which feeds an organ or region) to a reservoir at an appropriate elevation so that it drains by gravity. The flow rate is read from graduations on the reservoir or from one of the flow meters (described in this chapter) which is interposed. The reservoir must be refilled manually. (2) Air expansion chambers are used which permit constant pressure perfusion. In these, the peripheral end of the artery of an organ is connected to an air chamber, the lower portion of which contains blood exposed to the desired pressure in the chamber. Flow into the organ is indicated by one of the appropriate blood flow meters interposed between the organ and chamber. The supply of chamber blood for infusion is

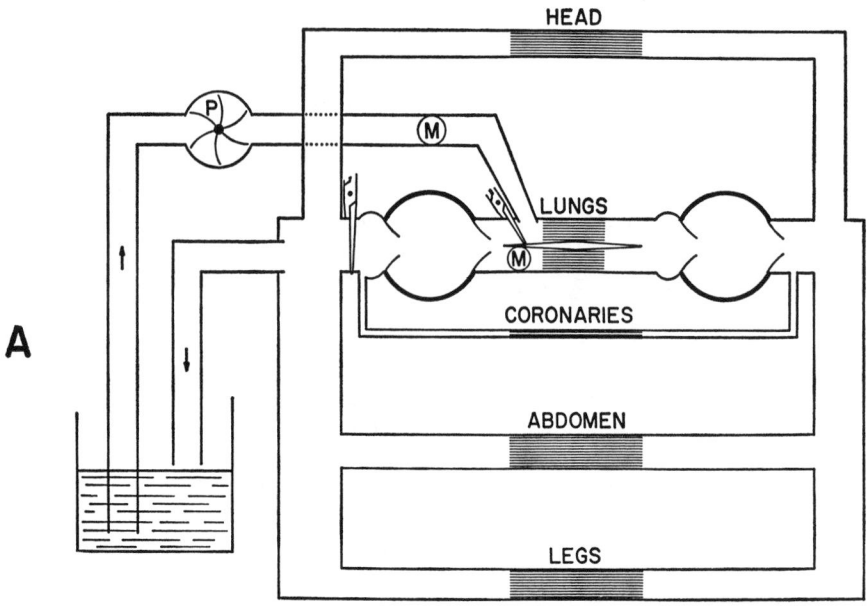

RIGHT HEART BYPASS

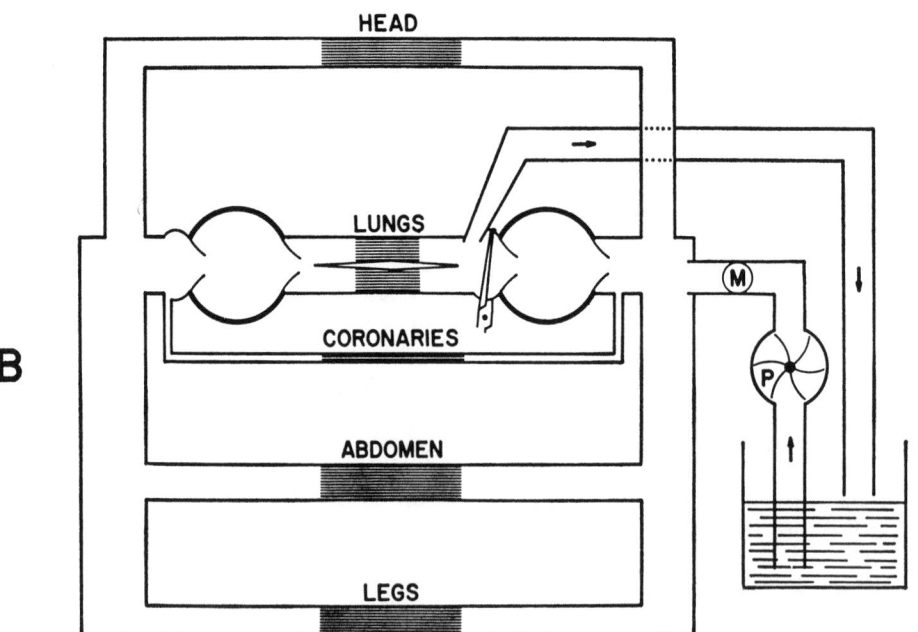

LEFT HEART BYPASS

FIG. 39.1. Schematic representation of techniques; *A* , for right heart bypass; *B*, for left heart bypass; *C*, for total cardiac bypass; *D*, for studying regional blood flow while either perfusion pressure or blood flow is maintained constant.

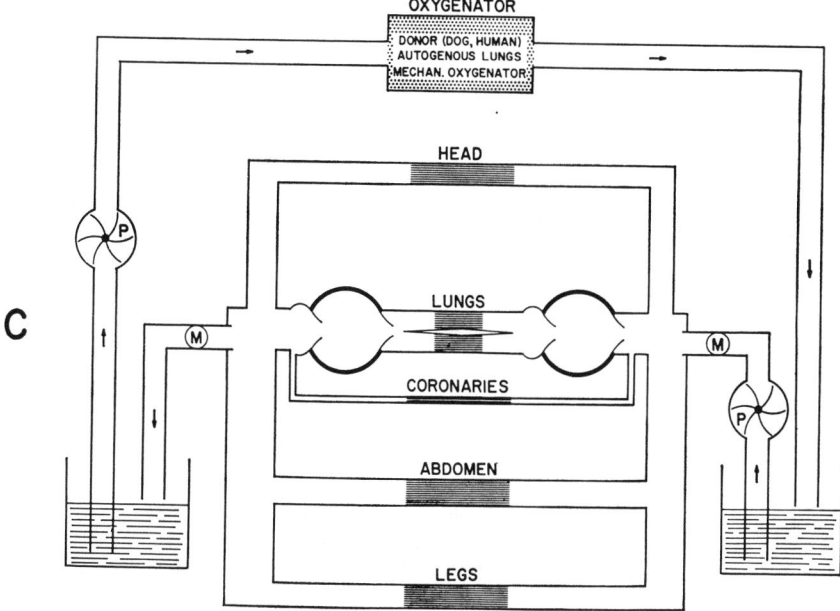

TOTAL HEART-LUNG BYPASS

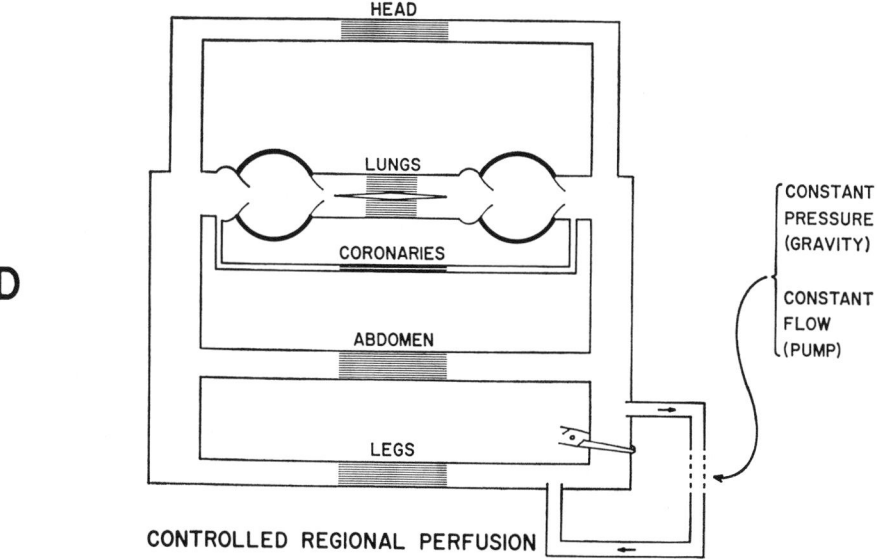

CONTROLLED REGIONAL PERFUSION

FIG. 39.1.

replenished by letting it flow into the chamber from a convenient artery under the animal's own blood pressure. (3) An end of a pump is connected to a local arterial source and the other end of the same pump to the artery of the organ or region being supplied. Either the perfusion pressure or flow rate can be varied separately. (4) The output side of a pump can be connected to a blood-air reservoir in which the air pressure is maintained

constant at any desired perfusion pressure level and whose outlet is connected to the organ being perfused.

These approaches obviously have the important advantage that they enable the investigator to study separately the peripheral factors in the organ or region that regulate flow.

MEAN FLOW RECORDERS (FIG. 39.2). Because of the imposed resistance to flow, most mean flow recorders are not suitable for use in the path of venous flow but are acceptable in the arterial system where a small drop in pressure across the meter is not so important. The types that have given much information regarding the operation of the cardiovascular system include the mechanical stromuhr, bubble flow meter, rotameter, and turbinometer. Their present operation is extensive. In use, they have the disadvantages that they require anesthesia, injection of anticoagulant, insertion between the cut ends of the vessel in which flow is being measured, and their response time is slow, the fastest (the rotameter) being of the order of 90 per cent complete in 1 second. Despite these disadvantages, and although arterial flow is highly phasic, these devices have been most helpful.

A. Mechanical stromuhr. The stromuhr of Ludwig is one of the oldest and best-known. It consists of an ingoing and an outgoing cannula which are inserted, respectively, into the proximal and distal sections of a divided artery. The blood flowing from the artery into the instrument enters a small pear-shaped flask of known capacity filled with oil. Upon the entrance of the blood, the

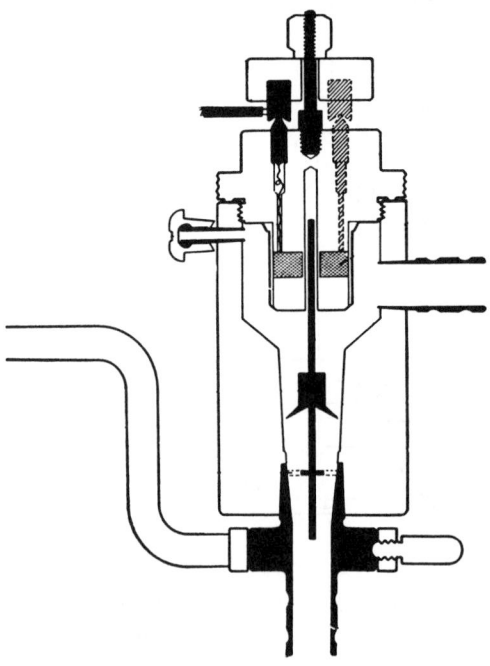

FIG. 39.2*A*. Full scale sectional view of 0-400 ml. per minute rotameter constructed of lucite or plexiglass, showing tapered flow chamber, metal float with soft iron upper rod extension, float rest at zero flow, and coil for detecting float position. Float is shown in position it would occupy in middle of flow range. (After Shipley and Wilson, Proc. Soc. Exper. Biol. & Med., 1951, **78**, 724.)

oil is forced over into another flask of identical size but which has previously been filled with blood. The entrance of the oil forces the blood in turn into the peripheral section of the artery. The position of the flasks can be reversed by rotating through a semicircle and the process of filling and emptying repeated, or by appropriate means the flow can be automatically reversed in direction through the flasks. From the number of fillings of the flasks during the period of observation, the volume of blood flowing in a unit of time is readily calculated.

B. Rotameter. This device originally developed for commercial use was first adapted in 1942 to quantitation of blood flow. Basically the device consists of a vertical transparent tube with tapered bore within which the height of a float is determined by the rate of flow. With upward flow through the tube, the float is lifted until it reaches a height determined by a balance of the downward force (weight of float minus weight of displaced fluid), and the upward force (pressure drop across the float times maximal cross-sectional area of float). As flow increases, the balance is altered, and the float rises to a new position at which the increase in the annular orifice is large enough to reduce the pressure drop across the float to that existing at the previous flow level. The position of the float may be read visually, or for continuous recording, the vertical position of the float is detected by an induction mechanism. It is possibly the best method for continuous and accurate quantitation of mean blood flow in the aorta and arteries. Flow quantitation is with an error of ±5 per cent.

C. Turbinometer. The turbinometer consists of a turbine of known capacity per revolution which is driven by the flowing blood stream. In the turbine is a rotating magnet which induces a recordable signal in an adjacent coil and which indicates the number of turbine rotations. Because of starting frictional resistance to turbine rotation, the turbinometer does not turn with less than 400 to 500 ml. blood flow per minute, and the pressure drop across it is quite high. Consequently, it can measure large flows only and is used exclusively in the aorta.

D. Bubble flow meter. Mean rate of blood flow in arteries has been measured by timing visually or photoelectrically the passage of an injected air bubble through a glass tube of known length and volume which is placed between the cut ends of the vessel. Because of the resistance to flow from the long (1 meter) tube used, the device cannot be used in veins. For quantitating flow in

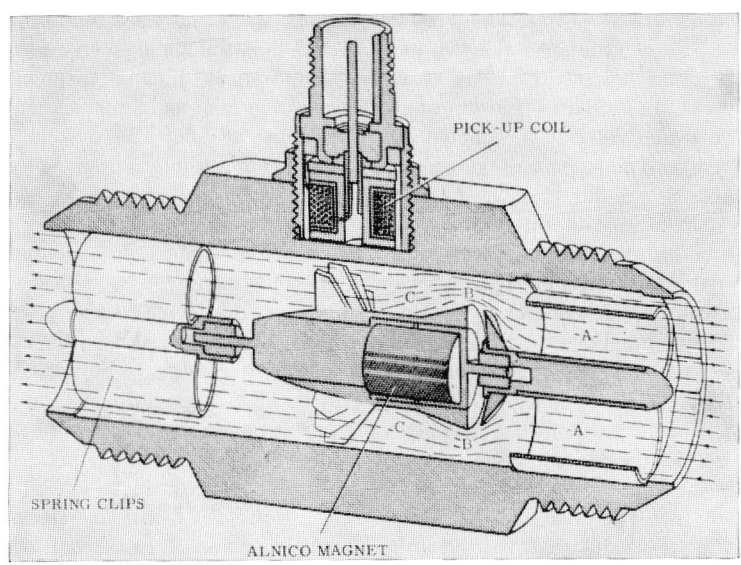

FIG. 39.2*B*. The Potter electroturbinometer. (After Sarnoff, Circulation Res., 1953, **1**, 724.)

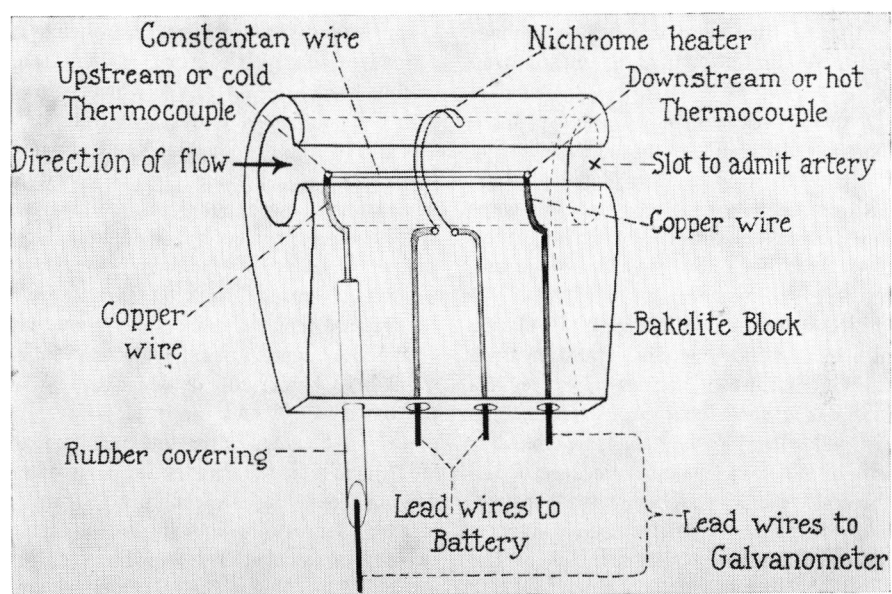

FIG. 39.2*C*. Diagram of direct current thermostromuhr. (Gregg, Coronary Circulation in Health and Disease, Lea & Febiger, Philadelphia, 1950.)

the smaller arteries, it is inexpensive and easy to use and has a linear calibration curve. However evidence has been presented that blood and bubble flow velocity are not equal. At low flows the bubble is slower and at high flows it is faster than blood velocity.

E. Thermostromuhr. Mean flow through arteries or veins has been determined by several types of thermostromuhrs which operate on the principle that when a circuit is formed of two wires of different metals and one of their junctions is at a higher temperature than the other, an electromotive force is produced in the circuit. The two thermal junctions are mounted in a plastic sleeve, and the proper temperature difference is created by a high frequency or direct current heater. This is either snugly fitted around an intact vessel or is inserted between the cut ends of a vessel so that the flowing blood is in close contact with the thermocouples and heater.

A part of the heat is carried away by the flowing blood, hence the rate of cooling of the thermal element depends upon the rate of blood flow. The cross-section of the vessel is held constant so that volume of flow is related to the differential temperature of the two junctions, provided environmental factors do not alter this relationship. However, several external and internal factors other than rate of blood flow influence significantly and unpredictably the flow readings by altering the relative rate of heat loss to the environment at the two junctions or the heat distribution between the junctions, so that its reliability is questionable.

PHASIC FLOW METERS (FIG. 39.3). These devices faithfully record the phasic or moment to moment changes in arterial and or venous flow during a cardiac cycle. The differential pressure and pendulum types must be used with heparin and inserted between the cut ends of a vessel; the electromagnetic and sonar flow meters are used to measure blood flow in intact vessels in unanesthetized active animals; the electromagnetic flow meter has been used in anesthetized humans.

A. *Differential pressure flow meters.* By introducing a device between two points in a flowing stream, a pressure difference is created which varies with the velocity of blood flow. The ways of creating the pressure differences are illustrated (fig. 39.3A). Of these, only the orifice meter and Pitot tube will be considered.

The orifice meter makes use of the velocity with which blood is flowing. The lateral pressure difference is determined between two regions above and below a region of constriction (the orifice) in a flowing bloodstream, the cross-sectional area of which is constant. Because of the higher stream velocity just below the constriction, the downstream lateral pressure is lower. The pressure difference is proportional to the flow.

With the Pitot tube method, the difference in pressure is determined in two tubes inserted into a vessel, one directed upstream, the other downstream. In the tube pointed upstream, the energy of movement is added to the existing potential energy (pressure on the wall) and a higher pressure is thus recorded than in the tube pointed downstream. In the tube pointed downstream, the kinetic energy of movement is deducted from the potential energy (pressure). The pressure difference is entirely a function of the velocity of flow at the two points.

In the past, the pressure difference which is proportional to flow has been optically recorded by a differential manometer. Recent replacement of the optical differential manometer by an electrical system and amplification has improved the fidelity of differential flow meters.

Until recently most of our information regarding phasic blood flow in the aorta, venae cavae, and various arteries has come from the use of these two flow meters. Both are quite satisfactory. The orifice meter causes a considerable pressure drop, the Pitot meter does not; hence, the former is adequate for arterial flow, the latter for venous flow. The question has been raised whether the orifice meter, by imposing resistance to flow gives a correct phasic flow curve in an artery such as a coronary, in which blood temporarily reverses its direction of flow during a portion of the cardiac cycle. However, recent experiments in the author's laboratory have shown that flow curves are similar with the orifice meter and with an electromagnetic flow meter in which no resistance to flow is imposed by the meter.

B. *Pendulum flow meters.* In principle first described in the 15th century, a small pendulum, paddle, reed, wire, or bristle which is introduced into a blood vessel is deviated from its resting position by the flowing blood, the amount of deviation being proportional to the velocity of flow. At least two successful types are in use. In one type, the electromagnetic pendulum flow meter, the pendulum is made of ferro-magnetic material which moves in an induction field. The induction changes are then amplified. In a second type, the bristle flow meter, the bloodstream deviates a small bristle, one end of which is inserted into the blood vessel and the other attached to the plate pin of a subminiature vacuum tube (fig. 39.3B). When the bristle is deviated by the flowing blood, the electron current from cathode to anode varies in proportion to the distance between them, which is determined by the degree of deviation. The electrical signal is amplified. These two types of devices have the advantages of smallness and compactness, good frequency and sensitivity, minimal resistance to flow, low drift and equal response to forward and backward flow. A big drawback is that the pendulum or bristle is very sensitive to position changes (gravity effect) as well as to flow.

C. *Sonar and electromagnetic flow meters.* The optimal flow meter for physiological investigation would be made up of a miniature sensing agent which is mounted chronically on the external surface of intact blood vessels. It would record instantaneous flow for extended periods,

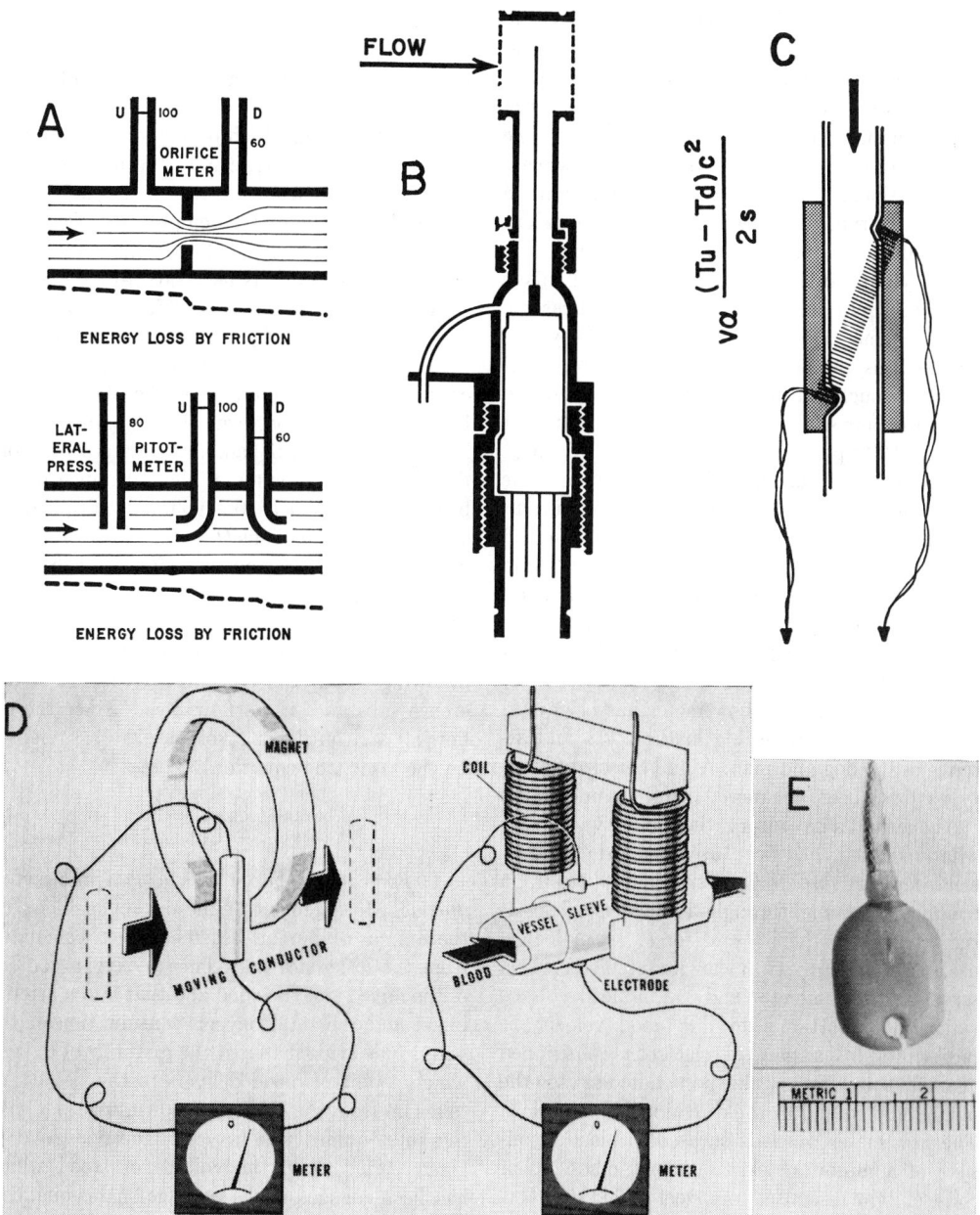

Fig. 39.3. Phasic blood flow meters. *A.* Schematic drawing illustrating the principle of the orifice meter and the Pitot tube (after Brecher, Venous return, Grune & Stratton, Inc., New York, 1955). *B.* Schematic diagram of the bristle flow meter cannula utilizing a subminiature vacuum tube and flow-sensing element (after Brecher, Venous return, Grune & Stratton, Inc., New York, 1955). *C.* Sonar flow meter principle (Franklin *et al.*, J. Appl. Physiol., 1959, **14,** 809). *D.* Electromagnetic flow meter principle. *E.* Electromagnetic flow meter probe.

weeks to months, without change in calibration, and would have sufficient sensitivity and frequency response to monitor flow in arteries and venous trunks. Two different types of flowmeter, the sonar and electromagnetic, have been developed in the attempt to satisfy these demands (figs. 39.3C and D).

An electrosonic meter has been used to measure flow in the arteries, aorta and vena cava, and to measure left ventricular diameter of unanesthetized dogs. Earlier models were developed by Kalmus with some miniaturization by Herrick. In principle, the transit time of sound moving downstream is determined by the velocity of sound in the motionless medium plus the velocity of the medium. The transit time of the sound upstream is determined by the velocity of sound in the motionless medium minus the velocity of the medium. Thus the difference in transit time of the ultrasonic waves upstream and downstream is proportional to the velocity of the medium. In practice, barium titrate crystals are mounted at diagonally opposed positions near the end of a lucite cylinder divided longitudinally and this is clamped about an artery. Bursts of ultrasonic waves (3 megacycles per sec.) emitted by one crystal pass through the vessel wall and diagonally through the stream of flowing blood to reach the opposite crystal. Bursts are emitted at about 12,000 per sec. with direction reversal at 800 per sec. The difference in transit time of the ultrasonic waves is converted into a direct current voltage, amplified and recorded. By turning off the ultrasonic pulse generator, the flow beam reaches a position which is the same as that following temporary mechanical occlusion of the vessel. This device appears to be usable on both artery and vein.

The electromagnetic flow meter has been used for pulsatile flow recording in the aorta and arteries of the dog and man. A number of different types have been produced, some commercially. In the author's laboratory, the Kolin type, somewhat modified, has been used. In principle, an electromotive force or voltage is induced in a conductor moving through a magnetic field at right angles to the lines of force. In biological use, blood moving within an intact blood vessel serves as the conductor and the induced voltage which is proportional to the blood velocity is picked up by a pair of electrodes positioned against the vessel wall, perpendicular to the magnetic field and to the direction of blood flow. The flow meter which is encased in plastic, consists of a miniature electromagnet made up of coils of wire mounted on steel laminations, a slotted plastic tube into which the vessel is inserted, two electrodes, and wires for energizing the electromagnet and for leading off the induced voltage (one-millionth volt) which is amplified and recorded. In use, the probe is implanted around an intact blood vessel by temporarily decompressing and forcing the vessel through the longitudinal slit in the probe. Its main advantages are its ability to measure mean and phasic flow in unopened large and small vessels of chronic animals, its linearity of calibration and its high frequency of response. The flow beam can be made to approximate the zero flow position by "electronic zeroing" or repeated mechanical

flow zeros can be easily obtained even in the exercising dog by temporary (3 to 4 sec.) inflation of a rubber pneumatic cuff just distal to the flow meter.

FICK PRINCIPLE. Much of our information concerning blood flow, especially the output of the heart is derived from the use of methods based on the Fick principle. To employ the Fick principle to determine blood flow through the whole body or an organ, it is necessary to have a substance that is either removed from or added to the blood during its period of flow through the vessels under study. The amount which is added or removed from the organ by the blood is equal to the difference between the amount brought into the organ and the amount carried away from the organ. The amount of the substance in the blood is expressed as the volume multiplied by the concentration. Thus $Q = F_1 \times C_1 - F_0 \times C_0$ in which Q = amount of reference substance picked up or released by the organ, F_1 = blood flow into organ, F_0 = blood flow out of organ, C_1 = concentration of reference substance in the inflowing blood, and C_0 = concentration of reference substance in outflow blood. Since the inflowing and outflowing volumes are assumed to be the same, the equation becomes

$$F = \frac{Q}{C_0 - C_1} = \frac{Q}{\Delta C}.$$

A. For cardiac output with oxygen and carbon dioxide. Measurement of the output of blood by the animal or human heart has been calculated from the difference between the oxygen content of the mixed venous blood and that of the arterial blood and the total oxygen consumption of the body. It is evident that if the quantity of oxygen which a unit of blood delivers to the tissues (or takes up from the lungs) is known, together with the total quantity of oxygen consumed over a given period, then the volume of blood which had been engaged in the carriage of this quantity of gas can be calculated. For example, the arterial blood contains about 19 volumes of oxygen per 100 ml. It gives up, let us say, 6 volumes to the tissues, i.e., the mixed venous blood coming to the lungs contains 13 volumes per cent. The arteriovenous (A-V) oxygen difference is, therefore, 6 volumes per cent. If the total quantity of oxygen consumed per minute is found to be 250 ml., then the cardiac output is:

(Total O_2 consumption per minute)

$$\frac{250}{19 - 13} \times 100 = \text{(Output per minute) 4.6 liters}$$

(Arteriovenous O_2 difference).

The oxygen consumption must be measured very accurately for several minutes and the subject must be in a steady state. The blood samples for determining arteriovenous oxygen difference should be obtained simultaneously. Arterial blood may be obtained from any artery but only *mixed* venous blood can be used since the quantity of oxygen contained in venous blood varies grossly depending upon the vascular bed from which it drains. Even the oxygen content of blood in the superior vena cava differs from that in the inferior vena cava by 1 to 2 volumes per cent. Mixing of the blood occurs in the right ventricle and is generally complete by the time the blood reaches the pulmonary artery where sampling must be made for accurate determinations.

The cardiac output can be calculated in a similar way from the total carbon dioxide elimination and the arteriovenous carbon dioxide difference (CO_2 in mixed venous blood less CO_2 in arterial blood). However, the vagaries of cardiac output calculation on this basis are such that the measurement is generally ignored. The unreliability of the Fick method when carbon dioxide is used is related to the fact that small changes in ventilation strongly influence carbon dioxide storage by the body and a steady state is hard to reach.

The direct Fick method was first employed in man in Germany in 1929 by Forssmann, who experimented upon himself, and a little later by Klein. Cournand and his associates established the safety of the procedure and stimulated widespread utilization of the method. The technique of cardiac catheterization has been described in detail by Cournand and others. A sample of mixed venous blood is drawn from the pulmonary artery by means of a catheter passed up an appropriate arm vein. The introduction of the catheter is guided by X-ray visualization (fluoroscope). A sample of arterial blood is obtained by arterial puncture. The blood samples can be analyzed for their oxygen contents, and after the total oxygen consumption has been determined in the usual way, calculation of the cardiac output is made from the formula already given. The oxygen contents can be measured with the Van Slyke apparatus or for more rapid determination, a photoelectric method has been developed (fig. 39.4). Blood for analysis is drawn through a cuvette which is transilluminated by a constant intensity light source. The light passing through a 628 filter falls upon a photomultiplier tube. This method has a high degree of accuracy and has proved only slightly less accurate than the Van Slyke procedure.

The method presupposes that the oxygen consumption and the A-V oxygen difference are obtained simultaneously and are constant during the time of measurement. Both cardiac and respiratory cyclic changes in the concentration difference of oxygen and the flow rate are capable of introducing large errors in cardiac output calculations. These changes do not appear to occur to any significant degree in man when a steady state has been achieved. A potentially serious error of the Fick application may occur if gas is stored in, or liberated from, the body, including

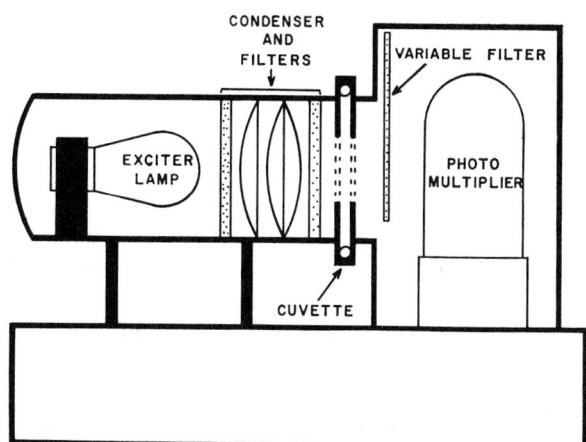
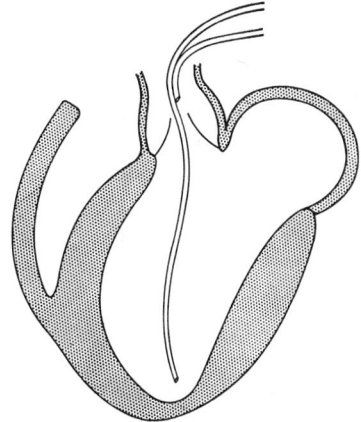

Fig. 39.4. *Left.* Drawing showing principle of the densitometer used to determine instantaneous cardiac output and continuous blood O_2 saturation. *Right.* Principle by which change in blood conductivity in a ventricular cavity is used to determine diastolic ventricular volume and stroke volume.

the lungs. This would occur when the relation of aerobic to anaerobic metabolism of the body is altered and, as a consequence, the level of blood oxygen is altered without relation to blood flow. Thus, the Fick calculation is dubiously related to cardiac output as the organism goes into or comes out of an anoxic state or in the presence of congenital heart disease with cyanotic episodes. In the latter instance, the shunts between the pulmonary and systemic circuits induce large errors in calculation of systemic flow. Special formulas have been developed to calculate the volume of blood flow through such shunts.

Cardiac output determined by the Fick method probably has an error of ± 10 per cent when very carefully done. However, it is to be remembered that the procedure gives rise to considerable apprehension in the patient and may in itself abnormally increase the cardiac output values.

B. For cardiac output with foreign gases. Most of the early figures for cardiac output were based on the Fick principle using a foreign gas. For this, the lungs are used as a gas aerotonometer to measure the gas tensions of mixed venous blood and, hence, its gas content. A subject breathes an inert foreign gas (i.e., one which becomes dissolved in plasma but does not combine with hemoglobin, lipoid or other constituents of the blood). If the rate of gas absorption by the blood, its alveolar tension and its stability in blood are known, then the quantity of blood which has passed through the lungs can be calculated.

Flow

$$= \frac{\text{rate of gas absorption}}{\text{alveolar concentration of gas} \times \text{blood solubility}}$$

This is the principle upon which a foreign gas method is based. Nitrous oxide (N_2O), ethyl iodide (C_2H_5I), and especially acetylene (C_2H_2) have been used in the past. The main difficulty of the method is that equilibrium between alveolar air and the venous blood must be effected before recirculation. Originally, it was felt that the circulation time was 25 to 30 seconds, and hence, that a respiratory mixture could be left in the lungs for that length of time without exposure to recirculated blood. However, the correct figure for circulation time is much shorter, 10 to 18 sec., which is often an insufficient time for equilibrium to be established; hence, the values for resting cardiac output established by this method are usually lower than normal and, at times, grossly in error. Recently nitrous oxide has been used to estimate not only cardiac output but the instantaneous capillary blood flow since it is so soluble that it is immediately picked up by blood entering the capillary bed of the lung (fig. 39.5). If a subject is in an airtight cha mbe and takes and holds a single breath of N_2O fo

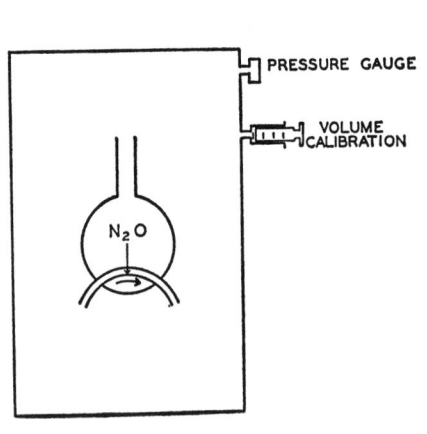

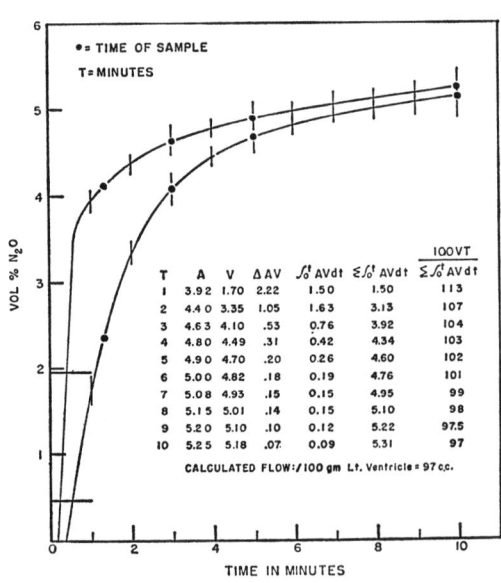

T	A	V	ΔAV	$\int_0^t AVdt$	$\Sigma \int_0^t AVdt$	$\dfrac{100VT}{\Sigma \int_0^t AVdt}$
1	3.92	1.70	2.22	1.50	1.50	113
2	4.40	3.35	1.05	1.63	3.13	107
3	4.63	4.10	.53	0.76	3.92	104
4	4.80	4.49	.31	0.42	4.34	103
5	4.90	4.70	.20	0.26	4.60	102
6	5.00	4.82	.18	0.19	4.76	101
7	5.08	4.93	.15	0.15	4.95	99
8	5.15	5.01	.14	0.15	5.10	98
9	5.20	5.10	.10	0.12	5.22	97.5
10	5.25	5.18	.07	0.09	5.31	97

CALCULATED FLOW:/100 gm Lt. Ventricle = 97 c.c.

Fig. 39.5. *Left.* Diagram illustrating the principle of measurement of pulmonary capillary blood flow (DuBois, J. Clin. Invest., 1957, **36**, 1566). *Right.* Graph indicating typical nitrous oxide saturation curves obtained in determining coronary flow per 100 gms. per left ventricle per minute in dog. *Upper curve* from carotid artery; *lower curve* from coronary sinus by catheter. (Gregg, Coronary circulation in health and Disease, Lea & Febiger, Philadelphia, 1950.)

8 to 10 sec., the chamber pressure falls at a rate which indicates the rate of absorption of the gas by the blood and, consequently, the rate of pulmonary capillary blood flow or cardiac output. Recirculation is not a problem during this short time. The instantaneous rate of blood flow can be calculated since the rate of N_2O absorption, the alveolar gas tension and its blood solubility are known.

C. For regional blood flow. Of the methods considered, except for the electromagnetic flow meter and sonar techniques, measurements of volume of blood flow passing through the splanchnic bed or kidney cannot be made directly even in experimental animals without destructive surgical procedures or unphysiological interference with function. The Fick principle has been used to determine mean blood flow in man and animal through the liver, and kidneys, as well as the coronary and cerebral circulation. The introduction of venous catheterization has made it possible to obtain blood issuing from the hepatic vein in intact animals and man, thus permitting the development of methods of measuring flow on the basis of the Fick principle. Bromsulphalein (BSP) has proved especially useful here because it is taken up by the liver with remarkable efficiency. Of the total removed from the blood each minute, when the plasma BSP concentration is maintained by constant intravenous infusion below 2 or 3 mg. per cent, no more than 5 per cent can be attributed to escape through extrasplanchnic portals. For practical purposes, therefore, the hepatic removal of BSP equals the rate of infusion as long as the plasma level is constant. The splanchnic blood flow may be calculated by dividing the removal rate by the difference between BSP concentrations in peripheral arterial and hepatic venous blood. The flow value is generally referred to as the estimated hepatic blood flow since sampling is made in only one of several hepatic veins. A number of other substances such as Rose Bengal and I^{131}, have been used in the same way to measure splanchnic blood volume.

Similarly, the blood flow through the human kidney can be determined. Diodrast, when in low concentration in the plasma, undergoes virtually complete clearance, i.e., it is removed from the plasma in a single passage of blood through the kidney. This substance is excreted largely by the tubules, only about 16 per cent being filtered through the glomeruli. Knowing the amount excreted in the urine within a time, and the plasma concentration, the quantity of blood that has passed through active renal tissue can be calculated. For example, if 600 mg. of Diodrast are excreted in the urine per minute, and each milliliter of plasma contains 1 mg., then to deliver 600 mg. of Diodrast, 600 ml. of plasma went through the kidney, or with a hematocrit of 40, about 1,000 ml. of blood flow.

Mean blood flow has been successfully determined through the coronary circulation with nitrous oxide inhalation and through the cerebral circulation with nitrous oxide or krypton inhalation. It is the only method available for such studies in man (fig. 39.5). In use in the heart or brain, several simultaneous arterial (any artery) and venous (coronary sinus for the heart and the internal jugular vein for the brain) samples are drawn from the beginning of N_2O inhalation (mixture of nitrogen, 64 per cent; N_2O, 15 per cent; O_2, 21 per cent) to the time of its equilibrium in the bloodstream or during denitrogenation after previous inhalation of the nitrogen mixture. Continuous simultaneous samples can also be drawn from the artery and vein for analysis. The flow per unit of time through these organs is equal to the amount of the substance taken up by that organ in a given time divided by the difference in concentration of the substance in the arterial blood and venous drainage of the organ in the same time period. The denominator in the Fick equation is found by computing the integrated difference between the concentrations of N_2O in arterial and venous blood during the period of equilibration with a low concentration of N_2O. The concentration of gas in the tissue at the time of equilibration (the numerator in the Fick equation) is unobtainable directly and is assumed to be equal to the product of the venous blood concentration of the gas (after equilibrium is established) and a partition coefficient (1.0 in case of the heart and 1.3 for the brain). When the equation is multiplied by 100, units for blood flow are obtained which are expressed as milliliters of flow per 100 grams of heart or myocardium.

As compared to direct measurement of cerebral and coronary flow with a rotameter, the method shows a reasonable accuracy and, in humans, has furnished almost all of our information regarding the cerebral and coronary blood flows.

INDICATOR DILUTION PRINCIPLE. The principle is based on observation of the rate at which a known quantity of material introduced into a vessel or heart cavity is diluted by blood flow through the vessel or cavity. In the principle as originally applied by Stewart and modified by

Hamilton, it has been shown that the average rate of blood flow can be stated:

$$F = E \bigg/ \int_0^\infty C\,dt$$

where F = average rate of flow, E = total quantity injected, C = instantaneous concentration of the injected material. From this relationship, it is possible to determine the average flow rate in almost any cavity or vessel of reasonable size if the amount of injected material is known and if the concentration-time function can be accurately determined.

For good quantitation, however, various precautions are necessary. The procedures and indicator substances used must cause little discomfort or injury; volumes of solution added or blood withdrawn for analysis should be minimal. In addition, the indicator should stay inside the blood vessels between the points of injection and sampling (any loss would be calculated as an increment of flow); the indicator should not diffuse into or out of red cells during its passage. Dilution of the indicator in the cavity or vessel can be determined in the same cavity or a small distance downstream in the vessel, or far removed from the injection site. In all cases, and especially the first, the injection must be made almost instantaneously, and in most sites, the injection should be made with special apertures in the catheter tip so that turbulence is induced and mixing is immediately complete, assuring an accurate dilution basis for the test. This in itself leads to certain difficulties when the injection is made into the systemic circulation. It has long been known that rapid intra-arterial injection is followed by some hemolysis which liberates vasoactive substances. This gives rise to a vasodilation, sometimes of considerable magnitude, in the organs deriving their blood from the ventricle, aorta, or artery in question, so that the quantity to be measured is altered at the very moment it is measured. Thus, although the methodology may give correct flows, they are too high. This obstacle is difficult to circumvent.

A. Indicator substances. A variety of indicator substances can be used to modify in a quantitative way, the optical, electrical, thermal, and radioactive characteristics of the passing blood. (1) The optical density of the blood is altered by the injection of plasma and dyes such as brilliant vital red, Evans blue (T 1824), Cardiogreen and Rie 1743. The latter two dyes are especially useful since they have a high extinction value around the isobestic point of reduced oxy-hemoglobin at 805 mμ and, therefore, they do not require constancy of oxygen saturation of the blood as do the other dyes. Thus, with their use the blood flow in the veins or in cyanotic patients can be determined. Of course, constancy of hemoglobin quantity in the light path is required during the registration of each dilution curve. (2) The electrical conductivity of the blood is changed by injection into it of hypertonic salt solution (fig. 39.4). It is critically important that calibration of this method be done with a sample of the subject's arterial blood and part of the hypertonic salt solution which was prepared for injection. Following salt injection, the increase in electrical conductivity is due partly to the increase in sodium chloride concentration and partly to red cell dilution. (3) A thermal dilution technique is employed in which cool (18 to 22°C.) sodium chloride or 5 per cent glucose is injected. One must be very careful of the obvious possibility of heat exchange between the cold injectate and the warm tissues of the central circulation. (4) Changes in radioactivity of the blood are induced by the injection of radioactive inorganic P^{32}, radioactive iodinated serum albumin, organic radioactive iodine, D_2O, potassium^{42} chloride, Rb^{86} chloride, Xenon^{133}, or 4-iodoantipyrine (I^{131}).

B. Indicator detectors. For recording continuously the different properties of arterial blood which are changed by such injections, four types of detectors are used. One type is inserted directly into the bloodstream through the vessel or cavity wall in a needle or catheter; this is used to indicate changes in conductivity (conductivity cell), in temperature (thermistor), and in the optical density of the bloodstream to the right ventricle. A second type of detector encloses a segment of unopened vessel monitoring changes in conductivity or optical density of the bloodstream using a photocell. In a third type, a catheter is inserted through which the blood is pushed or pulled to a monitoring device for analysis and then either discarded or returned to the body by vein or artery (fig. 39.4). The third type is the most widely used and follows optical changes and radioactive emanations of the blood. The changes in optical density and radioactivity concentration are detected by having the blood flow continuously, in the first case, past a photocell or photomultiplier tube and, in the second case, past a continuous scanner. Analysis can also be made with the Beckman spectrophotometer or by counts on individual samples drawn every second. The fourth type, easiest but empirical, is applied to the external intact skin. Radioactivity curves or opacity changes can be determined by this method (transillumination for opacity changes can be done on the pinna of the ear only). This type is obviously subject to many uncontrollable difficulties for much unrelated tissue is interposed between the detector and area in which flow is to be measured.

C. Uses. The various approaches have been used in a variety of situations. In general, the conductivity method has been used for determining cardiac output and diastolic volume of the heart; the thermal, dye, and radioactivity methods, for cardiac output and flow in arteries and veins. In addition, the radioactivity method has been applied to the fractional distribution of cardiac output to various organs of very small animals (as well as large animals). For this, simultaneous measurement of the flow fractions to the organs is based on the principle that for a short time (6 to 60 sec.) after a single intravenous injection of any foreign substance, the organ reservoir for its dilution is so large in relation to the inflow rate of the substance that it does not appear in the venous circulation and, consequently, its extraction ratio is 1. The substance is, therefore, distributed in the same manner as the cardiac output. Although sound in principle, the accuracy of the method has not yet been established. It would be expected to furnish only very rough values because of the anesthesia and trauma associated with the determination of the isotope content of the individual organs.

Figure 39.6 illustrates the principle applied to determination of cardiac output in the unanesthetized human. In this approach, a tracer material (Evans Blue dye, T1824) that affixes itself to the albumin of the blood plasma is introduced into the large veins near the superior vena cava and the diluted material that issues from the heart is continuously sampled at a peripheral artery (radial). This blood is drawn at a constant rate through the cuvette of a densitometer which gives a continuous record of the changing optical density of the blood induced by the injected dye. The dye dilution curve is plotted at one second intervals as the logarithm of deflection against time and the straight line downslope is extrapolated to 1.0 mm. deflection. The average height of this plot, calculated by area per unit of time, is then converted to an average concentration of dye in milligrams per ml. by means of the calibration curve and this value is used in the formula for calculating the cardiac output.

Most work with indicators deals with what happens when a "slug" of indicator is introduced

as rapidly as possible. A variation of this procedure is to give a constant rate of infusion of the indicator, and to observe its resultant plateau. Experiment and theory demonstrate, however, that such an equilibrium concentration or plateau is a very dubious possibility (fig. 39.6). This is because recirculation of the indicator prevents attainment of a plateau, and the curve must begin to rise, because of this, before it has stopped rising toward the equilibrium level. On the other hand, recirculation is easily detected with the "slug" injection technique.

The indicator dilution technique, especially dye dilution, is a standard procedure for measuring cardiac output. Its accuracy is about the same as that of the Fick procedure. It has the added advantages that cardiac output can be determined from only a few heart beats, and it is not necessary to immobilize the subject because of the presence of an intracardiac catheter; cardiac output measurements can be made during violent exercise on a treadmill.

PLETHYSMOGRAPHY. This is based upon the principle that if the venous return from an organ is occluded, any change in volume of the part which results during the period of occlusion must represent the amount of blood which has entered the part during that period. This change in volume presumably approximates the normal inflow into the organ if its venous outflow had not been occluded. The major portion of volume in a vascular bed is on the venous side and because it can take up large volumes of blood with minimal change in pressure, arterial inflow would not immediately be affected by increased venous pressure. Still, the time during which the vein is compressed and, consequently, the duration of the observation must obviously be brief, for interference with the venous flow will soon (about 15 seconds) slow the bloodstream and give a fallacious result. In use, an organ with its blood vessels intact is placed in an air-tight chamber. At the point where the vessels enter and leave the chamber, a soft material, e.g., sponge or tow packing smeared with vaseline, is used to form a hermetic seal which does not compress the vessels. A tube leads from the interior of the chamber to a tambour and recording apparatus. The excursions of the latter are calibrated to represent cubic centimeters of blood. To estimate the blood flow, the vein is suddenly clamped and the increase in volume of the organ recorded over a short period. This method has been adapted by Hewlett and Van Zwaluwenburg and others, to estimate the volume flow in the human hand and forearm.

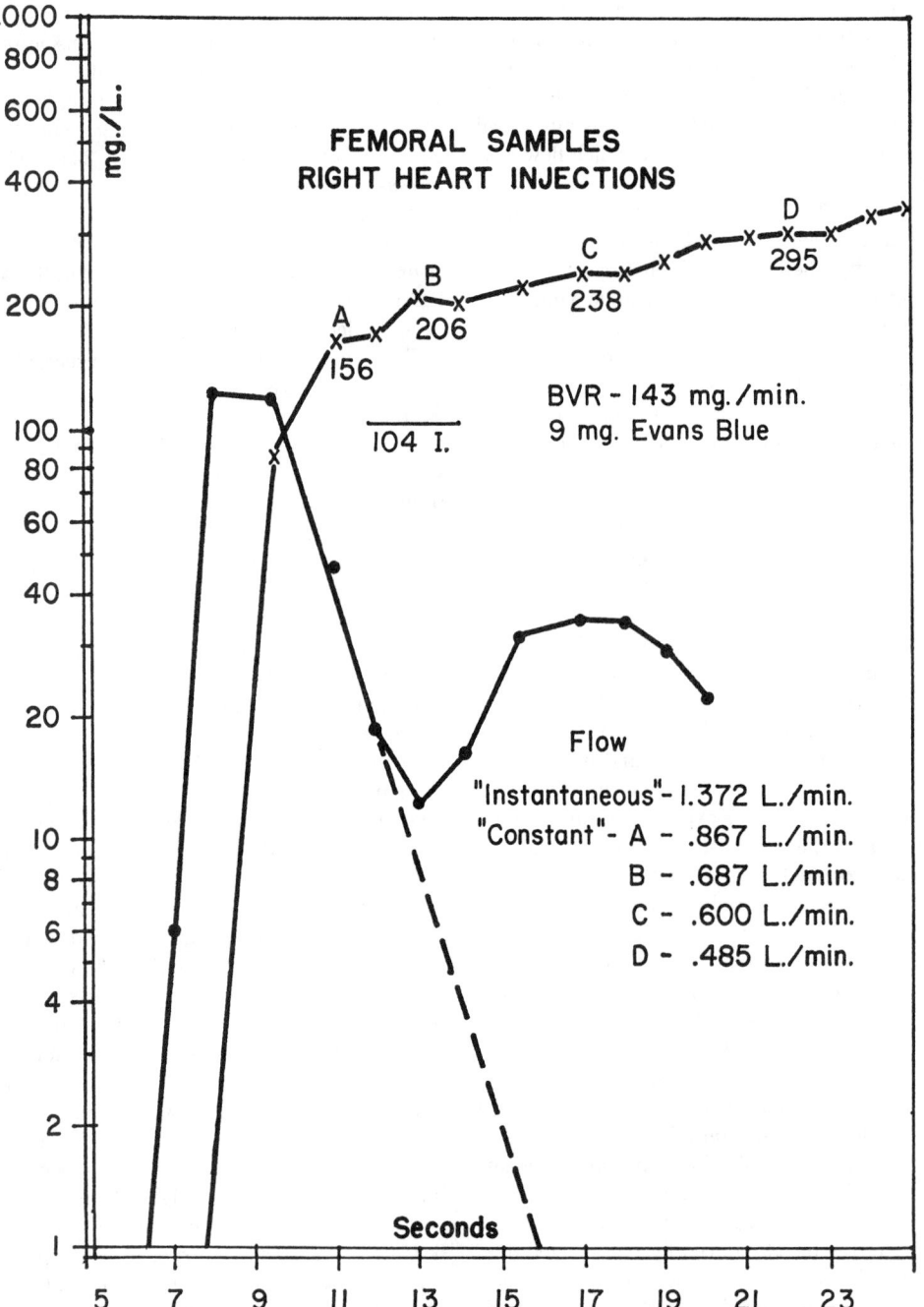

FEMORAL SAMPLES
RIGHT HEART INJECTIONS

A 156
B 206
C 238
D 295

104 I.

BVR - 143 mg./min.
9 mg. Evans Blue

Flow
"Instantaneous"- 1.372 L./min.
"Constant"- A - .867 L./min.
                 B - .687 L./min.
                 C - .600 L./min.
                 D - .485 L./min.

Seconds

Fig. 39.6. Concentration curves resulting from continuous infusions of brilliant vital red (BVR) and rapid injection of T1824 (Evans Blue), both started at zero seconds. Short horizontal lines and figures denote the expected concentration plateau levels of the continuous infusion on the basis of "instantaneous" injection (I) or the measured flow (M) plotted on three logarithmic decades. (Hamilton *et al.*, Am. J. Physiol., 1953, 175, 173.)

The chamber is filled with air or fluid. A cuff encircling the upper arm is employed to compress the veins (fig. 39.7). A number of variations of this type of plethysmograph, for the finger, toe, and leg, have been designed. Recently considerable doubt has been thrown on this classical method of measuring inflow by Gaskell and Burton, who found that, in the toe or finger, the very act of

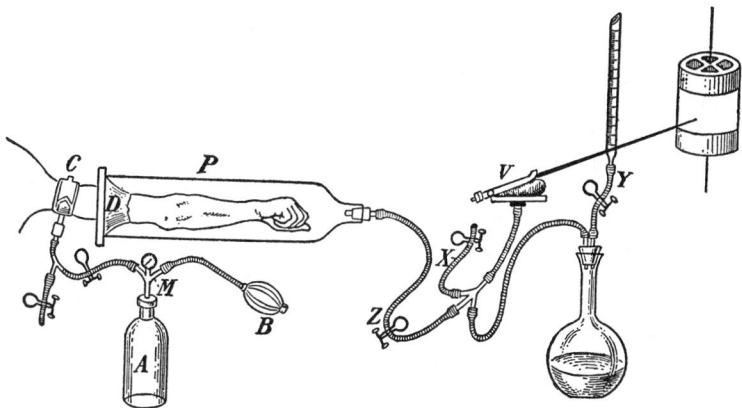

Fig. 39.7. Diagram showing Hewlett and Van Zwaluwenburg's method for estimating the rate of blood flow in the arm. (After Hewlett and Van Zwaluwenburg.)

collecting blood in the vessels (by change in limb posture) reduced the rate of arterial inflow as a result of venous distension. This was ascribed to a veni-vasomotor reflex from vein to artery. However, Greenfield and Patterson found no evidence for this in the forearm in which inflow was unaltered in the presence of venous back pressure sufficient to increase the resting forearm volume by 2 per cent. Animal experiments, in which arterial flow measured by an electromagnetic flowmeter was compared with plethysmograph flow, confirmed the accuracy of plethysmography. Actually two small errors were found but, since they are in opposite directions, they cancel each other out.

Although no entirely satisfactory method is yet available, ventricular volume in systole and diastole has long been determined by some form of plethysmography. It is not necessary to occlude the inflow or outflow since the heart, by contraction, induces change in its own volume (fig. 39.8). The plethysmograph or cardiometer is applied around both ventricular cavities in the isolated heart, heart-lung preparation or the open-chest dog. Changes in external volume of the ventricles create small pressure changes within the cardiometer which are recorded and calibrated against ventricular volume. Under special circumstances it is used to determine cyclic changes in right and left ventricular volume separately. The change in volume of the left ventricle alone can be recorded in the open-chest dog by shunting the systemic flow around the right ventricle; similarly, right ventricular volume change can be followed if the left ventricle is excluded from the circulation.

QUALITATIVE OR EMPIRIC METHODS. There are

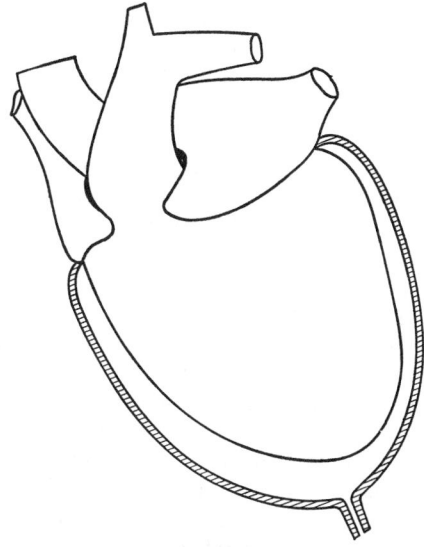

Fig. 39.8. Schematic drawing showing cardiac plethysmograph. A rubber cuff secures the chamber to the base of the heart at the A-V ring. Pressure-volume changes are tapped from the small outlet and recorded as in figure 18.7.

a number of methods using sound principles which, because they must be applied in a biological environment rather poor for their operation, give qualitative or directional trends, or which achieve their degree of validity from constants derived by comparison with a direct method.

A. The ballistocardiograph method. This method for determining cardiac output was originated by Henderson many years ago and has been elaborated and modified in recent years by Starr and his colleagues. The cardiac output is calculated from the record made by the recoil of the body caused by oppositely directed movements of the heart and the impact of the blood during systole. It involves the basic principle that "every reaction has an opposite and equal reaction." The apparatus or ballistocardiograph consists of a suspended table, braced to prevent any but a horizontal movement in the long axis of the body (fig. 39.9*A*). The patient lies supine on the table with his feet braced against a footboard. The movements of the table are opposed by a strong spring and magnified greatly. The normal ballistocardiogram shows three principal waves, *H*, *I*, and *J*, inscribed during systole. The stroke volume is calculated from the areas of the waves *I* and *J*, and by applying the following formula:

$$\text{Stroke volume} = 7\sqrt{[I + J]\,AC\,2/3}$$

where *I* and *J* are the areas of the waves so designated, *A* is the diameter of the aorta (calculated from age and surface area according to Bazett's data) and *C* the duration of the cardiac cycle; the minute volume is obtained by multiplying the value of the stroke volume by the pulse rate. To make them match accepted, simultaneously obtained, cardiac output values, different correction values are needed to apply to such calculations in normal and disease states.

This method should not be used for cardiac output. Such calculations of cardiac output from ballistic waves are based on an empirical procedure which cannot give valid values since the usual ballistocardiogram represents movements along the longitudinal axis of the body, but the blood ejected from the two ventricles moves simultaneously in several directions (3 dimensions) after leaving the heart. Since the amplitude of the deflections is influenced by the rate of blood acceleration, variation in pattern should reveal changes in force of ventricular contraction. It should, therefore, be possible to recognize empirical relationships between different types of cardiac dysfunction and characteristic ballistocardiographic patterns.

B. X-ray kymography. An indication of possible directional changes in ventricular blood volume has been obtained in various ways. The area of shadow on x-ray film during diastole has been used as a cross-section of the whole heart, and a fairly accurate normographic chart of the relation of this heart shadow to cardiac volume has been worked out for the anesthetized dog. Planimetric measurements of a cross-section of either the right or left ventricular cavity during systole and diastole have been made from successive motion picture frames following injection of contrast

medium into the right ventricle through a cardiac catheter or into the left ventricle by retrograde catheterization by way of the carotid arteries and the aortic valves. Except in right ventricular studies, these methods have never been validated against a direct measurement. Hence, interpretation of results should be made with great caution unless the change in size of the cardiac silhouette is very large.

C. Pulse pressure. From the time of Erlanger and Hooker, a large amount of experimental work has been applied to the possibility that the product of heart rate and the systemic pulse pressure to an organ (and, especially, in the case of the central aorta, to the body as a whole) might quantitatively represent the blood flow through that organ. To do this effectively, one must know the volume of blood required to expand the arterial tree as the pulse wave passes out over the arteries, and the volume of blood which drains out of the arterioles during systole. Such pressure-volume curves should be linear, if possible, but at least must be constant among animals or individuals. The distensibility of the four main divisions of the arterial tree (aortic arch, head, viscera and legs) and the effective pressure change in each area brought about by the pulse wave have been laboriously determined in animals. The arteriolar outflow during systole is calculated from Poiseuille's law (see ch. 36), on the basis that it is the product of the prevailing pressure and flow, with the assumption that the arterioles do not change in diameter. In dogs the pulse contour method gives results which compare reasonably well with those obtained simultaneously with the Fick, dye injection, or rotameter method. However, there are many circumstances in which the values are poor, such as in the presence of high aortic diastolic pressure, and following prolonged venous stasis. Why the distensibility of the arterial system varies spontaneously under circumstances such as these is not known. In humans the attempt has been made to "calibrate" the distensibility of the subject's arteries before an experimental investigation by first making an actual cardiac output measurement with the Fick or dye dilution technique. This is not helpful for it assumes that thereafter arterial distensibility will not change, a highly unlikely assumption.

D. Plethysmography. Two types of plethysmographs, the electrical impedance and the mercury strain gauge (Whitney gauge, fig. 39.9B) have been used successfully for indicating the blood flow through the extremities of man or

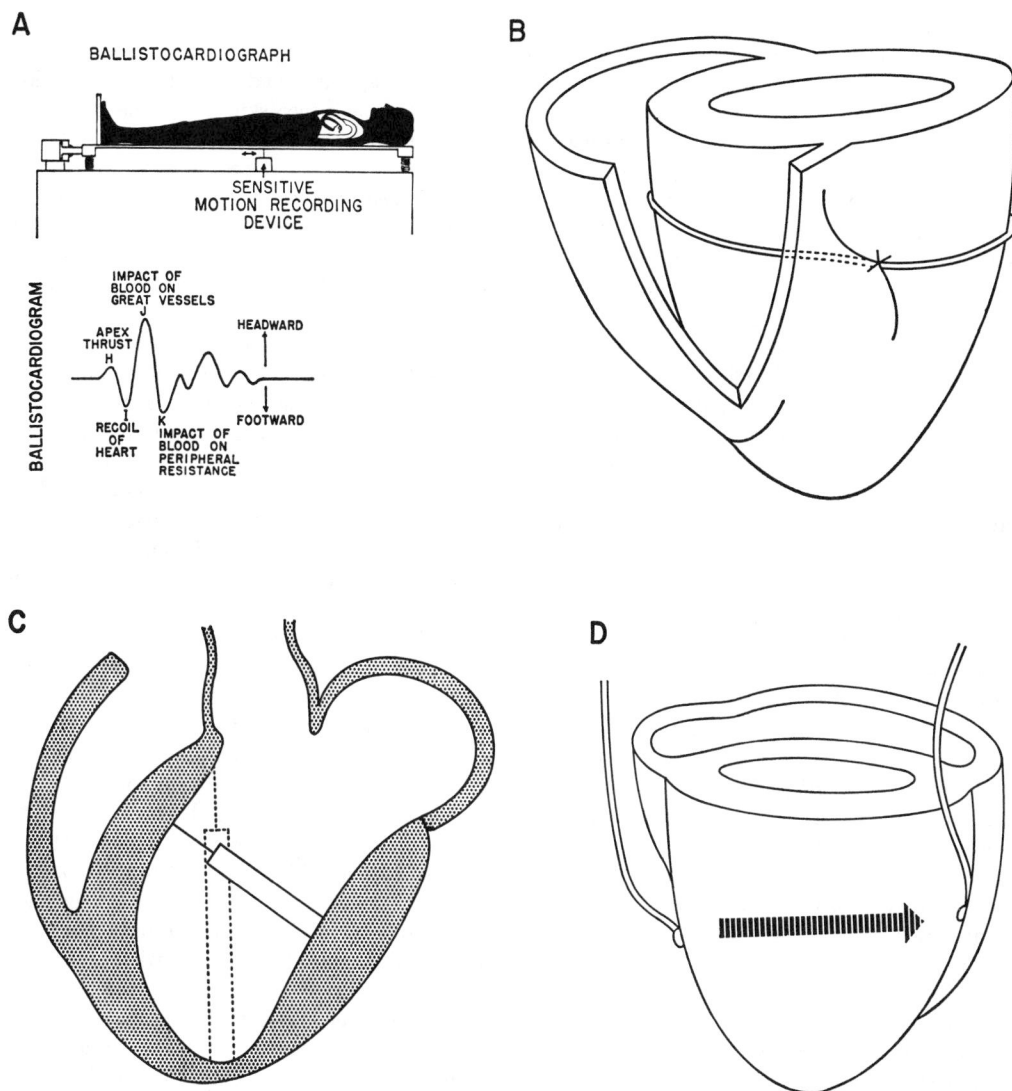

A BALLISTOCARDIOGRAPH

SENSITIVE MOTION RECORDING DEVICE

BALLISTOCARDIOGRAM

IMPACT OF BLOOD ON GREAT VESSELS
J

APEX THRUST
H

HEADWARD

FOOTWARD

RECOIL OF HEART
I

K
IMPACT OF BLOOD ON PERIPHERAL RESISTANCE

B

C

D

FIG. 39.9A. Schematic drawings showing the ballistocardiograph and typical ballistocardiogram (Modified after Rushmer, Cardiac Diagnosis, W. B. Saunders Company, Philadelphia, 1955). *B*. Principle of Whitney gauge as applied to a ventricle. As the mercury-filled rubber tube changes in length its electrical resistance is altered (Whitney, J. Physiol., 1953, **121**, 1). *C*. Variable inductance gauge used to measure a ventricular dimension (Rushmer, Circulation Res., 1954, **2**, 14). *D*. Sonar principle used to measure a ventricular dimension (Rushmer, Circulation Res., 1956, **4**, 684).

animal. In principle, the electrical impedance plethysmograph measures the change in electrical conductivity of an extremity induced by the changing number of ions brought to the segment by the heart action, i.e., the electrical impedance is a function of the volume of the part. Without venous occlusion, this represents volume pulsation of the extremity, with occlusion, the inflow of blood. For the Whitney gauge, a delicate rubber or plastic tubing is filled with mercury and sealed at each end with insulated wires. It is wrapped around a digit or an extremity in man,

or the aorta, left or right ventricle in the unanesthetized dog. Lengthening of the gauge reduces the cross-sectional area and increases the length of the mercury column producing a corresponding increase in electrical resistance. The gauge forms one arm of a Wheatstone bridge. Assuming that the organ enlarges during venous occlusion only in a diametrical direction, changes in circumference can be converted into volume changes. An index of ventricular cross-sectional area has also been obtained in active unanesthetized dogs by measuring the change in inductance of a variable inductance gauge implanted in a ventricle (fig. 39.9C), by the change in transit time of sound waves across the cavity (fig. 39.9D), and by the use of an electromagnetic principle.

A third type of plethysmograph utilizes a photocell to detect vascular changes by the absorption of light from transilluminated skin. Light from an illumination source enters the skin and scatters; the resulting variations in the photoelectric current caused by changes in blood flow can be recorded. Blood flow in skin areas, not accessible by other means, can be estimated by this method. The amplitudes of the photoelectrically recorded cutaneous pulses may be calibrated by use of a "filter" and correlated with finger blood flow measured by other methods. However, the volume pulse depends on the relationship between arterial inflow and venous outflow and, at best, is only a qualitative measure of actual blood flow.

E. Isotope disappearance rate. In 1951, Kety pointed out that radioactive indicators, which diffuse freely across cell membranes, could be used to measure local blood flow. The indicator must come into complete diffusion equilibrium between tissue and capillary blood for the disappearance rate to be determined by the blood supply. A small amount of radioactive ion is injected into a tissue (muscle, skin, myocardium, etc.) and the rate of disappearance from the area is followed by a counting device. In animal and human experiments, Walder demonstrated that there was a linear relationship between radioactive disappearance rates and directly measured blood flow in skeletal muscle; however at high rates of blood flow the clearance rate may remain fixed despite further increases in flow. For two reasons, much doubt has been expressed that disappearance rates measure blood flow: (1) in some instances, the rate of clearance does not parallel the blood flow simultaneously directly measured and (2) successively run tests, under the same conditions in the same area give different disappearance rates. Disagreements between direct blood flow measurements and disappearance rates may be explained by the fact that disappearance rates measure only a small area of capillary muscle flow while other methods determine total blood flow. Recently Xenon[133] has been used as a tracer since it is considered a more freely diffusible substance than Na[24] or I[131]. There is an indication that the disappearance rate of Xenon[133] may parallel other methods of measuring blood flow even at high flow values. The disappearance rate needs more investigative substantiation before it can be ac-

cepted as a quantitative method. It could be an extremely important research tool since it measures capillary, and not shunt, blood flow, can determine either skin or muscle blood flow separately in man, and is a convenient technique to use.

F. Thermal methods. Devices using the principle of heat clearance have been widely used to indicate directional changes in blood flow in a localized area of skin, muscle or internal organ, or through part or all of an extremity. One type of device consists of a thermocouple or thermistor (connected in series with a reference thermocouple or thermistor) mounted in the end of a hypodermic needle. The needle is inserted a variable distance into the tissue and a constant source of heat is used to raise the temperature of the test thermocouple 2 to 3° C above tissue temperature. The temperature difference between the test and reference junctions is essentially determined by the carrying away of the heat by the blood flow. The more rapid the blood flow, the smaller will be the junction temperature difference. A variation of this arrangement is to supply a variable amount of heat to the test junction at a rate just sufficient to maintain a small difference in temperature between the heat source and the reference junction. As blood flow through the tissue increases, progressively higher rates of delivery of heat will be required to maintain this constant temperature difference between heat source and "heat sink." The "rate of flow" will follow the magnitude of the electric current supplied to the heat source.

A second type of device has been much used in recent years to measure blood flow through part or all of an extremity. It is based on the theory that when the limb is in a water bath, the blood flow is equal to the amount of heat given out to the water, divided by the temperature difference of arterial and venous blood, times the specific heat of blood. However, the arteriovenous temperature difference is not measureable, and there is no guarantee that the ingoing and outgoing temperature reach water bath temperature. A variation is to circulate the water and to measure the heat exchange from the volume of water flow and temperature difference. As with the thermal needle, an index of blood flow can also be obtained by setting the calorimeter water temperature below mouth temperature and then measuring the amount of current necessary to keep the bath temperature constant.

This approach has been found very useful and has given much valuable information despite the fact that there is no good way of calibrating the deflections against known blood flows; zero flow is difficult if not impossible to obtain; in the case of the needle, the surrounding tissue is not normal and in addition to capillary flow, the device may be affected by flow in nearby veins.

G. Oxygen electrode. When a very small negative voltage is applied to a metallic electrode in a solution containing dissolved oxygen, there is a reduction of the oxygen at the electrode surface resulting in a small flow of current through the electrode. At such a voltage, the oxygen is reduced as quickly as it reaches the electrode surface and a straight line relationship exists between the oxygen concentration and the current that flows. In use, a platinum wire protrudes through a fine glass tip inserted into the skin; mercury makes contact between the platinum and the circuit. It is assumed that the electrode is in contact with a number of capillaries and that as blood flow increases, it will indicate the rising oxygen tension in the tissue. This has been used to indicate blood flow in the skin, skeletal muscle, and myocardium. It is at best a qualitative indication of tissue blood flow and has most of the disadvantages of the thermal methods.

Blood Velocity

Of the two measurements, volume flow of blood in milliliters per minute and the velocity of flow in centimeters per second, the former is probably more important. The major function of the circulation is to supply the metabolic needs of the tissues and volume flow is closely related to this, whereas measurement of velocity of flow alone does not necessarily tell us anything about the blood supply to the tissues. The relation between the observed velocity and volume flow is not consistent. For example, in the presence of local constriction in a vessel without constriction in other areas, flow velocity will increase, but flow will decrease. In the presence of general as well as local constriction, velocity and volume flow will both decrease. Despite this, knowledge of the flow velocity is highly important to an understanding of hemodynamics of the circulation. Flow velocity measurements have been made under direct vision, by use of the various flow meters that have been described, by observation of movement of injected substances, and finally, by determination of the differential pressure within an unopened and unrestrained vessel.

VISUALIZATION. There is a natural tendency to assume that when one actually sees the move-

ment of blood within a vessel, this must supply the most certain evidence of blood velocity. However, when this is done, one tends to be impressed by the movement of the red cells and not by that of the blood as a whole.

FLOW METERS. By insertion into or application onto a blood vessel of almost any of the flow meters described, one automatically measures the velocity of flow since the meter insures a fixed diameter through which the flow occurs. This is because $V = v/\pi r^2$, where V = velocity in millimeters per second, "v" volume flow of blood in milliliters through the meter per unit of time, and "r" the radius of the vessel.

MOVEMENT OF INJECTED MATERIALS. Various noteworthy attempts have been made to follow cyclic changes in velocity in the unopened vessel by recording the movements of various injected foreign materials such as air bubbles, dyes, and x-ray opaque fluid. The technique is difficult since the moving front of the injected material, i.e., the difference of optical density between blood and the contrasting medium, is often difficult to detect. This is because the velocity is not the same at different points along the radius of the blood column, the flow being much greater in the axial part of the stream than toward the periphery, and also because the flow is not always unidirectional. A mean or average velocity is obtained which is derived from the flow indicated by mean flow meters. It, of course, ignores very large fluctuations in velocity which occur during a cardiac cycle. The moment-to-moment or phasic velocity is recorded by those pulsatile flow meters with a frequency of response sufficiently rapid to follow it.

DIFFERENTIAL PRESSURE VELOCITY. The instantaneous blood velocity has been determined in the aorta and arteries from the instantaneous pressure difference between two points located along the axis of flow or along the vessel (ch. 36, fig. 36.9). Such pressure gradients have been measured by simultaneous recording of arterial pressure at the two points either with individual pressure manometers or by use of a double lumen catheter attached to a differential pressure strain gauge. In the double lumen catheter which has been used in the aorta of humans, the lateral opening of one catheter tip opens at a point about 5 cm. from the other. From the pressure gradients, velocity curves and flow curves have been calculated which agree well with those directly measured. A consideration of this highly technical approach is beyond the scope of this section.

A rough approximation to mean linear aortic

velocity in man can be made using the cardiac output and the cross-sectional area of the aorta (measured in a cadaver of the same size). The velocity in centimeters per second = cardiac output/cross-sectional area.

Circulation Time (C.T.)

Circulation time is defined as the shortest time which a particle of blood takes to go from one point in the circulation to another. Circulation time is most often determined for a portion of the circulation, such as, from the right to left side of the heart.

The circulation time of a particle of a substance can be accurately determined if it is injected instantaneously into a blood vessel, if it moves at the same rate as the blood stream and if its arrival further down the vessel is accurately detected. Practically, the situation is much more complicated. When a reasonable amount of a substance is injected, its arrival time is so spread out at the downstream detection point that detection is difficult. If the circulation time is made across an organ or a major portion of the circulatory system, the spreadout is even greater. In addition, if all the blood channels between the two points are not approximately uniform in length and diameter, only a part of the blood will pass from point to point at the rate indicated by the measurement. Despite these considerations, measurements of circulation time can be semi-quantitative.

The clinical methods for estimating circulation time use injected substances, such as decholin and ether, that signal their arrival by effects on special receptors, such as the taste buds in the tongue. With decholin, the normal range of arm to tongue (bitter taste) time is 8 to 17 seconds; with ether, the normal arm to lung (patient first smells ether) is from 4 to 8 seconds. For greater precision in experimental investigations, these classical methods have been superseded by the injection of dyes and radioactive tracers which can be easily and objectively detected by densitometers, conductivity cells and isotope counters. The main technical difficulty is the proper calculation of the average transit time. In a symmetrical curve, the mean (average of all transit times), the mode (time coordinate of the peak), and the median (time coordinate which halves the area) all coincide. But as the curve becomes asymmetrical, and particularly as the terminal portion stretches out more in time than the initial part, the three measures depart more and more from each other. The mean circulation time (MCT) it takes all dye to pass is computed as the center of gravity of the curve.

The significance of a change in circulation time is debatable. The circulation time between two points in the vascular system is equal to the volume of the vessels between the two points divided by the flow (fig. 39.10). The validity of this relationship has been checked in glass models and mathematically. It is obvious that a change in circulation time could be due to a change in volume of the vascular bed between the point of injection and sampling, as well as to change in flow. Since change in flow follows any vasomotor change, and since the resultant redistribution of pressures causes local volume change, both numerator and denominator of the ratio for circulation time (volume over flow) change simultaneously. They generally change in the same direction, and so the circulation time could be a very poor indicator of blood flow, volume of blood, or vasomotor change.

Volume of Organ, Vessel, Cavity and Region

Information is not abundant concerning regional blood volume, and the alterations that occur in normal humans and animals. Available information is based largely on some form of calculation, on the use of some form of plethysmography, and on the use of the dilution technique.

CALCULATION. For example, the blood volume of a single capillary may be derived from measurement of its length and diameter by microscopic inspection. Calculation of the total cross-sectional area of the capillary bed in man is based on the fact that the same volume of blood going through one part of the vascular bed, such as the aorta, goes through the total capillary bed, i.e., cross-sectional area of aorta times average velocity in

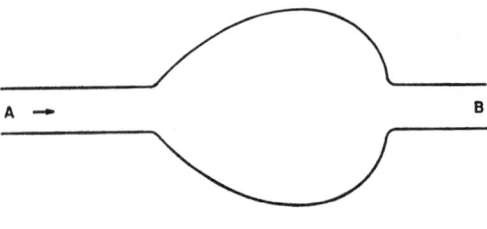

$$\text{CIRC. TIME IN SEC.} = \frac{\text{VOL. A TO B}}{\text{FLOW IN ml/SEC.}}$$

FIG. 39.10. Schematic diagram illustrating the relation between circulation time, volume flow, and the volume of the vascular bed.

the aorta = cross-sectional area of the capillary bed times the average velocity in the capillaries. Since the aortic velocity and cross-section, and capillary velocity (by inspection) can be determined experimentally, then cross-section of capillaries =

$$\frac{\text{cross-section of aorta} \times \text{aortic velocity}}{\text{average capillary velocity}}.$$

PLETHYSMOGRAPHY. The plethysmographs used are those already described to determine volume flow, but they are used without local venous occlusion. These have been used successfully on the heart, liver, spleen and vessels of animals. Dimensional, cross-sectional or possibly directional change in volume has been obtained in unanesthetized active dogs with the use of some of the various gauges previously described. For the heart cavities, large arteries and veins, the impedance plethysmograph, sonar cardiometer, strain gauge arch, Whitney gauge and mutual inductance coils are used; for organs, the sonar cardiometer, impedance plethysmograph and Whitney gauge are used. Most of these techniques are not applicable to man except under unusual conditions. However, determination of various in blood distribution in man can be made to some extent using plethysmography. For example, changes in quantity of blood in the lower extremities are determined by measuring the volume of the legs after occlusion of the circulation by applying pressure cuffs to the thighs and inflating them to a pressure greater than arterial. Changes in the quantity of blood in the trunk are determined by simultaneously recording the trunk volume with a plethysmograph and determining any change in pulmonary air volume by a spirometer. Variations in average blood volume in the heart are established by estimating the heart volume by x-ray. Values obtained by these techniques are admittedly rough but are helpful in establishing large directional or qualitative shifts in blood distribution resulting from change of position, fainting, injection of drugs, etc.

The plethysmograph is also used to measure the pressure-volume characteristics of the distensible venous system in a limb segment. The pressure in a congesting cuff on the limb proximal to the plethysmograph is increased 30 mm. Hg by increments of 5 mm. Hg, and the corresponding increases in limb volume with each pressure rise are recorded. The effective venous pressure can then be plotted against the volume in a graphic representation of the volume of blood that the venous system will accept with a given change of effective venous pressure. Venoconstriction or venodilation would result in lesser or greater distensibility, respectively, of the venous bed. Thus, an alteration in venous volume, determined by this method, implies a change in venous tone assuming that the volume of a blood vessel varies directly with the effective intravascular pressure, if other factors are controlled. A variation of this method is also used; the congesting cuff is inflated immediately to the highest pressure used and the increase in limb volume recorded. Results obtained with the two methods appear to be similar.

DILUTION TECHNIQUE. Provided certain conditions are fulfilled, the volume of a vascular compartment (cavity or vessel) can be measured in man and animal by analysis of a dilution curve obtained at the outlet of the compartment after rapid injection of an indicator at the inlet to the compartment. The blood content can be calculated from the following equation: $C = Q (60/T)$ where C = the cardiac output per minute, Q, the quantity of blood, and T, the circulation time. Thus, the volume is represented by the product of cardiac output and mean transit time of the indicator particles, both values being automatically available when cardiac output is quantitated with the dilution technique as described earlier in this chapter.

Calculation of a central blood volume from the cardiac output and mean transit time obtained following the injection of the indicator has been used experimentally and clinically for many years. Its accuracy has been established mathematically by perfusion experiments, by model systems, and *in vivo*. This measurement in the anesthetized dog has been compared to the determination of the actual amount of blood in the heart and lungs by injecting cells tagged with Cr^{51} and then calculating the local blood volume from the total radioactivity in the blended homogenate of these organs.

This is the only method presently available which can be used to quantitate regional blood distribution in man. In addition to central blood volume, it has been used to determine cardiac volume, systemic venous volume, and blood volume in other areas. For example, the systemic venous blood volume can be derived from a dilution curve recorded at the right atrium after injection into the femoral vein; the cardiopulmonary blood volume by injection into the right atrium and sampling at carotid artery or aorta. Since in practice adequate mixing at the sites of

TABLE 39.1

Regional distribution of blood volume

Vascular Compartment	Site of Injection	Site of Sample
1. Systemic venous blood volume and right side of the heart	Femoral vein	Pulmonary valves
2. Right side of the heart	Superior vena cava	Pulmonary valves
3. Systemic venous volume $(1 - 2)$		
4. Lungs and left side of the heart	Pulmonary artery	Aortic valves
5. Pulmonary artery to brachial artery	Pulmonary artery	Brachial artery
6. Left atrium to brachial artery	Left atrium	Brachial artery
7. Pulmonary blood volume $(5 - 6)$		

sampling and injection is essential, somewhat more accurate results are obtained by combinations of volumes in which adequate mixing is reasonably assured. Table 39.1 indicates how this may be accomplished.

REFERENCES

BAUMGARTNER, G., GRUPP, G., AND JANSSEN, S. Automatisch registrierendes Bubbleflowmeter. Pflügers Arch. ges. Physiol., 1955, 261, 575.

BRADLEY, S. E., INGELFINGER, F. J., BRADLEY, G. P., AND CURRY, J. J. The estimation of hepatic blood flow in man. J. Clin. Invest., 1945, 24, 890.

BRAUNWALD, E., FISHMAN, A. P., AND COURNAND, A. Estimation of volume of a circulatory model by the Hamilton and the Bradley methods at varying flow volume ratios. J. Appl. Physiol., 1958, 12, 445.

BRUNER, H. D. Bubble flow Meter. Methods in Med. Research, 1948, 1, 80.

CONRAD, M. C. AND GREEN, H. D.: Evaluation of venous occlusion plethysmograph. J. Appl. Physiol., 1961, 16, 289.

COURNAND, A. AND RANGES, H. A. Catheterization of the right auricle in man. Proc. Soc. Exper. Biol. & Med., 1941, 46, 462.

DENISON, A. B., SPENCER, M. P., AND GREEN, H. D. A square wave electromagnetic flowmeter for application to intact blood vessels. Circulation Res., 1955, 3, 39.

DUBOIS, A. B. AND MARSHALL, R. Measurements of pulmonary capillary blood flow and gas exchange throughout the respiratory cycle in man. J. Clin. Invest., 1957, 36, 1566.

ECKENHOFF, J. E., HAFKENSCHIEL, J. H., HARMEL, M. M., GOODALE, W. T., LUBIN, M., BING, R. J., AND KETY, S. S. Measurement of coronary blood flow by the nitrous oxide method. Am. J. Physiol., 1948, 152, 356.

ECKSTEIN, R. W., STROUD, M., III, DOWLING, C. V., AND PRITCHARD, W. H. Factors influencing changes in coronary flow following sympathetic nerve stimulation. Am. J. Phys., 1950, 162, 266.

FICK, A. Ueber die Messung des Blutquantums in den Herzventrikeln. Sitzungsb. der phys. med. Gesellsch. zu Würzburg, 1870, p. 16.

FISHMAN, A. P., MCCLEMENT, J., HIMMELSTEIN, A. AND COURNAND, A. Effects of acute anoxia on circulation and respiration in patients with chronic pulmonary disease studied during the "steady state." J. Clin. Invest., 1952, 31, 770.

FORSSMANN, W. I. Die Sondierung des rechten Hertzen. Klin. Wchnschr., 1929, 8, 2085.

FOX, I. J., BROOKER, L. G. S., HASELTINE, D. W., ESSEX, H. E., AND WOOD, E. H. A tricarbocyanine dye for continuous recording of dilution curves in whole blood independent of variations in blood oxygen saturation. Proc. Staff Meet. Mayo Clinic, 1957, 32, 478.

FRANKLIN, D. L., ELLIS, R. M., AND RUSHMER, R. F. Aortic blood flow in dogs during treadmill exercise. J. Appl. Physiol., 1959, 14, 809.

FRONEK, A. AND GANZ, V. Measurement of flow in single blood vessels including cardiac output by local thermodilution. Circulation Res., 1960, 8, 175.

FRY, D. L., MALLOS, A. J., AND CASPER, A. G. T. A catheter tip method for measurement of instantaneous aortic blood velocity. Circulation Res., 1956, 4, 627.

GASKELL, P. AND BURTON, A. C. Local postural vasomotor reflexes arising from the limb veins. Circulation Res., 1953, 1, 27.

GIBBS, F. A. A thermoelectric blood flow recorder in the form of a needle. Proc. Soc. Exper. Biol. & Med., 1933, 31, 141.

GILFORD, S. R., GREGG, D. E., SHADLE, D. W., FERGUSON, T. B., AND MARZETTA, L. A. An improved cuvette densitometer for cardiac determination by the dye-dilution method. Rev. of Sci. Instr., 1953, 24, 696.

GOODYER, A. V. N., HUVOS, A., ECKHARDT, W. F., AND OSTERBERG, R. O. Thermal dilution curves in intact animals. Circulation Res., 1959, 7, 432.

GREENFIELD, A. D. M. AND PATTERSON, G. C. The effect of small degrees of venous distension on the apparent rate of blood inflow to the forearm. J. Physiol., 1954, 125, 525.

GREEN, E. W., ZIEGLER, R. F. & KAVANAGH-GRAY, D., Clinical use of retrograde left ventricular catheterization in congenital heart disease (Abstract). Circulation, 1959, 20, 704.

GREGG, D. E., SHIPLEY, R. E., ECKSTEIN, R. W., ROTTA, A., AND WEARN, J. T. Measurement of mean blood flow in arteries and veins by means of the rotameter. Proc. Soc. Exper. Biol. & Med., 1942, 49, 267.

GREGG, D. E. AND GREEN, H. D. Registration and interpretation of normal phasic inflow into a left coronary artery by an improved differential manometric method. Am. J. Physiol., 1940, 130, 114.

GREGG, D. E., LONGINO, F. H., GREEN, P. A., AND CZERWONKA, L. J. A comparison of coronary flow determined by the nitrous oxide method and by a direct method using the rotameter. Circulation, 1951, 3, 89.

HAMILTON, W. F., HOWARD, A. R., AND DOW, P. Limitations of the continuous infusion method for measuring cardiac output by dye dilution. Am. J. Physiol., 1953, 175, 173.

HAMILTON, W. F. AND REMINGTON, J. W. The measurement of the stroke volume from the pressure pulse. Am. J. Physiol., 1947, 148, 14.

HAMILTON, W. F., MOORE, J. W., KINSMAN, J. M., AND SPURLING, R. G. Studies on the circulation. IV. Further analysis of the injection method and of changes in hemodynamics under physiological and pathological conditions. Am. J. Physiol., 1932, 99, 534.

HENSEL, H., RUEF, J. AND GOLENHOFEN, K. Human muscle and skin blood flow. Angiology, 1955, 6, 190.

HERTZMAN, A. B. The blood supply of various skin areas as estimated by the photoelectric plethysmograph. Am. J. Physiol., 1938, 124, 328.

HERTZMAN, A. B., RANDALL, W. C., AND JOCHIM, K. E. The estimation of the cutaneous blood flow with the photoelectric plethysmograph. Am. J. Physiol., 1946, 145, 716.

HEWLETT, A. W. AND VAN ZWALUWENBURG, J. G. The rate of blood flow in the arm. Heart, 1909, 1, 87.

HOLT, J. P. AND ALLENSWORTH, J. Estimation of the residual volume of the right ventricle of the dog's heart. Circulation Res., 1957, 5, 323.

HUFF, R. L., FELLER, D. D., JUDD, O. J., AND BOGARDUS, G. M. Cardiac output of men and dogs measured by *in vivo* analysis of iodinated (I^{131}) human serum albumin. Circulation Res., 1955, 3, 564.

IRISAWA, H., WILSON, M. F., AND RUSHMER, R. F. Left ventricle as a mixing chamber. Circulation Res., 1960, 8, 183.

KALMUS, H. P. Electronic flow meter. Natl. Bur. Standards (U. S.), Tech. News Bull. 1953, No. 2, 37,

KETY, S. S. AND SCHMIDT, C. F. The determination of cerebral blood flow in man by use of nitrous oxide in low concentrations. Am. J. Physiol., 1945, 143, 53.

KETY, S. S. Measurement of regional circulation by local clearance of radioactive sodium. Am. Heart J., 1949, 38, 321.

KLEIN, O. Zur Bestimmung des zirkulatorischen minutenvolumens beim Menschen nach dem Fickschen Prinzip. Munchen Med. Wchnschr., 1930, 77, 1311.

KOLIN, A. AND KADO, R. T. Miniaturization of the electromagnetic blood flow meter and its use for the recording of circulatory responses of conscious animals to sensory stimuli. Proc. Natl. Acad. Sc. 1959, 45, 1312.

KRAMER, K. AND ZIEGENRÜCKER, U. G. Die Bestimmung des Herzminutenvolumens unabhängig von der Sauerstoffsättigung des Blutes, an uneröffneten Arterien mit Hilfe eines neuen im nahen Infrarot absorbierenden Farbstoffes. Klin. Wchnschr., 1957, 35, 468.

LACY, W. W., UGAZ, C., AND NEWMAN, E. V. The use of indigo carmine for dye dilution curves. Circulation Res., 1955, 3, 570.

LASSEN, N. A. Muscle blood flow in normal man and in patients with intermittent claudication evaluated by simultaneous Xe^{133} and Na^{24} clearances. J. Clin. Invest., 1964, 43, 1805.

LITTER, J. AND WOOD, J. E., JR. The venous pressure-volume curve of the human leg measured in vivo. J. Clin. Invest., 1954, 33, 953.

LONGINO, F. H. AND GREGG, D. E. Comparison of cardiac stroke volume as determined by pressure pulse contour method and by a direct method using a rotameter. Am. J. Physiol., 1951, 167, 721.

MARSHALL, R. J., WANG, Y., AND SHEPHERD, J. T. Components of the "central" blood volume in the dog. Circulation Res., 1960, 8, 93.

McCLURE, J. A., LACY, W. W., LATIMER, P., AND NEWMAN, E. V. Indicator dilution in an atrioventricular system with competent or incompetent valves. A complete analysis of the behavior of indicator injected simultaneously or continuously into either chamber. Circulation Res., 1959, 7, 794.

McDONALD, D. A. The relation of pulsatile pressure to flow in arteries. J. Physiol., 1955, 127, 533.

MENDLOWITZ, M. AND FEITELBERG, S. A bloodless thermal recording digital flowmeter. J. Appl. Physiol., 1956, 8, 671.

MILNOR, W. R. AND BERTRAND, C. A. Estimation of venous blood volume in the dog by the indicator-dilution method. Circulation Res., 1958, 6, 55.

MIXTER, G. Respiratory augmentation of inferior vena caval flow demonstrated by a low-resistance phasic flowmeter. Am. J. Physiol., 1953, 172, 446.

MONTGOMERY, H. AND HORWITZ, O. Oxygen tension of tissues by the polarographic method: introduction: oxygen tension and blood flow of the skin of human extremities. J. Clin. Invest., 1950, 29, 1120.

PETERSEN, L. H., HELRICH, M., GREENE, L., TAYLOR, C., AND CHOQUETTE, G. Measurement of left ventricular output. J. Appl. Physiol., 1954, 7, 258.

PIEPER, H. AND WETTERER, E. Strompendel fur Elektrische Registrierung der Blutstromungsgeschwindigkeit. Ztschr. Biol., 1953, 105, 214.

REINDELL, H., WEYLAND, R., KLEPZIG, H., SCHILDGE, E., AND MUSSHOFF, K. Über Anpassungsvorgänge und Schädigungsmöglichkeiten beim Sportherzen. Schweiz. Ztschr. f. Sportmed. 1953, 1, 97.

RODBARD, S., GRAHAM, G. R., AND WILLIAMS, F. Continuous and simultaneous measurement of total coronary flow, venous return and cardiac output in the dog. J. Appl. Physiol., 1953, 6, 311.

ROSE, J. C., BROIDA, H. P., HUFNAGEL, C. A.,

GILLESPIE, J. F., RABIL, P. J., AND FREIS, E. D. A method for the study of the circulation in the dog using a mechanical left ventricle. J. Appl. Physiol., 1955, 7, 580.

ROSE, J. C., COSIMANO, S. V., HUFNAGEL, C. A., AND MASSULLO, E. A. The effects of exclusion of right ventricle from the circulation in dogs. J. Clin. Invest., 1955, 34, 1625.

RUSHMER, R. F., FRANKLIN, D. L., AND ELLIS, R. M. Left ventricular dimensions recorded by sonocardiometry. Circulation Res., 1956, 4, 684.

RUSHMER, R. F. Continuous measurement of left ventricular dimensions in intact unanesthetized dogs. Circulation Res., 1954, 2, 14.

SABISTON, D. C., KHOURI, E. M., AND GREGG, D. E. Use and application of the cuvette densitometer as an oximeter. Circulation Res., 1957, 5, 125.

SAPIRSTEIN, L. A. Regional blood flow by fractional distribution of indicators. Am. J. Physiol., 1958, 193, 161.

SARNOFF, S. J. AND BERGLUND, E. The Potter electroturbinometer. Circulation Res., 1953, 1, 331.

SCHLANT, R. C., NOVACK, P., KRAUS, W. L., MOORE, C. B., HAYNES, F. W., AND DEXTER, L. Determination of central blood volume. Comparison of Stewart-Hamilton method with direct measurements in dogs. Am. J. Physiol., 1959, 196, 499.

SCHREINER, B. F., JR., LOVEJOY, F. W., JR., AND YU, P. N. Estimation of cardiac output from precordial dilution curves in patients with cardiopulmonary disease. Circulation Res., 1959, 7, 595.

SHIPLEY, R. E. AND WILSON, C. An improved recording rotameter. Proc. Soc. Exper. Biol. & Med., 1951, 78, 724.

SMITH, H. W., RANGES, H. A., CHASIS, H., AND GOLDRING, W. The dispersion of glomerular activity in the normal and hypertensive kidney. Am. J. Physiol., 1941, 133, 450.

STARR, I., RAWSON, A. J., SCHROEDER, H. A., AND JOSEPH, N. R. Studies on estimation of cardiac output in man and of abnormalities in cardiac function from heart's recoil and blood's impact. Am. J. Physiol., 1939, 127, 1.

STEWART, G. N. Research on the circulation time and on the influences which affect it. IV. The output of the heart. J. Physiol., 1897, 22, 159.

VISSCHER, M. B. AND JOHNSON, J. A. The Fick principle: analysis of potential errors in its conventional application. J. Appl. Physiol., 1953, 5, 635.

WALDER, D. N. The local clearance of radioactive sodium from muscle in normal subjects and those with peripheral vascular disease. Clin. Sc., 1953, 12, 153.

WARNER, H. R., SWAN, H. J. C., AND WOOD, E. H. Quantitation of rapid stroke volume changes in man from aortic pulse pressure. Am. J. Physiol., 1952, 171, 777.

WEST, J. W. AND GUZMAN, S. V. Coronary dilation and constriction visualized by selective arteriography. Circulation Res., 1959, 7, 527.

WEVER, R. AND ASCHOFF, J. Durchflussmessung mit der diathermiethermostromuhr bei pulsierender stromung. Arch. ges. Physiol., 1956, 262, 152.

WHITNEY, R. J. The measurement of volume change in limbs. J. Physiol., 1953, 121, 1.

WOOD, E. H., BOWERS, D., SHEPHERD, J. T., AND FOX, I. J. Oxygen content of "mixed" venous blood in man during phases of respiratory and cardiac cycles in relation to possible errors in measurement of cardiac output by conventional application of the Fick method. J. Appl. Physiol., 1955, 7, 621.

WOOD, E. H. AND SWAN, H. J. C. Definition of terms and symbols for description of circulatory indicator-dilution curves. J. Appl. Physiol., 1954, 6, 797.

WOOD, J. E. AND ECKSTEIN, J. W. A tandem forearm plethysmograph for study of acute responses of the peripheral veins of man: The effect of environmental and local temperature change and the effect of pooling blood in the extremities. J. Clin. Invest., 1958, 37, 41.

Monographs and Reviews

ALGIRE, G. H. The transparent chamber technic for observation of the peripheral circulation. In Peripheral Circulation in Man. A Ciba Foundation Symposium, Little, Brown & Company, Boston, 1954.

ALLEN, G. Extracorporeal circulation. Charles C Thomas, Springfield, Illinois, 1958.

ARNULF, G. Systematic coronary arteriography with acetylcholine cardiac arrest. Progress in Cardiovascular Disease, 1959, 2, 197.

ASMUSSEN, E. AND NIELSEN, M. Cardiac Output during Muscular Work and Its Regulation. Phys. Rev., 1955, 35, 778.

BRECHER, G. A. Critical review of bristle flowmeter techniques. IRE Trans. on Med. Electronics, 1959, ME-6, 294.

BRECHER, G. A. Venous return. Grune & Stratton, New York, 1955.

DOW, P. Estimation of cardiac output and central blood volume by dye dilution. Physiol. Rev., 1956, 36, 77.

FULTON, G. P. AND ZWEIFACH, B. Factors regulating blood flow. Proceeding of the Third Conference on Microcirculatory Physiology & Pathology, American Physiological Society, Washington D. C., 1958.

GREGG, D. E. Thermostromuhr. Methods in Med. Research, 1948, 1, 89.

GREGG, D. E. Coronary circulation in health and disease. Lea & Febiger, Philadelphia, 1950.

HADDY, F. J. Vasomotion in systemic arteries, small vessels and veins determined by direct resistance measurements. Minnesota Med., 1958, 41, 162.

HAMILTON, W. F. The Physiology of the Cardiac Output. Circulation, 1953, 8, 527.

LEHMAN, J. S. Coronary arteriography: practical considerations. Progress in Cardiovascular Disease 1959, 2, 36.

MEIER, P. AND ZIERLER, K. L. On the theory of

the indicator-dilution method for measurement of blood flow and volume. J. Appl. Physiol., 1954, 6, 731.

MORRIS, L. E. AND BLUMGART, H. L. Velocity of blood flow in health and disease. Circulation, 1957, 15, 448.

NILSON, N. J. Oximetry. Physiol. Rev., 1960, 40, 1.

NYBOER, J. Electrical impedance plethysmography. The electrical resistive measure of the blood pulse volume, peripheral and central blood flow. American Lectures on Medical Physics, Charles C. Thomas, Springfield, Illinois, 1960.

RUSHMER, R. F. Cardiac Diagnosis. W. B. Saunders Co., Phila., 1955.

SCARBOROUGH, W. R. Current status of ballistocardiography. Progress in Cardiovascular Diseases 1959, 2, 263.

STEWART, G. N. Studies on the circulation in man. Harvey Lectures 1912, 8, 86.

CHAPTER 40

Blood Pressure Measurements

The development of adequate methods and the overcoming of instrumental obstacles are the essential preliminaries to the solution and consideration of problems dealing with the circulation. One must discuss the various devices and procedures that have been used to study the circulation and point out their respective merits and shortcomings. Indication will be made of the degree of adequacy and the principles upon which a limited number of these devices operate. Such consideration should reveal the proper basis for the interpretation of the present and subsequent studies of the circulation.

Of the three principal attributes of the circulation, blood pressure, flow and blood volume, the pressure is most easily determined and recorded. Measurements in both man and animals can be direct or indirect.

Direct Blood Pressure Measurements

In the direct approach, a catheter or needle is inserted into a vessel or heart cavity and connected to a hydrostatic column of fluid or to a special device. Pressures thus obtained in almost all parts of the cardiovascular system of animal and man have been quantitated and studied. Direct pressure measurements have value in determining certain aspects of function of the circulation. They should not, however, as is pointed out elsewhere, be used as an index of change in flow through or volume of a blood vessel or heart cavity. Whenever a change in volume is empirically deduced from a change in pressure, potentially active changes in caliber are ignored which are known to occur in every vessel except the capillaries.

MEANS OF PRESSURE PICK-UP. Most approaches have been worked out in acute experiments in anesthetized animals, but techniques are now widely used in chronic animal preparations and in humans without anesthesia, both at rest and during physical activity.

In techniques used only on animals, various regions of the circulatory system are made accessible by a previous operation so that pressures can be determined atraumatically and repeatedly over many months. These include the carotid loop (exteriorization of a carotid artery in a tube of skin) in the dog and rabbit, cardiopexy in the dog (attachment of the apex of the heart to the chest wall just under the skin to permit easy access to the left ventricle), an indwelling silver tube with one end sutured to the exterior surface of a vessel or cardiac cavity and the other end sutured just under the skin, and an indwelling polyvinyl tube filled with heparin with one end penetrating a vessel or cardiac cavity and the other plugged end protruding from the skin. In the last instance, the tube is connected directly to the appropriate pressure transducer; in the others, a needle and/or catheter connected to a pressure transducer penetrates the vessel or cavity.

A number of techniques are also applicable to both normal man and animal without previous preparation. Needles and catheters can be passed into many accessible veins and arteries. For the right side of the circulation, one procedure is to "float" a polyvinyl catheter with a balloon tip down the jugular vein into the right ventricle or pulmonary artery without benefit of fluoroscopy. The standard procedure, however, is to pass a catheter under fluoroscopy *via* the jugular vein (dog), or an arm or leg vein (human), into the venae cavae and their venous tributaries from the liver and kidney, or into the right atrium, right ventricle or pulmonary artery.

Various techniques have been used in man as well as in animals for direct measurement of pressures in the left heart, which is not normally accessible. A catheter passed by the right heart and impacted in a branch of the pulmonary artery is presumed by some to give an approximation of the pressure in the venous end of the pulmonary capillaries. Other approaches include transbronchoscopic and transesophageal entrance for pressure recording from the left atrium, left ventricle, and aorta, a percutaneous needle approach through the anterior chest wall for left ventricular pressure, retrograde femoral artery catheterization of the left ventricle through the aortic valves, and transeptal left atrial puncture. In the last technique, the left atrium is punctured by a retractable needle introduced through a cardiac catheter passed up a leg vein, the tip of which is positioned against the interatrial septum.

MEASUREMENT OF NONOSCILLATORY OR NEARLY NONOSCILLATORY PRESSURES. A vertical column of fluid with attached millimeter scale, and with some form of anticoagulant between it and the vessel whose pressure is being tapped, is the only device needed to determine the pressure in most intravascular pressure regions. To measure the pressure, the column is filled from a side tube, and the column is then allowed to seek its own level by drainage into the vessel (fig. 40.1). For the low pressure regions such as the venous system, atrium and pulmonary artery, the column is saline solution; for higher pressure as in the arteries, the column is filled with mercury to keep it short. This is generally in the form of a "U" tube. To minimize the pressure fluctuations, the tubing between the mercury manometer and the vessel is constricted to dampen the oscillations. By placing a float with a writing point on top of the saline or mercury, the venous or arterial blood pressure can be continuously recorded. Such a fluid manometer is the basic instrument for pressure recording and most complicated pressure devices are calibrated against such pressure indicators. Very often, complicated pressure devices are used when this simple arrangement would suffice. For measuring cerebrospinal fluid pressure, intravascular pressure in arterioles, capillaries and venules, and extravascular pressure in the tissue space in skin, muscle, kidney, subcutaneous tissue, etc., water or saline manometers are used in which little or no fluid enters or leaves the manometer. This is very important for the addition or removal of even small volumes of fluid may grossly affect the absolute pressure level obtained. The apparatus consists of a small hypodermic needle attached to a horizontal glass capillary tube partially filled with sterile saline to a reference line. Except for a water manometer, the rest of the system is filled with air. Upon insertion of the needle into the tissue, a pneumatic bulb connected to both the capillary tube and the manometer is compressed. When the meniscus is returned to the reference line, the pressure in the manometer equals tissue pressure. A correction must be made for the capillarity of the system. This method yields higher values for tissue pressure than those obtained with implanted perforated capsules (Guyton).

Since the pressures in veins and extravascular spaces change slowly, they can be accurately indicated visually with these two simple fluid manometer systems. When the mercury filled ma-

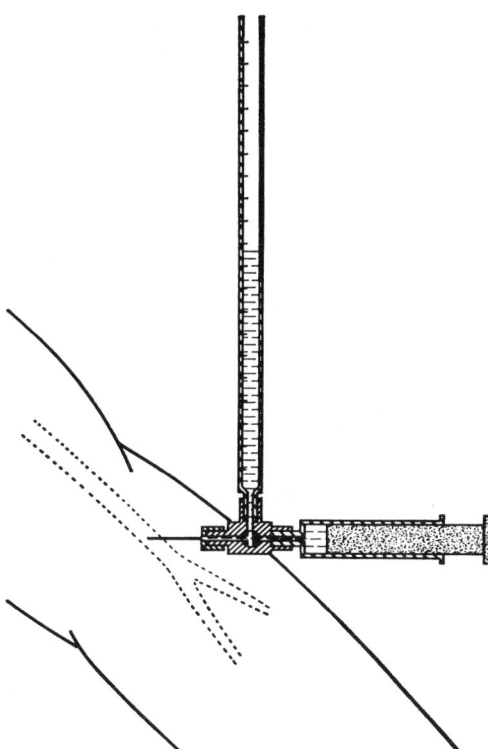

FIG. 40.1. Method for measuring pressure in a superficial vein using a vertical column of saline.

nometer is applied to an artery, a pressure is recorded which is a rough *mean* of the existing intra-arterial pressure. To accurately measure the widely fluctuating pressures during systole and diastole, in the arteries and in the ventricular cavities, or to continuously record electrically or photographically these, as well as nonoscillating pressures, more complicated and sophisticated instrumentation is necessary.

MEASUREMENT OF PRESSURE PULSES. The pattern of variation of pressure occurring with each heart beat (but not the pressure values) can be recorded from the surface of the accessible large arteries and veins without interference with them. In arteries, a crude representation of the pulse can be made by applying the principle that the relatively minute natural excursions of an artery are increased by applying an external pressure (usually a small button) which approximates the intra-arterial pressure. This amplified excursion of the vessel wall is further magnified by mechanical levers. In arteries, a more precise indication of the pressure pulse pattern is obtained by following the volumetric change in diameter of the artery by means of a cup system placed over it. An open cup or receiver is firmly pressed to the skin over an artery such as the carotid and connected by tubing to a highly sensitive pressure recorder. For registration of the venous pulse, the patient is placed in the recumbent position to neutralize the effects of gravity, and a cup receiver is applied snugly over the right supraclavicular fossa, the internal jugular bulb at the margin of the sternocleidomastoid muscle, or the suprasternal notch. In turn, this is connected by an air system to a sensitive pressure manometer.

Apparatus and requisite techniques for registering pressure curves in a proper manner have improved rapidly in the last few years because of increasing interest in cardiac catheterizations; chief improvements lie in the use of expedients for giving greater amplification, flexibility and ease of operation. The simple principles involved, however, are unchanged, and the classical curves of Wiggers and others, using older optical manometers, have not been improved upon.

Basically, all types of pressure apparatus involve measurement of the displacement of some type of elastic membrane which is moved by generation of pressure in a vessel or cavity. In one group of manometers, an essentially nondistensible conduit (needle, lead tube, cannula or catheter) is filled with fluid and connected to the membrane outside the body; this, in turn, is connected to a form of amplification and recording; in the other, a micromanometer membrane or its equivalent is mounted in a catheter tip at the pressure source, and the catheter serves only as a conduit for wires to the amplifying and recording assembly (fig. 40.2). The detection and transmission of the movements of the membrane can take place by mechanical, optical or electrical means, or by a combination of these principles. Owing to their technical imperfection, purely mechanical systems are now only of historical interest. Pretty much in the same category are manometers which combine optical and electrical systems.

Manometers with Fluid-Filled Conduit

A. Optical manometers (fig. 40.2). In the case of the optical type of manometer (which was largely used until recently), the entire system consists of a stiff rubber or metal membrane of minimum diameter connected to a nondistensible, fluid filled conduit of minimal volume, which is inserted into the source of pressure variation. Movements of the membrane induced by pressure change are recorded by reflecting from an attached mirror a weightless beam of light as a

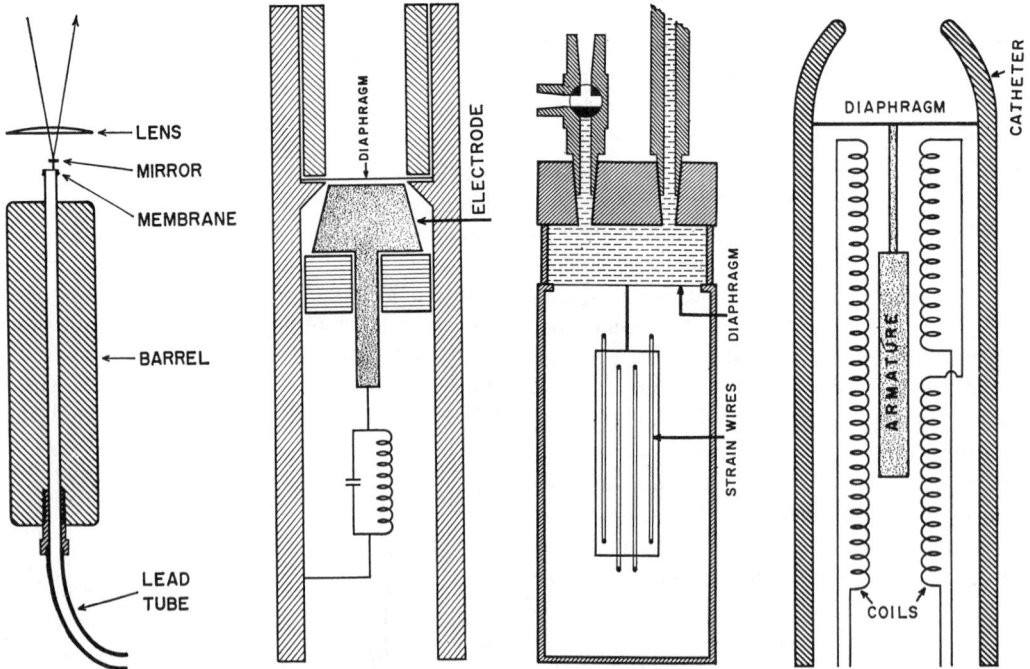

FIG. 40.2. Externally recording pressure gauges. *Left,* principle of the classical optical method for determining biological pressures. A flexible, short, nondistensible, lead tube, offering little damping effect, connects to the pressure source. *Center left,* capacitance transducer; *center right,* strain gauge transducer; and *right,* catheter mounted inductance transducer.

lever to give rapid response with adequate sensitivity. A number of different forms of such manometers have been developed and widely used.

B. Electrical transducers. The common feature of the methods dependent on electrical principles is that the movement of the manometer membrane is transformed into electrical energy which is then transferred to a recorder. In practice, the transformation of the pressure impulse is effected by a piezo-electric effect, or by a change in capacitance, resistance and inductance. The piezo-electric principle which depends on the difference in potential occurring in certain crystals exposed to mechanical pressure, is little used since stationary difference of crystal potential cannot be maintained and constant pressures cannot be accurately measured.

For most present day determinations of biological pressures, the pressure fluctuations in a cavity or vessel are transmitted to a membrane through a long nondistensible catheter filled with fluid. This activates an electronic pressure transducer in which movements of the stiff membrane, with minimal fluid displacement and high frequency of response, produce a change in capacitance, resistance or inductance.

One of the first of the electronic pressure transducers was devised by Lilly (1942), in which a stiff metal membrane separated from an electrode by a very small air gap, formed a condenser. Movements of the membrane relative to the electrode vary the capacitance which is measured by a radio frequency circuit. This device is rather temperature sensitive and has considerable zero pressure drift (fig. 40.2).

The electronic transducer in most common use today is the resistance wire strain gauge. Strain sensitive wire responds to a change in pressure with a change in the resistance to flow of an electric current. A membrane is displaced by increased pressure in a chamber attached to the pressure source (fig. 40.2).

MANOMETERS MOUNTED IN AN EMPTY CATHETER TIP. In this type of gauge, the pressure sensitive element is mounted in the catheter tip, the catheter contains no fluid, serving only as a conduit for wires leading to an amplifier. Inductance pressure gauges of this type are coming into use in which the variable mutual inductance between a pair of coils can be altered by changing the position of an iron core within its magnetic field. If the iron core connected to the center of an elastic membrane is mounted between two coils, movement of the membrane moves the core within the coils, changing their inductance. Change in inductance, monitored by an appropriate bridge circuit indicates the extent of membrane displacement (fig. 40.2). This instrument was first devised by Wetterer and has been considerably modified and improved by others. The strain gauge principle has also been applied to a micromanometer mounted in the end of a catheter. In this, a strain wire wrapped around a metal reed with multiple longitudinal slits is stretched by the pressure source.

Both the inductance and strain gauge type of micromanometer faithfully record the pressure pattern but are difficult and expensive to build. Inductance gauges have been used in animals and, at times, in humans, but their use has been limited because it has not been possible to determine accurately the zero pressure with the Wetterer type. Although the strain gauge type does not have this disadvantage and has been used with some patients, its initial expense is higher than the inductance type, and it has the added drawback that no way has been found to disconnect it from its catheter which wears out first.

AMPLIFICATION AND RECORDING. The signal from the various pressure transducers (except the optical manometer) is amplified electronically to drive a high frequency galvanometer or oscilloscope. The devices used to record the pressure pulses are the optical manometer with camera, the direct pen writing galvanometer, the optical galvanometer, and the cathode ray oscilloscopic camera. Many types of pressure transducer-amplifier combinations are available commercially. In terms of ascending order of frequency of response, the systems may be graded as follows: the direct writing galvanometer, the optical manometer, the optical galvanometer, and the oscilloscope. However, no ideal system exists at present. For any specific application, the combination of transducer, recorder, and amplifier is a compromise of sensitivity, stability, convenience of use, and frequency of response.

FREQUENCY OF MANOMETER SYSTEMS. The accuracy with which a manometer system records change of pressure without lag and with correct phasic relations depends on its natural frequency. Reasonably good reproduction of a wave form can be best recorded by a system which has uniform response to the tenth harmonic of its fundamental frequency. With a heart rate of 240 beats per minute, the pulse frequency is 4 per second, and its tenth harmonic is 40 cycles per second. With such a frequency, rapid changes in pressure are fairly well recorded.

The frequency response characteristics of the

entire system of transducer, amplifier, and galvanometer must be determined since the net frequency is limited by the lowest component of the system. The frequency of a manometer with a fluid filled conduit is governed by its effective mass and the elasticity of its membrane, i.e., frequency is increased by a decrease in the mass to be moved by the pressure and by a decrease in the size and distensibility of the membrane. In the case of the optical manometer, this is the sole determinant of frequency response since the rest of the system is a weightless light beam which does not affect the frequency. The normal frequency of such manometers is 120 to 160 double vibrations per second. In the case of the other types of manometer with a fluid filled conduit, the frequency is often limited as well by the type of recorder used and may vary from 5 to 100 cycles per sec. In the manometer in which the catheter is used only as a conduit for wires, the basic frequency is generally higher than in the other types and is determined largely by the characteristics of the membrane at the catheter tip since there is no fluid space central to the membrane.

The fact that a recording manometer system has an adequate frequency and sensitivity does not insure that the recorded pressures are free of artefacts. Impact of a cardiac cavity or vessel on the side or tip of the catheter often leads to very large artefacts in the recorded pressure curve, which invalidate a goodly portion of records taken in catheterization laboratories for diagnostic purposes. In the manometer with a fluid filled catheter, this type of artefact is maximal and, despite all precautions, it is very often impossible to obtain technically perfect records. The response characteristics of such curves can be somewhat improved by "critical damping" through mechanically constricting the conduit system. However, this is not to be recommended since it is almost impossible to maintain a fixed degree of damping, and slight increases in damping completely deform the pressure curve. In the pressure manometers in which the membrane is mounted in the catheter tip, the phasic pressure patterns invariably are excellent and artefacts are almost nonexistent. This is the pressure manometer of the future.

STANDARD ZERO REFERENCE PLANE FOR PRESSURE MEASUREMENTS. The numerical value obtained from pressure measurements in the cardiovascular system depends, of course, upon the horizontal plane to which zero pressure is referred. Most commonly, this has reference to the assumed level of the center of the atrium. The exact level is easy to establish in the open-chest animal or human, by adjusting the needle or catheter end attached to the recording manometer to the level of the midpoint of the atrium. This is zero pressure. When the chest is closed, it is difficult to determine precisely the proper zero point of reference and to obtain comparable figures in different subjects or in a series of measurements. It is not surprising, therefore, that many different reference planes or levels have been used. Possibly, the one closest to the truth is that described by Winsor and Burch. The reference level or heart level used is an axis running transversely through the thorax at the point of junction of a plane passing cross-sectionally through the fourth intercostal space adjacent to the sternum, with a frontal plane passing midway between the posterior surface of the body and the xiphoid process of the sternum. Horizontal planes passing through this axis are the zero pressure reference levels to be used for that particular position of the patient.

This method, however, measures the intravascular pressure against the atmospheric pressure as a reference. Most vessels are imbedded in tissues which have a significant tissue pressure that is either lower (in the thorax) or higher (in the abdomen and skeletal muscle) than the atmospheric pressure. For precise quantitation, the intravascular pressure should be measured against the extravascular or tissue pressure which is around the vessel. The terms effective, transmural, and net pressure, have been introduced to indicate the pressure difference between the intravascular and extravascular pressure. Precise determination of extravascular pressure is unreliable. The artefacts are especially large in measuring tissue pressure in solid organs, especially the heart muscle, and least in recording pressure surrounding the great vessels and the heart. Intrathoracic pressure is taken as an approximation for the latter, but even here, calculation of transmural pressure must be made on the basis of the immediately contiguous intrathoracic pressure since regional intrathoracic pressure is quite variable.

Indirect Blood Pressure Measurements

Human

Although the blood pressure can be determined in man by inserting a hollow, wide-bore needle into an artery and connecting it with a suitable manometer, such a method is usually reserved for human cardiopulmonary diagnostic work. Convenience and safety demand that any method for general clinical use must be indirect. The principle employed involves the balancing of air pressure against the pressure of the blood in the brachial artery. The air pressure is estimated by means of a mercury or an aneroid manometer.

The instrument used for this purpose includes a flat rubber bag covered by a nondistensible envelope of cotton fabric. The cavity of the bag is connected to both the manometer and a hand bulb or small pump by rubber tubing. By this means the bag can be inflated to any desired pressure. A small valve between the bulb or pump and the bag permits the escape of air, and the reduction of the pressure as required. The uninflated rubber bag (usually referred to as the cuff or armlet) which should be at least 12 cm. wide is wrapped snugly around the upper arm just above the elbow. The bag is then inflated until the air pressure within it overcomes the arterial pressure and obliterates the arterial lumen. The pressure is increased a little beyond this point and is then cautiously reduced again,[1] by the release of the valve, until the arterial pressure just overcomes the air pressure and blood escapes beyond the cuff into the peripheral section of the artery. At this instant the pressure in the bag is read from the manometer. Since the air pressure practically balances the systolic arterial pressure the manometer reading must indicate the value of the latter. It is essential to the method that the manometer reading be taken at the instant when the blood escapes beneath the cuff.

One of three methods, the *palpatory, oscillatory* or *auscultatory*, may be employed to determine when the blood first escapes beneath the cuff. In all three procedures the value for the lateral pressure in the brachial artery is obtained, whereas direct methods (which entail the introduction of a straight, unbranched cannula, or a large-bore needle into an artery) measure the end pressure. The latter is greater because it includes not only the lateral pressure on the elastic arterial wall, but also that derived from the conversion of the kinetic energy of the moving blood column as it meets the obstruction, and the increment of pressure caused by the reflected wave from the obstruction.

A. The palpatory method. In this method the examiner takes the manometer reading at the moment that the pulse is felt at the wrist as the index of the systolic pressure. This method is now

[1] Should deflation be carried out too rapidly the mercurial type of clinical manometer shows a considerable lag, due to the time required for the air above the mercury column to reach atmospheric pressure. With rapid deflation, particularly when the heart rate is slow, the actual point at which arterial pressure overcomes cuff pressure may be missed. The rate of deflation should not exceed from 2 to 3 mm. Hg per second.

rarely used since it lacks accuracy. It assumes that the first escape of blood beneath the cuff will cause pulsation in the peripheral artery, but there is no evidence that the amount of blood which escapes beneath the cuff when the artery first opens is sufficient to produce a pulse wave detectable by the finger. Definite pulsation may not occur until the cuff pressure has been lowered 5 to 10 mm. below the point when the artery first becomes pervious. This method therefore gives readings that are too low. Another disadvantage of the palpatory method is that the diastolic pressure cannot be measured.

B. The oscillatory method. In this method a tambour or capsule covered with a very delicate membrane, or a second bag connected with the cuff, is used to pick up and magnify the pulsations transmitted from the artery to the upper edge of the cuff or armlet. The pulsations appear as oscillations of the indicator needle on the clock-face dial of an aneroid manometer. Pressures are marked by figures on the dial; as the cuff is inflated or deflated, the needle moves to indicate the applied pressure at the moment. At pressures exceeding systolic the oscillations are minimal, but as the pressure is gradually lowered and the pulsations pass beneath the cuff, a sudden increase in their amplitude and duration occurs. This is the criterion of systolic pressure. The oscillations show little change in magnitude as the cuff is deflated further, until the pressure has fallen to the diastolic level at which they suddenly become smaller. At this instant the figure on the dial to which the needle points is noted.

C. The auscultatory method. This procedure is the one generally employed clinically. It was introduced in 1905 by the Russian physician Korotkow. Certain sounds heard during auscultation over the brachial artery distal to the cuff are taken as the criteria for the systolic and diastolic pressures. Under ordinary circumstances if a stethoscope is placed over the brachial or any other artery, no sound can be heard, the flow of blood through the channels being inaudible. If however the artery is compressed by the manometer cuff so as to completely arrest the flow of blood, a sharp light tapping sound, in rhythm with the heart beat, will be heard when the pressure in the cuff is released and falls just sufficiently to permit the arterial lumen to open. As the pressure in the cuff is progressively lowered the sound undergoes a series of changes in quality and intensity.

Four phases of the sound, each having its distinctive character, may be heard in succession in the normal individual, as the pressure is gradually reduced from about 120 to 80 mm. of mercury or less. These are described below with the average pressures at which they are normally heard:

Sounds of Korotkow

Phase   I. Sudden appearance of a clear, but
           often faint, tapping sound growing
           louder during the succeeding 10 mm.
           Hg fall in pressure.
Phase II. The sound takes on a murmurish
           quality during the next 15 mm. fall
           in pressure.
Phase III. Sound changes little in quality but
           becomes clearer and louder during
           the next 15 mm. fall in pressure.
Phase IV. Muffled quality lasting throughout
           the next 5 to 6 mm. Hg fall. After
           this all sound disappears.

The beginning of the first sound is taken as the
index of systolic pressure. As it is quite faint at its
commencement it may not be caught at this time
by the ear of the inexperienced, or if the observer's
hearing is distracted by other sounds.

The pressure at the time of complete disappearance of the fourth sound is usually taken as the index of the diastolic pressure. The sound coincides with the moment that the blood escapes beneath the armlet in a continuous stream rather than intermittently. There has been a difference of experimental data concerning whether the point of muffling of the Korotkow sounds or the disappearance of the sounds more closely estimates the diastolic blood pressure. It may be that the muffling of the sound correlates with diastolic pressure best in children and young adults while the disappearance of sounds should be used in older subjects (Moss and Adams).

It should be clearly understood that arterial blood pressure cannot be measured with precision by means of sphygmomanometers. The method is attended by inaccuracies caused by variations in heart rhythm, the presence of normal respiration, and resistance of the tissues of the part. To compensate for tissue resistance, a rule of thumb is that the inflatable arm bag should be approximately 20 per cent wider than the arm diameter, or approximately 12 cm. for adults, 8 cm. for children less than 8 years, 5 cm. for children less than 4 years, 2½ cm. for children less than 1 year. Despite use of such cuffs, a mean error of ±8 mm. Hg may be expected in individual readings of systolic and diastolic pressures. In general, the auscultatory method tends to underestimate systolic pressure and overestimate diastolic pressure. In the arms of people with much fat tissue, the error is further exaggerated; in arrhythmias, deep breathing, or abnormalities of the arterial wall, the errors are still larger. Increases in the resistance of the arterial wall, as a result of sclerotic changes or simple hypertonus of the muscular coat, give readings that are too high. Repeated compression and decompression just before the actual determination is made may soften the

artery or remove any spasm of its walls sufficiently to reduce this source of inaccuracy. Though lower readings as a rule are not obtained in a normal individual by repeated readings, in others with apparently normal arteries, the reading obtained after the third or fourth trial may, as a result of the reduction in tone of the vessel wall, be lower than the initial observation by several millimeters.

Determination of the blood pressure in the human thigh by the auscultatory method gives incorrectly high values and has led to the misconception that leg blood pressure is higher than arm blood pressure. Simultaneous direct intra-arterial measurements in the brachial and femoral arteries have shown the two pressure curves to be similar in all respects (Pascarelli and Bertrand).

Animals

Indirect methods of measuring blood pressure in animals involve inflating a cuff around a carotid loop in the dog (Van Leersum), or around the tail or foot of the rat, and detecting the onset of blood flow under the cuff as cuff pressure is lowered. In the dog this is done with the auscultatory method; in the rat, the volume of blood passing into the tail or foot when the cuff pressure drops below systolic, is insufficient to cause an audible sound. The first blood flow under the cuff and, hence the volume change, is detected in the tail by noting the onset of volume change in a small water-filled plethysmograph just beyond the cuff, or by having the expanding tail press on a carbon button causing a change in tone pitch in ear phones. In the foot, the increase in volume with the lowering of cuff pressure is indicated by the sudden decrease in current flow from a photocell which receives light through the foot.

Use of Simultaneous Measurements of Pressure, Flow, and Volume

In addition to the direct information supplied by blood pressure measurements, knowledge of its association with other phenomena in the circulation, such as blood volume and blood flow, has contributed greatly to advancement in this field. Some reference has already been made to this relationship in chapters 36 and 39. As has been pointed out here, differential pressure measurements in the aorta have enabled calculation of the patterns of flow velocity even in the aorta of man, and the use of such a principle when the pressure pick-up is mounted in a rigid sleeve or vessel, has permitted, in animals, not only patterns of flow velocity but also absolute values for phasic and mean flow. Pressure determination has been particularly useful in estimating the contractility of the heart muscle and the distensibility of the ventricles, arteries and veins. Because of its extreme importance, consideration of this subject will also be found in chapters 35 and 41.

REFERENCES

ALLISON, P. R. AND LINDEN, R. J. Bronchoscopic measurement of left auricular pressure. Circulation 1953, **7**, 669.

BURTON, A. C. AND YAMADA, S. Relation between blood pressure and flow in the human forearm. J. Appl. Physiol., 1951, 4, 329.

BURTON, A. C. Peripheral circulation. Ann. Rev. Physiol., 1953, **15**, 213.

COLERIDGE, J. C. G. AND LINDEN, R. J. The measurement of effective atrial pressure. J. Physiol., 1954, **126**, 304.

COURNAND, A., LAUSON, H. D., BLOOMFIELD, R. A., BREED, E. S., AND BALDWIN, E. deF. Recording of right heart pressures in man. Proc. Soc. Exper. Biol. & Med., 1944, **55**, 34.

FRANK, O. Ein neues optisches Federmanometer. Ztschr. Biol., 1925, **82**, 49.

FRY, D. L., NOBLE, F. W., AND MALLOS, A. J. An evaluation of modern pressure recording systems. Circulation Res., 1957, **5**, 40.

GAUER, O. H. AND GIENAPP, E. A miniature pressure recording device. Science, 1950, 112, 404.

GREEN, E. W., ZIEGLER, R. F., AND KAVANAGH-GRAY, D. Clinical use of retrograde left ventricular catheterization in congenital heart disease (Abstract). Circulation, 1959, **20**, 704.

GREGG, D. E., ECKSTEIN, R. W., AND FINEBERG, M. H. Pressure pulses and blood pressure values in unanesthetized dogs. Am. J. Physiol., 1937, 118, 399.

GREGG, D. E. AND DeWALD, D. The immediate effects of the occlusion of the coronary veins on the collateral blood flow in the coronary arteries. Am. J. Physiol., 1938, **124**, 435.

GREGG, D. E. AND ECKSTEIN, R. W. Measurements of intramyocardial pressure. Am. J. Physiol., 1941, **132**, 781.

GUYTON, A. C. A concept of negative interstitial pressure based on pressures in implanted perforated capsules. Circulation Res., 1963, **12**, 399.

HAMILTON, W. F., BREWER, G., AND BROTMAN, I. Pressure pulse contours in the intact animal; analytical description of the new high frequency hypodermic manometer with illustrative curves of simultaneous arterial and intracardiac pressures. Am. J. Physiol., 1934, **107**, 427.

KARVONEN, M. J., TELIVUO, L. J., AND JARVINEN, E. J. K. Sphygmomanometer cuff size and the accuracy of indirect measurement of blood pressure. Am. J. of Cardiol., 1964, **13**, 688.

LAMBERT, E. H. Strain gauges: resistance wire. Medical Physics, Vol. 2, p. 1090. The Year Book Publishers, Chicago, 1950.

LANDIS, E. M. The capillary pressure in frog mesentery as determined by micro-injection methods. Am. J. Physiol., 1925, **75**, 548.

LATEGOLA, M. AND RAHN, H. A self-guiding catheter for cardiac and pulmonary arterial catheterization and occlusion. Proc. Soc. Exper. Biol. & Med., 1953, **84**, 667.

LILLY, J. C., LEGALLAIS, V., AND CHERRY, R. A variable capacitor for measurements of pressure and mechanical displacements; a theoretical analysis and its experimental evaluations. J. Appl. Physics, 1947, **18**, 613.

MOSS, A. J. AND ADAMS, F. Muffling versus complete cessation of vascular sounds as an index of diastolic blood pressure. Circulation, 1963, **28**, 773.

MUNNELL, E. R. AND GREGG, D. E. The production of chronic systemic hypertension in the rat with a small adjustable renal artery clamp. J. Lab. & Clin. Med., 1950, **36**, 660.

PASCARELLI, E. F. AND BERTRAND, C. A. Comparison of blood pressures in the arms and legs. New Engl. J. Med., 1964, **270**, 693.

ROBERTS, L. N., SMILEY, J. R., AND MANNING, G. W. A comparison of direct and indirect blood-pressure determinations. Circulation, 1953, **8**, 232.

ROSS, J., BRAUNWALD, E., AND MORROW, A. G. Transseptal left atrial puncture. New technique for measurement of left atrial pressure in man. Am. J. Cardiology 1959 3, 653.

RUDOLPH, A. M. AND PAUL, M. H. Chronic catheterization of pulmonary and systemic circulations: a technique for repeated measurement of cardiac output and pulmonary and systemic pressures in the unanesthetized dog. J. Appl. Physiol., 1957, **10**, 327.

SODEMAN, W. A. Direct venous pressure determinations by use of a new instrument. Am. Heart J., 1952, **43**, 687.

SOULIE, P., LAURENS, P., BOUCHARD, F., CORNU, C., AND BRIAL, E. Enrigistrement des pressions et des bruits intracardiaques a l'aide micromanometre. Bull. et mém. Sod. méd. hôp. Paris, 1957, **22, 23, 24**, 713.

WARNICK, A. AND DRAKE, E. H. A new intracardiac pressure measuring system for infants and adults. Institute of Radio Engineers National Convention Record, Part 9, New York, 1958.

WETTERER, E. AND PEIPER, H. Eine neue manometrische sonde mit elektrischer transmission. Ztschr. Biol., 1952, **105**, 49.

WIGGERS, C. J. AND BAKER, W. R. A new universal optical manometer. J. Lab. & Clin. Med., 1924, **10**, 54.

WINSOR, T. AND BURCH, G. E. Phlebostatic axis and phlebostatic level. Reference levels for venous pressure measurements in man. Proc. Soc. Exper. Biol. & Med., 1945, **58**, 165.

WOOD, E. H. Physical response characteristics of pressure transducers for the reproduction of physiological phenomena. Communications and Electronics, 1956, **23**, 56.

Monographs and Reviews

American Medical Association, Recommendations for human blood pressure determination by sphygmomanometers. J. A. M. A., 1951, **147,** 632.

GREEN, H. D. Circulatory system: Methods. In Medical Physics, 1950, p. 208. Year Book Publishers.

HANSEN, A. T. Pressure measurement in the human organism. Acta physiol. scandinav., 1949, **19,** suppl., 68.

HARKEN, D. E. Technic of left heart catheterization. Methods in Medical Research, 1958, **7,** 94. Year Book Publishers.

NOBLE, F. W. Electrical methods of blood pressure recording. Charles C Thomas, Publisher, Springfield, Illinois, 1953.

RAPPAPORT, E. AND DEXTER, L. Pulmonary "capillary" pressure. Methods in Medical Research, 1958, **7,** 85.

CHAPTER 41

THE HEART AS A PUMP

Functional Anatomy

Knowledge of the functional anatomy of cardiac contraction is essential for an understanding of cardiac action. Actually, the two ventricles have different anatomical and functional characteristics. The energy released during systole of the heart represents the combined effects of various bundles of myocardial fibers. The contribution of each bundle depends not only on its contractile power but also on its anatomical orientation within the cardiac walls.

STRUCTURE. Four valve rings of dense connective tissue join to form a fibrous skeleton of the heart. The atria and arterial trunks are attached to the superior surface of this fibrous skeleton; to its inferior aspect are fastened the arteriovenous (A-V) valves and ventricular chambers. The atrial musculature is thin and arranged as bands radiating from the sulcus terminalis. The atria have two muscular systems, one common to both atria and encircling them, the other arranged at right angles and independent for each atrium. From a functional point of view, the ventricular musculature has two groups of myocardial bundles, the spiral muscles and the deep constrictor muscles (fig. 41.1). The superficial spiral muscles which arise from the mitral and tricuspid rings cover very thinly almost the entire surface of both ventricles to a depth of about 1 mm. They course diagonally around the surface of both ventricles to converge at the apex where they are strongly twisted and where they make up the full wall thickness. They penetrate to the interior of both ventricles to form there its inner thin layer of spiral muscle and the lower third of the interventricular septum. They spiral upward in reverse directions to form the papillary muscles from which fibrous tendons (chordae tendinae) attach to the valve leaflets (A-V valves). The inner and outer spiral muscles follow oblique directions about 90° apart since they spiral in opposite directions. As they contract, the oblique traction by the outer layer is opposed by tension in the opposite direction by the inner layer. The net result of their action is a shortening of the ventricular cavities longitudinally rather than a rotation of the ventricles. Interposed between the thin exterior and interior spiral muscles are the heavy constrictor muscles which make up the basilar two-thirds of the septum and lateral wall of the left ventricle. In the right ventricle these deep circular fibers from a thin middle layer but its contribution to thickness is small compared to that of the inner and outer spiral layers. Because the left ventricular wall contains a large mass of circularly arranged constrictor fibers, its contraction would be expected to result predominantly in a reduced ventricular diameter with minimal shortening from apex to base whereas in the right ventricle with its dominance of spiral muscle, the ventricle should shorten with little movements of its lateral wall.

ROLE OF THE PERICARDIUM. The pericardium is a double-walled sac containing a few cubic centimeters of serous fluid which gives a smooth lubricated surface for the heart's movements. Although its potential volume is larger than that occupied by the normal heart in diastole, still, after moderate enlargement of the contained heart, the interpericardial sac pressure rises greatly with small volume influence. Thus, in case of left ventricular stress and enlargement the pericardium restrains diastolic expansion especially of the right ventricle, and therefore, limits right ventricular work. This protects the left ventricle from overload and the pulmonary circulation from congestion. The pericardium also protects against tricuspid or mitral valve regurgitation at high ventricular filling pressures. The value of these mechanisms is probably limited to situations involving acute changes in heart volume; when cardiac enlargement develops more gradually the pericardium follows suit and stretches to accommodate the larger contents. Congenital lack of a pericardium is not uncommon in animals and humans who live to a ripe old age without evidence of cardiac distress.

ATRIAL AND VENTRICULAR BLOOD VOLUME. In man the atrial capacities are slightly greater than those of the corresponding ventricles, thus assuring the presence of sufficient blood to fill the ventricular cavities completely. In the dead human heart, the right atrium has 163 cc., the right ventricle 137 cc., the left atrium 140 cc., the left ventricle 120 cc.

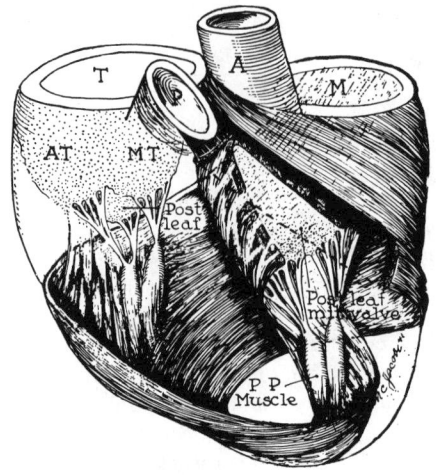

SUPERFICIAL BULBO SPIRAL   SUPERFICIAL SINO SPIRAL

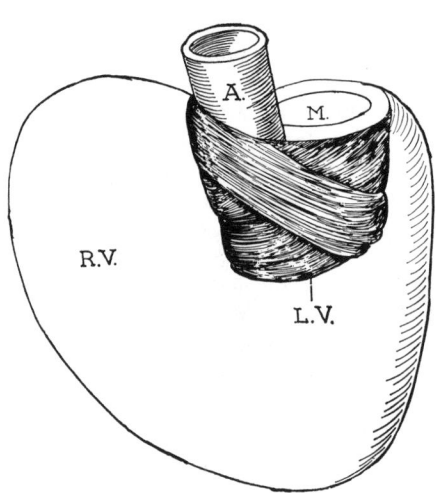 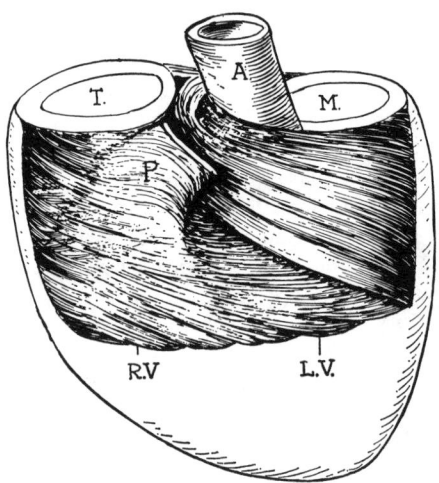

DEEP BULBO SPIRAL   DEEP SINO SPIRAL

Fig. 41.1. Demonstration of the superficial and deep ventricular myocardial bundles (Robb and Robb, Am. Heart J., 1942, **23**, 455).

Such *in vitro* measurements are of limited interest and do not give information as to the diastolic volume of the ventricles during life, or the portion of the diastolic volume which is expelled nor the portion which remains in the ventricle at the end of each heart beat. It is now well-established that the heart is not completely emptied of blood during ventricular contraction, i.e., a residual ventricular volume of blood remains at the end of ejection. Nylin was the first to demonstrate that the diastolic volume of the human heart under working conditions is about 540 cc., of which about 140 cc. is ejected by the two ventricles. The difference, 400 cc., is an estimate of the volume of blood which is normally available at the end of systole for refilling the two ventricles. However, what fraction of this is in the atria and what fraction is in the ventricles is not known. Observations in dogs indicate that the right ventricle and left ventricle both empty in a fractionate manner, ejecting 40 to 45 per cent of their end diastolic volume with each stroke and retaining a residual volume of 55 to 60 per cent. The stroke volume in the resting untrained human approximates 60 cc. On the basis of the dog, this would give a diastolic volume of 130 cc. in the human ventricle. Indeed, Folse and Braunwald reported left ventricular end-diastolic measurements in humans rather closely approximating this predicted value (90 ml./m.^{2} of body surface area; 37 per cent of which was discharged as forward stroke volume, leaving a residual end-systolic volume of 63 per cent). A note of caution is necessary, however, regarding the methodology of *in vivo* ventricular volume measurements. Two such methods are currently available: one is based on the indicator dilution technic, measuring during successive heart beats the decline in concentration of the indicator introduced into the ventricle; the other utilizes cineradiographic measurements following the injection of a radiopaque substance outlining the ventricular cavity. Theoretical objections to the former method include the demonstrated incomplete mixing of the indicator within the ventricular chamber, while angiographic methods must necessarily involve certain geometric assumptions, in addition to the unknown effect on the heart of the rapid injection of a relatively large volume of contrast material. Under these circumstances it would be desirable to see close agreement between results obtained by the two methods in the same experimental subject. In one such study, however, gross discrepancy was found between both end-diastolic and residual end-systolic volume values when calculated by the two different methods.

PATTERNS OF VENTRICULAR EMPTYING. Traditional concept has it that the ventricles eject blood primarily by shortening of the longitudinal axis accompanied by a rotational action comparable to a wringing out of a wet rag. Direct measurements, however, of changing ventricle dimensions in unanesthetized dogs by cinefluorographic techniques with contrast media, by intraventricular gauges and by external resistance gauges, indicate that the left ventricle resembles a cylinder with a conoid apical segment. The cylindrical portion is made of a strong cuff of deep fibers between thin layers of spiral muscle. The conoid section is made primarily of closely woven spiral muscle entering and leaving "the vortex." Left ventricular contraction involves primarily a reduction in transverse diameter. This action accounts for most of the power and volume of the ejection since the contained volume decreases with the square of the radius in a cylinder. There is relatively little rotation or shortening of the longitudinal axis. All this would be ex-

pected since the bulk of the fibers is circularly arranged.

By contrast, right ventricular ejection of blood can be effected by three means. (1) Longitudinal shortening of the chamber, i.e., base moving toward apex is the most obvious movement. This might be expected since the inner and outer layers of spiral muscle making up most of the right ventricle are oriented at about 90° from each other. Hence, simultaneous contraction of the two layers of spiral muscle produces shortening along the longitudinal axis of the right ventricle chamber. (2) The right ventricular chamber is roughly triangular in shape, being bounded by a convex septal well and a concave free or lateral wall which enclose a crescent shaped area between them. The free wall of the right ventricle moves toward the convex surface of the septum. This movement although slight could be extremely effective in moving blood, and it would operate like a bellows used to kindle a fire, i.e., since the sides of the ventricle or bellows are large compared to their enclosed space, slight movement toward each other should cause displacement of a large volume of blood. (3) Contraction of the left ventricle must produce a greater curvature of the septum, and thus, since this is attached to the right ventricular lateral wall, traction on it will add to the bellows action. The action of this or the other factors has not been quantitated. That it can be a potent mechanism, however, is borne out by the observation that right ventricular ejection can be maintained when the free wall of the right ventricle has been almost completely destroyed by cautery in the dog or by coronary occlusion in man.

The reduction in diameter and circumference necessary to eject the stroke volume is different in the two ventricles because of their shape and manner of contraction but they are small in both cases. With present methodology, it is not possible to quantitate the extent of myocardial fiber shortening associated with ventricular ejection of blood. However, some rough estimates are instructive. Under normal circumstances the ventricles function at relatively large diastolic and systolic dimensions since possibly half their contained volume is not ejected with each contraction. If the left ventricle is regarded roughly as a cylinder which ejects approximately half its contained volume of 130 cc., then the diameter can decrease from 5.2 cm. to 3.9 cm., and the circumference from 16.5 cm. to 12.1 cm.

The right ventricle has some semblance to a segment of a sphere, and a small shortening of its fibers will eject a large blood volume. If its volume is also 130 cc., and half is ejected, the diameter will decrease from 6.3 cm. to 5.1 cm., and the circumference from 19.8 cm. to 16.0 cm. The average shortening of the right and left ventricle walls might be estimated as 20 per cent and 25 per cent of the diastolic size. The extent of myocardial shortening also varies greatly for the same volume of ejection depending on the size of the cavity or the fiber length before ejection takes place. It takes a much smaller reduction in fiber length of a larger sphere or cylinder to eject the same volume. For example, if in a heart enlarged by congestive failure of the circulation the right ventricle contains 500 cc. blood, then ejection of 60 cc. will decrease the diameter from 9.8 cm. to 9.4 cm., or by 0.4 cm., and the circumference from 30.8 cm. to 29.5 cm.

It would be expected that the shortening of muscle fibers of the lateral wall of the right ventricle at different depths would be similar since the wall is so thin. In the left ventricle, however, the circumferentially arranged deep constrictor fibers form a cuff of muscle making up most of the muscle wall which is so thick that the inner layers near the endocardium have a much smaller radius and circumference than the outer layers near the epicardium. With the onset of contraction, the inner layers must shorten more than the outer layers in ejecting a particular volume. Thus, presumably, no two layers of the myocardial fibers shorten to the same extent during ejection.

Pressure and Volume Events of a Cardiac Cycle

It is important to consider the means by which the heart cavities are able to pump the necessary volume of blood from the systemic veins to the arteries and to impart to it a pressure sufficient to cause a continuous flow of blood through the capillaries. The sequence of events can be considered in terms of atrial, ventricular, and arterial pressures, and of variations in the volume of and means of emptying the cardiac cavities. The events of the cardiac cycle for both left and right hearts are depicted in figure 41.2. Terminology and symbols given to the various phases of the cardiac cycle by Wiggers are used. The curves are synthesized in part from records obtained in dogs. In the main, however, pressure values and temporal relations are based upon pressure pulses obtained from all four cardiac chambers, pulmonary artery and aorta, by direct needle puncture at the time of thoracotomy in human subjects clinically free of cardiovascular disease. The schematized volume curve is based on recordings

of volume of both ventricles in which a cardiometer has been placed around the ventricles up to their A-V junction in the open-chest dog. Left ventricular circumference and cross-sectional area recordings, by means of external resistance gauges attached to the heart, yield qualitatively similar curves in unanesthetized, closed-chest dogs.

SEQUENCE OF EVENTS. Ventricular contraction begins at "1", and almost instantly closure of the mitral valve occurs as the ventricular pressure curve exceeds the left atrial pressure curve. The "c" wave in the atrial curve begins at this time and is due to the rising pressure in the ventricle which is transmitted through the closed A-V valves which bulge into the atrium. It marks the onset of the left ventricular isometric or isovolumic contraction period which consists of a slow and then a rapid pressure rise. This period in which the ventricle is a closed cavity, ends at "2" the moment at which the ventricular pressure exceeds the aortic pressure. The aortic valves are forced open as indicated by the onset of the pressure rise in the aorta, and blood is discharged from the ventricular cavity. From the moment that the aortic valves open at "2", until they close at "4", ventricle and aorta are common cavities and, consequently, their pressure pulses have a similar contour. Ventricular volume starts now to decrease. The period of maximum ejection lasts until the peak of the aortic pressure pulse and is followed by a period of reduced ejection which is completed at the beginning of the incisura (3), a point which is often difficult to identify on the records. This is the end of ejection of blood and of ventricular systole. The ventricular cavity still retains more than half its original diastolic volume. During protodiastole (3 to 4), the pressure within the ventricle continues to decline and this phase ends at the moment of aortic valve closure (4), i.e., at the bottom of the incisura of the aortic pressure curve. Isometric or isovolumic relaxation (4 to 5) then follows. At this time, the atrium and ventricle are relaxed and the left ventricular cavity is completely closed off from the atrium and aorta and only partially filled.

During the preceding ventricular contraction, the left atrial pressure undergoes a temporary abrupt decline as a result of an artefact imposed by cardiac movement. As blood, however, pours into the cavity of the left atrium from the pulmonary veins, the atrial pressure rises continuously to the end of the isometric relaxation period forming the "V" wave. This atrial blood which

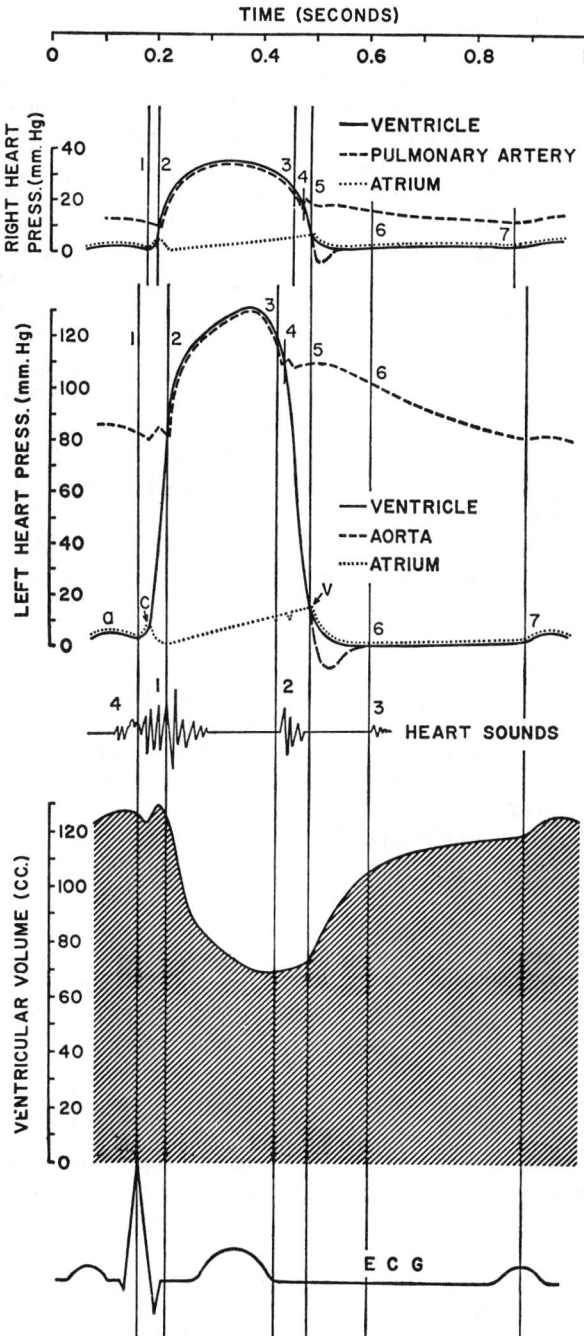

Fig. 41.2. Schematization of the sequential cardiac events relating pressure-volume changes to the phono- and electrocardiograms: *upper tracings*, right and left heart pressures; *middle tracings*, phono-cardiogram and ventricular volume; and *bottom tracings*, electrocardiogram. Vertical lines correspond temporally to the following: 1, onset of isometric ventricular contraction and closure of A-V valves; 2, end of isometric contraction and opening of semilunar valves; 3, incisura or end of ventricular ejection and ventricular systole; 4, closure of semilunar valves and onset of isometric ventricular relaxation; 5, opening of A-V valves and onset of rapid ventricular filling; and 6 and 7, slow ventricular filling or diastasis, ending with atrial contraction.

has accumulated during the previous ventricular contraction is now transferred to the ventricle. Ventricular filling begins at the time the intraventricular pressure drops below the intra-atrial pressure and the A-V valves reopen (5).

The period of rapid ventricular filling, i.e., the early diastolic inflow period is marked by a continuous decline in ventricular pressure and in the "V" wave of the atrial pressure curve (the so-called "Y" descent). Inflow into a ventricular cavity is regulated by mechanisms operating in both its systole and diastole. Since no blood enters the ventricles until it has passed through the atria, it is important to know their means of filling. It is not possible to measure flow into the atria, but since the right atrium is continuous with the venae cavae without intervening valves, vena caval flow should indicate right atrial flow. Caval flow into the right atrium shows three phases. It is reduced nearly to zero during atrial contraction. During ventricular diastole inflow is considerable, but the volume of atrial inflow is greater during ventricular systole when the A-V valves are closed and no blood can enter the ventricle, than during ventricular diastole when A-V valves are open and atria and ventricles form a common cavity. Atrial inflow during ventricular contraction is particularly effective in the presence of tachycardia in which the time available for diastolic inflow is shortened. The pistonlike downward movement of the atrioventricular junction during ventricular systole enlarges the atria and vena cava and attracts blood to them. The filling of the atria during ventricular systole depends on the quantity and pressure of blood available in the venous reservoir and the vigor with which ventricular systole moves the A-V junction. Thus, ventricular myocardial contraction is a very important means of actively filling the atria during systole and, therefore, in determining the extent of ventricular filling during the rapid filling phase.

Finally, attention is directed to the dashed and abruptly dipping line representing an alternate decline of the ventricular pressure and which, at times, indicates a negative intraventricular pressure has developed. Such a dip in the pressure curve of ventricular relaxation, although recorded for many years and considered an artefact, is now given more credence since (1) it can be recorded with a micromanometer (which is supposedly immune to artefacts); (2) recent experimental evidence indicates that the relaxing ventricle can develop suction under certain artificial experimental conditions. For example, in the beating mammalian heart, a moderate volume of fluid can be drawn into the ventricular cavity in the absence of a positive ventricular filling pressure and in the presence of an empty ventricle or one with some systolic residual volume. The time available during which suction could act is approximately 0.1 sec., i.e., the earlier part of the rapid inflow period. The quantitative contribution of the ventricle to ventricular filling under normal conditions is still unknown and, hence, the physiological significance of diastolic suction for the return of blood to the heart cannot be evaluated. Wiggers, in summarizing the problem, states "crucial evidence is still required that the small remnant of elastic recoil still operative at the end of relaxation can create sufficient suction to be of significance in filling the normally beating heart. Dynamically it must be shown that the concordant declines of atrial and ventricular pressures are due to a more rapid rate of ventricular relaxation than of filling from the atrium."

Diastasis, or the period of slowed ventricular filling, begins when the atrial pressure begins to rise during diastole (6). The end of diastasis (7) is marked by the onset of atrial contraction ("a" wave) which is reflected in the ventricle since the atrial and ventricular cavities are now continuous. The dynamic interval of atrial systole lasts until the peak of the atrial contraction wave while the inflow phase that follows ends at the onset of ventricular isometric contraction and completes the cardiac cycle.

ATRIAL CONTRACTION. The dynamic importance of atrial contraction on ventricular filling has been much debated. The older view that the chief function of the atria is filling the ventricles is not now acceptable since it is known that such filling occurs chiefly during the earlier portion of diastole when the difference between atrial and ventricular pressure is maximal. However, in hearts slowed by vagal stimulation to separate atrial and ventricular contraction and in hearts with 2:1 or more block, it can be demonstrated that atrial contraction has a small but significant effect on the ventricular volume curve obtained with a cardiometer. In open-chest dogs with surgically induced complete atrio-ventricular block and a fixed, slow ventricular rate, there is an increase in left ventricular end-diastolic pressure, stroke volume, stroke work and aortic systolic pressure when atrial systole precedes ventricular systole by an interval of 0.085 to 0.125 seconds, indicating enhanced ventricular filling through atrial contraction. Finally, atrial contraction and relaxation are instrumental in bringing about closure of the atrio-ventricular valves (see below).

PRESSURE AND TIME VALUES OF DYNAMIC AND ELECTRICAL EVENTS AND THEIR TEMPORAL RELATIONSHIP IN THE LEFT AND RIGHT HEART. For full details original articles should be consulted. However, certain features are obvious. The following table gives the approximate figures for the duration of the chief phases of the cardiac cycle of the left heart when the heart rate approximates 70 per minute in the human.

	Seconds
Atrial systole	0.11
Atrial diastole	0.71
Ventricular systole (total)	0.27
Isometric contraction period	0.06 (right ventricle, .02)
Ejection period	0.21
Ventricular diastole (total)	0.56
Protodiastolic period	0.02
Isometric relaxation period	0.05 (right ventricle, .02)
Rapid inflow period	0.16
Diastasis	0.23
Atrial systole	0.10

A. Pressure pulse values. Aortic pressure throughout the cardiac cycle is uniformly higher than in the pulmonary artery. The peak aortic pressure during systole of 120 mm. Hg is approximately five times that of 25 mm. Hg in the pulmonary artery; the relative end-diastolic pressures are 80 mm. Hg versus 10 mm. Hg; the relative pulse pressures are 40 mm. Hg versus 15 mm. Hg. The diastolic pressure in both cavities is quite low with a small pressure gradient from the left ventricle (0 to 5 mm. Hg mean diastolic, 5 to 12 mm. Hg end-diastolic) to the right ventricle (0 to 3 mm. Hg mean diastolic, 0 to 5 mm. Hg end-diastolic). The atrial pressure values are only a few mm. Hg and are uniformly somewhat higher in the left atrial (mean 2 to 12 mm. Hg) than in the right atrial (mean 0 to 5 mm. Hg) curve.

B. Asynchronisms of pressure pulses. While dynamic events on the two sides of the heart are generally similar, there is considerable asynchronism and some difference in duration of parts of the cardiac cycle. The onset of contraction of the right atrium precedes that of the left atrium while the onset of contraction of the right ventricle follows that of the left ventricle. Right

ventricular ejection begins earlier and is completed later than left ventricular ejection.

C. Electrocardiogram versus onset of pressure events. In man the interval between the onset of electrical and mechanical activity in the left atrium (rise of P wave versus onset of rise of atrial A wave) is of the order of 0.06 sec.; for the right atrium, the interval approximates 0.08 sec. For the left ventricle, the interval between the onset of ventricular depolarization (Q wave) and onset of left ventricular contraction (onset of pressure rise) approximates 0.04 sec.; for the right ventricle, the interval is about 0.05 sec. The T wave has a variable relation to the end of systole but terminates usually before the incisura of the aortic pressure curve.

The Movements of the Heart Valves

The chief factor concerned in the opening and closing of the valves is, as already indicated (p. 734), the difference in pressure upon their opposite surfaces. Some additional features of the valvular mechanisms must now be considered.

THE ATRIOVENTRICULAR VALVES (TRICUSPID AND MITRAL). The valve leaflets or cusps, three in number on the right and two on the left side, are attached by their bases to the fibrous rings surrounding the atrioventricular openings. Their free margins are connected through delicate tendons (chordae tendineae) to the papillary muscles which prevent inversion of the valves into the auricle during ventricular systole. The chordae tendineae are tightened at the commencement of systole by the contraction of the papillary muscles. The leaflets are composed mainly of a double layer of the endothelial lining of the heart, strengthened by a few connective tissue fibers. Their attached bases are thicker and contain more connective tissue, small blood vessels and delicate strands of smooth muscle. The latter, however, play no part in valve closure which is effected, as mentioned above, in a passive manner.

A. The mechanism of valve closure. According to traditional concept, an advancing gush of blood thrusts the A-V valves widely open during early ventricular diastole. During atrial systole the leaflets do not lie back against the ventricular wall but occupy a midposition as a result of two opposing currents. The inflowing blood pressing upon their atrial surfaces keeps them open, while eddies reflected in the reverse direction from the ventricular walls strike their ventricular surfaces and tend to close them. Thus, they float in a position of delicate balance. When,

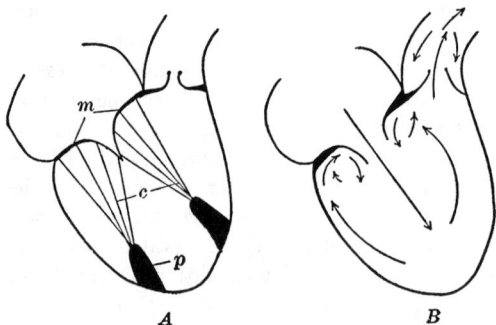

FIG. 41.3. Two diagrams showing mechanisms concerned in valve closure. *A*, showing relations of papillary muscles and chordae tendineae to valve flaps; *B*, partial closure due to eddy formation (after Wiggers, 1954.)

as a result of the fall in intra-atrial pressure at the end of atrial systole, the incoming jet is diminished in force and finally ceases, the back eddies persisting for a brief space and being unopposed, approximate the valves or bring them gently into apposition (fig. 41.3). The importance of atrial relaxation in closing the valves has been shown in open-chest dogs with surgically induced atrio-ventricular block, where a negative atrio-ventricular pressure difference was demonstrated during atrial diastole. The fact that the first heart sound has been found to be significantly delayed in the absence of atrial systole supports this view that normally the atrioventricular valves are closed or nearly so, before ventricular systole. They are not, however, firmly closed. This is effected by the rise in pressure in the ventricle when it contracts. Dean has shown by attaching a hair to the septal leaf of the valve and recording its movements, that if ventricular systole does not follow almost instantly upon the cessation of the flow of blood from the atrium, the valves start to reopen. In instances, therefore, in which ventricular systole is delayed, that is, when the A-V interval is prolonged, the reopening of the valves proceeds for an appreciable time. Then, when ventricular contraction occurs, a small amount of blood regurgitates into the atrium before the valves are swung closed by the rising intraventricular pressure. The backward flow of blood through the orifice may then give rise to a murmur just preceding the first heart sound (presystolic murmur).

These concepts have been derived mainly from observations and direct photography of valve action in isolated hearts and from correlation of heart sound with mechanical and electrical events of the cardiac cycle. However, cinefluorographic observations of the motions of the mitral valve cusps by means of attached radiopaque markers in intact anesthetized dogs, showed the edges of the valve cusps to be only slightly separated during ventricular filling. Since in both instances, it is not possible to rule out certain experimental artefacts, at present no choice can be made between the concept of wide valve excursion in isolated hearts and restricted valve movements in intact animals.

THE SEMILUNAR VALVES. The dynamics of aortic and pulmonary closure are essentially the same in principle as those described for the A-V valves. The valves form three small pockets open toward the arterial lumen. Back eddies which are set up during the ejection phase of systole prevent the contact of the valves with the arterial wall. When ejection ceases, the centripetal currents carry the valves into apposition and firm closure is effected by the higher pressure at this time upon their arterial surfaces.

Heart Sounds

METHODOLOGY. The sounds produced by the heart during a cardiac cycle consist of waves of greatly varying frequency. To pick these up, a simple form of stethoscope is used in which a small bell or disk placed over the chest conducts the sound waves through rubber tubes to ear pieces. Because of the intervening tissue, the intensity of the sounds is generally decreased and some components are accentuated and others depressed. The stethoscope itself does not amplify sounds accurately or conduct them accurately to the ear, the size and shape of the end pieces and the pressure exerted affecting the auditory characteristics of the sounds. Despite this, the sounds heard thus by ear give more practical information than is obtained by any other approach. The heart sounds have also been picked up by a microphone applied to the chest wall over the heart, amplified, and the frequency selectively filtered before it reaches the ear or is conducted to a loudspeaker. This is didactically helpful since many can listen simultaneously, but it does not give a better appreciation of the sounds as they actually occur.

Graphic registration of the heart sounds has been used to give a permanent record for study and to permit precise relations to be established between them and the events of the cardiac cycle, as recorded by other graphic methods such as the electrocardiogram and intracardiac and intravascular pressure curves. As already mentioned, this provides an accurate method of measuring the duration of ventricular systole. In the classical direct method, heart sounds at the chest level are conducted by a stethoscopic bell by means of a short rubber tube to a sound recorder, the coarsest vibrations being allowed to escape through a lateral opening. The recorder consists of a very fine rubber membrane with attached mirror whose movements are recorded on photographic paper. Einthoven introduced an indirect method in which the sounds picked up by a stethoscope fastened to the chest were transmitted to a microphone the movements of the disk of which produced changes in a simple electric circuit recordable by a string galvanometer (fig. 41.4). With the development of crystal microphones and proper vacuum tube amplification, a number of devices are available commercially in which the heart sounds are converted at the chest level into electrical variations which are amplified and recorded by high frequency oscillographs. In this electronic apparatus, the lower frequencies have generally been severely attenuated or filtered to resemble the effect of the human hearing mechanism with a stethoscope. The records are used to increase the acumen of clinical auscultation; the advantage is mainly in appreciating the timing and relation to each other of heart sounds and murmurs. But in the matter of increase in perception of faint murmurs, phonocardiography does not compare with the remarkable sensitivity and selectivity of the human ear.

For obvious reasons, sounds picked up from the surface of the thorax are not a true representation of the actual vibrations of the cardiac valves and walls. Thus, attempts have been made to move the pick-up device closer to the source of sound by placing microphones in the esophagus, by suturing microphones to the myocardium in experimental animals, by applying suction microphones directly to the surface of the human heart, and finally, by introducing the microphone into the cardiac chambers themselves. The latter technique aids in locating the site of production of normal heart sounds and serves as a valuable diagnostic tool in disease states in locating the origin of abnormal sounds and murmurs. However, use of data obtained thereby must be tempered by knowledge of the fact the catheter mounted device may itself, through the motion imparted to it in the cardiac cavities, produce sounds which are recorded as naturally occurring.

CHARACTERISTICS OF HEART SOUNDS. Two distinct sounds are heard by direct auscultation and occasionally a third is also audible during a cardiac cycle. A fourth sound is revealed by graphic

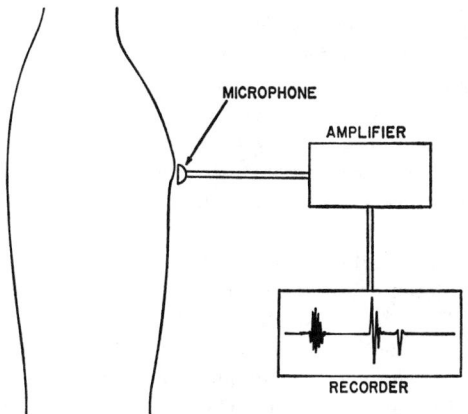

FIG. 41.4. Schematic diagram illustrating the recording of heart sounds. The signal from the microphone goes through an amplifier to give it the necessary amplitude to drive a recorder.

methods. The first two sounds occur mainly during ventricular systole, the other two sounds take place during ventricular diastole (fig. 41.2).

A. Origin of heart sounds and time relations. These vibrations arising in the heart are fundamentally the result of sudden displacement of blood (acceleration) or abrupt stoppage of blood (deceleration).

The temporal relations of human heart sounds to central hemodynamic events are illustrated schematically in figure 41.2. The large vibrations of the first sound begin with the rapid rise in intraventricular tension and by the beginning of ejection they have already reached a maximum. The beginning of the second sound coincides with the trough of the incisura of the aortic pressure. The third sound occurs near the end of the rapid inflow phase of diastole of the ventricles. The fourth sound begins near the middle of the atrial pressure wave and extends to the isometric phase of ventricular contraction.

B. First heart sound. The first sound is of relatively long duration, soft in quality and low in pitch. The second sound is shorter, sharper and of higher pitch. These characteristics are best imitated vocally by the syllables "lub" and "dup" separated by a brief pause. The two heart sounds mark the beginning and end of ventricular systole and the determination of the interval between their commencements (as determined by the phonocardiogram) is a reliable method for arriving at the length of ventricular systole in man although intracardiac phonocardiographic techniques indicate a time lag of the order of 0.02 seconds between the closure of the atrio-ventricular valves and the beginning of the first heart sound (see below). The pause between the end of the second sound and the beginning of the first coincides with ventricular diastole.

The first sound is heard most clearly and at maximum intensity over the 5th left intercostal space, i.e., with an area centered over the "apex beat." Here the mitral element of the sound predominates. Any abnormal sound produced at the tricuspid valve is detected by listening over the lower end of the sternum.

The principal factors entering into the production of the first sound are: (1) the closure of the atrioventricular valves and the tension set up in the valve leaflets and chordae tendineae as the intraventricular pressure rises (valvular element), (2) contraction of the ventricular muscle, and (3) the rush of blood from the ventricles and the shock transmitted to the walls of the aorta and the pulmonary artery (vascular element).

The vibration of the valves is the most important element of the first sound. Since the sound, as recorded by intracardiac phonocardiography, begins about 0.02 seconds after ventricular pressure excedes atrial pressure (i.e. after closure of the atrio-ventricular valves), the apposition of the valve leaflet margins is a silent event, and the sound is generated by vibrations set up in the valvular structures by the rising ventricular pressure. Dock has questioned whether the ventricular muscle produces a sound at all. He recorded the sound vibrations by means of a phonocardiograph applied to the surface of the heart and reported that no sound was produced when the empty heart contracted, valve action being abolished. Although he concluded from this that the normal first sound contained no muscular element, evidence from other sources is strongly opposed to such a conception. Wiggers and Dean, previously had recorded sound vibration from an isolated strip of myocardium. It has also been shown that when free movement of the valves of the beating heart is prevented, the booming character of the first sound still persists. Some have claimed that the first sound is not prolonged into the ejection period, and therefore, the impact of the blood upon the walls of the large vessels cannot contribute to the sound. But the observations of Straub and of Orias and Braun-Menendez indicate that the first sound does extend beyond the isometric period and that the vascular element is an important component.

The record of the first sound is composed chiefly of a series of from 9 to 13 vibrations, and has a duration of from 0.9 to 0.16 sec. These are of small amplitude to start with but rise to a "crescendo" which reaches its maximum at the end of the isometric period and is followed by a "diminuendo" of about the same duration. The main series is followed by a few final vibrations, variable in number. The vibrations are in general irregular, which places the sounds in the category of noises rather than of musical tones. The frequency is low varying from 33 to 110 per sec.

C. The second sound results from the vibrations set up in the blood column and arterial walls as the aortic and pulmonary valves are placed under tension following their closure. The duration of the second sound is about 0.10 sec. It commences about 0.09 sec. after the summit of the T wave of the electrocardiogram. The average frequency is about 50 per sec. In the pulmonary area (along the left upper border of the sternum) two components of the second sound can normally be heard ("split second sound"). Phonocardiographic records show that the first of the two components is synchronous with the dicrotic notch of the carotid arterial pressure pulse and therefore represents aortic valve closure; the second component is caused by closure of the pulmonary valve. The relative delay of pulmonary vs. aortic valve closure is enhanced during inspiration when the increased venous return to the right heart prolongs right ventricular ejection time; the situation is reversed during subsequent expiration, when the blood ejected by the right ventricle reaches the left side of the heart and causes prolongation of left ventricular ejection, moving aortic valve closure closer to pulmonary valve closure. Thus the splitting of the second heart sound widens during inspiration (average 0.05 sec.) and narrows or even disappears during expiration (average 0.02 sec.).

D. The third heart sound. Sometimes a faint third sound is heard in normal hearts which follows the second sound by about 0.08 sec. and lasts for about 0.04 sec. It is heard at the apex and is commonly found in young adults. Thayer found it present in 65 per cent of normal individuals. It may be made to appear or is intensified by procedures which increase the venous flow into the atria, e.g., exercise, recumbent position, etc. The sound was first described by Gibson and independently by Herschfelder; several explanations have since been given to account for it. By intracardiac phonocardiography it was demonstrated that the sound coincides with rapid, early ventricular filling and is recordable from the ventricular cavity and the ventricular surface but not from the atrium. It is suggested that the sound is produced by the vibrations of the ventricular wall as blood rushes into the ventricle.

E. The fourth heart sound, as a rule, is inaudible in normal subjects. Often, however, the phonocardiogram records a few small pre-systolic vibrations, usually consisting of two components. The first of these coincides with the atrial "a" wave and, by intracardiac phonocardiographic techniques, it can be recorded from within the atria, indicating that it is caused by atrial contraction. The second component follows the peak of atrial contraction and can be recorded more often from the ventricles than from the atria, suggesting that it is due to the impact of blood, expelled from the atria, against the ventricular wall.

F. Variations in the intensity of the heart sounds. It is the general belief that the first sound varies in intensity with the force of ventricular systole and the loudness of the second sound with the height of the arterial blood pressure. The experiments of Wiggers bear this out. The sounds were recorded graphically and correlated with the intraventricular and aortic pressure curves. It was found that the vibrations of the first sound were increased in amplitude and number when the tension developed by the cardiac muscle was increased. The intensity of the first sound is directly related to the rate of the pressure rise within the ventricle during the isometric period. The intensity of this sound is not dependent upon the volume of the systolic discharge but rather upon the diastolic pressures in the pulmonary and systemic circuits. Wiggers found that when the heart was slowed and the systolic discharge consequently increased but the diastolic pressure lowered, the intensity of the first heart sound was reduced while acceleration of the heart (reduced systolic discharge with raised diastolic pressure) increased its intensity. These experiments together with the observations that the first heart sound is believed to be largely on a valvular basis and is greatly influenced by the length of the P-R interval, strongly suggest that the intensity of the sound is ultimately conditioned by the position of the A-V valves at the onset of ventricular systole.

The intensity of the second sound, aortic or pulmonary, is increased by an elevation in the systemic or pulmonary pressures, respectively. Among the cardiovascular conditions associated with intensification of the second sound are, mitral stenosis and failure of the left ventricle which raise the pulmonary arterial pressure, and arterial hypertension which raises the aortic pressure.

REFERENCES

BAKOS, A. C. P. The question of the function of the right ventricular myocardium: an experimental study. Circulation, 1950, **1**, 724.

BERGLUND, E., SARNOFF, S. J., AND ISAACS, J. P. The pericardium in regulation of cardiovascular dynamics. Circulation Res., 1955, **3**, 133.

BERGLUND, E. AND SARNOFF, S. J. Role of the pericardium in regulation of ventricular stroke work and output when the left ventricle is acutely challenged. Am. J. Physiol., 1952, **171**, 708.

BING, R. J., HEIMBECKER, R. AND FALHOLT, W. An estimation of the residual volume of blood in the right ventricle of normal and diseased human hearts *in vivo*. Am. Heart J., 1951, **42**, 483.

BOYER, N. H. Studies of the third heart sound. Am. Heart J., 1942, **23**, 797.

BRAUNWALD, E., BROCKENBROUGH, E. C., FRAHM, C. J., AND ROSS, J. R., JR. Left atrial and left ventricular pressure in subjects without cardiovascular disease. Observations in eighteen patients studied by transseptal left heart catheterization. Circulation, 1961, **24**, 267.

BRAUNWALD, E., MOSCOWITZ, H. L., AMRAM, S. S., LASSER, R. P., SAPIN, S. O., HIMMELSTEIN, A., RAVITCH, M. M., AND GORDON, A. J. Timing of electrical and mechanical events of the left side of the human heart. J. Appl. Physiol., 1955, **8**, 309.

BRAUNWALD, E., MOSCOWITZ, H. L., AMRAM, S. S., LASSER, R. P., SAPIN, S. O., HIMMELSTEIN, A., AND RAVITCH, M. M. The hemodynamics of the left side of the heart as studied by simultaneous left atrial, left ventricular and aortic pressures: particular reference to mitral stenosis. Circulation, 1955, **12**, 69.

BRAUNWALD, E., FISHMAN, A. P., AND COURNAND, A. Time relationship of dynamic events in the cardiac chambers, pulmonary artery and aorta in man. Circulation Res., 1956, **4**, 100.

BRECHER, G. A. Cardiac variations in venous return studied with a new bristle flow meter. Am. J. Physiol., 1954, **176**, 423.

BRECHER, G. A. AND KISSEN, A. T. Ventricular diastolic suction at normal arterial pressures. Circulation Res., 1958, **6**, 100.

BROCKMAN, S. K. Dynamic function of atrial contraction in regulation of cardiac performance. Am. J. Physiol., 1963, **204**, 597.

COBLENTZ, B., HARVEY, R. M., FERRER, M. L., AND COURNAND, A. The relationship between electrical and mechanical events in the cardiac cycle of man. Brit. Heart J., 1949, **11**, 1.

COUNIHAN, T., MESSER, A., RAPPAPORT, M. B., AND SPRAGUE, H. B. The initial vibrations of the first heart sound. Circulation, 1951, **3**, 730.

CREVASSE, L., WHEAT, M. W., WILSON, J. R., LEEDS, R. F., AND TAYLOR, W. J. The mechanism of the generation of the third and fourth heart sounds. Circulation, 1962, **25**, 635.

DiBARTOLO, G., NUNEZ-DEY, D., MUIESAN, G., MacCANON, D. M., AND LUISADA, A. A.

Hemodynamic correlates of the first heart sound. Am. J. Physiol., 1961, **201**, 888.

Dock, W. Mode of production of the first heart sound. Arch. Int. Med., 1933, **51**, 737.

Dock, W. The forces needed to evoke sounds from cardiac tissues, and the attenuation of heart sounds. Circulation, 1959, **19**, 376.

Eckstein, R. W. Sounds due to muscular contraction and their importance in the auscultatory quality of the first heart sound. Am. J. Physiol., 1937, **118**, 359.

Folse, R. and Braunwald, E. Determination of fraction of left ventricular volume ejected per beat and of ventricular end-diastolic and residual volumes. Experimental and clinical observations with a precordial dilution technic. Circulation, 1962, **25**, 674.

Gouley, B. A. The aortic valvular lesion associated with Austin Flint murmur. Am. Heart J., 1941, **22**, 208.

Hallermann, F. J., Rastelli, G. C., and Swan, H. J. C. Comparison of left ventricular volumes by dye dilution and angiographic methods in the dog. Am. J. Physiol., 1963, **204**, 446.

Hawthorne, E. W. Instantaneous dimensional changes of the left ventricle in dogs. Circulation Res., 1961, **9**, 110.

Henderson, Y. and Barringer, T. B. The conditions determining the volume of the arterial blood stream. Am. J. Physiol., 1913, **31**, 288.

Henderson, Y. and Johnson, F. E. Two modes of closure of the heart valves. Heart, 1912, **4**, 69.

Hochrein, M. and Eckhardt, W. Dynamik Verschiedener Klappen-Fehler insbesandere der Mitral Stenose und Aorten Insuffizenz. Klin. Wchnschr., 1930, **9**, 12.

Holt, J. P., Allenworth, J., Diana, J., Collins, D., and Hines, H. Estimation of the residual volume of the right ventricle of the dog's heart. Circulation Res., 1957, **5**, 323.

Holt, J. P. Estimation of residual volume of ventricle of the dog's heart by two indicator dilution technics. Circulation Res., 1956, **4**, 187.

Irisawa, H., Wilson, M. F., and Rushmer, R. F. Left ventricle as mixing chamber. Circulation Res., 1960, **8**, 183.

Jochim, K. The contribution of the auricle to ventricular filling in complete heart block. Am. J. Physiol., 1938, **122**, 639.

Kagan, A. Dynamic responses of the right ventricle following extensive damage by cauterization. Circulation, 1952, **5**, 816.

Kountz, W. B., Gilson, A. S., and Smith, J. R. The use of the cathode ray for recording heart sounds and vibrations: I. Studies on the normal heart. Am. Heart J., 1940, **20**, 667; II. Studies on the muscular element of the first heart sound. Am. Heart J., 1941, **21**, 17.

Leatham, A. Splitting of the first and second heart sounds. Lancet, 1954, **2**, 607.

Little, R. C., Hilton, J. G., and Schaeffer, R. D. The first heart sound in normal and ectopic ventricular contractions. Mechanism of closure of the A-V valves. Circulation Res., 1954, **2**, 48.

McClure, J. A., Lacy, W. W., Latimer, P., and Newman, E. V. Indicator dilution in an atrioventricular system with competent or incompetent valves. A complete analysis of the behavior of indicator injected instantaneously or continuously into either chamber. Circulation Res., 1959, **7**, 794.

McKusick, V. A., Talbot, S. A., and Webb, G. N. Spectral phonocardiography; problems and prospects in the application of the Bell sound spectrograph to phonocardiography. Bull. Johns Hopkins Hosp., 1954, **95**, 90.

Moscovitz, H. L. and Wilder, R. J. Pressure events of the cardiac cycle in the dog. Circulation Res., 1956, **4**, 574.

Muiesan, G., MacCanon, D. M., Nunez-Dey, D., and DiBartolo, G. Hemodynamic correlates of the fourth heart sound. Am. J. Physiol., 1961, **201**, 1090.

Nylin, G. On the amount of and changes in the residual blood of the heart. Am. Heart J., 1943, **25**, 598.

Rappaport, M. B. and Sprague, H. B. Physiologic and physical laws that govern auscultation and their clinical application. Am. Heart J., 1941, **21**, 257.

Rappaport, M. B. and Sprague, H. B. The graphic registration of the normal heart sounds. Am. Heart J., 1942, **23**, 591.

Robb, J. S. and Robb, R. C. Normal heart. Anatomy and physiology of the structural units. Am. Heart J., 1942, **23**, 455.

Rushmer, R. F. and Thal, N. The mechanics of ventricular contraction: a cinefluorographic study. Circulation, 1951, **4**, 219.

Rushmer, R. F., Crystal, D. K., and Wagner, C. The functional anatomy of ventricular contraction. Circulation Res., 1953, **1**, 162.

Rushmer, R. F. Continuous measurements of left ventricular dimensions in intact, unanesthetized dogs. Circulation Res., 1954, **2**, 14.

Rushmer, R. F. Length-circumference relations of the left ventricle. Circulation Res., 1955, **3**, 639.

Rushmer, R. F. Anatomy and physiology of ventricular function. Physiol. Rev., 1956, **36**, 400.

Rushmer, R. F., Finlayson, B. L., and Nash, A. A. Movements of the mitral valve. Circulation Res., 1956, **4**, 337.

Samet, P., Bernstein, W. H., and Litwak, R. S. Electrical activation and mechanical asynchronization in the cardiac cycle of the dog. Circulation Res., 1959, **7**, 228.

Sarnoff, S. J., Gilmore, J. P., and Mitchell, J. H. Influence of atrial contraction and relaxation on closure of mitral valve. Circulation Res., 1962, **11**, 26.

Shaffer, H. A. Splitting of the second heart sound. Am. J. Cardiol., 1960, **6**, 1013.

Siecke, H. and Essex, H. E. Relation of the difference in pressure across the mitral valve to the amplitude of the first heart sound in dogs with atrioventricular block. Am. J. Physiol., 1958, **192**, 135.

Sloan, A. W. and Wishart, M. The effect on the human third heart sound of variations in the rate of filling of the heart. Brit. Heart J., 1953, **15**, 25.

Smith, H. L., Essex, H. E., and Baldes, E. J.

A study of the movements of heart valves and of heart sounds. Ann. Int. Med., 1950, **33,** 1357.

SMITH, J. R., EDWARDS, J. C., AND KOUNTZ, W. B. The use of the cathode ray for recording heart sounds and vibrations. III. Total cardiac vibrations in 100 subjects. Am. Heart J., 1941, **21,** 228.

STARR, I., JEFFERS, W. A., AND MEADE, R. H. The absence of conspicuous increments of venous pressure after severe damage to the right ventricle of the dog, with a discussion of the relation between clinical congestive heart failure and heart disease. Am. Heart J., 1943, **26,** 291.

SWAN, H. J. C. AND BECK, W. Ventricular nonmixing as a source of error in the estimation of ventricular volumes by the indicator dilution technic. Circulation Res., 1960, **8,** 989.

WIGGERS, C. J. AND DEAN, A. L. The movements of the mitral cusps in relation to the cardiac cycle. Am. J. Physiol., 1916, **40,** 206.

WIGGERS, C. J. AND DEAN, A. L. The nature and time relations of the fundamental heart sounds. Am. J. Physiol., 1917, **42,** 476.

WIGGERS, C. J. AND KATZ, L. N. The contour of the ventricular volume curves under different conditions. Am. J. Physiol., 1922, **58,** 439.

WIGGERS, C. J. Factors determining the relative intensity of the heart sounds in different auscultation areas. Arch. Int. Med., 1919, **24,** 471.

WIGGERS, C. J. Cardiac mechanisms that limit operation of ventricular suction. Science, 1957, **126,** 1,236.

WOLFERTH, C. C. AND MARGOLIES, A. The influence of auricular contraction on the first heart sound and the radial pulse. Arch. Int. Med., 1930, **46,** 1048.

Monographs and Reviews

BRECHER, G. A. Critical review of recent work on diastolic suction. Circulation Res., 1958, **6,** 554.

GREEN, H. D. Circulatory system. In Methods in Medical Physics. Vol. **2,** p. 209. The Year Book Publishers, Chicago, Illinois, 1950.

KJELLBERG, S. R., NORDENSTRÖM, B., RUDHE, U., BJÖRK, V. O., AND MALMSTRÖM, G. Cardiographic studies of the mitral and aortic valves. Acta Radiol. (Stockholm), 1961, Suppl. 204.

LEATHAM, A. Auscultation of the heart sounds. Lancet, 1958, **2,** 703.

LEATHAM, A. Auscultation of the heart murmurs. Lancet, 1958, **2,** 757.

LEVINE, S. A. AND HARVEY, W. P. Clinical auscultation of the heart. Ed. 2. W. B. Saunders Company, Philadelphia, 1960.

LEWIS, T. Diseases of the heart, described for practitioners and students. The MacMillan Company, London, 1933.

McKUSICK, V. A. (guest ed.). Symposium on cardiovascular sound. I. Mechanisms. Circulation, 1957, **16,** 270.

McKUSICK, V. A. (guest ed.) Second Symposium on cardiovascular sound. Circulation, 1958, **18,** 946.

ORIAS, O. AND BRAUN-MENENDEZ, E. The heart sounds in normal and pathological conditions. Oxford University Press, London, 1939.

WIGGERS, C. J. Physiology in health and disease. Ed. 5. Lea & Febiger, Philadelphia, 1954.

WIGGERS, C. J. Pressure pulses in the cardiovascular system. Longmans, Green & Company, Inc., New York, 1928.

WIGGERS, C. J. Circulation in health and disease. Ed. 2. Lea & Febiger, Philadelphia, 1923.

CHAPTER 42

Regulation of Pressure and Flow in the Systemic and Pulmonary Circulation

If all the vascular beds of the body were to open simultaneously to their full capacities, the total peripheral resistance would disappear and the cardiac output and blood pressure would be reduced to zero. In order, therefore, to permit the circulation pumps and vessels to carry out their functions, most blood vessels must be partially constricted much of the time. To effect this, vascular constriction must be precisely balanced against vascular dilation so as to permit the requisite cardiac output for tissue needs.

Body economy requires that blood flow through organs or regions be dictated by local function. In tissues with a high metabolic rate, such as active skeletal muscle and the myocardium, the volume of blood flow is very high and the arteriovenous (A-V) oxygen difference may be 70 per cent or more. In other tissues, such as skin, kidney, and the brain, blood flow is not determined by local metabolic demands. Here, with rather low metabolic requirements, the blood flow is high with a small A-V oxygen difference, because the specialized functions of temperature regulation, urine formation and neural activity require a very large blood flow beyond the oxygen requirements.

The size of vessels can be varied passively because of their content of elastic and collagenous tissue, and of smooth muscle, each of which can be stretched by an intravascular pressure. The walls of most vessels such as the aorta, arteries, arterioles, venules and veins, contain involuntary muscle fibers arranged in circular fashion. The walls of the arterioles are composed almost exclusively of this smooth muscle. Vascular contractility is dependent only on these smooth muscle cells and is based on their intrinsic "tone" and on their response to blood borne substances. In addition, like the cardiac muscle, the musculature of these vessels is supplied by two types of nerve fibers—inhibitory and excitatory. Those which cause contraction of the musculature are called vasoconstrictor; those which inhibit, and in consequence, cause relaxation of the muscle rings, are termed vasodilator. Both sets together are referred to as vasomotor nerves.

Since, according to Poiseuille's law, pressure, flow and resistance are intimately associated, it is necessary for proper study, as pointed out in chapter 36, to be able to measure the blood flow in the presence of a constant perfusion pressure, or to measure the blood pressure change in the presence of a constant blood flow. In no other way can one determine whether a variation in peripheral resistance arises through a change in blood flow as a result of heart action or through a change in state of vasomotion of peripheral vessels induced by local mechanisms. Ever since Poiseuille introduced the mercury manometer, in 1828, and later Ludwig added a float and a writing point, it has been easy to make pressure measurements, whereas, because of the slowness in development of methodology, flow measurements have not been too plentiful until recently.

Local Control of Vascular Smooth Muscle

The smallest blood vessels have an inherent, myogenic automaticity or basal degree of contraction of their contained smooth muscle which is independent of blood borne substances or nervous influences, but which can be altered by stimulation of nerve fibers, local electrical stimulation, or by changing the physical and chemical environment. The mechanism of this inherent vasomotion is unknown. Presumably, it arises from locally produced metabolites which can have complex effects. Locally, in the arterioles, precapillaries and capillaries, there are released 5-hydroxytryptamine, norepinephrine, acetylcholine, histamine, CO_2, lactic acid, products of nuclear metabolism and presumably many other substances, which can act in many different ways on these vessels. The extent of such basal vasomotion has been evaluated in sympathectomized, vascular areas where neurohumoral, constrictor influences are eliminated. Although large quantitative differences exist in different parts of the vascular tree, generally speaking, there is an inverse relation between the local, inherent activity of smooth muscle cells and the extent of neurohumoral control in any given vascular bed. The cutaneous arteriovenous anastomoses, such as in the paw of the cat, which are strongly controlled from the hypothalamic heat loss center, are maximally dilated when neurohumoral agents are eliminated, while elimination of the vasomotor nerves serving vitally important metabolic areas, such as the brain and myocardium, has scarcely any effect on the local blood flow. In areas such as skeletal muscle, neural elimination still leaves a very strong vessel tone in the dog and man, which is increased with time. Indeed, some investigators have expressed the belief that in skeletal muscle, blood flow is mainly under local control by metabolites, and not nerves, since subjects with sympathectomized legs do as well running (athletes and normals) before and after sympathectomy. Evidence suggests that reactivity to local metabolic effects is stronger in the metarterioles and precapillary sphincters, whereas constrictor fibers predominantly affect the arterioles, indicating that a difference in type of control may exist within the same vascular bed. Presumably, in all beds, there is some locally produced vasodilation which counteracts the centrally induced reduction in blood flow by constrictor nerves and protects the tissue against ischemia.

The Sympathetic Vasoconstrictor Fibers

DISTRIBUTION. These were discovered in 1852 by Claude Bernard, who stimulated the cervical sympathetic nerve in the rabbit and observed constriction of the vessels of the ear. They belong to the thoracicolumbar (sympathetic) division of the involuntary nervous system. The constrictor fibers arise from groups of nerve cells situated in the lateral horns of the spinal gray matter, extending in man from the 1st thoracic to the 2nd or 3rd lumbar segment, inclusive. All the arterioles of the body wherever situated are supplied with filaments which have their ultimate source in this relatively limited region of the central nervous system. They are distributed to the periphery in the manner elsewhere described for the thoracicolumbar outflow in general (see also ch. 12).

The vascular nerves of the limbs, as shown by Todd and Kramer and by Woollard, are distributed by two distinct modes. (1) A *proximal* innervation arises in the case of the vessels of the upper limb directly from the cervical part of the sympathetic chain—middle and inferior cervical ganglia. The fibers pass to the subclavian artery and are conveyed in a plexiform manner along the outer coat of this vessel and its branches, and into the arm along the axillary artery. The corresponding supply to the vessels of the lower limb is derived by extension from the aortic plexus in the abdomen. The fibers follow the common and external iliac arteries into the thigh. The sympathetic fibers derived in the manner just described do not extend beyond the larger vessels of the limbs (proximal portions of the brachial and femoral arteries). (2) A *distal* innervation is carried to the peripheral vessels via the spinal nerve trunks. These nerves reach the arteries at different levels and, penetrating the vascular wall, form a nerve net surrounding the muscular coat; the highest level of this type of innervation probably overlaps the region innervated by the proximal group of fibers mentioned above. The lowest levels supply the arterioles and capillaries. It is solely through such sympathetic fibers traveling with somatic nerve trunks that constrictor impulses are conveyed to the minute vessels of the limbs. Ganglion cells are absent from the vessels of the limbs. Section of a peripheral nerve, therefore, causes complete degeneration of vasoconstrictor fibers in the area of its distribution.

Vasoconstrictor fibers to the head and neck are conveyed from the sympathetic chain through plexuses investing the blood vessels, but also via peripheral nerve trunks (cervical and certain cranial nerves). The vessels of the abdomen and pelvis are supplied with fibers which pass along the vascular walls from plexuses surrounding the aorta and its branches. The sympathetic fibers to the heart arise chiefly in 5 upper dorsal segments of the cord, pass to the stellate ganglia and upper dorsal ganglia as white rami, and proceed to the heart by a complex plexus. There is no certainty that these fibers should be included here. They are included because with their stimulation norepinephrine is released in the heart, but no good evidence exists to prove that stimulation *per se* causes coronary artery dilation since each stimulation is overshadowed by a massive metabolic response and associated dilation.

SITE AND MODE OF ACTION. These nerve fibers constitute a group of powerful vasoconstrictor mechanisms. The physiological discharge rate of the vasoconstrictor fibers is 1 to 2 per sec. to maintain normal vessel tone and reaches 10 impulses per sec., with maximal physiological excitation. The chemical transmitter released at the smooth muscle cell is probably norepinephrine, since norepinephrine is released into the blood stream on intense sympathetic stimulation. However, such an overflow does not usually occur at physiological discharge rates. These constrictor fibers exert control over the resistance vessels (arterioles and adjacent smaller blood vessels) where the main drop in blood pressure from the arterial to the venous system occurs. This can be observed by noting the marked increase in blood flow in a vasoconstricted limb immediately following sympathetic blockade. Predominantly, the true arterioles are controlled by constrictor fibers while the capillaries are mainly regulated by local factors.

In addition, these fibers exert strong control over the heart size and the capacity vessels, mainly the veins, and can alter greatly the venous return to the heart and, thus, markedly influence cardiac output. To establish this capacitance action, pressure changes occurring in functionally isolated parts of the superficial and deep venous system of dog and man were used to indicate changes in venous constriction, and evidence of a reflex constriction to a variety of stimuli was obtained. Isolated venous segments in the intact forearm constrict after reflex sympathetic stimulation by cold, excitement, etc. Venoconstriction in the forearm occurs in response to pooling of blood in the leg. Similar observations have been made on the capacity vessels of the splanchnic area. These effects are abolished by constrictor fiber blockade by hexamethonium. Possibly the most clear-cut experiments in dogs on the quantitative importance of the sympathetic system in adjusting total vascular volume, and hence, venous return and cardiac output, are those in which a pump, with output which remained constant under marked variations of peripheral resistance, was substituted for the left ventricle of a dog. The pulmonary drainage of blood was carried to a reservoir by means of a plastic tube in the left auricle. The blood was pumped from the reservoir through a T tube in the descending thoracic aorta. Under equilibrium conditions (reservoir level remaining constant), if norepinephrine (which simulates sympathetic vasoconstriction in physiological dosages) was injected into the dog, there was not only an increase in vascular pressures but also approximately 250 ml. ($\frac{1}{6}$ of the dog's blood volume) was forced into the pulmonary drainage reservoir feeding the mechanical left ventricle. This could come only from the venous system and the right heart. When hexamethonium (simulating a functional sympathectomy) was injected instead of norepinephrine, the pressures fell and the dog took up 200 to 300 ml. of blood from the reservoir. Further work has extended these findings to man. In normal man, removal of large amounts of blood in 50 ml. increments produces little change in vascular pressure or hemo-

dynamics. But, if done following inhibition of sympathetic vasoconstrictor reflexes with hexamethonium, then with each 50 ml. of blood withdrawn, there is a perceptible decline in blood pressure. After removal of only 350 to 500 ml. of blood, the arterial pressure falls, by decrements, to collapse levels. During reinfusion, the process is reversed. Thus, sympathetic vasoconstrictor inhibition has converted the vasculature into a static system. In addition, using the pressure-volume apparatus of Litter and associates, which can be applied to the extremities of man, it is calculated that infused epinephrine and norepinephrine can shift as much as 500 ml. of blood from the veins of dependent limbs in a short period of time.

These effects of constrictor fibers on venous volume can considerably change venous return by very small changes in vein caliber. For example, if the veins contain 60 per cent of blood volume of which 1 to 2 per cent make up the stroke volume of the ventricles, a 1 to 2 per cent shortening of venous vascular smooth muscle would be estimated to double diastolic inflow to the heart; this same amount of constriction of the resistance vessels would only insignificantly increase the peripheral resistance.

Excitation of sympathetic vasoconstrictor fibers affects somewhat the aortic smooth muscle cells and possibly other arteries. Presumably, the effect is mainly a change in vascular distensibility and only secondarily are mild pressure changes along the arterial tree produced (see also ch. 47). In general, however, the effect is small. In vessels from the root of the aorta down to arteries of 1 mm., induced changes in diameter are probably less than 5 per cent of total diameter even with marked vasoconstriction or vasodilation.

FUNCTIONAL SIGNIFICANCE. Experimental evidence now indicates that these vasoconstrictor fibers are responsible for blood pressure homeostasis (vascular adjustments derived from the baro- and chemoreceptors), and for the regulation of heat loss by the skin blood flow. Thus, the commonest type of centrally induced vasodilation is caused simply by an inhibition of vascular tone. In fulfilling their role as the main neurogenic adjustors of the peripheral circulation, the vasoconstrictor fibers may show a generalized, strictly segmental, or regional function, depending upon the type of stimulus.

CENTRAL CONTROL. The control of the degree and sites of vasoconstriction depends predominantly on the influence of hormonal action and on the action of the central nervous system. In discussing the central control of the cardiovascular system, it should be emphasized that, in the past, relatively little work has been done in this field. This has been true ever since the discovery and location of the medullary vasomotor centers by Oswjannikow and by Dittmar in 1873. It was not until 1916 that Ranson and Billingsley published further significant work. Practically all the work in the field has been done by neurophysiologists with the result that generally only blood pressure and heart rate have been measured. More recently, circulatory physiologists have become interested in the problem, and with teams of neural and circulatory physiologists in operation, regional blood flows and direct effects on the heart have been studied with some progress.

However, at times, interpretation of results is difficult because of the types of central nervous changes that are necessarily induced experimentally. For such studies these include stimulation of outlying nerve fibers, ganglionic blockade, electrical exploration of the central nervous system, ablation of areas, and chronic implantation of stimulating electrodes. Each has its drawbacks in a physiological system. Ganglionic blockade is a pharmacological test used to identify vasomotor activity. Its action may be incomplete or not entirely selective. An electric shock is an artificial stimulus and its frequency and intensity may bear no relation to a physiological stimulus. Such stimulation experiments, in general, demonstrate what can happen in nerve fibers, and that in the central nervous system there are excitable areas in the region of the electrodes which, in turn, have synaptic continuity with the nervous pathways controlling the cardiovascular system. They do not necessarily indicate what role the excitable areas play in the intact human or animal. Ablation experiments obviate some of these difficulties but there is no surety that the cardiovascular changes induced by ablation are not in part due to injury to surrounding areas. Attempts have recently been made with the use of chronically implanted electrodes to simulate the hemodynamic responses normally occurring in excitement and exercise and then to show, by ablation of such areas, that the cardiovascular response disappears. This approach has considerable promise.

A. The spinal cord. The preganglionic sympathetic neurons may, under some circumstances, exhibit spontaneous activity independent of an excitatory drive from afferent fibers or central levels. This spontaneous discharge may arise from a changed oxygen and CO_2 tension which is prone to occur in a spinal preparation in which neuronal respiration and blood supply are without doubt considerably altered.

Various afferent impulses are able to call forth spinal vasomotor reflexes; the vasoconstrictor neurons form the efferent link. Pain or cold stimulation in the skin induces a segmentally arranged constriction of the intestinal vessels in such spinal animals. Vasodilation occurs when the skin is moderately heated. More intense and widespread effects are seen in human beings with chronic transverse lesions of the spinal cord. Guttman and Whitteridge showed the existence of powerful reflexes, in the spinal man, arising from the hollow viscera. In patients with high spinal transection, distension of the bladder would raise the blood pressure from normal levels to 300/140 mm. Hg. This is ascribed to the action of reflexes initiated by the tension in the bladder wall and mediated by the isolated spinal cord and the sympathetic outflow. There could also be demonstrated vasoconstriction in the hand and a fall in calf blood flow. These phenomena are consistent with a very widespread vasoconstriction as a result of afferent impulses which spread to an unusual extent in the isolated spinal cord.

B. Medulla. The constrictor sympathetic vascular effects are controlled primarily by areas in the medulla oblongata situated in the floor of the 4th ventricle. Local electrical stimulation has revealed a lateral "pressor area" and a medial "depressor area" causing vasoconstriction and vasodilation, respectively. The vasodilation is caused by inhibition of vasoconstrictor tone, specific vasodilator fibers not being involved. This area is defined simply as the vasomotor center but does not represent the highest centers of this system. The latter are situated in the hypothalamus and in the cerebral cortex. In the intact mammal, complicated afferent influences integrated in the cerebral cortex and hypothalamus modify and control the action of the vasomotor center.

The state of activity of the medullary vasomotor center depends upon afferent nerve impulses received from various organs and regions of the body, as well as from other nervous centers, respiratory centers, etc., and upon the chemical composition of the blood. In turn, the contractility of the heart, the relative peripheral resistance and, hence, the cardiac output, with its distribution to the various organs, are all mainly controlled by the medulla oblongata responding to impulses from all tissues of the body, including the spinal cord and other portions of the brain itself.

The vasomotor center exhibits inherent automaticity, since its continuous discharge goes on even after elimination of all incoming nerve influences. Section of the brain stem above the medulla does not affect blood pressure, indicating that upper areas do not dominate vasomotor outflow from the sympathetic nervous system. However, such control may be demonstrated by sectioning the cord in the lower cervical region. This interrupts the stream of vasoconstrictor impulses passing from the medullary to the spinal centers; the vessels dilate and the blood pressure falls. After a time, however, the blood pressure rises again; the spinal centers exhibit their inherent power of autonomous action, and assuming the duties hitherto exercised by the medullary centers, restore the vessels to their previous state of tonic constriction. The time required for the vessels to regain their tone after section of the cord varies considerably in different species.

The high degree of vasoconstrictor tone which is normally maintained is shown by the fact that section of the splanchnics doubles the flow in the vessels of the denervated area (Burton-Opitz). After the loss of tone resulting from cord section has been restored (see above) it falls again if the splanchnics are sectioned, but after a time a certain degree of tone is regained. This resides in the vascular muscle itself– *peripheral tone.* Apparently, a long period is required for the development of the intrinsic arteriolar tone.

C. The hypothalamus. In the hypothalamus, electrical stimulation shows the existence of both excitatory and inhibitory neurons which, presumably, have much to do with blood pressure regulation. It must be remembered that drastic redistribution of blood flow following extensive changes in the discharge of the constrictor fibers to some areas is often concealed behind slight blood pressure changes and, hence, blood pressure change alone is not a reliable guide. Recently, the hypothalamic area has been explored for structures from which a pure inhibition of sympathetic activity could be induced. Such a structure, of very restricted dimensions, has been localized in the anterior part of the hypothalamus, only a few millimeters from the relay station of the sympathetic vasodilator fibers (see next section). From this area, topical stimulation induces a generalized, often very marked, inhibi-

tion of sympathetic discharge affecting both resistance and capacitance vessels.

An immediate and persistent lowering of blood pressure in both normotensive and renal hypertensive dogs occurs following large bilateral coagulations involving the hypothalamic area. This lowering of blood pressure is small in magnitude but is as marked as that resulting permanently from bilateral sympathectomy and low cervical cord transection. Whether this lowering in blood pressure has a neural or an endocrine basis has not been determined. It is not due to the absence of the neurohypophysial antidiuretic principle because precipitation of a maximal diabetes insipidus (functional neurohypophysectomy) has been accomplished without affecting blood pressure. It is believed not to be due to a neighboring adenohypophysial hypofunction because the lowering of pressure following adenohypophysectomy is delayed rather than immediate as is the case following hypothalamectomy. It is perhaps associated with the immediate and marked decrease in basal energy metabolism which supervenes following appropriate hypothalamectomies.

In addition, there is a "heat loss center" in the anterior parts of the hypothalamus which controls the discharge to the vasoconstrictor fibers of the cutaneous blood vessels, and, thus, plays an important role in adjusting blood pressure. Electrical stimulation or local cooling of this area brings about a rise in blood pressure (vasoconstriction) while direct warming of this region produces a fall in blood pressure (vasodilation). The cutaneous arterioles and precapillary vessels, and, especially, the arteriovenous anastomoses (shunts), are the vessels most sensitively engaged in the control of heat loss. However, Keller has marshalled evidence to indicate that vasoconstrictor impulses responsible for the maintained contraction of cutaneous blood vessels *do not take* origin from the hypothalamus as evidenced by the following experiments. An asymmetry in the ear vessels and in skin temperature (Horner's syndrome) does not follow unilateral lesions in the hypothalamus or hemisection of the brainstem at a midbrain, pontile or upper medullary level; nor does a complete transection of the midbrain or pons result in generalized cutaneous vasodilation. Ipsilateral vasodilation does occur following hemisection of the lower medulla and this approximates in magnitude and duration that which follows hemisection of the cervical cord.

D. Cerebral cortex. Quite a number of studies of cortical vasoconstrictor fiber control are available but relatively little is known about the circulatory adjustments. Stimulation of the motor and premotor cerebral cortex results in marked elevation of blood pressure with constriction of the cutaneous, splanchnic and renal vessels, and, at the same time, a considerable vasodilation in the skeletal muscle. It is believed that these higher centers play significant roles in blood pressure response to pain and anxiety.

The Vasodilator Fibers

Dilator impulses emerge from the central nervous system by (1) the thoracicolumbar outflow, (2) the cranial outflow of the parasympathetic division reaching the periphery by way of the chorda tympani, glossopharyngeal and vagus nerves, (3) the sacral outflow of the pelvic nerve, and (4) the posterior spinal nerve roots—antidromic impulses.

THE SYMPATHETIC VASODILATOR FIBERS. The question of dilator fibers in the sympathetic system has been much debated. About 15 years ago, it was generally believed that they took an active part in regulation of vascular tone, their activity being governed by the medulla, and that such fibers were distributed to the skeletal muscles, the facial muscles, the buccal mucosa, the coronaries, the intestines, and to certain skin areas, such as the ear. These findings were based on direct stimulation of sympathetic fibers and the recording of volume changes by plethysmography. Direct measurement of blood flow (volume changes by plethysmography do not always mean change in blood flow), and location of an area of central control has led to considerable clarification. The control of the degree of vasodilation of blood vessels is, indeed, supplemented by a system of efferent dilator nerves transmitting from the central nervous system, but this seems to be distributed only to skeletal muscle. Electrical stimulation of the sympathetic fibers usually brings about vasoconstriction in the innervated area, since the action of the vasoconstrictor influence usually predominates over that of vasodilation. But, if the vasoconstrictor response is first blocked by ergotamine, electrical stimulation will produce vasodilation if the sympathetic outflow contains vasodilator fibers. The existence of a sympathetic vasodilator innervation to skeletal muscle of the dog and cat has been established by this technique. The vasodilator nerves may also be activated by topical stimula-

tion in the brain (hypothalamus), with the result that venous outflow from skeletal muscle of the hind leg of the dog may increase 4 to 5 times (as does the local lactic acid production), but the oxygen usage may decrease, suggesting that shunts are being utilized and capillary flow is reduced. In addition, such stimulation results in release of epinephrine from the adrenal glands. This increased rate of blood flow approximates maximum dilation achieved by other means, such as acetylcholine injection. Since blood flow in the human forearm increases during fainting, a potent means of vasodilation must be present in humans. Also, since the blood pressure falls, and the blood flow is greater in the normal forearm than in a nerve-blocked forearm during syncope, this might be explained by active vasodilation in the normal forearm excited by sympathetic fibers to the muscles. The transmitter is believed to be acetylcholine and the fibers are exclusively cholinergic; i.e., they are blocked by small amounts of atropine. They take their origin in the motor cortex, synapse in the hypothalamus, pass as a thin bundle through the ventrolateral portion of the medulla oblongata, and down to the lateral horn of the spinal medulla where they are relayed to lower motor neurons. This pathway is anatomically and functionally separate from the medullary vasomotor center which mediates vasoconstrictor activity. The functional significance of the vasodilator fibers is unknown, but it has been suggested that they are activated in response to cerebral activity, presumably in association with, or in anticipation of skeletal muscle activity.

PARASYMPATHETIC VASODILATOR FIBERS. The parasympathetic vasodilator fibers run to restricted cranial and sacral areas such as the cerebral vessels, tongue, salivary glands, external genitalia and, possibly, to the bladder and rectum. These fibers are probably not concerned with baro- and chemoreceptor control of blood vessels, nor are they tonically active. It is generally believed that these fibers are cholinergic, although their vasodilator effect is very resistant to atropine. Their distribution to a few areas with highly specialized functions makes it probable that their function is associated with the special tissue in which they are located.

ANTIDROMIC VASODILATOR IMPULSES. Stricker, many years ago, reported that stimulation of the peripheral segments of the cut posterior roots of the sacral nerves caused dilation of the vessels of the dog paw. This observation was at variance with the Bell-Magendie law which states that the posterior roots convey only centripetal impulses. However, in subsequent years, the former view has been fairly well documented. Since such fibers do not convey the induced impulses to the central nervous system, but rather the vasodilator impulses are conveyed along the fibers in a direction opposite to that in which ordinary sensory impulses travel, they are called antidromic.

The effective stimulus leading to vessel dilation may arise in or around dorsal root ganglia, or it may arise in the skin, to be conveyed antidromically to superficial blood vessels. The latter are also called axon reflexes, but they are obviously not true reflexes since no nerve cell is involved. The efferent and afferent limbs of the axon reflex are formed by the branching of a single nerve fiber. A stimulus applied to one branch sets up an impulse which travels centrally to the point of division where it is reflected down the other branch to an effector organ. The most familiar type of axon reflex is that which involves a sensory nerve fiber and through which vasodilation is effected.

Dorsal root dilation is of significance only in tissues with a relatively rich distribution of pain fibers, such as the skin and mucous membranes. Various substances have been indicated as the transmitter—a histaminelike substance, acetylcholine, and adenosine triphosphate. This local axon reflex in the skin is induced by any factor which causes damage to surface tissues—trauma, cooling, heating, frostbite. Thus, this local mechanism contributes to local defense and repair in surface tissues by creating an increase of local blood flow in response to the majority of harmful stimuli.

Adrenal Medulla versus Neural Control of Blood Vessels

Aside from direct neurogenic connections to the blood vessels, the presence in the blood stream of circulating catecholamines raises the question of their role in controlling the circulation. Presumably they appear through some form of hypothalamic stimulation. It has been widely assumed, but never proved, that the hormones secreted from the adrenal medulla markedly contribute to the vasomotor control of the blood vessels. Using a method that allowed a direct comparison of the individual actions of the hormone and vasomotor fibers on peripheral resistance in representative

vascular beds, it has been found that the blood vessels are completely dominated by their vasoconstrictor fibers. The contribution by the adrenal secretion is negligible, except in skeletal muscle, in which small physiological concentrations of epinephrine cause almost maximal vasodilation. On the basis of adrenal catecholamine secretion following maximal excitation of the vasomotor center, it is estimated that the maximal secretion is 2 to 3 μg./kg./min. Such concentrations of epinephrine and norepinephrine (probably 10 times the normal concentration), when injected intravenously, dilate the vessels of the skeletal muscles and probably those of the liver, but have insignificant vasoconstrictor effects in other regions when compared with the constrictor fibers.

The importance of the adrenal catecholamines for the motor control of the blood vessels is next to insignificant as compared with direct vasomotor innervation. However, a moderate secretion of epinephrine induces extensive metabolic effects in liver cells (which lack direct sympathetic innervation) and skeletal muscle which may produce the vasodilation. Norepinephrine secretion from the adrenal gland has relatively little influence on the blood vessels, either directly or through metabolic dilation (indirectly).

The vasomotor system of nerves discussed above is the main adjustor of the peripheral circulation, whereby the blood pumped by the heart is distributed throughout the body according to the needs of each individual tissue and of the organism as a whole. This vital role is accomplished by constant, moment-to-moment adjustments of the resistance in the local vascular beds, and it is mediated and regulated by the central nervous system through various reflex mechanisms (fig. 42.1).

Our knowledge and understanding of these reflex mechanisms is far from complete; the function of some of them is fairly well established, the existence of others is known without any certainty regarding their function, and it is safe to assume that there exist still others, totally unknown to us at the present time. Inevitably, in the ensuing parts, the lengthiest considerations will be given to the most completely studied mechanisms, but it should be clear that this is not necessarily proportional to their respective physiological importance.

Vasomotor reflexes can be elicited by the stimulation of practically any afferent nerve—somatic or visceral.

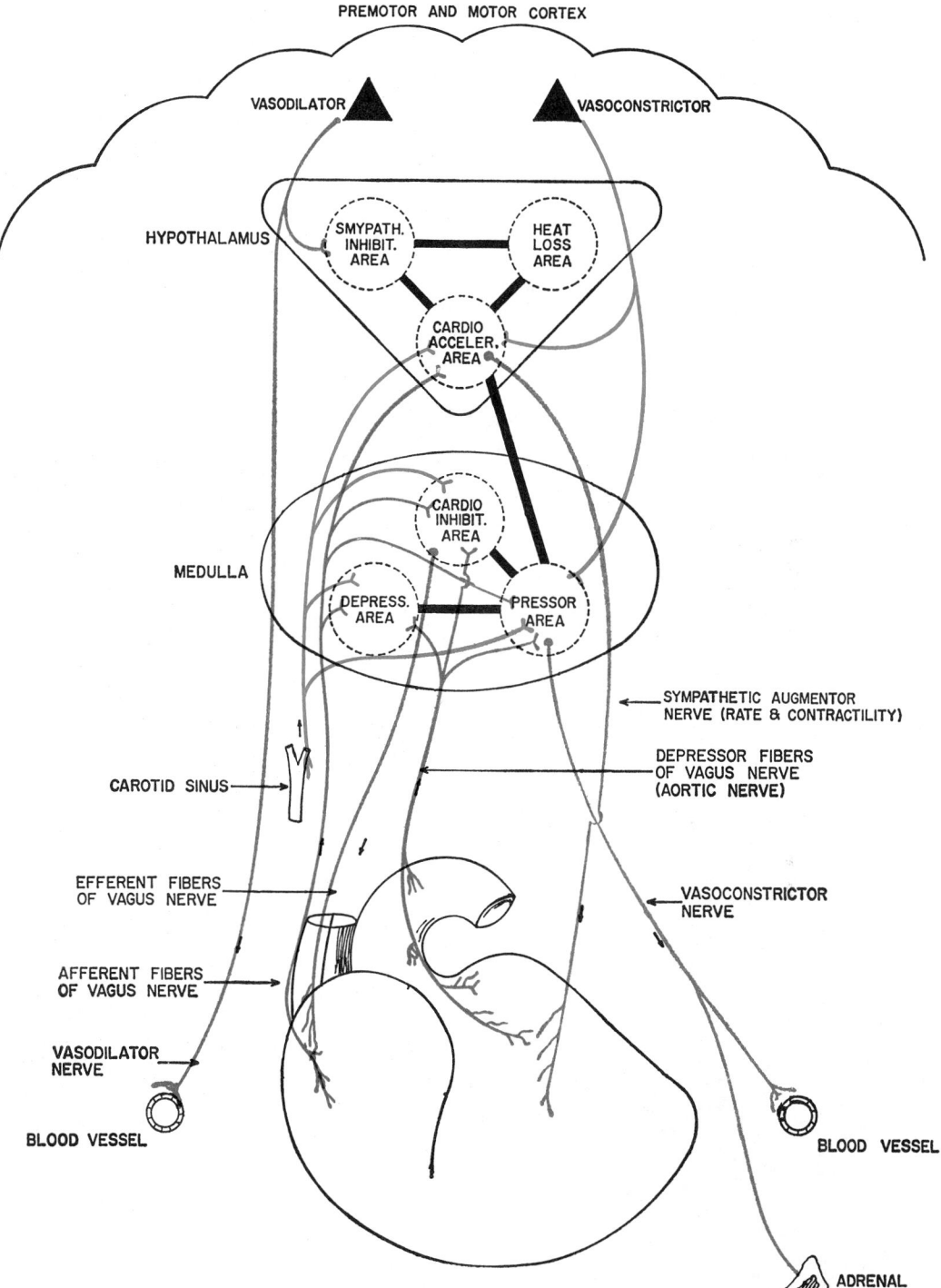

Fig. 42.1. Diagrammatic representation of cardiovascular reflex mechanisms.

Vascular Reflexes Resulting from the Stimulation of Somatic Nerves

Historically, these are among the earliest vascular reflex mechanisms known, although their importance in overall circulatory regulation is relatively minor.

Stimulation of the central end of a nerve, such as the sciatic, the median or a sensory cranial nerve, may result in either a rise or a fall in the arterial blood pressure according to the strength and type of the stimulus employed. The components of the reflex arc upon which the responses depend are, (1) afferent fibers in the peripheral nerve, (2) the vasomotor centers, and (3) the efferent vascular nerves, i.e., the vasoconstrictors or vasodilators. In order to elicit a pressor reflex, a stimulus much stronger than that necessary to provoke a depressor response must, as a rule, be applied; that is, one which would elicit pain in a conscious animal. In the elicitation of either reflex, the magnitude of the response is apparently dependent upon the number of afferent fibers involved. For example, stimulation of various nerves of the brachial or lumbar plexus causes practically equivalent depressions or elevations in the blood pressure when the number of afferent fibers in the respective nerves is taken into account.

It must be re-emphasized that not all the pressor or depressor impulses ascend to the medulla but that reflex arcs exist which have their centers within the cord; both vasoconstrictor and vasodilator reflexes can be elicited in an animal whose cord has been divided in the lower cervical region a short time previously.

From the results of experiments upon animals, it is to be expected that in the human subject a painful stimulus applied to a somatic nerve will be followed by a pressor response. The excitation of psychic centers and, also, the liberation of epinephrine are additional factors which play an important part in the pressor response resulting from painful stimuli. On the other hand, there are numerous afferent fibers in the hollow viscera which respond to stretch and result in a decreased blood pressure. Stimulation of the mesentery, peritoneum and abdominal viscera or of certain regions such as the anus, vagina, and spermatic cord may be followed by a fall in blood pressure. Finally, there may be obvious reflex effects which may or may not be associated with blood pressure changes. For example, in normal persons with bladder distention, there may be facial flushing but with evidence of widespread venous constriction. Following inflation of balloons placed in the esophagus, rectum or in an ileostomy, regional venoconstriction also can be demonstrated.

The Presso or Baroreceptors

Experiments have shown that the fundamental regulation of systemic blood pressure is reflexly controlled by the action of the arterial pressure itself on pressure sensitive receptors located in the vascular walls, especially of the aortic arch and carotid sinus areas.

THE AORTIC OR CARDIAC DEPRESSOR NERVE. The branch of the vagus which is known as the *aortic* or *cardiac depressor* nerve was first described by Cyon and Ludwig (1866). It is purely afferent and depressor in function; when it is sectioned, and its central (cerebral) end stimulated, a pronounced fall in pressure occurs (fig 42.2); excitation of the cardiac end, on the other hand, causes no effect. Two factors are involved in the depressor response following stimulation of the fibers. (*1*) *Slowing of the heart rate and increased force of the ventricular contraction.* The efferent fibers of the vagus of the same and of the opposite side constitute the efferent limb of the reflex arc through which this response is chiefly brought about; for its full elicitation at least one vagus must, therefore, remain intact. (*2*) *Vasodilation.* The vasomotor pathways constitute the efferent limb of this reflex. Vasoconstriction is inhibited and vasodilation results. The reflex effect upon the vessels cannot, therefore, be elicited after section of the spinal cord in the lower cervical region.

The receptors of the reflex (the terminals of the aortic nerve) are situated in the aortic arch and upper part of the thoracic aorta, in the ventricles and possibly also, according to Daly and Verney,

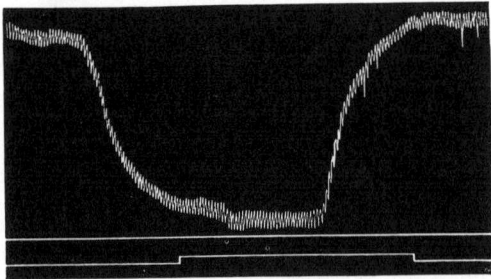

FIG. 42.2. Fall in arterial blood pressure resulting from stimulation of the central end of the cardiac depressor (aortic) nerve. The drum was stopped in the middle of the curve and the excitation maintained for 17 minutes. The line of zero pressure should be 30 mm. lower than here shown. (From Bayliss.)

in the coronary and pulmonary vessels (see fig. 42.3).

The fall in pressure is due mainly to dilation of the splanchnic vessels. The dilation is not, however, confined to these vessels but includes those of the skin and muscles. Cardiac slowing plays a minor role in the production of the fall in blood pressure, for almost as great an effect can be obtained after both vagi have been cut. The depressor reflex can be elicited by mechanical or electrical stimulation of the aortic wall itself wherein the special proprioceptors are located; stretching is an especially effective type of stimulus. It was shown that action currents ascend the nerve synchronously with the heart beats (fig. 42.4). The normal stimulus is evidently the pulsatile expansion of the aortic wall, a rise in general blood pressure increasing the intensity of the stimulus, a fall in pressure causing the reverse effect.

THE CAROTID SINUS MECHANISM. The carotid sinus is the term applied to the slight enlargement of the common carotid artery where it bifurcates into the internal and external carotids (fig. 42.3). The carotid sinus was shown by Hering in 1923 to play an important role in the regulation of the cardiac rate and arterial blood pressure. Compression of the carotid at its bifurcation (so as to raise the pressure within the sinus) causes a marked slowing of the heart rate, vasodilation (see p. 755), and a fall in blood pressure; these effects result even though mechanical stimulation of the vagus is carefully avoided. Electrical stimulation of the sinus wall produces similar effects. Pressure upon the common carotid some distance below the sinus (so as to reduce the blood pressure within the sinus itself) causes cardiac acceleration, vasoconstriction, and a rise in arterial pressure together with, as shown by Heymans, the liberation of epinephrine. The carotid sinus therefore constitutes a mechanism whereby both pressor and depressor effects are mediated. The effects are brought about through the following neural mechanism.

THE SINUS REFLEX ARC. The afferent fibers of the reflex arc are contained in the *sinus nerve*, a branch of the glossopharyngeal. This delicate filament descends between the internal and external carotids to the sinus where its fibers terminate in sensory organs (proprioceptors) situated between the connective tissue fibers in the adventitia of the sinus wall. Centrally the fibers of the sinus nerve make connections with the cardio-inhibitory and vasomotor centers. The efferent limb of the cardiac part of the reflex is, of course, the vagus. The efferent limbs of the vasodilator and

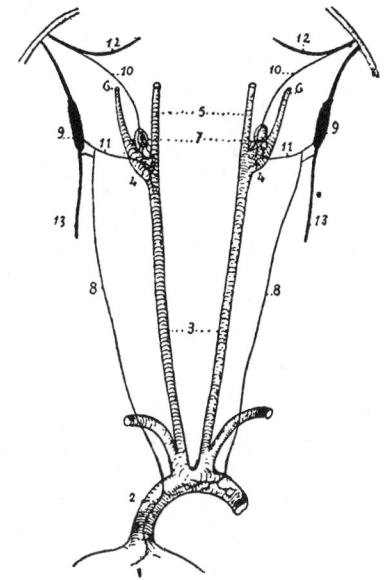

FIG. 42.3. Innervation of the carotid sinus and arch of aorta. 1, Heart; 2, arch of aorta; 3, common carotid; 4, carotid sinus; 5, external carotid; 6, internal carotid; 7, carotid bodies; 8, cardiac depressor nerve; 9, ganglion of vagus; 10, sinus nerve, branch of the glossopharyngeal nerve; 11, nerve branch connecting the carotid sinus with the vagus ganglion; 12, glossopharyngeal nerve; 13, vagus nerve. (After Heymans.)

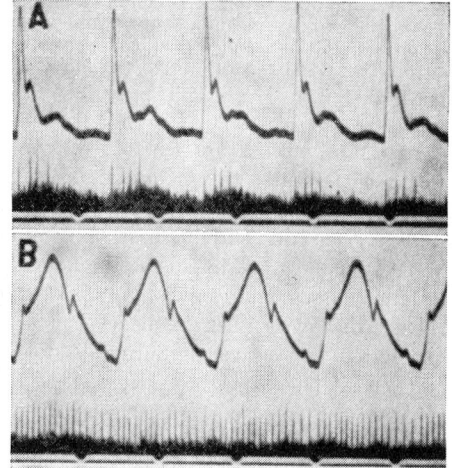

FIG. 42.4. The upper curve in each record represents the arterial blood pressure registered by a membrane manometer; the lower curve of each record shows the electrical discharge from a single fiber of the carotid sinus nerve of the rabbit. In the upper record (A) the mean arterial pressure was 55 mm. Hg; even at this low level a discharge of 4 impulses accompanied each ventricular systole. In the lower record (B) the mean arterial pressure was 135 mm. Hg; in this instance there was a more rapid and more continuous discharge from the end-organ. (Bronk and Stella.)

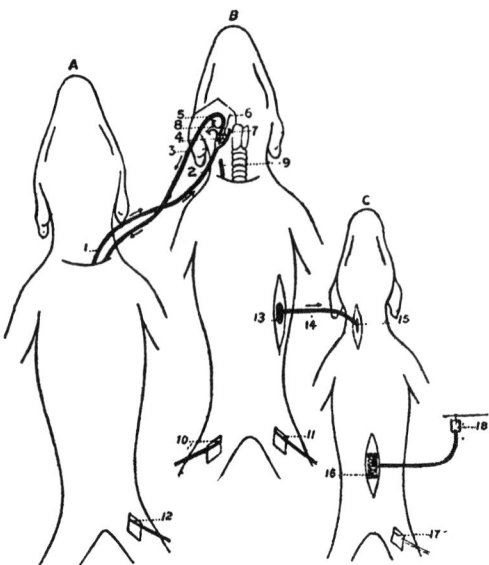

FIG. 42.5. Scheme of perfusion of the isolated carotid sinus of dog B, by dog A, and an anastomosis between the suprarenal vein of B and the jugular vein of dog C. 1, left carotid artery of dog A; 2, right carotid artery of B, anastomosed with carotid of A; 3, left external jugular vein of A; 4, isolated right carotid sinus of B; 5, lingual artery of B, anastomosed with jugular vein of dog A; 6, nerve supply to carotid sinus of B. The blood from dog A flows through the carotid sinus of dog B and back to A via the lingual artery of B and the external jugular of A. 7, internal carotid; 8, facial and maxillary arteries; 9, common carotid; 10, 11, 12 and 17, femoral arteries to manometers; 13, adrenal gland; 14 and 15, suprarenal-jugular anastomosis; 16, decapsulated spleen in plethysmograph; 18, piston recorder for plethysmograph. (After Heymans.)

vasoconstrictor reflexes are apparently sympathetic fibers, for these reflexes are abolished by complete removal of the sympathetic chains.

Study of the action currents passing along the sinus nerve shows that impulses stimulated by the arterial pressure pulse are discharged throughout the cardiac cycle, their frequency increasing during systole and decreasing during diastole. A rise in general blood pressure increases the rate of impulse discharge as well as the number of sense organs excited. The latter show slow adaptation so that though the stimulus (distension of the arterial wall) persists the impulse discharge shows little reduction in frequency, and when the pressure is very high, they extend with little reduction in rate throughout diastole. At low pressures, impulses are discharged only during systole.

The sinus reflexes have been studied exhaustively by Heymans and his associates. They carried out cross-circulation experiments which speak conclusively for the physiological impor-

tance of these reflexes in cardiovascular regulation (see fig. 42.5). The sinus of one dog (B) was isolated from the general circulation and perfused with the blood of another animal (A) in the manner shown in the figure. The nerve supply to the sinus was left intact. When the arterial pressure of dog A was raised, that of dog B, recorded in the femoral artery, fell. Conversely, a reduction in blood pressure of dog A caused a rise in the blood pressure of dog B. In the latter instance, epinephrine liberation also occurred which was a contributory factor in the blood pressure elevation as indicated by its pressor effect upon the circulation of dog C, connected to the suprarenal vein of B. These effects could not be obtained after denervation of the sinus.

The sinus and aortic nerves, or so-called "buffer" nerves, constitute a mechanism of the utmost importance in controlling the arterial blood pressure and in maintaining the circulation to the brain. The rise in diastolic pressure and the increase in heart rate which occur when the body changes from the recumbent to the sitting position or from the sitting to the standing position, are apparently brought about through these nerves; they therefore play an essential part in compensating for the effect of gravity upon the circulation.

An underfilled state of the vessels, as may result from hemorrhage or shock, or any other condition which tends to cause a fall in blood pressure, will call these mechanisms into play. A generalized vasoconstriction results to adjust the vascular capacity to the reduced blood volume and thus maintain the blood pressure. Excessive elevation of the blood pressure, on the other hand, is countered by a depressor reflex (see diagram fig. 42.1). The great importance of these reflex mechanisms in hemorrhage is shown by the fact that in an animal in which all four buffer nerves have been sectioned the rapid loss of only about $\frac{1}{10}$ of the blood volume proves fatal, whereas usually a reduction in blood volume of from 35 to 45 per cent is required to cause death. Mayerson found that tilting anesthetized dogs from the horizontal to the upright position caused a sharp drop in blood pressure followed within 10 sec. by a compensatory rise. After section of both sets of buffer nerves the compensatory rise did not, as a rule, occur.

Several workers have reported the occurrence of permanent hypertension in animals following bilateral section of the sinus aortic nerves. Pressures as high as 200 mm. Hg lasting over a period of 3 years have been reported. Other investigators who have carried out similar experiments find that the hypertension so produced is not permanent in the majority of animals, but tends to return to normal after a variable period. Such a result may be due to the regeneration of the sectioned nerves or to the reflex control of the circulation being assumed by some other mechanism.

MECHANISM OF ACTION. The mechanism of action of the blood pressure on the baroreceptors is complex and only partially understood. If deformation of the baroreceptive arterial walls from a raised arterial pressure is prevented, the baroreceptors no longer respond to the pressure change. Local application of drugs, such as epinephrine or norepinephrine, increases the smooth muscle tension in the arterial wall of the isolated carotid sinus preparation which, in turn, is associated with a large increase in impulse traffic along the baroreceptor fibers throughout the cardiac cycle, and a resetting of the baroreceptive mechanisms at a higher level, with resultant blood pressure adjustment. Sodium nitrite, which relaxes smooth muscle, reduces the intramural tension in these sensitive regions, decreases the impulse traffic, and resets the blood pressure regulation at a lower level. These experiments indicate that under normal conditions, the response of the baroreceptor area and the level of blood pressure maintained depend not only on the level of arterial pressure, but, possibly, even more so on the resistance of the baroreceptive arterial walls to deformation by the intravascular pressure.

Possible Other Arterial Baroreceptors

Possible additional arterial baroreceptor types have been studied in the common carotid artery, the thoracic, and mesenteric arteries. Experiments in which a sudden rise in intracranial pressure causes systemic hypertension, and sudden reduction in intracranial pressure leads to systemic hypotension, suggest, but do not prove, that pressure sensitive receptors are present in the cranial cavity. Such responses could be due to asphyxia of the medullary centers. Impulse output in the mesenteric baroreceptors exists throughout the cardiac cycle, and, if pressure is changed in the mesenteric artery or the artery is clamped, vasomotor reflexes are induced. These reflexes do affect the systemic blood pressure even when the sino-aortic nerves are cut. It is a segmental, reflex adaptation of the circulation and vasomotor state related to pressure changes in a given area. It apparently exists in the cat but not in the dog. Reflex responses can also be obtained in the innervated perfused hind leg of the open-chest dog, when the descending aorta between the left subclavian artery and the diaphragm is isolated and perfused at varying pulsatile pressures, or when epinephrine is added.

The importance of these afferent mechanisms in control of the circulation is not known.

Balanced and Reciprocal Vascular Reactions

In the intact animal the height of the blood pressure at any moment, insofar as the nervous control of the peripheral vessels is concerned, is apparently the algebraic sum of the effects of afferent impulses impinging upon the vasomotor centers. Under ordinary circumstances impulses arising from the carotid sinus and aortic arch play the most prominent roles, but impulses from skin, muscles and viscera and from higher nervous centers also exert an important influence. That pronounced effects upon the peripheral vessels can be produced by the radiation of impulses from higher centers is evidenced by such phenomena as blushing, pallor, erection, and certain types of syncope (fainting). When a dog is excited, similar vascular changes can be observed in the mucosa of the exteriorized colon and in splenic volume. Even very mild excitation of psychic centers exerts an influence upon the vascular mechanisms. The psychogalvanic reflex (due to changes in the electrical resistance of the skin) has a vascular basis. A reciprocal relationship also exists between splanchnic and cutaneous vascular areas on the one hand and the vessels of the muscles on the other. Epinephrine, for example, causes dilation of the latter vessels accompanied by vasoconstriction in the skin and abdominal viscera. Stimulation of the wall of a large vein or distension of the duodenum causes reflex constriction of the cutaneous vessels, and stimulation of the skin results in an increased amount of blood in the liver and in the renal cortex. Furthermore, the muscular and cutaneous tissues may show opposite vascular reactions. Thus, in the dog, cooling of the body causes constriction of the skin vessels and vasodilation in the muscles.

A mechanism also exists in the experimental animal whereby afferent impulses arising within an organ, although leading to generalized vasoconstriction, result locally in dilation and increased blood flow.

An interesting example of the complex nature of the reflex vascular adjustments has been described. An electrical record obtained from a nerve twig coming from a Pacinian corpuscle in the mesentery during perfusion of the mesenteric vessels showed an increase in the frequency of the afferent impulses when the perfusion pressure was raised. The impulse frequency was reduced by bleeding the animal and increased again when the blood was reintroduced into the body. It is suggested that the Pacinian corpuscles which lie in close relation to the vessels are stimulated when the latter dilate. Messages pass to the vasomotor center which then discharges vasoconstrictor impulses to the vessels of the area from which the afferent impulses arose. Thus, undue distention of the vessels and pooling of blood in the splanchnic region is prevented. It has also been shown that stimulation of the peripheral end of the splanchnic nerve causes a much greater rise in blood pressure than usual if the carotid sinuses have been excluded from the circulation (by clamping the carotids). This observation indicates that ordinarily the pressor effect of splanchnic stimulation is largely counteracted by a depressor reflex initiated from the sinus.

The Extraresistance (Cardiac) Effects of the Baroreceptor Reflexes

Too much attention has been paid in the past to the effects of baroreceptor reflexes on the level of blood pressure itself. The action of the baroreceptors is not confined to effects on arteriolar resistance. Much of the preoccupation with peripheral resistance has stemmed from the difficulty in measuring capacity and total flow of the vascular system, a situation which is now being alleviated. The ease of measurement of arterial blood pressure and the dramatic effects thereon from stimulation of the baroreceptor afferents have resulted in identifying circulation changes in terms of blood pressure and, hence, in terms of alterations of peripheral resistance. If vasoconstriction of arterioles were the sole result of baroreceptor stimulation, it is debatable whether any benefit would be conferred on the circulation as a whole. The last few years have seen considerable development in flow methodology and evidence, thus far, from such studies indicates that we have been too prone to ascribe changes in the circulation to blood pressure and arteriolar resistance alterations. The most important changes during reflex, systemic hypertension of sinoaortic origin are those of *venoconstriction* (effects on the capacity vessels) and direct sympathetic stimulation of the heart. Occlusion of the common carotid arteries causes systemic hypertension with resultant decrease in the plethysmographic volume of spleen, limb, kidney, and other parts of the circulation. If the systemic

hypertension is ascribed to widespread arteriolar vasoconstriction, cardiac output would be expected to fall or, at least, not to increase. However, total pulmonary, muscle and kidney blood flow have been shown to increase during carotid occlusion. There is always some increase in peripheral resistance but it is of less quantitative significance, since the cardiac output increases. Experiments, utilizing an extracorporeal circulation with exclusion of the heart and lungs to allow continuous measurement of alterations of intravascular blood volume and of venous return, have also demonstrated venoconstriction (decreased vascular volume) and an increased venous return to the heart when hypotension was induced in the isolated canine carotid sinus. The opposite effects occurred with carotid sinus hypertension. Venoconstriction has also been shown in the forelimb vascular bed of the dog during carotid baroreceptor stimulation. Some studies have failed to confirm these convincing data.

There is evidence that the sympathetics (from the stellates), and parasympathetics (vagal) to the heart, can significantly alter the atrial and ventricular contractility and that this occurs naturally by way of reflexes. In the open chest dog, stimulation of the cardiac nerve fibers previously isolated from the left stellate ganglion, increased systolic blood pressure, cardiac output and stroke volume with a decrease in heart size. The heart rate did not necessarily change. Since stellate stimulation largely elevated arterial blood pressure and cardiac output in the presence of a constant heart rate, after all known connections to the peripheral vasculature had been severed, it follows that the rise of blood pressure was caused by the augmented force of contraction giving an increased cardiac output and not by increased peripheral resistance. These results with cardiac fiber stimulation are similar to those obtained with carotid sinus hypotension. In the open chest dog, when both carotid sinuses were independently perfused under controlled conditions (in the presence of a high, but constant, heart rate) and the mean perfusion pressure and pulse pressure were greatly decreased, the arterial blood pressure, cardiac output and stroke volume rose appreciably. The calculated stroke work increased about 10 times, while the peripheral resistance was only about doubled. This indicates that the circulatory response to carotid sinus baroreceptor stimulation can be, dominantly, an increased cardiac action and, secondarily, an increase in peripheral resistance. Repetitive stimulation at different levels of carotid sinus hypotension produced a shift of the ventricular function curve to the left (more external work at a lower filling pressure). The reverse is also true, i.e., carotid hypertension reduces arterial blood pressure, cardiac output, stroke volume, and shifts the ventricular function curve to the right. The effector portion of this reflex appears to be the sympathetic fibers from the stellate ganglia to the heart, since, following their section these effects disappeared or could not again be induced.

In the open-chest dog with an electrically driven heart (at a constant high heart rate), distal stimulation of the cut vagi decreased mean atrial pressure, arterial pressure, cardiac output and stroke volume, while the ventricular function curve was shifted to the right. Carotid sinus hypertension (produced by the method described in the previous paragraph) gave similar findings. Carotid sinus hypotension enhanced the atrial pressure, arterial pressure, cardiac output and stroke volume. All responses were abolished by atropine. The change in response of atrial contractility is presumed to be reflexly induced, while the ventricular changes arise secondary to the changing atrial contribution to ventricular end diastolic pressure and fiber length.

Finally, observations in man are instructive (Fig. 42.6). Pressures within the carotid sinus regions were directly measured with indwelling catheters in conscious, supine man while the internal pressure was lowered by central, bilateral, carotid artery compression. As the carotid sinus pressure dropped from a mean of 100 to 40 mm. Hg., the arterial blood pressure and heart rate increased only mildly. There is no evidence that the pressor response is secondary to reduction in caliber of the limb and skeletal muscle vessels. The resistance to flow which they offer is actually slightly less than in the control state as the result of a mild increase in systemic blood pressure and in blood flow through the limbs. Simultaneous measurement of cardiac output would have been helpful here, since the increase in arterial blood pressure could arise from the increased cardiac output or from increased vessel resistance in another area.

Cardiovascular Reflexes of Chemoreceptor Origin

Just as the receptors in the root of the aorta and in the carotid sinus serve as outposts of the brain, testing the blood for its pressure level so that the vasomotor center may be advised, so, in similar fashion, the adjacent carotid and aortic bodies contain epitheloid cells and nerve endings

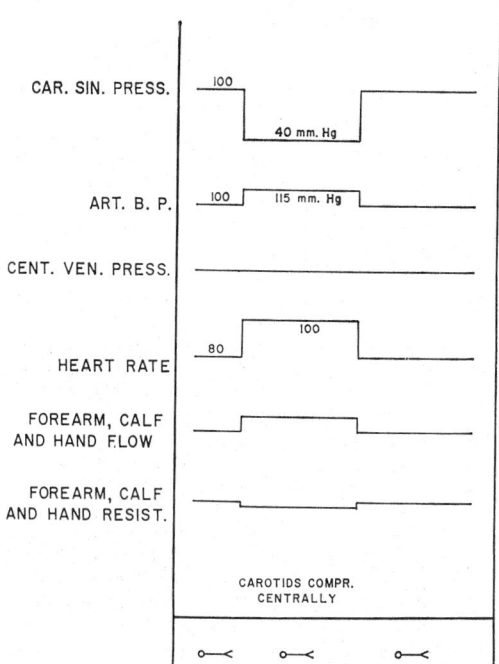

Fig. 42.6. Bilateral carotid artery compression in supine man producing carotid sinus hypotension, reflexly causes a rise in systemic pressure, a tachycardia and an increase in peripheral flow with concomitant decrease in peripheral resistance.

sensitive to the chemical composition of the arterial blood. The fibers of the aortic body run in the vagus while the fibers of the carotid body are branches of the glossopharyngeal nerves. The aortic body is connected with a branch of a fine artery arising from the aorta beyond its arch. The carotid body (glomus caroticum) is a small structure situated upon a branch of the occipital artery or upon a small vessel arising directly from the external carotid just above the bifurcation of the common carotid. It is composed of rounded clumps of polyhedral cells, and possesses a rich network of capillaries of sinusoidal character. Both the carotid and aortic chemoreceptors sample the blood for its pO_2, pCO_2, pH, and possibly for other qualities. Blood flow through the carotid body appears to be by far the largest for any body tissue. Calculations based on direct flow measurements indicate a flow of 2,000 ml. per 100 g. per min. (left ventricle = 80 to 100 ml. per 100 g. per min.) while the oxygen usage of 9 ml. per 100 g. per min., compares with that of the left ventricle. This flow can be cut to $\frac{1}{3}$ by stimulation of the cervical sympathetics. Reflex vasomotor effects evoked by chemoreceptor stimulation have been extensively studied. In general, the chemoreceptors are stimulated by anoxia, hypercapnia, and acidosis. The mechanism by which changes in blood chemical composition effect a response in these two structures is not clearly understood nor has the chemoreceptor intermediate that stimulates the nerve endings been identified, but it has been shown that electroneurographic evidence of chemoreceptor activity exists at CO_2 tensions above 30 mm. Hg and at O_2 tensions of approximately 90 mm. Hg or less. With increasing pCO_2 and decreasing pO_2, discharge of the chemoreceptors is diffuse, but the discharge with increasing CO_2 tension is rarely as great as that resulting from anoxia. According to Heymans, "it is doubtful that chemoreceptors exert any significant effects on the circulation at rest." However, acute hypoxia (inhalation of low oxygen mixtures or of nitrogen) causes systemic hypertension and vasoconstriction (decreased blood flow) in the limbs and intestine; responses are abolished if the chemoreceptor areas are blocked. It is unlikely that chemoreflexes cause systemic hypertension only by inducing an increase in arteriolar resistance, but there are no studies of the reflex effects of such stimulation on cardiac output or on the capacitance vessels. It is certain, however, that they contribute to the maintenance of the circulation following depletion of the blood volume. The latter can be shown in an animal in which, following massive hemorrhage, the blood pressure decreased to 70 mm. Hg. There was intense firing of the chemoreceptors which could be stopped by raising the oxygen tension while resection of the sinus nerves caused a further fall of blood pressure. The latter can only be due to withdrawal of chemoreceptor reflex vasoconstriction since the baroreceptors are not operative at this blood pressure level. Presumably the capacitance vessels (veins) are involved here as well as the resistance vessels, but this remains to be determined.

The Vascular Effects of Normal Variations in Blood Oxygen, Carbon Dioxide and pH

The cardiovascular effects of large changes in blood pO_2, pCO_2, and pH, are discussed in chapter 48. It is generally stated that both CO_2 and oxygen have dual effects. Although CO_2 may have a minor reflex effect through the aortic and carotid body chemoreceptors, it may also have a large direct central effect on the medullary centers which leads to peripheral vasoconstriction with rising blood CO_2 concentrations, while with decreasing blood CO_2 the center will ultimately cease giving out its normal tonic influence. It also

may have a large direct peripheral vessel effect, an increasing blood CO_2 causing peripheral dilation and a decreasing blood CO_2 leading to vasoconstriction. Similarly, the central effects of oxygen lack are supposedly largely mediated through the sinus and aortic bodies, a decrease in oxygen leading to reflex peripheral vasoconstriction, while in the periphery, local hypoxia has the effect of vasodilation. While these statements based on experimental data have been perpetuated, it is very difficult to make such a functional separation and yet retain some reasonable degree of normalcy in the experimental approach to the problem. Aside from the effects mediated through the chemoreceptors, it is doubtful that the relative effects of physiological variations in blood gases and pH on the vasomotor centers and the general peripheral circulation are known. However, for some individual organs or regions, one can distinguish between the local vascular effects of chemical changes in the blood and their central neural effects. For example, the main body of evidence indicates that small increases in carbon dioxide have a direct vasodilating action on cerebral and skin vessels in animals and in humans.

The complexity of the problem, even in individual regions, is indicated when one compares the effect of carbon dioxide on the vasomotor state in the extremities. The hindlimb of an animal perfused with blood from a heart-lung preparation shows vasodilation (greater blood flow at the same perfusion pressure) when the lungs are ventilated by air containing a small amount of carbon dioxide, or by air with some reduction in its oxygen content. The vasodilation must result from local chemical reactions. However, in human subjects with hypercapnia alone, induced from breathing a small concentration of carbon dioxide in the inspired air, the forearm's vascular resistance (mainly muscle) is greatly increased, for systemic blood pressure is increased with little or no change in local blood flow. In the same subjects in whom hypoxia was produced by breathing 5 to 10 per cent oxygen in nitrogen, forearm blood flow increases 100 per cent in the presence of a constant systemic arterial and venous pressure so that vascular resistance in the forearm is considerably reduced. Since the same results are observed in the nerve-blocked arm, the local change in vasomotor state is due to a humoral mechanism and not to a nervous mechanism. When the increased elimination of CO_2 during hypoxia is prevented by adding enough CO_2 to the oxygen-poor gas mixture to maintain the alveolar pCO_2 constant, vascular resistance in the forearm is not

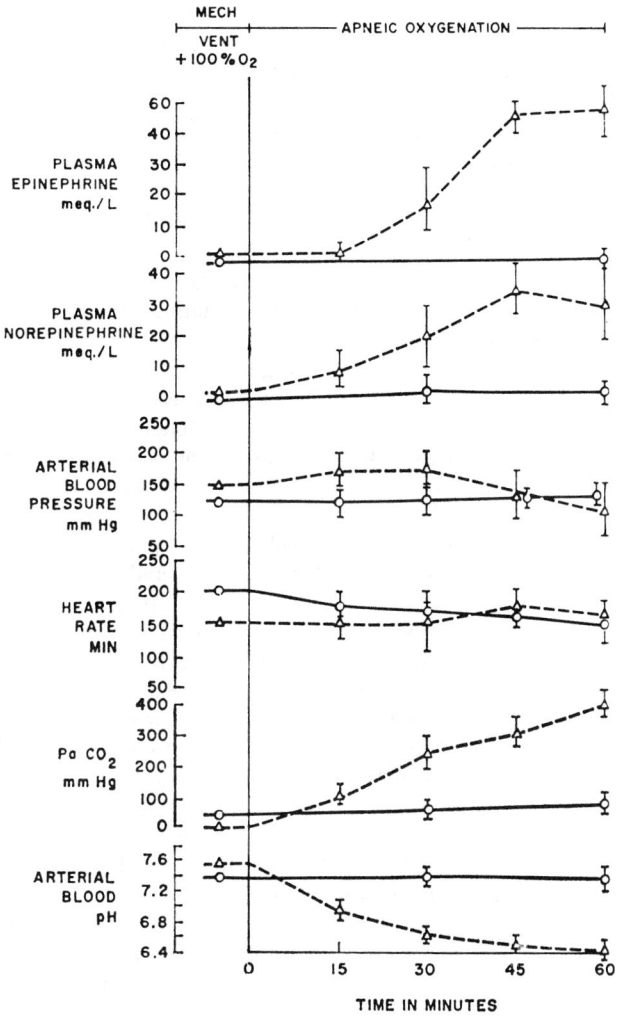

FIG. 42.7. Comparative changes in pH, pCO₂, blood pressure and catecholamine levels during apneic oxygenation with and without TRIS administration. (Nahas, Am. J. Physiol., 1959, **197**, 1308.)

significantly changed. This indicates that marked hypoxia does not affect local overall vessel resistance. Thus, in man, a humoral vasoconstriction occurs with hypercapnia; a humoral vasodilation occurs with hypoxia in the muscles of the forearm which is due to the hypocapnia resulting from the hypoxia rather than directly to the lack of oxygen. The exact mechanism is not clear. The CO_2 or altered pH could have had a local effect, but it is just as probable that a rapid change in arterial pCO_2 evoked biochemical changes in the blood which caused local vasoconstriction or dilation. Of several possible humoral vasodilators which are known, epinephrine, which causes vasodilation in skeletal muscle, might have been released by the lowered pCO_2.

In the past, it has been debatable whether the circulatory effects observed with respiratory or metabolic acidosis come from the elevated pCO_2, the fall in pH, or a combination of both, because there has not been any good way of separating these effects. However, with the use of the organic buffer Tris (hydroxymethyl) amino methane, reasonable experimental separation has been performed with the finding that the cardiovascular effects arise from the decrease in pH and not from the associated change in blood $PaCO_2$ (fig. 42.7). To make this study, the effects of metabolic acidosis were observed in dogs under apneic oxygenation with and without Tris injection. Apneic oxygenation is a condition of ventilatory arrest during which oxygenation of the blood is maintained while acute hypercapnia develops. This condition is produced by ventilating the dog with 100 per cent oxygen in an open circuit for one hour. During this time, oxygen replaces nitrogen throughout the body. After this period of denitrogenation, apnea is induced by succinylcholine, and the lungs are left connected to a reservoir of oxygen. Thus, the blood is maintained in full oxygen saturation, but blood CO_2 accumulates slowly. Without the presence of Tris in such dogs, there is a rise in CO_2, arterial, pulmonary artery and central venous blood pressures, $PaCO_2$, and plasma norepinephrine and epinephrine; the blood pH drops precipitously, the heart rate mildly. In similar dogs treated with intravenous drip of Tris, all these physiological variables remain close to their control values except $PaCO_2$ which rises from 38 to 82 mm. Hg. Since such a pCO_2 increase in the intact animal does produce the above circulatory changes when it is accompanied by a parallel fall in pH, the H^+ concentration increase during hypercapnia seems to be a determinant factor in the stimulation of the cardiovascular system. This type of experiment, however, still does not clearly separate the effects of CO_2 and pH, for the latter does change (7.45 to 7.31), and the vascular system may be very sensitive to it.

Reflexes from the Heart and Lungs

Despite a considerable lack in our knowledge concerning their functions, the carotid and aortic baroreceptor and chemoreceptor reflexes are the most completely studied and understood of vasomotor regulatory reflex mechanisms.

From various intrathoracic vessels (including the chambers of the heart) arise other reflexes affecting vasomotor tone. Although their importance in the regulation of the circulation may possibly be comparable to that of the previously mentioned reflexes, much less is known about their function. As a matter of fact, our present state of knowledge permits little more than an enumeration of various cardiopulmonary reflexes discovered up to date.

It is much more difficult to investigate cardiopulmonary reflexes than those related to the baroreceptors in the systemic circuit. This is because the operative procedures necessary to make interpretable experiments are so extensive and traumatic, and it is difficult to denervate the heart and/or lungs. Despite this, the usual technique so successful in other vascular beds, of eliciting reflexes by change of perfusion pressure in an isolated vascular bed, has been used with some success to indicate qualitatively, if not quantitatively, cardiopulmonary reflexes.

RIGHT HEART REFLEXES

Observations have shown conclusively that in the walls of the atria and great veins, there are receptors which have fairly large afferent nerve fibers and which respond to change of pressure in the atria by firing during atrial contraction (Type A), or during the passive distention of atrial diastole (Type B). These afferent fibers are in the vagi.

The existence of a right atrial reflex has been shown as follows: Blood returning through both venae cavae was collected and pumped into the right atrium, whence it passed through the right ventricle to the pulmonary artery, where it was collected and pumped into a donor dog's veins for oxygenation and returned by a pump to the recipient's left atrium. Increase of perfusion pressure in the right heart produced bradycardia and systemic hypotension which were abolished after vagotomy. Since atropine prevented the bradycardia resulting from the perfusion pressure elevation but did not affect the associated hypotension, a reflex peripheral dilation had occurred. The receptors were found to be in the atrium and not in the ventricle.

In 1915, Bainbridge showed that the intravenous injection of saline or blood produced tachycardia in the anesthetized dog and that this was abolished only by bilateral vagotomy. This is the one reflex which is known to most medical students. Yet, he left unanswered the question of the nature of the effective stimulus to the receptors and their location in the great veins or right side of the heart. Many subsequent investigators using more refined techniques have tried to pin-point the receptors involved and their location. Many are of the opinion that the receptors are in the right atrium, others that no such reflex exists. The answer must await the use of better techniques.

In anesthetized dogs, partial occlusion of the pulmonary artery leads to an increase in pulmonary blood flow. It has been shown that this reflex is dependent on an intact sympathetic innervation of the heart; the vagi and medullary centers are not involved. Presumably the increase in pulmonary blood flow is due to a reflex myocardial stimulation initiated by a rise in right ventricular systolic pressure and is mediated by the cardiac sympathetic nerves.

PULMONARY VESSEL REFLEXES

Most investigators now admit that the pulmonary blood vessels have tone and, therefore, the possibility that this tone can be altered. Daly has found evidence in the anesthetized dog that the pulmonary vascular resistance can be altered by extrinsic vasomotor nerves. Both vasoconstrictor and vasodilator responses have been demonstrated. Recently, direct evidence has been produced that stimulation of the carotid body chemoreceptors by perfusion with venous blood decreases pulmonary vascular resistance. This response was abolished by cutting the carotid sinus nerve or cervico-vagosympathetic trunks, or by injection of atropine. However, localization of the vascular area involved in the dilation was not possible.

A. Pulmonary depressor reflex. In perfusion experiments, blood is pumped from the right atrium of a donor dog through the cannulated left pulmonary artery of a recipient, the outflow from the recipient's left pulmonary vein (thus excluding the left atrium) being returned to the jugular vein of the donor. Marked elevation of the perfusion pressure at times decreases the systemic blood pressure and heart rate which effect is removed by cutting the vagi. In addition, injection of certain drugs into the pulmonary artery also causes a fall in systemic blood pressure and heart rate which is prevented by previous vagal section. This suggests a pulmonary depressor chemoreflex. The receptors concerned are believed to lie in the pulmonary veins.

B. Reflexes from the smaller pulmonary vessels. Despite a tremendous amount of investigation, it is problematic whether reflexes are initiated from the smaller vessels of the pulmonary circuit—arterioles, capillaries and venules. Embolization by clots, starch grain, glass and plastic beads has not determined conclusively whether the results have a mechanical or a reflex explanation. From the work of Daly, it is known that the sympathetic innervation of the vessels is largely vasoconstrictor and that stimulation of the stellates may, at times, reduce lung blood flow by as much as 30 per cent. Despite this, there is no knowledge that pulmonary vasoconstriction can be elicited from stimulation of pulmonary vascular receptors.

Halmagyi and coworkers have demonstrated an "alveolar-vascular reflex of the lung." If water is introduced into the airways of sheep, a reflex response occurs via the parasympathetic nervous system (blocked by atropine) producing pulmonary vasoconstriction. The vagus is not involved for vagotomy does not abolish the response; the reflex is therefore considered to be local in nature. This reflex would lead to a homeostatic redistribution of blood flow away from nonventilated lung areas.

LEFT HEART REFLEXES

A. Left ventricle. Daly and Verney were first to show that pressor receptors existed in the left heart. In an innervated heart-lung preparation in which the aortic pressure was kept constant, an increased pressure in the left side of the heart caused cardiac slowing. More recently, it has been shown that when the pressure is elevated in a vascularly isolated left heart, reflex bradycardia, systemic hypotension, and vasodilation of the leg vessels result. Since left atrial pressure elevation alone was ineffective, it is concluded the receptors were in the left ventricle. Upon vagal blockage the effect disappeared. These effects may also arise from pressoreceptors of the aortic arch which are known to extend into the left side of the heart.

Ross and coworkers studied this reflex by perfusing the systemic vascular bed, using an extracorporeal circulation; pressures could be varied independently in the innervated but isolated heart. Significant decreases in systemic vascular resistance occurred when left ventricular systolic pressure was elevated or when left ventricular diastolic and mean left atrial pressure were *also* elevated. Only minimal alterations in vascular resistance were observed to accompany right ventricular pressure elevations alone. Most important, the elevations in left intracardiac pressure produced a large increase in systemic vascular volume and a diminished venous return. This suggests that left ventricular baroreceptor stimulation reflexly inhibits venous tone. Informative experiments are those of Doutheil and Kramer, who varied the left ventricular stretch and pressure by an adjustable clamp on the aorta, while the systemic flow was metered, and its perfusion pressure maintained constant during aortic constriction by a very large pressure buffering chamber attached to the aorta. It was observed (fig. 42.8) that within 4 sec. after elevation of left ventricular pressure by mechanical constriction, the aortic flow starts to rise and is almost doubled, indicating massive peripheral dilation arising reflexly from the beginning of the aorta or in the left heart. The afferent pathway for this reflex was demonstrated to be the vagus nerve, for following its cervical section, the effect disappeared. To what extent this reflex is invoked under normal conditions is problematic, since a

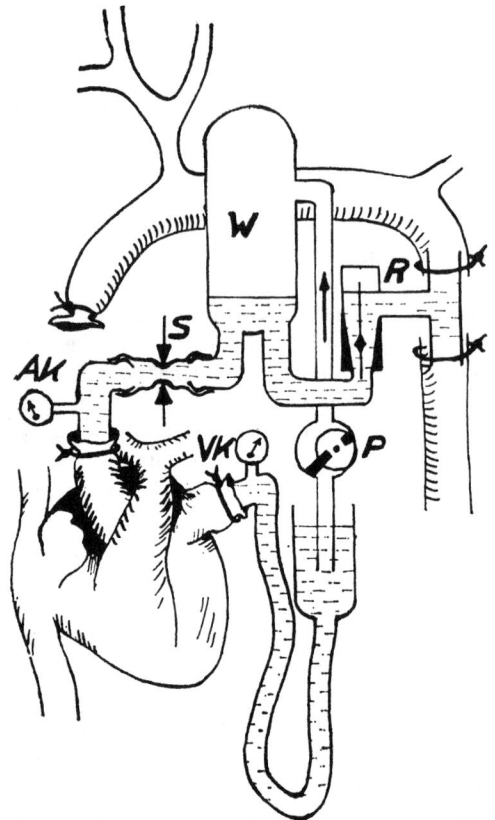

Fig. 42.8. Experimental device to show presence of left ventricular pressure (stretch) receptors by aortic compression. *S*, clamp; *AK* and *VK*, aortic and left atrial pressure manometers, respectively; *W*, constant pressure buffering chamber; *R*, systemic flow meter; *P*, pump. (Doutheil and Kramer, Pflüger's Arch. ges. Physiol., 1959, **269**, 114.)

rather large increase in ventricular pressure (and presumably, therefore, stretch) is necessary to elicit a systemic flow response.

B. Coronary chemoreflex (Bezold-Jarish reflex). In the dog or cat, the peripheral ends of the major coronary artery branches have been separately connected to systemic arteries. Injection of veratrine peripherally into the left circumflex artery causes a fall in blood pressure and heart rate. The systemic hypotension was shown to be independent of the bradycardia, being due to reflex vasodilation. This does not occur if the vagi are first cut. This does not occur upon injection into the right coronary artery or into the coronary artery branches supplying the atrial appendages. Thus, there are receptors in the left ventricular wall supplied by the left circumflex artery.

C. Left atrial receptors. Recent work has shown that left atrial vagal receptors (and also, possibly, receptors in the pulmonary veins) may be the sensory endings of a reflex which controls blood volume. It was first shown that negative pressure breathing causes diuresis. This was then related to the congestion of the thoracic blood vessels which arises from this procedure. Since the effect was removed by vagotomy, it was reasoned that pulmonary or cardiac vessel receptors of vagal origin exist which are responsive to stretch or pressure. Experimentally, it was shown that procedures which lead to an increase of the intrathoracic blood volume (negative pressure breathing), congestion of the pulmonary vascular bed by mitral stenosis through snares, embolization of the pulmonary capillary bed, or an inflated balloon in the left atrium, all cause marked diuresis which, in the balloon experiments, is prevented by previous cooling of the vagus nerves. However, in general the physiological purpose and quantitative effects remain unknown.

Intracardiac or arterial baroreceptors have been suggested as controlling aldosterone secretion from the adrenal cortex. Extensive denervation of the cervical carotid and aortic arch baroreceptor areas, bilateral vagotomy and bilateral splanchnic nerve resection failed to prevent the increase in aldosterone secretion seen in dogs with ascites secondary to thoracic inferior vena caval constriction.

Respiratory Reflexes

A. Vasoconstriction in the finger. Vasoconstriction occurs in a finger after voluntary deep inspiration or passive deep inflation of the chest with air under positive pressure. The vasoconstriction was determined by a finger plethysmograph in which a blood flow decrease was noted with inspiration which bore no relation to the respiratory fluctuations of systemic blood pressure. The receptors and afferent pathways of this reflex are unknown except that without doubt, they arise within the lungs.

B. Respiratory arrhythmias. Changes in heart rate caused by respiration can be demonstrated. Most investigations show that mild inflation causes cardiac acceleration and that this can be abolished by vagal section. It is believed, therefore, that the lungs are a constant source of impulses which exert an inhibitory influence on the cardiac vagal center, this influence being maximal during lung inflation and minimal during lung deflation. Presumably, the respiratory arrhythmia of the pulse has also a central initiating mechanism since increase of the carbon dioxide tension in the cerebral vessels augments the heart rate during each period of inspiratory discharge. It has not been established whether this central arrhythmia is due to diminution of vagal activity during inspiration, or augmentation of sympathetic accelerator activity.

Peripheral Vasculature Reflexes

Although little is known concerning reflexes originating in the peripheral blood vessels, recent interest has been aroused in sensory mechanisms that may lie in the peripheral vasculature. Haddy and Gilbert, using anesthetized dogs in which pressures were measured in the brachial artery, cephalic vein, and a small artery and a small vein of the paw, (with maintenance of a constant brachial artery flow by a pump) found that elevation of cephalic vein pressure produced dilation of the arteries and veins which was completely compensated for by constriction in the small vessel segment. After procaine nerve block the vessels respond like a passive elastic system. Therefore, the observed small vessel constriction must have been of venous origin. However, this local veno-vasomotor reflex has not been confirmed by Greenfield and Patterson using the plethysmograph.

Low Pressoreceptors in Man

Most of the previously described intrathoracic vascular reflexes were studied exclusively in experimental animals and their significance in the human remains to be confirmed. It is, therefore, of interest to mention recent experiments in man which have functionally implicated pressoreceptors in the thoracic portion of the central blood pool in adjustments of the circulation (fig. 42.9). When the legs of a recumbent man are passively raised, the blood flow through the skeletal muscles of the forearm is increased greatly as is the central pool of blood. Since at this time, the arterial blood pressure remains the same or even decreases, this dilation in the forearm is evidently not a consequence of arterial baroreceptor stimulation. Inflation of leg cuffs before trunk and leg elevation, or the use of sympathetic blockade to the forearm, eliminates the flow response. While the precise nature of the stimulus and accurate location of the receptors concerned in the reflex have not been determined, it seems likely that forearm dilation is due to stimulation of receptors in the low pressure area of the thoracic vascular bed. Rapid positive and negative pressure breathing causes a similar augmentation of blood flow in forearm and calf without changes in arterial

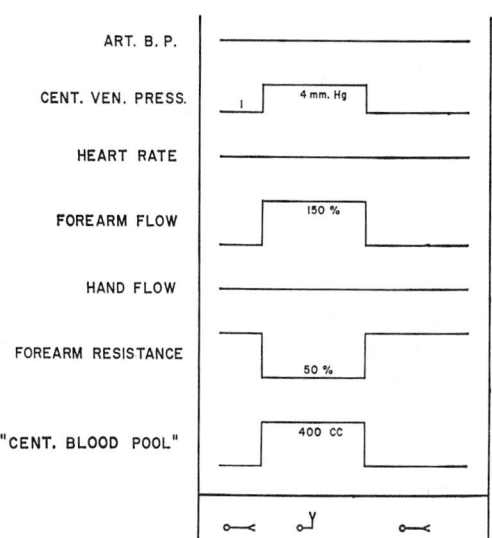

Fig. 42.9. Passive elevation of the legs in recumbent man produces elevations in the central blood pool and central venous pressure with increased peripheral flow, while heart rate and systemic arterial pressure are unchanged. The decreased peripheral resistance is felt to be secondary to reflex dilation.

blood pressure and heart rate. Presumably, this response is also to be explained through stimulation of pressoreceptors in the chest.

Summary

Change in activation of the vasoconstrictor fibers is responsible for blood pressure homeostasis and heat loss regulation of the skin blood flow. Centrally induced vasodilation is caused almost entirely by inhibition of constrictor tone. There may be a generalized or a strictly segmental or regional engagement, depending upon the type of stimulus. Together with the sympathetic vasodilator fibers to skeletal muscles, vasoconstrictor fibers may affect specific vascular areas in a discharge pattern causing marked redistribution of blood flow. The vasoconstrictor fibers are looked upon as the main neurogenic adjustors of the peripheral circulation showing prompt and retional adjustments of their impulse discharge to any change in environment, especially those changes that affect the hypothalamus and the vasoconstrictor center in the medulla.

In the nerves from the pressure or stretch sensitive vascular walls of the aorta and carotid sinus, an increased number of impulses is discharged with each rise of blood pressure; the impulse frequency, systemic blood pressure and heart rate can be varied at will when these areas are artificially perfused at different pressures and pulse pressures; section of the nerves results in a persistent hypertension. These presso- or baro-receptors are joined by the aortic and carotid sinus nerves with the nerve centers in the medulla oblongata which maintain systemic blood pressure at normal levels. Any arterial blood pressure deviation causes compensatory reflexes, through the baroreceptors, to reestablish a normal blood pressure. The efferent pathways to the heart for these baroreceptor vasomotor reflexes are the vagus and the sympathetic; in addition, the sympathetic vasoconstrictor fibers adjust the size of the "resistance" and "capacity" vessels in control of peripheral resistance to blood flow and the return of blood to the heart. The sympathetic fibers which control secretion of epinephrine and norepinephrine by the adrenal glands also stimulate these secretions and add a blood-borne hormone to the nervous influence, but as already indicated, this humoral influence is almost insignificant compared to that of the direct nerve effect.

The baroreceptors also react to nonspecific pharmacological agents. Baroreceptors exist in several other tissues—common carotid artery, thoracic and mesenteric arteries; these are probably not related to blood pressure homeostasis but may be engaged in local reflex adjustments of peripheral resistance and blood flow. Baroreceptor nerve endings are in the walls of the caval veins, heart (mainly the atria), and in the pulmonary circulation. Presumably, these receptors are primarily engaged in the reflex adjustment of venous return, heart rate, blood volume, and cardiac output. In the presence of marked hypotension from hemorrhage, chemoreceptors in the carotid and aortic bodies are excited to induce vasoconstriction in the resistance and capacitance vessels through the sympathetic constrictor fibers. Chemoreceptors are also present in the pulmonary and coronary circulations, but the physiological stimuli adequate for their activation are not known.

REFERENCES

ALEXANDER, R. S. Tonic and reflex functions of medullary sympathetic cardiovascular centers. J. Neurophysiol., 1946, **9**, 205.

ALEXANDER, R. S. The participation of the venomotor system in pressor reflexes. Circulation Res., 1954, **2**, 405.

AVIADO, D. M. AND SCHMIDT, C. F. Cardiovascular and respiratory reflexes from the left side of the heart. Am. J. Physiol., 1959, **196**, 726.

BACH, L. M. The reflex activation of the vasodilator fibers of the dorsal roots and their role in vasodilator tone. Am. J. Physiol., 1946, **145**, 474.

BAINBRIDGE, F. A. On some cardiac reflexes. J. Physiol., 1914, **48**, 332.

BARCROFT, H., BONNAR, W. M., EDHOLM, O. G., AND EFFRON, A. S. On sympathetic vasoconstrictor tone in human skeletal muscle. J. Physiol., 1943, **102**, 21.

BAYLISS, W. M. On the physiology of the depressor nerve. J. Physiol., 1893, **14**, 303.

BLACK, J. E. AND RODDIE, I. C. The mechanism of the changes in forearm vascular resistance during hypoxia. J. Physiol., 1958, **143**, 226.

BRONK, D. W., PITTS, R. F., AND LARRABEE, M. G. Role of hypothalamus in cardiovascular regulation. Res. Publ. A. Nerv. & Ment. Dis., 1940, **20**, 323.

BRONK, D. W. AND STELLA, G. J. Afferent impulses in carotid sinus nerve; relation of discharge from single end organs to arterial blood pressure. J. Cell. & Comp. Physiol., 1932, **1**, 113.

BRONK, D. W. AND STELLA, G. J. Response to steady pressures of single end organs in isolated carotid sinus. Am. J. Physiol., 1935, **110**, 708.

BURCH, G. E. AND MURTADHA, M. A study of the venomotor tone in a short intact venous segment of the forearm of man. Am. Heart J., 1956, **51**, 807.

BURTON-OPITZ, R. Venous pressures. Am. J. Physiol., 1903, **9**, 198.

CARPENTER, C. C. J., DAVIS, J. O., AND AYERS, C. R. Concerning the role of arterial baroreceptors in the control of aldosterone secretion. J. Clin. Invest., 1961, **40**, 1160.

CELANDER, O. The range of control exercised by the sympathico-adrenal system. Acta physiol. scandinav., 1954, (suppl. 116), 1.

CELANDER, O. AND FOLKOW, B. A comparison of the sympathetic vasomotor fiber control of the vessels within the skin and the muscles. Acta physiol. scandinav., 1953, **29**, 241.

COMROE, J. H. The location and function of the chemoreceptors of the aorta. Am. J. Physiol., 1939, **127**, 176.

CORCONDILAS, A., DONALD, D. E., AND SHEPHERD, J. T. Assessment by two independent methods of the role of cardiac output in the pressor response to carotid occlusion. J. Physiol., 1964, **170**, 250.

CROUCH, R. L. AND THOMPSON, G. K. Autonomic functions of cerebral cortex. J. Nerv. & Mental Dis., 1939, **89**, 328.

CYON, E. VON AND LUDWIG, C. Ber. Sachs. Ges., 1866, **18**, 307. (Quoted by Bayliss).

DALY, I. DE B. AND VERNEY, E. B. Cardiovascular reflexes. J. Physiol., 1926, **61**, 268.

DALY, I. DE B. AND DALY, M. DE B. The effect of stimulation of the carotid sinus baroreceptors on the pulmonary vascular bed in the dog. J. Physiol., 1959, **148**, 220.

DALY, M. DE B., LAMBERTSEN, C. J., AND SCHWEITZER, A. Observations on the volume of blood flow and oxygen utilization of the carotid body in the cat. J. Physiol., 1954, **125**, 67.

DAWES, G. S. Studies on veratrum alkaloids; receptor areas in coronary arteries and elsewhere as revealed by veratridine. J. Pharmacol. & Exper. Therap., 1947, **89**, 325.

DITTMAR, C. Vasomotor centre, location. Ber. sächs. Ges. (Acad.) Wiss., 1873, **25**, 449.

DOUTHEIL, U. AND KRAMER, K. Über die Differenzierung kreislaufregulierender Reflexe aus dem linken Herz. Pflüger's Arch. ges. Physiol., 1959, **269**, 114.

ECKSTEIN, J. W. AND HAMILTON, W. K. The pressure-volume responses of human forearm veins during epinephrine and norepinephrine infusions. J. Clin. Invest., 1957, **36**, 1663.

ELIASSON, S., LINDGREN, P., AND UVNÄS, B. Representation in the hypothalamus and the motor cortex in the dog of the sympathetic vasodilator outflow to the skeletal muscles. Acta physiol. scandinav., 1952, **27**, 18.

ELIASSON, S., FOLKOW, B., LINDGREN, P. AND UVNÄS, B. Activation of sympathetic vasodilator nerves to the skeletal muscles in the cat by hypothalamic stimulation. Acta physiol. scandinav., 1951, **23**, 333.

ELIASSON, S. AND STRÖM, G. On the localization in the cat of hypothalamic and cortical structures influencing cutaneous blood flow. Acta, physiol. scandinav., 1950, **20**, (suppl. 70), 113.

ELIASSON, S., LINDGREN, P. AND UVNÄS, B. The hypothalamus, a relay station of the sympathetic vasodilator tract. Acta physiol. scandinav., 1954, **31**, 290.

EULER, U. S. VON, LILJESTRAND, G., AND ZOTTERMAN, Y. Excitation mechanism of chemoreceptors of carotid body. Skandinav. Arch. Physiol., 1939, **83**, 132.

FOLKOW, B. Impulse frequency in sympathetic vasomotor fibers correlated to the release and elimination of the transmitter. Acta physiol. scandinav., 1952, **25**, (Suppl. 89–92) 49.

FRIEDEN, J. AND KELLER, A. D. Blood pressure in normotensive and renal hypertensive dogs following hypothalamic ablations and neurohypophysectomy. Army Medical Research Laboratory, Fort Knox, Kentucky, Project 6-64-12-028, Report 172, March 1955.

GILLIATT, R. W. Vasoconstriction in the finger after deep inspiration. J. Physiol., 1947, **107**, 76.

GILMORE, J. P., MITCHELL, J. H., AND SARNOFF, S. J. The carotido-vago-atrial and carotido-sympatho-atrial reflexes. Fed. Proc., 1960, **19**, 119.

GREENFIELD, A. D. M. AND PATTERSON, G. C. On the capacity and distensibility of the blood vessels of the human forearm. J. Physiol., 1956, **131**, 290.

GRUHZIT, C. C. AND MOE, G. K. Reflex vasodilatation induced by epinephrine. Am. J. Physiol., 1952, **171**, 730.

GUTTMAN, L. AND WHITTERIDGE, D. Effects of bladder distension on autonomic mechanisms after spinal cord injuries. Brain, 1947, **70**, 361.

HADDY, F. J. AND GILBERT, R. P. The relation of a venous-arteriolar reflex to transmural pressure and resistance in small and large systemic vessels. Circulation Res., 1956, **4**, 25.

HALMAGYI, D. F. J., COLEBATCH, H. J. H., STARZECKI, B., AND HORNER, G. J. Pulmonary alveolar-vascular reflex. J. Appl. Physiol., 1964, **19**, 105.

HEYMANS, C., DESCHAEPDRYVER, A. F., AND DE-

VLEESCHHOUWER, G. R. Abdominal baro- and chemosensitivity in dogs. Circulation Res., 1960, **8**, 347.

HEYMANS, C. AND VAN DEN HEUVEL-HEYMANS, G. New aspects of blood pressure regulation. Circulation, 1951, **4**, 581.

HOFF, E. C., KELL, J. F., HASTING, N., SHALES, D. M., AND GRAY, E. H. Vasomotor, cellular, and functional changes produced in kidney by brain stimulation. J. Neurophysiol., 1951, **14**, 317.

KELLER, A. D. Ablation and stimulation of the hypothalamus: Circulatory effects. Physiol. Rev., 1960, Supp. 4, **40**, 116.

KINMONTH, J. B., SIMEONE, F. A., AND PERLOW, V. Factors affecting the diameter of large arteries with particular reference to traumatic spasm. Surgery, 1949, **26**, 452.

KUNTZ, A. J. Anatomic and physiologic properties of cutaneo-visceral vasomotor reflex arcs. J. Neurophysiol., 1945, **8**, 421.

LANDGREN, S. AND NEIL, E. The contribution of carotid chemoceptor mechanisms to the rise of blood pressure caused by carotid occlusion. Acta physiol. scandinav., 1951, **23**, 152.

LINDGREN, P. AND UVNÄS, B. Activation of sympathetic vasodilator and vasoconstrictor neurons by electrical stimulation in the medulla of the cat and dog. Circulation Res., 1953, **1**, 479.

MAGOUN, H. W., RANSON, S. W., AND HETHERINGTON, A. Descending connections from hypothalamus. Arch. Neurol. & Psychiat., 1938, **39**, 1127.

MANN, M. AND WEST, G. B. Nature of hepatic and splenic sympathin. Brit. J. Pharmacol and Chemother., 1950, **5**, 173.

MARTIN, D. A., WHITE, K. L., AND VERNON, C. R. Influence of emotional and physical stimuli on pressure in isolated vein segment. Circulation Res., 1959, **7**, 580.

MAYERSON, H. S. Effect of gravity on the blood pressure of the dog. Am. J. Physiol., 1942, **135**, 411.

MCCUBBIN, J. W., GREEN, J. H., AND PAGE, I. H. Carotid sinus participation in experimental renal hypertension. Circulation, 1958, **17**, 791.

NAHAS, G. G. Effects of acute exposure to low oxygen tension on the circulation of vagotomized non-narcotized dogs. J. Appl. Physiol., 1956, **9**, 65.

NAHAS, G. G., JORDAN, E. C., AND LIGOU, J. C. Effects of a "CO_2 buffer" on hypercapnia of apneic oxygenation. Am. J. Physiol., 1959, **197**, 1308.

PAINTAL, A. S. A study of ventricular pressure receptors and their role in the Bezold reflex. Quart. J. Exper. Physiol., 1955, **40**, 348.

PAINTAL, A. S. A study of right and left atrial receptors. J. Physiol., 1953, **120**, 596.

RANDALL, W. A., AND ROHSE, W. G. The augmentor action of the sympathetic cardiac nerves. Circulation Res., 1956, **4**, 470.

RANSON, S. W. AND BILLINGSLEY, P. R. Vasomotor reactions from stimulation of the floor of the fourth ventricle. Studies in vasomotor reflex arcs. Am. J. Physiol., 1916, **41**, 85.

RICHINS, C. A. AND BRIZZEE, K. Effect of localized

cutaneous stimulation on circulation in duodenal arterioles and capillary beds. J. Neurophysiol., 1949, **12**, 131.

RODDIE, I. C., SHEPHERD, J. T., AND WHALEN, R. F. Reflex changes in human skeletal muscle blood flow associated with intrathoracic pressure changes. Circulation Res., 1958, **6**, 232.

RODDIE, I. C. AND SHEPHERD, J. T. The effects of carotid artery compression in man with special reference to changes in vascular resistance in limbs. J. Physiol., 1957, **139**, 377.

ROSE, J. C. AND FREIS, E. D. Alterations in systemic vascular volume of the dog in response to hexamethonium and norepinephrine. Am. J. Physiol., 1957, **191**, 283.

ROSS, J., JR., FRAHM, C. J., AND BRAUNWALD, E. The influence of the carotid baroreceptors and of vasoactive drugs on systemic vascular volume and venous distensibility. Circulation Res., 1961, **9**, 75.

ROSS, J., JR., FRAHM, C. J., AND BRAUNWALD, E. Influence of intracardiac baroreceptors on venous return, systemic vascular volume and peripheral resistance. J. Clin. Invest., 1961, **40**, 563.

ROTTA, A., CANEPA, A., HURTADO, A., VELASQUEZ, T., AND CHAVEZ, R. Pulmonary circulation at sea level and at high altitudes. J. Appl. Physiol., 1956, **9**, 328.

SARNOFF, S. J. AND YAMADA, S. I. Evidence for reflex control of arterial pressure from abdominal receptors with special reference to the pancreas. Circulation Res., 1959, **7**, 325.

SARNOFF, S. J. et al. The influence of carotid sinus pressure on myocardial contractility. Fed. Proc., 1959, **18**, 137.

SHIPLEY, R. AND GREGG, D. E. Cardiac response to stimulation of the stellate ganglia and cardiac nerves. Am. J. Physiol., 1945, **143**, 396.

STRICKER, S. Wien. Sitzber., 1876, **74**, (**III**), 173. (Quoted by Bayliss).

STROM, G. Vasomotor responses to thermal and electrical stimulation of frontal lobe and hypothalamus. Acta Physiol. scandinav., 1950, **20** (70), 83.

TAQUINI, A. C. AND AVIADO, D. M. Reflex stimulation of heart induced by partial occlusion of pulmonary artery. Am. J. Physiol., 1961, **200**, 647.

TODD, T. W. AND KRAMER, J. G. The distribution of nerves to the arteries of the arm, with a discussion of the clinical value of results. Anat. Rec., 1914, **8**, 243.

WAKERLIN, G. E., CRANDALL, E. E., FRANK, M. H., JOHNSON, B., POMPER, L., AND SCHMID, H. E. Experimental hypertension produced by constriction of carotid sinus area. Circulation Res., 1954, **2**, 416.

WILLIAMS, M. H. Mechanical vs. reflex effects of diffuse pulmonary embolism in anesthetized dogs. Circulation Res., 1956, **4**, 325.

ZINGHER, D. AND GRODINS, F. S. Effect of carotid baroreceptor stimulation upon the forelimb vascular bed of the dog. Circulation Res., 1964, **14**, 392.

Monographs and Reviews

ADAMS, W. R. AND VEITH, I. (editors). Pulmonary circulation. An international symposium. Grune & Stratton, Inc., New York, 1959.

AVIADO, D. M., JR. AND SCHMIDT, C. F. Reflexes from stretch receptors in blood vessels, heart and lungs. Physiol. Rev., 1955, **35**, 247.

BARCROFT, H. AND SWAN, H. J. C. Sympathetic control of human blood vessels. Edward Arnold & Company, London, 1953.

BAYLISS, W. M. The vaso-motor system. Longmans, London, 1923.

DAWES, G. S. AND COMROE, J. H. Chemoreflexes from heart and lungs. Physiol. Rev., 1954, **34**, 167.

DAWES, G. S. Reflex factors in the regulation of the circulation. Josiah Macy Foundation. Transactions of the Third Conference on Shock and Circulatory Homeostasis, 1953.

EICHNA, L. W. AND McQUARRIE, D. G. (editors). Symposium. Central Nervous System Control of Circulation. Physiol. Rev., 1960, **40** (suppl. 4).

FOLKOW, B. Nervous control of the blood vessels. Physiol. Rev., 1955, **35**, 629.

FOLKOW, B. Structural, myogenic, humoral and nervous factors controlling peripheral resistance. Proceedings of the Conference on Hypotensive Drugs and Control of Vascular Tone in Hypotension. Pergamon Press, London, 1956.

GAUER, O. H., AND HENRY, J. P. Beitrag zur Homöostase des extraarteriellen Kreislaufs. Klin. Wchnschr., 1956, **34**, 356.

GREGG, D. E. Coronary circulation in health and disease. Lea & Febiger, Philadelphia, 1950.

HEYMANS, C. AND NEIL, E. Reflexogenic areas of the cardiovascular system. J. & A. Churchill, Ltd., London, 1958.

LANDIS, E. M. AND HORTENSTINE, J. C. Functional significance of venous blood pressure. Physiol. Rev., 1950, **30**, 1.

LUND, A. Significance of the cerebral cortex to the vasomotor reaction of the extremities. Ejnar Munksgaards Forlag, Copenhagen, 1943.

PERIFIELD, W., AND RASMUSSEN, T. The cerebral cortex of man. The Macmillan Company, New York, 1950.

RUSHMER, R. F. AND SMITH, O. A. Cardiac control. Physiol. Rev., 1959, **39**, 41.

SCHMIDT, C. F. The cerebral circulation in health and disease, Charles C Thomas, Publisher, Springfield, Illinois, 1950.

UVNÄS, B. Sympathetic vasodilator outflow. Physiol. Rev., 1954, **34**, 608.

VON EULER, U. S. Noradrenaline. Chemistry, physiology, pharmacology and clinical aspects. Charles C Thomas, Publisher, Springfield, Illinois, 1956.

ZWEIFACH, B. W. Structural make-up of the capillary wall. Ann. New York Acad. Sc., 1955 **61**, 670.

CHAPTER 43

Regulation of Pressure and Flow in the Systemic and Pulmonary Circulation (Continued)

Arterial Blood Pressure

The first determination of arterial blood pressure was in 1733 when the Reverend Stephen Hales inserted a brass cannula into the central end of the femoral artery of a horse, connected it to a long vertical glass tube, and observed that a column of blood filled the tube to a height of 8 ft., 3 in. (185 mm. Hg).

SPECIES DIFFERENCES. The arterial blood pressure varies moderately between different warm-blooded species, and there is little or no relationship between the size of an animal and the height of its blood pressure. The blood pressure, in general, is higher in birds than in mammals, whereas that of cold-blooded animals is only about one-third as great. The carotid blood pressure (mean) of the unanesthetized, basal dog approximates 110 mm. Hg. The domestic cow has a mean blood pressure of about 135 mm. Hg. The following systolic pressures (mm. Hg.) have have been reported: mouse, 113; rat, 130; canary, 220; robin, 118; frog, 43; turtle, 44; and carp, 43. Of considerable interest is the arterial pressure in the carotid artery of the giraffe, because of the very long, vertical distance from heart to brain. In experiments performed on 4 standing, unanesthetized giraffes, the carotid pressure, corrected to heart level, ranged from 280/150 to 344/194 mm. Hg. The walls of the giraffe's left ventricle and the aorta are extraordinarily thick.

Arterial Blood Pressure in Man

A. Normal values. The average systolic pressure of young male adults at mental and physical rest in the sitting position (as usually measured in a routine medical examination) is usually given as 120 mm. Hg; the diastolic as 80, the mean pressure as 100, and the pulse pressure as 40. However, the range of normal blood pressures may be from 90 to 120 mm. Hg systolic, and 60 to 80 mm. Hg diastolic. Slight diurnal variations in blood pressure of from 5 to 10 mm. Hg systolic occur, the peak being in the afternoon and the lowest level in the early hours of the morning.

B. Age, sex and build. Age exerts a definite influence upon the blood pressure levels. At birth the systolic pressure measures from 20 to 60 mm. with an average of 40 mm. It rises rapidly, however, and has an average value of about 70 mm. at the end of a fortnight and 80 mm. at the end of a month. A slow steady rise takes place from this time until about the 12th year when it averages 105 mm. With the onset of puberty, a more sudden rise occurs which in boys reaches 120 mm. at about the age of 17. A steady though not great rise in blood pressure, from adolescence to old age, is the rule in health, the averages for the age of 60 being given as about 140 systolic pressure and 87 diastolic. In women up to the time of the menopause, the systolic pressure is from 4 to 5 mm. lower than for men of the same age. At the menopause, however, there is a somewhat abrupt rise, and the pressure remains a little above the male average from then on (table 43.1).

Comparing groups of markedly obese and normal persons, the former have a rather pronounced increase of systolic pressure. The incidence of abnormally high blood pressure (hypertension) is also definitely greater in overweight persons.

C. The effects of digestion, emotion, exercise and posture. The systolic pressure is influenced to a small but definite extent by meals. A rise of from 6 to 8 mm. is the usual effect, and this lasts for an hour or so. There is little change in the diastolic pressure; if anything, it is reduced, presumably as a result of vasodilation in the digestive organs and skin.

Quiet, restful sleep may be accompanied by a fall of from 15 to 30 mm. in the systolic pressure. The fall is most marked during the first hours, rising gradually again after this until the time of waking. If the sleep is disturbed and accompanied by imaginary motor activities, there may be no depression of the pressure, but rather an elevation, in some instances to as high as 200 mm. systolic and 105 mm. diastolic. Excitement, fear, worry, etc., markedly affect the arterial blood pressure, especially the systolic. The effects are brought about through increased cardiac action and changes in the state of the vessels through impulses playing upon the cardiac and vasomotor

TABLE 43.1

The average variations of blood pressure (after Hunter's compilation of observations on a quarter million healthy Americans)

(After Gager)

Age	Systolic Pressure	Diastolic Pressure	Pulse Pressure
10	103	70	33
15	113	75	38
20	120	80	40
25	122	81	41
30	123	82	41
35	124	83	41
40	126	84	42
45	128	85	43
50	130	86	44
55	132	87	45
60	135	89	46

centers in the medulla. The liberation of adrenaline into the blood stream may also be a factor.

Of all physiological conditions, exercise, if of a strenuous nature, has the most powerful effect upon the arterial blood pressure. During the muscular effort or even immediately before, i.e., at the instant that the exertion is contemplated, the systolic pressure commences to rise and may reach a height of 180 or 200 mm. Hg. Except in well trained persons or athletes, this is invariably associated with a large increase in heart rate to 150 or 180 per minute. In the trained individual, the blood pressure rise may be quite mild. The diastolic pressure shows a less pronounced rise (100 to 110) so that the pulse pressure is increased. In light exercise the diastolic pressure may remain at the normal level while the systolic rises several millimeters. Immediately after the exercise the pressure drops momentarily to normal or even slightly below. It then mounts rapidly to its previous high level, from which it gradually declines again, and in a healthy person reaches the normal within from 1 to 4½ minutes. The evanescent drop in pressure is explained as being due to the sudden relaxation of the abdominal muscles. The blood is drained into the venous reservoirs. These when deprived of their support (abdominal muscles) have their capacity increased and the blood flow into the right heart is temporarily curtailed. It is not until an appreciable time has elapsed to enable the increased venous capacity to become filled again by blood pouring in from the recently active muscles that an adequate flow into the right heart is restored.

The diastolic pressure is somewhat higher in the standing than in the sitting position and lowest in recumbency. This change is found to occur whether the postural change is brought about actively or passively and is evidently an overcompensation for the gravity effect. The systolic pressure usually rises but to a less extent than the diastolic, so the pulse pressure is reduced. Pressures, however, taken at as short an interval as 10 seconds after the erect position has been assumed show that the initial effect is a fall of from 6 to 22 mm. Hg in the systolic pressure. This is sufficient to stimulate the carotid sinus and aortic mechanisms and cause increased vascular tone with a consequent compensatory rise in pressure. Compensation is usually complete within 30 seconds. Reverting from the standing to the sitting or recumbent position has the reverse effect, fall in diastolic pressure and rise in pulse pressure. In persons with an abnormally and habitually low blood pressure, the systolic pressure may actually rise in the lying-down position and fall when the subject stands. The diastolic, on the other hand, is always lowered in recumbency and raised in the erect posture.

THE SYSTOLIC, DIASTOLIC, MEAN AND PULSE PRESSURES. Hales, in describing his experiment, speaks of the blood column after it had ceased to rise further in the tube, oscillating above and below a mean level. To quote his own words, "When it (the blood) was at its full height, it would rise and fall at, and after, each pulse, 2, 3 or 4 inches." By recording with an adequate pressure manometric system, these fluctuations are seen as waves synchronous with the heart beats (see fig. 43.4). The crest of the wave represents the maximal pressure, corresponding to the contraction or systole of the ventricle, and is called the systolic pressure. The trough of the wave, i.e., the point of minimal pressure, coincides with the end of the resting phase or diastole of the cardiac cycle, and is called the diastolic pressure. The mean pressure is usually given as half the sum of the values for the systolic and diastolic pressures. This would be strictly accurate only if the pulse wave inscribed a perfect triangle which, however, is not the case. The average pressure throughout the cardiac cycle, i.e., the true or geometric mean, is generally somewhat lower than this, lying nearer the diastolic than the systolic pressure. This can be obtained by integration of the curve.

The difference between the diastolic and systolic pressures is the pulse pressure. This is caused by the ejection of blood into the aorta during systole. Its magnitude, other things being equal, will vary with the quantity of blood ejected by the heart at each beat.

The systolic pressure reflects mainly the distensibility characteristics of the arterial system as it receives blood from the left ventricle. It would be expected to undergo wider variations under the stresses of every day life than the diastolic pressure. The latter represents the constant load which the arterial walls are called upon to bear and the resistance which the ventricular contraction must overcome to throw open the aortic valves. It shows a steady but slight decline from the larger to the medium sized vessels. The systolic pressure shows a fall between the larger and the smaller arteries which, though not great, is much more pronounced than that which occurs in the diastolic. On this account, the two pressures tend to become more nearly equal toward the periphery, the pulse pressure being reduced. Since the pulse pressure is the difference between the systolic and diastolic pressures, it may be reduced by an alteration in one or other of these. A rise in the systolic or a fall in the diastolic, will cause the pulse pressure to increase, while a fall in the systolic or a rise in the diastolic will lower the pulse pressure. If both systolic and diastolic pressures rise or fall to an equal extent, the pulse pressure remains unchanged. The mean pressure will rise as a result of a rise in either the diastolic or systolic pressure, or of both together, and will fall when a reduction of either or of both of these pressures occurs.

DETERMINANTS OF NORMAL ARTERIAL BLOOD PRESSURE

Several factors combine to maintain normal arterial blood pressure. They are, (a) the pumping action of the heart, (b) the peripheral resistance, (c) the quantity of blood in the arterial system, (d) the viscosity of the blood, (e) the elasticity of the arterial walls.

A. The pumping action of the heart. The means by which the cardiac contraction exerts its effect upon the arterial blood pressure is, obviously, through the *quantity* of blood which it is capable of discharging into the aorta in a unit period of time, i.e., upon the output of the heart per minute or stroke volume times heart rate. When more blood is forced into the already filled arterial system, it cannot escape at once from the system in the same amount as it is thrown into the aorta, so the arterial walls become stretched. The pressure rises until the velocity of flow through the arterioles is great enough to balance again the out-

flow from the system with the inflow. Hales grasped this fundamental fact when he wrote, "the real force (pressure) of the blood in the arteries depends on the proportion which the quantity of blood thrown out of the left ventricle in a given time bears to the quantity which can pass through the capillary arteries (arterioles) into the veins at that time."

B. The peripheral resistance. The peripheral resistance is dependent upon the caliber of the small vessels, mainly of the arterioles and, to a less extent, of the capillaries, and upon the viscosity of the blood. It has also been demonstrated by Haddy, that the macroscopic vessels (smaller arteries and veins) contribute significantly to resistance across systemic vascular beds. By far the greater part of the peripheral resistance of the circulatory system is constituted by the minute vessels of the muscles and of the abdominal structures. The importance in this connection of the latter—the so-called splanchnic area—can be demonstrated by tying off all branches of the aortic arch, except the carotids, and the abdominal aorta below the inferior mesenteric branch, when little or no change in peripheral resistance results; whereas an increase in the latter at once occurs when the blood supply to the splanchnic area is reduced by ligating the superior mesenteric artery. Stimulation of the great splanchnic nerve, which innervates the rings of muscle fibers in the walls of these vessels, causes their constriction, and consequently a reduction in the outflow from the arterial system. The pressure will continue to rise until inflow and outflow are again balanced. In the absence of compensatory changes in the other factors concerned in the maintenance of the pressure this remains at the higher level so long as the constriction persists. Dilation of the vessels, i.e., reduction in peripheral resistance, will of course be followed by the opposite effect. When the vessels of the splanchnic area are fully dilated they are capable of accommodating almost all the blood in the body; in such an event the blood pressure would fall to zero. The peripheral resistance might be compared to a dam in a river. If the dam is raised or lowered, and no change occurs in the supply of water flowing down the river to the dam, the water continues to rise or fall respectlvely (and its pressure in consequence increases or diminishes) until it reaches the new level. From then on the quantity of water which overflows in a given time is the same as it was at the original level.

The total peripheral resistance in animals or

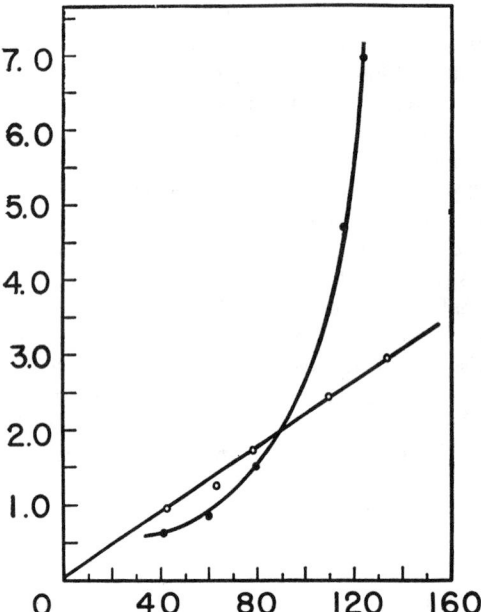

FIG. 43.1. Relationship between mean arterial pressure in millimeters of mercury (abscissa) and cardiac output in liters per minute (ordinate) in a typical experiment. Solid circles represent values observed with buffer nerves intact; open circles, values obtained after bilateral vagotomy and while a constant pressure of 210 mm. Hg. was exerted upon the isolated, innervated carotid sinuses (From Levy, Circulation Res., 1954, **2**, 372.)

in man can be calculated from the mean blood pressure (M) and the cardiac output (F), since all blood entering the aorta must, of course, pass through the peripheral vessels. This can be derived for the whole body from the simultaneously measured arterial pressure and cardiac output, and for an organ or region from the local arterial pressure and flow, but interpretation is valid only under strictly controlled conditions which have already been discussed. In general, in isolated organs, either pressure or flow should be kept constant while the other is varied. For total circulation, either this arrangement or possibly a complete pressure-volume curve for the systemic circulation can be used, before and after a test stimulus, with subsequent comparison of the two curves. There is a curvilinear relationship between pressure and flow in the aorta (fig. 43.1). This is also true in separate vascular beds where pressure and flow have been measured but the shape of the curves may be quite different.

Various terminologies have been used to define peripheral resistance. Green has used a unit of peripheral resistance (PRU) as equal to 1 mm. Hg./1 ml/min. Many authors take such a ratio

and by expressing P in dynes per square centimeter and F as milliliters per second, the peripheral resistance can be given in absolute units of force. Thus,

$$\text{Peripheral resistance (R)} = \frac{M(\text{mm. Hg}) \times 1332}{F(\text{ml./sec.})}$$

$$R = \frac{\text{dynes/cm.}^2}{\text{cm.}^3/\text{sec.}}$$

$$R = \frac{\text{dyne sec.}}{\text{cm.}^5}$$

1332 is a figure for the conversion of pressure to dynes.

The peripheral resistance so calculated is found to vary inversely with the size of the animal, i.e., directly with the surface area. It amounts normally to from about 600 to 2,000 absolute units in man, but may be over 5,000 in arterial hypertension in which F shows little change. The values for the dog and rabbit range from 2,000 to 9,000 and from 11,500 to 12,000, respectively. This means that the minute vessels in a large animal offer less resistance than do the fewer number in a smaller animal, even though the vessels of both are constricted to the same degree. This is due to the fact that the rate of flow in the smaller animal is greater in relation to the size of its vascular bed (cardiac output bearing a constant relationship to surface area which varies inversely with body weight).

C. The quantity of blood in the arterial system. In any closed system of rigid tubes fluid must fill it to capacity in order that a pressure can be developed within it. The arterial walls are distensible and elastic, and a certain degree of stretching of these must occur before any considerable pressure is created. The arterial system must be actually over-filled, and the greater the extent of the over-filling, the greater will be the blood pressure. Loss of blood, either of all its elements, as in hemorrhage, or of the fluid portion alone, if not compensated for sufficiently by readjustment of the other factors concerned in blood pressure maintenance, must inevitably result in a fall of pressure. Increasing the total amount of circulating fluid artifically as by the transfusion of blood or blood substitute will elevate the pressure again. In animals the blood pressure may be lowered by hemorrhage to half its normal value and restored again to its original level by re-introducing into the circulation the blood which has been removed or by the infusion of an effective blood substitute.

D. *The viscosity of the blood.* The greater the viscosity or "thickness" of any liquid the greater is the pressure required to force it along a length of narrow tube in a given time; or if the pressure remains constant the longer will be the time required for the liquid to traverse the tube. The frictional resistance which is developed between the parts of the liquid itself, that is, the internal friction is greater when the viscosity is high than when it is low. Viscosity depends upon the degree to which the molecules or particles of a fluid cohere. Blood is some 5 times more viscous than water.[1] With regard to the influence of viscosity upon the blood pressure, it is again a matter of outflow through the arterioles. If the driving force remains constant and the caliber of the vessels is unchanged, then the greater the viscosity the greater will be the frictional resistance developed in this region and the less will be the quantity of fluid that will pass through in a unit of time.

The blood owes its viscosity to its colloids (plasma proteins) and to an even greater extent its suspended corpuscles; friction is developed between the surfaces of the latter and the surrounding fluid. Changes in the concentration of the blood as a result of changes in its protein content or in the number of its corpuscles will therefore alter its viscosity; venesection by removing a quantity of blood and causing dilution of the remainder causes a fall in viscosity which may materially relieve the work of the heart. For these reasons the viscosity is low in anemia and high in polycythemia, leukemia and anhydremia. Also changes in its chemical composition or in its gas content may alter the viscosity of the blood. Carbon dioxide increases the viscosity, oxygen lowers it; venous blood is, in consequence, more viscous than arterial, and high blood viscosity is usual in congestive heart failure with cyanosis. Chloroform anesthesia and narcotization with morphine are said to increase the blood viscosity. It is also raised in hyperglycemia, hypercalcemia and in acidosis.

The viscosity of most liquids is reduced by a rise of temperature—hot syrup flows more freely than cold. In muscular exercise and in fever the blood temperature is raised, the viscosity of the blood is lowered, and the work which the heart is called upon to do in overcoming the frictional resistance in the smaller vessels is thereby appreciably reduced. Blood concentration, however, which occurs to some extent under these circumstances, tends to offset the effect of temperature.

[1] This is an average figure. Values obtained by different observers for the viscosity of blood, taking distilled water as unity, vary considerably but the majority range between 4.5 and 5.5.

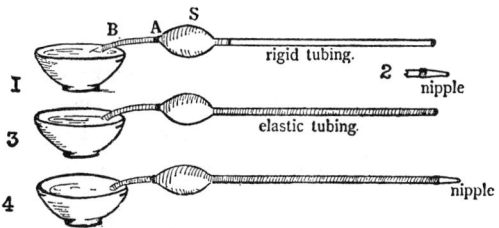

Fig. 43.2. Description in text.

E. *The elasticity of the vessel walls.* This is concerned mainly with the origin and maintenance of the diastolic pressure and with sustaining the mean pressure at a higher level than would be possible in a rigid system under otherwise identical conditions.

The elasticity of arterial tissue does not come into play to any notable extent with a pressure below from 30 to 40 mm. of mercury. Below this level there would be little stretching of the walls of the arteries which would then behave like a system of rigid tubes. At the usual diastolic pressure that exists, however, the walls are stretched and by virtue of their elasticity tend to recoil against the distending force. We have seen that the flow of blood is pulsatile in the arteries. Beyond the arterioles, i.e., in the capillaries and veins, the flow is continuous. The conversion of the pulsatile flow to a uniform one depends upon the existence of a diastolic pressure. The physical principles involved in the maintenance of the diastolic pressure and the disappearance of the pulse beyond the arterioles may be best illustrated by a simple artificial model similar in principle to one devised by Borelli for the same purpose some 300 or more years ago.

In figure 43.2 is represented a bulb syringe, S, valved at A, and having a short tube, B, which dips into a basin of water. Leading from the opposite pole of the bulb is a longer tube, C. When the bulb is alternately compressed and released fluid is drawn from the basin and discharged from the mouth of the tube. If the walls of the latter are composed of some rigid material (fig. 43.2, 1), it will be found that when the pump is worked the fluid issues from the tube in spurts or jets synchronous with each stroke, but no flow occurs between the strokes. An increase in the frequency or force of the strokes does not alter the intermittent character of the flow nor does lengthening the tubing. If the peripheral resistance of the vascular system be imitated by attaching a nipple of small bore to the mouth of the delivery tube so as to increase the resistance to the outflow of fluid, the issuing stream is finer and its velocity is increased, but it still remains intermittent (fig. 43.2, 2). Let the elasticity of the arterial wall now be imitated by replacing the rigid tube by one of rubber, yet let the mouth of the tube be left free and not constricted in any way (fig. 43.2, 3). The intermittent character of the stream is unaffected. However, if the small-bored nipple representing the peripheral resistance be fixed into the mouth of the elastic tubing the stream will be found to have lost its pulsatile character and to have become continuous (fig. 43.2, 4). Two factors are therefore necessary to produce this result, (a) *resistance to the outflow* and (b) *elastic tubing*. The reasons for this are clear. If the fluid has free egress from the tube most of that which enters it from the pump is discharged from the open end before the next beat occurs; the pressure, in consequence, does not rise to a sufficient height to distend the rubber wall, i.e., elasticity is not called into play, over-filling of the tube does not occur, and in consequence the latter acts simply as though it were composed or rigid material.

The foregoing facts apply directly to the arterial system. The elasticity of the vascular walls and the peripheral resistance are both essential for the maintenance of the diastolic pressure. As the contents of the ventricle are thrown into the already over-filled system during systole the added pressure which is then exerted upon the vascular walls causes their further distension. After the completion of systole the elastic walls rebound and, pressing upon the blood within their embrace, force it onwards through the peripheral vessels. In other words, the arterial lumen returns to its previous diameter and the energy that had been stored up during the stretching of the elastic tissue is in this way gradually expended during diastole.

The elastic recoil of the arterial wall thus acts in a sense as a subsidiary pump to drive the blood onwards in a continuous stream between the heart beats. Otherwise the pressure would fall to zero after each systole.

It is clear then that any increase in the elasticity of the arteries, other factors remaining unchanged, will tend toward a lowering of the diastolic pressure. If the aorta and its larger branches are stiffened (as a result of sclerotic changes), they cannot expand to the same degree as can healthy, resilient vessels, and therefore do not so readily accommodate the blood (60–100 cc.) ejected from the heart during systole. Such a state will lead to a rise in the systolic pressure. Normally, however, the cross-sectional area of the aorta increases considerably with age, so that it needs to expand much less to accommodate the systolic discharge.

THE INFLUENCE WHICH VARIATIONS IN SOME OF THE FOREGOING FACTORS EXERT UPON THE DIFFERENT PHASES OF THE ARTERIAL PRESSURE

A. Change in heart rate unaccompanied by an alteration in any of the other factors, e.g., output of heart per minute, peripheral resistance, etc., will cause a change in the diastolic pressure but relatively little change in the systolic thus giving a smaller pulse rate. During cardiac acceleration, for example, the diastolic period is shortened and less time is therefore allowed for the energy stored in the elastic walls during systole to become converted into energy of flow during diastole. In other words, the fall in pressure during diastole is halted at a higher level by the earlier arrival of the next beat. A decrease in heart rate will have the opposite effect; with the longer diastole the slope of pressure is enabled to reach a lower level. Since the quantity of blood entering the arteries per minute remains constant the quantity entering at each beat must vary inversely with the change in rate, which accounts for the relatively small change in the systolic pressure.

B. Alterations in the quantity of blood discharged per minute by the ventricle. If little change should occur in the heart rate and other factors remain unaltered, increase in the output per beat of the heart causes a rise chiefly of the systolic pressure. The diastolic pressure is raised less noticeably, consequently the pulse pressure is increased. The explanation for the less pronounced rise in the diastolic pressure is that, as a result of the high pressure at the end of the ejection period, the pressure gradient throughout diastole is steeper and more energy is expended in giving velocity to the blood; of the blood pumped into the arterial system during systole a larger proportion than ordinarily will therefore have passed through the arterioles by the end of diastole.

C. Changes in the peripheral resistance while other factors remain constant. Though these affect both systolic and disatolic pressures they show their influence predominantly upon the latter phase. The diastolic period is considerably longer even in a rapidly beating heart than the ejection period of systole and, as we have seen, the peripheral resistance is an important factor in the maintenance of the diastolic pressure. It follows therefore that any increase or decrease in the outflow from the arterial system will affect this pressure to a greater degree than the systolic. The mean pressure and pulse pressure vary accordingly. Aortic regurgitation produces an effect upon diastolic pressure similar to that caused by a reduction in the peripheral resistance but greater in degree. The mechanical principles involved are similar; an increased quantity of blood passes from the arterial system during diastole as a result of leakage through the incompetent aortic valves. The peripheral vessels are also usually dilated, which, combined with the high pulse pressure, may cause the appearance of a pulse in the capillaries especially if their emptying be aided by holding the arm above the heart level. Slight pressure upon a superficial capillary area such as at the base of the finger nail may then show alternate blanching and flushing synchronous with the heart beat. In aortic regurgitation the pulse pressure attains a magnitude seen in no other condition (80 or 110 mm. Hg) for not only is the diastolic pressure much reduced but the systolic pressure is raised as well, owing to the greater volume of blood ejected at each heart beat—that which has regurgitated through the aortic valves plus that received from the auricle. For these reasons, the carotids throb visibly. The pulse is of the collapsing type (water hammer or Corrigan's pulse). An arteriovenous aneurysm produces somewhat similar effects upon the arterial system.

D. A rise or a fall in blood viscosity. Other factors remaining unchanged, tend to affect the diastolic pressure in a manner similar to changes in the calibers of the peripheral vessels.

E. Increase in blood volume will raise both pressures, as a result of the overfilling of the arterial system and greater stretching of the elastic walls.

F. Increase in elasticity of the arterial walls. Obviously a condition such as arteriosclerosis, which renders arteries less resilient and more like rigid tubes will, tend toward a lowering of diastolic pressure. Yet as a matter of fact, in arteriosclerosis the diastolic pressure may be raised rather than lowered, since there is frequently an associated narrowing of the peripheral vessels which more than offsets the hardening of the walls of the larger arteries. When, however, the sclerosis is confined to the larger vessels and their branches while the peripheral vessels are free from proliferative changes which narrow their lumina the diastolic pressure is lowered. Diminished distensibility of the walls of the aorta and the larger arteries tends to increase the systolic pressure.

In the foregoing paragraphs variations in the several blood pressure factors and their effects have each been considered as being the only variable in a particular instance. The object of this was to disclose the value of each and the manner in which it acted. Yet it must be remembered that such a description is more or less artificial and that in health and even to a large extent under pathological conditions the various factors interact with one another—there is a give and take among them. When a change in the value of one factor occurs, readjustments of others take place to regulate the blood pressure and keep it within the normal limits. For instance, dilation of the vessels in one area may be accompanied by vasoconstriction in another. Reduction in blood volume as by hemorrhage, is followed by constriction of the peripheral vessels, while increased blood volume or a rise in viscosity will likely be followed by the opposite effect upon the vessels.

THE ARTERIAL PRESSURE PULSE. Pressure waves in the heart cavities, the aorta and almost any of its branches, and in the systemic venous system, can be readily recorded in the experimental animal and in humans by use of appropriate combinations of catheters or needles with pressure manometers of adequate frequency (see ch. 40). The form or pattern of the pressure curves can also be recorded from superficial vessels such as the radial artery, subclavian artery and vein, carotid artery, jugular vein, etc., by overlying cup-tambour arrangements or microphones (for details see ch. 40, and Wiggers).

A. Velocity. The pulse is the pressure change created by the ejection of blood from the heart into the already full aorta, and propagated as a wave through the blood column and arterial wall to the periphery. If the walls of the system were absolutely rigid, since liquids are incompressible, an impact delivered at one end would cause a pressure change to be transmitted almost instantaneously. In the case of elastic tubing, such as composes the vascular system, the pressure change is accompanied by an expansion of the tube's wall. From the equation of Bramwell and Hill ($Vp = K\sqrt{\Delta pV/\Delta V}$ in which Vp is pulse wave velocity and V is vessel volume, it is obvious that the velocity with which a pressure wave is transmitted peripherally, is largely determined by the elasticity of the vessel wall.

Because of their accessibility, pressure pulse wave velocities are generally measured in the brachial, radial or femoral arteries, although many measurements exist for the aorta. The usual order of time of arrival of the pressure pulse is brachial, femoral, radial. The velocity of the pulse wave can be determined by noting the difference in the time of arrival of the naturally occurring pulse wave at a near and at a far point of the vascular system. This can be done roughly by means of a pair of tambours overlying points on the two arteries and which are connected to writing levers or recorders. A more accurate way is to record directly the arterial pressures at the two points from indwelling needles connected to pressure manometers, or to record the transit

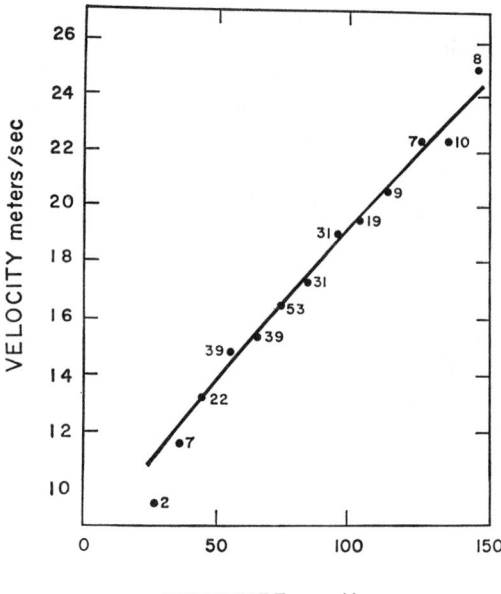

FIG. 43.3. Curve showing the relation between arterial blood pressure (abscissa) and pulse wave velocity (ordinate). (From Landowne, J. Appl. Physiol., 1958, **12**, 93.)

time of a mechanically induced external impact wave. The time difference divided into the distance traveled between two points gives the velocity of propagation of the wave. Thus,

Distance in millimeters

Time in seconds

= velocity in millimeters per second.

The rate of propagation of the pulse wave peripherally depends on the degree of vessel distention by internal pressure, and on its distensibility characteristics. Thus, the level of blood pressure, the basic structure of the vessel wall and its alteration by function or disease are the important determinants of pulse wave velocity. The normal velocity in the aorta approximates 3 to 4 meters per second; in the arteries of the limbs, it is 7 to 14 meters per second, the velocity of the pulse in the femoral artery being somewhat greater than in the brachial artery. In hypertension resulting from muscular exercise, the walls of the vessels are more strongly stretched and the pulse wave is transmitted at a higher speed. Vasodilation or low pressure from many causes reduces the velocity of the pulse wave. Figure 43.3 shows this strong relation between the pulse wave velocity and ambient intraarterial pressure in the brachioradial artery segment of normal individuals.

(Pressures below diastolic were obtained by temporary digital occlusion of the axillary or subclavian artery). This fact must be taken into account in the comparison of velocities at different ages and in different disease states. In addition, since the rate of transmission alters with the state of elasticity of the vessel wall, the velocity is increased with old age or when the elasticity is increased by disease, such as arteriosclerosis. In the brachial artery, speeds have been recorded of 5 meters per second at age of 5 years, 6 meters per second at middle age, and 8.6 meters per second at age of 84 years.

In the aorta (and arterial tree), the acceleration of the blood occurs almost simultaneously with the rise of the pressure pulse. This is to be expected since the latter causes the former. However, whereas the pressure wave travels in terms of meters per second, the movement of the red cells or plasma is much slower, at 10 to 20 cm. per second. Thus, although the pressure wave may reach the vessels of the foot in 0.2 second, it requires several heart beats for the blood entering the ascending aorta to reach the foot vessels. This is because the speed of the blood depends upon such factors as the blood pressure gradient, cross-sectional area of the vessel and viscosity, while the velocity of the pulse wave is determined almost entirely by the elasticity of the wall of the vessel.

B. Characteristics and transformation of the pressure pulse. Pressure curves simultaneously recorded from the aortic arch and a peripheral artery of the dog are shown in figure 43.4. It is obvious that the pressure pulse patterns are quite different. The aortic pressure rises quite abruptly, and after an anacrotic shoulder (abrupt change in gradient), rises still further to a systolic rounded peak. The pressure then drops slowly during the last half of systole until closure of the aortic valves, which is occasioned by a sharp incisura. During diastole, the pressure is first sustained and then drops smoothly. The extra-arterial forces which affect the aortic pulse pattern are by impact from the contracting atrium and the bulging of the aortic valves during the isometric contraction period. These waves appear on the aortic pulse preceding the main wave and are noticeable in the immediate aortic branches, but not beyond. A series of internal free vibrations are added at the incisura and at the first steep rise during ejection, as the pressure pulse reaches the main aortic branches. In the simultaneously recorded peripheral pulse, the onset of the pressure rise is delayed and rises a little more slowly but to a very peaked, earlier, and larger maximum, being about 30 mm. Hg higher than that in the aorta. The drop of pressure in the latter half of systole and in early diastole is much quicker. The dicrotic notch and its after wave are quite large. The remainder of the diastolic curve is uneventful. Thus, in the peripheral vessel the net effect is to augment the peak amplitude of the pulse wave, obscure the incisura, and to depress the remainder of the pulse curve. Pressure curves recorded from arteries intermediately situated such as the renal, mesenteric, and carotid, show a lesser augmentation of the peak systolic pressure and a smaller dicrotic wave; pulses recorded from more peripheral arteries such as the dorsalis pedis, show an exaggeration of these phenomena. The effects of the extra-arterial forces are gradually damped in the extensions of the aorta and are lost in the radial artery. In very small arteries (1.0 to 0.2 mm. in diameter) there is a reduction in both systolic (average 17 per cent) and diastolic (average 12 per cent) pressures, slowing of the systolic upstroke and smoothing out of the incisura.

The pressure pulse just described at the root of the aorta is basically triangular. This original pattern is largely retained as the pressure wave

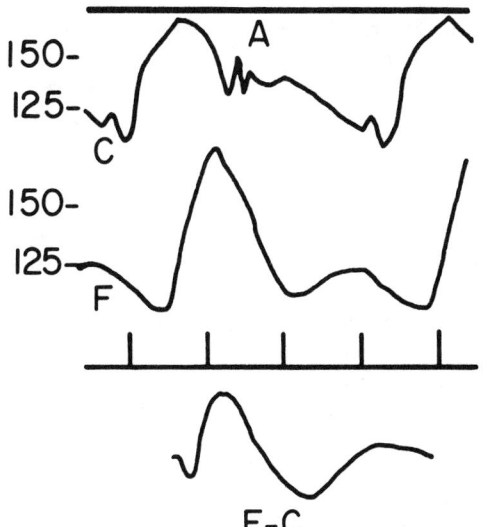

FIG. 43.4. Arterial pressure pulses recorded from the central aorta, *C*, and the femoral artery, *F*, in the anesthetized dog. Curve F-C beneath pulse tracings obtained by coordirectographic subtraction of the aortic pulse from the femoral pulse. This represents the reflected or standing wave in the distal portion of the arterial tree. Time 0.1 second; ordinate pressures in millimeters of mercury (after Alexander, R. S., Am. J. Physiol., 1949, **158**, 287).

is transmitted down the aorta and into some of its immediate branches. The temporal distortions of the pressure pulses in their transit from the central to the peripheral arteries are effected mainly as the result of damping from friction of the blood with the vessel wall, hysteresis of the vessel wall, differences in the distensibility of the vessels, and summation of reflected pressure waves. The viscosity of the blood in the smaller arteries acts to smooth out the abruptness of pressure changes; in arteries such as the femoral, there is a possibility of considerable lag in the response of its wall to internal pressure such as occurs in isolated vessel strips; and the greater distensibility of these arteries, taken *in toto*, gives the system a low natural frequency (3 to 5 cycles per second), which tends to smooth out or make less angular the basic central pressure pattern, slow down the rate of pressure elevation, and lessen the pressure peak obtained.

In addition to damping, the other major factor controlling the peripheral pattern is wave summation. The pressure wave leaving the aortic arch rebounds from areas of increasing resistance in the peripheral arteries and arterioles, and travels retrogradely along the arterial tree. These centrally reflected pressure waves can be obliterated by damping or may summate with or be subtracted from the peripherally directed pressure wave, depending upon the phasic relationships. They do not, in general, materially alter the central aortic pattern. The magnitude and pattern of such a reflected wave can be roughly ascertained by substraction of the peripheral pulse pattern from the central aortic pattern (see fig. 43.4). This reveals that the waves occur in both systole and diastole. The points of change in resistance and pressure reflection have not been firmly established, but best opinion favors a locus in the abdominal aorta, just below the diaphragm, and a point in the femoral system. Reflected components from these areas can be either negative or positive.

C. Determinants of aortic pulse pressure pattern. The aorta and its larger branches can be regarded as a large elastically distensible compression chamber with cardiac ejection entering at one end and drainage occurring at the other end. The chamber possesses varying degrees of distensibility, conforming to those existing in various portions of the aorta and its branches. The generated pulse pressure is caused by an imbalance between the ventricular outflow entering the aorta, and the peripheral run-off leaving the aorta with each systole. The systolic portion

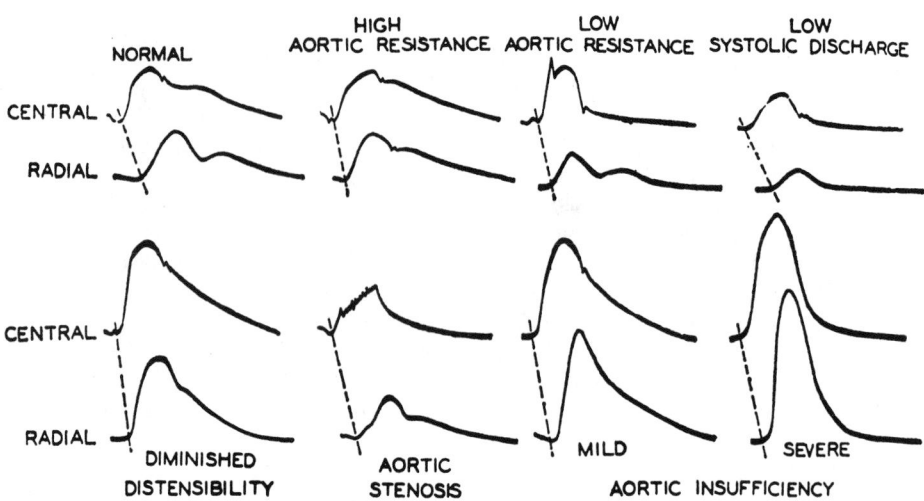

FIG. 43.5. Illustration of changes in contour and amplitude of subclavian and radial pulses under abnormal cardiovascular conditions. Discussion in text. Note changes in transmission rates. (Wiggers, Circulatory dynamics, Grune and Stratton, Inc., New York, 1952.)

largely expresses input into the aorta; the diastolic portion expresses decompression of the aorta or peripheral run-off, since, at this time, it is disconnected functionally from the ventricle. Four factors are of major importance in determining the pressure and increments of pressure from moment to moment: the elasticity or distensibility of the vessel walls, the volume of contained blood, the volume increment from cardiac ejection, and the decrement in volume caused by peripheral drainage. These relations are expressed by the equation:

$$E = \frac{\Delta P}{\Delta v} \cdot V$$

in which E = volume-elasticity coefficient, p = change in pressure, v = change in volume, and V = capacity of aorta in diastole. If the aorta and arteries constituted a simple elastic chamber, the pressure-volume relations (P/V) should be predictable from the preceding, and if P is known, V should become available. It would be helpful if such a relation could be used to indicate what is happening to the blood and whether the effect is centrally or peripherally induced. However, difficulties in such an approach are: (1) there is no way to quantitate V; (2) the pressure-volume relation of any part of the aorta is linear over only a limited pressure range; (3) distensibility is different in various regions of the arterial tree; and (4) changes have been revealed in the distensibility characteristics of the aorta by reflex stimulation and adrenalin injection.

D. *Usefulness of aortic or central artery pulse patterns.* Despite the difficulties in elucidating the

pressure volume relations in the aorta, pressure pulses from the large arteries, depicting fairly well the pattern of the central aortic pulse pressure, have been found useful in predicting hemodynamic changes. Such interpretation and extrapolation is based on experiments in dogs in which changes in peripheral resistance and cardiac activity have been deliberately induced and their effects on the pressure pulses separately determined. Figure 43.5 shows the human subclavian pulse obtained indirectly. The duration of systole and diastole can be determined. In the presence of a high peripheral resistance and in a normal vessel, the pulse shows a much steeper rise throughout systole. In the presence of a low aortic resistance but with good vascular volume, the curve has an initial early spike followed by a lower systolic tip, a rapid decline and a greatly reduced slope during diastole. When the stroke volume is low, as in hemorrhage, the systolic part is small, smooth and rounded, and diastole is almost flat. Decreased distensibility of the aorta is revealed by a rapid, sustained and large elevation of the pulse, a high incisura and a gradual decline during diastole. Distinctive pulse patterns caused by lesions of the aortic valves are also shown. These are considered in detail in chapter 49. Attempts to use central arterial pressure pulses to estimate stroke volume have been numerous but none have been successful (see ch. 44).

Arterial Blood Flow

With contraction of the human ventricle, a stroke volume or systolic discharge of 60 to 70 cc. is ejected into the distensible aorta within less than 0.25 seconds. Of this, at least 45 cc. is pushed into the aorta within the first 0.1 second. Space for this volume in the aortic arch is made by distending it and by removing some of its blood. The resulting pressure change travels as a wave throughout the length of the aorta and its branches to the capillaries (and sometimes through them), and expands the entire arterial tree radially and longitudinally. This enlargement results in a forward movement of blood from aortic valves to capillaries before the end of ventricular systole. As yet, too few studies of phasic flow have been made to justify a statement pertaining to the factors which determine the major characteristics of the flow patterns in the aorta. It is, however, worthwhile describing and considering them briefly.

PHASIC AORTIC FLOW. Aortic flow pulses have been measured in dogs and, also, incidentally in a number of human subjects at the time of surgical exposure of the aorta. The former will be considered since it has been possible to record simultaneously both pressure and flow pulses, and, at times, to record at least two flow pulses at different aortic levels. The phasic flows were recorded with an electromagnetic flow meter or sonar meter. Examples are shown in figure 43.6. The phasic flow in the ascending aorta is roughly triangular in shape 43.6A. Acceleration reaches a peak ejection rate early in systole following which there is a rapid deceleration ending in a momentary, small, high frequency backflow at the time of closure of the aortic valves. The flow curve is flat with almost zero velocity during most of diastole. The considerable modifying effect of the aorta upon the left ventricular ejection pulse is seen in figure 43.6B, taken near the terminus of the aorta. The flow pulse is now a series of smooth, highly damped oscillations of a frequency of 3 to 4 cycles per second which continue to extinction, but which are renewed with each heart beat. There is quite a large backflow in very early diastole. Flow pulses in the isthmal area of the aorta (proximal portion of descending aorta) are intermediate in pattern between the central and abdominal patterns. In figure 43.6C are the calculated blood velocity curve and the aortic differential pressure curve, the latter taken by a double lumen catheter with pressure pick up holes 6 cm. apart. This shows the positive and negative acceleration waves which act on the aortic blood column to produce the flow pulsations. The effects of inertia are seen throughout the cardiac cycle. The beginning upstrokes of both pressure and flow curves coincide quite well, but when the first positive wave of the ΔP reaches its peak, flow acceleration is maximal, and when ΔP is maximally negative, flow deceleration is maximal. This represents about a 90° phase lag.

PHASIC FLOW IN PERIPHERAL ARTERIES. Flow patterns and simultaneous intraarterial pressure curves characteristic of several peripheral arteries are illustrated in figure 43.7. There are certain distinguishing characteristics. A flow pattern is made up of waves whose directional changes have a qualitative correspondence with gradient changes in the simultaneously recorded intravascular pressure pulse and which may be characteristically distinctive for that artery and vascular bed. Since the flow velocity varies with the differential pressure existing at the site of the flow meter, similarity in contour of the flow and applied pressure pulse is one criterion for the comparison of flow curves from different arteries. Certain patterns, especially those of the superior mesenteric and renal arteries, have a well-rounded and sustained systolic portion in relative conformity to that of the pressure pulse. Those of the hepatic and common carotid arteries are less well-rounded; those of the brachial and femoral arteries have a sharp systolic peak. The flow pulse pressure is generally small in the renal and axillary patterns, and somewhat larger in the superior mesenteric and hepatic, while the femoral may be quite large. Backflow components are consistently found in the femoral and axillary patterns and, on occasion, in the common carotid, while the renal, hepatic and superior mesenteric flow curves exhibit only forward flow. However, the main feature which permits a separation of the flow curves is the variable relation of the early diastolic to presystolic flow rates. Comparison of this relation with similar early diastolic and presystolic points on the corresponding pressure curve, shows that the superior mesenteric, renal, hepatic, common carotid, and femoral patterns have, on this basis, a progressively graded dissimilarity to their respective pressure curves.

While a method of analysis and interpretation is not yet available by means of which the probable determinants of, and interrelated influences upon phasic flow can be quantitatively evaluated, a partial attempt has been made in at least one artery. The approach is too technical to be considered here and the interested reader is referred to the paper of Shipley et al.

ARTERY TO VEIN PRESSURE AND FLOW. Pressure gradients across the very small vessels of the periphery have been difficult to establish in reasonably normal, biological situations. Possibly

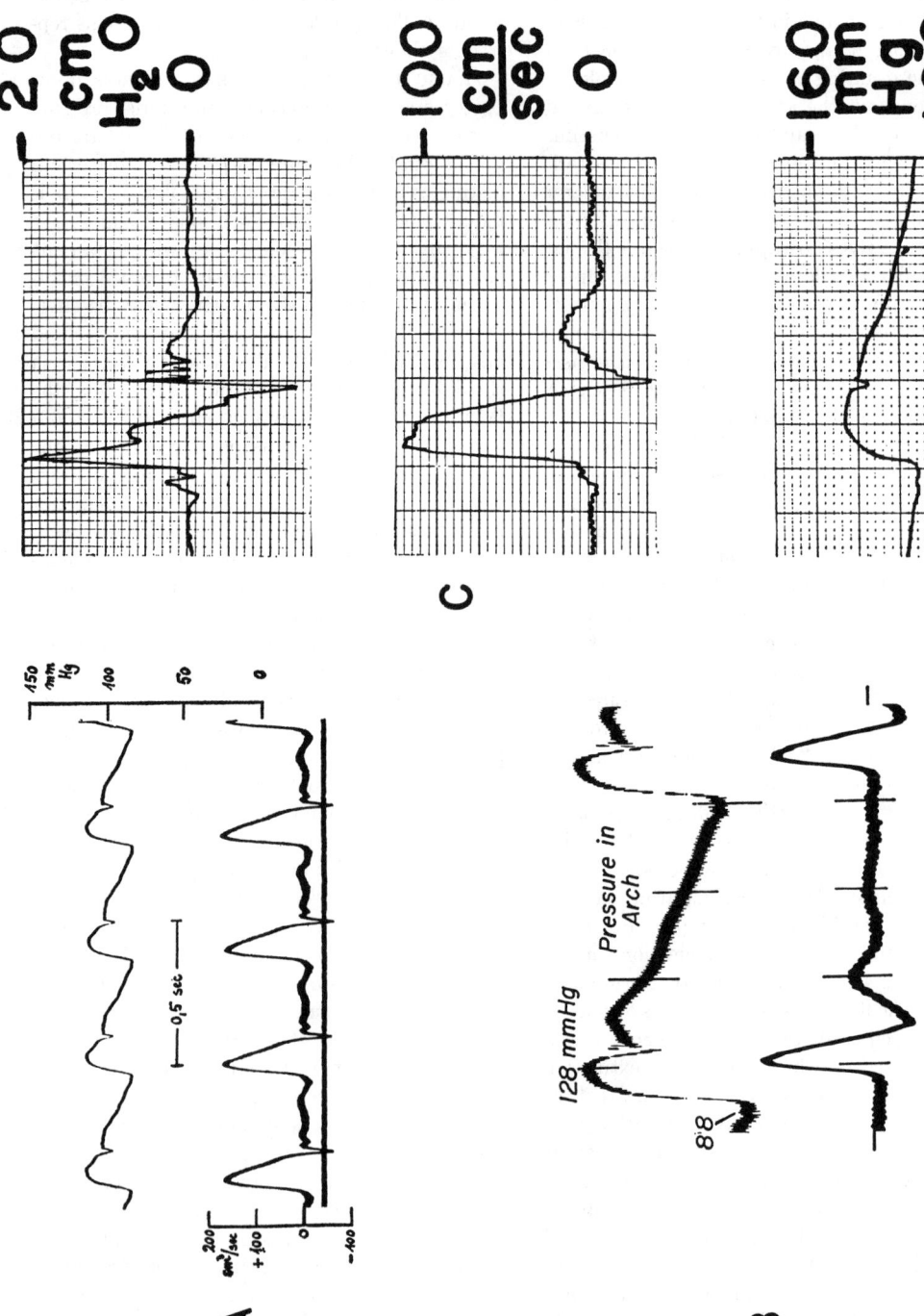

FIG. 43.6A. Tracings from bottom to top: flow in the ascending aorta, pressure in the aorta (from Wetterer, Minnesota Med., 1954, 37, 79). *B.* Tracing from top to bottom: pressure in aortic arch, flow in terminal aorta (from Spencer, Circulation Res., 1958, 6, 492). *C.* Simultaneous recording of (1) aortic axial pressure drop between two points 6 cm. apart, at level of subclavian artery, (2) com-

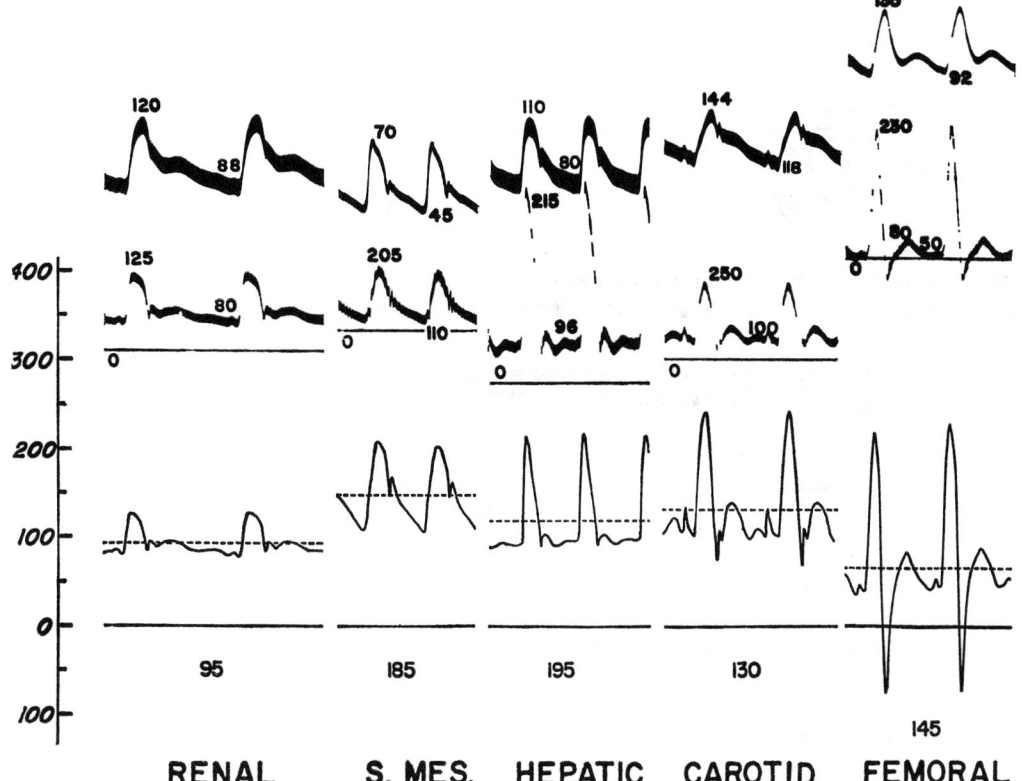

RENAL   S. MES.   HEPATIC   CAROTID   FEMORAL

Fig. 43.7. Phasic flow in peripheral arteries obtained by orifice meter (Shiple y and associates, Am J. Physiol., 1943, **138**, 718.

the closest approach to this is based upon the experimental approach of Haddy, in which arterial and venous pressure are measured in the quite small vessels (0.2 mm. diameter) of the dog forepaw, while constant blood flow is maintained by a pump (fig. 43.8). It can be seen that with the environmental temperature at 20° C., the pressure drop from small artery to small vein approximates 40 mm. Hg, and, from small vein to large vein, 6 mm. Hg. (fig. 43.9). Upon exposure to 0° C., the increase in pressure gradient is almost entirely through the small vessels with little gradient change between the small and large veins. Since the blood flow was maintained constant, the increase in pressure gradient represents directly active vasomotor resistance changes. Unfortunately, at present it is not possible by this technique to differentiate between changes in resistance of the arterioles and venules. Expansion, however, of this type of investigation would be most fruitful.

Venous Pressure

The functional importance of the venous blood pressure has long interested physiologists and clinicians. The superficial veins, which can be observed and whose pressure values and pulse pressure contours can be easily measured, have been considered to serve as reliable indicators of the functional status of the less accessible and deeper lying portions of the systemic venous system.

THE VENOUS PRESSURE PULSE. The venous pressure pulse is best determined with the subject in the recumbent position. Venous pressure is measured directly with an indwelling needle or catheter or indirectly (without pressure values) by applying a cup over a vein external to the chest, such as the jugular, and connected to a manometer or a microphone receiver. The venous pulse waves are usually timed against an electrocardiogram, arteriogram or phonocardiogram (see ch. 41). Two distinct types of pulsations, respiratory and cardiac, are seen in the peripheral and central veins. With inspiration, blood is aspirated into the chest and the external veins tend to collapse while internal veins expand; with expiration, venous inflow is impeded and the external veins become distended while the chest veins tend to become smaller. These changes

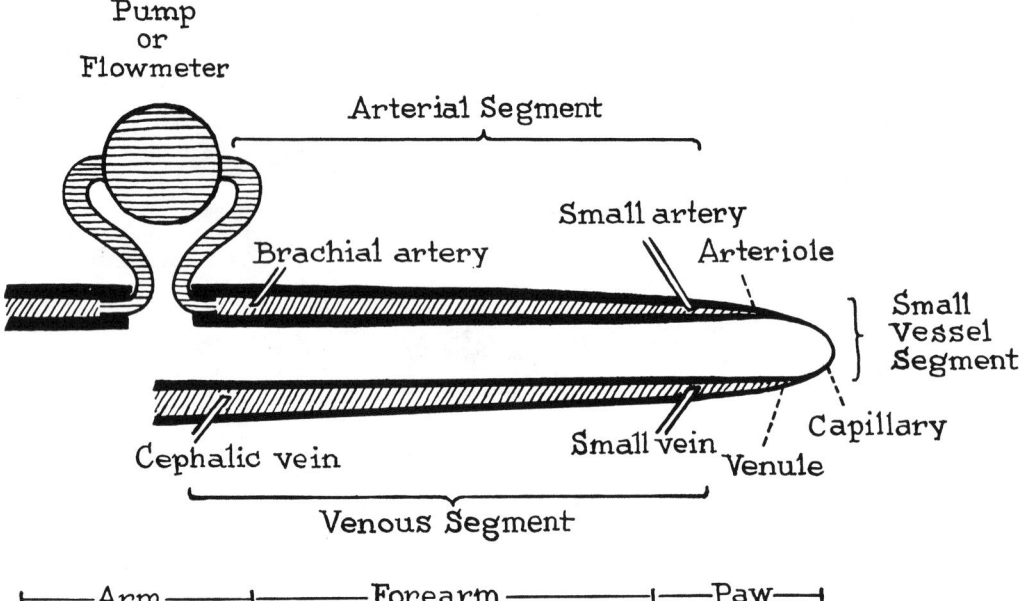

FIG. 43.8. Schema showing means of measuring pressure gradient and resistance across small peripheral vessels. (Haddy, Minnesota Med., 1958, **41,** 162).

make up the respiratory venous pulse. The cardiac venous pressure pulse represents a retrograde reflection of a somewhat distorted version of the right atrial pulse pattern (see ch. 41). These a, c, v, waves are clearly seen in the record obtained from a peripheral vein in figure 43.10.

Valuable information concerning the events of the cardiac cycle, both from the experimental and clinical point of view, can be obtained by a study of the jugular pulse records. The length of the P-R interval can be roughly estimated by noting the time interval between the jugular a and c waves. It is not difficult to decide whether the a-c interval is normal (around 0.16 second), or obviously prolonged (0.24 second or more). The orderly sequence of a, c, v, waves indicates a normal sequence of atrial and ventricular beats. With partial or complete heart block, the number of a waves is greater than the number of c-v complexes. With atrial fibrillation, the a waves are absent. Premature ventricular beats of atrial origin are preceded by an a wave; those arising in the ventricle are not. A giant a wave can arise from tricuspid stenosis, severe pulmonary hypertension, pulmonary stenosis, tricuspid atresia, nodal rhythm and partial heart block. The powerful right atrial contraction causing the giant a wave is due to the increased resistance to right ventricular filling. In tricuspid insufficiency, giant ventricular systolic (v) waves are seen. The systolic wave rises rapidly to a summit upon

which vibrations of the murmur are superimposed.

NORMAL VENOUS BLOOD PRESSURE AND ITS VARIATIONS. Using the techniques previously described, mean blood pressure in the large, superficial veins of unanesthetized man at rest and in the supine position, is found to be a function of distance from the right atrium. The average value decreases from 13.8 mm. Hg (188 mm. H_2O) in the dorsal venous arch of the foot to about 5.2 mm. Hg (70 mm. H_2O) in the jugular vein. The pressure change from the surface veins to the central veins and along the central veins has been precisely determined. Great care must be taken in measuring the peripheral venous pressure since, under some conditions in the supine position, the peripheral veins may become partially collapsed and, as a result, the peripheral venous pressure becomes independent of right atrial pressure. It is generally advisable to make the measurement with the arm well below heart level to prevent this venous collapse. With this precaution, the average pressure of 7.1 mm. Hg (97 mm. H_2O) in the antecubital vein drops to about 4.6 mm. Hg (63 mm. H_2O) in the vena cava opposite the right atrium (fig. 43.11). Thus, the over-all venous pressure gradient approximates 9.2 mm. Hg (125 mm. H_2O) with a pressure difference of only a few mm. H_2O occurring between the upper thoracic veins and the right atrium. Although venous pressure measurements in the same subject are quite constant, considerable variation (up to 100 mm. H_2O) may occur in the venous pressure from the same area in different persons.

Peripheral and central venous pressures are altered in the same direction under many circumstances. They do not appear to be related to age, sex or hypertension, but they are decreased in severe hemorrhage and surgical shock. They are increased by positive pressure breathing, the Valsalva maneuver, tilting, the excitement stage of anesthesia, the apneic phase of asthmatic attacks and in Cheynes-Stokes breathing. The main pathological condition in which central and peripheral venous pressures are elevated, sometimes as high as 22 mm. Hg (300 mm. H_2O) in the antecubital vein, is congestive heart failure.

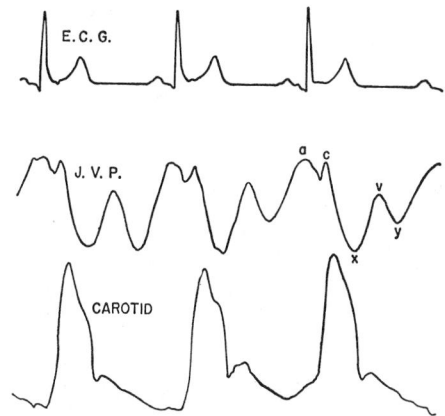

FIG. 43.10. The jugular venous pulse pattern (JVP) of a normal subject. An electrocardiogram (ECG) and carotid pulse tracing were simultaneously recorded. The presystolic "a" wave is caused by atrial contraction. The "c" peak is secondary to closure of the tricuspid valve although it may also represent transmission of the arterial pulse to the vein. The descending limb of the pulse tracing after the "c" wave is secondary to emptying of the vein into the right atrium. The negative "x" wave occurs during lowering of the atrioventricular septum and tricuspid valve during ventricular systole. Then the pressure rises, as the right atrium fills, to form the "v" wave. The second negative depression, the "y" wave represents the fall in jugular venous pressure as the tricuspid valve opens and the right atrium empties. (From Wood, P., Diseases of the heart and circulation, J. B. Lippincott Company, Philadelphia, 1956.)

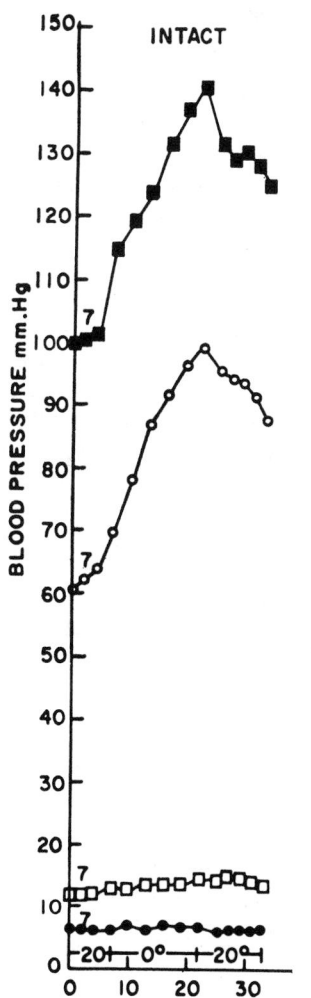

FIG. 43.9. Effect of temperature changes upon vascular pressures in the foreleg of the dog, flow rate being maintained constant (from Haddy, Circulation Res., 1957, **5**, 59).

DETERMINANTS OF VENOUS PRESSURE. The interplay of factors which determine systemic venous pressure and venous flow can be briefly stated. The veins are placed between the capillaries or the A-V anastomoses, and the right heart. The blood enters the venules with an appreciable pressure residuum (vis a tergo) from the arterial side, after it has passed through the capillaries. This pressure is met by the resistance to flow from the veins themselves and from the heart itself (the vis a fronte). The venous pressure is affected by internal factors which control the relation between the contained venous volume and the state of distensibility of its vessel walls. Finally, there are various external or extramural factors (vis a latere) such as the actions of respiration, muscle and gravity, which together represent the pressure effect of the surrounding tissues. Because their interplay is so complex, and flow methodology is generally so inadequate for normal situations, it is difficult to estimate their relative effect on venous pressure and flow. However, before considering the details of operation of these determinants, it must be emphasized that they act to insure that the pressure in the

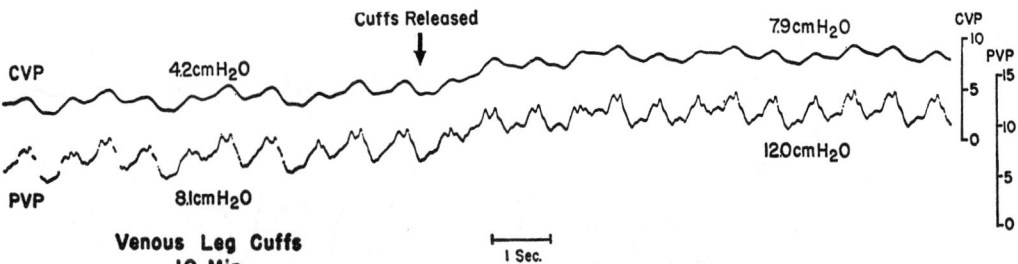

FIG. 43.11. Comparison of central venous pressure (CVP) and the peripheral venous pressure (PVP). After release of occluding cuffs at the thighs, the pressures return to control levels without a change in the pressure gradient. (From Gauer, O. H. and Sieker, H. O., Circulation Res., 1956, **4**, 75).

veins can never be less than the right atrial pressure, and whenever right atrial pressure increases, the peripheral venous pressure increases. This excess of pressure (10 to 12 mm. Hg or 125 mm. H_2O) in the various veins, over that in the right atrium, is an expression of the pressure gradient (P_1-P_2 in Poiseuille's formula). This, together with a reasonable venous cross-section, causes blood to flow from vein to atrium.

A. *The contraction of the left ventricle (the "vis a tergo")*. The energy of the ventricular contraction (the "vis a tergo") is expended in driving blood through the arterioles and onward through the capillaries and veins to the right atrium. By the time the blood reaches the venules, the remaining pressure may approximate 7 to 8 mm. Hg. When it reaches the right atrium, the energy has been almost entirely dissipated in overcoming the frictional resistance offered by the vascular channels; at this point, the pressure may be less than 1 mm. Hg.

B. *Quantity of blood flowing through the arterioles in relation to capacity of the veins*. Although the details are largely unknown, generally speaking, the more blood which is received from the arterial side, the greater will be the venous pressure. That is, with dilated arterioles, the difference between the arterial pressure on the one hand and venous pressure on the other, tends to be reduced; with constricted vessels the pressure difference will be increased. Rough estimates based on the volume-elasticity of the various compartments of the vascular system indicate that if a liter of blood is transfused into the circulation of man at rest, only 10 to 20 cc. would be found in the arterial tree and about 980 cc. in the extra-arterial system (systemic venous and pulmonary circuits), and that the pressure elevation in the whole system would be only 4 or 5 mm. Hg. In bleeding and transfusion experiments in man, the circulation behaves like an elastic container (ch. 36); with pooling of blood in the extremities by occlusive cuffs, the central venous pressure falls without any apparent sign of counter-veno motor control. This emphasizes the view that normal stresses to which the circulation is exposed, if they are not too abrupt or excessive, lead to only passive change in the resistance vessels and systemic venous system, and do not cause relaxation or strong contraction of the peripheral capacitance vessels.

This relationship, however, does not always hold because the veins are capable of adjusting their capacity to the quantity of blood received from the arterial system by reflex vasomotor activity. The smaller vessels may expand to accommodate the extra blood so that little change in venous pressure results, or they may reduce their capacities and maintain pressure in spite of a reduced volume of received blood.

The participation of venomotor tone in the control of the venous pressure and venous blood flow can be shown in animal experiments in which oxygen want, high CO_2, stimulation of the carotid sinus and excessive hemorrhage are effective in reducing the size of the capacitance vessels, but proper interpretation is difficult because of the often, unphysiological strength of the stimulus. In man, using strong stimuli such as the Valsalva maneuver, asphyxia, high G, or large blood losses, the veins constrict in what may be called an emergency reaction. In the latter case, the central venous pressure may be normal or even increased.

It is significant that the central and peripheral venous pressures do not necessarily shift in the same direction. The pressure gradient from very small veins (0.5 mm. diameter or less) to large central veins, is not necessarily constant and can be markedly affected by various states. With cold, hyperventilation and moderate exercise, only the peripheral venous pressure may rise significantly. This often independent action of local venous pressure and central venous pres-

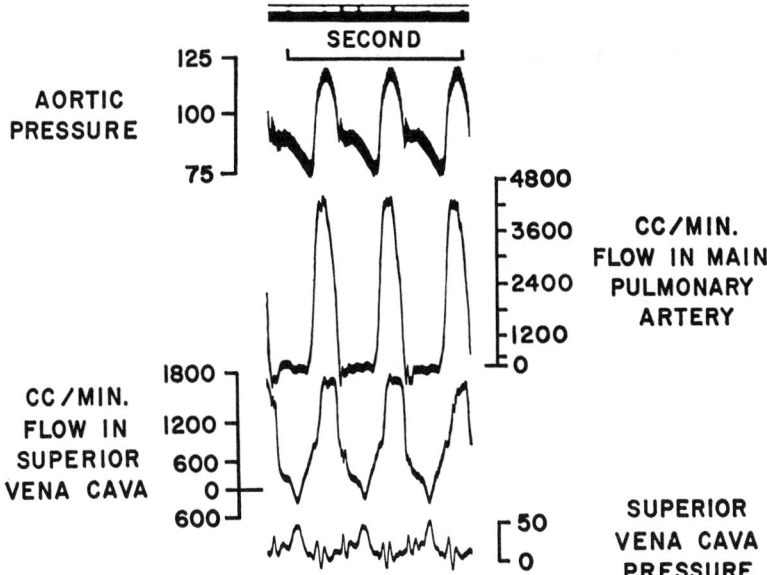

Fig. 43.12. Simultaneous recording in open chest dog of aortic pressure, superior vena cava pressure, and pulmonary artery pressure and superior vena cava flow with bristle flowmeter. Note acceleration of venous return during systolic ejection. (From Brecher, Venous Return, p. 111, Grune & Stratton, Inc., New York, 1956.)

sure indicates that reflex venomotor activity of the capacitance vessels in normal persons is highly selective and regional in operation and that local small vein or venule pressure is not necessarily an index of happenings in the central venous system. Hence, the state of distensibility of the arterioles, venules and small veins, and large central veins, are not necessarily related, and net effects are unpredictable.

C. The action of the right side of the heart upon the blood flow in the veins. Obviously, if the blood is not passed on again by the right heart as quickly as it is carried to it by the great veins, the venous pressure will rise. That is, there will be a tendency for the blood to be "dammed back." When the heart is beating vigorously and output and inflow are balanced, no rise in venous pressure occurs. In health the force of the ventricular contraction is nicely adjusted to the quantity of blood which pours into the atrium from the veins, and no accumulation occurs. If, however, the heart fails, the venous pressure rises and back pressure effects ensue.

There now appears to be good experimental proof that the activity of the right ventricle itself actually increases greatly vena caval flow into the right atrium. This is illustrated in the vena caval flow curves of figure 43.12, in which it can be seen that there is a larger forward flow of blood during right ventricular systole than during

diastole. Thus, venous inflow into the right atrium is large in the presence of closed tricuspid valves. The responsible force is believed to be right ventricular contraction itself. During such contraction, the descent of the atrioventricular junction enlarges the great venous reservoir which comprises the atria and venae cavae. Obviously, this could be a very useful mechanism for maintaining venous return during tachycardia. In slow hearts, most of atrial inflow occurs during the long ventricular diastole, but during a rapid heart rate the proportion of atrial inflow due to active systolic "injection" of blood from the veins into the right atrium, is greatly increased. Cineangiographic studies of lipiodol droplets injected into the venae cavae of anesthetized, supine cats confirm the predominantly systolic nature of superior vena caval flow during tachycardia; in the inferior vena cava, where flow is more rapid, the effects of heart rate on flow pattern are less clear-cut.

The influence of cardiac action upon the movement of blood in veins and atria does not necessarily imply that the ventricles exert an aspirating action during diastole. This problem has been debated many years and is considered in chapter 41 in some detail. In general, it can be said that under strictly controlled experimental conditions, there is some positive evidence for this. However, one must remember that there is no

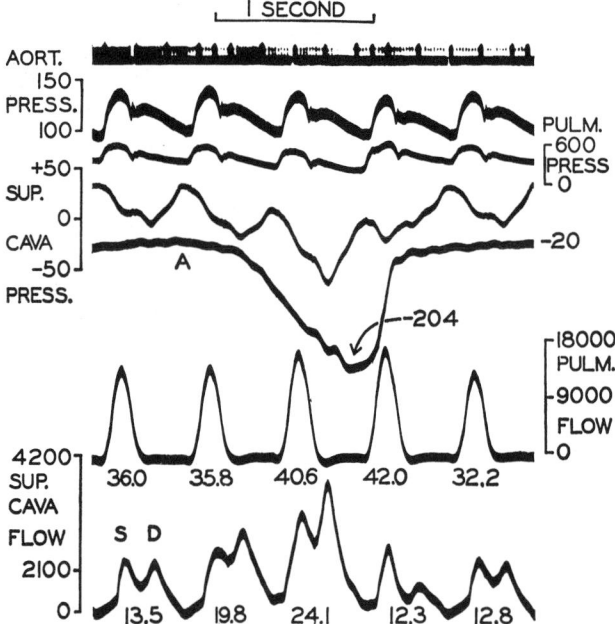

FIG. 43.13. Effect of spontaneous respiration on venous return and cardiac output (closed chest). Tracings from top to bottom: time and base line, aortic pressure in millimeters of mercury, pulmonary artery, superior vena caval and intrathoracic pressure in millimeters of water, pulmonary arterial and superior vena caval flows in cubic centimeters per minute A, beginning of inspiration, S, acceleration of superior vena caval flow during ventricular systole, D, acceleration of superior vena caval during ventricular diastole. Stroke volume (in cubic centimeters) under pulmonary arterial flow curve. Flow (in cubic centimeters) through superior vena cava during each cardiac cycle at bottom of record. Electrical frequency response of both flowmeters reduced from 400 to 40 cycles per second. Superior vena caval pressure curve damped. (Brecher, G. A., Venous Return, Grune & Stratton, Inc., New York, 1956.)

good quantitation of this and it would take place only in very early diastolic relaxation, which is a very short time period.

Sometimes when vigorous respiratory efforts are made, slight fluctuations of the venous pressure can be detected in the peripheral veins of the human subject. These variations rarely amount to more than 10 mm. of H_2O but may be considerably higher than this when dyspnea resulting from obstruction to the free entrance and egress of air from the lungs exists. Owing to the inertia of the blood column the aspirating effect is less evident the nearer to the periphery at which the pressure measurements are made.

The respiratory effects upon venous pressure and also presumably upon venous flow, can also be exaggerated in normal subjects by the following procedures. If a forced expiration is made with the glottis closed (Valsalva's experiment) the negative intrathoracic pressure can be abolished and a positive pressure of several millimeters of mercury substituted. The veins of the neck, face and limbs become distended with blood as a result of the impediment to the flow into the right auricle. The peripheral venous

pressure under these circumstances may rise to 400 mm. H_2O or more. In the converse experiment of Mueller in which a forced inspiration is made with the glottis closed, the powerful suction effect may cause a fall of 50 mm. H_2O or so in the venous pressure of a peripheral vein. The increase in negative intrathoracic pressure may be seen by means of the X-ray to exert an effect upon the ventricle which during diastole becomes somewhat enlarged beyond its usual size.

D. External forces. Natural and artificial respiration have a very large effect on central venous pressure and flow. Direct measurements of flow with the bristle flow meter in the closed-chest dog have shown flow to increase in both the superior and inferior vena cava during inspiration, and in turn, this effect is transmitted to the outlying veins (fig. 43.13). The interplay of mechanisms is as follows: the blood in the great veins at their entrance into the atrium has a small, but definite pressure of about 5 mm. H_2O transmitted from the arterial side. That is to say, if the thorax were opened so as to abolish the subatmospheric pressure within it, and a manometer placed in the inferior vena cava, a positive pressure of this magnitude would be registered. During inspiration, the pressure within the thorax is about -6 mm. Hg (81 mm. H_2O) below that of the atmosphere. During expiration it amounts to -2.5 mm. Hg (34 mm. H_2O). Their algebraic sum during inspiration (-6 mm. Hg $\div$ 0.5 mm. Hg), and during expiration (-2.5 mm. Hg $\div$ 0.5 mm. Hg), represents the transmural pressure expanding the intrathoracic structures and causing blood to enter the thorax. This especially expands the thin-walled intrathoracic veins. A similar effect but of less degree is exerted upon the walls of the atria. The diameters of the thick-walled ventricles, however, and the comparatively rigid coats of the larger arteries remain practically uninfluenced by the "negative pressure" during ordinary breathing. During expiration, the intravenous pressure within the abdomen exceeds the intraabdominal pressure by only about 1 mm. Hg. However, descent of the diaphragm during the inspiratory phase compresses the abdominal contents and, since the outlying veins have valves, blood is forced into the thorax. The recent extensive use of artificial respiration in surgical and medical situations has focused attention on the effects of such procedures on the circulation. In the closed-chest dog, intermittent, positive-atmospheric-pressure, artificial respiration (expiration occurring passively against atmospheric pressure) reduces significantly venous return to the right heart over that occurring with natural respiration. Intermittent positive-negative pressure respiration (use of mild suction during expiration) augments vena caval flow over that occurring during positive-atmospheric pressure respiration. In unanesthetized, normal humans continuous negative pressure breathing increases cardiac output and stroke volume, while continuous positive pressure breathing has the opposite effect. The use of positive-negative pressure respiration with particular attention to the negative pressure phase might be beneficial to patients in poor circulatory condition because it could be made to facilitate their venous return. In the presence of an open chest, the net caval flow increase of positive-negative pressure respiration as compared to positive-atmospheric pressure respiration is negligible. The untoward effects of artificial respiration arise because of the positive pressure applied during artificial inspiration; the intra pleural pressure, instead of decreasing, actually increases, and may even become positive. This decreases vena caval flow secondary to an induced increase in pulmonary vascular resist-

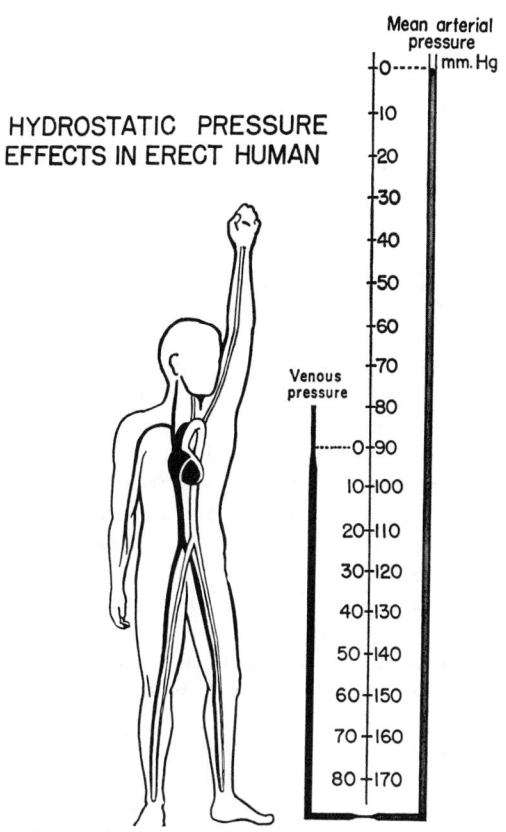

HYDROSTATIC PRESSURE EFFECTS IN ERECT HUMAN

FIG. 43.14. In erect position, arterial and venous pressures are both increased by about 85 mm. Hg. at the ankle. With the arm elevated over the head, the arterial pressure at the wrist is about 40 mm. Hg. and the effective venous pressure is zero down to a level just above the heart. (From Rushmer, Cardiac Diagnosis, W. B. Saunders Company, Philadelphia, 1955.)

ance and, in part, to the mechanical compression or "tamponade" of the heart and lungs caused by the expanding lungs. The mechanical aspects of respiration, however, are apparently not essential to maintenance of venous return or cardiac output, for in the presence of apneic oxygenation in dogs (a condition of induced ventilatory arrest with the trachea connected to a reservoir of oxygen), life continues and the cardiac output may even increase.

E. Posture and exercise. The venous pressure varies, of course, as a result of the gravity effect, i.e., with the position of the vein in relation to the right atrium, at which level, venous pressure is assumed to approximate zero (fig. 43.14). If man assumes the upright position and is motionless and relaxed, the measured pressure in an ankle vein approximates 85 to 90 mm. Hg. This is slightly more than the hydrostatic pressure from the vein to the heart level. This means that there is a continuous column of blood from the right atrium to the ankle. Similarly, the arterial blood pressure measured at the ankle will be increased over that at the heart level by an amount equal to the hydrostatic level. Thus, the arterial and venous pressures at the ankle are increased by the same amount, and the pressure difference between vein and artery is the same at ankle and heart level. This means that a favorable pressure gradient exists for venous flow. Below heart level, the veins increase in fullness and the venous pressure gradient responsible for venous return from periphery to the heart is the measured venous pressure minus the hydrostatic column. This is a small gradient but, since the veins are distended, resistance is quite low. In the upright position, veins from the upper part of the body empty towards the heart. These upper veins partially collapse and their intravascular pressure may approximate zero. Above heart level, the pressure gradient along the venous channels is the height of the hydrostatic column above heart level. This gradient is large but since the veins are partially collapsed, resistance is high.

There is, however, a special feature of the venous system which distinguishes it from the arterial system. This is the tendency of the veins to collapse. In the low pressure system, even in the recumbent position, the veins are not usually round but may be partially or fully, and intermittently collapsed. For surface veins, collapse arises from increase in atmospheric pressure; in the deeper veins, it is caused by the surrounding tissue pressure acting on the venous walls. This occurs during normal respiration in the neck veins and in the inferior vena cava below the diaphragm where this process is aided by the increased intra-abdominal pressure. With deep and prolonged inspiration, these veins may completely collapse. Such a collapse tendency may be greatly augmented by an increased gravitational stress. In the upright position, the pressure in the neck veins falls to 0 mm. Hg, and the atmospheric pressure on the outside of the neck causes these veins to collapse all the way up to the skull. This causes the pressure in these veins to remain at zero along their course. It is this tendency for collapse that causes resistance in the large veins for when distended, resistance is minimal. However, not all veins are collapsible, especially the venous sinuses in the skull, vertebral column, bones, liver and spleen, which are held open by firm-walled surrounding tissues. For example, the veins in the skull are in a non-collapsible chamber, and in the standing position a negative venous pressure of about 10 mm. Hg exists in the sagittal sinus because of the hydrostatic pressure difference between the top and base of the skull.

It is obvious from the preceding that the pressure gradient between two points in the venous system may give no information as to volume flow between the points, because of this tendency of the extrathoracic veins to collapse. Partial collapse can reduce blood flow despite an increase in pressure gradient along the vessel. Volume flow through partially collapsed veins is represented by a modification of Poiseuille's law to a tube with an elliptical cross-section. With venous pressure constant, volume flow in a partially collapsed vein is estimated to be about 25 per cent of that through the same vein when round.

Although a change in position does not alter the relative pressure gradients on the arterial and venous sides, still a normal return of venous blood is not necessarily insured. This would be the situation only if all the vasculature were made up of semi-rigid tubes and in which flow would depend only on the difference of artery and venous pressure at the level of the heart. This, however, is not true in a distensible system such as the veins. Owing to its much greater filling capacity, the volume on the venous side is greatly increased by this shift from horizontal to the erect position. In man, tilting into the feet-down position produces an immediate decrease of inferior vena caval flow which is more or less proportional to the degree of tilt. The decreased venous return under such conditions is of short duration because of a number of compensatory vasomotor mechanisms which operate very quickly. However, even with these compensations, the venous return is somewhat less than in the supine man. It is difficult to decide how effective are the active venomotor mechanisms in returning blood to the heart as man assumes the upright position. Direct information on venomotor control of the intestinal vessels, mostly in operated animals, indicates that they are capable of widespread constriction, but again, these situations can hardly be regarded as normal. In tilting the human subject into an upright posture, the blood pressure at the carotid sinus decreases mildly and the heart becomes smaller (fig. 43.15). About 400 cc. of blood leaves the thoracic compartment to accumulate mainly in the veins of the extremities (determined by leg plethysmographys). The pressure in them increases and the filling pressure of the heart drops.

Cardiac output drops mildly; stroke volume decreases considerably; the heart rate rises. There is also a decrease in blood flow through skin, skeletal muscle, liver and kidney. These changes are at least partially explainable on a mechanical basis, i.e., tipping into the erect posture might be regarded as a functional hemorrhage into the lower portions of the body. Since the pressure in a superficial arm vein maintained at heart level rises considerably (about 10 mm. Hg), possible widespread peripheral venous constriction has taken place to shift blood centrally to make more blood available to the heart for maintaining cardiac output, although its effect is not enough to maintain central venous pressure. That this limitation of peripheral blood flow is a reflex phenomenon has been shown by its absence in a sympathectomized extremity. The fact that application of a G suit before or after the subject has assumed the upright position, either prevents these changes, or re-establishes the original state of the circulation, mitigates against the role of the arterial baro-receptors and favors the stimulation of low pressor receptors. While their precise stimulus and accurate location are not known, they presumably belong to the many receptors demonstrated anatomically in the thoracic vascular bed. Atropine causes a decrease of the

central venous pressure which is only partly corrected by G suit inflation, suggesting venous pooling in certain parts of the body.

Since man spends most of his life in the erect position, there is no doubt regarding the practical effectiveness of these compensatory mechanisms. It is especially evident when one compares their behavior with that in persons with naturally occurring, or drug-induced, hypotension, who lose very large quantities of blood into their extremities and lose consciousness upon standing up. Despite this, venomotor compensation is still far from perfect in normal persons since an excess of, at least, 400 cc. of blood still remains in their extremities.

The circulation of animals such as the domestic rabbit, eel and snake, which have not acquired a compensatory mechanism, are placed at great disadvantage when the vertical position is assumed. The eel and snake can be killed by immobilization in the vertical head-up position. They literally bleed to death into their veins. Thus, in the human subject if, upon assuming the erect posture after a protracted confinement to bed, the muscles of the abdomen and limbs are weak and the tone of the nervous mechanism governing the peripheral vessels lowered, the hydrostatic effect is overcome with difficulty. The blood subsides into the capacious abdominal veins and capillaries and the right heart is no longer adequately supplied with blood. The arterial pressure falls and the cerebral blood flow becomes inadequate. The subject turns pale, sweats freely and feels giddy or perhaps nauseated, and in a complete faint loses consciousness (syncope). In this situation, and in various circulatory disorders, baths can obviously have a beneficial effect on venous return. Body immersion up to the heart level increases the pressure exerted on the body and reduces pooling in the abdomen and dependent parts. In man, increased gravitational stress in the head-foot direction (positive acceleration) leads to practically no venous return to the right heart. The increased hydrostatic pressure distends the veins so much that they contain almost all the blood volume, and active vasomotor influences are not sufficient to combat this very high hydrostatic pressure. Again this can be effectively combated by wearing an inflated pressure suit to compress the extrathoracic parts of the body and to force blood to flow centrally.

In exercise, a much greater volume of blood enters the central veins from the arterial side. The various mechanical assists already men-

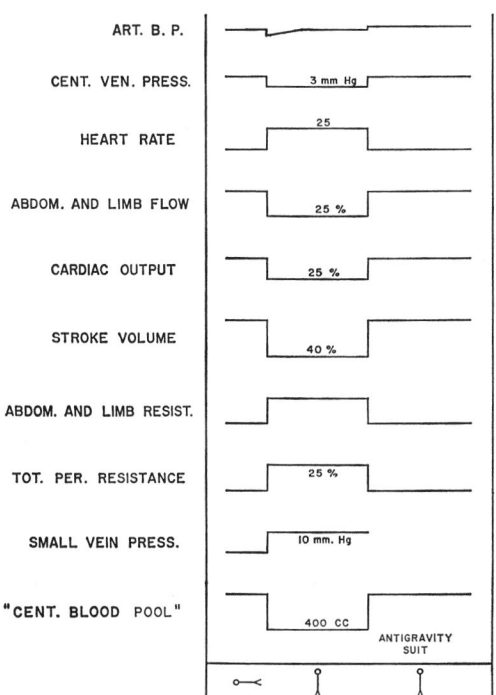

Fig. 43.15. Effect on various cardiovascular parameters in man of changing from supine to the upright position.

tioned, that increase the venous pressure gradient and venous blood flow toward the heart and decrease the venous reservoir, now operate even more effectively. In addition, the act of muscle shortening propels blood toward the heart. In animal experiments in which skeletal muscle is perfused with blood under a constant pressure, the arterial inflow decreases and venous outflow increases during muscle shortening; upon relaxation, the arterial inflow increases and the venous outflow decreases; the net result is to augment flow. The pressure within the active muscles surrounding the veins is thus a potent factor in regulating venous pressure and flow. Intra muscle pressure rises from a resting level of 2 to 5 cm. H_2O to as high as 50 cm. H_2O during exercise. The venous pressure in the ankle veins which, in the standing position approximate 80 to 90 mm. Hg, is now greatly reduced. By rhythmical action of the muscle, the venous valves are activated and the blood column broken up, and venous pressure at the ankle may decrease to as low as 30 mm. Hg (40 cm. H_2O). Although helpful, the presence of venous valves is not essential for this beneficial action of active muscle on venous return. Extravascular vessel compression will promote flow equally in both directions only if flow resistance is equal in both directions. Without the presence of valves, the resistance in the vessels on the capillary side of the venous system is lower than in the veins on the right cardiac side. Hence, rhythmical vein compression per se will drive blood toward the heart, and this has been shown experimentally to occur. It can also be observed clinically that in advanced age and under pathological conditions with incompetent or no venous valves, muscle movements improve venous return. Information on active changes in venomotor action in man is limited and is essentially contained in the observations that there is a drastic reduction in splanchnic blood volume with exercise and the pressure in the superficial veins (within a nonexercising area) increases by 10 to 13 mm. Hg over that in a standing position only.

Regulation of Pulmonary Pressure and Flow

Uniquely interposed between the right and left heart and entirely enclosed within the negative pressure confines of the thorax, the pulmonary circulation exhibits certain peculiarities uncommon to the other organ-perfused systems. For instance, (1) it is the only circuit in the body to receive the total cardiac output, (2) it operates at a perfusion pressure $\frac{1}{4}$ to $\frac{1}{8}$ that of the systemic circuit, (3) its mean transit time is equal to the systemic, albeit across a much reduced linear distance, reflecting the enormous surface area of the pulmonary capillary bed, (4) it is predominantly controlled by the beat to beat pressure differential between the pulmonary artery (right ventricle) and the left atrium upon which phasic, intrathoracic respiratory variations are superimposed, and (5) it is the only arterial circuit which carries desaturated hemoglobin and which, by virtue of the alveolar-capillary pressure difference, the desaturated hemoglobin and the huge surface area participates in large instantaneous gas exchanges.

PULMONARY RESISTANCE. To determine the mechanisms controlling pulmonary flow, it is necessary to know the resistance to flow. Classically, this should be simply the ratio of the difference of pressure across any portion of a vascular bed to the blood flow that develops; it is a convenient factor by which the pressure drop can be multiplied to give the flow. Such resistance gives information regarding the two factors upon which it depends, the viscosity and geometry of the vascular bed. Since, however, the relation of pressure and flow is not a straight line and when plotted does not pass through the origin, the mechanisms involved are not determinable from a single point relationship. To make the results interpretable, a vascular bed must be perfused in the control state and in the presence of a variable at the same pressure while flow is measured, or at the same flow while pressure is measured. In no other way can it be even roughly determined that a calculated change in resistance (Pressure/Flow) reflects vasomotor activity produced by the stimulus, or reflects only the passive change in resistance caused by alteration in left atrial pressure or in pulmonary flow. There is also an additional difficulty in measuring changing resistance in the pulmonary circulation, for here the relationship between pressure and flow is quantitatively quite different from that in the systemic circulation. The difference is that with the same volume perfusing both circuits, the pressure drop from the pulmonary artery to the left atrium is only about one-fifth that from the aorta to the right atrium. This is illustrated in figure 43.16 where the differential pressure between the pulmonary artery and the pulmonary veins is only about 15 to 20 mm. Hg. With present pressure methodology, figures of this magnitude can only be roughly determined. This means that while the systemic resistance at the arterioles is high and made up of relatively thick muscle cuffs, the resistance at the outlet of the small pulmonary artery branches has quite thin muscular coats with relatively large luminae. The tone of the terminal pulmonary vessels is thereby relatively low so that a rise in pulmonary venous pressure is readily transmitted to the arterial side, or so that a rise in blood volume injected into the arterial side will increase greatly the volume in the lungs. As a result of the high degree of distensibility of the pulmonary vascular bed, secondary to the opening up of fresh capillaries or further opening of those being used, the blood contained within the lungs shows wide variations under different conditions and on a passive basis.

PRESSURE PULSE IN THE PULMONARY CIRCUIT. Pressures in the pulmonary circuit are determined by means of intracardiac catheterization or by indwelling tubes already described. Pulmonary circuit pressures are much lower than those in the systemic arterial circuit. For the curves of figure 43.16, angiostomy cannulas were placed in the central pulmonary artery and pulmonary veins. Phasic pressure from the two vessels and also their differential pressure were recorded some days postoperatively in the unanesthetized dog. The results showed that the pulmonary artery pressure is 40/10 mm. Hg and the pulmonary vein pressure is 2 to 12 mm. Hg. The pattern of the pulmonary arterial pressure is distinctive showing a marked incisura low on the anacrotic limb. In late diastole, the pressure descent almost ceases and becomes horizontal. The pulse contours of the peripheral and central portions of the pulmonary artery display differences somewhat like those of the systemic circuit. The pulse wave velocity in the pulmonary artery in man, studied during thoracic surgical procedures, is about 2 meters per second at normal pulmonary arterial pressure levels. In patients with pulmonary hypertension, pulse velocity is increased to about 4 meters per second, indicating reduced distensibility of the pulmonary artery, since the pulse velocity is inversely related to distensibility. The contour of the pulmonary vein pressure curve clearly shows a, c, and v waves, and closely resembles pressure pulses taken from the left atrium. In open-chest dogs a 4 to 5 mm. Hg pressure gradient was found between mean pulmonary venular (small pulmonary venous) and mean left atrial pressures.

PHASIC BLOOD FLOW IN THE PULMONARY CIRCUIT. Figure 43.13 demonstrates that the flow through the main pulmonary artery is almost entirely during systole, the diastolic flow being flat and close to zero. This strongly suggests that

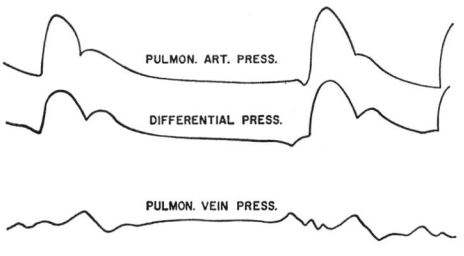

FIG. 43.16. Record from the unanesthetized dog showing the pressure pulse contours in the pulmonary artery, *upper curve*; pulmonary vein, *lower*; and the differential pressure between the two, *middle curve*. Pulmonary artery pressure, 28/10 mm. Hg.; mean pulmonary vein pressure, 10 mm. Hg.; differential pressure 5 to 10 mm. Hg. (From Hamilton, Am. J. Physiol., 1939, **125**, 130.)

there is little or no diastolic run-off of blood into the pulmonary capillaries. By the ingenious method of DuBois and associates, measurements of cyclic change in flow through the pulmonary capillaries has revealed that this is quite pulsatile with a very high peak flow during systole. By the end of diastole, pressures in the vascular bed are equilibrated and capillary flow practically ceases (figure 43.17). Flow curves in the pulmonary veins are not available.

THE EFFECTS OF THE RESPIRATION UPON THE PULMONARY AND SYSTEMIC BLOOD PRESSURES AND FLOWS. The effects of natural respiration on the hemodynamics of the pulmonary circulation are illustrated in figure 43.13. The pulmonary arterial pressure falls during inspiration and rises during expiration. One should expect that, as a result of the increased flow of blood into the right ventricle during inspiration (see superior caval flow) and the greater systolic discharge, both the pulmonary pressure and pulmonary flow would rise during this phase of respiration. However, only the pulmonary flow rises. Because of the traction exerted upon the circumference of the pulmonary vessels by the surrounding lung tissue, their capacity is increased. This more than compensates for the lack of change in the pressure gradient and for the greater amount of blood entering the pulmonary circuit during the inspiratory phase. During expiration these effects are reversed. The right systolic discharge is less but the capacity of the vascular bed of the lungs is at the same time reduced; an upward swing in pulmonary arterial pressure occurs. With maximal expansion of the lungs, or during a forced expiration with the glottis closed (Valsalva's experiment), the vessels are strongly compressed by the surrounding lung tissue, and the pulmonary arterial pressure rises sharply.

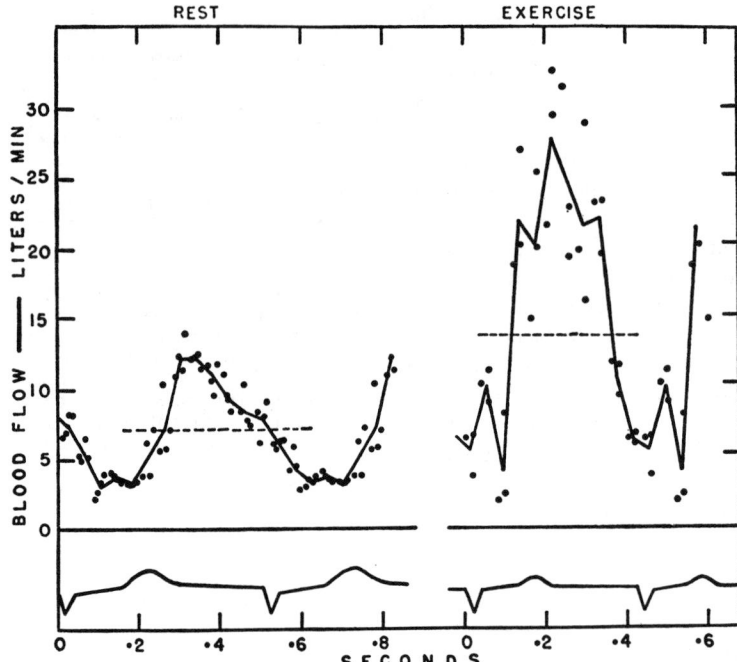

Fig. 43.17. Simultaneous pulmonary capillary blood flow curves at rest and during exercise. (DuBois, J. Clin. Invest., 1957, **36**, 1566.)

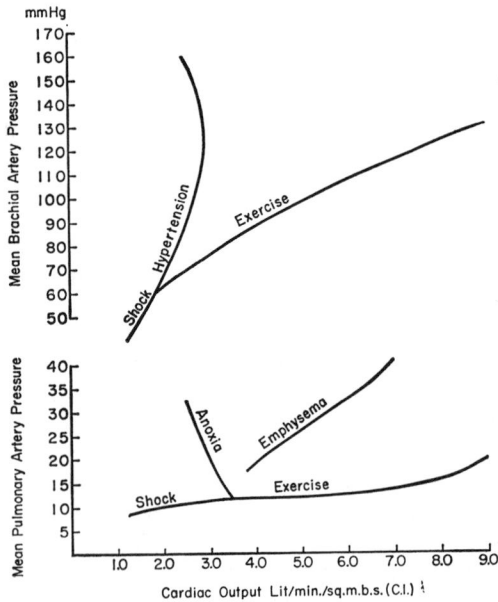

Fig. 43.18. The relationship of pressure to flow in the systemic circulation and pulmonary circulation in normal and abnormal states. Note the difference in response of the two circulations to exercise.

The increased capacity of the pulmonary vessels during inspiration reduces, momentarily, the flow of blood into the left atrium; the consequent reduction in the systolic discharge of the left

ventricle causes a fall in aortic pressure (figure 43.13). After a few beats of the right ventricle, the greater capacity of the pulmonary vessels again becomes filled and the flow of blood into the left chambers of the heart increases; the aortic pressure rises. The succeeding expiration, by reducing the capacity of the pulmonary vessels, drives blood to the left side and further increases the discharge into the aorta; the systemic pressure, in consequence, continues its rise until near the end of the expiratory phase. The large undulations which appear in the blood pressure tracings of animals are due to these effects. If the respiratory movements and the systemic blood pressure are recorded simultaneously, it is found that the blood pressure commences to fall at the commencement of inspiration and reaches its lowest point in the latter half of this phase; the blood pressure tracing then commences to rise and reaches its maximum toward the latter part of expiration. In this situation, it is presumed that the decrease and increase in peripheral resistance are on a passive basis but this has not been proved.

EFFECTS OF EXERCISE ON THE PULMONARY CIRCULATION. The general form of the curve relating pulmonary artery pressure and pulmonary blood flow in man and the intact dog at rest and exercise, is shown in figure 43.18. The curve indicates that pulmonary artery pressure is maintained below the upper limit of normal until the flow exceeds at least three times the base level whereupon it increases progressively. This absence of pressure rise with increased flow implies an expansion of the vascular bed from opening of new channels, widening of those already perfused, or a combination of both. Thus, the resistance decreases. It is believed (without proof) that this is on the basis of passive distension of the lungs, especially since the same relation holds when attempts are made to denervate the heart, when isolated lung lobes are perfused, or when variations in the quantity of blood in the lungs is induced by different procedures.

As pointed out earlier, to understand what is happening hemodynamically in the pulmonary circulation, it is more important here than in any other vascular bed to know both the pulmonary artery pressure and pulmonary vein (or left atrial pressure). This is because the pressure gradient is only a few millimeters of mercury, and a 5 mm. Hg-change in the pulmonary venous pressure could be transmitted back as a 5-mm. Hg rise on the pulmonary artery side without any active change in peripheral resistance in the lung vessels. So, unless it is known what is happening in the pulmonary veins, one is at a loss to ascribe the cause of a change in pulmonary artery pressure. Keeping this in mind, little or no evidence exists in the dog that various procedures that actively affect peripheral resistance in the systemic circuit have any effect in the pulmonary bed. For example, epinephrine injection in small or large doses into the pulmonary artery, has no effect on the pulmonary circulation in its first circuit. After it has entered the systemic circuit and increased pulse pressure and cardiac output, then the pulmonary vein pressure may increase 50 to 60 mm. Hg, but so does the pulmonary artery pressure by a like amount, so the pressure difference is not changed. Acetylcholine, aminophylline, angiotensin, histamine and stellate ganglion stimulation are also without effect on the differential pressure. Hence, the passive bag theory of pulmonary function has arisen.

EVIDENCE FOR AND AGAINST VASOMOTOR CONTROL OF THE PULMONARY CIRCULATION. The pressure in the pulmonary artery may increase as the result of back pressure from the left heart, an increase in pulmonary blood flow and vasoconstriction in the pulmonary vascular bed. Also, pressure changes follow alteration of intrathoracic pressure.

The pulmonary vasculature could respond to active vasoconstriction and contribute to an increase of pulmonary artery pressure. The small pulmonary vessels possess muscular coats and are equipped with dual nerve supply—sympathetic and parasympathetic, stimulation of the pulmonary nerves increases the pulmonary vascular resistance; stimulation of the baroreceptors gives increased pulmonary flow and decreased pulmonary arterial pressure; casts of the two sides of a lung are markedly different if one side is perfused with noradrenaline up to the time of plastic injection (the latter showing marked constriction in the vessels of less than 25 microns (μ) in diameter). Narrowing and gnarling of the small, muscular pulmonary arteries can be demonstrated angiographically in response to hypoxia and to the intrapulmonary arterial injection of catecholamines and serotonin in the closed-chest dog. However, since there is little doubt that wide variations in vascular resistance can normally occur in a purely passive way, and since it is impossible to establish accurately the pressure gradient when it is so very low, demonstration of an active part played by smooth muscle under normal conditions, in the walls of the small vessels, is difficult.

In normal subjects, hypoxia, induced by breathing 12 per cent oxygen in nitrogen, considerably increases pulmonary arterial pressure, mildly increases cardiac output, and is without effect on left atrial pressure or central blood volume. This suggests that the vasoconstriction induced is on an active basis. Although generalized, such vasoconstriction of the pulmonary bed would seem to serve no useful purpose; local hypoxia, however, could be helpful in regulating the distribution of blood by causing vasoconstriction which, in turn, diverts blood from the affected region to vessels in better aerated parts of the lung. In experiments in man and animals in which one lung was respired with an hypoxic mixture, the lung probably developed vasoconstriction, since the arterial saturation returned to normal. This would be the case if the vessels in the hypoxic lung constricted and forced the blood normally flowing through them into well-oxygenated channels. Final proof, however, that hypoxia induces active vasoconstriction in man is contained in the experiments in which acetylcholine (a drug with strong vasodilating effects on the systemic circulation) was infused into the right atrium, but in such quantities that no systemic effects were produced. In the presence of hypoxia induced by breathing a low oxygen mixture, infusion of acetylcholine decreased the elevated pulmonary arterial pressure but did not change the left atrial pressure, cardiac output, systemic blood pressure, or heart rate. This seems to indicate than an active vasoconstriction caused by hypoxia is relieved by the drug. This view is further substantiated by the observation that in emphysematous patients who represent a chronic and more limited form of hypoxia with some degree of arterial unsaturation, acetylcholine infusion lowers still further the arterial oxygen saturation. The site and mechanism of action are unknown but they could be many—a local reflex from alveoli or pulmonary veins, chemoreceptor stimulation of the sinus or aortic body, direct local action on pulmonary bed, and shift of systemic blood into the pulmonary circuit, etc. Presumably, the action is not related to sympathetic nervous control since the vasoconstrictor effect of hypoxia can be observed in man with a total sympathectomy. Serotonin (5-hydroxytryptamine) infused into the intact dog produces a considerable rise in pulmonary arterial pressure with only a modest increase of cardiac output and no change in pulmonary venous or left atrial pressures, indicating active vasoconstriction.

In summary then, experimental evidence demonstrates that human pulmonary vessels can constrict and dilate, but these functions have have been shown only under extreme conditions. Hence, the role played by active vasomotion in controlling the pulmonary circulation is not known, and since the present methods available for such study have serious limitations, this problem will be difficult to solve.

REFERENCES

ALEXANDER, R. S. Transformation of the arterial pulse wave between the aortic arch and the femoral artery. Am. J. Physiol., 1949, **158**, 287.

ALEXANDER, R. S. Standing wave components in arterial pulses of hypothermic dogs. Circulation Res., 1958, **6**, 580.

BRAMWELL, J. C. AND HILL, A. V. The velocity of the pulse wave in man., Proc. Roy. Soc. **93B**, 298, 1922.

BRECHER, G. A. Mechanism of venous flow under different degrees of aspiration. Am. J. Physiol., 1952, **169**, 423.

BRECHER, G. A. AND HUBAY, C. A. Pulmonary blood flow and venous return during spontaneous respiration. Circulation Res., 1955, **3**, 210.

BRIGDEN, W., HOWARTH, S., AND SHARPEY-SCHAFER, E. P. Postural changes in the peripheral blood flow of normal subjects with observations on vasovagal fainting reactions as a result of tilting, the lordotic posture, pregnancy and spinal anesthesia. Clin. Sc., 1950, **9**, 79.

CARO, C. G. AND HARRISON, G. K. Observations on pulse wave velocity and pulsatile blood pressure in the human pulmonary circulation. Clin. Sci., 1962, **23**, 317.

CHIDSEY, C. A., FRITZ, H. W., ZOCCHE, G. P., HIMMELSTEIN, A., AND COURNAND, A. Effect of acetylcholine on the distribution of pulmonary blood flow in chronic pulmonary emphysema. Malattie Cardiovascolari, 1960, **1**, 15.

COURNAND, A. Some aspects of the pulmonary circulation in normal man and in chronic cardiopulmonary diseases. Circulation, 1950, **2**, 641.

CULBERTSON, J. W., WILKINS, R. W., INGELFINGER, AND BRADLEY, S. E. The effect of the upright posture upon hepatic blood flow in normotensive and hypertensive subjects. J. Clin. Invest., 1951, **30**, 305.

DALY, I. DE BURGH. An analysis of active and passive effects on the pulmonary vascular bed in response to pulmonary nerve stimulation. Quart. J. Exp. Physiol., 1961, **46**, 257.

DALY, W. J. AND BEHNKE, R. H. The behavior of the venous reservoir as affected by atropine. Trans. Ass. Amer. Physicians, 1962, **75**, 277.

DOYLE, J. T., PATTERSON, J. L., WARREN, I. V., AND DETWEILER, D. K. Observations on the circulation of domestic cattle. Circulation Res., 1960, **8**, 4.

DUBOIS, A. B., AND MARSHALL, R. Measurements of pulmonary capillary blood flow and gas exchange throughout the respiratory cycle in man. J. Clin. Invest., 1957, **36**, 1566.

FISHMAN, A. P., MCCLEMENT, J., HIMMELSTEIN, A., AND COURNAND, A. Effects of acute anoxia on the circulation and respiration in patients with chronic pulmonary disease studied during the "steady state." J. Clin. Invest., 1952, **31**, 770.

FRANKLIN, D. L., ELLIS, R. M., AND RUSHMER, R. F. Aortic blood flow in dogs during treadmill exercise. J. Appl. Physiol., 1959, **14**, 809.

FRITTS, H. W., HARRIS, P., CLAUSS, R. H., ODELL, J. E., AND COURNAND, A. The effect of acetylcholine on the human pulmonary circulation under normal and hypoxic conditions. J. Clin. Invest., 1958, **37**, 99.

FRY, D. L., NOBLE, F. W., AND MALLOS, A. J. An electric device for instantaneous and continuous computation of aortic blood velocity. Circul. Res., 1957, **5**, 75.

GAUER, O. H., HENRY, J. P. AND SIEKER, H. O. Changes in central venous pressure after moderate hemorrhage and transfusion in man. Circulation Res., 1956, **4**, 79.

GAUER, O. H. AND SIEKER, H. O. The continuous recording of central venous pressure changes from an arm vein. Circulation Res., 1956, **4**, 74.

GREEN, H. D., LEWIS, R. N., NICKERSON, N. D., AND HELLER, A. C. Blood flow, peripheral resistance and vascular tonus with observations on relationship between blood flow and cutaneous temperature. Am. J. Physiol., 1944, **141**, 518.

GREGG, D. E., ECKSTEIN, R. W., AND FINEBERG, M. H. Pressure pulses and blood pressure values in unanesthetized dogs. Am. J. Physiol., 1937, **118**, 399.

HADDY, F. J., FLEISHMAN, M., AND SCOTT, J. B.,

JR. Effect of change in air temperature upon systemic small and large vessel resistance. Circulation Res., 1957, **5**, 58.

HAMILTON, W. F., WOODBURY, R. A., AND VOGT, E. Differential pressures in the lesser circulation of the unanesthetized dog. Am. J. Physiol., 1939, **125**, 130.

HAMILTON, W. F. AND DOW, P. An experimental study of the standing waves in the pulse propagated through the aorta. Am. J. Physiol., 1939, **125**, 48.

HELLEBRANDT, F. A., CRIGLER, E. F., AND KELSO, E. A. Variations in intramuscular pressure during postural and phasic contraction of human muscle. Am. J. Physiol., 1939, **126**, 247.

HICKHAM, J. B. AND CARGILL, W. H. Effect of exercise on cardiac output and pulmonary arterial pressure in normal persons and in patients with cardiovascular disease and pulmonary emphysema. J. Clin. Invest., 1948, **27**, 10.

HIRSCHMAN, J. C. AND BOUCEK, R. J. Angiographic evidence of pulmonary vasomotion in the dog. Brit. Heart J., 1963, **25**, 375.

HOLT, J. P. The effect of positive and negative intrathoracic pressure on peripheral venous pressure in man. Am. J. Physiol., 1943, **139**, 208.

HUBAY, C. A., WALTZ, R. C., BRECHER, G. A., PRAGLIN, J., AND HINSON, R. A. Circulatory dynamics of venous return during positive-negative pressure respiration. Anesthesiology, 1954, **15**, 445.

INOUYE, A. AND KOSAKA, H. A study with the electromagnetic flow meter of flow patterns in carotid and femoral arteries of rabbits and dogs. J. Physiol., 1959, **147**, 209.

JOHNSON, V., HAMILTON, W. F., KATZ, L. N., AND WEINSTEIN, W. Studies of the dynamics of the pulmonary circulation. Am. J. Physiol., 1937, **120**, 624.

KILBURN, K. H. AND SIEKER, H. O. Hemodynamic effects of continuous positive and negative pressure breathing in normal man. Circulation Res., 1960, **8**, 660.

KRAMER, K., OBAL, F., AND QUENSEL, W. Untersuchungen über den Muskelstoffwechsel des Warmblüters; die sauerstoffaufnahme des Muskels während rhythmischer Tätigkeit. Arch. ges. Physiol., 1939, **241**, 717.

KURAMOTO, K. AND RODBARD, S. Effects of blood flow and left atrial pressure on pulmonary venous resistance. Circulation Res., 1962, **11**, 240.

LAGERLOF, H., ELIASCH, H., WERKO, L., AND BERGLUND, E. Orthostatic changes of the pulmonary and peripheral circulation in man. A preliminary report. Scandinav. J. Clin. & Lab. Invest., 1951, **3**, 85.

LANDOWNE, M. Characteristics of impact and pulse wave propagation in brachial and radial arteries. J. Appl. Physiol., 1958, **12**, 91.

LEVY, M. N., BRIND, S. H., BRANDLIN, F. R., AND PHILLIPS, F. A. The relationship between pressure and flow in the systemic circulation of the dog. Circulation Res., 1954, **2**, 372.

LYNCH, P. R., CARTER, B. L., GIMENEZ, J., AND KRISCH, R. Venae cavae flow pattern in cats: as studied with high-speed cinefluorographic technique. Amer. J. Physiol., 1960, **199**, 1139.

McDONALD, D. A. The relation of pulsatile pressure to flow in arteries. J. Physiol., 1955, **127**, 533.

MOTLEY, H. L., COURNAND, A., WERKO, L., HIMMELSTEIN, AND DRESDALE, D. The influence of short periods of induced acute anoxia upon pulmonary artery pressures in man. Am. J. Physiol., 1947, **150**, 315.

OCHSNER, A., COLP, R., AND BURCH, G. E. Normal blood pressure in the superficial venous system of man at rest in the supine position. Circulation, 1951, **3**, 674.

PAGE, E. B., HICKHAM, J. B., SIEKER, H. O., McINTOSH, H. D., AND PRYOR, W. W. Reflex venomotor activity in normal persons and in patients with postural hypotension. Circulation, 1955, **2**, 262.

PATEL, D. J. AND BURTON, A. C. Active constriction of small pulmonary arteries in the rabbit. Circulation Res., 1957, **5**, 620.

PENTECOST, B. L., IRVING, D. W., AND SHILLINGFORD, J. P. The effects of posture on the blood flow in the inferior vena cava. Clin. Sci., 1963, **24**, 149.

POLLACK, A. A. AND WOOD, E. H. Venous pressure in the saphenous vein at the ankle in man during exercise and changes of posture. J. Appl. Physiol., 1949, **1**, 649.

RILEY, R. L., HIMMELSTEIN, A., MOTLEY, H. L., WEINER, H. M., AND COURNAND, A. Studies of pulmonary circulation at rest and during exercise in normal individuals and in patients with chronic pulmonary disease. Am. J. Physiol., 1948, **152**, 372.

RYAN, J. M., STACY, R. W., AND WATMAN, R. N. Role of abdominal aortic branches in pulse wave contour genesis. Circulation Res., 1956, **4**, 676.

SANCETTA, S. M. General and pulmonary hemodynamic effects of pure decapeptide angiotensin in normotensive man. Circulation Res., 1960, **8**, 616.

SHEPHERD, J. T., DONALD, D. E., LINDER, E., AND SWAN, H. J. C. Effect of small doses of 5-hydroxytryptamine (serotonin) on pulmonary circulation in the closed-chest dog. Am. J. Physiol., 1959, **197**, 963.

SHIPLEY, R. E., GREGG, D. E., AND SCHROEDER, E. F. An experimental study of flow patterns in various peripheral arteries. Am. J. Physiol., 1943, **138**, 718.

SPENCER, M. P., JOHNSTON, F. R., AND DENISON, A. B., JR. Dynamics of the normal aorta: "inertiance" and "compliance" of the arterial system which transforms the cardiac ejection pulse. Circulation Res., 1958, **6**, 491.

SPENCER, M. P. AND DENISON, A. B., JR. The aortic flow pulse as related to differential pressure. Circulation Res., 1956, **4**, 476.

STEAD, E. A., WARREN, J. V., MERRILL, A. J., AND BRANNON, E. S. The cardiac output in male subjects as measured by the technique of right atrial catheterization. Normal values with observations on the effect of anxiety and tilting. J. Clin. Invest., 1945, **24**, 326.

SUGIURA, T. AND FREIS, E. D. Pressure pulse in small arteries. Circulation Res., 1962, **11**, 838.

SWANN, H. G., MONTGOMERY, A. U., DAVIS, J. C., AND MICKLE, E. R. A method for rapid measurement of intrarenal and other tissue pressures. J. Exper. Med., 1950, **92**, 625.

WADE, O. L., COMBES, B., CHILDS, A. W., WHEELER, H. O., COURNAND, A., AND BRADLEY, S. E. The effect of exercise on the splanchnic blood flow and splanchnic blood volume in normal man. Clin. Sci. 1956, **15**, 457.

WALLACE, G. M. AND STEAD, E. A. Spontaneous pressure elevations in small veins and effects of epinephrine and cold. Circulation Res., 1957, **5**, 651.

WARREN, J. V., PATTERSON, J. L., DOYLE, J. T., GAUER, O. H., KEEN, E. N., MC GREGOR, M., AND GOETZ, R. H. Circulation and respiration in the giraffe. Circulation, 1957, **16**, 947.

WARREN, J. V., BRANNON, E. S., WEENS, H. S., AND STEAD, E. A. Effect of increasing blood volume and right atrial pressure on circulation of normal subjects by intravenous infusion. Am. J. Med., 1948, **4**, 193.

WARREN, J. V., BRANNON, E. S., STEAD, E. A., AND MERRILL, A. J. The effect of venesection and the pooling of blood in the extremities on the atrial pressure and cardiac output in normal subjects with observations on acute circulatory collapse in 3 instances. J. Clin. Invest., 1945, **24**, 337.

WEISSLER, A. M., WARREN, J. V., ESTES, E. H., MCINTOSH, H. C., AND LEONARD, J. J. Vasodepressor syncope. Factors influencing cardiac output. Circulation, 1957, **15**, 875.

WEISSLER, A. M., LEONARD, J. J., AND WARREN, J. V. Effects of posture and atropine on cardiac output. J. Clin. Invest., 1957, **36**, 1656.

WILKINS, R. W., CULBERTSON, J. W., AND INGELFINGER, F. J. The effect of splanchnic sympathectomy in hypertensive patients upon estimated hepatic blood flow in the upright as contrasted with the horizontal position. J. Clin. Invest., 1951, **30**, 312.

WOMERSLEY, J. R. Method for the calculation of velocity, rate of flow and viscous drag in arteries when the pressure gradient is known. J. Physiol., 1955, **127**, 553.

WOODBURY, R. A. AND HAMILTON, W. F. Blood pressure studies in small animals. Am. J. Physiol., 1937, **119**, 663.

Monographs and Reviews

BRECHER, G. Venous return. Grune & Stratton, Inc., New York, 1956.

BURCH, G. E. A primer on venous pressure. Lea & Febiger, Philadelphia, 1950.

BURTON, A. C. The relation between pressure and flow in the pulmonary bed. Pulmonary circulation, Grune & Stratton, Inc., New York, 1958.

COURNAND, A. Control of the pulmonary circulation in normal man. In Circulation. Proceedings of the Harvey Tercentenary Congress, London, 1957. Edited by J. McMichael. Blackwell Scientific Publications, Oxford, 1958.

DuBOIS, A. B. Instantaneous pulmonary capillary blood flow. Pulmonary circulation, Grune & Stratton, Inc., New York, 1958.

FRITTS, H. W. AND COURNAND, A. Physiological factors regulating pressure, flow and distribution of blood in the pulmonary circulation. Pulmonary circulation, Grune & Stratton, Inc., New York, 1958.

GAUER, O. H. AND HENRY, P. Beitrag zur homeostase des extra-arteriellen Kreislaufs. Volumenregulation als unabhangiger physiologischer Parameter. Klin. Wchnschr., 1956, 34, 356.

GAUER, O. H. Homeostasis of the extra-arterial circulation. First International Symposium on Submarine and Space Medicine, New London, Connecticut, 1958.

GREGG, D. E. Homeostasis of the arterial circulation. First International Symposium on Submarine and Space Medicine, New London, Connecticut, 1958.

HADDY, F. J. Vasomotion in systemic arteries, small vessels and veins determined by direct resistance measurements. Minnesota Med., 1958, 41, 162.

HEYMANS, C. The regulation of blood pressure and heart rate. American Lecture Series #43, Charles C Thomas, Publisher, Springfield, Ill., 1950.

LANDIS, E. M. AND HORTENSTINE, J. C. Functional significance of venous blood pressure. Physiol. Rev., 1950, 30, 1.

McWILLIAMS, J. A. Blood pressures in man under normal and pathological conditions. Physiol. Rev., 1925, 5, 203.

OPDYKE, D. F., ALEXANDER, R. S., REMINGTON, J. W., PETERSEN, L. H., HUGGINS, R. A., AND SMITH, E. L. Panel discussion: interpretation and significance of alterations in central pulse form. Fed. Proc., 1952, 11, 732.

RUSHMER, R. F. Cardiac diagnosis, W. B. Saunders Company, Philadelphia, 1955.

SJOSTRAND, T. Significance of the volume and distribution of the blood for the circulation. Physical Rev., 1953, 33, 202.

WETTERER, E. Die Wirkung der Herztätigkeit auf die Dynamik des Arteriensystems. Verhandl. deutsch. Gesellsch. für Kreislaufforschung, 1956, 22, 26.

WETTERER, E. Flow and pressure in the arterial system. Their hemodynamic relationship and the principles of their measurement. Minnesota Med., 1954, 37, 77.

WIGGERS, C. J. Circulatory dynamics. Grune and Stratton, Inc., New York, 1952.

WOOD, P. Diseases of the heart and circulation. Ed. 2, J. B. Lippincott Company, Philadelphia, 1956.

CHAPTER 44

The Output of the Heart and the Regulation of its Action

Nervous Control of the Heart

THE HEART RATE

In general, the rate of the heart bears an inverse relationship to the size of the animal, and a direct relationship to the metabolic rate. The heart rate in the canary, for example, is in the neighborhood of 1000 beats per minute, whereas that of the elephant is about 25. The average rate in adult man is around 70 per minute, but there is a rather wide variation between individuals, a rate considerably below or above this average being not uncommon. Muscular training tends to reduce the cardiac rate; athletes not infrequently having a pulse rate between 50 and 60. On the other hand, a rate between 80 and 90 is sometimes seen in other healthy persons. The rate diminishes progressively from birth, when it is around 130 per minute, to adolescence, but increases slightly again in old age. Among physiological conditions which temporarily increase the heart rate are *muscular exercise, emotional excitement and high environmental temperature.* It also increases somewhat during *digestion.* The rate is lowered during *sleep* (55 to 60). Among pathological conditions which cause an increase in cardiac rate are *hemorrhage, surgical shock, hyperthyroidism, fever* (an increase of 10 beats per 1° F. rise in temperature) and certain *cardiac arrhythmias,* e.g., paroxysmal tachycardia, atrial fibrillation, etc.

Tachycardia and *bradycardia* are general terms used to denote, respectively, any considerable increase in heart rate above, or reduction below the normal average.

Ordinarily the heart rate is not under voluntary control. However, several instances have been reported of individuals possessing the power of voluntarily accelerating the heart rate. In one such case the effect was brought about apparently through the discharge of impulses along accelerator nerves since other sympathetic manifestations, e.g., vasoconstriction, glycosuria and dilation of the pupils accompanied the increased pulse rate. Voluntary stopping of the heart is said to be within the power of certain practitioners of Yoga in India. Such claims have been supported by the testimony of physicians who observed disappearance of the heart sounds and of the radial pulse during such demonstrations. In one electrocardiographically controlled investigation, however, it became apparent that even though decreased venous return to the heart (brought about by tensing of the thoracic and abdominal muscles against the closed glottis) may result in marked diminution or even disappearance of heart sounds and pulse, electrocardiographic activity continues uninterrupted and finger plethysmography shows persisting pulsations.

The heart, as we know, beats rhythmically after its complete separation from the central nervous system, but in the intact animal this automatic action is under the continuous influence of nervous impulses. The nervous mechanism comprises groups of nerve cells in the medulla—the *cardiac centers;* various *afferent pathways* along which impulses are conveyed to these centers from numerous regions of the body; and the *vagus* and *accelerator* or *augmentor* nerves which transmit impulses from the centers to the heart.

THE VAGUS NERVES

The vagus nerves are cardio-inhibitory. This action was discovered by the Weber brothers in 1845. They convey fibers, belonging to the parasympathetic division of the involuntary nervous system, from a center in the medulla (*cardio-inhibitor center*) to the special tissues of the heart. The medullary center was located by Miller and Bowman in the dorsal nucleus of the vagus situated in the floor of the 4th ventricle. Weak electrical stimulation of this area produced slowing of the beat, and stronger currents, complete arrest of the heart. The cardiac fibers of the vagus separate from the trunk of the nerve in the neck between the origins of its superior and inferior laryngeal branches. Intermingling with fibers of the accelerator nerves they enter into the formation of the deep and superficial cardiac plexuses whence they are continued to the atrial muscle. Here they make connection with ganglion cells. Postganglionic fibers pass to the specialized tissue of the sino-atrial and atrioventricular (A-V) nodes where they are prolonged between the mus-

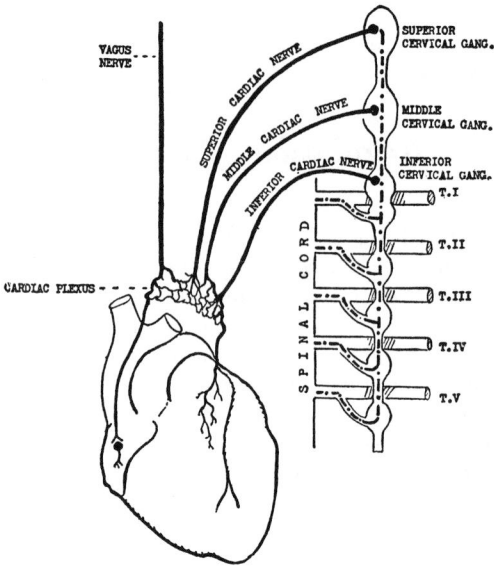

Fig. 44.1. Diagram of the cardiac nerves. *Broken lines* = preganglionic sympathetic fibers.

cle fibers. They form a rich plexus and are seen to end as ring-shaped or club-shaped structures ("boutons") upon the fibers of the specialized tissue. Many postganglionic fibers do not enter the nodal tissues but terminate in the atrial myocardium proper. Those which enter the atrioventricular node do not extend beyond the upper part of the bundle. None has been found to terminate in the ventricular myocadium (Nonidez), or in the lower part of the specialized conducting system.

THE ACCELERATOR OR AUGMENTOR NERVES

The accelerator fibers were described by Von Bezold in 1863. They belong to the thoraco-lumbar division of the involuntary nervous system and arise from cells situated in the lateral horns of the upper thoracic segments of the spinal cord. These cells constitute a spinal cardio-accelerator center. The preganglionic fibers enter the gangliated cord of the sympathetic to connect with cells in the *inferior, middle* and *superior cervical ganglia*. In many animals and also often in the human subject the inferior cervical and the first thoracic ganglia are fused into an irregularly shaped structure called the *stellate ganglion* from which accelerator fibers pass directly to the heart. The heart also receives accelerator fibers *directly* from the sympathetic chain as far down as the 4th or 5th thoracic ganglion. In order, therefore, to remove all accelerator influence

from the heart it is necessary, as shown by Cannon, Lewis and Britton, and by others in man, to interrupt these connections as well as to remove the stellate ganglia. The axons of the cells of the cervical ganglia (postganglionic fibers) form the *inferior, middle* and *superior cardiac nerves* (fig. 44.1). These fibers, especially those forming the nerves of the right side, terminate in the sino-atrial node. Those of the left side are distributed mainly to the A-V node and bundle. According to Nonidez, the sympathetic efferent fibers which reach the heart are contained mainly in the middle cardiac nerve. The superior cardiac nerve is distributed to the large arteries at the base of the heart while the inferior cardiac nerve is mainly afferent. The spinal accelerator center is subordinate to higher centers. The precise locations of the latter are not known, but the experiments of Beattie, Brow and Long indicate the presence of a center in the posterior hypothalamic region; and Green and Hoff observed changes in heart rate, in blood pressure and in limb and kidney volumes upon stimulating the cerebral cortex (motor and premotor areas) in cats and monkeys. A medullary center also probably exists.

TONIC ACTION OF NERVES

The separate effects of stimulation of the vagal and sympathetic fibers to the heart on the heart rate, conduction, distensibility and contractility of the heart have been considered in chapter 35. But their normal tone, reflex activation and control, and their interplay or balance remain to be considered.

A. The tone of the vagus. During the normal life of the animal the vagus nerves exert a continuous restraint upon the action of the heart. In other words the vagus, or rather the cardio-inhibitory center, possesses tone, impulses passing from it in a continuous stream to the heart. This effect, which may be compared to the action of a dragging brake, can be readily demonstrated in animals by cutting or freezing the nerves. The heart's action then immediately becomes greatly accelerated. The increase in rate following the removal of the vagal influence also occurs though the stellate ganglia have been previously excised; the result therefore cannot be due to an increased action of the accelerator nerves. The tonic action of the vagus nerves may be annulled by means of atropine, $\frac{1}{20}$ to $\frac{1}{15}$ grain being required in man to completely abolish their effects, the heart rate then increasing to 150 or 180 per minute. The difference between this rate and the normal resting rate of 70 per minute, therefore, represents the vagal effect which is being constantly exerted under ordinary circumstances. Various conditions, physiological and pathological, alter the tone of the vagus center. The tone is naturally higher in some species, e.g., the dog, which is capable of feats of endurance, than in others, e.g., the domestic rabbit. It also shows individual variations in man, athletes usually showing a higher tone than those who lead sedentary lives.

Vagal tone is apparently reflex in nature and dependent upon afferent impulses flowing to the vagus center especially along the sinus and aortic nerves. Section of these nerves causes an increase in heart rate and little further acceleration occurs as a rule when the vagi themselves are subsequently severed.

B. Accelerator tone. The existence of a tonic action of the accelerator nerves has been postulated on the basis of experiments showing that excision of the stellate ganglion was followed by a slowing of the heart rate. Gasser and Meek, for example, found that when the ganglia were removed but the vagi were left intact, an immediate and marked fall in rate (about 40 per cent) occurred; further slowing occurred later which was attributed to a rise in vagal tone. Slowing of the rate is produced, however, by excision of the ganglia, even though vagotomy has been performed previously; this fact of course precludes the possibility of the immediate reduction in rate following excision of the stellate ganglia being due to increased vagal tone. Bronk and his associates demonstrated the existence of accelerator tone in the cat by recording the action potentials from nerves leaving the stellate ganglion. A fairly continuous discharge of impulses at a rate of 5 to 20 per second was observed, suggesting the existence of accelerator tone.

A criticism of these experiments is that they were not performed under truly basal conditions—i.e., in conscious, fasting animals resting comfortably, with external visual and auditory stimuli reduced to a minimum and, in addition, apprehension of the animal eliminated through previous training to lie quietly during observation of the heart rate. Yet only under these circumstances can the presence or absence of true accelerator tone (as opposed to accelerator nerve activity under various experimental conditions) be ascertained. Murphy studied a group of dogs in this manner. The average "resting" heart rate before training was 90 to 112 per minute.

After several weeks of training the resting rate slowed and stabilized at 47 to 57 per minute. Cardiac sympathectomy was then performed. Following recovery of the animals from this procedure the basal rate was 50 to 58—i.e., not different from that observed prior to interruption of the accelerator fibers. It was concluded that in the truly resting state the accelerator nerves are not in tonic activity, but that the accelerator mechanism is more or less constantly involved in adapting the heart rate to the changing bodily conditions.

The foregoing illustrates rather well a difficult problem underlying many aspects of the regulation of the heart's performance discussed in this section: the interpretation and application of experimental data, by necessity obtained under certain special conditions, to the intact, functioning organism. Different experimental designs may lead to divergent conclusions as to the role of various factors in cardiac regulation.

CARDIAC REFLEXES

Under ordinary conditions, the activities of the cardio-inhibitory and cardio-accelerator centers which result in the continuous discharge of impulses along the corresponding cardiac nerves are in turn dependent to a very large extent, if not entirely, upon the reception of impulses by afferent paths. In other words, the maintenance of the tone of the centers, and so of the normal resting rate of the heart, and the alterations in rate which occur under various physiological conditions are in large measure either reflex in nature or due to impulses received from cerebral centers. The impulses which stream into the nervous centers arise in all parts of the body, the heart itself included. By these influences the tone of either center may be exalted or depressed, and corresponding changes produced in the cardiac rate. If the cardiac vagus on one side be cut and its central portion (i.e., the end leading to the brain) stimulated, a reflex through the cardio-inhibitory center and the opposite vagus occurs which alters the cardiac rate. The nature of the change in rate—whether acceleration or inhibition—which will result from stimulation of the central end of the vagus or of most other afferent nerves cannot always be foretold. Reflex slowing of the pulse can usually be demonstrated in the human subject by pressure upon the eyeball at the outer canthus (oculo-cardiac reflex), or by the stimulation of nasal branches of the 5th nerve. Stimulation of afferent fibers in the respiratory passages as by the inhalation of irritating vapors, e.g., anesthetics, is particularly likely to cause reflex inhibition of the heart. Extrasystoles and bradycardia have been demonstrated electrocardiographically in man during abdominal operations, the irregularities being the consequence, apparently, of visceral stimulation. Excitation of the central end of various peripheral nerves, e.g., the sciatic, causes reflex changes in the pulse rate. In these last instances acceleration is more readily obtained than inhibition. The irradiation of impulses on to the cardiac centers from the cerebral centers, e.g., from the motor area at the commencement of muscular exercise or from regions concerned with emotional manifestations, are held responsible for the changes in pulse rate which occurs under these conditions.

The pulse rate is generally inversely related to the arterial blood pressure, a rise or fall in pressure causing respectively a decrease or increase in heart rate. These adjustments are believed to be subserved by (1) a reflex whose afferent limb is constituted of afferent vagal fibers (aortic nerve) ending in the aortic arch and heart, (2) a reflex in which the sinus nerve forms the afferent limb. These mechanisms have been considered in chapter 42. Presumably, such changes in heart rate are brought about not simply by an increase or a decrease in tone of one or the other cardiac centers, but by reciprocal variations in the tone of both. For example, the slowing of the heart which results from a rise in arterial pressure is much less pronounced if impulses from the cardioinhibitory center have been prevented from reaching the heart by section of the vagi. After removal of the stellate ganglia, on the other hand, the cardiac response to a rise in blood pressure is reduced to a less extent. Obviously, the mechanisms concerned are not too well understood since a fall in blood pressure causes an increase in the rate of the heart even after it has been completely denervated.

Cardiac Output and Cardiac Work

The most important external manifestation of the heart is its output of blood and the work it performs. These measurements are obtained by the Fick procedure, by the dilution principle, and in some instances, by the foreign gas methods (ch. 39).

DEFINITIONS AND GENERAL CONSIDERATIONS

The output of the heart per beat is spoken of as the *systolic discharge* or the *stroke volume*, and the output per minute as the *minute volume*. The value of the latter is simply the product of the stroke volume and the pulse rate (pulse rate times stroke volume = minute volume); the minute volume divided by the pulse rate, therefore, gives the stroke volume. The quantity of blood ejected by each beat of the left ventricle in the average healthy man during rest is from 70 to 80 cc. An equal quantity is, of course, discharged at the same time by the right ventricle, making a total for the whole heart of from 140 to 160 cc. The contents of the left ventricle are ejected against a much higher mean arterial pressure than the contents of the right; the mean pressure in the pulmonary artery being about $\frac{1}{6}$ of that in the aorta. The minute volume is expressed in terms of one ventricle. The output of one ventricle obviously represents the quantity of blood flowing through the lungs, or through the systemic vessels, during the same period. An adult of sedentary occupation pumps at least 5500 liters of blood through his body daily—from left to right ventricle through the systemic vessels, and from right to left through the lungs.

The heart cavities are not believed to completely empty themselves during the resting state, but contain around 100 cc. of residual blood at the end of systole. Each ventricle has a normal capacity of approximately 200 cc.

The portion of the energy output of the left ventricle that appears as useful work can be roughly calculated from the product of mean aortic blood pressure and cardiac output. The work done by the right ventricle can be similarly calculated except that the mean pressure is that in the pulmonary artery. The end diastolic pressure in the left or right ventricle should be subtracted from the measured aortic pressure or pulmonary arterial pressure since the end diastolic ventricular pressure does not have its origin from ventricular systole. Preferably, the transmural pressure should be subtracted but this is difficult to obtain in man. Ordinarily the end diastolic pressure is small approximating up to 5 mm. Hg in the right ventricle and up to 10 mm. Hg in the left ventricle. However, under some conditions of heavy ventricular loading such as an A-V fistula, or congestive heart failure, the value may reach 30 to 40 mm. Hg, and hence, the correction is important. The simpler calculation also assumes that the velocity factor is but a very small part of the external work of the heart. Normally, this is of the order of 1 to 2 per cent. When cardiac output is quite large in the presence of a decreased systemic pressure, or

TABLE 44.1

Hemodynamic studies in man of the right and left heart during rest and exercise both at sea level and at high altitude

Condition	Treadmill Exercise kg. m./min./m.²	Heart Rate	Mean BP* mm. Hg	CI* L./min.	TPR* (Press.)/(Flow)	CWI* kg.-m./min./m.²	SVI* cc.	SWI* gm. m./min./m.²	O² usage, L./min./m.²	A-VO₂, cc./100 cc.
Right heart (average surface area, 1.83 m.²)										
Rest		73	16	3.4	2.6	0.63	47	8	0.132	4.1
Exercise	Leg movements	152	35	9.2	2	3.94	67	26	1.047	11.32
Left heart (average surface area, 1.74 m.²) Lima										
Rest		81	92	2.8	19	3.6	33	41		
Exercise	704 to 986	163	109	8.1	8	12.1	51	75	1.353	16.9
Left heart (average surface area, 1.62 m.²) Morococha										
Rest		83	101	4.2	15	6.0	51	72	0.209	5.7
Exercise	490 to 580	156	118	7.5	10	12.3	49	79	1.072	13.9
Exercise	695 to 749	175	125	15.2	5	26.4	88	151		

* BP, blood pressure; CI, cardiac index; TPR, total peripheral resistance; CWI, cardiac work index; SVI, stroke volume index; SWI, stroke work index.

especially if aortic or pulmonary stenosis occurs, the kinetic factor can be up to 50 per cent of the cardiac work. For a somewhat precise evaluation of the work done by either ventricle, the following formula may be used,

$$W = QR + \frac{wV^2}{2g}$$

in which W is work in gram meters; Q is cardiac output in cc. per beat; R is mean aortic blood pressure in meters Hg; w is mass of blood ejected in grams; and g is 9.8. The mean velocity (V) during systolic ejection in centimeters per second at the root of the aorta or pulmonary artery is equal to stroke volume in cubic centimeters divided by the product of the cross sectional area at the aortic or pulmonary root in square centimeters times the duration of ejection in seconds. The aortic or pulmonic diameter is obtained from cadavers. The kinetic factor is assumed to be the same for both ventricles since the cross-sectional areas of aorta and pulmonary artery are about the same.

To better compare cardiac output and cardiac work in different individuals, the values are generally expressed in terms of surface area and are spoken of as flow or work indices. Thus, the cardiac index (CI), stroke volume index (SVI), cardiac work index (CWI), and stroke work index (SWI) are obtained by dividing the cardiac output, stroke volume, cardiac work, and stroke work by the surface area of the body. An average surface area is 1.7 square meters. Normal values for the right and left heart obtained in man during catheterization studies are in Table 44.1.

THE OUTPUT OF THE HEALTHY HEART. NORMAL STANDARDS. PHYSIOLOGICAL VARIATIONS. The minute output of the heart under basal conditions[1] for the average size male adult is about 5.5 liters, and the CI is 3.2 liters. The CI is slightly lower for the female and considerably higher for children. Cardiac output can be quite variable in the same person from day to day unless extreme precautions are used to maintain the resting state.

A. Conditions in which cardiac output is not changed. The cardiac output is apparently the same when a person is asleep as when he is awake and in the horizontal position. It is unaffected by menstruation, by metabolic acidosis produced by the infusion of ammonium chloride or lactic acid, and by moderate variations in the external

[1] Body recumbent, at rest and at 20°C. for 15 to 20 minutes and 12 hours after food and drink.

temperature although it may be increased up to 30 per cent at environmental temperatures above 30°C., or by low temperatures that are associated with shivering. The native indigenous to high altitude undergoes considerable acclimatization by changes in his cardiovascular and respiratory systems so that at altitudes of, at least, 15,000 feet, the cardiac output is normal as are his heart rate and systemic blood pressure and systemic A-VO$_2$. However, the slightest exertion will increase his cardiac output which will be considerably higher in the sitting rather than in the reclining position, whereas in persons indigenous to sea level, such change in posture at sea level may decrease cardiac output.

B. Conditions in which cardiac output decreases. Normal. The cardiac output is decreased about 30 per cent in changing from the recumbent to the upright posture.

Pathological states. Atrial fibrillation and a very rapid heart rate may reduce cardiac output up to 50 per cent. In complete heart block and with an efficient myocardium, the output may be approximately normal, but when this exists in the presence of coronary sclerosis, myocardial degeneration, or after open heart surgery (cutting of the A-V bundle), the output may be greatly reduced. In other subjects, although the output at rest is normal, the inability of the heart to accelerate properly prevents an adequate output during muscular exertion. In congestive heart failure, cardiac output very often is reduced, and the increase in cardiac output which normally follows muscular effort does not occur or is slight. This type of failure is to some extent compensated for by a greater increase in the systemic A-VO$_2$ difference than occurs in healthy persons doing a similar amount of external work.

C. Conditions which increase cardiac output. Cardiac output may be increased 50 to 100 per cent by anxiety and excitement and, at least, 30 per cent by eating (during first 3 hours). Anxiety, apprehension, and excitement may increase cardiac output greatly presumably through the release and action of catecholamines. Anemia, pregnancy (in later months), metabolic alkalosis produced by infusion of sodium bicarbonate and low oxygen or high CO$_2$ in the inspired air are conditions which increase cardiac output up to 100 per cent. If prolonged or too severe, the output declines due to the injurious effect upon the heart muscle. In maximum exercise the cardiac output may be increased ninefold.

D. Effects of drugs upon the cardiac output. Adrenaline and *histamine* increase the oxygen consumption and the cardiac output; the effect upon the minute volume is, however, proportionately greater than that upon the oxygen consumption. *Acetylcholine,* whose effects in general are very evanescent, causes a slight increase in the minute volume. A decided rise in the cardiac output is produced by *nitrites* which, like acetylcholine, cause arteriolar dilation. The increase in the cardiac output caused by nitrites is probably a compensatory effect of the lower peripheral resistance, whereby the blood pressure is maintained near the normal level. *Digitalis* produces no immediate effect upon the minute volume in normal persons. In subjects with congestive heart failure and atrial fibrillation the output is as a rule, though not invariably, increased as the cardiac condition improves. *Strophanthin* acts similarly to digitalis. *Atropine* which increases the heart rate to 150 or 180 beats per minute does not increase, as a rule, the cardiac output. *Alcohol* in moderate dosage (35 cc.) causes no more than a slight rise in the cardiac output.

REGULATION OF CARDIAC OUTPUT AND CARDIAC WORK DURING EXERCISE AND EXCITEMENT

Reliable determinations of cardiac output and cardiac work during exercise and excitement are not too numerous. For mild to moderate exercise, measurements are generally made by the Fick procedure with the subject in the supine position and with indwelling cardiac catheters while he pushes bicycle pedals with his feet operating against a mechanical frictional resistance. For heavy as well as light external work, cardiac output is determined with the dilution technique while the subject runs on a treadmill. In strenuous exercise, the cardiac output may reach 35 to 45 liters per minute (table 44.1) or increase 7 to 9 times, while the body oxygen usage may increase 10 to 12 times.

Exercise and excitement make up the most important and continuous stress impacts of every day life. With present knowledge, it is impossible to portray sequentially the responses of the heart and circulation to these stimuli. A description of present information is, however, possible and some of it will stand a reasonable degree of integration. Many parameters of importance have been measured.

A. Heart rate. At the transition from rest to work, the pulse frequency rises very rapidly with heavy exercise, reaching levels of 160 to 180 per minute. During short exhaustive work, heart rates as high as 240 to 270 have been recorded in normal young people. This increase in heart rate is attributed to some form of autonomic control, but the mechanisms have not been established. The suspect Bainbridge reflex probably does not apply since this requires for its operation cardiac distension from increased venous return. As we shall see later, the heart is more apt to decrease in size. The tachycardia during exercise is attributed to a reflex through the carotid sinus and aortic baroreceptors resulting from a reduced arterial pressure as the result of vasodilation in the active muscle. However, the systemic blood pressure rises, not falls, during exercise. Finally, tachycardia is explained as related to direct regulation from the higher centers. In dogs subjected to total regional cardiac denervation, the abrupt, rapid increase in heart rate at the onset of exercise is absent; consistent with the view that under normal circumstances this response is mediated through the cardiac nerves. On the other hand, during exercise there is a gradual, slow (over a period of 1 to 2 min.) increase in the heart rate, proportional to the severity of the exercise but always less than that shown by dogs with intact cardiac nerves. The mechanism of this acceleration is unknown at the present time. Adrenalectomy is without effect, indicating that circulating catecholamines secreted by the adrenal medulla are not causative.

B. Ventricular pressure-volume relations. It has long been believed that the output of the heart is governed by its venous blood supply and that the increase in minute output during muscular work requires a regulating mechanism by which venous return is augmented. To effect this, the venous blood supply and pressure in the central veins must increase to such a height that the increased venous flow and ventricular filling pressure will dilate the heart and increase the length of its fibers during each diastole and by this stretch cause a greater ventricular response in the following systole.

A very large amount of experimental work has stressed this viewpoint. Howell and Donaldson (1884) first showed the intrinsic adaptation of the heart of the dog to an artificially increased venous return. Frank in 1895, in the frog heart, came to the conclusion that the magnitude of ventricular contraction is determined by the intra-cavity volume at the end of systole. In 1914, Patterson, Piper and Starling measured the pressure and volume of both ventricles with a cardiometer in a heart-lung preparation of the dog while the venous return was passively and progressively increased by elevating a blood infusion reservoir

connected to the right atrium. As the atrial pressure or ventricular filling pressure rose, the heart dilated and with each systole ejected a greater stroke volume at a greater ventricular pressure. This relationship called "Starling's Law of the Heart" indicated in a more formalized way that "the energy of contraction, however measured, is a function of the length of the muscle fibers," before contraction (fig. 44.2A). As these investigators indicated, this relationship is little more than the application to cardiac muscle of what was already known about skeletal muscle by Blix in 1895 and Flick in 1882. This relationship of ventricular pressure and volume has been confirmed for the whole heart in the open chest dog and for the left ventricle in the open and closed chest dog (fig. 44.2B).

Because of the difficulty of estimating volume of a single ventricle and the relative ease of pressure measurement, attempts have been made to correlate mean atrial pressure or end diastolic pressure of the associated ventricle with the stroke volume or stroke work. An elegant experimental preparation for this type of study by Sarnoff is in figure 44.3. At the outset it might be expected on mechanical and other grounds that neither mean atrial pressure nor end diastolic pressure would be a reliable substitute for the ventricular volume as a guide to the response of the ventricle. First of all, the two pressures do not always follow each other. They represent only an approximation to one of the variables that determine the end diastolic volume of a ventricle. The end diastolic volume is determined not only by the filling pressure but by its duration, the resistance of the ventricle to filling (its tone), and by the systolic volume of blood remaining in the heart after systole has ended (its systolic residue). Both the latter are independent of these pressures. Finally, the relationship between these pressures and the end diastolic volume is almost flat in the physiological range, i.e., it takes large changes in diastolic volume to induce almost no change in atrial or ventricular end diastolic pressure. Despite this, most experimenters found that under ordinary circumstances, mean atrial pressure or ventricular end diastolic pressure and the succeeding ventricular response of pressure, stroke volume or stroke work were usually altered together. Sarnoff, in particular, has greatly expanded this approach and has found that the curves expressing the relation of mean atrial pressure and stroke work are shifted in one direction by conditions improving myocardial performance (stimulation of cardiac fibers from the

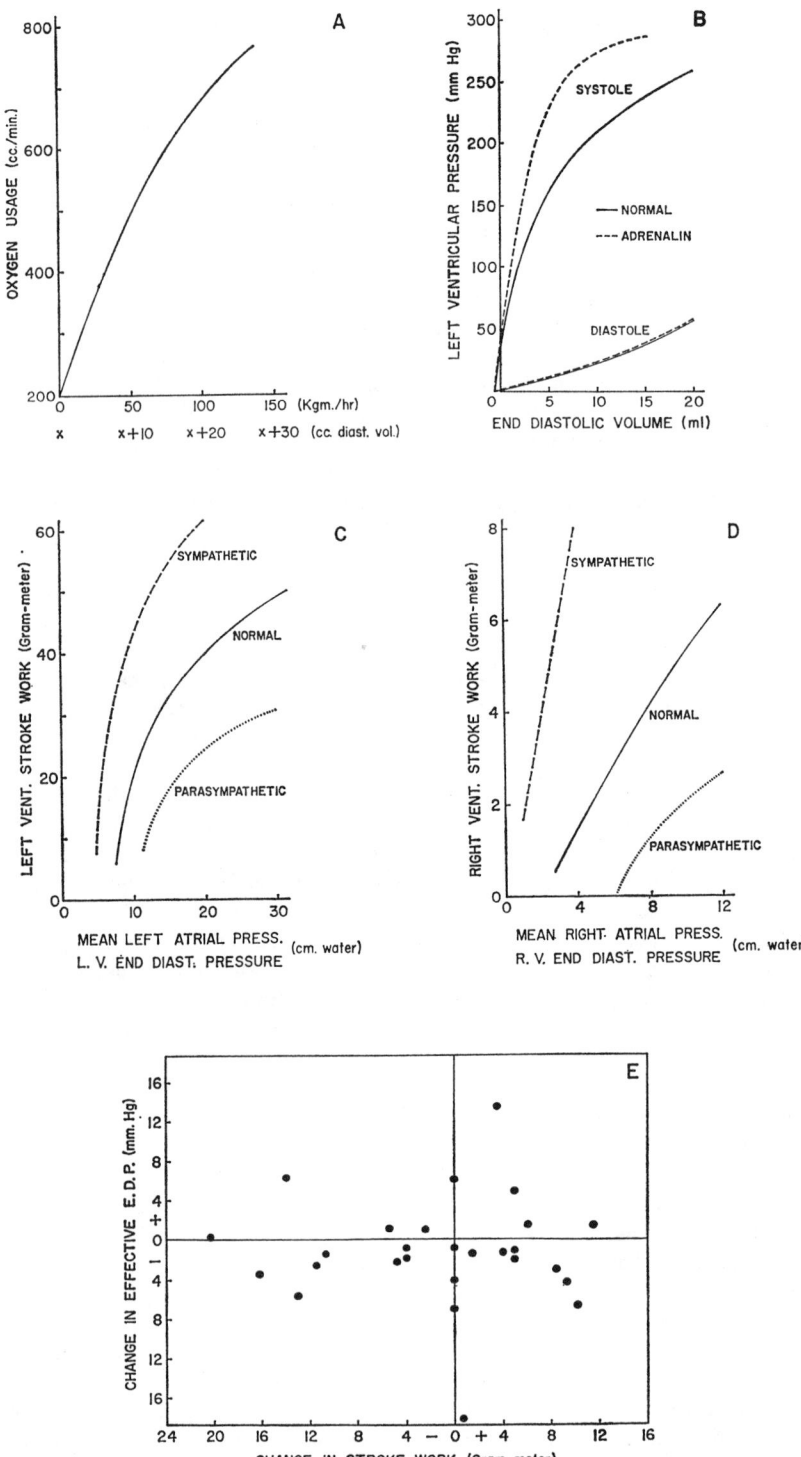

Fig. 44.2. Performance characteristics of the heart. A. Relation of O_2 usage to cardiac work and diastolic volume, i.e., the energy output of the heart, utilizing the "heart'lung preparation." (Starling and Visscher, J. Physiol., 1926, 62, 243.) B. Pressure-volume function curves of the left ventricle in the open-chest dog. C. Effect of sympathetic and parasympathetic cardiac nerve stimulation on the relation between mean left atrial pressure and left ventricular stroke work and relation between left ventricular end diastolic pressure and left ventricular stroke work. Note lack of depressant effect of vagal stimulation upon end diastolic pressure-stroke work relations. (Sarnoff, Am. J. Cardiol. 1960, 5, 579.) D. Response of right ventricular stroke work to mean right atrial pressure and to ventricular end diastolic pressure, and the effects of autonomic stimulation. The parasympathetic response is presented only for direction and does not indicate magnitude. (Sarnoff, Am. J. Cardiol. 1960, 5, 579.) E. Change in effective end diastolic pressure (EDP) versus stroke work in the normal dog before and within 1 minute after exercise. (From Gregg, et al. Physiol. Rev., 1955, 35, 130.)

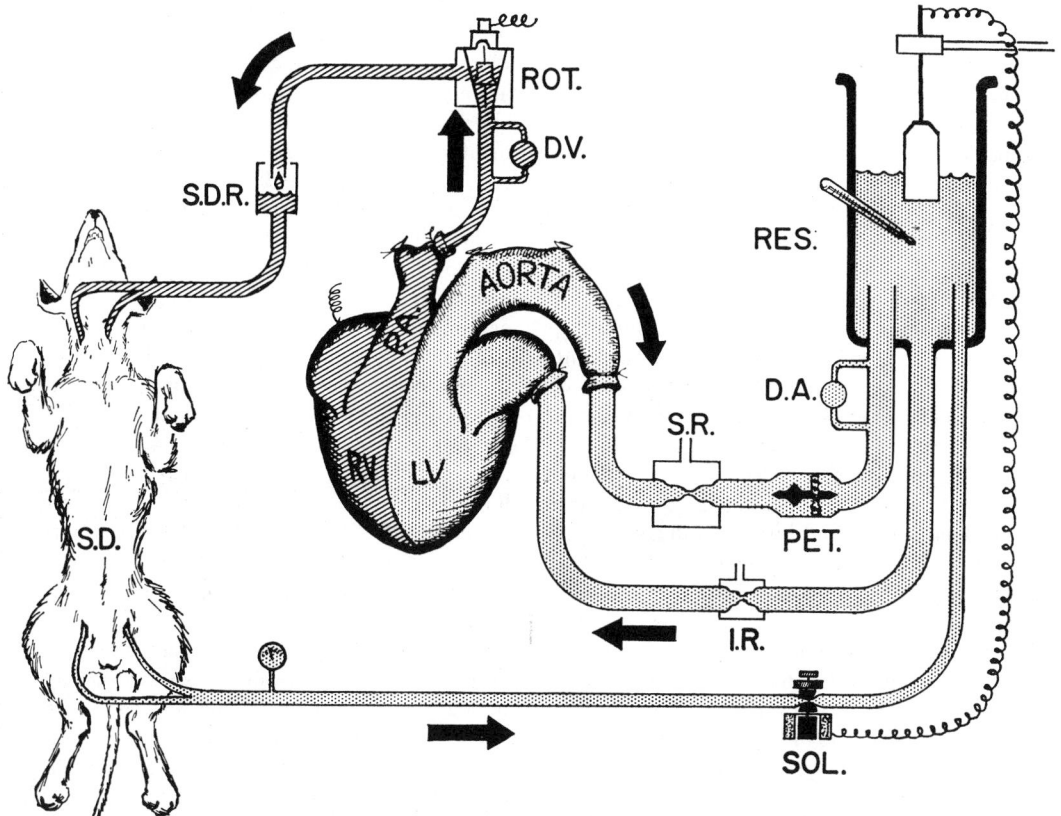

Fig. 44.3. Modern version by Sarnoff of isolated heart or heart-lung preparation. The coronary venous return is passed through a donor dog to maintain the blood at a normal biochemical environment before it is infused into the coronary system of the isolated heart. In older versions of the Starling isolated heart or heart-lung preparation in which the coronary venous blood circulating through the myocardial wall was simply reoxygenated and returned to the coronary system, progressive deterioration in performance characteristics developed within 60 to 90 minutes. *S-D*, support dog; *S-D-R*, support dog reservoir; *SOL*, solonoid valve electrically operated by microswitch at top of reservoir float; *S-R*, air-filled Starling resistance; *PET*, Potter electroturbinometer; *D-A*, arterial densitometer; *RES*, reservoir; *I.R.*, water-filled inflow Starling resistance; *D.V.*, venous densitometer; *ROT*, rotameter. (Sarnoff, *et al.* Am. J. Physiol., 1958, **192**, 141.)

stellate ganglia, reflex stimulation of the myocardium by a decrease in carotid sinus perfusion pressure, injection of epinephrine), while unfavorable conditions such as vagal stimulation, increase in carotid sinus perfusion pressure and coronary insufficiency shift the curves in the opposite direction. These ventricular function curves provide important objective evidence that ventricular control can involve changes in myocardial contractility, a concept now widely accepted (fig. 44.2C and *D*).

As one approaches the normal state, however, the evidence is equivocal for this relationship. The peripheral venous pressure in man during heavy work (2.8 liters oxygen per minute) can increase up to 7 mm. Hg. Variations of filling pressure, however, cannot be deduced from peripheral venous pressure because of the unknown pressure gradient from the periphery to central veins. In the dog exercising on the treadmill, in the human following injection of a small amount of epinephrine or exercising mildly while lying down, there may be no direct correlation between the increased cardiac output or cardiac work and the atrial or ventricular end diastolic pressure. Furthermore, intracardiac end-diastolic pressure measurements alone do not necessarily represent the effective transmural pressure, since it was shown in the closed-chest dog that under certain experimental conditions a rise in ventricular end-diastolic may be accompanied by a concommitant increase of the intrapericardial pressure. On the other hand, in subjects with an artificial pneumothorax, a linear relation was found between effective or transmural atrial pressure and stroke volume with an increase of 2 mm. Hg providing an increase in stroke volume of 40 per cent. In humans whose autonomic nervous system has been inhibited by a ganglionic blocking drug elevation of the left ventricular end-diastolic pressure, induced by blood transfusion, was accompanied by an increase of the cardiac output and stroke volume. This relationship also apparently holds in patients with high output failure and very large ventricular volumes.

C. Ventricular volume and stroke volume. As already indicated, comparisons of direct measurements of ventricular volume with pressure or with stroke volume or stroke work have not been made in the normal state in which the aggregate complications of venous resistance, intrathoracic pressure, vascular volume, changing heart rate, neurogenic factors, and humoral influences exist. However, highly suggestive evidence has been obtained by estimating the ventricular volume in systole and diastole. In dogs, this has been done by measuring the cyclic changes in an external ventricular dimension (using the mercury filled tube of Whitney or the sonar technique); or by measuring a changing internal ventricular dimension by an induction gauge. A limited amount of work is available in which stroke volume has been simultaneously determined by the sonar or electromagnetic flow meter technique applied to the aorta. In humans, the diastolic volume has been estimated from the X-ray silhouette while the stroke volume has been directly determined using the Fick or dye dilution principle. Recently, metallic clips have been sutured on the surface of both ventricles of patients undergoing certain cardiac operations. Following recovery, the external dimensions of the heart were studied by means of cineradiograms, measurements being made of the distances separating the clips during the cardiac cycle, at rest as well as during exercise. The essential findings follow:

In man and the dog, the left ventricular diastolic volume and stroke volume increase in the recumbent position as compared to the more or less upright position. Concurrently the central blood pool or thoracic blood volume increases by about 400 cc. The cardiac output and heart rate change in opposite directions on alteration of position, i.e., in the supine position the cardiac output increases and the heart rate decreases. Correspondingly, assuming the upright position is accompanied by a reduction in heart size and stroke volume.

In the resting dog, an increase in venous return induced by a rapid infusion of blood or by displacing blood from the splanchnic area into the thorax by abdominal compression increases the left ventricular dimension without significantly altering stroke volume or stroke work. Excitement or startle or the anticipation of exercise just before treadmill activity can lead to a transitory increase in stroke volume with enlargement of the left ventricle.

Nonexhaustive exercise by healthy dogs and normal untrained supine human subjects may be accompanied by increased cardiac output, primarily resulting from tachycardia with little or no progressive increase in stroke volume as the level of exertion increases. Stroke volume during such exertion may only occasionally exceed the resting recumbent values in healthy dogs or untrained human subjects, although with exercise performed in the upright position (when the resting stroke volume is smaller), a definite increase in stroke volume accompanies the increasing heart rate and cardiac output. Concurrently, the left ventricular dimension of the dog's heart remains the same or becomes smaller. However, trained athletes and patients with chronic volume loads such as in valvular insufficiency may increase cardiac output with a significant augmentation of stroke volume and a lesser degree of tachycardia. The relatively small hearts of untrained persons may show a tendency to reduce their diastolic size during exercise but the end diastolic size of the large hearts of athletes gets much smaller. The larger capacity of athletes, as compared to untrained subjects, for increasing cardiac output during exercise is explained by the larger stroke volume.

As mentioned previously, dogs subjected to total regional cardiac denervation show only a modest rise in heart rate during exercise. Since they are able to raise their cardiac output to a normal extent, this is achieved through augmentation of the stroke volume. Similarly, in dogs with surgically created complete atrioventricular block, whose ventricles are stimulated by an implanted electrical pacemaker, cardiac output remains constant over a wide range of varying heart rates, both at rest and during exercise, indicating a capacity for readjusting the stroke volume to the required flow.

Evidence for increased contractility of the myocardium during exercise is in the increasing rate of tension development, rate of blood ejection and rate of relaxation as seen in the ventricular pressure curves and the aortic flow curves.

The preceding evidence suggests, but does not offer quite certain proof, that the fundamental property of cardiac muscle of a relation between end ventricular diastolic size and energy release is not dominant, but rather that in the normal dog and man, an increase in cardiac output during exercise is achieved mainly by an increase in heart rate with a constant or slightly increased stroke volume. A little reflection will indicate, however, that this is a self-regulating mechanism and cannot alone explain the observed changes in cardiac output. When the heart accelerates, the output per beat can be kept constant only if the venous inflow is adequate; only under such circumstances can the minute volume be increased. If, for example, the beat of the heart has occurred at the end of a period of rapid filling, i.e., before or at the moment that the heart chambers are filled, simply increasing the heart rate will cause the beat to fall earlier in the period of rapid filling. Reduction in the stroke volume in proportion to the increase in rate must result and no increase in the minute volume can, therefore, occur. At very rapid heart rates, as in paroxysmal tachycardia, a point is reached at which the heart does not relax sufficiently between beats to take on an adequate load of blood, and the minute volume is actually reduced.

The contribution which cardiac acceleration can make toward the minute volume is, therefore, strictly limited, for rates from 180 to 200 are about the maximums to which the healthy heart can be speeded up. This is only about $2\frac{1}{2}$ to 3 times the normal rate. With a constant stroke volume, therefore, cardiac acceleration could not increase the minute volume more than about 3 times. Yet reliable data have shown that the cardiac output of untrained man doing strenuous exercise may increase ninefold (from 5 to 6 liters per min. at rest to 35 to 45 liters) and the oxygen consumption 12 times (from 250 cc. oxygen at rest to 3,000 cc.). In this circumstance, it must be concluded that the stroke volume increases 2 to 3 times (even at a maximum pulse rate) to account for up to 50 per cent of the cardiac output increase.

This is borne out by some of the data in table 44.1. The left ventricular response to treadmill exercise of natives of the Morococha, Peru region (elevation 14,900 ft.), and of natives of the Lima, Peru region (elevation 500 ft.), was studied at the elevation where they had always lived. It can be seen that at sea level, on the average, about half the increase in cardiac output comes from an increase in stroke volume from 41 to 75 cc. In one group at Morococha, exercising at a somewhat lower level of treadmill activity (490 to 580 kg.-m.

per min. per m.²), the cardiac output and cardiac work were almost entirely explainable by the increase in heart rate and systemic blood pressure. The data in the second group at Morococha obtained at a higher level of treadmill activity (650 to 749 kg.-m. per min. per m.²) represents an attempt to stress the left ventricle to maximum external effort. Each of the five persons in this group stated at the end of the exercise that he was "completely exhausted." Two of them attained a cardiac output approximating 35 liters per min. and a stroke volume of about 200 cc. On an average, the stroke volume increased from 53 to 88 cc., and accounted for about 66 per cent of the increase in cardiac output.

The preceding also indicates that the cardiac size decreases in exercise. If the ventricle does become smaller during diastole and systole, then the heart must possess an adequate residual volume to effect an increased stroke volume or a constant stroke volume. Presumably, as already pointed out, the human heart at the end of systole contains about 400 cc. blood divided equally among the four cavities. This will give each ventricle a residual volume of 100 cc. in the recumbent position and about 45 cc. in the upright position and which is used as the ventricle becomes smaller with exertion. This diminishes the volume reserve of the ventricles in severe exercise. Presumably, it is replenished during each diastole from the blood volume in the thoracic pool. The mechanisms for this are not understood, but it can be demonstrated that the stroke volume is directly, and the heart rate indirectly, related to the volume of blood in this central compartment. The skeletal muscles of the limbs and abdomen play an important role in translocating blood from the periphery to the central venous pool by their pumping action. In dogs with spinal cord transection, stimulation of the cord below the point of section produces an almost immediate increase in the cardiac output. This can be entirely prevented by blocking skeletal muscular contractions with decamethonium, whereas blockade of the sympathetic ganglia does not prevent the rise in cardiac output. The latter is therefore attributed to skeletal muscular activity, compressing the intramuscular and intraabdominal vessels and enhancing the venous return.

In summary, it can be stated that both changes in stroke volume and heart rate contribute significantly to regulation of cardiac output in man, but no firm conclusion can be drawn as to the relative role that stroke volume, heart rate and diastolic and systolic volumes play under various conditions of stress. Proper understanding will follow the development of adequate methodology for determining cyclic changes in ventricular volume and stroke volume in animals and especially in man.

D. *Body A-VO$_2$ difference.* Since the body oxygen usage can increase 12 times in exercise, it is important to know the mechanisms by which this amount of oxygen is supplied to the tissues. Continuous measurements of A-V O$_2$ difference from the onset of exercise have not yet been made and so it is not known how early these changes occur. The A-V O$_2$ difference is generally calculated from the body oxygen usage divided by the cardiac output, the former being determined by collection and oxygen analysis of the expired air and the cardiac output by the dilution technique, which does not require cardiac catheterization. The oxygen extraction rises but considerably more slowly than does the cardiac output, reaching in very heavy exercise a calculated maximum of 13 to 16 cc. per 100 cc. of blood. Since most of the increase in blood flow is presumably through the exercising muscle, this means that the oxygen extraction at times must be very nearly complete in the latter, a situation similar to that which has been observed in the heart muscle with maximal activity. In well trained subjects, it appears that the rise in A-V O$_2$ difference, as well as heart rate, are somewhat smaller, while the stroke volume is larger.

E. *Other hemodynamic variables in exercise.* In addition to the heart rate and stroke volume alterations occurring in exercise, many other changes are involved which may be mild or almost insignificant in light exercise, or which may be massive in strenuous activity (table 44.1). In the presence of heavy exercise and a very large increase in cardiac output, the CWI of the left ventricle may increase 4 times; the systemic blood pressure may increase considerably; the arterial pressure pulse may increase from 50 to 100 mm. Hg; the total peripheral resistance may decrease greatly. Presumably, the latter results mainly from vasodilation in the metabolically active beds for, since splanchnic blood flow in man is decreased in the presence of an elevated systemic blood pressure, resistance in the splanchnic bed must be increased. In the pulmonary circulation, the arterial pressure rises moderately, while the resistance decreases or undergoes little change. Finally, as pointed out earlier, the central venous, atrial, and ventricular end diastolic pressure do not necessarily increase. The alterations in many

hemodynamic parameters during exercise is indicated in figure 44.4.

The cause, sequence and relative importance of these and other factors in the control of cardiac output during excitement and muscular exercise is still an enigma. Following the discovery of the baroreceptors, it was quite natural that they be invoked as the major mechanism controlling cardiac output during exercise. This was especially felt to be so since, as already mentioned, it has been established experimentally in the dog that if the blood pressure in the carotid sinus is lowered, there results reflexly an increased heart rate, decreased systemic peripheral resistance, increased peripheral venomotor tone, increased cardiac contractility (presumably *via* catecholamine release in the heart) and increased cardiac output. This presupposes a fall in arterial blood pressure caused by the vasodilation in the working muscles as the factor which initiates the hemodynamic changes resulting in an augmented cardiac output. However, intra-arterial blood pressure in man and dog at the transition from rest to work has been shown not to fall and, of course, later in the working period it increases. Another important experiment has indicated that the output of the heart in exercise is not related to the extent of vasodilation for, if pneumatic cuffs are placed on the exercising extremities of man so that about 50 per cent of the working musculature is cut off, the oxygen usage may be halved, but the cardiac output and heart rate are not decreased.

F. *Simulated exercise.* Finally, attempts have been made to simulate in the normal animal the cardiovascular events which are known to occur in exercise with the hope that one might serve as the proper experimental substitute for exercise. These include increased venous return (already considered), decreased peripheral resistance through injection of isoproterenol, injection of autonomic hormones, electrically induced tachycardias at rates existing in exercise, chronic stimulation of the sympathetic nerves to the heart and chronic stimulation of the central nervous system. Left ventricular performance during exercise could be fairly accurately reproduced by isoproterenol infusion and stimulation of the hypothalamic region in the unanesthetized dog.

G. *The role of catecholamines.* The importance of the sympathetic nervous system in the regulation of the heart's performance has already been mentioned on several occasions throughout this section. The effects of sympathetic nerve stimulation are in all likelihood mediated through the

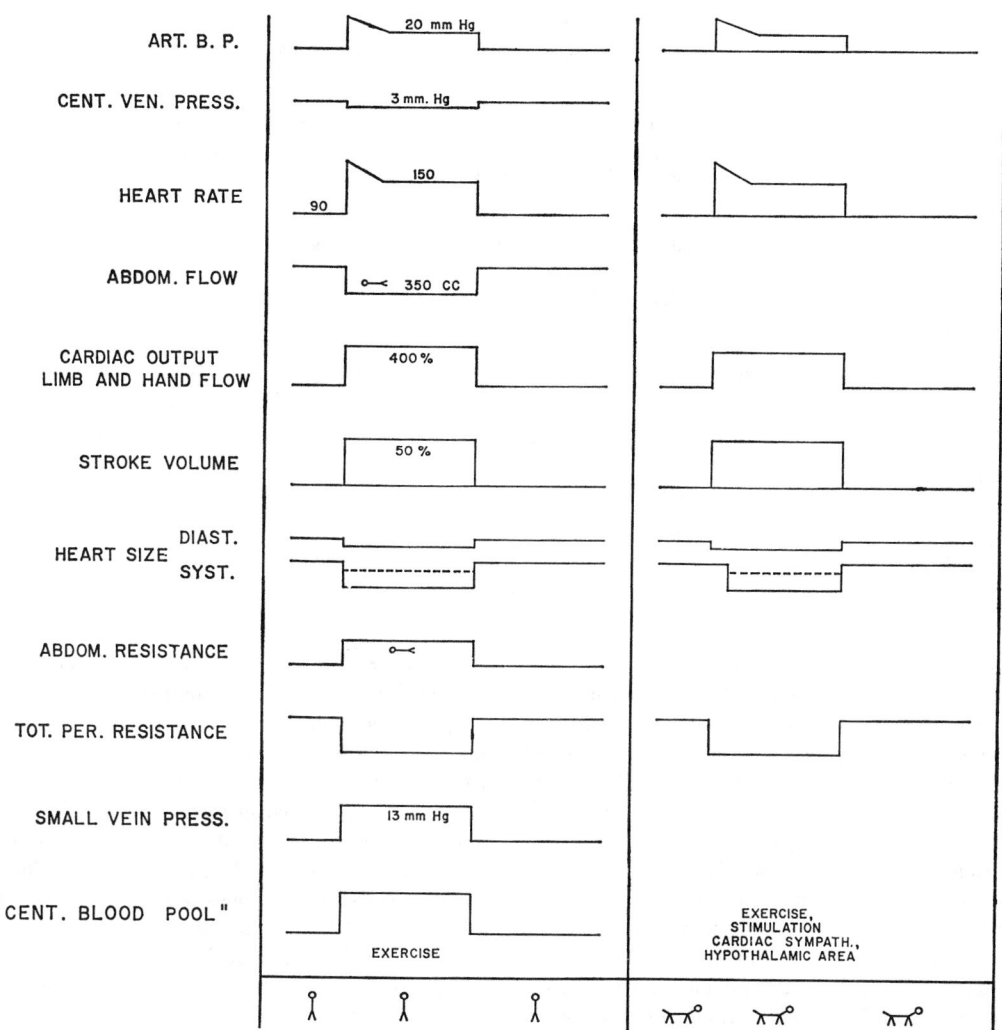

FIG. 44.4. *Left side,* hemodynamic responses in exercising man and *right side,* hemodynamic responses in the unanesthetized dog to exercise to stimulation of the cardiac sympathetic fibers and of the hypothalamic area. Dotted lines represent the less usual responses.

release of norepinephrine from the nerve endings. Evidence for this view may be summarized as follows:

The mammalian heart, including the human, like several other tissues and organs possessing a rich adrenergic innervation, contains significant stores of norepinephrine. The norepinephrine content of the tissues is closely related to the number of adrenergic fibers supplying them. It disappears completely following post-ganglionic sympathetic denervation. Similarly, the administration of reserpine results in practically complete disappearance of norepinephrine from the heart, and, in animals so treated, the positive chronotropic effect of accelerator nerve stimulation is blocked. The cardiac effects of stellate

ganglionic stimulation can be mimicked by norepinephrine infusion. Finally, during stellate ganglionic stimulation, norepinephrine can be recovered from coronary venous blood, in an amount proportional to the intensity of the stimulus.

REGIONAL DISTRIBUTION OF O_2 CONSUMPTION AND BLOOD FLOW. The preceding discussion indicates that despite much study of long familiar functions, their operation in the adjustments of oxygen and cardiac output to exercise is poorly understood. The response of oxygen usage and blood flow, of course, represents the average requirements of organs and regions of the body. At present, adequate knowledge is not available of the allocation of cardiac output in the resting or exercising animal, let alone man. Simultaneous

TABLE 44.2

Distribution of cardiac output and oxygen usage

Region	Weight		Blood Flow			Oxygen Usage			O₂ Extraction	
	Kg.	% Total	L./min.	% Total	cc./100 gm./min.	cc./min.	% Total	cc./100 gm./ min.	Venous O₂ cc./ 100 cc. blood	A-VO₂
Total	70	100	5.4	100		250	100		14.5	4.5
Brain	1.54	2.2	0.83	15	54	63	23	3.7	12.5	6.5
Convulsion			1.15	20	75					
Heart	0.33	0.5	0.22	4	70	23	9	7.0	7	12
Liver, Intestines	2.86	4.0	1.54	29	54	55	20	1.95	15	4.0
Kidney	0.33	0.5	1.43	27	430	20	7	6.0	17	2.0
Skeletal muscle	34.0	50.0	0.92	17	2.7	55	20	0.16	12.5	6.5
Exercise			35.0	80	100	2700	90	7.9	3	16.0

measurements of flow through major regions or organs such as the heart, kidney, brain, liver, intestines, cannot be made in the same person at the same time. Even in the experimental animal, until recently the only method available (based on the dilution principle) involved anesthesia and/or excitement so as to vitiate the interpretation of the findings. The advent of implantable sonar and electromagnetic flowmeters now makes it possible to measure blood flow simultaneously in a limited number of different vascular beds in intact, conscious animals under a variety of physiological conditions. Table 44.2 is presented showing data on distribution of flow and oxygen consumption in resting and exercising man, obtained by different types of measurement by different observers on different subjects. (In some instances, values are extrapolated from animals). The values are certainly not absolute but the general pattern of distribution may be right. The kidney blood flow of 400 cc. per 100 grams of tissue is about 6 times greater than that of any other organ (nearest is the heart with a flow of 70 cc.). The heart per unit of tissue, on the other hand, uses considerably more oxygen than any other organ. Four organs—brain, heart, liver and intestine, and kidney, make up about 7 per cent of body weight but receive 65 to 70 per cent of the output of the heart and account for 60 per cent of the total oxygen used at rest. The skeletal muscles representing 50 per cent of body weight receive only 20 per cent of cardiac output at rest and account for only 15 per cent of body oxygen usage, but

during exercise they may account for 80 to 90 per cent of the oxygen consumption and cardiac output. The brain which is only 2 per cent of body weight requires more than 20 per cent of the total oxygen used by the body and during convulsions (observed in monkeys), this fraction may increase to 40 per cent and the brain fraction of cardiac output from 14 to 20 per cent. Thus, the cardiovascular response is not limited to an adjustment of the cardiac pump, complicated as this may be. Certainly, real changes occur in the distribution of the output of the pump. There is, however, no integrated picture of the circulatory responses that occur and the underlying involvement of the central nervous system and peripheral mechanisms in the allocation of oxygen and cardiac output is unknown.

Cardiac Reserve

HEART RATE, VENTRICULAR VOLUME, BLOOD FLOW, CORONARY VENOUS O₂, VENTRICULAR EFFICIENCY

Present knowledge of the reserves available to the heart to cope with various stress impacts permits little more than their enumeration. The potential reserves are its heart rate, its systolic and diastolic volume, its blood flow, the oxygen content of the body mixed venous blood, the, cardiac work, the changing efficiency of the heart, and possibly the stores of catecholamines.

The reserve in heart rate is about 130 to 140 beats per min., resulting in a maximum heart rate of 210. The reserve in stroke volume is 80 to 100 cc. since each ventricle normally contains about 150 to 170 cc., of which 60 to 70 cc. is ejected during systole. This figure is somewhat lower than the measured figure of 190 cc. for maximum stroke volume in Peruvian natives in the mountains, exercising to exhaustion on a treadmill. Attainment of such an increased stroke volume indicates an increased contractility of the myocardium. The reserve in blood flow approximates 30 liters per min., since maximum cardiac output is about 35 liters per min. in man working to exhaustion, and the resting cardiac output is about 5 liters. The potential reserve of oxygen within the body is about 900 cc. This is based upon the fact the body mixed venous blood contains 15 to 16 cc. oxygen per 100 cc. blood, and the blood volume is 5500 cc. However, neither normal persons nor persons with heart disease utilize this oxygen to the full. With maximum exertion, the oxygen extraction approximates 14 to 16 volumes per cent. This is supplemented by the ability of the human body to take up a maximum of 3000 cc. oxygen per min., or an excess of about 2700 cc. over that in the basal state. The reserve work of the heart is at about 75 kg. per min., since the maximum left ventricle work recorded is about 80 kg. per min., and the resting left ventricle work approximates 5 to 6 kg. per min.

In the whole body, the efficiency value for performing external work is fairly easily obtained by measuring the external work performed by the subject and dividing this by the energy equivalent of the difference between total body oxygen consumption and the oxygen usage of the body during rest. For the beating left ventricle, the efficiency is calculated in a similar way by dividing the external work of the ventricle by the difference between the energy equivalent of its oxygen usage while beating and while at rest. The external work of the ventricle is determined by the method already indicated; the oxygen usage of the left ventricle is determined from the product of coronary blood flow through the left myocardium and the coronary A-V oxygen difference. This is converted to kilogram meters of work per minute by multiplying by 2.057 which is the energy equivalent of 1 cc. oxygen in kg.-m.

Accurate determination of ventricular efficiency in man is not possible since left ventricular weight cannot be determined and, hence, total left ventricular flow is not available. In the unanesthetized dog, efficiencies of 31 per cent are reported. In the anesthetized dog with good cardiac output and systemic blood pressure, efficiencies have been found to vary from 7 to 54 per cent.

By definition, mechanical efficiency is work done per unit of energy output. The work of the heart is performed during the first part of the period of systole, but as in skeletal muscle, energy is released by the heart (oxygen used) when it is doing no work. Oxygen is used before, during, and after ventricular systole. A certain amount of oxygen can be used during the early part of systole from the onset of the elevation of intraventricular pressure to the time of opening of the pulmonary and aortic valves (isometric contraction period) during which time no blood is moved and no external mechanical work is done. Also, during diastole, oxygen can be used but the muscle fibers are relaxed and not shortening. The cardiac efficiency will, therefore, vary in part with the extent of contribution of the oxygen consumption during the resting and isometric contraction periods to the total oxygen usage. In general, the former will tend to lower the calculated efficiency at low levels of work and to increase efficiency as the work is increased.

Published data on myocardial efficiency are of particular interest because they do not include oxygen values for the resting ventricle or ventricle doing no external work. The myocardium takes up considerable oxygen in diastole as well as systole. With our present poor methodology, separation can only be made by measuring oxygen uptake, first in the beating heart during repetitive systoles and diastoles, and then in the relaxed heart or during prolonged diastole, and finally, obtaining the oxygen usage during systole by difference. To do this, the coronary arteries are perfused with blood under constant pressure while coronary A-V oxygen difference and left coronary inflow are measured continuously, first in the beating heart and then in the heart stopped by vagal stimulation until a new equilibrium had been established, usually within 20 to 25 seconds. The resting metabolism (absence of heart rate, blood pressure and cardiac output) during cardiac arrest approximates 2.5 ml. oxygen per 100 grams left ventricle per min., or about 25 to 30 per cent of the value at the prior working level. This value during diastole averages about one-third that during systole for the same time period. These values in the vagal stopped heart have some interesting characteristics. Oxygen uptake is unaffected by ventricular diastolic size. They are not fixed but vary greatly with the control metabolic level in the beating heart before it is stopped.

TABLE 44.3

Effect of oxygen usage in the nonworking left ventricle on the calculated left ventricular efficiency

$$\text{Efficiency} = \frac{\text{Left ventricular work (kg.-m./min.) (100)}}{(\text{Total left ventricular } O_2 \text{ used } - \text{ resting } O_2 \text{ used)} \, 2.057}$$

$$\text{Efficiency} = \frac{1.2 \, (100)}{8.1} = 15\%$$

$$\text{Efficiency} = \frac{1.2 \, (100)}{8.1 - 2.3} = 22\%$$

$$\text{Efficiency} = \frac{1.2 \, (100)}{8.1 - 3.4} = 26\%$$

Under some circumstances, the oxygen usage in the resting heart may equal 50 per cent of that in the beating heart. In addition, in the nonworking but beating heart which has been emptied by hemorrhage and suction, the metabolism of 3.4 ml. per 100 grams of left ventricle per min., is considerably greater than that with vagal asystole. Adjustments of the mechanical efficiency taking into account the usual oxygen usage in the vagal arrested heart and in the beating empty heart, are in table 44.3. The apparent efficiency is increased thereby from an assumed efficiency of 15 per cent to 26 per cent. While it cannot be stated that alteration of the mechanical efficiency by these amounts is correct, the data do emphasize that until the oxygen usage of the myocardium doing no external work is known under various physiological conditions, calculation of or reference to figures for cardiac efficiency is premature.

REFERENCES

BAILIE, M. D., ROBINSON, S., ROSTORFER, H. H., AND NEWTON, J. L. Effects of exercise on heart output of the dog. J. Appl. Physiol., 1961, 16, 107.

BARGER, A. C., RICHARDS, V., METCALFE, J., AND GUNTHER, B. Regulatoin of the circulation during exercise. Cardiac output (direct Fick) and metabolic adjustments in the normal dog. Am. J. Physiol., 1956, 184, 613.

BARRATT-BOYES, G. B. AND WOOD, E. H. Hemodynamic response of healthy subjects to exercise in the supine position while breathing oxygen. J. Appl. Physiol., 1957, 11, 129.

BEATTIE, J., BROW, G. R., AND LONG, C. N. H. Physiological and anatomical evidence for the existence of nerve tracts connecting the hypothalamus with spinal sympathetic centres. Proc. Roy. Soc., 1930, 106B, 253.

BERTLER, A., CARLSSON, A., AND ROSENGREN, E. Release by reserpine of catecholamines from rabbits' hearts. Naturwissenschaften, 1956, 43, 521.

BEVEGÅRD, S., HOLMGREN, A., AND JONSSON, B. The effect of body position on the circulation at rest and during exercise, with special reference to the influence on the stroke volume. Acta Physiol. Scand., 1960, 49, 279.

BEVEGÅRD, S., HOLMGREN, A., AND JONSSON, B. Circulatory studies in well trained athletes at rest and during heavy exercise, with special reference to stroke volume and the influence of body position. Acta Physiol. Scand., 1963, 57, 26.

BRAUNWALD, E., FRAHM, C. J., AND ROSS, J., JR. Studies on Starling's law of the heart. V. Left ventricular function in man. J. Clin. Invest., 1961, 40, 1882.

BRAUNWALD, E., GOLDBLATT, A., HARRISON, D. C., AND MASON, D. T. Studies on cardiac dimensions in intact, unanesthetized man. III. Effects of muscular exercise. Circulation Res., 1963, 13, 448.

BRONK, D. W., FERGUSON, L. K., MARGARIA, R., AND SOLANDT, D. Y. The activity of the cardiac sympathetic centers. Am. J. Physiol., 1936, 117, 237.

CHAPMAN, E. M., KINSEY, D., CHAPMAN, W. P., AND SMITHWICK, R. H. Sympathetic innervation of the heart in man. Preliminary observations of the effect of thoracic sympathectomy on heart rate. J. A. M. A., 1948, 137, 579.

CHAPMAN, C. B., FISHER, J. N., AND SPROULE, B. J. Behavior of stroke volume at rest and during exercise in human beings. J. Clin. Invest., 1960, 39, 1208.

CHIDSEY, C. A., BRAUNWALD, E., MORROW, A. G., AND MASON, D. T. Myocardial norepinephrine concentration in man. Effects of reserpine and congestive heart failure. New Eng. J. Med., 1963, 269, 653.

DEXTER, L., WHITTENHOGER, J. L., HAYNES, F. W., GOODALE, W. T., GORLIN, R., AND SAWYER, C. G. Effect of exercise on circulatory dynamics of normal individuals. J. Appl. Physiol., 1951, 3, 439.

DONALD, K. W., BISHOP, J. M., CUMMING, G., AND WADE, O. L. The effect of exercise on the cardiac output and circulatory dynamics of normal subjects. Clin. Sc., 1955, 14, 37.

DONALD, D. E., AND SHEPHERD, J. T. Response to exercise in dogs with cardiac denervation. Am. J. Physiol., 1963, 205, 393.

VON EULER, U. S. Presence of a sympathomimetic substance in extracts of mammalian heart. J. Physiol., 1946, 105, 38.

FRANKLIN, D. L., ELLIS, R. M., AND RUSHMER,

R. F. Aortic blood flow in dogs during treadmill exercise. J. Appl. Physiol., 1959, 14, 809.

GASSER, H. S. AND MEEK, W. J. A study of the mechanisms by which muscular exercise produces acceleration of the heart. Am. J. Physiol., 1914, 34, 48.

GOODALL, McC. Studies of adrenaline and noradrenaline in mammalian heart and suprarenals. Acta physiol. scandinav., 1951, 24, suppl. 85.

GREEN, H. D. AND HOFF, E. C. Effects of faradic stimulation of the cerebral cortex on limb and renal volumes in the cat and monkey. Am. J. Physiol., 1937, 118, 641.

GUYTON, A. C., DOUGLAS, B. H., LANGSTON, J. B., AND RICHARDSON, T. Q. Instantaneous increase in mean circulatory pressure and cardiac output at onset of muscular activity. Circulation Res., 1962, 11, 431.

HICKHAM, H. D. AND CARGILL, W. H. Effect of exercise on cardiac output and pulmonary artery pressure in normal persons and in patients with cardiovascular disease and pulmonary emphysema. J. Clin. Invest., 1948, 27, 10.

HOLMGREN, A., JONSSON, B., AND SJÖSTRAND, T. Circulatory data in normal subjects at rest and during exercise in recumbent position, with special reference to the stroke volume at different work intensities. Acta Physiol. Scand., 1960, 49, 343.

HOLT, J. P., RHODE, E. A., AND KINES, H. Pericardial and ventricular pressure. Circulation Res., 1960, 8, 1171.

MARSHALL, R. J., WANG, Y., SEMLER, H. J., AND SHEPHERD, J. T. Flow, pressure and volume relationships in the pulmonary circulation during exercise in normal dogs and dogs with divided left pulmonary artery. Circulation Res., 1961, 9, 53.

McKEEVER, W. P., GREGG, D. E., AND CANNEY, P. C. Oxygen uptake of the nonworking left ventricle. Circulation Res., 1958, 6, 612.

McMICHAEL, J. AND SHARPEY-SCHAFER, E. P. Cardiac output in man by direct Fick method; effects of posture, venous pressure change, atropine and adrenaline. Brit. Heart J., 1945, 6, 33.

MILLER, F. R. AND BOWMAN, J. T. The cardioinhibitory center. Am. J. Physiol., 1915, 39, 149.

MURPHY, Q. The influence of the accelerator nerves on the basal heart rate of the dog. Amer. J. Physiol., 1942, 137, 727.

NAHAS, G. G. AND CAVERT, H. M. Cardiac depressant effect of CO_2 and its reversal. Am. J. Physiol., 1957, 190, 483.

NONIDEZ, J. F. The structure and innervation of the conductive system of the heart of the dog and rhesus monkey as seen with a silver impregnation technique. Am. Heart J., 1943, 26, 577.

PATTERSON, S. W., PIPER, H., AND STARLING, E. H. The regulation of the heart beat. J. Physiol., 1914, 48, 465.

RICHARDSON, D. W., WASSERMAN, A. J., AND PATTERSON, J. L., JR. General and regional circulatory responses to change in blood pH and carbon dioxide tension. J. Clin. Invest., 1961, 40, 31.

RILEY, R. L., HIMMELSTEIN, A., MATLEY, H. L., WEINER, H. M., AND COURNAND, A. Studies of the pulmonary circulation at rest and during exercise in normal individuals and in patients with chronic pulmonary disease. Am. J. Physiol., 1948, 152, 372.

ROTTA, A., CANEPA, A., HURTADO, A., VELASQUEZ, T., AND CHANEZ, R. Pulmonary circulation at sea level and at high altitudes. J. Appl. Physiol., 1956, 9, 328.

RUSHMER, R. F. Postural effects on the baselines of ventricular performance. Circulation, 1959, 20, 897.

RUSHMER, R. F., FRANKLIN, D. L., VAN CITTERS, R. L., AND SMITH, O. A. Changes in peripheral blood flow distribution in healthy dogs. Circulation Res., 1961, 9, 675.

RUSHMER, R. F., SMITH, D. A., AND FRANKLIN, D. Mechanisms of cardiac control in exercise. Circulation Res., 1959, 7, 602.

RUSHMER, R. F. Constancy of stroke volume in ventricular responses to exertion. Am. J. Physiol., 1959, 196, 745.

SARNOFF, S. J. AND BERGLUND, B. Ventricular function. I. Starling's law of the heart studied by means of simultaneous right and left ventricular function curves in the dog. Circulation, 1954, 9, 706.

SARNOFF, S. J. Certain aspects of the role of catecholamines in circulatory regulation. Am. J. Cardiol., 1960, 5, 579.

SARNOFF, S. J., CASE, R. B., WELCH, G. A., BRAUNWALD, E., AND STAINSHY, W. H. Performance characteristics and oxygen debt in a non-failing metabolically supported, isolated heart preparation. Am. J. Physiol., 1958, 192, 141.

SARNOFF, S. J., BROCKMAN, S. K., GILMORE, J. P., LINDEN, R. J., AND MITCHELL, J. H. Regulation of ventricular contraction. Influence of cardiac sympathetic and vagal nerve stimulation on atrial and ventricular dynamics. Circulation Res., 1960, 8, 1108.

SIEGEL, J. H., GILMORE, J. P., AND SARNOFF, S. J. Myocardial extraction and production of catechol amines. Circulation Res., 1961, 9, 1336.

STARLING, E. H. AND VISSCHER, M. B. Regulation of energy output of the heart. J. Physiol., 1927, 62, 243.

THIELEN, E. O., GREGG, D. E., AND ROTTA, A. Exercise and cardiac work response at high altitude. Circulation, 1955, 12, 383.

WANG, S. C. AND CHAI, C. Y. Central control of sympathetic cardio-acceleration in medulla oblongata of the cat. Amer. J. Physiol., 1962, 202, 31.

WANG, Y., MARSHALL, R. J., AND SHEPHERD, J. T. Stroke volume in the dog during graded exercise. Circulation Res., 1960, 8, 558.

WARNER, H. R. AND TORONTO, A. F. Regulation of cardiac output through stroke volume. Circulation Res., 1960, 8, 549.

WENGER, M. A., BAGCHI, B. K., AND ANAND, B. K. Experiments in India on "voluntary" control of the heart and pulse. Circulation, 1961, 24, 1319.

WIGGERS, C. J. AND KATZ, L. N. Contour of the ventricular volume curves under different conditions. Am. J. Physiol., 1922, 58, 439.

Monographs and Reviews

ASMUSSEN, E. AND NIELSEN, M. Cardiac output during muscular work and its regulation. Physiol. Rev., 1955, **35,** 778.

BEST, C. H. AND TAYLOR, N. B. Physiological Basis of Medical Practice, Ed. 6, 1955.

BING, R. J. AND MICHEL, G. Myocardial efficiency in metabolic factors in cardiac contractility. Ann. New York Acad. Sci., 1959, **72,** 555.

GREGG, D. E., SABISTON, D. C., AND THEILEN, E. O. Performance of the heart: changes in left ventricular end-diastolic pressure and stroke work during infusion and following exercise. Physiol. Rev., 1955, **35,** 130.

GREGG, D. E. Homeostasis of the arterial circulation. First International Symposium on Submarine and Space Medicine, New London, Connecticut, 1958.

HAMILTON, W. F. The Lewis A. Connor memorial lecture. The Physiology of the Cardiac Output. Circulation, 1953, **8,** 527.

KATZ, L. N., SARNOFF, S. J., GUYTON, A. C., GREGG, D. E., SABISTON, D. C., THEILEN, E. O., LORBER, V., RUSHMER, R. F., GAUER, O. H., RICHARDS, D. W., AND HAMILTON, W. F. Symposium on the regulation of the performance of the heart. Physiol. Rev., 1955, **35,** 91.

MARSHALL, R. J., AND SHEPHERD, J. T. Exercise and the circulation. Circulation, 1963, **27,** 323.

PICKERING, G. Starling and the concept of heart failure. Circulation, 1960, **21,** 323.

RUSHMER, R. F. AND SMITH, O. A. Cardiac control. Physiol. Rev., 1959, **39,** 41.

SCHMIDT, C. F. The adjustment of oxygen supply to oxygen demand in organs. Symposium on Stress. Army Medical Service Graduate School, WRAMC, 1953.

STARLING, E. H. Linacre lecture on law of the heart. Longmans, Green & Company, Inc., Cambridge, 1915; New York, 1918.

WIGGERS, C. J. Determinants of cardiac performance. Circulation, 1951, **4,** 485.

CHAPTER 45

The Coronary Circulation

General Consideration

Beginning with Harvey in the seventeenth century, the anatomical and dynamic details of this system have been gradually elucidated.

ANATOMICAL

Two coronary arteries, the right and left, carry blood to the myocardium. About 2 mm. from its ostium, the left coronary artery divides into the left circumflex and the anterior descendens branches. The former runs in the atrioventricular (A-V) groove to the left, ending in a posterior descending branch. The anterior descending branch runs downward in the interventricular groove toward the apex. Near its origin, septal branches are given off. The right coronary descends in the right (A-V) sulcus and ends posteriorly as several descending branches on the right and left ventricles. The subdivisions of the main coronary rami descend superficially in the general direction of the apex and give off myocardial branches which course directly into the ventricular muscle. At or near the apex, where the superficial muscles form a spiral and penetrate to form the innermost (subendocardial) layer of muscle, the terminal coronary arteries go along with the muscle to supply the inner layer of both ventricles and the papillary muscles. Anatomical studies in both the dog and human heart indicate that vessel branching within the myocardium is related to muscle bundles, but numerous communications exist between the different muscle layers.

As in any other vascular system, each of the two coronary arteries connects with its capillary bed, its superficial myocardial venous bed, and eventually with the right atrium (fig. 45.1). The epicardial branches of the coronary arteries and coronary veins also anastomose with each other and with extracardiac arteries and veins. There are numerous arteriovenous shunts. In addition to these pathways, the arterioles as well as the capillaries and superficial veins connect directly with both ventricular cavities by discrete, deep drainage channels, the arterioluminal, the arteriosinusoidal, and the Thebesian vessels which together comprise the deep coronary drainage circuit.

In man, approximately 50 per cent of hearts have the right coronary artery predominant; 30 per cent have a balanced coronary circulation; and 20 per cent have the left coronary artery predominant. The arterial pattern of the dog heart contrasts with the situation in man. In the dog, the left coronary artery nourishes about 85 per cent of the heart muscle, supplying the whole of the left heart as well as portions of the right ventricle.

PREPARATION AND METHODOLOGY

The objective of studies of the coronary circulation is knowledge of the determinants of coronary flow, of the oxygen uptake (coronary flow times the coronary arteriovenous oxygen difference) by the myocardium, and of their relation to the work of the heart in states of normalcy, of increased or decreased stress, and of disease in man. This objective is far from being realized.

The Pitot tube, orifice meter, rotameter, bubble flowmeter, and thermostromuhr are used to measure coronary flow by insertion between the cut ends of a coronary vessel. The thermostromuhr also measures flow in the intact coronary artery. The electromagnetic flowmeter has also been used successfully to quantitate coronary flow in the anesthetized (resting) and unanesthetized (resting and exercising) dog. In addition, the nitrous oxide method can be used in the normal dog and human being and, if used with care, reasonably accurate values can be obtained. Derivation of the coronary blood flow from indicator-dilution cardiac output curves (dye or radioisotope) has proved impractical since accurate definition of the component of the curve representing coronary blood flow cannot be made. Several methods have been studied utilizing radioactive substances and the Fick principle (injection of radioisotope intravenously, into a coronary artery or the left ventricle, with precordial counting and/or collection of samples from the coronary sinus, or measurement of radioactivity of excised heart muscle). The methods involving the myocardial uptake of a radioisotope and the technique using the rate of disappearance of a radioisotope injected into the myocardium need further experimental sub-

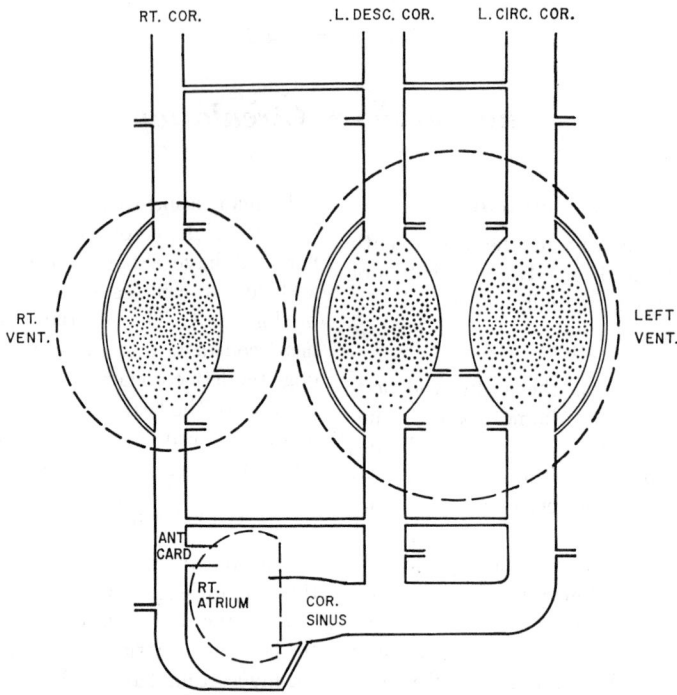

FIG. 45.1. Schematic representation of the coronary circulation. The areas enclosed within the circles depict the capillary beds, collateral communications and A-V shunts (Gregg and Sabiston, Circulation, 1956, 13, 916).

stantiation. In studies comparing the myocardial radioisotope uptake technique with direct methods of measuring flow and with the nitrous oxide method, the correlations are good. All except the bubble flowmeter, nitrous oxide, and radioisotope methods permit continuous recording of flow. All measure mean flow; the orifice meter, Pitot tube, and electromagnetic flow meter can be used for recording phasic flow. The oxygen saturation of coronary arterial and venous blood is obtained by continuous withdrawal of aliquots of blood (through indwelling tubes) and their analyses by the Van Slyke, Beckman, or oximeter techniques. The first two methods give average oxygen values over a period of time; the last permits continuous recording of the arteriovenous oxygen difference.

UTILIZATION OF THE SUPERFICIAL VERSUS THE DEEP DRAINAGE CIRCUITS IN THE NORMAL HEART. Venous drainage of the left coronary artery inflow is divided among three routes. Balance studies of coronary inflow and outflow have shown that most of the blood entering the left coronary artery drains into the coronary sinus. Studies using an isotope dilution technique demonstrated direct right ventricular drainage from the septal artery and direct left atrial drainage of the left anterior atrial artery, a branch of the left circumflex ar-

tery. These studies show that deep drainage channels account for approximately 15 per cent of the total left coronary artery inflow. A small portion of left coronary inflow is recovered in the superficial (anterior cardiac) veins of the right myocardium that drain into the right atrium. Most of the right coronary artery inflow appears in these anterior cardiac veins and the remainder (10 to 20 per cent) drains into the coronary sinus. Presumably a similar utilization of anatomical pathways exists in man. In man, it is reported that 16 per cent of left coronary flow enters the left ventricular cavity by the deep drainage channels. This has not yet been confirmed.

The deep drainage channels could have an important functional role if they served as arterial channels from the left ventricle to the myocardium during coronary artery constriction or occlusion, or as venous channels for the whole myocardium in the presence of extensive superficial vein constriction or occlusion. Regarding the first situation, essentially complete occlusion of the coronary arteries has been found at autopsy in patients who died from causes other than heart disease; however, the contribution of extracardiac arterial collaterals to the myocardial blood supply is not known. With functional separation of one or both coronary arteries from the aorta, no blood flow from the ventricles into the superficial coronary venous system can be demonstrated and the hearts do not survive. Regarding the second situation with acute closure of all visible superficial coronary veins, although such hearts may survive, large intra- and extracardiac superficial venous channels quickly appear. Hence, any conclusion regarding the utilization of deep coronary venous drainage channels in diseased hearts is difficult.

USE OF LEFT CORONARY ARTERY FLOW TOGETHER WITH THE CHEMICAL COMPOSITION OF CORONARY SINUS BLOOD AS AN INDEX OF LEFT VENTRICULAR METABOLISM. It is not possible to quantitate accurately the metabolism of the right ventricle in the dog because its superficial anterior cardiac veins have many exits into the right atrium and because their contained blood is grossly contaminated by blood from the left coronary artery. However, a large percentage of the drainage of the left myocardium is accessible. In most instances quantitative changes in the metabolism of the left ventricle can be obtained from measurement of the chemical composition of the coronary sinus blood together with measurement of the left coronary inflow. This is because: (1) coronary sinus blood is almost entirely from the left coronary artery; (2) by means of a special cannula which permits collection of all blood draining into the coronary sinus, the percentage of left coronary artery inflow recovered in the coronary sinus is quite high (80 to 90 per cent) and reasonably constant during the induction of a variety of physiological variables and drug injections; (3) the O_2 content of the venous blood from the left coronary artery not draining into the coronary sinus is generally only slightly less than that in the coronary sinus. These are very important and practical considerations because of the widespread use of these measurements in man and dog for just this purpose.

BASAL DATA. In the resting state, the coronary data for dog and man agree. With the left ventricular cardiac work index approximately 3.5 to 4.6 kg.-M./min./M², left coronary flow approximates 72 to 85 ml. per 100 grams of left ventricle per minute. In anesthetized and unanesthetized dogs, under stress conditions, values as high as 600 ml. per 100 g. of left ventricle per minute have been recorded. Although the heart can remove essentially all oxygen from the coronary blood in its passage through the myocardium, normally about two-thirds is extracted with an arteriovenous difference of 12 to 14 ml. and a coronary sinus value of 4 to 5 ml. per 100 ml. of

blood. This extraction changes little with increased stress, signifying that the oxygen supply is well balanced with metabolic demands.

Oxygen uptake per 100 grams of left ventricle is 8 to 10 ml. per minute. Oxygen consumption during systole averages about 3 times that in diastole.

MYOCARDIAL RESPONSE TO ANOXIA. The coronary vascular bed is very reactive to the stimulus of anoxia; occlusion of a cornary artery for as short a time as 5 seconds is followed by a temporary increase in blood flow. Reactive hyperemia is considered to be the excess blood flow (over the control flow that normally would have occurred) which follows release of an arterial occlusion (fig. 45.2). The amount and duration of the reactive hyperemic blood flow increase with lengthening periods of left circumflex artery occlusion up to 120 sec.; peak flows also increase but to a lesser degree. The theoretical blood flow "debt" (control blood flow multiplied by the duration of occlusion) is usually greatly overpaid. Reactive hyperemia in skeletal muscle vascular beds shows these same characteristics except the blood flow "debt" is variably under or overpaid (ch. 46). Coronary vasodilator agents do not consistently affect myocardial reactive hyperemia while Pitressin usually decreases the response.

The oxygen consumption during myocardial reactive hyperemia is measured by determining the left coronary artery blood flow (rotameter) and the oxygen saturation of the arterial and coronary sinus blood (measured continuously with a densitometer). The theoretical oxygen "debt" (control oxygen consumption times duration of left coronary artery occlusion) is overpaid for 15- and 30-second, but slightly underpaid for 10-second occlusions. In contrast to skeletal muscle, where the arteriovenous oxygen (A-V O_2) difference increases during reactive hyperemia, the myocardial A-V O_2 difference decreases during the period of increased blood flow. The rate of oxygen consumption during the increased blood flow period is greater than in the control state, showing that the myocardium has been stimulated to take up more oxygen. The basic hypothesis governing the calculation of the oxygen "debt" in these studies is erroneous, for the oxygen in the blood in the coronary vascular bed during arterial occlusion, the metabolic rate during the circulatory stasis, and changes in cardiac work are not considered. These errors would lead to overestimation of the oxygen debt and underestimation of the repayment. As further evidence that the myocardium develops an oxygen deficit, i.e., anaerobic

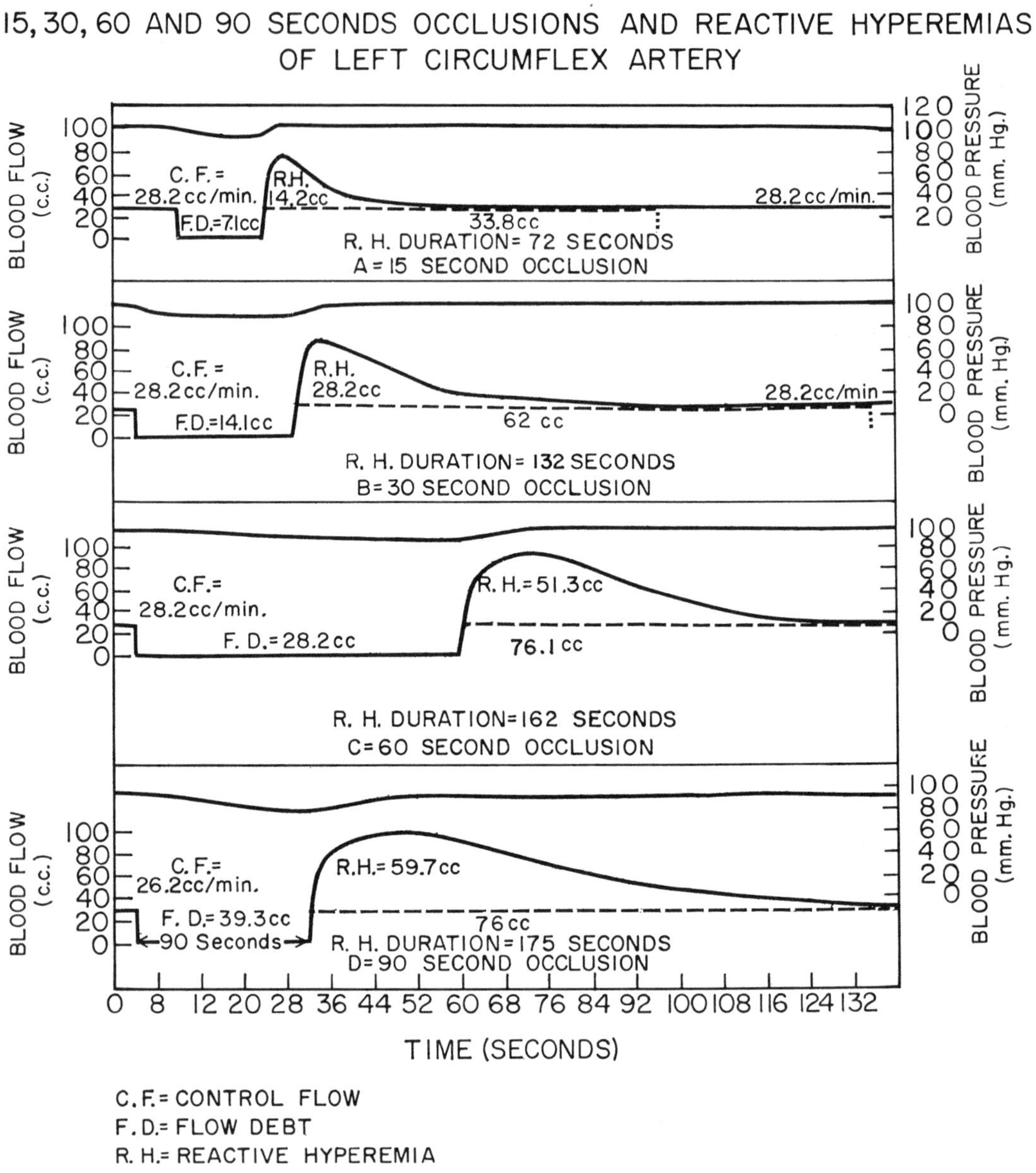

15, 30, 60 AND 90 SECONDS OCCLUSIONS AND REACTIVE HYPEREMIAS OF LEFT CIRCUMFLEX ARTERY

C.F. = CONTROL FLOW
F.D. = FLOW DEBT
R.H. = REACTIVE HYPEREMIA

Fig. 45.2. Myocardial response to anoxia. Tracings redrawn from original experiment (Coffman, and Gregg, Am. J. Physiol., 1960, 199, 1143).

metabolism occurs, it was found that lactic acid often increases in the coronary sinus blood in comparison to pyruvic acid levels, following the period of anoxia. Using the coronary sinus lactate to pyruvate ratio to reflect the state of oxidation of DPN, it has been demonstrated that anaerobic metabolism occurs in canine cardiac tissue during moderate muscular exercise and when breathing 10 per cent oxygen in nitrogen.

The *contracting* myocardium cannot withstand as long periods of arterial occlusion and oxygen deficit as *resting* skeletal muscle, and repays its oxygen "debt" with an increased blood flow but a decreased A-V oxygen difference

The Determinants of Coronary Flow

Consideration of the mechanisms that control the blood supply to the myocardium involves certain difficulties not encountered in similar investigations in other organs of the body. The myocardial wall of the left ventricle not only furnishes the pressure head for driving blood into the coronary arteries but also may either offer phasic resistance to coronary flow or actually aid flow by its muscular contraction around the coronary vascular bed. Similarly, the right ventricle rapidly changes resistance to right coronary flow at the same time that left ventricular contraction presents blood to it under a pulsatile head of pressure. However, coronary flow is related to the pressure difference (effective pressure) between the central coronary artery (identical to aortic pressure) and the right atrium divided by the sum of the viscous resistances to flow in the epicardial portion of the artery and in the peripheral coronary bed. Viscous resistance to flow (aside from change in hematocrit) is mainly governed by the mean caliber of the coronary vascular bed. The mean coronary diameter and, hence, flow are controlled by the effective intravessel pressure and by two peripheral mechanisms, i.e., active changes in the state of the small mass of intravascular smooth muscle built into the coronary vessels, and the mechanical or passive effect on flow exerted during ventricular systole by the large muscle mass around the coronary vessels. The peripheral mechanisms are

regarded as more important in controlling coronary flow than the central coronary or aortic pressure which does not change greatly even in exercise. It is estimated that doubling the aortic pressure might double the coronary flow, but doubling the average radius of the coronary bed might increase coronary flow about 16 times.

Insight into the complexity of the integrating action of these three flow determinants has been obtained from recording of the peripheral coronary pressure and the phasic, or moment-to-moment changes, in coronary inflow and outflow in the epicardial arteries and veins (fig. 45.3). At the onset of isometric contraction of the left ventricle, there is an abrupt decrease in left coronary inflow (*solid line*) or even the appearance of backflow. With the rise in aortic pressure, forward flow increases initially and rapidly, only to decrease to a new intermediate level in late systole. With the onset of isometric relaxation, coronary flow increases significantly, peaking at early diastole and then declining progressively

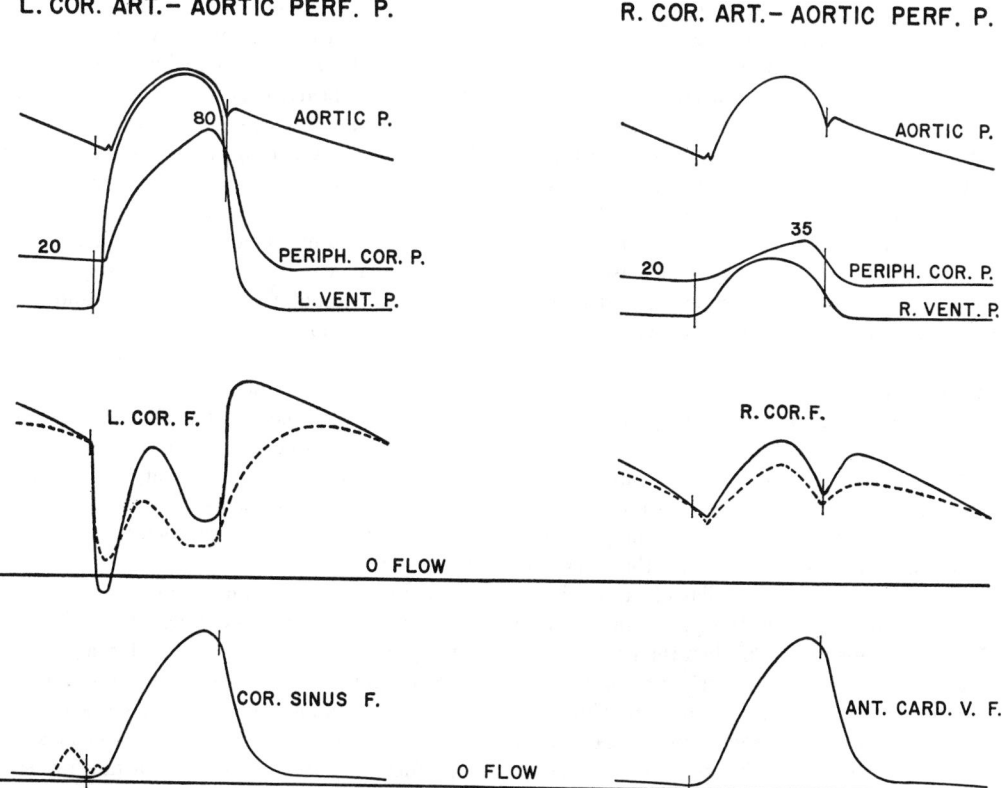

FIG. 45.3. Series of curves relating phasic variations in left and right coronary inflow and coronary sinus-anterior cardiac vein outflow to aortic pressure, ventricular pressure and peripheral coronary pressure. Coronary inflow (*solid lines*) and anterior coronary vein flow obtained with orifice meter, coronary sinus flow with pitot tube. *Broken lines*, estimated intramural velocity curves. (Gregg, D. E. Coronary Circulation. Encyclopedia of Cardiology, Vol. 1, Ch. 23, McGraw-Hill-Blakiston, New York, 1959).

The velocity of coronary inflow differs somewhat from the estimated intramyocardial flow (*dotted line*). The deficit during isometric contraction is caused by the compressing action of the myocardium on the coronary capillaries, forcing blood into the superficial vessels. Early in the period of ejection, the flow excess is caused by the uptake of blood in the superficial coronary arteries; in diastole, the excess is caused by the uptake of blood to fill the previously compressed capillaries. These demarcations of flow are much less obvious in the right coronary inflow pattern, which roughly resembles the prevailing aortic pressure curve. Thus, blood is flowing through the myocardium throughout the cardiac cycle, except possibly for a brief period in early systole in the left coronary artery. In the left coronary artery, the systolic rate of flow is less than that during diastole; in the right coronary artery, the systolic rate equals or exceeds the diastolic. In contrast to the left coronary inflow pattern, the flow curves in the coronary sinus and anterior cardiac veins rise and fall smoothly, with most flow occurring during systole and very little during diastole. In unanesthetized dogs, using electromagnetic flowmeters, data have been obtained clarifying left coronary blood flow during systole and diastole. In the resting dog, left coronary inflow during systole was 15 to 60 per cent of diastolic inflow. Under stress conditions (during excitement, chronic cardiac sympathetic nerve stimulation, or irreversible hemorrhagic shock), both the systolic and diastolic flow per heart beat increased by 300 to 400 per cent, the ratio between them remaining the same, approaching unity, or even reversing, so that systolic flow surpassed diastolic flow. Thus the strong contractions of the left ventricle, although impeding coronary flow, permit a large, but variable, systolic flow.

The preceding account indicates that the coronary bed has a fluctuating resistance to coronary flow. For the left coronary artery, the peripheral intracoronary pressure values at the height of systole and the low point of diastole approximate 80 and 20 mm. Hg, respectively, and inflow is cut off at these pressure levels when the left coronary artery is perfused under constant pressure. In the right coronary artery, the contour and time relations of the peripheral coronary pressure curve are similar, but the values for systole and diastole and for the cutoff of flow are considerably lower.

Elevation of right atrial pressure must increase coronary venous pressure and decrease the flow of blood in the coronary arteries provided no compensatory mechanisms set in. Such studies have not been made. However, mild elevation of the pressure in the coronary veins draining the left coronary artery, by coronary sinus constriction, may decrease coronary flow and increase coronary arteriovenous oxygen difference only slightly. Even marked constriction, or clamping, of the coronary sinus may cause only moderate reduction in arterial pressure and left coronary flow. The smallness of the effect on coronary flow, despite elevation at times of the coronary venous pressure to near aortic systolic level, is presumably caused by the compensatory increased functioning of collateral venous communications with the anterior cardiac veins, in which flow increases considerably. Similarly, right coronary inflow is not greatly reduced by clamping most of the anterior cardiac veins, presumably for the same reason.

The relation of coronary perfusion pressure to coronary flow (P/CF) is generally such that the calculated coronary resistance decreases as the coronary flow rises. This holds for almost any dynamic state of the coronary system (excised fibrillating or beating heart, heart *in situ*) and also exists in the pulmonary artery, peripheral vascular beds, and in an artificial set of rigid tubes. In the heart, it is impossible to say what fraction of the flow change is caused by passive dilation from the perfusion pressure per se, since the oxygen consumption per minute and per heart beat is elevated without any other observable systemic dynamic change. Accordingly, if a physiological variable alters coronary pressure and flow by about the same amount and hence the ratio is unaltered, it is impossible to know whether the change in coronary flow is due to a change in effective head of pressure alone or whether the variable directly affected resistance. However, a gross change in the vasomotor state of the bed occurs when coronary flow changes considerably with a constant pressure, or when flow and pressure change considerably in opposite directions.

Separation and quantitation of the determinants of coronary flow lying within the myocardial wall, i.e., the intravascular and extravascular muscle, are of extreme importance. To do this, continuous measurements are made in the open-chest dog while the left coronary artery is perfused with blood under a constant pressure; first it is done in the beating heart, and then during ventricular asystole induced by vagal stimulation or by disconnecting an external pacemaker which drives the ventricles, the latter manifesting complete atrioventricular heart block which had been surgically produced earlier. By either means, the mechanical effects of ventricular contraction are largely removed. Figure 45.4 illustrates that induction of ventricular asystole by vagal stimulation always increases immediately (within 1 second) left and right coronary inflow, in this instance from 56 to 78 and from 9 to 11 cc. per minute respectively. Thus, ventricular contraction acts to impede coronary flow through the ventricular wall. The extent of the rise of flow is taken to represent the magnitude of the mechanical or passive factors limiting coronary flow. The magnitude of this mechanical throttling effect on coronary flow during systole normally varies from 31 to 300 per cent and averages about 50 per cent. The new flow level represents that state of coronary dilation related to the condition of the intrinsic smooth muscle of the coronary vessels at the prevailing coronary pressure. The relative contribution of extravascular and intravascular resistance to an increase of coronary flow has been tested under the different conditions of increasing heart rate, decreased arterial blood oxygen saturation, aortic constriction, transfusion and drug injections. In all instances, the major portion of a flow increase is through active dilation and not through reduction in extravascular resistance. The largest reduction (40 per cent) in extravascular resistance came from a decrease in arterial oxygen saturation.

Determinants of Normal Cardiac Metabolism

METABOLIC PATTERNS IN THE HEART. The ability of the heart to do work depends basically on its biochemical activity leading to muscular contraction. Cardiac muscle has been found to have basic chemical patterns similar to those of skeletal muscle. The catabolism of fat, carbohydrate and protein produces free energy, about half of which is dissipated as heat and half is captured as phosphate bond energy which is used for muscle cell work and for various anabolic activities such as synthesis of glycogen, lipids, proteins and enzymes. These catabolic and anabolic reactions proceed simultaneously under the influence of a complex system of enzymes, coenzymes (from the vitamin B complex), and hormones.

Coronary sinus catheterization studies in man and dog have indicated that the heart is able to choose its fuel from a variety of foodstuffs. These include mainly glucose, lactate, pyruvate, esterified and nonesterified fatty acids and, to a lesser extent, acetate, ketone bodies and amino acids.

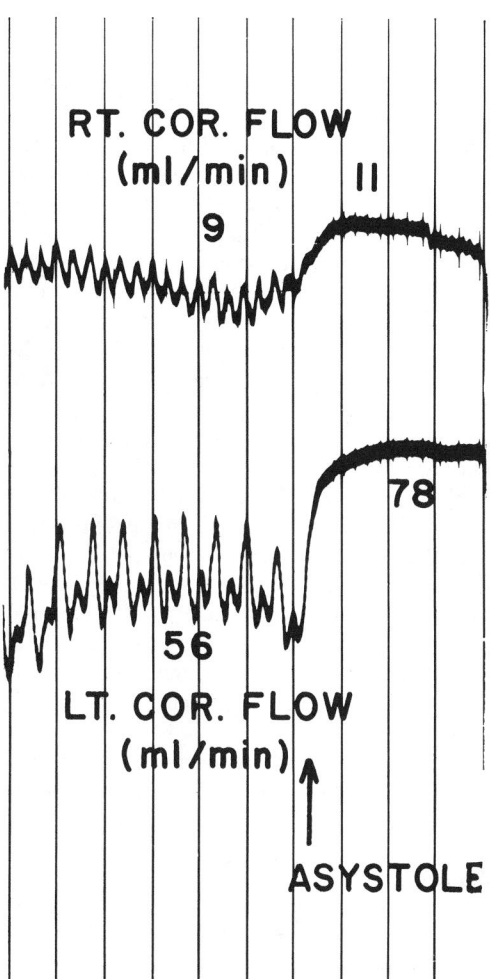

FIG. 45.4. Response of left and right coronary flow to vagal induced asystole. Note the prompt increase with the induction of asystole. Time lines are 1 sec. apart. (Sabiston and Gregg, Circulation, 1957, **15**, 14.)

To determine their quantitative contribution to the energy production of the heart, i.e., its oxygen consumption, measurements have been made of their cardiac extraction (coronary artery − coronary sinus difference), their total uptake [coronary flow times (coronary artery − coronary sinus difference of substance)], and the myocardial respiratory quotient (coronary sinus − arterial carbon dioxide difference) divided by (coronary artery − coronary sinus oxygen difference). Excellent correlation has been demonstrated between the myocardial respiratory quotient and the myocardial uptake of substance. The extent to which each substrate contributes to the energy requirement of the heart *in vivo* is influenced by its concentration (above threshold) in arterial blood. In addition, the state of nutrition of the organism markedly influences the kind of substrate used for energy production of the heart. Under postprandial conditions, or after glucose infusion, myocardial metabolism is mainly glucose, lactate and pyruvate, since its respiratory quotient approximates 0.9 with a high extraction of carbohydrate and a negligible uptake of amino acids. Even the substitution of 5 to 10 per cent oxygen for the normal 21 per cent in the inspirated air does little to change carbohydrate uptake by the normal heart. During overnight fasting, the heart derives much of its energy from fat, as indicated by a myocardial respiratory quotient of 0.8 with a low extraction and uptake of carbohydrate. With prolonged fasting, the extraction coefficient for carbohydrate practically disappears, those for fatty acids and ketones are maximal, and the respiratory quotient is 0.7. As regards the uptake of oxygen, the coronary A-V O_2 differences in man vary linearly with the arterial oxygen content through a range from mild anemia to marked polycythemia, so that the myocardial extraction coefficient $(A-V)/(A)$ is constant.

In addition to patterns of myocardial metabolism in the normal heart, other metabolic changes have been reported in some pathological and diseased states. Patients with heart failure and decreased cardiac work due to valvular disease show an increased carbohydrate uptake by the heart with a normal extraction of lactate and pyruvate and increased glucose extraction. The heart in the patient with diabetes mellitus, even in mild cases, appears to derive most of its energy from fat with a postabsorptive respiratory quotient of about 0.7, an increased uptake of fatty acids and a decreased carbohydrate uptake.

Thus, the heart demonstrates broad flexibility in the utilization of substrate for energy production without a change in work performance or work capacity. This makes it largely independent of fluctuations in its chemical environment. There is no evidence that substrate lack occurs in any clinical situation to the extent that it embarrasses the cardiac work capacity. Similarly, the metabolic disturbances such as diabetes mellitus which alter the fuel mixture available to the heart do not also alter cardiac function. It is, however, well to defer detailed consideration of other data because an interpretation must be based on the assumption that oxidation of foodstuffs to carbon dioxide and water is the sole factor in the determination of the myocardial respiratory quotient and of the myocardial extraction and uptake of

these compounds including oxygen. Without doubt, storage of and/or conversion into other compounds is occurring concurrently, and these activities are especially prominent in the presence of a changing cardiac level of activity or changing levels of blood substrate.

DETERMINANTS OF O_2 USAGE OF THE MYOCARDIUM. Our knowledge is only sufficient to introduce the subject. With present poor methodology, separation can be made only by measuring oxygen uptake, first in the beating heart during repetitive systoles and diastoles, and then in the relaxed heart or during prolonged diastole and, finally, obtaining the oxygen usage during systole by subtraction. Estimation of the metabolism of the myocardium in the absence of a heart beat, that is, during prolonged diastole, has been made in the vagal arrested heart as previously described under determinants of coronary flow. The oxygen saturation of the arterial blood and coronary sinus blood is also measured continuously. This permits left coronary arteriovenous oxygen differences as well as coronary inflow to be measured continuously first in the beating heart and then in the stopped heart until a new equilibrium is established, usually within 20 to 25 seconds.

Typical results are shown in figure 45.5. As coronary inflow rises immediately with asystole from 70 to 90 ml. per minute, the oxygen saturation of blood in the coronary sinus also rises from a low control value of 44 per cent to a very high value of 81 per cent, thus greatly reducing the coronary arteriovenous oxygen difference. The O_2 usage at rest is 35 per cent of that in the beating heart. Calculations in many experiments show that as the result of the combination of increased coronary flow and decreased coronary arteriovenous oxygen difference, the average oxygen usage per 100 grams of left ventricle per min. decreases from the average control level of 8.1 in the beating heart to 2.3 ml. in the resting heart. Individual values for the resting heart range from 1.0 to 4.0 ml. This oxygen consumption in diastole is about one-third that in systole for an equivalent time period.

Attention is also directed to the values for oxygen usage obtained in the same type of preparation in which the external work of the heart is reduced to zero by other means. In the potassium stopped heart, the oxygen usage of 2 ml. is about the same. In the beating heart emptied by suction and hemorrhage, and in the heart with induced ventricular fibrillation, the oxygen usages of 3.4 and 3.8 ml. are much greater. The oxygen values obtained in the resting heart have

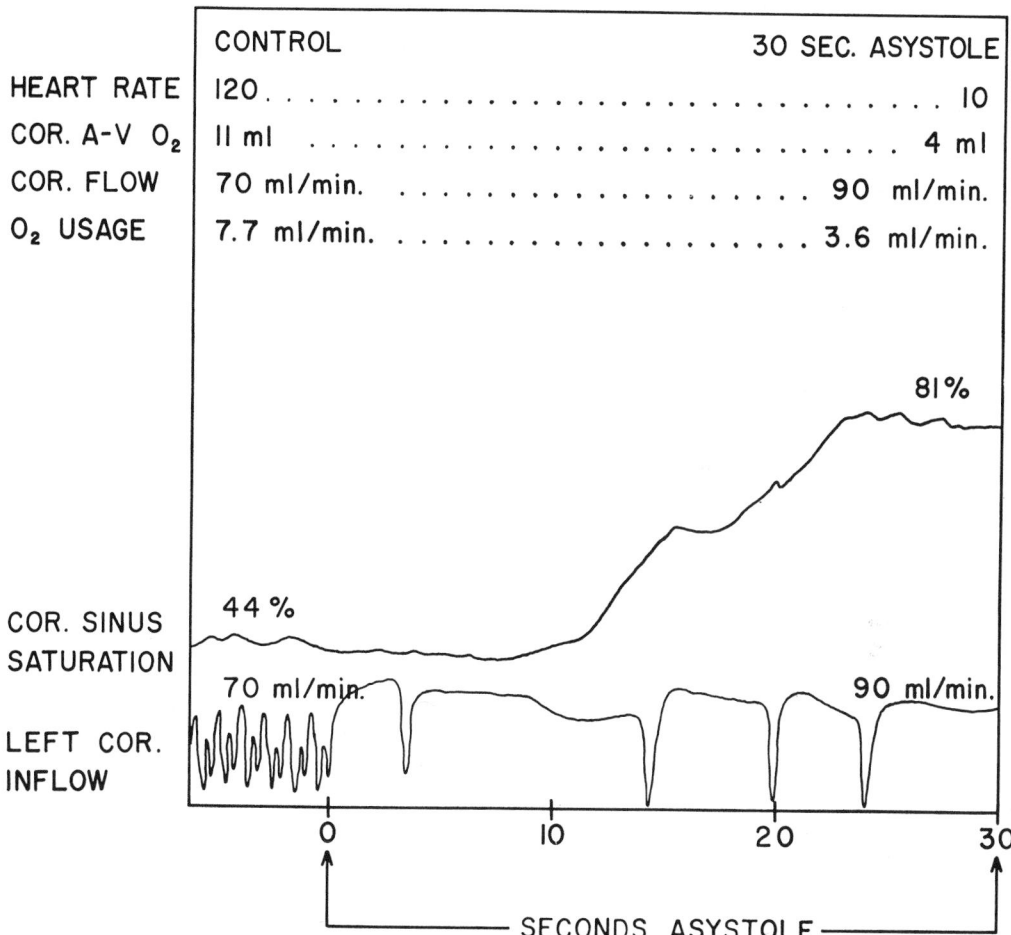

	CONTROL	30 SEC. ASYSTOLE
HEART RATE	120 10	
COR. A-V O₂	11 ml . . . . 4 ml	
COR. FLOW	70 ml/min. . . . . 90 ml/min.	
O₂ USAGE	7.7 ml/min. . . . . 3.6 ml/min.	

81%

COR. SINUS
SATURATION

44 %

70 ml/min.   90 ml/min.

LEFT COR.
INFLOW

0   10   20   30

SECONDS ASYSTOLE

Fig. 45.5. Reproduction of tracing from original record showing changes in left coronary inflow and coronary sinus oxygen saturation during prolonged ventricular asystole. (Gregg, D. E. Verh. Dtsch. ges. Kreislaufforschg. 1955, **21**, 22.)

some interesting characteristics. The oxygen uptake during vagal arrest or removal of the artificial pacemaker is unaffected by the ventricular diastolic size. In any one experiment, the value is not fixed but varies greatly with the control metabolic level in the beating heart. With intracoronary artery epinephrine or norepinephrine injection, the values are especially high and may equal 50 per cent of those in the control state. The implications of such experiments in relation to ventricular efficiency have already been considered in another chapter.

Patterns of Response of the Coronary Circulation

The preceding gives some idea of the fractionation of the control of coronary flow and oxygen uptake within the myocardium during a cardiac cycle. There are certain general patterns of hemo-dynamic responses of the heart and coronary circulation which follow primary changes in stress. The information has been obtained from both humans and animals and has been assembled from many laboratories (table 45.1).

Metabolites

The coronary flow is greatly increased and the coronary arteriovenous oxygen difference decreased by some chemical constituents of the blood, while others produce no response or a decrease in coronary flow; in any case there is little or no change in systemic dynamics (blood pressure, cardiac work, heart rate) or myocardial oxygen consumption. The coronary response to carbon dioxide and decreased pH is minimal; intracoronary injection of some intermediate metabolites will increase coronary flow and decrease oxygen extraction. Although it has not

TABLE 45.1
Circulatory responses to stress states

Arrows merely indicate direction of response, not magnitude, i.e., → no change, ↗ increase or ↘ decrease.

CONDITION	Cardiac Work	Cardiac Output	Coronary Flow	Cor. Press. Cor. Flow	Oxygen Usage	Coronary a-v O₂
↗ Blood CO_2, ↘ blood pH	→	→	→	→	→	→
Ischemia, mild anemia and anoxia, metabolites	→	→	↗	↘	→	↘
↗ Heart rate, ↗ CO (transfusion) ↗ C.W. Aortic coarctat. (mild)[1], thyrotoxicosis Cardiac sympathetic nerves, epinephrine and norepinephrine i.v. Severe anemia[2] and anoxia[2]	↗	↗	↗	↘	↗	→
Hypothermia, shock (hemorrhagic) Heart failure (extreme)[3]	↘	↘	↘		↘	→
Aortic coarctation (complete)	↘	↘	↗	↘	↗	→
Hypertensive cardiovascular disease	↗	→	→	↗	→	→

[1]Cardiac output → or ↘　　　[2]Cor. a-v O₂ ↘　　　[3]Cor. a-v O₂ ↗

been possible to demonstrate in the coronary sinus blood substances which would increase coronary blood flow, such metabolites could be metabolized or degraded rapidly and not be recoverable in venous blood. Adenosine and adenine nucleotides are very active coronary vasodilators. Although they are not found in coronary sinus blood, their derivatives, inosine and hypoxanthine, appear in measurable quantities during periods of myocardial hypoxia. If adenosine is added to coronary arterial blood, only inosine and hypoxanthine are recoverable in the coronary sinus blood. Thus it is possible that some metabolites may induce the vasodilation seen in myocardial hypoxia and yet not be recoverable in the coronary sinus blood.

HEART RATE

When the heart rate is increased considerably by electrical stimulation of the myocardium, aortic blood pressure, and minute cardiac output and work increase while the stroke volume and stroke work decrease. Simultaneously, minute coronary flow and oxygen usage increase, coronary resistance decreases, oxygen extraction is unchanged, but the coronary flow and oxygen consumption per beat decrease. Since acceleration of the heart means proportionally greater time per beat and per minute in systole than in diastole and since in systole coronary flow is less than in diastole, it would be anticipated that increased heart rate per se should reduce coronary flow. Since it does not, it must be that increased flow is due to arteriolar dilation from the increased metabolic activity. The same trend of flow and oxygen usage per beat and per minute also occurs at the faster heart rate when minute cardiac work is held constant or when comparisons are made at the same stroke work. This means that cardiac acceleration can augment the energy metabolism of the myocardium without manifestations of the extra energy as work.

TRANSFUSION

Augmentation of ventricular load by increasing venous return and hence circulating blood volume through infusion has a clinical counterpart in the load placed upon the human heart by transfusion or by an aortacaval fistula. The increasing coronary flow is partially explainable on a mechanical basis, since the slowing of the heart, which occurs under these circumstances, should increase coronary flow per beat and per minute by increasing diastolic time in which flow is greater. However, active dilation presumably results from the increasing local chemometabolic activity associated with the increased cardiac work. The coronary flow and oxygen are used economically, for the ratio of cardiac work to oxygen consumption increases.

Aortic Coarctation

With simulation of clinical coarctation by acute mechanical constriction (moderate) of the thoracic aorta just beyond the left subclavian artery, venous return to the heart by way of the inferior vena cava is decreased, but compensatory flow through various branches of the aortic arch may increase, so that cardiac output is maintained at the same level while the left ventricular workload is elevated. With greater aortic constriction, the net cardiac output decreases, causing the cardiac work to decrease. In either case the coronary dilation and increased flow arise in large part from *active* changes in the bore of the coronary bed related to the metabolic demands and in part passively from the increased blood pressure and moderately decreased heart rate. The cardiac oxygen consumption is increased much more by this augmentation of pressure work than with an equal increase of volume work following transfusion. No chronic studies of aortic coarctation have been made, because, owing to development of collateral circuits, the aorta may be first partially and then completely constricted at the arch without permanent development of hypertension proximal to the occlusion. In human coarctation not much change has been reported in coronary flow and oxygen uptake per unit of muscle, but this might be expected because systemic pressure was only mildly elevated. However, if true, the difference from the animal experiments might be explained by the fact that in these hearts, which are hypertrophied, there are fewer capillaries per unit of muscle to carry the oxygen and flow.

Hormones

A Thyroid. The myocardium participates in the increase in oxygen consumption characteristic of all body tissues in thyrotoxicosis. This hypermetabolism is accompanied by an increase in coronary blood flow, a decrease in coronary vascular resistance, and an increase in oxygen consumption per minute and per beat. Since there is an increase in oxygen usage per beat, cardiac oxygen utilization is presumably related not only to the increase in heart rate but to the general hypermetabolism of the myocardium as well.

B. Epinephrine and norepinephrine. The response of the systemic and coronary circulation to intracoronary artery injection of a minimal amount of epinephrine is similar to that indicated for stellate stimulation (see Nervous Influences). Probably the coronary changes can be similarly explained. With doses of 0.0002 mg. or less, coronary flow may increase without any change in blood pressure or heart rate and with an increased coronary arteriovenous oxygen difference. With the same or larger doses, as the systemic effects of the substance (increased aortic blood pressure, cardiac output, and changing heart rate) become evident, the coronary effects are exaggerated. In those instances in which it has been tested, norepinephrine affects the coronary circulation similarly. The circulatory responses to cigarette smoking or nicotine (i.e., increased heart rate, systemic blood pressure, cardiac output, cardiac work, left coronary blood flow, and decreased coronary vascular resistance), parallel those with epinephrine or norepinephrine injection and are presumably related to the release of norepinephrine. However myocardial oxygen consumption may increase, decrease or remain unchanged.

C. Acetylcholine. This hormone, when infused into a coronary artery, increases coronary blood flow in the anesthetized dog. If the dose is properly chosen, this response in the beating heart occurs without a significant change in blood pressure, heart rate, cardiac output, or cardiac work; myocardial oxygen consumption per beat and per minute have been shown to increase. However, when the hormone is infused intravenously into dogs with a constant heart rate and peripheral resistance, a decrease in myocardial oxygen consumption and ventricular contractility accompany the increased coronary blood flow. The oxygen consumption of the myocardium for a given amount of cardiac work is not changed. Although mechanical factors have been excluded, whether the effect of acetylcholine on coronary blood flow is directly on the intrinsic smooth muscle of coronary vessels or is induced through metabolic changes of the heart cannot be determined from the experimental data.

D. Pitressin and angiotensin. Of the hormones used clinically, pitressin and angiotensin increase coronary resistance to flow. Coronary flow decreases during pitressin infusion, the reduction occurring throughout the cardiac cycle in the presence of an increased central coronary pressure. There is a decrease in myocardial oxygen consumption and contractility, and in stroke work. Although a reduced metabolic influence is presumably the cause of the decrease in coronary blood flow, a direct effect on the coronary vascular bed has not been ruled out. Angiotensin produces an increase in coronary vascular resistance; its mode of action is unknown. An initial cardiac depression is followed by a positive inotropic effect. Blood pressure and cardiac work are increased.

Nervous Influences

No critical evidence has been adduced that stimulation of vagal fibers to the heart causes coronary flow changes not explainable on some other basis, such as a change in heart rate. However, stimulation of the cardiac fibers from a stellate ganglion in the anesthetized dog increases mean left coronary flow as the result of a decrease in systolic flow and a large increase in diastolic flow. This is in contrast to the unanesthetized dog where the ratio of systolic to diastolic flow is variable. Concurrently, left ventricular metabolism, cardiac output, and cardiac work increase while the systolic and diastolic sizes of the heart decrease. The decreased ratio of pressure to flow indicates an increased mean coronary bore. The major part of the dilation is explained by active changes in the coronary bed resulting from the release of an epinephrine-like substance (presumably norepinephrine) which directly enhances myocardial metabolism. This process is very wasteful because the oxygen uptake is greatly increased even when cardiac work is not permitted to rise. The fact that the central coronary pressure and heart rate do not necessarily change rules them out as a necessary part of the flow-controlling mechanisms. About 30 per cent of the flow increase is due to the marked shortening of systole and lengthening of diastole. When the heart rate and blood pressure are elevated, the systemic and coronary effects are greatly accentuated.

Experimental evidence has been accumulated that alpha and beta adrenergic receptors (ch. 12, p. 255) are present in the coronary vascular bed. Norepinephrine and epinephrine produce a relaxation of helical strips of coronary vessels (200 to 500μ in diameter); this relaxation can be prevented by beta adrenergic blockers (Zuberbuhler and Bohr). Also the decrease in coronary vascular resistance induced by intracoronary infusion of isoproterenol in the potassium arrested heart can be blocked with beta adrenergic blocking agents (Klocke and associates).

Reports have appeared suggesting that coronary flow can be influenced reflexly and adversely by impulses arising in various body regions, especially the heart, lungs, and abdominal viscera, but the importance of these reports is doubtful because of the methodology used.

Anemia

The coronary system participates actively in the circulatory adjustments to anemia. For hemoglobin values of 10 grams or more, the systemic circulation is essentially unaltered, and the compensation of the coronary system to the decreased oxygen-carrying capacity is similar to that with hypoxia, i.e., an increased coronary flow without change in oxygen uptake. When the hemoglobin values reach 6 to 8 grams, the response of the systemic circulation is manifested by tachycardia, increased cardiac output, cardiac work, and a fall in peripheral resistance. The coronary flow may now triple, coronary venous blood may contain less than 2 volumes per cent oxygen, the coronary arteriovenous oxygen difference may be 4 ml. or less, and oxygen uptake is considerably increased. The increase in coronary flow is related in part to the decreased blood viscosity and in larger part to the active dilation associated with myocardial hypoxia, which arises from the low hematocrit and from the increased metabolism. Ultimately, myocardial failure will occur in severe anemia when the coronary vessels have approached maximal dilation and cannot further compensate for the decreased oxygen-carrying capacity of the blood either by increased flow or by increased oxygen extraction. In the presence of coronary stenosis associated with anemia, the effect of coronary arteriolar dilation in increasing coronary flow is minimized by the high fixed resistance of the stenotic artery, and myocardial depression and failure occur at lesser degrees of anemia.

Valvular Lesions

Acute elevation of right ventricular pressure by pulmonary artery constriction initially decreases right coronary flow, to be followed quickly by a sustained increase in systolic, diastolic, and mean flow in the right coronary artery and, to some extent, in the left coronary artery. Upon release, right coronary flow temporarily increases still further. During the sustained response, the systemic blood pressure can be fairly well maintained. At the same time both the right ventricular work and metabolism increase, the former arising from the increased pulmonary artery pressure and cardiac output, the latter indicated by the increased right coronary flow and greater oxygen extraction from the coronary blood. The coronary response to elevation of left ventricular pressure by aortic constriction central to the coronary ostia is similar to that with pulmonary artery stenosis. In both instances, the sustained flow increase indicates a dominant influence of active coronary dilation over the increased mechanical flow-inhibiting effect of increasing extravascular compression which earlier was dominant. These maintained changes in the coronary circulation could well be the early response in the human being to gradual moderate stenosis of the corresponding valves.

Heart Failure

The heart shares with other types of muscle the characteristic that an optimum exists beyond which further stretching reduces the force of contraction and leads to myocardial failure. In acute heart failure with progressive deterioration of the myocardium from pulmonary artery stenosis, the changes in coronary flow and oxygen usage per minute and per beat may be in the same direction as those described for the right myocardium during pulmonary artery constriction, but of lesser magnitude. If the heart failure is severe enough, extravascular compression can become dominant over any active coronary dilation from metabolic processes, and coronary flow and oxygen usage may be normal or decrease, with the oxygen extraction at times reaching 90 per cent. The coronary circulation in the heart failing with severe aortic stenosis undergoes similar changes. When acute heart failure and chronic congestive failure simulating the human condition are induced by surgical complete heart block, changes in left coronary flow and ventricular oxygen consumption rather closely parallel alterations in the reduced left ventricular work. In chronic left heart failure due to rheumatic, arteriosclerotic, and hypertensive heart disease, the coronary circulation apparently responds by a slight increase in oxygen usage through maintenance of the left coronary flow and an increased coronary arteriovenous oxygen difference. The increased oxygen usage corresponds with that indicated above for the right heart in one stage of failure. Such hearts have considerable difficulty in transforming released energy into realizable work.

Studies of the coronary circulation in high-output failure from excessive transfusion or a chronic aortacaval fistula are not available.

Hypothermia

Hypothermia is often used during open heart surgery. The circulatory and metabolic adjustments of the heart during hypothermia have been partially explored. The associated changes that occur which tend to reduce the coronary flow are a diminution in blood and muscle temperatures, cardiac output, heart rate, cardiac work, and oxygen usage by the heart, and an increased blood viscosity, and a greatly lengthened period of ventricular systole. Opposing these factors are the relaxation of the major coronary vessels, which is known to occur with hypothermia, and dilation of the coronary bed caused by the hypotension per se. As a result of these determinants, coronary flow is decreased at low temperature. However, the percentage of reduction is greater in cardiac output than in coronary flow, which results in an increase in the coronary fraction of cardiac output at temperatures of 25 to 26° C. There is a decrease, increase or no change in peripheral resistance in the coronary bed, whereas in the systemic bed an increase in peripheral resistance occurs. Myocardial function appears to be adequate. However, many hearts are apparently not too far from failure, because if total venous inflow occlusion (which decreases coronary flow close to zero) is now added to permit open cardiotomy, myocardial failure supervenes, as evidenced by elevation in mean right atrial pressure and postmortem findings. This trend can be reversed by perfusion of the coronary system with small volumes of oxygenated blood.

Shock

Standardized oligemic shock in dogs is characterized during the hypotensive phase by a decrease in cardiac output, systemic blood pressure, cardiac work, stroke volume, stroke work, and by an increase in heart rate and an adequate central venous pressure. Coronary flow and coronary resistance are greatly decreased. Coronary flow is generally greater and the resistance generally less than can be accounted for by a simple decline in arterial blood pressure. At the same time, the oxygen uptake decreases, and the coronary arteriovenous oxygen difference is generally unchanged. (The coronary response to sustained hypotension through spinal anesthesia or injection of procaine and *Etamon* is similar.) With restoration to normal systemic blood pressure by reinfusion (intraarterial and intravenous routes are equally effective), coronary flow is greater and flow resistance is less than at an equivalent arterial blood pressure in the preshock state, and the augmented flow is maintained even if circulatory failure subsequently intervenes.

The fact that early in the hypotensive phase ventricular end-diastolic pressure does not rise indicates that the functional capacity of the heart is adequate for the work performed. At times after prolonged hypotension there may be evident cardiac dilation and elevated left and right atrial pressures, with the heart eventually proceeding to ventricular fibrillation or standstill, suggesting that myocardial depression or failure is partially responsible for the hemorrhagic shock syndrome. Gross and microscopic evidence of myocardial injury appears in both reversible and irreversible shock. Such myocardial depression could be caused by an insufficient coronary flow during either the hypotensive or the restoration periods. The high coronary flow during the restoration period would seem to preclude an insufficient coronary flow during this phase as an adequate explanation. During the hypotensive period, the actual coronary flow is greatly curtailed. The problem is whether the associated sizable reduction in coronary resistance is sufficient to permit enough blood to reach the myocardium to prevent it from failing. In some instances, at least, this loss of myocardial contractility is consequent upon an insufficient coronary flow, since the relation of atrial pressure to cardiac size can be reversed by increasing mildly with a pump left coronary flow without change in either the hypotension or blood volume.

Hypertensive Cardiovascular Disease

An exception to the general picture of coronary compensation to increased systemic stress appears to be the response of the chronically hypertensive heart. In essential hypertension with a normal cardiac output and elevated systemic blood pressure, the coronary flow and oxygen consumption per 100 g. of ventricular muscle are unaltered while coronary resistance increases. This increased resistance is also present in the renal and cerebral circulations. Since these hearts are generally hypertrophied, *total* coronary flow and oxygen usage are increased. This deviation (increased cardiac work with little change in coronary flow and oxygen usage per 100 g. of ventricular muscle) is explainable if it is assumed that such hearts with known coronary artery

disease have an increased amount of perfused fibrotic tissue.

Exercise

Correct values for left coronary flow and myocardial oxygen consumption during natural stress, such as exercise, have not been available because of technical difficulties of instrumentation and application. The data that have been obtained suggest that with a normal hematocrit and normal arterial oxygen content, maximal work is determined by factors within the muscle and not by limitation of coronary flow and oxygen supply.

Most of the information thus far considered is based upon observations in the open-chest dog. It is not known to what extent it applies to normal situations since it has been obtained under conditions far removed from normal as the result of insults from anesthesia, surgery and trauma. It is true that semiquantitative values for coronary flow and oxygen usage are available in the resting human and dog. No information exists, however, in normal humans and animals as to the regulation of the coronary circulation exposed to the stresses of every day life such as exercise and excitement.

A start is being made in alleviating this situation. Successful direct measurements of coronary flow have been made in normal unanesthetized dogs by applying chronically an appropriate electromagnetic flow meter (a somewhat modified Kolin type) directly to the circumflex branch of the left coronary artery. Although this gives correct flow values, very often it causes thrombosis within a few days because of the violent heart action. To remove the probe to a quiet area, it is applied to the left internal mammary artery just above the site of its chronic anastomosis to the peripheral end of the left circumflex coronary artery (see section on coronary artery collaterals in this chapter). Illustrated in figure 45.6 are the changes in phasic and mean coronary flow in such a dog 15 months after construction of the anastomosis and 7 weeks after implantation of the electromagnetic flow meter probe. First, the dog stood on a treadmill, then ran for 3 minutes at 12 miles per hour at a 5 per cent grade, and finally, stood at rest. Although not measured, the blood pressure and cardiac output obviously rose in this dog as they have in other dogs. A pulse pressure pattern has been sketched in for orientation purposes. The control flow is 46 ml. per minute, with most of this occurring during diastole. Within 15 to 20 seconds after the onset of exer-

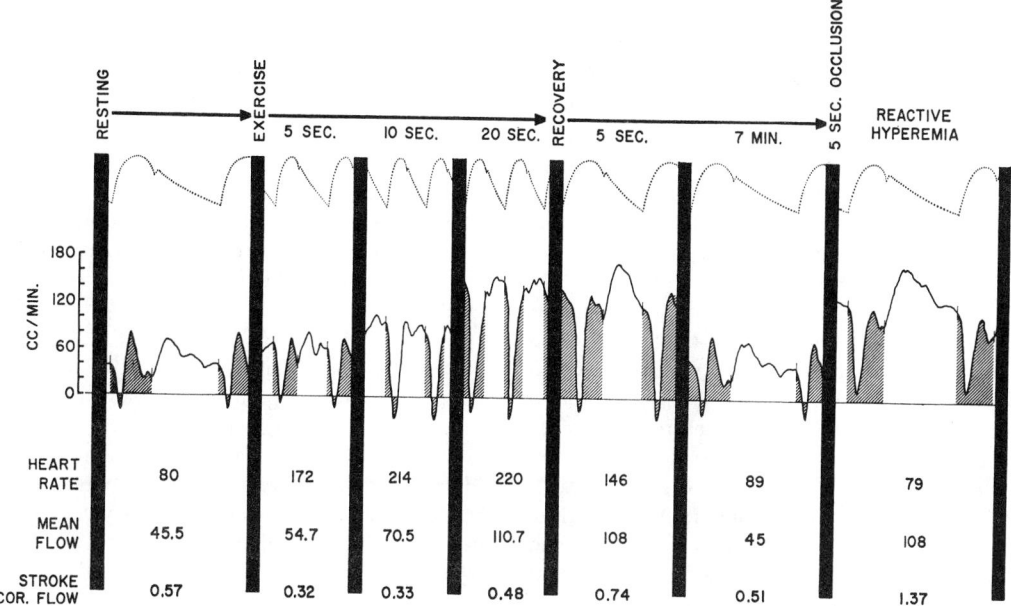

FIG. 45.6. Response of the unanesthetized, intact dog to exercise. Curves are redrawn from the original experiment. Phasic flow curves obtained with an electromagnetic flow meter monitoring an internal mammary-circumflex coronary anastomotic shunt. *Upper curve*, aortic pressure. *Lower curve*, phasic circumflex coronary flow. (Gregg, D. E. unpublished data).

cise, the changes in the coronary flow response are complete and do not change further during the 3-minute period of exercise. The changes include an increase in heart rate from 80 to 220 per minute, a reduction in duration of both systole and diastole per beat and an increase in mean flow from 46 to 111 ml. per minute. Calculation shows that the flow per heart beat is mildly decreased, and, hence, the mean flow increase is entirely on the basis of the increase in heart rate. Within 5 seconds after sudden stoppage of the treadmill, the patterns and flow have started to revert toward normal; the return to normal is completed within about 7 minutes. The last record was taken so that a comparison could be made between the maximum diastolic rate of flow during exercise and that during reactive hyperemia. It was taken shortly after the 7-minute recovery period and immediately following a 5-second occlusion by a pneumatic cuff of the coronary artery in which flow was being measured. Despite the slower heart rate, maximum diastolic flow during reactive hyperemia is about the same as that during exercise.

In other experiments, left coronary artery flow (electromagnetic flowmeter), cardiac output (a second flowmeter probe on the aorta), blood pressure (from a catheter in the aorta), and coronary sinus oxygen (from a catheter in the coronary sinus) have been monitored. In *mild to*

moderate exercise with little change in stroke cardiac output, with doubling of the heart rate, and with a mild blood pressure rise, coronary blood flow and myocardial oxygen usage *per heart beat* increased slightly, remained the same, or even decreased. During induced excitement of the dog or stimulation of the cardiac sympathetic nerves, there was a massive dilation of the left coronary vascular bed; an increased heart rate with a greatly increased myocardial flow and oxygen usage per heart beat occurred. Thus the coronary flow response to *mild to moderate* exercise is not similar to sympathetic stimulation of the heart in that stroke coronary flow and stroke oxygen usage are not always increased in the former. The exercise response does resemble the effects resulting from a mechanical increase in heart rate by means of an artificial pacemaker. Further experimentation may show that strenuous exercise always increases the coronary flow and oxygen usage per heart beat. The ultimate interpretation of these experiments on unanesthetized animals remains to be determined.

SUMMARY

Is there one over-all unifying mechanism controlling coronary flow? Is there a similar mechanism controlling the oxygen usage of the myocardium? The answer has been sought for many years. From the preceding discussion, it is apparent that when the primary change in stress is an increased heart rate, increased venous return (whole blood transfusion), increased cardiac work, aortic coarctation (moderate), thyrotoxicosis, cardiac action of fibers from the sympathetic nerves, intravenous injection of epinephrine or norepinephrine, severe anemia or anoxia, there is an increase in cardiac work and cardiac oxygen usage. Concurrently, coronary flow increases while coronary vascular resistance decreases. In situations of primary decrease in stress such as hemorrhagic hypotension, hypothermia, and extreme heart failure, the cardiac work and oxygen consumption decrease as does the coronary inflow. An exception to this general picture of coronary compensation to changing stress is that of complete aortic coarctation which may be characterized by a reduction in the output and work of the heart but an increased left coronary flow and oxygen usage. A second exception is that of chronic hypertension in which the cardiac work is increased, but cardiac output, oxygen usage and left coronary flow are unaltered while coronary resistance to flow increases. Thus, in most instances, coronary flow follows a primary change in cardiac stress. However, coronary flow correlates best with oxygen usage. This relationship is understandable since the oxygen consumption is derived from the product of the coronary flow and the coronary arteriovenous oxygen difference. Normally, most of the oxygen in the coronary blood is removed, and the level of coronary sinus oxygen is usually fairly constant under stress, i.e., it does not change more than 10 to 15 per cent. In those instances in which the coronary arteriovenous oxygen difference increases or decreases by this amount, it does not greatly affect the relation of coronary flow to oxygen usage since the change is generally small relative to the magnitude of the coronary flow change.

No final answer has been obtained as to the control of coronary flow. It has been variously related to the oxygen tension of the arterial blood, oxygen tension within the myocardium, and the action of local metabolites or vasodilating substances. Ultimately, at the cellular level, it is presumably related to the rate of reduction of cytochrome oxidase and the needs of the hydrogen transport system.

It would be expected that the oxygen consumption during systole when ventricular muscle is shortening and developing tension, would depend in some way on the dynamic adaptation of the ventricle to its work. The presence of some such correlation was first illustrated by the experiments of Evans and Matsuoka, and of Starling and Visscher, indicating in the isolated heart a linear relation between diastolic volume and oxygen usage. More recently, it has been found that oxygen usage correlates best with the total tension developed by the left ventricle.

Further experimental work in normal unanesthetized animals or man concerning the control of coronary blood flow will clarify many of the problems discussed above.

The Coronary Artery Collateral Circulation

The state of the human heart in the presence of naturally occurring coronary insufficiency or occlusion, or the state of the dog's heart in which coronary insufficiency has been experimentally induced, can be improved by augmentation of the naturally occurring coronary artery collateral circulation (by retrograde perfusion of the ischemic coronary bed with arterial blood) or by elevation of the ventricular fibrillation threshold. In addition, in man, positive and subjective benefit from drugs or surgical procedures could arise through psychogenic effects which are not necessarily related to the heart.

Information on the coronary collateral circulation is no better than the method used to obtain it and experimental tools for study of the collateral circulation are admittedly crude. These studies are concerned with measurements of the effects of various prophylactic and postcoronary occlusion procedures on the electrocardiogram, mortality, size of infarcts, exercise tolerance, and finally, on the injectable and functional collaterals in the presence of coronary occlusion or insufficiency. All are difficult to evaluate because of the considerable variability of the size of the naturally occurring collateral circulation.

The measurement which is most important, least subject to error, and which has yielded most information, is that of the collateral flow. This is determined by collecting the volume of blood that flows externally from a tube inserted into the peripheral end of an occluded coronary artery (retrograde flow). This is done acutely in the open-chest dog before, and sometime after, a variable has been chronically induced to improve collateral flow. This is collateral flow before it passes through a capillary bed. Collateral flow can also be measured after it has passed through a capillary bed and has appeared in the coronary sinus. This can be done when extracardiac tissue with a vascular stalk has been previously placed on the heart to stimulate collateral development. The coronary sinus flow is measured before and after clamping the potential extracardiac source of collateral blood. Any difference in flow would represent that which has traversed the capillary bed.

Natural Response of the Coronary Collateral Circulation

The natural responses of the coronary system during experimental coronary artery constriction and occlusion (which presumably also occur in the heart of man) have been studied extensively. Within 1 minute after occlusion of a left coronary artery branch, the intracoronary pressure beyond this point drops to about 35/25 mm. Hg; the ischemic muscle lengthens during systole of the left ventricle and useful function is lost. When the peripheral end of this ligated coronary artery is permitted to bleed externally, collateral arterial blood appears immediately, averaging about 3.0 ml. per minute for about 50 grams of potentially infarcted myocardium. Probably not more than 2.4 ml. of this blood (containing 0.5 ml. of oxygen) would perfuse the myocardial bed if the collateral flow were not permitted to bleed externally. This is because of the peripheral resistance existing beyond the point of occlusion. This level of collateral flow and oxygen content is estimated to be up to 40 per cent of that calculated as necessary to maintain indefinitely the viability of this myocardium. (The oxygen uptake of 50 grams of a heart with perfused coronary arteries at rest and doing no external work approximates 1.2 ml. as compared to the immediately available collateral oxygen supply of 0.5 ml.)

Hence, it is important to try to increase immediately this collateral or retrograde flow. The level of retrograde flow does not naturally increase and cannot be made to increase for 8 to 10 hours by drugs or by any known physiological means such as increased heart rate, increased flow in the other coronary arteries or induction of hypoxia or hypoxemia in the other coronary arteries. It can, however, be increased by passive elevation of arterial blood pressure (fig. 45.7). Why the collateral flow remains fixed, why the anastomoses function as a set of inert tubes, and why they do not participate in the vasodilatory response of the normal coronary bed is not known. It contrasts with the rapid development of collaterals in other vascular beds.

This retrograde flow can be greatly reduced by at least two conditions, namely, by excessive stretch of the non-ischemic myocardium and by the presence of reactive hyperemia in the other

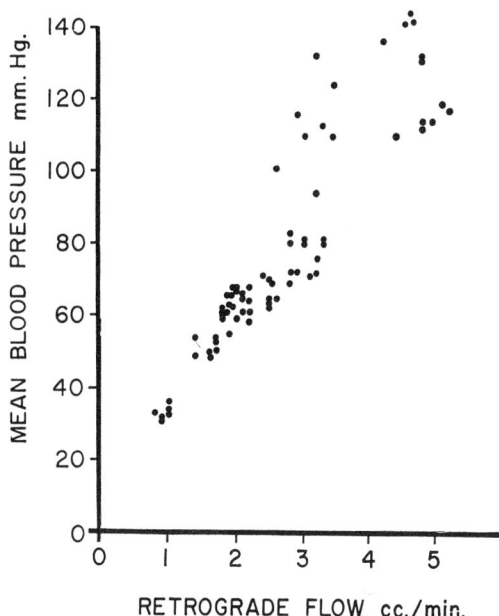

FIG. 45.7. Relation of retrograde coronary flow to mean arterial perfusion pressure in dogs. (Kattus and Gregg, Circulation Res., 1959, 7, 628.)

coronary arterial branches. One suspects that the reason for the decreased collateral flow in an occluded coronary artery branch while reactive hyperemia exists in the other coronaries is also the excessive stretch of the non-ischemic myocardium. Thus, the improvement that occurs in the human heart with drugs such as Neosynephrine in the presence of coronary insufficiency and infarction arises because of a good dynamic response in the non-ischemic but over-stretched myocardium. This would increase the collateral flow by increasing the coronary perfusion pressure and by decreasing the size of the heart.

Most hearts with an occluded coronary artery branch die within a number of hours. If they survive the first few hours, then within 12 hours, for some completely unknown reason, collateral flow starts to rise, doubling within 2 days, and within 3 to 4 weeks it may approximate 40 to 100 per cent of normal inflow into that coronary artery. At the same time the peripheral coronary pressure pulse beyond the point of ligation of the coronary artery branch may approximate in pattern and ordinate values the aortic pressure pattern simultaneously recorded.

This is the usual course of events. In other cases, stresses, some known but mostly unknown, prophylactically enhance the potential collateral circulation without the stimulus of coronary insufficiency or occlusion (Table 45.2). These are

TABLE 45.2

Prophylactic augmentation of coronary artery collaterals by natural stimuli

	Known stimuli	Incidence of injectable collaterals %	Retrograde flow ml./min.
Man	None	9	—
	Hypertrophy	26	—
	Valvular disease	28	—
	Cor pulmonale	73	—
	Anemia	39	—
	Coronary constriction	11 – 63	—
	Coronary occlusion	90 – 100	—
	High altitude (man & pig)	↗	↗
Pig	Anemia	100	—
Dog	Transfused anemia	↗	9 art.
Dog	Mild coronary constriction and exercise	→	3 art.

exemplified in man by the increase in the incidence of the injectable collateral bed in the presence of hypertrophy, valvular disease, cor pulmonale, anemia, and probably high altitude. This is exemplified in animals by an increase in both the injectable and functional collaterals in the presence of high altitude and transfused anemia. No good experimental evidence exists to indicate that physical exercise per se augments prophylactically the collateral flow as measured in a normal coronary artery immediately after its occlusion. Even with a combination of moderate coronary artery constriction and exercise, the retrograde flow does not increase.

DRUGS VERSUS CORONARY COLLATERAL FUNCTION

Since the vascular bed beyond an occluded coronary artery is presumably maximally dilated by anoxia, it is unlikely that a drug could improve a heart by immediately increasing flow to this area. Actually, the best experimental evidence offers no support for the belief that any drug penetrates the connecting collaterals or exerts any beneficial influence in the ischemic bed. It has not been possible to increase the flow of blood into this ischemic area within a short time after

coronary artery occlusion, or to retain myocardial shortening by the use of drugs that are known to dilate the normal coronary bed, such as papaverine, nitroglycerine, epinephrine, aminophylline, coramine, and khellin. In chronic experiments, cortisone and ACTH do not promote collateral flow or reduce the size of infarcts. The hypothesis that coronary occlusion reflexly decreases flow in other nonoccluded coronary arteries is negated by the experimental fact that flow in nonoccluded coronary arteries generally rises with coronary artery ligation. The alleged favorable effect on survival of prophylactic and therapeutic drugs, such as papaverine and quinidine, is best explained by their known action in raising the fibrillation threshold and in reducing the excitability of the myocardium.

NATURAL RESPONSE OF THE NORMAL BUT OVERSTRESSED PORTION OF THE MYOCARDIUM

Since the collateral flow does not increase for some hours, any early natural compensation must occur, not by improvement of the circulation in the affected area, but through enhanced action of the normal myocardium which is not involved. Nonfunction of involved muscle following coronary artery occlusion reduces the total myocardial force available for raising intraventricular tension; also intraventricular pressure must be spent in stretching the ischemic area and thus is lost for expelling blood into the aorta. The immediate consequences, which lead to a hypodynamic ventricle, are a reduction in left ventricular systolic pressure, aortic pulse pressure, systolic and diastolic pressures, duration of systole, stroke volume and stroke work. In this situation, left coronary inflow decreases considerably because of the mechanical reduction in size of its peripheral vascular bed. However, within a few minutes, the non-ischemic portion of the heart puts into operation compensatory mechanisms by means of which dynamic conditions are largely restored to normal, provided the non-ischemic myocardium is in a good responsive condition. Briefly, as the result of the lesser expulsion of blood with hypodynamic beats, the accumulating systolic remainder added to the oncoming blood stretches the viable muscle more and raises the ventricular end diastolic pressure or left atrial pressure. This combination of increased pressure in, and increased radius of, the ventricular cavity, causes the normal muscle to contract more vigorously, thereby restoring normal hemodynamics. In this situation of increased cardiac work per unit of functioning myocardium, coronary flow, arteriovenous oxygen difference, and metabolism of the left ventricle increase. The increase in oxygen uptake is equal to, and at times can be much more than that lost by the deletion of noncontractile muscle.

However, not all hearts react as well because the viable portion of the myocardium may not respond to stretch, or may respond only temporarily. This has been most thoroughly studied when the coronary obstruction has been induced by intracoronary injection of microspheres. This leads to acute or progressive heart failure associated with a profound hypotension with a decreased cardiac output, and the clinical signs and symptoms of shock. The clinical inference that this is due to the supervention of peripheral circulatory failure has not received heavy experimental support. On the contrary, experimental work favors the view that, in this situation, circulatory failure not due to severe irregularity of the heart beat is due, successively, to defection of useful contractions in the ischemic area, a loss of contractile energy through expansion of the affected area, and failure of the still viable fractions to compensate adequately.

EFFECTS OF DRUGS AND AN EXTRACORPOREAL CIRCULATION IN THE PRESENCE OF MYOCARDIAL INFARCTION WITH SHOCK

Since protracted hypotension can, at times, lead to myocardial damage and failure, and since experimentally, the coronary collateral flow varies passively with the systemic blood pressure, attempts have been made to improve such hearts experimentally and clinically by drugs or venoarterial perfusion.

The state of the heavily stressed normal myocardium could be improved with drugs either by increasing its oxygen supply or by using the available oxygen more economically. The major mechanism for increasing the oxygen supply is by increased coronary flow since, normally, most of the available oxygen is extracted from blood passing through the myocardium. The drugs would have to promote coronary flow in the non-ischemic myocardium in which oxygen usage, coronary flow and oxygen extraction are already at a high level. Whether any drug produces the desired type of dilation (active myocardial vessel relaxation, decreased extravascular compression, minimal increase in metabolism and cardiac work, minimal effect on other vascular beds), and whether it also increases ventricular efficiency, remains to be determined. In the normal dog, drugs such as papaverine, epinephrine, aminophylline, coramine, the adenosine nucleotides, and khellin augment the myocardial oxygen supply, but generally at a considerable expense to the heart, through increased cardiac work and metabolism. Persantin augments the oxygen supply to the myocardium; cardiac work and metabolism are little altered. Sublingual nitroglycerine is the only agent which has been found to definitely relieve the pain of angina pectoris. In normal man, sublingual nitroglycerine leads to an increased myocardial oxygen usage with little or no change in cardiac output and cardiac work, and with a decreased efficiency. In patients with coronary artery disease, resting coronary flow is normal. Following nitroglycerine, coronary flow and oxygen usage are unchanged, but systemic blood pressure, cardiac work and cardiac output are reduced; coronary resistance is not greatly changed, while efficiency is decreased. It would thus seem that the dilator capacity of the coronary tree with coronary artery disease is exhausted. The mechanism whereby nitroglycerine relieves pain is not that of general coronary dilation and is unknown. It is thought by some investigators to be due to the fall in blood pressure with a resultant decrease in cardiac work while the oxygen supply remains the same.

The incidence of cardiogenic shock complicating acute myocardial infarction has been reported as 12 per cent. Mortality associated with this complication may be in excess of 80 per cent. Vasopressor drugs have been widely employed in this situation. The improvement that occurs in the human heart with drugs such as neosynephrine, in the presence of coronary insufficiency and infarction, arises because of a good dynamic response in the normal but overstretched myocardium. This presumably augments the coronary collateral flow by increasing the coronary perfusion pressure and by making the heart smaller.

Although the use of vasopressor agents reduces mortality in myocardial infarction with shock, at least half fail to respond. In such patients, extracorporeal circulatory support is being tried whereby blood is pumped from a convenient vein into the aorta. The major objective is to produce a sustained increase in aortic pressure and, hence, an increase in coronary, cerebral, and other important regional circulations, yet without an increase in left ventricular work that might cause further cardiac deterioration. Conclusive evidence

of the benefit of this procedure has not yet been obtained.

Attempts to Improve Coronary Collateral Circulation

The state of the heart following coronary artery occlusion can be improved considerably by various physiological and surgical procedures. The principles of the procedures used, together with the surgical manipulations are shown in table 45.3. These include section of the cardiac sympathetic nerves, induction of myocardial hypoxia by various manipulations of the coronary venous system, production of chronic epicardial granuloma by mechanical and chemical means, application of extracardiac tissue to the heart, internal mammary artery ligation, sham operations, irradiation of the heart, coronary endarterectomy and coronary artery bypass.

Animals

Many of these procedures in the experimental animal are of positive benefit to the heart and give immediate or sustained protection against subsequent ligation of a major coronary artery ramus. This is illustrated in the data obtained in

TABLE 45.3

Procedures for improving coronary function (man and animal)

Approaches	Tissue
Section cardiac sympathetic fibres	
Myocardial hypoxia	Coronary sinus constriction or ligation, aorta - cor. sinus shunt pulmonary artery-left atrial shunt
Chronic pericardial granuloma via mechanical and chemical means	Talc, powdered bone, asbestos, mica, gelatin, sponge, silver nitrate, mechanical burrs
Application extra cardiac tissue to the heart	Spleen, omentum, fat, muscle, skin flap, intestine, lung, arterial implants
Internal mammary artery ligation	
Sham operation	
Coronary by-pass and endarterectomy	Internal mammary and carotid arteries

many laboratories (table 45.4). Ligation of a major ramus of the left coronary artery causes about a 70 per cent mortality within the first 1 to 2 hours, and chronically there is considerable infarction. When partial or complete occlusion of the coronary sinus precedes coronary artery ligation, or when a portion of the coronary bed is perfused in retrograde fashion by connecting the coronary sinus to an artery, the immediate mortality is reduced considerably. With the exception of section of cardiac sympathetic fibers and internal mammary artery ligation, all other procedures listed—chronic coronary venous maneuvers, application of various chemical and mechanical irritants, separately or in combination, and application of extracardiac tissue to the heart lead to a significant reduction in mortality and infarction. Irradiation of the normal canine heart before coronary artery ligation is another procedure which reduces mortality. There is an increase in the injectable and functional collaterals with the chronic coronary venous maneuvers and with the application of mechanical and chemical irritants to the heart. The level of collateral flow, 5 to 12 ml. in most instances, considerably exceeds the control flow of 3 ml. with acute artery ligation alone, and approximates that necessary to maintain viability in the potentially infarcted area. There is as yet no evidence that the protection of the heart afforded by "arterialization" of the coronary sinus arises from passage of blood retrogradely from vein to capillary. Such a procedure reduces left coronary inflow, hence, it is more likely that the benefit arises from the increased collateral flow which is associated with the induced myocardial hypoxia. In general, the over-all protection to the heart by the various procedures is probably on a collateral flow basis, but since sham operations involving manipulation of the heart also increase collateral flow, the possibility must be entertained that there may be no specific effect of some of the maneuvers; they may act by raising the ventricular fibrillation threshold, thus giving time for collaterals to develop.

In some procedures that apply extracardiac tissue to the heart, such as a pedicle skin flap, and in internal mammary artery ligation or its myocardial implantation, the collateral flow does not increase. These studies, however, are incom-

TABLE 45.4

Physiological effects of prophylactic procedures on coronary collaterals (dog)
Directional arrows merely indicate direction, not magnitude, i.e., → no change, ↗ increase or ↘ decrease.

Experiment	Procedures prior to ligation of coronary artery ramus	Acute ligation of coronary artery ramus				
		Mortality %	Infarction	Injectable collaterals	Retrograde flow ml./min.	Persistence of collaterals
Acute	None	70	—	—	3 art.	—
Chronic	None	70	Gross	—	50 art.	—
Chronic	Section cardiac sympathetic fibres	→	→	→	→	—
Acute	(Cor sinus constriction or ligation) (Aorta-coronary sinus shunt)	↘	—	—	15 ven.	—
Chronic	(Cor sinus constriction or ligation) (Aorta-coronary sinus shunt-Beck #2)	↘	↘	↗	7-12 art.	yes
Chronic	Irritants applied to heart -- Talc, asbestos, mechanical abrasion, mica, phenol, silver nitrate, etc.	↘	↘	↗	5-8 art.	yes
Chronic	Mechanical abrasion, asbestos, cor sinus reduced to 3 mm., fat-Beck #1	↘	↘	↗	8 art.	yes
Chronic	Extracardiac tissue -- muscle, lungs, intestine, omentum, pedicle, skin flap, internal mammary artery	↘	↘	↗	2 art.	—
Chronic	Ligation internal mammary artery	→	→	→	3 art.	—
Chronic	Sham operation	↘	↘	↗	7 art.	—
Chronic	Cor by-pass and coronary endarterectomy	—	—	—	—	—

plete. Prophylactic internal mammary artery implantation has been shown to increase the ventricular fibrillation threshold in dogs who have their anterior descendens artery ligated; in control animals in which thrombosis is induced in the arterial implant, the fibrillation threshold does not rise appreciably. The mechanism of the protective effect is unknown. Further work should be done to determine, in addition to the usual arterial collateral flow measurements, whether blood brought in by the extracardiac tissue actually flows through the capillary bed of the myocardium in the presence of chronic as well as acute coronary occlusion. If it does, then it should be possible to demonstrate its presence in the coronary sinus flow. Preliminary experiments indicate, however, that clamping of the extracardiac source of a myocardially imbedded artery, pedicle skin flap, etc., does not usually affect coronary sinus flow.

Man

All of the procedures listed in table 45.3 designed to promote collateral development, including the sham operation, have been applied to the heart of man suffering from coronary artery disease. All appear to increase to some extent the work and exercise tolerance and to decrease the cardiac pain. These observations are not necessarily explained on the same basis as the improvement in the collateral circulation which follows such procedures in the dog. This is because, in the dog, surgery precedes coronary artery ligation, whereas in the human, surgery follows coronary artery occlusion. Surgery in the dog is designed to promote collaterals in the presence of a normal coronary circulation. Surgery in the human is designed to promote collateral circulation after the coronary insufficiency has been naturally established. In man, hypoxia, the greatest known vessel dilator, and a natural stimulus to collateral development, has already been working for many months. To be effective, the surgical procedure must supply a stimulus to collateral development far more potent than hypoxia. This has never been demonstrated in animals in which coronary insufficiency has previously been induced.

The explanation of the results in man is not clear. Undoubtedly, some subjects are protected and live longer because of the known experimental fact that handling the heart enhances the ventricular fibrillation threshold. Some may be improved by procedures such as de-epicardialization which could obliterate the afferent pathways

for pain. However, results of the sham operation of Adams and of others, involving only a skin incision, strongly suggest that much of the positive benefit is on a psychogenic basis.

Coronary endarterectomy, which has been applied to man, is on a sound physiological basis, and its purpose is entirely different from the preceding. The surgeon directly re-establishes coronary flow through the original coronary artery by removing its atherosclerotic plug. It does not require collateral development and should be effective provided there exists a gross coronary insufficiency of blood beyond the obstruction, provided the vessel remains patent and thrombi do not form, and provided there are no sizeable atherosclerotic lesions beyond the region of the occluded coronary artery. Only a small group of patients have benefited from this type of operation and long term evaluation is not available. Patients must be chosen carefully for this procedure with the above criteria in mind.

Finally, bypass of a length of an occluded coronary artery by anastomosis of its peripheral patent end to a systemic artery has not yet been attempted in man. In dogs, a nonsuture anastomosis by intima to intima contact between the left coronary artery and the left internal mammary artery has been highly successful. In almost all of the dogs, the anastomoses have been demonstrated to be patent as evidenced by gross observation, angiography, and measurement of coronary blood flow through the anastomosis up to the time of dog sacrifice (12 to 24 months after operation). Since such an operation is almost always successful and without sequelae in the dog in which the anastomosed vessels are only 2 to 2.5 mm. in diameter, there should be no difficulty in the human heart in which the coronary artery branches have a much greater diameter. This procedure could, therefore, have a very practical application in the creation of a permanent new blood supply in the presence of coronary artery disease in man.

There is, however, a possible late complication to successful coronary endarterectomy or coronary bypass in man which must not be overlooked. In the presence of such a large new blood supply, the existing collateral flow might disappear. If another coronary occlusion subsequently occurs, the patient would be in difficulties because he had lost his collaterals.

Summary

From the preceding, it would appear that in the normal heart a moderate collateral circulation exists which functions immediately following a coronary artery occlusion. Different prophylactic procedures are successful experimentally in preserving life either by compensating for a deficit in the supply of collateral oxygen or by preventing ventricular fibrillation. This protection against occlusion of a coronary artery may be dependent upon a collateral development on the arterial side of the order of magnitude of that essential for viability. Human coronary surgery which follows coronary insufficiency has no counterpart in animal experiments and these human coronary experiments cannot as yet be interpreted on a physiological basis.

REFERENCES

ABRAMSON, D. I., TUCK, S., JR., BELL, Y., MITCHELL, R. E., AND ZAYAS, A. M. Effect of short periods of arterial occlusion on blood flow and oxygen uptake. J. Appl. Physiol., 1961, 16, 851.

ADAMS, R. Internal mammary artery ligation for coronary insufficiency. An evaluation. New England J. Med., 1958, 258, 113.

BAROLDI, G., MANTERO, O., AND SCOMAZZONI, G. The collaterals of the coronary arteries in normal and pathologic hearts. Circulation Res., 1956, 4, 223.

BARONOFSKY, I. D., SPROFKA, J. L., AND NOBLE, J. F. Use of intestinal loops for revascularization of the heart. Circulation Res., 1954, 2, 506.

BERNE, R. M. The effect of immersion hypothermia on coronary blood flow. Circulation Res., 1954, 2, 236.

BERNE, R. M., BLACKMON, R. J., AND GARDNER, T. H. Hypoxemia and coronary blood flow. J. Clin. Invest., 1957, 36, 1101.

BING, R. J., CASTELLANOS, A., GRADEL, E., SIEGEL, A., AND LUPTON, C. Enzymatic, metabolic, circulatory and pathologic studies in myocardial infarction. Tr. A. Am. Physicians, 1956, 69, 170.

BLUMGART, H. L., ZOLL, P. M., FREEDBERG, A. S., AND GILLIGAN, D. R. The experimental production of intercoronary arterial anastomoses and their functional significance. Circulation, 1950, 1, 10.

BRACHFELD, N., BOZER, J., AND GORLIN, R. Action of nitroglycerin on the coronary circulation in normal and in mild cardiac subjects. Circulation, 1959, 19, 697.

CANNON, J. A., LONGMIRE, W. P., AND KATTUS, A. A. Considerations of the rationale and technic of coronary endarterectomy for angina pectoris. Surgery, 1959, 46, 197.

CASE, R. B., BERGLUND, E., AND SARNOFF, S. J. Ventricular function. II. Quantitative relationship between coronary flow and ventricular function with observations on unilateral failure. Circulation Res., 1954, 2, 319.

COFFMAN, J. D. AND GREGG, D. E. Oxygen metabolism and oxygen debt repayment after myocardial ischemia. Am. J. Physiol., 1961, 201, 881.

COFFMAN, J. D. AND GREGG, D. E. Reactive hyperemia characteristics of the myocardium. Am. J. Physiol., 1960, 199, 1143.

COHEN, L. S., ELLIOTT, W. C., AND GORLIN, R. Measurement of myocardial blood flow using krypton 85. Am. J. Physiol., 1964, 206, 997.

DAY, S. B. AND LILLEHEI, C. W. Experimental basis for a new operation for coronary artery disease. A left atrial-pulmonary artery shunt to encourage development of interarterial intercoronary anastomoses. Surgery, 1959, 45, 487.

DENISON, A. B., JR., BARDHANABAEDVA, S., AND GREEN, H. D. Adrenergic drugs and blockade on coronary arterioles and myocardial contraction. Circulation Res., 1956, 4, 653.

DUFF, F., BERGLUND, E., AND BORST, H. Effects of heart rate on ventricular function and coronary circulation in dogs. Am. J. Physiol., 1955, 183, 611.

ECKENHOFF, J. E., HASKENSHIEL, J. H., LANDMESSER, C. M., AND HARMEL, M. Cardiac oxygen metabolism and control of the coronary circulation. Am. J. Physiol., 1947, 149, 634.

ECKSTEIN, R. W., STROUD M., III, ECKEL, R., DOWLING, C. V., AND PRITCHARD, W. H. Effects of control of cardiac work upon coronary flow and oxygen consumption after sympathetic nerve stimulation. Am. J. Physiol., 1950, 163, 539.

ECKSTEIN, R. W. Development of interarterial coronary anastomoses by chronic anemia. Disappearance following correction of anemia. Circulation Res., 1955, 3, 306.

ECKSTEIN, R. W. Effect of exercise and coronary artery narrowing on coronary collateral circulation. Circulation Res., 1957, 5, 230.

ECKSTEIN, R. W. AND LEIGHNINGER, D. S. Chronic effects of aorta-coronary sinus anastomosis of Beck in dogs. Circulation Res., 1954, 2, 60.

EVANS, C. L. AND MATSUOKA, Y. The effect of various mechanical conditions on the gaseous metabolism and efficiency of the mammalian heart. J. Physiol., 1915, 49, 378.

FOLTZ, E. L., PAGE, R. G., SHELDON, W. F., WONG, S. K. TUDDENHAM, W. J., AND WEISS, A. J. Factors in variations and regulations of coronary blood flow in intact anesthetized dogs. Am. J. Physiol., 1950, 162, 521.

FOWLER, N. O. AND HOLMES, J. C. Coronary and myocardial actions of angiotensin. Circulation Res., 1964, 14, 191.

FREIS, E. D., SCHNAPER, H. W., JOHNSON, R. L., AND SCHREINER, G. E. Hemodynamic alterations in acute myocardial infarction. Cardiac output, mean arterial pressure, total peripheral resistance, "central" and total blood volumes, venous pressure and average circulation time. J. Clin. Invest., 1952, 31, 131.

GOODALE, W. T. OLSON, R. E., AND HACKEL, D. B. The effects of fasting and diabetes mellitus on myocardial metabolism in man. Am. J. Med., 1959, 27, 212.

GORLIN, R., BRACHFELD, N., MACLEOD, C., AND BOPP, P. Effect of nitroglycerin on the coronary circulation in patients with coronary artery disease or increased left ventricular work. Circulation, 1959, 19, 705.

GREEN, H. D. AND WEGRIA, R. Effects of asphyxia, anoxia and myocardial ischemia on the coronary circulation. Am. J. Physiol., 1942, 135, 271.

GREEN, H. D., WEGRIA, R., AND BOYER, N. H. Effects of epinephrine and pitressin on the coronary artery inflow in anesthetized dogs. J. Pharmacol. & Exper. Therap., 1942, 76, 378.

GREGG, D. E. Physiology of the coronary circulation. Circulation, 1963, 27, 1128.

GREGG, D. E. AND SHIPLEY, R. E. Studies of the venous drainage of the heart. Am. J. Physiol., 1947, 151, 13.

GREGG, D. E. AND GREEN, H. D. Registration and interpretation of normal phasic inflow into a left coronary artery by an improved manometric method. Am. J. Physiol., 1940, 130, 114.

GREGG, D. E. AND SHIPLEY, R. E. Changes in right and left coronary artery inflow with cardiac nerve stimulation. Am. J. Physiol., 1944, 141, 382.

GREGG, D. E. AND SHIPLEY, R. E. Augmentation of left coronary inflow with elevation of left ventricular pressure and observation on the mechanism for increased coronary inflow with increased cardiac load. Am. J. Physiol., 1944, 142, 44.

GREGG, D. E., PRITCHARD, W. H., SHIPLEY, R. E., AND WEARN, J. T. Augmentation of blood flow in the coronary arteries with elevation of right ventricular pressure. Am. J. Physiol., 1943, 139, 726.

GREGG, D. E., THORNTON, J. J., AND MAUTZ, F. R. The magnitude, adequacy and source of the collateral blood flow and pressure in chronically occluded coronary arteries. Am. J. Physiol., 1939, 127, 161.

HACKEL, D. B., SANCETTA, S. M., AND KLEINERMAN, J. Effect of hypotension due to spinal anesthesia on coronary blood flow and myocardial metabolism in man. Circulation, 1956, 13, 92.

HALL, R. J., KHOURI, E. M., AND GREGG, D. E. Non-suture internal mammary-coronary artery anastomosis. (abstract). Circulation, 1959, 20, 791.

HARDIN, R. A., SCOTT, J. B., AND HADDY, F. J. Effect of cardiac cooling on coronary vascular resistance in normothermic dogs. Am. J. Physiol., 1960, 199, 163.

HARKEN, D. E. BLACK, H., DICKSON, J. F., III, AND WILSON, H. E., III. De-epicardialization: A simple, effective surgical treatment for angina pectoris. Circulation, 1955, 12, 955.

HERD, J. A., HOLLENBERG, M., THORBURN, G. D., KOPOLD, H. H., AND BARGER, A. C. Myocardial blood flow determined with Krypton 85 in unanesthetized dogs. Am. J. Physiol., 1962, 203, 122.

HUCKABEE, W. Relationship of pyruvate and lactate during anaerobic metabolism. V. Coronary inadequacy. Am. J. Physiol., 1961, 200, 1169.

JACOBS, H. I., ROSEN, V., AND AGRESS, C. M. Further evidence for a critical vessel caliber in experimental coronary shock. Circulation Res., 1953, 1, 466.

JELLIFFE, R. W., WOLF, C. R., BERNE, R. M., AND ECKSTEIN, R. W. Absence of vasoactive and cardiotropic substances in coronary sinus blood of dogs. Circulation Res., 1957, 5, 382.

KATTUS, A. A. AND GREGG, D. E. Some determinants of coronary collateral blood flow in the open chest dog. Circulation Res., 1959, 7, 628.

KATZ, A. M., KATZ, L. N., AND WILLIAMS, F. L. Regulation of coronary flow. Am. J. Physiol., 1955, 180, 392.

KLOCKE, F., KAISER, G., ROSS, J., AND BRAUNWALD, E. Studies on beta adrenergic receptor mechanisms in the coronary vascular bed. Fed. Proc., 1964, 23, 125 (Abstract).

KUHN, L. A., GRUBER, F. L., FRANKEL, A., AND KUPFER, S. Hemodynamic effects of extracorporeal circulation in closed chest normal animals and in those with myocardial infarction with shock. Circulation Res., 1960, 8, 199.

LEIGHT, L., DEFAZIO, V., TALMERS, F. N., REGAN, T. J., AND HELLEMS, H. K. Coronary blood flow, myocardial oxygen consumption and myocardial metabolism in normal and hyperthyroid human subjects. Circulation, 1956, 14, 90.

LEVY, M. N. AND MARTINS DE OLIVEIRA, J. Regional distribution of myocardial blood flow in the dog as determined by Rb[86]. Circulation Res., 1961, 9, 96.

LEWIS, F. B., COFFMAN, J. D., AND GREGG, D. E. The effect of heart rate and intracoronary isoproterenol, levarterenol and epinephrine on coronary flow and resistance. Circul. Res., 1961, 9, 89.

MACLEAN, L. D. AND PHIBBS, C. M. Relative effect of chronic ischemia and a myocardial revascularization procedure on the ventricular fibrillation threshold. Circulation Res., 1960, 8, 473.

MARCHIORO, T., FELDMAN, A., OWENS, J. C., AND SWAN, H. Measurement of myocardial blood flow: indicator-dilution technique. Circulation Res., 1961, 9, 541.

MCKEEVER, W. P., GREGG, D. E., AND CANNEY, P. C. Oxygen uptake of the non-working left ventricle. Circulation Res., 1958, 6, 612.

MOIR, T. W., DRISCOL, T. E., AND ECKSTEIN, R. W. Thebesian drainage in the left heart of the dog. Circulation Res., 1964, 14, 245.

OPDYKE, D. F. AND FOREMAN, R. C. A study of coronary flow under conditions of hemorrhagic hypotension and shock. Am. J. Physiol., 1947, 148, 726.

OSHER, W. J. Pressure-flow relationship of the coronary system. Am. J. Physiol., 1953, 172, 403.

PAUL, M. H., THEILEN, E. O., GREGG, D. E., MARSH, J. B., AND CASTEN, G. G. Cardiac metabolism in experimental ventricular fibrillation. Circulation Res., 1954, 2, 573.

RAYFORD, C. R., KHOURI, E. M., LEWIS, F. B., AND GREGG, D. E. Evaluation of the use of the left coronary artery inflow and the oxygen content of the coronary sinus blood as a measure of left ventricular metabolism. J. Appl. Physiol., 1959, 14, 817.

REGAN, T. J. AND STEVELMAN, H. Influence of varied concentrations of Pitressin on myocardial blood flow and oxygen uptake. Fed. Proc., 1962, 21, 105. (Abstract).

ROWE, G. G., HUSTON, J. H., MAXWELL, G. M., WEINSTEIN, A. B., TUCKMAN, H., AND CRUMPTON, C. W. The effects of 1-Hydrazinophthalazine upon coronary hemodynamics and myocardial oxygen metabolism in essential hypertension. J. Clin. Invest., 1955, 34, 696.

SABISTON, D. C. AND GREGG, D. E. Effect of cardiac contraction on coronary blood flow. Circulation, 1957, 15, 14.

SABISTON, D. C., THEILEN, E. O., AND GREGG, D. E. The relationship of coronary blood flow and cardiac output and other parameters in hypothermia. Surgery, 1955, 38, 498.

SABISTON, D. C., FAUTEUX, J. P., AND BLALOCK, A. An experimental study of the fate of arterial implants in the left ventricular myocardium. Ann. Surg., 1957, 145, 927.

SABISTON, D. C., JR. AND BLALOCK, A. Coronary thromboendarterectomy for angina pectoris. Postgrad. Med., 1961, 29, 439.

SARNOFF, S. J., BRAUNWALD, E., WELCH, G. H., JR., CASE, R. B., STAINSBY, W. N., AND MACRUZ, R. Hemodynamic determinants of oxygen consumption of the heart with special reference to the tension-time index. Am. J. Physiol., 1958, 192, 148.

SCHLESINGER, M. J. Significant variations in the anatomic pattern of the coronary vessels. Blood, heart and circulation. Publ. Am. Ass. Advance. Sci., 1940, 13, 61.

SCHREINER, G. L., BERGLUND, E., BORST, H. G., AND MONROE, R. G. Effects of vagus stimulation and of acetylcholine on myocardial contractility, oxygen consumption and coronary flow in dogs. Circulation Res., 1957, 5, 562.

SENDEROFF, E., KANEKO, M., BECK, A. R., AND BARONOFSKY, I. D. The effects of cardiac irradiation upon the normal canine heart. Am. J. Roentgenol. 1961, 86, 740.

SHIPLEY, R. E. AND GREGG, D. E. The cardiac response to stimulation of the stellate ganglia and cardiac nerves. Am. J. Physiol., 1945, 143, 396.

STARLING, E. H., AND VISSCHER, M. B. The regulation of the energy output of the heart. J. Physiol., 1927, 62, 243.

THEILEN, E. O., PAUL, M. H., AND GREGG, D. E A comparison of the effects of intra-arterial and intravenous transfusions in hemorrhagic hypotension on coronary blood flow, systemic blood pressure and ventricular end-diastolic pressure. J. Appl. Physiol., 1954, 7, 248.

VASTESAEGER, M., VAN DER STRAETEN, P. P., FRIART, J., CANDAELE, G., GHYS, A., AND BERNARD, R. M. Les anastomoses intercoronariennes telles qu'elles apparaissent a la coronarographie postmortem. Acta cardiol., 1957, 12, 365.

VIDONE, R. A., KLINE, J. L., PITEL, M., AND LIEBOW, A. A. The application of an induced bronchial collateral circulation to the coronary arteries by cardiopneumonopexy. II. Hemodynamics and the measurement of collateral flow to the myocardium. Am. J. Pathol., 1956, 32, 897.

VINEBERG, A. AND WALKER, J. Six months to six years experience with coronary artery insufficiency treated by internal mammary artery implantation. Am. Heart J., 1957, 54, 851.

WARTMAN, W. B., CAMPBELL, L. A., AND CRAIG,

R. L.: The effect of ACTH on experimental myocardial infarcts. Circulation Res., 1955, 3, 496.

WEGRIA, R. AND NICKERSON, N. D. The effect of papaverine, epinephrine, and quinidine on the fibrillation threshold of the mammalian ventricles. J. Pharmacol. & Exper. Therap., 1942, 75, 50.

WEST, J. W., BELLET, S., MANZOLI, U. C. AND MÜLLER, O. F. Effects of Persantin (RA8), a new coronary vasodilator, on coronary blood flow and cardiac dynamics in the dog. Circulation Res., 1962, 10, 35.

WIGGERS, C. J. AND GREEN, H. D. The ineffectiveness of drugs upon collateral flow after experimental coronary occlusion in dogs. Am. Heart J., 1936, 11, 527.

WOLF, M. M. AND BERNE, R. M. Coronary vasodilator properties of purine and pyrimidine derivatives. Circulation Res., 1956, 4, 343.

YONCE, L. R. AND HAMILTON, W. F. Oxygen consumption in skeletal muscle during reactive hyperemia. Am. J. Physiol., 1959, 197, 190.

ZOLL, P. M., WESSLER, S., AND SCHLESINGER, M. J. Interarterial coronary anastomoses in the human heart with particular reference to anemia and relative cardiac anoxia. Circulation, 1951, 4, 797.

ZUBERBUHLER, R. AND BOHR, D. F. Effects of catecholamines and angiotensin on coronary vascular smooth muscle. Fed. Proc., 1964, 23, 121 (Abstract).

Monographs and Reviews

AGRESS, C. M., KITCHELL, J. R., SCHERF, D., BINE, R., JR., BROTMAN, I., AND GOFMAN, J. W. Symposium on treatment of myocardial infarction. Am. J. Cardiol. 1958, 1, 224.

ALELLA, A., BRETSCHNEIDER, H. J., DELIUS, L., GIESE, W., HARDERS, H., HAUSS, W. H., LUBBERS, D., MATTHES, K., MEESMANN, W., MERCKER, H., MOLBERT, E., MULLER-MOHNSSEN, H., SCHMIER, J., SCHOEDEL, W., SCHOENMACKERS, J., AND WITZLEB, E. Probleme der Coronardurchblutung, Bad Oeynhausener Gesprache II, Springer-Verlag, Heidelberg, 1958.

BECK, C. S., BROFMAN, B. L., AND MAUTZ, F. R. Symposium on coronary artery disease. Dis. Chest, 1957, 31, 243.

BING, R. J. The coronary circulation in health and disease as studied by coronary sinus catheterization. Bull. New York Acad. Med., 1951, 27, 407.

BING, R. J. The Harvey Lectures, p. 27. The Academic Press, New York, 1956.

BLUMGART, H. L. Anatomy and functional importance of intercoronary arterial anastomoses (ed.). Circulation, 1959, 20, 812.

GREGG, D. E. Coronary circulation in health and disease. Lea & Febiger, 1950.

GREGG, D. E. Regulation of the collateral and coronary circulation of the heart. Lecture, Harvey Tercentenary Congress, London, 1957.

GREGG, D. E. The coronary circulation, Encyclopedia of Cardiology, Vol. I, Ch. 23, McGraw-Hill-Blakiston, New York, 1959.

GREGG, D. E. Physiology of the coronary circulation. Ann. New York Acad. Sci., 1960, **90**, 145–155.

GREGG, D. E. Physiopathology of different surgical approaches to human coronary atherosclerosis. Acta cardiol., 1959, **14**, Suppl. 8, 3.

GREGG, D. E. Some problems of the coronary circulation. Verh. der Deutsch. Gesellsch. fur Kreislaufforschg., 1955, **21**, 22.

GREGG, D. E., AND SABISTON, D., JR. Current research and problems of the coronary circulation. Circulation, 1956, **13**, 916.

KARDESCH, M., HOGANCAMP, C. E., AND BING, R. J. The survival of excitability, energy production and energy utilization of the heart. Clinical progress. Circulation, 1958, **18**, 935.

OLSON, R. E. AND PIATNEK, D. A. Conservation of energy in cardiac muscle. Ann. New York Acad. Sci., 1959, **72**, 466.

CHAPTER 46

Special Features of the Circulation in Different Regions: Brain, Skeletal Muscle, Skin

The Cerebral Circulation

The cerebral circulation has been investigated extensively in various experimental animals in the past. The traumatic procedures necessary for obtaining blood flow measurements, however, prohibited the study of the circulation in the human brain. This became possible only since the introduction, recently, of a method permitting indirect measurement of cerebral blood flow in unanesthetized human subjects.

The nitrous oxide method (Kety and Schmidt, 1948) is based on the Fick principle (see ch. 39). The subject breathes a gas mixture containing 15 per cent N_2O, while blood samples are obtained from a peripheral artery and from the internal jugular vein (representing mixed cerebral venous blood). Cerebral blood flow per unit weight of brain may be calculated from the arterial and venous gas concentrations and the partition coefficient for nitrous oxide between brain and blood. Results are usually expressed as milliliters of blood per 100 grams of brain per minute; in resting, normal young men the mean value is 54 ml. Assuming a weight of 1400 grams for the brain, total cerebral blood flow is about 750 ml. per minute.

In experimental animals, where it is possible to check the results obtained by this method against direct cerebral blood flow measurements, there is good agreement between the two. In recent years the nitrous oxide procedure has been modified and adapted to the use of various radioactively labeled materials. Consideration of the cerebral circulation here will be limited to information derived from studies in man.

Cerebral blood flow is determined by two opposing sets of forces: the effective perfusion pressure and cerebral vascular resistance (see fig. 46.1). Effective perfusion pressure is the gradient between arterial blood pressure and internal jugular venous pressure; cerebral vascular resistance is defined here as the sum of all factors opposing the flow of blood through the brain, such as intracranial pressure, blood viscosity and vascular diameter.

Internal jugular venous pressure for all practi-

cal purposes is negligible as compared to arterial pressure. Even the obstruction of the vein by means of a tourniquet placed on the neck, producing pressures up to 300 mm. of water, has no effect on cerebral blood flow (Moyer and associates, 1954a). Thus, arterial blood pressure is the sole important determinant of the driving force of blood flow across the brain.

The relation of arterial blood pressure to cerebral blood flow is determined by the level of the blood pressure itself. A lowering of the mean arterial pressure to a level of about 60 to 70 mm. Hg by means of high spinal anesthesia, paralyzing most of the sympathetic vasoconstrictor nerves has no effect on cerebral blood flow, which remains constant (Kleinerman and associates, 1958). This indicates a compensatory lowering of vascular resistance in the brain (see below). Similarly, an elevation of blood pressure is without effect on blood flow due to a secondary increase in resistance (Moyer and associates, 1954b). This autoregulation of the cerebral circulation becomes ineffective, however, when mean blood pressure falls below 60 mm. Hg. In this hypotensive range, a lowering of blood pressure results in a reduction of blood flow. Initially, this is compensated for by increased oxygen extraction by the tissues, but at mean pressure levels of about 30 mm. Hg, when cerebral blood flow is reduced to about 30 ml. per 100 grams of tissue per minute, signs of cerebral ischemia appear (Finnerty and associates, 1954). Conversely, raising the blood pressure under these conditions increases blood flow, unlike in the normotensive range.

As seen in fig. 46.1, several extravascular factors contribute to "cerebral vascular resistance". Intracranial pressure, exerted upon the freely collapsible capillaries of the brain is a force opposing the flow of blood. Any increase in this pressure, resulting from an expansion of the contents of the rigid cranial box (such as a brain tumor) elevates cerebral vascular resistance in a direct, linear manner (Kety and associates, 1948). In spite of this, cerebral blood flow does not diminish until intracranial pressure reaches very

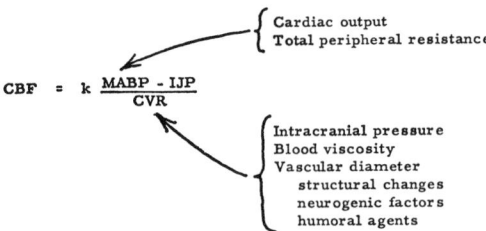

FIG. 46.1. Factors determining the cerebral blood flow. CBF, cerebral blood flow; MABP, mean arterial blood pressure; IJP, internal jugular venous pressure; CVR, cerebral vascular resistance. (From Kety, S. S., in Circulation, Proceedings of Harvey Tercentenary Congress, p. 329, 1958.)

high levels (about 450 mm. of water). The maintenance of normal flow is due to an increase of systemic blood pressure brought about by peripheral vasoconstriction. It has been suggested that the stimulus for the latter is ischemia of the medullary vasomotor center.

Viscosity of the blood increases resistance to flow: in polycythemia cerebral blood flow is considerably reduced; it is restored to normal levels after correcting the increased viscosity by phlebotomies (Nelson and Fazekas, 1956). In anemia, on the other hand, cerebral blood flow is increased in proportion to the decreased red cell mass; transfusion produces a return to normal flow (Robin and Gardner, 1953).

The most important component of cerebral vascular resistance is the diameter of the cerebral blood vessels. Their adjustment is responsible for the remarkable constancy of blood flow over a wide range of perfusion pressures, discussed above. The exact mechanism of vasomotor regulation in the brain is not known. Although the cerebral vessels are supplied by sympathetic fibers and norepinephrine is a powerful cerebral vasoconstrictor (King and associates, 1952), there is no evidence to show that they are physiologically active in man. Bilateral blocking of the stellate ganglia fails to produce any change in cerebral vascular resistance or blood flow, contrary to what might be expected if these nerves were normally contributing to the maintenance of cerebral vascular tone.

In contrast to this is the marked sensitivity exhibited by the cerebral vasculature to changes in arterial concentration of carbon dioxide and oxygen. Carbon dioxide is the most powerful cerebral vasodilator known. Inhalation of a gas mixture containing 5 or 7 per cent CO_2, which raises arterial pCO_2 by 9 mm. Hg, causes a 75 per cent increase in cerebral blood flow. Systemic

blood pressure rises without any change in cardiac output, indicating a peripheral vasoconstrictor effect, but cerebral vascular resistance falls, showing the specific vasodilator action of carbon dioxide on the cerebral vessels (Kety and Schmidt, 1948). Hyperventilation, which lowers arterial pCO_2, reduces cerebral blood flow.

These effects of carbon dioxide are not related to associated changes in hydrogen ion concentration. Intravenous infusion of sodium bicarbonate, which produces an increase of the total carbon dioxide content of the blood and a systemic alkalosis, has the same qualitative effect on cerebral vascular resistance as inhalation of 5 per cent CO_2, which also raises total blood carbon dioxide but results in acidosis. Conversely, an infusion of NH_4Cl duplicates the cerebral effects of hyperventilation: both procedures reduce the total carbon dioxide content of the blood, but the accompanying pH changes are in the opposite directions (Schieve and Wilson, 1953).

The vasodilator effect of carbon dioxide is a threshold phenomenon. No change in cerebral vascular resistance is detectable for arterial pCO_2 increases of up to 4.5 mm. Hg; beyond this point there is progressive vasodilation with further arterial pCO_2 increments (Patterson and associates, 1955). Decreasing the arterial CO_2 tension below normal produces cerebral vasoconstriction, but the reduction in cerebral blood flow is proportionately less than the increase resulting from hypercapnia (Wasserman and Patterson, 1961).

In view of the pronounced cerebral vasomotor activity of carbon dioxide on the one hand, and the absence of any demonstrable neurogenic control on the other, it is logical to postulate that cerebral blood flow is regulated, at least in part, by local carbon dioxide concentrations. It was calculated that a reduction in blood flow of about 30 per cent would be required for capillary carbon dioxide tension to reach the average vasodilator threshold level of 4.5. In all likelihood, however, a reduction of this magnitude is not necessary, since under physiological conditions any increase in carbon dioxide concentration would be accompanied by hypoxia (see below).

The cerebral vasomotor action of oxygen is qualitatively the direct opposite of that produced by carbon dioxide. Inhalation of a gas mixture containing 10 per cent oxygen, which reduces arterial oxygen content by about one-third, causes a 35 per cent increase in cerebral blood flow, despite a fall in systemic blood pressure and a decreased arterial pCO_2 and pH (due to increased pulmonary ventilation) (Kety and

Schmidt, 1948). The net effect of this degree of hypoxia on cerebral vascular resistance equals that produced by the inhalation of 5 to 7 per cent CO_2. Inhalation of high concentrations of oxygen which increase arterial pO_2, causes a reduction of cerebral blood flow, but recently it was stated that this does not occur if care is taken to prevent concomitant hypocapnia (Turner and associates, 1957).

If, as it may seem plausible, hypercapnia and hypoxia act synergistically on cerebral vascular resistance, possibly in combination with other metabolic products resulting from a diminished blood supply, this could well explain the mechanism of autoregulation exhibited by the cerebral circulation. Any impairment of blood supply resulting from a drop in perfusion pressure would automatically lead to an accumulation of metabolic products which, when present in sufficient concentrations, would act to restore blood flow by producing vasodilation. At the present time, however, this is still an unproved hypothesis.

Whatever is the exact mechanism of cerebral vasomotor regulation, cerebral blood flow shows a remarkable constancy under a variety of physiological conditions studied so far. In spite of the increased cardiac output and arterial blood pressure associated with physical exercise, cerebral blood flow remains unchanged (Hedlund and associates, 1962); there may be a slight increase in cerebral vascular resistance, probably due to the concomitant drop in arterial pCO_2 secondary to hyperventilation (Kleinerman and Sancetta, 1955). Intellectual efforts, such as mental arithmetics, have no effect on cerebral blood flow (Sokoloff and associates, 1955). Anxiety also seems to be devoid of influences on cerebral hemodynamics (Scheinberg and Stead, 1949). Natural sleep induces cerebral vasodilation and a small increase in blood flow without changes in arterial oxygen or carbon dioxide tensions (Mangold and associates, 1955). Eating does not affect cerebral blood flow (Rowe and associates, 1959). The effects of tilting from the supine to the upright position depend on the degree of tilting. Moderate elevations (20° from horizontal) have no effect on cerebral blood flow (Shenkin and associates, 1948), but more near-vertical positions which lower the mean arterial pressure at head level below 60 mm. Hg cause, as it might be expected, a reduction in blood flow despite a decrease in cerebral vascular resistance (Scheinberg and Stead, 1949).

The Cutaneous Circulation

THE ANATOMY OF THE CUTANEOUS CIRCULATION AND SKIN COLOR

The architecture of the vessels of the skin has the general pattern already described in Chapter 36. The arterioles upon approaching the bases of the papillae (the layer of the corium immediately underlying the epidermis) turn horizontally, and give rise to metarterioles from which originate, in turn, hairpin-shaped endothelial tubes—the *capillary loops*. The proximal or arterial limb of the capillary loop ascends in the papilla and then turns upon itself to form the venous limb. The latter on reaching the base of the papilla joins with the venous limbs of neighboring loops to form a *collecting venule*. The collecting venules anastomose with one another to form a rich plexus—the *subpapillary venous* plexus—which runs horizontally beneath the bases of the papillae and drains into deeper veins. The capillary loops can be seen readily in the living skin under the low power of the microscope. The vessels at the base of the human fingernail are shown diagramatically in fig. 46.2.

The color of the skin is dependent upon the capillary loops and the subpapillary venous plexus. The vessels of the plexus, though more deeply placed, present a greater area parallel to the skin, whereas the capillary loops are disposed chiefly at right angles to the skin surface. When little blood is contained in the superficial vessels, the skin is unusually pale and more transparent, and the deeper venous plexuses then contribute largely to the color of the skin, often adding a leaden tint to the pallor. When the overlying vessels are open and the skin is well

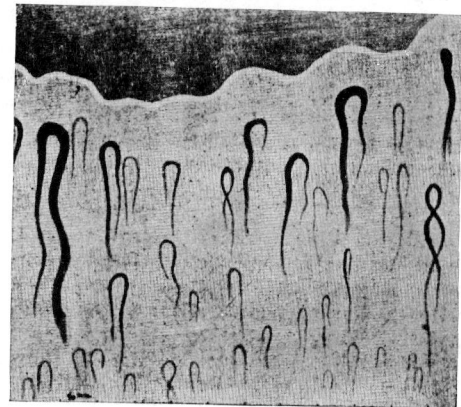

FIG. 46.2. The bed of the finger nail in a healthy subject, showing the capillary loops and the summits of the skin papillae. (After Lewis.)

supplied with blood, these deeper vessels are hidden from view.

Apart from pigmentary effects, and assuming the arterial blood to be normal, the *color* of the skin, i.e., the dominance of the reddish or of the bluish hue, depends upon the extent to which the oxyhemoglobin becomes reduced during the passage of the blood through the cutaneous vessels. The degree of reduction will depend, as a rule, upon the rate of blood flow. With rapid flow, the blood is more arterial in character, with slow flow, more venous, and the color of the skin varies accordingly.

The depth or intensity of the skin color is dependent upon the diameters and degree of engorgement of the superficial vessels.

Taking into account both the hue and the depth of color, an intense scarlet color of the skin indicates an increased blood flow and dilated vessels; a deep blue color accompanies a slowed blood flow and dilated vessels (such as would result from obstruction to the venous trunks), or arterial desaturation (cyanosis). Pallor or a light pink color of the skin is seen when the vessels are constricted or of moderate tone, and the blood flow normal or rapid. A slowed cutaneous blood flow and constricted superficial vessels tend to produce a leaden or ashen type of cyanosis for, as mentioned above, the dark blood in the deeper venous plexuses then becomes faintly visible.

EXPERIMENTAL INVESTIGATION OF SKIN BLOOD FLOW. Blood flow in the skin serves two main functions: (1) the regulation of body temperature, and (2) nourishment of the skin. The regulation of skin blood flow has been studied through the effects produced by direct or indirect warming or cooling, by pharmacological agents which act similarly to nervous system transmitters, by drugs which block the nervous supply or specific receptor sites, or by direct stimulation of nerves, baroreceptors or specific areas of the brain. Since the skin of animals (except for the paws) differs from human skin in possessing probably only vasoconstrictor fibers, data obtained from humans will be presented unless only animal studies are available. The skin of dogs and cats lacks eccrine glands, and sweating is absent (except in the paws). Techniques of blood flow measurement in human skin include plethysmography, continuous temperature recording, calorimetry, clearance rates of radioactive materials, oxygen polarography, blood oxygen saturation of cutaneous veins, pulse volume studies, and direct microscopic inspection of the vessels (ch. 39).

Human skin studies are limited because there is no direct method of blood flow measurement.

CONTROL OF SKIN BLOOD FLOW AND REGULATION OF BODY TEMPERATURE. Skin blood flow does not react the same in all areas of the body. The innervation of the cutaneous blood vessels differs regionally. Cutaneous vessels are regulated by the sympathetic nervous system; a parasympathetic supply has not been shown in any area. The sympathetic innervation has been demonstrated by blocking its effects with adrenergic or ganglionic blocking agents or sympathectomy. This presumably rules out a somatic or parasympathetic nervous system control of the vasomotor reflex being studied. The type of end-organ transmitter involved in the sympathetic responses is determined by the use of adrenergic or cholinergic (atropine) blocking agents. It should be pointed out that the sympathetic fibers travel with the main somatic nerves in the extremities so that both are blocked by anesthetization of the deep nerves.

A. Cutaneous Blood Flow in the Hand and Foot

Only a vasoconstrictor nerve supply with adrenergic sympathetic fibers has been identified in the hand or foot; its contribution to the regulation of body temperature has been shown to be of importance. The demonstration of specific cholinesterases by histochemical methods in the digital arteriovenous anastomoses suggests they may be cholinergically controlled. It has also been postulated that the sympathetic nerve supply to human fingers exerts a tonic dilator influence on vessels through the release of acetylcholine. The indirect evidence for this theory includes the dilation of vessels by extracts of human digital arteries, prevention of digital vessel dilation by atropine, and the presence in digital vessels of pseudocholinesterase activity.

Recently, a nonapeptide, bradykinin, has been suggested as an important factor causing active vasodilation in human forearm skin and, evidently, in any skin area containing sweat glands (palms and soles). During activity of the sweat glands, a proteolytic enzyme is released into the tissues where it acts on a decapeptide, bradykininogen to produce bradykinin (fig. 46.3). Bradykininogen is a normal component of the pseudoglobulin fraction of the plasma. Bradykinin is one of the most potent cutaneous vasodilators. Its concentration in human forearm skin reflexly vasodilated by body warming increases even before sweating or a rise in skin temperature has

SCHEMATIC DIAGRAM OF BRADYKININ FORMATION IN HUMAN SKIN

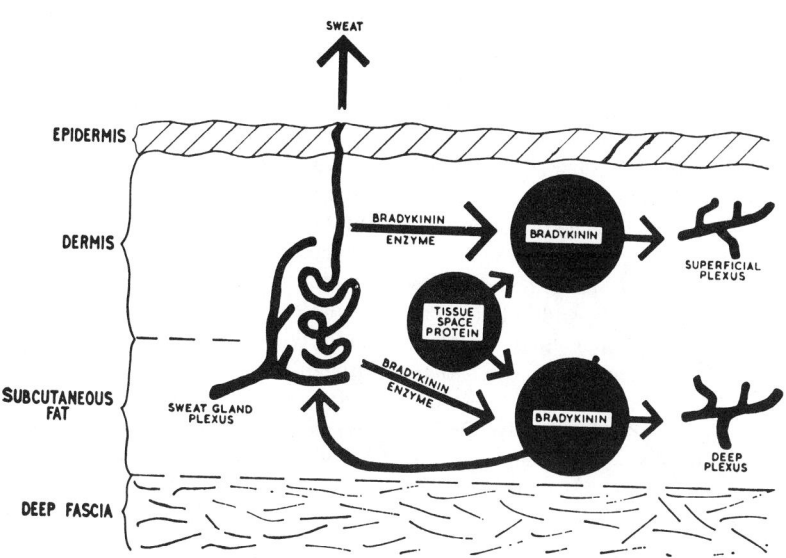

Fig. 46.3. Schematic diagram of bradykinin formation in human forearm skin during body warming. Sympathetic stimulation of the sweat gland releases a proteolytic enzyme which acts on a tissue fluid decapeptide (bradykininogen) to form a nonapeptide (bradykinin). The polypeptide has a vasodilator action of the cutaneous vasculature (from Barcroft).

occurred. The eccrine glands are presumably activated by a cholinergic substance *via* the sympathetic nervous system. This pathway is not believed to account for all reflex vasodilation for the vasodilation has been observed without an apparent change in sweat gland activity, and sweating may occur with no increase, or even with a decrease, in cutaneous blood flow.

A peptide-forming enzyme capable of releasing bradykinin has been isolated from carcinoid hepatic metastases and a vasoactive peptide, identical in many respects to bradykinin, has been isolated from the blood of these patients. Previously, flushes in carcinoid patients were considered to be due to serotonin.

Body warming elicits a reflex vasodilation in the hand or foot which has been shown to correlate with a release of vasoconstrictor tone (a decreased number of impulses traveling over the sympathetic nerve fibers). The reflex may originate either in cutaneous receptors or by central nervous system stimulation. The vessels, themselves, are also sensitive to warm temperature for the dilation following vasomotor nervous inhibition (by blocking agents) can be augmented by local heating of the hand. When the human body is cooled, the toe temperature approaches environmental temperature, whereas the finger tips cool but show more fluctuation in temperature

and blood flow. Similar cooling of the hands and feet occurs reflexly when cold is applied to one area of the body, such as the forehead. The transmitter substance involved in the cutaneous vasoconstriction mediated by the sympathetic nervous system is thought to be norepinephrine.

Since vasoconstrictor tone develops earlier and is more stable and less readily reversed by body warming in the feet than in the hands, it has been suggested that the lower extremities are concerned with gross adjustments while the upper extremities provide the fine regulation of body temperature.

If a finger is immersed in cold water, its temperature falls rapidly to the bath temperature and blood flow slows; the vessels then fluctuate in cycles of constriction and dilation. Both the sympathetic vasoconstrictive reflex and the local direct effect of cold on the vessels are involved in the reduction of blood flow. The vasodilatory mechanism during the cyclic changes remains partially unexplained. It is probably an effective protection against cold injury. Lewis thought it was secondary to a local or axon reflex (*via* the dorsal root vasodilator fibers); however the absence of sensory fibers reduces, but does not abolish, the response. As mentioned before, there is evidence for an active vasodilator innervation of the arteriovenous anastomoses which may take part in this cold vasodilation.

Arteriovenous (AV) anastomoses are communications between smaller arteries and arterioles and the corresponding venous channels, through which the blood may be shunted and capillary areas short circuited (fig. 46.4). The presence of a direct or indirect regulatory mechanism should be included in the shunt concept of AV anastomoses. These communications have been studied mostly in animals, especially the rabbit. In the rabbit ear, AV anastomoses have been observed to undergo rhythmic contraction and dilation, to contract after noxious stimuli, and to close during sleep. They react at a greater speed than arteries or arterioles and tend to act independently of neighboring vessels. Faradic stimulation of their nerve supply causes constriction of the anastomoses and disappearance of their rhythmic activity; destruction of their nerves leads to dilation. The nature of their nervous supply, sympathetic or parasympathetic, is unknown. The AV anastomoses react in the same manner as arterioles to the administration of epinephrine, norepinephrine, histamine, or acetylcholine, but close during hypoxia. In the rabbit ear, the AV anastomoses have been shown to be very effective in controlling the body temperature. An increased

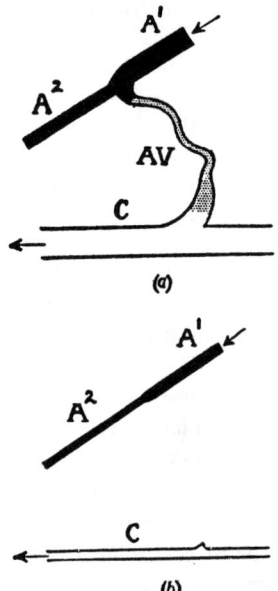

FIG. 46.4. Reaction of anastomosis and associated vessels to lowering of body temperature. A^1, artery; A^2, arteriole; AV, arteriovenous anastomosis; C, vein. Upper figure (*a*), anastomosis, open; lower figure (*b*), anastomosis closed. (After Grant.)

temperature induces vasodilation and a decreased temperature, constriction. When open, these channels would offer very low vessel resistance and large volumes of blood could flow through them for heat exchange. It has been demonstrated by a method involving the injection of microspheres that more than one third of the total flow through the rabbit ear or dog paw may pass through such shunts. The microspheres are suitably selected in size to pass through anastomotic vessels but not capillaries. Another function of the AV anastomoses may be in the regulation of vascular hemodynamics. For example, when open there would be more rapid flow through veins and vice versa.

Human digits and palms (glomus areas) and ears have large numbers of these potential shunts. The glomus areas contain muscular tufts and AV anastomoses, and receive a rich nervous innervation. In man, little information, except that mentioned previously, exists regarding the control or function of the AV anastomoses. Although studies suggest that they play a large role in the regulation of human body temperature by increasing or decreasing the radiation of heat, their participation in such reflexes has not been shown. The high rates and wide, rapid variations in digital blood flow (1 to 150 ml. per 100 ml. of skin per min.) are often attributed to these channels. The disappearance rate of a radioisotope from a depot in skin or muscle has been considered to represent capillary blood flow and not flow through anastomoses. For example the total plethysmographic blood flow of a finger may increase during body warming but the radioisotope disappearance rate does not change or slows. The disappearance rate is interpreted as demonstrating that the increase in total blood flow was through AV anastomoses. It is evident that new methods of study are needed to further our knowledge of these interesting communications.

B. Cutaneous Blood Flow of the Forearm

The blood flow of the forearm skin has been estimated to vary from 0 to 70.5 ml. per 100 ml. of skin per minute using rates determined plethysmographically before and after abolition of flow by epinephrine iontophoresis of the skin. The skin of the forearm has been shown to possess both a sympathetic vasoconstrictor and vasodilator nerve supply in contrast to that of the hand and foot. It was demonstrated that the increase in forearm blood flow secondary to body heating occurred in the skin and not in the muscles by the following: (1) iontophoresis of the forearm skin with epinephrine abolishes the increased forearm flow response, (2) venous oxygen saturation from cutaneous superficial veins rises while that from muscle veins remains stable during body heating, and (3) the temperature of the skin rises with body heating but that of muscle does not. By blockage of the forearm cutaneous nerve supply with local ring anesthesia or deep nerve blocks, the vasodilation reflex was prevented. The vasodilation could be partly blocked by atropine indicating cholinergic sympathetic fibers were involved. The experiments demonstrating the bradykinin mechanism and its activation by sympathetic sudomotor stimulation (as explained above) were performed in the forearm skin. Bradykinin vasodilation, the release of vasoconstrictor tone, and the direct effect of heat in relaxing the blood vessels may all play a part in the vasodilation which occurs in forearm skin during total body warming. A parasympathetic innervation has not been demonstrated.

The skin temperature and blood flow of the forearm decrease in response to body cooling. A longitudinal temperature gradient from the warmer trunk to the cooler hands and feet is maintained. The vasoconstriction in the forearm skin is evidently via sympathetic fibers as in the hands and feet.

In humans, subcutaneous injections of CO_2 cause a vasodilation, probably of small resistance vessels. Hyperventilation produces a decreased blood flow in normal and nerve blocked hands and fingers. In dogs, low pH solutions intra-arterially elicit a marked increase in cutaneous blood flow while alkaline solutions reduce flow.

Human skin studies utilizing the oxygen polarograph have shown that the oxygen tension increases with temperature elevations up to, but not over, about 43° C. It is postulated that heating causes an increase in the blood flow, a greater dissociation of oxygen from hemoglobin, and an increased supply of oxygen and blood to the skin. At higher temperatures, the oxygen utilization would outstrip the increased supply. The role of skin metabolism in the regulation of cutaneous blood flow has received little investigation.

C. Cutaneous Blood Flow to Other Skin Areas

Skin areas, other than the extremities, have received little study because of the lack of techniques for measuring blood flow. Most available studies have utilized the qualitative measurements of blood flow determined by the photo-

electric plethysmograph or surface temperature changes. The forehead skin is believed to have a weak or absent vasoconstrictor nerve supply. During cold exposure, the surface temperatures of the head and trunk fall relatively little and high rates of blood flow continue. This has been an important finding leading to the use of head gear to prevent heat loss in cold weather. Vasomotor reflexes to noise or distal application of cold, which severely decrease hand flow, have only a slight effect on forehead blood flow. India ink injections show the vascular plexus of the forehead to be very extensive while the rapid clearance of radioactive sodium and larger volume pulse measurements demonstrate the blood flow to exceed that in the skin of the calf, forearm and trunk. The forehead and cheek evidently do not possess glomi so all flow is through the capillary beds. Some pharmacological agents (nicotinic acid, histamine, papaverine, and Roniacol) increased the skin temperature in these areas but not in the toes. Adrenergic and ganglionic blocking agents had no effect on forehead skin temperature. It has been suggested that cholinergic sympathetic fibers maintain vasomotor tone in the forehead and cheek areas but experimental evidence for this is too indirect.

D. The Effect of Perfusion Pressure on Skin Blood Flow

The mechanical effects of perfusion pressure on blood flow were measured in isolated cutaneous beds of dog hind limbs. The *in situ* vascular bed was perfused *via* the saphenous artery from a reservoir of adjustable height to allow changes in perfusion pressure. When the rate of flow was plotted against changes in perfusion pressure, a parabolic curve (fig. 46.5) was obtained instead of a straight line. There was a progressive decrease in resistance to flow in the vessels as the perfusion pressure rose. With an increase of vasomotor tone in the vascular bed, the flow for any given pressure decreased. The nonlinear relation between flow and perfusion pressure may be secondary to a progressive decrease in viscosity of blood (because of a more axial flow of red cells) or to a mechanical dilation of blood vessels with the rising perfusion pressure.

E. The Cutaneous Veins

In dogs and cats, it has been shown that the superficial large and small veins of the skin have a nerve supply, undergo rhythmic changes in

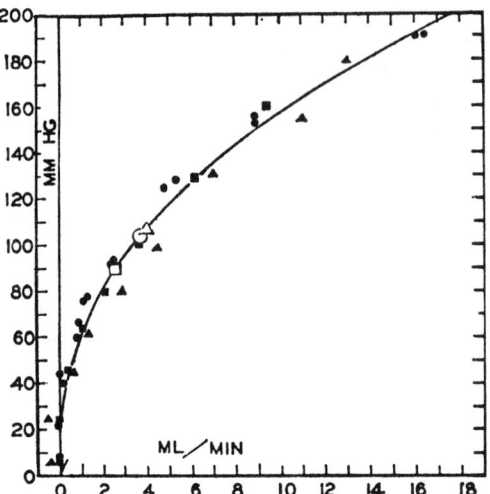

FIG. 46.5. Plot of relationship between perfusion pressure and blood flow through the skin supplied by the saphenous artery, in the hindlimb of a dog in which vasomotor activity remained practically constant at a high level. *Solid symbols* represent data obtained at different times during a 7-hour interval. *Hollow symbols* represent the animal's mean arterial blood pressure at these times. Ordinate scale represents the perfusion pressure in mm. Hg, expressed as the difference in pressure between arterial and venous pressures. Abscissal scale represents the blood flow in milliliters per minute. (Slightly modified from Green, Lewis, Nickerson and Heller.)

diameter, and respond to pharmacological agents. The small veins may contract separately and independently from the large veins or arterial vessels during sympathetic nerve stimulation. When the veins constrict, an increase in pressure results. Thus, a reduced blood flow may occur through the vascular bed without an obstruction or constriction of the arterial tree being present. In humans, forearm cutaneous vein segments, which were isolated *in situ* by pressure, have been demonstrated to constrict following a variety of normal and noxious stimuli. The venoconstriction was blocked by chemical or surgical sympathectomy or infiltration of an anesthetic solution around the vein. Venous tone was decreased during vasovagal syncope and by stroking the skin over the vein. The fact that cutaneous veins constrict by cooling and are not affected by warming is evidence for the existence of only a vasoconstrictor nervous supply. The active innervation of veins is evidently very important in the response of the cutaneous circulation to ordinary and abnormal stimuli although veins react more slowly than arteries or arterioles.

F. Vascular Responses of Skin to Stimulation by Mechanical and Other Agencies. Dorsal Root Vasodilator Fibers

1. THE WHITE REACTION. If the surface of the skin is stroked lightly with a blunt "pointed" instrument, a line of pallor appears in 15 to 20 sec. which traces the path taken by the instrument. The line attains its maximal intensity in ½ to 1 min., and then gradually fades to disappear in 3 to 5 minutes. The white reaction proper is due to direct stimulation of the capillary wall and has no nervous basis. It has been shown by Lewis to be due to the tension exerted upon the walls of the minute vessels—capillary loops, collecting venules and especially of the subpapillary venous plexus—which respond to the stimulus by contraction. The sharply delineated character of the white line, and the fact that it can be obtained after the circulation through the region has been occluded by compression of the larger vessels, show that it is an active capillary response, and not the result of arteriolar constriction.

2. THE TRIPLE RESPONSE. This comprises: (a) *the red reaction*, (b) *the flare*, and (c) *the wheal*.

(*a*) *The red reaction.* If the pointed instrument is drawn more firmly across the skin, especially of the forearm or back, a red instead of a white band appears after a somewhat shorter latent period (3 to 15 sec.), reaches its maximum in ½ to 1 min., and then gradually fades. Like the white reaction it is strictly localized to the line of stroke; it is due to *dilation* of the capillary vessels. The red reaction can be induced in its full intensity in the skin from which the circulation has been occluded, so it is due to active dilation of the capillary vessels and not merely a passive result of anteriolar dilation. *The red reaction is not dependent upon nervous mechanisms since it occurs after section and degeneration of the cutanous nerves.*

(*b*) *The spreading flush or flare.* If the stimulus is unusually strong, or is repeated often enough, the reddening of the skin is not confined to the line of stroke but surrounds it for a variable distance (1 to 10 cm.) according to the intensity of the injury inflicted. The temperature in the suffused area is definitely raised. This flare reaction appears a few seconds (15 to 30) after the local red line, and fades sooner. It is due to dilation of the arterioles, since it does not appear after the circulation of the part has been occluded by means of a tourniquet; also, unlike the red reaction, *the flare is dependent upon local nervous mechanisms* (*axon reflex*). *It occurs after the nerves are divided but not after they have degenerated.*

(*c*) *Local edema or wheal.* When the stimulus is still more intense, the skin along the line of the injury becomes blanched and raised above the surrounding area to a height of 1 or 2 mm. or even more. Such a wheal or welt can be produced in a normal person by the lash of a whip and other types of strong localized stimulation. In susceptible individuals, even light stimulation, such as drawing a pencil with moderate pressure over the skin of the back, will produce linear wheals surrounded by a diffuse red halo along the pencil's track. In this way letters or other designs may be embossed upon the skin (fig. 46.6). This phenomenon is spoken of as *dermographism or factitious urticaria.* The wheal is preceded by, but then completely replaces, the usual red reaction. It makes its appearance in 1 to 3 min. from the time of injury and is at its maximum height in 3 to 5 min. It is surrounded by the flare described above. The raised patch at first is clearly demarcated, but as time passes it increases in width and decreases in height, loses its sharpness and finally, though perhaps not for some hours, disappears. The wheal is due to the transudation of fluid from the minute vessels involved previously in the red reaction; it is, therefore, a localized edema. Increased permeability of the capillary wall is judged to be the immediate cause. Increased intracapillary pressure, distension of the capillary lumen, or reduction in pressure in extracapillary spaces are not responsible as shown by Lewis. That increased permeability rather than simply a rise in the filtration pressure is the dominating feature is also manifest by the high protein content of the transuded fluid. This more nearly approaches that of blood serum than the fluid of ordinary edema. Wheal production does not depend upon a nervous mechanism.

A considerable weight of indirect evidence has been presented by Lewis to support the conception that a diffusible substance is responsible for the three reactions comprising the triple response. This material, which he calls *H-substance,* is thought to be liberated by the injured cells of the epidermis lying beneath the horny layer and superficial to the papillae. The possibility that more deeply lying tissues, when subjected to injury, may release the substance is not excluded, but a needle which does not penetrate beyond the epidermis elicits the typical threefold reaction. The chemical substance closely resembles *histamine* in its action. It apparently causes the red

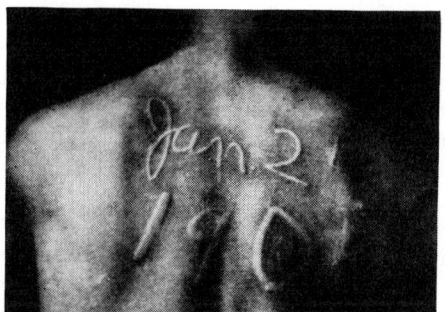

Fig. 46.6. Dermographism. (From Adami's textbook of Pathology, after Hyde and Ormsby.)

reaction and the wheal by a direct action upon the capillary wall. The flare is believed to be due to chemical stimulation of the sensory nerve endings of the skin, thus bringing about arteriolar dilation through the mechanism of the axon reflex. Although the evidence for this theory is indirect and actual proof of the existence of such a humoral mechanism is lacking, the results of Lewis's various ingenious experiments carry conviction.

The cutaneous reactions following injuries of various sorts, e.g., burning, freezing, electrical stimulation, are believed to be produced by the same humoral mechanism. The cardinal signs of inflammation—redness, heat and to some extent the swelling and pain—can be similarly explained, namely, direct action of the dilator H-substance upon the minute vessels, and an indirect effect through the medium of the axon reflex, upon the arterioles of the surrounding area. The ultraviolet light reaction in man is evidently secondary to a different mechanism. It has been shown that the ultraviolet light erythema is not reduced by pretreatment with antihistamines. Also histamine introduced into areas of ultraviolet erythema produces its usual triple response. Thus, Lewis's theory of all cutaneous inflammatory processes being secondary to release of the H-substance is not universally applicable.

Bradykinin has also been proposed as a humoral mediator in the inflammatory reaction. It is as potent a vasodilator as histamine, its ability to increase capillary permeability is greater than that of histamine, it causes pain on local injection, and it induces leukocytes to migrate to the area of injection. However the experimental evidence for bradykinin involvement in the inflammatory reaction is no better than for histamine and much more study is needed in this interesting area.

The dorsal root of the spinal cord contains vasodilatory fibers supplying mostly the cutaneous vessels. They do not convey impulses to or from the higher central nervous system centers for control of the cutaneous circulation. No true cutaneous vasomotor reflexes are seen after sympathectomy. Experiments have shown that the dorsal root vasodilator fibers do not engage in the baro- or chemoreceptor control of vascular tone, nor in the regulation of heat loss from the skin. The transmitter substance of these fibers is unknown but they probably act in an axon reflex arrangement to affect regional blood vessels. These are probably the fibers that, upon damage to the superficial tissues, are involved in the vasodilator (flare) reaction of the triple response. Any stimulus causing damage to the skin activates these fibers, such as severe cooling and heating. It was mentioned previously that an axon reflex may be involved in the cyclic vasodilation occurring when a finger is placed in cold water. Severe cooling would elicit the axon reflex in these fibers from the dorsal root with a consequent vasodilation in the finger. The latter would warm the finger stopping the axon reflex discharge and then vasoconstriction would recur.

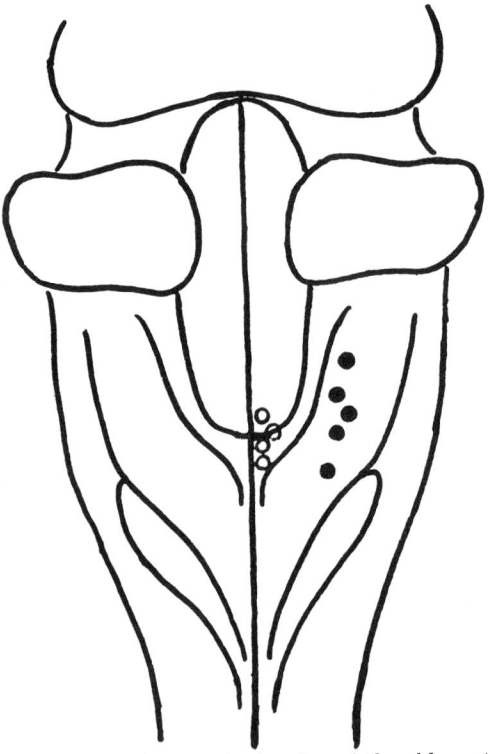

Fig. 46.7. Schematic drawing of the oblongate medulla showing the situation of points yielding skeletal muscle vasodilation secondary to inhibition of vasoconstrictor tone (*open circles*), and points yielding sympathetic vasodilator discharges (*black dots*). (From Lindgren and Uvnäs.)

G. Central Nervous System Control of Cutaneous and Muscle Blood Flow

The central nervous system regulation of blood flow is through the sympathetic fibers.

A variety of stimuli affecting peripheral receptors elicit spinal vasomotor reflexes; the efferent limbs are the cutaneous sympathetic vasoconstrictor fibers. These reflexes are usually segmentally or regionally arranged. Also, in certain animal preparations, the preganglionic sympathetic neurons in the lateral horns of the spinal medulla may exhibit spontaneous activity independent of afferent stimuli.

The vasomotor center located in the oblongate medulla is believed to be the primary controlling factor of cutaneous and muscle vessel vasoconstrictor tone. Experiments on dogs and cats have shown that stimulation of the midline of the oblongate medulla leads to vasodilation in both skin and muscle. This vasodilatory response is not blocked by atropine and, therefore, is secondary to a release of vasoconstrictor tone. Stimulation lateral to this vasodilator area elicits vasoconstriction in the same regions. Both these responses are absent in sympathectomized animals. The vasodilator and vasoconstrictor areas may act as an integrated unit and, evidently, are primarily involved in vascular reflexes arising from the baroreceptors in the carotid sinus and aorta. A decrease in blood pressure causes reflex vasoconstriction in the dog hindlimb *via* the carotid sinus baroreceptors while stimulation of the carotid sinus nerve induces vasodilation in skin and muscle.

The vasomotor center possesses automaticity for it continues discharging impulses without apparent afferent stimuli from the periphery or higher autonomic centers. The marked fluctuations from moment to moment that occur in the digital and forearm arteries and veins, and that disappear following sympathectomy, are thought to be secondary to the activity of the vasomotor center. The patterns of these continuous variations in pulse volume of the fingers, toes and ears, appear to correlate with the personality types (emotional stability or lability) of the humans studied.

Stimulation of a more lateral area to the vasomotor center invokes a vasodilation in skeletal muscle through the activity of the cholinergic (blocked by atropine) sympathetic fibers (fig. 46.7). The vasodilatory area of the vasomotor center has no anatomical or apparent functional connection with these cholinergic fibers which pass through, but do not synapse in, the oblongate medulla.

The anterior hypothalamus is often referred to as the "heat loss center" for it controls the vasoconstrictor fibers in association with the vasomotor center. Local heat applied to this area inhibits vasoconstrictor fiber discharge (vasodilation) while electrical stimulation excites the fibers (vasoconstriction). This center is thought to predominantly regulate the cutaneous vessels and, perhaps, the arteriovenous anastomoses. Sympathectomy also abolishes these effects of the hypothalamus. Stimulation of certain areas in the hypothalamus may elicit a vasodilation in muscle via the cholinergic fibers which synapse in this area. This muscle vasodilation is often associated with a vasoconstriction of the skin.

Many areas of the cerebral cortex have been found that influence, by excitation or inhibition, vasoconstrictor fiber discharge. For example, stimulation of the motor or premotor cortical areas results in cutaneous vasoconstriction. A muscle vasodilation also occurs but is evidently secondary to a baroreceptor reflex from a rise in blood pressure. The cholinergic vasodilator fibers to skeletal muscle are also represented near the motor cortex. These fibers, which probably are distributed only to muscle, synapse in the hypothalamus and mesencephalon and pass through the oblongate medulla as described above. Their function in man is not completely understood, but they appear to be involved in the control of the blood flow needs of muscle and not in the regulation of blood pressure. It is probable that the sympathetic vasodilator innervation of muscle is activated by emotional reactions and prepares for vigorous muscular effort.

Skeletal Muscle Circulation

Resting forearm skeletal muscle blood flow has been estimated to normally range from 1.8 to 9.6 ml. per 100 ml. of muscle per minute (compare to forearm skin flow on p. 844). The blood flow in skeletal muscle is affected and controlled by a multitude of factors. Many of these factors are poorly understood and their relative importance in the normal functioning of skeletal muscle is not known. Investigation of skeletal muscle blood flow is performed in man by techniques similar to those outlined under skin blood flow. The plethysmograph measures both the skin and muscle blood flow; the forearm is considered representative of muscle and the hand or foot,

of skin because of the relative amounts of each tissue in these regions. However, it has been shown that 60% of the total forearm flow may be in the skin under certain conditions. The skin may be iontophoresed with epinephrine to limit or abolish its blood flow in order to obtain forearm muscle flow determinations. However the depth of penetration of the epinephrine is a problem and may alter the muscle blood flow. In animals, blood flow may be measured by more direct methods and the results of central nervous system manipulations may be studied.

NERVOUS SYSTEM CONTROL OF SKELETAL MUSCLE BLOOD FLOW. Vasoconstrictor fibers have been shown to supply skeletal muscle by the demonstration of an increased blood flow in human forearms following nerve blocks, and by other indirect procedures. The transmitter substance for these constrictor fibers is presumably norepinephrine. Intra-arterial epinephrine has both a vasodilator and vasoconstrictor effect (see *beta and alpha receptors*, ch. 12, p. 255) on human skeletal muscle vessels, while norepinephrine has only a vasoconstrictor action. Vasodilator cholinergic sympathetic fibers also supply skeletal muscle as demonstrated by a responsiveness of the bed to acetylcholine, blocking of the vasodilator response with atropine, and the results of studies performed during vasovagal syncope. Despite a fall in blood pressure in vasovagal syncope, the forearm blood flow increases (and hand flow decreases). If the patient has had a sympathectomy, the forearm blood flow does not increase demonstrating that an active vasodilation *via* sympathetic nerve fibers had presumably occurred in the intact extremity. These vasodilator fibers appear to be activated by higher brain centers as described previously and do not participate in reflex blood pressure adjustments.

At present, the vasoconstrictor fibers are believed to be primarily concerned in postural and other homeostatic blood pressure adjustments. When the legs of a subject are raised, an increased blood flow occurs in the forearm but not the hand. This reflex has been shown to be secondary to an increased volume of blood in the thorax and an elevated central venous pressure which probably stimulates receptors in the low pressure vascular bed of the thorax. Since atropine does not abolish the forearm vasodilation, it is considered to be a result of a release of vasoconstrictor tone.

BLOOD GASES, pH, AND IONS AND SKELETAL MUSCLE BLOOD FLOW. The effect of blood gases and pH on skeletal muscle blood flow has been referred to in chapter 42 (p. 749). Studies in the dog forelimb show that many factors affect the vascular bed. Arteriolar dilation is elicited by increased blood levels of potassium, magnesium, acetate, citrate, pyruvate, AMP, ADP, ATP, hydrogen ions, increased plasma tonicity and decreased calcium blood levels. A decrease in hydrogen ions causes arteriolar constriction; elevated calcium concentrations or decreased plasma tonicity act similarly. Combinations of low potassium, increased calcium, low magnesium, and alkalosis produce more vasoconstriction than the ions alone. Changes in blood oxygen content induce only small changes in forelimb resistance. Studies on isolated vessels and in denervated, adrenergically blocked limbs demonstrate that the ions act directly on vascular smooth muscle. The importance of these studies is apparent when the many disease states with electrolyte abnormalities are considered.

Studies in man have shown that the increase in forearm blood flow during hyperventilation (increased pH, decreased arterial pCO_2) is (1) prevented by breathing air mixtures containing 5% CO_2, (2) occurs only in muscle and not in skin, and (3) is not abolished by blocking the nerve supply to the limb. This evidence points to a humoral mechanism which causes the increased forearm blood flow by a direct action on peripheral vessels. It is interesting that a similar increase in forearm blood flow is found when 5 to 10% oxygen is breathed. If CO_2 is added to the latter mixture, the blood flow response is greatly attenuated. Therefore the decreased peripheral resistance present in hypoxia may be secondary to hypocapnia.

Inhalation of 5 to 10% CO_2 (or intravenous sodium bicarbonate) does not increase skeletal muscle blood flow unless sympathetic blockade is present. Thirty percent CO_2 inhalation decreases forearm blood flow; nerve block or general anesthesia abolishes or even reverses the vasoconstriction. Intra-arterial sodium bicarbonate also increases forearm blood flow. Thus hypercapnia produces an *indirect* muscle vasoconstriction and a *direct* vasodilation. The vasoconstriction is believed to be elicited by the effect of increased CO_2 (or decreased pH) on the carotid or aortic body chemoreceptors.

A decreased pH of the blood by 0.08 units (intravenous lactic acid or ammonium chloride) or an increased pH (intravenous sodium bicarbonate) induces no change in forearm blood flow. If the sympathetic nerves are blocked, an increased or decreased pH leads to an increase in

blood flow; therefore a sympathetic vasoconstriction was concealing a direct vasodilation due to the local pH (or CO_2) effect.

In the above studies, the separation of the effects of arterial pCO_2 and pH on the peripheral blood vessels is difficult. In humans, local increase in pCO_2 or pH changes in either direction from normal produce vasodilation. Systemic increases in pCO_2 or changes in pH in either direction induce sympathetic vasoconstriction; systemic hypocapnia causes vasodilation. Data obtained in the dog hind limb does not entirely agree with these findings; the local effect of an increased hydrogen ion concentration is arteriolar dilation but a lowered pH caused by an increased pCO_2 has little effect. Before it can be decided whether pH or pCO_2 is the important variable, further study is necessary. It must be remembered that changing the pH of blood also affects pCO_2.

MECHANICAL EFFECTS ON SKELETAL MUSCLE BLOOD FLOW. When perfusion pressure is plotted against skeletal muscle blood flow (as determined in isolated muscle beds of the hindlimb of a dog), a parabolic-shaped curve is found in the upper and lower ranges (fig. 46.8), as in the skin vascular bed. These two normal relationships of pressure to flow are joined in the intermediate range by a sigmoid curve (a large drop in perfusion pressure changes blood flow little). It is postulated that the reason for the sigmoid curve is a reactive dilation at perfusion pressures below mean normal aortic pressure to maintain blood flow to the muscular bed. The two parabolic areas on the curve would represent perfusion pressures during two states of vasomotor activity of the vessels. Because of the shape of the curve, changes in vasomotor activity, secondary to a variable being tested, cannot always be predicted from the perfusion pressure and blood flow.

METABOLITES AND SKELETAL MUSCLE BLOOD FLOW; EXERCISE AND REACTIVE HYPEREMIA. The skeletal muscle vascular bed is subjected to very active and widely ranging fluctuations in blood flow. The idea has often been expressed that the formation of metabolites by the muscle cells is the main factor in controlling the bed. Since direct stimulation of an animal's curarized muscle still elicits an increased blood flow, while motor nerve excitation does not, it is felt that the hyperemia of contracting muscle is secondary to a local physicochemical change. Also, humans with sympathectomized extremities can perform as well as those with an intact innervation. Local or reflex warming or cooling has little effect on this intrinsic vasomotor tone of muscles. It has been

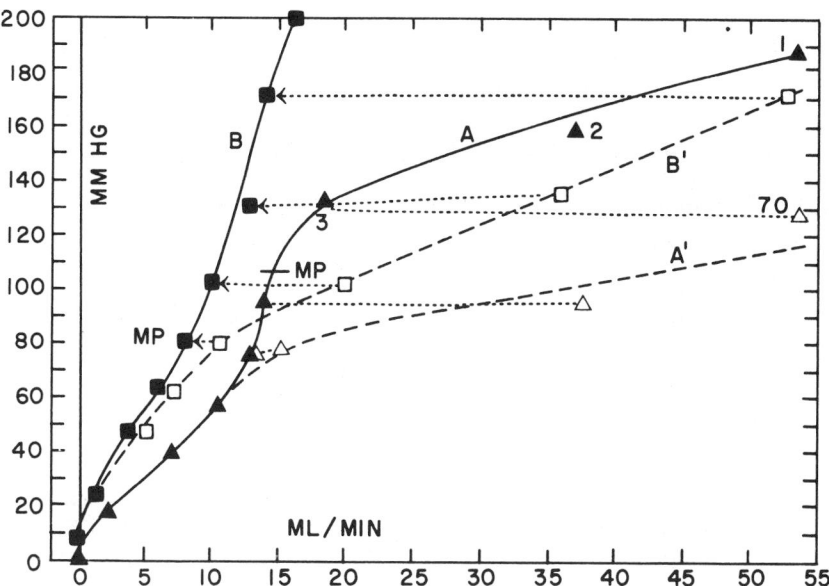

Fɪɢ. 46.8. Plots of relationship between perfusion pressure and blood flow in the portion of the canine quadriceps muscle supplied by the branches of the femoral artery between the inferior epigastric and saphenous branches. Plots A and B were obtained 6 hours apart in the same animal. A^1 and B^1, dashed lines, flow during first 2 seconds of perfusion at each pressure; A and B, solid lines, stabilized flows after maintenance of perfusion pressure for 10 to 20 seconds. Arrows indicate change of flow with time at each perfusion pressure. MP, represents the level of mean arterial pressure. Ordinate scale represents the perfusion pressure in mm.Hg, expressed as the difference between arterial and venous pressures; abscissal scale, blood flow in milliliters per minute (from Green, Lewis, Nickerson and Heller).

suggested that the metabolites, accumulated from muscle cell metabolism, may act directly on the smooth muscle cells of vessels or indirectly *via* a local nervous mechanism, such as peripheral ganglion cells or an axon reflex. The existence of ganglion cells among the muscle fibers has not been proven.

In the dog, muscular activity induces a dilation of the femoral artery which is mediated by an axon reflex (elicitable by acetylcholine). This mechanism, if it was shown to be present in the smaller arterial branches, could account for the vasodilation of exercise. In the cat limb, post exercise muscle hyperemia is blocked by substances (cocaine, botulinum toxin) which are likely to abolish such axon reflexes. The vascular reactivity is not paralyzed by these agents for the vessels continue to respond to epinephrine and acetylcholine. Since botulinum toxin specifically paralyzes cholinergic nerve endings, the fibers in the axon reflex may be cholinergic. However, a strong argument against this theory is that the vasodilation of exercise hyperemia is not blocked by atropine (although atropine does not block cholinergic fibers in all areas).

The role that local metabolites play in stimulating such axon reflexes is not known. Anoxia, increased CO_2 tension, lactic acid, hydrogen ions, bradykinin, histamine, acetylcholine, adenosine triphosphate, adenylic acid, and potassium ions have been suggested as the local determinant eliciting exercise vasodilation. Most of the metabolites have been studied by infusion into the muscular vascular bed or by examination of venous blood leaving the muscle following exercise hyperemia. Each one has received little support as the dilator agent, but a combination of two or more of these factors may provide the answer.

Bradykinin has been shown to be a very potent vasodilator in skeletal muscle by plethysmography and radioisotope disappearance rates. No change in oxygen consumption occurs despite the large increase in human calf blood flow. However there is no evidence for the presence of bradykinin activity in skeletal muscle; the venous blood draining exercising muscle does not contain increased bradykinin activity. These results do not rule out bradykinin as an agent affecting skeletal muscle blood flow, since the half-life of bradykinin in the blood is extremely short and only biological assay methods are available for its detection.

The circulation in human skeletal muscle has been studied by indirect methods during sustained muscular contraction. It was found that below a certain critical strength of sustained contraction of the calf muscle, blood flow was not decreased, but, above this critical point, the vessels were evidently compressed, for hyperemia followed release of the contraction.

With rhythmic contraction of calf or forearm muscles, blood flow was increased during and immediately following exercise. It was felt that increased flow (vasodilator metabolite mediated) alternating with decreased flow (mechanical compression of vessels) paralleled the relaxation and contraction of the muscle. Mechanical obstruction, metabolite formation, and the action of muscles on the venous flow are probably all intricately involved in the muscular blood flow of exercise. It has been shown that an increase in venous pressure may alter arterial inflow to muscle. The sympathetic nervous system probably does not have a significant effect on the circulatory changes during exercise, for vasodilation is similar during the after exercise in normal and sympathectomized limbs. Also, the vascular bed of the exercising hindlimb of the dog becomes less responsive to sympathetic stimulation as the strength of contraction and oxygen uptake increases.

The blood flow of exercising skeletal muscle in the dog, except during maximal exercise, is reduced by sympathetic nerve stimulation, intra-arterial norepinephrine or epinephrine infusions, and carotid sinus stimulation. However the hypothalamic vasodilator sympathetic pathway does not affect exercising muscle. Both resting and active skeletal muscle show autoregulation in the dog. An increased resistance occurs with a rise in perfusion pressure and vice versa; i.e. despite changes in blood pressure, the blood flow tends to remain stable. Theories to explain autoregulation involve a myogenic response of the vessel walls, release of vasodilator metabolites, or decreased oxygen. The level of metabolic activity does not affect autoregulation; the phenomenon also occurs in denervated muscles.

Following a period of complete occlusion of the arterial supply to a limb, the blood flow increases markedly and then returns to the control level. This phenomenon has been named "reactive hyperemia." For measurement of reactive hyperemia, the blood flow in excess of that expected (the control blood flow) is usually calculated. The response occurs both in skin and muscle and can be decreased in the skin by cooling, epinephrine, or tobacco smoking. The amount and duration of reactive hyperemia correlate with the previous length of arterial occlusion. This has been shown to be true for occlusion periods up to 10 minutes.

The blood flow and oxygen debt incurred during the period of occlusion are calculated by multiplying the control blood flow or oxygen usage before circulatory arrest by the duration of occlusion. This assumes that the blood flow and oxygen usage of the muscle would have remained at the previous control rates if the blood flow had not been occluded and that the metabolic rate of the muscle is not affected by the circulatory arrest. In the isolated gracilis muscle of the dog and in the human forearm, the oxygen debt is approximately repaid for different periods of occlusion, while the blood flow debt repayment ranges from 50 to 200 per cent of that expected.

The phenomenon of reactive hyperemia has also been demonstrated in the exercising dog hindlimb. Flow debts are underpaid or barely repaid. Oxygen debts are entirely or partially repaid depending upon the level of muscle performance and the duration of the ischemic period. In resting muscle and during light exercise, both increased blood flow and oxygen extraction are involved in repayment of the oxygen debts but during medium and strong exercise, the increased blood flow is most important. Since oxygen debts are often not repaid during strong exercise in the presence of a *decreased* arteriovenous oxygen difference, oxygen extraction is the limiting factor.

The metabolites incriminated as the cause of exercise hyperemia have also been postulated as eliciting reactive hyperemia. Since reactive hyperemia occurs in sympathectomized and denervated limbs, nervous system control is not considered as important. The mechanical effect of the lack of pressure in the vessels during the period of occlusion has been demonstrated to play a role in the dilation. If the forearm is "packed" with venous blood before the circulatory arrest, the ensuing reactive hyperemia is decreased. However, the peak flow of the reactive hyperemia is not altered so that intravascular pressure cannot be the entire cause of the dilation. Lewis and Grant postulated that H-substance was involved in the production of reactive hyperemia; some observers found an increased histamine concentration in the venous blood after circulatory arrest but others have not. However, antihistamines do not decrease or abolish the reactive hyperemia response. As in exercise hyperemia, the vasodilator metabolites and effects of pH cannot be ruled out by studying only the venous blood; tissue studies would probably be more informative. Failure to discover the causative agent of vasodilation in muscular exercise and following arterial occlusion has been a major obstacle to the understanding of muscle physiology and the diseases involving a decreased blood supply to human limbs. It seems likely that the study of aerobic and anaerobic tissue metabolism of skeletal muscle would be more profitable than blood flow studies, which evidently do not correlate with oxygen usage.

ARTERIOVENOUS ANASTOMOSES IN SKELETAL MUSCLE. The question of whether arteriovenous shunts actually exist as functional units in skeletal muscle is still unsettled to most physiologists. Microscopic studies on the circulation of rat skeletal muscle reveal many communications between small arteries and veins which do not enter the muscle proper. During inactivity, most of the flow is through these anastomoses and not to the muscle fibers. When the rats are bled in small amounts, the muscular arterioles close and flow in the capillaries ceases while it persists in the anastomotic channels. However, that such communications actually function in man and possess a means of shunt regulation has not been demonstrated. Indirect evidence for the existence of functional anastomoses is the decreased oxygen consumption and increased lactic acid production during vasodilation; such findings would occur if capillary flow were reduced. As mentioned previously, the disappearance rate of a radioisotope from a depot in skeletal muscle is thought to represent only capillary blood flow and not shunt flow. For example, during emotional stress, total forearm blood flow increases (plethysmograph) but radioisotope clearance from forearm muscle does not change. Such studies have led to the concept of a dual circulation in *resting* muscle; one circulatory pathway has been referred to as "nutritional" and the other, "nonnutritional."

SUMMARY

Although much investigative work has been performed, wide gaps still exist in our knowledge of the physiology of the cutaneous and muscle circulation. Most of the information concerning the control of these vascular beds has been gained from indirect and circumstantial evidence. The important limiting factor is the lack of a good technique for the direct measurement of blood flow in human skin and muscle. The indirect methods currently in use all have inadequacies. Another drawback is the difficulty in distinguishing the many variables (metabolic, nervous, temperature, bradykinin, arteriovenous anastomoses) that affect the cutaneous and muscle circulation. In human experiments, skin and muscle flow cannot be satisfactorily studied individually, and the contribution of the blood flow in bone, fat and subcutaneous tissue cannot be evaluated. The central nervous system control of the peripheral circulation has been investigated in animals only; much is known about efferent fibers but little concerning afferent pathways. The study of the metabolic control of blood flow in skin has been neglected while that of muscle has not advanced far enough. In conclusion, many isolated facts are known concerning the mechanisms controlling cutaneous and muscle vascular reactivity, but little is apparent of their integration in the homeostasis of these tissues.

Peripheral Vascular Disease

RAYNAUD'S PHENOMENON AND RAYNAUD'S DISEASE

A distinction must be made between Raynaud's disease and Raynaud's phenomenon.

Raynaud's disease is a primary affection, i.e., not associated with some other condition, first described by Raynaud in 1862. Young women are predominantly affected; the clinical manifestations are bilaterally symmetrical. The fingers, less commonly the toes, or, rarely, blush areas of the head are the seat of attacks of intermittent spasm of the small arteries. The affected areas become cold, numb, and waxy pale ("dead fingers") or cyanotic. The attack lasts as a rule for a few minutes, but may persist for an hour or two. The color change commences in the tips and spreads toward the bases of the digits. As the attack passes off the part may become cyanotic, then red and hot; the numbness may be replaced by burning pain. The pulse at the wrist or ankle is normal during the attack. Thromboses of small arteries may lead to ulcers, sclerodactyly, rarefaction of the terminal phalanges, and other trophic changes. Gangrene sometimes results.

In Raynaud's phenomenon, the attacks are secondary to some other abnormal state, e.g. trauma, neurogenic lesions, collagen diseases, occlusive arterial diseases, cryoglobulinemia, etc.

The *disease* has been generally attributed to hyperactivity of the vasomotor (vasoconstrictor) nerves. Sympathetic ganglionectomy is, therefore, frequently resorted to in an effort to abolish the attacks. Lewis has shown, however, that a typical attack may be induced in a subject upon whom this operation has been performed, by exposing the affected part to cold (as by immersing it in cold water). He concludes therefore that the fault lies not in the nervous control but in the vascular wall itself. The following observations cited by Lewis substantiate his view.

(1) If one finger of a subject with the disease be immersed in cold water, an attack confined to this finger may be induced. Such a localized result cannot be explained upon the basis of a nervous reflex.

(2) Novocaine anesthetization of the ulnar nerve of a normal person causes dilation of the vessels of the little finger (removal of vasoconstrictor tone). The vascular spasm in Raynaud's disease cannot be released in this way.

(3) If a subject suffering from Raynaud's disease affecting both hands, and upon whom a unilateral ganglionectomy has been performed, is seated in a cool room with both hands placed in cold water, the vascular spasm which results is more pronounced on the nonsympathectomized side. If, however, the rest of the body is warmed while the hands are immersed in cold water, the attack is more pronounced on the sympathectomized side. In the first experiment the greater degree of spasm on the nonoperated side is attributed to the added effect of a vasoconstrictor reflex. The lesser degree of spasm on the nonoperated side in the second experiment could be attributed to the inhibition of vasoconstrictor impulses. Though a nervous influence is evident in these observations the essentially local nature of the fault is also indicated.

Simpson and associates do not consider that Raynaud's disease is due *primarily* to a fault of the vascular tissue. These observers maintain that only in the advanced stages of the disease is the vascular wall itself abnormal and that in milder cases the fault is essentially vasomotor in character. They point out that Lewis' crucial experiments were performed upon severe or complicated cases of the disease.

Ganglionectomy, even though it may not remove the fundamental cause of the condition, does often exert a decidely beneficial effect. The attacks are less frequent and intense after the operation; since normal vasoconstrictor tone and, as just indicated, the reflex response to cold have been abolished, a more intense reaction of the arterial wall itself must occur before arrest of the circulation to the part can result. However, relapses often occurred 1 to 2 years following the operation in those who were benefited.

Peacock found that patients with Raynaud's disease, when compared to normal subjects, showed higher epinephrine and norepinephrien levels in venous blood from the hand after sympathetic stimulation; the amine oxidase content of the digital arteries, measured in only one patient, was low. He postulated that the intense vasoconstriction and high concentration of catecholamines may be secondary to incomplete destruction of the amines liberated from the peripheral sympathetic nerve endings in the vessel walls. Halpern and coworkers have implicated serotonin released from platelets during cold exposure as one factor in Raynaud's disease.

ERYTHROMELALGIA

Erythromelalgia is a rare but interesting condition characterized by attacks of painful redness of one or both feet, or occasionally of the hands. The etiology in idiopathic cases is unknown. Secondary erythromelalgia occurs in polycythemia vera, hypertension, and arteriosclerosis obliterans. The pain is burning in character and is induced by warming or exercising the part, or by allowing it to hang down. During an attack the involved part is warm or hot and the pulses are bounding. Rest, elevation of the part, or the application of cold tends to relieve the pain. Erythromelalgia has been attributed to vasodilation resulting from some abnormality of the vascular nerves. Lewis found, however, that the essential abnormality in these cases is not vasodilation, for an equivalent degree of vasodilation may occur in normal subjects in response to warmth or exercise, yet pain does not result. Erythromelalgia, or *erythralgia* as Lewis prefers to call the condition, is probably not of vasomotor origin. The abnormality in these cases is apparently a hypersensitive state of the cutaneous pain fibers to heat or tension. This "susceptible state" of the skin in erythralgia is analogous to that seen in inflammation, and to that which can be induced in normal people by certain types of cutaneous injury—exposure to ultraviolet light, repeated rubbing or stretching, burns, etc. In skin so injured, the pain fiber endings are very sensitive to warmth or to tension. Warming the part either by increasing the blood flow through its vessels, or by the application of heat causes burning pain. When the part is dependent, the engorged vessels cause tension upon the hypersensitive nerve endings resulting in pain.

Lewis suggests that in the pain associated with erythralgia and the above types of cutaneous injury, a chemical substance liberated in the skin serves as the immediate stimulus to the nerve endings. The pain which follows repeated rubbing or stretching of normal or erythralgic skin is prolonged and intensified by arresting the circulation to the part, giving support to this concept.

ACROCYANOSIS

In this disorder, the hands and less commonly the feet, are *persistently* cold, blue and sweaty. The etiology is unknown but patients with acrocyanosis often have an endocrine dysfunction. Exposure to cold intensifies the cyanotic color. In the case of the hands the cyanosis commences at about the level of the wrist and deepens as it is traced toward the fingers. There is puffiness of the fingers, but trophic disturbances are unusual. The milder forms of the disorder are closely allied, according to Lewis, to chilblains. The disorder is presumably due to increased tone of the cutaneous *arterioles* resulting from hypersensitivity to cold. The condition does not have a nervous basis; the fault is in the vascular wall itself, for the cyanosis persists unchanged after anesthetizing the ulnar nerve with novocaine. In acrocyanosis the cutaneous circulation is slowed as a result of arteriolar constriction; capillary dilation occurs with an increase in the quantity of blood in the skin. The slower blood flow, allows the hemoglobin to give up a greater part of its oxygen store, causing the blue tint of the skin.

THROMBOANGIITIS OBLITERANS (BUERGER'S DISEASE)

This is an *organic* vascular disease involving, as a rule, the medium and small arteries and the veins of the extremities. The condition in the majority of cases is confined to the limbs. Involvement of the distal arteries of the upper extremities is very common in contrast to arteriosclerosis obliterans. However, coronary, cerebral, renal and other systemic arterial involvement may occur. The lesions are focal in nature, interspersed with areas of normal vessel. In involved areas the vessels are stiffened and hard. The adventitia is thickened; the media shows muscle atrophy and an increase in connective tissue. Active proliferation of the intima occurs. Thrombosis follows the marked narrowing of the vascular lumen. The thrombi, not the intimal proliferation, are responsible for the final obliteration of the vessels. The acute lesion is characterized by *multiple microabscesses* in the thrombus; multinuclear giant cells may be present. Organization of the thrombus, i.e., its invasion by fibroblasts and its conversion into fibrous tissue, follows. Some restoration of the circulation through the vessel may occur later as a result of the formation of new channels within the substance of the organized thrombus. Whether or not such a process of revascularization results, the blood supply to the part is always greatly reduced.

Among some of the earlier manifestations of the condition are: fatigue of the limbs upon exertion; intermittent claudication; hypersensitive vasoconstrictor reactions to cold resulting in attacks of pallor, cyanosis, coldness and numbness, or dull aching of the extremities; superficial migratory phlebitis. A definite reduction in blood flow through the part may be demonstrated by plethysmographic or calorimetric methods. When the affected member is dependent, it becomes reddish or cyanotic, when raised above heart level, intensely pale and waxy in appearance.

As the pathological changes progress, the pulse disappears from the wrist or ankle, or even from the popliteal or brachial artery; ulcers and other trophic disorders appear and ultimately gangrene of the toes or fingers may develop. The vascular obliteration tends to creep upwards and amputation may be required at successively higher levels.

The cause of the disease is unknown; some believe it to be of infectious origin. Excessive use of tobacco is strongly suspected of being a predisposing factor. Buerger and others have remarked upon the very high incidence of the condition in Jews; of a series of 150 cases reported by Brown and Allen from the Mayo Clinic, over 50 per cent were Jews. The disease occurs almost exclusively in young males, whereas Raynaud's disease, with which it may be confused in its early stages, affects females predominantly. Other features distinguishing it from Raynaud's disease are the color changes produced by elevation of the limb and obliteration of the pulse in the larger arteries. Wessler has recently disputed the disease as an entity separate from arteriosclerosis obliterans but excellent evidence has been presented for its existence (McKusick).

It is only during the earlier stages of the condition, when vasospasm due to increased vasoconstrictor reactivity is a contributing factor and organic changes have not yet progressed to occlusion of vessels, that treatment can be expected to help. Remarkable improvement often follows the withdrawal of tobacco smoking. It has been reported that discontinuation of smoking in thromboangiitis obliterans causes a decrease in platelet adhesiveness. When vasospasm can be demonstrated, sympathectomy frequently results in improvement. Even when the larger arterial vessels are obliterated, sympathectomy, by removing the vasoconstrictor tone of collateral vessels, may be followed by a definite improvement in the blood supply to the part.

There are several methods to detect vascular spasm. The temperature of the part may be taken with a skin thermometer or a thermocouple before and after one of the following procedures which, normally, causes vasodilation and raises the temperature: (a) heating the entire body by a warm environment; (b) blocking sympathetic ganglia by local anesthesia or ganglionic blocking agents; (c) spinal anesthesia which temporarily paralyzes the vasoconstrictors; (d) anesthetization of a peripheral nerve; and (e) general anesthesia. A rise in temperature of the part, following one of these procedures, indicates the previous existence of vasospasm. The greater the degree of vasospasm the more pronounced and rapid is the temperature rise. If the occlusion is entirely organic in nature, no change in temperature results.

Instead of recording the skin temperature, the blood flow through the affected part may be estimated by the plethysmographic or calorimetric method before and after one of the procedures just enumerated.

ARTERIOSCLEROSIS OBLITERANS AND
INTERMITTENT CLAUDICATION

Intermittent claudication is a condition (described by Charcot in 1856) in which organic narrowing of the arteries of a limb and consequent restriction of its blood supply, causes pain or fatigue in the muscles during exercise. The usual etiology is arteriosclerosis and the lower limbs (*claudicare*, to limp) are most frequently affected.

Although the arterial tree is usually diffusely involved in arteriosclerosis obliterans, the *obstructing* lesions are frequently segmental. A "critical" degree of stenosis must occur before blood pressure and flow are decreased. This "critical" stenosis depends on the blood flow velocity (May et al.); i.e. the smaller the vessel or the longer the affected segment, the less the stenosis required to alter pressure and flow. About 90% of the aortic lumen must be occluded to produce hemodynamic changes. If an obstruction is complete, collateral blood vessels with low pressure provide the only blood supply to the area.

Blood flow, measured by plethysmography, is often normal at rest in patients with intermittent claudication; post-exercise or reactive hyperemia blood flow may be abnormal. Normally exercise causes a marked increase in radioisotope disappearance from muscle while steady muscle tension stops the clearance of the radioisotope. Walder has shown that, in patients with intermittent claudication, exercise slows or *stops* the radioisotope disappearance rate and the clearance ceases at a *lower* steady muscle tension. This would indicate that, during exercise, the developed muscle tension overcomes the lowered arterial pressure below a stenosed or obstructed arterial segment, blocking the blood flow.

Ejrup found that pedal pulses in patients with intermittent claudication diminished or disappeared following exercise; this is probably secondary to the redistribution of blood flow from the foot to the calf in these patients following exercise (Allwood). Another pathophysiological finding is that a good collateral circulation maintains adequate diastolic pressure below the stenosis to prevent blood flow past the stenotic area during diastole and a murmur is heard over the affected area only during systole. If the collateral circulation is insufficient, a continuous murmur will be heard.

In each patient, the pain of intermittent claudication always occurs after the same amount of exercise and disappears with rest. The pain cannot be secondary to muscular cramp for the muscles are flaccid during the attack. The abnormal stiffness of the arteries seems to preclude the possibility of vasospasm as a cause of pain; the smaller vessels are in all likelihood dilated rather than constricted during the attack.

The essential cause of intermittent claudication is a relative anoxia of the muscles—they are called upon to perform work for which the oxygen supply is inadequate. Lewis has shown that pain identical in character with that occurring in this condition can be induced by exercising any normal limb during the arrest of its circulation. When the circulation is restored, an immediate increase in the volume of the limb occurs which is taken to indicate that the vessels were dilated during the pain. In a patient suffering from the disease in one limb it was shown that the pain occurring in the limb during exercise was practically the same with regard to its time of onset, development and duration as that induced by exercising the sound limb while its circulation was arrested.

The fundamental importance of anoxia in the production of the pain is also evident from the observations of Pickering and Wayne who found that exercising the muscles of an anemic subject, in whom there was no evidence of arterial disease, caused the characteristic pain of intermittent claudication. Kissin also showed that exercise performed by normal persons during anoxia (induced by breathing an air mixture containing a low percentage of oxygen) caused the typical cramplike pain. The clinical experiments of Lewis indicate that the direct cause of the pain is not oxygen lack itself but the stimulation of sensory nerves by the metabolic products of muscular activity. Ordinarily these are removed by oxidation, but they accumulate when the blood supply is inadequate. He refers to the pain stimulus as "factor P". The evidence supporting this concept is as follows:

(1) The pain does not vary with the individual contractions but is a steady ache.

(2) Using a standard test (maximal grip exerted by thumb and index finger, recorded isometrically, and repeated at the rate of one per second) it was found that in normal subjects with the circulation to the arm arrested, the pain began about 35 sec. after the commencement of the exercise and took another 53 sec. to reach the point where it became intolerable. The pain disappears within 3 sec. after restoring the circulation—presumably as a result of the removal of "factor P". If, on the other hand, occlusion of the vessels is maintained, the pain persists. The onset of pain occurs after the same amount of exercise if the arterial occlusion of the limb has been present for a 10 min. period before the exercise.

(3) Lewis found that the time of onset of the pain is determined by the total amount of work performed rather than by the length of the exercise period. Thus, when the circulation of a normal limb is arrested, pain ensues after the same number of contractions of equal strength whether they are repeated in rapid or in slow succession. On the other hand, if a constant rate is maintained, the pain follows sooner with strong than with weak contractions. If, however, the circulation to the part is only partially obstructed (Katz and associates) or if air containing a low percentage of oxygen is breathed (Kissin), the amount of work necessary to cause pain is lessened by increasing the rate at which the contractions are repeated—the chemical factor presumably accumulating more rapidly as a result of the shorter time intervals allowed for its removal.

(4) If, after the pain has been relieved by restoring the circulation to the part, the vessels are again occluded and the limb exercised, the time of onset of the pain will vary with the length of time during which the blood has been permitted to flow (the shorter the flow period, the earlier the onset of pain). This result suggests that products accumulated during the previous exercise period, if not given sufficient time to be removed, are carried over to the second period and the concentration necessary for stimulation is reached sooner.

The nature of the chemical pain factor is unknown; Katz and associates believe it to be acid in character and novolatile. The ingestion of sodium bicarbonate was found to increase the amount of exercise required to cause pain.

COLLATERAL BLOOD FLOW

When the major artery to a vascular bed is occluded, smaller vessels arising from arteries above the occlusion supply the area with blood. This collateral flow may prove adequate for all functions. Some patients withstand an embolic femoral artery occlusion with no adverse effects to the limb. In dogs, ligation of the femoral artery rarely produces signs of ischemia. Since collateral arteries function within seconds of arterial occlusion, it is thought that these vessels pre-exist; however they increase in size following arterial occlusion. In patients with aortic bifurcation thromboses, aortography often reveals vessels as large as the femoral artery arising from the mesenteric arteries and supplying the limbs.

In normal young subjects, plethysmographic studies of calf blood flow show that mechanical compression of the femoral artery decreases flow to one sixth of the previous resting level with recovery to normal flow within 6 min. despite continued compression. The flow is non-, or only slightly, pulsatile. Reflex warming of the body and ganglionic blockade increase the collateral blood flow demonstrating that it is affected by the sympathetic nervous system. Exercise of the leg usually increases the collateral flow but the increase may be due to a rise in systemic blood pressure.

In animal experiments, flow from the artery distal to an occlusion (retrograde flow) or venous outflow following arterial occlusion has been used to estimate collateral flow. Both methods are inexact. Retrograde flow will vary with the amount of blood being used by the vascular bed below the occlusion; also, since there is no resistance to flow, the measurements may be erroneously high. Venous outflow from one vein does not equate with arterial inflow for there are often many other veins draining the area.

When the external iliac or femoral artery is acutely occluded in dogs or cats, the flow drops to one third of the previous resting level and then gradually rises to 50 to 100% of normal. In dogs with acute or chronic arterial occlusions, the blood pressure below the obstruction initially falls to low levels but approaches normal in a few weeks. The collateral flow (venous outflow) is affected by vasoactive agents, blood pressure alterations, sympathetic activity, and exercise, and shows the phenomenon of reactive hyperemia. Intravenous vasodilator drugs usually increase collateral flow but sometimes a decrease occurs. Since intra-aortic administration of drugs (above the occlusion) increases collateral flow more than infusions below the occlusion, the collateral vessels are directly affected. In cats, the collateral flow to the hind limb reacts in the same manner as that of the dog after chronic femoral artery occlusion but is much less reactive immediately following acute occlusion. The species difference may be secondary to a more ischemic, and consequently more vasodilated, vascular bed in the cat after acute femoral artery occlusion. In dogs, the oxygen saturation of the retrograde flow is the same as that of systemic arterial blood indicating the blood has not perfused a capillary bed. The arteriovenous oxygen difference of the limb with an acutely or chronically occluded artery is usually greater than in the unoccluded hind limb.

In summary, the collateral blood flow reacts in the same manner as normal blood flow although to a lesser degree. No method has been discovered to permanently increase collateral arterial supply to extremities. In cats with femoral artery occlusions chronic vasodilator therapy was ineffective. The collateral blood flow studies were performed in normal humans or animals; conclusions cannot be applied to patients whose collateral vessels might be afflicted with arteriosclerosis.

"Immersion Foot"; "Trench Foot"

During the Second World War this name was given to a state of the vessels and tissues of the feet brought on by severe and prolonged chilling from exposure to cold and dampness.

The hands may be affected by cold water in the same way as the foot but are rarely exposed to conditions of such extreme severity. It was seen most frequently in persons who had been shipwrecked and immersed for hours in the sea at northern latitudes. It may also result if the feet alone are kept cold and moist; sailors working in wet boots, or soldiers in wet trenches (trench foot) may be affected. In immersion foot, the feet during the period of exposure are swollen, numb and pulseless. Their color varies with the temperature from bright red to deep blue or waxy white, or may be mottled with areas of blue and white or blue and red. Within a few hours after removal from exposure, the feet become hyperemic and severely painful, the pain often being described as burning, scalding or stabbing in character. The swelling increases; blistering, ulceration, local wasting of muscles and, in the worst cases, gangrene result. Capillary damage permits fluid of high protein content to leak into the tissues. The hyperemic stage, which can last up to 10 weeks, often merges into one in which the feet are pale, cold and very sensitive to cold exposure. Damage to peripheral nerves and sympathetic fibers is a regular occurrence in severe immersion foot. Anesthesia, motor weakness, and muscular atrophy may last for many weeks.

During actual exposure, the vessels are in vasospasm and a decreased blood flow results. A decrease in tissue oxygen tension is found, most likely secondary to the lessened dissociation of oxygen from hemoglobin (the oxyhemoglobin dissociation curve is displaced to the left by cold). The metabolism of the tissue as a result of both the cold and the anoxia is greatly reduced. The vasoconstriction is both reflex (secondary to the action of cold on the general body surface) and local (direct effect of cold upon the vascular walls). The absence of vasodilator metabolites probably also contributes to the decreased blood flow. In the hyperemic stage, warming of the body overcomes the vascular spasm and there is maximum dilation of the vessels.

Since the intensity of hyperemia, tissue damage, and pain may be enhanced by high temperatures, the extremities should be kept in a cool but not cold environment. The rest of the body is kept warm to release vasoconstriction reflexly.

Frost Bite

Prolonged exposure to severe cold causes vasospasm and when freezing occurs the circulation in the small vessels of the part becomes completely arrested. Formation of ice crystals may occur but dehydration of the cells is probably the usual cause of damage. After the part has thawed, intense hyperemia usually follows. The increased capillary permeability secondary to the freezing and the high capillary pressure of the hyperemic stage cause edema of the part. Circulatory stasis results from the edema although in some cases it may be secondary to thrombosis. If the resulting ischemia is severe, gangrene follows. Measures are directed toward the reduction of these effects by thawing the part rapidly and by the administration of an anti-coagulant.

REFERENCES

Cerebral Circulation

HEDLUND, S., NYLIN, G., AND REGNSTRÖM, O. The behaviour of the cerebral circulation during muscular exercise. Acta Physiol. Scand., 1962, **54**, 316.

KING, B. D., SOKOLOFF, L., AND WECHSLER, R. L. The effects of 1-epinephrine and 1-nor-epinephrine upon cerebral circulation and metabolism in man. J. Clin. Invest., 1952, **31**, 273.

WASSERMAN, A. J. AND PATTERSON, J. L., JR. The cerebral vascular response to reduction in arterial carbon dioxide tension. J. Clin. Invest., 1961, **40**, 1297.

Cutaneous Circulation

ALLWOOD, M. J. AND BURG, H. S. Effect of local temperature on blood flow in the human foot. J. Physiol., 1954, **124**, 345.

ARMIN, J., GRANT, R. T., THOMPSON, R. H. S., AND TICKNER, A. An explanation for the heightened vascular reactivity of the denervated rabbit's ear. J. Physiol., 1953, **121**, 603.

BURCH, G. E., COHN, A. E., AND NEUMANN, C. The study by quantitative methods of the spontaneous variations in volume of the finger tip, toe tip, and postero-superior portion of the pinna of resting normal white adults. Am. J. Physiol., 1942, **136**, 433.

COFFMAN, J. D., WOOD, J. E., JR., AND WILKINS, R. W. Effect of cooling and of smoking tobacco upon the blood flow of reactive hyperemia of the foot, Circulation, 1958, **18**, 177.

DEAL, C. P., JR. AND GREEN, H. D. Effects of pH on blood flow and peripheral resistance in muscular and cutaneous vascular beds in the hind limb of pentobarbitalized dog. Circulation Res., 1954, **2**, 148.

DIJI, A. AND GREENFIELD, A. D. M. The local effect of carbon dioxide on the blood vessels of the human skin. J. Physiol., 1958, **140**, 42P.

DUGGAN, J. J., LOVE, V. L., AND LYONS, R. H. A study of reflex venomotor reactions in man. Circulation, 1953, **7**, 869.

EDHOLM, O. G., FOX, R. H., AND MACPHERSON, R. K. The effect of cutaneous anesthesia on skin blood flow. J. Physiol., 1956, **132**, 15P.

EDHOLM, O. G., FOX, R. H., AND MACPHERSON, R. K. Vasomotor control of cutaneous blood vessels in human forearm. J. Physiol., 1957, **139**, 455.

FOX, R. H. AND HILTON, S. M. Bradykinin formation in human skin as a factor in heat vasodilatation. J. Physiol., 1958, **142**, 219.

FROESE, G. AND BURTON, A. C. Heat losses from the human head. J. Appl. Physiol., 1957, **10**, 235.

GRANT, R. T. Observations on local arterial reactions in rabbit's ear. Heart, 1930, **15**, 257.

GREEN, H. D., LEWIS, R. N., NICKERSON, N. D., AND HELLER, A. C. Blood flow, peripheral resistance and vascular tonus, with observations on relationship between blood flow and cutaneous temperature. Am. J. Physiol., 1944, **141**, 518.

GREENFIELD, A. D. M., SHEPHERD, J. T., AND WHELAN, R. F. Circulatory responses to cold in fingers infiltrated with anesthetic solution. J. Appl. Physiol., 1952, **4**, 785.

HERTZMAN, A. B. Relative responses of dorsal metacarpal, digital and terminal arteries of the hand in vasoconstrictor reflexes. Am. J. Physiol., 1941, **134**, 59.

HERTZMAN, A. B. AND ROTH, L. W. Absence of vasoconstrictor reflexes in the forehead circulation. Effects of cold. Am. J. Physiol., 1942, **136**, 692.

HILTON, S. M. AND HOLTON, P. Antidromic vasodilatation and blood flow in the rabbit's ear. J. Physiol., 1954, **125**, 138.

HORTON, E. W. Bradykinin and the inflammatory response. In: Injury, inflammation and immunity. Thomas, L. (Ed.). Williams & Wilkins Co., Baltimore, 1964.

KELLEY, W. D. AND VISSCHER, M. Effect of sympathetic nerve stimulation on cutaneous small vein and small artery pressures, blood flow and hindpaw volume in the dog. Am. J. Physiol., 1956, **185**, 453.

LEE, J. S. AND VISSCHER, M. B. Microscopic studies of skin blood vessels in relation to sympathetic nerve stimulation. Am. J. Physiol., 1957, **190**, 37.

MELMON, K., LOVENBERG, W., DATES, J. A., GILLESPIE, L., JR. AND SJOERDSMA, A. Implication of the kallikrein system in production of the carcinoid flush. J. Clin. Invest., 1964, **43**, 1308 (Abstract).

MESCON, H., HURLEY, H. J., JR., AND MORETTI, G. The anatomy and histochemistry of the arteriovenous anastomoses in human digital skin. J. Invest. Dermat., 1956, **27**, 133.

MONTGOMERY, H. Oxygen tension of peripheral tissue. Am. J. Med., 1957, **23**, 697.

PAGE, E. B., HICKAM, J. B., SIEKER, H. O., AND MCINTOSH, H. D. Reflex venomotor activity in normal persons and in patients with postural hypotension. Circulation, 1955, **11**, 262.

PARTINGTON, M. W. The vascular response of the skin to ultra-violet light. Clin. Sc., 1954, **13**, 425.

RODDIE, I. C., SHEPHERD, J. T., AND WHELAN, R. F. Contribution of constrictor and dilator nerves to skin vasodilatation during body heating. J. Physiol., 1957, **136**, 489.

RODDIE, I. C., SHEPHERD, J. T., AND WHELAN, R. F. The vasomotor nerve supply to the skin and muscle of the human forearm. Clin. Sc., 1957, **16**, 67.

RONDELL, P. A., KEITZER, W. F., AND BOHR, D. F. Distribution of flow through capillaries and arteriovenous anastomoses in the rabbit ear. Am. J. Physiol., 1955, **183**, 523.

SENAY, L. C., JR., PROKOP, L. D., CRONAU, L. AND HERTZMAN, A. B. Relation of local skin temperature and local sweating to cutaneous blood flow. J. Appl. Physiol. 1963, **18**, 781.

SNELL, E. S. The relationship between vasomotor response in the hand and heat changes in the body induced by intravenous infusions of hot or cold saline. J. Physiol., 1954, **125**, 361.

SPEALMAN, C. R. Effect of ambient air temperature and of hand temperature on blood flow in hands. Am. J. Physiol., 1945, **145**, 218.

WERTHEIMER, L., REDISCH, W., HIRSCHHORN, K., AND STEELE, J. M. Patterns of surface temperature response to various agents. Circulation, 1955, **11**, 110.

WIJI, A. Local vasodilator action of carbon dioxide on blood vessels of the hand. J. Appl. Physiol. 1959, **14**, 414.

Skeletal Muscle Circulation

ABRAMSON, D. I., TUCK, S., JR., BELL, Y., MITCHELL, R. E., AND ZAYAS, A. M. Effect of short periods of arterial occlusion on blood flow and oxygen uptake. J. Appl. Physiol., 1961, **16**, 851.

ANREB, G. B., BARSOUM, G. S., SALAMA, F., AND SOUIDAN, Z. Liberation of histamine during reactive hyperemia and muscle contraction in man. J. Physiol., 1944, **103**, 297.

ANREP, G. B. AND VON SAALFELD, E. Blood flow through skeletal muscle in relation to its contraction. J. Physiol., 1935, **85**, 375.

BARCROFT, H., DARNHORST, A. C., McCLATCHEZ, H. M., AND TANNER, G. M. On the blood flow thru rhythmically contracting muscle before and during release of sympathetic constrictor tone. J. Physiol., 1952, **117**, 391.

BLACK, J. E. AND RODDIE, I. C. The role of CO_2 in the changes in forearm vascular resistance with anoxia. J. Physiol., 1958, **140**, 39P.

BROD, J., HEJL, Z., AND ULRYCH, M. Metabolic changes in the forearm muscle and skin during emotional muscular vasodilatation. Clin. Sci., 1963, **25**, 1.

CLARK, R. S. J. The effect of voluntary overbreathing on blood flow through the human forearm. J. Physiol., 1952, **118**, 537.

COFFMAN, J. D. Blood flow and oxygen debt repayment in exercising skeletal muscle. Am. J. Physiol., 1963, **205**, 365.

COFFMAN, J. D. AND JAVETT, S. L. Calf blood flow and oxygen usage during bradykinin infusions. J. Appl. Physiol., 1963, **18**, 1003.

COOPER, K. E., EDHOLM, O. G., AND MOTTRAM, R. F. The blood flow in skin and muscle of the human forearm. J. Physiol., 1955, **128**, 258.

DAWES, G. S. Vasodilator action of potassium. J. Physiol., 1941, **99**, 224.

DUFF, F., PATTERSON, C. G., AND WHELAN, R. F. The effect of intra-arterial antihistamines on hyperemia following temporary arrest of circulation in the human forearm. Clin. Sc., 1955, **14**, 267.

EDHOLM, O. G., MOREIRA, M. F., AND WERNER, A. Y. The measurement of forearm blood flow during a raised venous pressure. J. Physiol., 1954, **125**, 41P.

FOLKOW, B., HAEGER, K., AND KAHLSON, G. Observations on reactive hyperemia as related to histamine, on drugs antagonizing vasodilatation induced by histamine and on vasodilator properties of adenosine triphosphate. Acta physiol. scandinav., 1948, **15**, 264.

GRANT, R. T. Observations on the blood circulation in voluntary muscle in man. Clin. Sc., 1938, **3**, 157.

HADDY, F. J., SCOTT, J. B., FLORIO, M. A., DOUGHERTY, R. M., JR., AND HUIZENGA, J. N. Local vascular effects of hypokalemia, alkalosis, hypercalcemia and hypomagnesemia. Am. J. Physiol., 1963, **204**, 202.

HARPUDER, K., BYER, J., AND STEIN, I. D. The effect of intra-arterial injection of adrenalin upon blood flow of human forearm. Am. J. Physiol., 1947, **150**, 181.

HILTON, S. M. The effects of nicotine on the blood vessels of skeletal muscle in the cat. An investigation of vasomotor axon reflexes. J. Physiol., 1954, **123**, 289.

HILTON, S. M. Experiments on the postcontraction hyperemia of skeletal muscle. J. Physiol., 1953, **120**, 230.

HILTON, S. M. Femoral artery dilatation and postcontraction hyperemia of the leg muscles. J. Physiol., 1956, **131**, 31.

HIRVONEN, L. AND SONNENSCHEIN, R. R. Relation between blood flow and contraction force in active skeletal muscle. Circulation Res., 1962, **10**, 94.

LEWIS, T. AND GRANT, R. Observations upon reactive hyperaemia in man. Heart, 1925, **12**, 73.

LINGREN, P. AND UVNÄS, B. Vasoconstrictor inhibition and vasodilator activation—two functionally separate vasodilator mechanisms in the skeletal muscles. Acta physiol. scandinav., 1955, **33**, 108.

McADLE, L. AND RODDIE, I. C. Vascular response to CO_2 during anesthesia. Brit. J. Anesth., 1959, **30**, 358.

PATTERSON, G. C. The role of intravascular pressure in causation of reactive hyperemia in the human forearm. Clin. Sc., 1956, **15**, 17.

REMENSNYDER, J. P., MITCHELL, J. H., AND SARNOFF, S. J. Functional sympatholysis during muscular activity. Circulation Res. 1962, **11**, 370.

RICHARDSON, D. W., WASSERMAN, A. J., AND PATTERSON, J. L., JR. General and regional circulatory responses to change in blood pH and carbon dioxide tension. J. Clin. Invest., 1961, **40**, 31.

RODDIE, I. C., SHEPHERD, J. T., AND WHELAN, R. F. Humoral vasodilation in forearm during voluntary hyperventilation. J. Physiol., 1957, **137**, 80.

RODDIE, I. C., SHEPHERD, J. T., AND WHELAN, R. F. Reflex changes in vasoconstrictor tone in human skeletal muscle in response to stimulation of receptors in a low-pressure area of intrathoracic vascular bed. J. Physiol., 1957, **139**, 369.

STAINSBY, W. N. Autoregulation of blood flow in skeletal muscle during increased metabolic activity. Am. J. Physiol., 1962, **202**, 273.

WANG, S. C. AND BORISON, H. L. An analysis of the carotid sinus cardiovascular reflex mechanism. Am. J. Physiol., 1947, **150**, 712.

WOOD, J. E., JR., LITTER, J., AND WILKINS, R. W. The mechanism in limb segment reactive hyperemia in man. Circulation Res., 1955, **3**, 581.

YONCE, L. R. AND HAMILTON, W. F. Oxygen consumption in skeletal muscle during reactive hyperemia. Am. J. Physiol., 1959, **197**, 190.

YOUMANS, P. L., GREEN, H. D., AND DENISON,

A. B., Jr. Nature of the vasodilator and vaso-constrictor receptors in skeletal muscle of the dog. Circulation Res., 1955, **3**, 171.

ZWEIFACH, B. W. AND METZ, D. B. Selective distribution of blood through the terminal vascular bed of mesenteric structures and skeletal muscle. Angiology, 1955, **6**, 282.

Central Nervous System Control of Peripheral Circulation

ALEXANDER, R. S. Tonic and reflex functions of medullary sympathetic cardiovascular centers. J. Neurophysiol., 1946, **9**, 205.

CELANDER, O. The range of control exercised by the sympathico-adrenal system. Acta physiol. scandinav., 1954, **32**, suppl., 116.

CELANDER, O. AND FOLKOW, B. The nature and the distribution of afferent fibers provided with the axon reflex arrangement. Acta physiol. scandinav., 1953, **29**, 359.

DOLE, V. P., JR. AND MORISON, R. S. A note on the question of reflex activation of dorsal root dilators. Am. J. Physiol., 1940, **130**, 304.

ELIASSON, S., FOLKOW, B., LINDGREN, P., AND UVNÄS, B. Activation of sympathetic vasodilator nerves to the skeletal muscles in the cat by hypothalamic stimulation. Acta physiol. scandinav., 1951, **23**, 333.

FOLKOW, B., STRÖM, G., AND UVNÄS, B. Efferent nervous pathways involved in cutaneous vasodilatation induced by activation of hypothalamic heat loss mechanisms. Acta physiol. scandinav., 1949, **17**, 327.

FOLKOW, B. AND UVNÄS, B. Do adrenergic vasodilator nerves exist? Acta physiol. scandinav., 1950, **20**, 329.

FRUMIN, M. J., NGAI, S. H., AND WANG, S. C. Evaluation of vasodilator mechanisms in the canine hind leg; question of dorsal root participation. Am. J. Physiol., 1953, **173**, 428.

GREEN, H. D. AND HOFF, E. C. Effects of faradic stimulation of the cerebral cortex on limb and renal volumes in the cat and monkey. Am. J. Physiol., 1937, **118**, 641.

LUND, A. Function of cortical vasomotor centers elucidated through experimental studies on animals. Acta psychiat., et neurol., 1945, **20**, 213.

LUND, A. Significance of the cerebral cortex to the vasomotor reaction of the extremities. Ejnar Munksgaards Forlag, Copenhagen, 1943.

STRÖM, G. Influence of local thermal stimulation of the hypothalamus of the cat on cutaneous blood flow and respiratory rate. Acta physiol. scandinav., 1950, **20**, Suppl. 70, 47.

STRÖM, G. Vasomotor responses to thermal and electrical stimulation of frontal lobe and hypothalamus. Acta physiol. scandinav., 1950, **20**, Suppl. 70, 83.

WALL, P. D. AND DAVIS, G. D. Three cerebral cortical systems affecting autonomic function. J. Neurophysiol., 1951, **14**, 507.

Peripheral Vascular Disease

ALLWOOD, M. J. Redistribution of blood flow in limbs with obstruction of a main artery. Clin. Sci., 1962, **22**, 279.

BROWN, G. E. AND ALLEN, E. V. Thrombo-angiitis obliterans; clinical, physiologic and pathologic studies. W. B. Saunders Company, Philadelphia, 1928.

COFFMAN, J. D. Collateral circulation in the dog hind limb. Circulation, 1964, **30**, Supp. 3, 62.

ECKSTEIN, R. W., GREGG, D. E., AND PRITCHARD, W. H. The magnitude and time of development of the collateral circulation in occluded femoral, carotid, and coronary arteries. Am. J. Physiol., 1941, **132**, 351.

EISEN, M. E., TYSON, M. C., MICHAEL, S., AND BAUMANN, F. Adhesiveness of blood platelets in arteriosclerosis obliterans, thrombo-angiitis obliterans, acute thrombophlebitis, chronic venous insufficiency and arteriosclerotic heart disease. Circulation, 1951, **3**, 271.

EJRUP, B. Tonoscillography after exercise: new method for early diagnosis of organic arterial disease leading to intermittent claudication and for differential diagnosis of organic and functional arterial diseases with special type of apparatus adopted to this purpose. Acta med. Scandinav., 1948, **130**, Supp. 211, 1.

GREEN, H. D., COSBY, R. S., AND RADZOW, K. H. Dynamics of collateral circulations. Am. J. Physiol., 1944, **140**, 726.

HALPERN, A., KUHN, P. H., SHAFTEL, H. E., SAMUELS, S. S., SHAFTEL, N., SELMAN, D., AND BIRCH, H. G. Raynaud's disease, Raynaud's phenomenon, and serotonin. Angiology, 1960, **11**, 151.

KATZ, L. N., LINDNER, E., AND LANDT, H. On the nature of the substances producing pain in contracting skeletal muscle: its bearing on the problems of angina pectoris and intermittent claudication. J. Clin. Invest., 1935, **14**, 807.

KISSIN, M. The production of pain in exercising skeletal muscle during induced anoxemia. J. Clin. Invest., 1934, **13**, 37.

LEWIS, T. Clinical observations and experiments relating to burning pain in the extremities and to so-called "erythromelalgia" in particular. Clin. Sc., 1933, **1**, 175.

LEWIS, T. Experiments relating to the peripheral mechanism involved in spasmodic arrest of the circulation in the fingers, a variety of Raynaud's disease. Heart, 1929, **15**, 7.

LEWIS, T. Raynaud's disease, with special references to the nature of the malady. Brit. M. J., 1932, **2**, 136.

LEWIS, T. AND PICKERING, G. W. Observations upon maladies in which the blood supply to digits ceases intermittently or permanently, and upon bilateral gangrene of digits; observations relevant to so-called "Raynaud's disease." Clin. Sc., 1934, **1**, 327.

MAY, A. G., VANDEBERG, L., DEWEESE, J. A., AND ROB, C. G. Hemodynamic effects of arterial stenosis. Surgery, 1963, **54**, 250.

McKUSICK, V. A., HARRIS, W. S., OTTESEN, O. E., GOODMAN, R. M., SHELLEY, W. M., AND BLOODWELL, R. D. Buerger's disease: a distinct clinical and pathologic entity. J.A.M.A., 1962, **181**, 5.

MURDAUGH, H. V., JR. AND McINTOSH, H. D. Continuous arterial bruit as an index of collateral blood supply. New Engl. J. Med., 1958, **259,** 1170.

PEACOCK, J. H. Peripheral venous blood concentration of epinephrine and nor-epinephrine in primary Raynaud's disease. Circulation Res., 1959, **7,** 821.

PICKERING, G. W. AND WAYNE, E. J. Observations on angina pectoris and intermittent claudication in anemia. Clin. Sc., 1934, **1,** 305.

SHEPHERD, J. T. The effect of acute occlusion of the femoral artery on the blood supply to the calf before and after release of sympathetic vasomotor tone. Clin. Sci., 1950, **9,** 355.

SIMPSON, L., BROWN, G. E., AND ADSON, A. W. Raynaud's disease, evidence that is a type of vasomotor neurosis. Arch. Neurol. & Psychiat., 1931, **26,** 687.

THULESIUS, O. Hemodynamic studies on experimental obstruction of the femoral artery in the cat. Acta physiol. scandinav., 1962, **57,** Supp. 199, 1.

WALDER, D. N. The local clearance of radioactive Na^{24} from muscle in normal subjects and those with peripheral vascular disease. Clin. Sci., 1953, **12,** 153.

WASHBURN, B. Frostbite. New Engl. J. Med., 1962, **266,** 974.

WESSLER, S., MING, S., GUREWICK, V., FREIMAN, D. G. A critical evaluation of thromboangitis obliterans. New Engl. J. Med., 1960, **262,** 1149.

Cerebral Circulation

FINNERTY, F. A., JR., WITKIN, L., AND FAZEKAS, J. F. Cerebral hemodynamics during cerebral ischemia induced by acute hypotension. J. Clin. Invest., 1954, **33,** 1227.

HARMEL, M. H., HAFKENSCHIEL, J. H., AUSTIN, G. M., CRUMPTON, C. W., AND KETY, S. S. The effect of bilateral stellate ganglion block on the cerebral circulation in normotensive and hypertensive patients. J. Clin. Invest., 1949, **28,** 415.

KETY, S. S., AND SCHMIDT, C. F. The effects of altered arterial tensions of carbon dioxide and oxygen on cerebral blood flow and cerebral oxygen consumption of normal young men. J. Clin. Invest., 1948, **27,** 484.

KETY, S. S., SHENKIN, H. A., AND SCHMIDT, C. F. The effects of increased intracranial pressure on cerebral circulatory functions in man. J. Clin. Invest., 1948, **27,** 493.

KETY, S. S. AND SCHMIDT, C. F. The nitrous oxide method for the quantitative determination of cerebral blood flow in man: Theory, procedure and normal values. J. Clin. Invest., 1948, **27,** 476.

KLEINERMAN, J., SANCETTA, S. M., AND HACKEL, D. B. Effects of high spinal anesthesia on cerebral circulation and metabolism in man. J. Clin. Invest., 1958, **37,** 285.

KLEINERMAN, J. AND SANCETTA, S. M. Effect of mild steady state of exercise on cerebral and general hemodynamics of normal untrained subjects. J. Clin. Invest., 1955, **34,** 945.

MANGOLD, R., SOKOLOFF, L., CONNER, E., KLEINERMAN, J., THERMAN, P. G., AND KETY, S. S. The effects of sleep and lack of sleep on the cerebral circulation and metabolism of normal young men. J. Clin. Invest., 1955, **34,** 1092.

MOYER, J. H., MORRIS, G., AND SNYDER, H. A comparison of the cerebral hemodynamic response to aramine and norepinephrine in the normotensive and the hypotensive subject. Circulation, 1954, **10,** 265.

MOYER, J. H., MILLER, S. I., AND SNYDER, H. Effect of increased jugular pressure on cerebral hemodynamics. J. Appl. Physiol., 1954, **7,** 245.

NELSON, D. AND FAZEKAS, J. F. Cerebral blood flow in polycythemia vera. A. M. A. Arch. Int. Med., 1956, **98,** 328.

PATTERSON, J. L., HEYMAN, A., BATTEY, L. L., AND FERGUSON, R. W. Threshold of response of the cerebral vessels of man to increase in blood carbon dioxide. J. Clin. Invest., 1955, **34,** 1857.

ROBIN, E. D. AND GARDNER, F. H. Cerebral metabolism and hemodynamics in pernicious anemia. J. Clin. Invest., 1953, **32,** 598.

ROWE, G. G., MAXWELL, G. M., CASTILLO, C. A., FREEMAN, D. J., AND CRUMPTON, C. W. A study in man of cerebral blood flow and cerebral glucose, lactate and pyruvate metabolism before and after eating. J. Clin. Invest., 1959, **38,** 2154.

SCHEINBERG, P. AND STEAD, E. A., JR. The cerebral blood flow in male subjects as measured by the nitrous oxide technique. Normal values for blood flow, oxygen utilization, glucose utilization, and peripheral resistance, with observations on the effect of tilting and anxiety. J. Clin. Invest., 1949, **28,** 1163.

SCHIEVE, J. F. AND WILSON, W. P. The changes in cerebral vascular resistance of man in experimental alkalosis and acidosis. J. Clin. Invest., 1953, **32,** 33.

SHENKIN, H. A., SCHEUERMAN, W. G., SPITZ, E. B., AND GROFF, R. A. The effects of change of position upon the cerebral circulation of man. Am. J. Med. Sc., 1948, **216,** 714.

SOKOLOFF, L., MANGOLD, R., WECHSLER, R. L., KENNEDY, C., AND KETY, S. S. The effect of mental arithmetic on cerebral circulation and metabolism. J. Clin. Invest., 1955, **34,** 1101.

Monographs and Reviews

ABRAMSON, D. I. Vascular responses in extremities of man in health and disease. University of Chicago Press, Chicago, 1944.

ALLEN, E. V., BARKER, N. W., AND HINES, E. A. Peripheral vascular diseases. W. B. Saunders Co., Philadelphia, 1962.

BARCROFT, H. The circulation in the limbs. In Circulation, edited by J. McMichael. Blackwell Scientific Publications, Oxford, 1958.

BARCROFT, H., AND SWAN, H. J. C. Sympathetic control of human blood vessels. Edward Arnold & Company, London, 1953.

CLARK, E. R. Arterio-venous anastomoses. Physiol. Rev., 1938, **18,** 229.

FOLKOW, B. Nervous control of the blood vessels. Physiol. Rev., 1955, **35,** 629.

GREEN, H. D. AND KEPCHAR, J. H. Control of peripheral resistance in major systemic vascular beds. Physiol. Rev., 1959, **39,** 617.

HERTZMAN, A. B. Vasomotor regulation of cutaneous circulation. Physiol. Rev., 1959, **39,** 280.

LEWIS, T. The blood vessels of the human skin and their responses. Shaw, London, 1927.

LEWIS, T. Vascular disorders of the limbs. Macmillan & Company, Ltd., London, 1936.

LEWIS, T. Clinical Science, illustrated by personal experiences. Shaw, London, 1934.

LEWIS, T. Observations on some normal and injurious effects of cold upon the skin and underlying tissues. Brit. M. J., 1941, **2,** 795, 837, 869.

MERYMAN, H. T. Tissue freezing and local cold injury. Physiol. Rev., 1957, **37,** 233.

MONTGOMERY, H. Experimental immersion foot. Review of the physiopathology. Physiol. Rev., 1954, **34,** 147.

ORBISON, J. L. AND SMITH, D. E. The peripheral blood vessels. Williams & Wilkins Company, Baltimore, 1963.

SHEARD, C. Temperature of skin and thermal regulation of the body. In Medical Physics, edited by O. Glasser. p. 1523. Year Book Publishers, Inc., Chicago, 1944.

SHELLEY, W. B. AND ARTHUR, R. P. The Physiology of the Skin. In Annual Review of Physiology, edited by V. E. Hall. Annual Reviews, Inc., Palo Alto, California, 1958.

SHEPHERD, J. T. Physiology of the circulation in human limbs in health and disease. W. B. Saunders Co., Philadelphia, 1963.

SHERMAN, J. L. Normal arteriovenous anastomoses. Medicine, 1963, **42,** 247.

UVNÄS, B. Sympathetic vasodilator outflow. Physiol. Rev., 1954, **34,** 608.

CHAPTER 47

Special Features of Circulation in Different Regions (cont.). Splanchnic Circulation; Renal Circulation

The Splanchnic Circulation

The splanchnic circulation may be represented as consisting of three parts: (1) the mesenteric bed, supplying the gastrointestinal tract, (2) the splenic bed, and (3) the hepatic bed.

A unique feature of this circulatory system is that the combined outflow from two of the components (mesenteric and splenic) constitutes the major portion of the inflow of the third one (hepatic), through the portal vein. In its hemodynamic implications, this anatomical arrangement has been compared to the Wheatstone bridge in an electrical circuit (Bradley, 1958), because of the placement of the resistance vessels (fig. 47.1). This serves mainly to emphasize the large number of variables that influence blood pressure and flow in any one point of the system, and the potential fallacy of conclusions based upon measurements of a single variable, such as portal venous pressure.

As in other regions of the circulation, it is the measurement of blood flow that presents the greatest source of difficulties. Direct methods to this date can only be applied at the cost of considerable surgical and anesthetic trauma, and with various degrees of interference to flow (particularly venous flow) due to cannulation procedures. This latter obstacle has been eliminated by the application of noncannulating electromagnetic flow meters (Green and associates, 1959). Indirect methods, based on the Fick principle and the ability of the liver to clear certain dyes, such as bromsulphalein (Bradley and associates, 1945) or colloidal substances from the blood stream, do not have these disadvantages, but— aside from their failure to meet strictly the criteria of the Fick principle—can be used only for measurement of total splanchnic outflow (i.e., hepatic venous flow), not for that of its various components.

The Mesenteric Circulation

The nature of pressure-flow relationships in the intestinal vascular bed is controversial at the present time. According to one group of investigators, the mesenteric bed behaves in a passive manner, similar to other areas such as the skin. There exists a "critical closure" pressure of the order of 15 mm. Hg below which flow ceases; above this point, progressive increments of pressure result in greater and greater increments of flow: in other words, vascular resistance decreases with increasing perfusion pressure (Selkurt and associates, 1955; Hinshaw, 1962). The reasons for this deviation from Poiseuille's law (dilatation of blood vessels with increased intraluminal pressure and the opening up of "dormant" capillaries) have been fully discussed in chapter 46. This view is opposed by others who find evidence for mesenteric vascular autoregulation, such as is seen in the brain and kidney —i.e., a tendency to maintain blood flow (or possibly another variant, such as capillary pressure) constant in the face of a varying perfusion pressure. This implies an increase in vascular resistance as perfusion pressure is increased (Johnson, 1960; Texter and associates, 1962; Folkow and others, 1963). In all likelihood, differences in experimental methods, particularly in perfusion techniques, are responsible for the conflicting results.

Certain hemodynamic characteristics peculiar to the mesenteric circuit derive from the location of these vessels in the walls of viscera capable of actively or passively changing their intramural tension. Isolated, perfused intestinal loops exhibit two sorts of spontaneous contractile activity: rhythmic segmental contractions, and alterations of the muscular tone. Each of these has a definite influence on blood flow within the loop (Sidky and Bean, 1958). During segmental contractions, there is an increase in venous outflow and decrease in arteriolar inflow, proportional to the strength of the contraction; reverse changes occur during relaxation. In addition to these phasic changes associated with individual contractions, there is close relationship between mean blood flow per unit time and the frequency of rhythmic segmental activity. All other things being equal, the minute volume flow increases with increasing frequency of contractions.

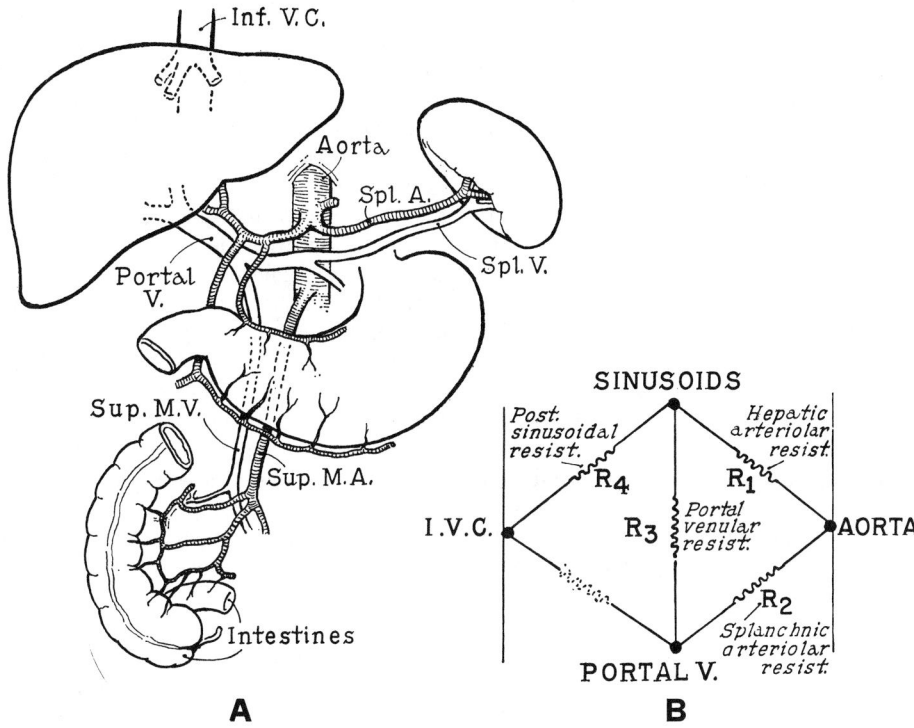

FIG. 47.1. The Splanchnic circuits. The vascular resistances in the splanchnic bed (*A*) are shown here in diagrammatic form (*B*). The resistances indicated are determinants of pressures in the portal vein and in the liver sinusoids, and of flows through the portal vein and hepatic artery. R_1, hepatic arteriolar resistance; R_2, splanchnic (i.e., mesenteric, pancreatic, gastric and splenic) arteriolar resistance; R_3, portal venular resistance; R_4, postsinusoidal or hepatic venular resistance. The dotted line represents a fifth resistance lying in the direct communications between the portal vein and inferior vena cava. (From S. E. Bradley, *Circulation*, Proceedings of the Harvey Tercentenary Congress, p. 356, 1958.)

Changes in the gut's muscular tone are of longer duration and involve greater lengths of intestine than segmental contractions. An increase of tonus results in reduction of both arterial inflow and venous outflow. Following cessation of tonic contraction, blood flow temporarily increases above precontraction levels, in a manner analagous to the reactive hyperemia observed in skin, skeletal muscle and myocardium (see ch. 46). Since segmental and tonic contractions occur independently from one another and may be more or less superimposed, their effect on intestinal blood flow can be quite complex. If these processes observed in the isolated loop also operate in the intact animal or man, the musculature of the intestine may emerge as a factor in the regulation of splanchnic and systemic blood flow.

Passive changes in intramural pressure, such as those occurring in acute distension, also influence intestinal circulation (Noer and associates, 1951). It was shown in serosal vessels of rabbit's intestine, that at intraluminal pressures of 15 to 20 mm. Hg, segmental contractions cease, accom-

panied by slowing of blood flow in the venules. With progressive rising of the pressure, circulation slows, then ceases, first on the venous, then on the arterial side. While such levels of intraintestinal pressures are clearly outside the physiological range, these circulatory changes are the basis of the massive trapping of blood and leakage of plasma into the wall and lumen of the gut observed during acute intestinal obstructions.

In the maintenance of normal mesenteric circulation, the hemodynamic characteristics of the local vascular bed and the possible influence thereon of the intestinal smooth musculature are supplemented by a rich network of vasomotor nerves. These nerves belong to the sympathetic nervous system; their preganglionic fibers are contained in the splanchnic nerves; the postganglionic fibers form large plexuses around the abdominal aorta and accompany its branches to all the viscera. The function of vasomotor nerves has been discussed in detail in chapters 42 and 46. Electrical stimulation of the splanchnic nerves in anesthetized dogs produces sharp decline in mesenteric artery flow, along with increasing the arterial (and portal vein) pressures, indicating that vasoconstriction has occurred. There is no evidence for the existence of vasodilator fibers in the splanchnic nerves (Deal and Green, 1956). Intra-arterially injected norepinephrine reproduces the effect of splanchnic nerve stimulation (see ch. 42), while section of the nerves or administration of ganglionic blocking agents increases mesenteric flow.

Vasomotor reactions in the mesenteric circuit are of considerable importance in various circulatory adjustments (see pp. 745, 746). Not all vasomotor activity, however, is necessarily mediated by the nervous system. In the dog, experimental elevation of the portal venous pressure results in a reduction of mesenteric blood flow greater than the decrease in mesenteric artery-portal vein pressure gradient, indicating that mesenteric vascular resistance had increased (Selkurt and Johnson, 1958). This change in resistance is shown to be independent from nervous activity and due to "myogenic" response of the arterioles to the pressure increase transmitted through the capillaries (Johnson, 1959). It is not known what role, if any, this venous-arteriolar response plays in the intact animal.

THE SPLENIC CIRCULATION

The nature of the intrasplenic circulation is a long-standing, unsettled controversy. Lack of agreement is centered around the manner of connection between arterial and venous capillaries: whether their lumina are continuous with one another ("closed circulation") or is arterial blood discharged directly into the meshwork of the splenic pulp from which it seeps back into the venous capillaries ("open circulation"). The basis for suspecting a discontinuity of the circulatory bed (unparalleled elsewhere in the body) is the presence of blood cells and intra-arterially injected foreign material in the splenic pulp, seen on histological examination; this is attributed to experimental artefacts by adherents of the "closed circulation" theory. Microscopic transillumination studies in the living animal (Whipple and associates, 1954) suggest that both open and closed circulatory patterns function simultaneously ("combined circulation"), but it is debatable whether these observations on mouse spleen are applicable to the human organ in view of the demonstrated structural differences between the two (Snook, 1950). Pressure-flow relationships in the perfused dog spleen show a continuous drop in vascular resistance, without any

plateauing, even at high pressure and flow rates. This great distensibility of the splenic intravascular space is probably due to the opening of the vascular sinuses.

In certain mammals (dog, cat, horse, guinea pig) the spleen serves as a reservoir of blood. Under ordinary circumstances, blood is stored in the distensible venous sinuses, to be released into the circulation when need arises (as during exercise, anoxia, hemorrhage).

Evidence indicates that this splenic emptying mechanism is under sympathetic regulation (Green and associates, 1960). Stimulation of splenic nerve fibers in the dog results in simultaneous decrease in arterial inflow, increase in venous outflow, and decrease of splenic weight. The inflow response can be reproduced by intra-arterial norepinephrine injection, while the outflow response can best be reproduced by injection of epinephrine. This suggests the existence of separate mechanisms for the control of splenic inflow and outflow: a norepinephrine-mediated arteriolar inflow constriction and an epinephrine-mediated emptying mechanism. This latter might be due either to venular relaxation causing passive elastic recoil of splenic tissues, or to primary contraction of splenic smooth muscle fibers.

In man, there is no evidence to indicate that splenic contractions take place under physiological circumstances, nor do injections of adrenaline raise the circulatory plasma or red cell volumes (Parsons and associates, 1948) as one would expect if the spleen served as an important blood depot.

THE HEPATIC CIRCULATION

In addition to receiving its arterial blood supply through the hepatic artery, the liver is also perfused by the mesenteric and splenic venous outflow through the portal vein. As pointed out earlier, this unique circulatory arrangement leads to considerable complexity of splanchnic hemodynamics, and information regarding the various factors determining blood flow through the liver is still fragmentary. The following may illustrate the difficulties encountered.

The hemodynamic properties of the portal venous bed of the isolated liver show a great deal of similarity to those of other vascular beds, such as the mesenteric described earlier. There is, in particular, a progressive decrease of vascular resistance with increase of perfusion pressures throughout the physiological pressure range (up to 12 to 13 cm. of H_2O) (Bauer and associates, 1956). This would indicate that relatively small changes of portal pressure are associated with marked flow effects and that, consequently, portal venous pressure is an important determinant of total hepatic flow.

As may be seen from figure 47.1, however, portal venous pressure is under the influence of a variety of factors. Mesenteric and splenic arteriolar tone regulate inflow, while the outflow is determined by venular tone and hepatic sinusoidal pressure. The latter, in turn, is dependent upon hepatic arteriolar tone and hepatic venous pressure (determined by inferior vena caval pressure) which regulate inflow and outflow in the sinusoids. Active contractions of the portal and hepatic veins are possible additional factors, all capable of altering portal venous pressure and thus influencing total hepatic flow.

Experimental separation of all these variables has not been possible up to now; nonetheless, certain important observations have been made. Continuous simultaneous direct measurements of hepatic arterial and portal venous flows in anesthetized dogs show the contribution of the portal vein to total hepatic flow as being approximately 65 per cent in one study (Selkurt and Brecher, 1956), and 80 per cent in another (Green and associates, 1959). The effective portal perfusion pressures under these circumstances are 6 and 8 mm. Hg, respectively. Unlike the portal venous bed, the hepatic arterial system seems to possess autoregulation—i.e. hepatic arterial flow tends to remain constant when the perfusion pressure is varied within the physiological range (Torrance, 1961). Splanchnic nerve stimulation causes an increase in both hepatic arterial and portal venous pressures, with a concomitant reduction in the corresponding flows. The calculated increases in resistance of the portal venous and hepatic arterial beds approximately equal one another, suggesting an equal degree of splanchnic vasomotor innervation. Compared to the mesenteric bed, they are both less sensitive to vasomotor stimulation. The effects of epinephrine and norepinephrine are similar to those of splanchnic nerve stimulation, causing, however, a less marked increase in the resistance of the portal bed. Thus, even though portal vein and hepatic artery pressures increase and hepatic arterial blood flow diminishes, portal flow does not change much and may even increase (Green and associates, 1959). In fact, the net effect of epinephrine in the resting, nonanesthetized human is an increase of total hepatic flow, as estimated by indirect Bromsulphalein retention (BSP) measurements, along with an elevation of

portal venous pressure (Bradley, 1952). Norepinephrine under similar conditions causes a decrease of estimated liver flow in man (Bearn and coworkers, 1951), while in normal, anesthetized dogs either no flow effect (Smythe and associates, 1953) or a decrease in flow (Turk and Shoemaker, 1962) was observed.

The hemodynamic properties of the hepatic vascular bed and the nervous and humoral controls exerted on it play an important part in circulatory homeostasis by adjusting splanchnic blood flow in response to varying body needs. Blood flow through the splanchnic bed is sufficiently large to enable it to serve as a reservoir. The circulating splanchnic blood volume in man at rest and in the anesthetized dog, measured by isotope dilution techniques, forms approximately 20 per cent of the total blood volume (about 1000 cc. in man) (Bradley and coworkers, 1953). Splanchnic blood flow (i.e., the total amount of blood perfusing the liver through the hepatic artery and portal vein), estimated by the BSP method, amounts to approximately 1,500 cc. per minute in man, or about 20 per cent of the resting cardiac output.

Changes in splanchnic hemodynamics occur under various physiological and pathological conditions. In man, occupation of the erect position is associated with widespread reflex vasomotor adjustments opposing the hydrostatic forces which would lower the blood pressure in the upper half of the body (see ch. 43). The splanchnic bed is an important effector end organ in these reflexes. Passive tilting of human subjects from supine to upright position causes a decrease of splanchnic blood flow without similar changes of mean blood pressure, indicating that an increase in splanchnic vascular resistance has occurred (Culbertson and associates, 1951). This channels blood to other vascular areas, notably those in the upper regions of the body. In subjects with previous splanchnicectomy, the same tilting procedure causes arterial hypotension and a proportional decrease of splanchnic blood flow without changing the vascular resistance (Wilkins and coworkers, 1951). This would indicate that the vasoconstriction is normally mediated through the splanchnic sympathetic nerves.

Vasomotor adjustments and redistribution of circulating blood are also prominent during exercise. In normal human subjects, performing light exercise in the recumbent position, circulating splanchnic blood volume and splanchnic blood flow decrease significantly (Wade and associates, 1956). As exercise is usually associated with an increase in arterial blood pressure and cardiac output (see ch. 39 and 44), the reduction in splanchnic flow must be caused by increased vascular resistance. The advantages for the organism of such vascular adjustments are evident; vasoconstriction diverts blood flow to those organs that need it most (e.g., the exercising muscles). Moreover, the extra blood derived from the reduction in circulating splanchnic blood volume serves to boost venous return, thereby contributing to the elevation of cardiac output.

Finally, the splanchnic circulation plays an important role in the response of the organism to a reduction of circulating blood volume, such as occurs after hemorrhage. This response is conditioned to a great extent by the amount of blood lost, and it may vary, accordingly, from transient vasomotor changes to a state of irreversible circulatory collapse resulting in death.

It might be expected from the splanchnic responses to tilting and to exercise that blood loss would produce vasoconstriction in the splanchnic bed, in order to maintain flow in other parts of the body such as the brain and heart. Actually, observations on the behavior of the mesenteric and splanchnic vasculature in response to hemorrhage are conflicting. Splanchnic blood volume and flow are reduced during hemorrhage but investigators using the BSP method for measuring splanchnic blood flow report no significant change in splanchnic resistance following removal of about one-third of the total blood volume of the anesthetized dog (Reynell and associates, 1955). This would indicate that the splanchnic bed, unlike the vasculature of the skin, skeletal muscles and kidneys, does not participate in the systemic vasoconstriction following hemorrhage. On the other hand, when superior mesenteric arterial flow is measured directly by means of an electromagnetic flowmeter, moderate, non-shocking hemorrhage produces an immediate increase in mesenteric vascular resistance, proportional to the magnitude of blood loss (Abel and Murphy, 1962). Removal of larger amounts of blood, resulting in irreversible shock, produces more marked but qualitatively similar changes in hemodynamic parameters. The metabolic consequences, however, are quite different. Splanchnic oxygen consumption is not affected by the moderate blood loss; the diminished flow is compensated for by increased oxygen extraction by the tissues (Hamrick and Myers, 1955). With more massive hemorrhage, however, blood flow is so reduced that this compensation is inadequate and splanchnic oxygen consumption falls, resulting in hepatic hypoxia. Hypoxia of the intestines and liver may be an important causative factor in determining the irreversibility of fatal hemorrhagic shock (Selkurt, 1959).

Renal Circulation

Renal circulation and renal function are so closely interrelated that reference to only one without consideration of the other always has to be artificial and incomplete. Also, much of our knowledge about renal blood flow stems indirectly from the behavior of some special functions of the kidney. The reader is referred to the chapter on "Urine Formation" where renal function, the anatomy and the clearance method for renal blood flow measurements are considered in detail.

METHODOLOGY OF RENAL BLOOD FLOW. The renal blood flow in man is usually measured by the clearance technique. There are some restrictions necessary in connection with this method: (1) rapid changes in the renal blood flow cannot be detected since a single clearance period covers 5 to 15 minutes and gives only average values during this time; (2) determinations can be carried out only when urine is produced at the same time, since, for the calculation of renal blood flow, it is necessary to know the amount of the clearance substance (usually paraminohippuric acid) which is excreted in the urine. For example, in shock and in certain renal diseases, when no urine is produced, renal blood flow cannot be evaluated by this method. (3) Urine formation is also interrupted when the arterial blood pressure is less than 50 mm. Hg, since the hydrostatic pressure in the glomerular capillaries is insufficient to produce a glomerular filtrate.

In order to get a more exact picture of the renal hemodynamics, it was necessary, therefore, to turn to animal experiments. Nearly all the direct and indirect methods for the measurement of blood flow described in chapter 39 have been applied in these animal experiments. However, these methods fail to elucidate the pattern of distribution of the *intrarenal* blood flow. During the last years, methods have been developed to separately determine the blood flow of the renal cortex and medulla. (1) Under certain circumstances the accumulation rate of a substance in a tissue can be used as a measure of the blood flow. This method has been applied to the determination of blood flow to the different renal areas. When radioactive albumin is introduced into the arterial circulation, the radioactivity builds up in the tissue. The rate of accumulation of the radioactivity is a function of the blood flow to the region. (2) Another method utilizes the translumination of the different parts of the kidney by implanted micro light sources.

Regional blood flow rate is calculated by means of local blood volume and local circulation time:

$$F \ (\text{ml}/100 \ \text{g/min}) = \frac{\text{vascular volume}/100 \ \text{g}}{\text{mean circulation time}}$$

Local vascular volume is calculated utilizing the ratio:

$$\frac{\text{Hemoglobin concentration in tissue}}{\text{Hemoglobin concentration in blood}}$$

$$= \text{vascular volume}/100 \ \text{g tissue}$$

To obtain mean circulation times of blood in the cortex and outer and inner medulla, dye-dilution curves in these areas were recorded simultaneously after a single injection of Evans blue or Cardio green into the renal artery (see Fig. 47.4). Recordings were taken by small photoelectric probes placed on the cortical surface and on one side of the papilla or further up into a calyx. Whereas in the cortex a photoelectric reflectometer was pierced under the capsule, the medullary photocells received light transmitted from a small tungsten bulb at the tip of a hypodermic needle pierced through the tissue. Local mean circulation times were calculated from the dye-dilution curves.

Recently Thorburne et al. used the inert gas method in conscious dogs to determine intrarenal blood flow distribution. After a single injection of Kr^{85} into the renal artery, the disappearance curve of the gamma emission was monitored with a scintillation probe placed on the body surface above the kidney. Assuming an equilibration of krypton between blood and tissue in a single passage through the capillary bed, and assuming an extremely small recirculation, the rate of disappearance from the kidney will depend upon the nutrient or capillary blood flow (F):

$$F \ (\text{ml}/100 \ \text{g/min}) = \frac{k \times \lambda \times 100}{P}$$

F = arterial inflow rate per 100 g tissue
k = slope of disappearance curve
λ = partition coefficient for the inert gas between tissue and blood
p = specific gravity of the tissue

In contrast to other organs, the decay curves obtained in the kidney are nonexponential and can be described by a series of exponentials, each

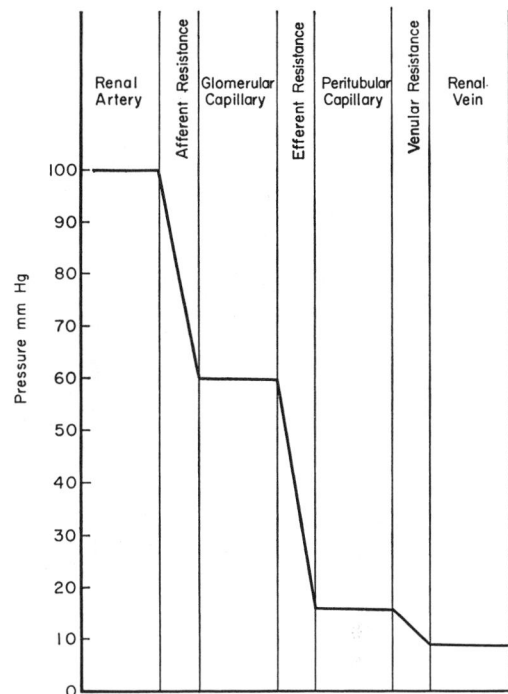

FIG. 47.2. Pressure gradients in the mammalian renal circulation.

associated with different blood flow rates through localized regions of the kidney. Four regions could be differentiated: (1) cortex, (2) juxtamedullary cortex and outer medully, (3) inner medully, and (4) perirenal and hilar fat.

NORMAL RENAL BLOOD FLOW. Under resting conditions, in the recumbent position, and with a normal mean arterial blood pressure, about 1,200 cc. of blood per minute pass through both human kidneys, or about 20 per cent of the cardiac output. This is called the renal fraction of the cardiac output. Since the average weight of both kidneys is about 300 gm., normally 1 gm. of kidney is perfused by 4 cc. of blood per minute. However, this value is only an average for the whole kidney since there are great differences in the distribution of the blood supply within various renal areas. Blood flow values per gram of tissue have been found to be similar in dogs (4 to 5 cc. per gm. per minute). However, smaller animals have a greater renal perfusion rate. Values up to 10 cc. per gm. per minute have been obtained in rats by the PAH clearance method. For a better comparison of values obtained from different laboratories, it has become the custom to express renal blood flow in cc. per gm. per minute.

In the kidney, there are two capillary beds connected in series: the glomerular capillaries and

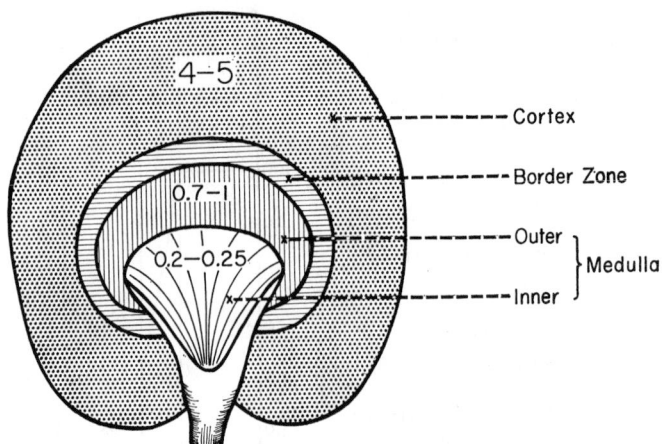

FIG. 47.3. Blood flow rates (cc. per gram per minute) in different areas of the dog kidney.

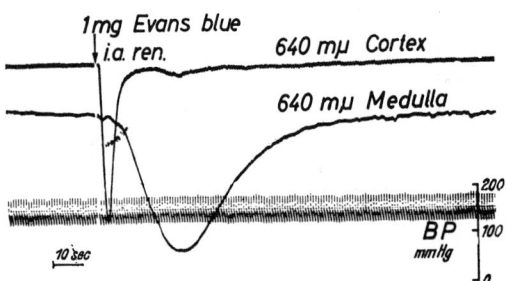

FIG. 47.4. Dye-dilution curves in the renal cortex and medulla of the dog after rapid injection of Evans blue into the renal artery (↓ i. a. ren.). The passage of Evans blue was measured by small photocells, which separately picked up reflected light from the cortex (*upper curve*) and transmitted light through the medulla (*middle curve*). The photocells were sensitive at the Evans blue absorption wave length (640 mμ). The lower curve represents systemic blood pressure (BP). (From Kramer, K., and associates, Pflüger's Arch. ges. Physiol., 1960, **270**, 251.)

the peritubular capillaries. They are separated by the vasa efferentia, which functionally and anatomically behave like arterioles. The main resistance to flow in the kidney is divided almost equally between the vasa afferentia (preglomerular) and vasa efferentia (postglomerular), and thus the main pressure drop occurs in these segments (fig. 47.2). It has been demonstrated by micropuncture studies in the cortex of mammalian kidney, that the hydrostatic pressure in the peritubular capillaries is usually 14 to 18 mm. Hg, and is about the same as the hydrostatic pressure in the proximal tubules. At the present time, there are no direct measurements of the hydrostatic pressure in mammalian glomerular capillaries. However, by indirect calculations, this pressure has been assumed to be normally in the range of 60 to 70 mm. Hg.

Ever since the investigations of Wirz and associates showed the significance of the renal medulla upon the concentrating mechanism of the kidney, and the functional difference of this area from the renal cortex, interest has grown in the distribution of total renal blood flow to the component parts of the kidney. Up to the present, all the data on the intrarenal distribution of blood flow are the results of experiments in dogs because of the operative procedures involved in obtaining these measurements. The results show that the perfusion rate in the renal cortical tissue is much greater than in the medulla (fig. 47.3), and indicate that only 1 to 2 per cent of the total renal blood flow passes through the inner medulla. This low blood flow in the inner medulla is associated with a low velocity of the blood in the vasa recta of the medulla. The mean circulation time of the blood through the vasa recta is about 50 seconds, and only about 2.5 seconds through the cortical capillaries (fig. 47.4). On the other hand, the vascular volume in the cortex and in the medulla seems to be the same; in both areas, the vascular volume has been calculated to be about 20 to 22 per cent of the tissue volume. More than one factor is known to cause this low velocity of blood in the vasa recta. The resistance to flow in these vessels is very high because of the unusual length (as compared to other capillaries) of the vasa recta, which may be as long as 20 mm. The composition of the blood is changed as it passes through the medulla, especially when the end urine is highly concentrated. The medullary blood becomes more and more dehydrated as it reaches the tip of the papilla, by transmembrane shunting of water from the descending to the ascending limb of the vasa recta. This water-

TABLE 47.1

Intrarenal circulation times, vascular volumes and blood flow rate

(From Thurau, Am. J. Med., 1964, *36:* 698)

Source	Weight (% of total kidney)	Intra-renal Circulation Times* (min.)	Vascular Volume		Blood Flow Rates			Investigator
			ml./100 gm. Tissue	ml./100 gm. Kidney	ml./100 gm. Tissue/Min.	ml./100 gm. Kidney/ Min.	% of Total renal blood flow	
Cortex	70	0.021	19.2	13.5	458	321.0	92.5	Kramer et al.
	75				472	354.0	94.1	Thorburn et al.
Outer medulla	20	0.086	19.2	3.9	112	22.4	6.5	Deetjen et al.
	15				132	20.0	5.3	Thorburn et al.
Inner medulla	10	0.75	22.0	2.2	29	2.9	1.0	Kramer et al.
	10				17	2.0	0.6	Thorburn et al.
					22			Lilienfield et al.
Compartment I + II		0.095 (0.073)		17.3		209.5	96.9	Ochwadt Ochwadt
Compartment III		1.4 (1.1)		6.1		6.5	3.1	Ochwadt Ochwadt

* Figures in parentheses represent values for erythrocytes; all other values were obtained from plasma.

shunt mechanism results in an increase of the blood viscosity. Thus, the unusual length of the vasa recta and increasing blood viscosity all contribute to the low velocity of medullary blood flow. Table 47.1 summarizes data on intrarenal circulation times, vascular volumes and blood flow rate.

INTRARENAL HEMODYNAMICS AND RENAL FUNCTION. Intrarenal hemodynamics and renal function are so interrelated that change in one will always affect the other. An increase in the cortical blood flow, if correlated with elevated glomerular capillary pressure, causes an increase in the glomerular filtration rate. In these circumstances, the excretion of osmotically active substances will be increased. This latter effect is partially caused by an increase in the tubular load, i.e., a greater amount of osmotically active substances offered to the tubules by the increased glomerular filtration rate. On the other hand, in the presence of an increase in cortical blood flow, there is a concomitant increase in the peritubular capillary pressure which, by itself, may affect the total excretion by means of decreased proximal tubular reabsorption.

Medullary blood flow seems to be important for the concentrating ability of the kidney. In the renal medulla, the osmotic pressure progressively increases from the base to the tip of the medulla and becomes a determinant in the concentration of the final urine delivered to the renal pelvis. An increase of blood flow in the medulla tends to wash out the osmotically active substances from this area, decreasing the osmotic pressure and causing a lower concentration of the final urine. In this manner, renal function is affected by primary changes in medullary blood flow and, conversely, medullary blood flow may be affected by primary changes in renal function. In water diuresis, the medullary blood flow is greater than in antidiuresis. The cortical blood flow and the glomerular filtration rate are unchanged under these circumstances.

AUTOREGULATION OF RENAL BLOOD FLOW. The blood flow (F) in an organ is directly proportional to the arteriovenous pressure gradient (Pa-v), and inversely proportional to the resistance (R), i.e., F = (Pa-v)/(R). In most organs, when only the arteriovenous pressure gradient increases, the blood flow increases more than the increase in pressure gradient, meaning that there has been a concomitant decrease in the resistance caused by the passive distention of the vessels with pressure. The pattern of behavior of the renal blood flow is different; it reacts in the manner just described at perfusion pressures only up to 90 mm. Hg. However, when the arterial perfusion pressure rises above 90 mm. Hg, the resistance increases so that the total blood flow in the kidney remains nearly constant (fig. 47.6, curve N). Above 250 mm. Hg, the blood flow again becomes directly dependent on the arterial pressure. This phenom-

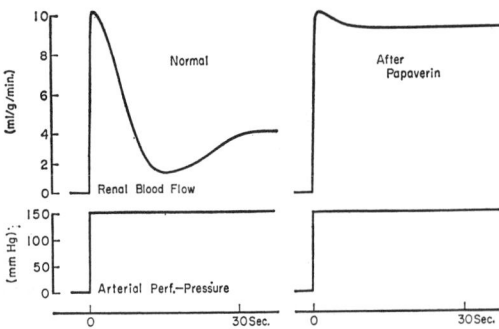

FIG. 47.5. Pattern of flow in the renal artery of dogs following sudden increase in the arterial perfusion pressure from 0 to 150 mm. Hg before and after vascular muscle paralysis by papaverine. The phasic changes in renal blood flow in the normal kidney, indicating a concomitant, inverse change in resistance can be abolished by papaverine. The steady state blood flow of 4 cc. per gram per minute at 150 mm. Hg in the control (autoregulated kidney) is increased under papaverine to about 9 cc. per gram per minute. (See also figure 26.6, difference between curve N and curve O at 150 mm. Hg). (Modified after Thurau, K. and Kramer, K. Pflüger's Arch. ges. Physiol., 1959, **269,** 77.)

enon is known as the autoregulation of renal blood flow because it is also present after cutting the renal nerves, after injecting ganglioplegic drugs, and in the isolated perfused kidney.

Simultaneous measurements of blood flow in the cortex and inner medulla of the kidney have shown that autoregulation is present solely in the cortex. Since only about 1 to 2 per cent of the total renal blood flow passes through the inner medulla, a solitary increase in medullary blood flow does not actually cause a measurable increase of total renal blood flow. Therefore, in the presence of a rising arterial perfusion pressure, the total renal blood flow remains nearly constant in spite of an increasing medullary blood flow. Hence, it is more accurate to limit discussion of autoregulation solely to the cortical blood flow.

There are at the moment, four theories which attempt to explain this special behavior of the renal blood flow.

A. Myogenic theory. When the arterial perfusion pressure is increased, the vessels become distended. The smooth muscles, especially in the preglomerular vessels, react to this distention by shortening, thereby constricting the vessels so that a new high resistance is established. This implies that the tonus of the vessels is increased by an autonomic myogenic reaction to increasing arterial perfusion pressure.[1] It has been demon-

[1] Contraction of the smooth muscles as the result of elevated intravascular pressure has been

strated in the dog kidney that when the arterial perfusion pressure is suddenly increased, the blood flow is only increased passively during the first 3 to 4 seconds. Following this, the resistance in the vascular bed increases to such an extent that the blood flow nearly ceases at about 15 seconds. After 20 to 30 seconds, the blood flow increases to the normal level of the autoregulation (fig. 47.5). This initial latency and the phasic changes of the resistance are in accord with the contracting properties of smooth muscle. The autoregulation can be abolished by drugs which paralyze the smooth muscles (potassium cyanide, papaverine, and procaine (novocaine) in high concentration). Likewise, the phasic changes of the resistance, caused by rapid pressure increases, are removed by these drugs (fig. 47.5).

There are experimental indications that the autoregulatory mechanism resides within the preglomerular vessels. The glomerular filtration rate is controlled, among other things, by the intraglomerular capillary pressure. The constancy of the glomerular filtration rate and its independence from arterial perfusion pressure changes above 90 mm. Hg, constitutes indirect evidence of a constant, intraglomerular capillary pressure. Furthermore, by paralyzing the vascular smooth muscles with papaverine, the glomerular filtration rate now becomes directly proportional to the arterial perfusion pressure. Thus, there is strong evidence to support the contention that the autoregulatory mechanism depends upon the integrity and reactivity of the preglomerular vascular muscles.

B. Cell separation theory. In a vascular system in which small vessels branch off from a large one, the small vessels receive cell poor plasma from the outer zone of blood in the large vessel, because the erythrocytes remain in the axial stream of the large vessel. This separation of plasma and erythrocytes at the bifurcation of vessels is called plasma skimming or cell separation. For the kidney, it is assumed that this cell separation takes place to an unusual degreee at the origin of the afferent arterioles. The blood remaining in the interlobular arteries becomes more

described for many vascular systems. In contrast to the kidney, these myogenic reactions are not powerful enough to constrict the vessel to such an extent that blood flow remains constant in spite of an elevated perfusion pressure. It is not necessarily true that the single muscle cell of the renal vessel reacts differently than in other organs. A spatial arrangement of the muscle cells, specially oriented, can increase the net effect of the single cell contraction on the diameter of the vessel.

and more concentrated with erythrocytes and flows through special erythrocyte-shunts directly into the veins without flowing through the peritubular capillaries, which are perfused only by cell poor plasma. The degree of the cell separation is supposed to be dependent on the arterial perfusion pressure, so that blood with a hematocrit up to about 80 per cent in the distal part of the interlobular arteries can be produced. In this range of hematocrit, the viscosity of the blood is high and varies greatly with small changes in hematocrit. This variable viscosity which is dependent on the arterial blood pressure, is believed to be the cause of the variable resistance responsible for the autoregulation. According to this theory, a cell-free perfusion of the kidney should not show any autoregulation. However, it has been demonstrated by different investigators that autoregulation does occur even when the kidney is perfused by dextran, a cell-free plasma, or blood with a very low hematocrit. It would, furthermore, be expected that the oxygen saturation of the blood in the distal peritubular capillaries should be lower than that in the mixed venous blood. However, investigations have shown that the oxygen saturation in this area is not different from that in mixed venous blood. Also, the passage times of plasma and erythrocytes from the renal artery to the renal vein are the same, but, according to the cell separation theory, they should differ.

C. Intrarenal pressure theory. By insertion of a 24 gauge needle into the renal tissue, it was found that the intrarenal tissue pressure measured in this way increases disproportionately with increasing arterial perfusion pressure. From this data, it is calculated that the elevated tissue pressure has a clamping effect on vascular geometry and resistance to flow. This assumes that the needle pressure selectively measures only normal tissue pressure and that no vessels have been ruptured by the needle insertion. In any case, measurements of the intracapillary and intratubular pressures in the rat kidney by the micropuncture technique have shown that these pressures do not change when the arterial perfusion pressure is elevated above 90 mm. Hg.

D. Intrarenal sodium feed-back theory at the level of the juxtaglomerular apparatus. The single nephron unit in the mammalian kidney is arranged in such a way that the end of the ascending limb of Henle's loop comes in direct contact with the vascular pole of its own glomerulum. At the point of contact the renin containing cells are located in the wall of the afferent arteriole.

The tubular cells, at the point of connection are called Macula Densa Cells and are in contact at their luminal side with tubular fluid, leaving the ascending limb of Henle's loop, and at the peritubular side with the granular cells of the afferent arteriole. Goormaghtigh suggested the Macula Densa Cells to be a sensing device by which changes in concentration of the tubular fluid could regulate the renin release in the afferent arteriole. Since renin is the enzyme necessary for angiotensin formation, preglomerular vasoactions could be initiated by such a mechanism. Recently it was shown by Thurau et al. that an increase in sodium concentration in the tubular fluid at the Macula Densa Cells leads to a reduction in glomerular filtration rate. Assuming the kidney showed no autoregulation, then the increase in arterial blood pressure would not only increase renal blood flow but also glomerular filtration rate and tubular sodium load. In order not to lose the excess filtered sodium, the metabolically linked tubular sodium reabsorption in the proximal tubule would have to increase instantaneously. Even if equal fractions of filtered sodium are reabsorbed in the proximal tubule, a greater amount of sodium during increased GFR would be delivered in the more distal tubular segments. Na-concentration at the Macula Densa Cells would therefore increase and reflect the increased GFR and RBF. The increased sodium concentration at the Macula Densa Cells lowers the glomerular filtration rate by preglomerular formation of angiotensin which leads to a preglomerular vaso-constriction and concomitantly to a fall in filtration rate. On the basis of this mechanism, renal autoregulation would primarily be a phenomenon which keeps sodium load as the major determinant for renal metabolism constant, and autoregulation of blood flow under normal conditions would be a consequence of such a regulation.

NERVOUS CONTROL OF RENAL BLOOD FLOW. The highly developed plexus renalis contains sympathetic and parasympathetic fibers. However, under normal physiological conditions, not too much is known of the significance of this rich nerve supply to the kidney. The interpretation of the results of experiments with regard to the nervous control of renal blood flow is complicated by the fact that the vascular system of the kidney has an autonomic and variable tonus which is independent of any innervation (see autoregulation of renal blood flow) and may interfere with nervous vascular reactions. For a better under-

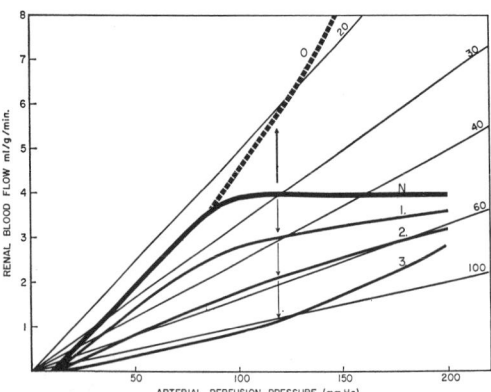

FIG. 47.6. Pressure-flow curves in the kidney. The thin lines through the origin of the graph represent equal resistances to flow expressed in terms of $\dfrac{\text{mm. Hg}}{\text{cc.}}$ per gram per minute.

Curve N. Pressure flow curve under normal conditions. The increase of resistance above 80 mm. Hg is independent of extrinsic factors (see autoregulation of renal blood flow). *Curves 1 to 3.* Pressure flow curves with increasing vascular tone secondary to various extrinsic factors such as increase sympathetic stimulation or epinephrine. With increasing extrinsically induced vascular tone, the pressure flow curves become more and more linear simultaneous to a decrease in autoregulation. *Curve O.* Pressure flow curve after paralyzing the smooth muscles of the renal vessels. Note the abolition of autoregulation; also note that under normal conditions (*curve N*), there is no myogenic tone in the renal vessels between 0 to 80 mm. Hg.

standing of this vascular behavior, see figure 47.6, which shows pressure flow curves resulting either from change of nervous vascular tonus or from autonomic tonus.

Much investigation has been going on to gain information about the nervous control of the renal blood flow under *resting conditions.* Renal blood flow has been measured before and after denervation of the kidney.

In *unanesthetized* man and animals in recumbency, the renal blood flow of the denervated kidney does not differ from that of the innervated kidney. This implies that under resting conditions there is no sympathetic nervous influence in the renal vascular bed. Furthermore, the nonexistence of a sympathetic tone of the renal vascular bed, under resting conditions, has been confirmed by animal experiments in which depressor reflexes in the systemic circulation were produced. Stimulation of the reflexogenic areas of the carotid sinus and aortic arch causes vasodilation in the kidney only when a sympathetic tonus of the renal vessel has been *previously* produced by asphyxia or by anesthesia.

In anesthetized animals, it has been shown that

the renal blood flow may increase after denervation; but, since the sympathetic tone in the peripheral vascular bed is usually augmented during anesthesia, the denervation, therefore, eliminates only the unphysiological sympathetic stimulation produced by the anesthesia, and thereby permits return of the blood flow to normal values. Accordingly, in a dog where one kidney is denervated, the renal blood flow decreases only in the innervated kidney during pentobarbital injection. The blood flow of the denervated kidney shows no change.

Neurogenic vasoconstriction of the renal vessels is produced by severe hypoxia, i.e., arterial oxygen saturation below 50 per cent. However, in the range of decreasing arterial oxygen saturation between 100 and about 50 per cent, there seems to be no change in renal blood flow, and this is true either in anesthetized dogs or in unanesthetized man. The vasoconstrictor effect of severe hypoxia can be eliminated in the dog by abolishing the chemoreceptors in the carotid sinus and aortic arch, indicating that the constrictor response to hypoxia is induced by stimulating the peripheral chemoreceptors.

Vasoconstriction in the dog kidney also occurs during hypercapnia while breathing a mixture of 5 to 30 per cent CO_2 in oxygen. In these experiments, the pH of the blood simultaneously decreased from 7.49 to 7.21. Since the constriction is abolished by renal denervation, hypercapnia and this degree of acidosis seem to produce only neurogenic rather than local vasoconstriction.

A decreased discharge rate of the pressoreceptors in the carotid sinus or aortic arch in dogs, caused by lowering the intrasinusal or intra-aortic blood pressure, or by damping the pulse pressure in these areas, leads to neurogenic vasoconstriction in the kidney as well as in other organs.

In connection with the nervous control of the renal blood flow, the question also arises as to whether or not there exists a nervous control of the function of the tubular cells. After denervation of the kidney, an increase of sodium excretion is often found, suggesting a decreased absorptive capacity of the tubular cells. However, in nearly all these experiments, the glomerular filtration rate simultaneously increased. It is well known that this increase of the glomerular filtration rate can cause an elevated sodium excretion without altered tubular function. Moreover, those experiments in which the excretion of electrolytes was increased *without* a corresponding increase in the glomerular filtration rate, by no means prove a primary changed tubular function after denervation. As yet, it is still unknown whether changes of the intrarenal distribution of blood flow occur after denervation since, for example, even small changes in medullary blood flow can affect the composition of the end urine.

Exercise, posture and central blood volume. Effects on renal blood flow. In the upright exercising man, renal blood flow is diminished when compared to blood flow under resting conditions while supine. If, however, exercise is performed in recumbency, the blood flow in the kidney remain nearly unaffected. Also, the dog, which usually does not change its posture during exercise, shows no change in renal blood flow when running 5.6 to 10 mph at a 15° slope on a treadmill.

These findings give rise to the supposition that the upright position *per se*, in which exercise is usually performed, leads to the decrease in renal blood flow. Indeed, it has been found that the usual response on changing from the recumbent to the standing position is a decrease in renal blood flow. Under the extreme conditions of prolonged standing, the renal blood flow may decrease by about 50 per cent of the control value. These changes are accompanied by similar reductions in glomerular filtration rate and urine output. Since the arterial blood pressure is little or unchanged, the reduction in renal blood flow is primarily caused by an elevated resistance to flow. This is only part of a generalized elevation in total peripheral resistance secondary to the upright position. This enhanced peripheral resistance is caused by an augmented neural vasoconstriction rather than by a humoral mechanism. The afferent mechanisms involved are poorly understood, but it is believed that this can be effected through reduction of central blood volume. The central blood volume in the thorax can be reduced to subnormal values by means of positive pressure breathing. It has been shown, that under these circumstances, the renal resistance to flow increases. Since the blood volume in the chest is also diminished in the upright position, this reduction in central blood volume, induced by changing from the recumbent to the standing position, may be one factor involved in the renal constrictor mechanism. Conversely, an increase in central blood volume above normal by blood infusion, tilting of the body to the head down position, or negative pressure breathing, should produce an neurogenic vasodilation in the kidney. But, as pointed out in the preceding section on nervous control of renal blood flow, under normal resting conditions there are *no* sympathetic discharges to the renal vessel, and hence

a neurogenic vasodilation is nonexistent. It is not surprising, therefore, than an increase in central blood volume fails to result in a renal vasodilation. However, there is another interesting effect of an increased central blood volume upon the kidney which should be briefly mentioned here. It has been found that elevation of central blood volume simultaneously increases the urine output. Since renal blood flow and also the glomerular filtration rate are not altered under these conditions, and, since the resultant diuresis is caused primarily by an increased free water excretion (i.e., without concomitant excretion of osmotically active substances), there is strong evidence that an increase in central blood volume inhibits antidiuretic hormone (ADH) secretion of the neurohypophysis. It is suggested that this ADH-inhibition is reflexly induced by stimulation of stretch receptors located predominantly in the left atrial wall and sensitive to an increase in central blood volume. Whether this mechanism has any significance in the regulation of the total blood volume, is the subject of present investigations.

Returning to the discussion of renal blood flow during exercise in man, there is no doubt that the change to the upright position *per se* is one factor involved in the decreased renal blood flow. But, reductions in renal blood flow down to 20 per cent of the control value, as measured in severe exercise in man, can hardly be explained by this orthostatic mechanism alone. It is a matter for further investigations to establish the other factors which determine the changes in renal blood flow during exercise.

The effect of some pharmacological agents upon renal circulation. Epinephrine and norepinephrine both have powerful vasoconstrictor effects upon the renal vessels. Each drug acts upon smooth muscles, and its action can be abolished by adrenergic blocking agents. Single intravenous injection of 2 μg. per kg. of epinephrine causes complete cessation of renal blood flow. During continuous intravenous infusion of low doses (10 to 15 μg. per minute) of epinephrine or norepinephrine in man, there occurs a 30 per cent decrease in renal flow without change in the glomerular filtration rate. The result indicates that low concentrations of the pressor agents predominantly produce efferent arteriolar constriction. Since the systemic arterial pressure is concomitantly elevated, a small rise in resistance must also occur in the afferent arterioles or, otherwise, there would occur an increase in the glomerular filtration rate. Similar results have been found in the denervated kidney in man. The effect of 2 to 10 μg. per minute of 1-norepinephrine, given intravenously, has been studied in the homotransplanted kidney of an identical twin recipient and in the innervated kidney of the donor. In both kidneys the renal blood flow decreased 25 per cent, when given 2 μg. 1-norepinephrine, and 50 per cent, when given 10 μg., without changes in the glomerular filtration rate, revealing the similarity in the response of the innervated and denervated kidney to 1-norepinephrine in unanesthetized man. Despite the decrease in renal blood flow following minute doses of epinephrine, there occurs a moderate swelling of the kidney. Experiments in dogs have shown a simultaneous increase in renal blood volume. It has, therefore, been concluded that an increase in resistance to flow also occurs in postcapillary segments (probably venular) which leads to an elevated intracapillary pressure and a resultant distention of the renal capillaries.

Pitressin is an extract of the posterior pituitaries of oxen and hogs with an antidiuretic-vasopressor action. Infusions of 1 to 2 mμ per kg. per hour, with which significant antidiuretic effects can be produced, have no effect upon the renal blood flow in man. Higher, nonphysiological doses, increase the resistance to flow in the kidney by direct action on the renal vessels. Repeated injections elicit tachyphylaxis.

The injection of serotonin (5-hydroxytryptamine) into the renal artery in dogs, produces constriction of the renal vessels. This constrictor effect has been shown in innervated as well as in denervated kidney and persists after the application of sympatholytic agents. Thus, serotonin probably acts directly on the smooth muscles. However, *intravenously* injected serotonin may be followed by a renal vasodilation reflexly induced by the action of this drug upon depressor receptors whose afferent fibers arise within the chest and are mediated through the vagus nerve. In patients with malignant carcinoid, the urinary excretion of serotonin or its metabolic products is elevated secondary to the high circulating blood level. In these patients, the glomerular filtration rate and renal blood flow are usually diminished.

1-Hydrozinophthalazine (Apresoline) produces a vasodilation in the kidney which persists for hours following a single injection. The mechanism of the vasodilatory effect is still unknown. It seems that Apresoline has no direct paralyzing effect upon the renal vessels since injection into the renal artery produces an initial vasoconstriction, followed in several minutes by the onset of vasodilation, the latter becoming more marked during the next 30 minutes and persisting for 2 to 3 hours.

REACTIVE HYPEREMIA. In both cardiac and skeletal muscles, and in some other organs, the blood flow temporarily increases over the control value after releasing an arterial clamp. This overshoot of blood flow, lasting from several seconds to several minutes, depends upon the duration of occlusion and may exceed the estimated blood flow debt incurred during the occlusion period. If the term reactive hyperemia is restricted to this overshoot, then by definition, the renal circulation does not show this phenomenon. After releasing an occlusion of the renal artery, there occurs a brief 3 to 5-second overshoot of blood flow (fig. 47.5), which, however, is independent of the duration of occlusion and is, in no instance, greater than the estimated blood flow debt. Furthermore, after interruption of the renal blood flow for several minutes, the re-established blood flow, following the initial overshoot, usually decreases temporarily to subnormal values.

HYPOTHERMIA AND RENAL BLOOD FLOW. At the onset of the cooling phase, as the body attempts to maintain a normal temperature (shivering phase), the renal blood flow increases 20 to 45 per cent above the control value. This has been observed utilizing para-aminohippurate (PAH) clearances in both anesthetized and unanesthetized man and animals. This initial increase in renal blood flow can be abolished by inhibiting shivering with d-tubocurarine. As the rectal temperature falls below 32° C. (90° F.), the renal blood flow progressively decreases and, at 27° C. (80° F.) is only 50 per cent of the normal value. This decrease in blood flow is also observed in the isolated dog kidney which was perfused by cooled blood, and in which the renal blood flow was directly measured. A major part of the decreased blood flow is caused by an increased resistance related to the augmented viscosity of cooled blood, but this factor alone, however, is insufficient to explain the degree of change in blood flow. It is still unknown which other nervous or humoral factors are involved.

Regional cooling such as the immersion of an extremity into ice water for some minutes, sufficient to produce a painful sensation, in man is attended by a 20 per cent decrease in renal blood flow. This is probably caused by a nervous reflex, stimulating sympathetic discharges to the renal vessels.

ARTERIOVENOUS OXYGEN DIFFERENCE AND OXYGEN UPTAKE OF THE KIDNEY. The oxygen difference between arterial and venous blood in the human kidney (A-V oxygen difference) is about 1.7 cc. per 100 cc. of blood, which is small compared with an A-V oxygen difference of 4 to 5 cc. per 100 cc. of blood between arterial blood and mixed venous blood of the right heart. From the renal A-V oxygen difference and the total renal blood flow (1,200 cc. per minute), the oxygen uptake of both human kidneys is calculated to be about 21 cc. per minute. In isolated dog kidney, as well as in dogs' kidneys *in situ*, the A-V oxygen difference has been found to be fairly constant in spite of renal blood flow changes, which means that the oxygen consumption in the kidney parallels the blood flow.

The observation of Zerahn that the oxygen uptake of an isolated frog skin above a resting level is proportional to active sodium transport, paved the way for an explanation of the direct relation between RBF and oxygen consumption. It is well established that renal sodium reabsorption is an active process and represents the overwhelming fraction of all tubular processes. Since under normal conditions, GFR varies with RBF, tubular sodium reabsorption is high at high RBF and accounts for the elevated oxygen consumption (see Fig. 47.7). The constant A-V difference

of oxygen only above 60 mm Hg BP is consistent with the onset of glomerular filtration at this range of BP, whereas below this pressure the A-V difference of oxygen is inversely correlated to RBF as in most other organs. It is clear that a direct correlation between RBF and oxygen consumption is only obtained as long as GFR changes with RBF. In osmotic diuresis and during ureteral occlusion oxygen consumption is lowered at an increased RBF since GFR is diminished.

The A-V oxygen difference in the renal medulla of anesthetized dogs has also been indirectly calculated by means of the oxygen tension of the final urine, which is assumed to be in equilibrium with the medullary venous blood. Usually, the oxygen tension in the urine is less than in the mixed renal venous blood and in these experiments, the difference during air breathing was 25 ± 3 mm. Hg. Thus, by this method, the A-V oxygen difference in the medulla has been calculated to be 8.5 cc. per 100 cc. of blood, which would indeed be very high. However, there are indications that oxygen pressure in the medulla may also be influenced by the counter-current exchange mechanism. In this case, oxygen pressure would progressively decrease to the tip of

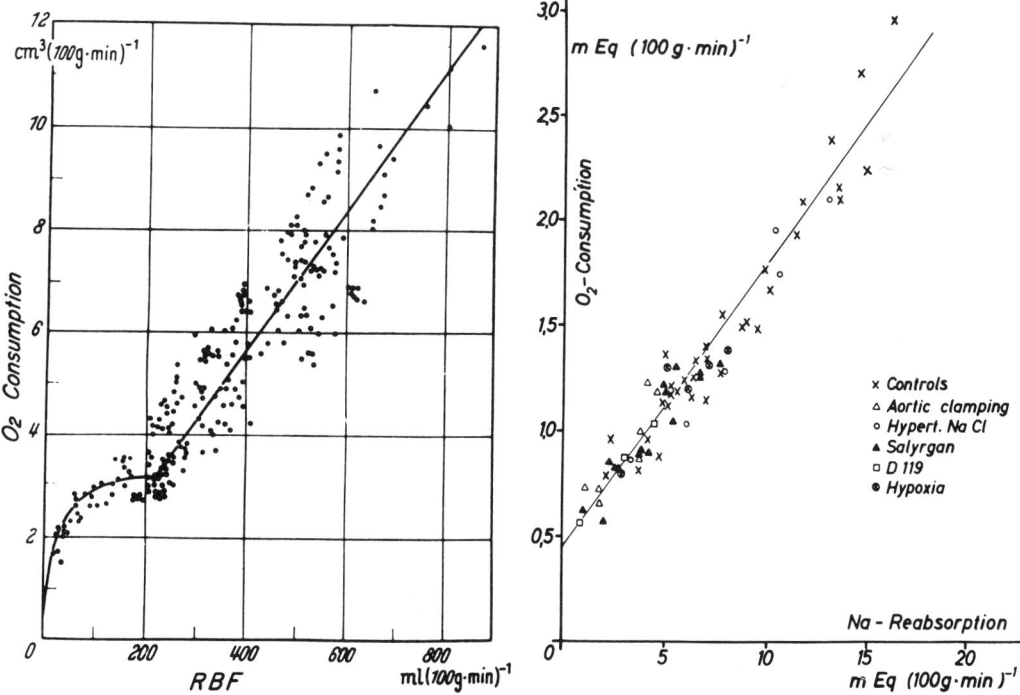

FIG. 47.7. Correlation of renal oxygen consumption with renal blood flow (left) and tubular sodium reabsorption (right). Note the exponential increase of oxygen consumption at low renal blood flow-values. Sodium reabsorption was varied by decreasing glomerular filtration rate (aortic clamp), hyperteronic sodium chloride infusion, saluretic drugs and hypoxia. (From Kramer and Deetjen, Proceedings of 1st International Congress of Nephrology, p. 687, Genéve/Evian, 1961.)

the medulla by transmembral shunting of oxygen from the descending to the ascending limb of the vasa recta. The low oxygen tension of the final urine would represent only the low oxygen pressure at the tip of the medulla rather than the oxygen pressure of the medullary venous blood and, therefore, could not be used for calculations of the medullary A-V oxygen difference.

Conclusions

Renal hemodynamics exhibit certain peculiarities which need re-emphasis. Under basal conditions, there exists no neurogenic tone in the renal vessels, and the kidney is protected against elevations of arterial blood pressure by an autonomic mechanism which usually maintains the cortical blood flow, the glomerular filtration rate and the intrarenal capillary pressure at constant levels. A neurogenic vasodilation is generally nonexistent and only vasoconstriction can be produced via the nervous system. This behavior is absolutely contrary to that of the coronary circulation where the experimental physiology, up to the present time, has demonstrated only dilatory reflex mechanisms. Renal hemodynamics are poorly understood by solely using measurements of the *total* renal blood flow. The renal artery supplies blood at varying flow rates to the differently functioning areas, and function and blood flow seem to be mutually interdependent; this has only been demonstrated in animals. The human kidney, however, still holds secret its distribution of intra-renal blood flow since, at the present time, techniques applicable for use in humans have not been developed.

REFERENCES

ABEL, F. L. AND MURPHY, Q. R. Mesenteric, renal, and iliac vascular resistance in dogs after hemorrhage. Am. J. Physiol., 1962, 202, 978.

AVIADO, D. M., JR., WUNCK, A. L., AND DeBEER, E. J. Effect of sympathomimetica on blood flow in anesthetized dog. J. Pharmacol. & Exper. Therap., 1958, 124, 238.

BEARN, A. G., BILLING, B., AND SHERLOCK, S. The effect of adrenaline and noradrenaline on hepatic blood flow and splanchnic carbohydrate metabolism in man. J. Physiol., 1951, 115, 430.

BERGER, E. Y., GOLDSTONE, M., AND HORWITZ, S. A. The effect of anoxic anoxia on the human kidney. J. Clin. Invest., 1949, 28, 648.

BERGSTRAND, A. AND STERKY, G. Renal function in hypothermia. Acta physiol. scandinav., 1954, 31, 13.

BERLINER, R. W. AND DAVIDSON, D. G. Production of hypertonic urine in the absence of pituitary antidiuretic hormone. J. Clin. Invest., 1957, 36, 1416.

BERNE, R. M. Hemodynamics and sodium excretion of denervated kidney in anesthetized and unanesthetized dogs. Am. J. Physiol., 1952, 171, 148.

BLATTEIS, C. M. AND HORVATH, S. M. Renal, cardiovascular and respiratory responses and their inter-relations during hypothermia. Am. J. Physiol., 1958, 192, 357.

BOYLAN, J. W. AND ANTKOWIAK, D. E. Mechanism of diuresis during negative pressure breathing. J. Appl. Physiol., 1959, 14, 116.

BRADLEY, S. E., MARKS, P. A., REYNELL, P. C., AND MELTZER, J. The circulating splanchnic blood volume in dog and man. Tr. A. Am. Physicians, 1953, 66, 294.

BRAUER, R. W., LEONG, G. F., McELROY, R. F., JR., AND HOLLOWAY, R. J. Hemodynamics of the vascular tree of the isolated rat liver preparation. Am. J. Physiol., 1956, 186, 537.

BRICKER, N. S., STRAFFON, R. A., MAHONEY, E. P., AND MERRILL, J. P. The functional capacity of the kidney denervated by autotransplantation in the dog. J. Clin. Invest., 1958, 37, 185.

BRICKER, N. S., GUILD, W. R., REARDEN, J. B., AND MERRILL, J. P. Studies on the functional capacity of a denervated homotransplanted kidney in an identical twin with parallel observations in the donor. J. Clin. Invest., 1956, 35, 1364.

BRODWALL, E. K. A study of renal function in orthostatic hypotension. Circulation, 1960, 21, 38.

CARLIN, M. R., MUELLER, C. B., AND WHITE, H. L. Effects of exercise on renal blood flow and sodium excretion in dogs. J. Appl. Physiol., 1950, 3, 291.

CHAPMAN, C. B., HENSCHEL, A., MINCKLER, J., FORSGREN, A., AND KEYS, A. Effect of exercise on renal plasma flow in normal male subjects. J. Clin. Invest., 1948, 27, 639.

CHARGILL, W. H. AND HICKAM, J. B. The oxygen consumption of the human kidney. J. Clin. Invest., 1948, 27, 528.

CHARGILL, W. H. AND HICKAM, J. B. The oxygen consumption of the normal and the diseased human kidney. J. Clin. Invest., 1949, 28, 526.

CHASIS, H, RANGES, H. A., GOLDRING, W., AND SMITH, H. W. The control of renal blood flow and glomerular filtration in normal man. J. Clin. Invest., 1938, 17, 683.

CORCORAN, A. C., BROWNING, J. S., AND PAGE, I. H. Renal hemodynamics in orthostatic hypotension. J. A. M. A., 1942, 119, 793.

CULBERTSON, J. W., WILKINS, R. W., INGELFINGER, F. J., AND BRADLEY, S. E. The effect of the upright posture upon hepatic blood flow in normotensive and hypertensive subjects. J. Clin. Invest., 1951, 30, 305.

DEAL, C. P., JR. AND GREEN, H. D. Comparison of changes in mesenteric resistance following splanchnic nerve stimulation with responses to epinephrine and norepinephrine. Circulation Res., 1956, 4, 38.

DEETJEN, P., BRECHTELSBAUER, H., AND KRAMER, K. Hämodynamik des Nierenmarkes. III. Mitteilung. Pflügers Arch. ges. Physiol., 1964, 279, 281.

EMANUEL, D. A., SCOTT, J., COLLINS, R., AND HADDY, F. J. Local effect of serotonin on renal vascular resistance and urine flow rate. Am. J. Physiol., 1959, 196, 1122.

FOLKOW, B. Intravascular pressure as a factor regulating the tone of small vessels. Acta physiol. scandinav., 1949, 17, 289.

FOLKOW, B., LUNDGREN, O., AND WALLENTINE, I. Studies on the relationship between flow resistance, capillary filtration coefficient and regional blood volume in the intestine of the cat. Acta Physiol. Scand., 1963, 57, 270.

FORSTER, R. P. AND MAES, J. P. Effect of experimental neurogenic hypertension on renal blood flow and glomerular filtration rates in intact denervated kidneys of unanesthetized rabbits with adrenal glands demedullated. Am. J. Physiol., 1947, 150, 534.

FRANK, M. A., SELIGMAN, A. M., AND FINE, J. Traumatic shock. XIII. The prevention of irreversibility in hemorrhagic shock by viviperfusion of the liver. J. Clin. Invest., 1946, 25, 22.

FREEMAN, O. W., MITCHELL, G. W., WILSON, J. S., FITZHUGH, F. W., AND MERRILL, A. J. Renal hemodynamics, sodium and water excretion in supine exercising normal and cardiac patients. J. Clin. Invest., 1955, 34, 1109.

FROHLICH, E. D. AND GILLENWATER, J. Y. Pressure-flow relationships in the perfusee dog spleen. Am. J. Physiol., 1963, 204, 645.

GOORMAGHTIGH, N. La Présence de cellules endocrines dans la paroi des artérioles du rein et leur comportement dans l'ischémie rénal. C.R. Soc. Biol., Paris, 1939, 132, 465.

GOORMAGHTIGH, N. Le cycle glandulaire de la cellule endocrine de l'artérile rénale du lapin. Arch. Biol., Paris, 1940, 51, 293.

GOTTSCHALK, C. W. AND MYLLE, M. Micropuncture study of pressures in proximal tubules and peritubular capillaries of the rat kidney and their relation to urethral and renal venous pressures. Am. J. Physiol., 1956, 185, 430.

GRECO, DEL F., MASSON, G. M. C., AND CORCORAN, A. C. Renal and arterial effects of serotonin in the anesthetized rat. Am. J. Physiol., 1956, 187, 509.

GREEN, H. D., LOCKSLEY, S. H., SEXTON, J., AND DEAL, C. P. Autonomic vasomotor responses in the canine hepatic arterial and venous beds. Am. J. Physiol., 1959, 196, 196.

GREEN, H. D., OTTIS, K., AND KITCHEN, T. Autonomic stimulation and blockade on canine splenic inflow, outflow and weight. Am. J. Physiol., 1960, 198, 424.

GRUPP, G. AND HEIMPEL, H. Zum Problem der reaktiven Hyperämie der Niere. Pflüger's Arch. ges. Physiol., 1958, 267, 426.

HADDY, F. S., SCOTT, J., FLEISHMAN, M., AND EMANUEL, D. Effect of change in blood flow rate upon vascular resistance. Am. J. Physiol., 1958, 195, 111.

HAMRICK, L. W., JR. AND MYERS, J. D. The effect of hemorrhage on hepatic blood flow and splanchnic oxygen consumption of the dog. Circulation Res., 1955, 3, 65.

HINSHAW, L. B. Arterial and venous pressure-resistance relationships in perfused leg and intestine. Am. J. Physiol., 1962, 203, 271.

HINSHAW, L. B., BALLIN, H. M., DAY, S. B., AND CARLSON, C. H. Tissue pressure and autoregulation in the dextran perfused kidney. Am. J. Physiol., 1959, 197, 853.

HULET, W. H. AND SMITH, H. W. Negative pressure respiration, water diuresis and natriuresis in normotensive, hypertensive and prehydrated normotensive subjects. J. Clin. Invest., 1959, 38, 1972.

JOHNSON, P. C. Autoregulation of intestinal blood flow. Am. J. Physiol., 1960, 311.

JOHNSON, P. C. Myogenic nature of increase in intestinal vascular resistance with venous pressure elevation. Circulation Res., 1959, 7, 992.

KAPLAN, S. A., WEST, C. D., AND FOMON, S. J. Effects of unilateral division of splanchnic nerve on the renal excretion of electrolytes in unanesthetized and anesthetized dogs: the mechanism of crossed stimulation. Am. J. Physiol., 1953, 175, 363.

KIIL, F., AUKLAND, K., AND REFSUM, H. E. Renal sodium transport and oxygen consumption. Am. J. Physiol., 1961, 201, 5111.

KRAMER, K., AND WINTON, F. R. The influence of urea and of change in arterial pressure on the oxygen consumption of the isolated kidney in dog. J. Physiol. 1937, 96, 87.

KRAMER, K. AND DEETJEN, P. Sodium reabsorption and oxygen consumption in the mammalian kidney. *In:* Symposium on Oxygen in the Animal Organism. New York, 1964. Pergamon Press.

KRAMER, K. AND ULLRICH, K. O₂-Saettigung und Hb-Gehalt des Capillarblutes der Nierenrinde. Pflüger's Arch. ges. Physiol., 1958, 267, 251.

KRAMER, K., THURAU, K., AND DEETJEN, P. Hämodynamik des Nierenmarks. I. Capilläre Passagezeit, Blutvolumen, Durchblutung, Gewebshämatokrit und O₂-Verbrauch des Nierenmarks in situ. Pflüger's Arch. ges. Physiol., 1960, 270, 251.

LASSEN, N. A., LONGLEY, J. B., AND LILIENFIELD, L. S. Concentration of albumin in renal papilla. Science, 1958, 128, 720.

LASSEN, N. A., MUNCK, O., AND THAYSEN, J. H. Oxygen consumption and sodium reabsorption in the kidney. Acta physiol. scandinav., 1961, 51, 371.

LAUSON, H. D. AND THOMPSON, D. D. Effects in dogs of decrease in glomerular filtration rate on cation excretion during intravenous administration of unreabsorbable anions. Am. J. Physiol., 1958, 192, 198.

LEVY, M. N. Oxygen consumption and blood flow in the hypothermic perfused kidney. Am. J. Physiol., 1959, 197, 1111.

LILIENFIELD, L. S. AND ROSE, J. C. Effect of blood pressure alterations on intrarenal red cell-plasma separation. J. Clin. Invest., 1958, 37, 1106.

LILIENFIELD, L. S., ROSE, J. C., AND LASSEN, N. A. Diverse distribution of red cells and albumin in dog kidney. Circulation Res., 1958, 6, 810.

LILIENFIELD, L. S., BAUER, M. H., AND MAGAN-

ZINI, H. C. Plasma flow in renal medulla. Circulation, 1959, **20**, 729.

LILLEHEI, R. C. Prevention of irreversible hemorrhagic shock in normal and Eck fistula dogs by controlled cross perfusion of the superior mesenteric artery. Am. J. Physiol., 1956, **187**, 614.

MAILLET, M. Innervation sympathique du rein: son role trophique. Acta neuroveg., 1959, **20**, 155.

MARSON, F. G. Effect of noradrenaline on urine and renal blood flow. Brit. J. Pharmacol., 1956, **11**, 431.

MEHRIZI, A. AND HAMILTON, W. F. Effect of levarterenol on renal blood flow and vascular volume in dogs. Am. J. Physiol., 1959, **197**, 1115.

MILES, B. E., VENTOM, M. G., AND deWARDENER, H. E. Observations on the mechanism of circulatory autoregulation in the perfused dog's kidney. J. Physiol., 1954, **123**, 143.

NOER, R. J., ROBB, H. J., AND JACOBSON, L. F. Circulatory disturbances produced by acute intestinal distension in the living animal. A. M. A. Arch. Surg., 1951, **63**, 520.

OCHWADT, B. Zur Selbststeuerung des Nierenkreislaufes. Pflüger's Arch. ges. Physiol., 1956, **262**, 207.

OCHWADT, B. Durchflusszeiten von Plasma und Erythrocyten, intrarenaler Hamatokrit und Widerstandsregulation der Isolierten Niere. Pflüger's Arch. ges. Physiol., 1957, **265**, 112.

OCHWADT, B. On the measurement of intrarenal blood flow distribution by wash-out techniques. *In:* Proceedings of 2nd International Congress of Nephrology, Prague, 1963.

PABST, K. AND THRON, H. L. Kaltediurese beim unnar kotisierten Hund. Pflüger's Arch. ges. Physiol., 1960, **270**, 585.

PAGE, I. H. AND McCUBBIN, J. W. Renal vascular and systemic arterial pressure responses to nervous and chemical stimuation of the kidney. Am. J. Physiol., 1953, **173**, 411.

PAGE, L. B., BAXTER, C. F., REEM, G. H., SCOTT-BAKER, J. C., AND SMITH, H. W. Effect of unilateral splanchnic nerve resection on the renal excretion of sodium. Am. J. Physiol., 1954, **177**, 194.

PAGE, L. B. Effects of hypothermia on renal function. Am. J. Physiol., 1955, **181**, 171.

PAPPENHEIMER, J. P. AND KINTER, W. B. Hematocrit ratio of blood within mammalian kidney and its significance for renal hemodynamics. Am. J. Physiol., 1956, **185**, 377.

PARSON, W., MAYERSON, H. S., LYONS, C., PORTER, B., AND TRAUTMAN, W. V., JR. Effect of the administration of adrenalin on the circulating red cell volume. Am. J. Physiol., 1948, **155**, 239.

RENNIE, D. W., REEVES, R. B., AND PAPPENHEIMER, J. R. Oxygen pressure in urine and its relation to intrarenal blood flow. Am. J. Physiol., 1958, **195**, 120.

REUBI, F. C. Renal hyperemia induced in man by a new phthalazine derivative. Proc. Soc. Exper. Biol. & Med., 1950, **73**, 102.

REYNELL, P. C., MARKS, T. A., CHIDSEY, C., AND BRADLEY, S. E. Changes in splanchnic blood volume and splanchnic blood flow in dogs after hemorrhage. Clin. Sc., 1955, **14**, 407.

RHOADS, C. P., VAN SLYKE, D. C., HILLER, A., AND ALVING, H. S. Effects of novocainization and total section of the nerves of the renal pedicle on renal blood flow and function. Am. J. Physiol., 1934, **110**, 392.

RITTER, E. R. Pressure-flow relations in the kidney alleged effects of pulse pressure. Am. J. Physiol., 1952, **168**, 480.

SARTORIUS, O. W. AND BURLINGTON, H. Acute effects of denervation on kidney function in the dog. Am. J. Physiol., 1956, **185**, 407.

SCHER, A. M. Mechanism of autoregulation of renal blood flow. Nature, 1959, **184**, 1322.

SELKURT, E. E. Effect of pulse pressure and mean arterial pressure modification on renal hemodynamics and electrolyte and water excretion. Circulation, 1951, **4**, 541.

SELKURT, E. E. Intestinal ischemic shock and the protective role of the liver. Am. J. Physiol., 1959, **197**, 281.

SELKURT, E. E. AND BRECHER, G. A. Splanchnic hemodynamics and oxygen utilization during hemorrhagic shock in the dog. Circulation Res., 1956, **4**, 693.

SELKURT, E. E., SCIBETTA, M. P., AND CULL, T. E. Hemodynamics of intestinal circulation. Circulation Res., 1958, **6**, 92.

SELKURT, E. E. AND JOHNSON, P. C. Effect of acute elevation of portal venous pressure on mesenteric blood volume, interstitial fluid volume and hemodynamics. Circulation Res. 1958, **6**, 592.

SHIPLEY, R. E. AND STUDY, R. S. Changes in renal blood flow, extraction of inulin, glomerular filtration rate, tissue pressure and urine flow with acute alterations of renal artery blood pressure. Am. J. Physiol., 1951, **167**, 676.

SIDKY, M. AND BEAN, J. W. Influence of rhythmic and tonic contraction of intestinal muscle on blood flow and blood reservoir capacity in dog intestine. Am. J. Physiol., 1958, **193**, 386.

SIEKER, H. O., GAUER, O. H., AND HENRY, J. P. The effects of continuous negative pressure breathing on water and electrolyte excretion by the human kidney. J. Clin. Invest., 1954, **33**, 572.

SMITH, H. W., ROVENSTINE, E. A., GOLDRING, W., CHASIS, H., AND RANGES, H. A. The effects of spinal anesthesia on the circulation in normal, unoperated man with reference to autonomy of arteries, and especially those of the renal circulation. J. Clin. Invest., 1939, **18**, 319.

SMYTHE, C. M., NICKEL, J. F., AND BRADLEY, S. E. The effect of epinephrine (USP), I-epinephrine, and 1-norepinephrine on GFR, RPF and urinary excretion of sodium, potassium and water in normal man. J. Clin. Invest., 1952, **31**, 499.

SMYTHE, C. M., GILMORE, J. P., AND HANDFORD, S. W. The effect of 1-norepinephrine on estimated hepatic blood flow in the normal anesthetized dog. J. Clin. Invest., 1953, **32**, 605.

SNOOK, T. A comparative study of the vascular arrangements in mammalian spleens. Am. J. Anat., 1950, **87**, 31.

STONE, J. E., WELLS, J., DRAPER, W. B., AND WHITEHEAD, R. W. Changes in renal blood flow in dogs during the inhalation of 30% carbon dioxide. Am. J. Physiol., 1958, **194**, 115.

SURTSHIN, A., MUELLER, C. B., AND WHITE, H. L.

Effect of acute changes in glomerular filtration rate on water and electrolyte excretion: mechanism of denervation diuresis. Am. J. Physiol., 1952, **169,** 159.

SURTSHIN, A., HOELTZENBEIN, J., AND WHITE, H. L. Some effects of negative pressure breathing on urine excretion. Am. J. Physiol., 1955, **180,** 612.

SWANN, H. Intrarenal pressure and renal blood flows. p. 76. Josiah Macy, Jr. Foundation III. Conference, 1951.

TEXTER, E. C., JR., MERRILL, S., SCHWARTZ, M., VAN DERSTAGEN, G., AND HADDY, F. J. Relationship of blood flow to pressure in the intestinal vascular bed of the dog. Am. J. Physiol., 1962, **202,** 253.

THOMPSON, D. D., KAVALER, F., LOZANO, R., AND PITTS, R. F. Evaluation of the cell separation hypothesis of autoregulation of renal blood flow and filtration rate. Blood flow, filtration rate and PAH extraction as functions of arterial pressure in normal and anemic dogs. Am. J. Physiol., 1957, **191,** 493.

THORBURN, G. D., KOPALD, H. H., HERD, J. A., HOLLENBERG, M., O'MORCHOE, C. C. C., AND BARGER, A. C. Intrarenal distribution of nutrient blood flow determined with krypton[85] in the unanesthetized dog. Circulation Res., 1963, **13,** 290.

THURAU, K. Renal sodium reabsorption and O_2 uptake in dogs during hypoxia and hydrochlorothiazide infusion. Proc. Soc. Exper. Biol. and Med., 1961, **106,** 714.

THURAU, K., KRAMER, K., AND BRECHTELSBAUER, H. Die Reaktionsweise der glatten Muskulatur der Nierengefässe auf Dehnungsreize und ihre Bedeutung für die Autoregulation des Nierenkreislaufes. Pflüger's Arch. ges. Physiol., 1959, **268,** 188.

THURAU, K. AND KRAMER, K. Weitere Untersuchungen zur myogenen Natur der Autoregulation des Nierenkreislaufes. Aufhebung der Autoregulation durch muskulotrope Substanzen und druckpassives Verhalten des Glomerulusfiltrates. Pflüger's Arch. ges. Physiol., 1959, **269,** 77.

THURAU, K., DEETJEN, P., AND KRAMER, K. Hamodynamik des Nierenmarks: Wechselbeziehung zwischen vasculärem und tubulärem Gegenstromsystem bei arteriellen Drucksteigerungen, Wasserdiurese und osmotischer Diurese. Pflüger's Arch. ges. Physiol., 1960, **270,** 270.

THURAU, K. AND SCHNERMANN, J. Die Natriumkonzentration an den Macula Densa Zellen als regulierender Faktor für das Glomerulumfiltrat (Mikropunktionsversuche). Klin. Wschr., 1965, **43,** 410.

TORRANCE, H. B. The control of the hepatic arterial circulation. J. Physiol., 1961, **158,** 39.

TURK, L. N., III, AND SHOEMAKER, W. C. Hepatic vascular response to norepinephrine. Am. J. Physiol., 1962, **202,** 1175.

ULLRICH, K. AND PEHLING, G. Activer Natriumtransport und Sauerstoffverbrauch in der äusseren Markzone der Niere. Pflüger's Arch. ges. Physiol., 1958, **267,** 207.

VAN SLYKE, D. D., RHOADS, C. P., HILLER, A.,

AND ALVING, A. S. Relationships between urea excretion, renal blood flow, renal oxygen consumption, and diuresis. The mechanism of urea excretion. Am. J. Physiol., 1934, **109,** 336.

WADE, O. L. ET AL. The effect of exercise on the splanchnic blood flow and splanchnic blood volume in normal man. Clin. Sc., 1956, **15,** 457.

WARREN, J. V., BRANNON, E. S., AND MERRILL, A. J. A method of obtaining renal venous blood in unanesthetized persons with observations on the extraction of oxygen and sodium paraaminohippurate. Science, 1944, **100,** 108.

WAUGH, W. H. Myogenic nature of autoregulation of renal flow in the absence of blood corpuscles. Circulation Res., 1958, **6,** 363.

WAUGH, W. H., AND SHANKS, R. G. Cause of genuine autoregulation of the renal circulation. Circul. Res. 1960, **8,** 871.

WEISS, S., PARKER, F., JR., AND ROBB, G. P. A correlation of the hemodynamics, function and histologic structure of the kidney in malignant arterial hypertension with malignant nephrosclerosis. Ann. Int. Med., 1932, **6,** 1599.

WHIPPLE, A. O., PARPART, A. K., AND CHANG, J. J. A study of the circulation of the blood in the spleen of the living mouse. Ann. Surg., 1954, **140,** 266.

WHITE, H. L. AND ROLF, D. Effects of exercise and some other influences on the renal circulation in man. Am. J. Physiol., 1948, **152,** 505.

WILKINS, R. W., CULBERTSON, J. W., AND INGELFINGER, F. J. The effect of splanchnic sympathectomy in hypertensive patients upon estimated hepatic blood flow in the upright as contrasted with the horizontal position. J. Clin. Invest., 1951, **30,** 312.

WINTON, F. R. Present concepts of the renal circulation. A. M. A. Arch. Int. Med., 1959, **103,** 495.

WIRZ, H. Druckmessung in Kapillaren und Tubuli der Niere durch Mikropunktion. Helvet. physiol. et pharmacol. acta, 1955, **13,** 42.

WIRZ, H., HARGITAY, B., AND KUHN, W. Lokalisation des Konzentrierungsprozesses in der Niere durch direkte Kryoskopie. Helvet. physiol. et pharmacol. acta, 1951, **9,** 196.

YAMADA, S. I. AND ASTIOM, H. Critical closing pressure and vasomotor tone in the hind leg and the kidney of the cat. Am. J. Physiol., 1959, **196,** 213.

ZERAHN, K. Oxygen consumption and active sodium transport in the isolated and short circuited frog skin. Acta physiol. scandinav., 1956, **36,** 300.

Monographs and Reviews

BRADLEY, S. E., INGELFINGER, F. J., BRADLEY, G. P., AND CURRY, J. J. The estimation of hepatic blood flow in man. J. Clin. Invest., 1945, **24,** 890.

BRADLEY, S. E. Methods for the evaluation of the splanchnic circulation. Circulation. Proceedings of the Harvey Tercentenary Congress, p. 355. Blackwell Scientific Publications, Oxford, 1958.

BRADLEY, S. E., INGELFINGER, F. J., AND BRADLEY, G. P. Determinants of hepatic hemodynamics. Visceral circulation, A Ciba Foundation Symposium, p. 219. J. & A. Churchill, Ltd., London, 1952.

KRAMER, K. Die Stellung der Niere im Gesamt-kreislauf Verhandl. deutsch. Ges. inn. Med., 65. Kongress, 1959.

PAGE, I. H. Serotonin (5-hydroxytryptamine); the last four years. Physiol. Rev., 1958, 38, 277.

SELKURT, E. E. Der Nierenkreislauf. Klin. Wchnschr., 1955, 33, 359.

SELKURT, E. E. The renal circulation, Handbook of Physiology Circ. II, 1963, 1457.

SMITH, H. W. The kidney. Structure and function in health and diseases. Oxford University Press, New York, 1951.

THURAU, K. Renal hemodynamics, Amer. J. Med., 1964, 36, 698.

WINTON, F. R. Physical factors involved in the activities of the mammalian kidney. Physiol. Rev., 1937, 17, 408.

CHAPTER 48

Regulation of the Circulation under States of Stress

Dilation and Hypertrophy of the Heart

CARDIAC DILATION. Dilation is an increased capacity of the cardiac chambers brought about by the elongation of the myocardial fibers. This increased capacity may result from many physiological or pathological factors. The force of ventricular contraction increases with increments in diastolic volume until overdistension occurs, and the force of contraction then decreases with a rise in diastolic pressure. An increased diastolic volume is a physiological means automatically brought into play to increase the cardiac work and to mobilize the energy reserves of the heart. The nearer the fibers approach their maximal physiological length during diastole, the greater will be the encroachment upon the heart's reserve. It has also been shown that the oxygen consumption of the heart muscle is proportional to its end diastolic volume (or its fiber length, fig. 48.1). Thus, the heart which is supporting a greater load expends a greater amount of energy to attain its cardiac output.

From the above discussion, it can be seen that cardiac dilation can be a compensatory mechanism of the heart in meeting everyday stresses although other factors (humoral and neurogenic) are also important. Dilation also occurs when an increased diastolic volume is secondary to a pathological state. An increased venous return to the heart, a reflux into the heart chambers, an increased outflow resistance, or intrinsic myocardial disease impairing the contractility of the muscle may induce dilation. Each of these causative factors involves an increase in work of the heart. However, the heart cannot continue to dilate indefinitely with an increase in work. A point is reached beyond which further dilation leads to a decline in work. The heart is unable to expel sufficient blood from its chambers, and the activity of the heart is no longer adequate to supply the peripheral tissues with their needs. Therefore, beyond this point, dilation becomes detrimental. It is claimed that the diseased heart reaches this detrimental point of dilation with less stretch in the myocardial fibers than the normal heart, but the experimental evidence for this is not adequate. Dilation can be, but is not always, a reversible phenomenon even when

caused by pathological states. The heart may continue to fail even when the underlying cause is removed.

CARDIAC HYPERTROPHY. The average weight range of the human adult heart is approximately 250 to 350 grams. In disease, 500 grams is not an unusual weight, and hearts weighing 1,000 gms or more are seen. The increased weight of the ventricular muscle is due to an increase in length and diameter of the individual muscle fibers. Linzbach found this was true of hearts hypertrophied up to 500 grams but, contrary to previous studies, reported a splitting of fibers longitudinally in hearts weighing over 500 grams. Thus, an increase in the number of fibers in the heart can also contribute to hypertrophy. With the increase in size of fibers, there is not a corresponding increase in the number of capillaries. Hypertrophy, then, differs from normal growth for, in the latter, the capillaries multiply and keep pace with the muscle as it grows; in hypertrophy the capillaries do not multiply and, per unit of muscle, actually decrease. This could become a limiting factor in the extent of development of hypertrophy especially in hearts with an already compromised blood supply.

Cardiac hypertrophy has been produced experimentally in animals by many methods. The most commonly used procedures are: constriction of the aorta, induction of aortic insufficiency or renal hypertension, or the administration of thyroid. Other methods include exercise (swimming, treadmill), induction of anemia, administration of somatotrophic hormone, exposure of the animal to reduced ambient pressure after explosive decompression, and coronary ligation. It must be remembered that the biochemistry and hemodynamics may differ when different methods of inducing myocardial hypertrophy are used.

The biochemical alterations in the myocardium in hypertrophy have received little study until recently. The electrolyte and fluid concentrations in the intra- and extracellular spaces have a normal relationship in the hypertrophied heart of rabbits following the production of aortic insufficiency. In rats which were exposed to reduced atmospheric pressure and increased envi-

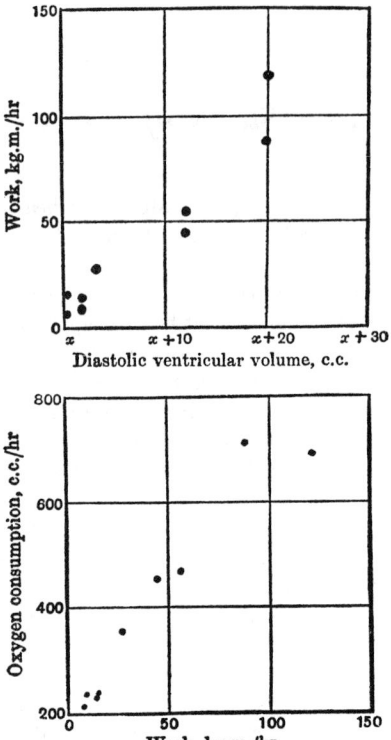

FIG. 48.1. Lower chart shows the work done plotted against the oxygen consumed. In calculating the work of the heart the velocity factor was neglected. Upper chart gives data from the same experiment, work being plotted against the diastolic volume of the ventricles. The volumes are expressed as x plus known values. The x represents the lowest value of the volume during the experiment, which is impossible to measure when a cardiometer is used to record heart volume. The cardiometer enables one to measure only an increase over this minimum value. The figure shows a direct correspondence between work done and ventricular volume. (After Starling and Visscher.)

ronmental temperature to produce hypertrophy, the total protein of the heart increased by 42 per cent. An increase in the fractions containing myoglobin, contractile protein and metachondria was found. The latter increase may indicate an expansion of the oxygen transporting and utilizing systems. The increased fractions in hypertrophy differ from those found in normal growth. This fact, plus the absence of capillary growth, indicate that hypertrophy is not caused by the same process which induces the left ventricle to become the more muscular of the two ventricles after birth.

Meerson has studied compensatory hyperfunction of the heart produced by experimental aortic stenosis in dogs and rabbits. He describes three

stages through which these hearts pass. During the transient breakdown stage (cardiac dilation and insufficiency), mobilization of creatine phosphate and glycogen occurs, ATP is synthesized by inefficient anaerobic pathways, and the rate of cardiac protein synthesis increases. During the following stage of relatively stable function (cardiac hypertrophy), myocardial glycogen, phosphocreatine, and ATP levels are normal as is protein synthesis. However, moderate hypoxia is indicated by a rise in lactic acid. The final stage of progressive cardiac insufficiency is characterized by a decreased rate of protein synthesis and a fall in ATP levels. Other groups have confirmed the findings concerning protein synthesis by using the same method (i.e., determining the extent of incorporation of a radioactive labelled amino acid into myocardial protein). The protein turnover rate was shown not to be increased indicating that the amino acids are used for net synthesis of protein and are not utilized to supply the increased energy requirements in cardiac hypertrophy. Other workers report a decrease in myocardial creatine phosphate and suggest an increased utilization of phosphate bond energy by the hypertrophied myocardium. The varying reports of myocardial constituents might be explained by differences in the methods used to produce hypertrophy in the experimental animals, or the different stages of hypertrophy at time of examination.

Most of the above experimental findings were studied in rabbit or rat hearts after short periods of cardiac stress to induce hypertrophy. In dogs who have had experimental aortic stenosis for 2.5 years, the hypertrophied left ventricle shows a 33 percent increase in DNA and RNA without a change in the ratio between them, a 6 percent increase in total nitrogen concentration with a 33 percent increase in non-protein nitrogen, a 37 percent decrease in adenosine triphosphatase activity of the actomyosin, a decrease in succinic dehydrogenase activity, and an increase in lactic acid dehydrogenase activity (Meerson). Some of these alterations have also been found in the hypertrophied myocardium of man. It is postulated that they reflect disturbances in structure and function of mitochondria and activation of the pyruvic-lactic acid pathway of metabolism. Progression of these changes may play a part in the development of chronic myocardial failure in hypertrophied hearts.

Meerson has also found a decrease in the norepinephrine concentration in the myocardium in experimental aortic stenosis in rabbits but no change in the acetylcholine concentration. He hypothesizes that there is an increased effect of the vagus nerve on the resting hypertrophied heart which is also evidenced by a depression of contractile function. Studies have shown that pharmacological blocking of the vagus nerve inhibits the development of cardiac hypertrophy induced by swimming in rats; this would support his theory that during the development of hypertrophy there is a decreasing effect of catecholamines with a predominance of a vagal regulation of the heart.

The mechanical factors leading to hypertrophy are the same myocardial stresses mentioned for dilation; hypertension and valvular disease lead the list of actual diseases. As in dilation, the chamber undergoing the stress may be the only one involved or all chambers may become hypertrophied, including the atria.

The factors which actually induce the cardiac muscle to hypertrophy are unknown. Experiments by Eyster and associates on the production of aortic insufficiency or stenosis in dogs illustrate the basis for the injury theory. These animals showed an early dilation of the heart (by roentgenograms) which disappeared within a few days and was followed by the development of hypertrophy. In dogs relieved of their aortic stenosis during the dilation phase, hypertrophy still developed. The sudden dilation of the heart was theorized to injure the myocardial fibers which led to their hypertrophy. These experiments have since been criticized and repeated. An increase in the heart weight-body weight ratio was found only when the cause of the heart stress was continued and not if the stress was removed during the dilation phase. The theory does not agree with clinical findings which often show dilation not followed by hypertrophy in patients. Other experiments in rats have shown that dilation of the heart caused by a reduced ambient pressure after explosive decompression was reversible and not followed by hypertrophy.

Another explanation for hypertrophy suggests that the greater surface area of the dilated muscle presents a greater area to be nourished which leads to fiber growth. A defective blood supply, due to either a deficient coronary circulation or an anemia, has been postulated as the cause of hypertrophy. Anoxia or ischemia as a cause has not been adequately investigated. A fourth theory would explain hypertrophy as essentially of hormonal origin in which the somatotrophic hormone of the anterior pituitary plays the leading role. Experiments on rats showed that this hormone produces an increased heart mass in the absence of an increased work load. Thyroxine was found to possess a lesser degree of this activity while cortisone inhibited the effect of the somatotrophic hormone. Since cardiac hypertrophy induced by thyroid treatment usually shows microscopic evidence of muscle tissue damage, injury may be the important factor. The work theory holds that hypertrophy is primarily due to the increased load on the heart, and experiments demonstrating a hypertrophy of animals' hearts under the stimulus of exercise are cited as evidence.

The above theories and our knowledge of the factors involved in the production of myocardial hypertrophy are inadequate. Animal experimentation is very difficult to evaluate since hypertrophy is usually judged on the basis of the heart weight to body weight ratio. Yet the fact that rat hearts have been shown to grow at 0.75 times the rate of growth of the body as a whole is usually not taken into account; this may apply to other species. The animals have often gained or lost weight during the experimental period. The degree of myocardial edema must also be taken into consideration as a cause of the increased bulk of the heart. Moderate hypertrophy must be present before microscopic findings are present; animal experiments usually deal with minimal hypertrophy. The most valid method would seem to be a long term study of a very large group of control and experimental animals of the same weight and breed with a comparison of their heart weights and microscopic findings. A definition of cardiac hypertrophy must take into account the presence of muscle edema, fat, and fibrotic tissue in the muscle being weighed. The effects of various methods of producing hypertrophy would have to be compared; hearts would also have to be examined at different stages of hypertrophy.

In human disease there is a marked difference in the degree of hypertrophy found in response to similar pathological stresses. Some patients with serious hypertensive disease demonstrate little or no hypertrophy at autopsy. Also, the clinical course of patients with heart disease shows no relation to the presence or absence of hypertrophy. A disease entity exists called "idiopathic" myocardial hypertrophy in which young people succumb to congestive heart failure and the only autopsy finding is myocardial hypertrophy.

Hypertrophy has been called a compensatory mechanism of the heart in response to an increased load whereby the increased mass of the heart permits it to release more energy. Several studies have shown that a hypertrophied animal heart has the ability to react to a further stress; i.e., it has a reserve. Rats who developed cardiac hypertrophy due to aortic constriction were able to raise their cardiac output more than control animals in response to overloading of their circulatory systems. From this experiment, it was concluded that a hypertrophied heart had a greater reserve power than the normal heart. Studies to prove that papillary muscles from hypertrophied hearts develop more tension per gram of muscle in response to electrical stimulation than normal papillary muscles have shown contradictory results. However, there is agreement that the hypertrophied heart does develop an increase in the absolute magnitude of tension. The fact that hypertrophy is beneficial to the heart has been questioned. It has been pointed out that the ST-T changes in the electrocardiogram in hypertrophy are similar to those of coronary insufficiency, that hypertensive patients without hypertrophy fare as well as those with increased mass of heart muscle, and that hearts developing hypertrophy after acute cardiac insults do not always improve.

Hypertrophy of the heart may be preceded or accompanied by dilation of the heart. It is claimed that dilation is the immediate response of the heart to stress while hypertrophy is a more gradually developing phenomenon due to chronic stress. Experimental data, with the above criticisms in mind, show hypertrophy developing as early as 2 days in rats, and in 2 to 3 weeks in dogs subjected to the stress of hypertension or valvular disease. However, the hypertrophy was based on heart weight to body weight ratios. It has not been adequately explained why some hearts show neither hypertrophy nor dilation, some only one, and some both of these phenomena under the same pathological conditions. Both have been shown to be occasionally reversible in animals and humans when the stress is removed.

The importance of hypertrophy lies in the fact that it is the response of the heart to most forms of stress. Our limited knowledge concerning the etiology and development of hypertrophy is a major stumbling block in the understanding of the physiology of the heart. It is apparent that improved methods of investigation and measurement of myocardial hypertrophy are needed.

Arterial Hypertension

The blood pressure may be persistently above or below the normal range. These departures from the normal are termed *hypertension* and *hypotension*, respectively. It is difficult to make a sharp separation between normal and abnormal, but an elevation above the average blood pressure level for a particular age group may be considered to be definitely abnormal. In the adult, elevations of systolic pressure above 140 mm. Hg and of diastolic pressure above 90 mm. Hg are usually considered hypertensive levels, although this sharp distinction is not reliable unless considered in relation to age. The clinical syndrome of hypertension appears to be a result of the elevated diastolic pressure. Usually, the systolic pressure is also raised, but it need not be. Systolic hypertension may also occur without a diastolic pressure elevation. Systolic hypertension alone is not believed to be clinically important unless very high levels threaten the integrity of the blood vessels. Systolic hypertension with a decreased diastolic pressure (an increased pulse pressure) often accompanies a variety of diseases such as hyperthyroidism, heart block with a slow rate, and aortic insufficiency.

Much research has been devoted to the investigation of the etiology of hypertension, especially in an attempt to delineate the factors involved in the essential (of unknown etiology) type. Renal, endocrine, cardiovascular, and neurogenic causes have received the most intensive study. Table 48.1 lists the more common types of human and experimental hypertension. Although the etiology of the most common disease, essential hypertension, remains obscure, much knowledge has been acquired concerning the other causes of high blood pressure.

EXPERIMENTAL RENAL HYPERTENSION

The experimental hypertension most similar to human hypertension is that following renal artery constriction. Moderate to severe chronic constriction of a renal artery in the dog, which causes a definite and immediate reduction in renal blood flow, is followed by a rise in systemic blood pressure. However, this hypertension usually persists for only a few weeks despite continued constriction of the renal artery. (In the monkey, rabbit, rat, goat and sheep, hypertension lasting many months generally occurs with chronic constriction of one renal artery.) In the dog, permanent systemic hypertension follows constriction of both renal arteries, constriction of one renal artery with subsequent removal of the other kidney, or wrapping of both kidneys in silk or cellophane. (Following wrapping, the hypertension presumably results from ischemia or a change in pulsatile flow induced by compression of the renal parenchyma by the thick membrane of connective tissue which develops under the silk or cellophane). This type of hypertension is benign and lasts for years. Its manifestations are almost identical with those usually seen in the benign phase of human essential hypertension, for there is an increase in systemic blood pressure and total peripheral resistance with left ventricular hypertrophy, but a normal heart rate, cardiac output, blood volume and renal excretory function (by the usual renal function tests which may not be sensitive enough to detect early changes). More extensive constriction of both main renal arteries produces hypertension, impairment of renal function, and appearance of some substance in the blood which causes development of a fulminating type of hypertension. This accelerated form of experimental hypertension closely resembles the malignant phase of essential human hypertension, with arteriolar hyaline degeneration and necrosis in all vascular beds. Even the kidney with the constricted renal artery may show severe vascular damage when the blood pressure is greatly elevated (in rats).

HUMORAL FACTORS. The pathogenesis of the early phase of sustained hypertension is not clearly understood but a neural reflex from the affected kidney is not the cause since renal denervation, splanchnic, and total sympathectomy fail to interfere with development of hypertension from renal artery constriction. The early phase of sustained hypertension is caused by some humoral mechanism, since release of the clamp or excision of the affected kidney restores a normal blood pressure.

The humoral pressor mechanism for the *early* period of hypertension is explained either by failure of the normal kidney to produce an essential agent which protects against hypertension, or by the release of a pressor substance from the affected kidney. Pressor enzymes and polypeptides may arise not only from the kidney but may also be of nonrenal origin.[1] An abundance of evidence supports the view that the pressor

---

[1] A vasoconstrictor substance (pepsitensin) closely resembling angiotensin in its effects has been obtained by the action of pepsin upon plasma globulin.

TABLE 48.1

Common clinical and experimental types of hypertension

Clinical Diseases	Experimental Causes
Unknown etiology	
Essential hypertension	
Renal hypertension	
Pyelonephritis	Renal artery stenoses
Glomerulonephritis	Wrapped kidneys
Unilateral or bilateral renal artery stenoses	Bilateral nephrectomy
Polycystic renal disease	
Endocrine hypertension	
Hyperaldosteronism	DOCA + salt
Cushing's syndrome	Aldosterone + salt
Pheochromocytoma	Adrenalectomy with regeneration + salt
Toxemia of pregnancy	Corticosteroids
Cardiovascular hypertension	
Atherosclerosis	Constriction of aorta
Coarctation of aorta	
Neurogenic hypertension	
Increased intracranial pressure	Cerebral ischemia
Carotid sinus sclerosis	Carotid sinus and aortic body denervation
Chronic porphyria	Experimental neurosis

---

mechanism of *acute* hypertension of renal origin is mediated by the release of a humoral substance, renin. Renin is a proteolytic enzyme with no direct pressor effect. It acts on an α-2 globulin substrate in plasma to produce angiotensin. The α-2 globulin is apparently produced in the liver, since it disappears from the blood after hepatectomy. Two different molecular forms of angiotensin have been obtained in purified form. The decapeptide, angiotensin I, is the initial product of the action of renin on its substrate, and lacks pressor activity. This decapeptide is transformed to the vasoconstrictor octapeptide, angiotensin II, by a chloride activated enzyme of the plasma. The octapeptide has been synthesized.

At present, many investigators are developing more accurate methods for the detection of renin or angiotensin in the blood of hypertensive patients and animals. Conflicting reports are numerous regarding the blood levels of these substances or pressor activity of the blood in

TABLE 48.2

Summary of effects of injections of renin on blood pressure and antirenin titer in 61 renal hypertensive dogs with hypertension of 4 to 36 months duration

Each symbol represents treatment results in one renal hypertensive dog. 0, no antihypertensive effect; +, decrease in blood pressure one-third toward normotension; ++, decrease in blood pressure two-thirds toward normotension; +++, decrease in blood pressure to normotension. Four different preparations of hog renins were used. Antirenin titer is expressed in antirenin units per milliliter. (From Wakerlin, G. E., Circulation, 1958, **17**, 653.)

Maximum antirenin titer	Antihypertensive Effect of Hog Renin			
	Crude, from cortex	Semipurified, from cortex	Crude, from whole kidney	Semipurified, from whole kidney
Au per ml.				
0			0000000	
1	00	0	0	
2		+	0	
3	++ +++	+	00	
4	0	+		
5	+++		0000	
6–7	0 ++	++ +++		0 0 +
8–10	++ +++ +++	+++	0 0+ +	0
11–14	+++ +++	++ ++ ++ +++ +++	0	+ ++
15–20		++ +++	000 ++	
21–30		++	0	
31–40			0	
41–60				++
61–100				
101–125	+++			

clinical or experimental situations.[2] At present, the mass of data cannot be evaluated and the question of involvement of the renin-angiotensin system in the various types of hypertension remains to be solved.

Failure to find renin consistently by assay methods in the blood of humans or animals who have renal hypertension of long standing has caused doubt that this theory explains the chronic phase of the disorder. Increased renin concentrations have usually been found in affected renal tissue of rats and dogs with chronic hypertension but not in their blood. Dogs with chronic experimental renal hypertension are usually not made normotensive by excision of the affected kidney. Destruction of the central nervous system by pithing rats produces a much greater fall in blood pressure in renal hypertensive than in normal rats, favoring neurogenic, rather than humoral, factors as the cause of chronic experimental renal hypertension (Taquini). When both normal and hypertensive rats were pithed while angiotensin was being infused intravenously, the pressure fell

[2] A collection of these studies appears in the Proceedings of the International Symposium on Angiotensin, Sodium, and Hypertension. Canad. Med. Assoc. J., 1964, **90**, 153.

more quickly and reached lower levels in the hypertensive rats. Thus the increased blood pressure in renal hypertensive rats would not be secondary to a simple direct constrictor action of angiotensin.

The blood pressure of a dog or monkey, hypertensive for months to years from constriction of the renal arteries, can be returned to normal by repeated injections of renin resulting in the development of antirenin in the blood (table 48.2). This is convincing evidence that a humoral mechanism is still active in elevating the blood pressure. Methods are now being studied to apply this technique in human hypertension.

Renin is confined to the cortex of the kidney, and has been demonstrated only in areas which contain glomeruli and not in purely tubular areas. As postulated many years ago, by Goormaghtigh, the juxtaglomerular cells may be the source of renin. These cells contain granules which exhibit histochemical properties similar to those of renin. There is a good correlation between the number of these granules and the renin content of the kidney (Marshall and Wakerlin). More recent studies by the Hartrofts and by Tobian demonstrate that the granularity of the juxtaglomerular cells increases or decreases when, according to the animal's blood pressure, renin would be expected to be increased or decreased. In addition, fluorescent antirenin antibodies have been demonstrated to attach to these granules. In human hypertension due to unilateral renal arterial stenosis (Goldblatt type kidney), a significant cellular hyperplasia of the juxtaglomerular bodies has been found. A lesser degree of hyperplasia is seen in the kidneys of hypertensive patients with pheochromocytoma, essential hypertension, and glomerulonephritis. No hyperplasia has been found in pyelonephritis or malignant hypertension (Sommers and Turgeon).

The stimulus for the production or liberation of renin by the kidney is not known. The immediate effect of constriction of the renal artery is a fall in pressure in the vessels of the kidney, and a reduction in blood flow. Page denies, however, that renal ischemia is responsible, for the renal blood flow may later return to normal. Anoxia of the renal tissue does not seem to be a necessary condition for the development of renal hypertension, because no increase over the normal was found in the arteriovenous oxygen difference of the affected kidney (Levy and associates). Moreover, anoxia induced by cyanide does not cause renin to appear in the circulation although a kidney so poisoned produces renin when the renal artery is clamped. It has been reported that removal of the upper quarter of the Goldblatt kidney a few weeks after hypertension develops, results in a return to normal blood pressure levels. This would suggest that an imbalance between renal mass and renal blood flow may be important (Schlegel and Okamoto).

Kolff and his associates have shown that the production of a "renin" response from constriction of canine renal arteries occurs irrespective of a pulsatile or nonpulsatile (using a depulsating chamber) renal blood flow. A decrease in perfusing pressure to the kidney causes the release of a reninlike substance but a reduction in pulse pressure alone is ineffective (Skinner). It is postulated that the release of renin from the kidney may be secondary to changes in the transmural pressure affecting renal vascular baroreceptors. The latter theory has been elaborated with the juxtaglomerular cells as the baroreceptors, because the granularity of these cells varies with changes in perfusion pressure.

Another interesting facet of the renin-angiotensin system is the fact that angiotensin induces hyperplasia of the zona glomerulosa of the adrenal cortex and hypersecretion of aldosterone. It has

been suggested that the system normally controls sodium balance and arterial blood pressure. Thus renin would be secreted in response to a fall in blood pressure or to sodium loss and vice versa. This mechanism would be active not only in hypertensive patients but also in edematous states such as cirrhosis with ascites. Much investigative work is being done in this area at present.

Constriction of the renal artery of one kidney in the dog without interference with the kidney of the opposite side is not followed by permanent hypertension, nor is the hypertension, even while it lasts, as great if a normal kidney is present. The return of the blood pressure to normal after excision of the affected kidney is much less rapid if the unaffected kidney is also removed. In order to demonstrate the maximum effect of the pressor substance liberated by the affected kidney, a recipient animal must first be nephrectomized. These facts are the basis for the "renoprival" theory which postulates that the presence of normal kidney tissue has a protective effect against hypertension. The normal kidney may produce some material which lowers the blood pressure, or it may destroy or excrete a pressor substance. Excretory removal is not likely, for the diversion of urine into the bloodstream does not result in hypertension. Since removal of a unilateral affected kidney causes the blood pressure to return to normal, and since antirenin, which lowers the blood pressure in chronic renal hypertension, has no effect when both kidneys are absent, it is considered that renoprival and chronic renal hypertension are probably unrelated in etiology.

Several substances which may protect against hypertension have been derived from the blood of nephrectomized animals and from the normal kidney. *Anephrotensin*, a peptide extracted from incubated serum, increases rapidly in rats after complete nephrectomy. Intravenous anephrotensin is pressor in nephrectomized or in desoxycorticosterone treated rats but is depressor in normal rats. It may be that anephrotensin is rendered non-pressor by the presence of normal kidney tissue. No theories have been offered to explain the depressor effect. A crude extract of the renal medulla has been shown to protect against renoprival hypertension and has no depressor effect in normal animals. A lipid has been found in the renal medulla of man and animals which has a direct effect on blood vessels, producing a sustained fall in blood pressure when given intravenously to animals (Hickler). Grollman has extracted a highly potent substance from ground kidneys which is an active antihypertensive agent when given orally to animals.

If both kidneys are removed from rats or dogs, hypertension will often develop if the animals are kept alive. However nephrectomized dogs usually require parenteral sodium or dietary protein before they develop high blood pressure. It has been reported that three patients without renal tissue developed hypertension only when overhydrated (Merrill and Schupals). The arenal state probably does not lead to hypertension if water and sodium balance are normal.

Braun-Menendez and his associates demonstrated the presence in normal kidney tissue of an enzyme which inactivates the pressor principle, angiotensin. This enzyme, called angiotensinase, is possibly responsible for the effect exerted by normal kidney tissue upon the development and severity of renal hypertension. Angiotensinase is also found in intestinal mucosa, pancrease, and the erythrocytes; minimal amounts are present in liver and serum. Attempts to obtain a material from extracts of normal kidney tissue to treat clinical hypertension have not, so far, been successful.

Two other possible humoral pressor systems in the kidney warrant brief mention. Helmer and associates found an increased concentration of sustained pressor substance (SPS) in the renal vein blood of chronic renal hypertensive rats. The relation between SPS and renin is not clear, but it may be a precursor or derivative of renin. Shorr and his colleagues suggest that hepatorenal factors enter into the mechanism of renal hypertension. They demonstrated that constriction of the renal artery by a clamp caused the appearance in the blood of a renal vasoexcitatory material (VEM or ferritin) which normally cannot be detected. A little later, a hepatic vasodepressor material (VDM) was found in low concentration in the blood; it increased progressively until in the chronic hypertensive phase, it counteracted the action of VEM. More evidence is needed before the VEM-VDM system can be assigned a pathogenetic role in renal hypertension.

In the later stages of experimental hypertension, although renal pressor substances may circulate in sufficient amounts to maintain elevated blood pressure, evidence suggests that other mechanisms are involved. Following injection of ganglionic blocking agents, a reduction in blood pressure does not occur in early renal hypertension or during renin infusion but does develop in late renal hypertension. This concurs with the established fact that in late renal hypertension the baroreceptor mechanism is reset at the higher blood pressure level, possibly due to changes in the walls of the carotid sinus from prolonged exposure to high blood pressure. The carotid-aortic reflex is the principal immediate depressor response to elevations of blood pressure. In chronic renal hypertension, it still responds to acute pressor stimuli but, presumably, not to the sustained pressor stimulus. In addition, there now occur generalized morphological vascular changes secondary to the hypertension which may act to perpetuate the disorder.

THE ENDOCRINES IN RELATION TO EXPERIMENTAL HYPERTENSION. Although the evidence points to angiotensin as acting directly upon the vessels and their controlling ganglia, the possibility must be considered that it exerts its effect by stimulating a ductless gland, such as the pituitary or adrenal, to secrete a vasoconstrictor substance. The endocrine glands could also cause hypertension by stimulating the kidney to produce a pressor agent.

The adrenal medulla probably does not play a role in experimental renal hypertension, for the hypertension is not prevented or modified in any way by bilateral excision of all medullary tissue. Tumors of the adrenal medulla, called pheochromocytomas, do produce a clinical syndrome in which hypertension is the outstanding feature. The elevated blood pressure is secondary to the excess production of catecholamines (which can be measured in the blood and urine).

Goldblatt has found that constriction of the renal arteries fails to cause a rise in blood pressure after bilateral removal of the adrenal cortex, even though the animal is maintained in good condition by a high salt and low potassium diet (ch. 76). But if cortin is administered to the adrenalectomized animals, unilateral renal artery constriction is followed by the usual hypertensive response. The blood pressure of hypertensive rats is lowered by adrenalectomy and is only partially restored by the administration of *desoxycorticosterone*. Since hypertension is not sustained, and evidently, vascular tone and responsiveness are decreased when the adrenals are absent, the adrenal cortex is said to have a "permissive" action in renal hypertension. There may also be an "additive" effect of the kidney and adrenal cortex, for the administration of desoxycorticosterone to uninephrectomized rats, or of desoxycorticosterone or aldosterone and renin to normal rats, produces a more severe hypertension with more intense vascular damage than either procedure alone. It has already been mentioned that renin has been found to stimulate growth of the zona glomerulosa of the adrenal cortex and secretion of aldosterone. However, these results should not be taken to imply that the renal principle mediates its action through the adrenal cortex, for Houssay and his colleagues found that in short term experiments in which a Goldblatt kidney was transplanted into a non-hypertensive animal, complete adrenalectomy or ligation of the adrenal veins of the latter did not prevent the rise in blood pressure.

Desoxycorticosterone is capable itself of inducing hypertension in normal animals, provided that the diet contains adequate amounts of salt. It is ineffective if the animal receives a salt poor diet. Damage to the renal vessels (nephrosclerosis) is caused by the administration of this hormone; it also increases the retention of salt (enhanced tubular reabsorption) and the volume of the extracellular fluids. Both the renal effect and the effect upon water and salt metabolism are probably responsible for the hypertension caused by this cortical hormone. Desoxycorticosterone also induces a humoral change favoring the formation of *anephrotensin*. This material increases slowly in rats after desoxycorticosterone treatment and may play a role in corticoid hypertension (Rosas and Croxatta).

It is pertinent that Tobian has found an increased concentration of water, sodium, potassium and magnesium in the aortic tissue of renal and desoxycorticosterone hypertensive rats; renal arteries from hypertensive patients also showed an increased sodium and water content. It is postulated that the electrolyte and fluid changes may lead to edema of the vessel walls. The narrowing of the vascular bed by this process could cause an elevated blood pressure secondary to the increased peripheral resistance. Other authors have reported a low serum magnesium and a high plasma sodium with a normal potassium in hypertensive patients. These studies were stimulated by the discovery of a clinical hypertensive syndrome associated with an excess production of the adrenal cortical electrolyte hormone, aldosterone. Patients with hyperaldosteronism show an elevated serum sodium with a low potassium and sometimes a low serum magnesium level. The hypertension in this syndrome may be cured by removal of the aldosterone producing tumor, hyperplastic adrenal tissue, or even normal appearing adrenal cortex. Peculiarly, it is more difficult to produce hypertension in animals

by the chronic administration of aldosterone than desoxycorticosterone.

Another type of experimental hypertension is associated with regeneration of the adrenal cortex after enucleation (Skelton). This hypertensive disease fails to occur in rats unless the salt intake is increased and uninephrectomy performed. Aldosterone, corticosterone and renin are evidently not involved. Once hypertension is established, salt deprivation or removal of the regenerated adrenal does not restore the blood pressure to normal. The pathogenesis of this type of hypertension remains unknown.

There is no evidence that the posterior lobe of the pituitary plays a role in the development of renal hypertension, but the anterior lobe appears to be implicated through its action upon the adrenal cortex. Ablation of the anterior lobe in animals with renal hypertension lowers the blood pressure, which is raised to its previous level by the administration of adrenocorticotrophin or of a crude anterior lobe extract. So far as is known neither the thyroid nor the sex glands are in any way responsible for renal hypertension.

NEUROGENIC FACTORS IN EXPERIMENTAL HYPERTENSION. Hypertension has been produced in animals by a variety of neurological manipulations. Russian researchers especially emphasize the problems of vasomotor control by the central nervous system. They postulate that a disturbance in the central nervous system is the primary factor in the pathogenesis of essential hypertension, and renal involvement is only secondary. In animals, they were able to produce stable hypertension by conflicting conditioned signals resulting in experimental neurosis. By indirect tests, early involvement of the central nervous system in essential and experimental hypertension was shown. This has led to the theory that, in man, excess nervous strain weakens the functional capacity of the brain cortex which is reflected in a decreased effectiveness of the cortical inhibitory centers controlling blood pressure. The nervous and emotional strain of modern civilization has frequently been suggested as an underlying factor in the development of essential hypertension; many groups have studied hypertensive patients in relation to emotional instability and strain, but conclusions cannot be drawn because of the presence of many experimental variables and the inconsistency of the results.

Denervation of the carotid sinus and aortic vasosensory areas in dogs produces chronic arterial hypertension (200 to 250 mm. Hg) for

1 to 3 years, and considerable tachycardia with extreme lability of the pressure and rate. In some dogs, the blood pressure and heart rate tend to return toward normal during sleep. Constriction of the internal and external carotid arteries bilaterally above the carotid sinus to approximately one-third normal size produces a pronounced increase in blood pressure in a large percentage of dogs for at least 4 years. However hypertension does not ensue if the carotid sinus nerves remain intact (Kezdi). Hypertension caused in this way differs from essential or renal hypertension, for cardiac output and limb blood flow are elevated (since stroke volume is unchanged, the rise in output is secondary to the increased heart rate), and total peripheral resistance is relatively unchanged.

Hypertension has also been produced in rats by subjecting them to loud noises, or by stimulation of the hypothalamus or certain areas of the cerebral cortex.

In dogs completely sympathectomized except for the renal innervation, cutting of the buffer nerves increases sympathetic vasomotor discharge to the kidney, resulting in chronic hypertension. Subsequent renal nerve section relieves the elevated blood pressure. Electrical stimulation of the renal sympathetic nerves induces hypertension as long as the stimulus is maintained (3 months). Blood pressure returns to normal levels upon cessation of stimulation.

Hypertension often accompanies a rapid increase in intracranial pressure in patients but is not present if the cerebrospinal fluid pressure rises slowly. Application of pressure to the dura or brain of animals results in a rise in blood pressure. Cushing attributed this type of hypertension to the increased pressure within the cranial cavity causing compression of the vessels and slowing of the blood flow supplying the medulla. The heightened blood pressure would then be secondary to a generalized vasoconstriction resulting from reduced oxygen supply to the vasomotor center. Another theory postulates that an intracranial baroreceptor responds to the rise in intracranial pressure by stimulating a generalized vasoconstriction via the medullary vasomotor center. Permanent hypertension from chronically raised intracranial pressure has been produced by injecting an inert substance such as kaolin into the cisterna magna of rabbits resulting in hydrocephalus (Dixon and Heller). However these experiments could not be reproduced (Foa et al.). In support of Cushing's medullary ischemic theory, sudden occlusion of the common carotid arteries in animals, after the vertebrals and other branches of the subclavian have been ligated, causes a pronounced rise in blood pressure. Even though the carotid sinus has been excised, chronic hypertension may be produced in dogs by a similar procedure which causes cerebral ischemia. However it was pointed out previously that hypertension does not occur following carotid artery constriction if the nerve supply of the vessels remains intact.

Hypertension may occur transiently during the acute phase of poliomyelitis especially when the brain stem is involved. Chronic hypertension may also develop following the infection. The etiology of the hypertension is unknown; hypoxia is evidently not a factor.

PRIMARY OR ESSENTIAL HYPERTENSION

As implied in the name "essential" or "primary", the etiology of this disease is unknown. The disease is more common in women than men, shows a definite genetic (Pickering, Platt) and familial tendency, and usually has its onset from the 3rd to the 5th decade. The systolic and diastolic pressures are elevated; elevation of the diastolic pressure is the characteristic diagnostic finding and the systolic pressure may be within normal limits. The immediate cause of the raised blood pressure has been considered to be an increase in the peripheral resistance, i.e. a vasoconstriction or narrowing in some way of the peripheral vessels. However some of these hypertensives have an elevated cardiac index and lower than normal peripheral resistance. In the patients with increased peripheral resistance it is not known whether there is hypertrophy or swelling of the vascular wall with a decreased diameter (mechanical theory) or whether the smooth muscle cells of the vessel wall react excessively to nervous and humoral influences (contractile theory).

The role of the kidney in essential hypertension is unknown. It has been mentioned that angiotensin stimulates the adrenal cortex to release aldosterone. Urinary aldosterone levels are usually elevated in malignant hypertension but only occasionally elevated in benign essential hypertension (Genest). Aldosterone secretion rates, studied by an isotope dilution technique, have been reported as normal in benign essential hypertension (Laragh). The place of both angiotensin and aldosterone in essential hypertension is being actively studied.

The role of salt intake in this disease is interesting. Studies have shown that population groups with a high salt intake have a high incidence of essential hypertension while in societies with a low salt intake, the disease is uncommon. Excessive salt feeding can induce hypertension in some animals. Dahl has shown that, in rats, the tendency to develop hypertension in response to the environmental factor of salt feeding may be genetically conditioned.

A hypertension similar to essential hypertension has been produced in the offspring of rats which were treated during pregnancy with various drugs, hormones, or diets (Grollman and Grollman). This is the first demonstration that environmental factors before birth may affect the fetus to produce hypertension. As in essential hypertension, the offspring do not develop an elevated blood pressure until maturity. Studies of this experimental form of hypertension may add greatly to our knowledge of the pathogenesis of essential hypertension.

The hemodynamic effects of hypertension primarily involve the left heart. The left ventricle must compensate for the increased load imposed by the elevated peripheral resistance which tends to limit its stroke output. A greater residual volume causes stretching of the myocardial fibers with an increased initial tension which leads to an augmented force of contraction to restore the stroke output. Humoral and neurogenic influences undoubtedly play a part in increasing the stroke volume (ch. 44). The work of the left heart increases as measured by cardiac output and mean arterial pressure in large series of catheterized patients. These calculations probably underestimate the situation for the kinetic energy of ejection becomes a large factor in the work of the left ventricle in hypertension. The increased heart work is nearly proportional to the blood pressure elevation, for the cardiac output has usually been normal when measured in patients. The oxygen consumption per unit weight of left ventricle in patients with chronic hypertension is normal. Due to the hypertrophy of the left ventricle seen in most hypertensives, the total weight, and therefore, the total oxygen consumption of the heart is increased. The pressures in the pulmonary circulation and right heart are normal unless failure of one of the ventricles is present. Most hypertensive patients have an increased total peripheral resistance which is probably uniformly distributed both in the splanchnic area and extremities. The distribution of cardiac output and the level of blood flow to various body regions remains essentially normal.

The pressure in the capillaries and small veins is within normal limits, and the slope of pressure

through these vessels is not materially different from that in health. The fall in pressure through the arterioles is much greater than in health (fig. 48.2). Ellis and Weiss found mean pressures of 155 and 12 mm. respectively in the brachial artery and in the capillaries—a fall of over 140 mm. Of this about 125 mm. must have occurred in the arterioles. Normally the fall of pressure in the latter vessels is less than half this figure (approximately 50 or 60 mm.).

In most cases of hypertension, there is no significant change in venous pressure, circulation time, blood volume or viscosity. With strenuous exercise, patients without cardiac symptoms show a normal increase in cardiac output and oxygen consumption, but no change in pulmonary artery or wedge pressures.

In hypertensive subjects the reactivity of the peripheral vessels to nervous stress or to cold, as by the immersion of a hand in ice water (cold pressor test), is usually greater than normal. Hypertensive subjects have also been shown to have exaggerated blood flow and/or blood pressure responses to angiotensin, epinephrine, norepinephrine, and serotonin. The greater decrease in skin blood flow during intravenous norepinephrine or angiotensin infusions in hypertensive patients occurs in nerve blocked areas indicating that the difference in neurogenic vasomotor tone between normotensives and hypertensives is not the responsible factor (Barany). An increased vasocon-

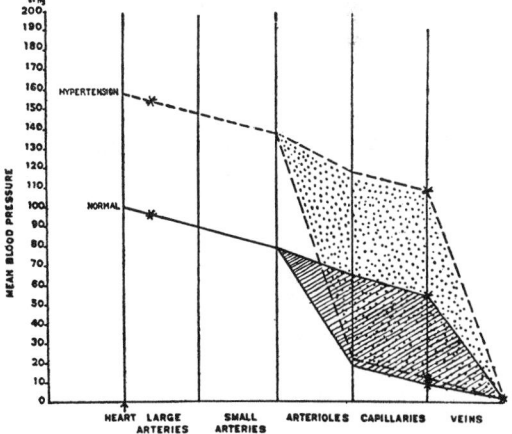

Fig. 48.2. Diagrammatic representation of fall in blood pressure in vascular circuit in subjects with hypertension compared with the normal. Shaded and stippled areas represent alteration in the pressure relationships in the skin vessels after the injection of histamine. The lower boundaries of these areas represent the pressure gradient under natural conditions; the upper boundaries this gradient after the injection of histamine (after Ellis and Weiss, modified).

striction or pressor response is not necessarily secondary to a hyperreactivity of the blood vessels since the rise in blood pressure in hypertensives, although greater in absolute values, is usually not proportionally greater than in normals. Since the radius of a vessel is such an important factor in peripheral resistance (Poiseuille's Law), a change in an already narrowed blood vessel (as may be present in hypertension) will produce a larger increase in resistance than the same change in a more dilated vessel. Until recently, an increased reactivity to norepinephrine of isolated blood vessels from hypertensive animals had not been demonstrated. Gordon and Nogueira showed that the initial tension exerted on aortic strips greatly influences their response to norepinephrine. At low initial tensions, aortic strips from hypertensive (renal artery constriction) rats and normal rats react the same to norepinephrine; at higher initial tensions, reactivity to norepinephrine is greater in the hypertensive vessels. These results support the theory of an increased reactivity of the vascular smooth muscle in the etiology of hypertension.

The cold pressor test is often employed for investigating the vascular responses. In most hypertensives the reaction is excessive; a sharp and inordinate rise in diastolic pressure occurs without an increase in cardiac output or pulse rate, which is taken as indicating a hypersensitive vasoconstrictor mechanism. Hines has studied this reaction in normal as well as in hypertensive subjects over a period of years, and has developed a classification of these groups: hyper-reactors, who respond to the test by a rise over 20 mm. Hg; normoreactors, who give a rise of between 10 and 20 mm. Hg; and hyporeactors, in whom the rise is less than 10 mm. Hg. The subjects with normal blood pressures who were hyper-reactors, showed

TABLE 48.3

The reaction of the diastolic pressure to the cold-pressor test, correlated with the subsequent development of hypertension (Hines)

Classification*	Cases	Hypertension 15 Years Later	
		Cases	Percentage
Hyporeactors............	36	0	0
Normoreactors..........	48	8	17
Hyper-reactors..........	57	31	54

* Blood pressure normal, less than 100 mm. Hg diastolic.

a definite susceptibility to the development of hypertension in later life (see table 48.3). In these, as well as in the hypertensive hyper-reactors, the magnitude of the response tends to increase progressively after 40 years of age. Actually the cold pressor test elicits a complex response of reflex vasoconstriction, pain perception and possibly an adrenergic discharge. Ganglionic blocking agents abolish the reaction.

MALIGNANT HYPERTENSION. Malignant or "accelerated" hypertension is a more severe, progressive form of arterial hypertension, characterized by rapidly advancing renal damage, usually, but not always, accompanied by retinal hemorrhages, exudates and papilledema. The papilledema (elevation of the optic discs) has been related to an increase in cerebrospinal fluid pressure induced by the marked diastolic blood pressure elevation. The clinical course is one of rapid degeneration with early demise due to cerebral, cardiac, or renal complications.

Contrary to the findings in benign essential hypertension, most investigators have found an increased adrenal secretion of aldosterone and some studies demonstrated increased renin or angiotensin blood levels in malignant hypertension. In aldosterone treated rats, renin injections induce a prolonged, significant increase in blood pressure, vascular damage, and death in a few days (Masson). This suggests that renin and aldosterone may both play an important role in experimental and clinical malignant hypertension. Although much more proof is necessary, it is postulated that renal damage from hypertension in the malignant disease leads to increased renin secretion and angiotensin formation. The angiotensin would maintain the elevated blood pressure and stimulate secretion of aldosterone by the adrenal cortex; the combined effects of increased levels of angiotensin and aldosterone would account for the accelerated course of the disease.

ECLAMPSIA GRAVIDARUM. Eclampsia is a state occurring in the last trimester of pregnancy, characterized by hypertension, headache, nausea and vomiting, albuminuria, edema, tremors, or convulsions ending in coma. The blood pressure may be extremely elevated, with the elevation developing rapidly. The diastolic pressure shows the more pronounced rise, indicating a generalized vasoconstriction. The cause of the widespread arteriolar spasm is unknown. It is not relieved by antiadrenergic agents or any substance acting at or below the level of the ganglia; a humoral mechanism is therefore suspected. The blood pressure, as a rule, falls after evacuation of the uterus, which points to the uterine contents being in some way responsible for the symptoms. Since death of the fetus does not result in an abatement of the condition, and it develops in association with hydatidiform moles, placental or uterine tissue is certainly incriminated. Hunter and Howard have obtained a pressor substance, *hysterotonin*, from amniotic fluid and freshly ground decidua (not placental tissue) of patients with eclampsia. It is apparently a polypeptide, constricts aortic muscle strips, and raises the blood pressure in pithed, nephrectomized cats. Uterine blood flow, measured by the nitrous oxide or radioactive sodium disappearance methods, has been decreased 50 to 60% in most cases of toxemia. Acute hypertension can be produced by compressing the aorta below the level of the renal arteries in pregnant, but not in nonpregnant, animals. Kumar induced chronic placental ischemia by clipping the uterine arteries and tying the ovarian arteries in dogs. This resulted in a decreased uterine blood flow, hypertension, proteinuria, but no gain in weight. Beyond these facts nothing is known for certain about the causative mechanism in eclampsia.

SUMMARY. Goldblatt's view is that the primary cause of essential hypertension in man is intrarenal obliterative vascular disease (usually arterial and arteriolar sclerosis) or any other condition that brings about the same disturbance of intrarenal hemodynamics. Although essential human hypertension is supposedly unassociated with obvious disturbance of renal function, this does not mean there is no functional disturbance of any kind, but that the usual tests for excretory function may not be adequate to disclose it. At autopsy, no evidence of *severe* renal arteriolar sclerosis was found in individuals who had had normal blood pressure, while moderate to severe renal arterial and arteriolar sclerosis occurred in almost 100 per cent of cases in which hypertension had existed. This is one of the strongest supports for renal vascular disease as a cause, not a result, of hypertension. Reviews of human unilateral renal hypertension confirm that interference with the renal blood supply can cause a form of human hypertension similar to that created experimentally and can be permanently cured by excision of the kidney. Reports of the ability to arrest the course of hypertension by transplanting a normal kidney and removing two diseased kidneys is a further verification.

The popular assumption that essential hypertension is mediated by a neurogenically maintained increase in peripheral arteriolar resistance lacks substantial experimental proof. Failure of total sympathectomy to cure essential hypertension is the strongest argument that the autonomic nervous system is not primarily involved in maintenance of increased peripheral resistance.

With the development of improved methods of measuring blood levels and production rates of renin, angiotensin, and aldosterone, the role of the kidney in many types of hypertension should be clarified. The response of animals with chronic experimental hypertension to antirenin is important evidence that the kidney is involved in long standing, as well as acute, hypertension. It is likely that no one mechanism can explain essential or other varieties of hypertension but that renal, endocrine, cardiovascular, and neurological factors all play an important role as pointed out in the "mosaic theory" of Page.

TREATMENT. The treatment of essential hypertension is predominantly medical, with the use of various pharmacological agents. Surgical treatment ranging from subdiaphragmatic splanchnicectomy to "total" (thoracolumbar and accessory ganglia) sympathectomy is usually reserved for selected patients; such surgery removes the sympathetic vasomotor tone from a large segment of the systemic vascular system resulting in a decreased peripheral resistance and an increased capacity of the vascular bed. Since sympathectomy does not offer better results than medical treatment, its popularity has declined. The ganglionic blocking agents, by reducing cholinergic transmission in the autonomic ganglia, produce a "chemical sympathectomy" and have the most profound effects of the pharmacological agents used. The blocking agents reduce both arteriolar and venous tone, producing an increased systemic vascular volume and a decreased diastolic pressure by a combination of venous pooling and failure of reflex vasoconstriction. Sympathetic tone of the blood vessels is reduced by a low dose of the drugs before a significant depression in cardiac output occurs. The cardiac output is decreased with higher doses by a blockage of sympathetic activity to the heart producing a decreased stroke volume and heart rate (Zimmerman). Because of postural hypotension and the side reactions from a concomitant parasympathetic blockage (constipation, urinary retention, mydriasis), these drugs are being used less frequently and in smaller doses, in combination with less potent antihypertensive agents.

Alkaloids of the plant, Rauwolfia serpentina Benth, are widely used antihypertensive preparations. Their action is very complex. Besides a sedative effect, Rauwolfia derivatives decrease sympathetic nervous tone. Catecholamines are released by these drugs from storage in hypothalamic centers and peripheral postganglionic sympathetic nerves. In animals, reflex pressor responses following carotid occlusion and central vagal stimulation are decreased. The lack of sympathetic transmitter substance, leading to a decrease in vasoconstrictor activity and peripheral resistance, may be the drug's main hypotensive action. Serotonin is also displaced from its binding sites in the brain which may lead to the sedative effect and relative parasympathetic overactivity (bradycardia). Hydralazine, another moderate hypotensive agent, possesses many complex actions. It has been shown to inactivate pressor materials derived from renin, to inactivate some decarboxylase enzymes, and probably to stimulate monoamine oxidase, the enzyme involved in inhibition or destruction of catecholamines and serotonin. The drug produces a prolonged dilation of constricted blood vessels and, unlike other hypotensive agents, increases renal plasma flow despite the decrease in blood pressure. Although its mode of action is not definitely known, it acts peripherally since it interferes with the hypertensive effects of pressor substances which are peripheral in action. Schroeder maintains that the relaxation of vasoconstriction is due not to sympatholytic activity but to a direct effect on the vascular smooth muscle cell which may be related to the drug's chelating action on trace metals.

The veratrum alkaloids are not widely used in the treatment of hypertension for the hypotensive dose approximates the emetic dose. The therapeutically used veratrum alkaloids or mixtures, produce a vasodepressor reflex by means of the baroreceptors of the carotid sinus, aortic arch and left ventricle, and not by their parasympathetic stimulatory effects. Some veratrum alkaloids do have an action directly on higher vasomotor centers.

Diuretics of the benzothiadiazine family (such as chlorothiazide) which inhibit renal tubular reabsorption of electrolytes have been found to have hypotensive properties. Their action has been assumed to be similar to the hypotensive effect of a low sodium diet (which is still a very useful treatment for hypertensive patients). The antihypertensive mechanism of these diuretics is believed to be a result of a decreased plasma volume with loss of sodium, chloride and water from the body and a subsequent decreased cardiac output and blood pressure. Restoration of the blood volume with dextran, early in treatment, restores the blood pressure towards previous hypertensive levels. However, the blood pressure reduction has been shown to be maintained even when the plasma volume, exchangeable sodium and cardiac output return to normal levels with more prolonged treatment. Therefore, other mechanisms may be operative in the antihypertensive action of these drugs besides a purely diuretic effect. The possibility that the peripheral resistance is lowered by reducing the sodium content in arteriolar walls is supported only by indirect evidence. Eckstein and his associates have shown that chlorothiazide reduces the peripheral vasoconstrictor response to norepinephrine in dogs; the effects of norepinephrine on heart rate and cardiac output were also modified. They suggest that chlorothiazide alters the sensitivity of the cardioregulatory reflexes.

Guanethidine is one of the most effective and widely used antihypertensive agents. It produces a predominantly postural hypotension without the annoying side effects of parasympathetic inhibition seen with the ganglionic blocking agents. In dogs, guanethidine produces complete blockage of the cardiac accelerator response before the myocardium is depleted of norepinephrine (Gaffney). Clinical doses in man do not deplete tissue catecholamines as evidenced by persistence of pressor responses to ephedrine and tyramine (Cohn). Therefore the reduction in blood pressure, postural hypotension, and blockage of the Valsalva blood pressure "overshoot" may not be dependent on depletion of catecholamine stores as reported by other groups. It is postulated that post-ganglionic sympathetic transmission is blocked but a direct effect on the myocardium or on smooth muscle has not been ruled out.

A large number of new agents are being tested in the treatment of hypertension, most of which are either serotonin, monoamine oxidase or catecholamine inhibitors. The role of serotonin in hypertension is unclear. Enigmatically, inhibitors of both monoamine oxidase (which destroys serotonin) and of serotonin itself lower blood pressure in hypertensive patients and are receiving clinical trials in treatment. There is evidence that monoamine oxidase inhibitors may possess ganglionic blocking activity.

The above-mentioned drugs are usually used in combination, in the lowest dosages necessary to reduce the blood pressure to reasonable levels for the patient concerned. Each agent seems to have an additive or potentiating effect on the other so that together smaller doses can be used with fewer side effects or toxic reactions than when each drug is used alone. Although the life of the patient may be prolonged by these agents, there is no definite evidence that the underlying hypertensive trait is reversed.

Hypotension

Hypotension is usually considered to be present in an adult when the systolic pressure is persistently below 90 to 110 mm. Hg, although such a definition is arbitrary, and hypotensive symptoms may not be experienced even at lower levels. On the other hand, patients with arterial hypertension may develop symptoms at higher systolic pressures.

PRIMARY HYPOTENSION. In the absence of an underlying disease, low blood pressure is referred to as "primary" or "essential" hypotension. The subjects with primary hypotension (who are usually emotionally labile, asthenic, young females) often suffer no ill effects beyond fatigue and weakness. The nonspecific symptoms may be more related to the individual's personality than to the hypotension. These patients are more likely to be free from cardiac and renal disease; for this reason, the condition is said to forecast longevity. Except for a hereditary predisposition, the etiological factors in primary hypotension are unknown.

SECONDARY HYPOTENSION. Low blood pressure may occur either as a temporary or persistent phenomenon in numerous disease states, such as acute fever, myocardial infarction, tuberculosis, adrenal or pituitary insufficiency, and debilitating diseases. The symptoms accompanying secondary hypotension usually result from the underlying disease rather than the low blood pressure. The determining factors are not well understood, but the hypotension is usually due to an inadequate cardiac output, a decreased peripheral resistance or blood volume, or a combination of these factors.

ORTHOSTATIC OR POSTURAL HYPOTENSION. In this interesting condition, the reflex mechanisms normally operating to maintain the blood pressure against the effect of gravity are apparently in abeyance, or their sensitivity greatly depressed. A profound fall in blood pressure occurs on assumption of the standing position; the systolic pressure may fall to 40 mm. Hg, and the diastolic to zero (as determined by the usual auscultatory method). The subject experiences dizziness and/or syncope. This syndrome may occur idiopathically with no known underlying disease, secondary to various nervous system diseases (diabetes mellitus with neuropathy, tabes dorsalis,

postinfectious neuritis, Wernicke's disease, myasthenia gravis, syringomyelia), following surgical sympathectomies, or during treatment with adrenergic or ganglionic depleting or blocking agents. In certain individuals, hypotension and syncope may occur before, during, or after micturition. Orthostasis, straining (Valsalva maneuver), or vasodepressor or cardioinhibitory reflexes initiated in the bladder have been implicated etiologically. In animal experiments, mechanical stimulation of the bladder produces cardioinhibitory effects. In some females in late pregnancy, the supine position may lead to hypotension and tachycardia. Stimulation of the nerve plexus behind the uterus has been blamed but it is more likely that compression of the inferior vena cava by the uterus leads to a decreased venous return, a decreased cardiac output, and thus a fall in blood pressure. A significant fall in blood pressure occurs in the pregnant animal following inferior vena cava ligation, but the absence of a hypotensive effect following the same procedure in the non-pregnant dog indicates that other factors are involved.

Idiopathic orthostatic hypotension is believed to be a definite syndrome usually accompanied by anhidrosis and impotence; the male between 40 and 70 years of age is most often affected. Since anhidrosis and failure of a reflex tachycardia on standing accompanies the postural hypotension, the abnormality is believed to be in the sympathetic nervous system. However, indirect evidence also implicates involvement of the parasympathetic system and the name "primary autonomic insufficiency" has been suggested. The site of the defect is unknown. Some patients demonstrate evidence of a diffuse degenerative central nervous system disorder which was presumably present early in the disease and could not be blamed on ischemia from hypotensive episodes.

Experimental studies on patients with chronic orthostatic hypotension have shown that they do not pool more blood in the lower extremities on assumption of the erect position than normals, but that there is an abnormal response to the usual shift in blood volume. The abnormality consists in the loss of reflex arteriolar and venous constriction which usually occurs on standing. Although the total amount of blood pooled in the legs is not excessive, an abnormally fast rate of pooling may contribute to the drop in blood pressure. The drop in blood pressure may be augmented by a fall in cardiac output, although the latter does not always decrease excessively (a large postural cardiac output fall may also be seen in normotensives without a significant change in blood pressure). In patients with postural hypotension, there is an absence of the normal rise in venous blood levels of epinephrine and norepinephrine during upright tilting. These patients also demonstrate a hyperreactivity to norepinephrine given parenterally. These findings suggest a failure of reflex release of norepinephrine from sympathetic nerve endings at effector sites in the vascular bed. Vasopressin, which usually does not have a pressor effect in man, sometimes raises the blood pressure in these patients. The increased reactivity to norepinephrine and vasopressin would be typical of the response of a denervated vascular bed. It has also been demonstrated that these patients can show the same defect in the supine position during exercise. Thus the defect occurs under circumstances in which venous pooling is not present. The fall in blood pressure during supine exercise can be explained by an absence of the usual compensatory vasoconstriction which occurs in the inactive muscular vascular beds. An abnormal renal transport of administered sodium has been demonstrated in these patients but whether this is a primary or secondary defect is unknown.

TREATMENT. Treatment of primary hypotension is usually unnecessary, while correction of the underlying disease should be attempted in secondary hypotension. Abdominal binders, elastic stockings, various sympathomimetic pressor agents, vasopressin, adrenal cortical sodium retaining hormones, or a high salt diet are often, but not always, helpful in chronic orthostatic hypotension. Sodium retaining hormones or a high salt intake are believed to act by increasing the blood volume and, hence, the blood pressure; however, the underlying abnormality is not corrected.

Hyperventilation, Hypoventilation and Hypercapnia

Circulatory adjustments result when the P_{CO_2} of arterial blood is increased or decreased. A decrease in P_{O_2} of arterial blood also elicits changes in the cardiovascular system, but a rise in P_{O_2} above that which is present in normal resting subjects at sea level has little or no effect. The patterns of response which need to be analyzed, therefore, are those related to hypocapnia (acapnia), hypercapnia, hypoxia (anoxia) and a combination of hypercapnia and hypoxia (asphyxia).

Hypocapnia can be produced by voluntary hyperventilation or by artificial respiration of anesthetized animals. Carbon dioxide depletion causes a lowering of the tonic activity of the vasoconstrictor center; arteriolar dilation results and the blood pressure falls. The heart rate may be accelerated reflexly from the fall in pressure in the sinoaortic zones. The *direct* effect of carbon dioxide lack upon the peripheral vessels is to increase their tone, but this effect is not evident in the pressence of the reduction in arteriolar tonus related to the central effects.

Dale and Evans found that when cats were severely overventilated the blood pressure fell to around 40 mm. Hg within a minute or two, and the depressor effect did not occur or was quite evanescent when a mixture of 5 per cent CO_2 in air was substituted for air as the ventilating gas. Depressor effects of hyperventilation with air also were present in decapitated animals thus indicating that the spinal vasomotor centers also are sensitive to changes in carbon dioxide tension. After destruction of the spinal cord hypocapnia caused a rise in blood pressure, as would be expected in view of the direct effects on peripheral vessels which in this case are not opposed by the central influences.

In the majority of human subjects in the standing position forced ventilation causes a fall in arterial blood pressure. The fall is attributed in part, at least in some subjects, to interference with the venous return which occurs as a result of the forcible expiratory movements (Vincent and Thompson), since the fall may occur when the subject breathes a mixture containing CO_2. Severe prolonged hyperventilation in some subjects may cause enough pooling of blood in dependent parts of the body to cause dizziness or even fainting since cerebral blood flow is decreased.

According to earlier views (Y. Henderson) shock could be produced by prolonged hyperventilation, however this does not appear to be the case in experimental animals if a method is used which does not obstruct flow of blood in the lungs. Although arterial pressure is lowered peripheral resistance also is lowered so that blood flow through most organs is maintained or even increased, and blood pressure is restored quickly when the hyperventilation is discontinued.

Hypercapnia causes increased tone of the vasoconstrictor center. Local effects of a rise in P_{CO_2}, as when metabolism in the tissues is increased are vasodilator, but this effect is not evident in the presence of moderate increases in P_{CO_2} achieved by rebreathing or adding CO_2 to the inhaled mixture. Mathison reported that when an animal breathed an air mixture containing 10 per cent CO_2 with an adequate percentage of oxygen the arterial blood pressure rose within less than a minute to double its previous height and intestinal volume fell. Injections of lactic acid or other organic acids into the blood stream produced effects similar to those of carbon dioxide excess.

In a decapitated animal a rise in blood pressure in response to CO_2 occurs when the percentage in respired air is increased to 20, whereas breathing air mixed with 5 per cent CO_2 may be sufficient to excite the medullary vasomotor center.

A moderate degree of hypoxia as produced by ascent to altitude or by breathing at sea level a gas mixture containing about 12 to 15 per cent O_2 causes a moderate increase in heart rate and elevation of the blood pressure. Breathing is stimulated so that a mild decrease in P_{CO_2} also occurs. A brief severe bout of hypoxia produced by breathing nitrogen for about 30 seconds causes marked cardiac acceleration while changes in blood pressure are somewhat variable. Breathing is stimulated, hence influences related to hypocapnia make the interpretations difficult. Heymans (1950) stated that cardiac acceleration in response to oxygen lack is due mainly "to reflex stimulation of the sympathetic centers (cardiac and adrenalinic centers) by way of the chemoreceptors", and that oxygen want effects these centers directly only if very marked. However, in experiments involving perfusion of the carotid bodies a lowering of the P_{O_2} in the perfused blood failed to elicit cardiac acceleration, and this was true when the systemic-arterial blood pressure was kept constant by the use of a mechanical compensator (Bernthal). Intravenous injection of sodium cyanide in the smaller doses which stimulate breathing also causes cardiac acceleration, however the effect of cyanide on heart rate is not exerted reflexly from the chemoreceptors (see Heymans, 1958).

In experiments on intact animals subjected to severe anoxia before and after adrenalectomy it is demonstrated that liberation of epinephrine is a factor in the production of cardiac acceleration (Van Loo and associates), however neural acceleration also is concerned. At present it must be concluded that the precise mechanism which sets off the acceleration in response to hypoxia is not known.

Cardiac output is increased in man as much as 50 per cent while breathing a gas mixture containing 8 per cent oxygen (Doyle and associates, 1952). Also, increases in cardiac output are pro-

duced by hypoxia in unanesthetized dogs (Nahas and associates, 1954).

In hypoventilation or asphyxia the combined effects of increased P_{CO_2} and decreased P_{O_2} are seen. Blood pressure is elevated; heart rate usually is increased. Cardiac output is elevated. The changes in the blood and the respiratory effects are described elsewhere (ch. 53 and 54). As asphyxia is prolonged blood pressure falls as a consequence of decreased strength of cardiac contractions and conduction in the atrioventricular portion of the conducting system may be impaired.

As asphyxia is progressive in an anesthetized dog which is allowed to rebreathe air from a small reservoir the blood pressure progressively becomes higher until it may reach a level double that in the period before asphyxia. Shortly, as rebreathing continues, the blood pressure suddenly falls. This is attributed to a weakening of the cardiac contractions due to anoxemia and not to release of arteriolar tonus, for if the volume of the kidney is recorded at this time, it is found that no change occurs.

As described above, the local effect of a deficiency of O_2 and an excess of CO_2 or rise in cH is to cause vasodilation while the effect of these changes in the vasomotor center is to promote vasoconstriction. In exercise large increases in P_{CO_2} and cH and decreases in P_{O_2} occur in the active muscles, and these changes promote a greater blood flow. Changes in P_{CO_2} and P_{O_2} in systemic arterial blood during exercise are not prominent since equilibrium with alveolar air of essentially normal composition still occurs (see control of pulmonary ventilation during exercise p. 1021 and of vasomotor reactions during exercise).

The persistent elevation of the blood pressure which results from a rise in intracranial pressure is attributed to compression of medullary vessels and hence interference with blood supply to the vasomotor centers. The rise in P_{CO_2} and cH in the vasoconstrictor center causes an increase in vasoconstrictor tonus and therefore a rise in arterial blood pressure to a level sufficient to restore blood flow to the brain. When the rise in intracranial pressure is rapid, as in the case of cerebral hemorrhage in man or when it is produced in experimental animals by introducing fluid into the subdural space, the rise in blood pressure is rapid and a decrease in heart rate is elicited from pressoreceptors. Hence, repeated recording of blood pressure and heart rate provides information concerning whether the rise in intracranial pressure is continuing.

Circulatory Adjustments to Climatic Conditions

Changes in environmental temperature elicit characteristic alterations in circulation. Adjustments in cutaneous blood flow, blood volume and cardiac output occur as a part of the process of heat regulation (see ch. 70). At present there is interest in the use of lowered body temperature to prevent or treat shock and to permit surgery on patients who might not be able to tolerate the stress of anesthesia and operations at normal body temperature. Therefore, it has become necessary to consider the circulatory effects of severely lowered body temperature.

Any mammal if exposed to a sufficiently low temperature will react by conserving its heat and increasing heat production; but if the cold is intense enough for a sufficiently long period the animal begins to cool. At a critical level of body temperature death occurs, but this level is lower for hibernators than for mammals which do not hibernate (Lyman and Chatfield, in *Physiology of Induced Hypothermia*). Species which hibernate evidently undergo adaptations which do not occur, at least in similar degree, in nonhibernators. If a nonhibernator is cooled progressively, death usually occurs due to ventricular fibrillation or asystole when the body temperature has reached the vicinity of 20 to 15° C. The heart of a hibernator (ground squirrel) can beat effectively at rates of 5 to 10 beats per minute at low temperatures and will continue to beat when removed from the animal and placed in cold unoxygenated saline, but the heart of a nonhibernator (white rat), under similar conditions, stops beating within a few minutes (Dawe and Landau, 1960).

As shown by Hook and Stormont (1941), and Hegnauer and associates (1950), heart rate in the dog decreases almost linearly with decreases in body temperature down to about 20 beats per minute at about 18 to 20° C. Blood pressure showed a progressive decrease but not as much as the decrease in heart rate down to about 24° C. Then as temperature was lowered further, the decrease in blood pressure paralleled the decrease in heart rate. Similar results have been obtained by others. As the heart rate decreases in hypothermia the durations of both systole and isometric relaxation as well as duration of diastole increase greatly (as much as 2½ times). When heart rate is decreased comparably by vagal stimulation,

most of the lengthening of the cycle is related to prolongation of diastole.

The cardiac output of dogs at a body temperature of 20° C. is about 15 per cent of normal due almost entirely to the decrease in heart rate since stroke volume may be normal. The tissues use less oxygen and the coefficient of oxygen utilization is increased. Although coronary blood flow is reduced it is adequate for the needs of the heart in the presence of reduced metabolism (Berne, 1954). During rewarming signs of circulatory inadequacy are noted and have been attributed to the peripheral vasodilation and to adrenal insufficiency related to lack of adrenal response to trauma during hypothermia.

Much attention has been given to the question of what causes ventricular fibrillation in hypothermic animals, and no definite conclusions have been reached. Absolute and relative refractory periods of cardiac muscle are lengthened and conduction is slowed. Excitability changes of the heart in hypothermia are varied. In some cases changes in threshold are not prominent while in others there is an abrupt loss of excitability. It is possible that the latter change is related to failure of repolarization of the fibers of the conducting system which sometimes occurs during cooling. The problem is discussed in detail by Hoffman (Symposium, *Physiology of Induced Hypothermia*). Covino (1958) reported that in hypothermic dogs which were about to fibrillate, calcium was shifting into the heart and potassium was leaving. He suggests a cause and effect relationship between these changes and ventricular fibrillation in hypothermic dogs, however several other factors including sympathetic neural activity, hydrogen ion shifts, and type of anesthetic agent also are considered to have an effect on the incidence of fibrillation.

Circulatory Responses to Gravitational Stress and Weightlessness

THE EFFECTS OF ACCELERATION. A constant speed, however great, has in itself no effect upon the circulation. As pointed out by Armstrong, we are travelling through space quite unaware of a speed of over 18 miles per second caused by the motion of the earth. But acceleration, that is, a change in velocity either in the line of our motion (*linear acceleration* and *deceleration*), or the movement of the body in a circular or curved course (*centripetal* or *central acceleration*), may cause profound effects upon the body as a result of the inertia of the blood and viscera. A third type of accelerated movement, known as *angular acceleration*, takes place when the body rotates about its own axis, as when a plane rolls or spins. The rate of angular acceleration is rarely great enough to cause any serious physiological disturbance, but this form of acceleration effects equilibrium and orientation. The development of the modern airplane, maneuvers of military flying, and space flights have brought prominently to the fore the importance and hazards of acceleration in relation to the circulation. According to Newton's Law, $F = MA$ where F = force, M the mass and A the linear acceleration. Therefore, $A = F/M$.

The effects of *horizontal linear acceleration* upon the body of a pilot are seen in catapulted take-offs, in picking up personnel from the ground or in gliders by high speed planes, and in launching of space flight ships. Deceleration, i.e., a sudden reduction in velocity, occurs in crash landings, parachute landings, reentry into the earth's atmosphere during space flights, or from parachute opening (especially at very high altitudes), etc. Vertical acceleration, as when the plane falls or pitches, owing to changes in air density, causes motion sickness.

Centripetal acceleration is the type which in military flying causes serious effects upon the circulation. It is defined as the acceleration of a body toward the center of a circle in the circumference of which it is moving at uniform velocity. The central force producing the acceleration (*centripetal force*) is resisted by an equal and opposite, radially acting force, generally called *centrifugal force*. This may be expressed, thus:—

$$F = MV^2/r$$

in which M is the mass, V the velocity and r the radius of the circular movement. At a linear or centripetal acceleration equal to that of gravity, namely, 32.2 ft. per second, the force exerted is equal to that of gravity. Gravitational force, like centrifugal force, is proportional to mass and is exhibited as weight. The force due to acceleration is, therefore, conveniently expressed in units of gravitational force and designated by the letter G. Thus an acceleration amounting to 2G indicates a force double that of gravity, i.e., a body acted upon by such a force would be doubled in weight. The centrifugal force is proportional to the square of the velocity. It can be calculated in G units from equation $G = V^2/32.2r$, where V is the velocity in feet, r the radius in feet of the curved course which the moving body takes, and

G, units of gravitational force per pound of mass.[3] Thus, the weight of a pilot's body subjected to a force of 2G is doubled, is tripled at 3G, quadrupled at 4G, and so on.

Acceleration which produces a force acting upon the airman in the long axis of the body from head to seat is called positive $(+G)$; that acting from seat to head is called negative $(-G)$. A pilot pulling out of a power dive, that is, changing direction at high velocity to a horizontal and upward direction in a banking maneuver has his head directed inward toward the center of the circular movement and is therefore subjected to a positive centripetal acceleration. If the force amounts to from 5 to $6 + G$ or more, and lasts for longer than 3 or 4 seconds, the phenomenon now generally referred to as "blackout" results, for his blood being acted upon by a force 5 or 6 times that of gravity "falls" or is "thrown" into the lower part of the body (the large vessels, it will be recalled, run in the general direction of the long axis of the body); the weight and, consequently. the hydrostatic pressure of the blood is increased (see fig. 48.3). In animal experiments it has been shown that as a result of the very high capillary pressure a marked increase in filtration of fluid from the blood into the extravascular spaces with hemoconcentration occurs. In man the skin of the lower parts of the legs may show numerous blood extravasations (petechiae). The movement of blood toward the feet reduces the venous return of blood to the heart, and, as a consequence, the pressure of blood in the cerebral and retinal vessels falls. Vision is temporarily lost and the pilot may become unconscious. The abdominal viscera are forced downwards and, drawing upon the diaphragm, may embarrass respiration. X-ray photography shows elongation of the heart and a reduction in cardiac volume.

"Negative" acceleration, as when a turn is made at high velocity with the plane in the inverted position, the pilot's head being directed outward, causes opposite effects upon the circulation and is likely to produce more serious injury, but fortunately, unlike positive acceleration, does not come into play in any necessary maneuver. "Negative" acceleration also occurs in spins resulting from some structural damage to the

---

[3] From the following equation the force developed during linear acceleration or deceleration can be calculated.

$$G = (V_x{}^2 - V_y{}^2)/32.2 \times 2 \times S$$

where V_y is the initial velocity, V_x the final velocity and S the distance travelled during the period of acceleration.

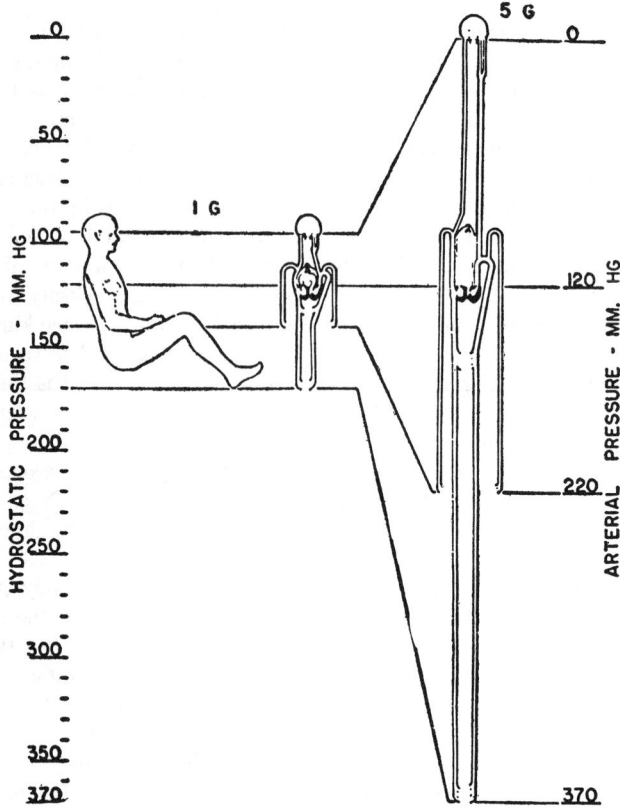

FIG. 48.3. Diagrammatic representation of the hydrostatic pressures in the vascular system of a man in the sitting position at 1 G and at 5 G. (Wood and associates.)

plane, when the tremendous force created may, through the increased weight of their bodies, prevent the pilot and other occupants of the plane from moving. In a turn with the head directed outward, the blood is driven toward the head resulting in effects sometimes called "red-out". The vessels of the head and neck become engorged, there may be small cutaneous hemorrhages, severe throbbing pain in the head is experienced and the eyes feel as though they were being extruded from their sockets. The abdominal viscera are pushed upwards against the diaphragm. The venous return to the heart is increased and the blood pressure in the cerebral vessels is raised considerably (as much as 65 mm. Hg). There may be mental confusion for a time. Cerebral hemorrhage may result, but since the hydrostatic pressure of the cerebrospinal fluid is also increased, it acts as a buffer which, to a large extent, protects the delicate walls of the small cerebral veins and capillaries, which are the most likely to rupture.

Large centrifuge machines have been devised for subjecting the body to positive acceleration and studying the effects produced. Instruments record blood pressure, cardiac action and blood content of the ear drum membrane automatically. Thus the tolerance of a pilot to +G can be measured (see fig. 48.4).

In order to prevent the physiological effects of positive acceleration, several types of double-walled suits have been designed which, by containing water or air under pressure, create a force to resist a rise in the hydrostatic pressure of the blood. The first suit of this kind to be employed in actual air combat was invented by Franks of the Royal Canadian Air Force. It envelops the abdomen and lower limbs; water is introduced into the space between its walls. During the development of centrifugal force a hydrostatic pressure, automatically graded to that exerted upon the blood, is applied through the tissues to the vascular walls. Thus, distension of the vascular bed of the lower part of the body and the accumulation of blood is prevented.

The effects of centripetal acceleration may also be minimized by the pilot assuming a crouching position with the trunk bent well forward and the thighs strongly flexed at the hips. The direction of the centrifugal force is then across the great vessels of the trunk rather than in line

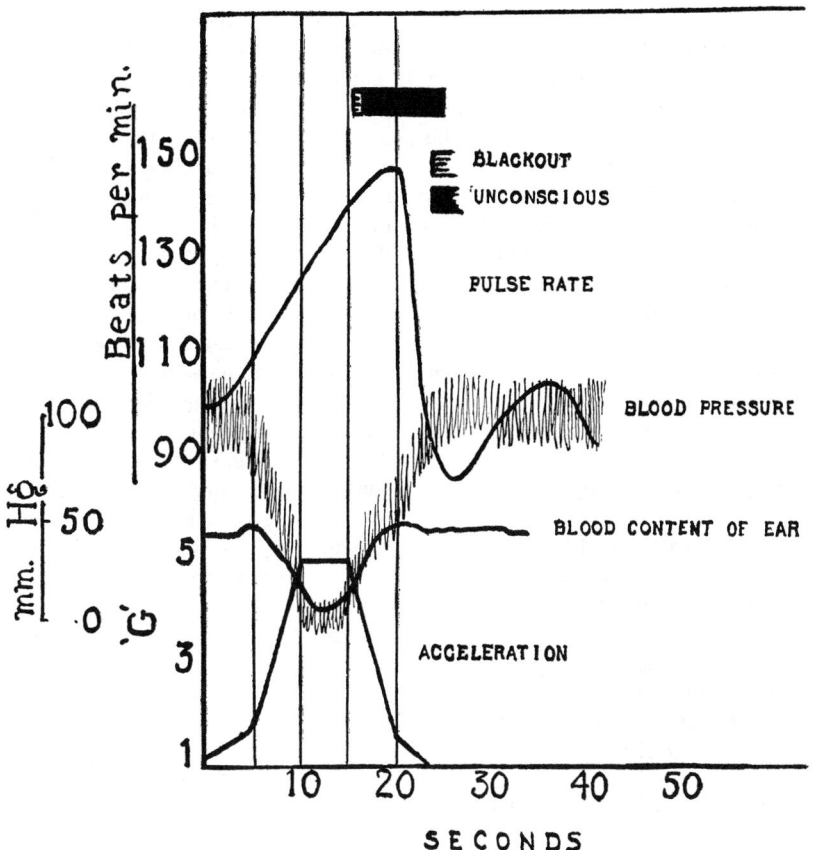

FIG. 48.4. Records of pulse rate, blood pressure and blood content of the ear of a normal subject exposed in the human centrifuge for 5 seconds to 5 G. (Drawn in part from graphs kindly furnished by Dr. W. R. Franks.)

with them, and runs from knee to hip more or less parallel to the vessels of the thigh; the movement of the blood along the veins of the thigh toward the heart is thus actually aided.

SPACE FLIGHTS. Space flights impose many problems on the circulatory system. The stresses of acceleration during take-off, the deceleration upon re-entry, and the absence of gravity during the flight are being actively studied.

The acceleration and deceleration due to take-off and landing of space ships presents no fundamental physiological difficulties. During space flights, the astronaut lies on his back so that the acceleration or deceleration thrust is imparted to his body in a transverse G force. In the recumbent position, the G force is perpendicular to the long axis of the body and the increased hydrostatic pressure effect is of little importance. In test subjects, the limit of tolerance to centrifugal forces in the direction of chest to back corresponds to an acceleration of 17 G for 4 minutes, and in the direction of back to chest, to an acceleration

of 11 G for 3 minutes. This is compatible with the acceleration and deceleration due to take-off and landing of space ships. Acceleration and deceleration are associated with an increased heart rate and increased mean, systolic, and diastolic blood pressures. It is probable that this is a sympathoadrenal response to the gravitational stress of acceleration and deceleration. Experiments to evaluate the human circulatory response to such stress have shown an increased output of both epinephrine and norepinephrine during and after centrifugation. The epinephrine release was found related to the anxiety associated with centrifugation for it was apparent during mock experiments. The norepinephrine release appeared closely related to the actual physical stress of centrifugation.

When the space ship has left the atmosphere of the earth and its propulsion is discontinued, it will behave like a celestial body in its orbit through the solar system. The orbit must lead the ship to its goal following the laws of gravitation.

Consequently, during the greater part of interplanetary flight, a gravity-free or a near gravity-free state is encountered. Its duration will vary from days (trip to the moon) to months (trip to Venus or Mars). Space flights to the time of this writing have lasted only two weeks.

On earth, gravity is omnipresent and is the only environmental factor which cannot be eliminated experimentally for any prolonged period of time. This is why our knowledge of the effects of gravity on the circulation is small. Apart from the few seconds in a free fall, such as in an airplane undergoing an almost vertical dive, there is only one way to escape gravity, and that is to leave the earth in a space ship. Experiments simulating a weightless environment have been performed by water immersion of man for varying lengths of time.

The circulatory changes caused by gravity are due to elastic deformation which body organs and blood vessels undergo. In the weightless state, the organs are without support and, hence, this might lead to mild derangement of body organs as they seek slightly altered positions. Direct disturbances of the circulation, however, by absence of gravity do not occur. The circulation operates by elastic forces delivered by the heart and the elasticity of the blood vessels. Although the blood loses its weight, it retains its mass, inertia, and other properties of a liquid. In general, it is believed it would resemble that of a man at sea level in the horizontal position except that flattening of the veins would not occur and the distribution of the blood would be the same in the horizontal and vertical, head up or down, position, or indeed, in any position. Finally, and most important, the absence of gravity leads to diminution of activity of the vasomotor system and of reflexes that have so much to do with normal compensatory responses of the circulatory system to stress. The execution of locomotion takes place under continuous guidance of a complex system of sensory receptors widely distributed over the body. Since the degree of activation of muscle is related to the weight of the body, and since this depends mainly on muscle proprioceptors, one could expect that muscle tonus will be reduced and the limbs relaxed and flaccid. In addition, since it will take no more energy to move a large object than a small object, and very little energy in either case, one might expect a further reduction in skeletal muscle activity with a fall in cardiac output and even atrophy of the heart and skeletal muscle. Some form of standard exercise is needed to prevent this.

As expected, the increased heart rate and blood pressure present during acceleration have been found to return to normal during the weightless period. Evidently no factors are involved in the gravity-free state other than those associated with a decreased workload or simple physical inactivity. Although only a short length of time was involved in the third manned U.S. orbital space flight, a tendency toward postural hypotension occurred for nearly 24 hours after landing. This was evidenced by a moderate increase in heart rate and a decrease in systolic blood pressure during quiet standing as compared with the preflight responses; an unusual degree of venous engorgement of the dependent extremities was also noted during standing. Orthostatic intolerance has been studied after water immersion, or bed or chair rest for long periods. The decreased orthostatic tolerance in these studies is associated with a fall in pulse pressure and systolic blood pressure and an increased heart rate on standing; an increased storage of catecholamines in the heart, a large reduction in plasma volume, a decreased tolerance to exercise, and a decreased oxygen consumption during exercise also occur. After water immersion of human subjects for 6 hours, there was a decrease in the urinary output of norepinephrine. Thus in a simulated weightless environment, the subsequent orthostatic intolerance is probably due to a decrease in sympathetic vasomotor nerve activity.

It had been considered that the decreased activity of the vasomotor system and orienting reflexes after weightlessness would become a problem during the deceleration of landing. However subjects are able to tolerate the stresses of re-entry after 4 weeks of bed rest and astronauts have landed without trouble from space flights. The orthostatic intolerance may prove to be a problem to astronauts who must be active upon landing.

Cardiovascular Effects of Ionizing Radiations

The effects of ionizing radiation upon the circulation of the skin and upon arteries and veins have been recognized and studied intensively over the past 60 years. It has been recognized only recently that whole-body radiation produces dysfunction of the entire cardiovascular system and that some form of cardiac failure may be a factor in causing radiation death in some species of animals. What role cardiovascular changes play in causing radiation death in man has not been studied in detail.

Ionizing radiation produces a variety of abnormalities of the cardiovascular system. These are caused by (1) a direct effect of radiation upon the tissues, (2) effects produced by the ionization of water by radiation, (3) effects produced by metabolites from damaged tissue, (4) effects produced by the autonomic and endocrine reactions to radiation, (5) effects produced by the marked changes in fluid balance of the irradiated animal, and (6) effects produced by other ill-defined but perhaps important abnormalities of the irradiated animal. Insufficient experimental data exist to define with precision the complete sequence of changes in the cardiovascular system or the exact mechanism by which these abnormalities are produced by ionizing radiation.

REACTION OF SKIN TO RADIATION. When the skin of man and animals is exposed to a sufficient dose of ionizing radiation (300 to 600r, depending upon the wave length) a characteristic sequence of changes is observed. There is usually an initial erythema during the 1st day which rapidly subsides, followed by a 2nd wave of erythema in the 2nd or 3rd week; a 3rd wave may be seen after 6 weeks. During the later waves of erythema the skin temperature is increased suggesting that a marked vasodilation with increased blood flow has occurred although there is no perceptible change during the latent periods. These changes in cutaneous circulation have been attributed to a combination of the direct effect of irradiation on the component cells of the blood vessels; by modification in the neuromuscular control of the peripheral vascular system (directly or indirectly produced by irradiation); and by the release of histamine and other tissue hormones by the damaged tissue surrounding the blood vessels. The relative importance of each of these in producing damage and dysfunction to the vascular system of the skin remains to be determined.

VASCULAR PHYSIOLOGY. Ionizing radiation produces diffuse and irregular damage to the arteries, capillaries, and veins of man and animals. It has been recognized only recently that, in addition to producing obliterative vascular lesions, irradiation produces significant physiological abnormalities of blood vessels. Arteries from irradiated dogs (total-body 300r) have an abnormal pressure volume curve, these vessels being more spastic than is normal upon removal from the body. Vessels from irradiated dogs likewise have a decreased vasoconstriction to 1-epinephrine and 1-norepinephrine when compared to control arteries. When a normal artery is irradiated *in vitro* two effects are noted. A slight constriction of the arterial wall occurs immediately upon beginning

of irradiation, which is completed in 30 to 45 seconds. This is a direct effect of the radiation. The flow through the vasa vasorum is decreased. This latter effect is secondary to ionization of the solution surrounding the specimen. Alterations in capillary permeability produced by irradiation play a significant role in producing changes in the red and white cell content of the peripheral blood. These studies have shown that ionizing radiations produce a variety of physiological abnormalities of the peripheral vascular system which are only beginning to be delineated.

CARDIOVASCULAR EFFECTS OF TOTAL-BODY RADIATION. The threshold dose of total-body X-ray or gamma radiation required to produce significant abnormalities of the cardiovascular system is below 300r and probably above 100r. Because of the tremendous species variation in these responses to irradiation it will be necessary to consider the response of man, when known, and other species separately.

Arterial blood pressure. Patients who are receiving x-ray therapy may develop a hypotensive episode shortly after irradiation which returns to normotensive levels within an hour or two. Rabbits develop hypotension immediately following total-body irradiation of as little as 50r. There is no change in blood pressure, cardiac output or total peripheral resistance of dogs during or for 5 hours following exposure to 1500r of gamma radiation. In the rat an initial hypotensive episode which occurs within the first 2 hours has been described. In both the rat and rabbit there is a rise in plasma histamine which is related in time to the initial hypotensive episodes in these species. This relation may be only fortuitous as there is evidence that the initial hypotension following irradiation is, in part, mediated by reflex mechanisms.

In most species recovery from an initial hypotension is prompt and blood pressure falls again only in the terminal period. VDM and VEM have been found in the blood of rats 6 to 10 days following irradiation.

Cardiac physiology and biochemistry. The isolated hearts of animals tolerate ionizing radiation in doses 10 times greater than the lethal dose for man without showing significant functional abnormalities. These data are strong evidence that irradiation does not directly injure the myocardium and the conduction system of the heart.

However, a series of changes in cardiac biochemistry and function following whole-body irradiation (700r) of the rat have been carefully defined by Caster and associates. These are most readily summarized by considering these changes chronologically: *0 to 2 days.* During the first 3 to 12 hours there are significant increases both in venous pressure and in the plasma volume of the tissues. By the 2nd day there is a loss in deoxyribonucleic acid (DNA) and lipid from the heart, a decrease in the area of the heart shadow and in the total body plasma volume, and the peripheral venous pressure has returned to normal. Electrocardiographic changes begin to appear. *3 to 5 days.* Both venous pressure and plasma volume drop to a minimum. Four days following radiation shows the beginning of a lineal decrease in DNA and actomyosin in the heart. *6 to 14 days.* By the 6th day the venous pressure increases abruptly and continues high until death. The plasma volume of the heart is increased by 50 per cent. The potassium, DNA and actomyosin concentrations of the heart reach minimum values and the percentage of fluid in the heart and lung increases. Cardiac arrhythmias appear more frequently by the 8th to 10th day and deaths occur frequently. The mechanical action of the heart (as indicated by the heart sounds) changes, and there is a significant shift in the electrical axis of the heart.

Electrocardiographic observations. Abnormalities in the T waves (depression and/or inversion), S-T segments (lowering) and miscellaneous arrhythmias have been observed in most species following total-body irradiation. The sequence of changes in the electrocardiogram of the rat following irradiation (700r) have been described by Caster and associates. In these studies the decrease in plasma volume rather than direct damage to the myocardium apparently played a major role in producing these changes.

Postmortem evidence. In many species the terminal findings include a marked pulmonary edema and enlargement of the right side of the heart. Blood vessel walls are diffusely and irregularly damaged.

Effects of Aging on the Circulation

With advancing age significant reductions occur in the functional capacities of many different organ systems. Oftentimes these changes are secondary to alterations in the circulation which result in impaired blood flow to specific organs and tissues. Because of its increased prevalence among the elderly, the disease process, arteriosclerosis, plays an important role in the functional impairments which accumulate with age. There are, however, progressive changes in the circulation which occur independently of the development of this disease. These changes will be described in this section.

Heart. Progressive changes take place in the heart which are not related to coronary artery disease, the most frequent cause of death in individuals over the age of 65. For example, there is a gradual accumulation of insoluble granular material in cardiac muscle fibers (Strehler et al., 1959). These granules make their first appearance at about the age of 20 and increase gradually so that by age 80 they may occupy as much as 5 to 10 per cent of the myocardial volume. These pigment granules are composed of protein and lipids and are believed to represent auto-oxidation products (Hendley et al., 1963) and may be associated with lysosome metabolism (Strehler, 1962; Samorajski et al., 1964). Their occurrence was not related to the presence of cardiac disease (Strehler et al., 1959). Animal experiments have shown that at higher ages the activity of important intracellular enzymes of the myocardium, such as succinoxidase, is significantly reduced when measurements were made on tissue slices or whole homogenates (Barrows and associates, 1958). However, no age differences were found in succinoxidase activity of isolated mitochondria (Barrows and Roeder, 1962). These findings imply that the age changes in this enzyme are due to the loss of myocardial elements rather than to an age impairment of basic biochemical processes.

Although average values for resting heart rate tend to diminish slightly with increasing age (Howell, 1950), the increased incidence of irregularities in rhythm in the aged (Blackburn et al., 1964) offers evidence of impairment in the mechanisms regulating rate.

Cardiac output under basal conditions diminishes by approximately 50 per cent between the ages of 20 and 80 years (Brandfonbrener and associates, 1955). Fig. 48.5 illustrates a series of measurements made on normal subjects by the dye injection technique. This curve illustrates the wide individual differences in the effects of age which are also found in observations on many other physiological variables. Thus, there are 80-year-old persons with cardiac outputs as high as the average 40-year-old. Cardiac outputs, calculated by an empirical formula from ballistocardiographic records, also show a significant reduction with age (Tanner, 1949).

Statistical analysis of resting blood pressure measurements in a sample of 79,757 apparently healthy people aged 20 to 106 years indicates a gradual rise in systolic pressure up to the age of 70 (Lasser and Master, 1959). After this age

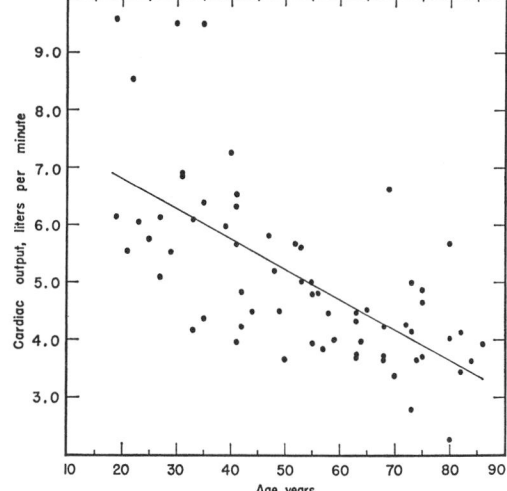

FIG. 48.5. Age changes in basal cardiac output in normal males. Each point represents an individual subject.

systolic pressure remains constant in men and declines in women. There is only a small rise in diastolic pressure (table 48.4). The increase in blood pressure with age may be a physiological adjustment to the large rise in peripheral resistance and the fall in cardiac output. With increased general peripheral resistance, blood pressure in the aged may be adjusted to higher levels in order to maintain flow in regions which exhibit a greater than average increase in vascular resistance. Hence the increase in blood pressure in the aged may not be detrimental to the individual, although it undoubtedly reduces the survival potential of the central vascular structures (Shock et al., 1965).

In experiments where simultaneous measurements of blood pressure and cardiac output were made it is possible to calculate left ventricular work from the equation $W = 14.3 \ \bar{p}_s$ stroke volume gm.-m./beat and stroke power from the equation $P = 1.40 \times 10^{-4} \times \bar{p}_s \times$ stroke volume/t_s watts where $\bar{p}_s$ = mean pressure during systole and t_s = duration of systole. Both ventricular work and power or rate of work diminish significantly with age (Landowne and associates, 1955). These observations reflect a decrease in left ventricular work since the calculated pressure increase is not proportional to the decrease in cardiac output. The duration of systole increase results in a decrease in calculated rate of work or power of the heart.

Other evidence of decreased power of the heart in advanced age is found in ballistocardiograph tracings. Starr and Hildreth (1952) recorded a

second ballistocardiogram after an interval of 10 to 14 years in 80 normal persons aged 20 to 60+. With increasing age, the I plus J amplitude diminished by roughly 50 per cent over the age span tested. These results are interpreted as a reduction in the force of ejection and a slowing of the contractile response of the ventricle. Such an adaptation would permit a weak heart to secure the maximum cardiac output possible.

The speed of circulation of the blood as measured by decholine, or by the mean transit time of dyes injected for the estimation of cardiac output, shows a significant slowing with age. The mean transit time of T-1824 from the antecubital vein to brachial artery increases from 19.0 seconds to 28.7 seconds between the ages of 23 and 82 years (Landowne and associates, 1955).

Age changes are also apparent in the electrocardiogram. The P-Q, P-R and QT intervals show a slight tendency toward prolongation, especially at low frequencies, in elderly subjects. The voltages of P, R and T waves decline after the age of 60. The mean electrical axis of the P wave, which is deviated to the left at birth, becomes vertical by the age of 40 and then shifts progressively to the left as age advances. The mean electrical axis of the QRS complex behaves in an opposite manner indicating a more hori-

TABLE 48.4

Mean blood pressure and standard deviation in apparently healthy persons, 20 to 106 years of age

Age Group	Males		Females	
	Systolic	Diastolic	Systolic	Diastolic
20–24	123±13.7*	76± 9.9	116±11.8	72± 9.7
25–29	125±12.6	78± 9.0	117±11.4	74± 9.1
30–34	126±13.6	79± 9.7	120±14.0	75±10.8
35–39	127±14.2	80±10.4	124±13.9	78±10.0
40–44	129±15.1	81± 9.5	127±17.1	80±10.6
45–49	130±16.9	82±10.8	131±19.5	82±11.6
50–54	135±19.2	83±11.3	137±21.3	84±12.4
55–59	138±18.8	84±11.4	139±21.4	84±11.8
60–64	142±21.1	85±12.4	144±22.3	85±13.0
65–69	143±26.0	83± 9.9	154±29.0	85±13.8
70–74	145±26.3	82±15.3	159±25.8	85±15.3
75–79	146±21.6	81±12.9	158±26.3	84±13.1
80–84	145±25.6	82± 9.9	157±28.0	83±13.1
85–89	145±24.2	79±14.9	154±27.9	82±17.3
90–94	145±23.4	78±12.1	150±23.6	79±12.1
95–106	146±27.5	78±12.7	149±23.5	81±12.5

* ± indicates standard deviation

From R. P. Lasser and A. M. Master, Geriatrics, 1959, 14, 345.

zontal position of the heart at advanced ages (Hiss et al., 1960; Simonson and Keys, 1952; Simonson, 1961). Vector analysis of conventionally recorded electrocardiograms show similar age changes. Both the QRS and T vector are rotated more anteriorly (larger azimuth angle), are smaller in magnitude and show a smaller angle between the vectors in old than in young men (Simonson and Keys, 1956). At present it is not possible to determine the relative importance of alterations in the electrical activity of the heart and anatomical and positional changes in producing the age changes in the electrocardiogram.

Blood vessels. With advancing age the chemical composition of certain blood vessels changes. Lansing and associates (1951) have shown that the elastin of the aorta undergoes an increase in specific gravity, calcium content and proportion of amino acids containing free carboxyl groups. There is an underlying shift in the amino acid composition of elastin, with an increase in aspartic and glutamic acid and a decrease in glycine, proline and valine. The deposition of collagen increases in the intimal and medial layers of blood vessels. Furthermore, the collagen in old blood vessels increases in resistance to solubilization by chemical treatment. It shows a denser aggregation of strands with increased chemical cross-linking. Recent studies have shown that certain aldehydes present in the blood can accelerate the formation of chemical cross-linkages in the collagen of blood vessels (Milch, 1963).

These structural and chemical changes form the basis for the increased rigidity of old blood vessels with an attendant increase in pulse wave velocity. Between the ages of 20 and 70 years the

pulse wave velocity in the aorta increases from about 5 m. per second to 11 m. per second (Hallock, 1934; Karnbaum, 1957). At lower intra-arterial pressures (diastolic) the pulse wave velocity in the brachial artery also increases with age, but at higher pressures (systolic) the age difference is much less. Thus, in older subjects, the artery behaves as if its fibers were initially more completely extended than in the young (Landowne, 1958). Although it has been traditional to regard estimates of pulse wave velocity as a measure of vascular elasticity, this simple interpretation can no longer be made. Many other factors, such as the thickness of the arterial wall, the diameter of the lumen, orientation of the fibers, and even the rate of development of the stress, also influence the distensibility characteristics of blood vessels in addition to the elastic modulus of arterial tissue.

The peripheral vascular system also shows significant age changes. Flow through a number of vascular beds is significantly reduced in old age. For example, plethysmographic studies of blood flow through the fingers show a fall from 4.77 to 2.76 ml. per 10 ml. finger volume per minute between the ages of 40 and 60 years (Ring and co-workers, 1959).

There is a rapid fall in the circulation to the brain from childhood through adolescence followed by a more gradual but progressive reduction throughout the remainder of life (Kety, 1956). Between the ages of 25 and 95 years the average fall in blood flow to the brain is approximately 25 per cent of the mean value at age 25.

Kidney blood flow, determined by the clearance of diodrast or para-aminohippuric acid (PAH), falls by about 60 per cent of the mean value at age 25 between the ages of 25 and 90 (fig. 48.6).

Although the total amount of blood available for perfusion, as indicated by the cardiac output, diminishes with age, there is not a proportional reduction in flow to all organs. As indicated above, the age reduction in blood flow to the kidney is greater than the reduction in cardiac output, or flow to the brain.

The simplest explanation of the differences in blood flow through different organ systems is to assume differences in the degree of structural changes such as arteriosclerosis in the vascular beds involved. However, this hypothesis is not in accord with observations which indicate that the reduction in blood flow in certain vascular beds is produced by a functional vasoconstriction that can be reduced by vasodilating agents. For example, the intravenous administration of a vaso-

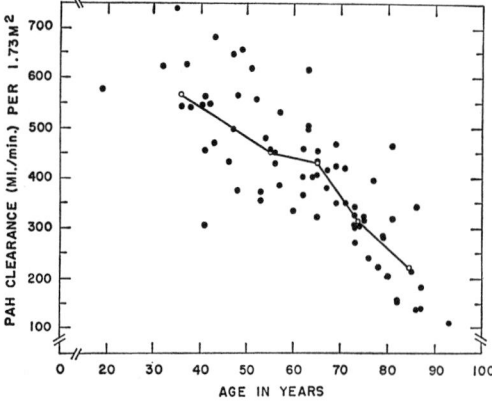

FIG. 48.6. Age changes in resting renal plasma flow in normal males, determined by clearance of PAH. Each point represents the mean of three 10-minute clearance periods on an individual.

dilating agent (pyrogen) produces proportional increases in renal blood flow in both young and old subjects (Shock, 1952). This increase in flow results from a decrease in renal arteriolar constriction. In the aged person, under resting conditions, a functional increase in vascular resistance reduces blood flow to the kidney, which makes a great proportion of the cardiac output available for perfusion of other organs such as the brain.

The response of peripheral blood vessels to both heat and cold shows a reduction with age. However, the primary change is in the speed of response, rather than the final degree of vasodilation or constriction attained.

Thus the marked increase in peripheral resistance calculated from measurement of blood pressure and flow which accompanies aging is due, at least in part, to functional changes in the degree of vasoconstriction of individual vascular beds, and not entirely to the increasing degree of sclerosis of the blood vessels.

Age changes in circulatory response to stress. Age changes in all organ systems become much more apparent when the individual is subjected to a physiological stress. Exercise places extra demands, especially on the circulatory system, which are met less effectively in the old than the young.

The maximum heart rate during maximum exercise is lower in the aged (160 per min. in 70-year-olds) than in the young (200 per min. in 20–30-year-olds) (Robinson, 1938; Åstrand, 1958; Strandell, 1963). In other words, the maximum heart rate that can be attained is reduced with age. When submaximal exercise of the same amount is performed by old and young subjects the increase in heart rate is greater in the old than in the young (Blackburn et al., 1964).

The increase in systolic blood pressure induced by heavy exercise is greater in old than in young men (Granath, Jonsson and Strandell, 1964).

One of the factors limiting physical performance in older subjects is their diminished ability to transport oxygen. Robinson (1938) showed that the increase in oxygen uptake during work proceeds at a slower rate in old than young subjects. He also found that the maximum amount of oxygen transported from the lungs falls from 53 to 26 cc. per kg. body weight per minute between the ages of 17 and 75. Furthermore, old subjects require more oxygen per kg. m. of work performed than do young at high or low work rates (Norris and Shock, 1960). There is a greater accumulation of lactic acid in the blood during and after exercise in old subjects than in young, which indi-

cates a greater degree of muscular anoxia in old than young.

The rate of recovery of oxygen consumption and carbon dioxide elimination following exercise also diminishes with age. Thus, advancing age places a limitation not only on total performance, but also on the rate of readjustment of physiological displacements produced. One of the characteristics of older subjects is their inability to increase their heart rate after severe exercise to as great an extent as younger people. Young men are able to increase their heart rate to a mean value of 200 beats per minute whereas by the age of 65 the maximum rate attained after exercise is only 160 on the average. Since the increment in cardiac output during exercise is controlled primarily by increase in rate rather than stroke volume, the aged individual is unable to maintain adequate blood flow to exercising muscles. It is therefore not surprising that the arteriovenous oxygen difference increases more in old than young under conditions of heavy exercise.

Performance on the standard Master step-test also shows impairment in normal aged subjects. Old subjects increase their systolic blood pressure and heart rate more after exercise and require a longer time to return to pre-exercise levels than do young.

Changes in posture also offer a challenge to the cardiovascular system. When subjects are passively tilted from supine to the upright position, older subjects showed a greater decrease and slower recovery of diastolic blood pressure and smaller increase in heart rate than did the young (Norris and associates, 1953).

The stress of a pain stimulus (Hardy-Wolf thermal stimulator) results in significant increments in heart rate. However, the variability of heart rate from beat to beat under these circumstances diminishes significantly with increasing age (Malmo and Shagass, 1949). It appears that the factors controlling heart rate are less sensitive to environmental changes in the old than in young.

Other evidence that regulatory mechanisms of the cardiovascular system suffer impairment with aging is provided by Frolkis (1962) who showed that after the administration of atropine the average increase in heart rate was 39 ± 3 beats per minute in young adults but only 20 ± 2 in old people. In young adults the administration of dihydroergotamine resulted in a decrease in heart rate that averaged 19 ± 3 beats per minute as compared to 11 ± 1 in the aged.

SUMMARY

In addition to the increased incidence of arteriosclerosis, age imposes gradual impairments in the functional capabilities of the cardiovascular system. Structural and metabolic changes occur in the myocardium. There is a gradual reduction in cardiac output as age advances. The systolic blood pressure rises with age, but there is little change in diastolic pressure. Mechanisms for the control of heart rate are less effective in old than young. In old subjects the duration of systolic is lengthened, and there is a decrease in left ventricular work even under resting conditions. There is a reduction in the force of ejection and a slowing of the circulation time.

The peripheral vascular system undergoes changes in structure, chemical composition and function. Large blood vessels become more rigid. The distribution of blood flow among different organs shifts with increasing age. Some organs, such as the kidney, show a functional vasoconstriction that diverts a greater proportion of the falling cardiac output to other organs such as the brain.

The reduced capacity for physical work in the aged is related to their inability to increase their heart rate, and thereby to increase cardiac output to meet the increased tissue demands for oxygen. Light exercise produces greater increments in heart rate and blood pressure in old than young. The rate of recovery of heart rate, oxygen uptake and carbon dioxide elimination after exercise, is slower in old than young subjects. Aging results in a general reduction in the reserve capacities of the cardiovascular system and an impairment in the effectiveness of mechanisms controlling heart rate and vasomotor tonus.

REFERENCES

ANDERSON, E., PAGE, E. W., LI, C. H., AND OGDEN, E. Restoration of renal hypertension in hypophysectomized rats by administration of adrenocorticotrophic hormone. Am. J. Physiol., 1944, 141, 393.

ARMSTRONG, H. G. Principles and practice of aviation medicine. Ed. 3. The Williams and Wilkins Company, Baltimore, 1952.

ÅSTRAND, I. Acta Physiol. Scand., 1958, 42, 73.

BÁRÁNY, F. R. Reactivity of the skin vessels to noradrenalin and angiotensin in arterial hypertension. Scandinav. J. Clin. and Lab. Invest., 1963, 15, 317.

BARROWS, C. H., JR. AND ROEDER, L. M. in Biological Aspects of Aging, edited by N. W. Shock, p. 290, Columbia Univ. Press, New York, 1962.

BERRY, C. A., MINNERS, H. A., McCUTCHEON, E. P., AND POLLARD, R. A. Aeromedical analysis *in* Results of the Third U.S. Manned Orbital Space Flight, October 3, 1962. Supt. Doc. U.S Government Printing Office, Washington, D.C., p. 23–36.

BEZNAK, M. Effect of growth hormone preparations on cardiac hypertrophy and blood pressure of hypophysectomized rats. Am. J. Physiol., 1956, 184, 563.

BEZNAK, M. Cardiac output during development of cardiac hypertrophy. Circulation Res., 1958, 6, 207.

BEZNAK, M. The role of anterior pituitary hormones in controlling size, work and strength of heart. J. Physiol., 1960, 150, 251.

BING, R. J., HAMMOND, M. M., HANDELSMAN, J. C., POWERS, S. R., SPENCER, F. C., ECKENHOFF, J. E., GOODALE, W. T., HAFKENSCHIEL, J. H., AND KETY, S. S. The measurement of coronary blood flow, oxygen consumption and efficiency of the left ventricle in man. Am. Heart J., 1949, 38, 1.

BLACKBURN, H., TAYLOR, H. L., AND KEYS, A. *in* International Studies of Coronary Heart Disease, edited by A. Keys, Acta Med. Scand., 1964 (in press).

BRAUN-MENENDEZ, E. AND VON EULER, U. S. Hypertension after bilateral nephrectomy in the rat. Nature, 1947, 160, 905.

BRAUN-MENENDEZ, E., FASCIOLO, J. C., LELOIR, L. F., AND MUNOZ, J. M. The substance causing renal hypertension. J. Physiol., 1940, 98, 283.

CARLSON, A. J. AND LUCKHARDT, A. B. Studies on visceral sensory nervous system. Am. J. Physiol., 1921, 55, 31.

COHN, J. N., LIPTAK, T. E., AND FREIS, E. D. Hemodynamic effects of guanethidine in man. Circulation Res., 1963, 12, 298.

CONN, J. W. Primary aldosteronism: a new clinical syndrome. J. Lab. & Clin. Med., 1955, 45, 3.

CONWAY, J. AND LOUWERS, P. Hemodynamic and hypotensive effects of long-term therapy with chlorothiazide. Circulation, 1960, 21, 21.

CUSHING, H. Some experimental and clinical observations concerning states of increased intracranial tension. Am. J. Med. Sc., 1902, 124, 375.

DAHL, L. K. AND SCHACKOW, E. Effects of chronic excess salt ingestion: experimental hypertension in the rat. Canad. Med. Assoc. J., 1964, 90, 155.

DEGRANDPRÉ, R. AND RAAB, W. Interrelated hormonal factors in cardiac hypertrophy. Experiments in nonhypertensive hypophysectomized rats. Circulation Res., 1953, 1, 345.

DIXON, W. E. AND HELLER, H. Experimentelle hypertonie durch Erhöhung desintrakraniellen Druckes. Arch. f. Exp. Path. u. Pharmakol., 1932, 265, 166.

ECKSTEIN, J. W., ABBOUD, F. M., AND PEREDA, S. A. The effect of norepinephrine on cardiac output, arterial blood pressure, and heart rate in dogs treated with chlorothiazide. J. Clin. Invest., 1962, 41, 1578.

EICH, R. H., PETERS, R. J., CUDDY, R. P., SMULYAN, H., AND LYONS, R. H. Hemodynamics in labile hypertension. Am. Heart J., 1962, 63, 188.

ELLIS, L. B. AND HAYNES, F. W. Postural hypotension with particular reference to its occurrence in disease of the central nervous system. Arch. Int. Med., 1936, 58, 773.

ELLIS, L. B. AND WEISS, S. J. The measurement of capillary pressure under natural conditions and after arteriolar dilatation; in normal subjects and in patients with arterial hypertension and with arteriosclerosis. J. Clin. Invest., 1930, **8**, 47.

EYSTER, J. A. E., MEEK, W. J., AND HODGES, F. J. Cardiac changes subsequent to experimental aortic lesions. Arch. Int. Med., 1927, **39**, 536.

FASCIOLO, J. C., HOUSSAY, B. A., AND TAQUINI, A. C. The blood-pressure raising secretion of the ischaemic kidney. J. Physiol., 1938, **94**, 281.

FOA, P. P., LIST, C. F., AND PEET, M. M. Possibility of producing arterial hypertension by intracisternal injection of kaolin. Proc. Soc. Exp. Biol. & Med., 1941, **46**, 696.

FRANK, M. H. Renin in experimental renal hypertension in monkeys. Circulation Res., 1963, **12**, 241.

FREIS, E. D., ROSE, J. C., PARTENOPE, E. A., HIGGINS, T. F., KELLEY, R. T., SCHNAPER, H. W., AND JOHNSON, R. L. The hemodynamic effects of hypotensive drugs in man. III. Hexamethonium. J. Clin. Invest., 1953, **32**, 1285.

FROLKIS, V. V. *in* Problems of Gerontology and Geriatrics, Vol. 2, edited by D. F. Chebotarev, p. 40, State Publ. House of Med. Lit. of Ukrainian SSR, Kiev, 1962.

GAFFNEY, T. E., CHIDSEY, C. A., AND BRAUNWALD, E. Relation between neurotransmitter store and adrenergic nerve block induced by reserpine and guanethidine. Circulation Res., 1963, **12**, 264.

GAUER, O. The physiological effects of prolonged acceleration. German Aviation Medicine, 1950, **1**, 554.

GAUER, O. AND HABER, H. Man under gravity-free conditions. German Aviation Medicine, 1950, **1**, 641.

GENEST, J., NOWACZYNSKI, W., KOIW, E., SANDOR, T., AND BIRON, P. Adrenocortical function in essential hypertension *in* Essential Hypertension, ed. Bock, K. D., Springer-Verlag, Berlin, 1960, p. 126.

GOLDBLATT, H., LYNCH, J., HANZAL, R. F., AND SUMMERVILLE, W. W. Studies on experimental hypertension: 1. The production of persistent elevation of systolic blood pressure by means of renal ischemia. J. Exper. Med., 1934, **59**, 347.

GOODALL, McC. Sympathoadrenal response to gravitational stress. J. Clin. Invest., 1962, **41**, 197.

GOODALL, McC., McCALLY, M., AND GRAVELINE, D. E. Urinary adrenaline and noradrenaline response to simulated weightless state. Amer. J. Physiol., 1964, **206**, 431.

GORDON, D. B. AND NOGUEIRA, A. Increased vascular reactivity in experimental hypertension. Circulation Res., 1962, **10**, 269.

GRANATH, A., JONSSON, B., AND STRANDELL, T. Acta Med. Scand., 1964, **176**, 425.

GRIMSON, K. S., BOUCKAERT, J. J., AND HEYMANS, C. Production of a sustained neurogenic hypertension of renal origin. Proc. Soc. Exper. Biol. & Med., 1939, **42**, 255.

GRIMSON, K. S. Role of the sympathetic nervous system in experimental neurogenic hypertension. Proc. Soc. Exp. Biol. & Med., 1940, **44**, 219.

GROLLMAN, A. Antihypertensive and pressor agents of renal origin. Canad. Med. Assoc. J., 1964, **90**, 299.

GROLLMAN, A. AND GROLLMAN, E. F. Teratogenic induction of hypertension. J. Clin. Invest., 1962, **41**, 710.

GROLLMAN, A., MUIRHEAD, E. E., AND VANATTA, J. Role of the kidney in pathogenesis of hypertension as determined by a study of the effects of bilateral nephrectomy and other experimental procedures on the blood pressure of the dog. Am. J. Physiol., 1949, **157**, 21.

HARTROFT, P. M., SUTHERLAND, L. E., AND HARTROFT, W. S. Juxtaglomerular cells as the source of renin: further studies with the fluorescent antibody technique and the effect of passive transfer of antirenin. Canad. Med. Assoc. J., 1964, **90**, 163.

HELMER, O. M. Renin activity in blood from patients with hypertension. Canad. Med. Assoc. J., 1964, **90**, 221.

HELMER, O. M. AND PAGE, I. H. Purification and some properties of renin. J. Biol. Chem., 1939, **127**, 757.

HENDLEY, D. D., MILDVAN, A. S., REPORTER, M. C., AND STREHLER, B. L. J. Gerontol., 1963, **18**, 144, 250.

HICKAM, J. B. AND PRYOR, W. W. Cardiac output in postural hypotension. J. Clin. Invest., 1951, **30**, 401.

HICKLER, R. B., LAULER, D. P., SARAVIS, C. A., VAGNUCCI, A. I., STEINER, G., AND THORN, G. W. Vasodepressor lipid from the renal medulla. Canad. Med. Assoc. J., 1964, **90**, 280.

HICKLER, R. B., THOMPSON, G. R., FOX, L. M., AND HAMLIN, J. T., III. Successful treatment of orthostatic hypotension with 9-alpha-fluorohydrocortisone. New England J. Med., 1959, **261**, 788.

HICKLER, R. B., WELLS, R. E., JR., TYLER, H. R., AND HAMLIN, J. T., III. Plasma catechol amine and electroencephalographic responses to acute postural change. Am. J. Med., 1959, **26**, 410.

HINES, E. A., JR. The significance of vascular hyperreaction as measured by the cold-pressor test. Am. Heart J., 1940, **19**, 408.

HISS, R. G., LAMB, L. E., AND ALLEN, M. F. Amer. J. Cardiol., 1960, **6**, 200.

HITCHINGS, G. H., DAUS, M. A., AND WEARN, J. T. Chemical changes in rabbit heart during hypertrophy. Am. J. Physiol., 1943, **138**, 527.

HOWARD, B. K., GOODSON, J. H., AND MENGERT, W. F. Supine hypotensive syndrome in late pregnancy. Obstet. and Gynec., 1953, **1**, 371.

HOWARD, J. E., BERTHRONG, B., GOULD, D. M., AND YENDT, E. R. Hypertension resulting from unilateral renal vascular disease and its relief by nephrectomy. Bull. Johns Hopkins Hosp., 1954, **94**, 51.

HUNTER, C. A., JR. AND HOWARD, W. F. A pressor substance (hysterotonin) occurring in toxemia. Am. J. Obstet. and Gynec., 1960, **79**, 838.

KAS'YAN, I. I. Cardiovascular and respiratory reactions of animals in sealed cabins during rocket flights up to an altitude of 212 kilometers. Fed. Proc., 1964, **23**, Part 2, T410.

KERR, A., JR. Cardiac dilatation and hypertrophy. Am. Heart J., 1957, **54**, 23.

KERR, A., JR., WINTERBERGER, A. R., AND GIAMBATTISTA, M. Tension developed by papillary muscles from hypertrophied rat hearts. Circulation Res., 1961, **9**, 103.

KEZDI, P. Chronic constriction of the external and internal carotid arteries in dogs: its effect on the blood pressure. Circulation Res., 1960, **8**, 930.

KHAIRALLAH, P. A. AND PAGE, I. H. Mechanism of action of angiotensin and bradykinin on smooth muscle in situ. Am. J. Physiol., 1961, **200**, 51.

KOLFF, W. J. Discussion of reports on renal factors in hypertension. Circulation, 1958, **17**, 676.

KOLFF, W. J. AND PAGE, I. H. Blood pressure reducing function of the kidney: Reduction of renoprival hypertension by kidney perfusion. Am. J. Physiol., 1954, **178**, 75.

KUMAR, D. Chronic placental ischemia in relation to toxemias of pregnancy. Am. J. Obstet. and Gynec., 1962, **84**, 1323.

LAMB, L. E. Aerospace medicine *in* Advances in Internal Medicine, Year Book Med. Publ., Chicago, Ill., 1965.

LARAGH, J. H., CANNON, P. J., AND AMES, R. P. Interaction between aldosterone secretion, sodium and potassium balance, and angiotensin activity in man: studies in hypertension and cirrhosis. Canad. Med. Assoc. J., 1964, **90**, 248.

LEVY, S. E., LIGHT, R. A., AND BLALOCK, A. The blood flow and oxygen consumption of the kidney in experimental renal hypertension. Am. J. Physiol., 1938, **122**, 38.

LINZBACH, A. Micrometric and histologic studies of cardiac hypertrophy. Virchows Arch. path. Anat., 1947, **314**, 534.

LUFT, R. AND VON EULER, U. S. Two cases of postural hypotension showing a deficiency in release of norepinephrine and epinephrine. J. Clin. Invest., 1953, **32**, 1065.

MARSHALL, J. AND WAKERLIN, G. E. Purification of renin. Fed. Proc., 1948, **7**, 78.

MARSHALL, R. J., SCHIRGER, A., AND SHEPHERD, J. T. Blood pressure during supine exercise in idiopathic orthostatic hypotension. Circulation, 1961, **24**, 76.

MASSON, G. M. C., MIKASA, A., AND YASUDA, H. Experimental vascular disease elicited by aldosterone and renin. Endocrinology, 1962, **71**, 505.

McCUBBIN, J. W., GREEN, J. H., AND PAGE, I. H. Baroceptor function in chronic renal hypertension. Circulation Res., 1956, **4**, 205.

MEERSON, F. Z. Compensatory hyperfunction of the heart and cardiac insufficiency. Circulation Res., 1962, **10**, 250.

MEERSON, F. Z., BELOSHAPKINA, T. D., LUSHNIKOV, E. F., LEIKINA, E. M., MARKOVSKAYA, G. N., AND CHERNYSHOVA, G. V. Function, structure and protein metabolism of hypertrophied myocardium. Vest. Akad. Medit. Nauk SSSR, 1963, **18**, 27.

MEERSON, F. Z., MANUKHIN, B. N., PSHENICHNIKOVA, M. G., AND ROZANOVA, L. S. Mediator metabolism of myocardium in compensatory hyperfunction and hypertrophy of heart. Fed. Proc., 1964, **23**, T593.

MERRILL, J. P., MURRAY, J. E., HARRISON, J. H., AND GUILD, W. R. Successful homotransplantation of the human kidney between identical twins. J.A.M.A., 1956, **160**, 277.

MERRILL, J. P. AND SCHUPAK, E. Mechanisms of hypertension in renoprival man. Canad. Med. Assoc. J., 1964, **90**, 328.

MILCH, R. A. Gerontologia (Basel), 1963, **7**, 129.

MINTON, P. R., ZOLL, P. M., AND NORMAN, L. R. Levels of phosphate compounds in experimental cardiac hypertrophy. Circulation Res., 1960, **8**, 924.

MUIRHEAD, E. E. AND KOSINSKI, M. Renal medulla and renoprival hypertension: relationship between corticorenal (renin) and medullorenal extracts. Circulation Res., 1962, **11**, 674.

PAGE, E. B., HICKAM, J. B., SIEKER, H. O., McINTOSH, H. D., AND PRYOR, W. W. Reflex venomotor activity in normal persons and in patients with postural hypotension. Circulation, 1955, **11**, 262.

PAGE, I. H. Production of persistent arterial hypertension by cellophane perinephritis. J.A.M.A., 1939, **113**, 2046.

PAGE, I. H. The mosaic theory of hypertension *in* Essential Hypertension, ed. Bock, K. D., Springer-Verlag, Berlin, 1960, page 1.

PAGE, I. H. AND SWEET, J. E. The effect of hypophysectomy on arterial blood pressure of dogs with experimental hypertension. Am. J. Physiol., 1937, **120**, 238.

PICKERING, G. W. Inheritance of high blood pressure *in* Essential Hypertension, ed. Bock, K. D. Springer-Verlag, Berlin, 1960, page 30.

PLATT, R. The nature of essential hypertension *in* Essential Hypertension, ed. Bock, K. D., Springer-Verlag, Berlin, 1960, page 39.

RATHER, L. J. Experimental cardiac hypertrophy: Rate of development and effect of adrenalectomy. Am. J. Physiol., 1949, **159**, 153.

ROBERTS, J. T. AND WEARN, J. T. Quantitative changes in the capillary-muscle relationship in human hearts during normal growth and hypertrophy. Am. Heart J., 1941, **21**, 617.

ROSAS, R. AND CROXATTO, H. Vasoactive substances in blood and urine of DOCA hypertensive rats. Circulation Res., 1962, **10**, 880.

ROSECAN, M., GLASER, R. J., AND GOLDMAN, M. L. Orthostatic hypotension, anhidrosis and impotence. Circulation, 1952, **6**, 30.

SAMORAJSKI, T., KEEFE, J. R., AND ORDY, J. M. J. Gerontol., 1964, **19**, 262.

SCHLEGEL, J. U. AND OKAMOTO, S. Some studies in experimental renal hypertension. J. Urol., 1961, **86**, 27.

SCHROEDER, H. A. AND PERRY, H. M., JR. Current status of therapy in hypertension. J.A.M.A., 1956, **162**, 1382.

SHOCK, N. W., SIMONSON, E., LANDOWNE, M., ANDRES, R., NORRIS, A., AND SWARTZ, F. C. *in* 2nd National Conference on Cardiovascular Diseases, Washington, D. C., 1964, p. 1201.

SHORR, E. *In* Hypertension, a Symposium, edited by E. T. Bell, University of Minnesota Press, 1951, p. 79.

SIMONSON, E. Differentiation Between Normal and Abnormal in Electrocardiography, C. V. Mosby Co., St. Louis, 1961, 328 pp.

SKELTON, F. R. Increased sensitivity to corticosterone as a possible factor in the development of adrenal regeneration hypertension. Circulation Res., 1960, **8**, 772.

SKINNER, S. L., McCUBBIN, J. W., AND PAGE, I. H. Renal baroceptor control of renin secretion. Science, 1963, **141**, 814.

SOBEL, H. AND COHEN, F. M. Proteins of heart in experimental cardiac hypertrophy in the rat. Proc. Soc. Exper. Biol. & Med., 1958, **99**, 656.

SOMMERS, S. C. AND TURGEON, C. Juxtaglomerular cell counts and human hypertension. Am. J. Path., 1961, **38**, 227.

STARLING, E. H. AND VISSCHER, M. B. The regulation of the energy output of the heart. J. Physiol., 1926, **62**, 243.

STEAD, E. A., JR. AND EBERT, R. V. Postural hypotension; a disease of the sympathetic nervous system. Arch. Int. Med., 1941, **67**, 546.

STICKNEY, J. C., NORTHRUP, D. W., AND VAN TIERE, E. J. Cardiac dilatation without hypertrophy from reduced ambient pressure in rats. Circulation Res., 1956, **4**, 217.

STRANDELL, T. Acta Med. Scand., 1963, **174**, 479.

STREHLER, B. L. Time, Cells and Aging, Academic Press, New York, 1962, 270 pp.

STRUGHOLD, H. Bioastronautics. Advances in research. School of Aviation Medicine, USAF, Randolph Air Force Base, Texas, 1959.

SUMNER, R. G. AND McINTOSH, H. D. Nucleic acid studies in experimental cardiomegaly. Circulation Res., 1963, **12**, 170.

TAQUINI, A. C., JR., BLAQUIER, P. C., AND BOHR, D. F. Neurogenic factors and angiotensin in etiology of hypertension. Am. J. Physiol., 1961, **201**, 1173.

TAYLOR, R. D. AND PAGE, I. H. Production of prolonged arterial hypertension in dogs by chronic stimulation of the nervous system. Circulation, 1951, **3**, 551.

TOBIAN, L. Sodium, renal arterial distension and the juxtaglomerular apparatus. Canad. Med. Assoc. J., 1964, **90**, 160.

TOBIAN, L., AND BINION, J. T. Tissue cations and water in arterial hypertension. Circulation, 1952, **5**, 754.

TOBIAN, L., AND BINION, J. Artery wall electrolytes in renal and DCA hypertension. J. Clin. Invest., 1954, **33**, 1407.

TYLER, H. R. AND DAWSON, D. Hypertension and its relation to the nervous system. Ann. Int. Med., 1961, **55**, 681.

WAGNER, H. N., JR. AND BRAUNWALD, E. The pressor effect of the antidiuretic principle of the posterior pituitary in orthostatic hypotension. J. Clin. Invest., 1956, **35**, 1412.

WAKERLIN, G. E. Antibodies to renin as proof of the pathogenesis of sustained renal hypertension. Circulation, 1958, **17**, 653.

WAKERLIN, G. E., BIRD, R. B., BRENNAN, B. B., FRANK, M. H., KREMEN, S., KUPERMAN, I., AND SKOM, J. H. Treatment and prophylaxis of experimental renal hypertension with "renin." J. Lab. & Clin. Med., 1953, **41**, 708.

WAKERLIN, G. E., BRANNICK, T. L., OSGOOD, B. G., AND BURNS, R. O. Treatment of experimental renal hypertension with anti-renin. Am. J. Physiol., 1950, **163**, 701.

WALTER, F. AND ADDIS, T. Organ work and organ weight. J. Exper. Med., 1939, **69**, 467.

WILKINS, R. W., CULBERTSON, J. W., AND HALPERIN, M. H. The hemodynamic effects of sympathectomy in essential hypertension. Ann. Int. Med., 1949, **30**, 291.

WOOD, E. H., LAMBERT, L. E., BALDES, E. J., AND CODE, C. F. Effects of acceleration in relation to aviation. Fed. Proc., 1946, **5**, 327.

ZIMMERMAN, B. G., BRODY, M. J., AND BECK, L. Mechanism of the cardiac output reduction by hexamethonium. Am. J. Physiol., 1960, **199**, 319.

Monographs and Reviews

ARMSTRONG, H. G. Principles and practice of aviation medicine. Ed. 3. The Williams & Wilkins Company, Baltimore, 1952.

BREST, A. N. AND MOYER, J. H. Newer approaches to antihypertensive therapy. J. A. M. A., 1960, **172**, 1041.

DESJARDINS, A. U. Action of roentgen rays and radium on the heart and lungs; experimental data and clinical radiotherapy. Am. J. Roentgenol., 1932, **27**, 149, 303, 477; **28**, 127, 271, 421, 567, 699, 843.

DRIPPS, R. D. (chairman and editor) The physiology of induced hypothermia symposium. National Academy of Sciences, National Research Council, Washington, D. C., 1956.

FREIS, E. D. Hemodynamics of hypertension. Physiol. Rev., 1960, **40**, 27.

GAUER, O. The physiological effects of prolonged acceleration. German Aviation Medicine, 1950, **1**, 554.

GAUER, O. AND HABER, M. Man under gravity-free conditions. German Aviation Medicine, 1950, **1**, 641.

GOLDBLATT, H. Factors regulating blood pressure. Fifth Conference, Josiah Macy, Jr., Foundation, New York, 1951.

GRANT, R. P. Aspects of cardiac hypertrophy. Am. Heart J., 1953, **46**, 154.

HEYMANS, C. AND NEIL, E. Reflexogenic areas of the cardiovascular system. J. & A. Churchill, Ltd., London, 1958.

HOOBLER, S. W. (editor). Proceedings of Conference on Basic Mechanisms of Arterial Hypertension. Circulation, 1958, **17**, 641.

KORNER, P. I. Circulatory adaptations in hypoxia. Physiol. Rev., 1959, **39**, 687.

KRAYER, O. AND ACHESON, G. H. The pharmacology of the veratrum alkaloids. Physiol. Rev., 1946, **26**, 383.

LANSING, A. I. (editor). The arterial wall. The Williams & Wilkins Co., Baltimore, 1959.

MICHAELSON, S. J. Hemodynamic effects of ionizing radiation; vertebrates. Handbook of Circulation, p. 196. W. B. Saunders Company, Philadelphia, 1959.

MOYER, J. H. (editor). Hypertension, the first

Hahnemann symposium on hypertensive disease. W. B. Saunders Company, Philadelphia, 1959.

NORMAN, T. D. The pathogenesis of cardiac hypertrophy. Prog. in Cardiovasc. Dis., 1962, 4, 439.

PAGE, I. H. AND BUMPUS, F. M. Angiotensin. Physiol. Rev., 1961, 41, 331.

PATT, H. M. AND BRUES, A. M. The pathological physiology of radiation injury in the mammal. II. Specific aspects of the physiology of radiation injury. Radiation Biology, Vol. 1: High Energy Radiation Part II. p. 976. McGraw-Hill Book Company, New York, 1954.

PROCEEDINGS of the International Symposium on Angiotensin, Sodium, and Hypertension. Canad. Med. Assoc. J., 1964, 90, 153.

REUBI, F. C. (chairman). Essential Hypertension, An International Symposium, ed. Bock, K. D., Springer-Verlag, Berlin, 1960.

SCHROEDER, H. A. AND PERRY, H. M., JR., Current status of therapy in hypertension. J. A. M. A., 1956, 162, 1382.

SIMONSON, E. AND BROZEK, J. Russian Research on Arterial Hypertension. Ann. Int. Med., 1959, 50, 129.

SMITH, D. J., MACMILLAN, W. H., SAUNDERS, H., AND DANIELL, H. W. Effects of ionizing radiation upon the cardiovascular, biochemical and hematological systems of man and animals: A review. Report No. 1, Contract AF 19(604)-1093, School of Aviation Medicine, USAF, 1955.

STARLING, E. H. The Linacre lecture on the law of the heart. Longmans, Green & Company, New York, 1918.

STRUGHOLD, H. Bioastronautics. Advances in research. School of Aviation Medicine, USAF, Randolph Air Force Base, Texas, 1959.

TOBIAN, L. Physiology of the juxtaglomerular cells. Ann. Int. Med., 1960, 52, 395.

WAKERLIN, G. E. Endocrine factors in renal hypertension. Physiol. Rev., 1955, 35, 555.

WARREN, S. Effects of radiation on normal tissues: VI. Effects of radiation on the cardiovascular system. Arch. Path., 1942, 34, 1070.

WIGGERS, C. J. Cardiac adaptation in acute progressive anoxia. Ann. Int. Med., 1941, 14, 1237.

WILKINS, R. W. New drugs for the treatment of hypertension. Ann. Int. Med., 1959, 50, 1.

ZWEIFACH, B. W. AND SHORR, E. Factors regulating blood pressure. Fifth Conference, Josiah Macy, Jr., Foundation, New York, 1951.

CHAPTER 49

Regulation of the Circulation under States of Stress—*Continued*

Shock and Hemorrhage

BASES AND PRINCIPAL CHARACTERISTICS

The state which commonly develops several hours after a severe tissue injury is referred to either as traumatic, or surgical, or wound, or secondary shock. The last designation contrasts it with primary shock which may supervene immediately following the injury. Primary shock has mainly a neural basis and, therefore, is also called neurogenic shock.

It is believed that the most characteristic feature of traumatic shock is a disparity between the circulating blood volume and the capacity of the circulatory system. When such a disparity develops, for any reason, the pressure in the great veins and right atrium becomes reduced and consequently the filling of the ventricles is inadequate. This leads to a decrease in stroke volume, cardiac output and arterial blood pressure. The fall in blood pressure elicits cardiac acceleration and vasoconstriction. The pale cold skin which is typical of shock is a manifestation of the cutaneous vasoconstriction. Also, the decreased rate of blood flow results in the hypokinetic type of hypoxia and associated cyanosis of the ears and finger tips. The acceleration of the heart rate results in encroachment on time for ventricular filling and this, along with the lowered venous pressure, contributes to lowering of the stroke volume and pulse pressure. A pulse pressure of less than 20 mm. Hg is not uncommon in shock.

Oliguria or anuria may occur in shock since there is inadequate pressure to maintain the glomerular filtration rate (GFR). Renal blood flow is decreased even more than the reduction in GFR. The nonprotein nitrogen of the blood increases and the alkali reserve falls.

The initiating mechanisms in traumatic shock are those which promote either a decrease in blood volume or an increase in the capacity of the cardiovascular system. Trauma may cause actual blood loss of varying degree, but in addition, it may cause extravasation of fluid into the damaged part. The importance of the loss of blood or plasma volume in the production of the signs and symptoms of shock is made evident by the dramatic improvement in the condition of the patient which occurs when the circulating blood volume is restored early after shock has developed. Later on when circulation has been inadequate for awhile the beneficial effect of transfusions is less, or the blood pressure may not be restored by this method.

Early in traumatic shock it appears that there is no serious defect in the heart itself as indicated by the response to transfusions; inadequate cardiac filling is the main problem. In so-called cardiogenic shock the circulatory failure is central, i.e., in the heart, and the right atrial pressure is not reduced. Actually, it may be increased. Obviously, the problem in this case is quite different than in traumatic shock.

If the essential feature in traumatic shock is the reduction in circulating blood volume then the severity will be related both to the amount of reduction and to the time which has elapsed since the reduction occurred. The production of shock by withdrawal of blood has been studied extensively in experimental animals, and it has been demonstrated that removal of a certain fraction of the blood volume for a certain time will result in the appearance of shock and subsequent death even though the blood be reinfused.

STAGES OF SHOCK

Wiggers (1950) differentiates between four stages in the progression of shock to the phase in which treatment is ineffective. In the *initial* or developing stage circulating blood volume is decreased but not sufficiently to cause serious symptoms. Next is the *compensatory* stage in which blood volume is reduced further, but blood pressure tends to be maintained within the normal range through vasoconstriction. At this stage blood flow through the skin and, perhaps, the kidneys is decreased while flow to the central nervous system and myocardium tend to be maintained. The volume of the spleen and other blood reservoirs typically is decreased. The *progressive* stage of shock is characterized by the fact that unfavorable changes are becoming more and more prominent:

falling blood pressure, increasing vasoconstriction, accelerated heart rate, decreased pulse pressure, oliguria, etc. Progression indicates that compensatory mechanisms are unable to cope with the reduced blood volume so as to maintain the circulation. When blood pressure is reduced to the range of 60 to 70 mm. Hg myocardial depression, a decrease in heart rate and, perhaps, a decrease in arteriolar tonus may become factors in promoting the hypotension. The last, or *irreversible*, stage is so designated because treatment no longer is successful in saving the life of the patient. Arterial blood pressure is not restored by the infusion of blood. Apparently, both a loss of arteriolar tonus and myocardial depression are factors in the inability of the circulatory system to respond to transfusions in a beneficial manner. The infused blood tends to remain in the capillary beds.

Theories Concerning the Cause of Shock

Shock can be produced in experimental animals by mechanical trauma which does not break the skin (e.g., pounding the limb of an anesthetized animal with a mallet) and by bleeding the animal to the extent of 40 to 60 per cent of its calculated blood volume. Blalock, using these methods, concluded that there is no essential difference between the shock induced by the two methods. He favored the view that fluid loss at the *site* of trauma was sufficient to set off the train of events leading to shock. However, Moon believed that a stage is reached in animals in shock when hypoxia of capillary walls causes increased permeability and thus promotes fluid loss into the tissues at sites remote from the injury. This theory seems to be losing ground.

The results of numerous studies of shock in animals can be summarized by stating that the decrease in blood flow in vital structures such as the myocardium, central nervous system and, perhaps, the liver which occurs when blood volume is inadequate leads to the development of changes which can not be reversed by present methods of treatment. It is possible that in irreversible shock vital cells have become irreparably damaged. However, the possibility remains that if the nature of the changes in the late stages of shock were understood better effective treatment could be achieved. Contrary to earlier theories shock does not appear to be due to hypocapnia (as suggested by Y. Henderson) or to paralysis of the vasomotor center (Crile) or to adrenal exhaustion (Swingle) or to fat embolism from damaged tissues (Porter). It is true that the adrenal cortex, adrenal medulla and the vasomotor system are subjected to increased demands in a patient in shock, but failure of any of these is not demonstrated to be the basis for irreversibility.

In the period from 1914 to 1921 Dale and Laidlaw, Cannon, Bayliss, and others searched for a toxic factor in the production of shock and gave special attention to histamine. This substance is produced in damaged tissues and causes certain changes in the cardiovascular system similar to those which are found in shock. However, it does not appear that enough histamine is produced over a long enough period in traumatized tissues to cause irreversible shock.

Shorr, Zweifach and associates reported the liberation of a depressor substance from the liver in animals in shock. This substance, initially called VDM (vasodepressor material) and later identified as ferritin, was considered to be responsible for the irreversible stage of shock. However, subsequent studies cast doubt on this interpretation. Injection of ferritin in very large doses does not cause symptoms of shock.

It has been suggested that bacterial toxins are concerned in the irreversibility of traumatic shock. Fine (1954) states that irreversibility to transfusion is present from the onset in septic shock whereas it does not develop until after a long delay in hemorrhagic shock. Even in hemorrhagic shock, according to Fine, a bacterial factor is encountered since antibiotics delay or prevent the development of irreversibility. Therefore, he believes that administration of antibiotics is important as a part of the therapy of both traumatic and hemorrhagic shock.

Burn Shock

Secondary shock results from extensive burns. In this case loss of fluid and plasma constituents into the damaged area is considered to be the initiating factor. Since blood cells, for the most part, are retained hemoconcentration is characteristic. Transfusion of plasma is quite beneficial under these conditions. The amount of loss of plasma volume is related to the extent of the burn. The possibility of a toxic factor in burn shock is even greater than in traumatic shock, however no specific substance has been demonstrated to be responsible for development of irreversibility. It seems that considerable amounts of histamine are produced in tissues and liberated following burns. Barsoum and Gaddum found the histamine content of patients suffering from extensive burns to be several times higher than the normal. Also, it is not uncommon for a patient with extensive burns to develop ulceration of the duodenum

(Curling's ulcer) which is attributed to the stimulating effect of histamine on gastric secretion. However, no clear correlation in time was found between the histamine concentration in blood and the onset of shock. Rose and Brown observed that the course of blood histamine concentration following burns could be divided into three stages (1) an early increase in some cases, (2) a marked decrease during the period of edema and plasma loss, i.e., during the time when shock was evident, and (3) a return to normal or above normal levels as the edema subsided and the patient was improving. These results do not support the view that histamine is the responsible agent in the development of shock following burns.

"Crush Syndrome"

A person who has had a limb compressed for some time, for example by a beam or pile of rubble, may pass into a state resembling shock. In the *crush syndrome* impairment of renal function is a prominent factor. The urine is brownish in color, contains dark granular casts and gives a positive test for myoglobin derived from the damaged muscles. In severe cases anuria develops, and death is due to the failure of renal function. The renal tubules are considered to be damaged by myohematin. The anuria, therefore, would be caused in a manner analogous to that resulting from the transfusion of incompatible blood, the difference being that in one the pigment is liberated from muscle and in the other from erythrocytes.

It appears that the blood flow to the renal cortex becomes reduced in the *crush syndrome* which seems to render the tubules more susceptible to the action of the blood pigment. Trueta and his associates found that the renal cortex had a reduced blood flow in tourniquet shock and stimulation of afferent nerves from the limb also causes renal vasoconstriction.

The renal pathological changes seen in the *crush syndrome* are described as lower nephron nephrosis (ch. 80). This consists of extensive degeneration or necrosis of tubular epithelium and is characteristic of a number of different conditions in which toxic substances reach the kidney in considerable quantities or when the renal blood flow is decreased severely for a relatively prolonged period.

Anaphylactic Shock

The anaphylactic reaction is one which follows administration of a foreign substance (usually protein in nature) to an animal which has been sensitized to it by a previous dose. The second dose may be quite small as compared with the initial dose. The first dose acts as an antigen; that is, it induces the production of antibody by the animal. Usually about 2 weeks must elapse between doses in order that the second dose may produce maximum effects. The severe form of the anaphylactic reaction is called anaphylactic shock. This shows different manifestations in different species. *In the dog* the primary change which may cause the death of the animal is constriction of the hepatic veins. This holds the blood back in the splanchnic organs and all of the manifestations of failure of venous return consequently appear. Cardiac output, arterial blood pressure and pulse pressure fall. Heart rate is accelerated. Respiration is stimulated. Salivation and vomiting are induced. *In the guinea pig* the most serious feature of the anaphylactic reaction is the contraction of bronchiolar smooth muscle. This leads to extreme dyspnea and death from asphyxia. The effect can be demonstrated in the perfused isolated lungs of a sensitized animal by the addition of antigen to the perfusion fluid. Histamine may be concerned, at least in part, in this reaction since the amount of this substance in the lungs and blood is increased during the anaphylactic reaction, and it has a potent stimulant action on the bronchiolar smooth muscle.

In the rabbit, the reaction may be general or purely local. When the foreign substance is injected subcutaneously into a sensitized animal, the skin and subcutaneous tissue at the site of the injection become edematous and swollen; a sterile abscess or slough appears. This was originally described by Arthus and is known as the Arthus phenomenon. When the antigen is administered intravenously, the blood pressure falls abruptly and the respirations become rapid. The bladder and intestine are evacuated. The animal may die within a few minutes from dilation and failure of the right ventricle secondary to the increased resistance in the pulmonary circuit caused by constriction of the arterioles. The arterioles in other parts of the vascular system are also constricted and emboli composed of clumps of leukocytes may be seen blocking the pulmonary and systemic capillaries.

The evidence indicates, with little doubt, that, in anaphylactic shock, the antibody-antigen reaction takes place in or on the tissue cells and not in the blood plasma. Dale showed for example, that when the uterus was removed from a sensitized guinea pig and its vessels freed from all traces of blood, it gave the typical anaphylactic contraction when the antigen was added to the bath in which it was immersed. Manwaring also found that the blood of the sensitized animal could be replaced by blood from a normal animal without affecting the first animal's sensitivity.

It is now generally accepted that the antigen-antibody reaction in some way brings about the liberation of histamine from the affected tissues and that the action of this amine is responsible for some of the anaphylactic manifestations. Nearly all the features, as seen in these three species, can be explained upon such a basis. In the dog and guinea pig, anaphylactic shock is associated with a rise in the histamine concentration of the blood and, although the whole blood of the rabbit shows no increase and is often reduced, the amine passes from the white cells (which contain it in especially large amounts) into the plasma. The species peculiarities of the anaphylactic manifestations can be accounted for largely by the amount of smooth muscle in the reactive tissues of these three species and by its susceptibility to the action of histamine. In the dog, the smooth muscle of the hepatic veins is especially well developed. In the guinea pig, the bronchioles are particularly susceptible to stimulation by histamine and, in the rabbit, the pulmonary arterioles show unusually thick muscular coats.

Though histamine liberation appears to be a major factor in the production of the phenomena of anaphylaxis, certain observations indicate that some other factor or factors are involved. Minute doses of histamine, for example, cause contraction of the isolated rat's uterus, whereas large doses of antigen are required to produce even a weak contraction. Also, the isolated guinea pig's uterus, poisoned by high concentrations of histamine, responds to a further dose by relaxation, but by contraction to a further dose of antigen.

Peptone solution, injected intravenously, produces in the dog effects almost identical with those of anaphylactic shock, including incoagulability of the blood due to the liberation of heparin from the liver. Sensitization by a previous dose is not necessary, however. Adding peptone to rabbit blood *in vitro* causes the liberation of histamine from the cells into the plasma.

In man, fatal anaphylactic shock may follow the injection of horse serum into a person who has been sensitized by a previous administration. Allergic reactions, in general, show many similarities to anaphylactic reactions and many observations suggest that the two are fundamentally allied, although in the case of allergic reactions, sensitization by an earlier exposure cannot always be demonstrated, the reaction appearing upon the first known contact with the foreign substance.

Congestive Heart Failure

Heart failure occurs when the heart muscle is weak or if the heart ceases to pump blood because of arrest or ventricular fibrillation or if cardiac filling is prevented. The heart may fail suddenly as a result of occlusion of a coronary artery or following rapid accumulation of fluid or blood in the pericardial sac, or failure may result from sudden overloading of a heart already weakened by chronic disease. In acute heart failure there is a sudden reduction in or cessation of cardiac output. Arterial blood pressure decreases, the pulse weakens or is not palpable, and vasoconstrictor reflexes are elicited from the pressoreceptors. The patient is in shock as far as conditions on the arterial side of the systemic circuit are concerned, but the venous pressure is not lowered as in shock related to decreased blood volume.

Chronic Congestive Heart Failure

A number of chronic diseases eventually lead to weakening of the heart muscle, and this results in the development of the syndrome which is known as chronic congestive heart failure. It is important to recognize that heart failure designates a clinical syndrome rather than any specific defect in the heart.

Weakness of the heart is not necessarily expressed as decreased cardiac output, since homeostatic mechanisms operate which tend to maintain whatever cardiac output is needed to meet the metabolic requirements of the tissues. Hence, in many cases of chronic congestive heart failure a normal cardiac output under resting conditions is observed in the presence of a moderately elevated venous pressure (Espersen; Altschule; McMichael, 1938 and 1947; Richards, 1949). The weakness of the heart is evident in that it pumps less blood than a normal heart would pump if it were subjected to the same (elevated) filling pressure. It will be noted that the definition of cardiac weakness implied in the preceding statement is that a weak heart is one which will show a lower than normal increase in output in response to a given increase in the venous pressure. Thus if cardiac output at various venous pressures is graphed, a curve would be obtained which lies somewhere below that for a ventricle of normal strength, and the weaker the ventricle, the lower will be this curve (see Youmans and Huckins, 1951).

Another way of thinking about the strength of the heart is in terms of its *reserve*. Although the moderately weakened heart can achieve a normal output under resting conditions or during mild exercise it has less reserve. As the level of muscular activity is increased a point would be reached at which cardiac output could not increase further, whereas the normal heart could continue to increase its output well beyond this amount as muscular activity is increased (Nielsen). Thus, the first indication of cardiac weakness is a reduction in the cardiac reserve, as determined by suitable exercise tests, and the severity of cardiac "disability" would be related to the degree of loss of the cardiac reserve.

When the cardiac reserve is diminished as a result of disease cardiovascular adjustments occur to maintain adequate output, and the heart and circulation are said to be in a state of compensation. When such adjustments are inadequate as manifested particularly by a considerable rise in venous pressure, increase in heart size (dilation) and other signs of congestion the condition is referred to as cardiac decompensation.

Congestive heart failure may develop in any person whose heart has been working for a more or less prolonged period against a high peripheral resistance (e.g., essential hypertension) or if the work of the heart has been above normal because of cardiac valvular defects (rheumatic fever) or because of prolonged continuous demands for increased cardiac output (hyperthyroidism, arteriovenous fistula). When the work of the heart is increased chronically, for any reason, a sequence of changes in heart muscle is induced which terminates eventually in its weakening. On the other hand, weakness of the myocardium may result from more specific causes such as inadequate blood supply, damage by certain toxins, etc.

Sequence of Changes in Congestive Heart Failure

The chief manifestations of chronic congestive heart failure are: increased extracellular fluid volume; increased blood volume; elevated venous pressure; dyspnea; cyanosis in some cases; enlargement of the liver and spleen; edema of the dependent parts of the body; and in some cases hydrothorax and ascites. The cardiac output in classical congestive heart failure in the patient at rest is within the normal range or decreased. However, in a group of conditions commonly referred to as "high output" heart failure specific stimuli are present which cause an elevated basal cardiac output.

Until a few years ago most discussions of the mechanisms involved in the development of the characteristic changes seen in congestive heart failure presented either or both of two theories: the "backward failure" theory, and the "forward failure" theory; however, it no longer seems profitable to describe these theories as such but rather to present the sequence of events now reasonably well established.

One of the most characteristic features of congestive heart failure is the increase in volume and pressure of blood in the pulmonary circuit and in the right atrium and systemic veins (Landis and others, 1946; McMichael, 1947). What causes these changes? According to the earlier theories a decrease in output of the left ventricle would, on purely hemodynamic bases, allow the pulmonary circuit to become congested to the extent that it occurs in congestive heart failure. Likewise, the rise in systemic venous pressure was attributed entirely to failure of the right ventricle to respond to its filling pressure in such a way as to keep the pressure down to normal levels. At the time of the actual onset of failure it was visualized that blood was returning to the corresponding ventricle more rapidly than it was being pumped out, and therefore, the pressure upstream from the ventricle was being permitted to progressively increase until the relatively high levels which occur in congestive heart failure were reached. In some explanations the ventricle was referred to as "damming back" the blood or causing "back pressure". It is apparent, however, that a cardiac ventricle behaves as a force pump and not as a dam (Starr, 1949). The ventricles do not create a back pressure by failing to pump; they allow the pressure to rise as they fail to force the blood on. Therefore, the term "back pressure" does not seem to be suitable to describe any of the hemodynamic changes associated with congestive heart failure. For example, the rise in pressure in a cistern which occurs as water runs into it faster than it is lifted out by a pump would not be called back pressure.

The concept that venous pressure can increase to very high levels as a consequence of failure of the ventricle to pump the blood which is flowing in by the venous system implies a continuing venous return in the presence of decreased cardiac output. However, the venous return is the same as the cardiac output for any prolonged period except as a shift of volume out of the arterial tree occurs when cardiac output and mean arterial blood pressure decrease. As arterial pressure falls the volume in the systemic arterial tree decreases and this is associated with a slight increase in pressure in the "low pressure" portions of the cardiovascular system (i.e., the great veins, atria and pulmonary circuit). The maximum increase in pressure which could occur in the atria, on purely hemodynamic bases, when ventricular output decreases is that which would occur following ventricular arrest. When this occurs flow from the arterial tree into the systemic veins and pulmonary system continues until equalization of pressure occurs at the static blood pressure level which is only about 8 to 10 cm. of water. Thus, a rise in venous pressure to the levels which commonly are seen in congestive heart failure is not produced simply by failure of the ventricles to pump the blood returning to them. The large rises in venous pressure are dependent in part upon elevation of the blood volume. Starr (1940) reported that the static blood pressure, i.e., that found throughout the circulatory system shortly after the heart ceases to beat, was considerably higher in patients who had died of heart failure than in those who died from other causes. The elevation of static blood pressure can be attributed to any of three changes: reduced capacity of the cardiovascular system; reduced distensibility; or increased volume of blood in the system. There is no reason for considering that either of the first two changes is characteristic of congestive heart failure. Blood volume, on the other hand, has been found to be elevated in congestive heart failure by most investigators who have studied it (Altschule, Borst).

The initial change in the cardiovascular system which leads to the classical syndrome of congestive heart failure must be assumed to be the decrease in left ventricular output related to weakening of the left ventricle or lack of filling of the left ventricle secondary to such changes as right ventricular failure or compression of the left ventricle from without (as from pericardial effusion). Then a series of changes is initiated which in mild or moderate cases leads to restoration of the cardiac output. Hence, when congestive heart failure is diagnosed some of the measurable changes are those which have occurred to counter a decrease in cardiac output. When cardiac output is found to be decreased in the patient at rest this indicates that the condition is so severe that compensatory mechanisms which serve to maintain cardiac output have been overtaxed. In other words a subnormal cardiac output in the patient at rest indicates virtual absence of cardiac reserve.

Patients with congestive heart failure usually have a decreased renal blood flow while the glomerular filtration rate is reduced to a lesser degree (Merrill, Bradley and Blake, Davies and Kilpatrick, Mokotoff and others). The load of sodium and chloride filtered at the level of the glomerulus is decreased in direct proportion to the reduction in glomerular filtration. This alone, if sodium reabsorbing capacity of the tubules were unaltered, would lead to a considerable reduction in in NaCl excretion. However it appears that tubular reabsorption of sodium also is stimulated. This change has been attributed to the action of aldosterone which is reported to be produced in increased amounts (Parrish, Lasche and others, Singer and Wener). Regardless of the mechanism, the ability of the kidney to excrete NaCl is markedly impaired in patients with congestive heart failure as indicated by the fact that they may show a positive salt and water balance despite a greatly restricted salt intake.

The decreased renal blood flow and glomerular filtration rate in congestive heart failure in the presence of an arterial blood pressure within the normal range indicates that the tonus of renal arterioles is increased. The increased filtration fraction (see ch. 79) may be related to efferent arteriolar constriction; since a change of this type causes a lowered renal blood flow without producing a corresponding decrease in glomerular filtration rate.

Patients with congestive heart failure do not show impairment of ability to excrete water in a degree that makes it necessary for them to restrict their water intake. The defect which leads to the increase in the amount of NaCl and water in the body and the corresponding rise in volume of the extracellular fluid compartment is the failure of the kidney to excrete NaCl. As the salt is retained water is held back with it. As a part of this secondary process the increased production of antidiuretic hormone (ADH) may be involved. It has been postulated that the reabsorption of sodium ion from the tubules is the primary change and that the chloride ion moves along with sodium because of its opposite charge. It is significant that the amount of edema in a patient with congestive heart failure can be controlled by directing attention to lowering the total amount of NaCl in the body, by any of several methods, while allowing him to drink water *ad libitum* (Futcher and Schroeder, Schroeder). In the reaction against the severe restriction of water intake, which occurred when it was recognized that there is no physiological basis for such a regimen, it was reported that forcing fluids was of benefit in treating congestive heart failure (Schemm, 1942 and 1944). It now appears that a low fluid intake is disadvantageous but that high fluid intake is not of value except to correct the ill effects of dehydration produced by a period during which fluid intake had been severely restricted.

High Output Circulatory Failure

Some patients who are diagnosed as having congestive heart failure have a basal cardiac output well above the normal range. Furthermore, effective treatment leads to a lowering of the basal cardiac output to normal levels. It is not reasonable to consider that cardiac weakness as such would lead to an increase in the basal cardiac output; therefore, in patients who have the high output type of circulatory failure it is reasonable to postulate a source of cardiac stimulation which is not present in normal persons.

The similarities between simple congestive failure, described in the preceding section, and high output failure are related to the fact that retention of NaCl and water occurs in both. The increase in extracellular fluid volume leads to many of the signs and symptoms which are common to the two syndromes. The two principal differences between the syndromes are (1) that in high output failure the peripheral resistance typically is low while in simple congestive heart failure it tends to be elevated, and (2) that the level of the basal cardiac output, by definition, is elevated in high output failure. Since a low peripheral resistance, as produced for example by an arteriovenous shunt, will elicit an increase in cardiac output, it is logical to consider that the decreased peripheral resistance is a primary change in the cardiovascular system in patients with high output failure and is the basis for the cardiac stimulation (Youmans and Huckins, 1951; Youmans, 1954 and 1957). Associated with the increased cardiac output there is a shortened circulation time, decreased arteriovenous oxygen difference, increased heart rate in some cases and, commonly, a widening of the pulse pressure.

There are several reasons for postulating that the decrease in peripheral resistance in high output failure is the initial change in the cardiovascular system that leads to the other changes characteristic of the syndrome. (1) In arteriovenous fistula, which may lead to high output failure, perhaps in its purest form (see Elkin and Warren, Holman, Cohen and others), the initial hemodynamic alteration obviously is the reduced resistance to outflow of blood from the systemic arterial tree. (2) Decreased peripheral resistance occurs in beriberi, severe anemia, hyperthyroidism, Paget's disease, patent ductus arteriosus, hyperthyroidism and certain types of chronic pulmonary disease, all of which may lead to high output failure. (3) The high cardiac output can be explained as a compensatory response to the low peripheral resistance. (4) The renal retention

of salt and water may be caused by a shunting of blood away from the kidney by a disproportionately large decrease in resistance in the extrarenal portion of the systemic circuit.

In 1937 Weiss and Wilkins emphasized the similarities between the effects of systemic arteriovenous fistula and chronic thiamine deficiency, and they observed that circulatory changes produced by large doses of thiamine in patients with beriberi heart disease are similar in important respects to those associated with closure of an arteriovenous fistula. The pattern of cardiovascular changes in beriberi heart disease is the typical high output failure syndrome (Porter and Downs, Weiss and Wilkins, Burwell and Dexter).

Davies and Kilpatrick found renal blood flow and glomerular filtration rate reduced in patients with high output failure due to chronic cor pulmonale. The average for 10 patients was about one half the average for normal individuals. If the renal blood flow in these patients is expressed as the per cent of the cardiac output, the range is 2.0 to 15 per cent with an average of 7 per cent as compared with an average of around 22 per cent in normal subjects. It is evident that the kidneys do not share in the increased circulation in high output failure associated with beriberi or cor pulmonale. This demonstrates that the extrarenal fraction of the peripheral resistance is disproportionately lowered in these diseases, just as it is in systemic arteriovenous fistula.

It seems probable that chronically increased demands upon the heart caused by a low peripheral resistance would lead eventually to development of cardiac weakness just as when increased cardiac work is related to other types of changes in the circulatory system. If this should occur, the sequence of changes seen in simple congestive heart failure would be expected to be superimposed upon those changes related to low peripheral resistance to produce the final picture in prolonged severe high output failure. In other words, early in high output failure the changes seen could be related entirely to compensation for low peripheral resistance while later the factor of cardiac weakness also probably would be present.

Consequences of Hypervolemia in Congestive Heart Failure

It is visualized that hypervolemia to some extent has a compensatory role in simple congestive heart failure and in the high output failure syndrome; however, the increase in blood volume may be great enough to lead to difficulties. The principal dangers in hypervolemia are, first, the possibility that the weakened left ventricle may become dilated to the extent that the dilation per se contributes to an acute decrease in cardiac output, and second, that the pressure in the pulmonary capillary bed may become increased to the point of producing transudation into the alveoli. The dangers of fluid administration to patients with hypervolemia are obvious, but the consequences of administration of vasoconstrictor drugs are less apparent. The ill effects of such drugs in hypervolemia are related to the fact that they promote a shift of blood from the systemic circuit into the already engorged pulmonary circuit, and this may cause a rise in pulmonary capillary pressure sufficient to produce pulmonary edema.

The degree of pulmonary congestion in a patient with chronic hypervolemia is least in the orthostatic position, but is increased when the patient lies down. Immediate transfer of blood from the systemic to the pulmonary circuit occurs as a result of the effects of gravity when the recumbent position is assumed. However, there is also a gradual increase in blood volume while the patient remains recumbent, as edema fluid moves from the interstitial space through the capillary walls; thus the blood volume shows nocturnal increases in patients with chronic hypervolemia and edema. The rise which occurs during the night, and the consequent increase in pulmonary engorgement, perhaps may explain the development of acute dyspnea.

Hemodynamics

The following is a discussion of the effects of arrhythmias, valvular disease, cardiac tamponade, and congenital heart disease on the hemodynamic function of the heart. In less than two decades, tremendous advances have been made in the study of these pathological entities by the development of catheterization techniques (including pressure measuring devices) for use in humans. Reference will at times be made to pertinent animal studies, but, mainly, the more important human data will be presented. However, it must be remembered that errors are inherent in measurements used for flow calculations on human subjects even when obtained by cardiac catheterization. In addition to the difficulties in measuring cardiac output by the Fick principle [including dye methods (ch. 39)], true controls are lacking (except those from a series of catheterized, normal subjects) for the patient cannot be his own control. As an example, an end diastolic ventricular pressure of 4 mm. Hg may be elevated since the patient's normal level (before compensation of the heart to the pathological stress) may have been 1 mm. Hg. This small pressure elevation could represent a significant diastolic volume increase. Since catheterization may be a frightening experience it is difficult to attain the necessary resting, steady state. Anesthesia cannot be used because it produces hemodynamic changes such as an increased cardiac output. When measurements are made "following exercise," the exertion is performed with the patient in the supine position (with catheter in place); therefore, the amount of exercise is usually mild.

Formulas have been derived for the calculation of flow through shunts and stenotic and regurgitant valves. These formulas often use the cardiac output, pulmonary wedge pressure, completely mixed venous blood samples and other measurements or calculations which possess their own errors. Clinically the information derived from these catheterizations is very practical and important, but physiologically it may represent only directional and semiquantitative hemodynamic changes. Therefore the results cannot be considered as precise as those obtained in animal experiments.

The pulmonary wedge pressure and the extent to which it represents the events in the pulmonary capillary bed, or the left side of the heart, has been discussed. The term "pulmonary circulation pressures" includes the pulmonary venous, wedge, and arterial pressures. The "filling pressure gradient" is the difference in pressure between the atrium and ventricle causing blood to flow from the former to the latter. Often a gradient cannot be measured across a normal or pathological valve by the techniques in present use. Yet a pressure gradient must exist in order for blood to flow. There is evidence that small pressure gradients (which may not be measurable by modern equipment) can lead to large blood flows (ch. 43). An important technique for measuring these pressure gradients by withdrawal of the catheter from one chamber to another with continuous measurements of pressures, is being replaced by the use of a double lumened catheter with an opening in each chamber.

HEMODYNAMICS IN ARRHYTHMIAS

The investigation by graphic methods, the etiology and the treatment of disorders of the heart beat have already been considered in chapter 23. In this section, the hemodynamic effects of arrhythmias on the circulatory system will be discussed. Stress on the heart is caused by arrhythmias possessing one or more of the following characteristics: (1) a very rapid rate, (2) an irregular rhythm with disruption of the normal atrial and ventricular coordination, or (3) a very slow rate. Whether the arrhythmia develops in a normal or diseased heart is often very important to the hemodynamic effects produced and, hence, must be considered in determining the actual alterations caused by the heart rhythm. If drugs, like digitalis (inotropic effect on the heart), quinidine (decreased peripheral resistance and increased cardiac output), or procaine amide (decreased blood pressure probably due to peripheral vasodilation) are used to revert the arrhythmia, the corrected hemodynamic effects cannot be attributed only to reversion of the arrhythmia. A consideration of the role of atrial contraction in the normal functioning of the heart becomes important in those arrhythmias interfering with atrial systole. Atrial contraction has been demonstrated to be very important; it brings the atrioventricular valves into closer apposition prior to ventricular contraction and it adds blood volume to the ventricles. However, there is no adequate evidence that a normal heart cannot function without contraction of its atria. On the other hand, improperly timed atrial systoles, occurring when the atrioventricular valves are closed, can lead to hemodynamic abnormalities.

PREMATURE CONTRACTIONS. Ferrer and associates have studied premature contractions during right heart catheterization in humans. When premature atrial or ventricular beats occur, the diastolic filling time is shortened, leading to a smaller stroke output and arterial pulse pressure. This is exaggerated with ventricular premature beats when atrial systole does not precede ventricular contraction. There is no augmentation of ventricular end-diastolic volume by atrial contraction and the atrioventricular valves do not close efficiently, resulting in regurgitation. The heart beat following a premature contraction may also vary in strength depending upon the regurgitant volume (which returns immediately to the ventricle) as well as the length of ventricular filling time. An imbalance in the output of the two ventricles has been shown to occur with coupled ventricular premature contractions. The small left ventricular contraction fails to develop enough systolic pressure to surpass the aortic diastolic pressure and open the aortic valve, yet the right ventricular systole opens the pulmonary valve because of the low pulmonary artery pres-

sure. Such imbalance of ventricular output could lead to pulmonary congestion. Levy and coworkers found unequal right and left ventricular ejections with electrically stimulated premature beats in open chest, anesthetized dogs. The imbalance in volume ejected was a result of differences in the diastolic pressure levels in the aorta compared with the pulmonary artery and was related to the peak systolic pressures which the corresponding ventricles developed. This was more exaggerated with ventricular premature beats because the percentage of control pressure developed by the stimulated ventricle was lower than that developed in the contralateral ventricle. The reason for this is unknown although the abnormal activation pathway of the ventricle is suspected. The difference between aortic and pulmonary blood flow was less marked with right ventricular premature beats due to the low pulmonary arterial pressure.

TACHYCARDIAS. The results of animal experiments by Starzl and associates on normal hearts in closed-chest animals showed that electrically induced atrial tachycardias at rates up to 190 per minute for short periods usually caused no alterations in cardiac output, systemic arterial blood pressure or systemic venous pressure, whereas the stroke volume and radiographic size of the heart decreased (fig. 49.1). If on the other hand, the ventricles were electrically stimulated to a tachycardia (made possible with stimulatory rates above the existing sinus rate), the cardiac output, stroke volume, and blood pressure decreased. The resultant atrioventricular asynchronism produced discordant positions of the A-V valves at the time of ventricular systole, varying from fully open to fully closed, thereby altering the end-diastolic ventricular volume. The strongest beats (largest stroke volumes) would occur after the longest diastolic filling times (largest end diastolic volumes), whereas shorter filling times would produce weaker beats. If the atrioventricular conduction pathways were then blocked and the ventricles driven at rates up to 190, the results resembled those described for atrial tachycardia. Nakano produced atrial or ventricular tachycardias at rates up to 280 beats per minute in anesthetized dogs. Early changes included a depressed ventricular function curve, decreased arterial pressure, stroke volume, and cardiac output and increased myocardial contractile force, pulmonary artery pressure and left and right atrial pressures. The magnitude of these changes was greater with the higher heart rates; ventricular tachycardia produced greater ab-

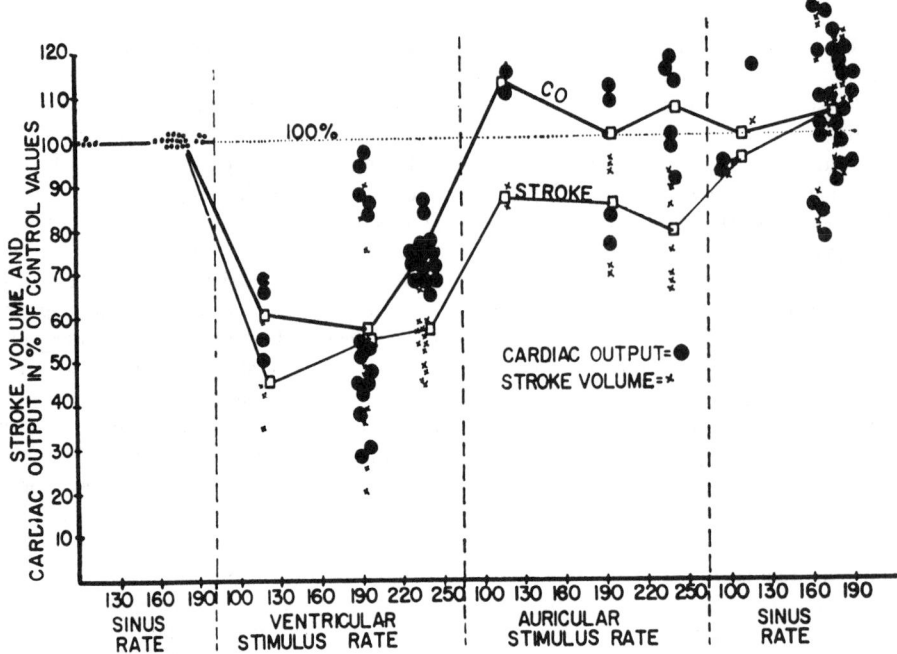

FIG. 49.1. The effect of atrial and ventricular tachycardia in the dog. Changes in cardiac output and stroke volume from the initial sinus rate values are shown with increasing rates of atrial and ventricular electrical stimulation. The changes are depicted as percentages of control values. Experiments were performed in closed chest dogs. In contrast to atrial stimulation, ventricular driving, irrespective of ventricular stimulation site, resulted in a reduction in cardiac output and stroke volume. (From Starzl, T. E. and associates, Circulation, 1955, **11**, 952.)

normalities than atrial tachycardia. The hemodynamic alterations are evidently secondary to the decreased stroke volume and cardiac output caused by impairment of ventricular filling; an increased heart rate results in a decrease in ventricular filling time with each beat. A progressive decrease in end-systolic, end-diastolic and stroke volume of the ventricles with progressive increases in heart rate has been shown by Bristow and coworkers. The initial hemodynamic changes of the rapid tachycardias are followed by a marked recovery of arterial pressure and cardiac output, probably through increased activity of the sympathetic nervous system.

Clinically the supraventricular tachycardias (atrial and nodal) cause circulatory failure if there is underlying heart disease, or if the tachycardia is prolonged in time. However, heart rates over 200 per minute were tolerated for hours and sometimes days in patients without heart disease. Ferrer and associates studied two patients during paroxysms of nodal tachycardia by right heart catheterization. An unaltered cardiac output with a decreased stroke volume was found. Right atrial pressure was elevated while blood pressure and peripheral resistance were normal. Since atrial systole followed ventricular con-

traction in these patients, the atrioventricular valves were probably not tightly opposed during ventricular systole. This could lead to tricuspid regurgitation and explain the elevated right atrial pressure.

Patients with atrial flutter have been studied in the same manner as above. Those without underlying heart disease, and one patient with a slow ventricular rate, were found to have normal cardiac outputs. When heart disease was present, atrial flutter with a rapid ventricular rate induced a marked decrease in cardiac output and stroke volume concomitant with a small systemic arterial pulse pressure, prolonged circulation time, dilated heart by roentgenograms, and a raised venous pressure in some patients. In all instances, after reversion to sinus rhythm, the resting cardiac output rose. This was found to be true in 2 patients after all medication had been discontinued. Since this rise in cardiac output occurred without a change in heart rate in 2 patients, and the ventricular diastolic filling time therefore remained constant, it was suggested that atrial flutter contributed to reduced blood flow by the continuous, rapid atrial contractions impeding venous inflow (each electrical flutter wave elicits a mechanical atrial systole). Atrioventricular valvular insufficiency was rarely present in atrial flutter. Pulmonary circulation pressures (pulmonary artery and pulmonary wedge pressures) were normal during atrial flutter in those without circulatory insufficiency.

IRREGULAR RHYTHM. Atrial fibrillation contrasts with the above tachycardias by having an irregular ventricular rhythm and absent atrial contractions. Atrioventricular regurgitation is present, even in the absence of elevated atrial pressures or heart failure, probably due to the lack of atrial contractions. The characteristics which distinguish atrial fibrillation from the regular tachycardias are beat-to-beat variations of ventricular rate or ventricular filling and emptying, and of arterial blood pressure (a changing resistance to ventricular ejection). It has been shown in animals and patients that the beat-to-beat changes were related not only to the previous diastolic filling time and end-diastolic volume, but also to the arterial pressure, end-systolic volume and the duration of systole of the preceding beat. In closed-chest dog experiments, acutely induced atrial fibrillation with rapid ventricular rate decreased cardiac output and blood pressure, and increased central venous pressure and the arteriovenous oxygen difference. Dilation of the heart could be seen by roentgenograms. On reversion to sinus rhythm the circulatory hemodynamics returned to the previous status. In patients studied by right heart catheterization (Ferrer and Harvey), tricuspid (and probably mitral) regurgitation and a decreased resting cardiac output were present. The variation in pulse pressure of the right ventricular contractions was marked, and totally ineffective beats occurred in which the pulmonic valve did not open. Left ventricular ejection occurred with every contraction. Therefore, stroke volume may be variable not only from beat to beat but also in one ventricle as compared with the other.

In patients, reversion to sinus rhythm is usually beneficial if the ventricular rate is rapid. Most show an increased cardiac output with a shortened circulation time and decreased atrial pressure. Exercise tolerance is often improved. It has been difficult to evaluate the results of reversion to sinus rhythm (i.e., is atrial fibrillation with a slow ventricular rate definitely detrimental to the circulatory status?) since drugs that affect the circulatory system were used and the heart rate usually slowed. With the recent innovation of direct current depolarization of the heart to produce reversion, it has been possible to study patients before and after reversion

under similar conditions of ventricular rate, drug effects, and oxygen consumption. Although there is not full agreement of all studies, most investigators have found a marked improvement in cardiac output and exercise tolerance upon the resumption of sinus rhythm in the majority of patients.

In summary, it can be said that atrial fibrillation with a rapid ventricular rate can lead to circulatory failure in diseased hearts or sometimes in normal hearts. The effect of the lack of atrial contraction has been discussed above. Since many patients in chronic congestive heart failure are benefited, and since the development of blood clots in the fibrillating atria is dangerous, reversion to sinus rhythm should be attempted.

BRADYCARDIAS. Up to this point, the arrhythmias which cause a rapid heart rate have been considered. Very little hemodynamic data is available concerning sinus bradycardia and partial heart block. A decreased cardiac output but a marked increase in stroke volume was present in one patient studied with sinus bradycardia. It is generally held that when the heart rate slows, there is an increase in end-diastolic volume due to the longer diastolic period. This increases the myocardial fibers' length and leads to a greater stroke volume. In this manner, the cardiac output is maintained at slow heart rates, probably as low as 30 to 40 beats per minute. Slower rates often lead to circulatory insufficiency secondary to a decreased cardiac output.

In experimental dogs, complete heart block can be produced by tying or cutting the atrioventricular conduction pathway. This usually results in average heart rates of 40 to 55. These dogs acutely manifest a decreased cardiac output proportional to the decrease in heart rate, an increased pulse pressure secondary to a decreased diastolic but normal systolic arterial blood pressure, a greater systemic arteriovenous oxygen difference and a rise in right atrial pressure. Within hours each of these factors tends to return toward normal. If the dog's ventricles are electrically stimulated to the preblock heart rate, the cardiac output and other abnormalities return immediately to normal levels. However, these dogs, especially if allowed normal exercise, usually develop severe cardiac failure within 3 months. In this respect they differ from humans who appear to better tolerate complete heart block. (Patients with congenital heart block may have a normal life span.)

Patients with complete heart block have been studied with right heart catheterization and by rapid biplane angiography. In patients with acquired complete heart block and without circulatory insufficiency, an elevation is found in right atrial systolic and mean pressure, right ventricular systolic and end-diastolic pressure, pulmonary arterial and wedge pressure, systemic artery pressure, and pulse pressure. A decreased cardiac output and cardiac index (cardiac output per square meter of body surface) with an increased stroke volume is present; the response of the cardiac output to exercise is impaired. However, the cardiac output (and cardiac index) was reported as normal, despite the above abnormal cardiac pressures, in some patients without underlying heart disease. In congenital heart block, the cardiac output may be normal and respond normally to exercise (the heart rate can increase); pressures in the pulmonary circulation are also normal. The low cardiac output of acquired heart block is due to the bradycardia and, probably, impaired contractility from underlying ischemic lesions of the heart muscle. Angiographic studies with timed electrocardiography have contributed to the understanding of the hemodynamic data in complete heart block. The timing of atrial systole in relation to ventricular systole determines the size of the atria and whether or not reflux of blood occurs into the great or pulmonary veins. When the atria contract against closed valves, or if more than one atrial systole occurs before a ventricular systole empties the ventricle, the right atrial pressure rises and reflux may occur.

In summary, complete heart block without underlying heart disease is compatible with a long and active life despite the presence of abnormal chamber pressures. Often such patients, especially if the heart block is of congenital origin, have a small increase in heart rate with exercise. If there is underlying heart disease, the prognosis is quite poor due to eventual circulatory failure from a chronic overload on the heart. Treatment of acute cases consists of administering epinephrine, isoproterenol, sodium lactate, methamphetamine, atropine, or corticosteroids and more recently potassium depleting diuretics have been recommended. Hypokalemia may enhance atrioventricular conduction. Isoproterenol is the only drug which has been studied and has been shown to augment the cardiac output not only by an increase in heart rate in some patients but also by a direct myocardial effect with an increased stroke volume in others. Treatment of chronic cases with circulatory failure or Stokes-Adams attacks involves the insertion into the left ventricular muscle of electrodes connected to a miniature,

battery operated, mechanical stimulator. With electric pacemakers, the resting cardiac output may be maintained at normal; their success has been remarkable. The optimal pacemaker rate at rest has been determined to be 70 to 83 beats per minute (Segel and associates). Higher rates do not further increase cardiac output. Evidently the site of stimulation of the left ventricle does not affect cardiac output suggesting that the pathway of ventricular excitation does not influence ventricular function in complete heart block (Fletcher and associates). In patients with a fixed ventricular rate from implanted pacemakers, large increases in stroke volume and, therefore, cardiac output occur with exercise and with infusions of norepinephrine (Judge and coworkers). When ventricular stimulation is properly timed to follow atrial systole, a small but significant increase in stroke volume of ventricular contractions is seen. This emphasizes the importance of atrial systole in the regulation of ventricular filling and stroke output.

Hemodynamics in Valvular Heart Disease

Rheumatic endocarditis is the most frequent disease leading to abnormalities of the heart valves. The mitral valve is most commonly affected followed by the aortic, and then the tricuspid valve. The pulmonic valve leaflets are rarely affected. Pulmonic valvular disease will be considered in the following section, Congenital Heart Disease. Other causes of valvular disease include syphilis, bacterial endocarditis, calcification of the valves and trauma.

When the valves become deformed by disease, they impede the flow of blood or allow leakage to occur. If there is narrowing of one of the orifices of the heart, the condition is spoken of as "stenosis." Stenosis of the valves is caused by fusion of the leaflets, rigidity of the cusps due to fibrosis and/or shortening and adherence of the chordae tendinae. When the valves are incapable of closing tightly, they are said to be "incompetent," "regurgitant," or "insufficient." They now allow blood to regurgitate in the opposite direction to that of the normal flow. Insufficiency of a valve may be due to deformity, rigidity, retraction, fusion of the cusps or chordae tendinae, or to a dilation of the ring of the valves. If the leaflets are deformed sufficiently to produce stenosis of a particular orifice, they may also be incapable of closing properly and regurgitation will occur as well. Therefore, stenosis and incompetence of a valve often occur together.

HEART MURMURS. When the valves become deformed, abnormal heart sounds appear. Such sounds are spoken of as murmurs or bruits. Presumably, heart murmurs result from the development of turbulence in rapidly flowing blood. The flow of blood through most cavities and channels is silent because the flow is laminar. Turbulence will appear when the Reynolds' number is exceeded (ch. 36). Practically speaking, cardiac murmurs appear in the presence of the following conditions, separately or in combination: high rates of flow through normal or abnormal valves; forward flow through a constricted, or an irregular valve or into a dilated vessel; back flow through a valve, septal defect or patent ductus arteriosus; presence of a loose, vibrating structure, such as a chordae tendinae. The impression should not be gained that all murmurs denote underlying cardiac pathology. Early systolic murmurs can be detected in a majority of children, especially those with thin chest walls. These murmurs are called functional and are most often heard at the pulmonary area. Early systolic murmurs are also audible in many normal persons following exercise and, presumably, arise from the increased flow rate. Hemic murmurs develop in anemic patients as the result of decreased blood viscosity and increased blood velocity in the presence of an augmented cardiac output.

TIME RELATIONS. The particular valve involved is determined from the relation of the murmur to the events of the cardiac cycle and from the point upon the chest wall where the sound is transmitted with the greatest intensity. For instance, the aortic valves should open fully during the ejection phase of ventricular systole so as to offer little or no resistance to the outflow of blood at this time. At the end of the period of ejection they should close tightly. If however the orifice is stenosed, the obstruction causes a murmur to be heard during ventricular systole which replaces or modifies the clear first sound. This is referred to as a *systolic murmur* (fig. 49.2). If, on the other hand, the valves are incompetent and do not come together at the end of the systolic discharge, a rush of blood from the aorta into the ventricle occurs in diastole, and a murmur modifies the normal second sound—diastolic murmur. The murmur may appear in early, mid-, or late diastole or may persist throughout almost the entire period. When stenosis and incompetence co-exist a murmur may be produced at the aortic orifice during both systole and diastole, in which event the two normal sounds are replaced by a to and fro blowing sound. A systolic murmur will also be caused by incompetence of the A-V

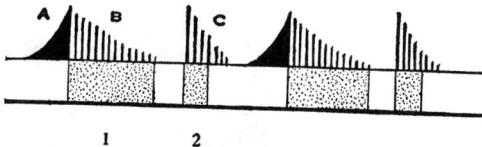

FIG. 49.2. Diagram showing the time relations of heart murmurs to the heart sounds. *A*, presystolic murmur; *B*, systolic murmur; *C*, early diastolic murmur. Numbers refer to normal heart sounds.

valves (mitral or tricuspid) since the rise in pressure during ventricular systole will drive blood backwards into the atrium and cause abnormal vibrations to be set up.

GALLOP RHYTHM. In addition to the clearly audible first and second heart sounds of each cardiac cycle, a third and even a fourth diastolic sound may be heard (see ch. 41). All four sounds are often seen in phonocardiographic tracings and may be heard in normal young persons. In certain conditions, three distinct heart sounds are heard which give rise to a rhythm not unlike the gallop or canter of a horse. Gallop rhythms appear to be the pathological counterparts of the normal third and fourth heart sounds.

In some cases, the abnormal sound precedes the first sound—the presystolic (atrial) type of gallop rhythm. Two sounds are heard in rapid succession followed by a pause, and then by the second heart sound (fig. 49.3). This type is associated with depressed atrioventricular conduction (ch. 37), bundle branch block, myocardial infarction or, most commonly, hypertensive cardiovascular disease. The extra sound is usually attributed to the actual muscular contraction of the atrium; more recent evidence favors a forceful movement of the ventricular wall apparently resulting from atrial ejection of blood into the partially filled ventricle. Normally, the ventricular contraction follows so closely upon atrial systole, that any sound that may be produced merges into the first heart sound. When, as a result of slowed conduction, the atrial and ventricular systoles are separated by an appreciable interval, the sound resulting from contraction of the atrium may become audible.

In other instances, the abnormal sound follows shortly after the second heart sound—early diastolic (protodiastolic) type of gallop rhythm (fig. 49.4). Most commonly, this gallop rhythm is associated with incipient or actual cardiac failure, therefore, it has a different clinical significance than the presystolic gallop. The cause of the protodiastolic gallop is unknown. It is not

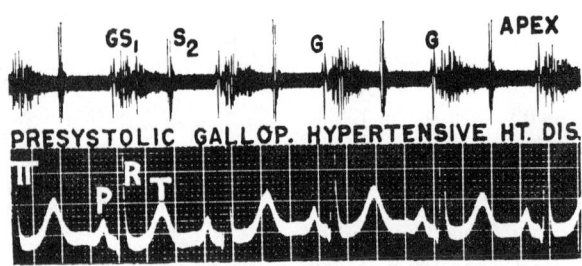

Fig. 49.3. Phonocardiogram (and electrocardiogram) demonstrating a presystolic gallop (G) in a patient with hypertensive heart disease. A systolic murmur is also present between the first (S_1) and the second heart sounds (S_2). (From Levine and Harvey.)

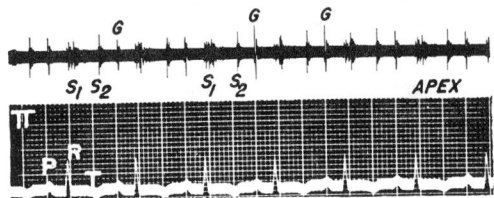

Fig. 49.4. Phonocardiogram (and electrocardiogram) demonstrating an early diastolic gallop (G). Note that the gallop sound occurs in early diastole nearer the second (S_2) than the first heart sound (from Levine and Harvey).

secondary to an asynchronous closure of the pulmonary and aortic valves. The sound occurs at the end of the period of rapid ventricular filling (as shown by correlative studies with intracardiac pressure curves). Most likely it is either produced by vibrations set up in the walls of the relaxed dilated ventricle by the shock of blood as it rushes from the atrium, or by a temporary reclosure of the atrioventricular valves (Dock).

Two variations of these gallop rhythms may occur. When both gallop sounds are present, a quadruple rhythm is produced. When the heart rate becomes very fast, a single, very loud sound may occur in mid-diastole. This is a result of the fusion of the two gallop sounds. It is probably not just an addition of the two sounds but is a new sound produced as a result of atrial contraction actually augmenting the phase of rapid ventricular filling.

Gallop sounds have been shown to vary in intensity with the respiratory cycle, posture, and pooling of venous blood in the legs. Each of these factors affects the venous return to the heart and therefore, atrial pressure and ventricular filling. In some instances, an abnormal sound is heard between the first and second heart sounds—the systolic type of gallop. In contrast to diastolic gallops, the systolic gallop is usually of little clinical significance. The origin of the extra sound is uncertain although it may be secondary to

vibration set up in a dilated vessel, pleuropericardial adhesions, or to other extracardiac factors.

MITRAL STENOSIS. Mitral stenosis is the most common valvular abnormality resulting from rheumatic involvement of the heart. Some degree of mitral regurgitation is also often present. The hemodynamic effects are due to the obstruction to flow between the left atrium and the left ventricle. The normal mitral valvular orifice in man varies between 4 and 6 cm.² When this is reduced to about 1.5 cm.², hemodynamic abnormalities may be found and at 1 cm.², they are severe enough to cause symptoms in most patients.

Mitral stenosis, by offering an obstruction to the flow of blood from the atrium into the ventricle, may cause a murmur to be heard at any time between the second and the first heart sounds (fig. 49.5). Since intensity of the murmur is dependent on both amount of flow and stenosis, it is not an indication of the degree of stenosis. The duration of the murmur is recognized as correlating better than the intensity with the size of the stenotic valve since a longer ventricular filling period must be accompanied by a longer murmur. Though the murmur may extend throughout diastole, it tends to be more intense toward the beginning and the end of this phase; it may be heard only during these times or be confined to one or the other of them. The late diastolic murmur (presystolic) disappears when auricular fibrillation supervenes and abolishes the propulsive action of atrial systole.

Braunwald and his associates have defined the hemodynamics of the cardiac cycle in mitral stenosis by catheterization of the left chambers of the heart in patients. Simultaneous inscription of atrial and ventricular pulse pressures (fig. 49.6) shows that the crossing of the left atrial and ventricular curve and the onset of the atrial "c" wave are delayed. Since the left atrial pressure at the end of diastole is higher than the ventricular pressure, the mitral valve cannot close until the ventricular pressure reaches that of the left atrium. Presumably, isometric contraction may begin while the valve is still open and left ventricular filling continuing. When the mitral valve reopens, the left atrial and ventricular curves diverge (instead of normally coinciding) for a pressure gradient is maintained to force blood across the stenotic valve. This pressure gradient results in a slight shortening of the isometric relaxation period and allows an early onset of mitral valve opening. Thus, the time for left ventricular filling may be increased by small amounts at either end of the ventricular filling period. The period of diastasis is usually absent and the atrial pressure curve shows a continuous decline in pressure during diastole until atrial contraction occurs. In the normal heart, left ventricular filling takes place early in diastole for the most part, but in mitral stenosis it is believed that filling continues throughout diastole.

Although little is understood concerning the sequence of hemodynamic events which may occur in any one patient, much data has been ac-

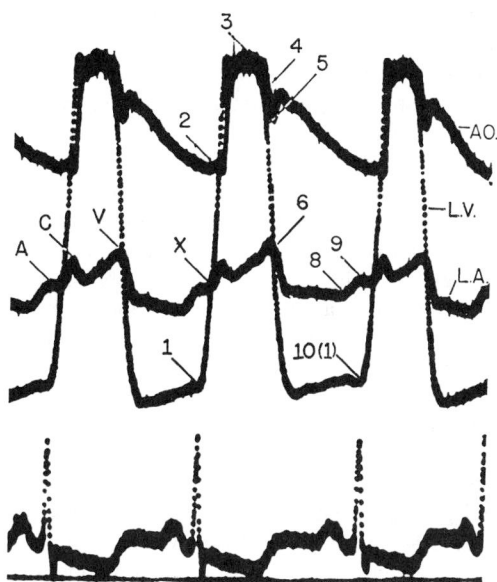

FIG. 49.6. The cardiac cycle of the left side of the heart in mitral stenosis. *A.O.*, aortic pressure curve; *L.V.*, left ventricular curve; *L.A.*, left atrial pressure curve; lower tracing is the electrocardiogram. 1, ventricular contraction onset; 2, end of isometric contraction period; 3, end of maximum ejection period; 4, end of reduced ejection period; 5, end of protodiastole (aortic valve closure); 6, end of isometric relaxation period; 8, onset of atrial contraction (the period of diastasis is absent); 9, peak of atrial contraction wave; and 10, onset of ventricular isometric contraction. See text for explanation (from E. Braunwald and associates, Circulation, 1955.)

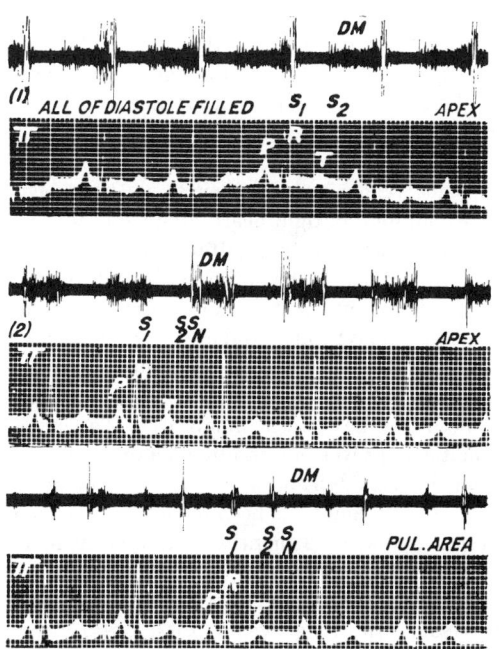

FIG. 49.5. Phonocardiogram (and electrocardiogram) depicting the murmur of mitral stenosis. Tracing (1) shows an apical diastolic murmur (*DM*) filling all of diastole with presystolic accentuation. The systolic interval between the first (S_1) and second (S_2) heart sounds demonstrates no murmur. Tracing (2) also is a diastolic murmur recorded at the apex and pulmonic areas from a patient with mitral stenosis. S_n denotes the "opening snap" of the mitral valves which is often heard in mitral stenosis. (From Levine and Harvey.)

cumulated from animal experiments and from catheterization studies in patients with mitral stenosis in different phases of the disease. Such data cannot take into account the effects of a concomitant, unmeasurable amount of mitral insufficiency, other valvular disease or myocardial insufficiency which are often present in the patients studied. In general, the asymptomatic patients show a normal cardiac output, a normal pulmonary artery and pulmonary wedge pressure and a normal pulmonary resistance at rest. The filling pressure gradient between the left atrium and the left ventricle is the only consistent abnormality in those patients that have had left heart catheterization. Often there is an abnormal response to exercise by an inadequate increase in cardiac output and a rise in pulmonary artery pressure. Since filling of the ventricle may take place during the entire period of diastole when a stenotic valve is present, an increased heart rate could decrease the cardiac output by shortening the period of diastole. Exercise results in an increased venous return to the right side of the heart. The increased right ventricular work load in pumping the blood against the raised pulmonary resistance may lead to decompensation and be an additional factor in the decrease in cardiac output.

Most patients with severe, symptomatic mitral stenosis show the following abnormalities at catheterization: a decreased cardiac output, stroke volume and vital capacity; an increased left atrial, pulmonary wedge, and pulmonary artery pressure; an increased left ventricular filling pressure gradient and an increased pulmonary arteriolar resistance. The work of the right ventricle is increased. A decrease in left ventricular coronary blood flow and decreased oxygen utilization per unit of left ventricular weight have also been demonstrated. The right atrial mean, and the right and left ventricular end-diastolic, pressures are normal unless myocardial failure has supervened. With exercise, the abnormalities in these patients are usually intensified.

From the above data, a scheme can be postulated for the hemodynamics in a patient with gradually increasing mitral stenosis. It has been shown by Gorlin and his associates that the dynamic effect of mitral stenosis is not linearly proportional to its degree but tends to be curvilinear. As the stenosis becomes tighter, a more than proportional rise in pressure is necessary to produce equivalent increases in flow across the valve. The left atrial pressure rises in order to produce the pressure gradient necessary to force blood into the left ventricle across the resistance created by the stenotic valve. There must be a corresponding increase in pulmonary vein, capillary, and finally, pulmonary artery and right ventricular systolic pressure to maintain the flow of blood to the left atrium from the right side of the heart. As the mitral valve narrows further, blood flow into the normal sized left ventricle is decreased despite a large pressure gradient from the enlarged left atrium, and cardiac output diminishes. The tissues of the body compensate for the decreased cardiac output by extracting more oxygen from each milliliter of blood, creating an increased arteriovenous oxygen difference. When the hydrostatic pressure in the pulmonary capillaries exceeds that of the plasma osmotic pressure, there will be transudation of fluid into the alveoli from the capillaries producing pulmonary edema.

The increased pulmonary artery pressure is not entirely due to the mitral valve obstruction. Parker and Weiss described a thickening of the pulmonary arterioles secondary to intimal proliferation. Necrotizing arteriolitis was also present along with pulmonary capillary elongation, dilation and basement membrane thickening. Whether these findings are related to the increased pressure and congestive phenomena of long standing mitral stenosis or represent changes from rheumatic involvement of the lung has not been settled. Curti and associates found no consistent correlation between the calculated pulmonary arteriolar resistance and the degree of disease of the pulmonary arterioles in lung biopsies. They postulated that active vasoconstriction may play a large role in the pulmonary resistance present in cases of mitral stenosis. It has been demonstrated that patients with high pulmonary artery pressure may show a decrease in pressure when acetylcholine is infused in the right atrium. Ischemia due to alveolar hypoventilation or the chronically increased pressure may be the stimulus which induces an increased pulmonary vascular tone. Whatever the cause of the lung pathology, the changes add another obstruction to the circuit in addition to the stenotic valve.

With the pulmonary artery pressure rise, the systolic pressure, and thus the work of the right ventricle, increases. When the right ventricle can no longer maintain its output against the increased pulmonary resistance, its end diastolic pressure rises, leading to right atrial and eventual systemic venous pressure elevations. Then, signs and symptoms of right heart failure appear.

Enlargement of the mitral orifice by finger fracture or incision has been performed in thousands of patients with symptomatic mitral stenosis. Hemodynamic studies before and after operation have demonstrated dramatic changes in some patients from such commissurotomies while others have been unimproved. The symptomatic improvement is often more impressive than the hemodynamic changes. The pulmonary vascular resistance has been reported to decrease over a period of 6 months to a year in many patients. Symptoms recur in a large percentage of patients after several years and reoperation is necessary. In recent years, total mitral valve replacement with a ball-valve prosthesis developed by Starr and Edwards has been performed in patients considered unsuitable for commissurotomy. Calcified or severely deformed valves do not function well after commissurotomy. Hemodynamic studies in patients in whom ball-valve prostheses have been inserted usually have shown a return to normal of left atrial, pulmonary artery and right ventricular pressures;

an increased pressure gradient between the left atrium and ventricle persists and is due to the prosthetic valve.

MITRAL INSUFFICIENCY. Mitral insufficiency often coexists with a stenotic mitral valve but may occur in the "pure" form. The usual etiology is rheumatic heart disease but other rarer causes are also seen. The magnitude of the regurgitant stream is determined not only by the size of the mitral valve opening, but also by the pressure relationships between the two chambers. Rodbard and Williams have suggested that contraction of the muscular ring at the base of the mitral valve decreases the size of the mitral leak during ventricular systole. The fact that simultaneous flow through two orifices favors the larger orifice (aortic valve) also lessens the amount of mitral regurgitation. However, since the pressure gradient from the left ventricle to the left atrium is

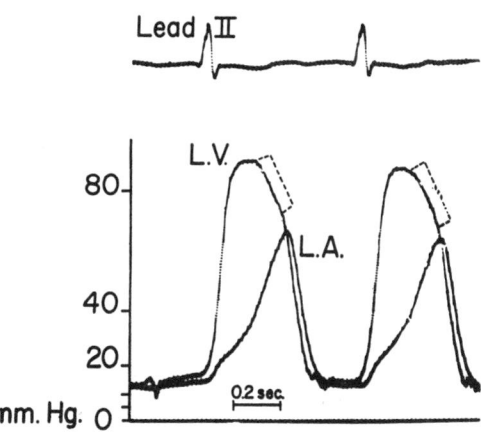

FIG. 49.8. Simultaneous left atrial and left ventricular pressures recorded at operation in a patient with mitral insufficiency. The atrial pressure curve rises to a high peak during ventricular ejection secondary to the regurgitation. An abnormally rapid fall in ventricular pressure (indicated by the brackets) is noted during late ventricular ejection. End diastolic pressures are elevated in both chambers; there is no diastolic pressure gradient across the mitral valve (from Ross, Braunwald, and Morrow).

much larger than from the left ventricle to the aorta, regurgitation is favored. The amount of reflux into the left atrium has been calculated in patients to sometimes exceed the aortic flow by as much as four times. Animal experiments, with the production of acute mitral insufficiency, have shown the heart to be able to compensate for large amounts of regurgitant flow. Wiggers and Feil demonstrated that reflux may occur during the entire period of systole, including isometric contraction, and continue into protodiastole in dog hearts with surgically produced acute mitral insufficiency. This explains why the murmur of mitral incompetence is pansystolic in time and often obscures the second heart sound (fig. 49.7). However, sometimes the murmur is maximal late in systole and may even be confined to late systole. The mechanism of this late systolic crescendo murmur is not understood.

Ross and associates studied the dynamics of the cardiac cycle in patients with mitral insufficiency by left heart catheterization. Left atrial pressure (fig. 49.8) rises little during isometric contraction followed by a rapid increase to a peak ("v" wave) during late ejection by the ventricle. The left atrial pressure slightly exceeds the left ventricular pressure during the "y" descent. An abnormally rapid fall in ventricular pressure during late ejection is coincident with the atrial "v" wave. The rapid fall is evidently due to the inability of the ventricle to maintain its ejection

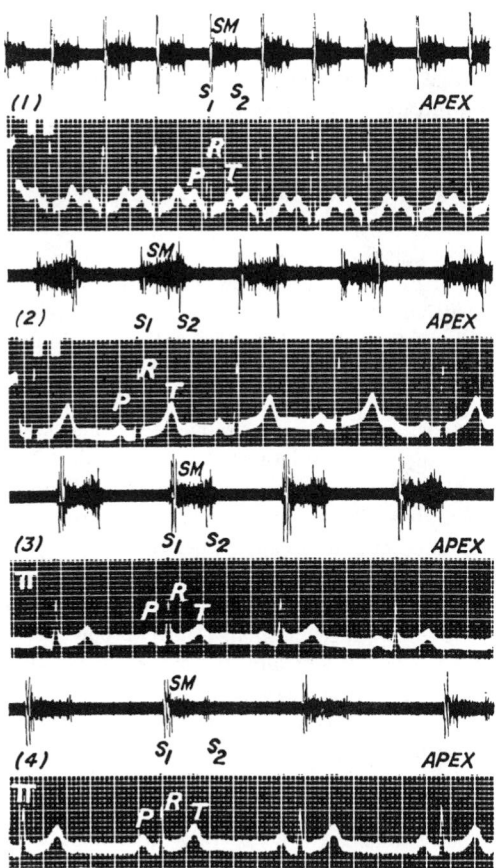

FIG. 49.7. Phonocardiogram (and electrocardiogram) demonstrating the murmur of mitral insufficiency. These 4 tracings show loud systolic murmurs (*SM*) at the apex in patients with mitral insufficiency. S_1 and S_2 denote the first and second heart sounds. The diastolic interval (S_2 to S_1) is clear (from Levine and Harvey).

pressure when regurgitant flow is maximal. Reflux of blood most likely begins during isometric contraction. The forward aortic output cannot begin until the intraventricular pressure exceeds the aortic pressure. It should be mentioned that the large "v" wave is not characteristic of mitral regurgitation for it has also been seen in predominant mitral stenosis. The "v" wave is responsible for a systolic atrial pulsation often seen in mitral insufficiency by fluoroscopy.

Cardiac output in patients with mitral insufficiency is usually decreased but may be normal or low normal. Since the left ventricle pumps blood into the left atrium and aorta, the total left ventricular stroke volume must increase or the aortic output will fall. The left ventricular tension and systolic pressure are increased by a greater diastolic volume leading to an elevated stroke output. The regurgitant flow work of the left ventricle may be very high; the total regurgitant work (flow and pressure) may constitute up to 77% of the total work of the left ventricle. Large regurgitant flow may exist without measurable increase in left ventricular end diastolic pressure. Braunwald and associates shunted blood from the left ventricle to the left atrium in dogs and suggested that the increased stroke volume was related to a more complete emptying of the ventricle; however, normal dog hearts are quite different from the hypertrophied, dilated, left atrium and ventricle seen in patients with diseased mitral valves.

The greater left ventricular diastolic volume may be brought about by a considerable increase in left atrial pressure. The left atrial pressure rises abnormally high during ventricular systole but may be normal during diastole; the mean pressure is usually elevated. There may or may not be abnormal pulmonary circulation pressures. When present, they are of less severe intensity than seen in mitral stenosis, and may be secondary to left ventricular failure, pathological pulmonary changes (as described for mitral stenosis), or to a left atrial pressure elevated to maintain sufficient diastolic blood flow through the mitral valve.

When the left ventricular end diastolic pressure rises to maintain the cardiac output in the presence of mitral incompetence, it may be due only to the attempt of the ventricle to maintain its stroke volume through the two orifices or, also, to intrinsic myocardial disease with impaired contractility. Whichever mechanism predominates, the end result is a further rise in left atrial pressure, eventually reflecting back to increase the peripheral venous pressure, as described for mitral stenosis.

Operative procedures to correct mitral insufficiency have consisted of suturing of the valvular commissures (annuloplasty), insertion of plastic leaflets or whole valves, or use of ball-valve prostheses. Long term followup to evaluate these procedures is not yet available.

AORTIC STENOSIS. Stenosis of the aortic valves may be classified as noncalcific or calcific. The former is predominantly due to rheumatic fever, but the etiology of the latter remains in doubt. Although the general opinion favors rheumatic endocarditis, atherosclerosis of the valves and bacterial endocarditis have been incriminated. The clinical picture and hemodynamic abnormalities of aortic stenosis may be imitated by supravalvular stenosis or by subaortic stenosis of the discrete type. Supravalvular stenosis may be produced by an annular constriction due to intimal and medial hypertrophy of the aorta, to a long tube-like narrowing of the ascending aorta due to medial proliferation, or to a thin membrane with a central opening just above the aortic valve. Subaortic stenosis may be caused by a membrane or diaphragm attached to the myocardium below the aortic valve. Brock has described an entity which causes functional subvalvular stenosis and pathologically shows only an enormous diffuse hypertrophy of the outflow tract of the ventricle; the hypertrophy often predominantly involves the ventricular septum. Recently, this diffuse subaortic stenosis has been found to have a high familial incidence. Supravalvular aortic and discrete subaortic stenosis produce the same clinical picture and hemodynamic abnormalities as valvular stenosis and will not be considered separately. The normal area of the aortic valve is about 3 cm.[2] Gorlin and associates estimated the "critical" orifice (below which significant hemodynamic changes take place) to be 0.5 cm.[2] Aortic stenosis produces a small orifice through which blood is ejected at high velocity during systole, presumably resulting in turbulent flow. The murmur (fig. 49.9) is usually mid-systolic for there is an interval between the first heart sound and the onset of the murmur determined by the time needed by the ventricle to raise its pressure sufficiently to open the aortic valve. The murmur increases to a maximum about midsystole and then diminishes to cease before the second heart sound. It is usually heard loudest over the aortic area and is transmitted into the neck vessels, but can also be loud at the apex. Subaortic stenosis, produces a loud, long systolic murmur which is best heard along the lower left sternal border or at the apex.

Those patients with aortic stenosis who are asymptomatic usually have a normal cardiac output and stroke volume. The systolic gradient of pressure between the left ventricle and aorta (by left heart catheterization) is the diagnostic feature present in all cases (fig. 49.10). This gradient may reach as high as 150 mm. Hg so that the brachial artery pressure is much lower than the ventricular systolic pressure. The left ventricular end diastolic pressure is usually normal. Musser and associates found an elevated left ventricular end diastolic pressure in patients who were thought not to be clinically in failure. They postulated that the concentric hypertrophy of the chamber decreased its capacity and perhaps small volume changes then led to large pressure changes. The workload of the left ventricle in patients with aortic stenosis has been calculated to be usually twice that of normals but may reach six times normal. Gorlin and coworkers found that, although the ventricular filling pressure rose in their patients, there was no change in effective or total stroke work or cardiac output with exercise. They suggested that this was secondary to the hydraulic obstruction rather than myocardial failure and that the hearts were on the plateau of their ventricular function curves.

The brachial artery pressure curve (which is similar to the aorta curve shown in fig. 49.10) in patients with aortic stenosis, shows a prolongation of the systolic upstroke time (end of diastole to peak of systole). There is an incisura on the ascending limb referred to as the "anacrotic notch." The latter has been shown by Katz and associates to be present in the central aortic pressure curve. They postulated that the vibration created by the suction action on the aortic walls of the rapid axial stream suddenly produced beyond the constriction was its cause.

With the above data in mind, a hemodynamic picture can be postulated for valvular aortic stenosis. Because of the obstruction between the left ventricle and aorta, the left ventricular systolic pressure must rise to force blood through the stenosed valves. The period of ejection is prolonged and blood is expelled at a high velocity. The percentage of the left ventricular work spent in giving velocity to the blood rises sharply. An increased diastolic volume causes a more forceful systolic contraction with restoration of normal cardiac output. Left ventricular hypertrophy develops to compensate for the increased workload and may be the reason the left ventricle is able to

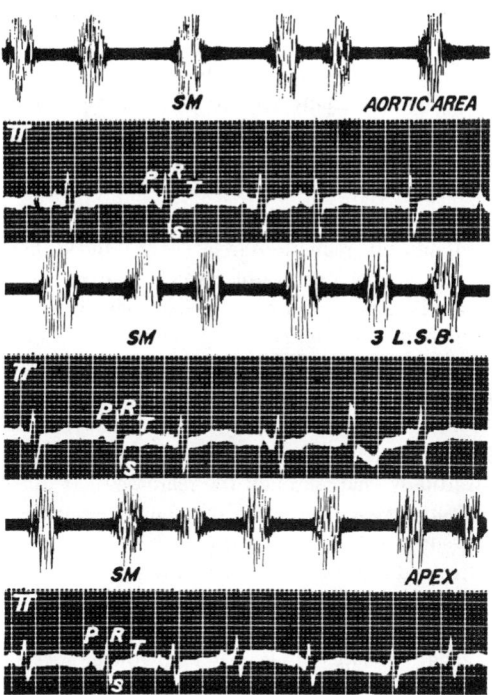

Fig. 49.9. Phonocardiogram (and electrocardiogram) showing the systolic murmur of aortic stenosis. The systolic murmur, with a midsystolic accentuation (often called "diamond-shaped") was recorded in three areas (aortic, left sternal border in the 3rd interspace, and apical). Note absence of diastolic murmur (from Levine and Harvey).

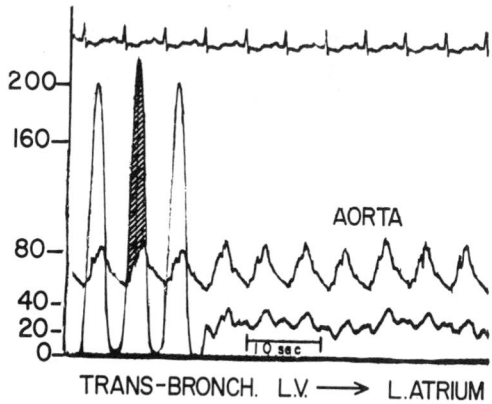

Fig. 49.10. Simultaneous pressure recordings in the left ventricle (*L.V.*) and aorta in a patient with aortic valvular stenosis. Catheterization of the left heart was *via* the transbronchial route. The electrocardiogram is shown above the pressure tracings. Note the very high left ventricular systolic pressure and systolic pressure gradient (hatched area) across the aortic valve. The aortic curve shows a small pulse pressure, prolonged systolic upstroke time, and an "anacrotic" notch. See text for further explanation (courtesy of E. Braunwald, Section of Cardiology, Clinic of Surgery, National Heart Institute).

sustain such high systolic pressures without failure.

The left ventricular systolic pressure may rise very high but finally the end diastolic ventricular pressure must increase in an attempt to maintain cardiac output. One of the reasons for failure of the left ventricle may be a decreased coronary supply. Animal experiments have demonstrated a significant reduction in coronary blood flow during ventricular systole which is due to increased coronary bed resistance associated with a very high intraventricular pressure. Also, since the aortic stenotic heart cannot usually increase its cardiac output with exercise, there would probably not be an increase in coronary flow. Elevation of the left ventricular diastolic pressure may eventually lead, through the increased left atrial pressure, to a rise in the pulmonary circulation pressures, an increased workload for the right ventricle and right-sided heart failure.

In diffuse subaortic stenosis, the area of narrowing and the pressure gradient are in the ventricular cavity. Exaggerated narrowing of the ventricular outflow tract occurs during systolic contraction. Brockenbrough and coworkers have shown that increasing the force of ventricular contraction decreases the size of the ventricular outflow tract. Thus, in these patients, the more forceful beat which follows the compensatory pause of an ectopic beat is associated with a larger ventricular pressure but a smaller arterial pulse pressure than with normal beats. The increased intraventricular pressure does not usually compensate for the decreased size of the outflow tract. It has also been demonstrated that the increased force of contraction induced by digitalis or isoproterenol results in unusually severe narrowing of the muscular outflow tract and an increased workload on the left ventricle without an

increase in cardiac output. Digitalis may therefore be detrimental in subaortic stenosis whereas it has no effect or improves ventricular function in valvular stenosis. Hernandez and coworkers have shown that 80% of the systolic output of the left ventricle in subaortic stenosis occurs during the first half of systole compared to about 60% in normal hearts or hearts afflicted with other diseases. A marked decrease in outflow occurs during the last half of systole. The mechanism is unknown; obstruction to flow may be more severe in the last half of systole or powerful, rapid contractions may produce total ejection early in systole. A *pulsus bisferiens* occurs in subaortic stenosis; the double-peaked pulse is sharp and bounding compared to the slow, plateau pulse of valvular stenosis. The pulsus bisferiens may be due to reflected pressure waves combining with the forward pressure wave, or to a negative dip in pressure with the rapid deceleration of blood flow during the last half of systole.

Patients with aortic valvular stenosis may have their valves opened by a surgical approach through the ventricle or aorta, often with the help of an extracorporeal pump-oxygenator. A dilator, finger, or knife is used as in mitral stenosis. In patients with severely deformed or calcified valves, prosthetic valve cusps or ball-valve prostheses are now being inserted. Clinical improvement has been excellent in many patients and a reduction in the left ventricular to aortic systolic pressure gradient has been found immediately after operation. Supravalvular stenosis is treated by excision of the stenosis; a graft must often be used to widen the aorta. In subaortic stenosis the hypertrophied tissue may be excised.

AORTIC REGURGITATION. Incompetent aortic valves most often result from rheumatic fever or syphilis; rarer causes are bacterial endocarditis, trauma, dissecting aneurysm of the aorta or congenital defects of the valves. The murmur (fig. 49.11) of aortic regurgitation is pandiastolic, beginning early after closure of the aortic valves, swelling quickly to a crescendo and then diminishing with the falling diastolic pressure. It is continuous throughout diastole because of a persistent pressure difference between the aorta and ventricle. This murmur is high pitched and usually of a very low intensity; it is often very difficult to hear. An apical presystolic murmur resembling that of mitral stenosis is sometimes heard in aortic incompetence. This murmur was described originally by Austin Flint and bears his name. According to the most generally accepted explanation, it is due to vibrations set up

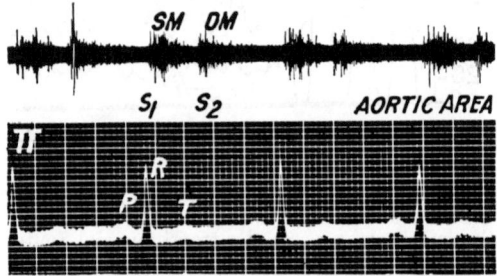

FIG. 49.11. Phonocardiogram (and electrocardiogram) demonstrating the murmur of aortic insufficiency. S_1 and S_2 denote the first and second heart sounds. An early, decrescendo diastolic murmur (*DM*) is recorded at the aortic area. A systolic murmur (*SM*) is also present (from Levine and Harvey).

in the anterior leaflet of the mitral valve as blood regurgitates through the aortic orifice into the path of the stream entering from the left atrium.

The hemodynamic effects of aortic incompetence are due to the regurgitation of blood from the aorta into the left ventricle. Wiggers and Maltby, in animal experiments, demonstrated that the magnitude of backflow varied with the size of the leak and could be 50% or more of the left ventricular output when the cusps were totally deficient. The pressure gradient existing in diastole between the left ventricle and the aorta, and the duration of the diastolic filling period are also important factors determining the amount of regurgitation. The left ventricle is called upon to accommodate, in diastole, not only the blood from the atrium, but that regurgitated as well. This leads to a high initial tension at the end of diastole and a greater stroke volume during systole; in time, dilation and hypertrophy develop to give a very large left ventricle. Welch and associates in dog experiments, have produced aortic regurgitation by a shunt from the aorta to the ventricle. Since the left ventricular end-diastolic pressure rose to higher levels than the left atrial pressure, they postulated that the mitral valve protected the pulmonary circulation and allowed a high left ventricular end-diastolic pressure to produce a more forceful contraction.

The left ventricle with aortic reflux demonstrates a much shorter isometric period and its pressure curve (fig. 49.12) rises abruptly. As the semilunar valves open, there is an "explosive" ejection of a large volume of blood into the aorta causing the abrupt increase in systolic pressure. A much greater proportion than usual of the ventricular contents is discharged during the first half of systole, and a much smaller proportion during the period of reduced ejection. It is at this time— the period of reduced ejection—that the sharp fall in pressure occurs and *not during diastole*. The pressure fall continues steeply into the period of isometric relaxation. Little further decline during the remainder of diastole occurs. Other factors contributing to the low diastolic pressure are the regurgitation itself and a peripheral dilation causing a rapid run-off of the blood. Gorlin and coworkers claim that peripheral vasodilation is a basic characteristic of aortic insufficiency which disappears when congestive heart failure develops with its usual systemic vasoconstriction. The pulsation in the capillaries seen in aortic regurgitation has been attributed by Lewis and Drury to dilation of the arterioles. Wiggers found that peripheral signs of aortic insufficiency could

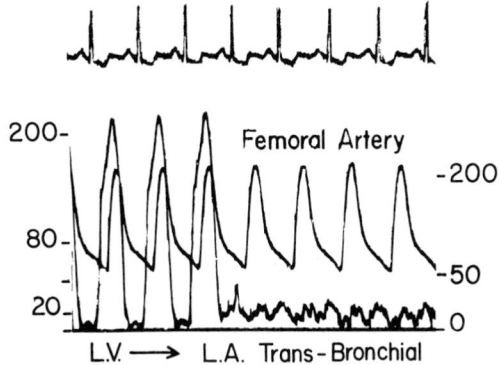

Fig. 49.12. Simultaneous recordings of the pressures in the left ventricle (*L.V.*) and femoral artery in a patient with aortic valvular insufficiency. The electrocardiogram is shown at the top of the figure. The calibration of the pressure for the left ventricle is on the left side and for the femoral artery on the right side. Note that the systolic pressures of the left ventricle and femoral artery are similar. The catheter has been withdrawn into the left atrium to obtain its pressure curve. The transbronchial route for left heart catheterization was used. See text for description of pressure curves (courtesy of E. Braunwald, Section of Cardiology, Clinic of Surgery, National Heart Institute).

be produced in an artificial model when central regurgitation was produced and the peripheral resistance kept constant. He, therefore, considered that they were due primarily to the low diastolic pressure and high pulse pressure. However, Myerson and associates have been able to produce all the peripheral phenomena of aortic insufficiency in a single extremity by the intra-arterial injection of mecholyl to cause vasodilation. Most cardiologists agree that peripheral vasodilation is a characteristic of aortic insufficiency.

The sudden ejection of a large volume of blood in early systole and the peripheral vasodilation also provide an explanation for the high-peaked character of the pulse tracing, and for the low position or absence of the dicrotic wave on the catacrotic limb (fig. 49.12). Also, the collapsing or water hammer character of the radial pulse (Corrigan's pulse), and the sound resembling a pistol shot, heard when a stethoscope is applied over an artery, are attributed to the very wide peripheral pulse pressure caused by these phenomena.

In most patients, catheterization studies show the effective cardiac output (aortic blood flow) to be normal at rest and usually to rise with exercise. This is in contrast to patients with aortic stenosis. Exercise may decrease the magnitude of the regurgitation by increasing the heart rate. In animal experiments, after production of acute aortic

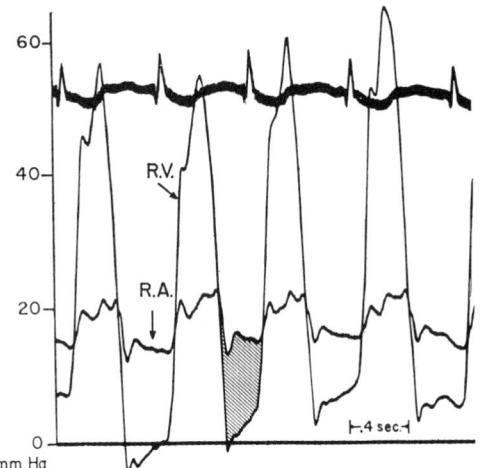

FIG. 49.13. Simultaneous pressure curves from the right atrium (*R.A.*) and right ventricle in a patient with tricuspid stenosis. The electrocardiogram is shown at the top of the tracing. Note that the right atrial pressure exceeds the right ventricular pressure throughout diastole creating the pressure gradient depicted by the hatched area. The right ventricular systolic pressure is elevated secondary to pulmonary hypertension from a concomitant mitral stenosis. For discussion of the pressure curves, see text (courtesy of E. Braunwald, Section of Cardiology, Clinic of Surgery, National Heart Institute).

insufficiency, an increase in heart rate reduced the regurgitant flow probably by a decrease in the diastolic filling time. The work of the left ventricle in patients with aortic valve incompetence is increased two to three times, and the left ventricular systolic pressure rises, as does stroke work, with exercise, again contrasting with aortic stenosis. Left heart catheterization usually reveals a normal left ventricular end-diastolic pressure but an increased left atrial pressure. Pulmonary wedge pressures, however, are normal in most patients but rise on exercise. No gradient of pressure is found across the aortic valve when aortic stenosis is absent. Patients have lived normal lives for years with aortic insufficiency. The reason for left ventricular failure occurring after a long asymptomatic period (except for symptoms related to the wide pulse pressure and peripheral vasodilation) is not clear. It may be secondary to many factors, such as over-stretching of the myocardial fibers, associated degenerative disease, or any added stress calling for an increased cardiac output. At this point, the left ventricular end-diastolic pressure rises and a pressure increase gradually occurs back through the pulmonary circulation to the right ventricle. Stretching of the mitral ring (with resultant regurgitation) by a

greatly dilated left ventricle may play a large role in the final picture.

Hufnagel and associates devised an operative approach to this disease by insertion of a rigid prosthetic plastic ball valve in the descending aorta. Clinical improvement has been satisfactory in many of the operated patients, but emboli often form in the aorta, seeding to various parts of the body. The valve is also a noise nuisance to the patient. With the use of open heart surgery, it has become possible to insert ball-valve prostheses, resuspend the patients own aortic cusps, or replace one or all cusps with prosthetic substitutes. Results reported with these procedures have been favorable.

TRICUSPID STENOSIS. Stenosis of the tricuspid valve is usually the result of rheumatic involvement but may also be congenital in origin. As an isolated lesion, it is rare; mitral stenosis is most often associated with it and, also, some degree of tricuspid insufficiency usually occurs through the stenotic valve. The murmur of a stenotic tricuspid valve resembles that of mitral stenosis, but is located parasternally in the 4th or 5th left intercostal space. It is low-pitched, rumbling, and is like the mitral stenotic murmur in its diastolic timing. Distinguishing features of the tricuspid murmur are an increase in intensity with inspiration and a soft or normal pulmonic component of the second heart sound.

Right heart catheterization studies on patients with tricuspid stenosis have helped to define the hemodynamics of the lesion. It must be remembered that few, if any, of the cases studied had "pure" tricuspid stenosis and that mitral disease often complicated the picture by raising the pulmonary circulation pressures. As in mitral stenosis, the main hemodynamic abnormality is that the atrium does not empty its contents normally into the ventricle. The increased resistance at the stenotic valve leads to an increased diastolic volume in the right atrium, which becomes dilated and hypertrophied. In order to propel the blood into the right ventricle, the pressure in the right atrium must be elevated. In patients, a high right atrial pressure is observed which exceeds the right ventricular pressure throughout diastole and, thus, creates a diastolic filling gradient across the tricuspid valve (fig. 49.13). The right atrial pressure is higher than the ventricular diastolic pressure even at the end of diastole. The latter chamber must raise its pressure to atrial level before the valve can close, causing a prolonged isometric contraction period. Because of the increased right atrial pressure, the peripheral venous pressure rises and, eventually, signs of right-sided heart failure (edema, hepatomegaly, and ascites) appear.

With exercise, patients show an increased right atrial pressure and an increase in the diastolic filling gradient. The right ventricular diastolic pressure would most likely be normal at rest and with exercise, but is usually elevated because of an associated mitral lesion in these patients. The cardiac output and stroke volume are decreased and, with exercise, a subnormal increase occurs. The low cardiac output is usually explained by the inability of the thin-walled, dilated right atrium to adequately fill the right ventricle. The lack of a normal increase in cardiac output during exercise may be secondary to a decreased diastolic filling time with an increased heart rate.

In tricuspid stenosis, the atrial pulse pressure (fig. 49.14) exhibits a very large "a" wave due to the contraction of a hypertrophied atrium, dilated by a large diastolic residual volume, against a narrowed outlet. These giant "a" waves propagate retrogradely through the venous system, causing a presystolic, pulsating liver, and can often be seen clearly in the jugular veins of the neck. Such giant "a" waves are not diagnostic of tricuspid stenosis for they may also be seen in other diseases, such as severe pulmonary hypertension. The peak atrial systolic pressure wave is thus very high and falls very rapidly with atrial relaxation. The "v" wave is usually small while the "c" wave may be absent. The right atrial pressure does not decrease rapidly when the tricuspid valves reopen, indicating impaired emptying of the right atrium, and ventricular filling probably takes place throughout diastole, as described for mitral stenosis.

The accentuation of the tricuspid stenosis murmur with inspiration is usually explained by the increased venous return secondary to the fall in intrathoracic pressure; this leads to a rise in right atrial pressure due to the stenotic valve. The right ventricular pressure falls with the decrease in intrathoracic pressure, and an increased pressure gradient and flow occur across the valve.

Tricuspid commissurotomy is now performed in this disease as in mitral stenosis. If the latter disease is also present, both valves may be opened at the same operation, but the mitral should be done first to avoid pulmonary congestion from a suddenly increased right ventricular output as the tricuspid stenosis is relieved. Prosthetic valves are used when necessary.

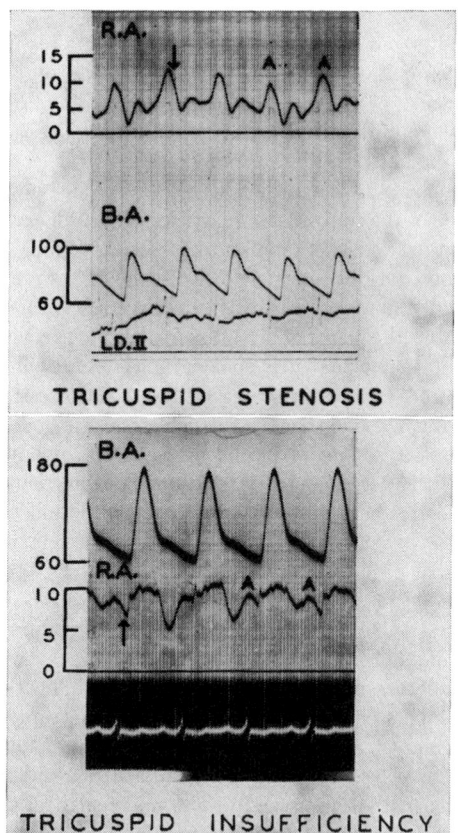

FIG. 49.14. Pressure tracings of the right atrium (*R.A.*) and brachial artery (*B.A.*) in a patient with tricuspid stenosis (*upper tracing*), and in a patient with tricuspid insufficiency (*lower tracing*). The electrocardiogram is shown in the lower section of each tracing. The *arrows* indicate the onset of ventricular systole and the letter *A* marks the peak of atrial systole. For discussion of atrial curves, see text (from Ferrer and associates, 1953.)

TRICUSPID INSUFFICIENCY. Organic tricuspid insufficiency is predominantly functional or rheumatic in origin, but trauma and bacterial endocarditis are rarer etiologies. It is sometimes present congenitally or in the syndrome associated with malignant carcinoid tumors. Functional tricuspid incompetence may occur whenever there is dilation of the right ventricle, and it is usually reversible. The murmur of an incompetent tricuspid valve resembles that of mitral regurgitation, being pansystolic. It is often accentuated early in systole and is heard loudest at the lower left sternal edge.

The pulse pressures of the right atrium and ventricle have been simultaneously and separately studied in these patients by right heart catheterization. The mean right atrial pressure is elevated. The right ventricular systolic pressure is usually very high while the end diastolic pressure may or may not be elevated depending on the presence of right ventricular failure, often from concomitant mitral disease. The atrial pressure curve (fig. 49.14) often shows a sharp spike at the onset of ventricular systole, probably due to the force of the contracting ventricle. Next a plateau-elevated curve, representing regurgitation of blood from the ventricle, occurs; the "x" wave is usually absent. This plateau curve may so resemble the ventricular pressure curve in severe insufficiency that it is spoken of as "ventricularization" of the atrial curve. The atrial pressure during the ventricular systolic period is higher than that of the presystolic period and is sustained to the end of isometric relaxation. The ventricular pressure then falls below the atrial level and the A-V valves open. The pressure in the relaxing ventricle continues to drop while the atrial pressure decreases at a slower rate and reaches its lowest value after the right ventricular pressure is minimal. Emptying of the right atrium reverses the decreasing ventricular pressure and the two chambers equalize their pressures, rising rapidly to complete the early diastolic dip. The diastolic dip, which is not always present in tricuspid insufficiency, is also seen in right ventricular failure and constrictive pericarditis but without the characteristic plateau pressure curve of the right atrium.

The cardiac output is decreased in most patients with tricuspid insufficiency and rises, although subnormally, with exercise. The peripheral arteriovenous oxygen difference is usually abnormal and increases further with exercise as the tissues extract more oxygen per unit of blood to compensate for the decreased blood flow. Patients with tricuspid insufficiency are often said to have a lower cardiac output than those with mitral incompetence because there is no ventricular pump to compensate for the tricuspid regurgitation of blood.

The enlarged right atrium, with its increased pressure, may never completely empty in tricuspid insufficiency and eventually cannot compensate despite the presence of hypertrophy and dilation. This leads to a high peripheral venous pressure with the development of edema, hepatomegaly, and ascites. In contrast to tricuspid stenosis, the enlarged, congested liver pulsates during systole. The usual explanation for the pulsating liver is that the reflux of blood into the atrium transmits a pulse wave to the organ, but Bloomfield and associates have measured in some

patients a pressure gradient from the right atrium to the peripheral veins suggesting there may actually be a reflux of blood into the inferior vena cava and into the liver. The right atrium may reach gigantic size in tricuspid insufficiency, as in stenosis, but, in contrast to the latter, the right ventricle also hypertrophies and/or dilates because of the increased workload imposed by pumping blood into both the right atrium and pulmonary artery.

Surgical treatment is similar to that for mitral insufficiency.

HEMODYNAMICS IN CARDIAC TAMPONADE

Pericardial effusions may develop during the course of an inflammation of the pericardium (pericarditis) due to a multitude of etiologies. Large amounts of fluid, up to a liter or more, accumulating slowly may not embarrass the heart, while acute effusions of much smaller amounts (often referred to as "tamponade") may compress the myocardium and interfere with its function. Chronic constrictive pericarditis is a fibrous, sometimes calcified thickening of the pericardium which adheres to the epicardium. Both conditions interfere with the normal cardiac action by restricting the ventricles, one by an increased intrapericardial pressure (effusion), the other by a stiffened pericardium (constrictive pericarditis). They produce a clinical syndrome characterized by systemic and pulmonary venous congestion with signs and symptoms of left and right sided heart failure. There is an absence of cardiac murmurs, but a prominent heart sound (*pericardial knock*) may be heard early in diastole. According to McKusick, this protodiastolic sound is probably related to the rapid ventricular filling and/or the abrupt halt (ventricle prevented from expanding by the tamponade or stiff pericardium) in ventricular filling.

The hemodynamic abnormalities of cardiac tamponade have been studied in both animal experiments and in patients. Pericardial effusion in dogs has been produced by infusion of air or saline into the pericardium while irritative substances, such as cellophane, have been used to induce chronic constrictive pericarditis. The syndrome produced in the dog is very similar to that seen in man. Metcalfe and associates, and Isaacs and co-workers, have shown that the main hemodynamic abnormality is a hindrance to the diastolic expansion of the heart and not a restriction of blood flow into the right atrium secondary to constriction of the venae cavae at their orifices. As successive amounts of saline or air were injected into the pericardium to raise the intra-pericardial pressure, the systemic and pulmonary venous, the mean atrial, and the pulmonary wedge pressures increased while peripheral blood pressure fell slowly at first and then precipitously. The cardiac output decreased secondary to a progressive fall in stroke volume and was insufficiently maintained by a concomitant rise in heart rate. The intravascular pressures (pulmonary and systemic, venous and arterial) tended to approach each other as the intrapericardial pressure increased. Isaacs and colleagues explained the restricted cardiac output by the pressure-volume curve of the pericardium which showed that large volume changes gave small increases in pressure when pressures and volumes were small, but as the curve rose, small volume increases caused large pressure increases (fig. 49.15). Thus, the circulatory effect would be due to a limitation of space available for expansion of the ventricle. Isaacs and associates also produced generalized and localized constrictive pericarditis in dogs by placing plastic casts in the pericardium. Hemodynamic changes were identical to those described for tamponade only when one or both ventricles were constricted. Isolated atrial involvement proved to be unimportant.

Catheterization studies in patients with chronic constrictive pericarditis and/or effusion have produced data comparable to that in the animal experiments. The mean atrial, systemic, pulmonary wedge, pulmonary artery diastolic and right ventricular end diastolic pressures all tend to be proportionally elevated in severe cases. Hemodynamic events are the same for both sides of the heart. The relationship of the left to the right atrial pressure is normal; the left usually being a few millimeters of mercury higher.

The ventricular pulse pressure curve is of low amplitude with a slightly elevated, normal or decreased systolic pressure. After the systolic pressure rise, there is a rapid fall in the ventricular pressure almost to or even below the baseline (?zero pressure), for the ventricle empties normally, creating a steep pressure gradient between the high atrial mean pressure and the ventricle. As a result, blood rushes into the ventricle causing a steep rise of the pressure curve to a higher than normal plateau for the remainder of diastole. This sharp fall and rise is called the diastolic "dip." Since the ventricular end diastolic (and mean diastolic) pressure approximates the mean atrial pressure (for the ventricle is prevented from distending by the thickened pericardium), filling of the ventricle occurs during the first part

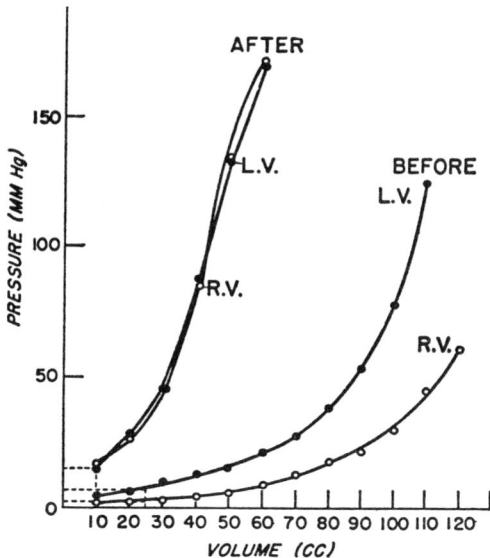

FIG. 49.15. Volume-elasticity curves of right and left ventricles before and after total pericardial constriction. These are volume-pressure curves obtained immediately after death from the right (*R.V.*) and left (*L.V.*) ventricles of the dog's heart within a normal pericardium (before) and from right and left ventricles within a generalized pericardial constriction (after). Increments of 10 cc. of saline were injected *via* the pulmonary artery or aorta into the closed ventricles while intraventricular pressures were recorded. It can be seen that, if the pericardium is thickened by scar so that it offers more resistance than usual, as the right ventricle volume increases against this increased resistance, greater than usual corresponding pressures are required (from Isaacs, Carter, and Haller).

("dip") of diastole with little further increase during the plateau phase. The atrial pressure curve shows two sharp drops to give a characteristic "M" shape: a large pressure decrease during the rapid ventricular filling, which coincides with the "dip" of the ventricular curve in time, amplitude and shape, and a smaller drop associated with ventricular ejection ("x" wave). Atrial systole is of high amplitude for the atrium is contracting against a nearly completely filled ventricle. The jugular venous pulse also reflects the sudden release of right atrial pressure due to rapid tricuspid inflow by demonstrating a characteristic diastolic collapse. The venous pulse shows a sharp *y* descent and deep *y* trough. Cardiac output and stroke volume have been normal in some patients but are usually decreased. With exercise, all elevated pressures rise further. In those that show some increase in cardiac output with exertion, the stroke volume did not increase indicating that the rise in cardiac output was secondary to an increased heart rate.

From the data presented above, hemodynamic sequelae can be postulated for both pericardial effusion and chronic constrictive pericarditis. The thickened pericardium or effusion interferes with diastolic filling of the ventricle so that greater than normal diastolic filling pressure gradients are needed to maintain cardiac output. As explained before, dilation of the ventricle normally leads to an increase in stroke output by increasing the myocardial fiber length resulting in a greater force of contraction. Presumably, such dilation is prevented by a constricting scar. Systemic and pulmonary venous pressure rise by unknown mechanisms, to increase the venous return to the heart and maintain cardiac output. The increased venous pressures lead to serous cavity effusions, anasarca, hepatomegaly and pulmonary congestion. The compensatory mechanisms probably become inadequate as scarring progresses, and cardiac output and stroke volume fall.

In cardiac tamponade and constrictive pericarditis, a *pulsus paradoxus* is often present. In normal persons, a small fall in systemic arterial blood pressure and a decrease in pulse volume occur with inspiration. The accentuation of this phenomenon is called pulsus paradoxus. The mechanism of the decrease in pulse volume has received much study. Dock has demonstrated, by producing pericardial distension with water in cadavers, that traction on the diaphragm results in a rise in pericardial pressure. During inspiration, descent of the diaphragm would stretch the tense pericardium and increase its pressure, impair cardiac filling and decrease stroke output. Pressure measurements in closed chest, living patients are needed to confirm this work. Katz and Gouchat demonstrated a decrease in the pressure gradient between the superior vena cava and the right atrium during inspiration; they postulated that a similar event occurring on the left side of the heart could explain pulsus paradoxus. Golinko and coworkers obtained experimental evidence to support this theory by actual left atrial and pulmonary venous pressure measurements in closed chest dogs with pericardial effusions. Under normal conditions, the decreased intrathoracic pressure of inspiration produces a small reduction in the pulmonary venous to left atrial pressure gradient, which by intefering with left atrial and ventricular filling causes the small decrease in pulse volume. Pericardial tamponade would interfere with transmission of the negative intrathoracic pressure to the left atrium but not to the pulmonary veins, thus accentuating the

normal phenomenon. However the cause of pulsus paradoxus is still unsettled, for Morgan and coworkers could not demonstrate in similar dog experiments that a pressure gradient is created by inspiration; during cardiac tamponade, an excellent correlation was found between pleural and pericardial pressure throughout the respiratory cycle.

The treatment of pericardial effusion is drainage of the fluid by needle tapping or surgery to create a pleuropericardial window. In chronic constrictive pericarditis, the two ventricles are decorticated of their thickened pericardium; the atria may be left alone. Following the surgical procedures, all pressures may return to near normal with a disappearance of the diastolic "dip", but most patients continue to show abnormal hemodynamics despite clinical improvement. The failure to attain normality is postulated to be due to incomplete decortication of the ventricles, persistent abnormalities of the lungs, or myocardial fibrosis. It should also be mentioned that the entire clinical and hemodynamic picture of chronic constrictive pericarditis and pericardial effusion can be produced by other conditions, the most common of which is diffuse myocardial fibrosis.

Hemodynamics in Congenital Heart Disease

The development of intracardiac catheterization to measure the pressures and oxygen contents of the various chambers of the heart has led to a better understanding of the hemodynamic effects of congenital lesions upon the heart. Various formulas have been developed for measurement of cardiac output, and systemic, pulmonary and shunt flows from the data obtained. It must be borne in mind in this section that many assumptions must be made in these formulas and that adequately mixed blood is often difficult to obtain when a shunt is present. Only the more common congenital entities involving the heart will be discussed. It is hoped that from the data presented, the main hemodynamic effects of the less common anomalies can be surmised.

pulmonic stenosis. Cardiac catheterization studies have shown that isolated pulmonary stenosis is a much more common congenital heart lesion than it was formerly considered. Acquired stenosis, due to rheumatic fever, bacterial endocarditis, or carcinoid tumors, is quite rare. The obstruction to right ventricular outflow usually occurs at the valves but is not uncommon in the outflow tract of the right ventricle (infundibular stenosis), and even occurs in the pulmonary artery, its main branches or in multiple peripheral branches. The outflow tract may be narrowed by muscular hypertrophy, and often a diaphragmatic stenosis is also present. The murmur of pulmonary valvular stenosis is located in the second or third left costal interspace, parasternally. It is often loud and rough with a pansystolic duration (fig. 49.16). Infundibular stenosis most often produces the same type of murmur over one or two lower interspaces. Multiple catheterization studies of patients with the various forms of pulmonic stenosis have been reported (fig. 49.17). The characteristic finding is an increased systolic pressure gradient across the stenotic area. In the normal heart, there is little or no measurable gradient in this area. The right ventricular systolic pressure and work are usually elevated, the amount of elevation presumably depending on the degree of stenosis. Right ventricular end-diastolic pressure is normal until failure intervenes. The right atrial mean pressure is normal to high.[1] The pulmonary artery pressure is normal or decreased, while pulmonary wedge pressure and vascular resistance are normal. (In stenosis of the branches of the pulmonary artery, the pulmonary artery pressure is elevated). The pulmonary blood flow is less than normal; saturation of pulmonary venous blood is within the normal range. Cardiac output is normal or low, although increases are found in the presence of minimal stenosis. Oxygen consumption increases with mild exercise showing that pulmonary artery flow can increase.

The pathophysiology of pulmonic stenosis is due to the obstruction to flow from the right ventricle to the pulmonary artery (fig. 49.18) leading to an increased volume of blood retained in the right ventricle. This increases the myocardial fiber length, the systolic pressure, and the work of the right ventricle, resulting in a compensatory increase in output to maintain the pulmonary blood flow and venous return to the left heart. Such dynamic changes lead to right ventricular hypertrophy; the work of the left ventricle is not increased. The right atrial pressure rises in order to maintain a filling pressure for its ventricle. With increasing degrees of stenosis, the right ventricular output falls and its end diastolic vol-

[1] The mean right atrial pressure may be high because of a large atrial pulse pressure (giant "a" wave) with an elevated systolic but normal diastolic level. The giant "a" wave is related to the contraction of the normal sized or enlarged atrium against the increased resistance to filling offered by the right ventricle.

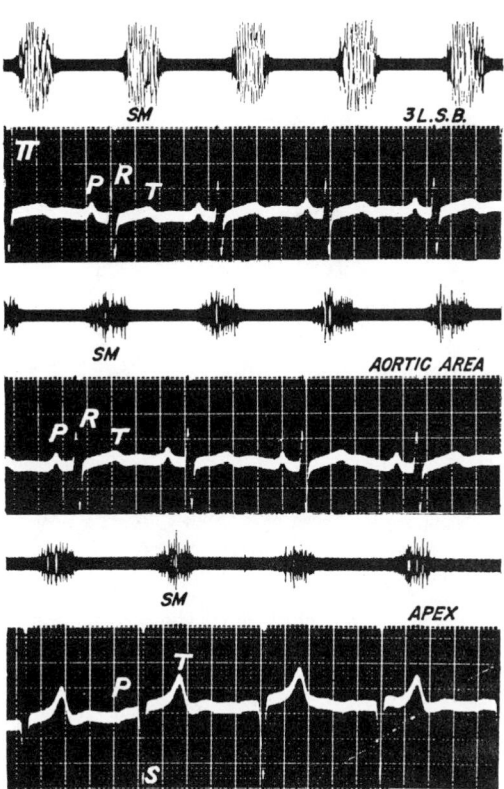

Fig. 49.16. Phonocardiogram (and electrocardiogram) showing the murmur of pulmonic stenosis. *Upper tracing* recorded in the 3rd left interspace at the sternal border; *middle tracing*, at aortic area; and *lower tracing*, at apical area. The systolic murmur (*SM*) is loudest at the pulmonic area and fills all of systole. The diastolic interval shows no murmur (from Levine and Harvey).

ume and pressure rise. The latter is reflected in the peripheral venous system by the development of right heart failure signs. Animal experiments and data from patients suggest that the presence of an atrial septal defect or patent foramen ovale in association with pulmonic stenosis acts as an escape valve for the increased load on the right heart by allowing a shunting of blood to the left atrium. Such cases, of course, may develop cyanosis.

The surgical approach to correction of pulmonary stenotic valves is an incision or excision of the valves by means of a transarterial or transventricular approach. Extracorporeal pump-oxygenators are now used more frequently in order to view the valve directly. Infundibular stenosis may be corrected by excision of the stenotic area or by an actual reaming out of the hypertrophied muscle. Stenosis of the branches of the pulmonary artery may be corrected by grafting procedures. Following the operation, the chamber

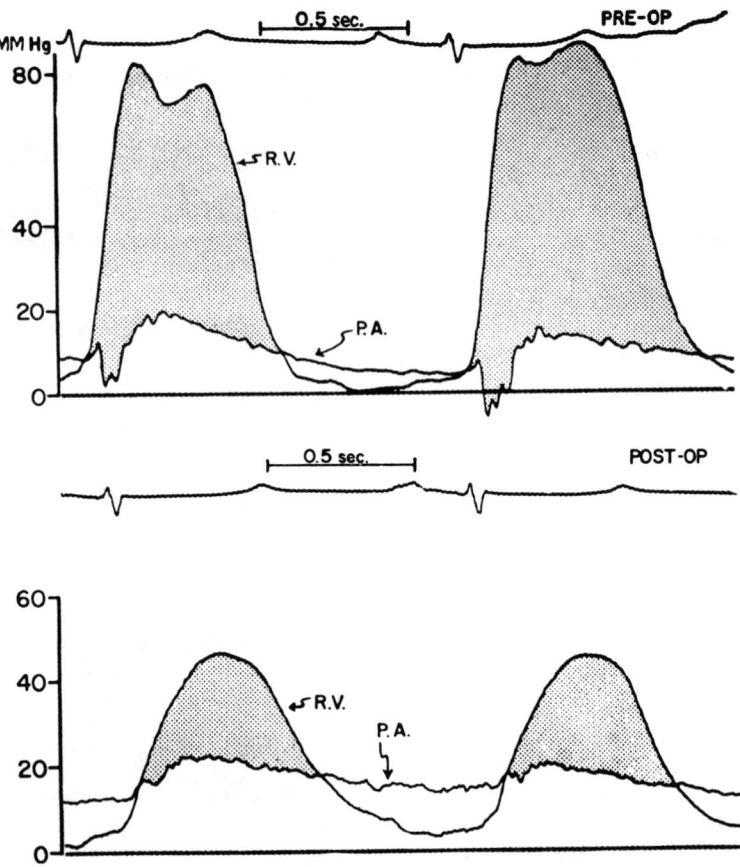

FIG. 49.17. Simultaneous pressure recordings in the right ventricle (*R.V.*) and pulmonary artery (*P.A.*) in a patient with valvular pulmonic stenosis. The electrocardiogram is shown above each pressure tracing. *Upper tracing* is preoperative and *lower tracing* is postoperative. The mean pulmonic valve systolic gradient is shown by the stippled area and fell from 45 to 19 mm. Hg postoperatively. Note the elevated right ventricular systolic pressure which decreased, but not to normal, following surgery (from Tanenbaum, Braunwald, and Morrow).

pressure may return to normal but often remains elevated. Most patients have improved markedly whether their pressures returned to normal levels or not.

PULMONIC INSUFFICIENCY. Insufficiency of the pulmonic valves, acquired or congenital, is a very rare lesion. Functional incompetence from dilation of the valvular ring is often seen in pulmonary hypertension secondary to mitral stenosis or pulmonary disease. A low-frequency, rumbling, decrescendo, diastolic murmur, which begins shortly or at a definite interval after the second heart sound, is located in the second or third left costal interspace parasternally, and may be transmitted to the apex. An increase in the loudness of the murmur with normal inspiration distinguishes it from the murmur of aortic insufficiency. When present in mitral stenosis, it is named the "Graham Steell" murmur, and was considered due to pulmonary regurgitation secondary to pulmonary hypertension. However, in most cases, the Graham Steell murmur is probably caused by aortic regurgitation (Brest et al.).

Several series of dog experiments with partial or complete pulmonic valvectomy or bypassing of the pulmonic valve (shunting of the total right ventricular output into the pulmonary artery) did not produce myocardial decompensation, even with strenuous exercise, for periods up to 18 months. The pulmonary artery diastolic and systolic pressures were found to approximate those of the right ventricle in these dogs. Changes in cardiac output were not consistent. The right ventricle was dilated (by fluoroscopy or at autopsy) or sometimes hypertrophied (at autopsy by heart weight to body weight ratios).

A few patients with isolated pulmonic insuf-

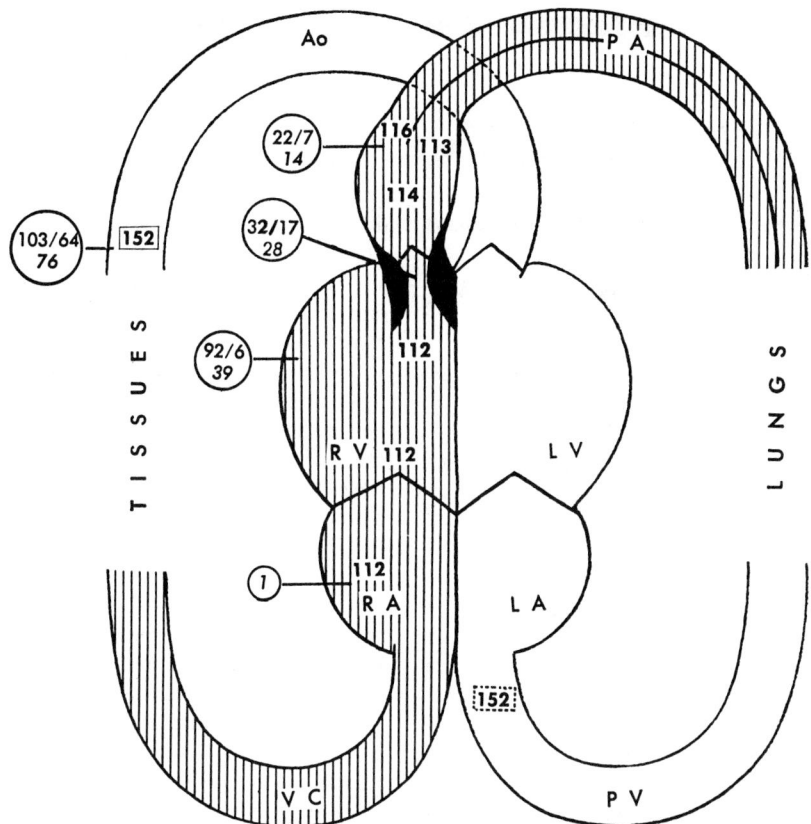

FIG. 49.18. Pulmonic stenosis. Figures within vessels or chambers denote the blood oxygen content in cubic centimeters per liter of blood. Circled figures indicate the blood pressure; systolic over diastolic and mean pressures are shown. The black shadow shows the area of pulmonic stenosis, infundibular in this patient. The pressure changes from the pulmonary artery to the right ventricle were determined by catheterization and localized the area of stenosis. The pulmonary artery is dilated as often seen in cases of pulmonic stenosis. Notice the marked degree of systolic hypertension in the right ventricle with a normal pulmonary artery pressure (from Cournand, Baldwin, and Himmelstein).

ficiency were studied by catheterization of the right heart. The right ventricular and pulmonary artery systolic and diastolic pressures were approximately equal (fig. 49.19). Mean right atrial pressures were normal. No evidence of right ventricular decompensation was shown unless pulmonary hypertension or another lesion co-existed. The pulmonary artery pulse pressure curve resembled the tracing seen in aortic insufficiency.

According to the above clinical and experimental data, pulmonic insufficiency evidently is easily compensated by the right ventricle. Usually there is not sufficient functional disturbance to produce symptoms or signs as evidenced by the few clinical reports. The patients, whose catheterization data are reported above, were asymptomatic for many years despite their incompetent pulmonary valves. However, insufficiency of the pulmonary valves may become significant if pulmonary hypertension is present. The increased

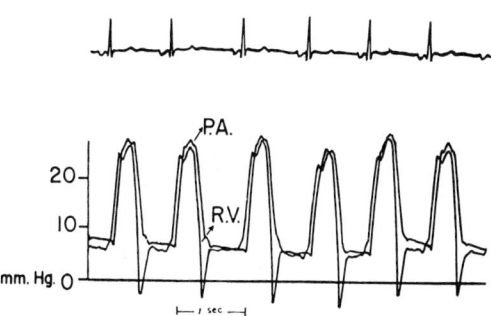

FIG. 49.19. Simultaneous pulmonary artery (*P.A.*) and right ventricular (*R.V.*) pressures obtained at right heart catheterization in a patient with congenital pulmonic valvular insufficiency. The pressures in the right ventricle and pulmonary artery are identical (28/7 mm. Hg). A diastolic pressure gradient is not present across the pulmonic valve indicating the absence of pulmonary stenosis (from Collins, Braunwald, and Morrow).

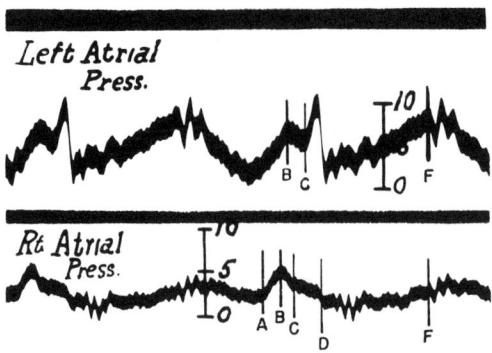

FIG. 49.20. Simultaneously recorded left and right atrial pressures in the open-chest dog. Vertical intercepts at *A*, *C*, *F*, beginning of atrial systole, onset of ventricular isometric contraction period, closure of aortic and pulmonary valves, respectively. For discussion, see text (from Opdyke and associates).

diastolic pulmonary artery pressure in the latter condition would lead to larger regurgitant flow. Right ventricular volume, stroke output and work would increase. Right ventricular hypertrophy was found in patients showing a combination of pulmonic insufficiency and hypertension.

ATRIAL SEPTAL DEFECT. Often referred to as the most frequent congenital heart lesion, atrial septal defect usually involves the foramen ovale and includes part of the septum secundum. Defects in the septum primum are less common and usually lie in the caudal part of the septum, involving the valvular rings. A patent foramen ovale (called "probe patent") is often found at autopsy, consisting of only a slit-like aperture which is functionally closed during life by the left to right atrial pressure gradient. Defects less than 0.5 cm. in diameter are usually hemodynamically insignificant, while those greater than 2 cm. almost always produce signs and symptoms. A loud systolic murmur, usually heard in the second or third left costal interspace, but also present in other areas, is the common finding and is felt to be caused by the large right ventricular outflow. An apical or pulmonic diastolic murmur may also be audible, presumably due to the large blood flow through the tricuspid valves or pulmonic insufficiency. The second heart sound in atrial septal defect is widely split and does not show the normal variation with respiration. The prolongation of right ventricular ejection, and therefore pulmonary valve closure, by an abnormally large right ventricular stroke volume has been suggested as the reason for the wide splitting. The reason for the absence of variation of the interval between aortic and pulmonic valve closure during

the respiratory cycle is not clear but has been attributed to reciprocal changes in the magnitude of the left to right shunt and the systemic venous inflow into the right ventricle during respiration. The two atria would act as a common reservoir for filling of the ventricles so that the normal difference in filling of the right and left ventricle during inspiration and expiration would be abolished. However, the magnitude of the left to right shunt would vary with respiration, diminishing during inspiration and increasing during expiration (Aygen and Braunwald).

Opdyke, Little and associates have studied the hemodynamic effects of the atria in dogs, with and without an atrial septal defect. With an intact atrial septum, the left consistently surpassed the right atrial pressure by a small, but significant, amount except for an occasional brief period before atrial systole (fig. 49.20). When intravenous infusions were given to increase the venous return to the heart, the pressure differential between the two atria was maintained. In another group of dogs, after creation of an atrial septal defect, the same left to right pressure differential existed. By tying the veins entering both atria in dogs with intact atrial septa, it was demonstrated that the left atriovenous system was less distensible than the right; more blood could be added to the right atrial chamber before a pressure rise occurred (fig. 49.21). This difference in distensibility could account for the pressure differential between the two atria. It was concluded that the pressure differential was solely a dynamic event since an equalization of pressures in the two atria occurred when ventricular asystole was produced; the gradient was then reestablished with the resumption of ventricular action. Two other reasons have been postulated for the difference in atrial pressures: (1) right atrial contraction slightly earlier than left atrial systole may transmit pressure to the left chamber, (2) and increased resistance to filling by the thicker left ventricle as compared to the right ventricle may result in a higher left atrial pressure.

Catheterization studies in patients have agreed with the above animal findings. When the catheter passes through the atrial septal defect, left and right atrial pressures can be compared. Findings vary, of course, with the size of the defect and with the presence or absence of pulmonary hypertension, which will be discussed below. In the absence of the latter, catheterization studies show (fig. 49.22): (1) a left atrial mean pressure which exceeds the right, the actual pressures being normal or elevated, (2) right atrial and ven-

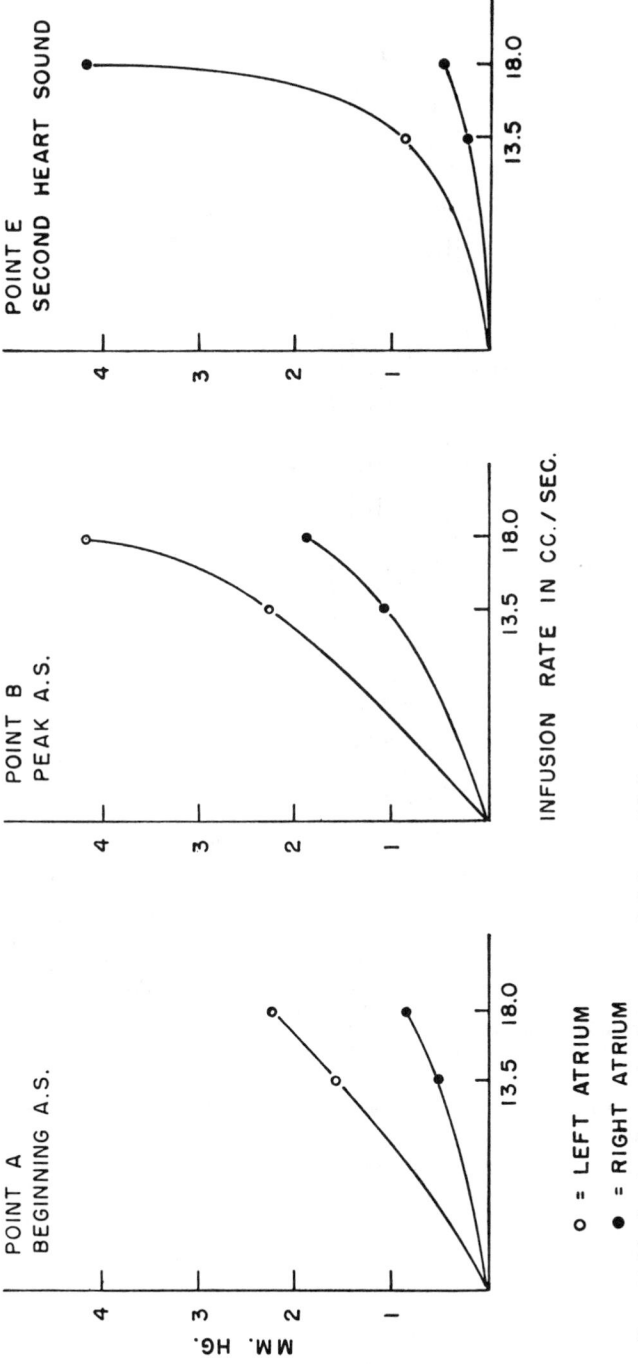

FIG. 49.21. Semi-volume elastic curves of right and left atriovenous-ventricular cavities at various points of the atrial cycle (*A. S.*, atrial systole). For discussion, see text. (Slightly modified from Opdyke and associates.)

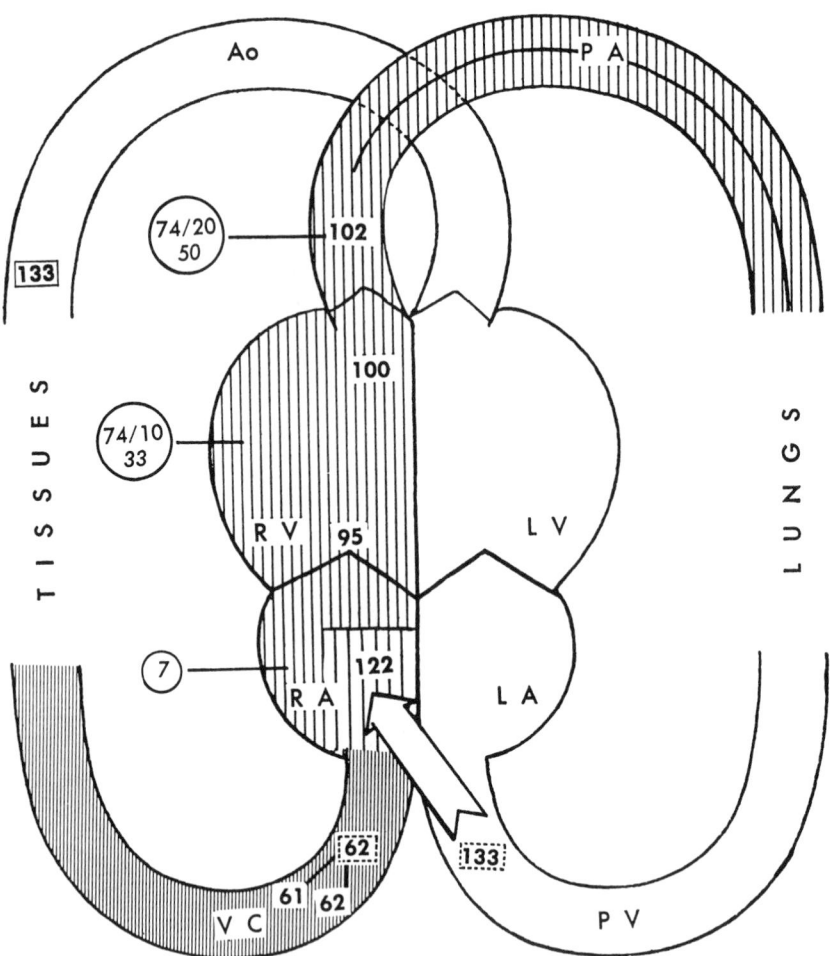

Fig. 49.22. Atrial septal defect. Numerical figures within vessels or chambers denote the blood oxygen content in cubic centimeters per liter of blood. Circled figures indicate the blood pressure; systolic over diastolic and mean pressures are shown. The presence of a shunt of well-oxygenated blood into the right atrium is diagnosed by the large difference in oxygen content between the blood samples from the venae cavae and the right atrium. Since the findings do not differentiate between an atrial septal defect and anomalous drainage of pulmonary veins into the right atrium, the shunt (denoted by the *arrow*) is depicted in an intermediate position. The pulmonary flow was calculated to be over twice the systemic flow. Pulmonary hypertension and an elevated right ventricular end diastolic pressure are also present (from Cournand, Baldwin, and Himmelstein).

tricular oxygen saturations higher than that of the superior vena caval blood due to the left-to-right shunt, (3) a left-to-right shunt flow which often is 3 times the systemic flow, (4) a normal or increased right ventricular systolic pressure (the latter may be due to a functional pulmonic stenosis from the excessive pulmonary blood flow in addition to the increased stroke volume of the right ventricle) (5) an increased workload of the right ventricle, especially in imparting velocity to the increased flow, (6) a markedly increased pulmonary blood flow which may be 2 to 4 times the systemic flow, but a normal or slightly elevated pulmonary artery pressure, and a normal or low pulmonary vascular resistance, (7) a normal,

but sometimes decreased, systemic flow, (8) an increased oxygen consumption with mild exercise, and (9) a normal peripheral arterial saturation.

From the above data, a hemodynamic picture can be postulated for atrial septal defect. Since the left exceeds the right atrial pressure, the shunt of blood is predominantly to the right atrium, although some reverse flow may occur. The right atrial pressure may rise to increase the filling pressure of the ventricle for the latter must eject not only the systemic venous return but also the large amount of shunted blood. The increased volume of blood stretches the myocardial fibers of the right ventricle to give an increased stroke output; this leads to an increased right ventricular workload and to a very large pulmonary blood flow. Large defects, therefore, may be associated with dilation of the right atrium, ventricle and pulmonary artery and right ventricular hypertrophy. The pulmonary vasculature is a low pressure, highly distensible system which, by a decrease in resistance, can accommodate the large excess flow with little change in pressure. The increased venous return to the left heart is divided between the shunt and the systemic blood flow, which may be normal or decreased. With large shunts, right ventricular output is augmented, but may not continue proportional to the increase in right atrial pressure; the right ventricle becomes less efficient at the higher filling pressures as the end diastolic pressure rises. This can eventually lead to the signs and symptoms of right heart failure since the peripheral venous pressure reflects the right chamber pressure elevations.

Pulmonary hypertension is a serious complication of atrial septal defects and other congenital heart diseases. An increased pulmonary artery pressure may be due to an increased pressure in the left atrium, a very large pulmonary blood flow (hyperkinetic), or a high pulmonary vascular resistance (obstructive). The role of an elevated pressure in the left atrium in congenital heart disease has received little study and is probably not of great importance. The pulmonary blood flow may increase as much as three-fold in adults without a rise in pulmonary artery pressure indicating the tremendous capacity of the pulmonary vasculature to accomodate large increases in flow. A high pulmonary vascular resistance may result from several factors: (1) failure of regression of the highly muscular, small pulmonary arteries seen in the fetal state; (2) an increased vascular tone; or (3) hyalinization and fibrosis of the muscular walls of small pulmonary arteries followed by intimal proliferation and local thrombus formation. The last cause is the most serious for it is presumably an irreversible pathological change. The time sequence over which these pathological changes occur in the various forms of congenital heart disease differs greatly. The etiology has not been elucidated despite much investigation. Hyalinization and fibrosis of the small pulmonary arteries usually do not develop until the third decade in patients with atrial septal defects. These changes appear earlier in ventricular septal defects but cannot be entirely secondary to an increased pressure in the pulmonary vessels, for this would not explain their development in atrial septal defects. In dogs,

similar pulmonary vascular changes can be produced by end-to-end anastomosis of a systemic arterial vessel to a pulmonary artery. This is more effective than a side-to-end anastomosis and could be explained by the lack of direct pressure thrusts in the latter. However, it has been pointed out that the changes seen in these dogs may be secondary to pulmonary vascular hemorrhages which are likely in this type of experiment. As mentioned, fetal lungs show highly muscular, small, pulmonary vessels; in ventricular septal defect, it is postulated that the increased pressure in the pulmonary artery does not allow normal regression of this fetal state. This is not, of course, an adequate explanation for the development of pulmonary hypertension in patients with atrial septal defects.

Once pulmonary vascular resistance increases in atrial septal defects, the increase may be progressive. The resistance raises the pulmonary artery pressure and decreases the pulmonary blood flow. The right ventricle has a further increase in its workload against pressure and shows a rise in systolic, and later, in end diastolic volume and pressure. The latter is reflected in the right atrium which must then raise its pressure to fill the ventricle. The elevated right atrial pressure decreases the pressure gradient and, thus, the shunt flow from the left atrium. These hemodynamic events may progress to a point where the shunt flow reverses, causing a decreased peripheral arterial saturation and cyanosis.

Atrial septal defects are also seen in combination with other congenital lesions, such as pulmonic stenosis, mitral stenosis (usually acquired and called Lutembacher's syndrome), Ebstein's disease, tricuspid atresia, and many others. These all affect the hemodynamic findings but, because of their rarity, will not be discussed.

The surgical correction of an atrial septal defect is performed by a closed or open technique, the latter with the aid of an extracorporeal pump-oxygenator. The defect is closed by direct suturing. After complete closure systemic blood flow often increases, pulmonary blood flow is markedly reduced, and right ventricular work and pressures are reduced. As the pulmonary blood flow decreases, the pulmonary vascular resistance often increases slightly in the postoperative period. If severe pulmonary hypertension is present, results are not so good, for the pulmonary vascular changes usually do not regress and right heart failure may develop. Patients with high pulmonary vascular resistance are refused operation for this reason. Pulmonary hypertension secondary to structural changes in the pulmonary vasculature has not been shown to regress following closure of atrial septal defects. An idea of the contribution of increased vasomotor tone to the pulmonary hypertension may be gained by having the patient breathe pure oxygen or by administration of a pulmonary vasodilator agent, although a correlation with postoperative results has not been extensively studied.

VENTRICULAR SEPTAL DEFECT. Ventricular septal defect is probably the second most common congenital heart lesion. Approximately 90 per cent of the defects occur in the membranous septum lying in the outflow tract of the left ventricle beneath the base of the aortic valve, and are usually separated from the latter by a band of connective tissue. Less common are defects of the muscular septum which are often multiple perforations, not usually functionally open because of the contraction of the musculature during systole. A pansystolic, loud, often coarse murmur is heard in the third to fourth left costal interspace parasternally. A mid-diastolic apical murmur may also be present, resulting either from a functional mitral stenosis or from rapid ventricular filling.

The hemodynamic effects of a ventricular septal defect are determined by the size of the defect, the pressure gradient across the defect and the relative resistances to flow of the pulmonic and systemic circulations. Small defects are usually asymptomatic with the murmur as the only sign present; such uncomplicated cases are called Roger's disease, after the man who first described the murmur. Because of the pressure differential, which may be over 100 mm. Hg between the left and right ventricle, large defects have much more profound hemodynamic effects than those seen in atrial septal defects.

Catheterization findings in patients with ventricular septal defect depend on the size of the opening and on the presence or absence of pulmonary hypertension. Small to medium defects (fig. 49.23) (less than 1 cm. per M^2 of body surface) show a pressure gradient across the defect, an elevated right ventricular systolic pressure, an increased oxygen content of right ventricular blood compared to right atrial blood, a shunt flow which may reach several liters per minute, and a large pulmonary blood flow with a normal or slightly elevated pulmonary artery pressure. The left and, also, the right heart have an increased workload and are usually hypertrophied. The left ventricle must pump blood into both the right ventricle and the aorta; it increases its output in

order to maintain systemic blood flow. Mean right atrial and pulmonary wedge pressures are normal, while pulmonary vascular resistance may be normal or low in the absence of pulmonary hypertension.

With very large ventricular septal defects, the systolic pressures tend to equalize between the right and left ventricle. The shunted blood flow into the low resistance right ventricular system is enormous in amount. There is a very large pulmonary blood flow and decreased pulmonary vascular resistance. Such defects usually lead to early failure of one or both ventricles unless pulmonary hypertension develops to decrease the amount of shunted blood. Pulmonary hypertension does not occur with small defects; with large defects it is often present from birth, or may develop later. Several investigators have found that the pulmonary vascular resistance remains stable, even though elevated, during the first two decades of life. In patients with pulmonary hypertension (fig. 49.24), the pulmonary artery pressure is increased but the pulmonary wedge pressure is normal (in the absence of left ventricular failure) demonstrating that it is an arteriolar resistance. There is a decreased pulmonary blood flow and an increased pressure workload of the right ventricle, leading to pressure elevations in this chamber which tend to decrease the shunt flow. As these hemodynamic events progress, the shunt flow may be reversed causing a decreased peripheral arterial saturation and cyanosis. The latter syndrome is indistinguishable from that described below as Eisenmenger's complex.

In summary, the amount of flow through a ventricular septal defect depends on the size of the defect and the resistances of the systemic and pulmonary circulation. Small defects present a large resistance to flow, meaning that a high pressure differential continues to exist between the two ventricles. Large defects allow a very large shunt flow which is decreased only by the development of increased pulmonary vascular resistance. However, the latter increases the workload of the right ventricle so that now both ventricles are severely hemodynamically involved.

Eisenmenger's complex, consisting of a ventricular septal defect, an aorta which overrides the ventricular septum and is therefore open to both ventricles, and right ventricular hypertrophy, will be briefly discussed, for it is often considered to be a severe form of ventricular septal defect. Substituting the word "syndrome" for "complex," Wood and others list any reversed shunt flow due

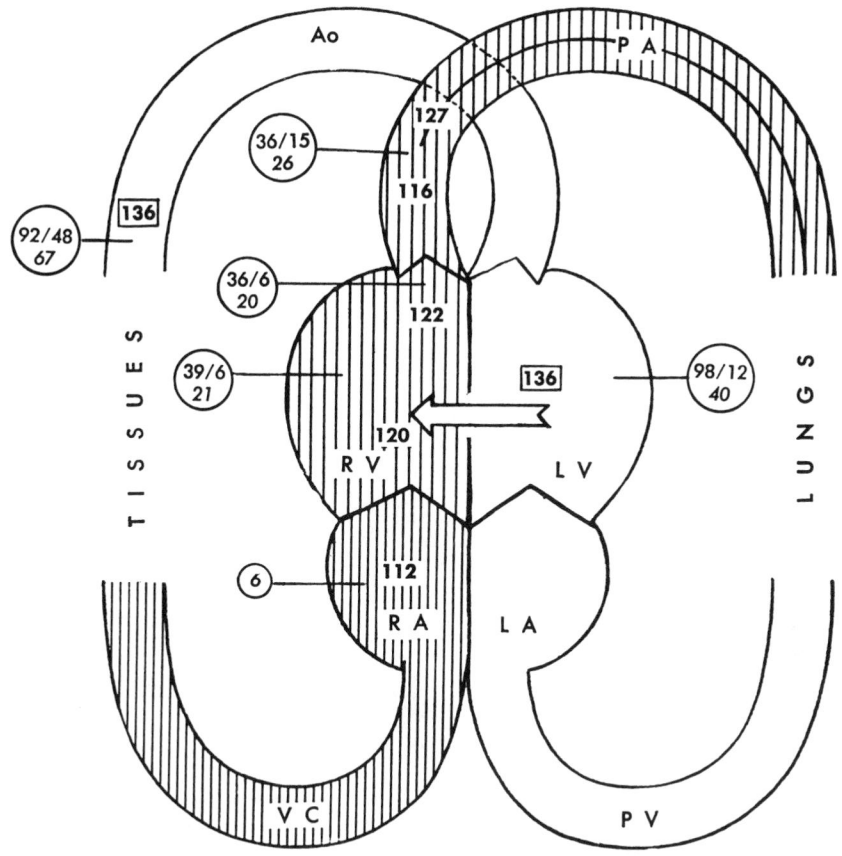

Fig. 49.23. Interventricular septal defect. Figures within vessels or chambers denote the blood oxygen content in cubic centimeters per liter of blood. Circled figures indicate the blood pressure; systolic over diastolic and mean pressures are shown. The increase in oxygen content in the right ventricle (compared to the right atrium) indicates a shunt of oxygenated blood (shown by the arrow) from the left ventricle. The estimated systemic and pulmonary blood flows were 3.57 and 6.14 liters per minute, respectively. This indicated a shunt flow of 2.57 liters per minute. Note the moderate elevation of right ventricular and pulmonary artery systolic pressures secondary to the shunt flow (from Cournand, Baldwin, and Himmelstein).

to pulmonary hypertension (such as occurs in patent ductus arteriosus, ventricular and atrial septal defects) under this classification. Since the upper portion of the ventricular septum has a spiral course whereby the aortic root may come in contact with both ventricles, a large ventricular septal defect located below the aortic valve may cause an apparent overriding of the aorta, i.e., the second component of the Eisenmenger's complex. The right to left shunt in this cyanotic disorder is probably not related to the dextroposition of the aorta but to the pulmonary hypertension which is always present. The aorta, unless it arises almost directly from the right ventricle, would receive little blood from the right side as long as the right ventricular systolic pressure remained well below that of the left ventricle. In patients with a large ventricular septal defect and an over-riding aorta, catheterization studies show a tremendous increase in pulmonary vascular resistance, an elevated right ventricular and pulmonic systolic pressure equal to the systemic systolic pressure, evidence of a right-to-left shunt by decreased arterial oxygen saturation, and a normal or low pulmonary blood flow. The oxygen saturation of the right ventricular blood is higher than that of the right atrial blood indicating that an admixture occurs through the septal defect. The right ventricular work is markedly increased which is reflected in the hypertrophy of this chamber. There is an increased oxygen consumption with mild exercise, although the cyanosis may deepen due to increased right-to-left shunting of blood.

In following children with ventricular septal defects, it has been found that spontaneous closure occurs in about 25% of small defects, and may also occur rarely with lesions large enough

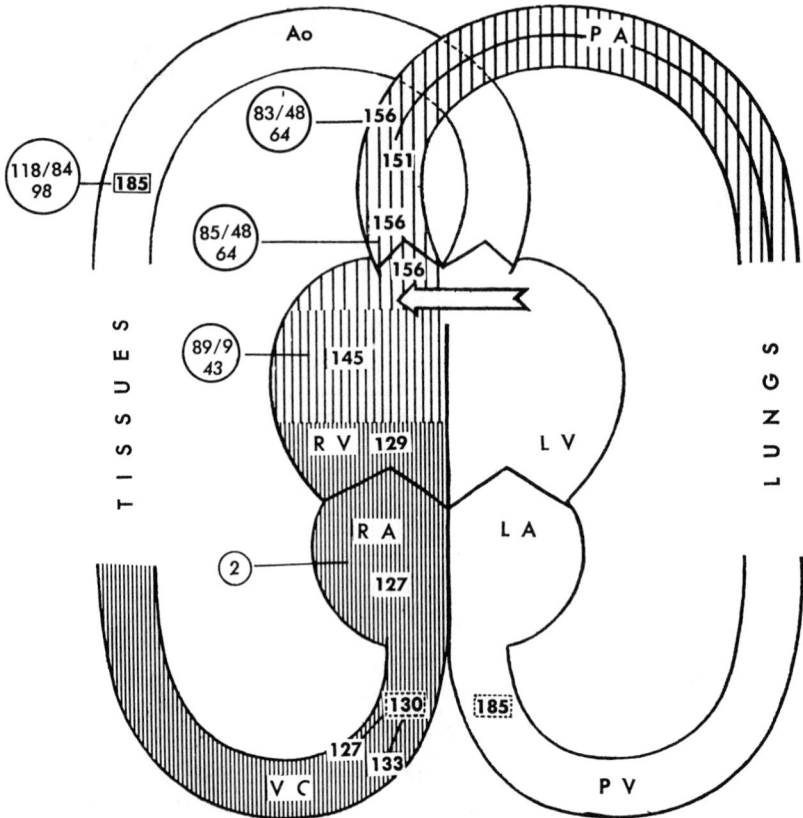

Fɪɢ. 49.24. Interventricular septal defect with marked pulmonary hypertension. Figures within vessels or chambers denote the blood oxygen content in cubic centimeters per liter of blood. Circled figures indicate the blood pressure; systolic over diastolic and mean pressures are shown. The increase in oxygen content in the right ventricle (compared to the right atrium) indicates a shunt of oxygenated blood (shown by the arrow) from the left ventricle. The lack of a systolic pressure gradient across the pulmonic valve rules out pulmonic stenosis. The high pressure in the pulmonary artery must be secondary to pathological changes in the pulmonary vasculature causing an increased resistance to flow. Note that the end diastolic right ventricular pressure is elevated slightly, indicating the presence of decompensation. The estimated systemic blood flow is 3.7 liters per minute and the pulmonary flow 6.95 liters per minute, giving an estimated shunt flow of 3.25 liters per minute (from Cournand, Baldwin, and Himmelstein).

to cause congestive heart failure in infancy. Closure may occur in three ways: (1) septal hypertrophy; (2) lengthening of ovoid slits as a result of normal growth, until their sides meet; (3) overlap of the defect by the medial leaf of the tricuspid valve.

The surgical correction of ventricular septal defect has been greatly enhanced by the use of extracorporeal pump-oxygenators and/or hypothermia. Under direct vision, the defect is sutured closed with or without the use of a synthetic patch. The ideal candidate for surgery would have a large shunt volume with a high pulmonary blood flow but normal or only slightly increased pulmonary vascular resistance. Following operation, patients who had an elevated pulmonary vascular resistance show little decrease when

catheterized several months later. Small defects with minor hemodynamic changes are usually not corrected because of the surgical risk. Cyanotic patients with right-to-left shunts from severe pulmonary hypertension including Eisenmenger's complex, do not benefit from closure of the defect. In patients with severe pulmonary hypertension, repair of the defect is usually indicated if there is a large left-to-right shunt. However, when a right-to-left shunt exists in the presence of pulmonary hypertension, operation is not indicated. Closure of the defect, in the latter circumstances, leads to a further increase in pulmonary and right ventricular pressure with a poor survival rate. Two procedures hold promise for the patients with severe pulmonary hypertension. The creation of pulmonary stenosis by banding the pulmonary artery in young patients with ventricular septal defects and pulmonary hypertension may prevent progressive changes in the pulmonary vasculature or even reverse existing changes. After a period of years of induced pulmonic stenosis, the ventricular septal defect may be closed surgically. Another promising approach is the use of perforated intracardiac patches to repair the defects; gradual closure of the defects would ensue, allowing a gradual adjustment of the right ventricle to the increased workload imposed on it.

TETRALOGY OF FALLOT. The tetralogy of Fallot is the most common of the cyanotic congenital heart diseases. Classically, it has been described as a combination of pulmonary stenosis, ventricular septal defect, right ventricular hypertrophy and dextroposition of the aorta, the latter overriding the ventricular septum. A right-sided aortic arch is also present in about a quarter of the cases. The pulmonary stenosis is most commonly of the infundibular type. Since the advent of cardiac catheterization studies, the concept of tetralogy as a single entity has been undermined. It is now considered that a spectrum of patients exists, ranging from severe tetralogy, with a large ventricular septal defect and severe pulmonic stenosis, to patients with either a large ventricular septal defect *or* a severe pulmonic stenosis as the *dominant* lesion. Between these two extremes are milder combinations of the two lesions. The dextroposition of the aorta is not considered as an important determinant in the hemodynamic picture (see ventricular septal defect). The right ventricular hypertrophy is not congenital in origin but results from the stress imposed on this chamber. There is usually a loud, harsh, systolic murmur in the second or third left costal interspace parasternally, presumably due to the pulmonary stenosis, but it is not pansystolic, ending before the aortic second sound.

Patients with large ventricular septal defects, but mild pulmonic stenosis, show a left-to-right shunt without cyanosis and the reader is referred to the above discussion of ventricular septal defects for the hemodynamic abnormalities. Similarly, patients with a severe pulmonic stenosis and a small ventricular septal defect behave hemodynamically as discussed under pulmonic stenosis but, in addition, have a right-to-left shunt with cyanosis.

When both the ventricular septal defect and the pulmonic stenosis are significant, the following catheterization data are found (fig. 49.25): (1) the pulmonary artery pressure is reduced as is the pulmonary blood flow, (2) the pulmonary capillary flow (from collateral circulation to the lungs) is often greater than the pulmonary artery flow; however, the effective pulmonary flow is still below normal, (3) the right ventricular systolic pressure is elevated, but the end diastolic pressure is usually normal; the right ventricular systolic pressure approximates the aortic systolic pressure, (4) right and left mean atrial pressures are similar, (5) the arterial oxygen saturation is decreased; left atrial samples of blood are usually more saturated than left ventricular samples showing that the shunt is mostly interventricular and not from the right ventricle into the aorta, and (7) the oxygen consumption with mild exercise does not rise but decreases, as does the peripheral arterial saturation, deepening the cyanosis.

In summary, a hemodynamic picture can be postulated for tetralogy of Fallot. The resistance offered by pulmonic stenosis causes the right ventricle to shunt blood mostly through the ventricular septal defect and somewhat into the dextropositioned aorta. The right ventricle hypertrophies in response to the increased workload but rarely dilates, for it can easily empty into the left ventricle or aorta. The systolic pressure of the right ventricle rises to the level of that in the left ventricle in order to eject its blood into the systemic circulation through the least resistant available opening, i.e., the aortic valve *via* the septal defect. The aortic blood is desaturated by the shunted venous blood. The pulmonary artery pressure and blood flow are markedly decreased because of the pulmonic stenosis, but the pulmonary capillary circulation may be augmented by a collateral flow from systemic arteries. The fact that some reversed shunt also occurs is established by the higher blood oxygen content of the right ventricle compared to that in the atrium. These patients cannot increase their oxygen consumption during mild exercise, probably because of the limited, circulating volume of mixed venous blood that can be propelled across the stenosed valve into the lungs.

It is well known that cyanotic children with tetralogy of Fallot may obtain relief from dyspnea and faintness after exercise by assuming a squatting position. Several investigations have been reported on the hemodynamic effects of squatting in these patients and in normal subjects. Squatting produces an increase in blood pressure, cardiac output, and central blood volume and a bradycardia. Most important, patients with tetralogy of Fallot show about a ten per cent increase in arterial oxygen saturation. It has been

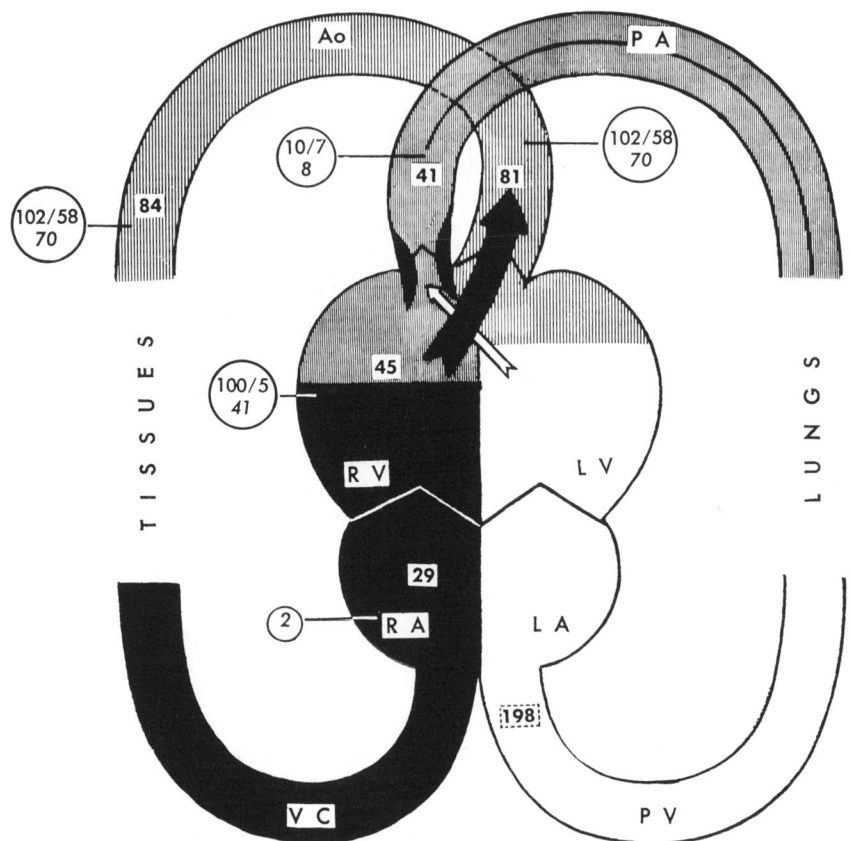

Fig. 49.25. Tetralogy of Fallot. Numerical figures within vessels or chambers denote the blood oxygen content in cubic centimeters per liter of blood. Circled figures indicate the blood pressure; systolic over diastolic and mean pressures are shown. Dark areas represent very low blood saturation as compared to white areas denoting high blood saturation. The large systolic gradient of the right ventricle to the pulmonary artery indicates a marked degree of stenosis. The systolic pressures in the right ventricle, aorta, and brachial artery are almost identical. From analysis of the oxygen data, it can be calculated that the left to right ventricular shunt is small, but the *right to left ventricular shunt* is large (indicated by *arrows*). Calculation of the systemic blood flow shows it to be somewhat reduced; the pulmonary blood flow is about half the systemic flow. Note that the aorta overrides both ventricles (from Cournand, Baldwin, and Himmelstein).

suggested that squatting removes the distending force of gravity on the systemic arterial bed by bringing the body closer to ground level (flexing the hips and knees, and arching the trunk forward). The change in the effect of gravity results in a shift of blood from the legs to the lungs and a rise in left ventricular output producing an increase in mixed venous oxygen saturation. O'Donnell and McIlroy determined that this does not account entirely for the improved arterial oxygen saturation. They postulate that changes in the peripheral and pulmonary vascular resistances lead to a decrease in shunt flow from right to left. Actual measurements to prove that changes in shunt flow occur during squatting have not been made.

The surgical correction of tetralogy of Fallot

has developed through three stages. The Blalock-Taussig operation, creating a channel similar to a patent ductus arteriosus between the aorta or subclavian artery and the pulmonary artery, supplies more blood to the lungs, but the results, although often good, are not excellent. The next procedure attempted was an indirect correction of the pulmonic stenosis. This produced slightly better results but with a higher operative mortality. The use of the extracorporeal pump-oxygenator has recently made a direct open approach possible to correct both the ventricular septal defect and the pulmonic stenosis. Since these patients do well without a correction of the dextropositioned aorta, this is further proof that it is probably not a significant hemodynamic determinant in this anomaly. Due to the high mortality in severely cyanotic infants following open heart surgery, some cardiologists recommend creation of an aorto-pulmonary shunt, and then total correction in future years.

PATENT DUCTUS ARTERIOSUS. Patent ductus arteriosus is next in frequency, after the septal defects, among congenital heart diseases. It is the persistence of a patent channel, joining the left pulmonary artery to the aorta (distal to the sub-clavian artery), which is normally found in the fetus and which closes within a few weeks after birth. The exact mechanism of the normal ob-literation of the ductus is not understood al-though it has been shown that the ducti constrict, when perfused with oxygenated blood, and dilate, if nitrogen replaces the oxygen; another theory asserts that high pressures maintain the ductus patent while low pressures lead to its closure. Classically, a "machinery" murmur (fig. 49.26) is heard throughout systole and diastole due to the continuous shunting of blood and is located in the second or third left costal interspace, para-sternally. This murmur is harsh in quality, in-creasing toward the end of systole, and waning during diastole.

The hemodynamic effects of a patent ductus arteriosus are secondary to the shunting of blood from the high pressure system of the aorta to the low pressure circulation of the pulmonary artery (fig. 49.27). The amount of blood shunted de-pends upon the size of the ductus and the pres-sure difference between the aorta and the pulmo-nary artery. Burwell, Eppinger, and Gross studied the hemodynamic changes in patients and dogs with patent ducti. In dogs, the left subclavian artery was sutured to the pulmonary artery to simulate the clinical situation. Such animals showed an increased left, but a decreased right, ventricular output. The shunted blood from the aorta to the pulmonary artery was calculated to be more than 50 per cent of the left ventricular output. Two of three dogs showed an increased mean pulmonary artery pressure, probably from the large pulmonary blood flow rather than an in-creased pulmonary resistance. Patients with pat-ent ductus were studied, while under anesthesia and during thoracotomy, before the ductus was tied. The oxygen content of the pulmonary artery was greater than that of the right ventricle. Blood flows through the shunt varied from 4 to 19 liters per minute, which was 45 to 75 per cent of the left ventricular output. The total pulmo-nary blood flow (right ventricular plus shunt flow) was 10 to 25 liters per minute. The left was

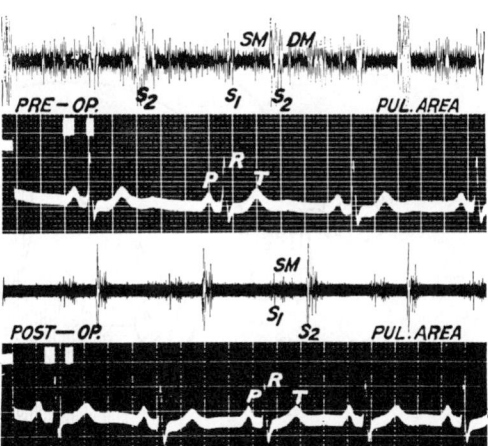

FIG. 49.26. Phonocardiogram (and electrocar-diogram) demonstrating the "machinery" mur-mur of patent ductus arteriosus. *Upper tracing* (recorded preoperatively) at the pulmonic area shows loud systolic (*SM*) and diastolic (*DM*) components of the continuous murmur. S_1 and S_2 denote the first and second heart sounds. *Lower tracing* (recorded after ligation of the ductus) shows persistence of a soft pulmonic systolic murmur (from Levine and Harvey).

2 to 4 times the right ventricular output. Arterial blood pressure showed a low diastolic level with a wide pulse pressure. Studies in unanesthetized subjects by other groups have demonstrated similar findings. The mean right atrial pressure was normal, while the right ventricular and pul-monary artery systolic pressures were normal or elevated. The pulmonary vascular resistance was increased when pulmonary hypertension was present.

In summary, the higher aortic pressure shunts blood through a patent ductus arteriosus to the low pressure pulmonary circuit during the entire cardiac cycle. Depending on the size, some shunts have been calculated to deliver up to 30 liters per minute to the pulmonary artery. This leads to an excess pulmonary blood flow and venous return to the left side of the heart. The increased volume return to the left ventricle results in a stretch of the myocardial fibers, whereby the left ventricle increases its output and maintains systemic blood flow at or near normal levels. This increased workload of the left ventricle may lead to its hypertrophy. The escape of blood from the aorta to the pulmonary artery causes a sharp fall in diastolic pressure, producing an increased pulse pressure and most of the peripheral signs of aortic insufficiency.

Patients with a patent ductus arteriosus may develop pulmonary hypertension for unknown

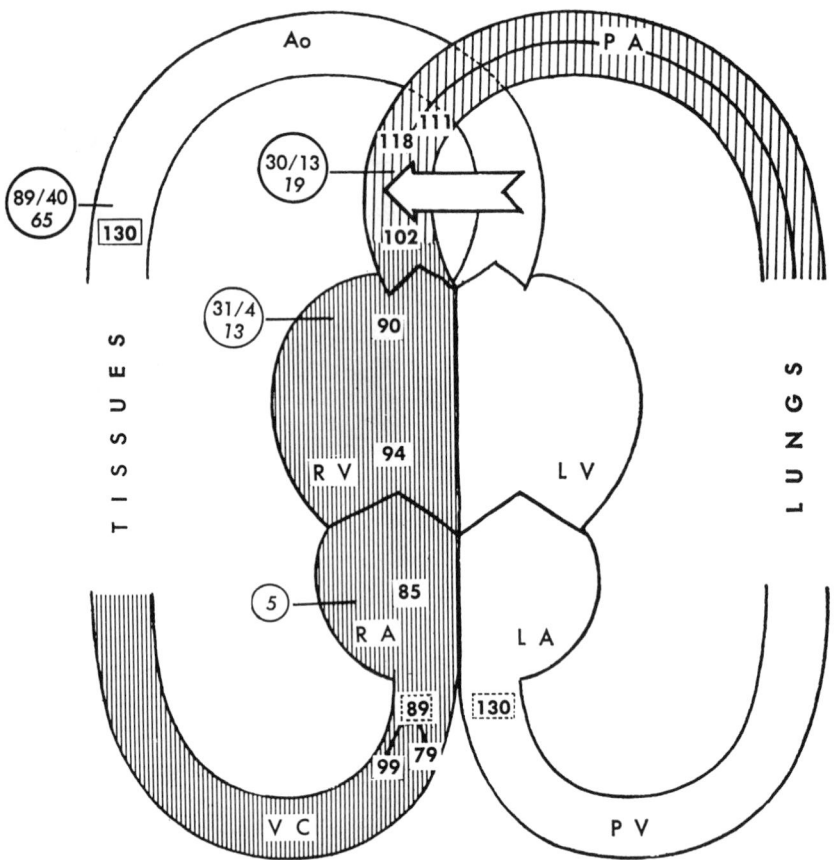

Fig. 49.27. Patent ductus arteriosus. Figures within vessels or chambers denote the blood oxygen content in cubic centimeters per liter of blood. Circled figures indicate the blood pressure; systolic over diastolic and mean pressures are shown. The large increase in oxygen content in the pulmonary artery demonstrates a shunt of oxygenated blood (indicated by the *arrow*) from the aorta. The estimated pulmonary blood flow as calculated from the oxygen content of the left pulmonary artery was 4.98 liters per minute, and the systemic cardiac output was 2.38 liters per minute. This means a shunt flow of 2.6 liters per minute existed. The slight increase in pulmonary artery pressures indicates the presence of a mild degree of pulmonary hypertension (from Cournand, Baldwin, and Himmelstein).

reasons, as discussed under atrial septal defect. It is believed that the pulmonary hypertension is present very early in life which implies that the fetal type pulmonary arteries with high pulmonary vascular resistance fail to regress in some of these patients. As the pulmonary vascular resistance increases, the pulmonary artery and right ventricular systolic pressures rise. This causes a decrease in the pressure differential between the aorta and pulmonary artery and a decrease in the shunt flow. When the pulmonary hypertension is more severe, the shunt flow may become partially, and then completely, reversed, producing a hemodynamic picture similar to Eisenmenger's complex, except that the cyanosis is limited to the lower body. Such patients usually have a very large ductus, right ventricular hypertrophy (secondary to the increased work of the right ventricle) and an atypical or absent murmur.

The surgical treatment of patent ductus arteriosus consists of cutting the ductus and suturing the aortic and pulmonary ends closed. After operation, the arterial diastolic pressure rises, the left ventricular output decreases and, in the majority of patients, the murmur disappears. Operation is usually not recommended for patients with severe pulmonary hypertension and reversal of ductal flow, since the ductus serves as an escape valve for the excess right ventricular pressure and output. Delayed closure, in such cases, by partial ligation or by a two-stage shunting operation has been suggested, but not tested in a sufficient number of patients. Postoperative catheterization data have shown a decrease in pulmonary artery pressure in patients with milder pulmonary hypertension not associated with reversal of ductal flow.

COARCTATION OF THE AORTA. Coarctation of the aorta is a congenital defect which is usually subdivided into "infantile" and "adult" types. Infantile coarctation consists of a long segment of narrowing in the distal aortic arch, from the left subclavian artery to the ductus arteriosus insertion, while the adult type is a shorter, more localized constriction at or distal to the ductus attachment. Since these two variations are often seen in different age groups than their label im-

plies, it has been suggested that such a classification be discarded because it serves no useful purpose to the surgeon who is attempting to correct the defect. A loud systolic murmur, due probably to the turbulence at the constricted area, extends from early systole slightly into diastole. It is most often loudest at the base of the heart but is also heard in the left interscapular area.

The hemodynamics of coarctation of the aorta involve an increased pressure workload on the left ventricle which has to pump its output

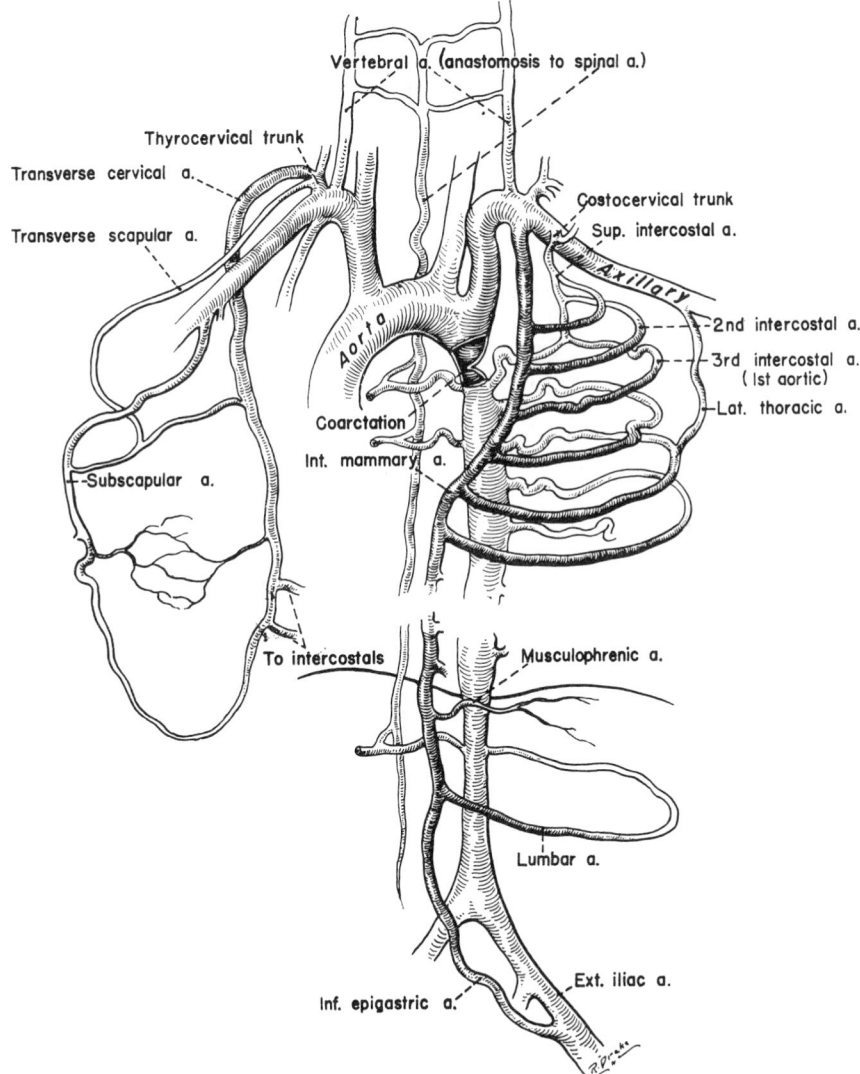

FIG. 49.28. Diagrammatic representation of routes of collateral circulation in coarctation of the aorta. The extensive collateral circulation between the subclavian arteries and their branches above the constriction and the branches of the descending aorta below the coarctation is shown. (From Edwards and associates. An atlas of congenital anomalies of the heart and great vessels. Charles C. Thomas, Publisher, Springfield, Illinois, 1954.)

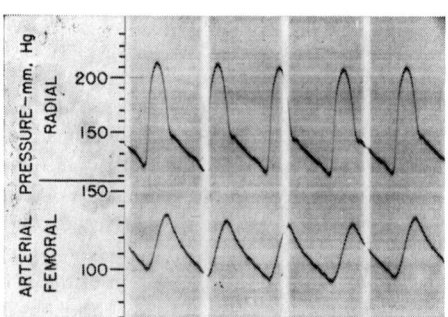

FIG. 49.29. Tracings of the intraradial and intrafemoral arterial pressures from a patient with coarctation of the aorta. The following points should be noticed: (1) the elevation of the systolic and diastolic pressures in the radial artery, (2) the smaller femoral systolic and pulse pressures, (3) the slight delay in onset of the femoral pulse wave compared to that of the radial pulse wave, and (4) the late peak of the femoral pulse as compared to that of the radial pulse (from Brown, Clagett, Burchell, and Wood).

through the narrowed area. This strain, which often leads to left ventricular hypertrophy, is somewhat relieved by the development of an extensive collateral circulation between the subclavian artery and its branches above the constriction, and the branches of the descending aorta below (fig. 49.28). In patients studied by catheterization techniques, the cardiac output is normal or increased. The blood flow is normal or elevated to the upper body and, due to the extensive collateral circulation, normal to the lower body. An elevated blood pressure occurs above the coarctation. There is a delay in onset of the femoral pulse (fig. 49.29) which normally precedes the radial pulse slightly. This delayed onset may not be palpable but the late systolic peak of the femoral pulse, as compared to the radial, is very noticeable. The femoral pulse curve shows a slow rise and fall with a decreased pulse pressure and an absent dicrotic notch.

Patient and animal studies purport to show that the upper body hypertension can be explained on a purely mechanical basis related to the degree of aortic constriction. Gupta and Wiggers thoroughly studied, in dogs, the hemodynamics of aortic constriction just beyond the left subclavian artery. As the degree of constriction was increased, systolic, diastolic and pulse pressures increased in the aorta above the constriction and decreased in the femoral artery. In chronic dogs (and patients), the femoral artery diastolic pressure usually is normal. They postulated that the hypertension above the constriction was not only secondary to the increased resistance but also to the reduced capacity and distensibility of the

aortic compression chamber, into which the left ventricle empties, and to the physiological reactions of the left ventricle, whereby its systolic discharge is increased. They explained the slow rise and fall of the femoral pulse and the maintenance of femoral artery diastolic pressure by the damping effect on the aortic pressure wave in its passage through the constricted area. In dogs with a constricted aorta, but with a subclavian to aorta shunt imitating the collaterals found in man, the systolic and diastolic pressures of the aorta above the constriction were decreased, while those of the femoral artery were increased when compared to the findings in coarcted dogs without such a shunt. The pulse pressure increased, but the contour of the femoral pulse wave did not return to normal. Thus, an artificial collateral circulation reduced the workload on the left ventricle and the elevated blood pressure of the upper body while increasing the blood flow to the lower extremities.

Experimentation on dogs and rats has produced evidence for and against renal ischemia as a factor in the upper body hypertension. In dogs with coarctation of the thoracic aorta, transplantation of one kidney to the neck and removal of the other kidney results in the return of carotid artery blood pressure to normal (Scott and Bahnson). In experimental coarctation in rats, there is an increase in norepinephrine responses and in perfusion pressure of the hindlimb blood vessels (Nolla-Panades). However it has been demonstrated that most patients with coarctation of the aorta have normal renal blood flow and hemodynamics; renal ischemia is not believed to be present. It has been shown that a decrease in perfusion pressure causes the release of renin from the kidney and may lead to hypertension (see Ch. 48).

Painter and associates have demonstrated, in patients, hypertrophy of the media and endothelial proliferation of arterioles in organs above and below the constricted aorta. An increase in peripheral resistance due to these changes could explain the finding of normal or even increased femoral artery diastolic pressures in most coarctation patients. The fact that hypertension does not usually exist in the lower body was explained by a metabolic arteriolar vasodilation compensating for the decreased blood flow.

Coarctation of the aorta has been corrected in hundreds of patients by excision of the involved area and anastomosis of the proximal to the distal end. If a long area of the aorta is involved, a graft is inserted. Following operation, the upper extremity hypertension may either decrease to normal levels or remain elevated. The persistence of this hypertension after removal of the constricted aortic area would argue for a renal etiology except that the increased pressure may have induced permanent arteriolar changes, thereby increasing the peripheral resistance.

REFERENCES

Valvular Heart Disease

BAILEY, C. P., AND LIKOFF, W. The surgical treatment of aortic insufficiency. Ann. Int. Med., 1955, **42**, 388.

BARGER, A. C., ROE, B. B., AND RICHARDSON, G. S. Relation of valvular lesions and of exercise to auricular pressure, work tolerance, and to development of chronic, congestive failure in dogs. Am. J. Physiol., 1952, **169**, 384.

BLOOMFIELD, R. A., LAUSON, H. A., COURNAND, A., BREED, E. S., AND RICHARDS, D. W., JR. Recording of right heart pressures in normal subjects and in patients with chronic pulmonary disease and various types of cardio-circulatory disease. J. Clin. Invest., 1946, **25**, 639.

BRAUNWALD, E., MOSCOVITZ, H. L., AMRAM, S. S., LASSER, R. P., SAPIN, S. O., HIMMELSTEIN, A., RAVITCH, M. M., AND GORDON, A. J. The hemodynamics of the left side of the heart as studied by simultaneous left atrial, left ventricular, and aortic pressures; particular reference to mitral stenosis. Circulation, 1955, **12**, 69.

BRAUNWALD, E., WELCH, G. H., JR., AND SARNOFF, S. J. Hemodynamic effects of quantitatively varied experimental mitral regurgitation. Circulation Res., 1957, **5**, 539.

BRÖCK, R. C. Functional obstruction of the left ventricle (acquired aortic subvalvular stenosis). Guy's Hosp. Rep., 1957, **106**, 221.

BROCKENBROUGH, E. C., BRAUNWALD, E., AND MORROW, A. G. Hemodynamic technique for detection of hypertrophic subaortic stenosis. Circulation, 1961, **23**, 189.

CURTI, P. C., COHEN, G., CASTLEMAN, B., SCANNELL, J. G., FRIEDLICH, A. L., AND MYERS, G. S. Respiratory and circulatory studies of patients with mitral stenosis. Circulation, 1953, **8**, 893.

DENIE, J. J. AND VERHEUGT, A. P. Supravalvular aortic stenosis. Circulation, 1958, **18**, 902.

DEXTER, L., HARKEN, D. E., COBB, L. A., JR., NOVACK, P., SCHLANT, R. C., PHINNEY, A. O., AND HAYNES, F. W. Aortic stenosis. A.M.A. Arch. Int. Med., 1958, **101**, 254.

FERRER, M. I., HARVEY, R. M., KUSCHNER, M., RICHARDS, D. W., JR., AND COURNAND, A. Hemodynamic studies in tricuspid stenosis of rheumatic origin. Circulation Res., 1953, **1**, 49.

FERRER, M. I., HARVEY, R. M., CATHCART, R. T., COURNAND, A., AND RICHARDS, D. W. Hemodynamic studies in rheumatic heart disease. Circulation, 1952, **6**, 688.

FRIEDBERG, C. K. Diseases of the heart. Ed. 2. W. B. Saunders Company, Philadelphia, 1956.

GORDON, A. J., JENKINS, G., GRISHMAN, A., AND NABATOFF, R. A. Tricuspid stenosis. Am. J. Med., 1957, **22**, 306.

GORLIN, R., AND GOODALE, W. T. Changing blood pressure in aortic insufficiency. New England J. Med., 1956, **255**, 77.

GORLIN, R. AND GORLIN, S. G. Hydraulic formula for calculation of the area of the stenotic mitral valve, other cardiac valves, and central circulatory shunts. I. Am. Heart J., 1951, **41**, 1.

GORLIN, R., HAYNES, F. W., GOODALE, W. T., SAWYER, C. G., DOW, J. W., AND DEXTER, L. Studies of the circulatory dynamics in mitral stenosis II. Am. Heart J., 1951, **41**, 30.

GORLIN, R., LEWIS, B. M., HAYNES, F. W., SPIEGL, R. J., AND DEXTER, L. Factors regulating pulmonary "capillary" pressure in mitral stenosis. IV. Am. Heart J., 1951, **41**, 834.

GORLIN, R., McMILLAN, I. K. R., MEDD, W. E., MATHEWS, M. B., AND DALEY, R. Dynamics of the circulation in aortic valvular disease. Am. J. Med., 1955, **18**, 855.

GORLIN, R., SAWYER, C. G., HAYNES, F. W., GOODALE, W. T., AND DEXTER, L. Effects of exercise on circulatory dynamics in mitral stenosis III. Am. Heart J., 1951, **41**, 192.

GREEN, H. D. The coronary blood flow in aortic stenosis, in aortic insufficiency and in arteriovenous fistula. Am. J. Physiol., 1936, **115**, 94.

HARVEY, R. M., FERRER, M. I., SAMET, P., BADER, R. A., BADER, M. E., COURNAND, A., AND RICHARDS, D. W. Mechanical and myocardial factors in rheumatic heart disease with mitral stenosis. Circulation, 1955, **11**, 531.

HERNANDEZ, R. R., GREENFIELD, J. C., JR., AND McCALL, B. W. Pressure flow studies in hypertrophic subaortic stenosis. J. Clin. Invest., 1964, **43**, 401.

HUFNAGEL, C. A., HARVEY, W. P., RABIL, P. S., AND McDERMOTT, T. F. Surgical correction of aortic insufficiency. Surgery, 1954, **35**, 673.

KATZ, L. N., RALLI, E. P., AND CHEER, S. The cardiodynamic changes in the aorta and left ventricle due to stenosis of the aorta. J. Clin. Invest., 1927–8, **5**, 205.

KILLIP, T., III, and LUKAS, D. S. Tricuspid stenosis. Circulation, 1957, **16**, 3.

LEATHAM, A. Auscultation of the Heart. Lancet, 1958, **2**, 703, 757.

LEVINE, S. A., AND HARVEY, W. P. Clinical auscultation of the heart. W. B. Saunders Company, Philadelphia, 1950.

LEWIS, T. AND DRURY, A. N. Observations relating to arteriovenous aneurism. Part I. Circulatory manifestations in clinical cases with particular reference to arterial phenomena of aortic regurgitation. Heart, 1923, **10**, 301.

McCORD, M. C. AND BLOUNT, S. G., JR. The hemodynamic pattern in tricuspid valve disease. Am. Heart J., 1952, **44**, 671.

McDONALD, L., DEALY, J. B., JR., RABINOWITZ, M., AND DEXTER, L. Clinical, physiological and pathological findings in mitral stenosis and regurgitation. Medicine, 1957, **36**, 237.

MOSCOVITZ, H. L., GORDON, A. J., BRAUNWALD, E., AMRAM, S. S., SAPIN, S. O., LASSER, R. P., HIMMELSTEIN, A., AND RAVITCH, M. M. The use of simultaneous left heart pressure pulse measurements in evaluating the effects of mitral valve surgery. Am. J. Med., 1955, **18**, 406.

Musser, B. G., Bougas, J., and Goldberg, H. Left heart catheterization. II. With particular reference to mitral and aortic valvular disease. Am. Heart J., 1956, **52**, 567.

Myerson, A., Loman, J., Rinkel, M., and Lesses, M. F. Human autonomic pharmacology. XVIII. Effect of intra-arterial injection of acetylcholine, acetyl-beta-methylcholine chloride, epinephrine and benzedrine sulfate. Am. Heart J., 1938, **16**, 329.

Opdyke, D. F., Duomarco, J., Dillon, W. H., Schreiber, H., Little, R. C., and Seely, R. D. Study of simultaneous right and left atrial pressure pulses under normal and experimentally altered conditions. Am. J. Physiol., 1948, **154**, 258.

Parker, F., Jr. and Weiss, S. The nature and significance of the structural changes in the lungs in mitral stenosis. Am. J. Path., 1936, **12**, 573.

Rodbard, S. and Williams, F. The dynamics of mitral insufficiency. Am. Heart J., 1954, **48**, 521.

Ross, J., Jr., Braunwald, E., and Morrow, A. G. Clinical and hemodynamic observations in pure mitral insufficiency. Am. J. Cardiol., 1958, **2**, 11.

Sepulveda, G. and Lukas, D. S. The diagnosis of tricuspid insufficiency. Circulation, 1955, **XI**, 552.

Starr, A., Edwards, M. L., and Griswold, H. E. Mitral replacement: late results with a ball valve prosthesis. Progr. Cardiovasc. Dis., 1962, **5**, 298.

Welch, G. H., Jr., Braunwald, E., and Sarnoff, S. J. Hemodynamic effects of quantitatively varied experimental aortic regurgitation. Circulation Res., 1957, **5**, 546.

Wiggers, C. J. and Feil, H. Cardiodynamics in mitral insufficiency. Heart, 1922, **9**, 149.

Wiggers, C. J. The magnitude of regurgitation with aortic leaks of different sizes. J. A. M. A., 1931, **97**, 1359.

Wiggers, C. J. and Malby, A. B. Further observations on experimental aortic insufficiency. IV. Hemodynamic factors determining the characteristic changes in aortic and ventricular pressure pulses. Am. J. Physiol., 1931, **97**, 689.

Wood, P. Diseases of the heart and circulation. Ed. 2. J. B. Lippincott Company, Philadelphia, 1956.

Shock and Hemorrhage, Congestive Heart Failure

Altschule, M. D. The pathological physiology of chronic cardiac decompensation. Medicine, 1938, **17**, 75.

Beecher, H. K. Early care of the seriously wounded man. J. A. M. A., 1951, **145**, 193.

Bolton, C. The pathology of cardiac dropsy. Brit. Med. J., 1917, **1**, 642.

Borst, J. G. G. The maintenance of an adequate cardiac output by the regulation of the urinary excretion of water and sodium chloride: an essential factor in the genesis of oedema. Acta med. scandinav., 1948, Suppl., **CCVII (207)**, 130.

Bradley, S. E. and Blake, W. D. Pathogenesis of renal dysfunction during congestive heart failure. Am. J. Med., 1949, **6**, 470.

Burwell, C. S. and Dexter, L. Beri-beri heart disease. Tr. A. Am. Physicians, 1947, **60**, 59.

Cohen, S. M., Edholm, O. G., Howarth, S., McMichael, J., and Sharpey-Schafer, E. P. Cardiac output and peripheral blood flow in arteriovenous aneurysm. Clin. Sc., 1948, **7**, 35.

Davies, C. E. and Kilpatrick, J. A. Renal circulation in "low output" and "high output" heart failure. Clin. Sc., 1951, **10**, 53.

Elkin, D. C. and Warren, J. V. Arteriovenous fistulas, their effect on the circulation. J. A. M. A., 1947, **134**, 1524.

Eppinger, E. C., Burwell, C. S., and Gross, R. E. The effects of the patent ductus arteriosus on the circulation. J. Clin. Invest., 1941, **20**, 127.

Erskine, J. M. The relation of the liver to shock. Internat. Abstr. Surg., 1958, **106**, 207.

Espersen, T. Studies on the cardiac output and related circulatory functions, especially in patients with congestive heart failure. Acta med. scandinav., 1941, **108**, 153.

Fine, J. The bacterial factor in traumatic shock. Charles C Thomas, Springfield, Illinois, 1954.

Futcher, P. H. and Schroeder, H. A. Studies on congestive heart failure. II. Impaired renal excretion of sodium chloride. Am. J. M. Sc., 1942, **204**, 52.

Green, H. H. (Ed.) Shock and circulatory homeostasis. Josiah Macy, Jr. Foundation, New York, Transactions of five annual conferences, 1952 to 1957.

Gregersen, M. I. Shock. Ann. Rev. Physiol., 1946, **8**, 335.

Gregersen, M. I. Blood volume. Ann. Rev. Physiol., 1951, **13**, 397.

Holman, E. Arteriovenous aneurysm; abnormal communication between the arterial and venous circulations. Macmillan Company, New York, 1937.

Holman, E. Clinical and experimental observations on arteriovenous fistulae. Ann. Surg., 1940, **112**, 840.

Landis, E. M., Brown, E., Fauteux, M., and Wise, C. Central venous pressure in relation to cardiac "competence", blood volume and exercise. J. Clin. Invest., 1946, **25**, 237.

Lasche, E. M., Perloff, W. H., and Durant, T. M. Some aspects of adrenocortical function in cardiac decompensation. Am. J. M. Sc., 1951, **222**, 459.

McMichael, J. Output of heart in congestive failure. Quart. J. Med., 1938, **7**, 331.

McMichael, J. Circulatory failure studied by means of venous catheterization. Advances Int. Med., 1947, **2**, 64.

Merrill, A. J. Mechanisms of salt and water retention in heart failure. Am. J. Med., 1949, **6**, 357.

Mokotoff, R., Ross, G., and Leiter, L. Renal plasma flow and sodium reabsorption and excretion in congestive heart failure. J. Clin. Invest., 1948, **27**, 1.

Nielsen, H. E. Clinical investigations into the cardiac output of patients with compensated heart disease during rest and during muscular work. Acta med. scandinav., 1937, **91**, 223.

PARRISH, A. E. The bioassay of adrenal corticoids in the urine of patients with congestive heart failure. J. Clin. Invest., 1949, **28**, 45.

PORTER, R. R. AND DOWNS, R. S. Some physiological observations on the circulation during recovery from vitamin B deficiency. Ann. Int. Med., 1942, **17**, 645.

RICHARDS, D. W., JR. Dynamics of congestive heart failure. Am. J. Med., 1949, **6**, 772.

SCHEMM, F. R. A high fluid intake in the management of edema, especially cardiac edema. Ann. Int. Med., 1942, **17**, 952; ibid., 1944, **21**, 937.

SCHORR, E., ZWEIFACH, B. W., FURCHGOTT, R. F., AND BAEZ, S. Hepatorenal factors in circulatory homeostasis. Circulation, 1951, **42**, 1951.

SINGER, B. AND WENER, J. Excretion of sodium-retaining substances in patients with congestive heart failure. Am. Heart J., 1953, **45**, 795.

STARR, I. Our changing viewpoint about congestive failure. Ann. Int. Med., 1949, **30**, 1.

STARR, I. Role of the "static blood pressure" in abnormal increments of venous pressure, especially in heart failure. Am. J. M. Sc., 1940, **199**, 40.

STARR, I., JEFFERS, W. A., AND MEADE, R. H., JR. The absence of conspicuous increments of venous pressure after severe damage to the right ventricle of the dog, with a discussion of the relation between clinical congestive failure and heart disease. Am. Heart J., 1943, **26**, 291.

STEAD, E. A., JR. Edema of heart failure. Bull. New York Acad. Med., 1948, **24**, 607.

WARREN, J. V. AND STEAD, E. A., JR. Fluid dynamics in chronic congestive heart failure. An interpretation of the mechanisms producing the edema, increased plasma volume and elevated venous pressure in certain patients with prolonged congestive failure. Arch. Int. Med., 1944, **73**, 138.

WEISS, S. AND WILKINS, R. W. The nature of the cardiovascular disturbances in nutritional deficiency states. Ann. Int. Med., 1937, **11**, 104.

WIGGERS, C. J. Physiology of shock. The Commonwealth Fund, New York, 1950.

YOUMANS, W. B. Mod. Concepts. Cardiovas. Dis., 1957, **26**, 389.

YOUMANS, W. B. Renal function in congestive heart failure. Ann. Int. Med., 1954, **41**, 739.

YOUMANS, W. B. Mechanism of high output circulatory failure. Ann. Int. Med., 1954, **41**, 747.

YOUMANS, W. B. AND HUCKINS, A. R. Hemodynamics in failure of the circulation. Charles C. Thomas, Springfield, Illinois, 1951.

Arrhythmias

BRISTOW, J. D., FERGUSON, R. E., MINTZ, F., AND RAPPORT, E. The influence of heart rate on left ventricular volume in dogs. J. Clin. Invest., 1963, **42**, 649.

DOCK, W., GRANDELL, F., AND TAUBMAN, F. The physiologic third heart sound: its mechanism and relation to protodiastolic gallop. Am. Heart J., 1955, **50**, 449.

DODGE, H. T., KIRKHAM, F. T., JR., AND KING,

C. V. Ventricular dynamics in atrial fibrillation. Circulation, 1957, **15**, 335.

FERRER, M. I. AND HARVEY, R. M. Some hemodynamic aspects of cardiac arrhythmias in man. Am. Heart J., 1964, **68**, 153.

FERRER, M. I., HARVEY, R. M., WEINER, H. M., CATHCART, R. T., AND COURNAND, A. Hemodynamic studies in two cases of W-P-W syndrome with paroxysmal A-V nodal tachycardia. Am. J. Med., 1949, **6**, 725.

FLETCHER, F. W., THEILEN, E. O., LAWRENCE, M. S., AND EVANS, J. W. Effect of pacemaker location on cardiac function in complete atrioventricular heart block. Amer. J. Physiol., 1963, **205**, 1232.

HANSEN, W. R., McCLENDON, R. L., AND KINSMAN, J. M. Auricular fibrillation: Hemodynamic studies before and after conversion with quinidine. Am. Heart J., 1952, **44**, 499.

HARVEY, R. M., FERRER, M. I., RICHARDS, D. W., AND COURNAND, A. Cardiocirculatory performance in atrial flutter. Circulation, 1955, **12**, 507.

IKKOS, D. AND HANSON, J. S. Response to exercise in congenital complete atrioventricular block. Circulation, 1960, **22**, 583.

JUDGE, R. D., WILSON, W. S., AND SIEGEL, J. H. Hemodynamic studies in patients with implanted cardiac pacemakers. New Engl. J. Med., 1964, **270**, 1391.

LEVINSON, D. C., GUNTHER, L., MEEHAN, J. P., GRIFFITH, G. C., AND SPRITZLER, R. J. Hemodynamic studies in five patients with heart block and slow ventricular rates. Circulation, 1955, **12**, 739.

LEVY, J. M., MESEL, E., AND RUDOLPH, A. M. Unequal right and left ventricular ejection with ectopic beats. Amer. J. Physiol., 1962, **203**, 1141.

LIND, J., WEGELIUS, C., AND LICHTENSTEIN, H. The dynamics of the heart in complete A-V block. An angiocardiographic study. Circulation, 1954, **10**, 195.

MORRIS, J. J., JR., ENTMAN, M. L., THOMPSON, H. K., JR., NORTH, W. C., AND McINTOSH, H. D. Cardiac output in atrial fibrillation and sinus rhythm. Circulation, 1963, **28**, 772.

NAKANO, J. Effects of atrial and ventricular tachycardia on the cardiovascular dynamics. Amer. J. Physiol., 1964, **206**, 547.

SEGEL, N., HUDSON, W. A., HARRIS, P. AND BISHOP, J. M. The circulatory effects of electrically induced changes in ventricular rate at rest and during exercise in complete heart block. J. Clin. Invest., 1964, **43**, 1541.

STACK, M. F., RADER, B., SOBOL, B. J., FARBER, S. J., AND EICHNA, L. W. Cardiovascular hemodynamic functions in complete heart block and the effect of isopropylnorepinephrine. Circulation, 1958, **17**, 526.

STARZL, T. E. AND GAERTNER, R. A. Chronic heart block in dogs. A method for producing experimental heart failure. Circulation, 1955, **12**, 259.

STARZL, T. E., GAERTNER, R. A., AND BAKER, R. R. Acute complete heart block in dogs. Circulation, 1955, **12**, 82.

STARZL, T. E., GAERTNER, R. A., AND WEBB, R.

C., JR. The effects of repetitive electric cardiac stimulation in dogs with normal hearts, complete heart block and experimental cardiac arrest. Circulation, 1955, 11, 952.

STEWART, H. J., DIETRICK, J. E., CRANE, N. F., AND THOMPSON, W. P. Studies of the circulation in the presence of abnormal cardiac rhythms. Observations relating to (Part I) rhythms associated with rapid ventricular rate and to (Part II) rhythms associated with slow ventricular rate. J. Clin. Invest., 1938, 17, 449.

WARREN, J. V., LEONARD, J. J., AND WEISSLER, A. M. Gallop rhythm. Ann. Int. Med., 1958, 48, 580.

Cardiac Tamponade

DOCK, W. Inspiratory traction on pericardium: cause of pulsus paradoxus in pericardial disease. Arch. Int. Med., 1961, 108, 837.

GOLINKO, R. J., KAPLAN, N., AND RUDOLPH, A. M. The mechanism of pulsus paradoxus during acute pericardial tamponade. J. Clin. Invest., 1963, 42, 249.

HANSEN, A. T., ESKILDSEN, P., AND GOTZSCHE, H. Pressure curves from the right auricle and the right ventricle in chronic constrictive pericarditis. Circulation, 1951, 3, 881.

HARVEY, R. M., FERRER, M. I., CATHCART, R. T., RICHARDS, D. W., AND COURNAND, A. Mechanical and myocardial factors in chronic constrictive pericarditis. Circulation, 1953, 8, 695.

ISAACS, J. P., CARTER, B. N., AND HALLER, J. A. Experimental pericarditis: The pathologic physiology of constrictive pericarditis. Bull. John Hopkins Hosp., 1952, 90, 259.

ISAACS, J. P., BERGLUND, E., AND SARNOFF, S. J. Ventricular function. III. The pathologic physiology of acute cardiac tamponade studied by means of ventricular function curves. Am. Heart J., 1954, 48, 66.

KATZ, L. N., AND GAUCHAT, H. W. Observations on pulsus paradoxus (with special reference to pericardial effusions): II. Experimental. Arch. Int. Med., 1924, 33, 371.

MCKUSICK, V. A. Chronic constrictive pericarditis. I. Some clinical and laboratory observations. Bull. Johns Hopkins Hosp., 1952, 90, 3.

METCALFE, J., WOODBURY, J. W., RICHARDS, V., AND BURWELL, C. S. Studies in experimental pericardial tamponade: effects on intravascular pressures and cardiac output. Circulation, 1952, 5, 518.

MORGAN, B. C., GUNTHEROTH, W. G., DILLARD, D. H., AND BREAZEALE, D. Relationship of pericardial to pleural pressure during quiet respiration and cardiac tamponade. Circulation, 1964, 30, Supp. III, 129 (Abstract).

SAWYER, C. G., BURWELL, C. S., DEXTER, L., EPPINGER, E. C., GOODALE, W. T., GORLIN, R., HARKEN, D. E., AND HAYNES, F. W. Chronic constrictive pericarditis: further consideration of the pathologic physiology of the disease. Am. Heart J., 1952, 44, 207.

Congenital Heart Disease

AYGEN, M. M. AND BRAUNWALD, E. The splitting of the second heart sound in normal subjects and in patients with congenital heart disease. Circulation, 1962, 25, 328.

BAHNSON, H. T., SPENCER, F. C., LANDTMAN, B., WOLF, M. D., NEILL, C. A., AND TAUSSIG, H. B. Surgical treatment and followup of 147 cases of tetralogy of Fallot treated by correction. J. Thoracic and Cardiovasc. Surg., 1962, 44, 419.

BING, R. J., VANDAM, L. D., AND GRAY, F. D. Physiological studies in congenital heart disease. III. Results obtained in five cases of Eisenmenger's Complex. Bull. Johns Hopkins Hosp., 1947, 80, 323.

BING, R. J., VANDAM, L. D., AND GRAY, F. D., JR. Physiological studies in congenital heart disease. II. Results of preoperative studies in patients with Tetralogy of Fallot. Bull. Johns Hopkins Hosp., 1947, 80, 121.

BLOOMFIELD, D. K. The natural history of ventricular septal defect in patients surviving infancy. Circulation, 1964, 29, 914.

BLOUNT, S. G., JR., MCCORD, M. C., MUELLER, H., AND SWAN, H. Isolated valvular pulmonic stenosis: clinical and physiologic response to open valvuloplasty. Circulation, 1954, 10, 161.

BLOUNT, S. G., JR., MUELLER, H., AND MCCORD, M. C. Ventricular septal defect. Am. J. Med., 1955, 18, 871.

BRAUNWALD, N. S., BRAUNWALD, E., AND MORROW, A. G. The effects of surgical abolition of left-to-right shunts on the pulmonary vascular dynamics of patients with pulmonary hypertension. Circulation, 1962, 26, 1270.

BRECHER, G. A. AND OPDYKE, D. F. Effect of pulmonary stenosis upon the circulation in the absence and presence of an interatrial septal defect. Am. J. Physiol., 1950, 163, 701.

BRENT, L. B., ABURANO, A., FISHER, D. L., MORAN, T. J., MYERS, J. D., AND TAYLOR, W. J. Familial muscular subaortic stenosis. Circulation, 1960, 21, 167.

BREST, A. N., UDHOJI, V., AND LIKOFF, W. A re-evaluation of the Graham-Steell murmur. New Engl. J. Med., 1960, 263, 1229.

BROWN, G. E., JR., CLAGETT, O. T., BURCHELL, H. B., AND WOOD, E. H. Preoperative and postoperative studies of intraradial and intrafemoral pressures in patients with coarctation of the aorta. Proc. Staff Meet. Mayo Clin., 1948, 23, 352.

BURWELL, C. S., EPPINGER, E. C., AND GROSS, R. E. The effects of patency of the ductus arteriosus on the circulation. J. Clin. Invest., 1940, 19, 774.

COLLINS, N. P., BRAUNWALD, E., AND MORROW, A. G. Isolated congenital pulmonic valvular regurgitation. Am. J. Med., 1960, 28, 159.

COURNAND, A., BALDWIN, J. S., AND HIMMELSTEIN, A. Cardiac catheterization in congenital heart disease. The Commonwealth Fund, New York, 1949.

COURNAND, A., MOTLEY, H. L., HIMMELSTEIN, A., DRESDALE, D., AND BALDWIN, J. Recording of blood pressure from the left auricle and the pulmonary veins in human subjects with interauricular septal defect. Am. J. Physiol., 1947, 150, 267.

CULBERTSON, J. W., ECKSTEIN, J. W., KIRKENDALL, W. M., AND BEDELL, G. N. General hemodynamics and splanchnic circulation in patients with coarctation of the aorta. J. Clin. Invest., 1957, **36,** 1537.

DAMMANN, J. F., JR., THOMPSON, W. M., JR., SOSA, O., AND CHRISTLIEB, I. Anatomy, physiology and natural history of simple ventricular septal defects. Am. J. Cardiol., 1960, **5,** 136.

DAMMANN, J. F., JR., McEACHEN, J. A., THOMPSON, W. M., JR., SMITH, R., AND MULLER, W. H., JR. Regression of pulmonary vascular disease after creation of pulmonary stenosis. J. Thoracic and Cardiovasc. Surg. 1961, **42,** 722.

DEXTER, L., HAYNES, F. W., BURWELL, C. S., EPPINGER, E. C., SOSMAN, M. C., AND EVANS, J. M. Studies of congenital heart disease. III. Venous catheterization as a diagnostic aid in patent ductus arteriosus, Tetralogy of Fallot, VSD and ASD. J. Clin. Invest., 1947, **26,** 561.

DONOVAN, T. J., HUFNAGEL, C. A., AND EASTCOTT, H. H. G. Techniques of endocardial anastomosis for circumventing the pulmonic valve. J. Thoracic Surg., 1952, **23,** 348.

DOW, J. W., LEVINE, H. D., ELKIN, M., HAYNES, F. W., HELLEMS, H. K., WHITTENBERGER, J. W., FERRIS, B. G., GOODALE, W. T., HARVEY, W. P., EPPINGER, E. C., AND DEXTER, L. Studies of congenital heart disease. IV. Uncomplicated pulmonic stenosis. Circulation, 1950, **1,** 267.

EVANS, J. R., ROWE, R. D., AND KEITH, J. D. Spontaneous closure of ventricular septal defects. Circulation, 1960, **22,** 1044.

FERGUSON, D. J. AND VARCO, R. L. The relation of blood pressure and flow to the development and regression of experimentally induced pulmonary arteriosclerosis. Circulation Res., 1955, **3,** 152.

FISH, R. G., TAKARO, T., AND CRYMES, T. Prognostic considerations in primary isolated insufficiency of the pulmonic valve. New England J. Med., 1959, **261,** 739.

FOWLER, N. O., MANNIX, E. P., AND NOBLE, W. Some effects of partial pulmonary valvectomy. Circulation Res., 1956, **4,** 8.

GROSS, R. E. The patent ductus arteriosus. Am. J. Med., 1952, **12,** 472.

GUPTA, T. C. AND WIGGERS, C. J. Basic hemodynamic changes produced by aortic coarctation of different degrees. Circulation, 1951, **3,** 17.

GUPTA, T. C. The effects of arterial and pulmonary shunts on the dynamics of aortic coarctation. Circulation, 1951, **3,** 32.

HANDELSMAN, J. C., BING, R. J., CAMPBELL, J. A., AND GRISWOLD, H. E. Physiological studies in congenital heart disease. V. The circulation in patients with isolated septal defects. Bull. Johns Hopkins Hosp., 1948, **82,** 615.

HIMMELSTEIN, A. AND COURNAND, A. Cardiac catheterization in the study of congenital cardiovascular anomalies. Am. J. Med., 1952, **12,** 349.

KOHOUT, F. W., AND KATZ, L. N. Pulmonic valvular regurgitation. Am. Heart J., 1955, **49,** 637.

LITTLE, R. C., OPDYKE, D. F., AND HAWLEY, J. G. Dynamics of experimental atrial septal defects. Am. J. Physiol., 1949, **158,** 241.

MARAIST, F., DALEY, R., DRAPER, A., JR., HEIMBECKER, R., DAMMANN, F., JR., KIEFFER, R., JR., KING, J. T., FERENCZ, C., AND BING, R. J. Physiological studies in congenital heart disease. X. The physiological findings in 34 patients with isolated pulmonary valvular stenosis. Bull. Johns Hopkins Hosp., 1951, **88,** 1.

McCORD, M. C., VAN ELK, J., AND BLOUNT, S. G., JR. Tetralogy of Fallot: Clinical and hemodynamic spectrum of combined pulmonary stenosis and ventricular septal defect. Circulation, 1957, **16,** 736.

NADAS, A. S., RUDOLPH, A. M., AND GROSS, R. E. Pulmonary arterial hypertension in congenital heart disease. Circulation, 1960, **22,** 1041.

NOLLA-PANADES, J. Hypertension and increased hindlimb vascular reactivity in experimental coarctation of aorta. Circulation Res., 1963, **12,** 3.

O'DONNELL, T. V. AND McILROY, M. B. Circulatory effects of squatting. Am. Heart J. 1962, **64,** 347.

OLESEN, K. H. AND FABRICIUS, J. Pulmonic valvular regurgitation during 27 years after gonorrheal endocarditis: report of case with catheterization data. Am. Heart J., 1956, **52,** 791.

PAINTER, R. C., HINES, E. A., JR., AND EDWARDS, J. E. Measurements of arterioles in coarctation of the aorta. Circulation, 1952, **6,** 727.

RUDOLPH, A. M. AND NADAS, A. S. The pulmonary circulation and congenital heart disease. New Engl. J. Med., 1962, **267,** 967.

RYTAND, D. A. The renal factor in arterial hypertension with coarctation of the aorta. J. Clin. Invest., 1938, **17,** 391.

SCHUSTER, S. R. AND GROSS, R. E. Surgery for coarctation of aorta: review of 500 cases. J. Thoracic and Cardiovasc. Surg., 1962, **43,** 54.

SCOTT, H. W., JR. AND BAHNSON, H. T. Evidence for renal factor in hypertension of experimental coarctation of aorta. Surgery, 1951, **30,** 206.

SELZER, A. Defects of the cardiac septum. J. A. M. A., 1954, **154,** 129.

SHARPEY-SCHAFER, E. P. Effects of squatting on the normal and failing circulation. Brit. Med. J., 1956, **1,** 1072.

SHEPHERD, JOHN T. The pulmonary circulation in the presence of interatrial, interventricular and interarterial communications. Pulmonary Circulation, edited by W. Adams and I. Veith. Grune & Stratton, Inc., New York, 1959.

SHEPHERD, J. T., WEIDMAN, W. H., BURKE, E. C., AND WOOD, E. H. Hemodynamics in patent ductus arteriosus without a murmur. Circulation, 1955, **11,** 404.

TANENBAUM, H. L., BRAUNWALD, E., AND MORROW, A. G. Determination of cardiac output and pressure gradients at operation; a technic for the immediate assessment of the results of operations for stenotic valvular disease. New England J. Med., 1958, **258,** 527.

WINCHELL, P. AND BASHOUR, F. Some physiologic features of atrial septal defect. Am. J. Cardiol., 1958, **2,** 687.

VI

RESPIRATION

CHAPTER 50

Uptake and Delivery of the Respiratory Gases

Introduction

The cells of higher animals continually use oxygen and produce carbon dioxide as a waste product. Breathing movements promote the transfer of oxygen from the atmosphere into the lungs and the removal of carbon dioxide from the lungs. Oxygen diffuses into the blood in the pulmonary capillaries to be carried to all parts of the body, where it diffuses from the capillary blood into the interstitial fluid and on to the cells. Carbon dioxide diffuses from the cells through the interstitial fluid to the blood in the systemic capillaries, and then is carried to the lungs where it diffuses into the alveolar air. The continual processes of respiration, regulated by a complex of "feed-back" and other mechanisms, play a major role in the maintenance of homeostasis. Under constant conditions the respiratory processes tend to attain a condition which may be called a "steady state," but not an "equilibrium with the environment" since at equilibrium all reactions would be at a standstill.

The major problems to be considered under the heading of respiratory physiology are: (1) the uptake of oxygen from alveolar air and its delivery to the tissues, (2) the uptake of carbon dioxide from tissues and its delivery to the alveolar air, (3) the mechanism of rhythmic inspiration and expiration, and (4) the mechanisms by means of which the amount of air breathed per minute is adjusted to the needs of the body. The actual chemical processes by which oxygen is utilized in the cells (cellular respiration) will not be discussed, since this subject is considered in detail in biochemistry texts. Some of the derangements of respiration are considered under the appropriate major headings, while others of a more general nature are described in the final chapter of this section.

It is assumed that the reader already will have knowledge of elementary biochemistry and human anatomy. Further, it is essential that the relation of carbon dioxide to the acid-base balance (ch. 34), the physiology of nerve, muscle, and reflex action (ch. 4) and the physiology of the autonomic nervous system (ch. 12) should be studied in advance in order to understand the chemical and neural control of respiration.

A system of notation for use in respiratory physiology, summarized in table 50.1, was agreed on by a group of physiologists meeting in Atlantic City in 1950. This system is now generally accepted, and will be followed in this section.

The Kinetic Theory of Gases

A quantity of gas when placed in a container of any size expands until it fills the confining vessel. This fact is explained upon the theory that the gas molecules are in continuous motion, moving through space at high velocity and being deflected from their course only upon coming into collision with other gas molecules or with the boundaries of the space itself which they strike and from which they rebound repeatedly. Such movements constitute a bombardment upon the confining walls which is responsible for the pressure of the gas. The greater the number of molecules in any given space, and the higher their mean velocity, the more frequent will be the impacts.

Boyle's Law. If the volume of a given mass of gas is reduced, the molecules are brought closer together and the rate of bombardment upon a unit surface increases, the increase becoming manifest as a rise in pressure. Robert Boyle first noted the quantitative relationship between pressure and volume: *at a constant temperature the pressure of a given mass of gas is inversely proportional to its volume;* i.e., the product of the pressure and the volume remains constant.

Avogadro's Law states that *equal volumes of different gases at the same temperature and pressure contain the same number of molecules.* Thus a gram-molecule of any gas at STPD occupies a volume of 22.4 liters. Since the force of an impact is related to the mass of the molecule as well as to its velocity, it follows that at a given temperature the molecules of a gas of low molecular weight are traveling faster than are those of a heavier gas. The mean kinetic energy of the gas molecules has a certain value which is related to temperature alone.

Law of Charles (or Gay-Lussac). A rise in temperature increases the velocity and kinetic energy of the gas molecules. The force of the impacts is thus increased, and at constant volume the rate of bombardment also is increased. For each rise in temperature of 1° C. a gas kept at constant volume increases its pressure by $\frac{1}{273}$ of its pressure at 0° C. If, instead, the pressure is held con-

TABLE 50.1*

Symbols and abbreviations used by pulmonary physiologists

(Based on report in Federation Proc. **9**: 602–605, 1950)

SPECIAL SYMBOLS

—Dash above any symbol indicates a *mean* value.
·Dot above any symbol indicates a *time derivative*.

FOR GASES				FOR BLOOD			
Primary Symbols (large capital letters)		**Examples**		**Primary Symbols** (large capital letters)			**Examples**
V	= gas volume	V_A	= volume of alveolar gas	Q	= volume of blood	Qc	= volume of blood in pulmonary capillaries
$\dot{V}$	= gas volume/ unit time	$\dot{V}_{O_2}$	= O_2 consumption/min				
P	= gas pressure	$P_{A_{O_2}}$	= alveolar O_2 pressure	$\dot{Q}$	= volume flow of blood/unit time	$\dot{Q}c$	= blood flow through pulmonary capillaries/min
$\overline{P}$	= mean gas pressure	$\overline{P}_{CO_2}$	= mean capillary O_2 pressure				
F	= fractional concentration in dry gas phase	$F_{I_{O_2}}$	= fractional concentration of O_2 in inspired gas	C	= concentration of gas in blood phase	Ca_{O_2}	= ml O_2 in 100 ml arterial blood
f	= respiratory frequency (breaths/unit time)			S	= % saturation of Hb with O_2 or CO	$S\overline{v}_{O_2}$	= saturation of Hb with O_2 in mixed venous blood
D	= diffusing capacity	D_{O_2}	= diffusing capacity for O_2 (ml $\dot{O}_2$/min/ mm Hg)	**Secondary Symbols** (small letters)			**Examples**
R	= respiratory exchange ratio	R	= $\dot{V}_{CO_2}/\dot{V}_{O_2}$	a	= arterial blood	Pa_{CO_2}	= partial pressure of CO_2 in arterial blood
Secondary Symbols (small capital letters)		**Examples**		v	= venous blood	$P\overline{v}_{O_2}$	= partial pressure of O_2 in mixed venous blood
I	= inspired gas	$F_{I_{CO_2}}$	= fractional concentration of CO_2 in inspired gas	c	= capillary blood	Pc_{CO}	= partial pressure of CO in pulmonary capillary blood
E	= expired gas	$\dot{V}_E$	= volume of expired gas				
A	= alveolar gas	$\dot{V}_A$	= alveolar ventilation/min	b	= blood in general		
T	= tidal gas	V_T	= tidal volume	s	= steady state		
D	= dead space gas	V_D	= volume of dead space gas				
B	= barometric	P_B	= barometric pressure				
STPD = 0°C, 760 mm Hg, dry							
BTPS = body temperature and pressure saturated with water vapor							
ATPS = ambient temperature and pressure saturated with water vapor							

* After Comroe *et al.* (1962).

stant, the volume increases by a corresponding amount. Taking $-273°$ C. as the absolute zero, it follows that *the pressure of a gas at constant volume (or the volume at constant pressure) is proportional to the absolute temperature.*

The *ideal gas law* is a quantitative expression of the foregoing principles:

$$PV = nRT$$

where P is the pressure, V is the volume, n is the number of gram-molecules of the gas, R is the

"gas constant," and T is the absolute temperature. When the units employed are atmospheres, liters and centigrade degrees, $R = 0.082$. For any real gas this expression is subject to small corrections related to the actual volume of the molecules themselves and the attractive forces between them.

Diffusion. In all circumstances, the gas molecules, as a result of their movement, will distribute themselves evenly throughout the space in which they are confined, and consequently the pressure will become equal throughout all parts of the space. This tendency of a gas to pass from a point of higher pressure to a point of lower pressure, and to distribute itself throughout the available space is called diffusion. However, the term applies equally to the distribution of dissolved molecules or ions in solution, and to the transfer of molecules across gas-liquid interfaces. The rate of diffusion of a *gas* at a given temperature is inversely proportional to the square root of its density. Thus hydrogen diffuses four times as rapidly as does oxygen.

Dalton's Law of Partial Pressures. If we should deal with a mixture of two or more gases, it would be found that each component of the mixture behaved as though present alone. Its molecules would become distributed evenly throughout the mixture, although its rate of diffusion would be retarded by collisions with other molecules. *Each gas in a mixture exerts a pressure according to its own concentration, independently of the other gases present.* The pressure of each constituent is referred to as its *partial pressure* or *tension* and the total pressure is the *sum of the partial pressures* of all the gases present.

Henry's Law. When a gas is brought into contact with water, gas molecules bombard the surface of the liquid and pass into it, but the dissolved gas molecules also tend to escape from the liquid. After a time their rate of escape equals their rate of entry. When this equilibrium is reached, the solution is said to be saturated. Each gas has its own characteristic solubility at a given temperature and pressure. If no chemical reaction is involved, but only physical solution, Henry's law states that *the concentration of a gas in solution at equilibrium is directly proportional to its partial pressure in the gas phase.* The solubility of oxygen, for example, is described by the expression

$$C_{O_2} = \alpha_{O_2} \cdot P_{O_2}$$

where C_{O_2} is its concentration in aqueous solution, P_{O_2} is its tension, and α_{O_2} is a constant which is characteristic of oxygen. If C_{O_2} is expressed in ml. (SPTD) per ml. of solution and P_{O_2} in atmospheres, α_{O_2} represents the solubility in ml. of oxygen gas per ml. of water and per atmosphere. This is called the solubility coefficient or absorption coefficient of oxygen.

The solubility of a gas is not affected by the presence of other gases; each gas in a mixture dissolves in accordance with its own partial pressure and absorption coefficient. The solubility is decreased slightly, however, by the presence of salts or other solutes. Hence the absorption coefficients are slightly lower for solution in blood plasma than for solution in water (table 50.2). The values for whole blood are influenced also by the presence

TABLE 50.2

Absorption coefficients of gases in water, blood plasma and whole blood, in ml. per ml. and per at.

	α_{O_2}	α_{CO_2}	α_{N_2}
Water, 20°C.........	0.0314*	0.872*	0.0155*
Water, 37°C.........	0.0237†	0.547†	0.0130‡
Plasma, 37°C.......	0.0213†	0.521†	0.0119‡
Blood, 37°C........	0.0235†	0.48†	0.0132‡

* Radford, 1964.

† Rossier *et al.*, 1960.

‡ Van Slyke *et al.*, 1934 (corrected to 37°C.).

of the erythrocytes. In general, the solubility of a gas is decreased by an increase in temperature.

Although carbon dioxide in solution combines with water to form H_2CO_3, this reaction does not cause deviations from Henry's Law. The two forms are present in a constant ratio, and the equilibrium is such that only one part in 680 is in the hydrated form at 38° C. (Roughton, 1943–44).

When the absorption coefficient is known, it is a simple matter to calculate the tension from the ml. of gas per ml. of solution and vice versa. Hence it is often convenient to use the value representing tension (in atmospheres or, more commonly, in mm. Hg) as a measure of the concentration of physically dissolved gas in a solution. If the liquid after equilibration were separated from the gas phase, this would not change the tension of the dissolved gas; hence the use of this measure does not require the presence of a gas phase. If the solution were subsequently exposed to a vacuum or to an atmosphere of other gases, however, the dissolved gas would tend to diffuse out of the solution. Hence the tension of a dissolved gas can be regarded as a measure of its tendency to escape from solution.

Aqueous tension. Water itself, when exposed to a vacuum or to an atmosphere of other gases, tends to evaporate until an equilibrium is reached between the gas phase and the liquid. Although it is common to speak of the air becoming saturated, the tension or vapor pressure of water attained at equilibrium is not affected by the presence or absence of other gases. It depends simply upon the temperature. At body temperature (37° C.) the aqueous tension of water is 47 mm. Hg. Substances in solution reduce the aqueous tension by small amounts.

The Exchange of Gases in the Lungs

The concept of tension gradients. Oxygen from the air in the aeveoli enters the blood in the pulmonary capillaries by diffusion through the alveolar and capillary membranes, while carbon dioxide diffuses in the reverse direction. The transfer of a quantity of gas by diffusion can occur only from a place of higher to a place of lower concentration, i.e., in the direction of a *concentration gradient*. Strictly speaking, such a gradient would be defined as a decrease in concentration per unit of distance. However, the actual distance traversed may not be precisely known and may not be of major interest. It is customary to refer to the total difference in oxygen tension between alveolar air and pulmonary blood plasma as the oxygen diffusion gradient. The direction of this gradient is from the higher (alveolar) toward the lower (capillary) tension. The carbon dioxide gradient, stated in the same terms, is in the opposite direction. Similar gradients exist between the blood plasma and the interstitial fluid, and in turn between the interstitial fluid and the interior of the respiring cells. In each case, the tension gradients are to be regarded as the driving forces for the exchange of gases. Combined forms of oxygen and carbon dioxide existing in the blood play no direct role in these exchanges; they serve only as reservoirs which, by dissociation and the laws of mass action, replenish and maintain the tensions of the physically dissolved gases.

The rate of diffusion of a gas through a liquid per unit of *tension* gradient is directly proportional to the solubility of the gas and inversely proportional to the square root of its molecular weight. Hence, at a given tension gradient and at body temperature, the diffusion rate of carbon dioxide in solution is about 20 times that of oxygen. The *diffusion coefficient* has been defined by Krogh as the volume in ml. of a gas which will diffuse 0.001 mm. distance over a square cm. of surface, per minute, at a pressure 1 atmosphere. It varies for different tissues and body fluids, and increases with rising temperature.

The Alveolar Air

The mixture of gases in the alveoli consists of inhaled air from which oxygen is being removed and to which carbon dioxide and water vapor are being added. Under resting conditions each inhalation brings into the respiratory system a volume of air representing less than 10 per cent of the total lung capacity, and not all of this reaches the alveoli. Hence the composition of the alveolar air shows only minor fluctuations with the respiratory cycle. The composition is not exactly the same in all parts of the lung, since there are variations in the effectiveness of ventilation. The average composition, however, is

maintained approximately constant by the mechanisms regulating the respiratory rate and volume.

A sample of expired air taken near the end of a normal expiration (end-tidal sample) is fairly representative of the average composition of alveolar air. The *Rahn sampler* is a device which automatically collects end-tidal samples, permitting continuous analysis and recording of the alveolar air (Rahn and Otis, 1949). In the older technique of *Haldane and Priestley*, allowance is made for small differences occurring during the respiratory cycle by taking two samples: one from the last part of a forced expiration following a normal inspiration; the other from a forced expiration following a normal expiration. The average of the two is taken to represent the mean composition of the alveolar air (Rossier, *et al.*, 1960). The *"functional"* alveolar oxygen tension can be obtained by an indirect method based on the *"alveolar air equation"*; this calculation requires analysis of the expired air (collected over a period of about 5 min.) and measurement of the arterial CO_2 tension. It is assumed that the mean CO_2 tension of the alveolar air is equal to that of the arterial blood (Riley *et al.*, 1946; Otis, 1964).

The air in the lungs has a temperature of about 37° C. and is usually considered to be saturated with water vapor. Its aqueous tension is therefore 47 mm. Hg.[1] When the air cools after exhalation, some of the water vapor condenses. The tension of water vapor in room air at 22° C. could be no higher than 20 mm. Hg and is usually much lower.

In the measurement of respiratory gases, the volumes are expressed dry (i.e., less the aqueous vapor) and at standard temperature and pressure. The individual gases are expressed as percentages of the dry volume. In order to arrive at the *tension* of a gas from its percentage by analysis, the figure for the barometric pressure less the aqueous tension must be used in the calculation. For example, if a sample of alveolar air (dry) is 5.6 per cent CO_2, and the barometric pressure is 760 mm. Hg, the *alveolar carbon dioxide tension* is calculated as follows:

$$P_{A_{CO_2}} = \frac{5.6}{100}\ (760 - 47) = 40 \text{ mm. Hg.}$$

---

[1] Christie and Loomis (1932), from direct measurements, obtained a slightly lower value for the aqueous tension of alveolar air (45 mm. Hg). They claim that the alveolar air is not fully saturated and that the temperature of the lung is lower than is usually assumed. Hyperpnea reduced the aqueous tension by as much as 7 mm. Hg. Holding the breath increased it by 0.5 mm. Hg.

In table 50.3 the *average* composition of alveolar air (at sea level) is compared with the known composition of dry atmospheric air. The latter does not show significant variations within the troposphere. Values for oxygen, carbon dioxide and nitrogen tensions also are given.

During voluntary hyperventilation the alveolar tension of CO_2 falls and that of oxygen rises. When the breath is held or during periods of apnea, changes occur in the reverse direction. At higher altitudes, the alveolar oxygen and nitrogen tensions are reduced along with the barometric pressure, but the alveolar P_{CO_2} does not show a proportionate decrease since it is controlled by the rate of ventilation of the lungs. The *per cent* of CO_2 therefore increases as the barometric pressure decreases and the oxygen and nitrogen *percentages* must accordingly decrease. When the P_{O_2} is reduced enough to reflexly increase the breathing, the P_{CO_2} begins to fall and the decrease in P_{O_2} is partially compensated.

Although a small but constant amount of nitrogen is physically dissolved in the blood (in accordance with Henry's Law), gaseous nitrogen is neither used nor produced in metabolism. Argon and other inert gases are usually included under "nitrogen," since no distinction need be made in discussions of respiratory physiology. It will be noted that the percentage of nitrogen is slightly higher in alveolar air than in the inspired air. This is due, not to any absolute increase in the quantity of nitrogen, but to the reduction of the total volume of the respiratory gases resulting from the fact that the oxygen consumption exceeds the CO_2 production.

BLOOD GASES

Oxygen and carbon dioxide tensions. The mixed venous blood, which enters the pulmonary arteries and is carried to the lungs, has an oxygen tension of about 40 mm. Hg. The gradient in oxygen tension from alveolar air to the blood as it enters the pulmonary capillaries is therefore about 60 mm. Hg. With this gradient as the driving force, oxygen diffuses across the alveolar and capillary membranes. Equilibrium is quickly established, and as the blood leaves the pulmonary capillaries it is nearly saturated with oxygen. A sample of blood obtained from a systemic artery is found to have an oxygen tension slightly lower than that of the alveolar air, not because of failure to attain equilibrium across the pulmonary membranes, but for reasons to be discussed later.

The venous blood has a CO_2 tension of about 46 mm. Hg; hence at the entrance of a pulmonary

TABLE 50.3

Atmospheric and alveolar air

	O_2	CO_2	N_2*
Atmospheric air			
Per cent (dry)	20.95	0.04	79.01
Tension, mm. Hg†,‡. .	157	0.3	593
Alveolar air			
Per cent (dry)	14.0	5.6	80.4
Tension, mm. Hg† . . .	100	40	573

* Includes other inert gases, 0.93 per cent.

† At sea level, barometric pressure 760 mm. Hg.

‡ Assuming absolute humidity of 10 mm. Hg.

capillary the diffusion gradient for the transfer of CO_2 to the alveolar air is only about 6 mm. Hg. However, since CO_2 is more soluble than oxygen, this gradient suffices for the removal from the blood of an amount of CO_2 almost equivalent to the oxygen absorbed, and equilibrium is reached before the blood leaves the pulmonary capillary. Within the limit of error involved in alveolar air sampling, the CO_2 tension of arterial blood is found to equal that of the alveolar air.

The great rapidity with which these exchanges occur is evident from estimates of the time spent by an individual corpuscle in traversing a pulmonary capillary. Roughton (1945) has estimated that the "transit time" is about 0.75 sec. under resting conditions and is reduced to about half this value by strenuous exercise.

Oxygen content and capacity. The amounts of gases in blood are commonly expressed in terms of *volumes per cent*, i.e., ml. of gas (STPD) per 100 ml. of blood. From the absorption coefficient of oxygen and the oxygen tension it can be calculated that the physically dissolved oxygen in arterial blood amounts to only 0.3 volumes per cent. If the transport of oxygen by the blood were dependent upon physical solution alone, an enormous cardiac output would be required to supply the amount of oxygen needed by the tissues. Actually most of the oxygen is carried in combination with hemoglobin,[2] and the total *oxygen content* of the arterial blood is about 20 volumes per cent. All of this oxygen can be removed from the blood by evacuation.

The oxygen content of blood is dependent upon the oxygen tension, but the relationship between these two variables is not linear. It is described by the *oxygen dissociation curve*, which will be discussed in detail in a later section. If blood is

[2] See ch. 27 for a discussion of the chemistry of hemoglobin.

TABLE 50.4

Average normal analytical values for arterial and venous blood

	Arterial	Venous
O_2 tension, mm. Hg.........	93	40
CO_2 tension, mm. Hg........	40	46
Dissolved O_2, vol. %........	0.3	0.1
Total O_2 content, vol. %....	19.8	15.2
O_2 capacity of Hb, vol. %....	20.1	20.1
O_2 saturation of Hb, %......	97	75
Hemoglobin, g. per 100 ml....	15	15
Dissolved CO_2, vol. %......	2.5	2.9
CO_2 content, vol. %.........	46	50
Plasma CO_2 content, vol. %..	56	60
Plasma CO_2 content, mM....	25	27
Plasma pH..................	7.40	7.37

equilibrated with air at 760 mm. Hg, the hemoglobin becomes saturated. The oxygen content of the blood, corrected by subtracting the small amount in physical solution, then represents the *oxygen capacity of the hemoglobin.* The oxygen capacity is a measure of the active hemoglobin content, since one gram of hemoglobin will combine with exactly 1.34 ml. of oxygen (STPD). Hemoglobin values calculated from precise measurements of oxygen capacity are often used as a basis for standardizing colorimetric methods for the determination of hemoglobin, but it must be remembered that many blood samples contain traces of inactive hemoglobin compounds such as methemoglobin and carboxyhemoglobin.

The ratio of the oxygen content (after correction for dissolved oxygen) to the oxygen capacity of the hemoglobin is a measure of the degree of saturation of the hemoglobin. This ratio is usually multiplied by 100 to give the *per cent saturation.* In arterial blood the hemoglobin is normally about 97 per cent saturated. The amount of oxygen given up by the blood as it passes through the tissues varies from one region to another and from time to time, depending upon the blood flow and the metabolic rate in the region concerned. Under resting conditions the average arteriovenous difference is about 5 volumes per cent. The mixed venous blood, then, has an oxygen content of about 15 volumes per cent and its hemoglobin is about 75% saturated. Samples of mixed venous blood can be obtained from human subjects by cardiac catheterization.

Average normal values for blood gases and hemoglobin content are summarized in table 50.4.

Carbon dioxide content. The tension of CO_2

in the alveolar air is lower than that of oxygen, but the absorption coefficient of CO_2 is much the higher of the two. The calculated amount of CO_2 present in *simple solution* in the arterial blood is 2.5 volumes per cent. This is distributed between the red cells and the plasma.

The total *carbon dioxide content* is the quantity of CO_2 that can be extracted from 100 ml. of blood by exposure to a vacuum after the addition of acid. In arterial blood this amounts to about 46 volumes per cent. A large fraction of it exists in the form of *bicarbonate* ions; some of this is in the plasma and a smaller portion is inside the erythrocytes. Another fraction is bound to hemoglobin in the erythrocytes as *carbaminohemoglobin.*

These various forms of carbon dioxide exist in equilibrium with each other in the blood, and all are involved in the transport of CO_2. When CO_2 enters or leaves the blood, a rapid readjustment of the equilibrium occurs.

Carbon dioxide-bicarbonate-pH relationships. The dissociation of a weak acid is described quantitatively by the *Henderson-Hasselbalch equation,* which is the logarithmic form of the law of mass action (see ch. 24). As applied to the carbonic acid-bicarbonate system, this equation is

$$pH = pK + \log \frac{[HCO_3^-]}{[H_2CO_3]}$$

where pK is the negative logarithm of the dissociation constant of carbonic acid.

Carbon dioxide forms carbonic acid by hydration:

$$CO_2 + H_2O \rightleftharpoons H_2CO_3 .$$

The hydrated and unhydrated forms reach an equilibrium, and the dissolved carbon dioxide is the sum of the two forms. However, the equilibrium point is so far to the left that only about 0.15 per cent is in the hydrated form at 38° C. Hence the concentration of the unhydrated form, designated $[CO_2]$, can be considered equal to the dissolved carbon dioxide with only a negligible error. The small concentration of H_2CO_3 is directly proportional to $[CO_2]$. Hence if an appropriate value for K is used, the equation can be written:

$$pH = pK' + \log \frac{[HCO_3^-]}{[CO_2]} .$$

The established value for pK' in *blood plasma* is

6.10^3 at $37°$ C. When the plasma pH is 7.4, therefore, the ratio of bicarbonate to dissolved carbon dioxide is 20 to 1. The concentrations of CO_2 and HCO_3^- can be expressed either in millimoles per liter or in volumes per cent of CO_2; the value for pK' is 6.10 in either case.

The dissolved carbon dioxide can be calculated from the CO_2 tension and the absorption coefficient α as determined on acidified plasma (table 50.2). The plasma $[HCO_3^-]$ can be obtained by subtracting the dissolved CO_2 from the total measured CO_2 content of the plasma. Incorporating these considerations, the equation becomes:

$$pH = 6.10 + \log \frac{[CO_2 \text{ content}] - \alpha P_{CO_2}}{\alpha P_{CO_2}}$$

If concentrations are expressed in volumes per cent and P_{CO_2} in mm. Hg, the value for α becomes 0.0686. In terms of millimoles per liter and mm. Hg, α is 0.0308 (since one mole of CO_2 at STPD occupies 22.26 liters).

This equation is very useful since if any two of the three variables are measured the third can be calculated. Its application to whole blood, however, is complicated since the carbon dioxide content of blood includes a considerable portion present as carbaminohemoglobin and the intracellular and extracellular concentrations of H^+ and HCO_3^- are complexly related.

Measuring Respiratory Gases

For many years the most widely used methods for the measurement of respiratory gases were those developed by J. S. Haldane at Oxford and by D. D. Van Slyke and his associates at The Rockefeller Institute. Numerous modifications of these methods have been described, and micro methods based on the same principles have been introduced. These methods depend upon the careful measurement of gas volumes and pressures and the selective absorption of carbon dioxide and of oxygen by appropriate reagents. In the analysis of blood the gases are first released by chemical treatment and vacuum extraction.

[3] Calculated from precise measurements of P_{CO_2}, pH, and CO_2 content or bicarbonate in plasma. K' therefore, is a composite constant including the true dissociation constant of H_2CO_3, the equilibrium constant for the hydration of CO_2, the activity coefficient of the bicarbonate ion, and a small correction for equating $[CO_2]$ with the dissolved carbon dioxide. The pK' value varies slightly with pH, probably because traces of carbonate and of plasma carbamino-bound carbon dioxide are included in the measurements of bicarbonate (Severinghaus *et al.*, 1956; Siggard Anderson, 1962a).

More recently, various electronic and other instruments have been devised for the measurement or continuous monitoring of oxygen, CO_2 and nitrogen in gas mixtures and of oxygen tension, hemoglobin saturation and CO_2 tension in blood. Some of the more important methods now in use will be outlined briefly. Detailed descriptions of these are available in a recent compilation by Consolazio *et al.* (1963) or in other references cited.

ANALYSIS OF GAS MIXTURES

Haldane method. (See fig. 63.8, ch 63). The gas sample is held in a sampling tube over mercury or in an oiled syringe. A 10 ml. volume is drawn into the gas buret and measured at the prevailing atmospheric pressure and temperature. CO_2 is absorbed by strong potassium hydroxide solution, and oxygen by an alkaline solution of potassium pyrogallate or of sodium hydrosulfite and sodium anthraquinone-β-sulfonate, the respective decreases in volume being recorded. The percentage of nitrogen is calculated from the volume of gas remaining unabsorbed. The inside of the buret is kept wet with dilute sulfuric acid to maintain a constant aqueous tension throughout; the results then represent percentages on a dry basis.

Scholander method. This is a rapid micro adaptation of the Haldane method employing an apparatus of very different design. A 0.5 ml. gas sample is introduced into a small reaction chamber connected to a micrometer buret. The buret is filled with mercury. The pressure of the sample is balanced against that of air in a compensating chamber by means of an indicating drop of fluid in a capillary tube connecting the two chambers. Absorbing solutions for CO_2 and oxygen can be tilted into the reaction chamber without altering the total volume. While a gas is being absorbed, mercury is forced into the reaction chamber from the micrometer buret at a rate sufficient to maintain a constant pressure. The volume of mercury introduced is then measured in terms of micrometer divisions.

The Pauling oxygen analyzer. This instrument measures the partial pressure of oxygen in a gas mixture. Its operation depends on the fact that oxygen is paramagnetic while most other gases are diamagnetic; i.e. the magnetic susceptibility of oxygen is very much greater than that of any other common gas. A small glass dumbbell filled with nitrogen or oxygen (depending on the range of the instrument) is suspended between the poles of a magnet by attachment to a vertically stretched silica fiber. By rotating around the fiber, the dumbbell can move in the magnetic field. The incoming gas surrounds the dumbbell, and the oxygen is attracted to the strongest part of the magnetic field. The dumbbell is subjected to a magnetic force depending on the difference between the magnetic susceptibility of its spheres and that of the gas which the spheres displace, and rotates as the spheres move farther into or out of the magnetic field. An equilibrium position is reached at which the magnetic rotational force is balanced by the restoring force of the twisted fiber. Thus the operation of the instrument is analogous to the measurement of the density of a liquid by weighing a solid body suspended in the liquid. A small mirror attached to the dumbbell reflects a light beam onto a scale which is calibrated to indicate oxygen tension. The Pauling analyzer has proved to be particularly useful for the analysis of expired air in studies of metabolism employing the open-circuit method.

The infrared CO_2 analyzer. CO_2 absorbs infrared radiation in proportion to its concentration. Rapidly responding instruments based on this property can be used for continuous monitoring of carbon dioxide in the expired air. The gas mixture is exhaled through a mouthpiece connected to the sampling tube, or a continuous sample is drawn into the analyzer through a very small polyethylene catheter. A beam of infrared radiation passes through the sample and then into a detector connected to an amplifier-recorder system. The instrument registers the infrared absorption and can be calibrated in terms of percent CO_2 (Collier et al., 1955).

The nitrogen analyzer. Gases subjected to electrical excitation ionize and emit radiation (spark, arc or glow discharge). The nitrogen analyzer contains an electrical discharge tube through which a slow, steady stream of the gas mixture is drawn. When a high potential is applied, nitrogen glows a bright orange-pink, oxygen a very faint green, CO_2 a dim blue, and water vapor red. The spectral region of 310–480 mμ includes some of the most intense nitrogen bands, but excludes the emission from oxygen and water vapor and most of that from carbon dioxide. A light filter selects this range and allows it to activate a photoelectric cell. The signal is amplified and indicated on a meter or recorder calibrated in per cent nitrogen. The response of the instrument is extremely rapid.

Gas chromatography. This recently developed technique seems destined to largely supersede other methods for the analysis of individual gas samples. The apparatus for respiratory gases employs gas-solid chromatography, and usually includes two columns connected in series, each with its own thermal conductivity detector. The gas sample is injected into a stream of helium entering the columns. CO_2 is separated from the other respiratory gases in the first column, and as the CO_2-laden portion of the helium carrier passes through the detector a variation in thermal conductivity is recorded as a peak, the size of which is proportional to the percent of CO_2 in the injected sample. Oxygen and nitrogen are separated and measured in the second column.

Other methods. The Van Slyke apparatus, the polarographic method for oxygen and the CO_2 electrode are applicable to gas mixtures, but more commonly are applied to the analysis of blood or plasma. These methods are described in the next section.

GASES IN BLOOD OR PLASMA

Handling blood samples. Blood for gasometric studies must be drawn and handled without exposure to air. It is sometimes drawn under oil or over mercury, but more commonly into a syringe which is immediately closed by replacing the needle with a cap. The syringe may then be stored briefly in ice water prior to the analysis. The sampling tube or syringe must contain an anticoagulant, usually a drop of heparin solution. Some workers use oiled syringes, but this is not necessary since wetting the barrel and plunger with heparin solution has been found to adequately protect the sample. When plasma is required, it is obtained by centrifuging the blood under a layer of mineral oil or, preferably, in a closed syringe with the plunger held in position by a plastic case fitted around its exposed portion (Peters and Van Slyke, 1932; Comroe, 1950).

Tonometers. As originally defined, a tonometer is an instrument for measuring tension. However, the first methods used for measuring gas tensions in blood required equilibration of the blood with a gas phase and analysis of the gas. Hence the vessel in which the equilibration was brought about came to be called a tonometer. Many forms of apparatus have been devised for this equilibration. For exampled, in experiments to establish the oxygen dissociation curve it is desirable to expose small volumes of blood to large volumes of gas mixtures. This can be done in a closed space, or a stream of gas can be passed over the blood. On the other hand, in the "bubble" method for measuring gas tensions a relatively large volume of blood is exposed to a bubble of air so small that the exchange of gases has a negligible effect on the composition of the blood.

The Van Slyke-Neill manometric apparatus (fig. 50.1). The analysis of blood or plasma is carried out by filling the reaction chamber with mercury and drawing in a 0.1–2.0 ml. sample, preceded or followed by reagents to free the gases. Carbon dioxide is released by lactic acid, and oxygen by potassium ferricyanide with saponin added to induce rapid hemolysis. The gases are extracted by lowering the mercury to the 50 ml. mark to create a vacuum and agitating the contents of the chamber with a shaking motor or a magnetic stirrer. The volume of the extracted gases is then reduced to 0.5 ml. or 2.0 ml. and the corresponding pressure is read on the manometer. A small amount of sodium hydroxide is introduced into the chamber to absorb the CO_2, and from the observed decrease in pressure at constant volume the CO_2 *content* of the sample is calculated. The *oxygen content* is determined in the same way by absorption with a sodium hydrosulfite-sodium anthraquinone-β-sulfonate mixture.

By this method the oxygen and carbon dioxide contents can be measured on a single blood sample. *Oxygen capacity* is determined on a separate sample by first equilibrating the blood with air to saturate the hemoglobin and then measuring its oxygen content. The *per cent saturation of hemoglobin* in the original sample can then be calculated. The *oxygen tension* can be determined from the standard oxygen dissociation curve, provided the pH of the blood also is carefully measured and the necessary correction applied (Severinghaus, 1958). This method gives reliable values for oxygen tension in the range between 0 and about 60–70 mm. Hg, but at higher levels the curve becomes too flat to allow accurate readings.

The *carbon dioxide tension* and the *plasma bicarbonate*[4] can be calculated from the carbon dioxide content and the pH of the plasma by use of the Henderson-Hasselbalch equation. The glass electrode technique (ch. 34) is the method of choice for the pH measurement; either plasma or whole blood may be used, but loss of CO_2 must be avoided. The *plasma CO_2 content* may be measured on separated plasma or may be calculated from the analysis of whole blood. However if whole blood is used it is necessary to determine the hematocrit (or the oxygen capacity) and the per cent saturation of hemoglobin as well as the CO_2 content. These data are needed since the CO_2 contained in the erythrocytes is proportional to the volume they occupy, and is influenced by the state of oxygenation of the hemoglobin as explained in a later section. In practice the calculations are greatly simplified by the use of line charts, called nomograms, which graphically represent the Henderson-Hasselbalch equation and the relations between plasma and

---

[4] The plasma bicarbonate represents the *alkali reserve* (ch. 34). Van Slyke and Cullen introduced a determination of plasma carbon dioxide capacity or combining power which, although inexact, is often used clinically as a measure of the alkali reserve. In this method the blood is drawn and centrifuged without strict anaerobic precautions, and the plasma is subsequently equilibrated with alveolar air at room temperature and analyzed for carbon dioxide content. From this the bicarbonate concentration at 20° C. is calculated. The variable losses, being accompanied by shifts of bicarbonate into the cells, are not accurately replaced by the equilibration, but the method usually gives values somewhat higher than the original bicarbonate concentration since the solubility of carbon dioxide is higher at the lower temperature.

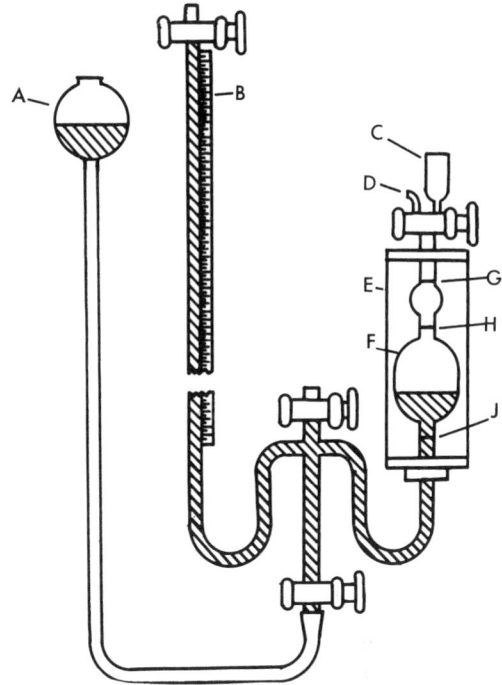

FIG. 50.1 Van Slyke-Neill manometric apparatus. *A*, leveling bulb; *B*, manometer; *C*, cup; *D*, waste tube; *E*, water jacket; *F*, reaction chamber; *G*, 0.5 ml. mark; *H*, 2.0 ml. mark; *J*, 50 ml. mark.

whole blood (Van Slyke and Sendroy, 1928; Singer and Hastings, 1948).

The Van Slyke volumetric apparatus operates on the same general principle as the monometric apparatus. It is less accurate and less versatile than the manometric, but is simpler to operate, and is widely used for measuring blood gases in clinical laboratories. After extraction, the gases are measured by observing the volume occupied at a fixed pressure (atmospheric), rather than the pressure exerted at a fixed volume (Peters and Van Slyke, 1932).

The Haldane method for blood gases. A 1–2 ml. sample of blood is placed anaerobically under an alkaline borate solution in a small flask. The buffer binds the CO_2. The flask is connected to a gas buret and a manometer, and the air pressure in the system is adjusted to that of the atmosphere. When the flask is agitated, any *reduced hemoglobin* present takes up oxygen and the volume of air in the system (readjusted to atmospheric pressure) is correspondingly decreased. A ferricyanide-saponin solution is then tipped into the flask from a side arm, releasing all of the combined oxygen. The increase in volume represents the *oxygen capacity*. The *oxygen content* is obtained by difference. Tartaric acid is then added to release the CO_2, and the increase in volume is observed. This method has the advantage that oxygen capacity, oxygen content and CO_2 content can all be measured on the same sample (Courtice and Douglas, 1947; Rossier *et al.*, 1960).

Ultramicro gasometric methods. Natelson (1957) devised a manometric apparatus similar in principle to that of Van Slyke and Neill, but adapted for measurements on 0.03 ml. quantities of blood or plasma. More recently, Van Slyke and Plazin (1961) described a modification of the Van Slyke-Neill apparatus applicable to 0.025–0.030 ml. samples. Volumetric procedures on the same scale, developed by Roughton and Scholander, employ a device consisting of a capillary buret sealed to the nozzle of a 1 ml. tuberculin syringe.

Blood gases by gas chromatography. For the analysis of blood by this method it is only necessary to supplement the gas chromatograph (described previously) with a blood gas releasing system. Samples of 0.2 ml. or less can be analyzed. The sample is mixed with releasing agents in a small chamber previously flushed with helium, and the evolved gases are carried into the chromatographic column by a stream of helium. An analysis can be completed in about 10 min.

The "bubble" method for oxygen and carbon dioxide tensions. A small bubble of air is equilibrated with blood at body temperature. The bubble is then analyzed by micro methods, and from the percentages of oxygen and CO_2 the corresponding tensions are calculated. If the volume of the bubble is kept very small in relation to the volume of blood, the amounts of oxygen and CO_2 exchanged during equilibration are insignificant and the results represent the original tensions in the blood. This method was introduced by Krogh in 1908, and several appropriate forms of apparatus have been devised. The Roughton-Scholander syringe analyzer is advantageous since it can be used for both the equilibration and the gas analysis (the "Riley technique").

Polarographic measurement of oxygen tension. If a platinum electrode in contact with a solution is made 0.6 to 0.7 volts negative to a chlorided silver electrode, dissolved oxygen molecules at the platinum surface receive electrons and are reduced to either H_2O_2 or OH^-. The current passing from the platinum is linearly related to the availability of dissolved oxygen molecules at its surface. When the platinum is in direct contact with the blood, however, the current flow is influenced by stirring and other factors which make adequate calibration difficult. In the Clark electrode the electrical cell is separated from the blood by a thin polyethylene membrane, permeable to oxygen (and CO_2) but impermeable to electrolytes and most other solutes. If the platinum surface area is very small and the membrane is of the right thickness, this electrode shows a fairly rapid response, is insensitive to stirring, and can be

calibrated to record *oxygen tension* in mm. Hg. It can be used to analyze either solutions or gas mixtures, and for monitoring *in vivo* (Torres, 1963; Charlton *et al.*, 1963).

The carbon dioxide electrode. This consists of a glass electrode, sensitive to pH changes, in contact with a thin layer of a solution containing a small concentration of bicarbonate ion and separated from the blood by a Teflon membrane. Since the membrane is permeable to carbon dioxide but not to ions, the pH of the sample cannot affect the pH at the glass electrode surface. The measured pH of the bicarbonate solution varies with the negative logarithm of the CO_2 tension, in accordance with the Henderson-Hasselbalch equation. The electrode is calibrated against solutions of known CO_2 tension (Severinghaus and Bradley, 1958).

Interpolation method for carbon dioxide tension and related variables. A graph showing the relation between log P_{CO_2} and the pH of a blood sample is a straight line. By equilibrating a blood sample at two known P_{CO_2} levels and measuring the corresponding pH values, two points of the graph are determined and the curve for the sample can be drawn. If the pH of the sample before equilibration is also measured, its P_{CO_2} can be found from the graph. Carbon dioxide-oxygen mixtures are used for the equilibrations so that the hemoglobin will be fully oxygenated; a small estimated correction can be applied if the sample initially is not completely oxygenated. Astrup (1961) described a capillary glass electrode and an equilibration unit, both thermostated at 38° C., with which the procedures can be carried out rapidly on a micro scale.

In addition to CO_2 tension, a number of other variables concerned with the acid-base balance can be calculated with the aid of a nomogram (Siggaard Anderson and Engel, 1960; Siggaard Anderson, 1962b). These include the standard bicarbonate of the plasma,[5] the buffer base and base excess (or deficit) of the blood, and the plasma bicarbonate, CO_2 content and CO_2 combining power. The three pH values are the only measurements necessary.

Photoelectric oximetry. An oximeter is a photoelectric photometer for measuring the fraction of hemoglobin in the oxygenated form. Oxyhemoglobin absorbs less visible red light (620–770 mμ), and therefore transmits and reflects more in this waveband, than does reduced hemoglobin. Infrared light of 805 mμ, however, is absorbed equally by oxygenated and reduced hemoglobin. A transmission oximeter measures light transmitted by

---

[5] Standard bicarbonate is defined as the bicarbonate concentration in the plasma of blood brought to a P_{CO_2} of 40 mm. Hg at 38° C. with the hemoglobin fully oxygenated. This variable is useful in studies of non-respiratory acid-base disorders since it is not influenced by variations in P_{CO_2} or oxygenation.

blood in both red and infra-red regions, and the oxygen saturation is determined from the ratio of the two readings. Some oximeters employ cuvettes in which the blood is contained or through which it is passed during either withdrawal from the body or diversion through an extracorporeal circuit. The ear oximeter is designed to record the oxygenation of the blood passing through the capillaries of the pinna. The ear is warmed to some extent by the earpiece, with the result that a localized vasodilation occurs. The capillary blood then is essentially arterial, since the oxygen utilization in this region is very small. A transparent pneumatic pressure capsule is interposed between the light source and the ear so that allowance can be made for the light absorbed by the bloodless (pressurized) ear (Wood *et al.*, 1960).

Instruments for reflection oximetry also are available, and are described in a monograph by Zijlstra (1958).

The Oxygen Dissociation Curve

The equilibrium between oxygen and hemoglobin is described by the oxygen dissociation curve, in which the per cent saturation of hemoglobin is plotted against the oxygen tension. Since oxygen tension must be regarded as the *independent* variable, it is represented on the abscissa while per cent saturation (the *dependent* variable) is on the ordinate. The equilibrium is influenced by such variables as hemoglobin concentration, temperature, pH and electrolytes; hence curves determined on pure hemoglobin solutions differ in their exact shape and position from those determined on whole blood. By equilibrating blood with known gas mixtures, Barcroft and Poulton (1913) determined the curves shown in fig. 50.2. For each curve the carbon dioxide was held constant while the oxygen tension was varied. It is evident that increasing the CO_2 tension increases the dissociation, thus shifting the curve to the *right* (the "Bohr effect"). This is due mainly to hydrogen ions produced by the dissociation of carbonic acid, but in part also to the formation of carbaminohemoglobin (Roughton, 1964). The hydrogen ion effect is related to the behavior of oxyhemoglobin and reduced hemoglobin as acids and the fact that the oxygenated form is a stronger acid than the reduced form, as discussed in a later section.

An increase in temperature also shifts the curve to the right (increasing dissociation). Variations in blood electrolyte concentrations ordinarily are too small to have measurable effects on the oxygen dissociation curve.

With changing oxygenation it is not possible to hold both the P_{CO_2} and the pH constant (without

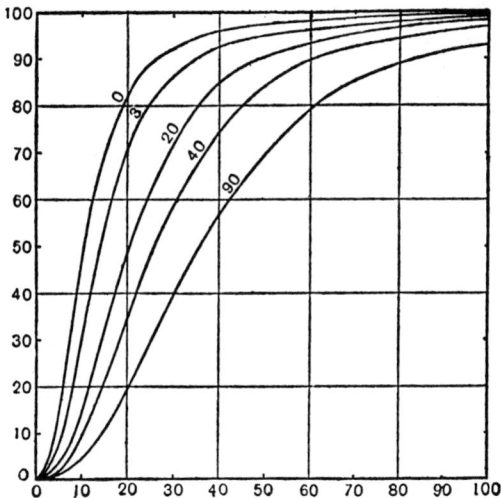

FIG. 50.2. Dissociation curves of human blood, exposed to 0, 3, 20, 40 and 90 mm. CO_2. Ordinates, percentage saturation. Abscissae, oxygen pressure. (After Barcroft and Poulton.)

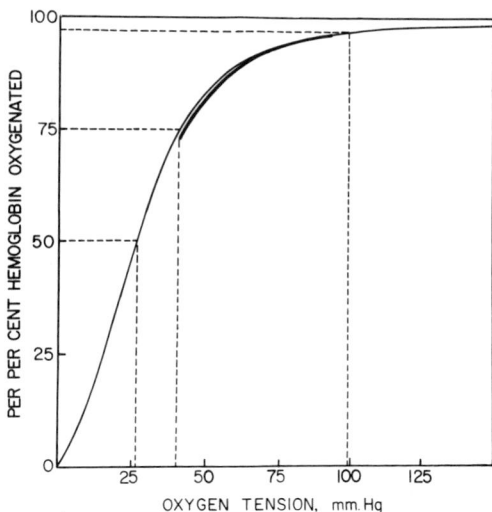

FIG. 50.3 Standard oxygen dissociation curve of human blood at 37° C. and plasma pH 7.40. Important points on the curve are the P_{O_2} at half-saturation (26 mm. Hg), 75 per cent saturation (40 mm. Hg) and 97 per cent saturation (99 mm. Hg). The heavy line represents the normal working range between arterial and mixed venous blood. It deviates slightly from the standard curve because the venous blood is 0.02–0.03 pH units more acid than the arterial blood.

adding acid or alkali); if P_{CO_2} remains constant the pH must shift slightly in the acid direction with increasing oxygenation since oxyhemoglobin is a stronger acid than reduced hemoglobin. It is now customary to use the *standard oxygen dissociation curve* at 37° C. and plasma pH of 7.40 (fig. 50.3). This has been established for human blood by careful measurements in several different laboratories, the observed values being subjected to pH and temperature corrections where necessary. Severinghaus (1958) has prepared a nomogram from which the corrections can be calculated and from which dissociation curves for various values of plasma pH and temperature can be derived. The reason for the sigmoid shape of the curve is discussed in ch. 27.

Individual variations and species differences. The position of the oxygen dissociation curve is conveniently established by determining the point at which the hemoglobin is *half-saturated.* On the standard curve (fig. 50.3) this occurs at an oxygen tension of 26 mm. Hg. The dissociation curve of the blood has been determined from time to time over a period of years in several persons and is found to be unaffected by age changes, but small variations occur in blood from different individuals. In the cases of human and canine blood the tension required for half saturation at 37° C. and at plasma pH 7.40 usually lies within the range of 25 to 30 mm. Hg. For blood from cats and sheep the value is about 1.5 times as large, indicating a lower affinity for oxygen. The curve for blood of pigs, bullocks and horses is similar to that of man. Since the hemes in blood of all species are chemically identical, the variations in affinity for oxygen are attributed to differences in the globin part of the molecule. This suggestion is supported by chemical findings on the protein structure of the hemoglobin of several species. The species differences in oxygen affinity are not correlated with the ability to withstand a lack of oxygen, indicating a preponderance of other factors in resistance to anoxia (Roughton, 1964).

Oxygen dissociation curve of fetal blood. The curve for fetal blood at pH 7.40 lies to the left of the standard curve, while the curve for maternal blood is in the normal position or sometimes a little to the right (Darling *et al.*, 1941). This means that the affinity for oxygen is higher in fetal than in maternal blood, a fact established for the human and several other species by various workers. The difference in affinity is thought to aid in the transfer of oxygen from the maternal to the fetal circulation in the placenta. The reason for the difference is uncertain, since fetal hemoglobin released from the cells by hemolysis and purified by dialyzing has the same dissociation curve as maternal hemoglobin (Allen *et al.*, 1953). However, fetal hemoglobin is known to differ from adult hemoglobin in certain physical and chemical properties (Schulman, 1959).

Oxygen and Carbon Dioxide Transport

Oxygenation of arterial blood. Under normal resting conditions the blood passing through an alveolar capillary is thought to reach equilibrium with the air in the alveolus well before arriving at the end of the capillary, despite the brevity of the transit time (fig. 50.4). If this were not so, the great reductions in transit time and in venous blood oxygen content which occur during severe exercise would lead to a considerable decrease in oxygenation of the arterial blood. Actually, severe exercise brings about only a very slight decrease in the oxygen tension of arterial blood while slightly increasing that of alveolar air; the alveolar-arterial Po_2 difference increases from 4–9 mm. Hg under resting conditions[6] to about 13–18 mm. Hg in severe exercise (Rossier *et al.*, 1960).

The existence of a measurable Po_2 difference between alveolar air and arterial blood is attributed to two factors: (1) *admixture of small amounts of venous blood* with the oxygenated blood and (2) *uneven effectiveness of ventilation* in relation to blood flow in different parts of the lungs. Sources of venous admixture normally include the bronchial and coronary circulations; pathologically there may also be pulmonary arterio-venous shunts. Blood from venous sources could decrease the arterial Po_2 significantly without causing a perceptible change in the Pco_2, since the total difference between venous and arterial Pco_2 is only 6 mm. Hg.

Uneven ventilation relative to blood flow would not be expected to measurably influence the arterial Pco_2 since underventilation of some alveoli (as compared with the mean for all alveoli) would be compensated for by overventilation of others. But an effect on arterial Po_2 occurs and is related to the shape of the oxygen dissociation curve. Because of the flattening of the curve at its upper end, increasing oxygen tension above 95 mm. Hg adds very little to the blood oxygen content; hence overventilated alveoli cannot supply extra oxygen sufficient to compensate for the effects of underventilated alveoli. The alveolar-arterial Po_2 difference decreases when the alveolar oxygen tension is reduced to a level falling on a steeper part of the oxygen dissociation curve.

[6] Slightly higher values are found by many investigators; the method used for sampling the alveolar air is of critical importance.

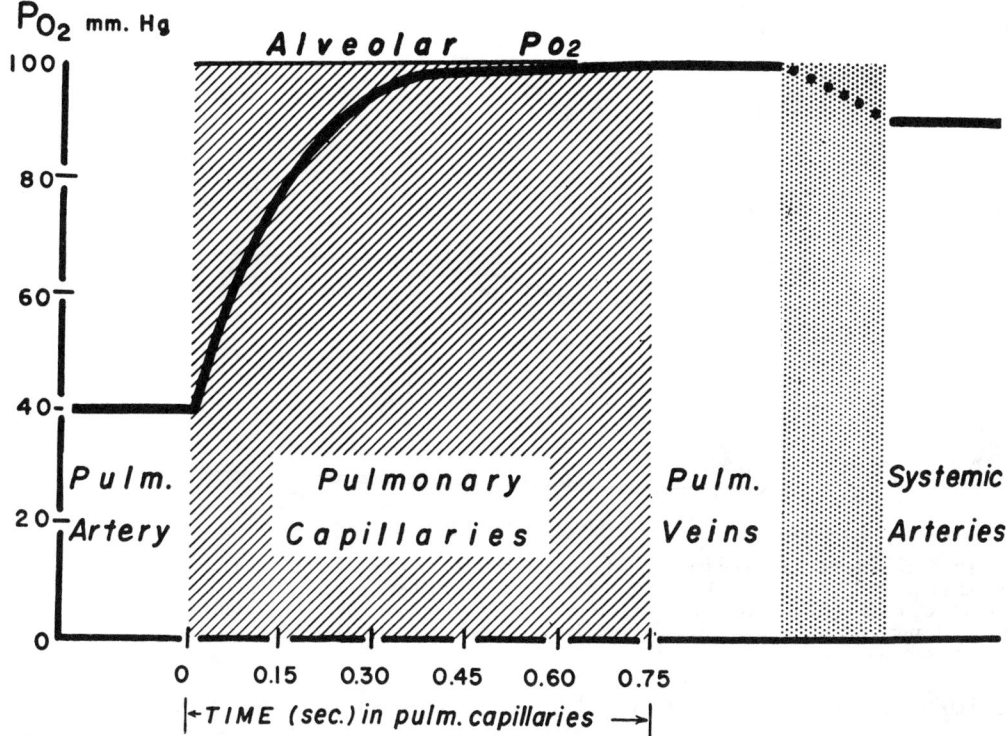

FIG. 50.4. Changes in P_{O_2} of blood during its passage through the lungs (from Comroe *et al.*, The Lung. 2nd ed. Year Book Medical Publishers, Chicago, 1962).

Although the alveolar-arterial P_{O_2} difference is small and of little consequence in normal subjects, it becomes a matter of importance in certain respiratory disorders. Methods have been developed to evaluate separately the effects of: (1) venous admixture, (2) uneven ventilation-blood flow relationships and, (3) impaired diffusion, since each of these may be a factor in respiratory dysfunction. With regard to the second of these, there is increasing recognition that ventilation and blood flow cannot be considered separately; the oxygen and CO_2 tensions in blood leaving the lungs are determined by the *ratio* between the ventilation of the alveoli and their capillary blood flow. Alveoli that are relatively overventilated waste a fraction of their ventilation, and alveoli that are underventilated waste a fraction of their blood flow, and both types of alveoli contribute to an alveolar or "physiological" dead space as well as to differences in gas tensions between alveolar air and arterial blood. In some disorders, ventilation/blood flow ratios are uneven enough to cause anoxemia or to exacerbate anoxemia resulting from decreased alveolar ventilation (Comroe *et al.*, 1962; Rahn and Fahri, 1964).

The working range of blood oxygenation. The normal range between arterial and mixed venous blood under resting conditions is shown in fig. 50.3. In arterial blood the hemoglobin is 96–97 per cent saturated with oxygen. In the tissue capillaries, outward diffusion of dissolved oxygen reduces the blood oxygen tension. Accordingly oxyhemoglobin dissociates, and the released oxygen diffuses away in the dissolved form. When the tension has been reduced to 40 mm. Hg, the level of saturation is about 75 per cent. A slight decrease in the blood pH occurs (0.02–0.03 pH units) due to the uptake of carbon dioxide; hence the physiological curve deviates slightly from the standard dissociation curve at pH 7.40.

Depending upon the particular tissue and its activity at the moment, the blood in its passage through the capillaries loses from a tenth to nearly all of its oxygen load. The figure used to express the proportion of the total oxygen content given up to the tissue is called the *coefficient of utilization.* Thus if the oxygen content of arterial blood is 19.5 volumes per cent and that of venous blood is 15 volumes per cent (i.e., an arteriovenous difference of 4.5 volumes per cent) the coefficient is 4.5/19.5 or 0.23. As indicated above, the coefficient varies considerably for different tissues and for the same tissue in accordance with blood flow and metabolic activity. During heavy exercise the over-all coefficient of

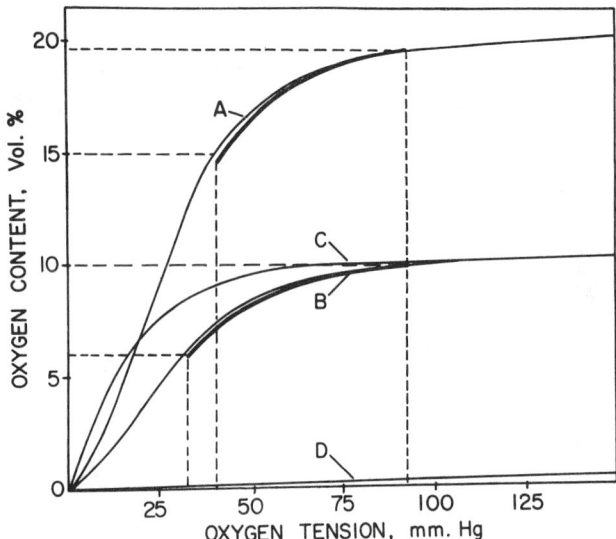

Fig. 50.5. Effects of anemia and of carbon monoxide on the oxygen dissociation curve of blood at pH 7.40 and 37° C. *A*, normal blood, 15 per cent hemoglobin; *B*, anemia, 7.5 per cent hemoglobin; *C*, carbon monoxide poisoning, 15 per cent hemoglobin half saturated with CO; *D*, curve representing oxygen in physical solution. Heavy lines indicate the working range in normal and anemic subjects.

utilization increases to about 0.6, and that of active muscle to as high as 0.8.

Certain features associated with the shape and position of the oxygen dissociation curve are of the utmost physiological importance. At the normal oxygen tension of alveolar air at sea level, the hemoglobin in the blood passing through the lungs becomes almost completely saturated. The flattening of the upper part of the curve means that relatively little reduction in the per cent saturation occurs until the alveolar Po_2 falls to about 60 per cent of its value at sea level. Such a decrease would occur on ascending to an altitude of about 10,000 ft, and at sea level is not uncommon in cardiopulmonary disease. Within this range, wide variations in alveolar Po_2 can occur with minimal changes in the total oxygen load of arterial blood. This circumstance constitutes a considerable safety factor. On the lower part of the curve, the steep slope means that in this region a given fall in oxygen tension causes the release of a relatively large volume of oxygen. The relation between oxygen content and oxygen tension therefore is such as to favor a nearly maximum *uptake* of oxygen in the lungs as long as the tension is above 60 mm. Hg and an adequate *release* of the gas at the lower tensions which prevail in the tissues. The slope of the curve would favor release at still lower tensions, but at some point the diffusion gradient would become insufficient to support the rapid transfer of oxygen into the cells.

The effects of increasing hydrogen ion concentration and Pco_2 on oxygen dissociation (shifting the curve to the right) tend to favor the release of oxygen to the tissues since carbon dioxide and sometimes lactic acid are produced by tissue activity. A slight increase in temperature, such as may occur in working muscle, has a similar effect. However, these shifts in the position of the curve are small and in working muscle are much less important than the opening up of additional capillaries induced by the changes in pH, Pco_2 and temperature. The influence of temperature is of some importance in hyperthermia, and requires particular consideration when patents are subjected to hypothermia for surgical procedures. Estimates of oxygen tension from oximeter readings taken during hypothermia would be higher than the true values if the effect of temperature were disregarded.

Oxygen content—Po_2 curves. When *per cent saturation* is plotted against oxygen tension, as in fig. 50.3, the importance of the hemoglobin concentration is not evident; the curve for blood from an anemic patient appears the same as that for normal blood. The difference becomes apparent if oxygen *content* is plotted against oxygen tension, as in fig. 50.5. Such a curve for blood of any hemoglobin concentration can be obtained from the standard curve by calculating the volumes per cent of oxygen combined with hemoglobin (per cent saturation × oxygen capacity) at each of a series of P_{O_2} values and adding the small concentration of dissolved oxygen present at that level. It is evident from fig. 50.5 that a 50 per cent decrease in hemoglobin, such as might occur in anemia, would halve the amount of oxygen delivered by 100 ml. of blood if the working range were unaltered. Partial compensation occurs by an increase in the coefficient of utilization, which in the diagram extends the working range downward to a tension of 32 mm. Hg, but the oxygen delivered by 100 ml. of blood is still not as much as in the normal subject. Additional compensation is achieved by a rise in the cardiac output, which increases the oxygen delivery by increasing the volume flow of blood through the tissues. The circulatory adjustments are aided by a decrease in blood viscosity (a consequence of erythrocyte depletion), which reduces the peripheral resistance.

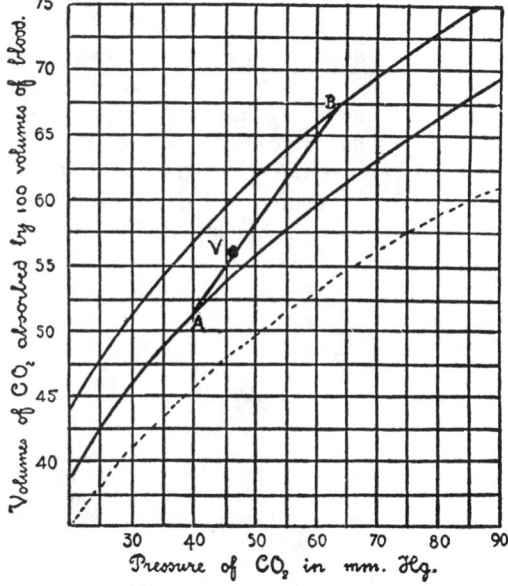

FIG. 50.6. Carbon dioxide dissociation curves of fully reduced human blood (upper solid line) in presence of hydrogen, and fully oxygenated human blood (lower solid line), in presence of air. Volumes of CO_2 along the ordinates; CO_2 tension along the abscissae. Line AVB is the so-called physiological dissociation curve of CO_2, i.e., as a result of the reduction of hemoglobin the relation of volumes of CO_2 to CO_2 tension is indicated at points along this line and not along the lower curve for oxygenated blood. At *A* (arterial point) are indicated the volume and tension of CO_2 in arterial blood. Point *B* indicates the conditions in fully reduced blood. Point *V* (venous point) represents the degree of reduction of hemoglobin which normally occurs in the body during the passage of blood through the systemic capillaries. The interrupted line below is the CO_2 dissociation curve for oxygenated dog's blood. (Modified from Christiansen, Douglas and Haldane.)

Effects of carbon monoxide. Hemoglobin and carbon monoxide react reversibly to form *carboxyhemoglobin*. As with oxygen, the hemoglobin becomes saturated in the proportion of one molecule of gas to one atom of iron, and the physicochemical aspects of the two reactions are very similar except that the affinity of hemoglobin for carbon monoxide is about 200 times its affinity for oxygen. When both gases are present they compete for the hemoglobin.

The presence of slightly less than 0.1 per cent of carbon monoxide in the inspired air over a period of a few hours (or a higher concentration for a shorter time) is sufficient to convert 50 per cent of the hemoglobin in the blood to carboxyhemoglobin, and at about this level the victim becomes incapacitated. By contrast, an anemic patient whose blood hemoglobin is reduced to 50 per cent of normal shows little evidence of anoxia. The major reason for this difference is shown in fig. 50.5. It will be seen that the position of the oxygen dissociation curve is shifted to the left by carbon monoxide, with the result that the ability to deliver oxygen to the tissues is greatly reduced. In other words, as the per cent of carboxyhemoglobin increases the remaining active hemoglobin holds more tightly to the oxygen with which it combines. This is explained as follows: in the hemoglobin molecule there are four hemes, each containing one atom of iron, and when one or more of the hemes is combined with carbon monoxide an interaction takes place which increases the affinity of the remaining hemes for oxygen (Roughton, 1964).

Carbon monoxide poisoning is discussed further in ch. 54.

Variation of blood CO_2 content with P_{CO_2}. Fig. 50.6 shows the manner in which the CO_2 *content* of the blood varies when the blood is exposed to gas mixtures of varying CO_2 *tension*. In the physiological range an increase in P_{CO_2} induces an almost proportional increase in CO_2 content; i.e., the curve is nearly a straight line in this region. A pH decrease, calculable from the Henderson-Hasselbalch equation, accompanies a P_{CO_2} increase but is very small in this range. The exact position of the CO_2 content-P_{CO_2} curve depends upon the total buffering power of the blood. Christiansen, Douglas and Haldane (1914) first noted that the curve is higher for reduced blood than for oxygenated blood. In other words, reduced blood has more buffering power than oxygenated blood and can carry more carbon dioxide at a given P_{CO_2}. This suggested that oxyhemoglobin may behave as a stronger acid than reduced hemoglobin. Thus oxygenation would cause the hemoglobin to release hydrogen ions, which would then be neutralized and would use up some of the buffer base (including some bicarbonate), and accordingly the position of the CO_2 content-P_{CO_2} curve would be shifted downward. Titration curves for oxygenated and reduced hemoglobin supported this interpretation. However, this mechanism is now known to be only a part of the explanation for the shift of the curve. The other factor is the effect of oxygenation in diminishing the power of hemoglobin to combine directly with carbon dioxide.

Transport of CO_2 as carbaminohemoglobin. Carbone dioxide combines with hemoglobin, not with the hemes as do O_2 and CO, but rather with free amino groups in the globin part of the molecule. The reaction can be represented as follows:

$$Hb\text{---}NH_2 + CO_2 \rightleftharpoons Hb\text{---}NHCOO^- + H^+$$

This occurs at a very rapid rate, requiring no enzyme, and the CO_2 does not go through the stage of H_2CO_3. The carbamino acid is almost completely ionized, but the pH change is minimized by the buffering power of the hemoglobin.

Carbamino compounds of CO_2 with amino acids are well known, and the technique of estimating them was adapted to the measurement of carbaminohemoglobin by Ferguson and Roughton (1934). Hemoglobin solutions containing bicarbonate were equilibrated with suitable tensions of CO_2 and then were mixed very rapidly with alkaline barium chloride. The alkali stabilized the carbamino compound, probably by inducing its complete ionization, and also converted the dissolved CO_2 and bicarbonate to carbonate which was then precipitated by the barium chloride. The $BaCO_3$ precipitate was removed by centrifuging. The carbaminohemoglobin, which remained in solution, could then be decomposed by acidification and the released CO_2 measured by the Van Slyke technique. It was found that *oxygenation of the hemoglobin* greatly reduced the amount of carbamino-bound CO_2. Although an increase in P_{CO_2} would be expected to favor the formation of carbaminohemoglobin, a decrease in pH has an opposite effect (by converting Hb—NH_2 to Hb—NH_3^+, which does not react with CO_2); hence the dissociation curve of carbaminohemoglobin is practically flat over the physiological range, and the variation in P_{CO_2} between arterial and venous levels has little effect on the carbamino reaction. The chief factor influencing the formation and breakdown of carbaminohemoglobin in the body is the variation in oxygenation. It has been estimated that 20 to 30 per cent of the carbon dioxide delivered to the lungs under resting conditions is transported as carbaminohemoglobin, although only 6 to 7 per cent of the CO_2 content of the venous blood is in this form (Davenport, 1958; Roughton, 1964).

Only traces of carbamino compounds are formed by the plasma proteins, and the concentrations do not vary significantly between arterial and venous blood.

Transport of CO_2 as bicarbonate. Carbon dioxide produced in the tissues diffuses into the blood in the capillaries as free CO_2 in solution. In the blood, a large part of it is converted to carbonic acid:

$$CO_2 + H_2O \rightleftharpoons H_2CO_3 \tag{1}$$

This reaction will take place in the absence of a catalyst, but the uncatalyzed reaction is much too slow to account for the rapid exchanges which take place in the body. The reaction rate is accelerated enormously (in both directions) by an enzyme called *carbonic anhydrase*, which is found inside the erythrocytes but not in the blood plasma.[7] The formation and decomposition of H_2CO_3 therefore occur primarily in the red cells.

The equilibrium point of reaction (1) lies far to the left. However, the hydration of CO_2 is followed by the rapid dissociation of carbonic acid:

$$CO_2 + H_2O \rightleftharpoons H_2CO_3 \rightleftharpoons H^+ + HCO_3^-$$

---

[7] Carbonic anhydrase is a protein of comparatively low molecular weight (about 30,000) containing one atom of zinc per molecule. It is present also in tissues such as gastric and intestinal mucosa, renal cortex, pancreas, brain, spleen, red muscle, liver and salivary glands, and in the oviducts of hens where its function appears to be concerned in the deposition of calcium in the egg shell. Its physiological significance in most of these situations is unknown. The enzyme is inhibited by sulfanilamide, cyanide, heavy metals, sulfocyanate, and certain other ions. Different sulfonamide drugs differ in their inhibitory potency. The ones most commonly used therapeutically are weak inhibitors, but some have been developed for this special purpose. Among these is acetazolamide (Diamox), which is used as a diuretic in cardiac insufficiency. It acts on the kidney, decreasing the tubular reabsorption of bicarbonate and thus increasing the excretion of sodium and potassium as bicarbonates. It also affects the brain (perhaps indirectly), and is used as an anticonvulsant. In experimental animals, large doses of Diamox initially induce a fall in CO_2 output, with recovery to the normal rate in about an hour. The compensation is brought about by a 40 per cent increase in the P_{CO_2} of the venous blood and a doubling of the ventilation rate (Roughton, 1964).

It is obvious that, by the law of mass action, an increase in Pco₂ and the removal of hydrogen ions would tend to drive the two reactions to the right. This is what happens as the blood is passing through the *tissue capillaries:* CO_2 diffusing into the blood increases the Pco₂ , and hydrogen ions are removed by the buffers, especially by hemoglobin since oxyhemoglobin is being converted to the reduced form, a weaker (less dissociated) acid. The opposite changes occur as the blood passes through the *alveolar capillaries:* the diffusion of CO_2 out of the blood reduces the Pco₂ , and the hemoglobin becomes oxygenated and releases hydrogen ions, with the result that the equilibrium is shifted to the left.

These interlocking reactions can be formulated as follows:

$$CO_2 + H_2O \rightleftharpoons H^+ + HCO_3^-$$

$$H^+ + HbO_2^- \rightleftharpoons HHb + O_2$$

Here oxyhemoglobin is represented as an ionized acid and reduced hemoglobin as unionized. It must be recognized that neither is *completely* ionized or unionized; this formulation merely symbolizes the fact that oxyhemoglobin is the stronger acid of the two. When the equilibrium shifts, most of the hydrogen ions released by one reaction are taken up by the other. The over-all equilibrium (the sum of the two reactions above) therefore is:

$$CO_2 + H_2O + HbO_2^- \underset{\text{lungs}}{\overset{\text{tissues}}{\rightleftharpoons}}$$

$$HCO_3^- + HHb + O_2$$

This is called the isohydric shift. The reaction does not go to completion in either direction, but the equilibrium is shifted to the right by conditions in the tissues and to the left by conditions in the lungs. Thus it can be said that CO_2 tends to drive out oxygen, and oxygen tends to drive out CO_2 . The shift occurs with very little change in the plasma pH.

The negative ions, HbO_2^- on the left and HCO_3^- on the right, are balanced by the presence of positive ions (mostly K^+) inside the red cells.[8] However, the cations take no active part in the reaction, and the common statement that they have been "captured" by oxyhemoglobin on the one hand or by bicarbonate on the other is likely to introduce confusion. It would be more accurate

[8] The cation content frequently is referred to as "base", but in modern acid-base theory the term base is reserved for substances able to accept protons (hydrogen ions).

to consider that *hydrogen ions* are captured either by reduced hemoglobin or by the bicarbonate system.

The "heme-linked" or "oxylabile" ionizing groups, i.e., those that dissociate to release hydrogen ions more readily in oxygenated than in reduced hemoglobin, are believed to be imidazole groups of the amino acid histidine, a constituent of the globin part of the molecule.

An over-simplification must be recognized in the above formulation. The hemoglobin molecule contains 4 hemes (ch. 27) and each heme appears to be associated with one ionizable hydrogen. Therefore, fully oxygenated hemoglobin should be represented as $H_4Hb_4(O_2)_4$, and there are intermediate forms such as $H_4Hb_4(O_2)_3$, etc. However, the simpler formulation is qualitatively satisfactory if the symbol Hb is understood to represent one heme and not a hemoglobin molecule.

The chloride-bicarbonate shift. Chloride and bicarbonate ions pass freely through the red cell membrane, while cations traverse it only very slowly. When the blood is in the tissue capillaries bicarbonate ions formed inside the red cells tend to diffuse out to the plasma. Since they cannot be accompanied by cations the red cells are left with a positive electric charge which tends to draw anions into the cells. Hence chloride ions, being the most abundant anions, migrate inward in exchange for bicarbonate. The reverse movements occur when the blood is passing through the lungs and intracellular bicarbonate is being converted to CO_2 . The intracellular-extracellular distribution of ions is described by Donnan's theory (ch. 34), which requires the following relations:

$$\frac{[HCO_3^-]_{\text{cells}}}{[HCO_3^-]_{\text{plasma}}} = \frac{[Cl^-]_{\text{cells}}}{[Cl^-]_{\text{plasma}}} = \frac{[H^+]_{\text{plasma}}}{[H^+]_{\text{cells}}}$$

This "Donnan ratio" varies from about 0.72 in arterial blood to 0.75 in venous blood (Davenport, 1958). It follows that: (1) the greater portion of the bicarbonate is carried in the plasma, and (2) the pH inside the cells is lower than that of the plasma by about 0.12–0.14 pH units. With the redistribution of ions occurring between the arterial side and the venous side of the circulatory system there is an alteration of osmotic relationships such that some water enters the cells along with the chloride, and a slight swelling of the cells occurs.

The exchanges occurring as the blood passes

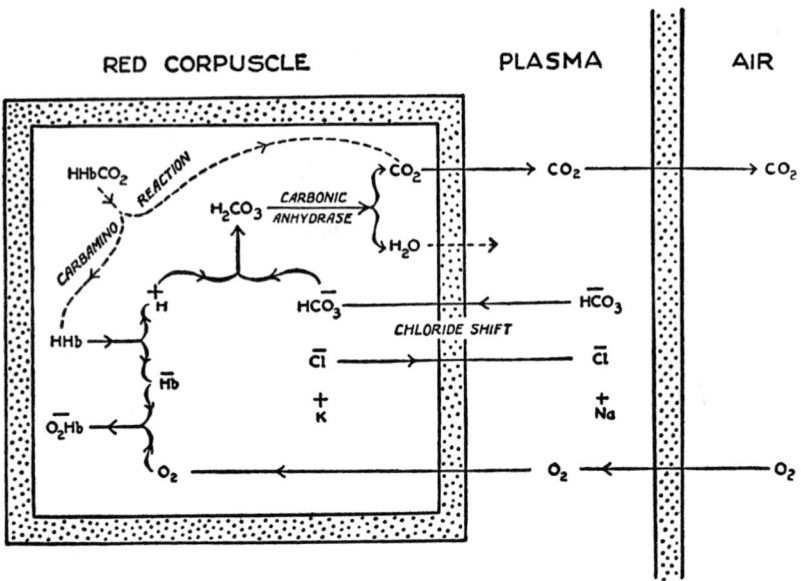

Fig. 50.7. Showing main processes occurring in the blood during the output of carbon dioxide and uptake of oxygen in the lung (after Roughton).

through the lungs are summarized in Roughton's diagram (fig. 50.7).

Gas Tensions in the Tissues

Oxygen tension. In the tissues oxygen is being supplied by diffusion and consumed within the cells; hence diffusion gradients are present and a uniform Po₂ cannot exist. At any given point within a tissue the Po₂ level represents a dynamic balance between oxygen supply and utilization. The rate of *supply* is influenced by the following factors: arterial Po₂ and oxygen capacity, blood flow, distance from a capillary, distance between capillaries, distance along the capillary, radius of the capillary, and the diffusion coefficient of oxygen in the tissue. The rate of oxygen *utilization* normally depends upon the energy requirement of the tissue; it varies with activity but is not limited by the availability of oxygen except when Po₂ is reduced to a very low level.

Davies and Bronk (1957) used a microelectrode for the polarographic measurement of Po₂ at the surface of the cerebral cortex in cats, and were able to demonstrate the existence of steep downward diffusion gradients as the electrode was moved away from an arteriole or a venule. Others have used modifications of this technique to record Po₂ in various parts of the brain and in other tissues.

The distribution of a gas in a tissue can be analyzed theoretically and its *average* tension estimated by calculation with the aid of a diffu-

sion model originally suggested by Krogh. It is assumed that the tissue is functionally divided into cylindrical segments, each supplied with a centrally situated capillary (Kety, 1957). Gleichmann *et al.* (1962) applied this reasoning to estimate the mean oxygen tension in the cerebral cortex of the dog, and compared the results with polarographic measurements of Po₂ at the surface of the cortex. The active surface of each electrode covered an area 2 to 4 mm. in diameter, and large vessels were absent from the areas chosen. The surface values agreed fairly well with those calculated for mean Po₂ in the tissue, and usually came close to the venous blood Po₂. The observed values were 25–42 mm. Hg in animals with ventilation rates approximately normal.

Other workers have reported lower Po₂ values from the surface of the cortex and from electrodes thrust into various parts of the brain. For example, Meyer and Gotoh (1961) reported surface values of 10–20 mm. Hg in cats and monkeys. Cater *et al.* (1961) made an extensive exploration of the rat brain, finding values of 33–60 mm. Hg at the cortical surface, 20–38 in gray matter of the cortex, 6–16 in white matter of the cortex, and 10–15 in hypothalamic nuclei. In rat muscle the values were 14–26, and in subcutaneous tissue there were wide variations from 8 to 62. Jamieson and Van den Brenk (1964) reported the following mean values for rat tissues: cerebral cortex 34, liver 13, kidney 17, and spleen 17 mm. Hg.

In the various tissues studied, rapid variations

in P_{O_2} occur in relation to metabolic, circulatory and respiratory changes induced by various means.

CO₂ tension. Diffusion gradients of P_{CO_2} must be assumed to exist between the tissue cells and the blood in the capillaries. With the aid of Krogh's diffusion model, Gleichmann *et al.* (1962) calculated the *average* P_{CO_2} in the cerebral cortex of the dog in each of a series of experiments. A statistical analysis of the data indicated that the average tissue P_{CO_2} is only about 0.7 mm. Hg higher than the mid-capillary blood P_{CO_2} (i.e., the average of arterial and cerebral venous values). CO₂ electrodes placed on the surface of the cortex gave values which in each experiment agreed closely with the estimated average tissue P_{CO_2}. The values ranged from 31 to 58 mm. Hg. Meyer and Gotoh (1961) found that the P_{CO_2} of the cerebral cortex fluctuates rapidly in relation to metabolic, circulatory and respiratory alterations.

Adjustments to Metabolic Requirements

Increased activity of any tissue entails an increase in oxygen consumption and CO₂ production. On the other hand, an increase in the oxygen supply above that which is adequate does not increase the oxygen usage. There are two ways in which an increased demand for oxygen may be met, (1) by increasing the blood flow through the tissue, and (2) by raising the coefficient of oxygen utilization. Both of these factors come into play, but the extent to which each operates is different for different tissues. The coefficient of oxygen utilization is increased by establishing a steeper P_{O_2} gradient between the capillary blood and the tissue cells; this is brought about by (a) a decrease in the intracellular P_{O_2} as utilization increases, (b) a shortening of the distance through which oxygen must diffuse, i.e., the opening up of more capillaries so that the radius of the cylinder of tissue supplied by each capillary is reduced, and (c) increased dissociation of oxyhemoglobin due to increased production of acids (carbonic and lactic) and a rise in temperature (Otis, 1963).

REFERENCES

ALLEN, D. W., WYMAN, J., JR., AND SMITH, C. A. The oxygen equilibrium of fetal and adult human hemoglobin. J. Biol. Chem., 1953, 203, 81.

ASTRUP, P. A new approach to acid-base metabolism. Clin. Chem., 1961, 7, 1.

BARCROFT, J. AND POULTON, E. P. The effect of carbonic acid on the dissociation curve of blood. J. Physiol., 1913, 46, iv.

CATER, D. B., GARATTINI, S., MARINA, F., AND SILVER, I. A. Changes of oxygen tension in brain and somatic tissues induced by vasodilator and vasoconstrictor drugs. Proc. Roy. Soc., B, 1961, 155, 136.

CHARLTON, G., READ, D., AND READ, J. Continuous intra-arterial P_{O_2} in normal man using a flexible microelectrode. J. Appl. Physiol., 1963, 18, 1247.

CHRISTIANSEN, J., DOUGLAS, C. G., AND HALDANE, J. S. The absorption and dissociation of carbon dioxide by human blood. J. Physiol., 1914, 48, 244.

CHRISTIE, R. V. AND LOOMIS, A. L. The pressure of aqueous vapor in the alveolar air. J. Physiol., 1932, 77, 35.

COLLIER, C. R., AFFELDT, J. E., AND FARR, A. F. Continuous rapid infrared CO₂ analysis. J. Lab. Clin. Med., 1955, 45, 526.

COMROE, J. H., JR. Measurements on arterial blood. Methods in Med. Research, 1950, 2, 138.

COMROE, J. H., JR., FORSTER, R. E., II, DuBois, A. B., BRISCOE, W. A., AND CARLSEN, E. The Lung, 2nd ed. Year Book Medical Publishers, Chicago, 1962.

CONSOLAZIO, C. F., JOHNSON, R. E., AND PECORA, L. J. Physiological measurements of metabolic functions in man. McGraw-Hill, New York, 1963.

COURTICE, F. C. AND DOUGLAS, C. G. The ferricyanide method of blood gas analysis. J. Physiol., 1947, 105, 345.

DARLING, R. C., SMITH, C. A., ASMUSSEN, E., AND COHEN, F. M. Some properties of human fetal and maternal blood. J. Clin. Invest., 1941, 20, 739.

DAVENPORT, H. W. The ABC of acid-base chemistry, 4th ed. University of Chicago Press, Chicago, 1958.

DAVIES, P. W. AND BRONK, D. W. Oxygen tension in mammalian brain. Fed. Proc., 1957, 16, 689.

FERGUSON, J. K. W. AND ROUGHTON, F. J. W. The direct chemical estimation of carbamino compounds of CO₂ with haemoglobin. J. Physiol., 1934, 83, 68.

GLEICHMANN, U., INGVAR, D. H., LÜBBERS, D. W., SIESJÖ, B. K., AND THEWS, G. Tissue pO_2 and pCO_2 of the cerebral cortex, related to blood gas tensions. Acta physiol. scand., 1962, 55, 127.

JAMIESON, D. AND VAN DEN BRENK, H. A. S. Effect of electrode dimensions on tissue pO_2 measurements *in vivo.* Nature, 1964, 201, 1227.

KETY, S. Determinants of tissue oxygen tension. Fed. Proc., 1957, 16, 666.

MEYER, J. S. AND GOTOH, F. Interaction of cerebral hemodynamics and metabolism. Neurology, 1961, 11, No. 4, part 2, p. 46.

NATELSON, S. Microtechniques of clinical chemistry. Charles C Thomas, Springfield, 1957.

OTIS, A. B. The control of respiratory gas exchange between blood and tissues. *In* The Regulation of Human Respiration (Ed. D. J. C. CUNNINGHAM AND B. B. LLOYD) p. 111. Blackwell, Oxford, 1963.

OTIS, A. B. Quantitative relationships in steady-state gas exchange. *In* Handbook of Physiology, Sec. 3: Respiration, Vol. I. (Ed. W. O. FENN AND

H. RAHN) p. 681. American Physiological Society, Washington, 1964.

PETERS, J. P. AND VAN SLYKE, D. D. Quantitative clinical chemistry, Vol. II. Williams & Wilkins, Baltimore, 1932.

RADFORD, E. P., JR. The physics of gases. *In* Handbook of Physiology, Sec. 3: Respiration, Vol. I. (Ed. W. O. FENN AND H. RAHN) p. 125. American Physiological Society, Washington, 1964.

RAHN, H. AND FARHI, L. E. Ventilation, perfusion, and gas exchange. *In* Handbook of Physiology, Sec. 3: Respiration, Vol. I. (Ed. W. O. FENN AND H. RAHN) p. 735. American Physiological Society, Washington, 1964.

RAHN, H. AND OTIS, A. B. Continuous analysis of alveolar gas composition during work, hyperpnea, hypercapnia and anoxia. J. Appl. Physiol., 1949, 1, 717.

RILEY, R. L., LILIENTHAL, J. L., JR., PROEMMEL, D. D., AND FRANKE, R. E. On the determination of the physiologically effective pressures of oxygen and carbon dioxide in alveolar air. Am. J. Physiol., 1946, 147, 191.

ROSSIER, P. H., BÜHLMANN, A. A., AND WEISINGER, K. Respiration (Ed. and translated by P. C. LUCHSINGER AND K. M. MOSER). Mosby, St. Louis, 1960.

ROUGHTON, F. J. W. Some recent work on the chemistry of carbon dioxide transport by the blood. Harvey Lectures, 1943–44, 39, 96.

ROUGHTON, F. J. W. The average time spent by the blood in the human lung capillary and its relation to the rates of CO uptake and elimination in man. Am. J. Physiol., 1945, 143, 621.

ROUGHTON, F. J. W. Transport of oxygen and carbon dioxide. *In* Handbook of Physiology, Sec. 3: Respiration, Vol. I. (Ed. W. O. FENN AND H. RAHN) p. 767. American Physiological Society, Washington, 1964.

SCHULMAN, I. Characteristics of the blood in foetal life. *In* Oxygen Supply to the Human Foetus. (Ed. J. WALKER AND A. C. TURNBULL) Blackwell, Oxford, 1959.

SEVERINGHAUS, J. W. Oxyhemoglobin dissociation curve correction for temperature and pH variation in human blood. J. Appl. Physiol., 1958, 12, 485.

SEVERINGHAUS, J. W. AND BRADLEY, A. F. Electrodes for blood pO$_2$ and pCO$_2$ determination. J. Appl. Physiol., 1958, 13, 515.

SEVERINGHAUS, J. W., STUPFEL, M., AND BRADLEY, A. F. Variations of serum carbonic acid pK′ with pH and temperature. J. Appl. Physiol., 1956, 9, 197.

SIGGAARD ANDERSON, O. The first dissociation exponent of carbonic acid as a function of pH. Scand. J. Clin. Lab. Invest., 1962a, 14, 587.

SIGGAARD ANDERSON, O. The pH-log pCO$_2$ blood acid-base nomogram. Scand. J. Clin. Lab. Invest., 1962b, 14, 598.

SIGGARD ANDERSON, O. AND ENGEL, K. A new acid-base nomogram. Scand. J. Clin. Lab. Invest., 1960, 12, 177.

SINGER, R. B. AND HASTINGS, A. B. An improved clinical method for the estimation of disturbances of the acid-base balance of human blood. Medicine, 1948, 27, 223.

TORRES, G. E. Validation of oxygen electrode for blood. J. Appl. Physiol., 1963, 18, 1008.

VAN SLYKE, D. D., DILLON, R. T., AND MARGARIA, R. Studies of gas and electrolyte equilibria in blood; solubility and physical state of atmospheric nitrogen in blood cells and plasma. J. Biol. Chem., 1934, 105, 571.

VAN SLYKE, D. D. AND PLAZIN, J. Micromanometric analyses. Williams & Wilkins, Baltimore, 1961.

VAN SLYKE, D. D. AND SENDROY, J. Studies of gas and electrolyte equilibria in blood. XV. Line charts for graphic calculations by the Henderson-Hasselbalch equation, and for calculating plasma carbon dioxide content from whole blood content. J. Biol. Chem., 1928, 79, 781.

WOOD, E. H., SUTTERER, W. F., AND CRONIN, L. Oximetry. *In* Medical Physics, Vol. 3. (Ed. O. GLASSER) p. 416. Year Book Medical Publishers, Chicago, 1960.

ZIJLSTRA, W. G. A manual of reflection oximetry. Van Gorcum and Comp. N. V., Assen, Netherlands, 1958.

CHAPTER 51

Pulmonary Gas Exchange

Total, Dead Space and Alveolar Ventilations

The lung is made up of tubes for airflow and alveoli for exchange of gases between air and blood. At the end of a normal expiration, the airways and alveoli are filled with alveolar gas. At the end of a normal inspiration, however, the airways are filled with moist room air and the balance of the inspired volume has been added to the volume of the alveolar spaces. During the subsequent expiration, room air is washed out of the airways by alveolar air and the cycle begins again. Therefore one expired breath (tidal volume) contains gas from two compartments, one filled with room air containing a negligible concentration of carbon dioxide, and the other filled with alveolar air with a partial pressure of carbon dioxide (P_{CO_2}) in equilibrium with arterial blood.

The volume of the airways of an adult man is about 150 cc. At a tidal volume of 500 cc. and a respiratory frequency of 12 per minute, the total ventilation is 6.0 l./min. of which the airway ventilation is $150 \times 12 = 1.8$ l./min. and the alveolar ventilation is $350 \times 12 = 4.2$ l./min. It is customary to refer to airway ventilation as "dead space" ventilation because it is not associated with exchange of gases with capillary blood. The terms "anatomic" and "physiologic" dead space ventilation are used to distinguish simple airway ventilation from ventilation of airways together with alveolar spaces which do not participate in gas exchange. A lung lacking its pulmonary artery, for example, would have only dead space ventilation despite its normal anatomic subdivision into airways and alveoli.

Anatomic dead space can be measured post mortem by making casts of the airways from mouth to terminal bronchioles and measuring their volume. It can also be measured approximately by the technique described in fig. 51.1. This requires measuring volume of expired air and nitrogen concentration in expired air simultaneously. A subject breathing room air (79% nitrogen) takes in a breath of 100% oxygen and then exhales slowly. The nitrogen meter records 0% nitrogen during the period of inspiration and during the first part of expiration as the dead space air is washed out. The meter then samples a mixture of rising nitrogen concentration as

dead space gas is mixed with alveolar gas. Ideally, if the inspired oxygen is evenly distributed throughout the alveoli, the meter then records an unvarying nitrogen concentration. The measurement of dead space is calculated to be the volume expired up to the time at which one-half the volume of the rising phase has been delivered. Measurements so made in normal subjects indicate that anatomic dead space at the end of a maximal expiration is about one-half its value at the end of a complete inspiration. This indicates the extent to which the airway volume is increased by elongation and widening as traction of airways by lung parenchyma increases with lung volume.

Total ("anatomic" plus "physiologic") dead space ventilation is readily measured provided the carbon dioxide content of alveolar air is known. This can be measured by sampling alveolar gas as described in a previous chapter. Since alveolar air is in equilibrium with arterial blood, the alveolar partial pressure can also be obtained from the arterial partial pressure. Mixed expired air is a mixture of room air from the airways and nonperfused alveoli, and of air from perfused alveoli. Its carbon dioxide partial pressure is lower in proportion to the dilution of the alveolar fraction by the dead space fraction. If, for example, the arterial P_{CO_2} is 40 mm. Hg and the partial pressure of carbon dioxide in mixed expired air ($P_{E_{CO_2}}$) is 30 mm. Hg, it must be concluded that alveolar gas was diluted one part room air (dead space) in three parts alveolar air (fig. 51.1).

The equation for calculating the ratio dead space volume/tidal volume is

$$\frac{V_D}{V_T} = \frac{P_{A_{CO_2}} - P_{E_{CO_2}}}{P_{A_{CO_2}}}$$

where V_D—dead space volume, V_T—tidal volume, $P_{A_{CO_2}}$—the partial pressure of carbon dioxide in alveolar gas or arterial blood and $P_{E_{CO_2}}$—the partial pressure of carbon dioxide in mixed expired air. In the instance cited,

$$\frac{V_D}{V_T} = \frac{40 - 30}{40} = .25.$$

If the minute ventilation were 6 l./min. and the

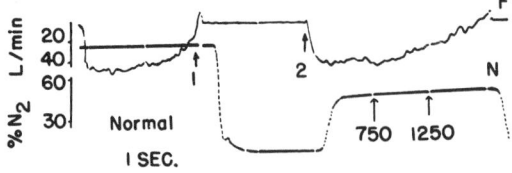

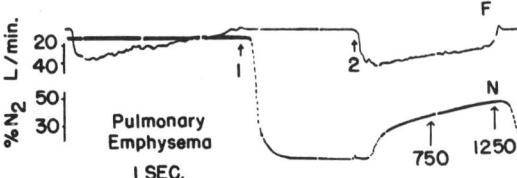

Fig. 51.1. Single breath nitrogen dilution method for: (a) measuring anatomic dead space, and (b) detecting nonuniform distribution of inspired air. F = respiratory flow, N = nitrogen concentration. Horizontal axis is time. Integration of F would give volume. Expiration after breathing room air is indicated to left of 1. Between 1 and 2, patient inspired one breath of oxygen and at 2 expiration began. See text for description of nitrogen curve and its use for measuring anatomic dead space. Nonuniform distribution of inspired oxygen is shown by continued increase of nitrogen concentration after rapidly rising phase. The increase in concentration between expired volume of 750 and 1,250 is 1% in normal subject and 9% in patient with emphysema. (From J. H. Comroe, and W. S. Fowler: Lung function studies. Amer. J. Med., 1951, 10, 408.)

TABLE 51.1

Frequency (breaths per min.)	Total Ventilation (l./min.)	V_T (cc.)	V_D (cc.)	Dead Space Ventilation (l./min.)	Alveolar Ventilation (l./min.)
10	6.00	600	150	1.50	4.50
15	6.00	400	150	2.25	3.75
20	6.00	300	150	3.00	3.00
30	6.00	200	150	4.50	1.50
40	6.00	150	150	6.00	0

respiratory frequency 12 per min., the tidal volume would be 500 ml. and the dead space volume 500 × .25 = 125 ml. Dead space ventilation would be 125 × 12 = 1500 ml./min. and the balance of 4½ l./min. would be alveolar ventilation. V_D/V_T does not exceed .30 in normal subjects.

The design of the lung is such that dead space ventilation is obligatory, i.e., the proportion of a tidal volume delivered to the alveoli is whatever exceeds the volume of the dead space. Table 51.1 shows how alveolar ventilation is affected by tidal volume when total ventilation and dead space volume are kept constant. It shows that dead space ventilation increases at the expense of alveolar ventilation as tidal volume approaches dead space volume. It is clear from this table that any increase in dead space, such as physiologic dead space or anatomic dead space in the form of breathing equipment, decreases alveolar ventilation unless total ventilation is increased. The patient with marginal ventilatory ability is therefore disadvantaged by any increase in dead space and may be assisted by decreasing his anatomic dead space. Tracheostomy reduces the anatomic dead space about 50% by eliminating ventilation of the mouth, larynx and pharynx. One of its favorable aspects is the increase in alveolar ventilation which results from reducing dead space.

Dead space ventilation is not altogether useless. Inspired air is warmed, saturated with water vapor at 37° C. and filtered. Panting, which is primarily dead space ventilation, is an important temperature regulating mechanism in some animals. The vital functions of ventilation, however, concern maintaining a sufficiently high partial pressure of oxygen in the alveoli and excreting carbon dioxide. These are accomplished exclusively by alveolar ventilation.

Alveolar Po2

Alveolar air contains four gases (O_2, CO_2, N_2, H_2O) the sum of whose partial pressures equals the barometric pressure (see previous chapters). The partial pressures of two of these, N_2 and H_2O, is fixed, for the pressure of water vapor in saturated air at body temperature (37° C.) is a constant (47 mm. Hg) and the nitrogen inspired into the lung is neither taken into the blood stream nor is it added to from the blood stream. The sum of the partial pressures of oxygen and carbon dioxide is therefore also a constant, approximately 150 mm. of Hg at sea level. This means that the subject breathing room air can vary his alveolar Po2 only by varying his alveolar Pco2.

Alveolar Pco2 is directly proportional to the rate at which carbon dioxide is produced by the tissues and inversely proportional to alveolar ventilation:

$$P_{ACO_2} \cong \frac{\text{Production}}{\text{Excretion}} \cong \frac{\text{Metabolic rate}}{\text{Alveolar ventilation}}$$

Clearly, therefore, at any metabolic rate, alveolar ventilation is the key to alveolar Po2. Insufficient alveolar ventilation causes hypoxia because carbon dioxide is produced more rapidly than it is excreted, alveolar Pco2 rises and alveolar Po2 must consequently fall. Conversely, increasing alveolar ventilation at a time when the rate of CO_2 production is constant lowers alveolar P_{CO_2} resulting in an increase in alveolar P_{O_2}.

Alveolar P_{O_2} ($P_{A_{O_2}}$) can be varied also by changing the total barometric pressure when the oxygen concentration (F) is kept constant (normally .2093), by changing the concentration in inspired air ($F_{I_{O_2}}$) or by changes in both pressure and concentration. For example, the Himalayan mountain climber can compensate for the fall in $P_{A_{O_2}}$ resulting from low barometric pressure by breathing mixtures in which oxygen concentration is increased at the expense of nitrogen concentration.

These factors upon which $P_{A_{O_2}}$ depend are included in the alveolar air equation, one form of which is as follows:

$$P_{A_{O_2}} = (BP - 47)F_{I_{O_2}} - \frac{P_{A_{CO_2}}}{R}$$

$$+ \frac{F_{I_{O_2}}P_{A_{CO_2}}(1 - R)}{R}$$

For the derivation of this and other equations used in respiratory physiology, the interested student is referred to Rahn and Fenn. The critical terms in the equation are the barometric pressure (BP), the concentration of oxygen in inspired air ($F_{I_{O_2}}$) and the partial pressure of carbon dioxide in alveolar gas ($P_{A_{CO_2}}$) or arterial blood. The final term

$$\frac{F_{I_{O_2}}P_{A_{CO_2}}(1 - R)}{R}$$

is numerically small and is 0 when the gas exchange ratio or respiratory quotient (R) is 1. It should be clear from substituting normal values for $P_{A_{CO_2}}$ (40 mm. of Hg) and R (.8) that $P_{A_{O_2}}$ can be increased to about 660 mm. of Hg at sea level (760 mm. Hg) by breathing 100% oxygen and to more than one atmosphere by placing the subject in a pressure chamber where the barometric pressure can be raised to two or three atmospheres (hyperbaric oxygen chamber). $P_{A_{O_2}}$ can be raised relatively little by increasing alveolar ventilation, for normal $P_{A_{CO_2}}$ is only 40 mm. Hg and $P_{A_{CO_2}}$ is rarely lowered to less than 20 mm. Hg during hyperventilation. On the other hand, CO_2 retention from alveolar hypoventilation can be sufficiently severe to double normal $P_{A_{CO_2}}$ thereby reducing $P_{A_{O_2}}$ substantially. Under normal circumstances, however, the regulation of respiration is such that increases in CO_2

production are attended by commensurate increases in alveolar ventilation and a normal $P_{A_{CO_2}}$ and normal $P_{A_{O_2}}$ are maintained.

The Alveolar-Arterial Partial Pressure Difference for Oxygen

The partial pressure of oxygen in alveolar gas ($P_{A_{O_2}}$) calculated from the alveolar equation is a mean value representative of all the alveoli. This value is invariably higher than the partial pressure of oxygen in arterial blood ($P_{a_{O_2}}$) by about 13 mm. Hg in normal individuals and by considerably greater amounts in certain abnormalities. The reasons for this difference in oxygen tensions are as follows (fig. 51.2):

Anatomic Shunts

Some blood passes from the venous to the arterial circulation without being exposed to the $P_{A_{O_2}}$ calculated by the alveolar equation (fig. 51.2). Some of this blood bypasses the lung entirely, the best known examples being blood from the coronary circulation draining directly into the left heart through the Thebessian veins, and venous blood in the bronchial veins draining into the pulmonary circulation distal to the capillary bed. It is estimated that less than 6% of the cardiac output follows these anatomic shunts. Clearly, they result in lowering the P_{O_2} of arterial blood below the P_{O_2} of pulmonary capillary blood in equilibrium with alveolar gas.

It is instructive to calculate the magnitude of this effect under specified conditions. Assuming, for example, that $P_{A_{O_2}}$ equals 100 mm. Hg, the oxyhemoglobin dissociation curve indicates that pulmonary capillary blood in equilibrium with this gas has an oxyhemoglobin saturation of 97%. If the capillary-venous difference in saturation is 25%, a common value, the venous saturation will be 72%. If venous shunts account for 6% of the cardiac output, leaving 94% to pass through the pulmonary capillaries, the resultant mixture will have a saturation of (.06 × 72) + (.94 × 97) = 4.32 + 91.18 = 95.50%. The partial pressure of oxygen at this saturation is 87 mm. Hg, 13 mm. Hg lower than in pulmonary capillary blood. There is normally, therefore, a difference between pulmonary capillary P_{O_2} ($P_{c_{O_2}}$) and arterial P_{O_2} ($P_{a_{O_2}}$) related to the magnitude of the venous admixture from anatomic shunts.

Physiologic Shunts

The lung has several million alveoli. Because of normal regional differences in compliances

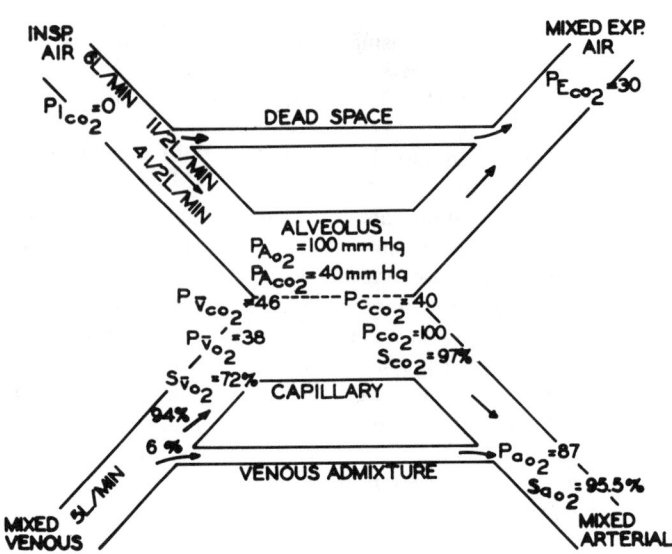

Fɪɢ. 51.2. Idealized schema of lung. Top half represents ventilation, bottom half perfusion. See text for meaning of symbols and concepts. Pc_{CO_2}, Pc_{O_2} and Sc_{O_2} are partial pressures of carbon dioxide and oxygen at the end of the pulmonary capillary, and saturation of blood at the end of the capillary, respectively.

and airway resistances, variations in ventilation inevitably result producing localized differences in $P_{A_{CO_2}}$ and consequently in $P_{A_{O_2}}$. The ultimate example of physiologic shunting is circulation through the capillaries of non-ventilated alveoli, the venous admixture effect of such blood comparing to that of blood coursing through anatomic shunts.

One of the interesting effects of regional differences in ventilation and $P_{A_{O_2}}$ is that Pa_{O_2} is lowered even if hypoventilation of some alveoli is matched by hyperventilation of others. This effect results from the nonlinearity of oxyhemoglobin dissociation. Consider, for example, arbitrarily dividing the pulmonary blood flow into three equal streams coursing through capillaries in equilibrium with alveolar oxygen partial pressures of 60, 80, and 100 mm. Hg. One might assume that the mixed blood collected from these would have a Po_2 of 80 mm. Hg, i.e. $(.333 \times 60) + (.333 \times 80) + (.333 \times 100) = 80$. The correct Po_2, however, would be found by calculating the Po_2 at the saturation of the mixed blood. This calculation is performed as follows. The dissociation curve indicates that saturations at Po_2 of 60, 80, and 100 mm. Hg are 89%, 94%, and 97%, respectively. The saturation of the mixture, therefore, would be $(.333 \times 89) = (.333 \times 94) + (.333 \times 97) = 29.6 + 31.3 + 32.3 = 93.2\%$. The Po_2 at a saturation of 93.2% is 75 mm. Hg, rather than 80 mm. Hg. It is clear, therefore, that a lung characterized by large

variations in $P_{A_{O_2}}$ inevitably delivers a blood mixture which is hypoxic relative to mean $P_{A_{O_2}}$.

The concept of anatomic and physiologic venous admixture is analogous to the concept of anatomic and physiologic dead space (fig. 51.2). The difference $Pc_{O_2} - Pa_{O_2}$ is a measure of venous admixture just as the difference $P_{A_{CO_2}} - P_{E_{CO_2}}$ is a measure of the admixture of dead space ventilation to alveolar ventilation. The fraction of the cardiac output which is venous admixture (Qva/Q_T) is proportional to the venous admixture effect on the saturation of capillary blood $(Sc_{O_2} - Sa_{O_2})$ divided by the total saturation difference between venous and capillary blood $(Sc_{O_2} - S\bar{v}_{O_2})$:

$$\frac{Qva}{Q_T} = \frac{Sc_{O_2} - Sa_{O_2}}{Sc_{O_2} - S\bar{v}_{O_2}}$$

In fig. 51.2, for example, $Qva/Q_T = 97 - 95.5/97 - 72 = 1.5/25 = .06$. This equation can be applied to any situation in which one wishes to measure relative flows of blood through two branches of a confluent system. It finds application clinically in calculating flows through the anatomic defects of children with congenital heart disease.

Alveoli can be classified by their ventilation-perfusion ratios, those with a high value contributing to the physiologic dead space and those with a low value contributing to the venous admixture-like effect of physiologic shunts. Inasmuch as normal alveolar ventilation is about

4 l./min. and cardiac output about 5 l./min., a normal ventilation-perfusion ratio for the entire lung is approximately 0.8.

Measuring dead space ventilation and measuring venous admixture is one means of detecting ventilation-perfusion abnormalities. There are other means. Non-uniform distribution of inspired air, for example, shows up on the nitrogen meter record of fig. 51.1 as a progressive increase in nitrogen concentration with time as the parts of the lung which are most poorly ventilated empty. Another popular method is to measure the concentration of nitrogen in alveolar air after the patient has breathed nitrogen-free oxygen for a specified period. Normal individuals have less than 2.5% nitrogen in alveolar air after breathing oxygen for seven minutes. Abnormal lungs with localized areas of hypoventilation, however, do not "wash out" nitrogen with this rapidity and consequently have elevated alveolar concentrations at the end of this time.

Low ventilation-perfusion ratios with increased venous admixture is the commonest cause of hypoxia in respiratory illness. Bronchiectasis, pneumonia, cystic fibrosis, emphysema are some of the conditions in which this mechanism plays a fundamental role.

Resistance to Diffusion of Oxygen from Alveolus to Capillary

The mechanism whereby oxygen passes from alveolus to pulmonary capillary was at one time a central issue preoccupying prominent departments of physiology at England's leading universities and prompting imaginative transcontinental expeditions to mountaintop laboratories. J. S. Haldane at Oxford University contended that oxygen is secreted into the capillaries against a partial pressure gradient, whereas J. Barcroft at Cambridge maintained that this transfer is entirely passive, following the laws of diffusion. The issue has been resolved conclusively in favor of the latter, partly because methods for measuring gas pressures in blood improved. It is now clear that venous blood is oxygenated because its P_{O_2} (about 40 mm. Hg at rest) is lower than alveolar P_{O_2}, that the rate at which oxygen diffuses is a function of the partial pressure difference between alveolus and capillary, and that, under normal circumstances, virtually complete equilibrium is reached between alveolar and pulmonary capillary P_{O_2} (fig. 51.2). When resistance to diffusion is abnormally high, however, or when transit time through the pulmonary circuit is shortened, a measurable alveolar-

capillary partial pressure difference may remain. Under these circumstances, the total alveolar-arterial partial pressure difference is the sum of a diffusion gradient between alveolus and capillary plus the capillary to arterial difference attributable to anatomic and physiologic venous admixture.

Separating the diffusion from the venous admixture component of the total alveolar-arterial P_{O_2} difference is necessary for purposes of measuring the pulmonary diffusing capacity for oxygen. Before passing to this topic, however, it should be clear that one of the causes of reduced P_{O_2} in arterial blood pathologically is incomplete equilibration of capillary blood with alveolar gas due to abnormal resistance to diffusion across the alveolar-capillary interface. Interstitial fibrosis is the classic clinical condition producing hypoxia from this cause. Increasing alveolar P_{O_2} by raising $F_{I_{O_2}}$ is the logical way of relieving severe hypoxia from this cause.

The Pulmonary Diffusing Capacity for Oxygen

The pulmonary diffusing capacity for oxygen (D_{O_2}) is the ratio of oxygen transfer in ml. of oxygen per minute ($\dot{V}_{O_2}$) from alveolar gas to capillary blood divided by the pressure (mm. Hg) required for this transfer:

$$D_{O_2} = \frac{\dot{V}_{O_2}}{P_{A_{O_2}} - \bar{P}_{C_{O_2}}}$$

where $P_{A_{O_2}}$ and $\bar{P}_{C_{O_2}}$ are partial pressures of oxygen in alveolar gas and pulmonary capillary, respectively. Inasmuch as the $P_{C_{O_2}}$ continuously changes as blood flows through the capillaries, a mean value ($\bar{P}_{C_{O_2}}$) must be obtained as described in a subsequent paragraph.

A normal D_{O_2} at rest is approximately 15 to 20 ml. of oxygen/min./mm. Hg P_{O_2} difference between alveolar and mean capillary oxygen tension. The diffusing capacity reflects resistance to diffusion per unit area as well as total surface area for diffusion. It is therefore reduced when the alveolar-capillary interface is thickened or where surface area for diffusion is attenuated. It rises during exercise by as much as three or four times, presumably because the dimensions of the diffusing surface enlarge as additional capillaries open around each alveolus or as existing capillaries enlarge. It increases from infancy to maturity and falls with age, probably reflecting changes in surface area for diffusion.

Measuring D_{O_2} requires knowing $\dot{V}_{O_2}$, or

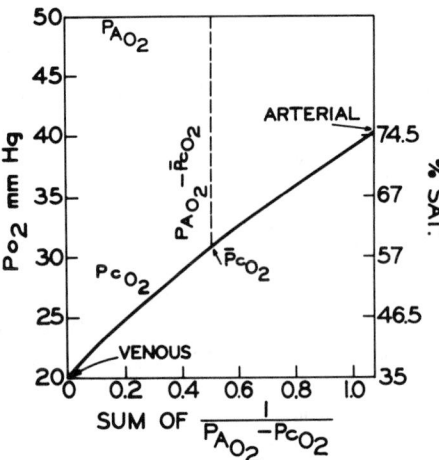

FIG. 51.3. Change in Po₂ and oxyhemoglobin saturation during passage of blood through pulmonary capillary. Data calculated by Bohr integration assuming conditions postulated in text. Time or distance along capillary is a function of the sum of $1/\text{PA}_{O_2} - \overline{P}c_{O_2}$ as explained in text.

metabolic rate, PA_{O_2} which can be calculated from the alveolar equation, and $\overline{P}c_{O_2}$ which cannot be measured directly but which can be estimated from arterial Po₂ as follows: It was indicated above that the total alveolar-arterial Po₂ difference is divisible into a diffusion and a venous admixture component. The key to measuring $\overline{P}c_{O_2}$ is to create circumstances under which the venous admixture component vanishes or becomes negligible, for under this circumstance arterial Po₂ (Pa_{O_2}) approaches Pc_{O_2}. This can be done by producing hypoxia sufficient to displace Pa_{O_2} to the steep part of the dissociation curve, i.e., the part for which substantial changes in saturation due to venous admixture result in relatively small changes in Pa_{O_2}. To illustrate, it was shown above that the capillary-arterial Po₂ difference is 13 mm. Hg if 6% of the cardiac output bypasses the lungs when PA_{O_2} and Pc_{O_2} are 100 mm. Hg, and when the arterial venous saturation difference is 25%. If this calculation is repeated at a saturation of 75% (Po₂ = 40 mm. Hg), the saturation of venous blood will be 50% (Po₂ = 26.5 mm. Hg), and the saturation of mixed arterial blood will be (.06 × 50) + (.94 × 75) = 3.00 + 70.50 = 73.5%. The Po₂ at this saturation is 39.5 mm. Hg, a difference of only 0.5 mm. Hg from the pulmonary capillary Po₂ (40 mm. Hg). By making the same calculation at a low Po₂, therefore, the venous admixture effect of 13 mm. Hg was reduced to 0.5 mm. Hg. The reason for this striking difference is the characteristic of oxyhemoglobin saturation

whereby a given change in saturation at high levels of saturation has a much greater effect on Po₂ than at low saturations.

Measuring Do₂ requires not only eliminating the effect of venous admixture on the alveolar-arterial Po₂ difference but creating a measurable difference between PA_{O_2} and Pc_{O_2}. This can be accomplished by breathing low concentrations of oxygen and by exercise. A low PA_{O_2} reduces the Po₂ gradient between alveolus and venous blood entering the capillary; the rate of diffusion is therefore slowed, the amount of oxygen taken up at any point along the capillary is less, and complete equilibration with alveolar gas is not achieved. Exercise increases cardiac output and pulmonary blood flow, thereby reducing time for equilibration of Pc_{O_2} with PA_{O_2}. Both exercise and hypoxia, therefore, foster an end-capillary $\text{PA}_{O_2} - Pc_{O_2}$ sufficiently large to be measured reliably.

In summary, by measuring the alveolar-arterial Po₂ difference at a high level of oxygenation to identify venous admixture, and at a low level of oxygenation during exercise, it is possible to create measurable differences between PA_{O_2} and Pa_{O_2} attributable to a difference between PA_{O_2} and Pc_{O_2}.

Bohr Integration

The final step in calculating diffusing capacity is to derive a mean Pc_{O_2} ($\overline{P}c_{O_2}$). This can be done if one knows the Po₂ at the arterial and venous ends of the pulmonary capillary as well as at all intermediate points. The former are measurable directly; the latter can be calculated from the oxyhemoglobin dissociation curve by Bohr integration (fig. 51.3). The fundamental premise is that distance or time (T) along the pulmonary capillary is proportional to the reciprocal of the tension difference between alveolar gas and capillary blood

$$\left(T \cong \frac{1}{\text{PA}_{O_2} - Pc_{O_2}} \right).$$

This is true because the rate of diffusion, i.e., the time (T) required for a given change in saturation (ΔSo₂) at a given point along a capillary, is proportional to the partial pressure difference between alveolus and blood at that point. Thus,

$$\frac{\Delta \text{So}_2}{T} \cong (\text{PA}_{O_2} - Pc_{O_2}).$$

The data of fig. 51.3 were calculated assuming

the subject was breathing 14% oxygen, had an alveolar Po_2 of 50, an arterial saturation of 75% (Po_2 = 40.5) and an arterial-venous saturation difference of 40%, i.e., mixed venous blood saturation of 35% and Po_2 of 20 mm. Hg. The end-gradient was 9.5 mm. Hg and the mean gradient calculated by Bohr integration 29 mm. Hg. Assuming an oxygen consumption of 1740 ml./min., the diffusing capacity would be

$$\frac{1750\ \text{ml./min.}}{29\ \text{mm. Hg}} = 60\ \text{ml./min./mm. Hg,}$$

a normal value during severe exercise.

Although the circumstances of exertion and hypoxia required for this measurement are so Spartan as to limit its applicability, this method nevertheless remains the only direct approach to measuring the pulmonary diffusing capacity for oxygen. Its ingenuity is obvious from the foregoing. The premise that hypoxia itself does not affect what is measured may not be justified.

Carbon Monoxide Diffusing Capacities

The use of carbon monoxide for measuring Do_2 is less trying on both subject and laboratory personnel. None of the methods require hypoxia or exercise and some methods do not require analysis of blood samples.

CO has a remarkable affinity for hemoglobin, its affinity being 210 times that of oxygen. The Pco of plasma is therefore extremely low at a given concentration of HbCO. Accordingly, plasma Pco can usually be assumed to be zero and the alveolar-arterial partial pressure difference becomes simply the alveolar Pco. Analyzing blood and performing the equivalent of the tedious Bohr integration are therefore unnecessary.

Dco can be converted to Do_2 by multiplying by 1.23. This figure indicates that oxygen is slightly more diffusible than CO. This is because diffusibility is directly proportional to solubility and inversely proportional to the square root of the molecular weight. Thus,

$$\frac{Do_2}{Dco} = \frac{\text{Sol } O_2}{\text{Sol } CO} \times \sqrt{\frac{\text{m. w. } CO}{\text{m. w. } O_2}} = \frac{0.0244}{0.0185}$$

$$\times \sqrt{\frac{20}{32}} = 1.23.$$

Diffusing capacity measured by whatever technique is subject to continuing scrutiny in efforts to define more precisely the significance of its measurement. The complexity of the problem is apparent if one recalls that the lung is not one alveolus, one capillary, one dead space and one venous admixture as idealized in fig. 51.2 but millions of alveolar-capillary relationships covering a spectrum of ventilation perfusion-relationships. Generally speaking, this spectrum is broader in disease than in health, further complicating the interpretation of measurements designed to clarify the status of the lung.

The concept of an alveolar-capillary "membrane" is itself deceptive. Oxygen and CO_2 diffuse through a number of layers in passing from air to hemoglobin or vice versa, including alveolar fluid, alveolar epithelium, tissue space between epithelium and capillary, capillary endothelium, plasma, red cell membrane and cytoplasm. There is evidence to suggest that the rate at which O_2 and CO combine with hemoglobin may limit Do_2 and Dco and that one therefore does not measure "membrane" properties so much as reaction rates. One can conceive of O_2 transfer from alveolar air to red blood cell as diffusion across a series of resistances, for Do_2 has the dimensions of Flow/Pressure and $1/Do_2$, therefore, the dimensions of Pressure/Flow or resistance. Roughton and Forster have subdivided total resistance into two resistances, one attributed to intracapillary processes (reaction rates with hemoglobin, diffusion in plasma and into red cell) and the other attributed to diffusion across the barriers separating air from plasma. Thus,

$$\frac{1}{D_L} = \frac{1}{Dm} + \frac{1}{\varnothing Vc}$$

where D_L is diffusing capacity of the lung, Dm is diffusion across "membranes," Vc is the capillary blood volume and $\varnothing$ is the amount of oxygen taken up per unit time per ml. blood of known hemoglobin concentration per ml. Hg Po_2. Experimental data suggest that the intracapillary component ($1/\varnothing Vc$) makes up a third or more of the total resistance. One of the interesting applications of this formulation is its use for measuring pulmonary capillary blood volume (Vc). Normal values are on the order of 60 to 110 ml.

Limitations and complexities not withstanding, however, it is clear that what diffusing capacity measures: (1) is reduced where histology of the lung suggests that the resistance to diffusion is increased by thickening or change in the characteristics of the layers separating alveolar gas from pulmonary capillary blood, and (2) varies directly with changes in size of the pulmonary-capillary surface area for diffusion.

Diffusion of CO_2

CO_2 is much more soluble in water than oxygen and its molecular weight is only slightly greater. A comparison of its diffusibility with that of oxygen is as follows:

$$\frac{D_{CO_2}}{D_{O_2}} = \frac{.592}{.0244} \times \sqrt{\frac{32}{44}} = 20.7.$$

Because of this greater diffusibility, end-capillary alveolar P_{CO_2} gradients are generally thought not to occur.

The dissociation curve for CO_2 is also very different from the oxyhemoglobin curve. Whereas the latter is nonlinear, the CO_2 curve is relatively linear within physiologic ranges of P_{CO_2} and CO_2 content. It was explained above that it is because of the nonlinearity of oxyhemoglobin dissociation that local differences in $P_{A_{O_2}}$ result in an alveolar-arterial P_{O_2} difference. Because CO_2 dissociation is more nearly linear, an alveolar-arterial P_{CO_2} difference from this cause is not likely to occur. Thus, neither a diffusion gradient nor a venous admixture effect influence alveolar-arterial partial pressure relationships. The validity of using arterial P_{CO_2} to measure alveolar P_{CO_2} rests on this statement.

Hypoxia

This chapter includes discussion of four different causes of low arterial P_{O_2} for a subject breathing room air at sea level: (1) alveolar hypoventilation, (2) increased anatomic shunts, e.g., right-to-left shunts in congenital heart disease, (3) ventilation-perfusion abnormalities increasing venous admixture, (4) increased resistance to diffusion. The following characteristics are helpful in distinguishing among these physiologically when they are present in pure form. Alveolar hypoventilation is invariably associated with elevated arterial and alveolar P_{CO_2} ; the other causes are not. Anatomic shunting is the only cause in which $P_{A_{O_2}}$ remains relatively low when the patient breathes air with a high P_{O_2}. The patient with hypoxia from a diffusion gradient commonly has a low alveolar P_{CO_2}, reflecting his attempt to raise alveolar P_{O_2} by increasing alveolar ventilation. His arterial P_{O_2} drops precipitously with exercise because the increased requirements for oxygen diffusion can be met only by steepening the P_{O_2} gradient across the alveolar-capillary walls. Moreover, his alveolar-arterial P_{O_2} difference remains high when he breathes an oxygen poor mixture. This procedure, however, lowers the alveolar-arterial P_{O_2} difference when venous admixture is the primary cause of hypoxia.

REFERENCES

FORSTER, R. E.: Exchange of gases between alveolar air and pulmonary capillary blood: Pulmonary diffusing capacity. Physiol. Rev., 1957, **37**, 391.

FOWLER, W. S. Intrapulmonary distribution of inspired gas. Physiol. Rev., 1, 1952, **32**, 1.

HENDERSON, Y. Adventures in Respiration. The Williams & Wilkins Co., Baltimore, 1938.

KROGH, M. Diffusion of gases through the lungs of man. J. Physiol., 1914–15, **49**, 271–300.

LILLIENTHAL, J. L., JR., RILEY, R. L., PROEMMEL, D. D., AND FRANKE, R. E. An experimental analysis in man of the oxygen pressure gradient from alveolar air to arterial blood during rest and exercise at sea level and at altitude. Am. J. Physiol., 1946, **147**, 199.

RAHN, H. AND FENN, W. O. A graphical analysis of the respiratory gas exchange. The Am. Physiol. Soc., Washington, D.C., 1955.

RILEY, R. L. AND COURNAND, A. "Ideal" alveolar air and the analysis of ventilation-perfusion relationships in the lungs. J. Appl. Physiol., 1949, **1**, 825.

RILEY, R. L. AND COURNAND, A. Analysis of factors affecting partial pressures of oxygen and carbon dioxide in gas and blood of lungs: Theory. J. Appl. Physiol., 1951, **4**, 77.

RILEY, R. L., COURNAND, A., AND DONALD, K. W. Analysis of factors affecting partial pressures of oxygen and carbon dioxide in gas and blood of lungs: Methods. J. Appl. Physiol., 1951, **4**, 102.

Monographs

BATES, D. V. AND CHRISTIE, R. V. Respiratory Function in Disease. W. B. Saunders Co., 1964.

COMROE, J. H. Physiology of Respiration. Year Book Medical Publishers, Inc., 1965.

DE REUCK, A. V. S. AND O'CONNOR, M. CIBA Foundation Symposium on Pulmonary Structure and Function. Little, Brown and Co., 1962.

CHAPTER 52

The Mechanics of Breathing

The mechanics of breathing have captured the interest of workers in both the basic sciences and clinic, important contributions having been made by both groups individually or working together. Fundamental concepts appeared in the German literature in the period 1915 to 1929 (Rohrer, et al.; Neergard and Wirz). Technical advances in simultaneously recording volumes, flows and small pressures with high fidelity have spurred rapid progress in this country and abroad, resulting in such feats as measuring the forces required for inflating the lung during the first breath of a newly born infant. Most prominently associated with this activity in this country have been groups originally associated with the Departments of Physiology at the University of Rochester, at the School of Public Health of Harvard University, and at the Graduate School of the University of Pennsylvania. Excellent reviews are included in four texts dealing with the respiratory system listed in the bibliography (Avery; Bates and Christie; Cherniak and Cherniak; Comroe, et al.)

The Muscles of Respiration

Supplying oxygen to the alveoli and removing carbon dioxide from the alveoli is accomplished by the flow of air in and out of the lungs with each breath. This is a mechanical process for which the muscles of respiration provide the force.

THE DIAPHRAGM

Quiet breathing results from alternate contraction and relaxation of the diaphragm and intercostal muscles. The former is attached circumferentially to fixed structures, vertebrae and sternum, and to relatively mobile structures, the lower ribs. It is normally dome-shaped (fig. 52.1), its fibers running nearly vertically upward near its periphery and horizontally at its tendinous central portion. Contraction during inspiration produces increased tension within itself and on its attachments. Its central tendon is therefore pulled down, increasing the vertical dimensions of the thorax, while the lower ribs are moved somewhat upward, increasing the lateral and anteroposterior dimensions of the lower chest.

The effectiveness of the diaphragm for changing the dimensions of the chest is related to the strength of its contraction and to its contour when relaxed. Strength of contraction, as in any muscle, is a function of the number of motor units activated and of the synchronization and frequency of their discharge. Interruption of both phrenic nerves immobilizes the diaphragm without changing its configuration. Increasing the circumference of the lower chest pathologically, as in obstructive pulmonary disease, flattens the diaphragm, consequently immobilizing it to varying degrees irrespective of how forcefully it contracts.

Descent of the diaphragm can be accomplished only by displacement of abdominal contents. This is made possible by relaxation of the muscles of the abdomen during inspiration. Although abdominal pressure does not normally interfere with the diaphragm's mobility, advanced pregnancy, extreme obesity, excessive flatulence, tight abdominal garments, and other circumstances can.

The diaphragm probably contributes more to inspiration than the intercostals. This statement rests on estimates of vertical displacement (about 1.5 cm.) and area (about 350 cm.²) of the diaphragm during quiet breathing. Since the volume of a single, quiet inspiration (tidal volume) is 500 to 700 ml., these estimates suggest that normal breathing is predominantly diaphragmatic. The relative proportions between diaphragmatic and intercostal contribution probably vary among different individuals and with different age groups. The ribs of infants, for example, are normally virtually horizontal. Inspiration must therefore result almost exclusively from increase in the vertical dimensions of the chest by contraction of the diaphragm.

THE INTERCOSTAL MUSCLES

The action of the diaphragm is straightforward and clearly inspiratory. The action of the muscles running between the ribs, however, is somewhat more complicated. The external intercostals run forward and downward whereas the internal intercostals run backward and downward, i.e., approximately at right angles to the external. Both groups originate and insert on adjacent ribs and can be expected to bring these ribs closer together

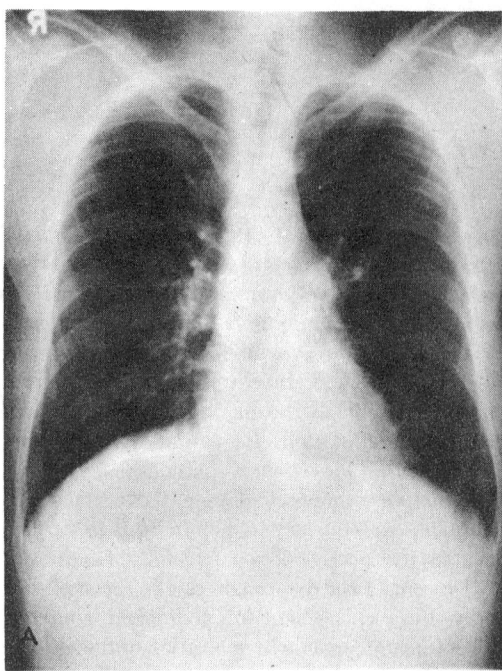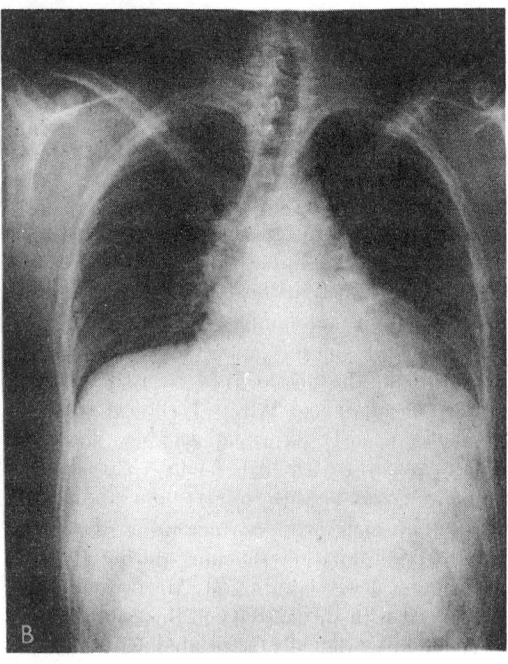

Fig. 52.1. Roentgenograms of the chest taken in the antero-posterior projection. Film on the left was taken after complete inspiration, when lungs contain the total lung capacity. Film on the right was taken after forced expiration, when lungs contain the residual volume. Note that the change in vertical dimensions of the chest is considerably greater than the change in transverse diameter.

when contracting. Whether a given rib moves upward, downward, or remains stationary, depends on the relative stability or fixation of adjacent ribs.

Inspiration is associated with electromyographic evidence of intercostal activity. The cephalad motion of the ribs indicates that the upper ribs are fixed relative to the lower. When contraction of the abdominal muscles fixes the lower ribs during cough or forced expiration, the rib cage moves down; and electromyography again shows intercostal activity. The intercostals contract during quiet inspiration, forced inspiration, and forced expiration, but not during quiet expiration (Campbell). Whether the internal and external groups have distinct functions in man is not clearly established.

Adequate breathing continues in the absence of either the diaphragm or the intercostals. In the absence of both, however, exogenous sources of power are usually needed for maintaining sufficient ventilation for life. Inasmuch as the intercostals and diaphragm are innervated from separate segments of the spinal cord (C3 and 4 for the phrenic nerves as compared to thoracic segments for intercostal nerves), paralysis of one is not necessarily associated with paralysis of the other.

THE MOTION OF THE RIBS

The ribs are more or less semicircular bones articulating with the vertebrae at one end and with the sternum or costal cartilages at the other. Rib motion, therefore, includes rotation around an axis joining these two points of attachment ("bucket-handle motion") (fig. 52.2). In addition, the motion of the ribs includes elevation and depression of the sternal end. Because this sternal end is lower than the vertebral end, elevating the shaft of the rib causes the sternum to protrude, increasing the anteroposterior diameter of the chest. Depression of the shaft of the rib correspondingly causes the opposite. Inspiration, therefore, is associated with an increase in the vertical diameter of the chest due to contraction of the diaphragm, with an increase in transverse diameter due to the "bucket-handle" action of the ribs, and with an increase in anteroposterior diameter due to the effect of rib motion on the sternum.

The motion of the ribs is not equivalent throughout the rib cage (fig. 52.2). The upper ribs are arcs of smaller circles and are more nearly horizontal than the lower ribs. Moreover, the lower ribs on inspiration are affected by displacement of all superior ribs; their motion is, therefore, the sum of the narrowing of many interspaces rather than only the adjacent one. Because of these differences, the changes in lateral diameter of the chest are greater in the lower than in the upper thorax (fig. 52.1).

As in the instance of the diaphragm, the contribution of costal motion to breathing depends on the force of intercostal contraction and on the position of the ribs prior to intercostal contraction. Accordingly, abnormal flaring or elevation of ribs and sternum interfere with the costal contribution to inspiration.

The Accessory Muscles

Electromyographic evidence from man and action potential recordings from the phrenic and intercostal nerves of animals indicate that: (a) quiet inspiration results from contraction of diaphragm and intercostals, and (b) quiet expiration occurs in the absence of any muscular contraction whatsoever. The accessory muscles are normally brought into play only for forced inspiration and expiration. Many such muscles could be listed. The distance runner struggling for air, for example, may use even the platysma for expanding his chest and the patient in paroxysms of cough probably contracts every muscle of trunk, thorax, and pectoral girdle during forced expiration. The principle accessory muscles, however, are the anterior neck muscles (sternocleidomastoids and scalenes), which are used during forced inspiration to stabilize and raise the first ribs and upper sternum, and the abdominal muscles, which are essential for forced expiration. The latter, together with the diaphragm, are used also for raising intra-abdominal pressure during defecation, urination, vomiting, parturition, cough, and the Valsalva maneuver. The patient with paralysis of abdominal muscles is therefore at a considerable disadvantage.

The Lung Volumes

The lungs and chest return passively to their original volume after inspiration. This end-expiratory volume is known as the functional residual capacity. It is the volume which reflects the equilibrium position of the chest and lungs when undisturbed by muscle contraction. It is also the volume into which each tidal volume is diluted during inspiration.

By adding the inspiratory capacity to this volume during a maximal inspiratory effort, the lung volume is increased by about $2\frac{1}{2}$ and contains the total lung capacity. On the other hand, delivering the expiratory reserve volume by forced

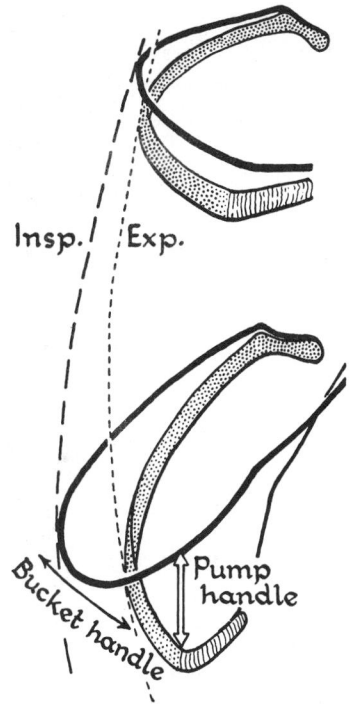

Fig. 52.2 Motion of upper and lower ribs. Solid outlines indicate position during inspiration. (From R. M. Cherniak and L. Cherniak, Respiration in health and disease, W. B. Saunders, 1961).

expiration reduces the end-expiratory volume by about one-half to the residual volume. The vital capacity is the volume which can be expired after a maximal inspiration by forceful expiration, i.e., it is the sum of the inspiratory capacity and the expiratory reserve. These relationshpis are shown in fig. 52.3.

The vital capacity and its subdivisions can be measured by collecting and measuring, in a spirometer, the volume of gas which flows into or out of the lungs during normal or forced inspiration and expiration. However, the residual volume, functional residual capacity, and total lung capacity cannot be directly recorded. These are commonly measured by "nitrogen wash-out" or "helium dilution." In "nitrogen wash-out" the subject is made to breathe nitrogen-free oxygen long enough (about seven minutes) to fully "wash-out" the nitrogen from his lungs. His expired air is collected, its volume is measured, and it is analyzed for concentration of nitrogen. The total amount of nitrogen collected is the product of the concentration and volume. Since the original concentration of nitrogen in the lungs is known (about 80%) the lung volume can be determined. Thus, if 50,000 cc. of expired air were collected over the seven-minute period and

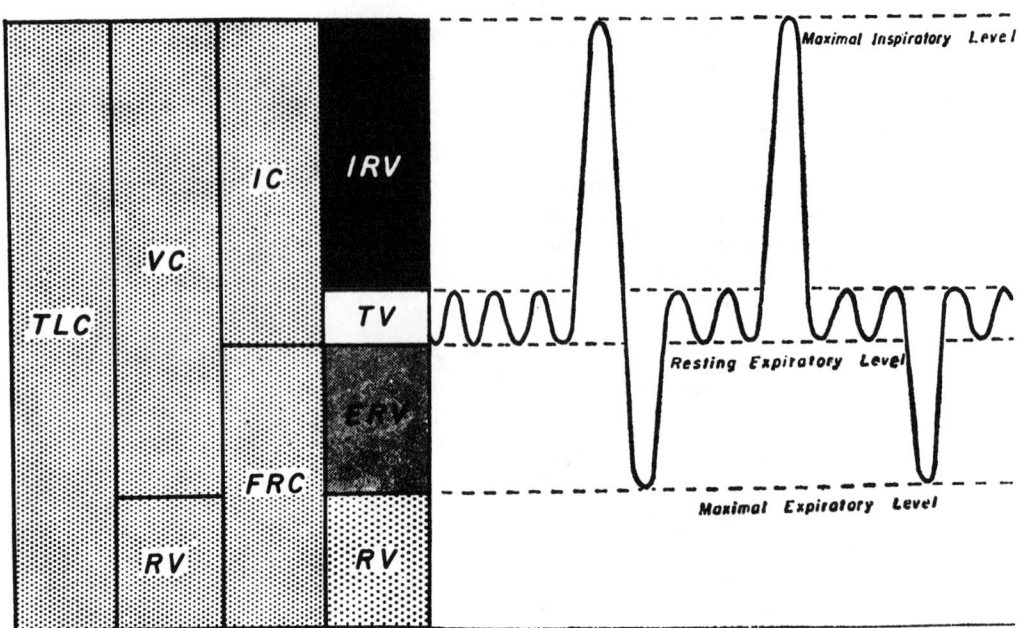

Fig. 52.3. The subdivisions of the total lung capacity. TLC = total lung capacity, VC = vital capacity, RV = residual volume, IC = inspiratory capacity, FRC = functional residual capacity, IRV = inspiratory reserve volume, TV = tidal volume, ERV = expiratory reserve volume. (From Comroe, et al. The Lung, Year Book Medical Publishers, Inc., Chicago, 1955.)

the concentration of nitrogen in the collected gas was 4%, the functional residual capacity would be $50,000 \times .04 \div .80$ or 2,500. Helium dilution is comparable in concept. A measurement is made of the dilution of helium which results from adding the volume of the lungs to a closed circuit containing a known amount of helium.

Whatever method is used, the functional residual capacity can be measured more reproducibly than the residual volume or total lung capacity because it is independent of muscular effort. The residual volume is usually calculated by subtracting the expiratory reserve from the functional residual capacity; the total lung capacity by adding the inspiratory capacity.

There are numerous normative data on lung volumes. One commonly used empiric prediction formula for adults is:

males, vital capacity = [27.63 − (0.112 × age)] × height in cms.;
females, vital capacity = [21.78 − (0.101 × age)] × height in cms.

These reflect the fact that vital capacity is related to age, sex, and height. A normal person's total lung capacity and residual volume can be estimated by knowing that the vital capacity comprises about 70% or 80% of the total lung capacity.

The vital capacity and total lung capacity are reduced by weakness of the normal and accessory muscles of inspiration and expiration, by immobilization of the ribs and sternum, or by space-occupying defects of the chest. The vital capacity is less in the supine position than in the upright position because the intrathoracic blood volume is increased in the supine position, displacing an equivalent volume of air.

The functional residual capacity is the volume to which the lungs and chest arrive in the absence of muscle contraction. It represents, therefore, an equilibrium position of the chest and lungs, intermittently disturbed by the forces of muscle contraction. Factors affecting this equilibrium and its disturbance are discussed below.

Pressures Required for Changes in Volume

The Lung

The chest wall, independent of the lung, and the lung itself are both hollow structures with elastic properties. Each has a certain volume when pressures inside and outside are equal and each responds to a distending or retracting force by a change in volume proportional to that force. The relationship between volume change and pressure required to inflate the lung alone is shown by the dotted line of fig. 52.4. It shows that the equilibrium volume of the lung, when no inflationary pressure is applied, is a small proportion of the total lung capacity (approaching 0 in the figure) and that increments in inflationary pressure produce specific increments of volume. The slope of this line indicates the compliance of the lung, i.e., the relationship between volume and pressure. Compliance is equal to the volume change in liters divided by pressure change in cms. of H_2O. Compliance decreases with inflation, indicating that as the lung inflates, progressively greater force is required for a given volume change. Under normal circumstances in man, it is not possible to measure the pulmonary compliance at volumes below the residual volume, for this would require opening the chest. Compliance is therefore usually measured over the relatively linear segment of the curve which includes the volumes of the lung during normal breathing, i.e., the functional residual capacity plus the tidal volume or more. Normal values in man are approximately 0.2 liters per cm. of H_2O.

The more a given lung is inflated the less is the compliance. It is less for small lungs than for large lungs (.0012 for rats as compared to .09 for dogs) and is reduced in man by circumstances which reduce the amount of lung, such as surgical removal of lung tissue. It is also reduced by change in the composition of lung tissue (pulmonary fibrosis) and progressively, with time, if the distension of the lung with each breath is unvarying.

The fact that compliance is less for small lungs than for large lungs, and less for a highly inflated lung than for less inflated lungs does not necessarily indicate fundamental differences in stiffness. True difference in elastic properties between one lung and another are reflected only when correction is made for differences in size or volume. One approach is to divide compliance by the functional residual capacity (so-called "specific" complicance); normal values in adults are between .05 and .06 liters per cc. of H_2O per liter. Another approach is to measure the increase in transpulmonary pressure required to inflate the lungs to a volume midway between any resting level and full inspiration; normal values in man are 7.58 ± 2.53 cms. of H_2O.

The Chest

The pressure-volume curve of the chest wall in the absence of the lung is displaced far to the left of the lung curve (fig. 52.4). This reflects the fact that the volume of the chest at a given distending pressure is considerably greater than the volume

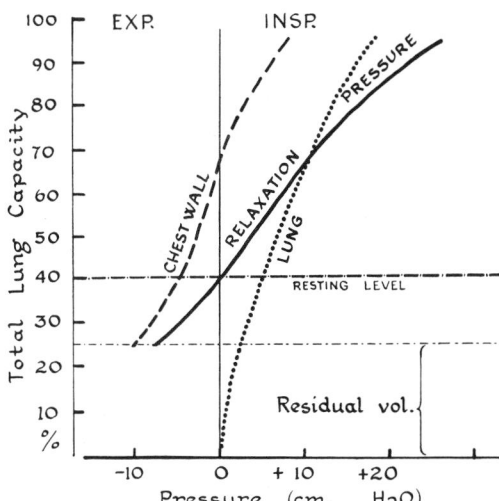

FIG. 52.4. Pressure-volume relationships of chest and lung in relaxed subject (relaxation pressure), in lung alone, and in chest wall alone. See text for explanation. (Adapted from H. Rahn, et al., Am. J. Physiol., **146:** 161, 1946).

of the lung at that pressure. Thus, although the volume of the lung when no pressure is applied is small, the volume of the chest is about 70% of the total lung capacity. It is necessary to apply negative pressure to the chest (inside negative with respect to outside) in order to reduce its volume to the functional residual capacity; positive pressure, on the other hand, (inside positive with respect to outside) is required for inflating the lung to the functional residual capacity. The compliance of the chest wall is about 0.2 l./cm. of H_2O.

The Lung and Chest

Up to this point, the lung and chest have been treated as separate structures. If the lung is now placed within the chest and its volume is to be the functional residual capacity, it will recoil and pull in on the chest with a force equal to the pressure required to distend it to the functional residual capacity (about 5 cms. of H_2O). This retracting force of the lung on the chest wall is the basis of negative (below atmospheric) pressure between the visceral and parietal pleurae (interpleural[1] "space"). As a result of it, the chest volume is less than it would be in the absence of the lung by a volume equal to the difference between

---

[1] "*Inter*pleural" is used here and subsequently to indicate between the visceral and parietal pleural surfaces. "*Intra*pleural" is more commonly used, referring to the pleural cavity. Inasmuch as there is normally no cavity or space as such, interpleural seems more appropriate.

the functional residual capacity and 70% of the total lung capacity.

The relaxation-pressure curve of an intact subject (fig. 52.4) depicts the relationship between pressure of air in the lungs and the volume of the lung-chest system when the subject is completely relaxed. The pressure is 0 at the functional residual capacity, for the elastic recoil of the lung is matched by an equal and opposite pull by the tensile properties of the relaxed chest wall. Increasing the volume of the chest and lung above the functional residual capacity requires increasing the air pressure. This pressure, or force, is equal to the force generated by contraction of the muscles of inspiration. Decreasing the volume of the chest and lung below the functional residual capacity requires reducing the intrapulmonary pressure below atmospheric pressure; this pressure is a measure of the force generated by the muscles of forced expiration. Fig. 52.4 shows that the force developed by the muscles of inspiration up to a volume comprising about 70% of the total lung capacity is expended only on the lungs. At higher volumes, however, force is needed both for expanding the lungs as well as the chest. During forced expiration, the energy of muscle contraction is expended exclusively on the chest wall. The compliance of the chest and lung (slope of the relaxation pressure curve) is about 0.1 l./cm. of H_2O, i.e., one-half the compliance of lung or chest individually.

It is apparent that the relationship between lung and chest can be compared to that between two opposing coiled springs whose equilibrium is disturbed in one direction or the other by a transient force equivalent to contraction of the muscles of respiration. The pressure which represents the recoil of the lung away from the chest wall (or the force required to keep the lung inflated at a given volume) can be measured in the intact chest by carefully placing a needle between the visceral and parietal pleurae, injecting a small bubble of air, and recording the pressure in the bubble with a manometer. It can be measured more conveniently and safely by measuring the pressure in a structure within the chest but outside the lungs. The esophagus is the most commonly used of these, pressure within it being recorded by having the subject swallow a small compliant balloon partially filled with air and recording the pressure within the balloon.

LUNG, CHEST, AND MUSCLE CONTRACTION

The maximum pressures which can be developed within the lungs by forcefully contracting the muscles of inspiration or expiration are shown in fig. 52.5. The expiratory pressures are greater as lung volume increases, partly because the muscles of forceful expiration are stretched to a length at which they can develop greater tension, and partly because the recoil of the lung-chest system toward a smaller volume is greatest when the chest and lung are fully expanded. The inspiratory pressures, represented by negative intrapulmonary pressure, are greater at low lung volumes because the muscles of inspiration are at a favorable portion of their length-tension relationship and because recoil of the chest toward a

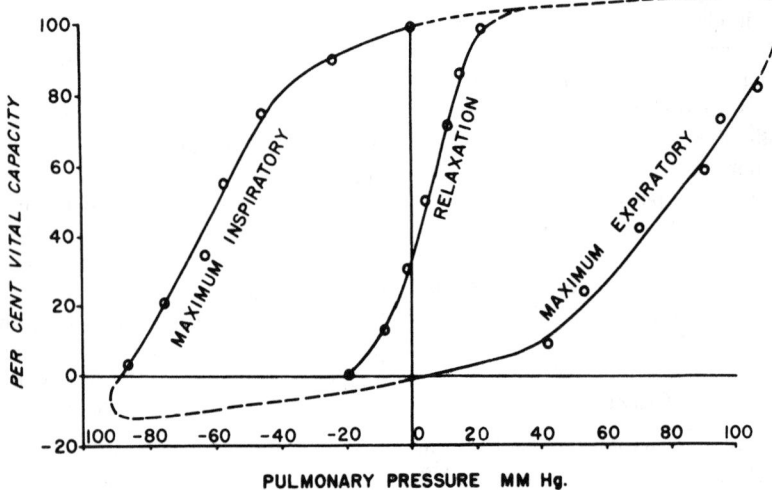

FIG. 52.5. Pressure-volume diagram of intact chest including the relaxation pressure curve (From Fenn, W. O., Am. J. Med. 10: 77, 1951).

more inflated state is maximal. The relative portion of the total pressure attributable to the muscle contraction and to recoil at each volume is represented by the difference between the relaxation pressure (recoil) and maximum pressure (recoil plus muscle contraction).

Ventilation

The volumes and pressures discussed in the previous section are independent of air flow or time. Ventilation has the dimensions of both volume and time. Normal ventilation in resting day-old infants (2.5 kg.) is about 500 ml. per min., with a respiratory rate of about 33 breaths per min. and a tidal volume of 15 ml. By adulthood (70 kg.) normal ventilation has increased to about 6,000 ml. per min., at a respiratory rate of

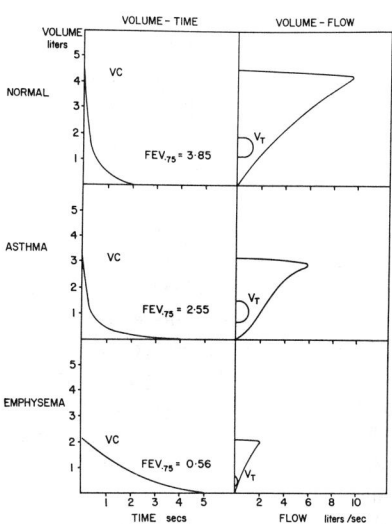

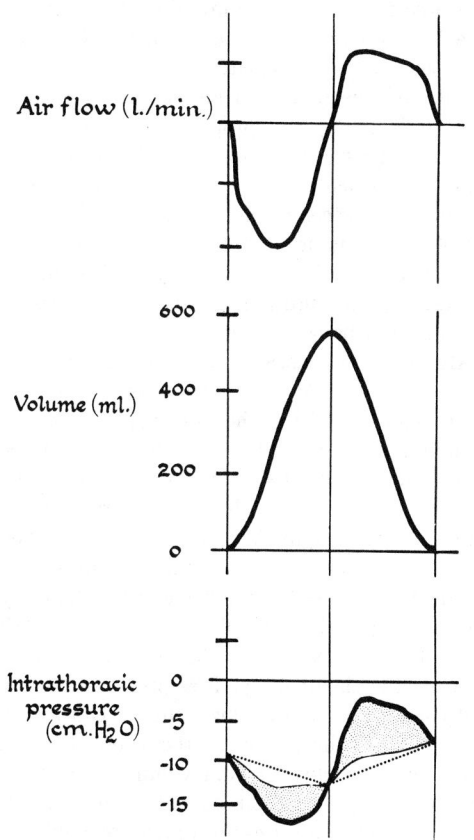

Fig. 52.6 One breathing cycle showing air flow, one tidal volume and intrathoracic pressures on simultaneous ordinates. Inspiration is indicated by downward deflection on flow tracing and upward deflection on volume record. See text for subdivision of intrathoracic pressure record. (From R. M. Cherniak and L. Cherniak, Respiration in Health and Disease, W. B. Saunders, 1961).

Fig. 52.7 Volume of air forcefully exhaled after maximal inspiration. Abscissa is time on left half of figure and flow on right half. VC = vital capacity, VT = tidal volume, FEV.75 = forced expiratory volume in .75 seconds: 1) Flow normally slows progressively as volume decreases, 2) peak flows attainable in asthma and emphysema are low, 3) flows during tidal ventilation are a small fraction of peak flows in normal individuals but a large fraction in emphysema, 4) because the functional residual capacity is so elevated, the patient with emphysema has a much reduced reserve of volume to which to inflate his lungs for attempting to increase flow. (From D. V. Bates and R. V. Christie, Respiratory Function in Disease, W. B. Saunders, 1964).

12 breaths per min. and a tidal volume of 500 ml. Thus, the infant ventilates about 200 ml. per min. per kg. as compared to less than one-half this amount in an adult.

The flow of air into and out of the lung varies from instant to instant during normal breathing (fig. 52.6). If one inspires maximally to the total lung capacity and then expires as forcefully as possible, the plot of volume and flow rate as functions of time appears as in fig. 52.7 (normal). One can calculate from such tracings that the maximum expiratory flow rate exceeds 400 l. per sec. and the proportion of the vital capacity exhaled in one sec., two sec., and three sec. exceeds 83%, 92%, and 97% respectively. These values are all used in comparing normal and abnormal patterns of ventilation. They are low where airway diameter is reduced, asthma and emphysema being the classic examples of obstructive respiratory abnormality (fig. 52.7).

Pressures Required for Ventilation

AIR FLOW

Ventilation, or air flow in and out of the lungs, occurs as a result of a pressure difference between the alveolar and oral ends of the airways. During normal inspiration, the pressure of air in the alveoli falls transiently below atmospheric pressure. It equals atmospheric pressure at the end of inspiration and rises above atmospheric pressure during expiration. The velocity of air flow is proportional to the pressure difference. The relationship between pressure difference and flow depends on the type of flow. Two types or patterns are commonly recognized, laminar flow and turbulent flow. The equation for laminar flow is expressed in Poiseuille's law, in which the pressure (P) difference between the two ends of a tube through which there is flow is directly proportional to the volume flowing per unit time (Q), to the viscosity of the fluid (v), to the length of the tube (L) and inversely related to the fourth power of the radius (r):

$$P_1 - P_2 = \frac{Q8LV}{2\pi r^4} .$$

It is apparent from this equation that pressure is extremely sensitive to radius, a 2-fold decrease in radius of an airway, for example, requiring a 16-fold increase in pressure if flow is to remain constant. It is also apparent that pressure is directly and simply related to flow, e.g. doubling pressure doubles flow ($P_1 - P_2 = KQ$) in which K is a constant incorporating the other terms.

As flow increases in a tube of given dimension, a rate is reached at which the flow pattern ceases to be laminar and becomes turbulent. Turbulence occurs when the product of density (d), linear velocity (V), and diameter (D) divided by viscosity (v) exceeds 2,000.

$$\text{Reynolds number} = \frac{dVD}{v} .$$

The relationship between pressure and flow in the presence of turbulence is exponential, pressure being related not simply to the velocity of flow but to the square of velocity, e.g., doubling flow requires a four-fold increase in pressure:

$$(P_1 - P_2 = KQ^2)$$

Calculations of Reynolds numbers in different parts of the airways suggest that flow is predominantly laminar during quiet breathing but predominantly turbulent during even moderate hyperventilation. Inasmuch as turbulence is favored not only by the factors included in calculating the Reynolds number but also by irregularities and branching of tubes, it is reasonable to assume that even during quiet breathing the pressures for moving air are required for both laminar and turbulent flows. It is estimated that about 10% of flow resistance is due to turbulence during quiet breathing.

RESISTANCE TO AIR FLOW

$$\text{Resistance} = \frac{\text{pressure}}{\text{flow}} = \frac{\text{cms. H}_2\text{O}}{\text{l. per sec.}}$$

Flow resistive pressures of the airways can be measured if flow and pressure difference between alveoli and environment are known. Regional resistances at intermediate points between the alveoli and the room can also be determined if pressure is known at appropriate sites. By measuring pressures in the pharynx with a small balloon, in the trachea by inserting a needle between the first and second tracheal rings, and in the alveoli by an indirect method described below, oral or nasal resistances, pharyngeal-laryngeal resistances, and intrapulmonary airway resistances can all be calculated.

Alveolar pressures are measured with a body plethysmograph. A subject is enclosed in an airtight chamber and breathes into and out of this chamber. The air within the chamber will be compressed and its pressure will rise whenever the external dimensions of the chest increase more rapidly than an equivalent volume of air is taken from the chamber into the lungs. This occurs during inspiration when the fall in intrapulmonary pressure required for air flow is associated with rarefaction of gases within the lung until flow of air from the chamber equalizes pressures in lung and chamber at a new lung volume. During expiration, the dimensions of the chest decrease more rapidly than the tidal volume is exhaled; the chamber pressure consequently falls as intrapulmonary pressure rises until pressure equilibration is again restored at the end of expiration. The plethysmographic pressure, therefore, reflects intrapulmonary pressure, the precise relationship being defined by calibration. An equivalent experiment can be conducted recording volume change in the plethysmograph at constant pressure rather than pressure at constant volume. Resistances can be calculated if instantaneous flow is recorded simultaneously with pressure.

Normal values (cms. of H_2O/l./sec.) for total airway resistance during panting are 1.50 ± .49 cms. of H_2O/l./sec. Normal values during quiet breathing are 1.26 ± .39. Resistances for women are about 20% higher than for men, presumably because the airways of women are narrower.

About 20% of the oral-alveolar air flow resistance can be attributed to flow through the mouth, 27% to flow through the glottis and larynx, and about 53% to flow through the airways below the second tracheal cartilage. During quiet breathing through the nose, on the other hand, the nasal passages contribute about two-thirds of the total air flow resistance. Resistance offered by the larynx and glottis during normal expiration is about twice its value in inspiration. Resistances are least, therefore, during inspiration, using oral rather than nasal breathing and in men rather than women.

Resistance of Lung (Viscous Resistance)

Alveolar pressures during ventilation are reflected in interpleural pressures. In addition, however, interpleural pressures register the force required for overcoming the viscous resistance of the lung. This latter has been estimated variously to comprise a negligible to substantial (28%, 21%, and 30% to 40%) proportion of the total pulmonary resistance, i.e., air flow resistance plus tissue viscous resistance. Although this figure, as many others concerning respiratory mechanics, are educated approximations, it is clear that interpleural pressure during ventilation represents: (a) compliant characteristics of the lung, (b) air flow resistances through the respiratory tract, and (c) tissue resistance of the lung.

These three components of the total pressure difference between atmosphere and esophagus are represented in fig. 52.6 (intrathoracic pressure). The elastic component is indicated by the thin solid line. It is not a straight line (cf. dotted line) because the relationship between lung volume and time is not linear. The shaded portion is the additional pressure required for air flow and tissue components. It is higher during expiration than during inspiration because air flow resistance is higher.

Resistance of Chest (Viscous Resistance)

Resistance of tissues of the chest have also been estimated. Thirty per cent to 40 per cent of the total respiratory resistance is attributed to

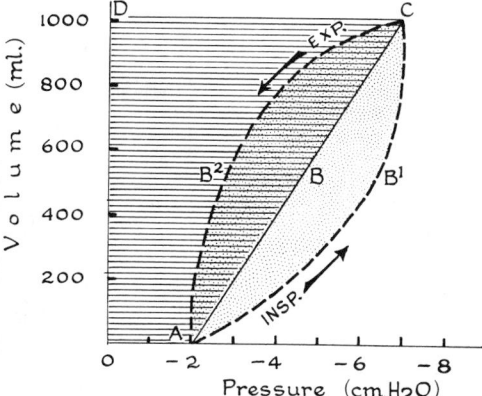

Fig. 52.8. The relationship between lung volume and transpulmonary pressure during one inspiration and expiration of 1,000 ml. See text for explanation. (From R. M. Cherniak and L. Cherniak, Respiration in Health and Disease, W. B. Saunders, 1961).

this source both during quiet oral breathing (0.4 l./sec.) and during mild hyperventilation (flows of 1 l./sec.) (fig. 52.8).

Inertia of Air, Lung, and Chest

The final component of the total mechanical force for respiration, inertia, has been measured for lung and air. At atmospheric pressure, a force of only approximately 0.01 cm. of water is required to produce a volume acceleration of 1 l./sec./sec. Clearly, this is a small component of the forces required for ventilation.

The Work of Breathing

The chest and lungs are a pump operating against resistances to generate the pressures outlined above. The concept of work is useful in expressing the energy required or expended for breathing.

$$\text{Work} = \text{force} \times \text{distance}.$$

Force is equivalent to pressure (cm. of water), and volume (ml.) to distance, i.e., ventilating 1 l. of air with a force of 1 cm. of water pressure is equivalent to moving 1 ml. of water (1 g.) 1,000 cm. or doing 1 g.-m. of work.

The total work of breathing has been estimated by placing a relaxed subject in a respirator and continuously measuring the pressure gradient between mouth and outside of the patient's body simultaneously with volume. At a tidal volume of 500 ml. and a frequency of 15 breaths per min., the work on the lungs, chest, abdomen, and air was approximately 0.32 kg.-m./min. The work

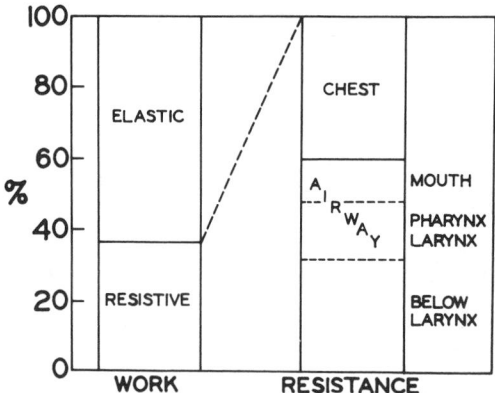

FIG. 52.9. Subdivision of respiratory work and resistance. Values for work bar for subject breathing 15 breaths per min. at a tidal volume of 500 ml. Values for resistance bar for subject breathing through mouth. Viscous resistance of lung was assumed to be 0. (See text.)

done to stretch chest and lungs, i.e. elastic work, was about 63% of the total work (fig. 52.8).

The work of breathing can be conceptualized by graphic representation. The work done on the lungs during a single breath is shown in fig. 52.9. Oral-esophageal pressure difference is plotted on the horizontal axis and volume at any pressure on the vertical axis. Point A is the plot of pleural pressure at the end of expiration when flow is 0, and volume is the functional residual capacity. Point C plots pleural pressure at the end of inspiration when flow is 0 again, and volume is the functional residual capacity plus 1,000 ml. The line AC is, therefore, the compliance of the lung. It is assumed to be straight because compliance is relatively linear over this range of lung volumes. The elastic work (pressure × volume) done on the lungs is represented by the area of the trapezoid $ABCDO$.

The pressures actually recorded during a breathing cycle are indicated by the loop AB^1CB^2. The area AB^1CB represents the nonelastic, i.e., flow resistive, work done on the lungs and air during inspiration. The area CB^2AB represents the nonelastic work done on lungs and air during passive expiration. This is a portion of the elastic energy stored in the lungs at the end of inspiration. The balance of the elastic energy, AB^2CDO, is not recovered during expiration and in this sense is "lost," possibly as heat.

The shape of the loop AB^1CB^2 reflects nonelastic pressures. It is, therefore, broad or more circular when flow rate is high (hyperventilation) or resistance increased (airway narrowing). Because

the force required to stretch the lungs (elastic properties) is independent of the rate at which the lung is inflated, progressively increasing rates of ventilation augment flow-resistive work without affecting elastic work. Increased depth of breathing, on the other hand, increases elastic work, particularly since compliance decreases at higher lung volumes.

Breathing is most economical when the balance of elastic and resistive work yields the lowest sum compatible with ventilation sufficient to meet the body's metabolic requirements. It might be assumed that this would result in low tidal volumes and rapid breathing rates, for this type of breathing would sharply reduce elastic work. However, as will be brought out later, carbon dioxide excretion and oxygen supply are a function not of total ventilation but of alveolar ventilation. A tidal volume equal to the dead space (150 ml.), for example, might accomplish a normal total ventilation (6 l./min.) at minimal elastic work but would be entirely wasted because no carbon dioxide would be excreted and alveolar oxygen pressure would not be maintained. It is one of the important facts of biologic economy that quiet respiration is accomplished at a tidal volume and frequency such that the sum of elastic and flow resistive work at an adequate alveolar ventilation is minimal. This has been shown for man as well as for other animals.

The work of breathing can be expressed in terms of oxygen utilization. This is about 0.5 ml. of oxygen per liter of ventilation in normal individuals. At a normal ventilation of 6 l./min. this is equivalent to 3 ml./min. or about 1% of normal total requirements (300 ml./min.). The oxygen cost increases with ventilation in a nonlinear manner, indicating progressively rising cost with the hyperventilation of exercise. One estimate of oxygen utilization for breathing during severe exercise at a ventilation of 160 l./min. is 406 ml./min.

Patients with obstructive disease expend a considerably larger proportion of their basal energy for breathing and are at a particular disadvantage when faced with the need for increasing ventilation. The work of breathing in these patients may be so increased that the muscles of respiration produce more carbon dioxide during increased ventilation than is eliminated by the increment in alveolar ventilation. A rise in the carbon dioxide retained within the body results. This consideration of respiratory work indicates the gravity of the problem faced by the patient with obstructive respiratory disease.

EFFICIENCY

The efficiency of the muscles of respiration can be calculated from the work they perform and the oxygen cost of doing this work:

$$\text{Efficiency} = \frac{\text{mechanical work}}{\text{oxygen used}}$$

Values for mechanical work are about .03 kg.-m./l. as compared to .6 kg.-m./l. for the work equivalent of oxygen utilization. The efficiency, therefore, is about 5%. This low mechanical efficiency indicates that most of the energy for respiration is in the form of heat.

Interpleural Pressures

The pressure within the chest but outside the lungs measures both the elastic recoil of the lungs and the flow-resistance of air and lungs. It is, therefore, most negative at high volumes, high inspiratory flow rates, and high inspiratory resistances. It is subatmospheric throughout inspiration and expiration (fig. 52.6) except when the energy stored in the lungs at the end of inspiration is inadequate for the work of expiration. This occurs during forced expiration, cough, sneeze, and expiration through narrowed airways. In these instances, active work is done during expiration which must be added to the work of inspiration for calculating the total work of breathing. It would appear graphically as an area extending to the left of the vertical axis in fig. 52.9.

The fact that interpleural pressure is subatmospheric has important implications. There will be flow into the thorax from any site at or above atmospheric pressure provided a flow-way is present. Accordingly, air flows into the chest from the atmosphere and creates an interpleural space (pneumothorax) when the chest wall is perforated; venous blood flows toward the thorax and right auricle down the pressure gradient from abdomen or other body part to the chest. This gradient with respect to the abdomen is increased during inspiration not only because intrathoracic pressure falls, but because the descent of the diaphragms raises abdominal pressure by a few centimeters of water above atmospheric pressure. Reducing or reversing this gradient by performing the Valsalva maneuver can compromise venous return sufficiently to cause hypotension and syncope.

Another important indirect consequence of negative interpleural pressure concerns its effect on the patency of airways. To the extent that these are exposed to interpleural pressures, they are subjected to a transmural force. This force is a distending force at high lung volumes and rapid inspiration, a weaker distending force during passive expiration as interpleural pressure falls, and a compressing force during forceful or high resistance expiration when interpleural pressure rises above atmospheric pressure.

The pressure gradient across the airway wall depends not only on interpleural pressure but also on the pressure within the airway. This is atmospheric when there is no air flow and the glottis is open. During ventilation, it is most nearly atmospheric in the larger airways closer to the atmosphere and most nearly interpleural in the finer airways farther downstream on inspiration and farther upstream on expiration. Accordingly, the airways subjected to the greatest transmural pressures are the larger ones. Providing these with supporting cartilage is, therefore, good teleology. Despite their cartilaginous support, however, these can be shown roentgenographically to undergo visible narrowing during forced expiration—a change which increases flow resistance.

Airway patency is preserved not only by negative interpleural pressure and by cartilage, but by radial traction from the elastic tissue within which the airways are suspended. This traction is a function of the relationship between length and tension of the lungs' elastic fabric, the number of elastic strands pulling on the airway per unit area of surface, and the degree to which the lung is stretched (lung volume). The significance of this support is shown in normal breathing by progressive slowing of air flow during forced expiration (fig. 52.7), indicating narrowing of the airways as lung volume decreases. This narrowing is particularly pronounced in emphysema (fig. 52.7) where loss of elastic properties of lung tissue and the thinning out of parenchymal strands surrounding airways predisposes them to collapse especially during expiration. This may be so pronounced that air flow ceases during expiration at lower volumes no matter the force with which the muscles of expiration contract. A vicious cycle results: as expiratory effort increases, interpleural pressure rises, airways undergo additional compression, and airflow is further slowed. Breathing at pathologically high lung volumes, one of the hallmarks of obstructive abnormality, is a logical recourse.

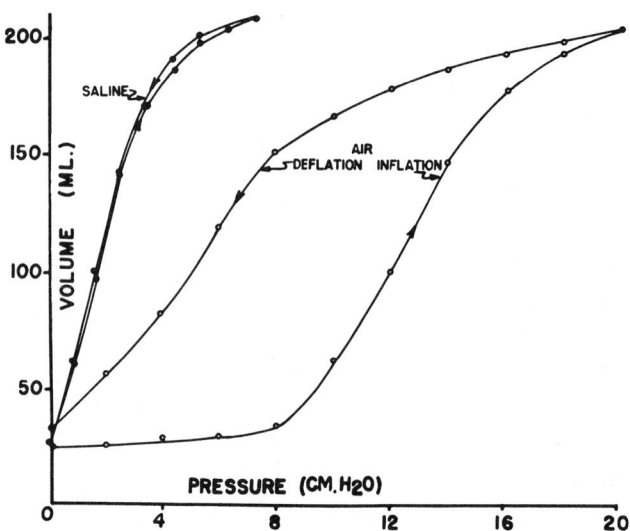

FIG. 52.10. Air versus saline filling, excised cat lungs at room temperature. Saline curves obtained from excised gas-free cat lungs suspended in saline bath at room temperature and filled from a saline reservoir. Air curves taken from the gas-free state, obtained with the lungs hanging in air and filled from an air reservoir maintained at a constant pressure. Volumes all taken relative to the initial volume of the lungs as removed from the animal. During inflation with air the volume equilibrated slowly and the lungs filled irregularly. During deflation, equilibrium was reached rapidly and the lungs emptied uniformly. (From E. P. Radford, in Tissue Elasticity, p. 185, Am. Physiol. Society, 1957).

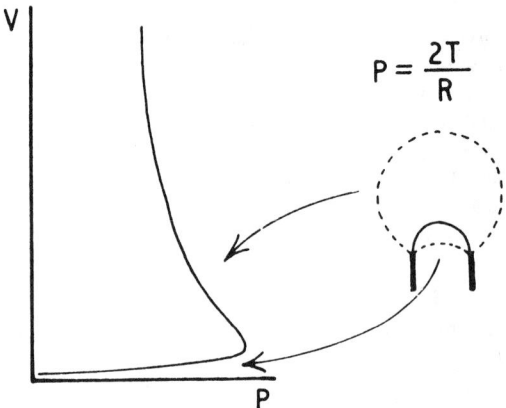

$$P = \frac{2T}{R}$$

FIG. 52.11. Volume-pressure curve for a bubble on a tube. As pressure rises, volume changes little until a critical point is reached, at which volume increases without further pressure rise. This point is reached when radius of curvature (R) passes through a minimum value equal to the radius of the tube. Thereafter, at a constant tension (T) in the wall of the bubble, pressure falls as radius or volume of the bubble increases. Alveoli of the deflated lung "pop" open when the lung is gradually inflated as though following this law. (From J. Mead, The mechanics of respiratory structures in the Ciba Symposium on Pulmonary Structure and Function. Reuck and O'Connor, Little, Brown and Co., Boston, 1962).

Hysteresis and Surface Activity

The change in volume of the lung with pressure has been described during inspiration (fig. 52.4). During expiration, when the lung is allowed to deflate, the curve of its volume-pressure behavior does not retrace itself, but is displaced to the left forming a loop (fig. 52.10). The area of this loop represents an amount of energy which is unaccounted for (hysteresis), i.e., at any volume the product of volume and pressure is less on expiration than during inspiration. The explanation for this "loss" is unclear. It is related, however, to a force, surface tension, present at the interface of air and the fluid lining the alveolar walls. This is clearly shown in fig. 52.10 in which the normal hysteresis of air-filled lungs is seen to be virtually eliminated by substituting saline for air. Some of the concepts relating to this important observation are the following.

The lung is comprised of several million more or less polygonal or spherical alveoli interconnected by tubes. It is tempting, therefore, to assume that some properties of the lung compare to those of a physical model made of a T-tube with an inflated bubble or balloon at each end of the top of the T. If the bubbles or balloons are inflated so that the pressure (P) is uniform throughout and if the stem of the T is then clamped off, one balloon or bubble may empty into the other rather than remain inflated. The reason for this instability of the system is explained by the relationship between pressure (P), intramural tension (T), and radius of curvature (r) of curved surfaces. This is stated in the La-Place equation: $P = (2T/r)$. If one assumes that at inflation the tension within the walls of the bubbles and the radii of curvature are precisely equal, the bubbles will both remain inflated. If, however, the radius of one bubble decreases slightly, the pressure in this one will rise if intramural tension remains constant and air will flow into the other bubble whose radius will increase, lowering its pressure (fig. 52.11). This phenomenon is not normally seen in the lung, i.e., once the lung is inflated, it remains so throughout rather than collapse in one area (atelectasis) and over-inflate in another.

The stability of the lung is partly due to the fact that intramural tension (T) is small for the surfaces of the alveoli. This property is attributed to a substance in the fluid lining the air spaces which reduces surface tension. The bubble of fluid which opens up into the airway is, therefore, low in its intramural tension and therefore low in its tendency to contract or deflate.

A substance with surface tension reducing properties appears to be a normal constituent of lung tissue extracts. Such extracts have a surface tension approximately $\frac{1}{10}$ the surface tension of water and $\frac{1}{40}$ the surface tension of other body fluids. Phospholipids or lipoproteins have been implicated, lecithin being specifically identified among this group of compounds. Extracts from lungs of children suffering from inability to maintain the inflation of their lungs (respiratory distress syndrome) are deficient in this surface active agent.

Not only do the surface active materials decrease surface tension, but they decrease it more when surface area is small than when it is large. Surface tension is consequently less in small alveoli than in large ones. Assuming alveoli change in size during inspiration and expiration, surface tension is less at the end of expiration than at the end of inspiration. This decrease in surface tension with deflation and size balances the increase in pressure one would anticipate from the LaPlace equation if surface tension remained constant and radius decreased. Stability is promoted, therefore, both because surface tension is generally reduced and because it adjusts itself to surface area.

It appears, therefore, that the mechanical properties of alveoli reflect those of at least two concentric layers: one is a film characterized by surface activity which normally stabilizes the air spaces of inflated lung and has its own pressure volume characteristics on inflation and deflation; the other is the alveolar epithelium together with the collagen, elastin, and other tissue possessing its independent mechanical attributes.

The First Breath

Breathing motions of a sort go on *in utero*, for material injected into the amniotic fluid can be recovered from the lungs after birth. Therefore the lungs contain fluid before the first breath. The following are some of the mechanical considerations pertaining to their dramatic change to organs of respiration.

To the extent that the spaces of the lung are distended with fluid, the pressure required for expansion conceivably is less, for some of the smaller airways will have a larger radius and, by the LaPlace equation, will enlarge with less pressure. In point of experimental fact, lungs containing some fluid expand at a lower pressure than airless lungs containing no added fluid.

The chest is compressed by pressures up to 95 cm. of H_2O during vaginal delivery. Some fluid is expressed from the lungs by this force in babies born with cephalic presentations. The balance of fluid must pass into the circulation either directly across the alveolar epithelium into the pulmonary capillaries or indirectly through the lung lymphatics into the systemic circulation.

The change from the airless to air filled state is precipitous; it occurs in less than one second after onset of breathing. The functional residual capacity at 10 min. of age is about 17 ml./kg., is about 30 ml./kg. after 30 min., and is at this same value four days later. Interpleural pressures recorded through an esophageal balloon during the first inspiration vary from -10 to -70 cm. of H_2O. The first expiration is associated with positive interpleural pressures as high as 20 cm. of H_2O. Presumably these pressures are the result primarily of diaphragmatic and abdominal muscle contraction.

REFERENCES

ADRIAN, E. D. AND BRONK, D. W. The discharge of impulses in motor nerve fibers. J. Physiol. (Lond.), 1929, **67**, 119.

AVERY, M. E. The Lung and Its Disorders in the Newborn Infant. W. B. Saunders Co., Phila. and London. 1964.

AVERY, M. E., FRANK, N. R., AND GRIBETZ, I. The inflationary force produced by pulmonary vascular distention in excised lungs. J. Clin. Invest., 1959, **38**, 456.

BALDWIN, E. DE F., COURNAND, A. AND RICHARDS, D. W., JR. Pulmonary insufficiency: 1. Methods of analysis, physiologic classification, standard values in normal subjects. Medicine, 1948, **27**, 243.

BATES, D. V. AND CHRISTIE, R. V.: Respiratory Function in Disease. W. B. Saunders. 1964.

BRONK, D. W. AND FERGUSON, L. K.: The nervous control of intercostal respiration. Amer. J. Physiol., 1935, 110, 700.

BUYTENDIJK, H. J.: Oesophagusdruck en Longelasticiteit. Thesis, University of Groningen, 1949, Groningen, Oppenheim, 1949.

CAMPBELL, E. J. MORAN: The Respiratory Muscles and the Mechanics of Breathing. Lloyd-Luke, Ltd. 1958.

CHERNIAK, R. M. AND CHERNIAK, L.: Respiration in Health and Disease. W. B. Saunders. 1962.

COMROE, J. H., JR., FORSTER, R. E., DU BOIS, A. B., BRISCOE, W. A., AND CARLSEN, E.: The Lung. 2nd Ed., Yearbook Publishers, Inc. 1962.

CROSFILL, M. L. AND WIDDICOMBE, J. G.: Physical characteristics of the chest and lungs and the work of breathing in different mammalian species. J. Physiol. (Lond.), 1961, 158, 1.

DAYMEN, H.: Mechanics of air flow in health and in emphysema. J. Clin. Invest., 1951, 30, 1175.

DU BOIS, A. B., BOTHELHO, S. Y., AND COMROE, J. H., JR.: A new method for measuring airway resistance in man using a body plethysmograph: Values in normal subjects and in patients with pulmonary disease. J. Clin. Invest., 1956, 35, 327.

FAWCITT, J., LIND, J., AND WEGELIUS, C.: The first breath. Acta Paediat. (Suppl. 123), 1960, 49, 5.

FENN, W. O.: Mechanics of respiration. Am. J. Med., 1951, 10, 77.

FERRIS, B. G., JR. AND POLLARD, D. S.: Effect of deep and quiet breathing on pulmonary compliance in man. J. Clin. Invest., 1960, 39, 143.

FERRIS, B. G., JR., MEAD, J., AND OPIE, L. H.: Partitioning of respiratory flow resistance in man. J. App. Physiol., 1964, 19, 653.

FRANK, N. R., MEAD, J., SIEBENS, A. A., AND STOREY, C. F.: Measurements of pulmonary compliance in seventy healthy young adults. J. Appl. Physiol., 1956, 9, 38.

JAEGER, M. J. AND OTIS, A. B.: Measurement of airway resistance with a volume displacement body plethysmograph. J. Appl. Physiol., 1964, 19, 813.

KARLBERG, P., CHERRY, R. B., ESCARDO, F. E., AND KOCH, G.: Respiratory studies in newborn infants. II. Pulmonary ventilation and mechanics

of breathing in the first minutes of life, including the onset of respiration. Acta Paediat., 1962, 51, 121.

MARSHALL, R. AND DU BOIS, A. B.: Measurement of the viscous resistance of the lung tissues in normal man. Clin. Sci., 1946, 15, 161.

McILROY, W. B., MEAD, J., SILVERSTONE, N. J., AND RADFORD, E. P., JR.: Measurement of lung tissue viscous resistance using gases of equal kinematic viscosity. J. Appl. Physiol., 1955, 7, 485.

MEAD, J.: Measurement of inertia of the lungs at increased ambient pressure. J. Appl. Physiol., 1956, 9, 208.

MEAD, J.: Volume displacement plethysmograph for respiratory measurements in human subjects. J. Appl. Physiol., 1960, 15, 736.

MEAD, J.: Mechanical properties of lungs. Physiol. Rev., 1961, 41, 281.

MEAD, J.: Mechanics of respiratory structures, in "Ciba Foundation Symposium on Pulmonary Structure and Function." P. 111. (ed. A. V. S. DE REUCK AND M. O'CONNOR.) Little, Brown and Co. 1962.

NEERGAARD, K. V. AND WIRZ, K.: Über eine Methode fur Messung der Lungen elastizität am lebenden Menschen, insbesondere beim Emphysem. Z. Klin. Med., 1927, 105, 35.

NEERGAARD, K. V. AND WIRZ, K.: Die Messung der Strömungswiderstände in den Atemwegen des Menschen, insbesondere bei Asthma und Emphysem. Z. Klin. Med., 1927, 105, 51.

OTIS, A. B.: The work of breathing. Physiol. Rev., 1954, 34, 449.

PATTLE, R. E.: The lining layer of the lung alveoli. Brit. Med. Bull., 1963, 19, 41.

RADFORD, E. P., JR.: Recent studies of mechanical properties of mammalian lungs, in "Tissue Elasticity." P. 177. (ed. REMINGTON, J. W.) Am. Physiol. Soc., Washington, D. C. 1957.

ROHRER, F., NAKESONE, K., AND WIRZ, K.: Physiologie der Atembewegung, in "Handbuch der Normalen und Pathologischen Physiologie II" P. 70. Berlin: Springer. 1925.

SALAZER, E. AND KNOWLES, J. H.: An analysis of pressure-volume characteristics of the lungs. J. App. Physiol., 1964, 19, 97.

SMITH, C. A.: The Physiology of the Newborn Infant. Chas. C Thomas, Springfield, Ill. 1959.

Chapter 53

The Control of Breathing

Control of Inspiration and Expiration

As described in chapter 51, inspiration during eupnea is accomplished by contraction of certain muscles, such as the diaphragm and interosseus external intercostals, which may be called *primary* muscles of inspiration; while expiration is the result of the elastic recoil of the lungs and thoracic cage, and the action of gravity when the inspiratory muscles relax. With increased demands for ventilation, additional muscles, collectively called *accessory* muscles of inspiration, are activated to produce a more rapid and deeper inspiration; certain muscles also contract during expiration to accelerate the return of the chest to the resting end-expiratory position. In eupneic breathing, therefore, for inspiration and expiration to occur it is necessary simply for the motor neurons supplying the primary muscles of inspiration to show intermittent bursts of activity.

The initial observation which is important in considering regulation of breathing is that apnea occurs when the CO_2 tension of the blood is below certain levels if at the same time the O_2 tension is above certain levels. This situation can be produced simply by hyperventilating with atmospheric air, or an even longer period of apnea can be produced by hyperventilating with oxygen. After hyperventilation is terminated apnea will supervene until CO_2 tension becomes elevated to a certain level or until O_2 tension becomes lowered below certain levels. Thus it is seen that the initiation of breathing after hyperventilation depends upon stimuli which derive either from a rise in CO_2 tension or from a fall in O_2 tension or from an interaction of these changes.

The relative importance of CO_2 and O_2 in influencing breathing in an individual at sea level (ambient pressure of 760 mm. Hg) is illustrated when the percentages of these gases in inspired air are altered. If the O_2 percentage is increased above the amount normally found, even up to 100%, negligible influences on rate and depth of breathing are observed. Also, if the amount of O_2 in inspired air is moderately lowered, namely, down to about 18%, typically, little or no change in breathing is observed. Some persons will show stimulation of breathing as the O_2 is lowered to

around 16% and levels of 10 to 12% regularly cause hyperpnea. From these facts it is apparent that reduction in O_2 tension is not an important factor in regulation of breathing until the tension is reduced below some critical level which is somewhat lower than that found in normal resting subjects breathing air at a pressure of one atmosphere. Any slight increase in the CO_2 tension of arterial blood, on the other hand, causes an increase in breathing and a decrease in CO_2 tension is associated with apnea even when the O_2 tension is moderately below that which is found normally at sea level. Such facts provide a basis for the interpretation that the inspiratory process at sea level in normal subjects is related to the action of CO_2 on certain neurons in the respiratory center in the medulla oblongata, causing them to discharge; and the termination of inspiration, resulting in expiration, occurs as a result of "feedback" of inhibitory influences to these neurons. This mechanism serves to keep the CO_2 tension of arterial blood at a constant level of about 38 to 40 mm. Hg in the presence of wide fluctuations in O_2 tension of arterial blood as long as the latter are at levels from about 80 to 90 mm. Hg and up.

The Respiratory Center

It is customary and convenient to speak of the collections of nerve cells in the brain stem which are concerned with the integration of the activity of the muscles of respiration as the *respiratory center*. But the use of the term should not be taken to imply that the controlling nervous elements are a compact circumscribed mass, or confined to a closely restricted area. Section through the brain at any level rostral to the upper border of the pons usually does not alter significantly the respiratory rhythm. But sections at various levels behind this cause pronounced disturbances in respiration. If a cut is made through the medulla caudal to the tip of the calamus scriptorius, all breathing ceases.

Legallois (1824) located the respiratory center in the lower part of the medulla oblongata, and Flourens (1842, 1858) found a small spot about the size of a pin's head just beneath the forepart

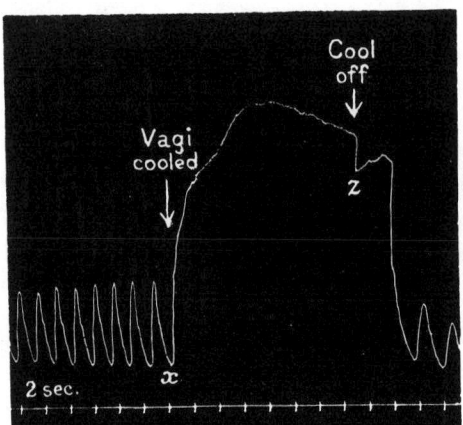

FIG. 53.1. Showing apneusis. Section of the brain stem along a plane passing dorsally immediately behind the posterior colliculi; and ventrally 2.5 mm. below the upper border of the pons. Between x and z the vagi were blocked by cold. Time: 2 sec. (After Stella.)

of the *calamus scriptorius* in the floor of the fourth ventricle, on either side of the midline. He showed that after bilateral destruction of this area, which he named *noeud vital* (vital knot), the breathing ceased. It appears, however, that the respiratory failure in these animals could have been secondary to circulatory failure related to loss of vasomotor tone.

Markwald (1887) described powerful and prolonged tonic inspiratory movements or "cramps" which supervened after bilateral section of the vagus nerves and division of the brain stem immediately behind the posterior colliculi. He concluded that a center inhibitory to inspiration was located in the latter situation, but that the vagi also had an inhibitory action, consequently the inspiratory "cramps" appeared only after vagal influence had been abolished as well. Markwald's observations were confirmed shortly afterwards by other experimenters. The subject was studied further by Lumsden (1932), who found that the prolonged inspiratory movements occurred only if the section passed through the pons a few millimeters behind its anterior border and occurred whether or not the vagi were divided. The inspiratory cramps or *apneuses*, as Lumsden preferred to call them, last for several seconds. He postulated their dependence upon an *apneustic* or *inspiratory center* at the level of the striae acusticae, which was dominated normally by an inhibitory or *pneumotaxic center* situated in the upper part of the pons. The duty of the latter center was, through its inhibitory influence, to help to transmute the apneustic movements into

the rhythmical movements characteristic of normal respiration. After section of the brain stem behind the striae acusticae, the respirations consisted of a series of gasps occurring at relatively long intervals. Lumsden concluded that these represented the activity of a primitive *gasping center* situated in the lower part of the medulla from which the two higher centers had evolved. It was considered to be of little importance in higher animals.

Lumsden's results were confirmed in the main by Stella and by Pitts, Magoun and Ranson. Stella, however, found in contradiction to Lumsden, that section through the pons (i.e., separation of the pneumotaxic center) did not result in apneusis unless the vagal influence was abolished also (see fig. 53.1). The results of Pitts and his associates are in essential agreement with those of Stella. They found that animals decerebrated through the upper part of the pons maintained a normal type of respiration which responded in the usual way to chemical and peripheral nerve stimulation so long as the vagi were intact, but immediately developed apneustic respiration and a complete cessation of rhythmical movements when both vagi were severed. Stimulation of the central end of one of the cut vagi temporarily restores the respiratory rhythm. The apneustic center is, therefore, under a double inhibitory influence, either one of which is capable of converting the apneustic type of respiration to the rhythm of normal or nearly normal respiration. The vagal impulses influencing the apneustic center are initiated by the stretch of the lung towards the latter part of the inspiratory phase of normal breathing. Studies by Cohen (1958) indicate that the pneumotaxic center shows rhythmic activity synchronous with breathing when its connections with the respiratory center are intact but fails to show rhythmicality when these pathways are cut.

The apneuses, like normal respirations, are affected powerfully by the CO_2 tension of the blood, being increased in depth by having the animal breathe an air mixture containing a high concentration of CO_2 and reduced in depth, or prevented from occurring, by carbon dioxide lack. According to Stella, the pneumotaxic center is bilateral but its connections with the apneustic center are mainly homolateral, i.e. uncrossed.

Pitts, Magoun and Ranson describe the respiratory center in the cat, which they locate in the reticular formation of the medulla, as consisting of an inspiratory and an expiratory division; both centers are bilaterally represented. The *inspiratory center* occupies the rostral half or two thirds of the reticular formation overlying the olivary nuclei on both sides, i.e., beneath the caudal third of the floor of the fourth ventricle (fig. 53.2). When stimulated a maximal co-ordinated inspiration results, involving both diaphragm and thorax. If stimulated during apneusis, the magnitude of the inspiratory movement is increased; if stimulated during an interval between apneuses, an apneustic movement is produced. The expiratory center lies in the reticular formation dorsal to the inspiratory center. Electrical stimulation within this area causes expiration; if stimulated during inspiration or during apneusis, these movements are inhibited. Regular respirations—inspiration alternating with expiration—are induced by rhythmical stimulation of the inspiratory center; expiration then occurs passively. Rhythmical stimulation of the expiratory center also produces regular respiration, spontaneous inspirations then alternating with the expiratory movements. Intimate synaptic connections exist between the diffusely distributed neurons within each center and between the two oppositely acting centers on the same side, as well as between similarly acting centers on opposite sides of the medulla. Thus, unilateral stimulation of a small area of the inspiratory center causes maximal contraction of all the inspiratory muscles. Excitation of one center causes simultaneous activation of its fellow of the contralateral side, accompanied by reciprocal inhibition of both oppositely acting centers. Thus, the alternating rhythm of inspiration is established and sustained, and the respiratory movements synchronized on the two sides of the body. The functional importance of the bilateral connections is demonstrated in a striking manner by making a deep longitudinal cut through the midline of the caudal part of the medulla; then the respiratory rhythms on the two sides of the body become asynchronous (see fig. 53.3).

The similarity in the effects of stimulation of the expiratory center and of the central end of the vagus, namely, inhibition of inspiration and of apneusis, has led Pitts and his colleagues to the conclusion that the vagal respiratory effects are mediated through the expiratory center. The influence of the pneumotaxic center probably is exerted in the same way.

The respiratory center is connected with the motor neurons of the phrenic and intercostal nerves in the cervical (C. 3, 4 and 5) and upper thoracic segments of the cord (T. 2-6) by descend-

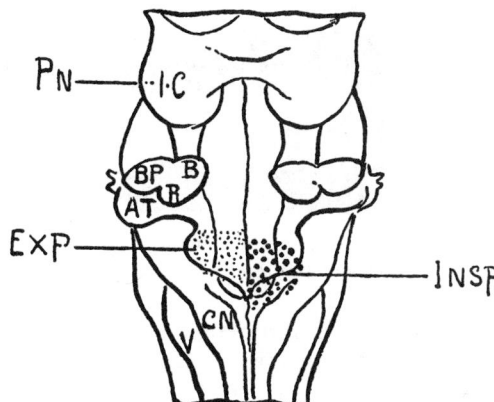

FIG. 53.2. Dorsal view of lower brain stem of cat showing location of pneumotaxic (Pn.), inspiratory (Insp.) and expiratory (Exp.) centers. Extent of expiratory center shown in light stippling, inspiratory center in heavy stippling. Though the centers are bilateral each is outlined on one side only, for the sake of simplicity. IC, inferior colliculus; AT, acoustic tubercle; B, brachium conjunctivum; B.P., brachium pontis; R, restiform body; CN, cuneate nucleus. (Redrawn from Pitts, Magoun and Ranson.)

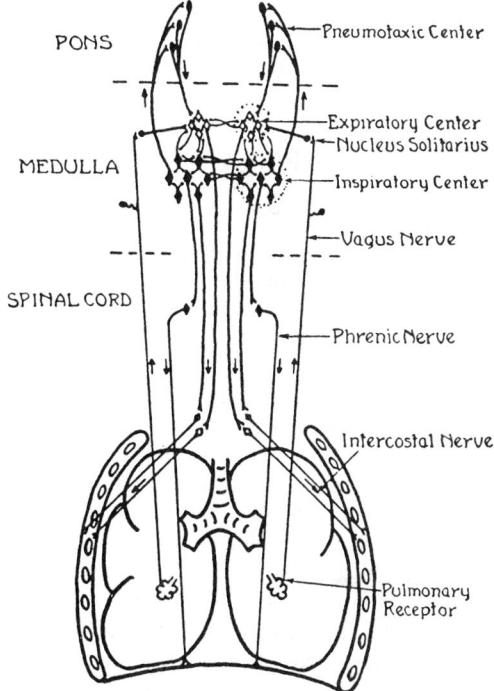

FIG. 53.3. Diagram illustrating the chief nervous connections responsible for the control of the respiratory rhythm. Inspiratory and expiratory centers in the medulla on the right side surrounded by dotted circles. (After Pitts, slightly modified.)

ing tracts which run in the anterior columns and in the ventral parts of the lateral columns of the spinal cord.

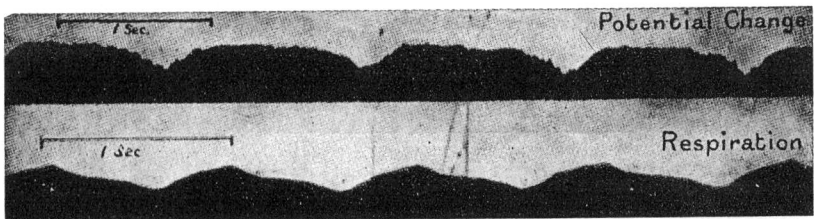

FIG. 53.4 Comparison of electrical potential wave rhythm and rhythm of respiratory movements. (After Adrian and Buytendijk.)

THE SPONTANEOUS ACTIVITY OF THE MEDULLARY RESPIRATORY CENTERS

This has been a subject of interest to physiologists for many years. Some investigators, such as Coombs and Pike, and Schafer, have denied that the center is capable of spontaneous activity, maintaining that afferent impulses, especially those set up in the lung by the stimulus of stretch and conveyed by the vagus, and those initiated from proprioceptors in the respiratory muscles and travelling by the posterior nerve roots, were essential. However, the results secured within recent years by means of improved methods of investigation leave little reason to doubt that, in certain species at least, the brain stem continues to discharge impulses to the respiratory muscles after all or nearly all afferent paths have been severed. For example, rhythmical bursts of impulses can be recorded from the central stump of the phrenic nerve of a decerebrate animal after section of the vagi, glossopharyngeal and other cranial nerves entering the pons and medulla, and division of the spinal cord below the level of the 7th cervical segment. Such an extensive operation would certainly interrupt all important afferent paths including those from the carotid sinus and the aortic arch. It is not to be supposed, of course, that the respirations would be normal after such a radical procedure, for even if not essential for maintaining the activity of the center, afferent nerve influences are of the utmost importance in the regulation of that activity and the production of the normal respiratory rhythm. Evidence for automaticity of the respiratory center of a cold-blooded species has been secured by Adrian and Buytenijk. They succeeded in recording rhythmical action potentials from the excised brain stem of the gold-fish; the potential changes had the same range of frequency as the respiratory movements (fig. 53.4).

The spontaneous respiratory activity is apparently dependent primarily upon the inspiratory center, the expiratory center playing an inhibitory role to interrupt intermittently the inspiratory discharge. As shown by Cohen (1958) impulses are not discharged spontaneously from the pneumotaxic center. Pitts and his colleagues suggest that the pneumotaxic center is excited from the inspiratory center, that a proportion of the impulses discharged from the latter region ascend to the pontine center whence impulses descend to the expiratory center; a discharge of *inhibitory* impulses is transmitted from the latter to the inspiratory center. As the discharge of impulses from the expiratory center ceases, the inspiratory center resumes its activity, and the cycle is repeated. A rise in the rate of discharge of the inhibitory impulses will increase the rate of breathing, while a reduction in the frequency of the discharge will be followed by slowing of the respirations.

It appears, then, that in the intact animal the automatic alternating rhythm of the medullary centers is maintained largely by inhibitory impulses from the pneumotaxic center and vagal afferents impinging upon the expiratory centers, which in turn inhibit, intermittently, the activity of the inspiratory centers. The vagal influence is evoked by inflation of the lungs (i.e., by inspiration); expiration, a passive act, follows (ch. 51). Under ordinary physiological conditions the vagal regulating influence appears to play the dominant role.

Of the two main methods which have been used for localizing inspiratory and expiratory centers, namely stimulation versus "sounding" for action potentials, the latter would seem to be somewhat more suitable. Stimulation serves to expose only a dominant or major influence. Neurons having opposite effects could be present and could be stimulated simultaneously, but the effects of the dominant one of the two groups would be expected to appear. Hence, inspiration elicited from a given site would not rule out the possibility that expiratory neurons are present in this region, nor could an expiratory response elicited from a specific site prove that no inspiratory neurons were being stimulated simultaneously. According to Brookhart (1940) lower strengths of stimuli applied to the regions in which the inspiratory center and expiratory center are supposed to be located will elicit various types of effects, and somewhat stronger stimuli are required to produce the effects reported by Pitts and coworkers. On the other hand the recording of a burst of impulses only during one phase of the respiratory cycle would constitute evidence that only the inspiratory or expiratory neurons, depending on the time relations, were activated at that site under the conditions of the experiment. When the "sounding" method is used, according to Gesell, Bricker and Magee (1936), for the most part, impulses are recorded from a given site during both inspiration and expiration. This would indicate that expiratory and inspiratory neurons are intermingled and would tend to make one doubt that there are anatomically discrete expiratory and inspiratory centers.

A difficulty with the "sounding" method for determining the location of inspiratory and expiratory neurons of the respiratory center is that impulses may be picked up directly from motor neurons. Achard and Bucher (1954) investigated the region of the respiratory center with needle electrodes and determined by subsequent histological examination the precise cells from which recordings were obtained. Any purely inspiratory activity obtained by them was from *motor neurons* involved in inspiration, while action currents recorded from numerous other electrodes located in the area of the respiratory center did not permit a distinction between respiratory rhythms and the continuous asynchronous "background" activity in the reticular substance. It must be concluded, therefore, that the question of the precise location of inspiratory and expiratory neurons within the medulla has not yet been answered.

The relative importance of the pneumotaxic center in maintaining rhythmic breathing after vagotomy seems to differ according to the species of animal studied and the conditions of the experiments. According to Hoff and Breckenridge (1954) in dogs, and under certain conditions in cats, midpontine section combined with bilateral vagotomy does not cause cessation of breathing. This has been confirmed by Wang and coworkers. In fact vagotomy has been reported to have no effect on breathing in some instances in animals having the brain stem sectioned in the midpontine region. Hoff and Breckenridge have returned to the view that the cause of the rhythmic discharge of respiration lies within the medulla itself. "Just

how the rhythm of respiration develops within the medulla is still problematical, and it may well be possible that within the confines of the medulla itself anatomical pathways are to be found wherein reciprocating self-limiting circuits, akin to those postulated between medulla and pons in earlier hypotheses, determine the rhythm of breathing."

The situation at present can be summarized by stating that the presence of a respiration-regulating group of neurons in the upper pontine region, the so-called pneumotaxic center, has been clearly demonstrated and has an important role in regulation of rhythmic breathing in the intact animal. However, it seems to be clearly demonstrated, also, that rhythmic breathing still can occur when both this mechanism and the vagal reflexes are eliminated. Finally, the precise manner in which the pontine elements influence respiration has not been determined. In figures 53.5 and 53.6 are shown two recent attempts to explain the organization of the respiratory center.

Profound inhibition of breathing can be produced by stimulation of the anterior cingulate cortex on the medial surface, and the orbitoinsulotemporal polar cortex on the ventral surface of the cerebral hemisphere. In man, arrest of breathing has been produced in patients under light pentothal anesthesia from the anterior cingulate and posterior orbital surface, and in the conscious patient from the same areas and from the anterior insula and the ventromedial aspect of the temporal pole. Acceleration of respiration has been observed in carnivores on stimulating the motor cortex, the anterior ectosylvian and the sylvian gyri, and the middle and anterior portion of the cingulate cortex. Precisely what role these cortical areas play in the control of breathing is not clear at present. (See Handbook of Physiology, Sec. 1, Vol. 2, pages 1347–1351.)

The Nature and Location of CO_2-Sensitive Cells in the Medulla

That cells in the respiratory center show increased rates of discharge in response to an increase in CO_2 tension or hydrogen ion concentration in them, or in their immediate vicinity, is generally accepted. The precise mechanisms of central sensitivity to changes in cH and P_{CO_2} however are not known. One may recall that before the discovery of carotid bodies (which anatomically are not very far from the respiratory center) it was believed that oxygen lack had a stimulant effect directly in the respiratory center,

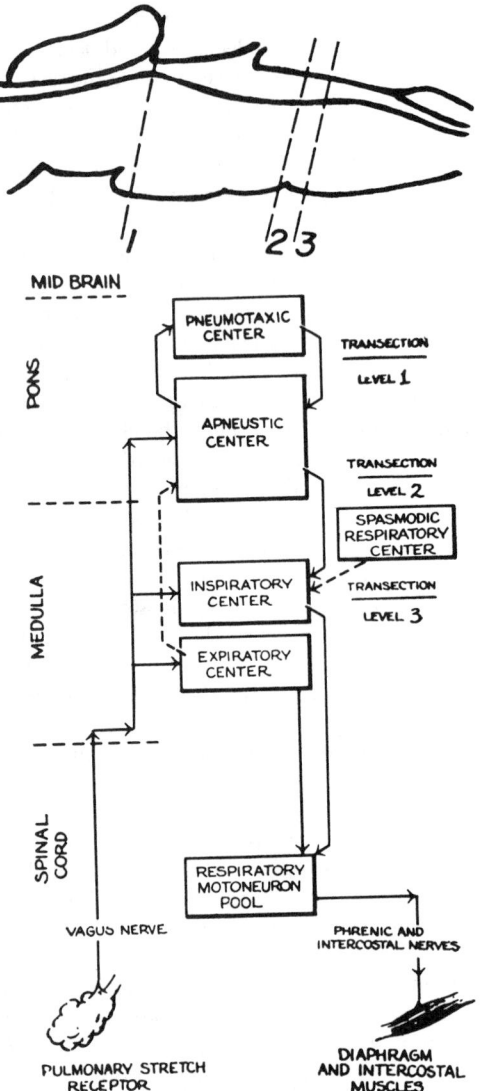

FIG. 53.5. Schematic representation of organization of central respiratory mechanisms in the brainstem of the cat. Key to transection levels is indicated above. In vagotomized cats transection rostral to level 1 allows eupnea to be present; transection between level 1 and 2 causes apneustic breathing to appear; transection between 2 and 3 results in eupneic breathing or gasping or occasionally Biot's breathing, and transection caudal to level 3 is followed by absence of respiration (reproduced by permission from Wang, Ngai, and Frumin).

and it is known now that such effects are on a reflex basis. Likewise it is theoretically possible, that special sensitivity to changes in CO_2 tension or cH is not a feature of the neurons of the respiratory center but rather of other cells which exert an influence on cells of the respiratory center.

Leusen (1954) showed that an increase in the hydrogen ion concentration in cerebrospinal fluid perfusing the cerebral ventricles stimulated ventilation, and he believed that this effect was exerted directly upon the respiratory center. However, Loeschcke (see Grodins, 1964) showed that local application of acid to the floor of the fourth ventricle failed to stimulate breathing, hence he postulated the existence of a CSF-bathed chemosensitive area outside the respiratory center. Subsequently, Mitchell et al. (1963) reported that specific areas on the ventrolateral surface of the medulla (bounded medially by the pyramidal tracts, laterally by the roots of the 8, 9, 10, and 11 cranial nerves, rostrally by the pons, and extending caudally about 6 mm.) show chemosensitivity similar to that exhibited by the receptors of the carotid bodies. Application to this area of pledgets containing CSF which was equilibrated with high Pco_2, or having a high cH, or containing nicotine or acetylcholine, produced hyperpnea, whereas local cooling or application

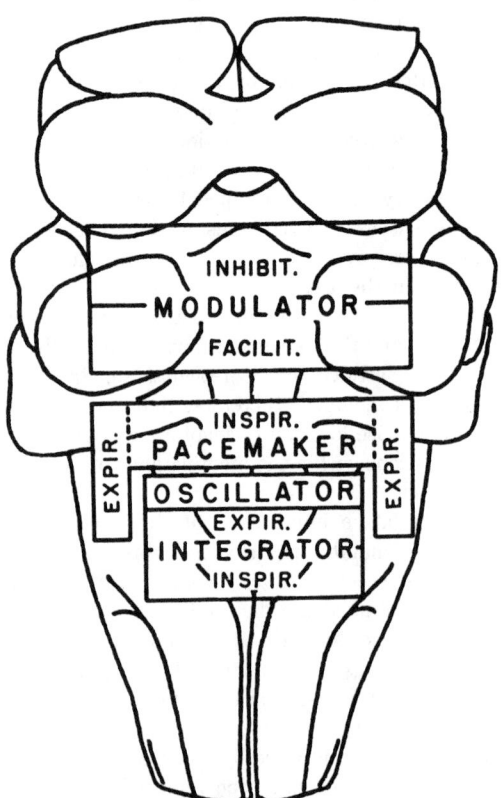

FIG. 53.6. Schematic representation of functional concept of central regulation of respiration. Relative locations in the brain-stem of a cat of the regions which subserve the various functions are indicated (reproduced by permission from Brodie and Borison).

of procaine caused inhibition of respiration. The authors postulate that all medullary CO_2 sensitivity is mediated via these "receptors" on the ventrolateral surface of the medulla. It would seem that studies of effects of ablation of these areas, although technically difficult, would be essential in obtaining a definite answer to this question.

Hering-Breuer Reflexes

The Hering-Breuer reflexes are effects on the respiratory cycle which are elicited by inflation and deflation of the lungs. The receptors concerned are in the lungs, and the afferent pathways are in the vagus nerves. The function of these reflexes apparently is to regulate the respiratory cycle rather than to alter significantly the pulmonary ventilation for any prolonged period. The observations made by Hering and Breuer in 1868 were that inflation of the lungs causes arrest of inspiration, expiration then ensuing, and deflation of the lungs has an inspiration-exciting effect. They found that these effects were abolished when the vagus nerves were sectioned. Another way to demonstrate the effects of lung distention is to block the airway at the beginning of either inspiration or expiration. When inflow of air is prevented, a stronger inspiratory effort results than in the preceding cycle, and when egress of air is blocked at the end of inspiration a longer interval than the preceding one occurs before the onset of the next inspiratory effort. In eupnea apparently the inflation effect during inspiration alone is a factor. As inspiration proceeds, distention of the lungs occurs, and impulses are carried by vagal afferents to the respiratory center where they cause inhibition of the inspiratory neurons, thus terminating inspiration. Once the lungs begin to deflate impulses are no longer set up in the vagal afferents and, consequently, the inspiratory neurons again are free to discharge.

The mechanical problem in studying the Hering-Breuer reflexes can be circumvented in the case of the rabbit since this animal has a slip of muscle on the posterior surface of the diaphragm which can be dissected free and recorded from separately from the remainder of the diaphragm. This diaphragmatic slip of muscle can be used as an indicator of the degree of activation of inspiratory muscles. If the lungs are distended, the rate and amplitude of contraction of the slip decrease, and if the lungs are deflated, an increase in rate and amplitude of contraction of the slip is observed (fig. 53.7).

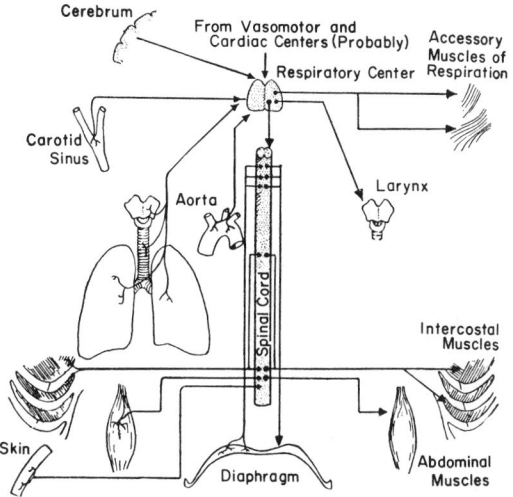

FIG. 53.7. Record of contractions of isolated slip of a diaphragm of a rabbit to illustrate Hering-Breuer reflexes. Upstroke is produced by contraction of the slip, i.e., inspiration. *Above* at + the trachea was occluded at the end of expiration, and at 0 the obstruction was removed. *Below* at + the trachea was occluded at the end of inspiration, and at 0 the obstruction was removed (after Head).

The stimulating effect of lung deflation on inspiration is related under ordinary conditions to failure in the production of the normal amount of inspiration-inhibiting influence at the end of inspiration. However, severe deflation, as from pneumothorax, results in activation of other receptors, and reflex stimulation of inspiration follows. Finally, if lung inflation is severe, not only is inspiration inhibited but active expiration is elicited reflexly. This may not require a third type of receptor, but may be simply the result of greater degree of activation of the same kind of receptors which are concerned in the reflex inhibition of inspiration. The role of vagal reflexes in regulating inspiration and expiration has been described in detail by Wyss (1954).

A physiological role of the Hering-Breuer reflexes is to regulate the extent of lung inflation so that the tidal volume tends to fall within a certain range. Also, these reflexes serve to insure filling and emptying of the lungs despite a considerable increase in resistance in the airway. As would be expected, the typical result following bilateral vagotomy is an increase in the depth of breathing. The inspiratory act under these conditions is seen to be unnecessarily long since the chest tends to remain in the inspiratory position for a short period after ingress of air has stopped. This is an inefficient process since muscular work is being done while no air is being moved. Also, a decrease in respiratory rate develops in most

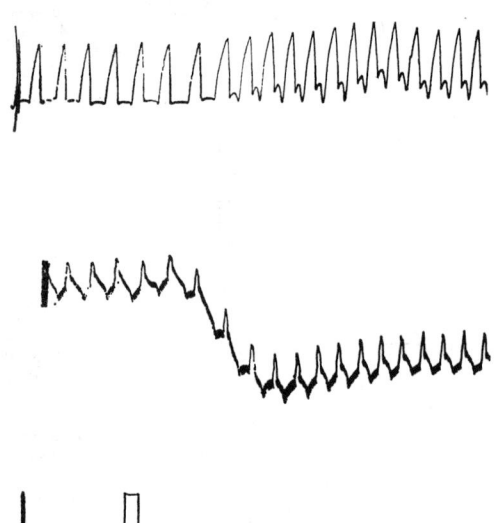

FIG. 53.8. Effects on blood pressure (*below*) and respiration (*above*) following injection of 0.1 mg. per kg. of nitroglycerin into dog anesthetized with alpha-chloralose. The respiratory stimulation can be prevented if the fall in arterial blood pressure is counteracted by means of rapid infusion of blood from a pressure-regulating device (from studies by Schopp, Gilfoil and Youmans).

animals after vagotomy. This probably is a compensatory change, secondary to the increased depth, which results in an amount of pulmonary ventilation similar to that which was present before vagotomy. An increased depth of breathing without a decrease in rate would soon wash out CO_2 so that the stimulus to the respiratory center would be removed, hence the rate soon would decrease to cause restoration of normal CO_2 levels. It should be mentioned, however, that the effects of vagotomy on rate and depth of breathing vary greatly depending upon the anesthetic agent which is used; and furthermore, changes are progressive for a prolonged period following vagotomy.

The effects on respiration of direct stimulation of the central end of the vagus nerve sectioned at the cervical level are somewhat unpredictable since the nerve contains several types of afferent fibers which carry impulses to the respiratory center. These include (1) aortic arch afferents, (2) aortic body afferents, (3) inspiration-inhibiting fibers activated normally during lung inflation, (4) inspiration-exciting fibers activated physiologically by excessive lung deflation, (5) fibers concerned with visceral pain, and possibly still other types of fibers. However, strong stimulation of the central end of the vagus nerve usually causes apnea, and this may persist for a

few seconds after cessation of stimulation. This result could be elicited if the effects of stimulation of (1) and (3) above were sufficient to override the effects of stimulation of (2) and (4).

The Hering-Breuer reflexes are basically proprioceptive in nature. In this case contraction of skeletal muscle not only increases the tension in muscles and shortens them but elastic objects, the lungs, also are put under greater tension. The lungs also are supplied with receptors from which information is carried back to the same neurons that activated the muscles. The muscles of respiration, like skeletal muscle in general, are supplied with proprioceptive innervation through which their contraction is regulated in the same way as described for the limb musculature.

Reflex Effects from Baroreceptors

A sudden rise in pressure in the sino-aortic zones elicits reflexly a decrease in rate and depth of breathing. If the pressure rise is considerable, apnea may be produced. Typically, adaptation is rather rapid so that breathing is restored even though the new pressure level is maintained. Part of the recovery of respiration is related to adaptation in the receptors themselves, but also it occurs as a consequence of the rise in P_{CO_2} during apnea. The opposite change, a sudden fall in pressure in the sino-aortic zones, elicits hyperpnea. Thus, any sudden change in blood pressure per se tends to elicit respiratory responses. During rapid bleeding or following injection of vasodilator drugs, such as nitroglycerin or bethanechol (a choline derivative), respiration is stimulated (fig. 53.8), and the effect is prevented in considerable part by sino-aortic denervation (Schopp, Gilfoil and Youmans, 1957). The respiration-stimulating effect of nitroglycerin which still remains after denervation can be partly or completely prevented if a device is used to prevent the fall in arterial blood pressure.

Schmidt in 1941, and later Aviado and Schmidt (1955) have suggested that the effects on respiration elicited from the pressoreceptors serve no physiological purpose; however, this mechanism probably is of importance in influencing the venous return (Youmans, 1958). Vasodilation promotes pooling of blood, especially in the abdominal viscera, and increased respiratory activity promotes the movement of blood from the abdominal portion of the inferior vena cava on into the thoracic portion. The concept of the respiratory pump, as a factor in aiding venous return, introduced by Donders in 1859, seems accurate according to the studies reviewed by Brecher (1956). Conversely, the respiratory inhibition during a rise in blood pressure, especially in a person in the orthostatic position, would favor pooling of blood in the splanchnic region so that venous return would be decreased; thus cardiac output would be lowered, and the rise in blood pressure would be counteracted. In short, one may interpret the respiratory responses from pressoreceptors, along with effects on heart rate and arteriolar tonus elicited at the same time, as being concerned with the stabilization of arterial blood pressure. However, characteristics of these reflexes are such that they are useful only in counteracting sudden changes of brief duration; they are overridden easily by other influences.

Control of Activity of the Abdominal Muscles

In the resting, supine subject, abdominal muscles may be completely inactive throughout the breathing cycle (Campbell, 1958). In moderate hyperpnea they become active during expiration, and in more severe hyperpnea they show a rapidly augmenting activity during the early part of expiration, with a decrease well before the next inspiration begins. Abdominal muscles usually are active during expiration in the subject in the standing position, and they contract in response to continuous positive pressure breathing in a subject in the supine position. The degree of their response to positive pressure is proportionate to the level of pressure applied. Gesell and Moyer (1941) reported that the contraction of abdominal muscles in response to positive pressure breathing in dogs did not occur after bilateral vagotomy at the cervical level. Their discussion was based on the tacit assumption that vagotomy had this effect because of elimination of impulses from the lungs. Apparently, no one had questioned the source of this reflex effect on abdominal muscles until recently. Studies by the Wisconsin group (Youmans et al., 1963) revealed that positive intrapulmonary pressure elicits contraction of abdominal muscles in dogs with closed chest, but does not do so if the chest is open, even though lung distention in the latter case is greater, hence Hering-Breuer reflexes apparently are not concerned. Bishop (1964) likewise has concluded that, the abdominal muscle response to positive pressure breathing "is not a simple corollary of the Hering-Breuer reflex but is a separate reflex served by its own vagal pathway."

Results of extensive studies (Youmans et al., 1963) indicate that activity of abdominal muscles may be increased selectively on a reflex basis when volume of blood in certain "low pressure" portions of the cardiovascular system is reduced. Although it is clear that anything which stimulates breathing tends to cause appearance of, or an increase in, activity of abdominal muscles, on the other hand, a number of procedures, which lead to changes in amplitude of contractions of abdominal muscles, do so without causing corresponding changes in tidal volume. In experiments on dogs it was found that several procedures (including bleeding, tilting the animal to the head-up position, aortic occlusion, and positive pressure breathing) cause marked changes in amplitude of steady-state contractions of abdominal muscles, while having little or no effect on tidal volume. In fig. 53.9, a schematic representation is shown of main factors and mechanisms concerned with influencing the activity of abdominal muscles. In addition to the well known influences from chemoreceptors and baroreceptors, acting by way of the respiratory center, it is postulated that atrial mechanoreceptors (extensively studied by Paintal and others) are concerned with reflex inhibition of tonus of abdominal muscles. Any decrease in volume of the atria is envisaged as causing an increase in tonus of abdominal muscles through withdrawal of this inhibitory effect. The consequent rise in intraabdominal pressure serves to reduce the capacity of the venous system and hence promotes better cardiac filling. The influences from alterations in cardiac filling apparently can be exerted independently of the effects on amplitude of breathing (as shown for example by the fact that occlusion of the postcaval vein causes an immediate increase in activity of abdominal muscles, while occlusion of the ascending aorta causes immediate inhibition of such activity, yet minimal and similar effects on inspiration occur). Therefore, it is necessary to assume, as shown in fig. 53.9, that impulses from atrial mechanoreceptros can be channeled to the motor neurons which innervate the abdominal muscles without influencing the respiratory center. The only new concept presented in the schema is that atrial mechanoreceptors (activated by increased atrial volume) are concerned with reflex inhibition of tonus of abdominal muscles. Campbell (1958) suggested the possibility that changes in activity of abdominal muscles during the respiratory act may be determined in part by reflexes which do not operate through the respiratory center. He further state

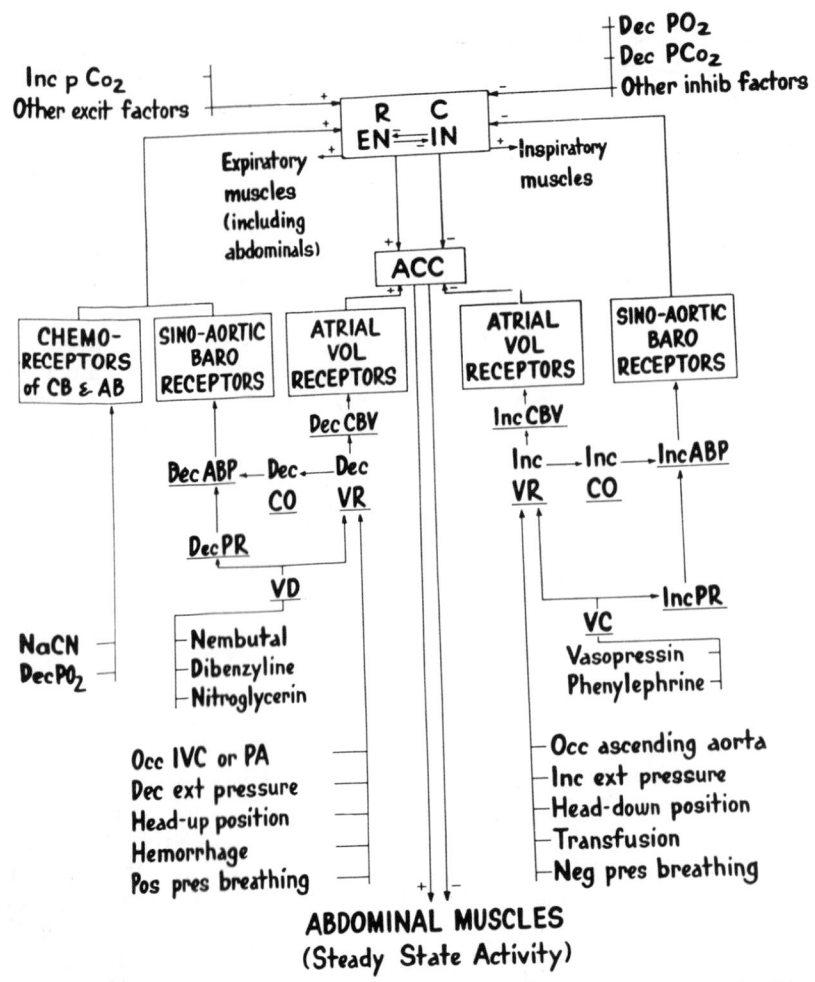

ABDOMINAL MUSCLES
(Steady State Activity)

FIG. 53.9. Schematic representation of main factors and mechanisms concerned with altering the level of activity of abdominal muscles in response to cardiorespiratory changes. The *left side* of the diagram illustrates excitatory influences which affect the ACR either through the respiratory center or more directly. The *right side* shows opposite changes which promote a decrease in the ACR. *RC*, the respiratory center; *EN*, expiratory center; *IN*, inspiratory center; *ACC*, abdominal compression center; *CB*, carotid body; *AB*, aortic body; *CBV*, central blood volume; *ABP*, arterial blood pressure; *CO*, cardiac output; *VR*, venous return; *PR*, peripheral resistance; *VC*, vasoconstriction; *VD*, vasodilatation; *IVC*, postcaval vein; *PA*, pulmonary artery; +, excitatory influence; −, inhibitory influence.

that some of the control of abdominal muscles may be for the purpose of modulating changes in abdominal pressure, because of the effects on circulation, and that receptors in the circulatory system, in either the abdominal or thoracic cavities, might be involved. Bjurstedt (1953), more specifically postulated that tonus of abdominal muscles may be influenced reflexly from receptors [in] the circulatory system that are sensitive to [chang]es in filling. As to the question of an ab[domin]al muscle tonus center (ACC in the [diagram]a), it is noteworthy that Gesell, Magee and [Moye]r (1940) observed steady state "expira[tory] discharge in neurons in the medulla and [not]ed that these units may be concerned with

posture rather than with exhalation. More recently Haber et al. (1957) recorded two types of "expiratory" patterns from neurons in the medulla, which they differentiate as early versus late. The late "expiratory" discharges are similar to Gesell's steady state type. Since they occur at maximum frequency in the anesthetized dog well after the end-expiratory position has been reached (at a time when there is no movement of air and when abdominal muscular activity and intra-abdominal pressure are maximal) it would seem to be at least as appropriate to call them abdominal compression discharges as to call them expiratory discharges. Haber et al. (1957) also found that the neurons are carbon dioxide sensi-

return, introduced by Donders in 1859, seems accurate according to the studies reviewed by Brecher (1956). Conversely, the respiratory inhibition during a rise in blood pressure, especially in a person in the orthostatic position, would favor pooling of blood in the splanchnic region so that venous return would be decreased; thus cardiac output would be lowered, and the rise in blood pressure would be counteracted. In short, one may interpret the respiratory responses from pressoreceptors, along with effects on heart rate and arteriolar tonus elicited at the same time, as being concerned with the stabilization of arterial blood pressure. However, characteristics of these reflexes are such that they are useful only in counteracting sudden changes of brief duration; they are overridden easily by other influences.

Control of Activity of the Abdominal Muscles

In the resting, supine subject, abdominal muscles may be completely inactive throughout the breathing cycle (Campbell, 1958). In moderate hyperpnea they become active during expiration, and in more severe hyperpnea they show a rapidly augmenting activity during the early part of expiration, with a decrease well before the next inspiration begins. Abdominal muscles usually are active during expiration in the subject in the standing position, and they contract in response to continuous positive pressure breathing in a subject in the supine position. The degree of their response to positive pressure is proportionate to the level of pressure applied. Gesell and Moyer (1941) reported that the contraction of abdominal muscles in response to positive pressure breathing in dogs did not occur after bilateral vagotomy at the cervical level. Their discussion was based on the tacit assumption that vagotomy had this effect because of elimination of impulses from the lungs. Apparently, no one had questioned the source of this reflex effect on abdominal muscles until recently. Studies by the Wisconsin group (Youmans et al., 1963) revealed that positive intrapulmonary pressure elicits contraction of abdominal muscles in dogs with closed chest, but does not do so if the chest is open, even though lung distention in the latter case is greater, hence Hering-Breuer reflexes apparently are not concerned. Bishop (1964) likewise has concluded that, the abdominal muscle response to positive pressure breathing "is not a simple corollary of the Hering-Breuer reflex but is a separate reflex served by its own vagal pathway."

Results of extensive studies (Youmans et al., 1963) indicate that activity of abdominal muscles may be increased selectively on a reflex basis when volume of blood in certain "low pressure" portions of the cardiovascular system is reduced. Although it is clear that anything which stimulates breathing tends to cause appearance of, or an increase in, activity of abdominal muscles, on the other hand, a number of procedures, which lead to changes in amplitude of contractions of abdominal muscles, do so without causing corresponding changes in tidal volume. In experiments on dogs it was found that several procedures (including bleeding, tilting the animal to the head-up position, aortic occlusion, and positive pressure breathing) cause marked changes in amplitude of steady-state contractions of abdominal muscles, while having little or no effect on tidal volume. In fig. 53.9, a schematic representation is shown of main factors and mechanisms concerned with influencing the activity of abdominal muscles. In addition to the well known influences from chemoreceptors and baroreceptors, acting by way of the respiratory center, it is postulated that atrial mechanoreceptors (extensively studied by Paintal and others) are concerned with reflex inhibition of tonus of abdominal muscles. Any decrease in volume of the atria is envisaged as causing an increase in tonus of abdominal muscles through withdrawal of this inhibitory effect. The consequent rise in intraabdominal pressure serves to reduce the capacity of the venous system and hence promotes better cardiac filling. The influences from alterations in cardiac filling apparently can be exerted independently of the effects on amplitude of breathing (as shown for example by the fact that occlusion of the postcaval vein causes an immediate increase in activity of abdominal muscles, while occlusion of the ascending aorta causes immediate inhibition of such activity, yet minimal and similar effects on inspiration occur). Therefore, it is necessary to assume, as shown in fig. 53.9, that impulses from atrial mechanoreceptros can be channeled to the motor neurons which innervate the abdominal muscles without influencing the respiratory center. The only new concept presented in the schema is that atrial mechanoreceptors (activated by increased atrial volume) are concerned with reflex inhibition of tonus of abdominal muscles. Campbell (1958) suggested the possibility that changes in activity of abdominal muscles during the respiratory act may be determined in part by reflexes which do not operate through the respiratory center. He further stated

would appear that if CO_2 is to be administered to stimulate breathing, there would be little use for any mixture containing less than 5% or more than 10% CO_2.

It is generally agreed that the primary site of action of CO_2 in producing effects on breathing is in the respiratory center or in the immediate vicinity of the center. Cells in a respiratory center which has been isolated from extrinsic neural influences, still show alterations in rates of discharge in response to corresponding changes in CO_2 tension of the blood reaching them, and injection of bicarbonate directly into the respiratory center causes an increased activity of these neurons.

Considerable attention has been given to the question of the precise mechanism by means of which CO_2 exerts its stimulant action. It has been debated whether CO_2 itself has such an effect, or whether the effect is exerted indirectly as a consequence of the concomitant increase in hydrogen ion concentration. There is evidence, analyzed by Gray (1950), that both a rise in Pco_2, and in cH, in the respiratory center, contribute to and supplement each other in causing an increase in pulmonary ventilation.

Another mechanism, reflex in nature, is available for the stimulation of breathing as a consequence of a rise in the Pco_2 of arterial blood. The chemoreceptors, already described as concerned with producing circulatory adjustments in response to changes in Po_2 and Pco_2, when subjected to a sufficient rise in Pco_2 will elicit an increase in RMV. The extensive literature dealing with chemoreceptors has been summarized by Heymans and Neil (1958) and additional facts have been added by several authors in the proceedings of the J. S. Haldane Centenary Symposium (Cunningham and Lloyd, 1963). The fact of reflex stimulation of breathing in response to rises in Pco_2 of the blood flowing to the aortic and carotid bodies has been demonstrated by a number of methods and is generally accepted. A question which has been vigorously disputed, however, is whether the respiratory center in the intact subject is more sensitive than the chemoreceptors. In other words does the chemoreceptive reflex mechanism constitute the ne of defense against a rising Pco_2 in blood or does the respiratory center have ater sensitivity. Heymans has supported w that the chemoreceptors are concerned flex drive of breathing even under resting ns at sea level, while Schmidt and Comroe

favor the interpretation that these receptors are activated in significant degree only after considerable increases in arterial Pco_2. The details of the argument are reviewed by Heymans and Neil, who conclude that the question remains open as to how much the chemoreceptors participate in the response to moderate hypercapnia in the intact animal. However, the majority viewpoint seems to be that the normally sensitive respiratory center responds to rising CO_2 and through increased ventilation prevents a rise in Pco_2 of arterial blood sufficient to elicit a response from chemoreceptors. If, on the other hand, the respiratory center is rendered relatively insensitive to CO_2, for example, by anesthetic agents and narcotic drugs, respiration is depressed, and Pco_2 rises to a level sufficient to set up chemoreceptive drive of breathing. According to the latter interpretation the CO_2-induced chemoreflex constitutes a secondary line of defense to help insure pulmonary ventilation when the sensitivity of the respiratory center is reduced.

The lowering of Pco_2 in arterial blood can be achieved by voluntary hyperventilation or by excessive artificial ventilation of anesthetized subjects. Following hyperventilation, apnea is observed, and breathing is resumed when either Pco_2 rises to approximately the level found in the subject under resting conditions or when the Po_2 of arterial blood drops to a level sufficient to set up reflex drive of breathing on an O_2 lack basis, whichever occurs first. After one has hyperventilated moderately with atmospheric air, oxygen lack develops quickly as the store of oxygen in the lungs is absorbed and utilized; breathing is resumed in response to the oxygen lack stimulus before the Pco_2 has been restored to the normal resting level. Then the oxygen lack is relieved by a few breaths, and apnea appears again. Gradually, the Pco_2 level becomes restored and takes over as the sole drive. This is the basis for the appearance of a few cycles of periodic breathing after hyperventilation. As would be expected if one hyperventilates with 100% O_2, rather than air, just as much CO_2 is blown off as before, with a given degree of respiratory activity, but the Po_2 in alveolar air is quite high at the end of the period of hyperventilation. Consequently a longer time will be required for the O_2-lack stimulus to appear than for the Pco_2 level to be restored. Therefore, following hyperventilation with 100% O_2 the elevation of Pco_2 may be the initial factor in the restoration of breathing.

Respiratory Adjustments to O_2

The Po_2 in inspired air can be reduced by lowering the atmospheric pressure in a decompression chamber in which the subject has been placed, or he may breathe prepared gas mixtures having various ratios of O_2 to N_2. Since O_2 tension is lowered in proportion to the decrease in barometric pressure with altitude, one may indicate the altitude at which the experimentally induced Po_2 would be encountered. Thus a certain altitude, as far as Po_2 is concerned, is simulated by the experimental conditions. For example, if one breathes a mixture of 10.5 per cent O_2 and 89.5 per cent N_2 at 760 mm. Hg pressure, the Po_2 is about ½ that in atmospheric air at the same pressure. This approximates the Po_2 found in atmospheric air at an altitude of 18,000 feet where the barometric pressure is about 380 mm. Hg. The details concerning respiratory responses to Po_2 lower than that of room air at sea level have been described by Dripps and Comroe (1947) and by Rahn and Otis (1949). The major observations may be summarized as follows. Some subjects show a slight stimulation of breathing when the O_2 is lowered to 16 per cent to 18 per cent; while others do not respond until a level in the range from 16 per cent down to 12 per cent, or even lower in occasional subjects, is reached. At levels of 10 per cent or below, breathing is stimulated but irregularities may develop. As the O_2 tension in inspired air is lowered and respiratory minute volume increases, the CO_2 tension in alveolar air and arterial blood falls. Thus at the same time that the oxygen-lack stimulus is operating to cause an increased RMV, the CO_2 and cH drives of breathing are being withdrawn. It is apparent, therefore, that the stimulating effects of oxygen-lack *per se* on breathing could be recorded if the fall in CO_2 tension were prevented, as by adding the appropriate amount of CO_2 to the inspired air. In the discussion of hyperventilation it was noted that a relatively slight reduction in CO_2 tension (3 to 4 mm. Hg) results in apnea when there is no accompanying O_2 lack. At altitude, therefore, where the CO_2 tension is lowered more than this (secondary to increased RMV), it must be assumed that respiratory drive is entirely on an oxygen-lack basis or that a readjustment in sensitivity to CO_2 tension has occurred. Acutely, the former seems to be true, while after prolonged exposure to low oxygen tension the latter change apparently occurs.

Papers on respiration written before the discovery of the chemoreceptors of the carotid bodies refer to a stimulant action of oxygen-lack on the respiratory center. It is now believed that a lowered O_2 tension in the medulla does not result in stimulation of breathing; and decreases in O_2 tension of arterial blood, within ranges that the animal can tolerate for significant periods, do not cause stimulation of breathing if the carotid and aortic bodies have been denervated. Thus, the only sensitive mechanism which responds to oxygen-lack and elicits an increase in RMV is the chemoreceptor reflex. Here, too, as in the case of the CO_2 effect, the precise level at which a lowered arterial O_2 tension elicits stimulation of breathing is disputed. Comroe and Schmidt (1938) first reported that the O_2 tension in blood perfusing the carotid bodies was lowered to about 50 mm. Hg before the receptors were activated, but others have reported the threshold to be above 100 mm. Hg Po_2. Experiments showing the effects on RMV of blocking the chemoreceptors do not serve to establish the level of activity under normal resting conditions if anesthetic agents are used, since, as already explained, these substances usually cause depression of the respiratory center so that some part of the drive of breathing is transferred to the chemoreceptors. If oxygen lack stimulates breathing only through activation of chemoreceptors, then depression of breathing should be produced as a result of breathing mixtures containing more O_2 than that found in atmospheric air. To be relevant to the question the experiment must be performed on normal, resting subjects at a barometric pressure of approximately one atmosphere, and the gas to be tested should differ from the control only in that an inert gas, such as nitrogen, is substituted for oxygen. Loeshke (1953) reported an 8 per cent reduction of RMV for about a minute when 32 per cent O_2 in N_2 was substituted for room air in unanesthetized man, and this was followed by a rise until equilibrium was reached after about 4 minutes. On returning to room air, RMV increased a little for a few minutes and then returned to the control level. Dripps and Comroe (1947), however, reported only 3.1 per cent reduction in RMV caused by inhalation of 100 per cent O_2, whereas Baker and Hitchcock (1957) found an increase in ventilation in response to 100 per cent O_2. The results cited indicate that if there is any drive of breathing related to O_2-tension effects in normal subjects at sea level it is so small that it can be detected only by very careful measurements. Furthermore, it is possible that even the slight increases in ventilation which have been reported are not related to the removal of chemoreceptor drive, but rather to a rise in Pco_2 tension in the respiratory center secondary to the vasoconstriction produced by high O_2 tension in the arterioles of the brain. (See Kety, S. S. and Schmidt, C. F., 1948.)

According to studies reported recently by Witzleb at the Haldane Centenary Symposium (Cunningham and Lloyd, 1963) in cats under chloralose-urethane anesthesia, which were artificially ventilated, excitation of chemoreceptors usually was apparent at an arterial Po_2 tension of about 100 mm. Unless the anesthetic agents, or other conditions of the experiment, sensitize the chemoreceptors to O_2 in some way, this result would indicate that influences from chemoreceptors, though slight, are concerned in regulation of respiration, even when the O_2 tension of arterial blood is within the range which occurs in a subject breathing air at sea level.

Physiology of the Chemoreceptors of the Carotid and Aortic Bodies

The typical responses to significantly lowered oxygen tension in inspired air include: (1) stimulation of breathing, (2) cardiac acceleration and, (3) a rise in arterial blood pressure. It is now clear that both the stimulation of breathing and vasoconstriction, which in turn causes an increase in blood pressure, can be attributed to reflex effects elicited from chemoreceptors of the carotid and aortic bodies, whereas the cardiac acceleration cannot be so explained. Several researchers have demonstrated by experiments employing perfusion of the carotid bodies, that a lowering of oxygen tension in them does not cause cardiac acceleration. (See M. deBurgh Daly and J. N. Scott in Cunningham and Lloyd, 1963.) Actually, cardiac inhibition occurs, but much of this effect must be attributed to baroreceptor reflexes. Since one of the changes elicited reflexly from the carotid bodies is vasoconstriction, the arterial blood pressure rises as a result of the increased peripheral resistance, hence if the baroreceptors of the carotid sinuses and aortic arch and their innervation are intact, reflex bradycardia is elicited. However, even when the rise in arterial blood pressure is buffered, lowering of the oxygen tension in the blood perfusing the carotid bodies does not elicit cardiac acceleration, provided the animal is also being artificially respired. Daly has concluded that the cardiac acceleration which occurs in response to hypoxia is secondary to the respiratory stimulation. He presents evidence that the increase in respiratory movements reflexly elicits the acceleration.

From the studies of Daly, Bernthal and others, it is clear that reflex effects on heart rate from the carotid bodies cannot be determined, unless the arterial blood pressure is kept constant and artificial respiration is utilized. When these conditions are met, a reduction in oxygen tension of blood perfusing the carotid body usually causes a moderate decrease in heart rate.

Sodium cyanide injected intravenously causes cardiovascular and respiratory changes similar to those occurring in response to hypoxia (respiratory stimulation, increase in arterial blood pressure, cardiac acceleration). Since cyanide prevents the utilization of oxygen by tissues, it is possible that the mechanisms concerned in the response to it are the same as those involved in responses to inadequate oxygen supply. Also the responses to cyanide (when it is introduced into the blood perfusing the carotid body) are similar to those produced by decreasing the oxygen tension of the perfusing blood. Several other compounds have been shown to have a stimulant action on chemoreceptors of the carotid bodies, and several theories have been advanced to explain how either oxygen lack or inability to use oxygen in the presence of an oxygen excess can be transduced into impulses in the afferent fibers which innervate chemoreceptors.

Recent work done in Anichov's laboratory, and other studies reviewed by him, indicate that widespread effects result from stimulation of carotid body chemoreceptors. He states that the machinery of the "stress" reaction, extensively described by Selye, is set in motion, and that ACTH, epinephrine and norepinephrine are liberated.

Ordinarily the chemoreceptors of the aortic bodies (which are much less accessible and hence have not been studied so extensively) have been considered to be of the same type as those of the carotid bodies. However, Comroe and Mortimer (1964) have reported that, in dogs, hyperpnea can be elicited from the carotid bodies and aortic bodies, but from the latter arterial hypertension and tachycardia are elicited—which are the opposite effects of those elicited from the carotid bodies.

Effects of Hydrogen Ion Concentration and the Interactions between Respiratory Drives

Since changes in Pco_2 are accompanied by changes in pH, a question may be raised whether changes in hydrogen ion concentration as such have an influence upon breathing. Gray (1950) has emphasized the point that in metabolic acidosis pulmonary ventilation is greatly increased while arterial Pco_2 is below normal. Obviously then if it is true to begin with that only three drives (Po_2, Pco_2, cH) operate to control breathing, increased acidity per se is capable of stimulating breathing since neither of the other two factors has changed in a direction which would cause such stimulation. Gray further states that an increase in RMV is not regularly associated with an increase (and in fact may occur in the presence of a decrease) in drive related to any one of the three factors considered to be concerned with the control of pulmonary ventilation, however, at least one of three changes must be present: (1) rise in arterial Pco_2, (2) decrease in arterial Po_2, or (3) increase in arterial cH. It is envisaged that any one of these may assume the major role in driving respiration under certain circumstances. In the case of administering CO_2 the arterial cH increases almost linearly with the increase in arterial Pco_2 so that, according to Gray's multiple factor theory, the stimulation of breathing is greater than would be produced by either the rise in Pco_2 alone or the rise in arterial cH alone.

The evidence seems to be sufficient to establish that the level of pulmonary ventilation in subjects at rest is determined by either the arterial Pco_2 tension, the arterial Po_2 tension, the arterial cH or by interaction of these three drives. The relationship between each of these drives and the other two has been discussed at length in physiological literature. Gray advanced the hypothesis that effects of the three factors are simply *additive*; and, in line with this view he presents an equation for calculation of the ventilation ratio (ratio of alveolar ventilation under new conditions to alveolar ventilation under control conditions) from the changes in Pco_2, Po_2 and cH of arterial blood.

According to Gray's theory if Pco_2 is lowered further below the level which leads to apnea because of lack of a CO_2 stimulus to the respiratory center, the Pco_2 effect is further subtracted. Stated in another way, if breathing is put on an oxygen-lack drive, the lower the Pco_2, the lower will be the amount of respiratory stimulation because of the lesser Pco_2 effect to be added to the oxygen-lack drive. In experiments by Nielsen and Smith (1952) the alveolar Po_2 tension was maintained at constant low levels, eliciting O_2-lack drive, while the effects of adding CO_2 were tested. It was found that CO_2 had no effect, or only a slight effect, on the ventilation under these condi-

tions until a threshold value of arterial Pco_2 of about the same magnitude as that which causes initiation of breathing under normal conditions was reached. Hence, it appears that the CO_2 level does not at all influence the level of ventilation when breathing is being maintained by the hypoxic stimulus. Christensen (1954) comments that it is difficult to see how Gray's multiple factor theory can explain an unchanged ventilation when the alveolar and arterial Pco_2 are changed between 21 and 33 mm. Hg at a constant alveolar Po_2. It seems possible that just as Po_2 is not a factor in respiratory regulation when it is above a certain level, Pco_2 may not be a factor at all when it is below a certain level.

Immediate respiratory responses to exposure to a given reduction in Po_2 in inspired air are of lesser degree than those which are seen after chronic exposure. Acclimatization occurs so that during prolonged exposure pulmonary ventilation is increased, as indicated by a further lowering of the alveolar Pco_2 beyond that observed initially. Rahn and Otis (1949) suggest that a rise in alkalinity of the blood due to decreased oxyhemoglobin saturation inhibits the respiratory stimulation that would be expected to result from the decrease in Po_2 *per se*. Regardless of the mechanism of acclimatization which occurs during chronic exposure to lowered Po_2 in inspired air, when it has occurred, there is increased pulmonary ventilation, lowered alveolar Pco_2, increased alveolar Po_2 beyond that observed initially, and a lowered alkali reserve. During the process of acclimatization, alkali is removed by urinary excretion. The pH of the blood is within the normal range. It appears that other more complex changes in respiratory control are involved in the gradual adjustments to hypoxia. For example, the alveolar Pco_2 which is lowered initially may return to or even exceed the level in normal subjects at sea level, hence sensitivity of the regulatory mechanism to CO_2 must have become readjusted. In short, in acute hypoxia the CO_2 drive may be largely or completely eliminated, but it must be assumed that the CO_2 drive is in some degree restored during acclimatization.

Mechanisms of Hyperpnea during Exercise

During exercise pulmonary ventilation increases, and the rise is quite proportionate to the amount of increase in muscular activity. Since an increased rate of production of CO_2 and of acid metabolites and an increased rate of utilization of oxygen occur as a consequence of increased

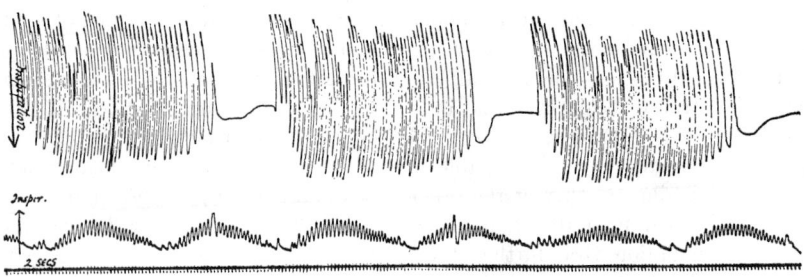

FIG. 53.10 Two examples of periodic breathing. (After Lewis.)

muscular activity, *a priori* it is logical to think that the respiratory stimulation is induced by the same three factors which are considered to operate in the resting subject. However, a number of studies show that muscular exercise is not regularly associated with either a decrease in arterial Po_2, or a rise in arterial Pco_2 or cH. In individual experiments none of these factors shows a change during exercise in the direction needed to elicit increased respiratory activity (Grodins, 1950).

The Pco_2 of *mixed venous* blood is increased and the Po_2 decreased during exercise, but no respiration-influencing receptor located on the *venous* side of the systemic circuit has been demonstrated. (The presence of bodies similar to the aortic bodies around the pulmonary artery and receiving a blood supply from it have been described, and if such receptors exist they might be expected to elicit stimulation of breathing during exercise). There is evidence that respiration is stimulated reflexly by impulses arising in the working muscles or the joints which are acted upon by these muscles. Still another possibility is that during voluntary activity impulses are directed in descending nerve tracts into the respiratory center to exert a stimulant effect, but there appears to be no evidence that this is the mechanism (see Kao in Cunningham and Lloyd, 1963). In any case it appears that accessory respiratory drives are brought into play during exercise so that increased ventilation may occur even before a change in Pco_2, Po_2 or cH have had time to occur at the sites upon which these stimuli act. The factors which are concerned in the stimulation of breathing, which most respiratory physiologists believe must be present in exercise over and above that related to the three chemical stimuli which operate under resting conditions, are referred to by Grodins (1950) as the *exercise stimulus*. It is probable that afferent influences from various sources are concerned and

also that chemical excitants not yet identified play a role.

Periodic Breathing

Under certain conditions irregular or "periodic" breathing may develop. There are two major types: Biot's breathing and Cheyne-Stokes breathing. In Biot's breathing there are periods of variable length during which breathing is present, and these alternate with apneic periods of different lengths. The transitions from the periods of activity to apnea and back are abrupt. In contrast to this in Cheyne-Stokes breathing, although periods of respiratory activity alternate with apneic periods, the amplitude of breathing increases gradually to a maximum and then decreases gradually until the next period of inactivity. Biot's breathing has been observed in meningitis and other pathological conditions affecting the medulla. Cheyne-Stokes respiration has been observed in a number of different circumstances, some of which are pathological and some physiological (fig. 53.10).

Cheyne-Stokes breathing occurs in some normal subjects at moderately high altitudes, (for example, 12,000 to 15,000 feet) and it may be seen in normal sleeping infants. Experimentally, it may be produced in normal subjects following a prolonged period of voluntary hyperventilation, and it can be produced by having the subject breathe deeply through a tube of a certain length. In the latter case, the dead space is increased by a specific amount, and if there is too little or too much increase in dead space, Cheyne-Stokes breathing will not develop. Several drugs, notably morphine, may cause the appearance of Cheyne-Stokes breathing. The condition is commonly seen in persons suffering from chronic congestive heart failure, and in such cases the periodicity tends to be aggravated by sedation or during sleep.

The basis for Cheyne-Stokes breathing after

hyperventilation, as explained on page 1018, appears to be that oxygen-lack drive makes its appearance and is relieved several times before the P_{CO_2} finally is built back up to levels sufficient to drive normal respiration. The oxygen-lack drive presumably is via the chemoreceptors. However, there is evidence that two or more types of initial defect may cause Cheyne-Stokes breathing. For example, during periodic breathing there also are cyclic changes in the blood pressure level; and in some instances, the rise in mean arterial blood pressure occurs during the phase of respiratory activity while in other cases the rise in blood pressure is during the apneic phase. These two types most likely are related to quite different basic mechanisms. The former has been demonstrated to occur in dogs having the sino-aortic pressoreceptors and the carotid and aortic bodies denervated or isolated (Youmans and Schopp, 1957) hence chemoreceptive drive could not have been a factor. It is still probable, however, that the other type of periodicity is dependent upon a seesawing between reflex and central drives. Guyton (1956) has described experiments in which he found that Cheyne-Stokes breathing was produced if the time required for blood to flow from the heart to the brain was prolonged by increasing the length of the channels. Since circulation time is increased in chronic heart failure, this may be the change that initiates periodic breathing in patients suffering from this condition.

Eyster (1906) produced periodic breathing in dogs by elevating the intracranial pressure. His records show that breathing occurred when blood pressure rose above the level of the intracranial pressure, and apnea was present when the pressure was below this level. In clinical cases with increased intracranial pressure, Eyster observed the same pattern of cyclic changes in respiration and blood pressure as that produced experimentally in dogs.

Dyspnea

Dyspnea literally means difficult breathing. When the respirations cannot be carried out with ease and practically unconsciously, the individual is said to be dyspneic. The term therefore implies a subjective element. Dyspnea thus differs from hyperpnea. The latter term means simply increased pulmonary ventilation, and this may occur quite unconsciously or if the subject is aware of the augmentation of the breathing, there is not necessarily any sensation of difficulty or distress. When the hyperpnea becomes extreme and yet leaves the need for which it has been instituted unsatisfied, discomfort or distress is experienced, and the term dyspnea is applicable. Meakins offers the following concise definition: "Dyspnea is the consciousness of the necessity for increased respiratory effort."

Causes of Dyspnea

Since the respiratory and circulatory functions are directed toward the acquisition of oxygen and the elimination of carbon dioxide, dyspnea may result if either of these functions be disturbed to such an extent that the normal gaseous exchanges cannot be accomplished. On the other hand, the oxygen requirement and the carbon dioxide production may be so great that the *normal* respiratory and circulatory mechanisms find difficulty in meeting the demands of the moment. Or again the supply of oxygen itself may be inadequate as a result of a low oxygen tension in the atmosphere (e.g., high altitudes). In considering the causes of dyspnea we must, therefore, in many instances look beyond the lungs themselves.

The fundamental or immediate causes of dyspnea can in most instances be reduced to the following categories. (1) Stimulation of the respiratory center either (a) reflexly from the carotid and aortic bodies (anoxia or increase in H-ion concentration due to fixed acids), (b) directly, by CO_2 excess, (c) a combination of (a) and (b) as in asphyxial states, or (d) by impulses from cerebral centers or by afferent impulses, especially of a painful character, from abdominal or peripheral regions. (2) Hypersensitivity of the Hering-Breuer reflex, thus bringing about earlier inhibition of the inspiratory phase and causing, as a consequence, a more rapid shallow type of breathing.

The abnormal conditions chiefly associated with dyspnea are:

(1) Prevention of adequate oxygenation of the blood in the lungs (arterial hypoxia, ch. 54).

(2) Interference with the transport of the respiratory gases. Anoxia of the hypokinetic or anemic type (a) slowing of the circulation as in cardiac failure, (b) severe anemia, breathlessness chiefly on exertion.

(3) Restriction of the action of the diaphragm or intercostals.

(4) *Acidosis*, reduced alkali reserve or retention of CO_2.

(5) Increased metabolism.

(6) *Nervous conditions*, e.g., emotional disturbance, neurasthenia, hysteria, encephalitis, or the direct stimulation of the respiratory center by cerebral tumor, hemorrhage or edema.

Dyspnea due to Pulmonary Diseases

Dyspnea is a feature of various respiratory diseases.

(a) In some instances, e.g., laryngeal or bronchial obstruction and asthma, the dyspnea is due to a combination of anoxia and CO_2 retention.

(b) In other instances owing to the reduced distensibility of the lungs resulting from edema, congestion, inflammation, fibrosis, etc., the Hering-Breuer reflex is thought to be abnormally sensitive.

(c) Limitation of the movements of the diaphragm and chest wall. In emphysema, for example, owing to the loss of lung elasticity the resting position of the chest is one of nearly full inspiration. The diaphragm is fixed and the thorax elevated. Any further enlargement of the chest entails unusual effort on the part of the intercostal muscles (see also ch. 51) and the enlistment of the accessory muscles of respiration. Expiration involves active contraction of the expiratory muscles.

Cardiac Dyspnea

Dyspnea upon exertion is a feature of certain chronic pulmonary and heart lesions, e.g., mitral stenosis. Stimulation of the carotid and aortic bodies by oxygen want or of the respiratory center by carbon dioxide excess is not, in most cases of cardiac failure, responsible for the dyspnea, since the oxygen saturation of the arterial blood may not be reduced to any important degree, and the carbon dioxide tension is within or even below the normal range. Pulmonary engorgement leading to diminished distensibility of the lung is considered by Meakins, Christie and associates to be the prime cause of cardiac dyspnea. Though the reduction in the vital capacity may be roughly proportional to the dyspnea, the two do not bear the relationship of cause and effect, since the subject's vital capacity is always greater than the volume of air required for the exertion which causes the dyspnea. Due, however, to the diminished distensibility—the stiffness of the lung—a greater inspiratory effort is expended in breathing the extra volume of air which the muscular exertion demands. The lung might be compared to

stiffened bellows leather; more force is required to distend it. The recoil of the lung is also moderately reduced so that expiration instead of being a passive act now requires the aid of the contraction of expiratory muscles in order to "squeeze" the air from the lungs. The intrapleural pressure, therefore, instead of remaining "negative" throughout the respiratory cycle becomes positive toward the end of expiration (Christie and Meakins). The decreased distensibility of the lung, for the same reason that it increases the difficulty of enlarging the volume of tidal air, reduces the vital capacity. In other words the dyspnea and reduced vital capacity are due to a common cause. The reduced distensibility possibly also has the effect, as already mentioned, of increasing the sensitivity of the Hering-Breuer reflex with the production of shallow breathing.

When pulmonary edema supervenes in patients with congestive heart failure, interference with the absorption of oxygen and the production of arterial hypoxia (stimulation of carotid body) may possibly be a factor. Hindrance to the absorption of oxygen, caused by the presence of exudate in the alveoli and the edematous swelling of the alveolar walls, is accompanied by little or no interference with the elimination of carbon dioxide; this is probably due in part to the much greater solubility of carbon dioxide than of oxygen and, in consequence, to the freer diffusion of the former gas through the edema fluid. In congestive heart failure arterial hypoxia with a normal or even a subnormal carbon dioxide content of the arterial blood may exist even in the absence of pulmonary edema.

Experimental support can be cited for the view that reduced distensibility of the lungs as a result of congestion is an important factor in cardiac dyspnea. It has been mentioned elsewhere (p. 1037) that distension of the pulmonary bed causes rapid shallow breathing. The production of multiple emboli in the pulmonary capillaries by the intravenous injection of starch granules causes congestion of the lungs and rapid shallow breathing, and Partridge found that after rapid breathing has been induced in this way, the impulses recorded from the vagus nerve are of higher frequency than those resulting from inflation of normal lung to an equal degree. It has also been shown that in man pulmonary congestion does actually reduce the distensibility of the lung tissue.

Harrison and his colleagues found in subjects with cardiac failure the CO_2 content of the jugular blood to be within normal limits and observed no significant reduction in the cerebral blood flow (i.e., through the respiratory center).

Though there is much to be said for the reflex origin of cardiac dyspnea, not all are agreed as to its paramount importance. McMichael, for example, in a clinical study found a reduction in cardiac output in those subjects showing hyperpnea (which is always associated with the dyspnea) during rest. The hyperpnea showed a closer correlation with the cardiac output than with the vital capacity which, he points out, is contrary to what might be expected were congestion of the lungs the dominant causative factor. He is inclined to believe that the hyperpnea and dyspnea of the cardiac patient *during rest* is due to reduced blood flow through the respiratory center, resulting in a high CO_2 tension, and possibly to the accumulation of acid products of its own metabolism.

Orthopnea. In congestive heart failure with dyspnea at rest the breathlessness is usually more pronounced in the recumbent than in the sitting position. When propped up with pillows, the patient may be quite comfortable but becomes dyspneic when he lies down. Many theories have been advanced in attempts to explain the less difficult breathing in the upright position. Among these are:

(a) Removal of the weight of the abdominal viscera which interferes with the descent of the diaphragm in the recumbent position.

(b) Reduction in the intracranial venous pressure and the improved draining of blood from the medulla and in consequence, augmentation of the flow through the respiratory center.

(c) Draining of blood from the pulmonary circuit. This is probably the most important factor. The vital capacity is less in the recumbent than in the sitting posture. This is true even for the normal person but in cardiac cases the effect is accentuated by the pulmonary vascular engorgement and decreased distensibility of the lung induced by recumbency.

Cardiac asthma (paroxysmal nocturnal dyspnea). In some patients with severe chronic congestive heart failure acute dyspnea which may terminate in pulmonary edema comes on during the night. The patient has a feeling of suffocation. He assumes the upright position and may go to the window for air. These attacks are related to excessive engorgement of the lungs with blood so that pulmonary capillary pressure rises to the point of producing transudation into the alveoli. As indicated above the volume of blood in the lungs increases when one changes from the upright to the recumbent position. Patients with chronic

heart failure already have an elevated venous pressure which increases further when they recline. The key question is with regard to the fact that paroxysmal nocturnal dyspnea comes on after a delay usually of several hours since the effects of changing from the upright to the recumbent position insofar as they are related to gravity might be expected to occur within seconds or minutes. The clue to this problem probably is provided in the observation that edema fluid in patients with congestive heart failure is transferred from the interstitial spaces into the blood, and a rise in blood volume occurs slowly during the night. This leads to a further elevation of venous and pulmonary capillary pressure. The paroxysm could be set off in two ways. The pressure in the pulmonary capillaries could rise to the point of producing transudation and hence impairment of exchange of O_2 and CO_2. On the other hand, the venous pressure might reach the critical level at which overdistention of the heart would result in a decrease in the output of the heart. Once this occurs a vicious cycle is produced: decreased output leads to further elevation of venous pressure, and elevation of venous pressure leads to further overdistention of the heart and decreased output. In either case the change to the orthostatic position would be beneficial in that the blood would tend to remain in the dependent part of the body and thus decrease the volume and pressure of blood in the heart and lungs. Also, it should be noted that acute cardiac decompensation, produced by exceeding the critical pressure on the curve which relates cardiac output to venous pressure, leads to a rise in pulmonary capillary pressure and hence to acute pulmonary edema.

Dyspnea in Anemia

The anemic subject at rest typically is not dyspneic. The hemoglobin, though reduced in amount, becomes fully saturated with oxygen in the lungs. The oxygen tension and consequently the quantity of the gas in simple solution in the arterial blood are normal. The arterial blood of a patient whose hemoglobin is 30 per cent of the normal value will, however, contain only a little over 6 volumes per cent of oxygen. In the healthy resting body the blood in its passage through the capillaries gives up about 5 volumes per cent. If the velocity of blood flow through the tissues in anemia were the same as during health, a unit volume of blood would tend to give up an equivalent amount of oxygen. If this occurred there would be a reserve of only 1 volume per cent, i.e., the venous blood would be almost completely reduced, and the tissues including the carotid and aortic bodies, would suffer at all times from anoxia. The circulation rate (cardiac output) is, however, increased in severe anemia so that each unit of blood gives up a smaller proportion than this of its oxygen load. The chemoreceptors apparently are not stimulated, and the patient is not dyspneic while resting even though his hemoglobin is greatly reduced. Fahr and Ronzone reported a case in which the hemoglobin was 12 per cent of the normal and the arterial blood contained only 2.2 volumes per cent of oxygen. There was no dyspnea during rest. Not only is the output of the heart increased, but a redistribution of the blood flow occurs. The vessels of the skin are constricted, and a greater proportion of the total blood volume is driven through other regions. The extent to which the circulatory readjustments can compensate for the blood defect is limited, therefore during exertion the extra demand for oxygen cannot be met. Oxygen want follows, the respiratory mechanism is stimulated; hyperpnea and dyspnea result.

It is to be remembered that in anemia the carriage of carbon dioxide may also be interfered with since hemoglobin plays an important role in the transport of this gas (see ch. 50).

Dyspnea due to Increased Metabolism

Muscular exercise is an outstanding cause of a great increase of metabolism. Reflexes initiated in the active muscles, and from the walls of the great veins as a result of the high pressure of blood entering the right side of the heart, and possibly as well the irradiation of impulses from the motor cortex, are thought to play an important part in the hyperpnea of exercise (p. 1021). As the severity of the exercise is increased, hyperpnea merges into dyspnea. The athlete and the untrained person differ widely in respect to the degree of muscular exertion which will produce this physiological type of dyspnea. The difference depends upon the following factors:

(a) *Vital capacity.* In the average normal man the pulmonary ventilation increases from 4- to 5-fold before the dyspneic point is reached. The athlete on the other hand, since his vital capacity is greater, shows a correspondingly greater increase in his pulmonary ventilation before dyspnea supervenes. The existence of any pulmonary condition which reduces the vital capacity will depress the level of the dyspneic point.

(b) *Circulation rate.* The trained man's circulation rate increases to a greater degree than the untrained, and so more oxygen is delivered to his tissues.

(c) *Neuromuscular integration.* Co-ordination of the several muscles in a given muscular act is more precise in the trained than in the untrained man. There is thus less waste of effort. In the performance of a given amount of work, therefore, the untrained man consumes a greater volume of oxygen, i.e., he is a less efficient machine.

A pathological increase in metabolism, e.g., hyperthyroidism, fever, etc., does not, in the absence of some respiratory or circulatory abnormality, cause dyspnea during rest. The increase in metabolism would need to be around 300 per cent before dyspnea might be expected to occur and such a metabolic level is never reached in these or any other pathological condition. Nevertheless, in hyperthyroidism dyspnea will follow upon a degree of exertion which would cause no distress in a healthy person, for the greater metabolic rate, due to the disease, added to that of the exercise will increase the metabolism sufficiently to raise the pulmonary ventilation above the dyspneic point. The dyspnea of hyperthyroidism, when pulmonary and cardiovascular complications are absent, therefore, is like that of anemia in that it is evident only upon exertion.

Dyspnea due to Acidosis

The importance of the part played by pulmonary ventilation in resisting a rise in the hydrogen ion concentration of the body fluids has been dealt with elsewhere (ch. 34). Little more need be said here. Nonvolatile acids, e.g., lactic in muscular exercise, β-hydroxybutyric and acetoacetic acids in diabetes, and retained acids in nephritis, react with bicarbonate. The alkali reserve becomes reduced, but the ratio,

$$\frac{H_2CO_2}{NaHCO_3} = \frac{1}{20}$$

is maintained through the stimulating effect of CO_2 upon the respiratory center. It is thus that the CO_2 of the alveolar air (and so of the arterial blood) is kept at a level proportional to the reduction in the denominator of the equation. When this can no longer be effected, i.e., when the hydrogen ion concentration of the blood rises, the acidosis being then uncompensated, the center is stimulated both directly and through reflexes initiated from chemoreceptors of the carotid and aortic bodies.

J. B. S. Haldane produced a severe acidosis and dyspnea in himself by the ingestion of acid-forming salts ($CaCl_2$ and NH_4Cl). But as a matter of fact, the production of fixed acids in diseased conditions rarely causes such a high degree of hyperpnea that dyspnea results, unless the circulatory and respiratory mechanisms are very inefficient or the metabolic rate is increased. According to Means the "alkali reserve" must drop to around 12 volumes per cent before dyspnea supervenes as a result of the acidosis itself. In milder grades of acidosis, however, dyspnea occurs upon exertion. The hyperpnea due to the increased metabolism of the exercise is then added to that due to the acidosis, with the result that the dyspneic point is soon reached.

In severe diabetic acidosis *air hunger*, or Kussmaul breathing, may be seen in the comatose patient.

Carbon dioxide retention may, as in emphysema, be accompanied by a compensatory rise in bicarbonate and a normal blood reaction (compensated CO_2 excess); dyspnea is not a notable feature in this condition. In other instances of CO_2 retention, compensation is incomplete (uncompensated CO_2 excess or gaseous acidosis) and dyspnea results. In others, again, the CO_2 retention is due to the depression of the respiratory center itself, as in morphine narcosis; in such instances, although compensation is incomplete, dyspnea of course does not occur.

REFERENCES

ADRIAN, E. D. J. Physiol., 1933, **79**, 332.

ADRIAN, E. D., AND BRONK, D. W. J. Physiol., 1928, **66**, 81.

ADRIAN, E. D., AND BUYTENDIJK, F. J. J. J. Physiol., 1931, **71**, 121.

ARCHER, O., AND BUCHER, V. Helv. Physiol. Acta, 1954, **12**, 265.

BAKER, S., AND HITCHCOCK, F. J. Appl. Physiol., 1957, **10**, 363.

BARCROFT, J., AND MARGARIA, R. J. Physiol., 1931, **72**, 175. Ibid., 1932, **74**, 156.

BATTRO, A., AND LABOURT, F. E. Rev. argent. cardiol., 1943, **10**, 83.

BAXTER, D. W., AND OLSZEWSKI, JERZY. J. Neurophysiol., 1955, **18**, 276.

BEAN, JOHN W. Am. J. Physiol., 1952, **171**, 522.

BISHOP, B. J. Appl. Physiol., 1964, **19**, 224.

BJURSTEDT, H. Physiol. Acta. Scandinav., 1953, **29**, 145.

BRECKENRIDGE, C. G., AND HOFF, H. E. Am. J. Physiol., 1953, **175**, 449. Ibid., 1954, **178**, 521.

BRODIE, D. A., AND BORISON, H. L. Am. J. Physiol., 1957, **188**, 347.

CHATFIELD, P. O., AND PURPURA, D. P. Am. J. Physiol., 1953, **172**, 632.

CHRISTIE, R. V., AND MEAKINS, J. J. Clin. Invest., 1934, **13**, 323.

CHURCHILL, E. D., AND COPE, O. J. Exper. Med., 1929, **49**, 531.

COLLIP, J. B. J. Physiol., 1920–21, **54**, 58.

COMROE, J. H. Physiol. Rev., 1944, **24**, 319.

COMROE, J. H., JR. AND MORTIMER, L. J. Pharm. & Exper. Therap., 1964, **146**, 33.

COMROE, J. H., AND SCHMIDT, C. F. Am. J. Physiol., 1938, **121**, 75. Ibid., 1943, **138**, 536.

COOMBS, H. D., AND PIKE, F. H. Am. J. Physiol., 1918, **45**, 569.

CROMER, S. P., AND IVY, A. C. Proc. Soc. Exper. Biol. & Med., 1931, **28**, 565.

DALE, H. H., AND EVANS, C. L. J. Physiol., 1920, **54**, 167.

DAVIS, H. L., FOWLER, W. S., AND LAMBERT, E. H. Am. J. Physiol., 1956, **187**, 558.

DOUGLAS, C. G., AND HALDANE, J. S. J. Physiol., 1909, **38**, 401. Ibid., 420.

DRINKER, C. K. Am. Rev. Tuberc., 1948, **58**, 1.

DRIPPS, R. D., AND COMROE, J. H. Am. J. Physiol., 1947, **149**, 277.

EYSTER, J. A. J. Exper. Med., 1906, **8**, 565.

FAHR, G. AND RONZONE, E. Arch. Int. Med., 1922, **29**, 331.

FIELD, H., JR., AND BOCK, A. V. J. Clin. Invest., 1925, **2**, 67.

FINLEY, K. H. Arch. Neurol. & Psychiat., 1931, **26**, 754.

FLOURENS, J. P. M. Compt. rend. Acad. sc., Paris, 1858, **47**, 803.

FREY, J. S., AND GESELL, R. Proc. Soc. Exper. Biol., 1947, **6**, 106.

GESELL, R. Physiol. Rev., 1925, **5**, 551.

GESELL, R. AND MOYER, C. Am. J. Physiol., 1941, **131**, 674.

GESSELL, R., BRICKER, J., AND MAGEE, C. Am. J. Physiol., 1936, **117**, 423.

GESELL, R., BRASSFIELD, C. R., AND LILLIE, R. H. J. Comp. Neurol. 1954, **101**, 331.

GESELL, R., MAGEE, C., AND BRICKER, J. Am. J. Physiol., 1940, **128**, 615.

GRAY, J. S. Pulmonary Ventilation, Am. Lecture Series. Charles C Thomas, Springfield, Ill., 1950, Science, 1946, **103**, 739.

GUYTON, A. C., CROWELL, J. W., AND MOORE, J. W. Am. J. Physiol., 1956, **187**, 395.

HABER, E., KOHN, K. W., NGAI, S. H., HOLADAY D. A., AND WANG, S. C. Am. J. Physiol., 1957, **190**, 350.

HALDANE, J. B. S. J. Physiol., 1921, **55**, 265.

HALDANE, J. S. J. Physiol., 1895, **18**, 201, 430.

HALDANE, J. S., AND POULTON, E. P. J. Physiol., 1908, **37**, 390.

HALDANE, J. S., AND PRIESTLEY, J. G. J. Physiol., 1905, **32**, 225.

HARRISON, T. R. AND ASSOCIATES. Arch. Int. Med., 1932, **50**, 690. J. Clin. Invest., 1932, **11**, 133.

HARROP, G. A. J. A. M. A., 1923, **80**, 1641.

HEAD, H. J. Physiol., 1889, **10**, 1:279.

HENDERSON, V. E., AND GRAIGIE, E. H. Am. J. Physiol., 1936, **115**, 520.

HENDERSON, V. E., AND SWEET, T. A. Am. J. Physiol., 1929, **91**, 94.

HERING, E., AND BREUER, J. Sitz. Akad. Wiss., Wien, 1868, **57**, 672. Ibid., **58**, 909.

HEYMANS, C., AND BOUCKAERT, J. J. J. Physiol., 1930, **69**, 254. Ibid., 1933, **79**, 49.

HEYMANS, C., BOUCKAERT, J. J., AND DAUTRE-BANDE, L. Compt. rend. Soc. biol., 1931, **107**, 54.

HEYMANS, J. F., AND HEYMANS, C. Arch. internat. pharmacodyn., 1927, **33**, 273.

HOFF, H. E., AND BRECKENRIDGE, C. G. A.M.A. Arch. Neurol. & Psychiat., 1954, **72**, 11.

JACOBS, M. H. Am. J. Physiol., 1920, **51**, 321. Ibid., **53**, 457.

KAO, F. F. Am. J. Physiol., 1956, **185**, 145.

KAO, F. F., AND RAY, L. H. Am. J. Physiol., 1954, **179**, 249.

KETY, S. S., AND SCHMIDT, C. F. J. Clin. Invest., 1948, **27**, 484.

LEUSEN, I. Am. J. Physiol., 1954, **176**, 39.

LEUSEN, I. Am. J. Physiol., 1954, **176**, 45.

LILJESTRAND, G. Acta. physiol. scandinav., 1951–54, **23–24**, 225.

LILJESTRAND, A. Acta physiol. scandinav., 1953, **29**, 321, Suppl. 106.

LOESHKE, G. C. Pflüger's Arch. ges. Physiol., 1953, **257**, 349.

LUMSDEN, T. J. Physiol., 1932, **58**, 81, 111.

MARKWALD, M., Ztschr. Biol., 1887, **23**, 149. Ibid., 1890, **26**, 259.

McMICHAEL. J. Clin. Sc., 1939, **4**, 19.

MEAKINS, J. C. J. A. M. A., 1934, **103**, 1442.

METZ, B. Am. J. Physiol., 1958, **192**, 101.

MITCHELL, R. A., LOESCHCKE, SEVERINGHAUS, J. W., RICHARDSON, B. W., AND MASSION, W. H., Ann. N. Y. Acad. Sci., 1963, **109**, 661.

MONNIER, M. Rev. neurol., 1938, **69**, 517.

MORGAN, D. P., KAO, F., LIM, T. P. K., AND GRODINS, F. S. Am. J. Physiol., 1955, **183**, 454.

NGAI, S. H. AND WANG, S. C. Am. J. Physiol., 1957, **190**, 343.

NIELSEN, M., AND SMITH, H. Acta. physiol. scandinav., 1951–52, **23–24**, 293.

NIELSON. M. Skand. Archinav. Physiol. (Suppl. 10), 1936, **74**, 87.

PARTRIDGE, G. J. Cell. & Comp. Physiol., 1933, **2**, 367. Canad. M. A. J., 1935, **33**, 11.

PEMBREY, M. S., AND ALLEN, R. W. J. Physiol., 1950, **21**, xviii.

PITTS, R. F. Physiol. Rev., 1946, **26**, 609.

PITTS, R. F., MAGOUN, H. W., AND RANSON, S. W. Am. J. Physiol., 1939, **126**, 673, 689. Ibid., **126**, 654.

PORTER, W. T. J. Physiol., 1895, **17**, 455.

RAHN, H., AND OTIS, A. B. Am. J. Physiol., 1949, **157**, 145.

ROSENTHAL, J. Hermann's Handb. der Physiol., 1882, **4**, (2) 157.

SCHMIDT, C. F., DUMKE, P. L., AND DRIPPS, R. D., JR. Am. J. Physiol., 1939, **128**, 1.

SCHOPP, R. T., GILFOIL, T. M., AND YOUMANS, W. B. Am. J. Physiol., 1957, **189**, 117, 123.

SCOTT, R. W. Am. J. Physiol., 1918–19, **47**, 43. Ibid., 1917, **44**, 196.

SEEGERS, W. H. J. Biol. Chem., 1940, **136**, 103.

SHARPEY-SCHAFER, E. J. Physiol., 1932, **75**, 130.

SMITH, D. L., MAASKE, C. A., AND JULIAN, F. Am. J. Physiol., 1955, **181**, 341.

STELLA, G. J. Physiol., 1938, **93**, 10, 263.

STEWART, G. N., PIKE, F. H., AND GUTHRIE, C. C. J. Exper. Med., 1908, **10**, 490.

TANG, P. C. Am. J. Physiol., 1953, **172**, 645.

TURNER, J. K. Fed. Proc., 1961, **20**, 120.

VON EULER, U. S., LILJESTRAND, G., AND ZOTTER-MAN, Y. Skandinav. Arch. Physiol., 1939, **83**, 132.

WANG, S. C., NGAI, S. H., AND FRUMIN, M. J. Am. J. Physiol., 1957, **190**, 333.

WATT, J. G., DUMKE, P. R., AND COMROE, J. H., JR. Am. J. Physiol., 1943, **138**, 610.

WEISS, S., AND ROBB, G. P. J. A. M. A., 1933, **100**, 1841.

WHALEN, W. J. Am. J. Physiol., 1955, **183**, 445.

WINTERSTEIN, H. Pflüger's Arch. ges. Physiol., 1911, **138**, 167.

WITZLEB, E., BARTELS, H., BUDDE, H., AND MOCHIZUCKI, M. Pflüger's Arch. ges. Physiol., 1955, **261**, 211.

YAMAMOTO, W. S. Am. J. Physiol., 1957, **191**, 423.

YOUMANS, W. B. Anesthesiology, 1958, **19**, 552.

YOUMANS, W. B., AND SCHOPP, R. T. Proc. Soc. Exper. Biol. & Med. 1957, **95**, 100.

Monographs and Reviews

AVIADO, D. M., JR., AND SCHMIDT, C. F. Physiol. Rev., 1955, **35**, 247.

BRECHER, G. Venous Return. Grune & Stratton, Inc., 1956.

BJURSTEDT, H. Ann. Rev. Physiol., 1957, **19**, 151.

CAMPBELL, E. J. M. The Respiratory Muscles and the Mechanics of Breathing. Lloyd-Luke, London, 1958.

CHRISTENSEN, H. The chemical and nervous control of respiration, in Handbook of Respiratory Physiology. p. 103, United States Air Force School of Aviation Medicine. Randolph Field, Texas, 1954.

COMROE, J. H. Physiology of Respiration. Year Book Medical Pub. Chicago, 1965.

CORDIER, D., AND HEYMANS, C. Le centre respiratoire. Hermann, Paris, 1935.

CUNNINGHAM, D. J. C. AND LLOYD, B. B., eds. The Regulation of Human Respiration. Blackwell Scientific Publications, Oxford, 1963.

DAWES, G. S., AND COMROE, J. H., JR. Physiol. Rev., 1954, **34**, 167.

DRIPPS, R. D., AND SEVERINGHAUS, J. W. Physiol. Rev., 1955, **35**, 741.

FENN, W. O., AND RAHN, H., eds., Handbook of Physiology, Sec. 3, Vol. I, Respiration, Amer. Physiol. Soc., 1964.

GESELL, R. Physiol. Rev., 1925, **5**, 551. Ann. Rev. Physiol., 1939, **1**, 185.

GRAY, J. S. Pulmonary Ventilation and Its Regulation. Charles C Thomas, Springfield, Ill., 1950.

GRODINS, F. S. Physiol. Rev., 1950, **30**, 220.

GRODINS, F. S. Regulation of pulmonary ventilation. The Physiologist, 1964, **7**, 319.

HALDANE, J. S., AND PRIESTLY, J. G. Respiration. Oxford University Press, 1935.

HARRISON, T. R. Failure of the Circulation. Williams & Wilkins Company, Baltimore, 1939.

HEEMSTRA, H. Ann. Rev. Physiol. 1956, **18**, 121.

HEYMANS, C. New England J. Med., 1938, **219**, 157.

HEYMANS, C., AND BOUCKAERT, J. J. Le sinus carotidien et la zone homologue cardioaortique. Doin, Paris, 1933.

HEYMANS, C., AND NEIL, E. Reflexogenic Areas of the Cardiovascular System. J. A. Churchill, Ltd., London, 1958.

KROGH, A. The Comparative Physiology of Respiratory Mechanisms. University of Pennsylvania Press, Philadelphia, 1941.

Magoun, H. W., ed. Handbook of Physiology, Sec. 1, Vol. II, Neurophysiology, Amer. Physiol. Soc., 1960.

Means, J. H. Dyspnea. Medicine, 1924, 3, 309.

Millikan, G. A. *In* Handbook of Respiration Data in Aviation. National Res. Council, Washington, D. C. W. B. Saunders Company, Philadelphia, 1958.

Nahas, C. G., ed. Regulation of Respiration. Ann. N. Y. Acad. of Med., 1963, 109, 411–948.

O'Leary, J. L., and Coben, L. A. 1957. Physiol. Rev., 1958, 38, 243.

Otis, A. B. Ann. Rev. Physiol. 1958, 20, 159.

Pi-Suñer, A. Physiol. Rev., 1947, 27, 1.

Rossi, G. F., and Zanchetti, A. The Brain Stem Reticular Formation: Anatomy and Physiology. Arch. Ital. de Biol., 1957, 115, 199 (see pages 263–265).

Schmidt, C. F., and Comroe, J. H., Jr. Physiol. Rev., 1940, 20, 115. Ann. Rev. Physiol., 1941, 3, 151.

Winterstein, H. Ergebn. Physiol. 1955, 328.

Wyss, O. A. M. Respiratory center and reflex control of breathing. Helvet. physiol. et pharmacol. acta, 1954, Supplement 10.

Youmans, W. B., Murphy, Q. R., Turner, J. K., Davis, L. D., Briggs, D. J., and Hoye, A. S. Am. J. Physical Med., 1963, 42, 1.

CHAPTER 54

Hypoxia, Asphyxia, Dysbarism, Oxygen Therapy, and Resuscitation

Types of Hypoxia

The terms *hypoxia* and *anoxia* are synonymous, although the former etymologically is more suitable. Both terms are in common use and will be used interchangeably in the following discussion. The most useful definition of hypoxia is that it refers to any condition in which there is an inadequate *supply* of oxygen to the tissues. According to this definition it is synonymous with *oxygen lack* or *oxygen want*. Upon the basis of three quite different categories of causes Barcroft classified anoxia into *anoxic*, *anemic* and *stagnant* types. The categories described by him still need to be differentiated, but changes in the names of two of them seem to be preferable. A fourth type, caused by cyanide (p. 1045) and known as histotoxic anoxia, was added by Peters and Van Slyke; however, there is no oxygen lack in this case, but rather inability of the cells to utilize the oxygen brought to them, with the result that oxygen tension of the tissues is actually elevated. Hence it would seem to be preferable not to classify cyanide poisoning as a form of hypoxia. For reasons which will become apparent in the subsequent discussion *arterial hypoxia* is preferable to anoxic anoxia in Barcroft's classification, and *hypokinetic hypoxia* is a better term for stagnant anoxia. The three major types of oxygen lack, together with the principal causes of each, are listed below. Also, it should be realized that two or more of these types or causes can be present simultaneously, and each type may be either acute or chronic.

Oxygen Lack: Major Types and Causes

ARTERIAL HYPOXIA *is characterized by a lower than normal* Po_2 *in arterial blood.* (Oxygen capacity of blood and rate of blood flow are normal or elevated).
A. Low Po_2 in inspired air
   1. Altitude
   2. Breathing in closed space[1]
   3. Breathing artificial gas mixture containing lower Po_2 than that found in atmospheric air.

[1] Arterial Pco_2 is increased.

B. Decreased pulmonary ventilation
   1. Airway obstruction[1]
   2. Weakness or paralysis of respiratory muscles[1]
   3. Depression of respiratory center by drugs[1]
   4. Pneumothorax
C. Inadequate oxygenation in (abnormal) lungs.
   1. Poor mixing[1]
   2. Impaired diffusion (alveolar-capillary block)
   3. Bronchiolar constriction (asthma)[1]
   4. Filling of alveoli with fluid. Pulmonary edema, pneumonia, pulmonary hemorrhage, drowning.[1]
D. Venous-arterial shunts. Various types of cardiac or vascular abnormalities in which unoxygenated blood is mixed with oxygenated blood.

ANEMIC HYPOXIA *is characterized by a lowered oxygen capacity of the blood.* (The Po_2 of arterial blood and rate of blood flow are normal or elevated)
A. Less than normal hemoglobin content. *Anemias* of all types.
B. Hemoglobin combined with something other than oxygen, e.g. *carbon monoxide*.
C. Hemoglobin altered so that it can not combine with O_2. *Methemoglobin* found after poisoning with chlorates, nitrites, ferricyanides, acetanilid, etc.

HYPOKINETIC HYPOXIA *is characterized by a decreased rate of blood flow.*
A. Generalized. Congestive heart failure, hemorrhage, shock, etc.
B. Localized. Vasospasm, thrombosis, embolus.

Some confusion has arisen in the use of the term *anoxemia*. In some of the medical dictionaries and textbooks it is defined as synonymous with arterial hypoxia while some authors (Comroe and Dripps, 1950) use it as referring to a diminution of oxygen in the blood whether it be related to decreased Po_2 or decreased hemoglobin. In any case it would seem to be preferable to use the more specific terms, arterial hypoxia and anemic hypoxia, since these are not ambiguous.

ASPHYXIA. *Asphyxia* refers to conditions in which hypoxia is combined with *hypercapnia*—an increased CO_2 tension in the arterial blood and hence in the tissues also. It will be noted that a number of the causes of arterial hypoxia also lead to hypercapnia, while in some cases, notably at altitude, hypercapnia is not a factor. The opposite change, a lowered CO_2 in the body, is referred to as *hypocapnia* or *acapnia*. The reactions in asphyxia are related to effects of decreased arterial and tissue Po_2 and increased arterial and tissue Pco_2. Asphyxia of some degree is present in a number of those conditions listed in the classification of causes of oxygen lack, since elimination of CO_2, as well as uptake of oxygen, is impaired. Respiratory stimulation and dyspnea are prominent, and although the stimulation is derived from both the lowered Po_2 and increased Pco_2, the latter is more important. Cyanosis, being related to the presence of an increased amount of reduced hemoglobin in the blood in the cutaneous capillaries (p. 1045), also is characteristic of asphyxial states as well as those in which arterial anoxia is present without hypercapnia. Blood pressure tends to be elevated due to the stimulant action of CO_2 on the vasoconstrictor center, except in the terminal stages. Chronic adjustments to asphyxia include the increase in erythrocyte count, hematocrit, hemoglobin and oxygen capacity of the blood, which are induced by the lowered Po_2 tension, and renal excretion of acid to compensate for the rise in cH produced by retention of CO_2.

Tensions and Volumes Per Cent of Oxygen in the Blood in Hypoxia

In the *arterial* type of hypoxia both the Po_2 and the volumes per cent of O_2 are lowered. The blood has a normal or elevated O_2 capacity (20 volumes per cent or more), but it is not exposed to Po_2 which is high enough to produce the usual degree of saturation (95 + per cent). However, even though the blood is carrying less than a full load of O_2, when it reaches the capillaries in tissues which are functioning at a lower than normal oxygen tension it can unload as much oxygen per 100 ml. of blood as occurs normally. That is, normally about 20 volumes per cent would be present in the arterial blood and 15 volumes per cent in mixed venous blood, while in arterial hypoxia arterial blood capable of holding 20 volumes per cent would actually contain 15 and give off 5 so that the mixed venous blood would contain only 10 volumes per cent. In the latter case 50 per cent desaturation of hemoglobin would be produced at the tissue level as compared with 25 per cent in the normal.

In *hypokinetic* hypoxia both the Po_2 and volumes per cent of O_2 in the arterial blood are normal; however, as the blood flow through the tissues is slower than in the normal state and the cells continue to use oxygen at an essentially normal rate, the Po_2 in the tissues becomes lowered, and this causes the unloading of more O_2 per unit volume of blood flowing through the tissues. In very active tissues which are subjected to a severely deficient blood flow, virtually all of the oxygen in the blood delivered to the tissue may be extracted. This indicates that the Po_2 in such tissues approaches zero. Such a situation can not exist for more than a very short time before damage to the tissue results.

In *anemic* hypoxia the arterial Po_2 is normal so that saturation of hemoglobin approaches 100 per cent, but the volumes per cent of O_2 carried is reduced in proportion to the reduction in the amount of hemoglobin. Hence if blood carrying, for example, 10 volumes per cent of O_2 at full saturation of the hemoglobin gives up 5 volumes per cent per 100 ml. of blood flowing through the tissues, it is apparent that the O_2 in the tissues is so low as to cause 50 per cent desaturation. Again this is to be contrasted with the normal state in which, on the average, only about 25 per cent desaturation occurs as blood flows through the tissues.

Arterial Hypoxia at Altitude

Arterial hypoxia, uncomplicated by hypercapnia, is observed in individuals breathing air at high altitudes or in decompression chambers. Knowledge of both the acute and chronic adjustments to altitude is of great interest since man ascends rapidly in airplanes or resides for years at levels of 15,000 to 18,000 feet.

The per cent composition of atmospheric air is the same at altitude as at sea level. But the barometric pressure decreases with altitude. It is noteworthy that at an altitude of 18,000 feet the barometric pressure is about 380 mm. Hg or one-half of that at sea level. The oxygen tension, therefore, is diminished to one-half of that at sea level, since the Po_2 at any altitude is calculated by multiplying the barometric pressure by .2094. Thus, a second vertical scale showing oxygen tension could be derived simply by multiplying each of the figures in the barometric pressure scale by .2094.

At altitude as one breathes air containing a lower Po_2 than that of air at sea level the alveolar Po_2 becomes lowered. The decrease in alveolar

Po$_2$ at altitude if severe enough is counteracted in part by an increase in pulmonary ventilation, although this response is not as prominent immediately as it is after some delay.

Conditions at altitude can be simulated in an air tight chamber from which the air has been partially evacuated. At a given barometric pressure a certain altitude is simulated as far as gas tensions are concerned. Chambers have been constructed in such a way that they may be very rapidly, i.e., explosively, decompressed and the reactions of the subject followed from moment to moment. During acute exposure to simulated altitude, produced by rapid decompression of a chamber containing the subject, alveolar ventilation is increased so that alveolar Pco$_2$ is lowered, and the amount of decrease is proportional to the reduction in ambient pressure (increase in altitude). For example, shortly after decompression to a simulated altitude of 18,000 feet the alveolar Pco$_2$ is in the range of 27 $\pm$ 2 mm. Hg, and the alveolar Po$_2$ is in the range of 42 $\pm$ 3 mm. Hg. The alveolar Po$_2$ is less than half that found at sea level. At this point it should be noted that the water vapor tension in alveolar air, being determined by body temperature which is constant, remains at 47 mm. Hg at all altitudes, and when expressed in terms of per cent, it increases in direct proportion to the decrease in total pressure in the alveoli. For example, at sea level the per cent of water vapor is 47/760 $\times$ 100 whereas at 18,000 feet it is 47/380 $\times$ 100. At an altitude where the barometric pressure is only 74 mm. Hg, water boils at body temperature and the alveoli are filled with water vapor.

Immediately after sudden exposure to altitude, respiratory adjustments occur; however, conditions continue to change from one 5-minute period to the next for a period of 30 to 60 minutes (Riley, Otis and Houston, 1954). Some of the bases for these changes already have been discussed.

The immediate circulatory adjustments to acute arterial hypoxia are an increase in heart rate and blood pressure, and the onset of cyanosis as a result of an increase in the amount of reduced hemoglobin in arterial blood. The amount of desaturation can be estimated from the alveolar Po$_2$ and the oxygen-hemoglobin dissociation curve.

In the normal subject breathing air (about 21 per cent O$_2$) about 95 per cent saturation of the hemoglobin of arterial blood with oxygen is attained. In a person breathing air at any given altitude somewhat less than 95 per cent saturation would occur but might be achieved if the O$_2$ per cent in inspired air were increased sufficiently. It is found that at 18,000 feet it would be necessary to breathe about 45 per cent O$_2$ in order to attain 95 per cent saturation, and at about 34,000 feet, 100 per cent O$_2$ is needed. It follows that at altitudes higher than 34,000 feet some degree of arterial hypoxia will occur even when the subject breathes pure O$_2$, and at very high altitudes intolerable degrees of oxygen lack would be experienced even when breathing 100% O$_2$. The limit at which aviators can fly in nonpressurized cabins breathing 100 per cent O$_2$ is in the range of 40,000 to 45,000 feet. Above this level cabins containing gases under pressures higher than that of the ambient air are required.

Several mountain climbing expeditions have been made in the past by different groups of physiologists for the purpose of studying the effects of low oxygen tensions upon the respiratory functions and of determining the factors underlying the phenomen of acclimatization. An expedition was made to Monte Rosa (15,000 feet) in 1894 by Mosso and by others subsequently; to the peak of Teneriffe (12,000 feet) in 1910 by Zuntz, Barcroft and associates, and in 1911 to Pike's Peak (14,100 feet) by the Anglo-American expeditions of which Haldane, Douglas, Henderson and Schneider were members. In 1921 to 1922 Barcroft headed a party to Cerro de Pasco (14,200 feet) in the Peruvian Andes. A Himalayan expedition was led by Hartman in 1931, and in 1935 Dill led a party to the Chilean Andes. Recently, Pugh (1957) has reported observations made on Mt. Everest during the successful British expedition of 1952.

GENERAL SIGNS AND SYMPTOMS

Airplane ascents, if made rapidly without the use of oxygen, may result in sudden loss of consciousness due to the reduction in oxygen supply to the brain. When the ascent is made more slowly, or the altitude is not so great as to cause immediate loss of consciousness, the aviator may at first experience sensations of excitement, exhilaration and well being. As higher altitudes are reached effects of a more serious nature develop, often insidiously. Mental and sensory dullness, muscular weakness, headache, vomiting, cyanosis, dyspnea and perhaps a tendency toward periodic breathing may be induced. A common and dangerous effect is the development of fixed ideas which may result in the performance of foolhardy and ill-judged actions.

When a person climbs to a mountain height, the time taken in the journey allows a certain degree of physiological readjustment to take place, and the symptoms are usually less intense. But, as in the case of the aviator, mental features, e.g., a feeling of elation, exhilaration, talkativeness and sometimes emotional outbursts, laughing or crying, quarrelsomeness or the development of fixed ideas are prominent. Mental tasks, e.g., calculations, memory tests, and telling the time from the mirror image of a clock face are performed less efficiently. Similar effects upon the mind are produced upon persons exposed to low oxygen pressures within a steel cabinet. The mental effects as pointed out by Barcroft are not unlike those caused by drunkenness. To quote his words,

"Alcohol affects different persons in different ways; so on my journeyings in high altitudes I have seen most of the symptoms of alcoholism reproduced. I have seen men vomit, I have seen them quarrel, I have seen them become reckless, I have seen them become morose. I have seen one of the most disciplined of men fling his arms about on the ledge of a crevasse to the great embarrassment of the guide. I have seen the most loyal companion become ill-tempered and abusive to the point at which I feared international complications would arise."—Lessons from High Altitudes.

Complete prostration may follow the earlier symptoms. If the individual remains at the high altitude the symptoms pass off after a time, as he becomes acclimatized to the low oxygen tension.

At a simulated altitude of about 20,000 feet (i.e., in a decompression chamber) most subjects experience failing vision, incoordinations, and inabilitity to write or to execute simple mental tasks within 15 minutes or so after the extra oxygen supply has been cut off; at 26,000 feet none are able to retain "effective consciousness" for this length of time without oxygen.

CHANGES ASSOCIATED WITH ACCLIMATIZATION

At an altitude of 14,200 feet as at Cerro de Pasco where Barcroft and his party carried out their investigations, the barometric pressure is around 440 mm. Hg. The partial pressure of oxygen is therefore about 92 mm. Hg. The oxygen tension of the alveolar air is not as far below that of the atmosphere as at sea level, and varied among the greater number of the party from 55 to 60 mm. Hg. The closer approximation of the atmospheric and alveolar oxygen tensions at high altitudes is due to the increased breathing which is brought about through the action of the lowered oxygen tension in the blood. The oxygen tension is slightly lower in the arterial blood than in the alveolar air which indicates that the passage of the gas is due purely to diffusion and not to an active secretion by the pulmonary epithelium. If this occurred, as has been suggested (Haldane), one would expect the arterial oxygen tension to be higher than that of the alveolar air. Alveolar carbon dioxide tension also, as a result of the increased pulmonary ventilation, is lower than that at sea level; it varied in different individuals of Barcroft's party from 23 to 29 mm. Hg. At 14,200 feet the arterial blood is from 85 to 88 per cent saturated with oxygen.

A marked increase in the number of red cells (see ch. 27) and a corresponding increase in hemoglobin content of the blood occur at high altitudes. The blood volume is also augmented. The natives of mountainous regions have a red cell count of from 6 to 8 million per cubic millimeter. The greater quantity of hemoglobin of course raises the oxygen capacity of the blood and so tends to compensate for its lowered oxygen saturation. That is, the *total* oxygen content of the arterial blood tends in spite of the low saturation to rise. Nevertheless, it may not be evident at first sight how a rise in the oxygen capacity is of advantage, for blood of normal hemoglobin content even when only 80 per cent saturated possesses a quantity of oxygen which is quite adequate for the needs of the tissues. It has already been pointed out, however, that the important factor in supplying the tissues is the oxygen pressure gradient between the plasma in the capillaries and the tissue cells. So then, if there are a greater number of red cells, each will be required to give up less of its oxygen store in passing through the capillaries to furnish a given quantity of oxygen (see anoxia due to anemia, p. 1031). Consequently the saturation and the oxygen tension of the venous blood will be maintained at a higher level than otherwise would be possible. This means that the mean intracapillary oxygen pressure will also be higher, and as a result the tissues are more effectively supplied with oxygen.

The reduction in the alveolar carbon dioxide results in a corresponding decrease in the carbon dioxide tension of the arterial blood. The ratio $H_2CO_3/NaHCO_3$, which tends to be altered by the loss of carbon dioxide, is adjusted by a decrease in the excretion of acid and ammonia in the urine, a consequent lowering of the "alkali reserve" and depression of the CO_2 dissociation curve (p. 979). The actual pH of the plasma changes little if at all. Up to about 12,000 feet if any change occurs it is toward the alkaline side; above this level the blood reaction shows little further change or tends to return to normal. Lactic acid, which was thought at one time to be produced in excess as a result of the anoxia is actually formed in smaller amounts at high altitudes than at sea level. Even during severe exercise at 15,000 feet and higher altitudes the lactic acid concentration in the blood is lower than during exercise of comparable severity at sea level.

Barcroft and his party observed a shift to the left in the oxygen dissociation curve of hemoglobin, i.e., the affinity of hemoglobin for oxygen was increased. The shift in the dissociation curve is ascribed by Barcroft to an increased alkalinity of the *interior of the red cell.* This increased alkalinity is in turn a direct result of the rise in the number of red cells. The buffering power of the blood is increased through the greater facility offered for the action of the "chloride shift" mechanism (ch. 34 and 50). In other words, when a given amount of carbon dioxide is liberated by the tissues, it is distributed among a greater number of red cells than under normal circumstances; therefore, the alkalinity of each cell is reduced to a proportionately less extent. There have been conflicting reports concerning this question of the shift in the oxygen dissociation curve. Some observers have been unable to confirm Barcroft's finding, while others claim that a shift to the right occurs. The truth appears to be that up to about 14,000 feet the affinity of hemoglobin for oxygen increases, but at higher levels the dissociation curve tends to assume the form found at sea level, and at altitudes of 19,000 feet there is a definite shift to the right.

One might suppose that an increased circulation rate would be an important adjustment to the rarefied atmosphere whereby an adequate oxygen supply to the tissues would be maintained, but except for a temporary increase during the first few days no change in cardiac output occurs at altitudes of less than 14,000 or 15,000 feet. Above 15,000 feet the greater degree of anoxia results in an increase in the minute output of the heart. Before acclimatization, the pulse rate during rest increases by from 15 to 20 beats per minute at altitudes between 15,000 and 18,000 feet. At greater altitudes, especially in persons in poor physical condition, the increase in rate may be greater than in the normal. The acceleration of the pulse, according to Barcroft, is a signal of distress flown by the heart laboring under the effects of the anoxia, rather than an indication of an increased minute volume. The blood pressure shows little or no change up to 15,000 feet; a small rise may occur at higher altitudes.

Those who have lived all their lives at very high altitudes (around 14,000 feet) have a larger vital capacity than dwellers at sea level. Barcroft reports that a native of Cerro de Pasco of 5 feet, 3 inches in height had a chest of a man of 6 feet. Moderate altitudes, up to about 7500 feet, appear to have little or no effect upon the chest development.

Although anoxia is the most serious effect of high altitudes with which the mountain climber or aviator has to contend, rapid ascents, as by airplane, cause other important physiological disturbances which should be mentioned, namely: (1) expansion of gases in the gastrointestinal tract, (2) aeroembolism (see below) and (3) pressure disturbances in the ears (ch. 19).

Expansion of gases in the gastrointestinal tract. Like the gases of the atmosphere those in the stomach and intestine increase in volume in proportion to the reduction in pressure. Gas having a volume of 1 liter at sea level expands to 2 liters at the pressure (375 mm. Hg) existing at 18,000 feet, to 4 liters at 34,000 feet to 6 liters at 42,000 feet (pressure 128 mm. Hg). Distention of stomach and intestine will result unless the abdomen is supported by a belt or other means, or the gases are freely evacuated. In rapid ascents distress or even severe pain results if there is any hindrance, as by an obstruction in the colon, to the ready passage of flatus.

Dysbarism

The term *dysbarism*, or decompression sickness (see Behnke, 1965), refers to the signs and symptoms which result when the total pressure of ambient gases suddenly is reduced. It refers to the effects of reduction in pressure as such. Dysbarism is seen in deep sea divers or caisson workers when they pass too quickly from the high pressure in which they have been working to the ordinary pressure of the atmosphere, hence the name *caisson* disease has been used. The "bends" is a popular name for the condition. In dysbarism the *percentage* reduction in pressure is a more important factor than the absolute amount of decrease. A sudden reduction in pressure to approximately 45 per cent of the pressure with which the subject was equilibrated ordinarily is necessary in order to cause dysbarism. A diver who has been exposed to a pressure of, for example, 8 atmospheres usually can be subjected to a quick reduction in pressure to 4 atmospheres without developing symptoms, then after he has been at this pressure long enough to approach equilibrium with the surrounding pressure he can be quickly lowered to 2 atmospheres where he remains for a time and next the pressure can be lowered to 1 atmosphere.

The cause of symptoms during rapid decompression is the formation of bubbles of gas in fatty tissues and blood. The gas is mainly nitrogen. The total amount of nitrogen dissolved in the body when one is exposed to a gas mixture having the same percentage composition as atmospheric air is several times that of O_2 and double that of CO_2. Also nitrogen diffuses less readily and, unlike O_2, it is not used in metabolic processes. When body fluids are saturated with N_2 at a given pressure and the ambient pressure suddenly is lowered, N_2 is evolved in gaseous form just as CO_2 is evolved from carbonated water when the cap is removed from the bottle containing it. Bubbles in the blood tend to lodge in the smaller vessels and obstruct the flow of blood. Symptoms vary depending upon the sites where the bubbles lodge. Fatty tissue usually is the site of bubble formation since N_2 is 5 times more soluble in oil than in water. The involved tissues include subcutaneous tissue, bone marrow, adrenal cortex, myelin sheaths, etc. Bubbles in the myelin sheaths of sensory nerves cause pain (bends), paresthesias, itching, etc., and those in myelin sheaths of motor nerves may cause temporary paralysis. It has been recognized for many years that obese persons are more susceptible to "the bends" than lean persons.

In rapid ascents in airplanes dysbarism is not a problem up to 20,000 feet since the reduction in pressure is less that 55 per cent; and, in fact, symptoms ordinarily do not appear below 30,000 feet. Above this level, however, dysbarism is common. The tendency to develop decompression illness is greater the more rapid the ascent. The most effective way to prevent or diminish the effects of rapid decompression is to have the aviator breathe 100 per cent oxygen or an oxygen-helium mixture for a time before the flight and thus wash much of the nitrogen out of the body. When this is done the aviator should be able to ascend quite rapidly to 40,000 feet (continuing to breathe 100 per cent O_2) without discomfort.

The effects of aeroembolism in flyers during rapid ascent take the form most commonly of severe pain in one or more of the large joints and itching of the skin or cutaneous sensations of heat or cold. Other more serious symptoms such as paralysis, intense burning pain in the chest, or pulmonary edema may, though rarely, occur. The symptoms are rarely as severe as in compressed air illness, since the amount of gas which can be released is not as great in the decompression which occurs in ascent to altitude.

The *explosive decompression* technique which is used to study adjustments to lowered Po_2 in the inspired air also is useful in the study of dysbarism. A rate of ascent can be simulated in this way which is much faster than any which has been attained even in rockets. Many thousands of flying personnel have been subjected to explosive decompression. The subject is instructed to breathe with mouth open. As the gas in the lungs expands during decompression it rushes out through the open airway. Gas in the sinuses also expands suddenly and exhausts through the natural channels, but if these openings are not patent severe pain is produced.

Experimental animals have been found to have an astonishingly high tolerance to explosive decompression at simulated high altitudes (from sea level to 50,000 feet—750 to 87 mm. Hg). The rate of decompression in the experiments of Whitehorn and his associates ranged from about 1100 mm. Hg per second to as high as 33,000 mm. Hg or more per second. That is to say, decompression from 750 mm. Hg to 87 mm. Hg was brought about in the latter instance in 0.02 second. Then the animal was quickly recompressed and the effects of anoxia thus prevented. The chief effects observed in these experiments were distension of the hollow viscera and lungs, fixation of the expanded thorax in the inspiratory position and of the diaphragm in the expiratory position, due to upward pressure of the distended stomach and intestines, sharp but temporary fall in blood pressure with cardiac slowing, hemorrhages into lungs and hollow organs, or rupture of the latter. The fall in blood pressure seems to be due to decreased cardiac filling caused by the increased intrathoracic pressure, due in turn to the rise of the diaphragm. The cardiac slowing does not occur after bilateral section of the vagus nerves. In no instance out of some 700 decompressions on several different species of laboratory animal did a fatality occur from a single decompression. The injuries which are most likely to occur from explosive decompression are damage to ears and lungs, though rupture of the stomach or intestine may result.

Respiration in a Sealed Cabin

In flight beyond the earth's atmosphere the passengers must be in a sealed compartment. The total pressure of gases in the compartment could be reduced quickly to one half that at sea level without causing any difficulty in normal subjects providing the Po_2 were kept up to a

TABLE 54.1

Daily metabolic turnover

(Man 70 kg. RQ = 0.82. Food: Protein 80 grams, Carbohydrate 270 grams, Fat 150 grams)

	Input			Output		
	grams	%		grams	%	
Gases	862	24.04	(Oxygen) 603 l.	982	27.39	(Carbon Dioxide) 496 l.
Liquid	2200	61.37	(Water)	2542	70.91	(Water)
Solids	500	13.95	(Food)	27	0.75	(Urea)
	23	0.64	(Salts)	23	0.64	(Salts)
				11	0.31	(Unaccounted for)
	3585	100.00		3583 plus 2830 Kcal	100.00	

level sufficient to prevent arterial hypoxia. This could be done if the per cent of O_2 were about 35 to 40 at a cabin pressure of 380 mm. of Hg. However, it might be preferable to maintain ambient gases at the level normally encountered at sea level.

The sealed cabin must contain apparatus for absorbing the CO_2. A rise in CO_2 content up to 2 per cent at 380 mm. Hg pressure would appear to be permissible even for indefinitely long periods. Circulation of the gas in the cabin through cannisters, such as are used in the closed CO_2-absorption methods of administering anesthetic gases, could accomplish CO_2 removal quite readily. The cabin would need to be equipped with instruments for continuous monitoring of Po_2 and Pco_2. For long term space flight the idea of using the photosynthetic process to take up CO_2 and produce O_2 has been advanced.

Average values for the daily metabolic turnover of a "standard" man are presented below (compiled by H. G. Clamann, United States Air Force School of Aviation Medicine, Randolph Field, Texas). Calculations of what supplies must be taken in a sealed cabin for trips of any duration can be made on the basis of such data (table 54.1).

Pneumonia

In *lobar pneumonia* the oxygen saturation of the arterial blood varies in different cases from normal to less than 70 per cent. The signs and symptoms of anoxia usually appear when the saturation is around 85 per cent. Cerebral symptoms, e.g., sleeplessness and delirium, cyanosis and dyspnea increase with the oxygen desaturation. In 33 cases

reported by Stadie with a saturation as low or lower than 80 per cent only 1 recovered. In lobar pneumonia the carbon dioxide content of the arterial blood is reduced on the average by about 15 per cent (Meakins and Davies). The "alkali reserve", however, is normal or only slightly reduced. The blood pH may in some cases be increased. From these findings it appears that there exists a partially compensated alkalosis, induced by the hyperventilation (blowing off of carbon dioxide) elicited by reduced oxygen tension of the arterial blood. The increased ventilation of the alveoli also increases the percentage of oxygen in the alveolar air, but this cannot, as we shall see presently, increase appreciably the oxygen in the arterial blood.

In *bronchopneumonia* a higher degree of oxygen desaturation of the arterial blood is usually present than in the lobar type. The cyanosis may be extreme. There is often *retention* of carbon dioxide when a rise in plasma bicarbonate results, to compensate, in part at least, the gaseous acidosis. The carbon dioxide content of the arterial blood may be 80 volumes per cent or more and the carbon dioxide dissociation curve well above the normal level.

The causes of hypoxia in pneumonia. Two main factors concerned in the production of the hypoxia are the passage of blood through unaerated (consolidated) portions of the lung and shallow breathing. Typically the blood of pneumonia patients has a normal oxygen capacity and the oxygen dissociation curve at a given carbon dioxide tension is not appreciably different from that of normal persons.

In *lobar pneumonia* during the stages of engorgement and red hepatization the alveoli of the affected portion of the lung are poorly aerated. Mucus blocks the bronchioles and the *air spaces* are filled or their walls coated with exudate. But a large proportion of the vessels of these unaerated regions are still pervious. Consequently blood traversing such areas must remain poorly oxygenated. This blood with a low oxygen saturation and a high carbon dioxide content mixes with blood which has passed through aerated regions. The general arterial blood therefore has its oxygen saturation reduced in proportion to the amount of unsaturated blood with which it is mixed (see also Shunt, p. 1042). When the pneumonic area passes into the stage of gray hepatization the vessels of the affected lobe become obliterated to a large extent and the pulmonary blood then passes through aerated regions (fig. 54.1). That is, the arterial blood is no longer vitiated by blood from non-aerated areas. Therefore in a typical case of lobar pneumonia when the disease is confined to a single large area and the breathing is not shallow, there is little anoxemia at this stage. If however, bronchopneumonic areas co-exist, the respiratory functions will be affected as described below. (See Oxygen Therapy, p. 1047).

In *bronchopneumonia*, patches of lung tissue are cut off from their air supply. The fine bronchioles become plugged with mucus, groups of alveoli become filled with exudate and the alveolar walls are edematous and thickened. Yet, obliteration of the vessels to any great extent does not occur. Blood continues to flow through unaerated areas. This blood which has a low Po_2 on mixing with that from aerated alveoli lowers the saturation of the general arterial blood.

SHALLOW BREATHING. In pneumonia breathing is frequently very rapid and shallow. Instead of the tidal air being around 500 ml. as in health it may be reduced to 250 ml. or less. It will be recalled that about 150 ml. are required to fill the anatomical dead space, therefore only 100 ml. will enter the air sacs of the healthy parts of the lung. The expansion of the lungs is not equal in all its parts. The alveoli towards the hub of the radiating rays expand less than those near the periphery. Those parts, such as the apex, which are indirectly expanded have even in health a tendency to be ventilated less than those which are directly expanded. In shallow breathing, these differences are greatly exaggerated. Although the tidal volume is only half the normal, the total quantity of air breathed per minute (minute volume) is, as a result of the increased respiratory rate, much greater than normal. Since a proportion of the al-

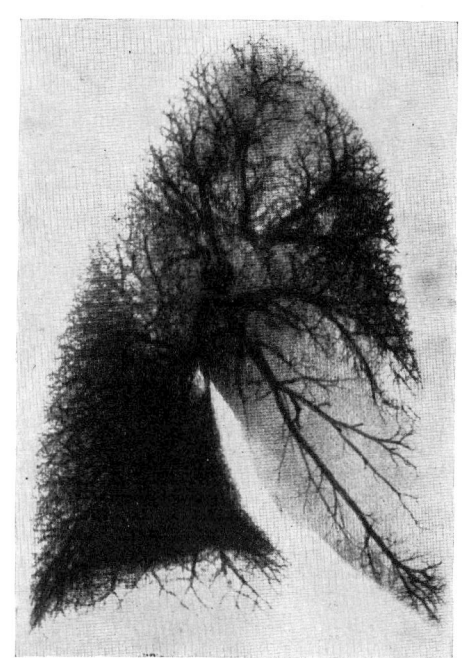

FIG. 54.1. X-ray photograph of lung (injected with barium) from a case of lobar pneumonia (after Gross). *Upper right hand area.* Consolidated area—red hepatization. The main vessels are constricted and the finer vascular structure is less dense than in the normal lung. *Lower right hand area.* Consolidated area—gray hepatization. The main vessels are patent but the finer vessels have been occluded. *Lower left hand area.* Healthy portion of lung except for compensatory congestion; the vessels are dilated.

veoli are very poorly ventilated or not at all, owing to the unequal expansion of the lung, those in other areas tend to be overventilated. The O_2 tension in the latter is therefore raised. But so far as the oxygenation of the blood is concerned the overventilation of some alveoli cannot make up for the underventilation of others. We know that the hemoglobin is nearly saturated already at the ordinary alveolar oxygen tension of 100 mm. Hg. As already mentioned the dissociation curve of hemoglobin in pneumonia does not differ appreciably from that in health, and the most, therefore, that could be expected from a rise in the alveolar O_2 tension would be an increase of 2 per cent or less in oxygen saturation of the blood traversing overventilated regions and a slight increase in the amount of O_2 held in simple solution. In other words, the blood flowing through the poorly ventilated parts of the lung will have a low saturation since the O_2 tension is low, while that flowing through the overventilated parts will be little above the normal. The net result will be a low oxygen saturation of the mixed arterial blood

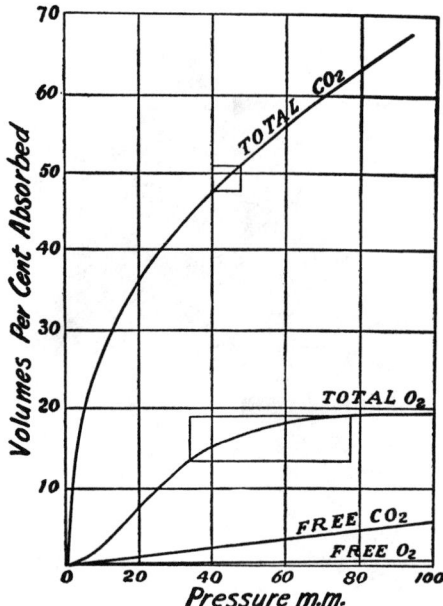

FIG. 54.2. Carbon dioxide and oxygen dissociation curves. The small rectangles indicate the extent of the variation of the O_2 and CO_2 of the subject's blood when at rest. (From L. J. Henderson.)

Matters are different in the case of CO_2 elimination. The shape of the CO_2 dissociation curve which shows a progressive slope throughout the entire range of CO_2 tensions is quite unlike that for oxyhemoglobin (fig. 54.2). The greater total ventilation results in a lowering of CO_2 tension in the overventilated parts of the lung and, consequently, in a "blowing off" of CO_2 from the blood circulating through these regions. CO_2 is retained in the blood circulating through poorly ventilated regions. In the patient with lobar pneumonia the amount of CO_2 blown off may exceed that retained; the net result will be a lowering of the CO_2 content of the arterial blood. In bronchopneumonia a larger proportion of the pulmonary blood circulates through non-aerated areas. As a consequence, CO_2 retention is greater, and a normal or a higher than normal CO_2 content of the blood is more usual.

The cause of shallow breathing in pneumonia. Pleuritic pain, by restricting the respiratory excursions, may result in this type of breathing. In other instances it may be of a reflex nature resulting from the inflammatory process which, through a reduction in the distensibility of the pulmonary tissue perhaps exalts the sensitivity of the afferent vagal endings in the alveolar walls. Thus the inspiratory movement possibly is terminated before a full excursion has been completed

(see Hering-Breuer reflex, p. 1013. In support of a reflex origin may be mentioned the experiments of Dunn and of Binger, Brow and Branch who produced this type of breathing in animals by the intravenous injection of potato starch granules. These, acting as small emboli, plugged the pulmonary capillaries. The rapid shallow breathing was immediately abolished by section of the vagi or prevented if the nerves had been cut before the injection. Also, in pneumonia it has been found that oxygen inhalations, even though they may restore the oxygen saturation of the arterial blood to normal, do not necessarily abolish the shallow breathing. This constitutes further evidence for the existence of a nervous element in the production of this type of breathing. Shallow breathing may also result from other diseases involving the alveoli, e.g., inflammation by irritant gases (phosgene and chlorine), pulmonary edema, miliary tuberculosis and pulmonary emboli, which would be expected to stimulate afferent nerve endings.

Bronchial Asthma

This is a paroxysmal disease in which acute oxygen want is caused by a spasm of the smooth muscles of the finer bronchioles. Edema of the bronchiolar mucosa is probably also present. The alveoli are poorly ventilated, and some may be completely cut off from their air supply. The high percentage of carbon dioxide and low percentage of oxygen in the alveolar air result in a low oxygen saturation of the arterial blood and the retention of carbon dioxide. The acidosis related to CO_2 retention is met by the excretion of a highly acid urine and a rise in the "alkali reserve". An intense plum-colored cyanosis may develop. The continued stimulating effect of oxygen want and carbon dioxide excess upon the respiratory mechanisms causes severe dyspnea.

Difficulty is experienced both in inspiration and expiration, but since there is a natural tendency for the bronchioles to narrow during expiration and dilate during inspiration, the greatest respiratory effort is exerted during expiration. The respiratory muscles contract with great force, and the accessory muscles of respiration are brought into play. The expiratory muscles compress the chest; the abdominal muscles contract in the attempt to squeeze the air from the lungs. The intrapulmonary pressure is greatly elevated, and the air escapes through the constricted tubes with a distinct wheezing sound. Due to the difficulty and prolongation of the expiratory phase normal deflation of the lungs cannot occur before the next inspiration ensues. The lungs, therefore, remain somewhat expanded even at the end of expiration. That is, during the asthmatic paroxysm a very large volume of residual air is present in the lungs (fig. 54.3). The tidal volume and the vital capacity are greatly reduced. The changes in volume of the overdistended lung are small and not commensurate with the excursions of the thoracic walls. As a consequence, the high value of the intrathoracic negative pressure induced during inspiration causes the structures at the root of the neck to be drawn toward the thoracic cavity to take up the space which the lungs are unable to fill. During expiration the veins of the neck and face become engorged. The restricted movements of the lung also greatly reduce the effect of mechanical mixing upon the lung air, the process of diffusion being depended upon to a larger extent for the freshening of the alveolar air.

Causation

Asthma often shows a strong hereditary tendency. The bronchiolar spasm may be of a *reflex nature* and due to the stimulation of hyper-

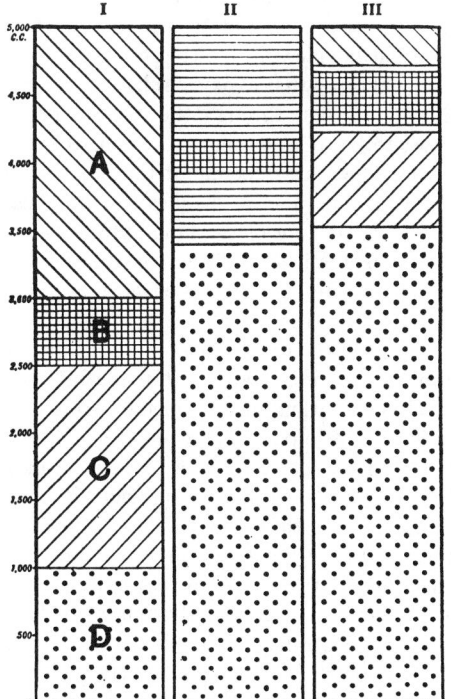

Fig. 54.3. Diagram showing subdivisions of the lung air in asthma (*II*) and emphysema (*III*) compared with the normal (*I*). *A*, Inspiratory reserve volume; *B*, tidal volume; *C*, expiratory reserve volume; and *D*, residual volume. (After Coke.)

sensitive afferent vagal endings in the larynx, or of trigeminal fibers by some nasal abnormality; the bronchoconstrictor impulses travel via efferent vagal fibers. On the other hand, the bronchiolar spasm may be an *allergic phenomenon*, i.e., the result of sensitization to some foreign protein. This is the most common cause of the condition. It is then frequently associated with other allergic conditions, e.g., hay fever, urticaria or eczema either in the patient himself or in members of his family. The foreign protein may be inhaled. Pollens of various grasses and flowers, the dandruff of animals, e.g., horse, cat or dog, or feathers are among the most common excitants; or the exciting cause may be some kind of food or the protein of bacteria within the respiratory tract itself. The sensitivity of certain individuals to foreign proteins presents many features resembling those of anaphylactic shock in animals. Sudden death may result from the injection of horse serum (e.g., diphtheria antitoxin or antitetanic serum) into an asthmatic subject. A guinea pig when injected with a protein to which it has previously been sensitized dies rapidly from anaphylactic shock. The bronchiolar muscle is strongly contracted. The air is trapped so that the lungs are maximally distended and do not collapse when the thorax is opened. Even when the pulmonary tissue is deeply incised the air does not escape from the distended lung. This manifestation of anaphylaxis is associated with (and perhaps due to) the liberation of histamine. It is well known that anaphylaxis and histamine administration produce almost identical effects in the guinea pig (fig. 54.4).

The *treatment* of asthma resolves itself into the relief of the paroxysm and the removal of the underlying cause. Epinephrine or ephedrine acts by inhibiting the bronchiolar muscle during the attack. Atropine blocks the action of the bronchoconstrictor (vagal) fibers. Of the three drugs, epinephrine is the most effective. In the allergic form of the disease every effort is made to identify the offending protein. Antihistaminic drugs have been employed with varying degrees of success.

Chronic Emphysema

The lungs in emphysema (Greek *em* + *physema*, a blowing) are in a state of extreme distention as a result of the enlargement of the air sacs. The latter, however, show fewer alveoli in their walls owing to the atrophy of the interalveolar septa. Contiguous air sacs within a lobule coalesce or even adjacent lobules may fuse to form large

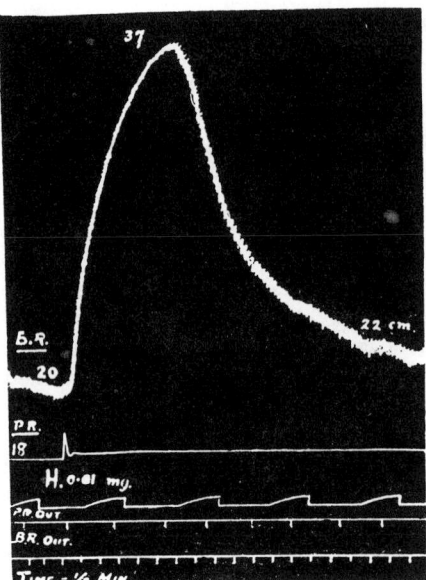

FIG. 54.4. Guinea pig. Reaction of bronchial muscle to 0.01 mg. histamine. (After Thornton.)

air spaces. For this reason the total respiratory surface is reduced. The alveolar and capillary walls become thickened and the interstitial pulmonary tissue increased. Many capillaries become occluded. The pulmonary elastic tissue is reduced in amount so that the lungs, when removed from the thorax, do not collapse normally but remain in an overexpanded state. The peripheral lobules, which in health expand to the greatest extent, are those mainly affected in emphysema, the enlarged lobules appearing as blebs upon the surface of the lung.

The chest is what is known as barrel-shaped. The ribs are more horizontal than normally, the thoracic spine is bowed backwards (kyphosis) so that the anteroposterior diameter of the chest is as great as or exceeds the transverse. The position of the chest is one of nearly full inspiration. The midposition of the diaphragm is at a much lower level than usual and its excursions above and below this level are restricted. The respiration is therefore mainly costal. In some instances the diaphragm is practically fixed or indeed may be drawn up during inspiration (paradoxical movement). The residual air is 2 or 3 times the normal, and the inspiratory reserve volume is reduced. The tidal volume is normal or only moderately reduced and the vital capacity (fig. 54.3) is lowered by from 20 to 60 per cent. Owing to the loss of the elasticity of the lung, expiration is no longer simply a passive movement but is aided

by a forcible contraction of the expiratory muscles. When the patient is asked to make a deep inspiration, he does not expel all the air during the next expiration. Several respirations occur before the chest returns to its original size. Expiratory reserve volume is greatly decreased, and residual volume is markedly increased (fig. 54.3). These phenomena are due to the fact that the inelastic lungs have been overstretched and are brought back to their original volume with difficulty.

In emphysema there are anoxemia and retention of carbon dioxide. The oxygen saturation of the arterial blood runs from a little below normal to around 75 per cent or even less. The carbon dioxide tension in the alveolar air in well marked cases is from 50 to over 60 mm. Hg (7 to 8 per cent) and the carbon dioxide content of the arterial blood correspondingly high.

Owing to the obliteration of many capillaries in the lungs, the resistance in the pulmonary circuit is increased, a greater burden being thus put upon the right ventricle.

The cause of the impaired gaseous exchange is not altogether clear. Thickening of the alveolar and capillary walls and the obliteration of capillaries have been considered to be factors. Yet if this were so one would not expect the retention of carbon dioxide which, owing to its greater solubility (30 times that of oxygen) has a much higher rate of diffusion through the pulmonary membrane, to be so much more pronounced than the anoxia. The sharp rebound at the end of inspiration which occurs in the healthy lung causes mechanical mixing of the lung air and is an important factor in the efficient ventilation of the alveoli. The absence of this effect in the emphysematous lung and its greater dependence, in consequence, upon the slower process of diffusion is probably an important factor leading to the defective aeration of the blood. According to Christie, the impaired gaseous exchange is due mainly to the fact that, as a result of the loss of elasticity, the intrathoracic pressure is not distributed evenly throughout the lung. As a consequence, the outlying alveoli which are largely functionless with obliterated vessels are ventilated to a greater extent than the relatively healthy ones more centrally placed. Owing to the shapes of the respective dissociation curves such underventilation of the functioning alveoli will tend to have a greater effect in preventing the elimination of CO_2 than in interfering with the absorption of oxygen. Other factors which are probably of importance are the slower rate of diffusion of CO_2, owing to its larger molecule, in the alveolar air, and the increased residual volume.

The red cell count, hemoglobin content, and consequently the oxygen capacity of the blood, are increased above the normal in emphysema. The cyanosis (p. 1046) is often pronounced, yet the patient's dyspnea is less than might be expected from his color and from the carbon dioxide retention which exists. This is explained by the well established fact that in emphysema the respiratory center is less sensitive to carbon dioxide. A normal person when breathing a carbon dioxide rich mixture (8 per cent) increases his pulmonary ventilation by 300 per cent or more; the breathing of the emphysematous patient, on the other hand, shows relatively little change as a result of breathing a much stronger mixture (see fig. 54.5).

Causation

Two factors are concerned in the production of emphysema (a) reduction in the elastic tissue of the lung and (b) increased distention of the alveolar spaces.

It is very questionable whether, in the absence of some abnormality of the lung tissue itself, emphysema can result from increased intrapulmonary pressure, such as occurs in those following certain occupations, e.g., glass blowers and the players of wind instruments. The study of groups of men following such occupations does not indicate that emphysema is produced in this way. Emphysema has, however, been induced in animals by stenosis of the trachea or bronchi or by the insertion of a valved apparatus into the trachea which allowed the free ingress of air but offered an obstruction to expiration.

Asthma and chronic bronchitis frequently are forerunners of emphysema. In the former condition the spasm of the bronchiolar muscle exerts a valvelike action. In chronic bronchitis mucous plugs would act similarly. Coughing, it has been supposed, places a strain upon the alveolar walls. But during the phase of coughing when the glottis is closed the alveolar walls are supported. When the glottis opens, the air escapes from the alveoli if the obstructing material has been dislodged, and no strain upon the alveolar wall would result. If, however, the air remains entrapped its sudden re-expansion (rebound), as the pressure in the surrounding pulmonary tissue falls at the end of a cough, may injure the alveolar membrane and start the emphysematous process.

What may be termed a physiological or *compensatory* emphysema occurs when part of the pulmonary surface is reduced as by the collapse

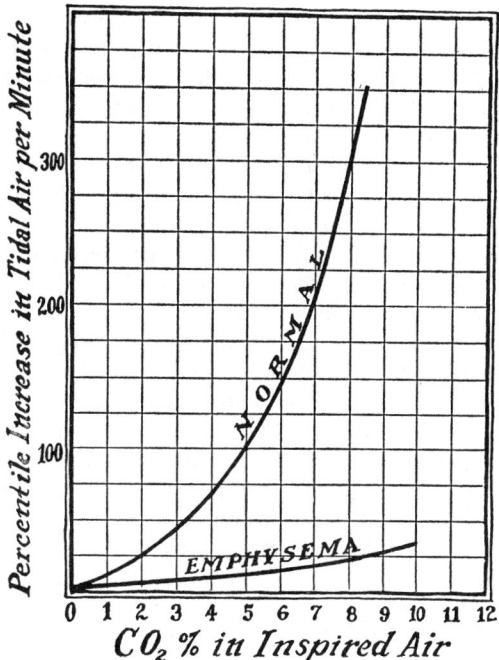

FIG. 54.5. Chart showing the percentile increase in tidal air per minute as the percentage of inspired carbon dioxide is raised. Note that when the normal subject inspires air containing 8 per cent carbon dioxide, the tidal volume is increased about 300 per cent, whereas in the emphysematous subject it is increased only about 25 per cent. (After R. W. Scott.)

of a part or the whole of one lung. This is more in the nature of an hypertrophy. A similar enlargement of both lungs occurs at high altitudes.

A type of emphysema also occurs in the elderly—*senile or postural emphysema*—and is secondary to the change in the shape of the thorax which becomes more barrel-shaped and increased in capacity. The lungs enlarge to fill the increased space. This condition is associated with few symptoms. There is little reduction in the vital capacity, and the oxygen saturation of the arterial blood is practically normal.

Atelectasis

Any condition which lowers the pressure within the alveoli or increases the pressure upon the lung surface, may lead to collapse of the lung. Thus pleural effusions, pneumothorax, tumors, etc., pressing from without or the isolation of the alveoli from their air supply by the obstruction of a bronchus will result in collapse of the lung or of the portion of the lung affected. Atelectasis (Greek *ateles*, incomplete; *ektasis*, distention) is also the term applied to the condition in the newborn in which, as a result of the blockage of a bronchus or of a group of bronchioles by mucous secretion, or owing to weak inspiratory movements, a portion of the lung fails to become distended with air.

Absorption of air from isolated alveoli and other closed spaces. When a bronchus or bronchiole in a previously distended lung is obstructed the imprisoned air soon becomes absorbed from the affected alveoli. Collapse of the air sacs cannot take place until this has occurred. Absorption is brought about in the following way, as pointed out by Henderson. The air in the isolated alveoli has a total pressure of 760 mm. Hg. The partial pressures are in round numbers, O_2, 100 mm.; N_2, 570 mm. CO_2, 40 mm. and aqueous vapor, 47 mm. In the venous blood the total pressure is 703 mm., the nitrogen and aqueous vapor being the same as that of the alveolar air, but the partial pressure of oxygen is only 40 mm. and of carbon dioxide 46 mm. An interchange of the latter gases therefore occurs between the alveolar air and the venous blood. It might be thought that the imprisoned air would then be in equilibrium with the blood and no further absorption occur. But the alveolar air loses more oxygen than it gains carbon dioxide whereupon its volume is reduced. The atmosphere acting upon the body surface and through the yielding soft tissues compresses the air so as to maintain its total pressure practically constant at 760 mm. As a result of the absorption of oxygen the percentage and consequently the partial pressure of carbon dioxide and of nitrogen are increased. These gases now diffuse into the blood. The volume of the alveolar air is further reduced thereby but its total pressure still remains unaltered. The percentage and therefore the partial pressure of oxygen rises and more of this gas passes into the blood. The process continues in this manner until no air remains, and the walls of the original space are ultimately approximated by the pressure of the atmosphere. Air is absorbed from the pleural cavity or from any other closed cavity of the body in the same way (Henderson and Henderson). The absorption of the air confined within the pleural cavity permits the lung, if the air pressure had caused its collapse, to re-expand.

The collapse and shrinkage of the lung which results from blockage of a bronchus increases the intrathoracic negative pressure, since the closed thoracic box is less completely filled. The diaphragm is therefore drawn upwards and uncollapsed portions of the lungs are expanded to a greater extent (compensatory emphysema) in order to fill the unoccupied space.

Shunt

In the fetus the vessels of the airless lungs are bypassed by the greater part of the blood brought to the heart. That is to say, most of the blood is shunted to the arterial side through channels which normally close at, or shortly after, birth. It is clear that if one or more of these channels should persist after birth, or if the interventricular septum is defective so that a large part of the venous blood does not traverse the lungs, but is short circuited from the right to the left heart or directly into the aorta, the oxygen saturation of the arterial blood will be seriously reduced. Arterial hypoxia evidenced by cyanosis (p. 1045) and dyspnea (p. 1023) will result (fig. 54.6). These will be especially pronounced upon exertion since the unsaturation of the polluting venous blood will be thereby increased.

The fetal circulation. Before the congenital abnormalities are described, the fetal circulation and the circulatory readjustments which occur at birth, or shortly thereafter, will be briefly reviewed.

In the fetus the oxygenated blood from the placenta is carried by the *umbilical vein* to the liver, where it separates into two streams, one of which is distributed to the left ⅔ or so of the liver; the remainder passes directly via the *ductus venosus* into the inferior vena cava, thus mixing with blood returning from the lower part of the body. The portal vein supplies the rest of the liver. That portion of the blood from the umbilical vein which has traversed the vessels of the liver is also delivered by the hepatic veins into the inferior vena cava. The hepatic veins are a number of small vessels and two much larger ones; the latter form a junction with the ductus venosus just before the latter joins the inferior vena cava. The blood in the vena cava beyond this point is, therefore, partly oxygenated (from placenta via umbilical vein and ductus venosus) and partly reduced, having traversed the tissues of the lower limbs, intestines and liver. The caval blood, upon reaching the right auricle, separates into two unequal parts. The much larger stream passes directly through the foramen ovale (*via sinistra*) into the left auricle; the smaller stream enters the right ventricle. The blood which has reached the left auricle, after being joined by a small but by no means inconsiderable volume of blood returned from the pulmonary tissue, flows into the left ventricle, and is discharged into the aorta and distributed to the brain by the brachiocephalic artery, and to the myocardium by the coronary arteries. The remainder flows down the aorta.

The blood returned from the head and entering the right auricle by the superior vena cava, together with the small fraction of blood of the inferior vena cava which was not directed through the foramen ovale, enters the right ventricle and is ejected into the pulmonary artery. A smaller part, yet, as shown by Franklin and his associates, more than has been generally supposed is conveyed to the lungs by two branches of the latter vessels. The main stream, discharged from the right ventricle, passes by a wide vessel, the *ductus arteriosus*, into the aorta, and mixing with the blood coming from the left ventricle, is distributed throughout the body. That portion which is supplied to the lower limbs is returned by two vessels—the *umbilical arteries*—to the placenta.

During birth, or very shortly after, the three umbilical vessels close (even though the cord has not been tied or broken) by the contraction of smooth muscle in the vascular walls. The flow through the ductus venosus ceases as a result of contraction of a smooth muscle sphincter at the point where it leaves the umbilical vein. This occurs in the sheep fetus, according to Franklin and his associates, in from 5 to 25 minutes after the umbilical vessels have closed. Within 5 minutes or so after the commencement of breathing the foramen ovale closes, and a little later (apparently never before the obliteration of the foramen ovale) the ductus arteriosus becomes occluded. All the blood from the right side of the heart is normally from now on directed through the lungs. Franklin and his associates found, however, in the case of the new-born lamb, that should the general condition of the latter seriously deteriorate, the ductus arteriosus may open again. The mechanism of closure of the ductus appears to be initiated in some way by the action of the oxygenated blood upon the vascular muscle and not through a nervous mechanism. In the lamb this channel has never been observed to close before occlusion of the umbilical vessels.

Congenital Cardiac Defects

Patent ductus arteriosus, or foramen ovale, interventricular septal defects, stenosis of the pulmonary artery and coarctation of the aorta (narrowing of aorta in the neighborhood of the ductus arteriosus) are among the congenital defects most commonly met with.

The development of the direct Fick method (p. 704) (utilizing catheterization of the right side of the heart) for determining the cardiac output has provided means of the greatest value in diagnosing congenital defects of the circulation. It is now possible to obtain samples of blood for gas analysis from the right ventricle, the pulmonary artery,

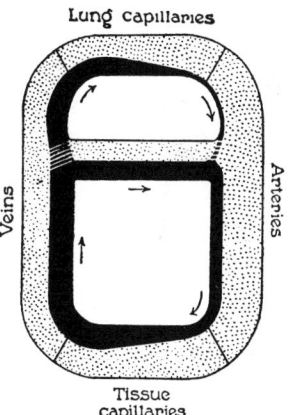

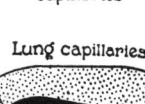

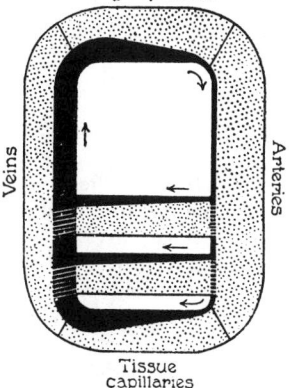

Fractional total hemoglobin in reduced form

Fractional total hemoglobin in oxygenated form

Fig. 54.6. Diagram (upper) showing the proportion of oxyhemoglobin to reduced hemoglobin in different parts of the circulation in an instance where a portion of the blood passes through unaerated channels (shunt) from the venous to the arterial system. Lower diagram represents a case in which the oxygen unsaturation of the blood is abnormally high in a part of the peripheral capillaries but normal in the arterial blood (stagnant type of anoxia). (After Lundsgaard and Van Slyke.)

and many sites in the systemic circuit, including the left ventricle. (See fig. 54.7.)

Patent foramen ovale or other defect in the interauricular septum. In patency of the foramen ovale, the opening is guarded by a valvelike membrane which prevents blood from passing from the left to the right auricle, and none passes in the opposite direction unless the pressure in the right auricle is high. With other defects of the interauricular septum, a shunt from right to left with cyanosis may occur, but if there is mitral stenosis and a large defect (*Lutembacher's syndrome*) the high

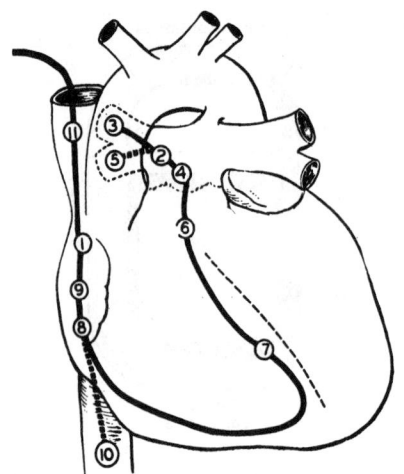

FIG. 54.7. Numbers from 1 to 11 indicate the positions from which blood samples may be taken by means of the intracardiac catheter. (After Groom and associates.)

pressure in the left auricle causes a shunt from left to right.

Patent ductus arteriosus. Blood enters the pulmonary system from the arterial side; the oxygen content in the pulmonary artery is increased, but is normal in the right auricle and ventricle.

If a *defect of the interventricular septum* exists alone, the oxygen content of the blood in the right ventricle and pulmonary artery is increased but not of that in the right auricle.

Neither of these last two defects, if it exists alone, will cause cyanosis, since the shunt is from left to right (arteriovenous shunt). Rarely, however, in the case of a patent ductus arteriosus, the direction of flow is reversed temporarily at certain times (during crying or coughing), blood passing from the pulmonary artery into the aorta.

Often the abnormalities are multiple. For example, a patent foramen ovale, together with stenosis of the pulmonary artery, results in the passage of venous blood to the arterial side, i.e., through the auricular defect; slight or moderate cyanosis is seen. The combination of congenital defects, originally described by John Hunter and later by Fallot, and now generally known as the *tetralogy of Fallot*, consists of, (a) an interventricular septal defect, (b) narrowing of the pulmonary artery, or stenosis of its orifice, and (c) dextroposition of the aorta, the orifice of this vessel being shifted to the right to straddle the septal defect. (d) The fourth element making up the tetrad is right ventricular hypertrophy. The blood flow through the lungs and the pulmonary pressure are reduced. Owing to the high pressure developed in the right ventricle blood is driven through the defect into the overriding aorta. If the pulmonary stenosis is very severe, the ductus arteriosus must be patent in order to provide sufficient blood flow

through the lungs to support life. Cyanosis and dyspnea are usually pronounced. Blalock and Taussig have devised an operation for the correction of the chief effects of these conditions. It consists of anastomosing a large branch of the aortic arch (usually carotid or subclavian) to the right or left pulmonary artery.

Another combination of defects has three features of the tetralogy of Fallot, namely, defect of the intraventricular septum, dextroposition of the aorta and right ventricular hypertrophy, but pulmonary stenosis is absent. It is known as *Eisenmenger's complex*. The shunt is from left to right in early life, but later, when as a result of the large volume of blood entering the right ventricle from the left side as well as through the normal channels this chamber enlarges and hypertrophies, the high pressure developed may force venous blood into the overriding aorta; cyanosis then appears.

In those congenital cardiac anomalies showing cyanosis, the arterial oxygen saturation is found to be, during rest, from 45 per cent in severer degrees of cyanosis to 90 per cent in the milder cases. The red cell count, however, is likely to be increased, and the hemoglobin concentration may be high as 26 grams per cent. The arterial oxygen content, i.e., the volumes of oxygen per 100 ml. of blood, in those with the higher hemoglobin concentration is, consequently, much higher than normal and may reach a value of 29 volumes per cent, as against the normal maximum of 22 volumes per cent (see Cyanosis, p. 1045). Exercise, which in normal subjects causes little or no change in arterial oxygen saturation, produces a profound fall in the congenital heart cases, amounting in some to a reduction of over 30 per cent.

Carbon Monoxide Poisoning

References to carbon monoxide poisoning are contained in the earliest medical writings. This gas was used by the Greeks and Romans for the execution of criminals and as a means of committing suicide. Today, carbon monoxide is the most important gaseous poison against which physicians have to contend. During times of peace it accounts for more deaths than all the other gases combined. Carbon monoxide combines with the hemoglobin of the blood and thus renders it unavailable for oxygen carriage. The affinity of hemoglobin for carbon monoxide is approximately 300 times its affinity for oxygen. Therefore, when the atmosphere contains only a very small percentage of CO, the hemoglobin takes up the poisonous gas and in so doing loses its ability to combine with an equivalent volume of oxygen.

Recovery from carbon monoxide poisoning is usually complete when the exposure has not been too long or the concentration too high. It is important that the carbon monoxide hemoglobin should be broken up as soon as possible since injury to the tissues is produced by the anoxia. It is possible to displace the carbon monoxide by oxygen if the tension of oxygen is sufficiently high and that of carbon monoxide low. Mixtures with a high percentage of oxygen and from 6 to 7 per cent carbon dioxide combined with artificial respiration are used in the treatment of CO poisoning. The carbon dioxide, as well as acting as a respiratory stimulant, reduces the affinity of hemoglobin for carbon monoxide. Recently, administration of oxygen under pressures greater than one atmosphere has been advocated by Smith (1965). Intravenous injections of methylene blue have been advocated but are valueless. Carbon monoxide, as well as its action in displacing oxygen from hemoglobin, has histotoxic properties, inhibiting the tissue respiratory enzymes. This fact has no practical bearing, however, upon carbon monoxide poisoning in man, for the concentrations at which such action occurs is many times greater than could ever occur in the body.

Cyanide Poisoning

No interference with oxygen carriage is caused by cyanide, but there is inhibition of tissue respiration. Cyanide inhibits the action of cytochrome oxidase, carbonic anhydrase and probably of other enzyme systems. It follows from this that any antidote for cyanide poisoning must have one of two actions. Either the cyanide must be removed or detoxified or the inactivated catalyst must be replaced. Methylene blue does act as a catalyst for certain biological oxidations, and this led to its use as an antidote for cyanide poisoning. When methylene blue is given to the intact animal, there is a marked rise in body temperature which is due to increased metabolism. Sahlin in 1926 provided the first experimental demonstration that methylene blue antagonizes the action of cyanide in the intact animal. He used rats and the observation has been confirmed on other animals—dogs, rabbits, mice. The evidence suggests that methylene blue acts by removing the cyanide from tissue. Methylene blue and cyanide do not combine directly, but methylene blue forms methemoglobin which combines with the cyanide to form cyanmethemoglobin. The cyanmethemoglobin is relatively nontoxic and is broken down slowly, the detoxification probably being brought about by conversion of the cyanide to thiocyanate (Smith and Malcolm). Other substances which form methemoglobin (Hug; Wendel) such as sodium nitrite, amyl nitrite, pyrogallol, etc., are also effective in the treatment of cyanide poison-

ing. Such methods of course are limited by the quantity of hemoglobin that can safely be converted to methemoglobin.

A number of sulphur compounds have been found effective in cyanide poisoning. Chen, Rose and Clowes showed that sodium thiosulphate and sodium tetrathionate may protect dogs against as much as three times the lethal dose of cyanide.

Cyanosis

Cyanosis (Greek, *cyanos*, blue) may be defined as the diffuse, dusky or bluish color of the skin and mucous membranes caused by the presence in the blood of the superficial capillaries (subpapillary venous plexus) of reduced hemoglobin above a certain definite amount.[2] Cyanosis is seen in the arterial and hypokinetic types of anoxia but not in the anemic or histotoxic forms. It seems scarcely necessary to state that the retention of carbon dioxide in the blood has no *direct* effect upon the production of cyanosis. The blue color of the skin depends fundamentally upon the *absolute* amount of reduced hemoglobin in the capillary blood and *not* upon the *relative proportions* of reduced hemoglobin and oxyhemoglobin. For example, in anemia the hemoglobin content of the blood may be only 20 per cent of the normal. In the capillary blood all of this could be in the reduced form, yet cyanosis would not result, since the absolute amount of reduced hemoglobin (i.e., "blue" pigment) would be insufficient to produce any blue discoloration. On the other hand, in polycythemia the hemoglobin may be 100 per cent above normal. Cyanosis will occur when the hemoglobin of the capillary blood is only 20 per cent reduced, for the absolute concentration of reduced hemoglobin will then be raised to threshold value. The greater quantity of the bright-colored oxyhemoglobin present exerts little or no influence; that is, it does not, as might be expected, tend to neutralize the color effect of the reduced hemoglobin.

Normal blood contains about 15 grams of hemoglobin per 100 cc. Lundsgaard found that the capillary blood must contain approximately

---

[2] The presence of abnormal compounds of hemoglobin, e.g., methemoglobin and sulfohemoglobin, resulting from the action of various toxic substances, causes a type of cyanosis (enterogenous cyanosis), but these will not be considered here (see pp. 524 and 525). Cyanosis may result from anoxia of either the arterial or hypokinetic type. It obviously cannot occur in the anemic type, which is due essentially to a low hemoglobin concentration, in the histotoxic type in which the hemoglobin gives up less of its oxygen store than in health, nor in the arterial and hypokinetic types if a severe grade of anemia exists.

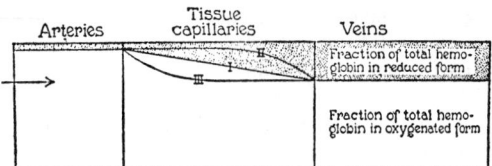

FIG. 54.8. Diagram showing hypothetical variations in the shape of the reduction curve of oxy-hemoglobin during the passage of the blood through tissue capillaries. (After Lundsgaard and Van Slyke.)

5 grams of reduced hemoglobin per 100 cc. before cyanosis will appear. When fully saturated (20 volumes per cent), ¾ gram of hemoglobin will take up 1 cc. of oxygen. Five grams of hemoglobin, therefore, hold about 6.7 cc. of oxygen, and 5 grams of reduced hemoglobin are formed when the blood contains 13.3 volumes per cent of oxygen. Cyanosis may therefore be expected to appear when the blood in the capillaries is on the average around 7 volumes per cent unsaturated. As a result of certain modifying factors (p. 1047) the precise level of capillary unsaturation at which cyanosis makes its appearance varies in different cases between 6 and 7 volumes of oxygen per cent.

The oxygen unsaturation of the capillary blood does not of course occur abruptly at the arterial end but is progressive from point to point along the course of the vessel. The loss of oxygen may be uniform from the arterial to the venous end of the capillary as shown in Curve I, figure 54.8, or the desaturation may occur mainly toward the venous end (Curve II) when the capillary blood would approximate arterial blood in its content of reduced hemoglobin. Under other circumstances the greatest oxygen loss may occur toward the arterial end (Curve III) when the unsaturation of the capillary blood throughout would approach that of venous blood. It is difficult to obtain data from which the true curve may be drawn. The simplest of these curves (Curve I) is assumed and the average unsaturation of the capillary blood is taken as midway between that of arterial and venous bloods respectively. Thus

$$\tfrac{1}{2}(A + V) = C$$

where A and V represent the unsaturation in volumes per cent of arterial and venous bloods respectively and C the average unsaturation of the capillary blood.

For example, in a normal person the arterial unsaturation is 0.5 volume per cent (19.5 volumes per cent saturation), another 5 volumes per cent

are given up in the capillary, the venous unsaturation is therefore 5.5 volumes per cent. So

$$\tfrac{1}{2}(0.5 + 5.5) = 3.0 \text{ volumes per cent average}$$
$$\text{unsaturation of capillary blood}$$

$$(3.0 \times 0.75) = 2.2 \text{ gram reduced Hb}$$

We have seen that the average unsaturation of the capillary blood must be between 6 and 7 volumes per cent (approximately 5 grams of reduced Hb) before cyanosis appears. This degree of unsaturation of the capillary blood may be brought about either by an increase in the arterial unsaturation (arterial type of anoxia) or as a result of a greater amount of oxygen being lost from the blood in its passage through the capillaries (hypokinetic type of anoxia). That is, by an increase in the venous unsaturation (V) alone. In order to produce an average unsaturation of from 6 to 7 volumes per cent in the capillary blood the arterial unsaturation would need to be from 4 to 4.5 volumes per cent, or the unsaturation of the venous blood—that in the arteries being normal—11 to 13 volumes per cent. Meakins and Davies found that when the veins of the arm were obstructed in normal individuals cyanosis was just detectable when the venous blood reached an unsaturation of 11.4 volumes per cent.

These facts may be clarified by examples. If the blood as it leaves the lungs contains only 15.5 volumes per cent of oxygen, i.e., if it has an unsaturation of 4.5 volumes per cent and the tissues abstract the usual quantity of oxygen, namely 5 volumes per cent, the unsaturation of the venous blood will be 9.5 volumes per cent and that of capillary blood

$$\tfrac{1}{2}(4.5 + 9.5) = 7 \text{ volumes per cent}$$

$$(7 \times 0.75 = 5.2 \text{ grams Hb}).$$

If on the other hand the arterial unsaturation is around the normal value of 0.5 volume per cent but as a result of slowing of the circulation each unit volume of the blood gives up a greater quantity of oxygen, and the venous unsaturation is increased to say 13 volumes per cent, the average unsaturation of the capillary blood will be

$$\tfrac{1}{2}(0.5 + 13) = 6.7 \text{ volumes per cent}.$$

In either of these instances slight cyanosis would be expected to appear.

Let us now consider what occurs when the hemoglobin percentage is above or below the normal value.

In *anemia* the amount of hemoglobin is below

normal, and the oxygen capacity of the blood is correspondingly lowered. If the hemoglobin content be only 30 per cent of the normal, the volumes per cent of oxygen in the arterial blood, though the latter be fully saturated, will be only about 6 volumes per cent, i.e., the quantity of hemoglobin in 100 cc. of blood is less than 5 grams. It is obvious that such a person could not become cyanotic even if, as a result of defective oxygenation of the blood or of slowing of the circulation, all his hemoglobin were in the reduced state. A patient whose hemoglobin was, say, 60 per cent (oxygen capacity 12 volumes per cent) would, like one with a normal hemoglobin content, become cyanotic when his arterial blood reached an unsaturation of about 4.5 volumes per cent, that is when his capillary blood had an average unsaturation of around 7 volumes per cent. But the oxygen want of the anemic subject would be greater than that of the subject with a normal hemoglobin content since in the case of the former 4.5 volumes per cent constitute nearly 40 per cent of the oxygen capacity of his blood. In a less enlightened age when bleeding was resorted to for the relief of cyanosis, the brilliant success of that procedure is not to be wondered at—nor that the patient died. In the hypokinetic type of anoxia the unsaturation of the venous blood of a subject with 60 per cent hemoglobin content could not reach the value necessary to produce cyanosis until all the hemoglobin was in the reduced state. Thus $\frac{1}{2}(1 + 12) = 6.5$ volumes per cent unsaturation of the capillary blood.

In *polycythemia*, in which the hemoglobin content is, say, double the normal (oxygen capacity 40 volumes per cent), cyanosis occurs in very mild degrees of anoxemia. At an arterial unsaturation of 4.5 volumes per cent the polycythemic subject would have the same degree of cyanosis as an ordinary person with this quantity (5 grams) of reduced hemoglobin in his blood. But in the polycythemic subject with a hemoglobin content of 200 per cent, 4.5 volumes per cent is only 11 per cent of the oxygen capacity of his blood; in the person with a normal hemoglobin content it constitutes 22.5 per cent. The oxygen want in the former would be relatively slight as compared with that of the latter. Or put in another way and including the anemic subject—if the anoxemia were of the same degree in each, the anemic person would show little or no cyanosis; the polycythemic, a cyanosis of high degree and the normal subject a color intermediate in intensity. In a person with an abnormally high blood count a degree of slowing of the peripheral blood flow

which would be without effect upon one possessing a normal hemoglobin content will result in cyanosis. Thus in regions such as the face, ear lobes and hands, where the cutaneous vessels are well filled with blood, cyanosis is readily induced in the polycythemic subject by exposure to cold. In certain conditions associated with arterial anoxemia, e.g., emphysema (p. 1039) and congenital heart disease the red cell count is increased, and the cyanosis, in consequence, enhanced. It will be evident from these examples that the presence of cyanosis indicates anoxia but the absence of cyanosis does not rule out the possibility of anoxia.

The Factors Which Influence the Depth of Cyanosis Caused by a Given Quantity of Reduced Hemoglobin

(a) *The state of cutaneous capillaries.* When these are dilated more of the dark colored blood will be present in the skin than when they are constricted. In the former instance cyanosis will of course be more pronounced. Increased carbon dioxide tension in the peripheral blood causes capillary dilation, therefore, when retention of this gas accompanies oxygen want, as in venous congestion of superficial regions, etc. the cyanosis is intense. If the peripheral vessels are strongly constricted, as in shock, cyanosis may be inconspicuous.

(b) *Pigmentation and thickness of the skin.* These factors obviously will modify the depth of the cyanotic color. Cyanosis is more clearly evident in regions where the skin is thin and unpigmented. The yellow discoloration of the skin caused by an excess of bilirubin in the blood (jaundice) tends to modify the cyanotic tint, but since the former stains the skin itself, while the discoloration due to reduced hemoglobin is confined to the capillary vessels, jaundice is likely to be just as intense in regions where the skin is thick as in those where it is thin. The cyanotic discoloration can be temporarily abolished by pressure upon the skin whereas the icteric staining cannot. Cyanosis does not appear in the conjunctivae but these are deeply colored in jaundice.

Oxygen Therapy

Oxygen administration is of great value in combating acute arterial anoxia as may occur in pneumonia, pulmonary edema, or obstruction to breathing, as well as in states such as congestive heart failure, or coronary thrombosis when, though the arterial blood contains the usual amount of oxygen, the tissues, owing to impairment of the peripheral circulation, suffer from a deficiency of oxygen.

The chronic anoxia due to anemia, in which the hemoglobin is saturated with oxygen to the normal degree, is treated preferably by measures directed to the disease itself rather than by oxygen therapy. In failure of the peripheral circulation, the inhalation of 100 per cent oxygen will increase the oxygen content of the blood to revive a flagging respiratory center. But the anoxia due to a shunt of blood from the right to the left side of the heart (p. 1042) or through a similarly completely unaerated portion of the lung will not be much benefited by oxygen inhalations; it is not possible to make the blood supplying healthy and well aerated alveoli absorb any important amount of *extra* oxygen and so compensate for the shunted blood.

When, however, the diffusion coefficient of oxygen (ch. 50) through the alveolar membrane is reduced as a result of edema, thickening or a coating of fluid, oxygen administration by raising the pressure of the gas in the alveolar air will increase its rate of diffusion across the pulmonary epithelium. The oxygen saturation of the blood flowing through the damaged pulmonary tissue is increased.

Consequently, in broncho- or lobar pneumonia when such changes are responsible for the anoxemia, in emphysema or in pulmonary edema whether from cardiac or pulmonary disease or from gas poisoning, the success of oxygen administration is often spectacular. Anoxemia apparently promotes an increase in transudation of fluid into the alveoli. In other words, a vicious circle may be established—edema inducing anoxemia and the latter increasing the edema—which is broken by oxygen administration.

Anoxemia due to rapid *shallow breathing* is relieved by oxygen treatment since the oxygen tension of poorly ventilated alveoli is raised thereby. The shallow breathing itself is likely to persist since it is primarily due to the local process in the lung acting upon the nerve endings rather than to the anoxemia. Therefore this type of breathing could, no more than the pulmonary lesion itself, be expected to be abolished by oxygen treatment.

It has been said that when the arterial blood contains the normal quantity of oxygen, namely about 19.5 volumes per cent (saturation 97.5 per cent) as in the hypokinetic type of anoxia of congestive heart failure, oxygen inhalation cannot be of any great value, since the oxygen saturation can be raised only to 100 per cent, and the total oxygen content increased by 2.2 volumes per cent

(an increase of 1.7 volumes in simple solution together with 0.5 volumes combined with hemoglobin). That is, the total oxygen content of a person breathing 100 per cent oxygen will be 21.7 volumes per cent. But this increase of 2.2 volumes per cent (representing an increase in O_2 content of 11 per cent) is as pointed out by Comroe and Dripps of the highest importance in anoxia, for it raises very considerably the pressure at which oxygen is delivered to the tissues. For example, when a patient is breathing ordinary air, every 100 cc. of blood in passing through the capillaries loses 7 volumes of O_2 (normal about 5 vols.), and, therefore, leaves the venous end of the capillary with a content of 12.5 vols. per cent, is 63 per cent saturated, and has a P_{O_2} of around 32 mm. Hg. Now when 100 per cent oxygen is breathed the extra 2.2 volumes per cent in the arterial blood is given up on entering the capillaries, which reduces the oxygen saturation only to that existing under ordinary conditions in the arterial blood, namely, 97.5 per cent. But the tissues owing to the slowing of the circulation abstract a further 4.8 volumes per cent to satisfy their need of 7 volumes per cent. The venous blood, therefore, contains 14.7 volumes per cent of oxygen, and is over 73 per cent saturated, instead of about 63 per cent without oxygen administration; the P_{O_2} is nearly 40 mm. Hg. Thus the tissues are supplied with oxygen at a virtually normal head of pressure. In congestive heart failure, therefore, especially if there is generalized edema, the administration of oxygen is often of great benefit.

Methods of Administration

Oxygen is given usually by means of a nasal or oral-nasal catheter, by a specially designed face mask, or the patient is placed in a hood-tent or airtight cabinet in which the O_2 percentage is maintained at the required concentration. Carbon dioxide (5 to 10 per cent) is sometimes added, especially in CO poisoning, persistent hiccough and postoperative atelectasis, in order to encourage lung expansion. In an oxygen tent the patient's own breath may raise the CO_2 to the range of 1 to 2 per cent.

In normal persons the breathing of 100 per cent oxygen often causes a slight initial reduction of breathing of about 3 per cent. In anoxia, a much more pronounced depression or even complete cessation of breathing may occur. This so-called *oxygen apnea* may be very alarming, especially during anesthesia. But it is a sure indication of the existence of anoxia and the need for oxygen therapy. Before oxygen administration the center had been driven by impulses from the peripheral chemoreceptors; the relief of the anoxia has abolished this source of stimulation. In chronic anoxia, such as may be seen in congestive heart failure and pulmonary emphysema, especially when there is also carbon dioxide retention, the patient may pass into coma when oxygen is administered. The unfavorable effects following administration of O_2 under these conditions are attributable to the further rise in Pco_2 which occurs as a result of the depression of breathing.

Another effect of oxygen inhalation is the elimination of nitrogen. A man of average weight (70 kg.) breathing oxygen eliminates about 18 ml. of nitrogen per minute. The rate of removal of the gas from all tissues is not however the same; it is removed most rapidly from the blood and the most vascular parts of the brain. Pure oxygen is, therefore, administered to divers to prevent decompression sickness, and to pilots before high altitude flights.

Helium (atomic weight 4, $\frac{1}{7}$ density that of nitrogen) is lighter than any other gas except hydrogen. Barach has applied this physical fact to reduce the respiratory effort in asthmatic attacks, in those suffering from laryngeal or tracheal obstruction and in certain other types of dyspnea. A gas mixture is used in which helium is substituted for nitrogen (oxygen, 21 per cent; helium, 79 per cent). For the relief of anoxemia the oxygen percentage may be increased to 60 or 70 per cent.

Effects of prolonged breathing 0.5 to 1 atmosphere of O_2. Ill effects other than the "oxygen apnea" described above may result from prolonged administration of oxygen. Commonly subjects complain of substernal distress in 4 to 16 hours after beginning to breathe 100 per cent O_2 at sea level. The symptom usually persists for some hours after the patient resumes breathing of atmospheric air. The pain evidently is related to tracheobronchitis, and it is not a problem unless oxygen tension in inspired air is in excess of 0.5 of an atmosphere. Other manifestations of toxicity produced by breathing 70 to 100 per cent O_2 at a pressure of 1 atmosphere include fatigue, paresthesias in the hands and feet, joint pain, anorexia, nausea and vomiting. The causes of these symptoms are unknown (Comroe and Dripps, 1950).

In the ordinary clinical management of patients when oxygen is given in a tent or by nasal catheter oxygen toxicity does not become a factor since the O_2 content in inspired air is rarely, if ever, increased to above 50 per cent. Higher levels

can be achieved if a close-fitting mask is used in the absence of rebreathing or if the subject is placed in an enclosure into which oxygen is introduced.

Effects of oxygen pressures greater than one atmosphere. By placing the patient in a pressure chamber it is possible to administer oxygen under a pressure of more than one atmosphere. Recently this method has been used for treatment of carbon monoxide poisoning, and its usefulness for other purposes is being investigated extensively (see Lambertsen, Bond, and Jacobsen, II). When oxygen is breathed at pressures around 2 to 4 atmospheres severe symptoms indicating dysfunction of the higher central nervous system are experienced. These include mood swings, indifference, loss of judgment, somnolence, irrational apprehension and finally convulsions of the grand mal type. The latter are followed by automatism and amnesia. Vertigo also is a common symptom of oxygen poisoning. The cause of the symptoms is not clear. Reduction in the CO_2 carrying capacity of the blood, with a corresponding rise in CO_2 tension and cH in the tissues and venous blood, has been shown to occur in experimental animals; but it is not known if the symptoms in man are related entirely to these changes (Bean, 1945).

Mice die within 20 to 25 minutes when exposed to an oxygen tension of 8 atmospheres, whereas a pressure of 8 atmospheres of air is tolerated well.

Effects of breathing air at very high pressures (nitrogen narcosis). The inert gases, including nitrogen, at certain pressures display the typical properties of anesthetic agents. Whereas surgical anesthesia is produced in patients breathing 80 per cent of an atmosphere of nitrous oxide or xenon, about 38 atmospheres of nitrogen has been calculated to be necessary to have this effect. In experimental animals a pressure of 30 atmospheres of nitrogen is required to abolish righting reactions. However, symptoms referrable to impairment of function of the central nervous system occur in an individual exposed to 6 atmospheres of nitrogen (the equivalent of about 200 feet below the surface of water). Helium-oxygen mixtures have less anesthetic action than nitrogen-oxygen mixtures, hence divers breathing helium-oxygen can descend to much greater depths without the development of mental aberrations.

Resuscitation

Until the last few years Schafer's prone pressure method of artificially inflating the lungs was

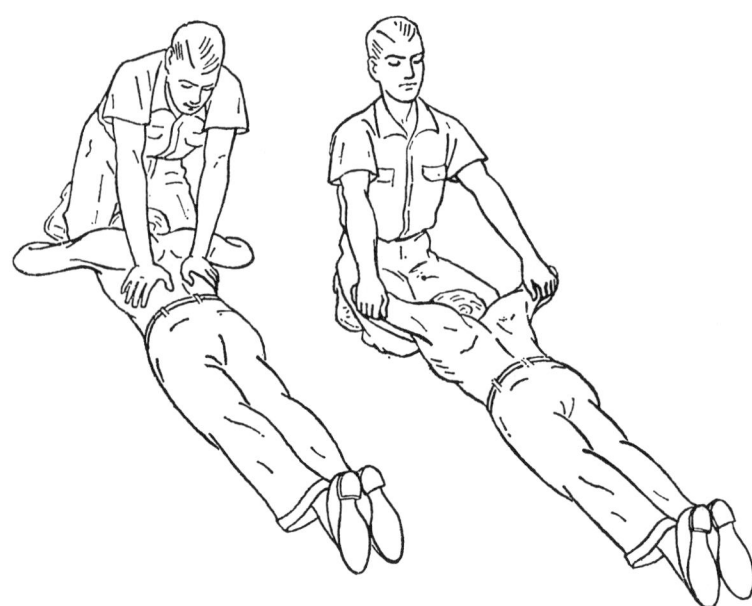

Fig. 54.9. Illustrating the Holger-Nielsen method of resuscitation. (From *First Aid. Metropolitan Life Insurance Company.*)

most widely practiced. But today either the *Holger-Nielson* or the *mouth-to-mouth method* is preferred.

HOLGER-NIELSON OR BACK-PRESSURE-ARM-LIFT METHOD. After loosening the clothing around the neck and chest, drawing the tongue well forward, and wiping fluid, mucus, etc., from the mouth and throat in order to allow free passage of air, the subject is laid in the prone position (chest down). The arms are abducted at the shoulders to lie at right angles to the trunk and bent at the elbows (see fig. 54.9). The head is turned to one side with a cheek resting on the hands. The operator places himself in front of the subject with one knee resting beside his head and near his forearm. The foot of the operator's other side is planted near the subject's opposite forearm. Then the operator places his hands, with fingers spread apart, upon the subject's back, thumbs touching, and on an imaginary line joining the axillae. He then sways forward, bringing his weight to bear through his arms and hands upon the subject's back. The operator should hold his arms straight at the elbows. This movement compresses the chest and imitates natural expiration. The operator then seizes the subject's arm above the elbows and draws them forward, at the same time as he himself straightens up. This position which expands the chest and simulates natural inspiration is held for two seconds. He then swings forward again

and repeats the first phase. The double movement is repeated about 12 times a minute.

MOUTH-TO-MOUTH METHOD. In a symposium published in the May, 1958 issue of the Journal of the American Medical Association it is stated that mouth-to-mouth resuscitation is superior to all manual methods for all age groups. It is reported to be the only technique capable of producing adequate ventilation in all cases. The single most important factor preventing adequate ventilation in this and some other methods, is mechanical obstruction of the airway by the tongue. Proper extension of the neck and elevation of the jaw eliminates this obstruction. To perform mouth-to-mouth resuscitation the subject is placed in the supine position with the head extended and the rescuer at the side of the head. The rescuer grasps the lower jaw of the subject between his thumb and index finger and lifts it vertically upward. The other thumb and index finger are used to clamp off the nostrils. The rescuer then places his mouth over the subject's mouth and exhales into the airway a volume about two times the normal tidal volume (fig. 54.10). Volume and pressure required are easily judged by the rescuer. He inflates the subject's lungs and thorax and notes the expansion of the chest. The rescuer then removes his mouth from that of the subject to allow him to exhale. The procedure should be performed about 12 to 20 times per minute.

The effectiveness and ease of performance of this type of resuscitation is improved by the use of an anesthesia face mask, or an oropharyngeal airway or an endotracheal tube.

During recent years several methods have been developed for the long continued application of artificial respiration by various mechanical devices. This work was begun by Thunberg in Lund who devised an apparatus called the barospirator. The subject was placed inside a metal chamber in which the pressure was raised and lowered rhythmically by means of the stroke of a large piston. The interchange of air within the lungs was caused by a rise and fall of pressure of the air in the external atmosphere. This apparatus was effective and a model was built large enough to accommodate patient, nurse and doctor. All three were ventilated without movement of the chest. A certain amount of discomfort was experienced in this cabinet due to the change in pressure on the two sides of the eardrum during the increase and decrease of air pressure. A more generally applicable model was produced by Drinker at Harvard. In this type the patient's head remains outside the cabinet (fig. 54.11). The chest is expanded by reducing the pressure within the cabinet and as the pressure is raised again, the natural elasticity of the lung causes expiration. Forced expiration, however, may be produced by raising the pressure above atmospheric. Patients have been adequately ventilated with this apparatus for many months. Some difficulty is occasionally encountered in the regulation of the rate and depth of respiration, but by determining the oxygen saturation of the arterial blood or watching for signs of cyanosis an observer can usually regulate the ventilation quite satisfactorily.

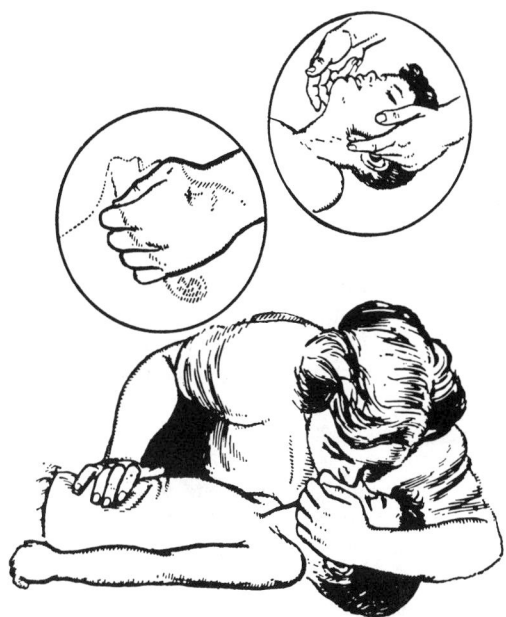

FIG. 54.10. Mouth-to-mouth method of artificial respiration. (Courtesy of Dr. John Henderson and Duell, Sloan, Pierce and Company Publishers, New York.)

Two other types of apparatus should be mentioned; (1) the jacket model of Sahlin which operates like the Drinker machine but is applied only to the chest, and (2) the Bragg-Paul pulsator which consists of a hollow elastic bandage placed around the chest. The bandage, when inflated by an electrically driven bellows, compresses the chest, which returns to the midposition by virtue of its own elasticity during the intervals between the compressions.

The pulmotor and other similarly devised resuscitators, which force air into the chest and suck it out again as though the lungs were rubber bags, though so appealing in their mechanical

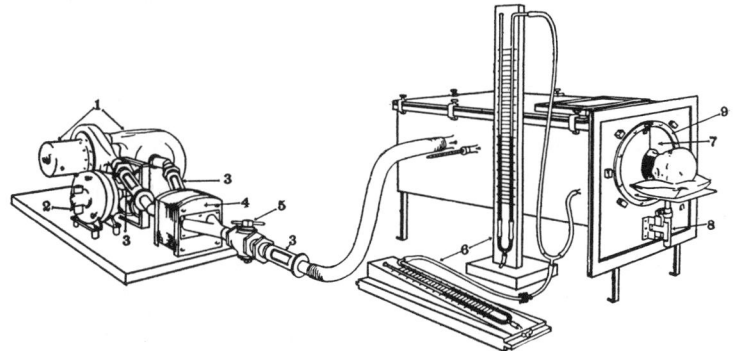

FIG. 54.11. The Drinker respirator. *1*, pumps; *2*, motor; *3*, vents; *4*, alternate; *5*, valves; *6*, manometers; *7*, external shutters; *8*, adjustment for head rest; *9*, adjustable ring to hold collar in place. (After Shaw and Drinker.)

efficiency, are physiologically unsound. They are not only less effective than other methods but may be actually harmful. The pulmonary tissue may be torn. Those machines which inflate the lungs with an oxygen-carbon dioxide mixture, and permit expiration to take place simply by interrupting the air current and thus permitting collapse of the thorax, are much sounder in principle.

A mixture of oxygen and carbon dioxide (5 per cent or 10 per cent of the latter) commonly is used for resuscitation. The high tension of CO_2 combined with the rhythmical inflation and deflation of the lungs, which presumably cause the discharge of afferent impulses, encourages the return of spontaneous breathing.

Resuscitation of the newborn. Asphyxia in the newborn infant is usually due to the failure of the lungs to expand fully, alveoli in areas of the pulmonary tissue remaining in the fetal state (atelectasis). The methods of resuscitation which may be effective in the adult are likely to fail. Cutaneous stimulation, e.g., slapping, hot or cold water, are time honored devices which are usually unsuccessful. The object aimed at should be the expansion of the collapsed alveoli, and when the infant makes no respiratory effort this is best accomplished by the insufflation of the lungs with a carbon dioxide-oxygen mixture, carried out by the passage down the trachea of a tube, to the outer end of which a rubber bag filled with the gas mixture is attached. When the breathing is not completely suspended but is weak, and the infant cyanosed, inhalations of a carbon dioxide-oxygen mixture are employed. Also mouth-to-mouth resuscitation is quite effective in infants.

REFERENCES

BARACH, A. L. Ann. Int. Med., 1931, **5,** 428.

BARACH, A. L., AND RICHARDS, D. W. Arch. Int. Med., 1931, **48,** 325.

BARCROFT, J., BINGER, C. A., BOCK, A. V., DOGGART, J. H., FORBES, H. S., HARROP, G., MEAKINS, J. C., AND REDFIELD, A. C. Phil. Trans. Roy. Soc., 1923, **B211,** 351.

BEHNKE, A. R., in Hyperbaric Oxygenation, ed. by LAMBERTSEN, C. J., BOND, G., AND JACOBSEN, J. H., II. Ann. N. Y. Acad. Sci., 1965, **117,** 843.

BINGER, C. A. L., AND MOORE, R. L. J. Exper. Med., 1927, **45,** 633.

BLALOCK, A., AND TAUSSIG, H. B. J. A. M. A., 1945, **128,** 129.

BOYCOTT, A. E., DAMANT, G. C. C., AND HALDANE, J. S. J. Hyg., 1908, **8,** 342.

CHEN, K. K., ROSE, C. L., AND CLOWES, G. H. A. Am. J. M. Sc., 1934, **188,** 767.

CHRISTIE, R. V. J. Clin. Invest., 1934, **13,** 295.

DALY, I. DEB. Tr. Med.-Chir. Soc., Edinburgh, 1936, 139.

DUNN, J. S. Quart. J. Med., 1920, **13,** 129.

GROOM, D., WOOD, E. H., BURCHELL, H. B., AND PARKER, R. L. Proc. Staff Meet. Mayo Clin, 1948, **23,** 601.

GROSS, L. J. A. M. A., 1919, **9,** 632.

HARROP, G. A. J. A. M. A., 1923, **80,** 1641.

HENDERSON, Y. J. A. M. A., 1924, **83,** 758. Ibid., 1928, **90,** 583. Ibid., 1929, **93,** 96. Brit. Med. J., 1931, **2,** 687. New England J. Med., 1932, **206,** 151.

HENDERSON, Y., AND HENDERSON, M. C. Arch. Int. Med., 1932, **49,** 88.

HENDERSON, Y., HAGGARD, H. W., CORYLLOS, P. N., AND BIRNBAUM, G. L. Arch. Int. Med., 1930, **45,** 72.

HUG, E. Compt. rend. Soc. biol., 1933, **112,** 511.

LUFT, U. L. Physiological aspects of pressure cabins and rapid decompression. *In* Handbook of Respiratory Physiology, p. 129. United States Air Force School of Aviation Medicine, Randolph Field, Texas, 1954.

MEAKINS, J., AND DAVIES, H. W. J. Path. & Bact., 1920, **23,** 451.

PUGH, L., J. Physiol., 1957, **135,** 590.

RILEY, R. L., OTIS, A. B., AND HOUSTON, C. S. Respiratory features of acclimatization to altitude. *In* Handbook of Respiratory Physiology, p. 143. United States Air Force School of Aviation Medicine, Randolph Field, Texas, 1954.

SAHLIN, B. Skandinav. Arch. Physiol., 1926, **47,** 284.

SCOTT, R. W. Arch. Int. Med., 1920, **26,** 545.

SMITH, G. in Hyperbaric Oxygenation, ed. by LAMBERTSEN, C. J., BOND G., AND JACOBSEN, J. H., II. Ann. N. Y. Acad. Sci., 1965, **117,** 684.

SMITH, R. G., AND MALCOLM, R. L. J. Pharmacol. & Exper. Therap., 1930, **40,** 457.

STADIE, W. C. J. Exper. Med., 1922, **35,** 377.

WARNER, W. P., AND GRAHAM, D. Arch. Int. Med., 1933, **52,** 888.

WENDEL, W. B. J. A. M. A., 1933, **100,** 1054.

WHITEHORN, W. V., LEIN, A., AND EDELMANN, A. Am. J. Physiol., 1946, **147,** 289.

WHITEHORN, W. V., LEIN, A., EDELMANN, A., AND HITCHCOCK, F. A. Am. J. Physiol., 1947, **148,** 253.

WHITEHORN, W. V., LEIN, A., AND HITCHCOCK, F. A. J. Aviation Med., 1947, **18,** 102.

Monographs and Reviews

ABBOT, M. E. S. Atlas of Congenital Cardiac Disease. American Heart Association, New York, 1936.

BALDWIN, E. DEF., COURNAND, A., AND RICHARDS, D. W., JR. Medicine, 1948, **27,** 243.

BARCLAY, A. E., FRANKLIN, K. J., AND PRICHARD, M. M. L. The Foetal Circulation and Cardiovascular System. Blackwell Scientific Publications, Oxford, 1946.

BARCROFT, J. The Respiratory Functions of the Blood. Cambridge University Press, London, 1925.

BLALOCK, A. Harvey Lectures, 1945–1946, **41,** 90.

BURCHELL, H. B., PARKER, R. L., DRY, T. J., WOOD, E. H., PENDER, J. W., AND PUGH, D. G. Proc. Staff Meet. Mayo Clinic, 1948, **23,** 482.

CATCHPOLE, H. R., AND GERSH, I. Physiol. Rev., 1947, **27,** 360.

COMROE, J. H., AND DRIPPS, R. D. The Physiological Basis of Oxygen Therapy, Am. Lecture

Series. Charles C Thomas, Springfield, Ill., 1950.

COURNAND, A., BALDWIN, J. S., AND HIMMELSTEIN, A. Cardiac Catheterization in Congenital Heart Disease. Commonwealth Fund, New York, 1949.

FRANKLIN, K. J., AND ASSOCIATES. The Circulation in the Foetus. Blackwell Scientific Publications, Oxford, 1946.

FULTON, J. F. (Ed.) Decompression Sickness. W. B. Saunders Company, Philadelphia, 1951.

HALDANE, J. S., AND PRIESTLEY, J. G. Respiration. Clarendon Press, Oxford, 1935.

HARVEY, N. E. Harvey Lecture, 1943–44, **40,** 41.

HILL, L. Caisson Sickness. Edward Arnold & Company, London, 1912.

IVY, A. C. High altitude problems in aviation. Fed. Proc., 1946, **5,** 319.

KOUNTZ, W. B., AND ALEXANDER, H. L. Emphysema. Medicine, 1934, **13,** 251.

LAMBERTSEN, C. J., BOND, G., AND JACOBSEN, J. H., II. Hyperbaric Oxygenation. Ann. N. Y. Acad. Sci., 1965, **117,** 843.

LUNDSGAARD, C., AND VAN SLYKE, D. D. Cyanosis. Medicine, 1923, **2,** 1.

MEAKINS, J. C., AND DAVIES, H. W. Respiratory Function in Disease. Oliver, Edinburgh, 1925.

SCHNEIDER, E. C. Physiol. Rev., 1921, **1,** 631.

STONE, LL. J. Advances Int. Med., 1955, **VII,** 243.

VAN LIERE, E. J. Anoxia; Its Effect on the Body. University of Chicago Press, 1942.

WHITTENBERGER, J. L. Physiol. Rev., 1955, **35,** 611.

CHAPTER 55

Cytoarchitecture of Protein Secretory and Active Transport Cells

Digestion and absorption of food and the formation of urine are complex phenomena from the standpoint of biochemical analysis. However, these activities are carried out by a population of cells which exhibit only two basically different patterns of subcellular organization. A small investment of time devoted to a consideration of these two characteristic cytoarchitectural plans will facilitate the assimilation of the complex body of subject matter related to biochemical and physiological manifestations of the cells concerned.

The cytological appearance of protoplasm devoted primarily to protein synthesis is dominated by the presence of a high concentration of ribosomes in the cytoplasm and a "cart wheel" or "clock-face" nucleus (i.e., one with prominent peripheral chromatin clumps and a large nucleolus). The highest degree of organization of protein-producing protoplasm is seen in cells which secrete their products soon after synthesis, such as the various zymogen-producing cells of the alimentary tract. The cytoplasm of such cells not only possesses a high concentration of *ribosomes*, but also contains a broad, long membranous sac which serves to transport the protein from the site of synthesis to the intracellular storage depot. These two closely associated activities of the cytoplasm, namely protein synthesis and bulk transport, require that the ribosome be attached to the outer (non-luminal) aspect of the membranous sac. This ribosome-encrusted portion of the sac has been named *rough-surfaced or granular endoplasmic reticulum* by electron microscopists (Palade *et al.*). This same component of the cell was called the *microsomes* by the cell fractionation chemists who first isolated them by differential centrifugation. More recently chemists have been able to separate the ribosomes from the membranous elements, and to show that the capacity to incorporate amino acids into protein resides in the ribosome, not in the membranous derivatives (Palade *et al.*). The

traditional histologic names for the organelle responsible for protein synthesis include ergastoplasm, basophilic substance and chromidial substance. In fig. 55.1 it should be noted that the rough-surfaced endoplasmic reticulum is compactly stacked in the basal half of the cell. This arrangement may be achieved simply by folding the long, broad ribosome-studded sac alternately from right to left across the width of the cell. The blind end of the sac envelopes the nucleus. This nuclear envelope is closely applied to the peripheral surface of each chromatin clump of the nucleus. Passages between adjacent chromatin clumps are guarded on the cytoplasmic side by pores in the nuclear envelope. These nuclear pores are believed to facilitate the distribution of template or messenger RNA from the sites of synthesis in the nucleus to the sites of action, the ribosomes of the cytoplasm. If the reader within the past several years has not reviewed the subject of the role of the nucleic acids in protein synthesis, it would be advisable to do so, since developments in this area have profoundly affected cell biology (Watson).

Although the ribosomes are confined to the basal half of the cell, the membranous sac extends into the apical or supranuclear region and converges towards the cell center along a tight zig-zag course, and by so doing forms the Golgi apparatus. The latter organelle is responsible for packaging the protein secretory product which it has received via the lumen of the endoplasmic reticulum from the sites of synthesis. The Golgi apparatus gives rise to spheroidal vesicles which enlarge as they become filled with secretory product. When a vesicle enlarges to a diameter of about 1 or 2 μ it is separated from the Golgi tubules as an independent vesicle and thereafter displaced towards the free surface of the cell. Release of the secretory product from the major digestive glands is synchronized so that delivery of the zymogen to the lumen of the alimentary tract coincides with passage of food. Within a

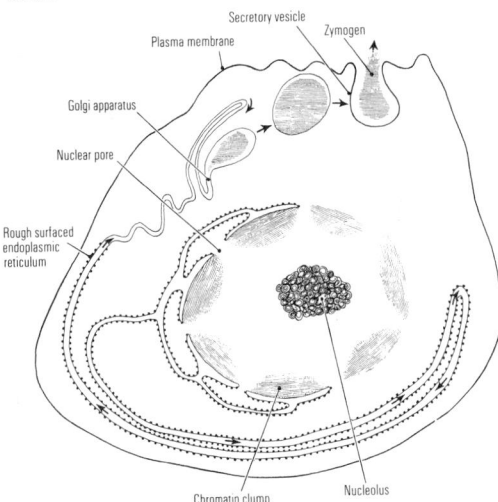

FIG. 55.1. *Intracellular route* of flow of the zymogen from the sites of synthesis, the ribosomes, to the free surface of the cell.

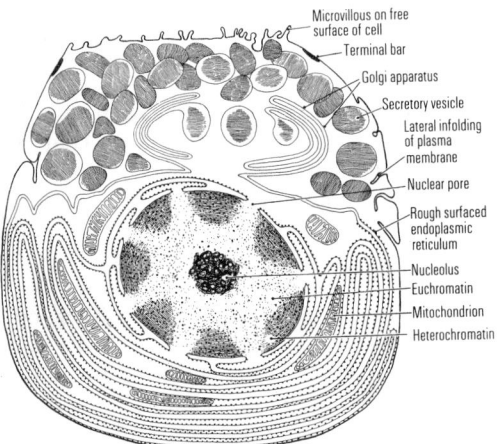

FIG. 55.2. A profile sketch of the *protein-secretory cell* prototype based upon electron micrographs of zymogen producing cells as seen at about 20,000 × magnification.

short period of time after having received the appropriate nervous or hormonal stimulus, most of the secretory vesicles make contact with the plasma membrane at the free surface of the cell (fig. 55.1). As the membrane bounding the vesicle fuses with the plasma membrane, the zymogen escapes into the lumen of the duct and is conveyed to the intestinal cavity.

It should be emphasized that the ribosomes and the membrane-bound sac (including the endoplasmic reticulum and Golgi apparatus) represent two distinct organelles or functional components which characteristically occur in intimate association in the zymogen-producing cells, as illustrated in fig. 55.2. This group of cells would

include the serous cells of the salivary glands, the source of salivary amylase (ptyalin), the chief cells of the stomach, the source of the proteolytic enzyme pepsin, and the acinar cells of the pancreas, the source of several different hydrolytic enzymes (chymotrypsin, trypsin, amylase, lipase, elastase and RNase). Electron microscopic examination of various cells *other* than those which secrete protein has revealed that the ribosomes and the endoplasmic reticulum often occur in the cytoplasm *dissociated* from one another. For example, at an early stage in the development of most cells ribosomes occur in high concentration arranged in rosette-like clusters called polysomes and not associated with membranous tubules. Such a distribution pattern is seen in fig. 55.3, which is based upon the electron microscopic appearance of the developing red blood cell. This cell retains all of the protein (hemoglobin) synthesized by the polysomes; hence, has no need for a bulk transport apparatus and, indeed, elements of the endoplasmic reticulum and Golgi apparatus are rarely seen in these cells. As another important example of protoplasm in which ribosomes and endoplasmic reticulum are dissociated from one another, the steroid hormone-producing cells may be cited. Electron microscopic examination of the cytoplasm of the adrenal cortical cells which produce the gluco- and mineral corticoids and the interstitial cells of Leydig which produce the male sex hormone, testosterone, has revealed the presence in high concentration of smooth-surface (ribosome-free) elements of the endoplasmic reticulum.

From the standpoint of cellular physiology the

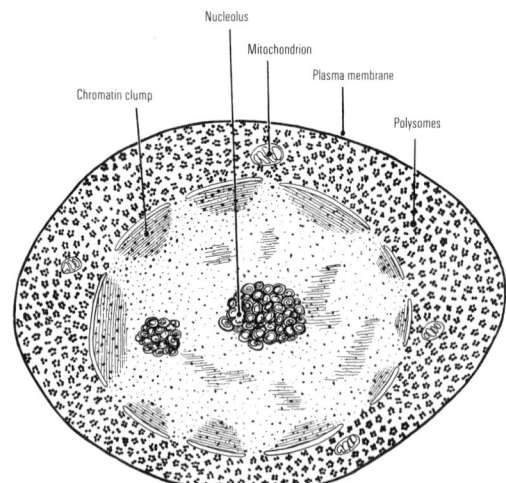

FIG. 55.3. A profile sketch of the *developing red blood cell* based upon electron micrographs at about 20,000 × magnification.

most important problem solved during the evolution of vertebrates was the development of homeostatic mechanisms, i.e., those which help to maintain constant the composition of the fluids which bathe all of the cells of the organism. Towards this end there was evolved: an integument essentially impermeable to water, a new organ of respiration (the lungs) for the efficient exchange of CO_2 and O_2 between air and blood, a new vehicle for oxygen delivery (a hemoglobin-filled corpuscle) permitting the efficient exchange of gasses between blood and all tissues, an additional vascular circuit, the pulmonary circulatory system, to serve the new organ of respiration, and finally, to guard the portals of entry (the intestines) and exit (the kidneys) into the extracellular fluid compartment and vascular system, an epithelium specialized to perform active transport functions.

Active transport was first demonstrated in isolated kidney preparations with the aid of the indicator dye, phenol red (Chambers *et al.*). Segments of renal tubules were excised from chick embryos and placed in a balanced salt solution. Spontaneously the cut ends of the tubules became closed off or "healed" and thus, there existed a closed lumen or cavity within the tubule the contents of which were controlled by the activity of the tubular epithelium. When phenol red was added to the bath maintained at 37° C., within a few minutes dye-tinted vacuoles were observed traversing the cytoplasm of the renal tubular epithelium, from the peripheral margin of the cells to the "free" or luminal surface. The concentration of dye increased rapidly

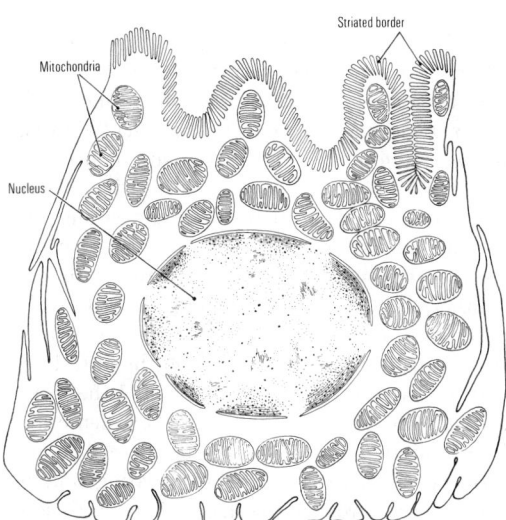

FIG. 55.4. A profile sketch of an *active transport cell* prototype based upon a composite of electron micrographs of the parietal cell of the stomach and absorptive cell of the intestines.

within the lumen of the tubule. Particularly significant was the observation that whenever metabolism of the cells was arrested by various means, e.g. oxygen or glucose deprivation, temperature depression or through action of a metabolic inhibitor such as phylorizin, dinitrophenol or cyanide, ability to concentrate the dye was lost. Subsequent experiments have established that active transport requires energy or in other words must be driven by adenosine triphosphate (ATP)-generating organelles, the mitochondria (4). *Therefore, cells which are devoted exclusively to the performance of active transport functions*

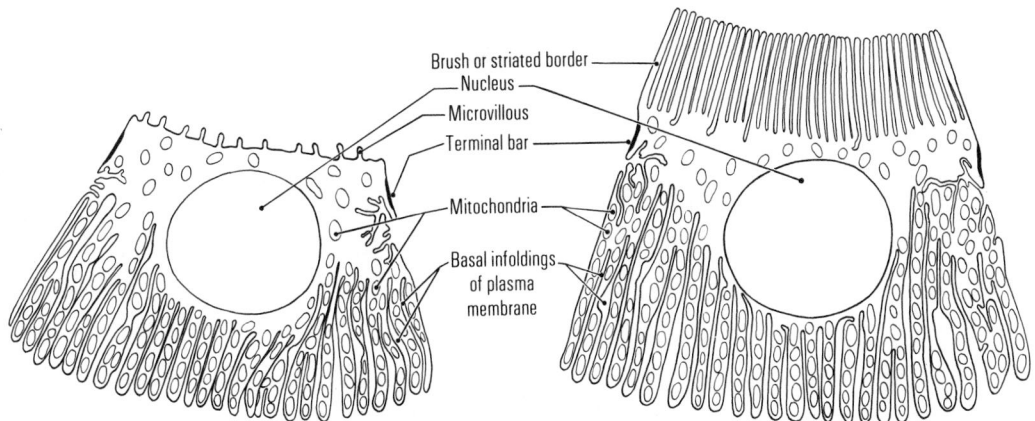

FIG. 55.5. A profile sketch to show the basal infoldings of the plasma membrane and mitochondrial distribution as seen in electron micrographs of the epithelial cells that line the distal convoluted tubules of the kidney and ducts of the salivary glands.

FIG. 55.6 A. profile sketch based upon the electron microscopic appearance of the epithelial cells that line the proximal convoluted tubules of the kidney.

may be identified cytologically by virtue of the presence in high concentrations of mitochondria and an extensive plasma membrane along the border of the cell across which the gradient of transport is maintained. These features are represented in figs. 55.4, 55.5 and 55.6, line drawings based upon the electron microscopic appearance of several different active transport cells (Kurtz). As the three sketches are compared with one another, it will become evident that the cells differ with respect to polarity. In fig. 55.4 which represents the absorptive cell of the intestines and the parietal (HCl-secreting) cell of the stomach amplification in extent of the cell membrane is seen at the luminal surface of the cell in the form of a *striated border.* The repeating unit of the striated border is the microvillous, a slender evagination 1 μ in height and 0.1 μ in diameter. The epithelium of the distal convoluted tubule of the kidney and of the salivary ducts of the salivary glands lack striated borders but possess deep infoldings of the plasma membrane along the basal aspect of the cell (fig. 55.5). These basal infoldings of the plasma membrane partition the cytoplasm into narrow compartments, the long axes of which are perpendicular to the base of the cell. Mitochondria are arranged end-to-end, single file, within each cytoplasmic compartment. The presence of basal infoldings is characteristic of cells which maintain concentration gradients of ions or molecules between the cytoplasm and the blood stream, whereas the presence of a striated border is characteristic of cells which maintain concentration gradients between cytoplasm and the contents of the lumen of the viscus. The *proximal* convoluted tubule of the kidney represents the most highly differentiated active transport cell and possesses a brush border as well as basal infoldings of the plasma membrane (fig. 55.6).

REFERENCES

CHAMBERS, R., BECK, L. V., AND BELKIN, M. Secretion in tissue cultures. I. Inhibition of phenol red accumulation in the chick kidney. J. Cell. Comp. Physiol., 1935, 6, 425–439.

Electron microscopic anatomy (ed., Kurtz, S. M.) Academic Press, New York, 1964.

PALADE, G. E., SIEKEVITZ, P., AND CARO, L. G. "Structure, chemistry and function of the pancreatic exocrine cell," Ciba Foundation Symposium on the Exocrine Pancreas, 1962.

WATSON, J. D. Molecular biology of the gene. W. A. Benjamin, Inc., New York, 1965.

WILSON, T. H. Intestinal absorption. W. B. Saunders Co., Philadelphia, 1962.

VII

DIGESTION

CHAPTER 56

Salivary Secretion

The Salivary Glands

Only mammals possess true salivary (digestive) glands. Oral mucous glands, however, are found in all terrestrial vertebrates. Among mammals there is considerable variation in the number of salivary glands and also in the cellular structure of individual glands. In addition, the products of secretion by salivary glands may vary not only from species to species, but even from one salivary gland to another in the same animal.

In man, salivary secretion is provided, for the most part, by three pairs of glands, the *parotid*, *submaxillary* and *sublingual* glands. Also located within the oral and pharyngeal cavities are numerous other smaller glands that contribute to the production of saliva. These smaller glands include the lingual mucous glands located along the borders and at the root of the tongue, lingual serous (Ebner's) glands located in the vicinity of the vallate and foliate papillae of the tongue, and numerous small mucous glands in the mucous membrane covering the cheeks, hard and soft palate, and the walls of the pharynx.

The production of saliva by the salivary glands provides the first digestive juice that comes in contact with food. In addition to containing salivary amylase that initiates starch digestion, the salivary secretions play an important role in oral hygiene, the sensitivity of taste perception, the process of deglutition, and also serve as a medium for the excretion of certain inorganic and organic substances. The mechanism of secretion of saliva and the various factors that regulate its production are similar to other digestive glands in many respects.

GENERAL FORM AND LOCATION

The *parotid glands* are the largest of the salivary glands and in the adult weigh from 20 to 30 g. each. The parotid gland is located at the side of the face below and in front of the ear. Its shape is somewhat prismatic or cuneiform, with the lateral surface being just below the skin of the cheek. The anteromedial and posteromedial surfaces extend medially to form the wedge-shaped retromandibular process. The antero-medial surface slightly overlaps the masseter

muscle and is in contact with the posterior border of the ramus of the mandible. Posteriorly, the gland is in contact with the mastoid and styloid processes and the anterior border of the sterno-mastoid muscle. The parotid gland is enclosed in a sheath which limits the swelling of the inflamed gland. Because of this facial presentation of the gland, relatively small degrees of swelling are often conspicuous, as in a patient with mumps. As the anteromedial surface of the gland is in intimate contact with the masseter muscle and the ramus of the mandible, movement of these structures when chewing usually aggravates the pain and tenderness of a swollen parotid gland.

The duct system of the parotid gland originates in the *acini* of the gland. Ducts from neighboring *alveoli* join to form ducts of larger caliber which unite again to form still larger ducts. The fine ducts that drain the acini are known as *inter-calated* ducts. The intercalated ducts empty into *intralobular* ducts and these into *interlobular* or excretory ducts. Thus, by a progressive converg-ence of the several orders of ducts, the gland's secretion is conducted finally into a single large duct which opens into the oral cavity. This gen-eral arrangement of the ductal system is similar to the stem branching of a bunch of grapes—the rounded alveoli at the ends of the finest channels corresponding to the grapes. The term *racemose* (Latin for bunch of grapes) has been applied to glands exhibiting such a structure, and acinus (Latin for grape) identifies the smallest group of secretory cells of such a gland.

The parotid duct, also known as *Stensen's duct*, emerges from the anterior border of the gland near its upper end and runs transversely across the surface of the masseter muscle, at the anterior border of which the parotid duct abruptly turns medialward, pierces the buccal fat pad and the mucosa to open into the oral cavity at a point latter to the crowns of the second upper molar. The parotid duct is approximately 35 to 40 mm. long and about 3 mm. in diameter. The wall of the duct is tough due to the presence of a thick layer of fibrous tissue.

The *submaxillary glands* are shaped somewhat like a flattened walnut and weigh 8 to 10 g. each.

They are located in the submaxillary triangle medial to the mandible. The posterior end of the gland lies very close to the sternomastoid muscle. Like the parotid glands, the submaxillary glands have a racemose structure. The duct system is similar to that of the parotid glands and collects in a large, single submaxillary duct known as *Wharton's duct*. The submaxillary duct emerges from the deep surface of the gland and runs forward and inward between the mylohyoid muscle below, and the hypoglossus and the genioglossus muscles above, to reach the floor of the mouth. It opens by a small orifice on the summit of a soft papilla known as the *caruncula sublingualis* by the side of the frenulum of the tongue. The submaxillary duct is 40 to 50 mm. in length and the walls of the duct are relatively thin.

The *sublingual glands* are the smallest of the paired salivary glands and weigh from 2 to 3 g. each. The sublingual glands are elongated in shape and lie immediately under the mucous membrane of the floor of the mouth under

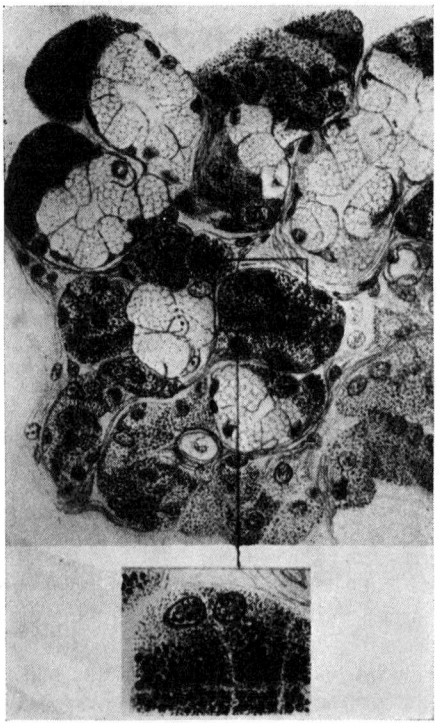

FIG. 56.1. Microscopic section of human submaxillary gland showing both mucous and serous groups of cells. The mucous cells are lightly stained and appear transparent. The serous cells are darker and some appear as demilune cells in the upper left area of the microscopic section. The insert is an oil immersion view showing zymogen granules in serous cells. (From Stormont in Cowdry's *Special Cytology*.)

the tongue. The structure of the sublingual glands is racemose like the parotid and submaxillary glands. Instead of being drained by a single, large duct, the sublingual glands are drained by 5 to 15 or more small, short ducts (*ducts of Rivinus*) that arise from the upper border of the gland and open on small papillae along the crest of the *plicae sublingualis*. The anterior portion of the gland is often drained by a single, larger duct, also known as *Bartholin's duct*, which opens alongside the submaxillary duct on the sublingual caruncle. Unlike the parotid and submaxillary glands, the capsule of the sublingual glands is poorly developed.

MICROSCOPIC ANATOMY

The racemose structure of the salivary glands is found on histological section to consist of acini, a tubule system and excretory ducts. The secreting epithelium of the acini is composed of two types of cells, *mucous* and *serous*, that can be differentiated from one another on the basis of nuclear appearance. The nucleus of the mucous cell is small, darkstained, indented and compressed against the lower pole of the cell. The serous cell possesses a larger, centrally placed vesicular nucleus. Four different types of cells may be distinguished in the lining of the salivary ducts. In addition, *myo-epithelial* cells which have been described in detail by Zimmerman (1927) have been demonstrated between the basal membrane of the alveoli and ducts.

Alveolar Structure

The acini of the salivary glands are composed of cells that are more or less pyramidal in shape. The apices of adjacent cells of an acinus converge upon a minute central lumen; the basal aspects of the cells form the periphery of the acinus. The central lumen is continuous with that of the excretory duct system.

The alveoli of the parotid gland in *man* consists entirely of serous cells. When parotid secretion is collected separately from that of the other salivary glands, it has a characteristic watery character or serous secretion. In the human submaxillary gland serous and mucous elements are seen in a ratio of about 4:1. More often than not the mucous alveoli are "capped" by a single layer of flattened serous cells, referred to as serous demilunes (fig. 56.1). The secretion of the serous demilune is believed to reach the lumen of the alveolus by means of small canaliculi between the mucous cells lining the alveolus. The alveolar structure of the sublingual glands is similar to the submaxillary gland except that the ratio of serous to mucous elements is about 1:4.

The mucous cells have large, translucent granules which readily transmit light, so that in thin sections they appear transparent. The serous cells have small granules that are more opaque and appear darker in sections than the mucous cells. The serous cells secrete a thin, watery fluid containing the starch-splitting enzyme, amylase, also known as *ptyalin*.

The myo-epithelial, or basket cells, are flat and somewhat star-shaped with long processes, and as previously mentioned, lie between the basement membrane and the secretory cells of the alveolus. They are also found in the intralobular salivary ducts between the basement membrane and cells lining the lumen. The myo-epithelial cells are modified epithelial cells and are thought to have a contractile function, although there is no clear evidence of this. The myo-epithelial cells of the salivary glands may serve a function similar to the myo-epithelial cells of the mammary gland. In the mammary gland, these cells are well developed and it has been established that their contraction results in the expulsion of preformed milk from the ducts. This is observed in the lactating breast and is known as "let down." It has been observed that stimulation of the sympathetic nerve supply to the salivary glands sometimes causes a sudden gush of saliva from the gland. This suggests that some previously secreted saliva is being expressed from the ducts by contraction of the myo-epithelial cells.

The cytoplasm of both the serous and mucous cells show a glandular structure. The fine granules of the serous cells are believed to furnish the enzymes of the secretion and are called zymogen granules. The mucinogen granules of the mucous cells provide the mucin that renders the secretion viscous. When the glands are in a resting state, the granules accumulate and the fine zymogen granules may load the cytoplasm to such an extent that the nucleus is almost obscured. The concentration of secretory granules, mucous as well as serous, is low soon after meals and gradually increases prior to the next meal. The *ultrastructure of the serous cells* of the salivary glands has been found to be quite similar to the acinar cells of the pancreas. See chap. 55 entitled, "Cytoarchitecture of protein secretory and active transport cells."

Nerve fibers have been observed penetrating the basement membrane of a salivary acinus and ending as fine filaments on the basal surface of the acinar cells (Scott and Pease, 1957). The electron microscope reveals the myo-epithelial cell to have a close resemblance to a smooth muscle cell (Porter 1954). This similarity tends to support the theory that the myo-epithelial cells have a contractile function.

Ductal Structure

Four different types of cells are found in the salivary ducts. In the *intercalary ducts* that lead directly away from the alveoli, the epithelium is *cuboidal* in character. These small cuboidal cells are practically filled by a large nucleus. The cytoplasm is scanty and rarely are any cytoplasmic granules observed. The *intralobular ducts* are lined by *columnar* cells that present a peculiar rod-shaped appearance, resembling in this respect some of the cells of the renal tubules. These cells have a centrally placed nucleus and there is a marked striation of the basal one-third of the cell. Electron micrographs reveal that the marked striation observed by the light microscope in the basal third of the columnar cells lining the intralobular ducts is due the alignment of mitochondria by infoldings of the plasma membrane. This arrangement, which greatly increases the surface area of the cell, suggests that it facilitates the transport of materials into or out of the cells. See also the preceding chapter. The *interlobular* or excretory ducts of the salivary glands are lined by a *two-layered epithelium* composed of a *columnar* superficial layer and a *flattened* deep layer. This type of lining of the excretory ducts is continued to near the termination of the duct, where it empties into the mouth. At this point, the lining of the duct changes to a layered, *stratified, squamous epithelium*. The fact that the cells that line the various portions of the salivary ducts differ in structure suggests that their functions may be different. The rod-shaped epithelium of the intralobular ducts is particularly suggestive of a secretory or reabsorptive function.

INNERVATION OF THE SALIVARY GLANDS

The salivary glands are supplied with efferent nerves from both the *parasympathetic* and *sympathetic* divisions of the *autonomic nervous system*. Functions regulated by the parasympathetic nerve supply are: secretion by the acinar cells and vasodilatation of the blood vessels. Functions regulated by the sympathetic nerve supply include secretion by the acinar cells, vasoconstriction of the vascular supply, and presumably, contraction or motor function by the myo-epithelial cells.

The origin of the parasympathetic supply is in *bulbar centers*, which consist of a group of nerve cells which run forward from the anterior end of the glossopharyngeal nucleus to the sensory nucleus of the facial nerve. The anterior (rostral) part is termed the *superior salivary nucleus*, and governs secretion by the submaxillary and sublingual glands; the posterior (caudal) part, called the *inferior salivary nucleus* controls secretion by the parotid gland.

The *submaxillary and sublingual glands* receive secretory impulses through the *chorda tympani nerve*. The course of the autonomic innervation is: from the *superior salivary nucleus* the axones arise and enter the *nervus intermedius of Wrisberg* (ch. 6) which terminates at the genicular ganglion. The preganglionic fibers by-pass the geniculate ganglion and continue a short distance with the motor fibers of the facial nerve. In the facial canal, just behind the ear drum, the chorda tympani arises from the facial nerve and passes forward across the inner aspect of the ear drum, then through the skull via the petro-tympanic fissure. Next the chorda joins the lingual branch of the trigeminal nerve and thereby is conveyed to the submandibular ganglion, located in the floor of the mouth. The preganglionic fibers carried by the chorda tympani end in the submandibular ganglion by making synapse with the cell bodies of the neurones of the ganglion. The axones arising from the latter constitute the postganglionic fibers which terminate by fine arborizations around the serous cells of the submandibular gland (fig. 56.2 and 56.3).

The parasympathetic or bulbar fibers to the *parotid* gland arise in the medulla from the *in-*

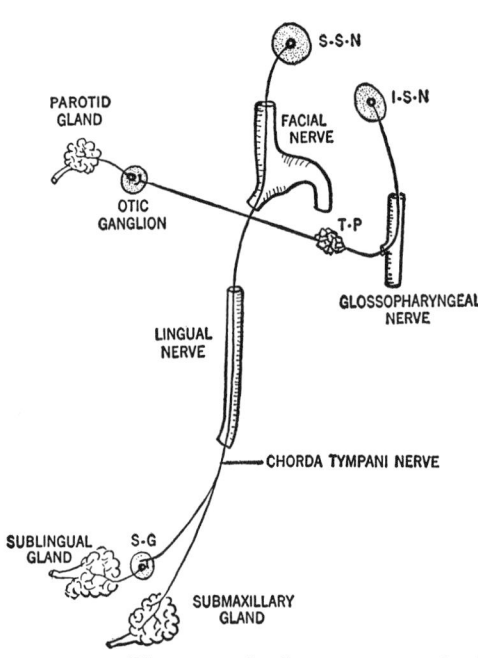

FIG. 56.3. Diagram of the parasympathetic nerve supply of the salivary glands. S-S-N, superior salivatory nucleus; I-S-N, inferior salivatory nucleus; S-G, submaxillary ganglion; T-P, tympanic plexus.

ferior salivary nucleus. They pursue the first part of their course in the *glossopharyngeal nerve* but they follow a devious path before finally terminating around the gland cells. At the jugular foramen, they separate from the glossopharyngeal (Petrous ganglion) in its *tympanic branch* (Jacobson's N.) and after passing into the trunk of the *lesser petrosal nerve* are conveyed to the *otic ganglion*. There, they communicate with ganglion cells from which postganglionic fibers arise. The latter are transmitted by the *auriculo-temporal* branch of the fifth nerve to the gland cells.

The *sympathetic nerve supply* (preganglionic fibers) to the salivary glands is derived from the lateral horn within the first and second thoracic segments of the spinal cord. Axones from the lateral horn cells leave the cord via the ventral roots, enter the paravertebral sympathetic trunk and continue craniad to the superior cervical ganglion where synapse is made with the cell bodies of the second order neurone. From the latter, axones arise and follow the external carotid artery to the parotid gland. Whether or not these fibers innervate more than vascular musculature is a moot question.

The great physiologist, R. Heidenhain (1878) suggested that each individual cell was innervated by both parasympathetic and sympathetic fibers.

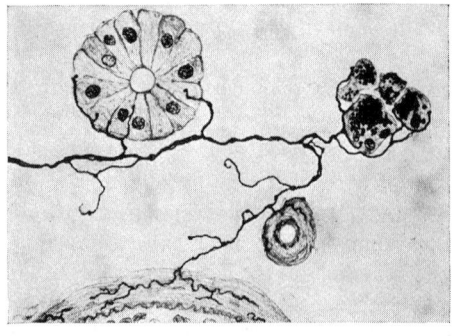

FIG. 56.2. Showing distribution of parasympathetic secretory nerves to cells and blood vessels of submaxillary gland of rabbit. (From Stormont in Cowdry's *Special Cytology*.)

He differentiated fibers into *trophic* and *secretory* types. He considered fibers which, when stimulated, produced the secretion of organic matter as trophic in nature and those which, on stimulation, caused the secretion of water and salts as secretory fibers. The observation that stimulating different nerves caused secretion of different types of saliva caused Heidenhain to believe that the chorda tympani nerve to the submaxillary gland contained chiefly secretory fibers since its stimulation produced an abundant, watery secretion. Stimulation of the sympathetic nerve supply produced a very small amount of highly viscous secretion (containing a high concentration of organic matter) suggesting that the sympathetic nerves consists mainly of "trophic" fibers.

Heidenhain's theory was challenged by Langley and Fletcher (1890), and later by Carlson and his co-workers (1907–1908), who demonstrated the importance of the blood supply to the gland in determining the composition of its secretion. Langley came to the conclusion that there is only one kind of secretory nerve for the secretory glands and that the changes in composition seen on stimulating different nerves depended upon the effects which these nerves have on the blood vessels of the salivary glands. If stimulation of a particular nerve, for example the sympathetic, caused not only secretion but constriction of the blood vessels, so as to limit the blood supply to the gland, the gland then would put out the usual amount of solids but a smaller amount of water, resulting in a highly viscid secretion. On the other hand, in the absence of sympathetic stimulation, the vessel would become dilated increasing the blood flow to the gland, in response to which the gland would put out a more watery fluid. This was in accordance with the fact that the parasympathetic nerves convey secretory fibers, whereas the sympathetic nerves convey vasoconstrictor fibers to the salivary glands.

Rawlinson (1933–1935), working in Babkin's laboratory, found that prolonged stimulation of the chorda tympani nerve with the cervical sympathetic trunk cut, caused the mucous alveolar cells of the submaxillary gland of the cat to decrease in size and become irregular in shape. The longer the chorda tympani was stimulated, the greater were the changes, and the more profuse the secretion. There was no definite or constant changes in the serous cells. On the other hand, stimulation of the cervical sympathetic trunk caused no changes in the mucous alveolar cells. After prolonged stimulation the serous cells were diminished in size, and clear vacuoles appeared in their cytoplasm. Furthermore, injection of massive doses of adrenalin caused marked changes in the serous cells, but had practically no effect on the mucous cells. These experiments were interpreted to indicate that the chorda tympani, which conveys the parasympathetic innervation to the submaxillary gland of the cat, is distributed to the mucous cells, and the sympathetic nerves to the serous cells.

Recent studies of the electrophysiology of the salivary glands by Swedish investigators contest the latter interpretation. Lundberg (1957–1958) found that characteristic electrical changes could be produced in a single cell of the cat's submaxillary gland by stimulation of either the sympathetic or the parasympathetic nerves which suggests that each cell receives a dual innervation. It has also been found (Emmelin, 1955) that once the gland is responding maximally to parasympathetic stimulation, stimulation of the sympathetic does not augment the secretion as it would do if it activated glandular elements not innervated by the parasympathetic. It was found that when one drug (acetylcholine, adrenalin or noradrenalin) had been given in a dose to produce its maximal effect on isolated preparations of submandibular gland, the addition of another did not further increase the oxygen consumption. Hokin and Sherwin (1957) have also presented evidence that acetylcholine and adrenalin act on the same cells of the salivary gland. They measured the incorporation of P^{32} into phospholipids and the secretion of amylase by slices of parotid glands of rabbits. Both acetylcholine and adrenalin stimulated the process; however, when one drug was producing a maximal effect, the addition of the other did not increase the response. These experiments by Strömblad, and Hokin and Sherwin suggest that acetylcholine and adrenalin produced their effects on the same cells. Nevertheless, the secretion elaborated by a given cell under the influence of innervation may differ considerably in composition from that produced by the same cell under sympathetic innervation.

Afferent nerve fibers from the salivary glands are found in the *chorda tympani* and the *glossopharyngeal nerves*. These fibers carry pain impulses from the salivary glands. Claude Bernard (1858) showed that stimulation of the submaxillary gland in a nonanesthetized dog caused evidence of pain. Swelling of the gland, as occurs in mumps or when the main salivary duct is obstructed, is also known to be painful.

Blood Supply and Lymphatic Drainage

Blood flow within the salivary glands, as we shall see later, has an intimate relationship to the process of salivary secretion. The arterial supply to the parotid gland is from the *posterior auricular* artery. The arteries to the submaxillary gland are derived from the *external maxillary* (facial) and *lingual* arteries, while the arterial supply to the sublingual gland is supplied from the *sublingual* and *submental* arteries. In the case of the submaxillary and sublingual glands the main arterial supply enters the gland at the hilus. The parotid gland does not have a well-defined "hilus," and correspondingly point of entrance of its arterial supply is subject to variation.

Within the gland substance, the arterial supply travels with the interlobular ducts into the lobules. Within the lobules, the arteries break up to form a rich capillary plexus about the ducts. Consistent with the observation that the ducts perform active transport functions is the fact that the vascularization of the ducts is much richer than that of the alveoli. Arteriovenous anastomoses similar to the juxta-glomerular vessels in the kidney have been described by Spanner (1937). The function of such arteriovenous anastomoses is not known. The capillary plexuses about the alveoli and ducts collect in venules which, in general, accompany the ducts out of the lobules. Near the hilus of the gland, Spanner has described large sacculated veins which he suggests serve a reservoir function and tend to back up pressure in the capillary circulation during secretory activity. Because of this suggested function, these sacculated, venous structures have been referred to as "throttle" veins. Similar veins are found in the penis. In studies on the circulation within the salivary glands, Burgen and Seeman (1958) have found that most of the blood profusing the gland went to capillaries in the duct system and that the flow in these was mainly counter-current to the flow of the saliva.

Lymph spaces are found around the alveoli which drain into lymphatics that accompany the ducts and vessels. Lymphatic drainage from all of the salivary glands is into the superficial and deep cervical glands.

Formation of Saliva

The mechanisms of salivary secretion that result in the formation of saliva have been studied extensively but still are only incompletely understood. An indication of the complexity of the situation is found in the observations that the salivary glands are morphologically complex structures, with a dual innervation from the autonomic nervous system, and that the composition of saliva may vary from gland to gland in the same animal. It was originally thought that the formation of saliva was accomplished by processes similar to those that result in the production of urine by the kidney. It was assumed that saliva was an ultrafiltrate of the blood. The ultrafiltration theory was disproved by Ludwig (1851) when he showed that the submaxillary gland could secrete against a pressure greater than its arterial blood pressure.

It is now recognized that the mechanism of salivary secretion is one that requires energy for the production and secretion of organic substances by the alveolar elements and for the "active transport" of inorganic substances across cell membranes against concentration gradients by the duct epithelium.

The evidence that salivary secretion is a process that requires energy has been accumulated in a number of ways. Northup (1935) has shown that the salivary gland utilized a metabolic process to obtain energy for the work of secretion that is in many ways similar to that of muscle. He compared the glycogen, phosphocreatin, and lactic acid content in a submaxillary gland that had been stimulated simultaneously by its parasympathetic and sympathetic nerve supply to the unstimulated gland on the opposite side. The stimulated gland showed a marked decrease in its content of glycogen and phosphocreatin and an increase in lactic acid when compared with the unstimulated gland on the opposite side.

The *respiratory quotient* (RQ) of slices of maxillary gland suspended in Ringer's solution was found by Deutsch and Raper (1938) to be between 0.6 and 0.8. When they added acetylcholine and eserine to the Ringer's solution, the rate of respiration was increased, but in the absence of glucose the RQ did not change. If glucose was added to the slices during incubation, the RQ increased to 1.0. Epinephrine had an effect similar to that of acetylcholine. Thus, the source of energy for salivary gland metabolism is glucose, although fructose and other compounds can serve as suitable substrates for the gland's metabolic function.

Barcroft (1914) reports the oxygen consumption for the resting submaxillary gland of the dog to be from 22 to 27 $\mu l./g./min.$ In the submaxillary gland of the cat, Stromblad (1959) obtained a value of 20 μl./g./min. When the gland is stimulated by injecting acetylcholine, or by parasympathetic stimulation, the oxygen consumption increases to 130 to 175 μl./g./min. Atropine can block the metabolic effects of acetylcholine. Metabolic poisons such as cyanide, iodoacetate and fluoride are also capable of blocking the metabolic effect of acetylcholine.

It has also been shown (Hokin and Hokin, 1959) that acetylcholine and adrenalin will increase the incorporation of radioactive phosphorus into the phospholipids of the rabbit parotid and submaxillary in guinea pig parotid gland slices. Atropine and ergotamine are capable of blocking this effect. A large proportion of the total respiration of the salivary glands must be attributed to the duct epithelium since these cells possess mitochondria in very high concentration (see the previous chapter).

The principal role of acinar cells in the formation of saliva is to contribute certain organic substances to the secretion. The organelles that participate in protein secretion have been considered in the previous chapter. Ribosomes synthesize the protein; the endoplasmic reticulum and Golgi apparatus are responsible for intracellular bulk transport of the secretory product. The endoplasmic reticulum delivers the protein to the Golgi apparatus, which in turn packages the product. The packaged product, or secretory granule, is held in the apical regions of the cell until the gland receives the signal from its autonomic nerve fibers whereupon the granules discharge their contents into the lumen of the duct.

It is now recognized that the intralobular ducts contribute considerably to the formation of saliva. Certain histological observations point up the importance of the salivary ducts. For example, in newborn rats and dogs, the acini of the salivary glands are extremely immature or absent altogether, whereas the ducts show a considerable degree of maturation. In these species, the secretion of saliva during infancy is as abundant as it is in adulthood. Thus, undoubtedly, in the immature rat and dog, most of the water is secreted by the ducts.

Since saliva is hypotonic to blood serum, this must be accounted for either by the reabsorption of electrolytes in the ducts or by the lack of transfer of electrolytes into the saliva across the cellular membrane. To elucidate the role of the salivary ducts in the formation of saliva, Burgen and Emmelin devised an ingenious method to demonstrate the site of entry of various substances into the saliva by the ductal epithelium. The method consisted of rapidly injecting a small amount of an isotope into the arterial blood supply of the salivary gland when the gland is secreting at a steady state. The appearance of the isotopic substance in the collected saliva is then determined. The amount of isotope used is quite small and thus the secreting gland is exposed to the isotope only briefly. After passage through the gland, the isotope is diluted in the animal's blood and body fluids. The appearance time of the isotope in the saliva is only a matter of seconds and an indication of the site of its passage across the ductal epithelium to enter the saliva. Thus, the more rapid the appearance of the substance in the saliva, the larger the order of duct representing the site of transfer. When two or more isotopic substances are injected simultaneously, the same relationship holds; i.e. the substance that appears first in the saliva was transported by the ductal epithelium at a point along the duct system that is distal to that at which the other substance was transported. Using this technique, the appearance time of water, chloride, bromide, iodide, sulfate, bicarbonate, sodium, potassium, urea, and four amino acids have been determined in parotid saliva of the dog. None of the four amino acids, valine, methionine, isoleucine and tyrosine, nor sulfate were detected in any appreciable amounts in the saliva. All of the other isotopes appeared after a more or less brief latent period of 2 to 10 sec. Following the appearance of the isotopic substance, its concentration rapidly increased to a peak in 5 to 6 sec., then gradually declined during the next 2 to 3 min. (fig. 56.4).

Isotopic water appeared first in the saliva, indicating that it was capable of being transported across the ductal epithelium at a more distal site than any of the other substances. Bicarbonate was found to enter the saliva at the same point as water and had a similar time concentration pattern. Chloride and bromide appeared next, indicating that they entered the saliva through the epithelium of somewhat smaller ducts than those of water and bicarbonate. Sodium and potassium ranked third in order of appearance, iodide and urea, fourth. It will be noted from fig. 56.4 that the declining slope of the potassium curve after it reaches a peak is quite slow. This slow decline of the potassium concentration is taken as evidence that potassium is also secreted into the saliva by the acinar cells.

The fact that anions can enter the ducts at a more distal site than cations suggests that anionic

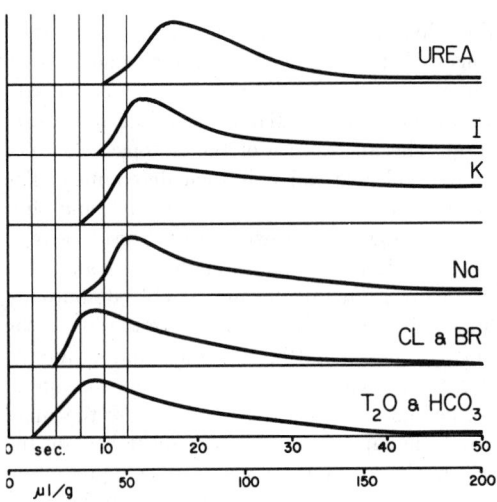

In man, the amount of saliva secreted in 24 hr. amounts to 1000–1500 ml. (about 1 ml./min.). A large proportion of this 24-hr. volume is secreted at meal-time, when the secretory rate is highest. In the absence of stimulation, as during sleep, the secretory rate is low and may not exceed 0.25 ml./min. Schneyer and Levin (1955) have determined the amounts of secretion each of the salivary glands contribute to the total output of all of the glands under "resting" conditions and found that the parotids contribute approximately 25 per cent, the submaxillary gland 70 per cent and the sublinguals 5 per cent. In the dog, the maximum secretory rate of the parotid gland is approximately 0.5 ml./g. of gland/min., whereas the maximum rate of the submaxillary gland is approximately one ml./g. of gland/min. The cow may secrete as much as 60 l. of saliva per day.

Ordinary mixed saliva contains about 99.5 per cent water and 0.5 per cent total solids. The specific gravity of mixed saliva is usually between 1.002 and 1.012. The volume of saliva secreted depends primarily upon the ability of the salivary glands to secrete water. The osmolarity of saliva from all of the salivary glands in man is slightly hypotonic to that of plasma. Thus, some osmotic work is required for the secretory process. The osmolarity of saliva can be increased by dehydration, and then decreased by subsequent hydration by drinking large amounts of water.

FIG. 56.4. Secretion patterns of various isotopic substances, after injection into the arterial blood supply of the parotid gland of the dog. The appearance of the isotopes was determined in single drops of saliva secreted by the gland. Note that tritiated water and bicarbonate appeared first and urea last. Except for potassium, the outflow curves of all other substances were similar (re-drawn from Burgen and Emmelin, 1961).

exchange may occur at this point. If cations are unable to enter the duct at some point, the only explanation of anion entry would be by an anionic exchange mechanism. It will be discussed later that there is a reciprocal relationship between bicarbonate and chloride that is controlled by the arterial pCO_2. The bicarbonate-chloride exchange may occur in the more distal part of the salivary ducts.

According to these data, at least five functionally distinct segments exist along the salivary tree in the dog parotid gland. The authors point out, however, that data from experiments of this type do not directly demonstrate sites of bulk transfer of ions. Also these sites are differentiated from one another histologically on the basis of quantitative rather than qualitative differences.

Composition of Saliva

The composition of saliva is variable but it consists mainly of water, inorganic constituents commonly found in the plasma, and certain organic constituents that will be described in more detail later. The variability of the composition of saliva is accounted for by the fact that the different salivary glands contribute different constituents and the final composition is adapted to stimuli evoking the secretion. In addition, the concentration of many of the common inorganic constituents depends upon flow rate.

Human mixed saliva is slightly acid in reaction. In a large series of normal persons, Starr (1922) found the pH of mixed saliva to vary between 5.75 and 7.05. However, in 86 per cent of the people he studied, the pH varied between 6.35 and 6.85. Schmidt-Nielsen (1946) found that the pH of parotid saliva from normal individuals varied from 5.45 to 6.06, with an average pH of 5.81. The pH of submaxillary saliva averaged 6.39 and the range varied from 6.02 to 7.14. The pH of saliva is dependent mainly upon the relative concentrations of free and combined CO_2, that is upon the ratio of $H_2CO_3/NaHCO_3$. Thus, for the true pH value to be obtained, the juice must be collected without loss of CO_2. The older figures in the literature of 7.50 to 8.00 for the pH of saliva are too high; the reason is that the precaution to prevent loss of CO_2 was not taken. The pH of the saliva varies directly with the CO_2 content of the blood. This means that when the CO_2 tension in the blood is high, more CO_2 finds its way into the salivary secretion to lower its pH and vice versa. Forced breathing causes a lessened amount of CO_2 in the saliva and, consequently, a rise in its pH. On the other hand, conditions associated with the retention of CO_2 in the blood increase the loss of the gas in the saliva. Ingestion of sodium bicarbonate, although it reduces the acidity of the urine, increases that of the saliva, since a rise in CO_2 tension in the blood results.

The *bicarbonates*, and to some extent, the *phosphates*, act as "buffers" in saliva. This buffering action is such that the pH of saliva remains relatively constant under all ordinary conditions. Even when relatively strong solutions of acid or alkali are introduced into the mouth, the reaction, except for such a short period, is not altered. The "acid-mouth" so often mentioned in dentifice advertisements as an abnormal condition and the possibility of altering the reaction of the oral secretions is very remote. Attempts to change the pH of saliva experimentally, by flooding the mouth with acid or alkaline solutions, are followed by contrary effects upon the salivary reaction. Acid solutions cause a rise in pH; alkaline solutions a fall. These changes last only about ten min. The reaction then returns to normal. Salivary pH is little effected by respiratory acidosis or alkalosis. Saliva becomes alkaline in the mouth due to loss of dissolved CO_2.

Inorganic Constituents

Bicarbonate concentrate in saliva increases with salivary flow. At low rates of secretion, the bicarbonate concentration may be from 5 to 10 mEq/l. With increased rates of secretion, the bicarbonate concentration *exceeds* that of the serum. In human parotid saliva, the bicarbonate concentration may go as high as 60 mEq/l. Sublingual saliva has a low bicarbonate concentration. Sympathetic stimulation produces saliva from the submaxillary gland of the cat with a higher bicarbonate concentration than that resulting from chorda stimulation. Salivary bicarbonate is derived from both gland metabolism and the transfer of bicarbonate from the plasma to the saliva.

The concentration of bicarbonate in saliva is directly influenced by the pCO_2 of the arterial blood. Conditions that produce an increase in arterial pCO_2 cause an increase in salivary bicarbonate and vice versa. With changes in bicarbonate concentration, there is a reciprocal change in the chloride concentration and the total anionic concentration is not markedly altered. Thus, with an increased arterial pCO_2, bicarbonate enters the saliva and exchanges for chloride. The site of this anionic exchange is probably in the more distal parts of the striated salivary ducts.

Phosphate concentration in saliva is about twice that of plasma and relatively independent of flow rate. Approximately 80 per cent of the phosphate is present as inorganic phosphate. The organic phosphate in saliva is acid-soluble and partially split by phosphatases.

Chloride concentration of saliva from different glands may show considerable variation. In general, there is nearly a linear relationship between the chloride concentration and flow rate. At all flow rates, however, the salivary chloride concentration is *below* that of plasma and may vary between 5 and 70 mEq/l. An exception to this general observation is sublingual saliva from the cat, which has a higher chloride concentration than that of plasma. Sublingual saliva of man has a higher chloride concentration than parotid or submaxillary saliva.

Sympathetic and parasympathetic stimulation of the submaxillary gland of the dog and cat produces similar chloride concentrations. Desoxycorticosterone causes a fall in salivary chloride accompanied by a decrease in concentration of salivary sodium and an increase in salivary potassium. In patients with salt depletion there is usually little change in the salivary chloride. Thus, the salivary chloride concentration tends to be independent of plasma chloride concentration.

Salivary secretion of *bromide* is similar to that of chloride. However, the salivary/plasma ratio tends to be slightly higher. Little is known about the secretion of fluoride by the salivary glands except that it is secreted in the saliva at a lower concentration than the other halides. McClure (1941) has reported that the salivary concentration of fluoride in children is from 0.006 to 0.015 mEq/l. Because of the relationship of fluorides to dental caries, more information is needed on the salivary secretion of fluoride.

Sodium concentration in saliva is highly dependent upon the rate of saliva flow. At low flow rates, the concentration may be less than 5 mEq/l., whereas at high flow rates it may exceed 100 mEq/l. Thus, it is impossible to give a "normal" sodium concentration for saliva. Resting saliva in normal children contains from 2 to 15 mEq/l. of sodium. In children with cystic fibrosis of the pancreas, the sodium concentration is increased and reaches levels from 20 to 45 mEq/l.

Potassium concentration of saliva is relatively high and exceeds that of the blood plasma. All of the main salivary glands of man secrete potassium at a concentration higher than that of plasma. Ordinary mixed saliva usually contains 8 to 20 mEq/l. of potassium which is 1.5 to 4 times the concentration in plasma. Values as high as 50 to 60 mEq/l. have been found in the submaxillary and sublingual saliva of rats. The potassium concentration of saliva resulting from sympathetic stimulation is about twice that obtained with parasympathetic stimulation.

The concentration of *calcium* in human parotid saliva, like sodium, increases with flow rate. At high flow rates, a concentration of 3 to 4 mEq/l. may be found.

Organic Constituents

Salivary proteins account for the physical characteristics of saliva. Parotid saliva has a low viscosity and is watery in character, whereas submaxillary saliva usually is viscous and sticky due to its mucoprotein content. With increasing flow rates, the concentration of protein increases. However, with prolonged stimulation, the quantity of protein secreted per unit of time progressively decreases. This suggests that protein production by the salivary glands is relatively slow compared with the rate of protein secretion. Stimulation of the sympathetic nerves to the submaxillary gland of the cat or dog produces a saliva rich in proteins. The concentration and character of the proteins differ from that obtained by parasympathetic stimulation.

The proteins of saliva are extremely complex in nature and the older classification of them into albumins and mucins is inadequate. Electrophoretic, ultracentrifugation and immunological methods have been used in attempts at identification and classification of salivary proteins. The electrophoretic pattern of salivary proteins differs greatly from that of serum. In human parotid saliva, the main electrophoretic peak is *amylase*. In submaxillary saliva, the major component is a *mucoprotein* of low mobility.

Free amino acids are found in saliva. Their concentrations are usually 10 to 20 per cent of the plasma levels. When plasma levels of free amino acids are raised, the concentration of the amino acids increase in saliva. *Urea, uric acid* and *creatine* are also found in saliva.

Amylase is the main digestive enzyme of parotid saliva in man. Amylase is also found in the saliva of apes, rabbit, guinea pig, rat and mouse. Very little amylase is found in parotid and submaxillary saliva of the dog, cat, cow, horse, sheep and goat. Apparently, starch digestion by salivary amylase is not too important in some animals. Amylase can be crystallized from saliva by successive acetone and ammonium sulphate precipitation. It is a carbohydrate-free protein with an optimum pH of 6.9 and requires chloride ions for its activation.

Lysozyme is an interesting enzymatic substance found in saliva. This enzyme, which appears to be a mucoprotein, has the ability of lysing certain bacteria. Lysozyme is bacteriolytic for organisms belonging to the genera *Bacillus, Micrococcus, Staphylococcus, Streptococcus, Proteus* and *Brucella*.

Two additional organic constituents of saliva that are of interest are *kallikrein* and the specific *blood group substances*. When saliva is injected intravenously into an animal, it produces a fall in blood pressure for a brief period. The substance responsible for this has been found to be due to kallikrein, an enzyme that acts on plasma protein to produce a vasodilator polypeptide. This polypeptide is known as *kallidin* or *bradykinin*. It has been suggested that the vasodilatation in the salivary gland during secretory activity is due to kallikrein release. The soluble specific blood group substances found in saliva have the same characteristics as the agglutinogen on the erythrocyte. These substances can be demonstrated by the direct precipitin reaction with type specific sera. In man, the A, B, O and Le^a substances have been demonstrated. The concentration of the blood group substances in saliva is from 10 to 20 mg/l. It appears that most of the blood group substances come from the mucous cells of the submaxillary gland whereas little is produced by the parotid.

Glucose is normally absent from saliva and even in patients with diabetes, none or only small amounts are found.

Regulation of Salivary Secretion

Saliva is secreted continuously, but the rate of secretion may vary greatly due to the influence of conditions that are capable of stimulating or inhibiting the process of secretion. The *continuous secretion* of saliva in the absence of any known stimulating factors is called "spontaneous" secretion. The continuous or spontaneous secretion of saliva is important in keeping the mucous membrane of the mouth and pharynx moist at all times. Examples of spontaneous or continuous salivary secretion in animals include the parotid gland of the sheep and ox and the sublingual gland of the cat. The mechanism of spontaneous secretion is not known but it has been suggested that it is due to the constant release of minute amounts of acetylcholine within the gland. However, atropine has no effect on this type of secretion. Cyanide and other metabolic poisons stop spontaneous secretion, indicating that the process is dependent upon metabolic function.

During mastication of food the rate of salivary secretion is greatly increased. The character of the secretion is adapted in some degree to the type of food undergoing mastication. This will be discussed in more detail later. During sleep the rate of salivary secretion is low. Sexual excitement in many animals is associated with an increase in salivary flow.

There are at least two ways of regulating the secretion of the digestive glands; one is through the nervous system and the other is by means of hormones. In the case of the salivary glands, it is believed that the regulation is exclusively through the nervous system. At any rate, all efforts to date to find a salivary hormone have failed.

In the normal life of the animal the secretion of saliva is brought about reflexly in two ways: either through the stimulation of the nerves of the mouth by the presence therein of food or other substances, or by the stimulation of some organ of special sense other than that of taste. The former type of reflex is termed *unconditioned* or *inherent;* the latter, *conditioned* or *acquired.* A reflex of one type does not, of course, exclude the other and, as a matter of fact, both are called into play together under ordinary circumstances.

REFLEX SECRETION OF SALIVA

In addition to the unconditioned salivary reflex brought about by materials placed in the mouth, the salivary glands can be excited readily by the artificial stimulation of afferent nerve supplying structures in the mouth. The conditioned salivary reflex depends upon afferent impulses arising from outside the oral cavity. The various salivary reflexes and pathways involved will now be discussed in detail.

The Unconditioned Salivary Reflex

Materials placed in the mouth call forth, after a short latent period (2 to 3 sec), a secretion of saliva which varies in *quantity* and *quality* with the physical and chemical nature of the substance introduced. The effect which sensations of taste produce upon the secretion of saliva are well

known. Among edible substances, those, generally speaking, which are the most palatable or arouse the sensation of taste with the greatest intensity, are the most potent salivary stimulants. Materials which are entirely inedible will, if unpleasant to the taste—acids especially—cause profuse salivation. In these instances, the secretions depend mainly upon the stimulation of the taste fibers, and the stimulus is chemical in nature. Materials such as dry sand, inedible powders (whether soluble or insoluble) or any other material which is capable of stimulating in a purely physical way, will evoke a secretion. The mere movements of the jaws and of the tongue over the mucosa of the mouth will have such an effect. A secretion occurs when any substance is chewed, whether or not it is edible or possesses taste. The chewing of Indian rubber (or gum), for instance, the manipulations of the dentist, the contact of his instruments with the oral mucosa, or the grinding of a tooth are familiar and effective salivatory stimuli. The salivary glands thus can be readily excited by the artificial stimulation of afferent nerves supplying structures in the mouth.

The reflexes are brought about through the salivary centers. The *efferent* limbs of the reflex arcs, including the secretory fibers of the chorda tympani and the tympanic branch of the glossopharyngeal, respectively, have been considered under the section dealing with innervation of the salivary glands. Mention was also made of afferent pathways. The *afferent* pathways are represented in the trunks of the chorda tympani, the pharyngeal branches of the vagus and glossopharyngeal nerves, and the lingual, buccal and palatine branches of the trigeminal nerve. The taste fibers of the chorda tympani which are distributed to the anterior two-thirds of the tongue arise from cells located in the geniculate ganglion. The central processes of the cells of the geniculate ganglion enter the pons via the nervus intermedius of Wrisberg. These processes enter the solitary tract and make connections with neurones of the superior salivary nucleus. The afferent fibers of the glossopharyngeal nerve concerned in the salivary reflex, carry sensations of taste from the posterior third of the tongue. The cell bodies of these afferent neurones are located in the petrous ganglion. The central processes of these cells enter the solitary tract at the level of the medulla oblongata and thereby reach the inferior salivary nucleus (p. 1064). The lingual fibers whose cells of origin are located in the Gasserian ganglion furnish the general buccal mucosa with general somatic afferent fibers (for touch, pain, etc.). Secretion of saliva may be induced by stimulation of the central end of any of these three groups of afferent fibers. Less readily, salivation can be elicited through stimulation of nerves in other regions. For example, experimental stimulation of the central end of the vagus, sciatic, or indeed of practically any sensory nerve of the body may cause salivation. According to some, stimulation of afferent nerves of the gastric mucosa is particularly likely to initiate a reflex secretion in the mouth. In disease, stimuli arising in the esophagus may cause profuse salivation (esophago-salivary reflex). Stimulation of trigeminal terminals in the nasal mucosa will also evoke a secretion of saliva (Babkin).

The Conditioned or Acquired Reflex

The secretion which flows into the empty mouth when "the mouth waters" is the result of a conditioned reflex. The stimulus which initiates such a reflex is not applied to the nerves of the mouth, but is received by one or other of the organs of special sense, particularly those of sight and smell. A conditioned reflex may also be elicited through the sense of hearing, or through sensory impressions arising from stimuli applied to the skin. In brief, a conditioned reflex is one in which the cerebral centers play an essential part, and in which training and experience are the basis for the development of the reflex process. Conditioned reflexes are taken up in detail in ch. 9.

ADAPTABILITY OF THE SALIVARY REFLEX

It has been mentioned previously that saliva varies in both quantity and quality with the physical and chemical nature of the substance stimulating the secretion. This remarkable adaptability or purposeful character of the salivary reflex has been observed by Pavlov. The physical and chemical qualities of the juice, to some extent, are conditioned by the agent evoking salivation. For instance, if clean pebbles are placed in a dog's mouth, they are expelled—merely allowed to drop out of their own weight. Little or no secretion occurs, since none is required; but if the stones are crushed and given as a powder, a profuse water salivation follows to rid and cleanse the mouth of the useless material. The juice, in this instance, is poor in organic material and resembles that obtained upon electrical stimulation of the chorda tympani nerve or of the parasympathetic fibers to the parotid. Strong acid produces an abundant saliva which, according to

Pavlov, is relatively rich in proteins; this exerts a buffer action which reduces or annuls the injurious effect of the acid. The salivary response provides a lubricant which is curiously appropriate in volume and viscosity for the food to be swallowed. A chunk of meat, given to a dog, is very quickly coated with a viscous, mucin-rich saliva and swallowed. If the meat is first dried and powdered, or if a dried biscuit is fed to the animal, an abundant watery saliva is produced such as is characteristic of parotid or chorda saliva. Milk evokes a secretion of saliva rich in mucin. In general, food produces a saliva rich in organic material, mucin and ferments, whereas inedible substances tend to elicit a watery saliva. The salivary responses in man are less well defined.

Babkin (1950), who has confirmed and extended the foregoing observations has offered the following interpretation: "It was evidenced from the facts observed that a salivary gland does not secrete as a unit, but that the different sets of epithelia of which the glands are composed contribute different components to the secretion and furthermore, that local productivity depends upon the intensity of the excitation received from the salivary center. The salivary center may be regarded as a compound structure consisting of several parts. Each peripheral stimulus transmitted through the appropriate taste or other sensory nerves of the mouth cavity act on different parts of the salivary center, and these in their turn, excite reflexly and selectively the various epithelial groups in the salivary glands. Moreover, it must not be forgotten that the brain possesses not one, but two salivary centers, parasympathetic and sympathetic. The parts of these centers innervating different epithelial groups may be stimulated reflexly in various combinations and this will be reflected in the composition of the saliva secreted."

PARALYTIC SALIVARY SECRETION

Claude Bernard observed in 1864 that if he cut the chorda tympani nerve in a dog or a cat, in about twenty-four hours the submaxillary gland began to produce a scanty secretion of thin, turbid saliva; the turbidity was due to the presence of leukocytes. The secretion increased until the seventh or eighth day, at which time it reached a plateau and began to diminish about the third week. It stopped some six weeks after the nerve was cut. During this time the gland increased in size, and no secretion could be obtained on stimulation of the mouth. Stimulation of the sympathetic, however, produced a flow of saliva. Division of the sympathetic nerve or extirpation of the cervical ganglion did not evoke a paralytic secretion. Rawlinson repeated these observations in Babkin's laboratory and found, on examination of the gland, that there was evidence of secretory activity during the paralytic secretion in the serous cells. Moreover, these cells were more excitable than normal on stimulation by adrenalin or electrical stimulation of the sympathetic nerves. Evidently cutting the chorda tympani causes some alteration in the gland alveoli which greatly increases the excitability of the sympathetic nerve endings on the serous or demilune cells. It has been suggested that paralytic secretion is due to continuous activity of the postganglionic neurons of the chorda tympani when they are disconnected from their preganglionic fibers, thus causing a continuous release in small amounts of acetylcholine in the gland. The heightened irritability of the sympathetic innervation is thought to be due to this minute amount of neurohormone. This explanation of the mechanism of paralytic secretion is similar to the phenomenon of augmented secretion, which will be discussed later. Recent observations, however, indicate that the release of adrenalin from the suprarenal glands play an important and essential role in paralytic secretion. Emmelin (1952) points out that only under conditions where a pronounced supersensitivity has been established by denervation and an increase in release of adrenalin occurs does paralytic secretion exist. Removal of the adrenal glands from the animal or the injection of sympatholytic agents as dihydroergotamine abolishes paralytic secretion. Thus it appears that paralytic secretion is due to adrenalin secreted by the animal's suprarenal glands, and that the degree of response will depend upon the level of sensitivity of the denervated salivary gland. Atropine has no effect on paralytic secretion.

Salivary Response to Electrical Stimuli

The importance of neural mechanisms in the control of salivary secretion has long been recognized; thus, exprimentation by applying electrical stimulation to the parasympathetic and sympathetic nerves supplying the salivary glands has contributed greatly to our knowledge of salivary secretion. Histological and electrical changes can be produced in the acinar cells by electrical stimulation. In addition, stimulation of the salivary nerves may affect structures other than the secreting cells and thus modify secretion. For instance, marked vascular changes within the gland

can result from electrical stimulation. In addition, electrical stimuli can presumably cause contraction of the myo-epithelial cells and produce a temporary acceleration of the flow of saliva being secreted.

Electrical stimulation of the nerves to the salivary gland produces different results in different species of animals. Stimulation of the parasympathetic nerves usually produces an abundant flow of quite watery saliva regardless of the gland or species studied. Stimulation of the sympathetic secretory fibers to the submaxillary or sublingual glands, although causing an abundant secretion in the cat, causes only a scanty and very viscid secretion in the dog. Even in the cat, in which the secretion is very abundant, the composition of sympathetic saliva is different from that obtained on stimulation of the parasympathetic nerves.

There is no clear proof that the sympathetic trunks contain secretory fibers for the parotid gland (Babkin, 1950). Stromblad (1955) obtained only a scanty secretion from the parotid gland of cats on administration of adrenalin or on stimulation of the sympathetic trunk in the neck. This is the more remarkable since the other salivary glands of the cat respond well to sympathetic stimulation. Stromblad suggests that the secretion observed on sympathetic stimulation may have been produced by stimulation of the contractile elements in the glands causing an expression of saliva from the ducts rather than a true secretion.

Parasympathetic Stimulation

It has been previously mentioned that stimulation of the parasympathetic nerve supply to the salivary glands produces a prompt and abundant flow of watery saliva from the gland. Vascular vasodilatation within the gland also occurs. The secretory effect of parasympathetic stimulation was discovered by Ludwig (1851) when he observed a flow of saliva from the submaxillary gland on stimulation of the chorda tympani nerve. The vasodilator effect, associated with chorda tympani stimulation, was described by Claude Bernard in 1858. Although it was originally thought that separate vasodilatory fibers existed in the parasympathetic nerve supply, most workers today consider the vasodilatation as secondary to the process of secretion and due to the release of vasodilator agents from the activated secretory cells.

The marked secretory effect that can be obtained on parasympathetic stimulation is illustrated by the fact that a salivary gland can secrete an amount of saliva equal to its own weight in just a few minutes. With repetitive parasympathetic stimulation, the rate of salivary secretion within certain limits is proportional to the rate of stimuli being applied. In the cat, the maximal secretory response from the submaxillary gland is obtained with a rate of 10 to 12 stimuli per sec. When the maximal rate of secretion has been attained by parasympathetic stimulation, this rate cannot be exceeded by the addition of other stimuli as adrenalin or acetylcholine or even by stimulation of the sympathetic nerve supply to the gland.

Parasympathetic stimulation results in the release of acetylcholine from the terminals of the postganglionic neurons that innervate the acinar cells. The released acetylcholine is the chemical transmitter that causes secretion. Lundberg (1955) has estimated that each alveolar cell is supplied with from five to ten parasympathetic fibers. He introduced a small intracellular electrode into an acinar cell and found that the hyperpolarization resulting from parasympathetic stimulation increased with increasing strengths of single shocks serving as the stimulus. Apparently, acetylcholine released at the postganglionic neuron terminals does not diffuse to adjacent cells but acts locally on the cell at its site of liberation.

By histochemical techniques, Snell and Garrett (1956) have demonstrated true cholinesterase in the fine network of neural fibers around the acinar cells. Another bit of evidence that indicates that acetylcholine acts locally and does not diffuse to neighboring cells is the finding of Hillarp (1949) that after destruction of some of the parasympathetic fibers, stimulation of the nerve caused cytological changes interpreted as being evidence of secretory activity in only some of the acini. Neighboring acini appeared to be at rest and unaffected by the stimulation.

Emmelin and Muren (1950) have demonstrated that acetylcholine is released from the submaxillary gland of the dog and cat on chorda tympani stimulation. They used an isolated perfused submaxillary gland and collected the venous blood from the gland after stimulation. Electrical stimulation of the parasympathetic nerve supply to the salivary glands and the injection of acetylcholine into the vascular supply of the gland both cause secretion. Both produce the same type of saliva, and Lundberg has demonstrated that the electrical response to acetylcholine and electrical stimulation are the same.

SYMPATHETIC STIMULATION

Stimulation of the sympathetic nerve supply to the salivary glands produces a much smaller and more variable response than stimulation of the parasympathetic. Different responses are found in different species and even from one gland to another in the same animal. In the cat, sympathetic stimulation usually produces an increase in secretion from the submaxillary gland and little effect is noted upon the parotid gland. In the rabbit, on the other hand, the response from sympathetic stimulation is more marked from the parotid gland than the submaxillary gland. As early as 1851, Ludwig observed a flow of saliva from a submaxillary gland on stimulation of the cervical sympathetic trunk. Claude Bernard in 1858 called attention to the fact that marked vasoconstriction also occurred with stimulation of the cervical sympathetic trunk.

The marked vasoconstriction that occurs on sympathetic stimulation is capable in itself of altering salivary secretion. With marked vasoconstriction, the blood supply to the gland may be restricted to such an extent that secretion may be inhibited. Matthews (1898) suggested that sympathetic stimulation produced the temporary flow of saliva from the submaxillary gland of the cat and dog due to the activation of contractile elements in the gland and that the increase in the flow rate that was noted was due simply to the expelling of saliva already present in the ducts. Lundberg (1955) has demonstrated changes in membrane potentials of single acinar cells of the submaxillary gland of the cat as a result of stimulation of the sympathetic nerve supply.

AUGMENTED SALIVARY SECRETION

It has long been known that if one stimulates a secretory nerve to one of the salivary glands, a subsequent stimulus of the same strength to the same nerve will evoke more saliva than the first stimulus, provided the second stimulus is applied within a few minutes after the first has ceased. Likewise, if one stimulates a parasympathetic nerve and then follows that by stimulation of the sympathetic, the sympathetic stimulation will produce more saliva than a sympathetic stimulus of the same strength not preceded by parasympathetic stimulation. Similarly, stimulation of the sympathetic augments the response to parasympathetic stimulation. In the case of the submaxillary gland, augmented secretion has been observed in the following situations by different investigators: chorda after chorda, chorda after sympathetic, sympathetic after chorda, and sympathetic after sympathetic. In short, augmented secretion is observed after any two successive stimulations of the same or of different secretory nerves of the salivary glands, provided the second stimulus is not too long delayed.

Augmented secretion was studied extensively by Langley (1889), and more recently by Babkin (1950) and his coworkers. The explanation of this phenomenon is perhaps to be found in the interaction of the neurohormones of the parasympathetic and sympathetic nerves, acetylcholine and noradrenalin (or adrenalin). Although acetylcholine is considered generally to act antagonistically to noradrenalin, it is nevertheless true that minute amounts of acetylcholine increase the excitability of sympathetically innervated structures to epinephrine or norepinephrine; likewise, minute amounts of epinephrine or norepinephrine increase the excitability of parasympathetically innervated structures to acetylcholine. In the salivary glands, in particular, where there is reason to believe that many cells are activated by both adrenergic (sympathetic) and cholinergic (parasympathetic) nerves, adrenalin or noradrenalin and acetylcholine would appear to act synergistically. The augmented secretion observed on chorda after chorda or on sympathetic after sympathetic stimulation, would appear to be a simple case of summation. We may assume that whether the sympathetic or the chorda has been stimulated, some neurohormone persists for a time after the stimulus has ceased, and this, added to the neurohormones released by subsequent stimulation, augments the total amount of neurohormone present.

ELECTRICAL PHENOMENA ASSOCIATED WITH SALIVARY SECRETION

Stimulation of the autonomic nerves to the salivary glands causes characteristic changes in the electrical potentials that may be observed by placing electrodes in various positions on or within the gland, and connecting them to a suitable recording device. With one electrode on the hilum and another on the outer surface of the submaxillary gland, stimulation of either the sympathetic or parasympathetic nerves causes the hilum of the gland to become electropositive to the outer surface after a comparatively long latent period. The latent period is 0.2 to 0.3 sec. with the parasympathetic, and somewhat longer when the sympathetic is stimulated. Following parasympathetic stimulation, the hilum positivity rapidly declines and may change to a negative

potential; there is another sharp rise in hilum positivity when the current is turned off. The potential caused by sympathetic stimulation is more consistently hilum-positive.

Since the submaxillary gland is composed of several different types of cells, each of which may have its own electrical characteristics, it is doubtful what significance should be ascribed to the external secretory potential. More precise information may be obtained from the use of microelectrodes with the tip placed in the interior of a single cell. With these, Lundberg (1957) has obtained three types of response representing presumably three types of cells: mucous cells, serous cells, and duct cells. In all cases the interior of the cell was electro-negative to the external medium. In the case of the mucous cells, stimulation of either the parasympathetic or sympathetic caused a sustained increase in internal negativity or "hyperpolarization" of the cell membrane. This followed a time course roughly parallel to that already described for the external secretory potential. When the microelectrode was in what was believed to be a serous cell, the parasympathetic caused hyperpolarization, but the sympathetic caused a decrease in the internal negativity of the cell (apparent depolarization). With the electrode in what was thought to be a cell of a salivary duct both sympathetic and parasympathetic nerves caused apparent depolarization.

In the sublingual gland, microelectrodes picked up currents corresponding to those obtained from alveolar cells of the submaxillary but the external secretory potential was of a polarity opposite to that of the submaxillary gland, that is, the hilus became electronegative. This difference was believed to be due to differences in the cellular composition of the two glands and not to any difference in the electrical response of corresponding individual cells.

These electrical phenomena are remarkable in several respects. Evidently they are not anologous to the familiar action potentials of nerve and muscle. They appear not to be concerned with the excitatory process (which must be quite different in gland cells and in muscle cells) but are concerned with the functional work of the cell. Lundberg has presented good evidence that the hyperpolarization, associated with secretory activity, is caused by an active transport of chloride ions through the outer cell membrane which is triggered by the release of a neurohormone at the autonomic nerve endings. The apparent depolarization, when it occurs, is not a self propagating disturbance of the cell membrane of the sort we are accustomed to associate with depolarization, but is probably due to the sustained activity of an ion transport mechanism in the duct cells opposite to that causing hyperpolarization in the alveolar cells.

As a corollary to these observations, Lundberg (1958) has suggested that secretion of water and salt by the alveolar cells is accomplished through the activity of an acitve chloride ion transport mechanism in the outer cell membrane which "pumps" chloride ions into the cell from the surrounding interstitial fluid. Electrical forces cause sodium to accompany chloride and osmotic forces take in water. As a result of the increased hydrostatic pressure within the cell, the salt and water escape through the inner membrane (where there may also be an ion pump) into the lumen of the alveolus. He has suggested further that the rodded epithelial cells of the ducts actively absorb sodium from the secretion. Sodium absorption at this point would account for the apparent depolarization of these cells (decreased internal negativity) and also for the fact that saliva may be hypotonic with respect to the blood.

LIMITATIONS OF ELECTRICAL STIMULATION

It should be remembered that electrical stimulation of a nerve trunk is highly artificial. All of the fibers in the nerve are stimulated even though they may be wholly unrelated in function. This is a situation that never occurs under conditions of normal reflex stimulation. It may be assumed that when the secretory fibers are stimulated reflexly, whether these are sympathetic or parasympathetic, the blood supply to the gland is adjusted to the needs at the moment, whatever they may be. Another point that should be clarified is the watery character of the secretion obtained on parasympathetic stimulation, in spite of the fact that these nerves are believed to cause secretion of mucus. Undoubtedly, mucus is secreted even on artificial stimulation, but secretion of water and mucus in the proper proportions to produce an ideal lubricant for the food must depend on normal reflex stimulation.

Functions of Saliva

Saliva has many functions, but its main functions are to aid in digestion and to provide a protective secretion in the mouth that keeps the mucous membranes moist and aids in oral hygiene. Saliva is not essential to life, but its absence results in a number of inconveniences. The more important functions of saliva are discussed below.

PREPARATION OF FOOD FOR SWALLOWING

Lubrication is perhaps the most important function of saliva. When food is introduced into the mouth, salivary secretion is increased. The saliva thus provided serves to moisten the food and to partially dissolve it. The mucous membrane of the mouth is moistened and this greatly facilitates chewing and the further mixing of saliva with the food. Through movements of the tongue, the moistened and masticated food is formed into a plastic mass or bolus. The mucous of the saliva lubricates the bolus and the epithelium of the pharynx, thus enhancing deglutition of the bolus. Claude Bernard observed that when deprived of parotid secretion, a horse will have such difficulty chewing and swallowing dry hay and oats that the animal will develop anorexia.

SOLVENT AND CLEANSING ACTION

Taste is chemically mediated, therefore, as a prerequisite to stimulation of the taste buds, any substance must be dissolved. It follows that deprivation of saliva would greatly limit taste sensibility. It has been mentioned previously that saliva contains little or no glucose and that the concentration of sodium is considerably below that of plasma. This is probably significant in the perception of the taste of sweet or salty substances.

The constant flow of saliva exerts a very necessary cleansing effect on the mouth and teeth, which are rinsed and kept comparatively free from food residues, shed epithelial cells, foreign particles, etc. In this way, saliva inhibits the growth of bacteria by removing the material that may serve as culture media. In addition, lysozyme in saliva serves a protective function through its ability to lyse certain bacteria. One has but to consider the foul condition of the mouth in certain fevers when salivary secretion is suppressed to realize its importance in oral hygiene. When salivation is suppressed, decomposing organic materials swarming with bacteria (sordes), tend to coat the teeth and lips and must be removed by artificial means. Thus, saliva plays a very essential role in maintaining good oral hygiene. The moistening of the mucous membranes of the mouth and lips by saliva also aids in articulation. When the supply of saliva is insufficient, public speakers must sip water frequently in order to counteract the desiccating effect of evaporation from the mouth.

Digestive Functions

The starch molecule is acted upon by salivary amylase and ultimately split into molecules of the dissacharide, maltose. However, the passage of food through the mouth is too rapid to permit any substantial action by salivary amylase. That the enzyme continues to act upon the starchy food during its passage through the stomach has been debated. The salivary amylase requires for its activity an alkaline, neutral, or but faintly acid medium; therefore, it was thought that the highly acid gastric juice would promptly arrest salivary amylase activity. It has been shown, however, that the latter part of the meal, which usually consists of carbohydrate, may remain in the fundus of the stomach, protected for some time from the acidifying action of the gastric juice, by a layer of food ingested previously. For example, Walter Cannon (1911) noted that in cat stomachs that were carefully removed and frozen at various times after a meal, the inner layers of food in the cardiac end remained neutral or weakly alkaline for hours and only the outer layers were slightly acidified. For this reason, it is likely that under favorable circumstances considerable digestion of starch is accomplished during this period. Bergeim (1926) found that 76 per cent of the starch of mashed potatoes was transformed into maltose in the human stomach.

When boiled starch is placed in a test tube in mixed human saliva and kept at body temperature, a slow conversion of the starch into maltose takes place. The reaction may be identified by the use of iodine. In the presence of iodine, boiled starch becomes blue. One of the first effects of salivary action is a physical change in the starch, by which the latter loses its opalescent appearance and becomes dissolved, yet continues to yield a blue reaction to iodine. Presently, however, the starch begins to break down and is partially converted into a dextrin which yields a red color in the presence of iodine, hence is known as erythrodextrin. Small amounts of maltose may also be detected. Still later achrodextrins are formed which yield no color in response to iodine. In the body, starch is entirely converted into maltose and isomaltose, which in turn are split by maltase into molecules of glucose. At the outset of starch digestion, traces of glucose may be detectable, since traces of maltase are present in saliva. The foregoing may be summarized as follows:

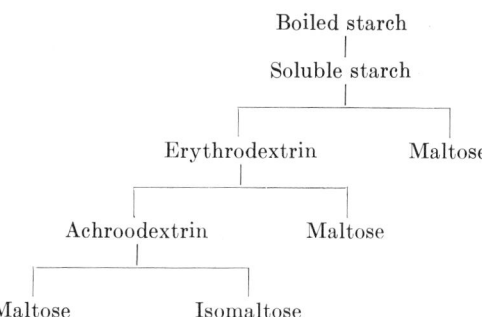

Salivary amylase has no action upon cellulose. For this reason starch for human consumption must be cooked in order that the cellulose envelopes surrounding the starch grains may be broken. Boiling also causes hydration of the starch molecule and renders it more easily digested by amylase.

Excretory Function

Many substances, both organic and inorganic, are excreted in the saliva. Drugs such as mercury, potassium iodide, lead, etc., when introduced into the body, are excreted in part in the saliva. Severe inflammation of the oral mucous membrane may develop as a result of the excessive excretion of mercury via the saliva. After entering the mouth via the saliva of persons with lead poisoning, lead sulfide is deposited in the gums and appears as a blue line. Sulfur derived from organic materials is deposited in the tartar on the lingual side of the teeth near the gum line. This explains why discoloration of the gums does not occur where teeth are absent. In patients with chronic nephritis the saliva contains a high percentage of urea. Small amounts of sugar sometimes appear in the saliva of patients with severe diabetes. As a result of administration of an overdosage of parathormone the calcium concentration of saliva may become elevated.

Alkaloids such as morphine, and antibiotics such as penicillin, streptomycin, and aureomycin are also excreted in saliva. The fact that ethyl alcohol is excreted by the salivary glands has prompted the recommendation that the alcohol content of saliva be used for medico-legal purposes.

Several types of microorganisms, some intensely virulent (e.g. the viruses of hydrophobia and poliomyelitis), are excreted in the saliva. The latter disease has been reproduced in monkeys by injecting the saliva of an infected person. In this connection, it may be added that mumps, which is usually looked upon as a specific inflammation of the parotid gland, is in reality a systemic disease since other organs, including the ovary or testicle, breast, pancreas, and meninges, are often also inflamed. The parotid may become inflamed secondarily as a result of passage of the infectious agent through the gland into the saliva.

In spite of their versatility in regard to excretory functions, this role of the salivary glands is not an indispensable one. The kidney represents the major organ of excretion. Doubtless all the excretory functions of the body could be carried on effectively in the absence of the excretory function of salivary glands.

REGULATION OF WATER BALANCE

When the water content of the body is adequate, saliva is secreted continuously. However, when large quantities of fluid are lost from the body, either through sweat, the bowels, the kidneys, evaporation from the lungs, loss of blood, or when water intake is curtailed; the salivary glands, in common with the other tissues, are subjected to the dehydrating effect. Injection into the veins or ingestion of strong salt solution has a similar effect. Salivary secretion is suppressed, drying of the oral mucous membranes occurs and the constant stimulation of afferent nerves in the mouth and pharynx arouse the sensation of thirst (ch. 62). Thirst may be looked upon as an essential part of a protective mechanism against the depletion of body fluid. It serves to warn the individual that the body's water supplies require to be replenished.

Effects of Chemicals and Drugs upon Salivary Secretion

Many chemicals and drugs are capable of affecting salivary secretion. In order for such agents to stimulate secretion they must produce an effect that is the same as the action of sympathetic or parasympathetic nerve fibers. Thus, drugs that mimic sympathetic or parasympathetic nerve stimulation result in an increase in salivary secretion. *Sympathomimetic* agents that stimulate salivary secretion include adrenalin, noradrenalin, synephrine and amphetamine. *Parasympathomimetic* agents causing salivary secretion include acetylcholine, methancholine (mecholyl) and pilocarpine. Cholinesterase inhibitors known as *anticholinesterases* provoke salivary secretion because they increase the effects of acetylcholine and parasympathetic stimulation.

Sympatholytic and *parasympatholytic* drugs, which block the effects of adrenalin and acetylcholine respectively, produce inhibition of sali-

vary secretion. Ergot, dibenamine and dehydroergotamine are examples of sympatholytic agents that inhibit secretion. Parasympatholytic or *anticholinergic* agents such as atropine, scopolamine, and methylscopolamine produce a marked suppression of salivary secretion. Many anticholinergic agents used therapeutically (e.g. in the treatment of duodenal ulcer), inhibit salivary secretion and produce dryness of the mouth as a disturbing side effect.

The salivary secretion caused by various surgical anesthetics such as ether, chloroform, and cyclopropane, is reflex in origin due to the anesthetic coming in contact with the buccal mucosa. Because excessive salivery secretion can be troublesome to the anesthetist, atropine and scopolamine have long been used as a premedication to anesthesia to suppress salivary secretion. When deep anesthesia has been induced excessive secretion stops due to central inhibition.

Disturbances of Salivary Secretion

Disturbances of salivary secretion can be divided into those conditions which result in an absence or decrease in salivary secretion (*hyposalivation*) and those that result in an increase in salivary secretion (*hypersalivation*). Temporary suppression of salivary secretions due to emotional states such as anxiety or fear, the presence of fever, or as a result of dehydration are not uncommon. Suppression of salivary secretion may also result from obstruction of the salivary ducts due to calculi formation. This condition is known as *sialolithiasis*. In patients with Bell's palsy, in which there is a peripheral paralysis of the facial nerve, secretion of the salivary glands on the paralyzed side is decreased.

Permanent suppression of salivary secretion (*xerostomia* or *aptyalism*) is rare and may be associated with congenital hypoplasia or absence of the salivary glands. Steggerda (1941) has reported an interesting case of a university student in whom the orifices of the ducts of the salivary glands were not demonstrable. The chronic dryness of the subject's mouth was not necessarily related to thirst. The student had learned to take a few swallows of water approximately every hour to relieve his uncomfortable xerostomia. When he became "actually thirsty" he would drink about 250 ml. of water. This occurred approximately four times a day. He found that it was necessary to take small sips of water frequently during his meals to facilitate mastication and swallowing. The water intake of this subject was studied over a period of a number of days and found not to be different from that of four students who served as controls.

Hyposalivation may also result from surgical procedures or x-ray therapy in areas where the principal salivary glands are located. In xerostomia, the patient complains of difficulty in masticating and swallowing food. Articulate speech is also difficult unless the subject takes frequent sips of water. In such patients, there is also an increase in dental caries.

Hypersalivation, or *sialorrhea*, is sometimes observed during pregnancy. The cause of the excessive salivation is not known. It may be particularly troublesome because the patient may secrete as much as three to four liters of saliva per day. Neoplasms of the mouth or tongue, or even a carious tooth, may result in hypersalivation due to reflex stimulation of the salivary glands due to local irritation. Excessive salivation is not uncommon in diseases of the esophagus, stomach and pancreas. Neoplasms of the esophagus, or even esophageal spasm, may result in reflex stimulation of salivary secretion (esophagosalivary reflex). This reflex may be elicited readily in a normal person by the passage of a stomach tube or an esophageal sound. Patients with gastric or duodenal ulcer and pancreatitis may also have excessive salivary secretion.

The reflex stimulation of secretion that results from stimuli arising in the stomach, esophagus, duodenum or pancreas may be excessive and pass down the esophagus, without the individual's knowledge, and collect above the cardiac sphincter. The secretion occurs as a rule shortly after a meal and a short time later, a large quantity of fluid may have accumulated. It may then be brought into the mouth in one or two gushes without any vomiting effort or even nausea. The condition is spoken of as *water-brash*.

Various neurological disorders, such as the Parkinsonian syndrome, are associated with excessive salivation. The psychotic state of schizophrenia may also be associated with excessive salivation.

An interesting disorder of salivary secretion is known as the *chorda tympani syndrome*. This syndrome results from a surgical or traumatic severance of the chorda tympani nerve. The regenerating chorda nerve fibers become misdirected and grow into nerves innervating sweat glands in the submental region. When the subject eats, or when salivary secretion is otherwise stimulated reflexly, sweating occurs in the submental area on the affected side. Both the salivary glands and the sweat glands are innervated by cholinergic fibers. In the chorda tympani syndrome, impulses intended for the salivary glands are transmitted to the sweat glands and they respond by secreting sweat.

REFERENCES

BARCROFT, J. The respiratory function of the blood. University Press Cambridge, 1914.

BERGEIM, O. Intestinal chemistry. III. Salivary digestion in the human stomach and intestines. Arch. int. Med., 1926, **37**, 110.

BERNARD, C. De l'influence de deux ordres de nerfs qui determinent les variations de couleur du sang veineus dans les organes glandulaires. C. R. Acad. Sci., 1858, **47**, 245.

BERNARD, C. Du role des actions réflexes paralysantes dans les phénoménes des sécrétions. J. Anat., Paris, 1864, **I**, 507.

BURGEN, A. S. V. AND SEEMAN, P. The role of the salivary duct system in the formation of the saliva. Can. J. Biochem. Physiol., 1958, **36**, 119.

CARLSON, A. J., GREER, J. R., AND BECHT, F. C. The relation between the blood supply to the submaxillary gland and the character of the chorda and the sympathetic saliva in the dog and cat. Am. J. Physiol., 1907–1908, **20**, 180.

DEUTSCH, W. AND RAPER, H. S. The respiration and metabolism of submaxillary gland tissue of the cat. J. Physiol., 1938, **92**, 439.

EMMELIN, N. "Paralytic secretion" of saliva. An example of supersensitivity after denervation. Physiol. Rev., 1952, **32**, 21.

EMMELIN, N. On the innervation of the submaxillary gland cells in cats. Acta Physiol. scandinav., 1955, **34**, 11.

EMMELIN, N. AND MUREN, A. Acetylcholine release at parasympathetic synapses. Acta physiol. scand., 1950, **20**, 13.

ERNSTER, L. Distribution and interaction of enzymes within animal cells. Biochem. Soc. Symp., 1959, **16**, 54. Cambridge University Press.

HEIDENHAIN, R. Ueber secretorische und trophische Drüsennerven. Pfluger's Arch. ges. Physiol., 1878, **17**, 1.

HILLARP, N.-Å. The functional organization of the peripheral autonomic innervation. Acta physiol. scand., 1949, **17**, 120.

HOKIN, L. E. AND HOKIN, M. R. The mechanism of phosphate exchange in phosphatidic acid in response to acetylcholine. J. Biol. Chem., 1959, **234**, 1387.

HOKIN, L. E. AND SHERWIN, A. L. Protein secretion and phosphate turnover in the phospholipids in salivary glands in vitro. J. Physiol., 1957, **135**, 18.

LANGLEY, J. N. On the physiology of the salivary secretion. V. The effect of stimulating the cerebral secretory nerves upon the amount of saliva obtained by stimulating the sympathetic nerve. J. Physiol., 1889, **10**, 291.

LANGLEY, J. N. AND FLETCHER, H. On the secretion of saliva, chiefly on the secretion of salts in it. Phil. Trans. Roy. Soc. London, Ser. B., 1890, **180**, 116.

LUDWIG, CARL. Neue Versuche über die Beihilfe

der Nerven zur Speichelabsonderung. Z. rat. Med., N. F. 1851, **1**, 255.

LUNDBERG, A. The electrophysiology of the submaxillary gland of the cat. Acta Physiol. scand., 1955, **35**, 1.

LUNDBERG, A. Secretory potentials in the salivary glands of the cat. Acta Physiol. scand., 1957, **40**, 21, 35 and 101.

MATTHEWS, A. The physiology of secretion. Ann. N. Y. Acad. Sci., 1898, **XI**, 293.

McCLURE, F. J. Fluorine in human saliva. Amer. J. Dis. Child., 1941, **62**, 512.

NORTHUP, D. The secretory metabolism of the salivary glands. Amer. J. Physiol., 1935, **114**, 46.

PALADE, G. E. A small particulate component of the cytoplasm. J. Biophys. Biochem. Cytol., 1955, **1**, 59.

PORTER, K. R. Electron microscopy of basophilic components of cytoplasm. J. Histochem., 1954, **2**, 346.

RAWLINSON, H. E. Cytological changes after autonomic and adrenalin stimulation of the cat's submaxillary gland. Anat. Rec., 1933, **57**, 289.

RAWLINSON, H. E. The changes in the alveolar and demilune cells of the simple and stimulated paralytic submaxillary gland of the cat. J. Anat., Lond., 1935, **70**, 143.

ROBERTSON, J. D. The ultrastructure of cell membranes and their derivatives in *The structure and function of subcellular components*. Biochem. Soc. Symp., 1959, **16**, 3. Cambridge University Press.

SCHMIDT-NIELSEN, B. The pH in parotid and mandibular saliva. Acta physiol. scand., 1946, **II**, 104.

SCHNEYER, L. H. AND LEVIN, L. K. Rate of secretion by individual salivary gland pairs of man under conditions of reduced exogenous stimulation. J. Appl. Physiol., 1955, **7**, 508.

SCOTT, B. L. AND PEASE, D. C. Electron microscopy of the major salivary glands of the rat. Anat. Rec., 1957, **127**, 364.

SNELL, R. S. AND GARRETT, J. R. Histochemical appearances of cholinesterase in the submaxillary and sublingual salivary glands of the rat. Nature, 1956, **178**, 1177.

SPANNER, R. Der Abkürzungskreislauf der Glandula submaxillaris. Z. Anat. Entwick., 1937, **107**, 124.

STARR, H. E. Studies of human mixed saliva. I. The determination of the hydrogen ion concentration of human mixed saliva. J. Biol. Chem., 1922, **54**, 43.

STEGGERDA, F. R. Observations on the water intake in an adult man with dysfunctioning salivary glands. Am. J. Physiol., 1941, **132**, 517.

STRÖMBLAD, B. C. R. Oxygen consumption of the normal and denervated submaxillary gland in vitro. Acta. Physiol. scand., 1957, **40**, 130.

STROMBLAD, B. C. R. Gaseous metabolism of the normal and denervated submaxillary gland of the cat. J. Physiol., 1959, **145**, 551.

STROMBLAD, S. Sensitivity of the normal and denervated parotid gland to chemical agents. Acta Physiol. scandinav., 1955, **33**, 83.

Monographs and Reviews

BABKIN, B. P. Die äussere Sekretion der Verdauungsdrüsen. Springer, Berlin, 1928.

BABKIN, B. P. Secretory mechanism of the digestive glands, 2nd ed., pp. 664–824. Paul B. Hoeber, New York, 1950.

BURGEN, A. S. V. AND EMMELIN, N. G. Physiology of the salivary glands. The Williams & Wilkins Company, Baltimore, 1961.

CANNON, W. B. The mechanical factors of digesgestion. p. 64. Longmans, Green and Co., New York, 1911.

LUNDBERG, A. Electrophysiology of salivary glands. Physiol. Rev., 1958, **38**, 21.

PAVLOV, I. P. The work of the digestive glands, 2nd ed., p. 71. Lippincott, Philadelphia, 1910.

STORMONT, D. L. The salivary glands. Cowdry's special cytology. 2nd ed., vol. 1, p. 91. Paul B. Hoeber, New York, 1932.

ZIMMERMAN, K. W. Die Speicheldrüsen der Mundhöhle und die Bauchspeichedrüse. Von Möllendorffs Handbuch der Mikroskopischen Anatomie des Menschen, Vol. 5, part 1, 161. J. Springer, 1927. Berlin. (Cited by Babkin, 1950.)

CHAPTER 57

Gastric Secretion

In 1824, an English chemist named Prout, discovered that the highly acid nature of gastric juice was due to the presence of hydrochloric acid. William Beaumont, from 1825 to 1833, contributed greatly to the knowledge of gastric secretion by his pioneering and classical experiments on Alexis St. Martin, a Canadian Indian who had a fistulous opening into his stomach as a result of a gunshot wound. Since that time, physiologists have been intensely interested in the phenomena of an animal tissue secreting such strong concentrations of a mineral acid. Even today, the study of the mechanism of secretion of hydrochloric acid by the gastric mucosa, and the various factors that regulate gastric secretion represents one of the most active areas of investigation in the field of gastrointestinal physiology.

Laymen also have had an intense interest in gastric secretion as evidenced by their consciousness of "acid stomach," "acid indigestion," and the misconceptions that such diverse conditions as "coated" tongue or excess flatus ("gas") is due to the production of too much or too little acid by the stomach.

Structure of the Gastric Mucosa

The surface epithelium of the gastric mucosa consists of a single layer of tall columnar cells that secrete mucus. The lining of the stomach thus differs markedly from that of the esophagus, which is a stratified squamous epithelium, and that of the small intestine with an absorptive epithelium arranged in finger-like protuberances, 0.2 to 0.5 mm. in height. The junction of the esophageal mucosa with that of the stomach is abrupt. The esophago-cardiac line of junction is irregular or zig-zag, and is often referred to as the "Z" or "Z-Z" line. At the pylorus, the mucous membrane of the stomach makes junction with that of the duodenum.

The mucous membrane of the stomach is separated from the outer muscular gastric wall by the *muscularis mucosae* and a supporting stroma of connecting tissue. When the stomach is empty, the mucous membrane is thrown into numerous longtitudinal folds called *rugae;* these tend to disappear when the stomach is distended.

The surface of the gastric mucosa is marked by slight linear depressions into small polygonal areas called *areae gastricae*, giving the surface a mammilated appearance; the areas measure from 1 to 6 mm. in diameter. The surface is constantly covered by a thick layer of tough, tenacious mucus secreted by the surface epithelial cells. The layer of mucus varies in thickness from 0.5 to 2.5 mm. Beneath the surface layer of epithelium, are located various types of tubular glands which vary in structure and in composition of their secretion in different parts of the stomach. When the mucus is removed, the *gastric foveolae* may be seen with the aid of a hand lens. The gastric foveolae are separated from one another by a distance of approximately 0.1 mm.; thus, there are 90 to 100 per mm^2. Opening into the bottom of each foveola are 3 to 7 individual gastric glands. The lining of the gastric pit is a continuation of the tall columnar surface epithelium.

The gastric mucosa can be divided into several areas, each of which contain a particular type of gland. The *cardiac area* is the zone, 1 to 4 cm. wide, that guards the esophageal orifice. The *fundic area* is the largest area of the stomach, accounting for 60 to 80 per cent of total mucosal surface, interposed between the cardiac and the *pyloric areas*. The lower limit of the fundic area is marked by the *incisura angularis* on the lesser curvature of the stomach, and a line extending diagonally toward the pylorus to the greater curvature. The junction of the pyloric and fundic area is not sharply demarcated and is frequently referred to as the *transitional zone*. The distal part of the pyloric zone extends to the pylorus which communicates with the first part of the duodenum. The pyloric area is about 15 per cent of the total gastric mucosal area. On the lesser curvature, where the mucous membrane is more firmly attached to the muscular wall of the stomach, the rugae form parallel longtitudinal folds and this area is sometimes referred to as the *"Magenstrasse."*

The *gastric glands* are tubular in structure and extend from the bottom of the gastric foveolae to the muscularis mucosae where they terminate in a blind bulbar end known as the *fundus* of

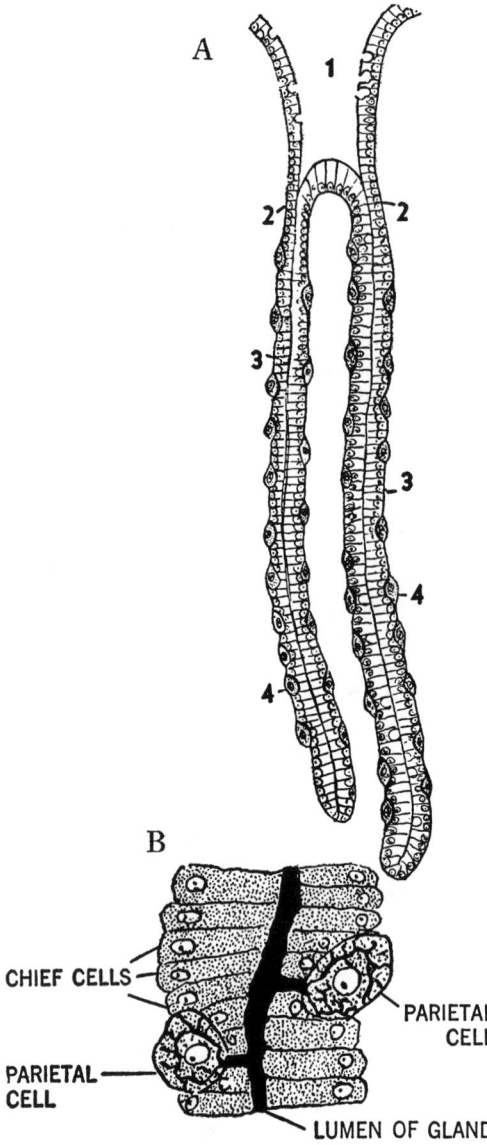

Fig. 57.1. *A*, gland from the fundus of the stomach. 1, crypt or foveola on the mucous surface connected to the neck (2) by the isthmus; 2, neck of gland containing mucin-secreting cells; 3, chief cells; 4, parietal cells. *B*, enlarged drawing showing intercellular and intracellular canaliculi.

the gland. The main tubular portion of the gland is known as the *body*. The *neck* of the gland connects the body to the *isthmus* which communicates with the gastric crypt. The total number of gastric glands has been estimated at 35,000,000.

Each area of the gastric mucosa is characterized by its glandular structure. The *cardiac glands* in the cardiac area tend to be short and tortuous, and are made up mostly of mucous cells, although a few pepsinogen cells are also present. Similar

glands, minus the pepsinogen cells, are found in the esophagus. The *fundic glands* tend to be straight, slender structures with narrow lumen. Three types of cells make up the fundic glands: *mucous* cells, *pepsinogen* or chief cells, and *parietal* or oxyntic cells. The mucous cells may be further divided into isthmus cells and neck cells. Although the isthmus cells are of the mucous type, they probably secrete very little mucus, inasmuch as they contain little of the granular material commonly considered to be converted into mucus. The cells of the neck are true mucous-secreting cells but they secrete a different type of mucus from that of the surface epithelial cells. The mucus of the neck cells is soluble, and constitutes a part of the soluble mucus of gastric juice. An important characteristic of the isthmus and neck cells is their frequent mitoses. It is believed that after birth these cells may develop into pepsinogen cells and thus replace chief cells.

In the neck region are also a great many parietal cells. These cells do not form a part of the gland wall but appear to lie outside, giving the gland a nodular appearance (fig. 57.1). They can be distinguished from their neighbors not only by their location, but by their staining characteristics. The parietal cells secrete the hydrochloric acid and most of the water of the gastric juice and, because of this, they are also known as the "oxyntic" or acid-secreting cells. Among the several observations which indicate the parietal cell origin of HCl is the direct correlation between the number of parietal cells and the titratable acidity and total chloride content of gastric juice from different regions of the gastric mucosa during secretion. Although separated from the lumen of the tubules by the chief, or pepsinogen cells, the parietal cells transmit their secretion into the lumen through delicate *canaliculi* lying between the chief cells. These canaliculi are extensions of a system of exquisitely fine canals which lie within the protoplasm of the parietal cells and possess definite walls. Numerous transparent, smooth-surfaced vesicles are seen in the protoplasm of the cells during rest. Depletion of this vesicular material occurs during activity. The distribution of parietal cells in the human stomach is shown in fig. 57.2.

The body of the gland which makes up the remainder of the tubule is composed principally of pepsinogen cells called *chief cells*. Parietal cells are also present, but in diminishing numbers, as the fundus of the tubule is approached. In addition to *pepsinogen*, the chief cells probably produce *renin* (in the calf), which coagulates milk, and is believed to be produced only in young animals, and a special gelatin-splitting enzyme known as *gelatinase* (in the pig), which liquifies gelatin at a rate about 400 times that of pepsin. It is not known whether each of these enzymes is produced by a different type of chief cell or whether they are produced by the same cell. Since the chief cells appear to be morphologically identical, there is no anatomical evidence for assuming that they differ from one another in their secretory products. No mitoses are seen in the chief cells.

Another type of cell occasionally found in the fundic glands is the argentaffin cell. With ordinary staining methods these cells are inconspicuous. However, after fixation in potassium bichromate, they stand out due to their dark yellow color. The granules contained in their protoplasm are easily impregnated with silver and this characteristic gives the cells their name. The exact function of argentaffin cells in the gastric mucosa is not known.

The *pyloric glands* are located in the pyloric area but they also extend into the transitional zone separating the pyloric area from the fundic area of the stomach. The pyloric glands tend to be somewhat shorter and are more tortuous than the fundic glands. The foveolae in the pyloric region tend to be deep. These glands are lined exclusively by mucous-secreting cells that resemble those of the cardiac glands. An occasional argentaffin cell may be noted in the fundus of the pyloric glands.

The electron microscope has provided additional information on the structure of the gastric mucosa. The presence of intracellular canaliculi in the parietal cells is a constant finding. At the free or luminal surface of the parietal cell, as in the case of certain other active transport cells, there is a striated border. The intracellular canaliculus simply represents an invagination of this striated border. The presence of a very high concentration of mitochondria also is consistent with the cell's role in transport of ions against a concentration gradient (fig. 57.3).

Recent studies correlating structural change with gastric secretion (Sedar and Friedman, 1961; Sedar, 1962; Rohrer et al., 1965) have demonstrated that during gastric secretion stimulated by histamine, insulin hypoglycemia or vagal stimulation, definite and characteristic changes occur within the parietal cell (fig. 57.4). Most prominent is a change in the structure of the intracellular canaliculi. The microvilli lining the walls of the canaliculi are markedly increased,

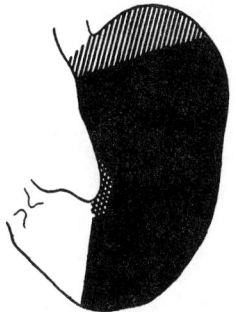

FIG. 57.2. Diagram showing the distribution of the parietal (acid-secreting) cells in the human stomach. In the black area the proportion of parietal cells was maximal and was taken as 100 per cent; in the cross-hatched area on lesser curvature the percentage of parietal cells was 75 per cent, in the shaded area at the fundus, 50 per cent, and in the white area 0 to 1 per cent. (After Berger, Am. J. Anat., 1934, 54, 87.)

to the point that the lumen of the canaliculus is almost occluded by these protoplasmic projections. The increased number of microvilli provides a tremendous increase in the surface area of the wall of the canaliculus, which is presumed to be the site of movement of hydrochloric acid and water from the cell into the canaliculus. During secretion of hydrochloric acid, the smooth-surfaced vesicles, which are randomly distributed in the cytoplasmic matrix in the resting cell, become concentrated adjacent to intracellular canaliculi. With continued secretion of hydrochloric acid, these smooth-surfaced elements decrease in number. In some instances it has been possible to observe these vesicles communicating with areas of the canalicular wall between adjacent microvilli.

Regardless of the stimulus to secretion, whether it be histamine, insulin hypoglycemia or vagal stimulation, the structural changes just described are similar. Not all parietal cells, however, show these changes during secretion. Some 20 to 25 per cent of cells in a biopsy specimen may appear to be in the resting state. Thus, stimulation apparently does not activate all parietal cells simultaneously. When acetazolamide, a powerful carbonic anhydrase inhibitor, is administered to a dog to prevent the gastric secretion of HCl, and then histamine or some other stimulus is used in an attempt to provoke secretion, the structural changes associated with secretion do not occur.

Innervation of the Gastric Glands

The gastric mucosa is innervated by both the sympathetic and parasympathetic divisions of

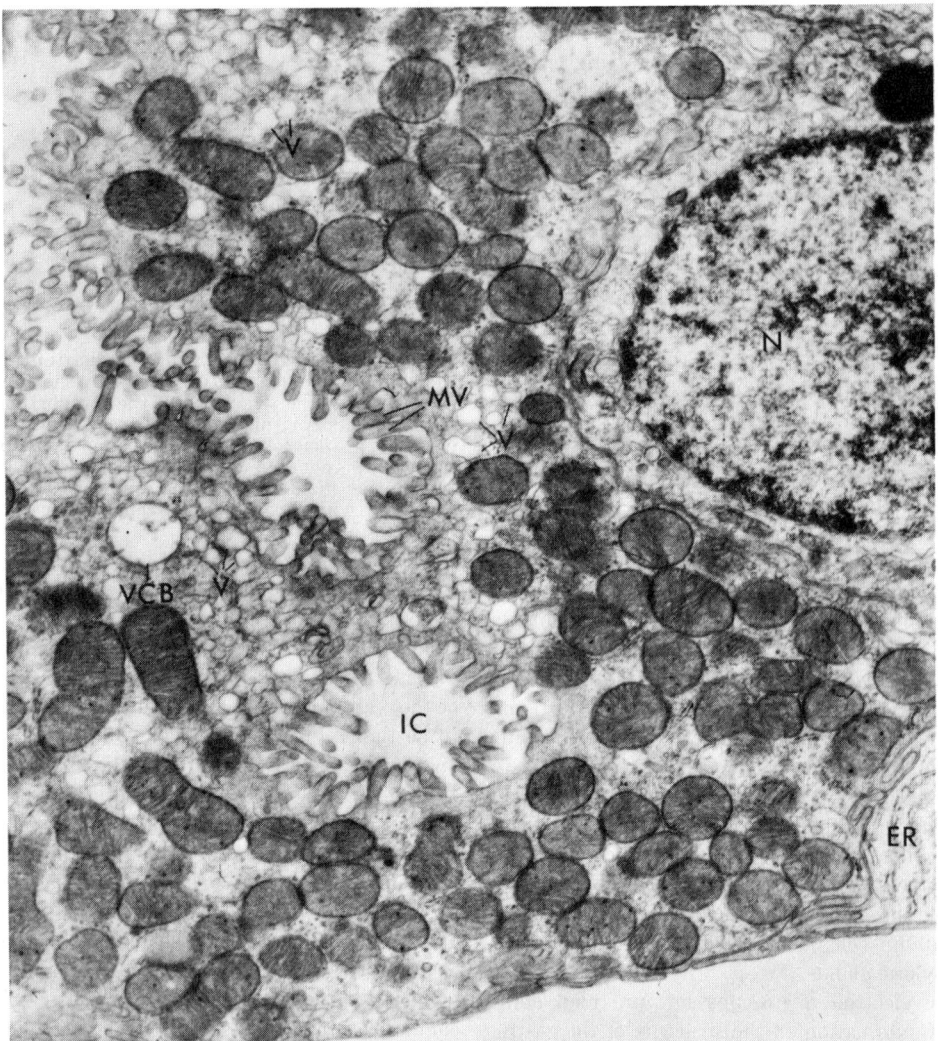

Fig. 57.3. Electromicrograph of part of a non-secreting human parietal cell. The specimen was obtained by biopsy. Secretion was suppressed by administering 0.5 mg. of atropine sulfate. The gastric juice contained no free acid and had a pH of 6.6 at the time of biopsy. The intracellular canal system (IC) is evident demonstrating patent lumen with projecting microvilli (MV). Throughout the cytoplasm are many small vesicular structures (V) whose content appears less dense than that of surrounding cytoplasm. Note the large vacuole containing body (VCB). Nucleus (N) and some endoplasmic reticulum (ER) of adjacent chief cells are also included in electromicrograph. (Approx. × 22,800). From Rohrer et al., Am. J. Digest. Dis., 1965, 10, 16.

the autonomic nervous system. The *efferent sympathetic supply* arises from neurones located in the latter horn of the fifth to tenth thoracic segments of spinal cord. The *preganglionic fibers* emerge from the cord in the anterior spinal nerve roots and pass to the ganglia of the thoracic sympathetic chain. Here, some form synapses but most continue in the thoracic splanchic nerves to the celiac plexus and form synapses with the ganglia within the celiac plexus. From the celiac ganglia, the *postganglionic fibers* ac-

company the arterial vascular supply of the stomach. The *afferent sympathetic fibers* from the stomach travel the same course just outlined, in reverse, to the ganglion cells in the posterior spinal nerve roots. The afferents do not synapse in, or arise from, the sympathetic ganglia.

The *efferent parasympathetic supply* to the gastric mucosa originates in the dorsal vagal nucleus in the floor of the fourth ventricle. The *preganglionic fibers* reach the stomach via the

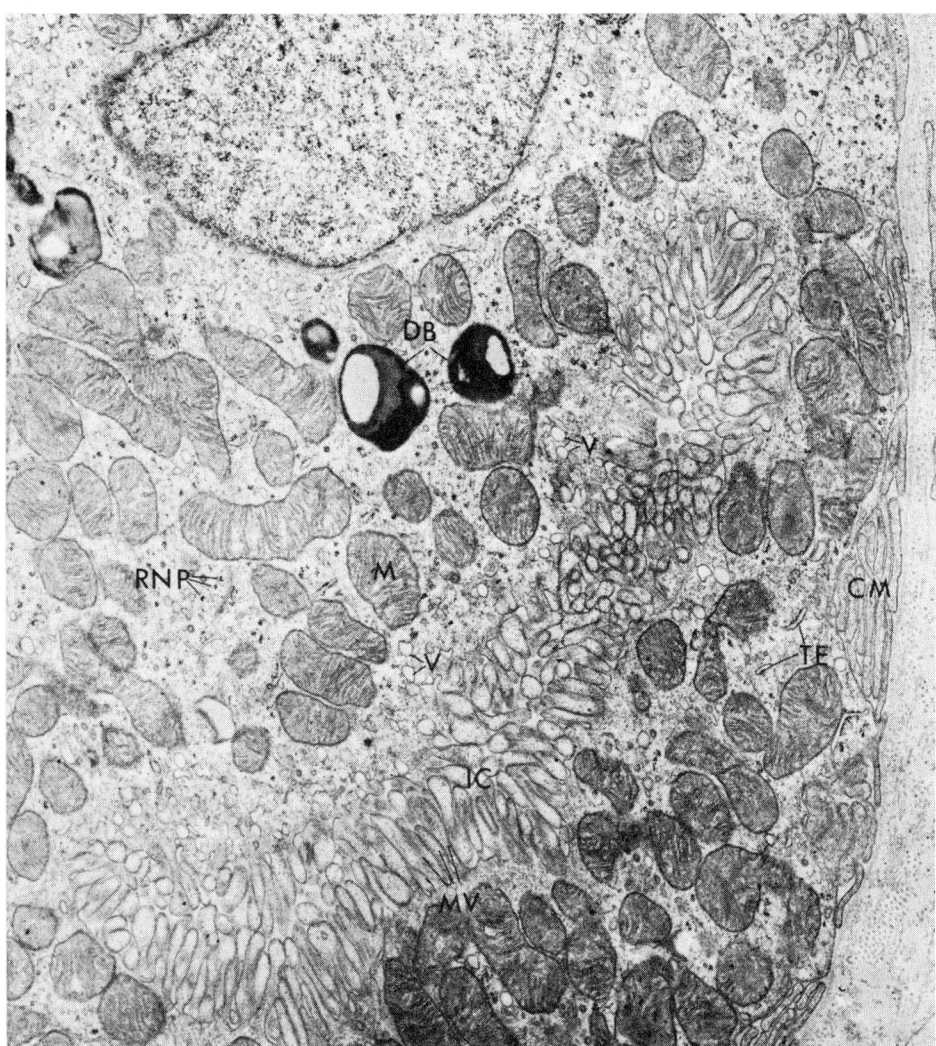

Fig. 57.4. Part of parietal cell from same subject as in fig. 57.3. Biopsy was taken after maxima histamine stimulation, when gastric juice contained 104 mEq/l. HCl and had pH of 1. Intracellular canaliculus (IC) appears very complex, and lumen is filled with microvilli (compare with fig. 57.3). Vesicular components (V) appear decreased in number and are oriented about intracellular canal. In cytoplasm are mitochondria (M), a few scattered tubular elements (TE), ribonucleoprotein granules (RNP), and 2 dense bodies (DB). An infolded cell membrane (CM) is noted on right. (From Rohrer et al., Am. J. Digest. Dis. 1965, **10**, 17.)

right and left vagus nerves. The left vagus supplies preganglionic fibers to the anterior surface, and the right vagus to the posterior surface of the stomach. In addition, both vagi send branches to the celiac plexus. The parasympathetic preganglionic fibers accompany the vascular supply and the sympathetic fibers into the muscular layers of the wall of the stomach, to form synapses with the ganglion cells of the myenteric plexus of Auerbach and the submucosus plexus of Meissner. The *postganglionic fibers* supplying the mucosa are thus very short, whereas the pre-

ganglionic fibers are quite long. *Afferent parasympathetic fibers* are found in the vagus. The neurons of these fibers are located mainly in the *ganglion nodosum*. The central processes of these afferent neurons terminate in the dorsal nucleus of the vagus, completing the reflex arc.

The vagi are important secretory nerves to the stomach. The cephalic or psychic phase of gastric secretion is mediated via the vagi. An intact vagal innervation is also important in the release of *gastrin* from the gastric antrum. Stimulation of the vagus nerve causes the secre-

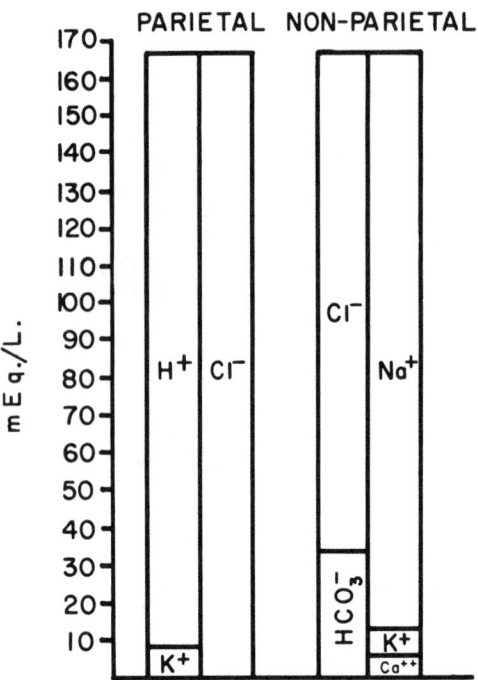

FIG. 57.5. The computed ionic concentration of the principal ions in the parietal and non-parietal secretions of the gastric gland. (Redrawn from Ivy, Grossman and Bachrach in *Peptic ulcer*, The Blakiston Company, Philadelphia, Toronto, 1950, p. 26.)

tion of strongly acidic gastric juice rich in pepsin. This effect is mediated through acetylcholine. Atropine, which blocks postganglionic parasympathetic stimulation, inhibits gastric secretion stimulated via the vagi.

According to Alley and Babkin, the glands of the lesser curvature respond more readily to vagal stimulation than do those of the greater curvature, and secrete a more highly concentrated juice, an observation which may have bearing on the development of gastric ulcer (p. 1112). Baxter has shown that stimulation of the sympathetic nerve supply to the mucosa causes the secretion, mainly from the pyloric glands, of an alkaline mucoid juice which is very low in peptic activity. The sympathetic response is unaffected by atropine, but is annulled by ergotamine (which paralyzes motor and secretory sympathetic fibers). Vineberg's results indicate that the vagus controls the secretion of mucin by the mucous neck cells and the surface epithelium of the gastric mucosa. The influence exerted by the sympathetic upon the peptic and oxyntic cells of the gastric body is not definitely known. According to some observers, its effect upon these elements is inhibitory.

Origin and Composition of Gastric Juice

Gastric juice is the product of secretion by the surface epithelium and the various gastric glands. The composition of gastric juice varies, depending on the individual contributions of the various secreting structures. The major constituents of gastric juice are: water, hydrochloric acid, and other inorganic constituents such as sodium, potassium, calcium, phosphate, bicarbonate and sulfate. The major organic constituents include various enzymes, at least two types of mucus, the *intrinsic factor* of Castle (ch. 30), and blood group substances.

It is convenient to think of gastric juice as a mixture of parietal cell secretion and secretion from non-parietal structures. HCl is secreted by the parietal cell at a *constant concentration* but at a *variable rate*. The non-parietal secretion is produced at a more constant rate but its composition may vary considerably. Thus, the acidity of the gastric juice will depend upon the rate of parietal cell secretion.

It has been estimated that the volume of gastric juice secreted by man in a 24-hr. period amounts to 1200 to 1500 ml. The amount will vary, depending upon the diet and other stimuli provoking gastric secretion. When gastric juice is collected for a 12-hr. period during the night, by means of a naso-gastric tube with constant suction, the average volume obtained is about 400 ml. Fasting human gastric juice collected from healthy young adults has an acidity of 40 to 60 mEq/l., a pH of 0.9 to 1.2, and a specific gravity of 1.002 to 1.004.

Hydrochloric Acid and Neutral Chloride

The composition of pure parietal secretion can be arrived at only by computation, inasmuch as no means is available for collecting pure parietal secretion that is not contaminated, at least to some extent, with secretions from non-parietal cells. Figure 57.5 illustrates the computed ionic composition of parietal and non-parietal secretions of the gastric glands. The best evidence indicates that pure parietal secretion consists of HCl with a concentration of approximately 0.166 N. It is further believed that the composition of parietal secretion remains constant, and is independent of rate of secretion, nature of stimulus, or strength of stimulus. The concentration of hydrochloric acid in gastric juice collected from man or a dog may vary from 0 to 150 mEq or more per liter. Other things being equal, the concentration of acid increases with increasing rates of secretion, up to a maximum of about 150 mEq/l. The chloride ions that accompany the hydrogen ions into the gastric juice to form HCl are not passively carried along by the hydrogen ions. Two important observations that indicate that the chloride ion of the HCl in gastric juice is secreted by an active, energy consuming mechanism are: (1) chloride ion is transported against a concentration gradient, from a plasma concentration of about 110 mEq/l. to a concentration in gastric juice up to 166 mEq/l., and (2) chloride ion is transported against an electro-chemical gradient (the luminal surface of the gastric mucosa is negative to the serosal surface with a potential difference of 30 to 50 mV). The chloride ion of HCl is considered to be secreted by a "chloride pump."

It is interesting that the mechanism (chloride pump) for transporting chloride ions into the gastric juice is also capable of transporting *bromide* and *iodide* ions. Hydrobromic acid may be recovered from the gastric juice of patients who have taken bromide salts. When radioactive iodine, I^{131}, is administered intravenously to a patient, radioactivity rapidly appears in the gastric juice.

A small part of the chloride of gastric juice is balanced against metallic ions, principally sodium. This constitutes the so-called *neutral chloride*. The concentration of other negative ions in the juice is negligible, thus the osmotic activity of gastric juice is primarily due to the acid, plus the neutral chloride. Since gastric juice is practically isotonic with blood, the ionic concentration of total chloride in the gastric juice differs but little from that of the total base of the blood; for example, in some experiments of Gilman and Cowgill (1933) the gastric chloride was 168 mEq/l. and the total base of the blood was 160 mEq/l.

In highly acid gastric juice, the neutral chloride is present only in small amounts, but in a less acid secretion it may constitute a major portion of the total chloride. When it is present in large quantities, its source becomes a matter of considerable interest. The source of neutral chloride has been a matter of widespread discussion and controversy but current thinking tends to the view that it is secreted by the non-parietal cells (mucous cells of the surface epithelium and chief cells of the gastric glands), along with sodium, calcium, potassium and the organic materials secreted by these cells; and that a certain, perhaps smaller, amount enters the gastric contents by diffusion from the interstitial fluid. In impure gastric juice, a large part of the neutral chloride may represent swallowed saliva and regurgitated duodenal contents, or perhaps even salt taken with the food.

GASTRIC ENZYMES

A number of enzymes found in gastric juice have been believed to be of gastric origin and play a role in gastric digestion. Except for pepsin, the specific cellular origin of these enzymes is not known, although some authors have postulated that rennin and gastric lipase are derived from the chief cells of the fundic glands of the stomach.

Pepsin

The principal proteolytic substance in acid gastric juice is pepsin. Pepsin is derived from the chief cells of the fundic glands. The zymogen granules in the cytoplasm of these cells represent the mother substance of the active ferment. In this form, the enzyme is inactive and referred to as *pepsinogen*. Pepsinogen is relatively resistant to heat and alkali and can withstand short exposures to temperatures of 70° C. or a pH of 11 without loss of activity. The enzyme becomes active only in acid media. At a pH below 6, pepsinogen is transformed into pepsin by an autocatalytic reaction. The optimum pH for peptic activity is about 2.0. At a pH of 5.0, the action of pepsin is almost abolished. Pepsin produces digestion of protein by attacking those peptide linkages in which the amino groups are attached to aromatic amino acids. The products of protein digestion by pepsin consist mainly of proteoses and peptones and relatively few amino acids and polypeptides. Both pepsinogen and pepsin have been isolated in the form of a crystalline protein. The crystals of pepsin are doubly refracting hexahedra. Pepsin is constantly present in acid gastric juice and probably is secreted continuously. During interdigestive periods, pepsin is stored in the chief cells of the fundic glands, as evidenced by the accumulation of zymogen granules. Details of the synthesis of pepsinogen from amino acids by the chief cells, or the mechanism of release of pepsinogen from the cells during secretion are not known. The major stimulus to pepsin secretion is vagal impulses. Gastric secretion induced by sham feeding, electrical stimulation of the vagus nerves, or insulin hypoglycemia results in a gastric juice containing high peptic activity. Pilocarpine and acetylcholine are potent stimuli of pepsin secretion.

Histamine produces a gastric juice of low pepsin concentration.

Most stimuli of gastric secretion produce a juice that is initially high in peptic activity. Gastric secretion in response to a meal will show the highest concentration of pepsin in the first hour. As the volume of gastric juice increases, the concentration of pepsin falls. During the later stages of digestion, when the volume of gastric juice diminishes, the concentration of pepsin increases. Since pepsin is a preformed secretory product and cannot be elaborated as rapidly as it is secreted, depletion of cell stores of pepsinogen occurs during the initial period of gastric secretion. Prolonged stimulation of gastric secretion, however, does not result in disappearance of peptic activity from gastric juice.

Proteolytic activity in blood serum and urine, presumably due to the presence of pepsinogen, has been demonstrated. Apparently, a small amount of pepsinogen is secreted directly into the blood by the chief cells. Pepsinogen can withstand the slightly alkaline pH of blood and its molecular size (42,500) would permit it to be filtered by the renal glomerulus. In serum and urine, pepsinogen is converted to pepsin on acidification and its proteolytic activity can be demonstrated. The name *uropepsin* has been given to the protease in urine. The protease, uropepsin, is of gastric origin, as proven by Bucher and Ivy (1947) who demonstrated that uropepsin disappeared from the urine of gastrectomized cats. In general, high gastric secretory rates are associated with increases in the concentration of uropepsin in the urine. However, the correlation is so poor that the measurement of uropepsin has no value clinically in assessing gastric secretory function. In patients with pernicious anemia, Farnsworth and associates (1945) have demonstrated that the pepsin-like substance in urine is significantly reduced.

Although the proteolytic activity of acid gastric juice is considered to be due principally to pepsin, there is evidence that gastric juice contains other acid proteases of gastric origin. The evidence that other acid proteases exist in gastric juice consists mainly of the demonstration of several pH activity optima for acid proteolysis, ranging approximately from 1.8 to 4.5 (Hollander, 1962). Other proteolytic enzymes described in gastric juice include *cathepsin* with a pH activity optimum of about 4.0; *gastricin*, most active at pH 3.0 and found in gastric juice of man but not in the juice of rats, hogs or dogs; and *parapepsins I* and *II*, which like *gelatinase*, have been found only in porcine gastric secretion. Hollander has pointed out that the several pH activity optima for acid proteolysis may result from the combination of various substrates with a single enzyme, rather than a multiplicity of them. This could occur if a single enzyme molecule had two or more active centers, each of which attacks a different type of peptide linkage and so possesses its own characteristic pH activity curve.

Rennin

This enzyme is the milk-curdling ferment. Rennin has been isolated from the gastric secretions of the calf. The optimum pH for the action of rennin is between 6.0 and 6.5. The presence of calcium ions are necessary for the action of rennin on milk. Gastric rennin, when added to milk kept at body temperature, causes a change in the soluble *casein*, splitting it into a *proteose-like* substance (whey protein) which remains in solution, and *paracasein*. The latter is soluble alone but upon combination with calcium forms an insoluble compound, *calcium paracasein*, which precipitates as a curd. The protein (paracasein) of the curd subsequently undergoes peptic digestion in the usual manner. The softer and more finely flocculent the character of the curd that is formed, the more readily is it attacked by the proteolytic ferments. According to Pavlov, the admixture of mucus with the milk renders the resulting curd softer in consistency.

Rennin is not found in the gastric juice of man, either infants or adults. The clotting and digestion of milk in man is affected by pepsin. With an optimum pH of 6.0 to 6.5, rennin would be inactive at the usual pH of the gastric contents of the normal adult.

Lipase

A gastric lipase has been described in gastric juice. The enzyme is a tributerase and may be similar to plasma lipase which is also a tributerase. The optimum pH for the action of gastric lipase is between 4.0 and 5.0 and is inactive at a pH of 2.5. The origin of lipase found in gastric juice is unknown. Many observers consider its presence in gastric juice due to regurgitation of duodenal contents into the stomach. When compared to pancreatic lipase, gastric lipase is a weak fat-splitting enzyme.

Other Gastric Enzymes

A number of less important digestive enzymes have been detected in gastric juice. Their presence in gastric juice in minute amounts suggests that they are of doubtful digestive significance.

Lysozyme (pH optimum 5.3) is a carbohydrate-splitting enzyme. In gastric juice from normal individuals, it is found in small amounts. Its cellular origin is unknown. The lysozyme content of gastric juice has been found to be increased in patients with gastric ulcer. This increase in lysozyme concentration is probably secondary to the inflammatory reaction produced by the ulcer.

Gelatinase is an enzyme that acts specifically upon gelatin and its action is about 400 times that of pepsin.

Urease can be isolated from the gastric mucosa and gastric juice. Urease is found also in bacteria contaminating the gastric mucosa. The hydrolysis of urea by urease to produce ammonia probably plays a negligible role in gastric secretion, which will be discussed later.

Carbonic anhydrase is found in gastric juice in small amounts and its presence is thought to be due to disintegration of desquamated surface epithelial cells. In addition to being present in the surface epithelial cells, carbonic anhydrase is found in high concentrations in the parietal cells where it plays an important role in the process of HCl formation. The relationship of carbonic anhydrase to secretion of acid will be considered in detail later.

Gastric Mucus

Two types of gastric mucus occur in gastric juice. *Visible* mucus is secreted by the surface epithelial cells of the gastric mucosa and is thick, viscous, and even jelly-like. It forms a transparent coating over the surface of the gastric mucosa 2 to 3 mm. in thickness. Mucus secretion from the surface epithelium is stimulated by various chemicals applied to the surface of the gastric mucosa, e.g., alcohol, ether, clove oil, phenol red, etc. In addition, such tactile stimuli as rubbing the mucosa with a brush, or even roughage in the diet, cause secretion of mucus by the surface epithelial cells.

Soluble, or transparent, mucus is secreted by the cells of the pyloric and cardiac glands and also by the mucus neck cells of the fundic glands. It is therefore a constituent of pure gastric juice (dissolved mucin). Vagal stimulation evokes a secretion of mucin from the mucin-secreting cells of the tubules. Mucin is a glycoprotein. Ivy found that the secretion collected from pouches fashioned from the pyloric part of the stomach of dogs was mucoid, viscous, tenacious,

and transparent, with a pH of 7.0 to 7.5. Gastric mucin has a high acid combining power. It coats the interior of the stomach and, by reducing the free hydrochloric acid, serves to protect the mucosa from the action of the gastric juice. Quite apart from its power to lower the acidity of the gastric juice, Babkin and Korarov found that mucin inhibits peptic activity. This anti-peptic action of mucin is due to its constituent, mucoitin-sulfuric acid, the main monomer of goblet cell mucus. By virtue of its high viscosity, mucin effectively lubricates and protects the gastric mucosa from mechanical injury.

Brunschwig and associates (1939) demonstrated the presence of a *gastric secretory inhibitor* that they isolated from the gastric juice of patients with pernicious anemia. Blackburn and Code (1948) also demonstrated the presence of a gastric secretory inhibitor in human gastric juice, and determined that the active material was in the mucin fraction of the juice. The exact nature of this gastric secretory inhibitor is not known, but gastric juice from patients with achlorhydria or pernicious anemia shows greater inhibitory potency than juice from a normal individual. Smith and his associates (1958), using more refined extraction techniques, have isolated an inhibitor from normal human gastric juice and have demonstrated that as little as 1.0 mg./kg. of body weight injected intravenously, effectively inhibits gastric secretion in Heidenhain pouch dogs stimulated by a meat meal. A gastric secretory inhibitor has also been isolated from human saliva.

Mechanism of Hydrochloric Acid Secretion

The precise manner in which the gastric mucosa secretes hydrochloric acid is still unknown, however, the following facts have been established. Taken together they point in a general way to the processes which must be involved in the secretion.

1. It is generally, although not universally, agreed that the acid is formed by the parietal cells of the gastric glands (Davies, 1951; for a dissenting opinion, see Rehm and Dennis, 1957). It is not believed to be produced in the protoplasm of these cells but to appear first in the secretory canaliculi which communicate with the lumen of the gland. This conclusion is based on the observation that the parietal cell shows an alkaline reaction while secreting acid.

2. The acid, as secreted by the parietal cell, has a uniform concentration of approximately 0.17 molar. The theory of the constancy of the

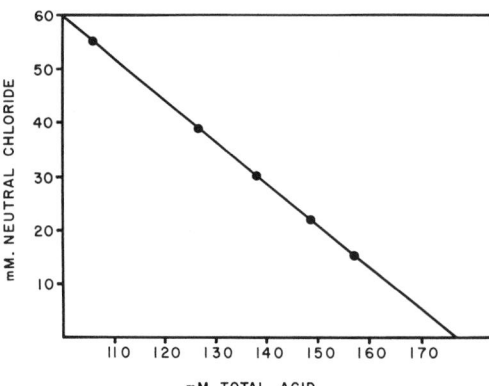

FIG. 57.6. Showing neutral chloride as a function of acidity (after Hollander).

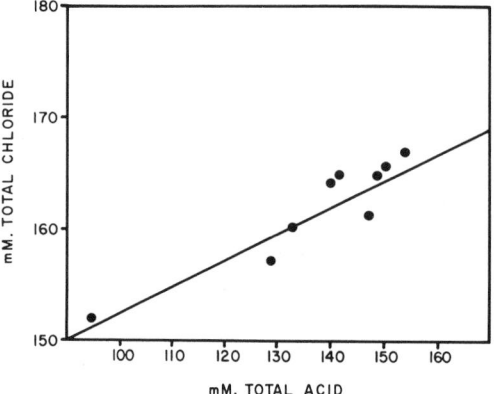

FIG. 57.7. Total chloride as a function of acidity (after Hollander).

concentration of hydrochloric acid as secreted by the parietal cells was first put forward by Pavlov and has since been supported by many investigators, including Hollander and Cowgill (1931). This theory is mainly based on the observation that the nearer one approaches to a pure parietal secretion, the nearer the concentration of hydrochloric acid approaches 0.17 molar. The acidity, when plotted against the neutral chloride, gives a straight line expressing the inverse relationship between them. When extrapolated, this line comes to a point representing a zero value for neutral chloride and an acidity of around 170 mEq/l. Since neutral chloride and acid chloride are inversely related, the total chloride tends to remain relatively constant. However, since some of the nonparietal secretion contains relatively little chloride, the total chloride increases somewhat with increasing rate of parietal secretion and, therefore, with increasing total acidity (figs. 57.6, 57.7).

A somewhat different opinion was expressed by Fisher and Hunt (1950), who made a study of the extensive data of Ihre (1938) on gastric secretion in human subjects. They mathematically tested various assumptions regarding the composition of parietal secretion in the gastric juice and concluded that the most probable concentration of hydrochloric acid in human parietal secretion is 160 mEq/l., and that the secretion contains, in addition, 10 mEq/l. of neutral chloride. This does not necessarily mean that human parietal secretion differs from that of experimental animals but merely that different methods of estimation give different results. The precise values are, of course, not known.

3. The secretion of hydrochloric acid involves expenditure of energy; that is to say, no simple chemical reaction which could proceed spontaneously can explain the formation of hydrochloric acid by the gastric glands. One estimate is that the secretion of one gram-molecular equivalent of hydrochloric acid requires expenditures of 10,000 gram-calories of energy.

4. The energy is derived from oxidation, probably of glucose, and requires the activity of the enzymes ordinarily active in such oxidation.

5. For every hydrogen ion produced, a bicarbonate ion is released into the interstitial fluid and ultimately into the blood. This requires a continuous supply of carbon dioxide. The carbon dioxide may be derived from the metabolism of the parietal cell itself if the secretory rate is low, but at higher rates of secretion the metabolic carbon dioxide has to be supplemented with carbon dioxide from the circulating blood. The need for carbon dioxide arises from the fact that, whatever the reacting system may be, removal of hydrogen ions results in accumulation of an excess of hydroxyl ions; if these were not neutralized, the resulting alkalinity would soon destroy the secreting cells. The fact that secretion of hydrochloric acid into the gastric juice results in secretion of an equivalent amount of bicarbonate into the blood explains the so-called alkaline tide seen in the urine during digestion (Bence-Jones, 1849).

6. Carbonic anhydrase (ch. 33 and 50) is present in high concentration in the parietal cells (Davenport, 1939), and participates in the overall process, though probably not directly in secretion of hydrogen ions. Its apparent function is to aid in the hydration of carbon dioxide, to produce the carbonic acid that is utilized in neutralizing the hydroxyl ions produced during

secretion. Secretion of hydrochloric acid is greatly depressed and in some subjects, totally inhibited, by the administration of large doses of Diamox, which is an inhibitor of carbonic anhydrase (Janowitz et al., 1957). Although excised frog gastric mucosa will secrete in the absence of carbon dioxide, the tissue is destroyed by the alkalinity resulting from the loss of hydrogen ions (Davies and Longmuir, 1948). In the living animals, at least in mammals, some mechanism apparently exists to prevent secretion under these circumstances, and this protects the secreting tissue from self destruction.

7. The overall reaction can be summarized by the equation:

$$CO_2 + H_2O + NaCl \rightleftharpoons HCl + NaHCO_3$$

This equation is not intended to describe the chemical reactions in detail, but merely to indicate the beginning and end products and their quantitative relationships. It indicates that: the ultimate source of the hydrogen ions is water; the ultimate source of the chloride ions is the salt of the blood; for each mole of hydrochloric acid produced, a mole of sodium bicarbonate has to be formed. The intermediate steps, the source or sources of the energy, and the enzymes and substrates concerned in the intermediate reactions, all of which constitute the real problem of the secretion of hydrochloric acid, are not even suggested. The fact that the reactions of this equation would ordinarily progress to the left is a simple qualitative proof that energy is required for the secretion of hydrochloric acid.

8. Rehm (1950) and his co-workers have shown that there is a natural, maintained potential difference across the gastric mucosa, the secretory surface being negative in an external circuit to the nutrient surface. When the two sides of the mucosa are connected electrically, a continuous current can be maintained representing about 10 per cent of the metabolic energy. This natural potential decreases with the onset of acid secretion. The rate of acid secretion can be increased or decreased by passing an electric current from a battery through the mucosa so as to increase or decrease, respectively, the potential difference across the tissue. Experiments with metabolic inhibitors show that most of the pathways of aerobic metabolism, and the related phosphorylations, are required to maintain the potential difference and the acid secretion. The facts prompted Rehm to propose a theory of acid secretion in which it is assumed that electrical

energy is utilized in the separation of hydrogen ions during the secretion of hydrochloric acid. It seems more likely that here, as elsewhere, the potential difference is the result of, rather than the cause of, the activity.

As to the intermediate steps between carbon dioxide and water at one end of the reaction, and hydrogen ions and bicarbonate at the other end, Davies (1951), after reviewing the history of research in this field from Claude Bernard's time until 1951, had this to say: "The available evidence shows that two related mechanisms of acid secretion are possible. In mechanism 1, the metabolic hydrogen atoms from glucose and water, which are transported by the dehydrogenases, become oxidized to hydrogen ions at the cytochrome level, and the electrons react with oxygen and water to form, first hydroxyl ions, and then bicarbonate ions by further reactions with carbon dioxide. This process uses the oxidation reduction energy from the level of atmospheric oxygen to that of the cytochromes. In mechanism 2, phosphate bond energy, generated by reactions at lower oxidation reduction levels is utilized to concentrate hydrogen ions, formed by ionization from water, in an electron cycle mechanism in which hydrogen ions are reduced to covalent hydrogen atoms, transported by a carrier system and oxidized to hydrogen ions at high concentration as a result of coupled phosphorylation. Kinetic and thermodynamic considerations show that the hydrogen carrier and electron transport systems could be oxaloacetate-malate and cytochrome b, or perhaps fumerate-succinate and cytochrome c. Both mechanisms require a spatial array of enzymes in the paracanalicular zone of the oxyntic cells, and in both cases, chloride ions move in the opposite direction to, and as a result of, the movements of the electrons carried by the cytochromes."

Davenport (1957), writing six years later, had this to say: "In agreement with Conway" (1953) "and many others, I suspect that the secretory process is a cyclic oxidation and reduction. A carrier molecule within the cell combines with high energy phosphate. The product is oxidized and the energy contained within it is dissipated in transporting the newly released proton" (hydrogen ion) "against a concentration gradient into the gastric juice. Then the carrier is reduced by substrate and is ready to re-enter the cycle. Two minor problems remain. For each proton secreted an electron must be taken up by oxygen, and the pH of the cell must be kept down by intracellular neutralization using the carbon dioxide mechanism" ... "Carbonic anhydrase which occupies a peripheral position is involved, an enzyme behaving like succinoxidase is there, and it is likely that some sulfhydryl compound is essential." Davenport, like Davies, recognized the need for assuming appropriate orientation of the various components involved in the reaction. Dr. Davenport's concept is illustrated in fig. 57.8 and 57.9.

Davies (1951) considers that "the rate of

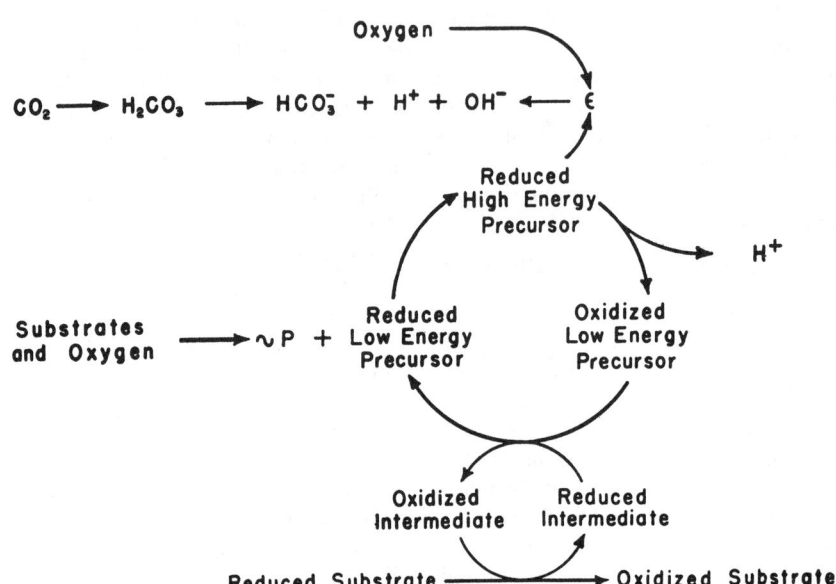

Fig. 57.8. Schema of a possible mechanism of gastric acid secretion showing the four essential parts: a) generation of high energy phosphate bounds from substrate and oxygen, b) cyclic oxidation and reduction generating hydrogen ions, c) removal of electrons to oxygen, and d) intracellular neutralization by carbon dioxide. From Davenport, 1957. (Courtesy of University of Wisconsin Press.)

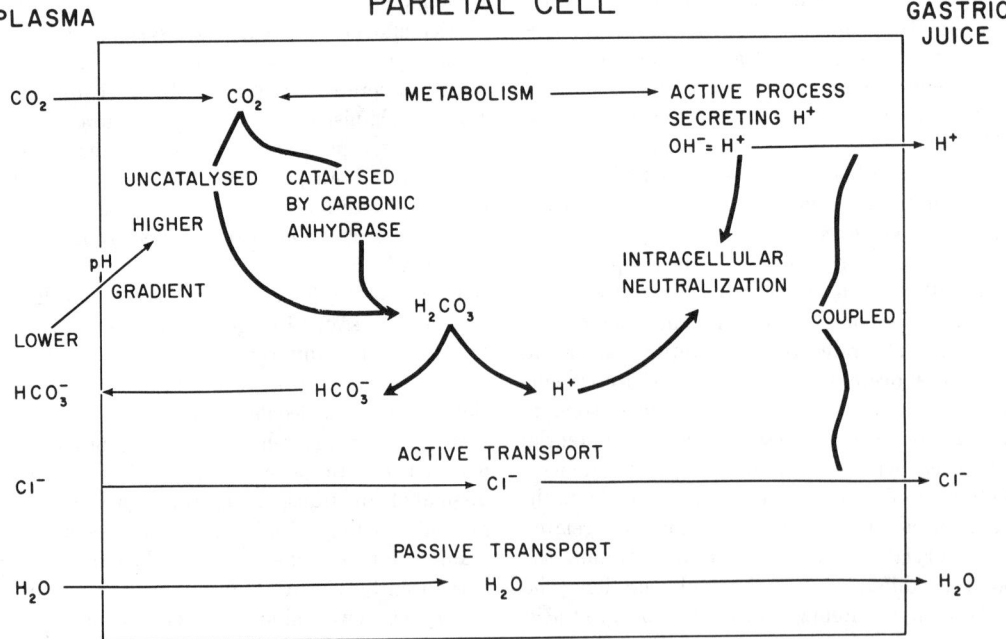

Fig. 57.9. Illustrating the role of carbon dioxide in intracellular neutralization during secretion of acid by the gastric mucosa (redrawn from Davenport, 1962.)

transport of water by oxyntic cells is so enormous that it could not be handled molecule by molecule by any known enzyme systems. The water must be moved in bulk, and probably flow osmotically as a result of the secretion of the hydrogen and chloride ions by the oxyntic cells."

Regulation of Gastric Secretion

Gastric secretion is regulated by both neural and humoral mechanisms. The gastric mucosa is innervated by both divisions of the autonomic nervous system. The parasympathetic (vagus) innervation provides the pathways for secretory stimuli to the gastric mucosa. Sympathetic pathways regulate gastric secretion indirectly, due to their control over vasomotor mechanisms and blood flow to the mucosa.

A number of humoral mechanisms also are involved in the regulation of gastric secretion. Examples include the release of *gastrin* from the gastric antrum which *stimulates* gastric secretion, and the release of *enterogastrone* from the mucosa of the upper small bowel which *inhibits* gastric secretions. Both neural and humoral mechanisms of regulating gastric secretion will be discussed in detail when the various phases of gastric secretion are considered.

Methods of Study

Studies of the regulation of gastric secretion offer some difficulty because gastric juice is secreted in small amounts in the fasting stomach, and that secretion is always contaminated with food during digestion. Most of our knowledge regarding the regulation of gastric secretion has resulted from the development of experimental surgical techniques to study separately the various neural and humoral mechanisms involved. Pavlov (1910) devised a method for collecting pure gastric juice from an animal that had been fed. This was accomplished by making an incompletely separated pouch of part of the stomach, now known as the *Pavlov pouch*. He divided the stomach by an incomplete incision into a larger and smaller portion. The mucous membrane was completely divided but an isthmus of the muscular wall was retained to connect the two parts and serve as a pathway for the vagus nerve fibers that supply the gastric glands. The cut edges of each part were then stitched together so as to restore the continuity of the main stomach wall and to make a closed cavity of the smaller portion or pouch, except for a small outlet that was brought out through the abdominal

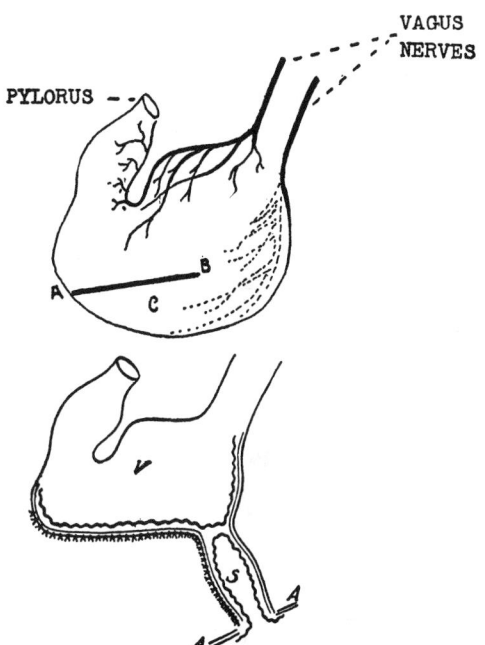

Fig. 57.10. The Pavlov pouch. Upper drawing shows line of incision to form a flap. C, corpus of stomach. Lower drawing shows the completed operation. S, pouch; the mucous membrane has been reflected to form a partition between the main cavity of the stomach and the miniature stomach. A, A, abdominal wall. (After Pavlov).

wall to provide drainage from the pouch (fig. 57.10). The Pavlov pouch, as originally devised, consisted of a part of the body and fundus of the stomach to produce a *vagally innervated* pouch. Numerous modifications of the Pavlov pouch have been devised; most of them designed to retain a greater portion of the vagus nerve supply to the pouch than did the original operation devised by Pavlov. A Pavlov pouch, or any of its modifications, responds to all the nervous and humoral stimuli that affect the main stomach, and makes possible the collection of pure gastric juice which can be then analyzed to determine the influence of various stimuli upon the volume and composition of the juice. Although a gastric pouch gives information regarding the secretory activity of only that particular portion of the stomach from which it is excised, pouches may be prepared from any of the regions of the stomach. Consequently, the method makes possible investigation of the function of any part of the gastric mucous membrane.

If a pouch is completely separated from the main stomach by dividing the isthmus between the two, leaving only the blood supply intact, it is known as a *Heidenhain pouch*. The Heiden-

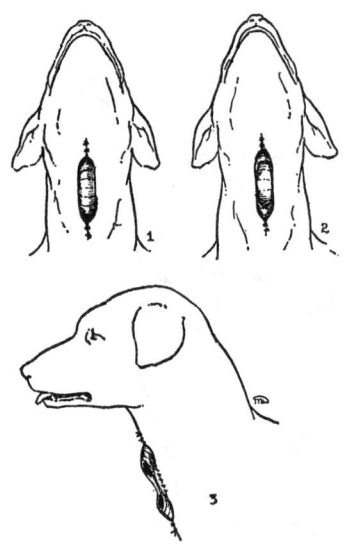

FIG. 57.11. A two-stage operation for making an esophageal fistula. 1. First stage, showing esophagus exteriorized. 2. Second stage, performed four or five days later, showing excision of elliptical segment of anterior esophageal wall. 3. Completed operation, lateral view. (After Dragstedt and associates.)

hain pouch is useful for investigating the secretion of a *vagally denervated* portion of the stomach. It continues to receive its sympathetic nerve supply through the periarterial nerve plexuses. If an attempt is made to cut the sympathetic fibers as well by stripping the arteries, the pouch is known as a *Bickel pouch* (Bickel and Katsch, 1912).

Farrell and Ivy (1926) prepared a *completely denervated pouch* of the stomach by *transplanting* a portion of the stomach of a dog into the subcutaneous tissue of the animal's abdominal wall. After the pouch had established a new blood supply, they severed its connections from the original nerve and blood supply of the stomach. Such a preparation responds only to humoral stimulation, and has been of fundamental importance in demonstrating the chemical nature of many of the stimuli which affect the stomach. "Pouches" have also been made of the entire stomach (the Fremont pouch, Pavlov, 1910) by cutting the stomach from the esophagus and duodenum and connecting these two organs by means of an end-to-end anastomosis. The cut end of the stomach is closed with sutures and a fistulous opening is made from some part of the stomach through the abdominal wall.

Another of Pavlov's devices for the study of the regulation of gastric secretion was esophagostomy. In this operation, the esophagus is divided

by a transverse incision and the cut ends are brought to the outside through a wound in the neck (fig. 57.11). After healing, all the food which the animal eats escapes from the lower end of the upper segment of the esophagus, and the animal can be fed by placing food in the lower segment through its exposed upper end. The maneuver of feeding such an animal with the consequent loss of food is known as "sham" feeding. The animal is able to experience all the sensations of eating without getting any food into the stomach. Gastric juice is collected from the stomach by means of a gastric cannula.

The surgical techniques described above have contributed greatly to our knowledge and understanding of the various factors that regulate gastric secretion. Such studies have been done more often in dogs than other experimental animals and the knowledge so obtained has been applied to man. It should be pointed out that dogs tend to secrete gastric juice only intermittently. Pavlov observed in the dog that except for the secretion of some alkaline mucus, the gastric glands, in the absence of food or psychic influences, remained at rest. These observations were confirmed by Babkin. In man, gastric juice is secreted continuously in fairly large amounts. This observation, however, does not necessarily indicate a fundamental difference between the activities of the gastric glands of the human and canine stomach. The shorter intervals between meals and psychic influences, which are impossible to eliminate in the case of the human subject, are probably responsible for the continuous apparently spontaneous secretion. Gastric secretion in man is maintained even during sleep.

In the human, gastric juice can be collected through a stomach tube. The secretion may be stimulated by means of a test meal or by use of one of the gastric secretagogues, such as histamine. Methods of studying gastric secretion in man will be taken up in detail later. Intubation techniques can also be used in unoperated animals, but it is simpler and just as satisfactory for most purposes, to prepare the animal with a gastric fistula in such a way as to avoid the use of a stomach tube.

Phases of Gastric Secretion

It is convenient when discussing the gastric secretory response of an animal or man to a meal, to divide the total response into different phases. By dividing the secretory response into *cephalic, gastric* and *intestinal* phases, the inter-relation-

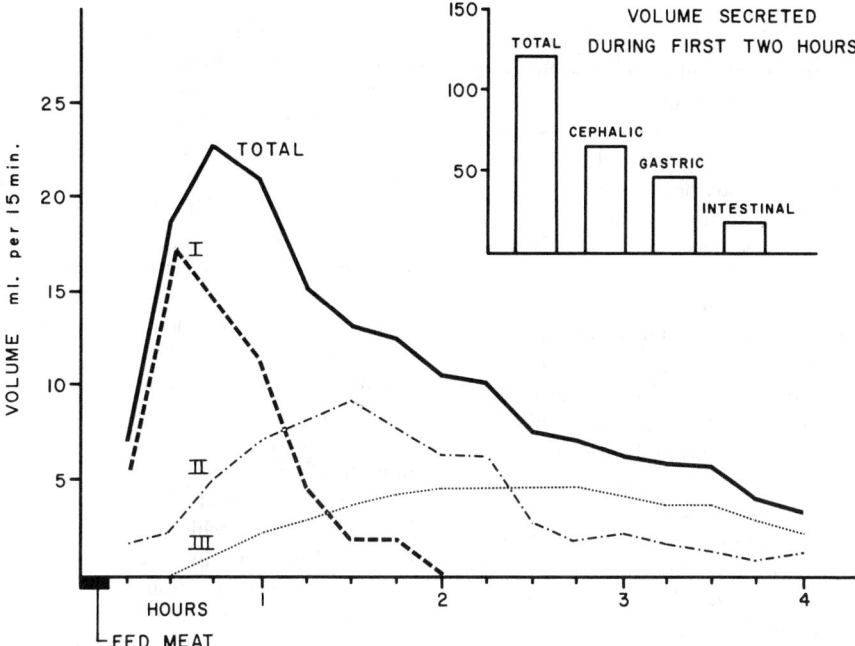

Fig. 57.12. Reconstructed curves to show the approximate distribution between the several phases of gastric secretion in the dog after a meal of 300 gm. of meat. 1. Cephalic or initial reflex phase; 2. gastric or pyloric phase; 3. intestinal phase (redrawn from Thomas and Friedman, 1951.)

ships of the various regulatory mechanisms of stimulation and inhibition can be defined more precisely. The cephalic, gastric and intestinal phases of gastric secretion in the dog have been studied extensively. The volume of gastric secretion resulting from these different phases in the dog is illustrated in fig. 57.12. In man, gastric secretion tends to be continuous. For this reason, a fourth phase of gastric secretion, the *interdigestive* phase, is recognized. An estimate of the volume of gastric secretion of the various phases in man is shown in table 57.1.

CEPHALIC PHASE

Upon eating a meal, gastric secretion is initiated prior to the food arriving in the stomach by afferent impulses arising in the head (thus the term cephalic) which converge on the vagus nucleus, and efferent stimuli are sent to the gastric mucosa via the vagi. The cephalic, or *initial reflex phase*, of gastric secretion results from the sight, smell, or taste of food, or from the act of eating and is prevented by section of the vagus nerves. If the secretion results from the sight or smell of food without food making actual contact with the mouth, it is referred to as *psychic* secretion. Pavlov referred to the secretion produced during the initial reflex phase as "appetite juice."

The fact that there can be an abundant secre-

TABLE 57.1

Volume of different phases of gastric secretion in man

Period or Phase	Amount (cc.)
Interdigestive.........	30–60 cc./hr.
Cephalic..............	50–150 cc./20 min.
Gastric...............	225–350 cc./5 hr.
Intestinal.............	200–300 cc./5 hr.

From Ivy, Grossman and Bachrach in *Peptic Ulcer*, The Blakiston Company, Philadelphia, 1950, p. 32.

tion of gastric juice even though there is no food in the stomach is readily demonstrated by means of sham feeding. When an animal provided with an esophagostomy is sham-fed, secretion of gastric juice begins within 5 min. and may continue for as long as 1½ hr. If the vagus nerves have been previously cut, sham feeding has no effect on gastric secretion, proving that secretion in this instance is the result of reflexes for which the vagus nerve serves as the efferent pathway. Pavlov demonstrated that gastric juice collected from an animal that was sham fed contained a very high concentration of both hydrochloric acid and pepsin. A similar type of gastric juice is secreted by the empty stomach on electrical stimulation of the vagus nerves.

Psychic Secretion in Man

In man, the cephalic phase causes the secretion of from 50 to 150 ml. of gastric juice within 20 min. Richet (1878) observed that in a subject who had suffered esophageal stricture, and into whose stomach an artificial opening (fistula) had been made for feeding purposes, the secretion of gastric juice occurred when food was taken into the mouth. Carlson conducted more extensive studies upon a subject who had had a similar operation performed because of an obstructed esophagus resulting from the ingestion of a corrosive in childhood. This subject, therefore, was already prepared, like Pavlov's dogs, for sham feeding, the only difference being that there was no opening in the neck, it being necessary for the subject to spit out the food after chewing it. All of the findings of Pavlov were, in the main, confirmed in Carlson's subject. The influence of appetite or the desire for food in particular was evident. The subject especially enjoyed desserts and fruits. The curve of gastric secretion showed the most pronounced rise when sweets or fruits, such as oranges, were chewed. Carlson noted, however, that the response to sham feeding in his subject did not last as long as Pavlov had observed in his dogs. When the subject was fed in the laboratory, there was no evidence that the sight or smell of food (conditioned stimulus) evoked a response. However, when the subject was sent from the laboratory to select his meal from a nearby cafeteria, there was a definite response to the sight and smell of food. Several other observers have reported the existence of definite conditioned reflexes for gastric secretion in man.

The psychic effect upon gastric secretion has been demonstrated also by Bennett and Venables (1920), upon subjects during hypnosis. A suggestion made to the subject that he was eating a savory food resulted in the secretion of gastric juice. The mere suggestion of nauseating substances inhibited secretion (see below). In experiments upon medical students, Hawk and his associates (1920) showed that a meal which had a disgusting appearance and a foul smell (indole was scattered over a dirty tablecloth) retarded digestion.

Janowitz and his colleagues have made some interesting observations in a female subject who had a complete stenosis of the esophagus following a lye stricture and had to have a gastrostomy for feeding purposes. They studied the effects of various types of meals on the cephalic phase of gastric secretion and found that an unappetizing meal consisting of cereal gruel evoked essentially no response, whereas a meal selected by the subject evoked a high secretory response. The routine hospital ward diet evoked an intermediate response (fig. 57.13). The latent period of the cephalic phase response was less than 5 min. The duration of the response ranged from 30 to 120 min. following cessation of sham feeding and varied with the type of meal.

The application of these experimental results to dietetics is obvious. Foods agreeably flavored and attractive in appearance, impressions received from a meal prepared in a pleasing way and, probably, sensations aroused by the surroundings but not directly concerned with the food itself, all have an effect upon gastric secretion. The impulse which guides the gourmet is sounder physiologically than that which impels the glutton. The question of calories and the relative digestibilities of the various foodstuffs should not be allowed to obscure the psychic element entirely in these matters for the "delights of the table" have true digestive value. These facts are expressed in the words of Pavlov, "Appetite spells gastric juice" or in the hospitable words of Macbeth "Now good digestion wait on appetite and health on both." Good gastronomical custom seems guided by this truth, for it has decreed that the meal shall begin and end with the more strongly flavored and appetizing dishes.

GASTRIC PHASE

Pavlov observed that if food were placed in the stomach without allowing the animal to smell or taste it, there was a secretion of gastric juice beginning about 15 min. after the food has been introduced; usually this required that the animal be fed through a gastric fistula while asleep. Pavlov considered this to be the gastric phase of gastric secretion. Babkin (1950) described gastric secretion of this type as the second, or *chemical phase* of secretion. Edkins, (1906) following the example of Bayless and Starling (who discovered secretin), suggested that a similar excitant for gastric secretion might be produced by contact of food with the gastric mucosa. Extracts of the pyloric mucous membrane prepared by Edkins did indeed stimulate secretion of gastric juice. He proposed that the stimulating substance be known as *gastrin*. With the discovery of gastrin, the gastric phase of gastric secretion was considered for many years to have only a humoral mechanism. Recent evidence indicates the gastric

AVERAGE VOLUME RESPONSE TO SHAM FEEDING IN GASTRIC FISTULA SUBJECT

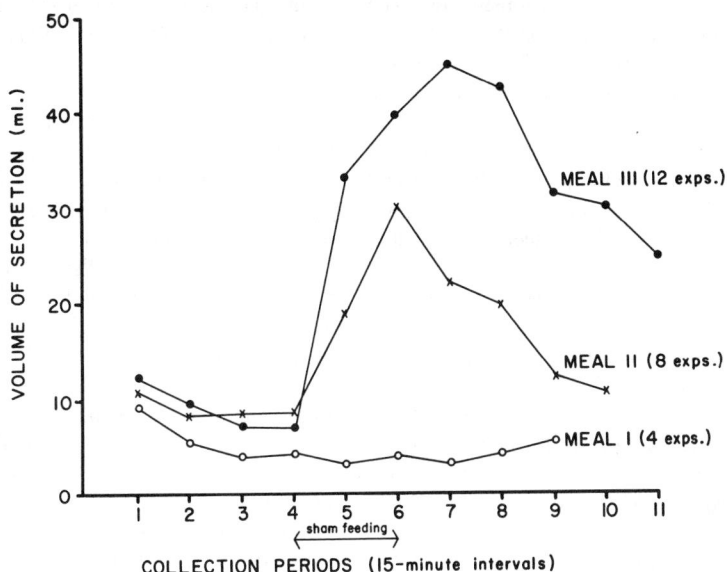

FIG. 57.13. Illustrating the volume response to sham feeding of different types of meals to a patient with a gastric fistula. Meal I consisted of cereal gruel; meal II was a routine hospital ward diet; meal III consisted of foods selected by the subject. (Redrawn from Janowitz et al., Gastroenterology, 1950, **16**, 106.)

phase is under both neural and humoral control (Grossman, 1963).

Gastrin was long believed to be a non-specific tissue extract and to owe its activity to histamine (Sacks et al., 1932), a common constituent of such extracts, but recent work has shown that gastrin is a true hormone. It is elaborated by the pyloric mucous membrane of the stomach and is absorbed and carried in the blood to the gastric glands, stimulating them to secrete (Komarov, 1942). The evidence on this point consists of the fact that extracts have been prepared in a number of laboratories, both in America and in Europe, which stimulate gastric secretion but do not depress blood pressure as histamine does. Furthermore, the activity of such a preparation is not destroyed by histaminase, an enzyme which inactivates histamine. Recently, Gregory and Tracy (1964) have reported the isolation of two gastrins from the hog antral mucosa that are almost identical peptides and have the same amino-acid constitution: aspartic acid (1), glutamic acid (6), glycine (2), alanine (1), methionine (2), tryptophane (2), tyrosine (1), proline (1), and phenylalanine (1). The calculated molecular weight for each gastrin is 2114. Both gastrins are powerful stimulants of acid secretion in dog

and man. It is not known whether either of these gastrins are the same as the antral hormone that is released into the circulation, or whether one is formed from the other during the extraction process. Gastrin-like activity is chiefly obtained from the pyloric portion of the stomach and in lesser amounts from the duodenum and upper small bowel of man (Lai, 1964). None is obtained from the fundus of the body of the stomach or the pancreas, or in significant amounts from other tissues.

The controversy that existed over the nature of gastrin is reminiscent of the efforts of Popileski during the early part of the century to prove that secretin was a non-specific tissue extract. He did, in fact, come to the conclusion that secretin was identical with histamine. Although erroneous on this point, his efforts inadvertently led to the discovery of the gastric secretagogue-action of histamine, an observation that enjoyed great service in physiology and the practice of medicine (Popileski, 1920).

Secretion formed by pure gastric stimulation, excluding the nerves, contains less pepsin than that secreted during the initial reflex phase and resembles the secretion produced in response to histamine. Indeed, the action on gastric glands of the most highly purified preparations of gastrin, so closely resembles the action of histamine as to suggest a close relationship between the two substances. Babkin (1938, 1950) has suggested that histamine is liberated in the vicinity of the parietal cells by vagus stimulation. Linde (1950) has gone even further and concluded, on the basis of his experiments with an antihistamine, that gastrin, as well as vagal stimulation, acts by liberating histamine. According to this concept, both acetylcholine and gastrin possess the capacity to liberate histamine in the vicinity of the parietal cell, the histamine then acting as a stimulus to secretion of water and acid. Whether or not this is the correct explanation, the work of Ivy and his co-workers leaves little doubt that histamine, or something very similar to it, is involved in some way in the secretion of hydrochloric acid by the stomach (Ivy and Schayer, 1957; Schayer and Ivy, 1957, 1958).

The effective stimulus for the normal gastric phase of gastric secretion is the presence of food in the antrum. In addition to the chemical substances in the food, such as meat extractives, products of protein digestions and soaps, which excite gastric secretion when present in the antrum, mechanical stimulation of the pyloric portion is also a highly effective stimulus. Simple distention with a balloon causes release of gastrin, as does the presence of solid objects such as bone chips or even brass or steel shavings. It is probable that the harmful effects of a coarse diet in peptic ulcer disease is caused more by the mechanical stimulation of the antrum by indigestible food particles than by its irritation of the ulcer surface itself.

Considerable evidence has accumulated in recent years indicating that the gastric phase of gastric secretion is not a pure chemical phase, but that its full functioning is dependent in some way upon the nervous system. Uvnas (1942) and Linde (1950) in Sweden, have brought forward evidence suggesting that efficient functioning of the reflex phase is dependent to some extent on the presence of gastrin. Different investigators have suggested that: (1) gastrin is released by stimulation of the vagus nerves; (2) that gastrin is necessary for the secretory effect of the vagus nerves on the gastric glands; (3) that a certain amount of vagal activity is necessary for the secretory effect of gastrin on the gastric glands; and (4) that gastrin is released by local reflex mechanism involving the presence of cholinergic nerve endings in the antral mucosa.

Only the first and last statements are supported by enough experimental evidence to be accepted as fact (Robertson et al., 1950; Gregory and Ivy, 1941; Zeljony and Savich, 1911). Thomas (1952) after reviewing the experimental evidence came to the following conclusions:

(1) Gastrin is released from the pyloric mucosa by local mechanical and chemical stimuli acting through a cholinergic nervous mechanism that probably comprises Meissner's plexus and its local and central connections.

(2) Stimulation of the vagi facilitates the nervous mechanism involved in the release of gastrin and may cause the release of some gastrin in the absence of specific local stimuli.

(3) Neither gastrin alone, nor vagal stimulation alone, can cause maximal stimulation of the gastric glands to secrete hydrochloric acid. Abundant secretion is obtainable only when nervous and hormonal stimuli act simultaneously.

These considerations help to elucidate the rationale for use of the operations of vagotomy, on the one hand, and of subtotal gastric resection on the other. If the nervous and hormonal mechanisms of stimulation were independent of each other, we should expect that cutting the vagus nerves would influence only the initial reflex phase of gastric secretion and leave the gastric phase in full effect. In reality, however, all phases of gastric secretion are profoundly depressed by vagotomy, and in some patients permanent achlorhydria has been reported. Likewise, resection of the antrum, or subtotal gastric resection, theoretically should affect only the gastric phase. Experience indicates however, that the cephalic phase too, is influenced profoundly.

As originally noted by Pavlov and subsequently confirmed by many investigators (Wilhelmj et al., 1936; Dragstedt et al., 1951; Oberhelman et al., 1952), the pyloric mucosa not only has the capacity to stimulate gastric secretion but also to inhibit it. Pavlov described the phenomenon as follows: "with the same dogs, we have also discovered a new form of autoregulation on the part of the stomach, which concerns the secretion of hydrochloric acid. It appears that acid prevents the further secretion of gastric juice when it has accumulated in any considerable quantity within the cavity of the organ." Dragstedt showed that hydrochloric acid in the stomach has to be in contact with the pyloric mucosa in order to produce inhibition. Whether it releases an inhibitory hormone or merely stops production of gastrin by the pyloric mucosa is still unknown. Acid in the duodenum also inhibits gastric secretion (Wilhelmj et al., 1934; Uvnas et al., 1956) provided the pH of the duodenal contents is lower than 2.5 or below (Pincus et al., 1942).

INTESTINAL PHASE

In Pavlov's laboratory it was observed that the presence of certain food substances in the small intestine also stimulated gastric secretion. This so-called intestinal phase has been extensively investigated by Babkin (1928, 1950) and his co-workers and others. The latent period of the intestinal phase is 2 to 3 hr. but once secretion is initiated, it may last for 8 to 10 hr. The following substances have been observed to excite gastric secretion when placed in the small intestine: water, extractive substances of meat, products of protein digestion, (for example, peptone and amino acids), milk, alcohol, histamine, saponin, adrenalin, $\frac{1}{10}$th normal hydrochloric acid, 10 per cent glycerin solution, and magnesium sulfate. The intestinal phase is characterized by less secretory activity than either the cephalic or gastric phases and for this reason, the interpretation of results of studies of the intestinal phase have been more difficult.

Experiments on the intestinal phase of gastric secretion have been conducted primarily on animals in the fasting state with the stomach empty. Because of the long duration of the intestinal phase of gastric secretion from previous feedings, it is customary to fast the animal (dog) at least 24 hr. The results obtained might have been otherwise had the intestinal phase been permitted to follow the cephalic and gastric phases as in the intact situation. The known tendency of stimuli of different sorts to act synergistically in the gastrointestinal tract suggests, but does not prove, that the stimuli normally causing an intestinal phase may be much more effective in the presence of the residual stimuli of the cephalic and gastric phases. Other factors are also important. For example, in the experiments of Beamer et al. (1944), introduction of a peptone solution into the intestine caused no gastric secretion unless bile was present. In the presence of bile, flow of gastric juice commenced after a latent period of about 2 hr. The long latent period is also characteristic of the intestinal phase of gastric secretion described by Webster and Armour (1932).

The cause of the intestinal phase is unknown, except that it is due to chemical stimuli. The evidence on this point was obtained ingeniously by Gregory and Ivy (1941). They used a denerv-ated pouch of the type described by Farrell and Ivy. This completely denervated gastric pouch secreted when food was placed in the intestine, proving that it was secreting in response to some chemical substance circulating in the blood. The nature of the stimulus is unknown but may be a hormone or it may be secretagogues absorbed with the food from the intestine, as suggested by Babkin (1950).

Perhaps one reason for the somewhat erratic behaviour of the intestinal phase of gastric secretion is the ease with which inhibition of secretion may be induced by placing certain substances in the intestine. The inhibitory effect of acid has already been mentioned, although acid in certain concentrations may stimulate gastric secretion, if the intestinal pH is lowered to 2.5 or below, it acts as an inhibitor. The most potent inhibitor of gastric secretion is fat in the intestine. Fat in the stomach is without inhibitory effects, but as soon as it passes the pylorus, gastric secretion begins to diminish and if the quantity of fat is large, it may cease altogether. The inhibition lasts as long as the fat remains in the intestine, but after the fat is absorbed, the inhibition is followed by a pronounced increase in gastric secretion, the so-called rebound phase of fat inhibition. The inhibition and subsequent stimulation of secretion of fat is known as the *biphasic* effect of fat. The stage of increased secretion which follows the inhibition is believed to be due to release of gastrin by the soaps which have regurgitated into the stomach from the intestine during digestion of the fat. Were it not for the rebound phase, fat would be a most successful substance for controlling gastric secretion; even so, it can be used successfully if given in small amounts at frequent intervals over a long period of time. The use of cream in this way is the basis of one form of treatment of peptic ulcer.

Enterogastrone: The mechanism of inhibition of gastric secretion by fat was elucidated by Lim (1933; see also Kosaka and Lim, 1930), who were able to prepare an extract of the intestinal mucosa which previously had been stimulated by the presence of fat. When injected intravenously this intestinal extract effected inhibition of gastric secretion. Kosaka and Lim named the inhibitory substance "enterogastrone." Chemical and physiological characterization of enterogastrone has been pursued primarily by Ivy and his students, who in addition discovered the humoral mechanism by which fat in the lumen of the stomach reduces gastric *motility* (Farrell and Ivy, 1926; see also Ivy and Gray, 1937).

Enterogastrone has never been obtained in pure form, hence its chemical composition is unknown. Since motility and secretion are differentially affected, in proportions that vary with the preparation, it is probable that more than one substance is involved. Enterogastrone, or a derivative thereof, is excreted in the urine and is given the name *urogastrone*.

INTERDIGESTIVE PHASE

Even after prolonged fasts, hydrochloric acid is found in the gastric juice of man as well as in that of the dog. Both Pavlov and Babkin believed that hydrochloric acid was not secreted in the gastric juice during the interdigestive period. When acid was detected in gastric juice of the dog after a prolonged fast, it was thought to result from either swallowing of saliva, regurgitation of duodenal juices, or extraneous stimuli such as the sight or smell of food. In man, Hoelzel (1926) found variable amounts of hydrochloric acid in gastric juice throughout a fast period of 40 days. In both man and dog, the interdigestive secretion of HCl apparently occurs in an intermittent or periodic fashion. The causes of such secretion are not known, but mechanisms involved apparently include both humoral and neural stimuli. A subcutaneous autotransplanted gastric pouch in a dog, devoid of all original extrinsic nerve and vascular supply, during a fast will secrete acid intermittently. This indicates that the stimuli for secretion must be humoral in nature. The role of the neural pathways is suggested by the fact that following vagotomy in man, interdigestive secretion of hydrochloric acid is inhibited but not completely abolished. With intact vagal innervation, conditioned reflexes in both man and the dog undoubtedly play a part. In addition, in man, psychic stimulation is also probably important.

The Normal Course of Gastric Secretion

With the discussion of the various phases of gastric secretion as background, we may now consider the sequence of events affecting the secretion of gastric juice following an "average" meal. First, there is the sight and smell and the taste of food which, if agreeable, and if the individual has an appetite, will initiate the psychic or cephalic phase of gastric secretion. This phase is augmented when the food is actually chewed and swallowed. The first juice secreted has powerful digestive action, particularly upon the protein constituents of the food and releases from the food chemical excitants for the second, or chemical, phase of secretion. These, along with the mechanical action of such food particles as enter the pyloric antrum, cause the release of gastrin. This augments and prolongs the secretion due to the cephalic phase and initiates the gastric phase. The gastric phase of secretion continues as long as food remains in the stomach. As soon as the stomach is empty and the buffering substances present during digestion are no longer available, the pH of the antrum or the duodenum falls to a point at which the inhibitory effect of acid becomes evident and that period of gastric secretion is brought to an end. During the gastric phase of secretion, some chyme enters the small intestine where, after a variable latent period of one to two hr., it initiates the intestinal phase of gastric secretion. This phase probably accounts for less than 20 per cent of the total acid secreted by the stomach. In duration, however, the intestinal phase exceeds the other phases, in fact, it may persist for as long as five hours. Following the completion of the intestinal phase, the interdigestive phase occurs. During the interdigestive phase, gastric secretion of minimal amount occurs intermittently.

Effects of Various Chemicals and Drugs on Gastric Secretions

Numerous chemical agents and various drugs are known to affect gastric secretion. In general, agents which have a parasympathomimetic action stimulate gastric secretion and those with a parasympatholytic action suppress gastric secretion. Pharmacological agents that produce either stimulation or inhibition of the sympathetic nervous system have little direct effect on gastric secretion but may influence secretion due to their effects on blood flow to the stomach. Various preparations of *bitters* are without any appreciable effect upon secretion unless they contain alcohol. *Condiments* have little direct effect but act indirectly by adding flavor to the food, stimulating the taste buds, and thus encouraging psychic secretion. Liver extract, meat, products of protein digestion (especially peptone), and vegetable extracts are generally powerful excitants of the gastric glands—an action which they owe to the presence of secretagogues. These secretagogues cause the liberation of gastrin from the antrum and thus potentiate the gastric phase of gastric secretion.

SECRETORY STIMULANTS

Histamine is one of the most powerful stimulants of gastric secretion. Even endogenous histamine liberated within the body, e.g., in dermographism, or even by the immersion of the hand in cold water at a temperature of 10° C., causes a detectable gastric secretory response within 15 min. Administration of exogenous histamine is commonly used in gastric analysis, which will be discussed in detail later. Anti-histamine agents, such as neoantergen and benadryl, do not inhibit gastric secretion evoked by histamine. Histamine is effective when administered subcutaneously in very small doses. Even a few tenths of a mg. (0.2 to 0.3 mg. of histamine base) will cause a copious secretion in dogs or man. A similar dose given rapidly intravenously has little effect on gastric secretion. If given very slowly, over a period of an hour, intravenous histamine is as effective as subcutaneous histamine in stimulating gastric secretion. It is thought that histamine acts directly on the

parietal cell to stimulate secretion of acid. Large amounts of histamine are found in the gastric mucosa, and during active secretion histamine can be detected in low concentrations in the gastric juice and the urine. Histaminase, an enzyme that destroys histamine, is not found in the gastric mucosa.

The effects of histamine on gastric secretion have been studied extensively. There is a specific dose-response relationship, as illustrated by Code and associates in fig. 57.14. By increasing the dose of histamine in a step-like manner, the parietal cells can be stimulated to produce a "maximal secretory response." The latter is not equivalent to the *secretory capacity* of the stomach, for it has been shown that through the administration of a parasympathomimetic drug such as acetyl-beta-methyl-choline chloride (Mecholyl), and sham feeding, it is possible to

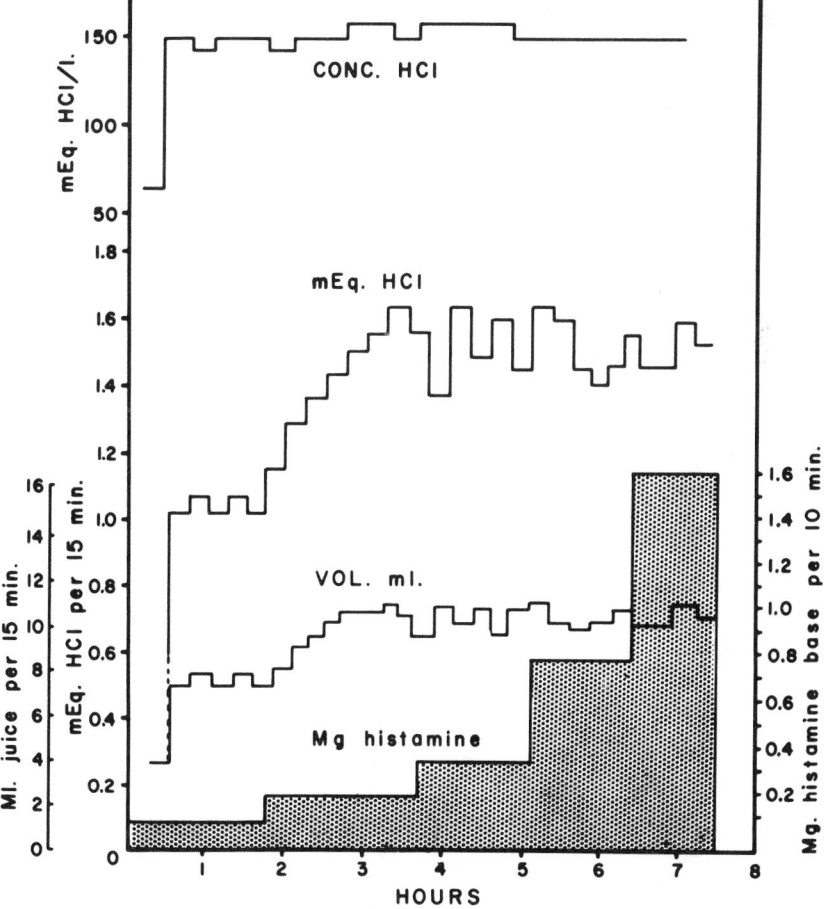

FIG. 57.14. Illustrating the dose-response relationship of a Heidenhain pouch to histamine given subcutaneously every 10 min. Note that after a dose of 0.4 mg. of histamine base per 10 min. was reached, no further increase in gastric secretion occurred, even with increasing amounts of histamine administration. (Redrawn from Code et al., Gastroenterology. 1949, **13**, 576.)

stimulate secretion beyond the level achieved by prior histamine administration (Marks et al., 1960). Even so, the maximal secretory response to histamine has been shown to correlate well with the total number of parietal cells in the gastric mucosa. Cox (1952) has attempted to calculate the number of parietal cells in the gastric mucosa on the basis of sampling representative fields using human autopsy material. Accordingly, the average size of the parietal cell population is 1.18 billion in the adult male and 0.84 billion in the adult female. In 15 patients with duodenal ulcer the average number of parietal cells was 1.8 billion (1.9 billion for 11 males and 1.52 billion for 4 females). In 13 cases of gastric ulcer (sex not stated), the average number of parietal cells was 0.8 billion. Card and Marks (1960) studied patients before and after partial gastrectomy for duodenal ulcer by measuring the maximal secretory response to histamine and counting the number of parietal cells in the portion of the stomach that was resected. When the reduction in secretory response after partial gastrectomy was compared to the estimated number of parietal cells in the resected portion of the stomach, a good correlation was found and indicated that one billion parietal cells can secrete, on the average, 25 mEq HCl per hour (fig. 57.15). Marks and his associates (1960) have studied the maximal secretory response to histamine in the dog, and compared this to the "parietal cell mass." A linear relationship was

demonstrated. These investigators found that, in the dog, one billion parietal cells, when responding maximally to histamine, secreted on the average 9.8 mEq HCl/30 min.

Histalog, an analog of histamine, (3-beta-aminoethylpyrazol) is also a powerful gastric secretory stimulant. It is frequently used in place of histamine for gastric analysis, as histalog does not produce the undesirable side effects caused by histamine.

Caffein and *alcohol* are strong secretory stimulants. The latter has a pronounced secretagogue action causing the secretion of a juice of high acidity and rich in mucin. It is possible that alcohol exerts its secretory action through the liberation of histamine, for it has been shown that the histamine output of the perfused lung of the guinea pig is increased by the addition of alcohol (2 to 6 per cent) to the perfusion fluid.

Parasympathomimetic agents such as acetylcholine (usually), Mecholyl (acetyl-beta-methylchlorine-chloride), pilocarpine and nicotine are secretory stimulants.

There is a widespread clinical impression that smoking tobacco increases gastric secretion and gastric acidity. Conflicting results have been reported by equally competent investigators, but the available evidence suggests that smoking one or two cigarettes increases gastric acidity in a majority of persons, whereas smoking several cigarettes or smoking for a long time depresses gastric secretion. Such a result would be in accord

THE RELATIONSHIP BETWEEN THE MAXIMUM ACID OUTPUT AND THE PARIETAL CELL MASS

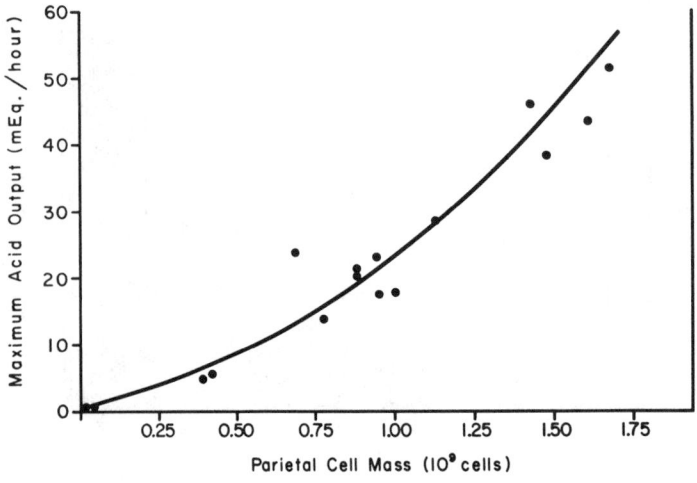

Fig. 57.15. The relationship between the "maximum acid output" and the parietal cell mass calculated for the resected portion of each of 17 human stomachs. The figure indicates that one billion parietal cells can produce approximately 25 mEq of HCl/hour. (Redrawn from Card and Marks, Clinical Science, 1960, **19**, 156.)

with the known fact that nicotine in small doses stimulates autonomic ganglia whereas larger doses causes depression.

SECRETORY DEPRESSANTS

Alkalis of the absorbable type administered in large doses, in general exert a depressing effect upon the secretion of gastric juice. Sodium bicarbonate, for instance, a favorite ingredient of digestive mixtures, was investigated by Pavlov in dogs and found to be definitely inhibitory. This observation has been confirmed by Farrell (1928). The inhibitory effect does not occur unless the dose is excessive. When administered repeatedly in small doses, sodium bicarbonate may augment gastric secretion (Boyd, 1925). This seems to be true also of other absorbable alkalis; massive single doses suppress, whereas small repeated dose tend to augment the flow of gastric juice. The inhibitory effect of large doses of alkali does not persist after their discontinuance; on the contrary, hypersecretion not uncommonly follows ("acid rebound"). The value of alkalis in gastric disorders depends chiefly, however, upon their antacid properties, i.e., upon their ability to neutralize or buffer the acidity of the gastric contents rather than to depress secretion. For this purpose, the non-absorbable alkalis, such as aluminum hydroxide and magnesium silicate are preferable to such substances as sodium bicarbonate and calcium carbonate which can be absorbed from the intestine. In the doses necessary to exert an appreciable effect on gastric acidity, soluble alkalis can cause profound changes in the acid-base balance of the body and have been known to produce severe alkalosis. The insoluble antacids do not affect the acid-base balance of the body and because of their slower and more prolonged action, they are less likely to cause an acid-rebound in the stomach. Incidentally, the acid rebound effect now is believed to be due to the temporary absence of the inhibitory effects of acid in the antrum following neutralization of the gastric contents by the alkali.

Acids depress gastric secretion. Introduction into the stomach of a one per cent solution of hydrochloric acid causes the complete inhibition of gastric secretion. Regarding the mechanism for this inhibition it has been thought that acidification of the gastric antrum either inhibits the release of gastrin from the antrum or causes the liberation of an inhibitory humoral substance from the antrum. Acid introduced into the small intestine will also exert an inhibitory effect upon gastric secretion. When introduced into the dog's duodenum, HCl will suppress secretory activity within a Pavlov pouch even after the latter had been stimulated by a meat meal.

Belladonna or its alkaloids, *atropine* and *hyoscine*, and *hyoscyamus* or its alkaloid *hyoscyamine*, are secretory depressants. These agents are capable of abolishing the cephalic phase of gastric secretion through their action on the vagus nerves. Atropine reduces but does not suppress secretion due to histamine, alcohol or caffeine.

Atropine, although it depresses gastric secretion, is not recommended for control of gastric acidity because of its severe side effects, such as acceleration of the heart, dilatation of the pupil, paralysis of accommodation, etc.

Certain *synthetic anticholinergic agents* which inhibit gastric secretion with minimal side effects are available. These agents are commonly used in the control of gastric acidity in patients with duodenal ulcer. Many of these agents have a greater inhibitory action than atropine on gastric secretion and motility, and have less effect on other peripheral structures than atropine does; so that their use for regulation of gastric secretion becomes feasible. In general, these parasympatholytic drugs can be divided into *tertiary* and *quaternary* amines. The tertiary amines produce few side effects but usually are not too potent as secretory inhibitors. The quaternary amines, on the other hand, are potent secretory inhibitors, and when given in adequate therapeutic doses, effectively suppress gastric secretion. Such agents are particularly valuable in controlling the cephalic and interdigestive phases of gastric secretion. Mild side effects such as dryness of the mouth, blurring of vision, or slowing of the urinary stream are not uncommon, however.

Influence of Vitamins and Hormones on Gastric Secretion

VITAMINS

Little is known of the effect of vitamins or vitamin deficiency on gastric secretion. Achlorhydria has been observed in severe thiamine deficiency (beri-beri). It has been claimed that achlorhydria can be cured by administration of vitamin A (Földes and Vajda, 1951; Schödt, 1936). Dyer and Roe (1941) found that acute or chronic vitamin A deficiency had no effect on the ability of rats to secrete hydrochloric acid or mucin in their gastric juice when the amount of secretion was expressed in terms of body weight.

Babkin and his associates (1940) found that vitamin D in excessive doses depressed gastric secretion. Apparently, this was due to the considerable increase in blood calcium concentration resulting from administration of the vitamin. Only the reflex phase of secretion was affected by the hypercalcemia in their experiments. Other studies on the effects of the blood calcium level on gastric secretion indicate that the normal blood calcium level of 10 mg. per cent is optimum for secretion of gastric juice. Any considerable change in this level, whether in the direction of increase or a decrease, depresses gastric secretion.

HORMONES

The effect of changes in blood calcium on gastric secretion has already been mentioned. These changes can be induced by administration of *Parathormone* as well as by administration of vitamin D, and with the same results. *Hypophysectomy* causes characteristic changes in the chief cells of the gastric glands, consisting of a decrease in the size of the nucleus, and loss of most of the pepsinogen granules. Secretion of hydrochloric acid is also reduced by hypophysectomy in rats (Jones and Harkins, 1958). *Adrenalectomy* also causes involution of the zymogen cells and reduction of pepsin in the gastric secretion (Baker and Abrams, 1954). Gastric acidity is diminished following adrenalectomy; indeed in human subjects, adrenalectomy profoundly reduces the level of gastric secretion (Gray, 1958).

Adrenalin, noradrenalin and *pituitrin* do not influence gastric secretion directly. However, by reducing blood flow through their vasoconstrictive action, these hormones limit the secretory capacity of the stomach.

Considerable interest has been aroused in stimulation of gastric secretion by *adrenocorticotrophic hormone* (*ACTH*), the adrenal steroids, and the various synthetics that stimulate the action of the steroids. Gray and his associates (1955) have noted particularly an increase in the output of *uropepsin* in circumstances in which it may be assumed that adrenal cortical activity is increased, either through natural stimuli such as are involved in stress or through the administration of ACTH, the steroids themselves or their synthetic counterparts. Gray and others have also reported an increase in gastric acid secretion under similar circumstances, but negative results have also been reported. Thus, although the evidence is conflicting, it appears that when given in sufficiently large doses over a considera-

ble period of time, the corticords promote hydrochloric acid and pepsin secretion and this may aggravate duodenal ulcer disease.

Serotonin is a substance, possibly a hormone, secreted by certain enterochromaffin cells found principally in the intestinal mucosa, which greatly augments intestinal motility when given intravenously. Among its numerous physiological actions is the inhibition of gastric secretion, particularly that activated reflexly or by cholinergic drugs. The effect of serotonin is of interest in connection with the action of *reserpine*, which has been used as a tranquilizer and in the treatment of high blood pressure. Although therapeutic doses of reserpine are said not to influence gastric secretion, acid production by the stomach is increased under the prolonged influence of high levels of reserpine. The suggestion that reserpine's effect on gastric secretion is mediated through serotonin is doubtful since serotonin inhibits gastric secretion. It is more likely that some other factor is operative in the reserpinized subject (Haverback et al., 1957).

Insulin may be considered with the hormones, although its effect on gastric secretion is not strictly a hormonal influence on the stomach. Insulin, in a dosage sufficient to lower the blood sugar to about 50 mg. per cent, has an effect on the gastric glands similar to that of stimulation of the vagus nerves; namely that the output of acid and pepsin is increased. By an ill-understood mechanism, vagal stimulation also causes hypoglycemia. Hypoglycemia activates sympathetic as well as parasympathetic centers. Insulin convulsions are merely a further manifestation of this general excitatory effect of hypoglycemia of rapid onset. Release of gastrin by the pyloric antrum may be reduced by insulin, as well as by vagal excitation, both of which are associated with hypoglycemia.

Our understanding of the action of insulin on gastric secretion is complicated by observations which indicate that the hormone exerts an inhibitory effect in addition to the excitatory influence just described. The duration of the inhibitory influence is brief (15 to 30 min.) in man, but as long as one hour in dogs. The inhibitory effect of insulin has been demonstrated during intravenous glucose administration, thus ruling out hypoglycemic mediation. Insulin inhibition effectively controls gastric secretion induced by vigorous histamine stimulation.

Since the effect of insulin on gastric secretion is dependent upon the integrity of the vagus nerves, the "insulin test" has been used as a means of determining the completeness of therapeutic vagotomy in human subjects (Hollander, 1946). A positive insulin test is proof of the presence of intact vagus fibers but a negative result is less conclusive, since some subjects with intact vagi fail to secrete in response to insulin. The test has, nevertheless, been of great value in the surgical control of duodenal ulcer.

The inhibitory effect of *enterogastrone* on gastric secretion has already been referred to. Enterogastrone is released from the mucosa of the upper small bowel, principally the duodenum, in response to the presence of fats or hypertonic solutions of sugars or saline. Commercial preparations of enterogastrone have not been successful in the control of gastric hypersecretion in peptic ulcer disease. This may be due to the lack of a suitable commercial preparation, or it may be that the hypersecretion of ulcer disease is a sign of the failure of the gastric glands to respond to normal inhibitory mechanisms, of which enterogastrone is one. Enterogastrone is effective mainly against the chemical phases of gastric secretion. Experimental evidence suggests that enterogastrone acts by preventing the release of gastrin from the gastric antrum. It has little influence on the initial reflex phase; as will be discussed presently, the initial reflex phase is abnormally prolonged and augmented in patients with duodenal ulcers.

Effect of Emotional States on Gastric Secretion

Evaluation of the effects of emotional stress is obviously limited by the animal's ability to express emotional reactions. In general, irrespective of the nature of the emotion, whether it be deemed fear, anger or frustration, the effect on gastric secretion is one of inhibition. Beaumont (1833) observed, in Alexis St. Martin, that anger and fear caused suppression of gastric secretion. In his book, "Bodily Changes in Pain, Hunger, Fear and Rage," (1915), Walter B. Cannon focused attention on the inhibitory effects of intense emotions. Thus, for years later, this observation dominated considerations of the effect of emotional states on gastric function. That certain types of emotional disturbances stimulate gastric function, in fact increase secretion of hydrochloric acid, was first demonstrated by Wolf and Wolff (1943) in studies on their modern Alexis St. Martin, Tom Little. Tom had a gastric fistula which made it possible to observe changes in the gastric mucosa and to note increases and decreases in the secretion of hydrochloric acid. When exposed to sudden fear or pain, Tom's stomach became pale and ceased to secrete hydrochloric acid in accordance with the concept popularized by Cannon; however, when a situation developed which caused prolonged resentment or deep seated chronic anger, the opposite effects were observed; the gastric mucosa became congested and the secretion of hydrochloric acid was increased. Subsequently, similar results have been observed by a number of investigators on human subjects and on animals. Although there are individual variations, the weight of evidence indicates that chronic anxiety, anger, resentment and fear, if sufficiently prolonged, tend to produce effects on gastric function characteristic of increased activity of the parasympathetic division of the autonomic system including increased secretion of hydrochloric acid by the stomach.

The central mechanism for these effects is doubtless situated partly in the hypothalamus. This portion of the brain has been shown repeatedly to be a center for the coordination of impulses involved in emotional expression (Bard, 1928, 1929; Fulton and Ingraham, 1929). Clark (1932) refers to the hypothalamus as a visceral correlation center and Hess (1947) has said that "in the diencephalon the functions of the various autonomic organs are synthesized into cooperative action." MacDonald (1951), citing the work of Hess, suggested that the hypothalamus is "the head ganglion of the autonomic system."

It has long been known that stimulation of the posterior portion of the hypothalamus brings about visceral responses characteristic of the activity of the sympathetic division of the autonomic nervous system. Evidence that the vagi, or other parasympathetic nerves, could be activated from the hypothalamus, has not been so abundant but it is becoming increasingly apparent that parasympathetic effects can be obtained from various regions of the hypothalamus by appropriate stimulating techniques (Strom and Uvnas, 1950). Thus, we see that mechanisms exist for the alteration of visceral function, presumably including gastric secretion, as a part of the general phenomena associated with emotional expression.

Emotional perceptibility, as distinguished from emotional expression, resides in the cortex. Widespread connections between various parts of the cerebral cortex and the hypothalamus are thought to exist. The rhinencephalon has a dominant role in modifying responses to visceral and sexual experiences (MacLean, 1949). The tracts that connect the hypothalamus directly, or by way of the thalamus, with the neopallium have been analyzed in detail by Murphy and Gellhorn (1945). They studied the distribution of action potentials resulting from the local application of strychnine to various points in the cortex, thalamus and hypothalamus. In discussing their results, they state that certain of the conducting paths that they demonstrated may be said to be tracts of preferential discharge of low resistance. These were paths from the hypothalamus to the cortex and from the cortex to the hypothalamus, both by way of the thalamus; also included were two-way paths between the hypothalamus and the thalamus. The authors suggest that these two-way conduction paths between cortex and hypothalamus may constitute, under some circumstances, "reverberating circuits," by which they mean closed chains of neurons over which impulses may be maintained long after the exciting stimulus has subsided.

Loss of Gastric Juice from the Body

When abnormally large quantities of gastric juice are lost from the body, as in pyloric obstruction with persistent vomiting, or in intestinal obstruction high in the small bowel, a profound effect upon the acid-base balance of the body is produced. There is a fall in blood chloride leading to a state of compensated or uncompensated alkalosis. Because calcium salts are less soluble in alkaline body fluids, tetany due to calcium deficiency may occur in uncompensated alkalosis (ch. 34). Dragstedt and Ellis (1930) have shown that, in animals, drainage of the gastric juice to the exterior through a fistula results in a reduction of blood chloride and alkalosis, marked dehydration, and a rise in non-protein nitrogen in the blood, leading to severe depression and death.

Gastric Analysis

The study of gastric secretion in the human subject requires use of a gastric tube to obtain gastric contents unless one, like Beaumont, were fortunate enough to have access to a patient with a gastric fistula, such as Alexis St. Martin. St. Martin was a French Canadian who was accidentally wounded by the discharge of a musket loaded with duckshot. The shot tore a hole in his left side and carried away a portion of the anterior wall of the stomach. On recovering from this wound, he was left with a permanent gastric fistula and much of our early knowledge of gastric function we owe to the careful observations that

William Beaumont made on his patient. At the time Beaumont was a military surgeon in the United States Army. Since then, other studies on patients with gastric fistula have been made. A. J. Carlson (1923) had three such subjects available in his physiology laboratory at the University of Chicago. In more recent times, Wolf and Wolff (1943) have reported their observations on their now famous patient, Tom Little.

A great variety of stomach tubes have been used for gastric analysis in the past. The tendency in recent years has been to use tubes of smaller size; number 12 French gauge is often used. Recently, disposable plastic tubes have come into common use. They have the advantage over rubber tubes in that the wall of the tube is thinner and the size of the lumen greater for a given outside diameter. Since they are cheap, they need not be re-used and hence, are thrown away and not re-sterilized. Many of the disposable gastric tubes are not radiopaque and have the disadvantage that the tip of the tube cannot be localized by fluoroscopy.

It is common practice to perform gastric analysis in the morning; the subject reporting to the laboratory after an overnight fast. In patients with duodenal ulcer or other diseases who are receiving drugs that influence gastric secretion, such medications are discontinued 12 hours prior to the test. The gastric tube is usually passed through the nose, particularly if the tube is to remain in place for a long period of time. A tube passed through the nose will cause less discomfort over a period of time than one in the mouth and is less likely to be bitten or otherwise damaged by the patient. Oral intubation, however, can be used, and after the tube has been introduced into the stomach, the portion passing through the mouth is maintained between the cheek and the outer surface of the molar teeth by hooking it over the last molar tooth. This keeps the tube out of the center of the pharynx and avoids constant stimulation of the sensitive mucous membrane of the uvula. Most gastric tubes are marked, indicating the distance from the nares or the incisor teeth to the diaphragmatic hiatus. If oral intubation has been used, this distance is approximately 40 cm. If the tube has been passed through the nose, the distance is approximately 45 cm. When quantitative studies of the gastric secretion are to be done, it is necessary that the distal portion of the gastric tube, containing multiple perforations, be localized carefully in the stomach by fluoroscopy. This, of course, requires a radiopaque gastric tube. One must be sure that the tip of the tube is not coiled up in the gastric fundus, but lies along the lesser curvature with the tip resting in the antrum. The multiple perforations in the gastric tube will then be in the proper position for maximal recovery of gastric secretions.

MEASUREMENT OF GASTRIC ACIDITY

The words "free acid," "combined acid," and "total acid" were coined at a time when we had little understanding of the nature of gastric acidity, and little knowledge of ionization and the nature of buffers. These terms were based on the concept that a certain fraction of the hydrochloric acid existed free in solution, a certain other fraction existed in combination with protein or other acid-absorbing substances, and that these fractions could be distinguished by the use of indicators. We realize now that indicators merely tell us when the solution has reached a certain pH.

It is customary to titrate the acidity of the gastric contents with a standard alkali. The acidity is first titrated to a pH of 3.5 using di-methylamino-azobenzine as an indicator. This indicator changes from red to yellow somewhere between a pH of 3.0 and 3.5. The amount of acid indicated by titration to this level is spoken of as "free" hydrochloric acid. Free acid may be defined as the acid equivalent of the amount of standard alkali necessary to bring the pH of the solution to 3.5. It is expressed in *clinical units* (which is the number of ml. of 0.1 normal NaOH needed to titrate 100 ml. of gastric contents to the desired pH). Titration is then continued with phenolphthalein as the indicator. This indicator changes to a pink color between pH 8.0 and 9.0. The amount of standard alkali needed to titrate to this pH is a measure of the "total" acidity, also expressed in clinical units. The difference between free and total acidity is the "combined" acid. The combined acid is a measure of the buffering capacity of the gastric contents, and will be influenced by the type of food and the amount of mucus and other buffers that happen to be present. In addition to the titration pro-cedure described above, it is customary to measure the pH of the gastric contents using a glass electrode and pH meter. pH, it will be remembered, is the negative logarithm of the hydrogen ion concentration. The glass electrode measures the hydrogen ion *activity* and not true concentration. Activity can be converted to

concentration by a connection factor, the ac-tivity coefficient. Thus, from the pH value, one can calculate the hydrogen ion concentration in terms of moles per liter. The pH value is particularly useful when the acidity is low (James, 1957).

It should be remembered that the expression of gastric acidity in terms of free acid and total acid is an expression of the *concentration* of HCl in the gastric contents. More quantitative data can be determined by expressing the gastric secretion in terms of *milliequivalents* or *milligrams* of hydrochloric acid secreted *per unit of time*. The advantage of expressing gastric secretion of hydrochloric acid in this manner will be apparent when we discuss the various methods of gastric analysis.

MEASUREMENT OF PEPTIC ACTIVITY

Measurement of the peptic activity of gastric secretion is a useful determination to assess the digestive function of the gastric juice. The earliest method of determining peptic activity of gastric juice was introduced by Mett in 1889. Egg white was drawn into a glass tube of 1 mm. bore and a few inches long. The albumin was coagulated by placing the tubes in water at a temperature of 85° C. and leaving them until the water had cooled. The tubes were then broken into sections about an inch long and immersed in gastric juice diluted 1:15 with N/20 HCl and incubated at a temperature of 37 C. for 24 hr. After this time, the length of the column of digested albumin at each end of the tubes is measured in millimeters under the low power of the microscope and the average of the number of measurements taken. The peptic power of the sample is expressed in accordance with Schutz's law which states that the amount of proteolytic enzyme present is proportional to the square of the number of millimeters of digestive albumin. Therefore, if the average length of the digestive columns is 2.5 mm. the peptic power of the undiluted juice will be $2.5^2 \times 16 = 100$, which is the average normal value.

Anson and Mirsky's (1932) method of deter-mining peptic activity utilizes hemoglobin as a substrate. After the juice has acted upon the hemoglobin for 10 min., the undigested protein is precipitated with trichloroacetic acid and removed by filtration. The quantity of protein-split products, which is a measure of peptic activity, is estimated colorimetrically after the addition of phenol reagent.

More recently, I^{131}-labeled albumin has been used as a substrate for the measurement of peptic activity. Klotz and Duval (1957) have described a simple rapid method based upon use of the following reaction mixture, one ml. of clear centrifuged gastric juice, one ml. of radioactive iodionated albumin of known specific activity (approximately 0.03 μc/ml.), one ml. of 6 per cent bovine albumin which serves as a carrier, and 3 ml. of Sorensen's phosphate buffer, pH 2.0. After incubating for 15 min. at 37° C., one ml. of 50 per cent trichloroacetic acid is added which precipitates the proteins and stops peptic activity. The preparation is centrifuged and the clear supernatant decanted. By means of a scintillation counter the radioactivity of the supernatant is determined. Only the I^{131} that was released as a result of the enzymatic hydrolysis of albumin would be present in the supernatant. The number of counts obtained for the supernate is divided by the number obtained from one ml. of the substrate I^{131} albumin diluted to the same volume of the supernate. This value (per cent activity) is then compared to values on a standard curve of reference obtained by the use of twice-crystallized pepsin as a source of peptic activity. With this method 1.0 mg. of crystallized pepsin will digest or release approximately 56 per cent of I^{131} from the I^{131}-labeled albumin. The peptic activity of gastric juice of patients with duodenal ulcer is often in excess of 1.0 mg. pepsin per ml. of juice.

Methods of Gastric Analysis

Many methods of gastric analysis have been devised for the assessment of gastric secretory function. Commonly used methods include: measuring gastric secretion under basal conditions, that is, without the use of any stimuli; determining the gastric secretory response to a test meal, or to various potent gastric secretory stimulators such as histamine or its analog, histalog, caffeine, or insulin; and the measurement of gastric secretion for a 12-hour period during the night (nocturnal secretion).

It is customary for the patient or subject to report to the laboratory after an overnight fast. After intubation and localizing the tip of the tube in the stomach, the residual gastric contents are aspirated. The volume and acidity of the fasting gastric contents vary a great deal in normal individuals, but it is rare in man to find the stomach completely empty or entirely devoid of hydrochloric acid. Usually 20 to 40 ml. of

gastric juice are found in the fasting human stomach. The acidity of the fasting secretion will ordinarily range from 20 to 30 mEq/l. of so-called free hydrochloric acid.

Response to Test Meals

The secretory response to a test meal has long been employed as a method of gastric analysis. After the stomach has been emptied, the patient is given a small meal called a "test meal," a great variety of which are in use. Typical test meals are: 300 ml. of oatmeal gruel; a piece of dry toast and a cup of tea; a shredded wheat biscuit or a piece of toast with 350 to 400 ml. of water; two slices of bread without the crust or 2 pieces of Zwieback with 350 ml. water (Ewald test meal); 200 ml. of a 10 per cent solution of peptone; and 8 Arrowroot cookies with 400 ml. of water (modified Ewald meal).

It is the custom in many institutions to do gastric analysis using the modified Ewald test meal in the following manner. The patient reports to the laboratory after an overnight fast and the test meal consisting of eight Arrowroot cookies and 400 ml. of water is administered. One hour later the gastric tube is passed, and the contents of the stomach removed completely by aspiration. The total volume, free and total hydrochloric acid, are then measured. Such a "spot check" of the concentration of hydrochloric acid after a test meal can be likened to one determination of the patient's blood pressure. Upper limits of normal for the concentration of free hydrochloric acid is usually taken as 60 mEq/l. Values above this are considered evidence of "hyperacidity"; values below 20 are taken to indicate "hypoacidity." The volume of the gastric contents aspirated one hour after the test meal is administered is a function of gastric motility. In normal individuals, one hour after ingesting the 400 ml. meal usually less than 100 ml. remains. When pyloric obstruction exists, or when gastric emptying is delayed, larger volumes will be recovered after one hour.

Using the modified Ewald test meal and method of gastric analysis just described, Vanzant, Alvarez and their associates at the Mayo Clinic (1932) studied the results of 3,746 records of "normal" individuals. The majority of the subjects, 3,381, were examined by them, and 365 additional cases were obtained from the literature. Of these patients that sought medical attention with a variety of complaints, none had any evidence of disease of the stomach, duodenum, gallbladder or colon. Most of the patients were considered to have "functional" gastrointestinal symptoms.

Their findings showed that the free acid of the

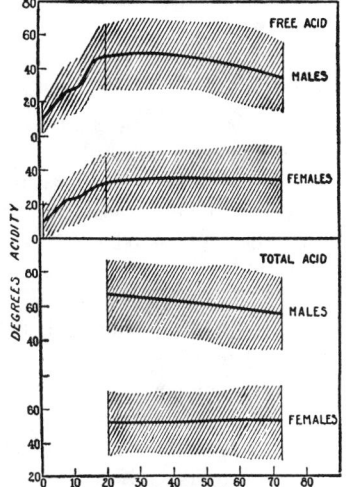

FIG. 57.16. Normal standards. The shaded areas represent the limits within which lay 80 per cent of the data for free and total acid at the different ages. The heavy lines represent modes. (After Vanzant, Alvarez and associates.)

stomach increased rapidly through childhood and the teenage years to reach adult levels at about the age of 20 years. In men between 20 and 40 years of age free acidity ranged between 45 and 50 units. In the aged, values of 30 to 35 units were obtained. The average value for women was approximately 35 units throughout adult life (fig. 57.16).

It was found also, that the incidence of an absence of free HCl in the sample obtained one hour after the test meal increased with age in both men and women. The absence of free HCl in the one-hour sample was termed "apparent achlorhydria." If samples obtained after the injection of histamine failed to exhibit free HCl then the subject was considered to have "true achlorhydria" (fig. 57.17). Unfortunately, histamine was used in only a few patients mentioned above.

If no free acid appears in the gastric contents after a test meal, it does not necessarily prove that the subject is achlorhydric, that is, one who secretes no hydrochloric acid. To detect true achlorhydria, it is necessary to use a more powerful secretory stimulant such as histamine or one of its analogs.

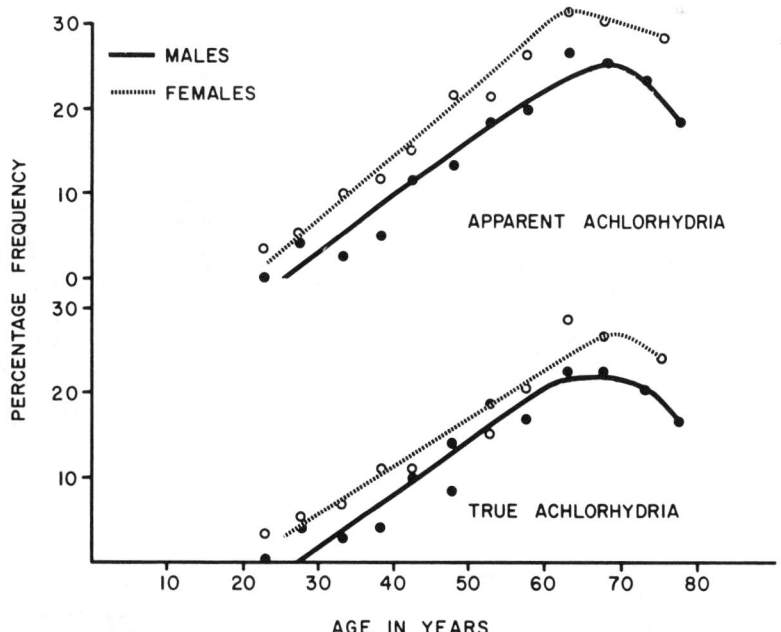

FIG. 57.17. Curves showing the relation between the incidence of true and apparent achlorhydria and age. (After Vanzant, Alvarez and associates.)

Fractional Gastric Analysis

Fractional gastric analysis was introduced by Rehfuss (1914) and his associates and is now in common use. After the residual fasting gastric contents have been removed, gastric secretions are collected by continuous manual aspiration for two 15-min. periods. At the end of this 30-min. control period, the test meal is administered and samples of gastric juice are aspirated at 15-min. intervals for a period of 2 to 2½ hr. These samples are then analyzed for free and total acidity and for peptic activity. Other tests may be done as indicated.

In a normal person, if the free and total acidities of the gastric contents are determined every 15 min. for a period of 2 to 3 hr. after the ingestion of a test meal, and the results are plotted against time along the base line, with HCl concentrations on the vertical axis, a curve is obtained as shown in fig. 57.18. The curve for total acidity commences to rise a short time after the meal and about one hour later reaches a maximum which varies from 35 to 70 in different persons. The curve maintains its maximal height for half an hour or less and then commences to decline, reaching the resting level again in from 2½ to 3 hr. after the ingestion of the test meal. The curve of free acidity runs parallel to, but at a lower level, than that of total acidity; the values ranging in different normal persons between 20 and 40 mEq/l. After the ingestion of foods such as meats, which vigorously stimulate gastric secretion, the values obtained are higher, averaging from 80 to 120 mEq/l. for total acidity and from 60 to 100 mEq/l. for free acidity.

The figures given above represent the range of the majority of normal persons; but gastric acidities show very wide individual variations in health, being influenced markedly by age and sex.

One-Hour Basal Gastric Analysis

The one-hour basal gastric analysis test has proved to be a reliable, quantitative measurement of gastric secretion. The patient reports to the laboratory after an overnight fast and is shielded from the sight or odors of food during the procedure. Smoking is not permitted prior to the test. After the gastric residium is aspirated, two 15-min. samples are collected (with the patient on his left side) by constant manual aspiration and the volume, free and total acidity are immediately determined to make sure that gastric secretion is stable. The patient is instructed to expectorate all saliva during the test. After this 30-min. control period, four 15-min. samples are collected by constant manual aspiration. The volume and free and total acid are determined for each 15-min. sample during the one-hour test period. Knowing the volume and concentration of acid in the gastric juice, one can calculate the mEq of HCl secreted in each 15-min. period. In normal individuals, this usually amounts to less than 3 mEq (109 mg.) per hour, while in patients with duodenal ulcer the one-hour basal gastric analysis usually shows an excess of 5 mEq (182 mg.) per hour. (See table 57.2 from Levin, Kirsner and Palmer, 1951.)

Nocturnal Gastric Secretion

A method of gastric analysis currently in use at many institutions is the measurement of gastric secretion during a 12-hr. nocturnal period. On the day of the test, the patient is given a clear liquid diet at noon and at 5:00 p.m. At 7:30 p.m. the patient is intubated and the tip of the gastric tube is localized in the gastric antrum. The tube is usually passed through the nose, as this is more comfortable for the patient when the tube is to be kept in place overnight. The tube is taped securely to the side of the face to prevent it from moving during the 12-hr. test period. At 8:00 p.m., the gastric contents are completely aspirated and the gastric tube is connected to a low pressure vacuum pump at a negative pressure of approximately 30 in. of

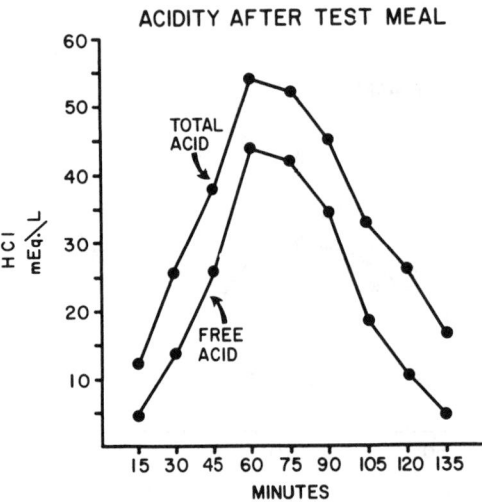

ACIDITY AFTER TEST MEAL

FIG. 57.18. The normal curve of gastric acidity following a test meal as determined by fractional gastric analysis (redrawn from Maclean).

TABLE 57.2

One-hour basal and histamine gastric secretion

Age Group	Number of Cases		Basal Secretion			Histamine Response		
			Volume	Free HCl conc.	Free HCl output	Volume	Free HCl conc.	Free HCl output
			(*ml.*)	(*c.u.*)	(*mg.*)	(*ml.*)	(*c.u.*)	(*mg*)
20–29	49	Mean	77.6	33.9	96.4	124.8	76.7	357.3
		S.E.	±6.2	±4.4	±16.2	±8.5	±4.7	±28.0
30–39	80	Mean	77.2	31.4	99.2	137.8	76.1	409.0
		S.E.	±4.6	±1.9	±11.7	±6.6	±3.4	±27.8
40–49	80	Mean	90.6	31.5	112.2	147.4	72.2	427.5
		S.E.	±4.8	±3.1	±13.2	±7.6	±4.7	±20.5
50–59	80	Mean	77.2	28.9	87.6	127.2	66.9	347.8
		S.E.	±4.4	±3.0	±11.3	±7.7	±4.2	±50.2
60+	30	Mean	65.1	16.1	42.4	108.3	44.3	231.6
		S.E.	±7.7	±4.0	±10.7	±13.6	±7.8	±41.9
Average.......	(total) 319)	Mean	79.4	25.8	93.8	133.1	69.9	372.9
		S.E.	±2.3	±1.8	±6.0	±3.5	±2.0	±2.8

From Levin, Kirsner and Palmer, Gastroenterology, **19**, 89, 1951.

water. Gastric secretions are collected from 8:00 p.m. to 8:00 a.m. The patient is advised to expectorate all saliva and he is shielded from the sight and odor of food throughout the period of the test. A considerable amount of supervision is required during the 12-hr. collection period. At least once each hour, the tube should be checked to make sure that it has not changed position. To prevent the tube from becoming plugged with mucus, it is advisable to "crack" the tube at least once each hour. This is done by disconnecting the proximal end of the gastric tube from the vacuum pump and injecting 20 to 30 ml. of air to make sure that the tube is cleared. At the end of the 12-hr. collection period, the gastric tube is removed and the usual measurements of total volume, free and total acidity and pepsin concentration are measured.

Normal individuals secrete approximately 1.5 mEq/hr. during the 12-hr. nocturnal period. However, the volume secreted and the output of HCl is usually greater during the first half of the night than during the last half. The total output of HCl during the 12-hr. period for normal individuals is usually 15 to 20 mEq or 550 to 750 mg. (36.46 mg. equals 1 mEq HCl). Patients with duodenal ulcer will secrete from three to ten times this much HCl during the 12-hr. period. The average volume, concentration, and mg. of free HCl obtained in normal individuals, and in patients with duodenal ulcer, gastric ulcer, and gastric carcinoma is shown in table 57.3 (from Levin, Kirsner and Palmer, 1949).

TABLE 57.3

Nocturnal gastric secretion

	Volume	Free Acid	Free HCl
	cc.	*Cl units*	*mg.*
Normal....................	581	29	661
Duodenal ulcer.............	1004	61	2242
Gastric ulcer...............	600	21	454
Gastric carcinoma..........	483	14	245

From Levin, Kirsner and Palmer, Gastroenterology, **12**, 561, 1941.

The Histamine Test

Histamine is a powerful stimulant of gastric secretion and has many advantages over the ordinary test meal:

(a) Histamine is capable of evoking secretion of HCl when a test meal fails to do so. It is thus of value in distinguishing true anacidity from false anacidity.

(b) The secretory response is not affected by conditions such as appetite or other psychic factors which influence the response to the test meal.

(c) With test meals, varying amounts of salivary secretion (that cannot be measured) are added to the volume of gastric contents; it is therefore impossible to determine accurately the quantity of gastric juice secreted.

(d) Swallowed saliva and the test meal itself partly neutralize the acid.

(e) In the histamine test, the gastric glands respond promptly, maximal acidity being reached within 15 to 20 min.; therefore, almost pure gastric juice is obtained for analysis and neutralization factors and gastric evacuation exert a minimum effect.

As with other methods of gastric analysis, the histamine test is performed in the morning after an overnight fast. After intubation and aspiration of any residual gastric contents, two 15-min. samples are obtained by constant hand aspiration to determine the level of gastric secretion in the basal state. At the end of the 30-min. control period, histamine, in a dose of 0.01 mg./kg. is administered subcutaneously. This dose of histamine should be calculated on the basis of histamine base in the histamine preparation being used (0.275 mg. histamine diphosphate = 0.1 mg. histamine base; 0.166 mg. histamine dihydrochloride = 0.1 mg. histamine base). After the histamine is given, four 15-min. samples are obtained. The maximal effect of histamine will be noted in the second and third samples. The results are expressed in terms of mEq or mg. of HCl secreted in the 1-hr. period following the histamine administration. Normal individuals will usually secrete 8 to 12 mEq (292 to 438 mg.) of HCl in one hour in response to histamine (table 57.2) while patients with duodenal ulcer usually respond by secreting twice this amount or more in the same time.

Histamine is a potent vasodilator and its use in some patients, particularly in a dose of 0.01 mg. histamine base per kg. body weight or larger, causes such unpleasant side effects as headache, flushing, tachycardia, and apprehension. The analog of histamine, 3-beta-amino-ethyl-pyrazole, Histalog (Eli Lilly), produces few, if any, side effects, but like histamine is a potent stimuli for HCl secretion. Histalog is used frequently instead of histamine in gastric analysis, and with a dose of 1 mg./kg. will give comparable results to 0.01 mg./kg. histamine.

Chronic Gastric and Duodenal Ulcer (Peptic Ulcer)

Peptic ulcer is the most common ulcerative disorder of the upper gastrointestinal tract. Duodenal ulcer is said to occur at one time or another in approximately 10 per cent of all males between the ages of 20 and 50 years. Duodenal ulcer is more common in males (6 or 7:1) than females, whereas gastric ulcer occurs with about equal incidence in both sexes. Epi-

gastric pain, coming on usually in from ½ to 1½ hr. after a meal, and vomiting, are the chief clinical features of *gastric ulcer*. In a certain proportion (about 20 per cent) of cases blood appears in the vomitus (hematemesis). In *duodenal ulcer* pain occurs usually within from 2 to 3 hr. after a meal, when the stomach is nearly empty. The onset of the pain is therefore earlier after a light than after a heavy meal. The pain is relieved by taking food.

Pathogenesis

It is generally agreed that the dominant factor in the development of gastric and of duodenal ulcer is the action of the pepsin-hydrochloric acid of the gastric juice. The term peptic ulcer is therefore well chosen. The importance of this factor is evidenced by the following facts:

(1) Apart from the ulcerations caused by some specific disease, e.g., tuberculosis, syphilis, carcinoma, etc., ulcer of the gastrointestinal tract is confined to those regions which are exposed to the action of acid. (a) *Gastric ulcers*, in the great majority of cases, involve the pyloric part of the stomach; they are most frequently situated on the lesser curvature near the incisura angularis or on the anterior or posterior wall in close proximity to this limited area. They are rarely seen in the dome of the fundus or on the upper part of the greater curvature; these regions, it will be noted, are not in contact with acid for any length of time. (b) *Esophageal ulcers*, in the lower part of the esophagus into which highly acid juice frequently regurgitates, especially in patients with hiatal hernia, and the adjacent part of the stomach wall, i.e., the cardia, are sometimes the site of ulceration. (c) *Duodenal ulcer* occurs practically exclusively within the first inch or less of the duodenal cap, and nearly always upon its anterior or posterior wall, that is, where the chyme, before it has been neutralized by the alkaline juices of the duodenum, comes into contact with the mucosa. (d) *Stomal ulcers* after gastrojejunostomy may occur in the jejunal mucosa in the region of the anastomosis, i.e., where the gastric juice first impinges. (e) *Diverticulum ulcers* are occasionally seen in a Meckel's diverticulum which contains ectopic gastric glands. The ulcer's site is either in that part of the mucosa of the diverticulum, which does not itself contain acid-secreting glands, or in the ileum at the point where the diverticulum opens into it. Matthews and Dragstedt (1932), experimenting with dogs, produced an "artificial

Meckel's diverticulum" by transplanting a pouch of the gastric wall into the ileum; an ulcer developed in the ileum just beyond the transplant in every experiment. (f) The *Mann-Williamson ulcer* is an experimental ulcer produced in dogs by excising the duodenum and transplanting it into the ileum, thus diverting its alkaline juices away from the region of the pylorus. The cut end of the jejunum is anastomosed to the pylorus. A high percentage of dogs subjected to the operation devised by Mann and Williamson (1923) will develop chronic ulcers in the jejunum just beyond the pylorus. However, Fawley and Ivy (1926) found that this operation, if combined with excision of the fundus, or if the alkaline secretions are drained into the stomach, does not cause a jejunal ulcer.

These observations emphasize a curious fact that the commonest situations of ulcer are not in the mucosa which secretes the acid, but in neighboring parts which *normally secrete a neutral or alkaline fluid*—the pyloric region, duodenal cap, cardiac region, esophagus, jejunum or ileum. The pyloric type of gland extends farther up the lesser curvature than up the greater curvature. It has even been suggested that the occurrence of ulcers in the body of the stomach, i.e., in the acid-secreting part of the mucosa, is actually dependent upon the presence of patches of aberrant pyloric glands.

Ulcers also have been produced by inducing continuous secretion of hydrochloric acid by implanting *histamine in beeswax* under the skin. This results in the continuous absorption of histamine and consequent continuous stimulation of the acid-secreting cells of the stomach. Ulcers also occur in the duodenum. True peptic ulcer does not develop in the absence of hydrochloric acid. Although a small acute or subacute ulcer may sometimes develop in the absence of acid, a large chronic ulcer of the duodenum is almost never seen with anacidity, as for example, in pernicious anemia.

(2) There is a definite tendency toward hypersecretion in most duodenal ulcer patients, though not in patients with gastric ulcer. The evidence on this point has been nicely summarized by Grossman (1951) as follows: "Patients with gastric ulcer show a distinct difference from those with duodenal ulcer in this regard. In gastric ulcer patients there is little or no tendency to secrete excessive amounts of acid, whereas this tendency is distinctly present in duodenal ulcer patients. Thus, both experimentally and clini-

cally, the ulcer associated with hypersecretion of acid is duodenal in location. This hypersecretion of duodenal ulcer patients manifests itself in all types of gastric secretory studies, whether these studies are on the interdigestive secretion during the day or night, or on the secretion in response either to a meal or to drugs such as histamine, insulin or caffeine. The difference between normal persons and duodenal ulcer patients is greatest in studies on the basal or interdigestive secretion and in the response to caffeine. The response of the ulcer patient to caffeine deserves special mention because it is characterized by being abnormally prolonged as well as elevated.

"There is no sharp dividing line between the secretory level of duodenal ulcer patients and that of normal persons. Some duodenal ulcer patients secrete no more acid than the average normal person; some normal persons secrete as much acid as the average duodenal ulcer patient. Only a small percentage of duodenal ulcer patients secrete acid at rates higher than the highest level encountered in normal subjects. The difference between the acid secretory rates in normal persons and patients with duodenal ulcers is a statistical phenomenon; the *average* secretory rate of normal persons is distinctly below the *average* for patients with duodenal ulcer. The difference is statistically highly significant; that is the probability of its having occurred by chance or random sampling error is low."

In duodenal ulcer the typical findings upon gastric analysis are: a fasting juice of greater volume than normal and of high acidity; and a curve of gastric acidity after a test meal which rises well above (60 mEq/l.) the normal maximum.

High gastric acidity is less commonly associated with gastric ulcer; according to Vanzant, the acidity is actually a little below the normal average. True anacidity, however, is rarely, if ever, found. Atkinson and Henley (1955) also found the acidity in gastric ulcer patients to be below the average of normal subjects but Ihre (1938) found it to be essentially normal. The relatively low gastric acidities found in gastric ulcer are probably the result of an associated gastritis and do not necessarily indicate that hyperchlorhydria did not precede the development of the ulcer.

(3) Stimulation of gastric secretion, as by the continued administration of histamine or of caffeine, is one of the most effective experimental means of producing gastric ulcer. Although gastric

ulcers are produced experimentally by means of a constant drip over the gastric mucosa of a solution of hydrochloric acid, some pepsin must be furnished by the stomach itself. Irrigation of a loop of jejunum with acid alone will not cause ulceration but this is readily produced by the addition of pepsin to the perfusion fluid.

(4) Measures directed toward the prevention of excessive gastric secretion and toward the neutralization of the acidity of the gastric contents are of outstanding value in encouraging the healing of the ulcer.

Though the importance of acid in the production of ulcer cannot be denied, this factor cannot be solely concerned. For one thing, many persons who show hyperchlorhydria do not develop ulcer. Why in these instances is the gastric mucosa immune to the action of the pepsin-hydrochloric acid? Indeed, the question has often been asked: "Why does not the pepsin-hydrochloric acid of even normal gastric juice digest the gastric or duodenal mucosa?" It is also an extraordinary fact, firmly established by several workers, that the tissue of other parts of the intestinal tract or of other organs, though susceptible to the action of acid in their normal situations, are not digested when transplanted into the wall of the normal stomach. Dragstedt and Vaughn, for example, removed areas from the gastric wall of dogs and then sutured portions of the duodenum, ileum, jejunum, colon, spleen or kidney into the gaps. In no case was the transplanted tissue digested. In the case of the kidney and spleen, their gastric surfaces became covered with a layer of gastric epithelium. Sections of transplanted intestinal mucosa were found to be perfectly normal after a period of nine months.

On the other hand, as shown years ago by Claude Bernard (1859), the intact leg of a living frog is digested when introduced through a fistula into the stomach of a dog. Pavy (1923) showed the same thing for the rabbit's ear, and Dragstedt and Vaughn have demonstrated that the intact limb of a live frog placed in an extract of frog's gastric mucosa is digested.

Until comparatively recently there has been no convincing or even very plausible answer to the question of why the stomach does not digest its own wall. One explanation offered was that the greater alkalinity of the blood coursing through the vessels of the gastric tubules as a result of the loss of H^+ ions served to neutralize the effect of the acid juice. Others suggested that the immunity of the gastric mucosa to

autodigestion is due to its containing an anti-pepsin. Two possible mechanisms that have been suggested are based upon: (1) the presence of high concentrations of urease in the gastric mucosa, and (2) the protective action of the alkaline mucus secreted by the mucosa.

Urea-Urease-Ammonia Mechanism

The presence of ammonia in the gastric contents was observed many years ago (1852) by Bidder and Schmidt, but little significance was attached to the finding until Luck and Seth demonstrated the production of ammonia in gastric tissue by the action of urease upon urea (urea + urease → NH_3 + CO_2), and pointed out the possible role of this mechanism in neutralizing gastric acid. A rise in blood urea, as in renal insufficiency or after the oral administration of urea, is followed by a corresponding increase in the urea + ammonia in the gastric wall, and a rise in the ammonia concentration of the gastric juice. In the gastric mucosa the concentration of urease is higher than in any other tissue; it is found in greatest amounts in the cells of the surface epithelium. FitzGerald and his associates have made an extended study of this mechanism. Although urease is found in the gastric mucosa, as well as in bacteria on the mucosa surface, it is doubtful if the production of ammonia plays a significant role in the neutralization of gastric acid in a normal individual. The amount of ammonia usually produced is insignificant compared to the amount of HCl produced.

The Mucus Barrier

Another factor which is even more important is the presence of the protective layer of mucus which normally covers the entire gastric mucosa. Hollander (1951) has pointed out that the mucus "adheres to the underlying tissue with great tenacity, is capable of maintaining a considerable thickness instead of flowing off rapidly as the acid secretion does, is generally impermeable to destructive chemical agents because of its cohesiveness and is impermeable to pepsin because of its absorptive properties." Hollander also calls attention to the remarkable capacity of the surface layers of the gastric mucosa to regenerate and to secrete a fresh layer of mucus, should the mucus barrier be broken down at any point.

Other Factors Concerned in the Production of Ulcer

Bacterial infection, and interference with the **blood supply** to the mucosa, either as a result of emboli, thrombosis or chronic vasospasm have been thought by some to be responsible for ulcer production. Except perhaps in rare instances, these are no longer believed to play a role. *Tobacco smoking* has been thought, in some instances at any rate, to encourage ulcer formation or to interfere with the healing of an ulcer already formed; however, if smoking is conducive to gastric or duodenal ulceration, the manner in which it acts is not clear. *Trauma*, although not essential to the production of ulcer, is probably often a contributory factor. It is not difficult to believe that in the presence of other causative factors, rubbing of food against the gastric mucosa or the passage of coarse, indigestible material into the duodenal cap, will encourage the production of ulcer or retard the healing of an existing one. Mann and Bollman point out that the site of duodenal ulcer corresponds to the area of mucosa upon which the gastric contents impinge and, when the gastric movements are vigorous, this may occur with considerable force. They found that experimental production of ulcer was considerably delayed if the propulsive force of the stomach was reduced by making an hourglass constriction in the prepyloric region. Ivy and his associetes have shown that, in the rabbit, coarse food retards the healing of an area of the stomach wall from which the mucosa has been denuded. The possible effect of trauma upon the blood supply of the gastric mucosa is referred to elsewhere.

The role of stress in the etiology of peptic ulcer— psychovisceral disease. As our knowledge of the control of visceral function has increased, it has become more and more evident that experiences with a high emotional content can adversely affect visceral function to the extent of causing organic disease. Whether or not this takes place, depends as much upon the individual and his reaction to his experiences as upon the experiences themselves, but in any case the emotional factor is predominant. Disease traceable to the individual's reactions to his environment, particularly his emotional reactions, are known as psychosomatic disease. They might better be called psychovisceral diseases (Thomas, 1955), because they generally affect some part of the viscera rather than the external body structures.

The fact that emotional states have an influence on gastric secretion has already been mentioned. The possibility is suggested that various forms of stress can, through this mechanism, cause gastric hypersecretion and thus promote the development of gastric or duodenal

ulcers. In this connection some observations of Harvey Cushing (1932) are significant. He reported three cases of acute perforated ulcers with death following removal of cerebellar tumors which possibly had caused injury to the hypothalamus. He concluded that there was a parasympathetic center in the diencephalon, apparently situated near the tuber cinereum from which fibers passed backward to the medulla for relay to the vagus and other autonomic centers. He noted that experimental lesions anywhere in the intracranial course of these fibers were prone to cause gastric erosions, perforation or ulcers. Similar observations have been reported by Keller (1933–1934) and his associates. It may also be recalled that the stimulation of the hypothalamus in the region of the tuber cinereum is followed by increased movements of the stomach, and that hypersecretion and gastric hypertonus are frequently features of duodenal ulcers. That emotional stress is frequently associated with duodenal ulcer is well known. Dragstedt has said "for a number of years many investigators have commented on the high incidence of ulcers in those persons whose occupations involve unusual anxiety, stress and strain, and on the tendency for healed ulcers to recur during periods of great emotional tension." "On the basis of available experimental evidence of the genesis of ulcers—it seems most probable that the central nervous system plays an undoubted role in causing the disease through increasing the volume of gastric juice."

Reference should be made also to the probable role of the pituitary and adrenal hormones in the response of the viscera to environmental stimuli. These glands are surely involved in reactions of the body as a whole to stress. Specific effects on the gastrointestinal organs of the hormones that are probably released in these reactions are little known or understood, but it is known that acute gastrointestinal ulceration and mucosal hemorrhages are of common occurrence in severe nonspecific types of stress. Although these have generally been interpreted as being due to activation of autonomic nerves, the work of Gray and his associates (1955) indicates that the adrenal hormones secreted in response to corticotrophin (ch. 76) may increase gastric secretion, and thus play a part in causing duodenal ulceration.

The role of emotional factors (particularly emotionally induced hypersecretion) in gastric ulcer is not so evident, although Dragstedt and associates (1954) believe that gastric stasis, which tends to cause a prolonged gastric phase of secretion, may be a factor in the production of gastric ulcers. There is no assurance that the etiology of gastric ulcer is the same as that of duodenal ulcer. Indeed there is reason to believe that the two may have quite different causations since gastric ulcer is about as common in women as in men, whereas duodenal ulcer occurs with a much higher frequency in men.

The Cause of Pain in Duodenal Ulcer

As mentioned previously, duodenal ulcer is characterized by pain which appears several hours after a meal. Pain of duodenal ulcer may occur at night, awakening the patient, but rarely occurs in the morning prior to breakfast. The pain is of a burning character and is usually felt somewhere in the epigastrium. Although it is evident that the pain appears at a time when the ulcerated surface is exposed to unneutralized acid from the stomach and can be induced experimentally by introducing acid into the stomach or duodenum, the mechanism of its production is obscure. The viscera are not supplied with pain fibers, which can be demonstrated in the healthy subject by any of the ordinary methods of producing pain. The intestines can be cut, burned, or pinched, without causing any other sensation than that due to contraction of the smooth muscle in the wall of the gut. Muscle spasm or stretching of the wall causes a characteristic type of pain which is different from that of ulcer pain.

One suggestion as to the cause of ulcer pain is that contact of acid with the ulcerated surface stimulates local reflex mechanisms which initiate muscle spasm in the smooth muscle in the vicinity of the ulcer. The difference in the quality of ulcer pain from ordinary muscle cramp may be due to the greater excitability of the sensory nerves induced by the inflammatory process. Another explanation utilizes this increased excitability and presumes that the threshold has been lowered sufficiently so that direct chemical trauma is capable of causing the sensation of pain, the pain in this instance being attributed to the action of acid on the exposed nerve endings or nerve fibers in the ulcer. One argument in favor of the direct acid irritation theory is that the pain is continuous and not intermittent as is the pain of muscle spasm, e.g., intestinal or biliary colic.

Pain caused by ulcers may be relieved by the administration of alkali or drugs that inhibit secretion or motility of the stomach, such as the belladonna alkaloids and the numerous synthetic parasympatholytic drugs. The pain is also relieved by sympathectomy or vagotomy. The former operation is effective because the visceral afferent fibers, including the pain fibers, from the abdominal organs accompany the sympathetic nerves. The latter has an effect like the parasympatholytic drugs: it diminishes gastric secretion and motility. It is interesting to note that pain can be induced in a vagotomized subject by introducing a large volume of acid into the stomach. Presumably, the acid overflows into the duodenum and initiates the usual mechanism of ulcer pain. The success of this experiment is a strong argument in favor of the direct acid irritation theory. The fact that the vagi have no profound influence on the smooth muscle of the small intestine does not preclude the possibility the duodenal musculature undergoes spasm in response to local irritation.

A point in favor of the muscle spasm theory is the fact that the parasympatholytic drugs relieve the pain of ulcer even when they fail to suppress greatly the secretion of acid. However, this effect, as well as that immediately following vagotomy, may be due to the delayed emptying of the stomach which these procedures induce, thus causing the acid to remain in the stomach where it does not make contact with the ulcer.

Physiological Principles in Treatment of Duodenal Ulcer

The medical treatment of peptic ulcer is directed toward the relief of pain, reduction of the acidity in the gastric and duodenal contents, protection of the ulcerated surface from mechanical trauma, and so far as possible, elimination of environmental stress. A conscientious program of medical therapy supervised by the physician and closely followed by the patient, is effective in controlling the symptoms of duodenal ulcer in approximately 85 per cent of patients. Relief of pain and reduction of acidity are accomplished by administration of alkalis or antacids, with the non-absorbable alkalis being preferable. Parasympatholytic drugs are also effective, particularly the quaternary amines. These agents should be used in effective doses that commonly produce mild side effects. It should be remembered that certain foods, particularly proteins, can act as effective buffers of acid and that fats have an inhibitory effect on gastric secretion. For this reason, milk is usually given in small amounts at frequent intervals. Antacids are most effective when they are given in small amounts at frequent intervals also. Winkelstein (1951) has advocated the continuous intragastric drip of milk and alkalis to control gastric acidity.

The diet for ulcer patients is selected with the idea of reducing, so far as possible, stimulation of gastric secretion and mechanical irritation of the ulcer. Stimulation of the cephalic phase of secretion is avoided by eliminating highly spiced foods, and foods which appeal to the appetite such as broiled steaks. Stimulation of the gastric phase, as well as mechanical irritation of the ulcer, are avoided by eliminating coarse and indigestible foods such as raw vegetables and fruits. The use of tobacco and alcohol in moderation is permitted by some physicians, yet forbidden by others. Rest and a placid way of life are desirable but cannot always be achieved. As a protection against environmental stress and the effects of charged emotions, many physicians use mild sedation in the form of barbiturates in the initial phase of their treatment of a patient with duodenal ulcer.

The medical treatment of both duodenal and gastric ulcer is essentially the same. It should be pointed out, however, that whereas a duodenal ulcer almost is never malignant, from 5 to 10 per cent of gastric ulcers are malignant. Thus, if what appears to be a simple gastric peptic ulcer does not heal within 3 to 4 weeks after adequate medical treatment, the possibility of a malignant lesion should be seriously considered.

Duodenal ulcer may become a chronic disease with periodic exacerbations. In addition, serious complications of the ulcer may develop. In general, medical treatment is best for an uncomplicated ulcer, whereas surgical treatment is usually reserved for the management of complications of the ulcer.

The surgical treatment of peptic ulcer is most often recommended for complications such as hemorrhage (especially in patients over 50 years of age), penetration or perforation, obstruction at the pylorus, and for patients in whom adequate medical treatment is unable to control symptoms. This latter situation is frequently referred to as "intractable" peptic ulcer.

The surgical treatment for gastric ulcer is usually partial gastric resection and re-establishment of gastrointestinal continuity by means of a gastroenterostomy. The surgical treatment for duodenal ulcer has varied during the years, but in general, three surgical approaches to the reduction of gastric acidity have been used. The first surgical procedure to gain popularity was simple gastroenterostomy. In this operation, an anastomosis between the stomach and jejunum was made in order to permit gastric emptying through the surgically created stoma and bypass the duodenum. Although gastroenterostomy proved to be effective for many patients, the incidence of a stomal ulcer was so high that the operation of simple gastroenterostomy has been abandoned by most surgeons. With the advent of more effective anesthesia, the introduction of antibiotics, and improvements of surgical techniques, subtotal gastric resection became a popular method of treatment of duodenal ulcer. In this operation, the pyloric portion and a large part of the body or fundus of the stomach are removed and continuity of the intestinal tract re-established by a gastrojejunostomy. The duodenal stump is closed, leaving the ulcer undisturbed. This operation is directed primarily at the gastric phase of gastric secretion with the removal of a large portion of the gastric mucosa containing parietal cells. Since experience had shown that removal of the antrum alone did not affect adequately a reduction in gastric acidity, it became the custom to take out a large part (60–80 per cent) of the body and fundus of the stomach as well.

Dragstedt (1944, 1945, 1946) popularized the operation of double vagotomy or vagectomy. In this operation an attempt is made to sever completely the vagus nerves immediately above or below the diaphragm, and to remove enough of the vagus trunks to prevent regeneration. The objective of this surgical procedure is to eliminate the cephalic phase of secretion which Dragstedt believes to be responsible for the hypersecretion in duodenal ulcer patients. The operation is not recommended for gastric ulcer. Due to the marked effects of vagotomy on gastric motility, causing delay in gastric emptying and stasis of gastric contents, it is necessary to do some type of drainage procedure when vagotomy is done. Thus, double vagotomy alone results in a profound suppression of gastric motility as well as secretion and the resulting gastric stasis proved to be a double hazard to the patient: there was danger of overdistention and atony of the stomach and the retained food in the antrum acted as a stimulus to the release of gastrin and thus increased the gastric phase of secretion. These problems have been met by performing at the same time as the vagotomy, a gastric drainage operation as previously mentioned. When a gastroenterostomy is done, this facilitates gastric emptying and encourages regurgitation of intestinal contents into the stomach, thus tending to lower gastric acidity.

More recently, the operation of antrectomy plus vagotomy has become popular with surgeons.

This procedure is directed at reducing both the cephalic and gastric phases of gastric secretion. By removing only the antrum, the patient is left with a larger gastric pouch, permitting him to eat more normal-sized meals, and postoperative complications do not occur as frequently as with the more extensive surgical procedure of subtotal or partial gastrectomy.

Radiation therapy has also been used for the treatment of peptic ulcer. The technique consists of delivering a dose of 1600 to 2500 roentgens to the stomach through anterior and posterior portals. X-ray therapy to the gastric mucosa has been shown by Richetts and associates (1948) to result in atrophy of the gastric mucosa and an associated suppression of gastric secretion. Suppression of gastric secretion is variable after x-ray treatment, but it has been reported that medical therapy combined with x-ray therapy increased the incidence of healing of ulcer from 70 per cent in patients treated by medical therapy alone to 94 per cent in those with combined medical and x-ray therapy. The incidence of recurrences was reduced from 66 to 32 per cent during a 2½ yr. period.

REFERENCES

ALLEY, A. The secretory activity of the gastric mucosa in the region of the lesser curvature. Tr. Roy. Soc. Can., 1933, 27, Sec. V, 71. The effect upon the gastric juice secretion of various cooked preparations of haddock and of lobster. Am. J. Digest. Dis. & Nutrit., 1934, 1, 182.

ALLEY, A., MacKENZIE, D. W., JR., AND WEBSTER, D. R. Dissociation of the functional properties of the gastric glands under the influence of fat. Am. J. Digest. Dis. & Nutrit., 1935, 1, 333. Inhibitory effects of histamine. Am. J. Digest. Dis. & Nutrit., 1935, 1, 787.

ANSON, M. L. AND MIRSKY, A. E. J. Estimation of pepsin with hemoglobin. J. Gen. Physiol., 1932, 16, 59.

ATKINSON, M. AND HENLEY, K. S. Levels of intragastric and intraduodenal acidity. Clin. Sc., London, 1955, 14, 1.

BABKIN, B. P. The value of histamine as a test of gastric secretion from a physiological point of view. Canad. M. A. J., 1930, 23, 268. Does the stomach secrete gastric juice continuously? Contrib. to the Med. Sciences in honor of Dr. Libman, Internat. Press, New York, 1932, 1, 113.

BABKIN, B. P. Modes of stimulation of the gastric secretion. Nature, 1934, 134, 1005. The "chemical" phase of gastric secretion and its regulation. Am. J. Digest. Dis. & Nutrit., 1934, 1, 715.

BABKIN, B. P. The abnormal functioning of the gastric secretory mechanism as a possible factor in the pathogenesis of peptic ulcer. Canad. M.A.J., 1938, 38, 421.

BABKIN, B. P., KOMAROV, O., AND KOMAROV, S. A. Effect of activated ergosterol and of parathyroid

hormone on gastric secretion in the dog. Endocrinology, 1940, 26, 703.

BABKIN, B. P. AND KOMAROV, S. A. The influence of gastric mucus on peptic digestion. Canad. M.A.J., 1932, 27, 463. (See also, WEBSTER, D. R. AND KOMAROV, S. A. Mucoprotein as a normal constituent of the gastric juice. J. Biol. Chem., 1932, 96, 133. Komarov, S. A., Isolation of mucoitinsulfuric acid from canine gastric juice. J. Biol. Chem. 1935, 109, 177. The influence of mucoitinsulfuric acid on peptic digestion. Am. J. Digest. Dis. & Nutrit. 1936, 3, 164.)

BAKER, B. L. AND ABRAMS, G. D. Effect of hypophysectomy on the cytology of the fundic glands of the stomach and the secretion of pepsin. Am. J. Physiol. 1954, 177, 409.

BARD, P. A diencephalic mechanism for the expression of rage with special reference to the sympathetic nervous system. Am. J. Physiol., 1928, 84, 490. The central representation of the sympathetic system. Arch. Neurol. & Psychiat. 1929, 22, 230.

BAXTER, S. G. Sympathetic secretory innervation of the gastric mucosa. Am. J. Digest. Dis. & Nutrit., 1934, 1, 40.

BEAMER, W. D., FRIEDMAN, M. H. F., THOMAS, J. E., AND REHFUSS, M. E. Factors responsible for the intestinal phase of gastric secretion. Am. J. Physiol. 1944, 141, 613.

BEAZELL, J. M. AND IVY, A. C. The influence of alcohol on the digestive tract. Quart. J. Stud. on Alcohol, 1940, 1, 45.

BENCE-JONES, H. Contributions to the chemistry of the urine. Paper III, Part I. (1849). On the variations of the acidity of the urine in the state of health. Phil. Trans. Roy. Soc. London, p. 235. Cited by Davies, 1951.

BENNETT, T. I. AND RYLE, J. A. Studies in gastric secretion: V. A study of normal gastric function based on one hundred healthy men by means of the fractional method of gastric analysis. Guy's Hosp. Rep., 1921, 71, 286.

BENNETT, T. I. AND VENABLES, J. F. The effect of emotions on gastric secretion and motility in the human being. Brit. M.J., 1920, 2, 662.

BIDDER, F. AND SCHMIDT, C. Die Verdauungssafte und der Stoffwechsel. p. 45, G. A. Reyher, Leipzig, 1852.

BLACKBURN, C. M. AND CODE, C. F. The inhibition of gastric secretion in dogs by human gastric juice and gastric mucin. Am. J. Physiol., 1948, 155, 427.

BOYD, T. E. Influence of alkalis on secretion and composition of gastric juice, effect of prolonged administration of sodium bicarbonate and calcium carbonate. Am. J. Physiol., 1925, 71, 455.

BRUNSCHWIG, A., VAN PROHASKA, J., CLARKE, T. H. AND KANDEL, E. V. A secretory depressant in gastric juice of patients with pernicious anemia. J. Clin. Invest., 1939, 18, 415.

BUCHER, G. AND IVY, A. C. Disappearance of uropepsin from the urine of gastrectomized cats. Am. J. Physiol. 1947, 150, 415.

CARD, W. I. AND MARKS, I. N. The relationship between the acid output of the stomach following the "maximal" histamine stimulation and the parietal cell mass. Clin. Sc., 1960, 19, 147.

CLARK, W. E. LE GROS. The structure and connections of the thalamus. Brain, 1932, **55**, 406.

CODE, C. F., BLACKBURN, C. M., LIVERMORE, G. R., AND RATKE, H. V. A method for the quantitative determination of gastric secretory inhibition. Gastroenterology, 1949, **13**, 573.

COX, A. J. Stomach size and its relation to chronic peptic ulcer. Arch. Path., 1952, **54**, 407.

DAVENPORT, H. W. Gastric carbonic anhydrase. J. Physiol., 1939, **97**, 32.

DAVIES, R. E. AND LONGMUIR, N. M. Production of ulcers in isolated frog gastric mucosa. Biochem. J., 1948, **42**, 621.

DRAGSTEDT, L. R. Supradiaphragmatic section of the vagus nerves in the treatment of gastric ulcer. Gastroenterology, 1944, **3**, 450. Removal of the vagus nerves of the stomach in gastroduodenal ulcer. Surgery, 1945, **17**, 742. Section of the vagus nerves to the stomach in the treatment of peptic ulcer. Surg. Gynec. & Obst., 1946, **83**, 547.

DRAGSTEDT, L. R. Pathogenesis of gastroduodenal ulcer. Arch. Surg., 1942, **44**, 438.

DRAGSTEDT, L. R. AND ELLIS, J. C. The fatal effect of the total loss of gastric juice. Am. J. Physiol., 1930, **93**, 407.

DRAGSTEDT, L. R., OBERHELMAN, H. A., EVANS, S. O. AND RIGLER, S. P. Antrum hyperfunction and gastric ulcer. Ann. Surg., 1954, **140**, 396.

DRAGSTEDT, L. R. AND VAUGHN, A. M. Gastric ulcer studies. Arch. Surg., 1924, **8**, 791.

DRAGSTEDT, L. R., WOODWARD, E. R., OBERHELMAN, H. A., JR., STORER, E. H., AND SMITH, C. W. Effect of transplantation of antrum of stomach on gastric secretion in experimental animals. Am. J. Physiol., 1951, **165**, 386.

DYER, H. AND ROE, J. H. Relation of nutrition to gastric function; effect of vitamin A deficiency. Am. J. Digest. Dis., 1941, **8**, 833.

EDKINS, J. S. On the chemical mechanism of gastric secretion. Proc. Roy. Soc., London, Ser. B, 1905, **76**, 376. The chemical mechanism of gastric secretion. J. Physiol., 1906, **34**, 133.

FARNSWORTH, E. B., SPEER, E. AND ALT, H. L. Pepsin-like substance in urine of patients with pernicious anemia and of normal subjects. Proc. Central Soc. Clin. Res., 1945, **18**, 52.

FARRELL, J. I. Contributions to physiology of gastric secretion; response of glands to substances applied to gastric mucosa. Am. J. Physiol., 1928, **85**, 672.

FARRELL, J. I. AND IVY, A. C. Studies on the motility of the transplanted gastric pouch. Am. J. Physiol., 1926, **76**, 227.

FAULEY, G. B. AND IVY, A. C. Fundusectomy prevents postoperative jejunal ulcer. Proc. Soc. Exper. Biol. & Med., 1926, **34**, 152.

FISHER, R. B. AND HUNT, J. N. The inorganic components of gastric secretion. J. Physiol., 1950, **111**, 138.

FÖLDES, F. AND VAJDA, G. Effect of vitamin A on the secretion of gastric juice in deficient hydrochloric acid production. Brit. M.J., 1941, **1**, 317.

FULTON, J. F. AND INGRAHAM, F. D. Emotional disturbances following experimental lesions of the base of the brain (pre-chiasmal). Am. J. Physiol., 1929, **90**, 35.

GILMAN, A. AND COWGILL, G. R. Osmotic relations between blood and body fluids II. The osmotic relation of blood and gastric juice. Am. J. Physiol., 1933, **103**, 143.

GRAY, S. J. The effect of steroids on the gastrointestinal tract. Am. J. Gastroenterology, 1958, **30**, 266.

GRAY, S. J., RAMSEY, C. AND REIFENSTEIN, R. W. Hormonal influences upon the stomach. Am. J. Gastroenterology, 1955, **24**, 244.

GREGORY, R. A. AND IVY, A. C. Humoral stimulation of gastric secretion. Quart. J. Exper. Physiol., 1941, **31**, 111.

GREGORY, R. A. AND TRACY, H. J. The constitution and properties of two gastrins extracted from hog antral mucosa. Gut, 1964, **5**, 103. A note on the nature of the gastrin-like stimulant present in Zollinger-Ellison tumours. Gut, 1964, **5**, 115.

GREGORY, R. A., TRACY, H. J., FRENCH, J. M. AND SIRCUS, W. Extraction of a gastrin-like substance from a pancreatic tumour in a case of Zollinger-Ellison syndrome. Lancet, 1960, **1**, 1045.

GROSSMAN, M. I. Integration of neural and hormonal control of gastric secretion. The Physiologist, 1963, **6**, 349.

HAVERBACK, B. J., BOGDANSKI, D. AND HOGBEN, A. Inhibition of gastric acid secretion in the dog by the precursor of serotonin (5-hydroxytryptophane). Gastroenterology, 1957, **34**, 188; (see also 1957, **32**, 1058).

HAWK, P. B., MILLER, R. J., BERGHEIM, O., AND REHFUSS, M. E. The psychic secretion of gastric juice in normal men. Am. J. Physiol. 1920, **52**, 1. See also Proc. Soc. Exper. Biol. & Med. 1920, **17**, 97.

HESS, W. R. Vegetative Functionen und Zwischenhirn. Helvet. Physiol. et Pharmacol. Acta, Suppl. IV, Ed. VII, pp. 1–65, 1947.

HOELZEL, F. The effect of variations in protein intake on the acidity of the fasting stomach. Am. J. Physiol., 1926, **77**, 166.

HOLLANDER, F. The insulin test for the presence of intact nerve fibers after vagal operations for peptic ulcer. Gastroenterology, 1946, **7**, 607.

HOLLANDER, F. The mucous barrier in the stomach. In Peptic ulcer (DAVID SANDWEISS, ed.), p. 65, W. B. Saunders Company, Philadelphia, 1951.

HOLLANDER, F. Recent advances in the physiology of gastric secretions. Ann. New York Acad. Sci. 1962, **99**, 4.

HOLLANDER F. AND COWGILL, G. R. Studies in gastric secretion. I. Gastric juice of constant acidity. J. Biol. Chem. 1931, **91**, 151.

IHRE, B. Human gastric secretion. A quantitative study of gastric secretion in normal and pathological conditions. Acta med. scandinav., Suppl., 1938, **95**, 1.

IVY, A. C. AND BACHRACH, W. H. An abnormal mechanism for the excitation of gastric secretion in the dog. Am. J. Digest. Dis., 1940, **7**, 76.

IVY, A. C. AND GRAY, J. S. Enterogastrone. Cold Spring Harbor Symposia, 1937, **5**, 405.

IVY, A. C. AND SCHAYER, R. W. Fed. Proc., 1957, **16.** 65.

JANOWITZ, H. D., DREILING, D. A., ROBBIN, H. L., AND HOLLANDER, F. Inhibition of formation of hydrochloric acid in the human stomach by Diamox. Gastroenterology, 1957, 33, 378.

JANOWITZ, H. D., HOLLANDER, F., ORRINGER, D., LEVY, M. H., WINKELSTEIN, A., KAUFMAN, M. R., AND MARGOLIN, S. G. A quantitative study of the gastric secretory response to sham feeding in a human subject. Gastroenterology, 1950, 16, 104.

JONES, T. W. AND HARKINS, H. M. Evaluation of mechanisms involved in gastric acid secretion of pylorus ligated rats. Gastroenterology, 1958, 35, 309.

KAY, A. W. Effect of large doses of histamine on gastric secretion of HCl. An augmented histamine test. Brit. J. Med., 1953, 2, 77.

KELLER, A. D., HARE, W. K., AND D'AMOUR, M. D. Ulceration in digestive tract following experimental lesions in brain stem. Proc. Soc. Exper. Biol. & Med., 1933, 30, 772. Ulceration of the digestive tract following hypophysectomy. Am. J. Physiol., 1934, 109, 63.

KIRSNER, J. B., LEVIN, E., AND PALMER, W. L. Observations on the excessive nocturnal gastric secretion in patients with duodenal ulcer. Gastroenterology, 1949, 11, 598.

KLOTZ, A. P. AND DUVALL, M. R. The laboratory determination of pepsin in gastric juice with radioactive iodinated albumin. J. Lab. & Clin. Med., 1957, 50, 753.

KOMAROV, S. A. Studies on gastrin. I. Methods of isolation of a specific gastric secretagogue from the pyloric mucous membrane and its chemical properties. Rev. Canad. Biol., 1942, 1, 377.

KOSAKA, T. AND LIM, R. K. S. Demonstration of the humoral agent in fat inhibition of gastric secretion. Proc. Soc. Exper. Biol. & Med., 1930, 27, 890.

LAI, K. S. Studies on gastrin: Part II. Quantitative study of the distribution of gastrin-like activity along the gut. Gut, 1964, 5, 334.

LEVIN, E., KIRSNER, J. B., AND PALMER, W. L. The nocturnal gastric secretion in patients with gastric carcinoma: A comparison with normal individuals and patients with duodenal ulcer and with gastric ulcer. Gastroenterology, 1949, 12, 561.

LEVIN, E., KIRSNER, J. B., AND PALMER, W. L. A simple measure of gastric secretion in man: Comparison of one hour basal secretion, histamine secretion and twelve hour nocturnal secretion. Gastroenterology, 1951, 19, 88.

LIM, R. K. S. Observations on the mechanism of inhibition of gastric function by fat. Quart. J. Exper. Physiol., 1933, 23, 263.

LINDE, S. Studies on the stimulation mechanism of gastric secretion. Acta. physiol. scandinav., Suppl. 74, 1950, 21, 1.

LUCK, J. M. AND SETH, T. N. Biochem. J., 1924, 18, 227; 19, 357.

MACDONALD, D. A. The control of the autonomic nervous system by the hypothalamus. Lancet, 1951, 1, 627.

MACLEAN, P. D. Psychosomatic disorders and the visceral brain. Psychosom. Med., 1949, 11, 338.

MANN, F. C. AND WILLIAMSON, C. S. Experimental production of peptic ulcers. Ann. Surg., 1923, 77, 409.

MARKS, I. N., KOMAROV, S. A., AND SHAY, H. Maximal acid secretory response to histamine and its relation to parietal cell mass in the dog. Am. J. Physiol., 1960, 199, 579.

MATTHEWS, W. B. AND DRAGSTEDT, L. R. Surg. Gynec. Obstet. 1932, 55, 265.

MURPHY, J. P. AND GELLHORN, E. Further investigations on diencephalic-cortical relations and their significance for the problem of emotion. J. Neurophysiol., 1945, 8, 431.

OBERHALMAN, H. A., JR., WOODWARD, E. R., ZUBIRAN, J. M. AND DRAGSTEDT, L. R. Physiology of the gastric antrum. Am. J. Physiol., 1952, 169, 738.

PAVY, 1923. Cited by Dragstedt and Vaughn, 1924.

PINCUS, I. J., THOMAS, J. E., AND REHFUSS, M. E. A study of gastric secretion as influenced by changes in duodenal acidity. Proc. Soc. Exper. Biol. & Med., 1942, 51, 367.

POPIELSKI, L. Imidazolyläthelamin und die Organextracte. I. B-1 als mächtigen erreger der Magendrüsen. Pflüger's Arch. ges. Physiol., 1920, 178, 214.

PROUT, W. On the nature of the acid and saline matters usually existing in the stomachs of animals. Philosoph. Trans. Royal Soc. London, Part I, 1824, p. 45.

REHFUSS, M. E. A new method of gastric testing with a description of a method for the fractional testing of the gastric juice. Am. J. Med. Sc., 1914, 147, 848.

REHM, W. S. A theory of the formation of hydrochloric acid by the stomach. Gastroenterology, 1950, 14, 401. See also Am. J. Physiol., 1949, 159, 586.

RICHET, J. Anat. et Physiol., 1878, p. 526. (Cited by Carlson, 1923).

RICKETTS, W. S., PALMER, W. L., KIRSNER, J. B., AND HAMANN, A. Radiation therapy in peptic ulcer: An analysis of the results. Gastroenterology, 1948, 11, 789.

ROBERTSON, C. R., LANGLOIS, K., MARTIN, C. G., SLEZAK, G., AND GROSSMAN, M. I. Release of gastrin in reponse to bathing the pyloric mucosa with acetylcholine. Am. J. Physiol., 1950, 163, 27.

ROHRER, G. V., SCOTT, J. R., JOEL, W., AND WOLF, S. The fine structure of human gastric parietal cells. Am. J. Digest. Dis., 1965, 10, 13.

ROTH, J. A. AND IVY, A. C. The effect of caffein on gastric secretion in the dog, cat and man. Am. J. Physiol., 1944, 141, 454.

SACKS, J., IVY, A. C., BURGESS, J. P., AND VANDOLAH, J. E. Histamine as the hormone for gastric secretion. Am. J. Physiol., 1932, 101, 331.

SCHAYER, R. W. AND IVY, A. C. Evidence that histamine is a gastric secretory hormone in the rat. Am. J. Physiol. 1957, 189, 369.

SCHÖDT, E. Über die behandlung Verschiedener Magen-krankheiten mit Vitamin A. Ztschr. klin. Med., 1936, 130, 163.

SEDAR, A. W. The fine structure of the oxyntic cell in relation to functional activity of the stomach. Ann. New York Acad. Sci., 1962, 99, 9.

SEDAR, A. W. AND FRIEDMAN, M. H. F. Correlation of the fine structure of the gastric parietal cell (dog) with functional activity of the stomach. J. Biophys. Biochem. Cytol., 1961, 11, 349.

SEGAL, H. L., MILLER, L. L., AND MORTON, J. J. Determination of gastric acidity without intubation by use of cation exchange indicator compounds. Proc. Soc. Exper. Biol. & Med., 1950, 74, 218.

SEGAL, H. L., MILLER, L. L., AND PLUMB, E. J. Tubeless gastric analysis with an Azure-A ion exchange compound. Gastroenterology, 1955, 28, 402.

SMITH, W. O., HOKE, R., LANDY, J., CAPUTTO, R. AND WOLF, S. The nature of the inhibitory effect of normal human gastric juice on Heidenhain pouch dogs. Gastroenterology, 1958, 34, 181.

STROM, G. AND UVNÄS, B. Motor responses of gastrointestinal tract and bladder to topical stimulation of the frontal lobe, basal ganglia and hypothalamus in the cat. Acta Physiol. scandinav., 1950, 21, 90.

THOMAS, J. E. Some recent progress in gastrointestinal physiology. Rev. Gastroenterology, 1952, 20, 174.

THOMAS J. E. The autonomic nervous system in gastrointestinal disease. J. A. M. A., 1955, 157, 209.

UVNÄS, B. The part played by the pyloric region in the cephalic phase of gastric secretion. Acta physiol. scandinav., 1942, 4, Suppl. 13, 1.

UVNÄS, B., ANDERSON, S., ELWIN, C., AND MALM, A. The influence of exclusion of the antrum-duodenum passage on the hydrochloric acid secretion in Pavlov pouch dogs. Gastroenterology, 1956, 30, 790.

VANZANT, F. R., ALVAREZ, W. C., EUSTERMAN, G. B., DUNN, H. L., AND BERKSON, J. The normal range of gastric acidity from youth to old age. Arch. Int. Med., 1932, 49, 345.

VINEBERG, A. M. The activation of different elements of the gastric secretion by variation of vagal stimulation. Am. J. Physiol., 1931, 96, 363.

WEBSTER, D. R. AND ARMOUR, J. C. Effect of pyloric obstruction on the gastric secretion. Tr. Roy. Soc. Canada, 1932, 26, sec. V., 109.

WILHELMJ, C. M., NEIGERS, I., AND HILL, F. C. A comparison of intragastric and duodenal factors in lowering the acidity of gastric contents. Am. J. Physiol., 1934, 107, 490.

WILHELMJ, C. M., O'BRIEN, F. T., AND HILL, F. C. The inhibitory influence of the acidity of the gastric contents on the secretion of acid by the stomach. Am. J. Physiol., 1936, 115, 429.

WINKELSTEIN, A. Continuous intragastric drip therapy for peptic ulcer. In Peptic ulcer (DAVID SANDWEISS, ed.), p. 377. W. B. Saunders Co., Philadelphia, 1951.

ZELJONY, G. P. AND SAVICH, V. V. Concerning the mechanism of gastric secretion. Proc. Soc. Russ. Physicians, St. Petersburg, January–May, 1911. (Cited by Babkin, 1928).

ZOLLINGER, R. M. AND ELLISON, E. H. Primary peptic ulcer of jejunum associated with islet cell tumors of pancreas. Ann. Surg., 1955, 142, 709.

Monographs and Reviews

BABKIN, B. P. The digestive work of the stomach. Physiol. Rev., 1928, 8, 365.

BABKIN, B. P. Die Äussere Sekrection der Verdauungsdrüsen, Springer, Berlin, 1928.

BABKIN, B. P. Secretory mechanism of the digestive glands, 2nd ed., p. 72, Paul B. Hoeber, New York, 1950.

BEAUMONT, W. Experiments and observations on the gastric juice and the physiology of digestion. Facsimile edition reprinted on the occasion of the XIIIth International Physiological Congress. Boston, 1929.

BERNARD, C. 1859. (Cited by Dragstedt and Vaughn, 1924.)

BICKEL, A. AND KATSCH, G. 1912. Chirurgische Technik zur normalen und pathologischen Physiologie der Verdauungs apparates. (Cited by Babkin, 1950).

CANNON, W. B. Bodily changes in pain, hunger, fear and rage. Appleton-Century-Crofts, Inc., New York and London, 1915.

CARLSON, A. J. The secretion of gastric juice in health and disease. Physiol. Rev., 1923, 3, 1.

CODE, C. F. Histamine and gastric secretion. Churchill, London, 1956.

CONWAY, E. J. The biochemistry of gastric acid secretion. Am. Lecture Series. Charles C Thomas, Springfield, Ill., 1953.

CUSHING, H. Peptic ulcer and the interbrain (Fourth Balfour Lecture, University of Toronto). In The pituitary body, hypothalamus and parasympathetic nervous system. Charles C Thomas, Springfield, Ill., 1932.

DAVENPORT, H. W. Metabolic aspects of gastric acid secretion. In Metabolic aspects of transport across cell membranes (Q. R. MURPHY, ed.), p. 295. University of Wisconsin Press, Madison, Wisconsin, 1957.

DAVENPORT, H. W. Physiology of the digestive tract. Year Book Medical Publishers, Inc., Chicago, 1962.

DAVIES, R. E. The mechanism of hydrochloric acid production by the stomach. Biol. Rev. Cambridge Phil. Soc., 1951, 26, 87.

GREGORY, R. A. Secretory mechanisms of the gastrointestinal tract. Edward Arnold Publishers, Ltd., London, 1962.

GROSSMAN, M. I. A critical analysis of various theories of the pathogenesis of peptic ulcer. In Peptic ulcer (DAVID SANDWEISS, ed.), p. 65. W. B. Saunders Company, Philadelphia, 1951.

IVY, A. C., GROSSMAN, M. I., AND BACHRACH, W. H. Peptic ulcer. Blakiston Company, Philadelphia, 1950.

JAMES, A. H. The physiology of gastric digestion. Edward Arnold and Company, London, 1957.

LILLIBRIDGE, C. B. The fine structure of normal human gastric mucosa. Gastroenterology, 1964, 47, 269.

PAVLOV, I. P. The work of the digestive glands. Griffin, London, 1910.

REHM, W. S. AND DENNIS, W. H. A discussion of theories of hydrochloric acid formation in the light of electrophysiological findings. In Metabolic aspects of transport across cell membranes, p. 303. University of Wisconsin Press, Madison, Wisconsin, 1957.

WOLF, S. AND WOLFF, H. G. Human gastric function. Oxford University Press, 1943.

CHAPTER 58

Pancreatic Secretion

Structure of the Pancreas

The pancreas is both an endocrine and exocrine gland. It is an elongated structure 5 to 6 in. in length, which extends from the duodenum obliquely upward behind the stomach, across the posterior abdominal wall to the spleen at the level of the first and second lumbar vertebrae. It develops from two outgrowths (ventral and dorsal) of the primitive gut. The ventral pancreatic bud arises with the hepatic diverticulum, and together they grow into the ventral mesentery. The dorsal pancreatic bud enters the dorsal mesentery and as a result of the rotation of the gut together with its mesenteries as well as growth of the pancreatic anlages themselves, the two portions of the pancreas meet along the left border of the duodenum and soon fuse with one another. The duct of the ventral pancreas becomes confluent with that of the dorsal anlage, usually near its origin. In keeping with the fact that the proximal portion of this duct was developed in conjunction with the liver bud, the definitive pancreatic duct (of Wirsung) enters the duodenum in close association with the common bile duct. That portion of the duct of the dorsal rudiment which lies between the duodenum and the point of anastomosis with the ventral duct is normally retarded in subsequent development and becomes the accessory duct (ductus pancreaticus accessorius or *duct of Santorini*).

For descriptive purposes the adult pancreas is divided into a *head, body* and *tail*. The more massive portion of the gland, the head, is flattened dorsoventrally and lies within the concavity of the duodenum to which it is attached by numerous blood vessels, the pancreatic ducts, and loose connective tissue. The uncinate process is a hooklike medial projection from the lower part of the head. The body of the pancreas represents most of the remainder of the gland; it is somewhat prismatic in shape and presents an anterior, a posterior and an inferior surface. The tail is the pointed, tongue-like left end of the gland, which lies in contact with the spleen.

The pancreas is a racemose gland, its alveoli resembling those of the salivary gland in their general arrangement and design. When studied microscopically, the pancreas is seen to be made up chiefly of groups of cells forming acini which tend to be spherical or ovoid in general contour; in the closely packed tissue of the pancreas they are actually polygonal. Groups of acini form primary lobules, also polygonal in contour, which are imperfectly separated from other primary lobules by incomplete connective tissue septa. Numerous adjacent primary lobules form a secondary lobule. The secondary lobules are completely surrounded by connective tissue and can be dissected out as separate structures connected to the rest of the gland by ducts, nerve fibers, lymphatic vessels and blood vessels. The pancreatic tissue proper is composed of acinous cells, islet cells (ch. 67), and duct cells. The acinous cells, owing to the spherical shape of the acini, tend to be pyramidal, with the truncated apex of the pyramid directed toward the lumen of the acinus. They are large cells with a well developed nucleus and abundant granular cytoplasm. The granules, called *zymogen granules*, vary in number and position in the cells depending on the state of activity of the gland but tend to be more abundant in the apical region of the cell which is adjacent to the lumen of the acinus.

An interesting feature of the duct system of the pancreas is the manner in which the small or terminal intralobular ducts end in relation to the acinus. Cells, corresponding in structure to the cells of the terminal ducts, may be seen in microscopic sections within the acini; these are called *centroacinar cells*. Most investigators have concluded that the terminal duct cells extend into the lumen of the acini where they form a sort of lining.

Innervation of the Pancreas

The pancreas receives an abundant nerve supply from both the vagi and splanchnic nerves. According to Richins (1945), who made his studies on cats by strictly morphological methods, the entire extrinsic nerve supply to the pancreas passes through the celiac plexus and reaches the gland by way of the nerve plexus surrounding the arteries, chiefly the superior pancreaticoduodenal artery. The vagus fibers end in the intrinsic ganglia of the pancreas. From these the parasympathetic path is continued through postganglionic unmyelinated fibers to the acinous cells, islet cells and the smooth muscles of the ducts. According to Richins, the efferent splanchnic fibers destined to supply the pancreas all end in the celiac and associated ganglia. From there the sympathetic path is continued through unmyelinated, postganglionic fibers which are distributed solely to the pancreatic blood vessels. However, the presence of cholinergic secretory fibers in the splanchnic nerves of the cat, which do not synapse in the celiac ganglia, is indicated by the physiological studies of Babkin and others (1939). Myelinated visceral afferent fibers from the pancreas are also present in the splanchnic nerves.

Guillaumie (1934), who used physiological methods on dogs, reached conclusions quite different from Richins regarding the course of the vagus fibers. Confirming, with few exceptions, the early observations of Popielski (1896), she concluded that a majority (80 per cent) of the vagus fibers to the pancreas course along the lesser curvature of the stomach, cross the pylorus, and after proceeding a certain distance in the duodenal wall, enter the pancreas by way of the nerve plexus which surrounds the major pancreatic duct. According to her findings, any method of collecting pancreatic juice in which the ducts are severed or separated from the intestine involves a partial denervation of the pancreas. The remaining 20 per cent of the vagus fibers, according to this author, traverse the hepatic plexus and join the pancreas in the region of the pylorus.

It is often incorrectly stated that the pancreas receives all, or the greater part, of its vagus nerve supply from the right vagus. This error arises from the tendency to overlook the fact that after the vagi merge in the esophageal plexus, the right and left nerves can no longer be distinguished. Two or more trunks emerge from the esophageal plexus. The trunk that occupies the more posterior position at the level of the diaphragm, although referred to by some anatomists as the right vagus, contains fibers from both the right and left vagi as they occur in the neck. When stimulated in the neck, the right and left vagi are equally effective in modifying pancreatic function.

The intrinsic ganglia of the pancreas undoubtedly develop in association with the enteric nerve plexuses. It would be interesting to know whether they retain connections with this plexus and whether such connections have anything to do with the effects of intestinal stimuli on pancreatic secretion. In this relation, it is interesting that, in addition to the rich plexus of nerve fibers surrounding the pancreatic ducts, there are many nerve fibers in the loose areolar tissue between the pancreas and duodenum.

Pancreatic Juice

The pancreas secretes a colorless, odorless, alkaline fluid of low viscosity, tasting strongly of sodium bicarbonate. Some specimens have been described as having a faint straw color. Exceptional specimens having a high concentration of enzymes may be viscous and may even jell at low temperatures. Pure pancreatic juice collected from dogs without loss of carbon dioxide has a pH between 8 and 8.3 and a specific gravity that ranges from 1.007 to 1.042, but usually falls between 1.010 and 1.018. The osmolar concentration of the juice is the same as that of the blood when the two are collected simultaneously from the same animal. When the osmolar concentration of the blood is altered experimentally, the pancreatic juice shows a corresponding change.

Electrolyte Composition

The distinguishing chemical characteristic of the juice is its *high bicarbonate content*. This is in contrast to the strongly acid character of the gastric juice which is secreted at the same time. The fact that the pancreas secretes base while the stomach is secreting acid is a factor in maintaining the acid-base balance of the rest of the body. Likewise, the fact that the two secretions are mixed in the intestine helps to maintain the normal pH of the intestinal contents. It is now well established that the bicarbonate and chloride concentrations of pancreatic juice vary in a reciprocal manner, so that the sum of the two expressed in milliequivalents is approximately constant and nearly the same as the total base of the blood plasma. In human pancreatic juice, Janowitz and Dreiling (1962) have found the sum of bicarbonate and chloride concentrations to remain remarkably constant at different secretory rates. They reported a value of 154 ± 10 mmoles/kg. H_2O. Also, within physiological limits, the bicarbonate concentration increases and the chloride concentration decreases with increasing rates of secretion. This relationship holds over a wide range of secretory rates and is

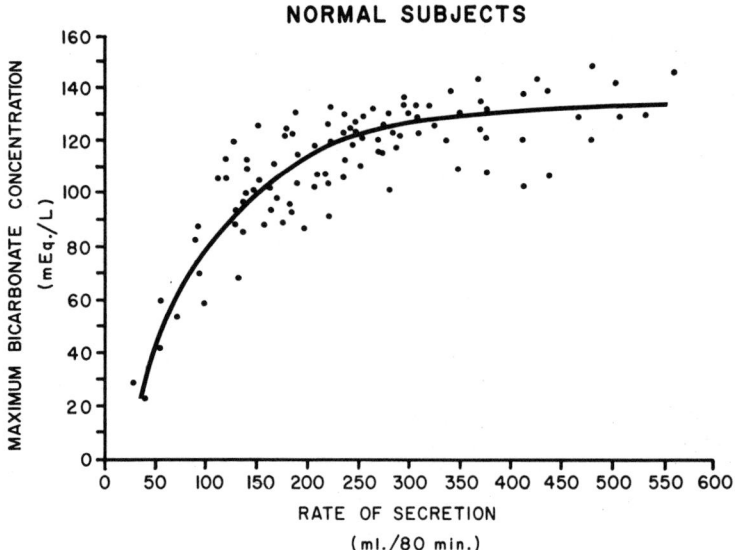

FIG. 58.1. Maximum bicarbonate concentration observed at different rates of pancreatic secretion in normal subjects following stimulation of the pancreas with intravenous secretin. (Redrawn from Dreiling and Janowitz, 1959.)

such that a straight line results when the logarithm of the bicarbonate concentration in mEq/l. is plotted against the *reciprocal* of the rate of secretion expressed as cubic centimeters of secretion per kilogram of body weight per minute; the slope indicates an inverse relation. The rate of increase in bicarbonate concentration with the rate of increase of secretion varies with different animals, therefore the rate of secretion cannot be estimated from the bicarbonate concentration of an unknown sample. However, it is possible to say that if the bicarbonate concentration is high, the pancreatic juice was secreted at a relatively rapid rate. The maximum bicarbonate concentration in juice collected from different dogs ranges between 135 and 148 mEq/l. and the maximum rate of secretion is about 0.1 ml./kg./min., or about 1 ml./min. for a 10 kg. dog; higher rates than this are occasionally seen. The relationship of bicarbonate concentration to flow rate in pancreatic juice collected from man is illustrated in fig. 58.1. In addition to chloride and bicarbonate, the pancreatic juice contains a small amount of phosphate, but less than that occurring in blood plasma.

The principal bases of pancreatic juice are sodium and potassium. Small amounts of calcium, magnesium and zinc are also found in pancreatic juice. The concentrations of sodium and potassium are approximately equivalent to those of the blood plasma and are independent of secretory rate. The calcium concentration is only 1.5 to 2.0 mEq/l. as compared to about 4.5 to 5.5 for blood serum. The low calcium concentration compared to that of the blood is attributed to the fact that much of the blood calcium is combined with protein and is not in a diffusible state. The electrolyte composition of a sample of human pancreatic juice secreted at a relatively high rate is illustrated in fig. 58.2.

PROTEIN CONTENT

The protein content of pancreatic juice varies over a wide range but in an orderly manner with the conditions governing secretion. In 200 samples of dog's pancreatic juice collected under different conditions, the protein content in different samples varied between 0.1 per cent and 10 per cent. Concentrations found in human pancreatic juice collected through accidental or surgical fistulas are nearer the lower extreme, ranging from 0.1 to 0.3 per cent. The protein in the juice consists mainly of enzymes. Using electrophoresis, a method by which the proteins in a mixture can be separated by means of their different mobilities in an electrical field, it has been possible to determine that there are at least ten distinct proteins in pancreatic juice, with the possibility of still others that fail to separate out in the time during which the electrical field is maintained (Grossberg, Komarov, and Shay, 1952). This method of separating the proteins of pancreatic juice also separates the enzymatic activity; proteolytic activity is found in one component, lipolytic activity in another, and amylolytic activity in another, confirming the belief that the proteins dealt with in the electrophoretic procedure are the actual enzymes of the juice. When different methods are used to stimulate secretion of the juice the electrophoretic patterns differ, depending upon the method used. For example, a meat meal produces pancreatic juice having a different protein composition from that secreted in response to stimulation by means of urocholine and secretin. This suggests that the relative concentration of the different enzymes in the juice can be made to vary by using different stimuli to cause secretion.

PANCREATIC ENZYMES

The enzymes of pancreatic juice are capable of digesting all three types of foodstuff, that is, the juice contains proteolytic, amylolytic and lipolytic enzymes. The proteolytic enzymes, as they occur in the pancreatic tissue and freshly secreted pancreatic juice, possess no proteolytic activity and are referred to in that state as zymogens. In the older literature, the proteolytic activity was attributed to trypsin, the corresponding zymogen being trypsinogen. Kunitz and Northrup (1934) have shown that what was called trypsin or trypsinogen consists of at least two components, for one of which they retained the name *trypsin* and for the other they coined the name *chymotrypsin*. The zymogen of chymotrypsin is known as chymotrypsinogen. These substances have been isolated and obtained in crystalline form and many of their properties determined by Kunitz and Northrup.

TRYPSINOGEN. The molecular weight of *trypsinogen* is not definitely known but it is approximately 25,000. Trypsinogen isolated from different species have slightly different molecular weights as estimated by chemical analysis (Desnuelle and Rovery, 1961). The molecular weight of bovine trypsinogen has been estimated at 23,800 and porcine trypsinogen at 24,900. Trypsinogen is a single polypeptide chain containing 229 amino acid residues (Neurath, 1964). Cleavage of trypsinogen between residues 6 and 7 yields active trypsin. As an enzyme trypsin hydrolyzes native protein, producing proteoses and peptides. It accelerates coagulation of the blood, in which it acts as a thrombokinase, but has only a feeble action in clotting milk. In its action on proteins, trypsin

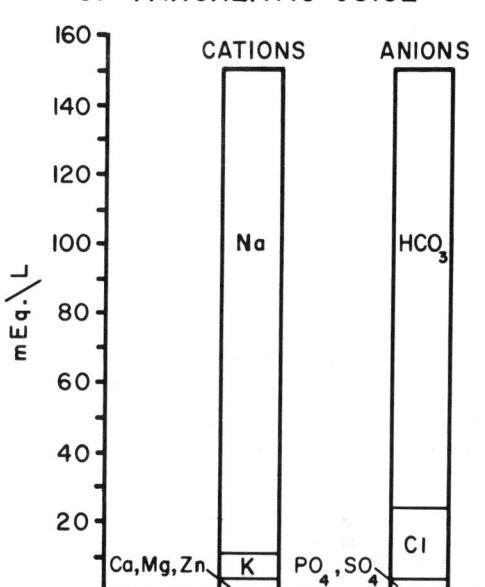

FIG. 58.2. Example of the electrolyte composition of human pancreatic juice secreted at a high flow rate of 3.5 ml./min.

hydrolyzes only those peptide bonds whose carbonyl group is contributed by an amino acid that has a positively charged side group as arginine or lysine. Trypsin cleaves peptide bonds that occupy an internal position in a polypeptide chain and is referred to as an "endopeptidase." Its optimum pH for digestion of casein lies between pH 8 and 9. When pure, it is reversibly inactivated by heat in acid solution; it slowly decomposes in alkaline solution.

Trypsinogen is indistinguishable on chemical analysis from trypsin, but has different solubilities and a different crystalline form, and it exhibits no proteolytic activity. It changes spontaneously in solution to active trypsin, but the change is accelerated by acid or by exposure to concentrated magnesium sulfate, calcium chloride, active trypsin or to certain activating enzymes called *kinases*. The effectiveness of trypsin in the activation of trypsinogen is of great importance because such autocatalytic reactions progress with great rapidity once they are started and require only minute amounts of activating agents to set them going. Spontaneous activation of trypsinogen is suppressed in crude extracts (and doubtless also in living pancreas) by the presence of an inhibitor which inactivates small amounts of trypsin. The trypsinogen, as secreted in the living animal, is activated on contact with the intestinal mucosa by means of an enzyme in the mucosa called *enterokinase*. Enterokinase does not appear in the intestinal secretion in the absence of pancreatic juice but is present in intestinal mucosal extracts. A similar substance is present in pancreatic extracts. Kunitz has observed that certain common molds (penicillium) produce an enzyme capable of activating trypsinogen.

CHYMOTRYPSINOGEN. Chymotrypsinogen has a molecular weight of approximately 25,700 and, like trypsinogen, is a single polypeptide chain containing 246 amino acid residues, or 17 more than trypsinogen (Neurath, 1964). When cleaved between residues 15 and 16, chymotrypsinogen is converted to the active enzyme chymotrypsin. The "active centers" of both trypsin and chymotrypsin are remarkably similar. In each enzyme a "histidine region" and a "serine region" have been localized and found to be connected by disulfide bonds (from two half-cystine residues) that lock the histidine and serine residues in a fixed position.

Chymotrypsinogen is converted to chymotrypsin by active trypsin only, but indirect activation can be accomplished by enterokinase if trypsinogen is also present. If chymotrypsinogen is activated rapidly by fairly large amounts of trypsin, π-chymotrypsin is formed which then changes spontaneously to δ-chymotrypsin, as a result of the π-chymotrypsin acting upon itself. If smaller amounts of trypsin are used the major products are α-, β-, and γ-chymotrypsin which appear to have essentially the same molecular weight as chymotrypsinogen and π- and δ-chymotrypsin. A sixth type, known as chymotrypsin (and chymotrypsinogen) β, also has been isolated. Alpha chymotrypsin is the active enzyme first crystallized by Kunitz and Northrup. The nature of the structural differences among the various chymotrypsins, other than in their crystal form, is unclear. The activity of chymotrypsin is comparable to that of trypsin but it has different specificities, for example, it coagulates milk but not blood. Chymotrypsin digests casein somewhat more rapidly than does trypsin, but the digestion is carried much further by a mixture of the two enzymes than by either alone, indicating that the two enzymes attack different linkages in the protein molecule. Chymotrypsin acts preferentially on peptide bonds whose carbonyl group is adjacent to an amino acid residue that has a six-carbon ring in its side group as tyrosine and phenylalanine. Like trypsin, chymotrypsin is also an "endopeptidase," and cleaves peptide bonds that occupy an internal position in a polypeptide. Chymotrypsin is reversibly inactivated by boiling in acid solution. Its optimum activity occurs in the same pH range as that of trypsin, i.e., 8 to 9 for casein digestion.

OTHER PROTEOLYTIC ENZYMES. The peptides resulting from protein digestion by trypsin and chymotrypsin are further digested by enzymes known as *peptidases*. Most of these come from the intestinal mucosa, but one has been identified and isolated from pancreatic juice: an enzyme known as *carboxypeptidase*, an "exopeptidase" which splits off the end amino acid containing a free carboxyl group from polypeptides. In fresh pancreas it occurs in an inactive form, procarboxypeptidase and, like chymotrypsinogen, it is activated by trypsin.

Pancreatic juice also contains *ribonuclease* and *desoxyribonuclease*, which partially hydrolyze the corresponding nucleic acids into mononucleotides. The action of these enzymes has not been clearly characterized. The optimum pH for desoxyribonuclease is in the neighborhood of 7. *Elastase* (Balo and Banga, 1949), and more recently, *collagenase* (Houck and Patel, 1962), have also been demonstrated in pancreatic juice.

LIPASE. *Pancreatic lipase* in pancreatic juice accounts for the ability of the juice to emulsify and hydrolyze fats. This enzyme is known principally through its activity and has not been isolated in a pure state or crystallized. Pancreatic lipase hydrolyzes fat only in the presence of bile salts or other substances with similar properties, for example, some of the synthetic detergents. Bile salts in high concentration inhibit the action of lipase, as do salts of certain heavy metals, e.g., copper, iron and cobalt; it is also inhibited by the halogens, fluorine, iodine and bromine. The pH at which pancreatic lipase exhibits its optimum activity varies with the substrate, but is always on the alkaline side of neutrality. Pancreatic lipase hydrolyzes triglycerides to free fatty acids and glycerol.

Pancreatic juice also contains two phospholipases. *Phospholipase A* splits a fatty acid off of lecithin or cephalin to form lysolecithin or lysocephalin. *Phospholipase B* is capable of splitting a fatty acid off of lysolecithin to form glyceryl-phosphoryl-choline.

AMYLASE. *Pancreatic amylase* is an α-amylase, as is salivary amylase. Amylase has been isolated in crystalline form from human pancreas. The molecular weight is approximately 45,000. Pancreatic amylase splits an α-1,4-glycosidic bond to hydrolyze starch to maltose. The amylolytic activity has an electrophoretic mobility in human serum similar to that of γ-globulin. Amylase is excreted in the urine and the amylolytic activity of urine is an excellent indicator of the amount of amylase released from the pancreas into the blood. Pancreatic amylase is secreted in active form but becomes inactive if dialyzed against distilled water—owing to the removal of neutral salts which are thus proved to be essential for the activity of the enzyme. The most efficient activating ion is chloride. The optimum pH for activity of pancreatic amylase varies between 6.5 and 7.2, depending upon the kind and concentration of neutral salts present in the solution. The enzyme digests glycogen as well as starch, and under favorable conditions, the end product in both instances is maltose.

The importance of the pancreatic enzymes in digestion is evidenced by the fact that when pancreatic juice is excluded from the intestine by pancreatectomy or ligation of the ducts there is serious impairment of digestion and absorption of the various foodstuffs. This is most pronounced in the case of fat and protein, unabsorbed fat particularly appearing in large amounts in the stools; this condition is known as *steatorrhea*. The bicarbonate of the juice also serves to neutralize the gastric juice as it enters the intestine, and to establish in the intestine a pH more favorable for intestinal digestion than would otherwise be the case.

Mechanism of Pancreatic Secretion

It has long been assumed that the inorganic constituents of pancreatic juice are secreted by the same cells that produce the enzymes, namely the acinous cells. However, the fact that fluid secretion and enzyme secretion are separately regulated raises a theoretical objection to this view. All current theories of stimulation require that cells shall respond to a stimulus with a characteristic type of functional activity regardless of the nature of the stimulus. In the other digestive glands, about which we have more information, each component of the secretion that is independently regulated is formed by a different type of cell. We must also take account of the clinical observation that in certain types of pancreatic disease enzyme secretion may be depressed or absent, whereas secretion of fluid and bicarbonate

remains normal (Lagerlöff, 1939; Friedman and Snape, 1950). On the other hand, in glands injured by alloxan, fluid secretion may be subnormal, whereas enzymes are secreted normally. This latter observation, reported by Grossman and Ivy (1946), contains a hint as to a possible solution of the problem. Histological examination of the glands which failed to respond normally to secretin showed no injury to the acinous cells but the cells of the intralobular ducts appeared abnormal; in particular they exhibited vacuolization. The intralobular duct cells are continuous with the centroacinar cells that line the alveoli and are identical with these cells in their cytological structure. It is now thought that cells of this type secrete water and bicarbonate and that the acinous cells secrete mainly enzymes.

In discussing details of the mechanism of pancreatic secretion, the secretion of fluid and electrolytes will be considered separately from the secretion of enzymes. The evidence presented above indicates that pancreatic juice, like gastric juice, is a mixture of secretory products from different glandular structures that are under the influence of separate regulatory mechanisms. The secretion of fluid, electrolytes, and enzymes constitutes the exocrine function of the pancreas.

Secretion of Fluid and Electrolytes

The fluid and electrolyte composition of pancreatic juice consists mainly of a watery solution of sodium bicarbonate. Pancreatic juice is isotonic with plasma in both health and disease. We have observed that the total anion concentration remains remarkably constant but that bicarbonate concentration increases with increases in flow rate, and that the chloride concentration varies inversely with the concentration of bicarbonate. The concentration of sodium and potassium in pancreatic juice are essentially the same as plasma.

To explain these observed facts, Dreiling and Janowitz (1959) have proposed a theory that the pancreas secretes a single bicarbonate fluid, isotonic with the blood, i.e., 165 mEq/l., and that this fluid, as it passes through the interlobular ductules, is equilibrated with the serum and undergoes a bicarbonate-chloride shift. It is proposed that the water and bicarbonate are secreted by the centroacinar or the intralobular ductule cells. The extent of the bicarbonate-chloride exchange in the interlobular ductules depends upon the rate of secretion, the flow rate through the duct system, the surface area of the duct system, and the relative masses of acinar and ductular parenchyma.

Further evidence that an exchange between bicarbonate and chloride occurs as pancreatic juice is passing through the ductular systems is provided by recent experiments by Perrier, Dreiling and Janowitz (1964). These investigators made a "stop-flow" analysis of pancreatic juice stimulated by secretin in anesthetized dogs. The accessory pancreatic duct was ligated and the main pancreatic duct cannulated at its point of entry into the duodenum. Control samples of pancreatic juice were collected at 2-min. intervals and then obstruction to the outflow was produced by clamping the tube inserted into the main pancreatic duct. After a period of 4 to 5 min. the clamp was removed and collections of juice were continued. In 15 experiments it was found that a significant fall in HCO_3^- concentration occurred in the samples collected immediately after the obstruction to pancreatic flow was removed. In 12 of the 15 experiments there was a rise in Cl^- concentration. The temporary obstruction to pancreatic flow did not produce any significant change in flow rate or Na^+ and K^+ concentrations. Although these experiments do not localize the precise site of the bicarbonate chloride exchange, they indicate that HCO_3^- may leave and Cl^- may enter the pancreatic juice during its passage through the ductular system.

The bicarbonate in pancreatic juice is thought to come from both metabolic CO_2 and HCO_3^- from the blood plasma. The pancreas contains an abundance of carbonic anhydrase, suggesting that it plays a role in the formation of bicarbonate. It has been demonstrated that acetazolamide (Diamox), a potent carbonic anhydrase inhibitor, is capable of inhibiting the secretion of bicarbonate by the pancreas (Dreiling and Janowitz, 1959). The recent demonstration by histochemical techniques that carbonic anhydrase in the pancreas is localized in the epithelium of the ductules and that little or none can be demonstrated in the acinar cells (Becker, 1962), lends further support to the theory that the origin of bicarbonate is in the intralobular ductule cells and not in the acinar cells.

If the concentration of sodium or potassium is increased in the plasma by injecting hypertonic NaCl or KCl the concentration of these cations is increased in the pancreatic juice to the same degree (Ball, 1930). In addition, if radioactive sodium is administered intravenously, it appears in pancreatic juice within 3 min. and after 15 min. the activities of the isotope in pancreatic juice and serum are essentially the same (Montgomery, Sheline and Chaikoff, 1941). These observations suggest a rapid equilibration, probably by diffusion, between sodium and potassium of the serum and sodium and potassium in pancreatic juice.

SECRETION OF ENZYMES

It is now well established that the pancreatic enzymes are produced by and secreted from the acinar cells. As in the case of other digestive glands, secretion of enzymes by the pancreas involves at least three distinct processes: (1) synthesis within the cell of the enzymes or their precursors, (2) storage of the enzymes within the cell in the form of zymogen granules, and (3) discharge of the enzymes from the secretory cells into the ducts. These various processes will now be considered.

Synthesis is a continuous process, dependent upon the availability of various amino acids that are required for the synthesis of the enzymes. The work of Magee and his associates (1955, 1956, 1957, 1958) indicates that the nature of the dietary protein, and in particular its amino acid composition, has a profound effect on the total concentration of enzymes in the pancreas and on the relative concentration of different enzymes. For example, Magee and Anderson (1955) found that, in animals fed a high protein diet (casein), the trypsin and lipase content of the resting pancreas was greater than in animals fed a low protein diet. Daily administration of urocholine (a parasympathomimetic drug), or of DL-valine, also had an effect similar to casein. Since DL-valine is a powerful stimulant for release of pancreozymin, and since the parasympathomimetic drugs stimulate enzyme *secretion*, these authors conclude that the stimuli for enzyme *secretion* (casein, urocholine, DL-valine) also stimulate enzyme synthesis. A similar interpretation could be given the earlier work of Grossman, Greengard and Ivy (1943), who reported changes in enzyme content of the pancreas with changes in diet.

Interesting light has been shed on the synthesis of enzymes by the recent studies of L. E. Hokin (1951, 1952) and Mabel Hokin (1956) on pigeon and mouse pancreas *in vitro*. It was found that pigeon pancreas slices would synthesize amylase *in vitro* in glucose solutions, in serum, in amino acid solutions and in saline. Synthesis was most rapid in solutions of amino acids and least rapid in normal saline; it proceeded at an intermediate rate in serum. One can see here the effect of an increased concentration of reacting substances (amino acids) on synthesis of protein by the cells of the pancreas. Although pancreozymin and parasympathomimetic drugs caused discharge of amylase from the cells into the surrounding medium (secretion), the rate of synthesis of the enzymes was not materially affected. This is not in accord with the conclusions of Magee and his associates, but does not invalidate their conclusions, since the experimental conditions were different—particularly with regard to the time during which the stimulus could act. It was found that certain amino acids were essential for synthesis but others could be supplied from sources in the medium. The amino acids essential for maximum synthesis were: tryptophane, arginine, threonine, valine, tyrosine, lysine, leucine, histadine, isoleucine, and phenylalanine. Similar results were obtained on mouse pancreas, except that there was no acceleration of synthesis on addition of amino acids if the animal had been fed before being killed for removal of the pancreas. However, if the animal had been starved for 24 hours, addition of amino acids to the medium increased the rate of synthesis by 25 per cent.

The synthesized material appears within the acinous cells as *zymogen granules*, which accumulate in the resting gland until they come to occupy most of the available space within the cells (Heidenhain, 1883; Hirsch, 1939, 1957; Sluiter, 1944). Under the influence of appropriate stimuli the zymogen granules diminish in number and in size; at the same time enzymes appear in the secretion. Stimuli such as HCl and secretin, which produce a watery secretion with a low enzyme content, have little effect on the granules, whereas stimuli which call forth secretion rich in enzymes deplete the granules and, if they act over a long period of time, may leave the cells amost free of zymogen granules.

According to the observations of Hokin and Hokin (1956) on pancreatic and salivary gland slices *in vitro*, effective stimuli for secretion of enzymes cause a remarkable increase in the rate of turnover of phosphorus and its incorporation into the other soluble phospholipids. In the pancreas, secretin has no such effect, although it does increase the uptake of oxygen by about 10 per cent. They conclude that "all active transport of proteins out of the cell involves the breakdown and resynthesis of the glycero-phosphate bonds in phospholipids."

The recent observations of Palade, Siekevitz and Caro (1962) have shed considerable light on morphological changes associated with secretion by the acinar cell. These investigators have used electron microscopy and autoradiography to study intracellular synthesis, storage, and transport of enzymes. Radioactive carbon-labelled leucine was injected into guinea pigs. Pancreatic tissue was obtained at different time intervals for examination by electron microscopy and autoradiography. Within three minutes, high specific activity was found in the RNA particles or ribosomes attached to the α-cytomembranes (endoplasmic reticulum). From the ribosomes α-chymotrypsinogen of high specific activity was obtained by means of column chromotography. The labelled enzyme is then transferred into cisternae formed from the α-cytomembranes. These structures have been termed "rough-surfaced cisternae," due to the attached ribosomes. Just how the enzyme is transferred from the ribosome across the cisternae membrane is not known. In the region of the Golgi apparatus, the enzyme content of the rough-surfaced cisternae is transferred to smooth-surfaced vacuoles. This occurs about 20 min. after the administration of the labelled amino acid. It is in the smooth-surfaced vacuoles that the enzyme is concentrated and stored. The filled vacuoles are recognized by light microscopy as "zymogen granules." The stage of storage in a "mature" zymogen granule is reached in about 45 min. In this form, enzymes can remain in storage for hours until discharged into the acinar lumen. The process of discharge of the contents of the zymogen granules is thought to involve a coalescence of the membrane of the zymogen granule with the plasma membrane of the cell. The various stages of the process just described are illustrated in fig. 58.3. Whether or not the mechanism of secretion proposed by Palade, Siekevitz and Caro for α-chymotrypsinogen also applies to amylase, lipase, and other pancreatic enzymes is not known. It should be remembered, however, that the pancreatic acinar cell is capable of secreting enzymes at a high rate, even after zymogen granules have been depleted. Thus, other pathways than via storage in a zymogen granule probably exist for the secretion of pancreatic enzymes.

Regulation of Pancreatic Secretion

The pancreas is under the control of both *nervous* and *humoral* mechanisms that regulate pancreatic secretion. The nervous control of pan-

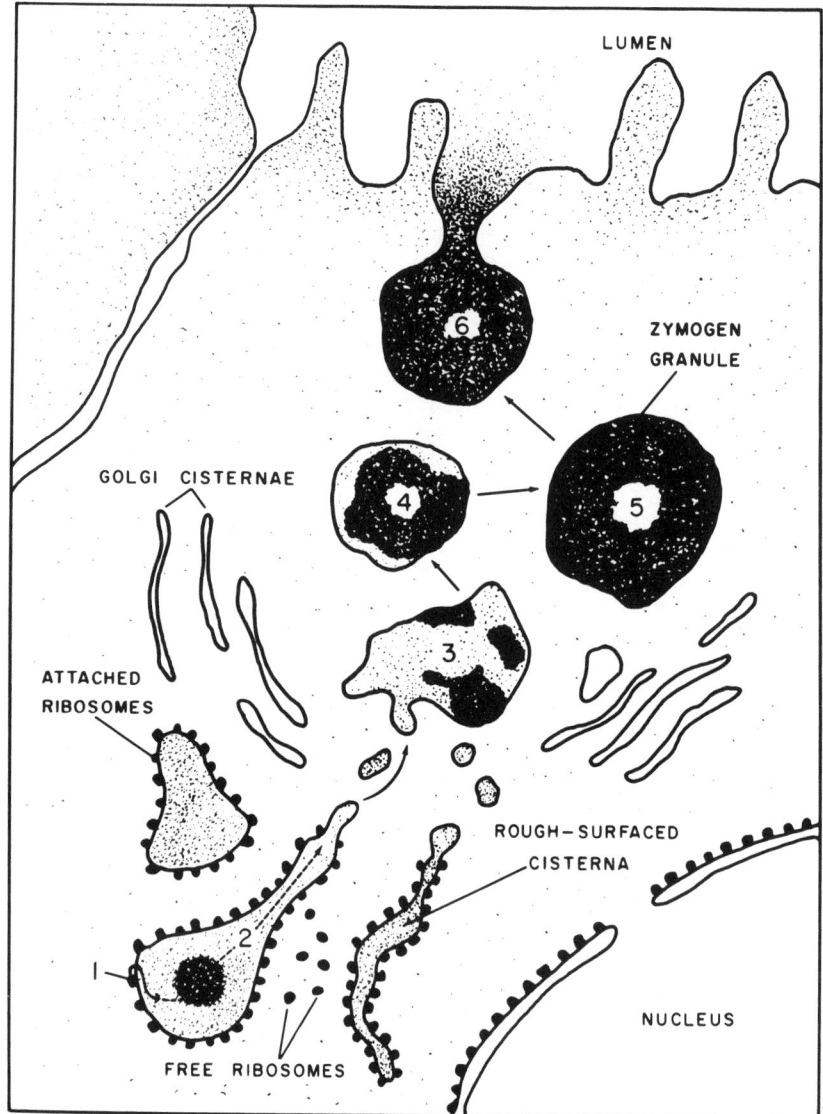

Fig. 58.3. Diagram illustrating the various stages of synthesis, storage and secretion of pancreatic enzymes by the acinar cell of the guinea pig. (1) Enzymes are synthesized by the ribosomes and transported into a rough-surfaced cisterna. (2) Enzymes are transferred from the rough-surfaced cisterna into a smooth-surfaced vesicle. (3) and (4) Near the Golgi apparatus, enzymes are concentrated within the smooth-surfaced vesicles to become (5) a mature zymogen granule. (6) Illustrating the "secretion" of enzymes into the lumen of the acinus. (Redrawn from Palade, Siekevitz and Caro, 1962.)

creatic secretion is provided by both the sympathetic and parasympathetic divisions of the autonomic nervous system. In addition, there is evidence that a *local cholinergic mechanism*, independent of vagal innervation, may play a role in regulating pancreatic secretion. Humoral control of pancreatic secretion is provided by the hormones *secretin* and *pancreozymin*. Before discussing these regulatory mechanisms in detail, the question of whether pancreatic secretion is continuous or intermittent will be considered.

Intermittent or continuous secretion? Claude Bernard believed that the pancreas secreted only when stimulated as, for example, during digestion. Heidenhain noted, however, that the secretion was continuous in herbivorous animals but he agreed with Bernard that in the dog and cat and other carnivora there was no secretion without stimulation. Proof has since been obtained that secretion is continuous in rabbits, white rats, white mice, guinea pigs and frogs. Baxter (1931) found that secretion in the rabbit continued even after removal of the small intestine and after decapitation. The idea that the pancreas of the fasting dog does not secrete unless stimulated by means of food or other external agents has had to be modified in the light of subsequent work. Boldyreff (1916) observed pancreatic secretion in fasting animals, at intervals associated with periods of secretory and motor activity in other organs of digestion, which we now recognize as hunger periods. This periodic secretion was studied thoroughly by Scott and his coworkers (1940, 1941) and they found that, although periodic secretion did occur, it was associated with hunger activity of the stomach only about half the time. Continuous secretion is the rule in human patients with pancreatic fistulas and McClure (1937) states that pancreatic enzymes are always found in the intestinal contents collected by intubation of normal subjects.

NEUROGENIC REGULATION

The effects of *sympathetic stimulation* on pancreatic secretion are variable. Both augmentation and decrease in flow rate have been reported in the literature. Atropine is said to block the effects of sympathetic stimulation, causing an increase in flow rate, indicating that cholinergic secretory fibers are present in the sympathetic innervation of the pancreas. As in the stomach, sympathetic stimulation can influence pancreatic secretion indirectly, due to changes in blood flow through the organ. Sympathetic stimulation may also alter the flow rate due to effects on the pancreatic ducts, since constriction of the ducts would slow the passage of pancreatic juice.

Stimulation of the vagus or *parasympathetic* innervation of the pancreas results in the secretion of enzymes but has little or no effect on the secretion of bicarbonate. Acetylcholine is the mediator of the vagal effect. Vagotomy and atropine markedly depress the secretion of enzymes by the pancreas. The effects of vagal stimulation on pancreatic secretion can be demonstrated easily in the experimental animal. In a dog with an esophagogastrostomy and pancreatic fistula, sham feeding produces a prompt secretion of enzymes by the pancreas. Insulin hypoglycemia, known to produce vagal stimulation, also results in the secretion of enzymes. Electrical stimulation of the peripheral segment of the cut vagus produces a similar response. Cholinergic drugs, as pilocarpine, stimulate pancreatic secretion of enzymes whereas atropine and anticholinergic agents produce inhibition.

The presence of a gastro-pancreatic reflex has been demonstrated by White, Lundh and Magee (1960). In dogs, these investigators found that distending the fundus of the stomach with a balloon caused an increase in volume and enzyme output in pancreatic juice. Vagotomy abolishes the gastro-pancreatic reflex for a few weeks but then it returns, suggesting that local reflex pathways exist which are independent of vagal innervation.

HUMORAL REGULATION

The two hormones, *secretin* and *pancreozymin,* provide for the humoral regulation of pancreatic secretion. Both of these hormones can be extracted from the mucosa of the duodenum and upper small bowel. The specific cells in the mucosa that produce secretin and pancreozymin are not known. Under normal circumstances, secretin and pancreozymin are released into the blood by appropriate stimuli and carried to the pancreas to produce their effects. Dilute hydrochloric acid in the duodenum is a potent stimulus for the release of secretin. Peptones or products of protein digestion serve equally well for the release of pancreozymin. Secretin acts on the ductule or centroacinar cells to stimulate them to secrete water and bicarbonate while pancreozymin stimulates the acinar cells to secrete enzymes.

SECRETIN. The discovery of secretin in 1902 by Bayliss and Starling was an event of great historical significance inasmuch as secretin was the first chemical substance known to be secreted into the blood and act as a stimulus to an organ at a distance from the site of its formation. Recognizing this fact, Bayliss and Starling coined the word *hormone* to characterize this and similar substances. Before the discovery of secretin it was known that acid in the intestine induced secretion of pancreatic juice in animals in which all the nerves to the pancreas and to the intestine had been severed. While workers in Pavlov's laboratory in St. Petersburg were busily searching for the unknown nervous pathways which, they supposed, conveyed impulses to the pancreas after all the known fibers had been cut, Bayliss and Starling in England did the simple experiment of making an acid extract of the mucous membrane of the intestine and injecting it into an animal. This caused the pancreas of the injected animal to secrete. The excitement in Starling's laboratory can well be imagined. A "chemical reflex" had been discovered, something hitherto unknown in physiology. They called the new substance *secretin*. The response in Pavlov's laboratory was less enthusiastic; the idea that something other than the nervous system could regulate body function was not in keeping with Pavlov's philosophy, nevertheless he ultimately accepted the fact with good grace.

Although it is probably true that the pancreatic response to Bayliss and Starling's extract was as much due to impurities as to the secretin that it contained, subsequent research has shown that such extracts do contain an active principle which, when highly purified, has a powerful secretory effect on the pancreas. The purest secretin available stimulates only the pancreas and liver; in both organs, it causes a dilute, watery secretion and has little or no influence on the secretion of organic solids. Secretin is probably a polypeptide with a molecular weight of about 5,000. It has been obtained in a highly purified state by Hammarsten and his coworkers (1928, 1933) and by many others subsequently. Jorpes and Mutt (1956) of the Karolinska Institute in Stockholm have made a preparation of which 0.1 mg. contains 70 "clinical units" [1] or an amount that will cause the human pancreas to secrete at a rapid rate for an hour or more. Since one clinical unit is equal to sixteen cat units, less than 0.0001 mg. of the preparation should cause detectable secretion in a cat. Greengard, Stein and Ivy (1941) have shown that secretin is destroyed by an enzyme found in the blood and urine, which they called *secretinase*.

PANCREOZYMIN. The crude extract prepared by Bayliss and Starling caused the pancreas to secrete enzymes as well as water and bicarbonates. Since purified secretin seemed to stimulate only the output of water and bicarbonate, a search was made by Harper and Raper (1943) for the material in the extracts which stimulated secretion of enzymes. They succeeded in separating a fraction which did not increase the volume of pancreatic juice but did greatly increase the enzyme concentration. This substance they called *pancreozymin*. Their observations were quickly confirmed by Greengard and others (1944).

It has long been known that hydrochloric acid in the intestine liberates secretin into the blood, thus causing the pancreas to secrete. It was not known whether other pancreatic stimuli liberated secretin or pancreozymin, or depended on some other mechanism for their effect. In 1951, Wang and Grossman succeeded in preparing a function-

[1] A clinical unit of secretin is equal to 1 dog unit (Ivy et al., 1930) or 16 cat units (Wilander and Agren, 1932). A dog unit is the amount that will increase the rate of secretion in a 10 to 12 kg. dog by 10 drops in 10 min. A cat unit is the least amount that will cause detectable secretion in a cat.

ing, nerve-free transplant of the canine pancreas. They imbedded a portion of the pancreas in the tissue of the mammary gland, leaving its nerve and blood supply intact for the time being. After it had established a new blood supply in its new location, the original nerves and blood vessels were cut, leaving a piece of pancreas whose activity could be influenced only through chemical substances reaching it by way of the blood stream. The flow of pancreatic juice from this transplant was increased by all the common pancreatic stimuli, including distilled water, hydrochloric acid, soaps and peptones. The enzyme concentration was also increased by these same stimuli, thus proving that both secretin and pancreozymin are released by all the ordinary stimuli used to excite pancreatic secretion.

INTERACTION OF NERVOUS AND HUMORAL REGULATORY MECHANISMS

Although the various nervous and humoral regulatory mechanisms have been discussed as separate or individual factors capable of influencing pancreatic secretion, the student should not be misled in thinking each regulatory mechanism acts independently of all others. The pancreatic response to a meal indicates that in all likelihood there is a high degree of interdependence between the neural and humoral mechanisms. Grossman (1962), after recently reviewing the evidence concluded, "Re-examination of the evidence concerning the relative roles of nervous and hormonal factors in regulating pancreatic secretion indicates that re-evaluation of current concepts is needed. While there is convincing evidence that the hormones secretin and pancreozymin participate importantly, there are equally cogent reasons for believing that cholinergic mechanisms, probably largely independent of the vagi and splanchnics, cooperate in an essential manner. The profound inhibitory effect of anticholinergic drugs on the volume and enzyme content of pancreatic juice secreted in response to a meal must, until a satisfactory alternative explanation is given, be taken to mean that cholinergic mechanisms are importantly involved, either as independent mechanisms additional to the hormones or, more probably, as cooperative neuro-hormonal actions. This cooperation may involve either the release of the hormones or their action on the pancreas, or possibly both."

RESPONSE TO A MEAL

Pancreatic secretion is always increased after meals. This occurs in response to specific stimuli associated either with the act of eating or the presence of food in the gastrointestinal tract. Proof that the act of eating serves as a stimulus to the pancreas was obtained in Pavlov's laboratory (later confirmed by Ivy, 1926) by means of sham feeding (ch. 57), that is, feeding a dog provided with an esophagostomy so that the food did not reach the stomach. In these circumstances, the pancreas begins to secrete within $1-1\frac{1}{2}$ min. after feeding and continues for 12–20 min. The volume secreted is small, but the concentration of enzymes is increased over the fasting secretion. The short latent period, as well as direct experimental evidence, has served to prove that the secretion is not due to gastric hydrochloric acid entering the duodenum (Tonkish, 1924). The response is abolished by cutting the vagus nerves. Food and food products in the stomach apparently do not have any direct stimulating effect on the pancreas; however, they become effective stimuli when the gastric contents enter the intestine.

All the major constituents of the gastric chyme influence the secretory activity of the pancreas in one way or another after they have entered the intestine; these include water, hydrochloric acid, products of protein digestion, fats, fatty acids, soaps and products of starch digestion. Each of these substances has a different effect on the pancreas, producing a characteristic type of pancreatic juice. Hydrochloric acid produces an abundant secretion of dilute alkaline fluid containing a minimum amount of enzymes. Fatty acids and soaps, although producing an abundant secretion, increase the concentration of enzymes, whereas the products of protein digestion when used in the absence of other stimuli produce only a small amount of secretion which is highly concentrated in enzymes; fats are said to act in a similar manner.

Adaptation of Pancreatic Enzyme Secretion to Diet

It has been stated that the total enzyme concentration of pancreatic juice is determined to a great extent by the type of stimulus used to provoke secretion. This mode of adaptation is an established fact, and its mechanism is well understood (see above under *secretin and pancreozymin*). Another type of adaptation, which involves changes in enzyme composition, is more controversial. Pavlov, as a result of certain errors in enzyme determinations in his laboratory, came to the conclusion that the relative concentration of the different enzymes of pancreatic juice was

adapted to the nature of the food undergoing digestion. For example, according to his concept, a meal consisting largely of carbohydrate would call forth secretion of pancreatic juice containing a large amount of amylase, whereas a fat meal would call forth secretion of lipase, etc. Babkin, using more precise methods in the same laboratory, found that this was not true, but that the enzymes tended to be secreted in parallel concentration regardless of the nature of the immediate stimulus to secretion. This concept has been challenged recently, especially by Guth, Komarov and their coworkers (1956, 1958), who find that there may be considerable variation in the relative concentration of the different enzymes in different samples of pancreatic juice, even when taken on the same day from the same animal. Although the differences they found are statistically significant, the fact remains that a large increase in enzyme concentration involves all the enzymes of the juice, although not necessarily all equally.

Efforts to determine whether the composition of the juice can be altered by a prolonged change in the diet have given confusing results. It has been established that a diet low in protein gives rise to considerable alteration in the enzyme composition of the juice (Grossman et al., 1943), as does deficiency or *excess* of certain amino acids (Magee et al., 1956, 1957, 1958). However, it is not clear that this represents an adaptation in any accepted sense of the word; rather it suggests that the pancreatic cells, which have the task of synthesizing the relatively enormous amounts of protein secreted in the pancreatic juice, are hampered in their work if they are not supplied with adequate and appropriate building material (Hokin, 1952). The pancreatic cells cannot "make bricks without straw" any more than could the Israelites of old.

Methods of Collecting Pancreatic Juice

In order to obtain pancreatic juice for study, it is necessary to make some kind of pancreatic fistula, by which the pancreatic juice may be conducted to the exterior of the body, rather than allowed to enter the duodenum, as in the intact situation. The first such fistula was described by Regner de Graaf in 1664. He cannulated the pancreatic duct of a dog with a quill from a wild duck, which he selected "because that kind of bird hath longer and thinner (quills) than all others." The cannula was brought out through the abdominal wall and the pancreatic juice collected in a small vessel attached to its outer end. Of great historical interest is the permanent fistula devised by Pavlov in 1879 (see Pavlov, 1910). Pavlov cut out a rhomboid portion of the duodenal wall surrounding the opening of the major pancreatic duct and, after repairing the duodenum, transplanted the excised papilla, with the duct attached, into the skin of the abdominal wall. It is now customary to collect pancreatic juice from animals through a duodenal fistula which is provided with a metal or plastic tube that can be closed when the fistula is not in use (Thomas, 1951). The opening of the duct can be seen through the fistulous opening into the duodenum and a glass or metal cannula inserted into the duct. If the accessory duct is tied at the time the fistula is made, the total secretion of the pancreas can be collected in this manner over a period of hours.

In man, pancreatic secretions can be obtained by intubating the duodenum with a long plastic or rubber tube. It is customary to use a double lumen tube; one lumen for the collection of duodenal contents, and the other for aspirating gastric secretions. The lumen used for gastric aspiration has multiple perforations and when connected to a constant suction pump permits little gastric juice to contaminate the secretions of the pancreas. With this method it is impossible to obtain uncontaminated specimens, due to the presence of duodenal mucosal secretions, bile and probably some gastric secretions escaping from the stomach. Even so, surprisingly good samples, which have a minimal amount of contamination, of pancreatic juice can be obtained. This is particularly true when the pancreatic secretory rate is high, as is the case with stimulation by secretin.

Pancreatic Fistula

The digestive disturbances following ligation of the ducts or removal of the pancreas are also observed when the pancreatic juice is diverted from the intestine through a complete fistula. Such fistulas, however, give rise to other, more serious complications which tend to obscure the digestive disturbances. Within a few days after the fistula has been made the secretion becomes continuous, increases in amount, and its composition changes. The concentration of total solids falls to 1 or 2 per cent, owing chiefly to the almost complete absence of protein (Babkin, 1928). These changes are associated with changes in the

microscopic appearance of the pancreas (Heidenhain, 1883). The acinous cells decrease in size and lose most of their granules. The animal loses weight rapidly, refuses to eat, and dies.

In animals with complete fistulas, Johnston and Ball (1930) found a decrease in chloride and an equivalent increase in the bicarbonate concentration of the pancreatic juice as drainage progressed. The increase in bicarbonate is not a constant finding, since Heidenhain obtained some specimens of juice which did not effervesce on addition of acid, and some samples collected by Johnston and Ball had a pH as low as 7.16. The total base of the juice remains normal, or nearly so, and because of this and the hypersecretion, there is a substantial loss of base (Na, K, Ca) from the body, giving rise to changes in the blood that ultimately prove fatal.

The most important blood changes are: lowered plasma volume (dehydration), decrease in chloride, decrease in bicarbonate, and a decrease in total base (Elman and McCaughan, 1927; Gamble and McIver, 1928; Dragstedt et al., 1930). The pH of the blood may increase or decrease, probably depending on the relative amounts of chloride and bicarbonate lost; excessive vomiting is common and this tends to increase the loss of chloride. Hypersecretion of the stomach has been observed in pancreatic fistula and this would add to the chloride loss when vomiting is present. It may also account for the hypersecretion of the pancreas when HCl from the stomach enters the intestine. In one group of animals studied by McCaughan (1929), the blood chemistry remained approximately normal; the animals, nevertheless, died within 5 to 8 days (the usual survival time), apparently because of dehydration. Changes in blood chemistry corresponding to those seen in experimental animals, but usually less severe, have been observed in human patients with pancreatic fistula (Miller and Wiper, 1944).

Administration of sodium chloride or sodium bicarbonate, intravenously or by mouth, prolongs the life of experimental animals with pancreatic fistula, sometimes indefinitely, but the ideal treatment is return of the secreted juice to the gastrointestinal tract. For animals with an incomplete fistula of the Pavlov type, the administration of sodium bicarbonate, and a diet that does not stimulate excessive secretion such as bread and milk may be all that is required.

A summary of the results observed in experimental pancreatic insufficiency is presented in tables 58.1 and 58.2.

TABLE 58.1

Results of pancreatic insufficiency

Procedure	Functional Changes		
	Absorption deficit	Duodenal ulcer	Fatty liver
Pancreatectomy	100% of animals (severity variable)	Rare	92% (Dragstedt)
Ligation of ducts	100% of animals (severity variable)	33% (Dragstedt)	50% (Dragstedt)
Total fistula	100% of animals (severity variable)	Limited by early death; otherwise probably 100% (Dragstedt)	None
Mann-Williamson operation	Some deficit (no exact data)	90–100%	No data

TABLE 58.2

Blood changes resulting from pancreatic insufficiency

Procedure	Blood Changes			
	Enzymes	Salts and Water	Sugar	Fat
Pancreatectomy	No change	No change	Hyperglycemia	Hypolipemia
Ligation of ducts	Increase in blood amylase ("diastase")	No change	No change—hyperglycemia possible late effect	Hypolipemia in 50 per cent
Total fistula	No change	Decrease in total base, decrease in Cl, decrease in HCO_3 dehydration; pH variable.	No change	No change

Tissue Damage by Pancreatic Enzymes

Under certain conditions pancreatic enzymes may escape into the tissues surrounding the acini, or into the blood. In explanation of this, we may assume that the enzymes, as they are being synthesized, appear first in solution in the cell protoplasm before being concentrated as zymogen granules. Some sort of equilibrium must exist between enzymes in solution and enzymes in the form of the more or less solid granules. We can only speculate on the concentration of dissolved enzymes that may be present at any time, but there is strong indirect evidence that the concentration is considerably increased by stimuli which cause discharge of enzymes into the ducts. Simple diffusion of dissolved enzymes through the cell membrane of the acinous cells will explain the presence of enzymes in the minute quantities found in the blood in the normal fasting state. The rate of diffusion will vary with: (1) the concentration gradient between the cells and the blood, (2) the hydrostatic pressure gradient between the interior and exterior of the cell, and (3) the permeability of the cell membrane. The increases in enzyme concentration in the blood which are seen during active secretion in response to food, or pancreozymin or parasympathomimetic drugs (Cherry and Crandall, 1932; Zucker et al., 1932), are probably reflections of the increased concentration of enzymes within the cells. If such secretion is accompanied by closure of the ducts, as for example, by inflammatory edema or spasm due to morphine, the increase in hydrostatic pressure within the acini will accelerate the diffusion. Cell damage, from whatever cause, can further augment the diffusion by increasing the permeability of the cell membrane.

As a practical matter we see increases in concentration of pancreatic enzymes in the blood during digestion, after administration of certain drugs (notably morphine (Lagerlöf, 1945; Ryan et al., 1949)), in acute pancreatitis, in carcinoma of the pancreas, and in many other conditions associated with injury to the cells or obstruction of the ducts, provided only that the damage is not so severe as to destroy the ability of the cells to synthesize enzymes. In order for tissue digestion to occur, it is necessary that the inactive proenzymes be activated. The mechanism of activation of extracellular pancreatic enzymes is obscure; probably tissue kinases that may be released from injured cells play a part in activating the proteolytic enzymes. It is commonly believed that reflux of bile (Bernard, 1856; Opie, 1910) into the pancreatic ducts may cause sufficient tissue damage to activate the proteolytic enzymes, whereas the bile itself serves to activate the lipase. In acute pancreatitis, from whatever cause, there is always the danger of extensive tissue destruction and fat necrosis brought about by activated pancreatic enzymes.

Tests of Pancreatic Exocrine Function

Pancreatic exocrine insufficiency may be caused by a number of diseases affecting the pancreas. Since the pancreas is the principal source of lipase furnished to the upper small bowel for the digestion of fats, an insufficient amount of pancreatic juice and its contained lipase results in maldigestion of fats and causes steatorrhea. The gastric juice provides pepsin and secretions from the small bowel (succus entericus) provide proteolytic enzymes so that maldigestion of proteins is not as marked as the defect in fat digestion. Amylase provided by the salivary glands and various disaccharidases provided by the small intestines also promote digestion of carbohydrates, even in severe exocrine insufficiency of the pancreas. Thus, the principal clinical manifestation of pancreatic exocrine insufficiency is an excess of fat excreted in the feces.

Fecal Fat Excretion

A commonly used test for the detection of pancreatic exocrine insufficiency is the quantitative measurement of fecal fat excretion. The amount of fat excreted in the feces may be determined chemically, or an isotope tagged fat may be used to measure fecal fat excretion.

Normal individuals on an average diet seldom excrete more than 6 or 7 gm. of fat in the feces in a 24-hr. period. Patients with exocrine insufficiency of the pancreas may excrete up to 50 gm. of fat per 24 hr., depending upon the dietary fat intake and the severity of the insufficiency. It is customary to place patients with steatorrhea suspected of having pancreatic insufficiency on a diet containing a known amount of fat. A diet containing 100 gm. of fat per day is frequently used. After being on this diet for 2 to 3 days, the patient is given a capsule containing carmine, a red dye that is not absorbed, for the purpose of "marking" the stool. The carmine capsule is given on the morning of the second or third day before breakfast and stool collections are started when the dye appears in the stool. Another carmine capsule is given 48 or 72 hr. after the first, depending on the collection period desired, and all stools are saved until the second "marker" appears in the feces. All stool specimens are saved, thoroughly mixed, and small aliquots are used for the chemical determination of fat.

Fecal fat excretion can also be determined by use of a radioactive tagged fat; I^{131}-triolein is commonly used. A known quantity of radioactivity, usually 15 to 20 μc. of I^{131}-triolein, is administered in a test meal and the appearance of radioactivity in the blood and fecal samples is determined by counting the specimens in a well-type scintillation counter. In patients without pancreatic insufficiency, at least 10 per cent of the administered dose of radioactivity will appear in the venous blood within 6 hr. and less than 5 per cent of the dose will be excreted in the feces. In patients with exocrine insufficiency of the pancreas, usually less than 10 per cent of the administered dose will appear in the blood and more than 5 per cent will be excreted in the feces.

Shingleton and his associates (1957) have shown that in patients with pancreatitis and those with carcinoma of the pancreas, the I^{131}-labeled fat test is of value in detecting exocrine insufficiency of the pancreas. Haines and his associates (1962) also have used I^{131}-triolein in the study of pancreatic function in patients with fibrocystic disease of the pancreas.

Secretin and Pancreozymin Tests of Pancreatic Function

Since secretin and pancreozymin in injectable form have become available, tests of pancreatic function using these hormones as stimuli have been developed. Secretin was first available in a form pure enough for use in humans and more experience has accumulated with it. The secretin test was introduced by Ågren, Lagerlöf and Berglund (1936) and has been used extensively in this country and abroad. It is wise to test the patients for hypersensitivity to the secretin preparation before conducting the test. To perform the test, a double-lumen tube is passed through the patient's nose or mouth into the stomach and duodenum, one lumen opening into the stomach for draining gastric juice and the other into the duodenum for collecting the pancreatic and duodenal secretions. It is important that the double-lumen tube be positioned accurately by means of fluoroscopy. The gastric and duodenal secretions are collected separately. Gastric juice is usually aspirated continuously by a low pressure vacuum pump while the duodenal contents are aspirated manually. Samples are collected during 10 or 20 min. intervals. After a control period of approximately 30 min., to provide for clearing of the duodenal samples of gastric juice, secretin, in a dose of 1 clinical unit

per kg. body weight, is given slowly intravenously over a 4 to 5 min. period. The duodenal contents are then collected in separate 10 to 20 min. samples for a period of time, usually 60 or 80 min. Volume, pH, bicarbonate and enzyme determinations are made on the samples collected from the duodenum.

With normal function, there is a rapid increase in flow rate following secretin injection, with the maximum flow rate usually being reached in 20 min. A flow rate of 1 to 2 ml./kg. weight/30 min. is usually obtained in normal individuals. The bicarbonate concentration increases with the flow rate and may go as high as 140 to 150 mEq/l. As the flow rate increases, there is an associated decrease in enzyme concentration. In patients with obstruction of the pancreatic ducts due to neoplasm or calculi, there is a reduction in flow rate. In diseases of the pancreas associated with destruction of the secreting parenchyma, such as pancreatitis or fibrocystic disease, a reduction in flow rate also is observed. In inflammatory diseases of the pancreas, the bicarbonate concentration may be markedly reduced. A concen-

SECRETIN-PANCREATIC RESPONSES

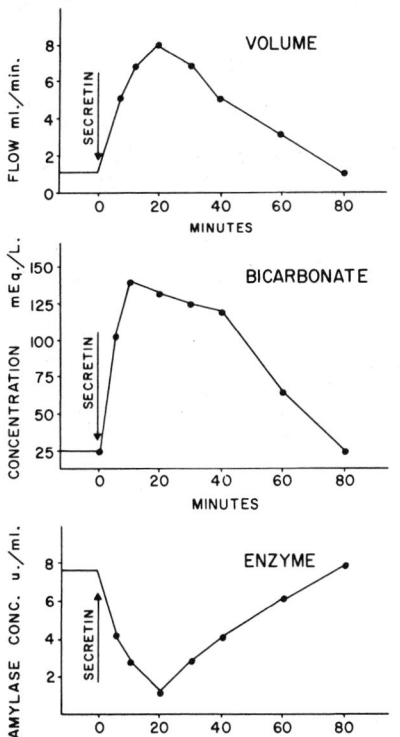

PANCREOZYMIN-PANCREATIC RESPONSES

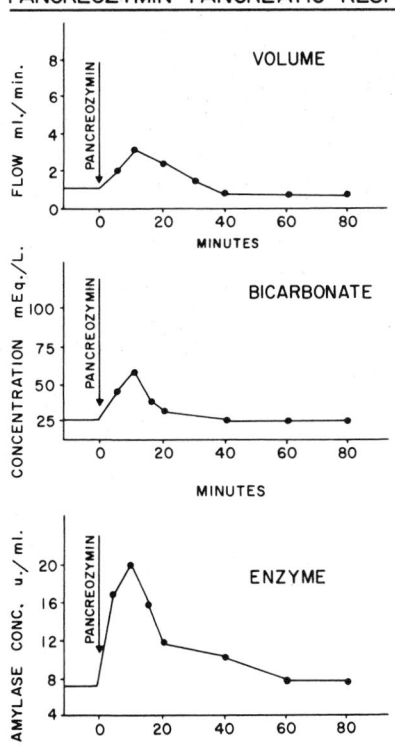

Fig. 58.4. Volume, bicarbonate, and amylase response following the administration of secretin and pancreozymin to a normal subject. The hormones were administered intravenously in a dose of 1 unit/kg. (Redrawn from Dreiling, Janowitz and Perrier, 1964).

tration of 90 mEq/l. is usually taken as the lower limit of normal for bicarbonate.

When pancreozymin is used as a stimulus for pancreatic secretion to test pancreatic function, the procedure of the test is the same as that described for the secretin test. As a matter of fact, secretin and pancreozymin are frequently used together in testing pancreatic function. There is some disagreement as to which hormone should be administered first when they are used together. English and European workers have tended to give secretin first, followed by pancreozymin in 30 min. (Burton et al., 1960), while workers in the United States seem to prefer the reverse order, giving pancreozymin first, followed 10 min. later by secretin (Sun and Shay, 1960). Dreiling and Janowitz (1962) have used both sequences of secretin-pancreozymin and pancreozymin-secretin in testing pancreatic function and have come to the conclusion that the addition of pancreozymin to the standard secretin test technique does not significantly improve the diagnostic accuracy of the procedure.

The separate effects of secretin and pancreozymin on pancreatic secretion of man are illustrated in fig. 58.4.

REFERENCES

ÅGREN, G., LAGERLOF, H., AND BERGLUND, H. The secretin test of pancreatic function in the diagnosis of pancreatic disease. Acta med. scandinav., 1936, 90, 224.

BABKIN, B. P., HEBB, C. O., AND SERGEYEVA, M. A. The parasympathetic-like effect of splanchnic nerve stimulation on pancreatic secretion. Quart. J. Exper. Physiol., 1939, 29, 217.

BALL, E. G. Composition of pancreatic juice and blood serum as influenced by the injection of organic salts. J. Biol. Chem., 1930, 86, 449.

BALO, J. AND BANGA, I. Die Zerstörung der elastischen Fasern der Gefässwand. Schweiz. Z. Path. Bact., 1949, 12, 350.

BAXTER, S. G. Continuous pancreatic secretion in the rabbit. Am. J. Physiol., 1931, 96, 343.

BAYLISS, W. M., AND STARLING, E. H. The mechanism of pancreatic secretion. J. Physiol., 1902, 28, 325.

BECKER, V. Histochemistry of the exocrine pancreas, In The exocrine pancreas, p. 56. Little, Brown and Co. Boston, 1962.

BOLDYREFF, W. N. Fonction périodique de l'organisme chez l'homme et les animaux d'ordre supérieur. (Pancréas comme principal agent du processus de l'assimilation dans tout les corps). Quart. J. Exper. Physiol., 1916, 10, 175.

BURTON, P., EVANS, D. G., HARPER, A. A., HOWAT, H. T., OLEESKY, S., SCOTT, J. E., AND VARLEY, H. Test of pancreatic function in man based on the analysis of duodenal contents after administration of secretin and pancreozymin. Gut, 1960, 1, 111.

CHERRY, I. S. AND CRANDALL, L. A., JR. Specificity of pancreatic lipase; its appearance in the blood after pancreatic injury. Am. J. Physiol., 1932, 100, 266.

DESNUELLE, P. AND ROVERY, M. The proteins of the exocrine pancreas, in Advances in protein chemistry, vol. 16, p. 139–195. Academic Press. New York, 1961.

DRAGSTEDT, L. R., MONTGOMERY, M. L., AND MATTHEWS, W. B. Fatal effect of total loss of pancreatic juice. Proc. Soc. Exper. Biol. & Med., 1930, 28, 110.

DREILING, D. A. AND JANOWITZ, H. D. The secretion of electrolytes by the human pancreas: The effects of Diamox, ACTH, and disease. Amer. J. Digest. Dis., 1959, 4, 137.

DREILING, D. A. AND JANOWITZ, H. D. Measurement of pancreatic secretory function, In The exocrine pancreas, p. 225. Ciba Foundation Symposium, Little, Brown and Company. Boston, 1962.

ELMAN, R. AND McCAUGHAN, J. M. On the collection of the entire external secretion of the pancreas under sterile conditions and the fatal effect of total loss of pancreatic juice. J. Exper. Med., 1927, 45, 561.

FRIEDMAN, M. H. F. AND SNAPE, W. J. Dissociation of secretion of pancreatic enzymes and bicarbonate in patients with chronic pancreatitis. Gastroenterology, 1950, 15, 296.

GAMBLE, J. L. AND McIVER, M. A. Body fluid changes due to continued loss of external secretion of the pancreas. J. Exper. Med., 1928, 48, 837, 849, 859.

GREENGARD, H., GROSSMAN, M. I., WOOLLEY, J. R., AND IVY, A. C. Confirmation of presence of pancreozymin in duodenal mucosa. Science, 1944, 99, 350.

GREENGARD, H., STEIN, I. F., AND IVY, A. C. Secretinase in blood serum. Am. J. Physiol., 1941, 133, 121. Modification of the pancreatic response to secretin by urine and urine concentrates. Am. J. Physiol., 1941: 134, 245.

GROSSBERG, A. L., KOMAROV, S. A., AND SHAY, H. Distribution of proteins and enzymatic activities in electrophoretic components of canine pancreatic juice. Am. J. Physiol., 1952, 168, 269.

GROSSMAN, M. I. Nervous and hormonal regulation of pancreatic secretion, In The exocrine pancreas, p. 220. Ciba Foundation Symposium, Little, Brown and Company. Boston, 1962.

GROSSMAN, M. I., GREENGARD, H., AND IVY, A. C. The effect of dietary composition on pancreatic enzymes. Am. J. Physiol., 1943, 138, 676. See also Am. J. Physiol., 1944, 141, 38.

GROSSMAN, M. I. AND IVY, A. C. Effect of alloxan upon external secretion of the pancreas. Proc. Soc. Exper. Biol. & Med., 1946, 63, 62.

GUTH, P. H., KOMAROV, S. R., SHAY, H., AND STYLE, Z. C. Relationship between protein nitrogen, proteolytic, amylolytic and lipolytic enzymes in canine pancreatic juice obtained under various conditions of stimulation. Am. J. Physiol., 1956, 187, 207. See also Am. J. Physiol., 1958, 192, 1.

HAINES, R. D., HIGHTOWER, N. C. JR., CROZIER, W. A., AND EIBAND, J. M. Pancreatic replacement therapy in fibrocystic disease. J.A.M.A., 1962, **180**, 1000.

HAMMARSTEN, E., JORPES, E., AND ÅGREN, G. Versuche zur Reinigung von Sekretin. Biochem. Ztschr., 1933, **264**, 272.

HAMMERSTEN, E., WILANDER, O., AND ÅGREN, G. Versuche zur Reinigung von Sekretin. Acta med. scandinav., 1928, **68**, 239.

HARPER, A. A. AND RAPER, H. S. Pancreozymin, a stimulant of the secretion of pancreatic enzymes in extracts of the small intestine. J. Physiol., 1943, **102**, 115.

HIRSCH, G. C., JUNQUEIRA, L. C. V., ROTHSCHILD, H. A., AND DOHI, S. T. Die Pankressaft-Sekretion bei der Ratte. I. Pfluger's Arch. ges. Physiol., 1957, **264**, 78.

HOKIN, L. E. The synthesis and secretion of amylase by pigeon pancreas in vitro. Biochem. J., 1951, **48**, 320.

HOKIN, L. E. Amino acid requirement of amylase synthesis by pigeon pancreas slices. Biochem. J., 1952, **50**, 216.

HOKIN, L. E. AND HOKIN, MABEL R. The actions of pancreozymin on pancreas slices and the role of phospholipids in enzyme secretion. J. Physiol., 1956, **132**, 442.

HOKIN, MABEL R. The formation of amylase by mouse pancreas in vitro J. Biol. Chem., 1956, **319**, 77.

HONG, S. S. AND MAGEE, D. F. Influence of dietary amino acids on pancreatic enzymes. Am. J. Physiol., 1957, **191**, 71.

HOUCK, J. C. AND PATEL, Y. M. The collagenolytic activity of pancreas. Ann. N. Y. Acad. Sci., 1962, **93**, 331.

IVY, A. C. Contributions to the physiology of the pancreas. Ann. Clin. Med., 1926, **4**, 798.

JANOWITZ, H. D. AND DREILING, D. A. The pancreatic secretion of fluid and electrolytes, In The exocrine pancreas, p. 115. Ciba Foundation Symposium, Little, Brown and Company. Boston, 1962.

JOHNSON, C. G. AND BALL, E. G. Variations in inorganic constituents of the pancreatic juice during constant drainage of the pancreatic ducts. J. Biol. Chem., 1930, **86**, 643.

JORPES, E. AND MUTT, V. Secretin, pancreozymin and cholecystokinin; their physiology and future clinical usefulness. Nord. Med., 1956, **56**, 1511.

KUNITZ, M. AND NORTHRUP, J. H. Isolation, crystallization and general properties of a new preoteolytic enzyme and its precursor. J. Gen. Physiol., 1934, **18**, 433. See also J. Gen. Physiol., **21**, 60; **22**, 429; **17**, 591; **19**, 991; and Science, **78**, 558; **80**, 190.

LAGERLÖF, H. The secretin test of pancreatic function. Quart. J. Med., 1939, **8**, 115.

LAGERLÖF, H. Normal esterases and pancreatic lipase in the blood (a second secretin test). Acta med. scandinav., 1945, **120**, 407.

MAGEE, D. F. AND ANDERSON, E. G. Changes in pancreatic enzymes brought about by changes in the nature of the dietary protein. Am. J. Physiol., 1955, **181**, 79. See also Hong and Magee, 1957, and Wang, 1955 (cited by above).

MAGEE, D. F. AND HONG, S. S. Changes in pancreatic enzymes brought about by amino acid additions to the diet. Am. J. Physiol., 1956, **184**, 449.

MAGEE, D. F. AND WHITE, T. T. Effect of alteration in dietary protein levels on pancreatic enzymes in the rat. Am. J. Physiol., 1958, **193**, 21.

McCAUGHAN, J. M. Lethal factors in complete pancreatic drainage. Changes in chemistry of the blood. The mechanism of death. Proc. Staff Meet. Mayo Clin., 1929, **4**, 199.

MILLER, J. M. AND WIPER, T. B. Physiologic observations on patients with external pancreatic fistulas. Ann. Surg., 1944, **120**, 852.

MONTGOMERY, M. L., SHELINE, G. E., AND CHAIKOFF, I. L. Elimination of sodium in pancreatic juice as measured by radioactive sodium. Am. J. Physiol., 1941, **131**, 578.

NEURATH, H. Protein-digesting enzymes. Scientific American, 1964, **211**, 68.

PALADE, G. E., SIEKEVITZ, P., AND CARO, L. G. Structure, chemistry and function of the pancreatic exocrine cell, In The exocrine pancreas, p. 39. Ciba Foundation Symposium. Little, Brown and Company. Boston, 1962.

PERRIER, CLAUDE V., DREILING, D. A., AND JANOWITZ, H. D. A stop-flow analysis of pancreatic secretion; the effect of transient occlusion on the electrolyte composition of pancreatic juice. Gastroenterology, 1964, **46**, 700.

POPIELSKI, L. Uber secretorische Hemmungsnerven des Pankreas. Zentralbl. Physiol., 1896, **10**, 405.

RICHENS, C. A. The innervation of the pancreas. J. Comp. Neurol., 1945, **83**, 223.

RYAN, J. D., DOUBILET, H., AND MULHOLLAND, J. H. Observations on biliary-pancreatic dynamics in a normal human. Gastroenterology, 1949, **13**, 1.

SCOTT, V. B., COLLIGNON, U. J., BUGEL, H. J., AND JOHNSON, G. C. Relation of external pancreatic secretion to variations in blood sugar. Am. J. Physiol., 1941, **134**, 208.

SCOTT, V. B., GRAHAM, J. S., AND McCARTNEY, D. H. Exocrine pancreatic secretion in fasting dogs. Am. J. Digest. Dis., 1940, **7**, 533.

SCOTT, V. B., SCOTT, C. C., AND BUGEL, H. J. Relation of fasting external pancreatic secretion to hunger. Am. J. Physiol., 1940, **131**, 60.

SHINGLETON, W. W., BAYLIN, G. J., ISLEY, J. K., SANDERS, A. P., AND RUFFIN, J. M. The evaluation of pancreatic function by use of I^{131}-labeled fat. Gastroenterology, 1957, **32**, 28.

SLUITER, J. W. Das Restitutions problem in der Pancreaselle. I. Die Bedeutung des Golgi-Apparates. Ztschr. Zellforsch., 1944, **33**, 187.

SUN, D. C. H. AND SHAY, H. Pancreozymin-secretin test. Combined study of serum enzymes and duodenal contents in the diagnosis of pancreatic disease. Gastroenterology, 1960, **38**, 570.

TONKISH, ANNA. Zur Physiologie des Pankreas. Pfluger's Arch. ges. Physiol., 1924, **206**, 525.

WANG, C. C. AND GROSSMAN, M. I. Physiological determination of release of secretin and pancreozymin from intestine of dogs with transplanted pancreas. Am. J. Physiol., 1951, **164**, 527.

WHITE, T. T., LUNDT, G., AND MAGEE, D. F. Evidence for the existence of a gastropancreatic reflex. Am. J. Physiol., 1960, **198,** 725.

ZUCKER, T. F., NEWBURGER, P. G., AND BERG, B. N. The amylase of serum in relation to functional states of the pancreas. Am. J. Physiol., 1932, **102,** 209.

Monographs and Reviews

BABKIN, B. P. Die aussere Sekretion der Verdauungdrusen., 2nd ed. Julius Springer. Berlin, 1928.

BABKIN, B. P. Secretory mechanism of the digestive glands, 2nd ed. Hoeber. New York, 1950.

BERNARD, CLAUDE. Leçons de physiologie experimentale, 1856, Vol. 2, p. 278 (Cited by Opie, 1910).

Ciba Foundation Symposium on The Exocrine Pancreas (ed. A. V. S. DE REUCK AND M. P. CAMERON). Little, Brown and Company. Boston, 1962.

DEGRAAF, REGNER. English translation quoted by J. F. FULTON, Selected readings in the history of physiology. Chas. C Thomas. Springfield, Ill., 1930. (1664).

DREILING, D. A. AND JANOWITZ, H. D. Electrolyte secretion of the pancreas. A new hypothesis of the mechanism of secretion by the pancreas. Proceedings, World Congress of Gastroenterology, 1958. Williams & Wilkins Co., Baltimore, 1959, p. 243.

DREILING, D. A., JANOWITZ, H. D., AND PERRIER, C. V. Pancreatic inflammatory disease: A physiological approach. Hoeber Medical Division, Harper and Row. New York, 1964, p. 130.

FLOREY, H. W., WRIGHT, R. D., AND JENNINGS, M. A. The secretions of the intestine. Physiol. Rev., 1941, **21,** 36.

GREENGARD, H. Hormones of the gastrointestinal tract, In The Hormones (Ed. G. PINCUS AND K. V. THIMANN). Academic Press. N. Y., 1948.

GROSSMAN, M. I. Gastrointestinal hormones. Physiol. Rev., 1950, **30,** 33.

GROSSMAN, M. I. The physiology of secretin. Vitamins and Hormones, 1958, **16,** 179.

GUILLAUMIE, M. Recherches expérimentales sur le rôle du nerf vague dans le fonctionnement exocrine du pancréas. Brenner et Cie. Paris, 1934.

HIRSCH, G. C. Form-und Stoffwechsel der Golgi-Korper. Protoplasma-Monographie, 19. Borntrager. Berlin, 1939.

IVY, A. C. The role of hormones in digestion. Physiol. Rev., 1930, **10,** 282.

MCCLURE, C. W. Functional activities of the pancreas and liver. Medical Authors Pub. Co. New York, 1937.

OPIE, E. L. Disease of the pancreas. Its cause and nature, p. 140. Lippincott. Philadelphia, 1910.

PAVLOV, I. P. The work of the digestive glands. Translation by W. H. THOMPSON, 2nd ed. Lippincott. Philadelphia, 1910.

STILL, E. U. Secretin. Physiol. Rev., 1931, **11,** 328.

THOMAS, J. E. The external secretion of the pancreas. Am. Lecture Series. Charles C Thomas. Springfield, Ill., 1950.

THOMAS, J. E. Methods for study of external secretory function of the pancreas. In methods in medical research, Vol. IV, pp. 149–166 (ed. MAURICE B. VISSCHER). Year Book Publishers, Inc. Chicago, Ill., 1951. Also see Gastroenterology, 1959, **36,** 362.

WALDSCHMIDT-LEITZ, E. Enzyme actions and properties. Wiley. New York, 1929.

CHAPTER 59

The Liver and Biliary System

The liver is both a secretory and excretory organ. Therefore, bile is a mixture of secretory and excretory products consisting of water, bile salts, bile pigments, inorganic salts, and a mixture of lipid material including fats, cholesterol and lecithin. In most animals and man, bile is formed continuously by the liver. In its transport to the intestinal tract, bile first passes along the bile capillaries, then the hepatic and cystic ducts to the gall bladder where it is stored. The expulsion of bile from the gall bladder and its passage along the common bile duct into the duodenum is intermittent, related in time to the arrival of food in the intestine, and is quite independent of the formation of bile by the liver.

Secretion of Bile

The steady flow of bile from the liver serves as an avenue for the secretion of certain substances important in digestion, and for the excretion of others. Before considering the composition of bile, the factors regulating its flow and the mechanisms involved, a brief consideration of the lobular pattern of the intra-hepatic architecture is in order.

The Hepatic Lobule

Microscopic sections of the normal human liver reveal a rather characteristic arrangement of the hepatic cells. Groups of cells appear to be arranged in a lobular fashion around a *central vein*, with the periphery of the lobule delineated by the presence of *portal triads*. A portal triad consists of a small arteriole of the hepatic artery, a venule derived from the portal vein, and a bile ductule. The central vein of the hepatic lobule drains into the hepatic vein.

It was originally thought that the liver cells were arranged in cords, two cells thick, with a bile capillary embedded in the center of the cord between the cells. These cords of liver cells were supposed to extend from the periphery of the lobule to the central vein and to be surrounded by sinusoids containing blood. However, recent investigations by Elias (1949, 1953) have caused us to change our concepts of the normal intra-hepatic architecture. It is now realized that liver cells are not arranged in cords as previously supposed, but in the form of *plates* one-cell thick that

provide a honeycomb or sponge-like architecture. Throughout this sponge-like structure, the cell plates are tunneled by a communicating system of cavities known as *lacunae*. The lacunae contain the blood *sinusoids* which have a basement membrane formed of *Kupffer cells*. The very narrow space separating the sinusoidal wall from the liver cell plates is known as *Disse's space*.

The formation of bile is accomplished by two types of cells, the *reticuloendothelial cells*, which help to line the liver sinusoids, and the *liver cells* proper. The sinusoids convey blood from the portal vein and hepatic artery to the hepatic vein. The reticulo-endothelial cells known in the liver as Kupffer cells are not confined to the liver but occur also in the spleen and bone marrow, where they likewise help to line vascular channels. Another name for the Kupffer cells is "stellate cells," so-called because the cells are frequently star-shaped when seen in the endothelial lining of the liver sinusoid. Similar cells occur free in the connective tissues and elsewhere in the body, and together comprise what is known as the reticulo-endothelial system. In general, these cells have a phagocytic function; their role in the production of bile will be considered later.

The *biliary canaliculi* are located within the liver cell plates, and are arranged in a communicating system surrounding the hepatic cells. The liver cell thus forms a narrow wall between the blood stream on the one hand and the bile stream on the other, and it is not surprising that bile sometimes escapes from or through the liver cells into the blood.

The electron microscope has provided new information regarding the relationship of the liver cells to the biliary canaliculi. The bile canaliculus is a space less than 1 μ in diameter between neighboring liver cells. The boundaries of the canaliculus are formed by the plasma membrane of the liver cells, and small finger-like projections or microvilli extend from the liver cells into the lumen of the canaliculus. It will be recalled that this arrangement is characteristic of surfaces across which fluid transfer occurs. In the pericanalicular area, the cytoplasm of the liver cell is different from the rest of the cell. In the pericanalicular zone, a membrane system of lamellas and vacuoles is always present. This is the Golgi complex. Free ribosomes, vacuoles, and dark, rounded bodies occur in the pericanalicular zone. It is thought that these structures, as in the pancreatic acinar cell, are related to the secretory functions of the hepatic cells. (Schaffner, 1965).

The Composition of Bile

Table 59.1 gives the composition of human liver bile (parts in 1000). Liver bile has a pH which varies between 8.0 and 8.6. The reaction of human gall bladder bile is neutral or very slightly alkaline; that of the dog (or cat) is definitely acid—with a pH between 5.0 and 6.0. The chief biliary components are: the *bile salts, bile pigments, cholesterol,* and *lecithin.* These organic materials make up over 60 per cent of the total biliary solids. As a result of the absorption of water and inorganic salts, gall bladder bile is several times more concentrated in organic solids than liver bile. The biliary constituents may vary independently of one another.

Bile Electrolytes

The electrolyte composition of bile is related to flow rate, in a manner similar to that observed in the pancreas. In turn, flow rate is related to the availability of bile salts. The principal cations in bile are sodium and potassium; the principal anions are bicarbonate and chloride. It will be seen later that the bile salts come from both hepatic synthesis and the re-excretion of bile salts absorbed from the intestine. It has been estimated that 85 to 90 per cent of the bile salts excreted in the bile are reabsorbed and returned to the liver for re-excretion. Other factors regulating bile flow will be discussed in more detail later, including neural stimuli, humoral agents such as secretin, and changes in vascular perfusion.

If bile salts are prevented from entering the intestinal tract due to removal through a biliary

TABLE 59.1

Constituents of bile

Water	976.22
Solids	23.78
Mucin and pigments	5.00
Bile salts	9.00
Fatty acids from soaps	1.23
Cholesterol	0.63
Lecithin \ Fat /	0.60
Inorganic salts	7.32

fistula, biliary flow gradually decreases. To overcome this problem, Wheeler and Ramos (1960) infused sodium taurocholate intravenously at a constant rate to dogs who had been prepared with biliary fistulae. They were then able to obtain multiple bile samples for measurement of electrolyte concentration without interfering with flow rate. In their excellent study of bile salts and electrolyte composition of bile samples collected from their dogs, they found that the taurocholate concentration of the bile was equal to the difference between the cations (Na^+ and K^+) and the anions (Cl^- and HCO_3^-). This relationship was maintained over a wide range of taurocholate concentrations (40 to 280 mEq/l.).

A characteristic alteration in the bile electrolyte composition was observed with increasing flow rate. As the flow rate increased, the taurocholate concentration decreased, indicating that the bile salt was excreted at a constant rate. With increase in bile flow, there was a striking increase in bicarbonate concentration and pH, similar to that observed in the pancreas. Chloride concentration also increased with increased flow rates. The changes observed in chloride and bicarbonate concentration and pH at different flow rates are illustrated in fig. 59.1. When secretin was administered intravenously to the dogs or when 0.05 N HCl was infused into the duodenum, the highest flow rates were obtained. When acetazolamide (Diamox) was administered intravenously, a choleresis or increased flow rate occurred, but in every instance there was a decrease in bicarbonate concentration and pH and an increase in chloride concentration. These effects of acetazolamide on bicarbonate and pH are again similar to that observed in the pancreas. Observations such as these suggest that sodium bicarbonate secretion in the bile may be similar to that observed in the pancreas, and that with passage through the biliary ducts, an exchange between bicarbonate and chloride occurs.

The osmolarity of the bile samples showed little variation, despite marked differences in electrolyte composition, bile flow, or time of collections. In all samples, the osmolarity of the bile was essentially that of plasma.

The Bile Salts

The most important secretory products of the liver are the bile acids which appear in the bile as salts of sodium or potassium. There are a variety of bile acids to be found in the bile of different species of animals, all of which are formed by conjugation of an amino acid with cholic acid. The structural formula of cholic acid contains the tetracyclic carbon group characteristic of the sterols; this is shown in skeleton form.

Cholic acid

Cholic acid is, therefore, related to cholesterol, to the male and female sex hormones, and to cortisone and other adrenal steroid fractions. It is highly probable that cholesterol is a precursor of cholic acid in normal metabolism. Bloch and his associates (1943) have demonstrated the production of cholic acid from cholesterol. When cholesterol containing deuterium was fed to dogs, cholic acid containing the isotope was isolated from the urine.

The acids of human bile are glycocholic and taurocholic acids, in which the cholic acid is conjugated with glycocoll or with taurine. Taurine is related to cystine, a sulfur-containing amino acid. Glycine we are familiar with as the simplest amino acid, and one which can be synthesized by the body. The bile acids, therefore, all contain nitrogen, and taurine contains sulfur in addition. The bile acids are presumed to be synthesized in the liver cells, but positive proof of their origin is not available.

Little can be said concerning the *site of origin* of the cholic acid; whether it is formed by the hepatic epithelium, or is merely brought preformed to the liver from other body tissues is not known. Some is formed in the body, as is indicated by the fact that the bile salts continue to be discharged from a biliary fistula during long periods of starvation. Apparently, it is derived also from the food, since increased excretion follows the ingestion of protein material. Though the supplies of glycocoll and taurine within the body are apparently plentiful, the supply of cholic acid is limited. Experiments in which taurine was fed alone caused no increase in the excretion of bile salts, whereas cholic acid ingestion alone caused a rise in the excretion of taurocholic acid. It is possible to deplete the taurine stores by feeding cholic acid for several days to a dog with a biliary fistula. When cystine disulphoxide, cysteine, cysteinesulfinic acid, or cysteic acid is then fed with cholic acid, an increase in the taurocholic acid of the bile follows (Virtue and Doster-Virtue,

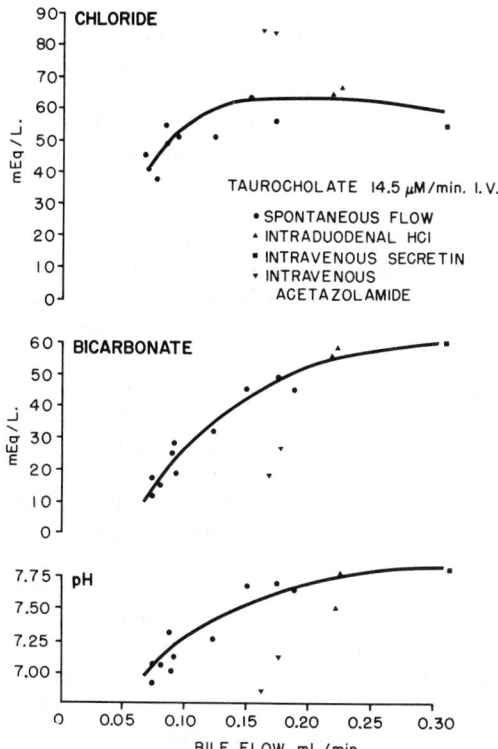

FIG. 59.1. Relationship between bile flow and composition. Sodium taurocholate was administered by a constant intravenous infusion at a rate of 14.5 micromoles per minute. Maximal flow, pH and bicarbonate concentration were observed after intravenous secretin or intraduodenal HCl. After intravenous acetazolamide, the chloride concentration was higher and the bicarbonate concentration lower than at comparable spontaneous lows. (Redrawn from Wheeler and Ramos, 1960.)

1939). This result suggests that taurine is produced in the body from such compounds. Under these circumstances taurine is evidently supplied from the body sources, whereas cholic acid must be furnished in the diet. The quantity of cholic acid available apparently determines the level of bile acid production (Whipple, 1922).

So far as is known, the liver is the only situation where the *conjugation* of taurine or glycocoll with cholic acid, and the production of the respective bile acid can take place. The following observations suggest that their formation is a specific function of the liver: (1) When liver function is depressed by injury, or by the establishment of an Eck fistula, the output of bile salts may be reduced by 50 per cent or more (Smyth and Whipple, 1924). (2) Bile acids appear in the blood of dogs when the common bile duct is ligated. On the other hand, no accumulation occurs in the blood after removal of the liver.

THE CIRCULATION OF BILE SALTS. After their passage into the intestine, the bile salts undergo reabsorption and are carried in the portal blood stream back to the liver for re-excretion. This portal-biliary circulation of the bile salts is intimately connected with the absorption of fat (p. 1187). When bile salts are fed to an animal they can be recovered almost quantitatively from a biliary fistula. This indicates that in the intact animal, the reabsorption of bile salts is almost complete (about 90 per cent). Under ordinary circumstances, comparatively small amounts (about 10 per cent) of bile salts are formed afresh, i.e., their concentration in the bile is maintained largely as a result of their being circulated over and over again through the portal and biliary systems. Nevertheless, if the bile is prevented from entering the intestine by draining it to the exterior through the fistula, its concentration in bile salts does not become materially reduced. Experiments by Berman and associates (1941) indicate that a homeostatic mechanism regulates synthesis of bile acids in such a way that the amount synthesized balances the amount lost. Thus, if an animal is fed an excess of bile acids, synthesis is depressed until the excess amount has been eliminated. On the other hand, if bile acids are drained away by removing bile from the body, synthesis of bile acids is increased.

Test for bile salts. Pettenkoffer's test. Five ml. of the fluid to be tested are mixed in a test tube with a few drops of a 10 per cent solution of cane sugar. One or two ml. of concentrated sulfuric acid are introduced beneath the surface of the mixture. The appearance of a red ring at the junction of the two liquids indicates the presence of bile salts; upon agitation, the color diffuses through the solution. The color is due to the formation of cholalic acid from the bile acids, and its combination with the furfural resulting from the decomposition of the cane sugar. A few drops of a 1:1000 aqueous solution of furfural itself may be employed (Mylin's modification) instead of the sugar solution.

Rowntree and associates (1927) have developed a method for the quantitative estimation of bile salts in blood based upon the Pettenkoffer reaction. The bile salts are extracted from the blood with alcohol and the test is performed upon the extract. The color is compared in a colorimeter with that produced under similar conditions in a standard solution of pure glycocholic acid. The results are expressed in terms of glycocholic acid. Normal human blood contains from 2.5 to 6.0 mg. per cent of bile acids. In obstructive jaundice the value is increased, sometimes several-fold.

The Bile Pigments

The biliary pigments are *bilirubin* and *biliverdin*. Bilirubin ($C_{33}H_{36}N_4O_6$) is the chief pigment in human bile and in the bile of the carnivora. Biliverdin ($C_{33}H_{36}N_4O_8$) is an oxidative derivative of bilirubin, and although it is present in only small amounts of human bile, it is the chief pigment of birds' bile. The pigments constitute from 15 to 20 per cent of the total solids in liver bile.

The readiness with which the bile pigments are oxidized, and the color changes which they undergo in the process, are the basis for Gmelin's test for bile in body fluids. If, for example, a fluid containing bile is passed through filter paper, and a drop of fuming nitric acid is then dropped upon the wet surface of the filter, the pigment is oxidized and a series of concentric rings of different colors appears—yellow, yellowish-red, violet and blue-green from the center outwards. Besides biliverdin, other derivatives of bilirubin are found in the body. *Urobilinogen* (cf. below and ch. 27) is a reduction product of bilirubin; upon oxidation it yields *urobilin*. *Bilicyanin* and *bilifuscin* are formed by the oxidation of biliverdin. The latter two pigments are not found in bile but may be present in gallstones.

ORIGIN OF THE BILE PIGMENTS. Bile pigments are derived from the free hemoglobin resulting from the destruction of red cells in the body and, in smaller amounts, from other chromoproteins. The red cells have a life span of about 100 to 120 days. Those that perish are disposed of by the reticuloendothelial cells distributed throughout the body. From these cells an average of about 8 g. of hemoglobin is released per day; this yields about 300 mg. of bile pigments. In order to produce bile pigment from hemoglobin, the hemin portion must be separated from the protein (globin) portion of the hemoglobin molecule. Oxidation scission of the iron-porphyrin follows. This involves opening the tetrapyrrole ring at the alpha position and the "shelling out" of iron. The resulting iron-free pigment is probably biliverdin, which is later reduced to bilirubin by the addition of one hydrogen atom. All these reactions are presumed to take place in the reticuloendothelial cells, but the order in which they occur is not known (Drabkin, 1951). In particular, it is not known if the splitting of the hemin moiety on the protein portion of the molecule must take place before the porphyrin ring is open. In any case, the bilirubin is not carried in the blood as such, but as a bilirubin protein complex; the bilirubin is bound to albumin for transport to the liver for excretion.

The bilirubin is taken out of the blood and transferred into the bile through the activity of the liver cells. The pigment is separated from the plasma in the process and, in the liver cells, is conjugated with glycuronic acid, forming bilirubin glycuronide (Schmid, 1956, Billing et al., 1957). The conjugation of bilirubin is accomplished by a microsomal enzyme, *glucuronyl transferase*, which utilizes uridine diphosphoglucuronic acid as a donor. The lipid-soluble unconjugated bilirubin is thus converted to a conjugated water-soluble form. Since bilirubin is capable of combining with two molecules of glucuronic acid, either the mono- or diglycuronide may be formed. The conjugation also may take place in the kidney but apparently does so only to a slight extent. The iron is stored in the liver, spleen and other tissues and, with the globin, is eventually utilized for synthesis of new hemoglobin. The chemical relationship between bilirubinglobin and the various bile pigment derivatives is shown schematically below.

could not be excreted through the liver, they accumulated in the blood and produced a condition analogous to jaundice. Mann and his associates also showed, by a spectroscopic method, that the blood of the splenic vein of a normal animal has a higher bilirubin concentration than does the blood in the corresponding artery.

CIRCULATION OF THE BILE PIGMENTS. URO-BILINOGEN AND UROBILIN. The bilirubin that enters the intestine undergoes reduction by bacteria to form *urobilinogen* (also called *stercobilinogen*). A part of this is excreted in the stools, and by exposure to air, is oxidized to *urobilin* (*stercobilin*). The latter can be detected spectroscopically or by the green fluorescence which it gives with a solution of alcoholic zinc acetate. A certain proportion of the urobilinogen is reabsorbed into the portal circulation and passes to the liver, where it is reconverted in part to bilirubin in the bile (fig. 59.2). It is then almost entirely re-excreted both as bilirubin and as urobilinogen. Any urobilinogen which escapes into the general circulation and is excreted by the kidney becomes oxidized to *urobilin* after the urine has been voided. Normally, however, no urobilin, or mere traces (0.5 to 2. mg.), appears in the urine. Only traces are present in normal blood. Bilirubin itself does not normally appear in the urine, so the

Bilirubinglobin

biliverdin $\xrightarrow{\text{reduction}}$ bilirubin $\xrightarrow{\text{reduction}}$ urobilinogen $\xrightarrow{\text{oxidation}}$ urobilin

It is evident from the distribution of the reticuloendothelial system that bile pigments may be formed, not only in the liver, but also in the spleen and bone marrow and at various other places in the body. This was not generally recognized until the experiments of Whipple and Hooper (1913) and the more conclusive experiments of Mann and his associates (1924, 1925, 1926). The former attempted to isolate the liver from the general circulation, whereas the latter removed the liver completely. In either case, bile pigments continued to be formed and, since they

color of urine is due to neither of these pigments. The urobilinogen normally present in bile merely represents re-excretion of this pigment after its absorption from the intestine, as shown by Elman and McMaster (1925, 1926). When the entire output of bile was collected through a biliary fistula (i.e., none was allowed to enter the intestine), there was complete disappearance of urobilinogen from the bile after the pigment already present in the intestine had been carried away in the feces. The fistula bile remained free from urobilinogen unless infection of the biliary

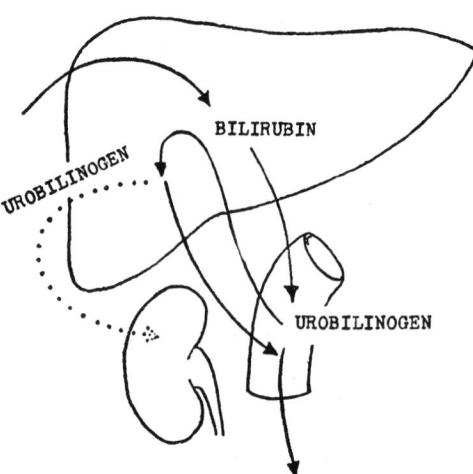

FIG. 59.2. Diagram illustrating the formation of urobilinogen from bilirubin in the intestine, its excretion in part in the feces and its absorption in part into the portal blood. Normally, the absorbed pigment except in negligible amounts is practically all re-excreted in the bile. The dotted lines indicate its passage into the blood, and its excretion by the kidney in cases of liver damage, excessive blood destruction or in the early stages of obstructive jaundice.

tracts had occurred, under which circumstance bacterial action in these situations caused its formation. When a part of the bile was allowed to enter the intestine, or bile was fed by mouth, the derived pigment invariably appeared in the fistula bile.

Complete experimental obstruction of the common bile duct, since it prevented the re-excretion of the urobilinogen absorbed from the intestine, also resulted in its accumulation in the blood and its excretion in the urine. These effects, however, can only occur for a short time after the duct has been obstructed, and are due to the absorption of pigment remaining in the intestine from the period prior to obstruction. After the pigment has been cleared from the intestine, the urine, although it may contain large amounts of bilirubin, is quite free from the derived pigment. Depression of the excretory function of the liver by such hepatic poisons as chloroform, carbon tetrachloride, phosphorus, etc., caused urobilinogen to appear in the urine; hepatic damage from other causes, e.g., infectious hepatitis, is also associated with the urinary excretion of urobilinogen, even though the injury is slight and there is no bilirubinuria. When bilirubin formation is increased by hemolytic agents, urobilinogen production is also increased; the liver, even though its function is normal, is unable to re-

excrete the excess pigment absorbed from the intestine, and urobilin appears in the urine.

The availability of unconjugated and conjugated bilirubin C^{14} has made it possible to study the enterohepatic circulation of bile pigments in a more precise manner. Lester and Schmid (1963) administered both conjugated and unconjugated bilirubin C^{14} to rats which had been prepared with an external biliary fistula. The labeled bilirubin was introduced into the duodenum through a transoral tube. A perianal plastic receptacle permitted separate collection of urine and feces. These investigators found that both of the labeled pigments were absorbed and appeared promptly in the bile. The urinary excretion of the isotope was less than 5 per cent of the dose. Because essentially all of the labeled pigment re-excreted in the bile was conjugated, it could not be decided whether the unconjugated and conjugated bilirubin had been absorbed intact or had undergone chemical modification during the absorptive process. The experiments were repeated in a strain of Wistar rats known as Gunn rats, that have a congenital deficiency of hepatic glucuronyl transferase. Due to the absence of the specific intrahepatic enzyme necessary for conjugation of the bilirubin, these animals have a hyperbilirubinemia of the unconjugated type. Although they are unable to conjugate bilirubin, they are able to excrete conjugated bilirubin. Thus, if conjugated bilirubin was unaltered in the absorptive process, it should be excreted in the bile of the Gunn rats. It was found, after intraduodenal administration of either unconjugated or conjugated bilirubin C^{14}, that no radioactive pigment appeared in the bile, indicating that conjugated bilirubin had been altered in the absorptive process.

The absorption of urobilinogen C^{14} has also been studied (Lester and Schmidt, 1964). In rats, it has been found that significant quantities of intact urobilinogen is absorbed from the intestine and re-excreted predominantly in the bile.

In man, Lester and Schmidt (1963) have demonstrated that unconjugated bilirubin is readily absorbed from the intestine but little, if any, conjugated bilirubin is absorbed. Evidence indicates that conjugated bilirubin remains intact during its transit through the biliary tree and small bowel. Conjugation prevents reabsorption of the pigment, thus the enterohepatic circulation of bilirubin is minimal.

When bacteria in the terminal ileum and colon reduce bilirubin to urobilinogen, it is not known if the glucuronide ester remains intact during these reductive steps. Conjugated forms of urobilinogen have not been isolated, but if they do occur, Lester (1964) indicates that minimal absorption of intact urobilinogen glucuronide would be anticipated.

In rare instances, urobilinogen is formed in situations other than the intestinal tract and independently of bacterial action. Rabinowitch (1930), for example, has reported a case in which large quantities of urobilinogen were present in the urine. A sterile ovarian cyst containing an old blood clot and a high percentage of urobilinogen was revealed by operation. When the cyst was removed, the urobilinogen disappeared from the urine.

Lecithin and Cholesterol

Lecithin is present in human liver bile to the extent of from 0.02 to 0.05 per cent. The *cholesterol* content is normally from 0.04 to 0.16 per cent. The cholesterol is present in the free state, i.e., not in the form of esters. The percentages of these materials in the bile of the gall bladder are, as a result of the absorption of water and salts through the gall bladder mucosa, much higher than the percentages in liver bile. The ratio of the concentration of cholesterol in bile to that of the bile salts is from 1:20 to 1:30. The ability of the bile to hold cholesterol in solution is, in large degree, dependent upon the bile salts. If the ratio falls to 1:13, precipitation of cholesterol occurs. Andrews and associates showed that if bile is dialyzed against water, bile salts are removed and the bile becomes turbid, as a result of cholesterol precipitation. The importance of this observation in relation to gallstone formation is considered on p. 1166. The fatty acid concentration of the bile is of as much, if not more, importance than the bile salt concentration in holding cholesterol in solution. Little is known concerning the origin and function of the biliary cholesterol. It may be derived from the stroma of disintegrated red cells or from nervous tissue, which contains it in large amounts. According to Gardner, the cholesterol of the bile does not vary with changes in the total blood cholesterol, nor is its concentration raised by increasing the cholesterol content of the diet. It continues to be excreted upon a cholesterol-free diet. A biliary-portal circulation of cholesterol has been shown to occur, i.e., excretion in the bile, reabsorption from the intestine, and reexcretion by the liver.

Bile Proteins

The study of proteins in bile of animals or man has been difficult because the bile pigments interfere with colorimetric methods of analysis, and the bile salts and other constituents interfere with chemical methods of analysis. In an attempt to overcome these difficulties, Verschure (1956) used paper electrophoresis and made analysis of normal human bile, bile obtained at autopsy, and bile from post-operative drainage of the common bile duct. He was able to identify four bands after staining the paper with azocarmine-B and designated the bands as P1, P2, P3 and P4. The P1 band moved most rapidly toward the anode and was considered to be a lipoprotein. The P2 band had an electrophoretic mobility similar to that of serum albumin. The P3 band was a mixture of proteins of the alpha and beta mobility. The P4 band remained at the point of application.

The interpretation of electrophoretic patterns of bile is difficult, because in a complex mixture such as bile, the demonstration of a mobility similar to that of some protein in the serum does not necessarily mean the same protein exists in the bile. Furthermore, the fact that the electrophoretic bands take up protein stains is no definite evidence of their protein nature.

Immunologic techniques have, however, demonstrated the presence of normal plasma proteins in human bile. Rawson (1962) has identified albumin and γ-globulin in human bile obtained at autopsy, and from the fistula drainage of patients who had undergone biliary surgery. Russel and Burnett (1963) have used the Ouchterlony gel diffusion technique, immunoelectrophoresis, and gel electrophoresis for the identification of plasma proteins in human bile. Samples of bile were obtained from both the gall bladder and common hepatic duct in patients undergoing laparotomy for various reasons. Bile samples were obtained from patients with gallstones as well as from patients who had a normal gall bladder and biliary system. Antihuman bile serum was developed in rabbits after injecting concentrated or alum-precipitated whole human bile. Rabbit antihuman serum was also used as a source of antibodies for the identification of serum proteins in bile. With these immunological techniques, Russel and Burnett have definitely identified albumin, γ-globulin and other plasma proteins in bile, confirming the findings of Rawson. No differences between normal bile and that obtained from patients with gallstones were found.

The presence of plasma proteins in the bile of patients with inflammatory disease of the gall bladder or biliary system on postmortem would not be too surprising, as one would expect plasma proteins to escape through the mucous membrane lining the biliary system and gall bladder. The presence of plasma proteins in normal bile is not as easily explained. However, the liver synthesizes large quantities of albumin and the presence of albumin in normal bile during life might be anticipated. On the other hand, γ-globulin is not formed in the liver. Russel and Burnett point out that the hepatic pericellular space (the space of Disse) communicates freely with the liver sinusoids as well as the biliary canaliculi, but that molecules with a molecular weight greater than 15,000 are unable to pass from blood to bile. Thus, further investigation is needed to determine the pathway by which plasma proteins gain entry into the bile in the absence of disease.

Regulation of Bile Secretion

Bile is secreted continuously. This is consistent with the fact that bile is an excretion as well as a secretion. On a normal feeding schedule, more bile is secreted during the daylight hours than during the night. This is because more bile is secreted after meals than in the fasting state, and meals are normally eaten in the daytime. If an animal is fed at regular intervals throughout the 24 hr., as much bile is secreted at night as in the daytime. The stimulating effect of food on the volume output of bile is due mainly to its protein content. Kocour and Ivy (1937) studied a variety of foods for their effect on the output of bile and found that only meat and liver were consistently effective. Fat had some tendency to increase the output but was unreliable. Glucose, given orally, tended to decrease the output of bile, provided the bile secreted was not returned to the intestine. When the secreted bile was returned to the intestine, the glucose had no consistent effect on the output.

Before discussing in detail the various agents influencing the flow of bile, it is well to define some of the terms that will be used. A more extensive list of terms with definitions is given by Ivy (1944). A *cholagogue* is any agent which increases the flow of bile into the intestine. The bile may come from the gall bladder, so the word does not necessarily signify an increase in the secretion of bile by the liver. A *choleretic* is an agent which increases the output of bile from the liver without necessarily changing its concen-

tration; thus a choleretic will usually increase the output of bile solids, as well as of the liquid portion of the bile. A *hydrocholeretic* causes an increase in the volume of bile without a corresponding increase in the output of bile solids.

The natural bile salts have a powerful choleretic action on the liver. No doubt a great part of the increase in the flow of bile after a meal is the result of the discharge of bile from the gall bladder, which increases the amount of bile acids in the intestine and consequently in the portal blood. Certain oxidized bile acids, notably dehydrocholic acid, act as hydrocholeretics and are sometimes used in therapy to produce an abundant flow of dilute bile. The hydrochloric acid of the gastric juice, when present in the intestine, increases the volume of flow of bile. This is probably a result of the release of secretin, or a more specific hormone, from the intestinal mucous membrane by the action of the acid.

Although the intravenous injection of various secretin preparations is followed by an increase in bile flow, there is some doubt as to whether the action is really due to secretin. Friedman and Snape (1945) found that the effect of an intestinal extract on the secretion of bile by the liver was not always proportional to its secretin content, as judged by its effect on the pancreas. Their experiments suggest that there may be a specific liver hormone (*hepatocrinin*) in intestinal extracts. Since foods also caused release of secretin from the intestine, it may be that some part of the action of food, aside from the action of hydrochloric acid, may also be attributed to secretin or hepatocrinin—as the case may be. At any rate, the purest secretin available increases the secretion of bile by the liver, although it does not contract the gall bladder. Studies by Grossman and his co-workers (1949) indicate that secretin acts as a hydrocholeretic in man.

Secretin causes only a moderate increase in bile flow, and none at all if the liver is already secreting vigorously. The maximal rate of flow that can be induced by secretin is only about one-tenth the rate that can be attained by the administration of bile acids and this ratio cannot be increased by increasing the dose of secretin. The increase in the amount of bile formed is usually less than the increase in the amount of pancreatic juice secreted in response to a given dose of highly purified secretin, and the latent period of the liver is no longer than that of the pancreas (Friedman, 1950). These facts suggest that secretin is not a major factor in the regulation of bile secretion. On the other hand, if hepatocrinin exists as a separate hormone, it may be a major factor.

In addition to humoral and hormonal factors affecting the secretion of bile, the nervous system may take part in the regulation of bile flow. The secretion of bile is increased by stimulation of the vagus nerves, but the principal effect of the autonomic innervation on bile secretion appears to be inhibitory. Denervating the liver, insofar as this is possible, causes an increase in bile flow; distention of the colon or stimulation of any one of a number of visceral afferent nerves causes inhibition of the flow of bile from the liver. It is not known whether the inhibitory effect is due to direct inhibition of the liver cells or to alterations in hepatic blood flow.

MECHANISM OF BILE SECRETION

In considering the mechanism of bile secretion it is convenient to divide the bile constituents into two classes (Brauer, 1958): Class A, which includes water, the inorganic salts, and other highly diffusible constituents; and Class B, which includes the bile pigments, bile acids and certain foreign substances such as Bromsulphalein, which may be used in liver function tests and appear in the bile. There is good evidence that water is secreted by the liver cells by an active process involving expenditure of energy. Pure mechanical filtration is ruled out, for bile may be secreted under a pressure which is higher than the pressure of the blood in contact with the liver cells. As pointed out by Brauer, in order for a filtration process such as is utilized in the kidney to be effective, it would be necessary for the capillary pressure to exceed the maximum pressure of bile in the bile ducts by an amount at least equal to the colloid osmotic pressure of the blood; this condition is not attained in the liver. The flow of bile has been shown to be independent of blood flow or of blood pressure, so long as the oxygen supply is adequate. Another bit of evidence is that cooling the liver greatly reduces the rate of flow of bile. For example, in the rat liver, a 10° C. reduction in the perfusion temperature between 18° and 38° C. reduces bile flow by a factor of 4. Such a change in temperature should have little or no effect on a pure mechanical process. Ether anesthesia also reduces the flow of bile. The situation is not so clear with respect to the inorganic salts, and it may be supposed that they are transferred along with the water. The evidence suggests that there is a free interchange of inorganic

salts between the blood and the bile as the bile passes through the bile ducts; thus osmotic equilibrium is established between the blood and the bile.

It is interesting to note that, if the concentration of salts in blood plasma is increased so as to make the blood hypertonic, vacuoles appear in the polygonal cells of the liver. This is taken as evidence that these cells are involved in secretion of water into the bile. These hepatic cells secrete the water, as is further evidenced by the fact that, in certain forms of toxic hepatitis in which only the polygonal cells are damaged, a sharp reduction in the volume of bile is one of the earliest signs (Brauer, 1958). Bile may be reabsorbed into the blood if the pressure of bile in the bile ducts is elevated above a certain critical level, but at normal pressures reabsorption of bile is negligible.

Organic constituents of the bile are actively secreted. They appear in such concentrations in the bile relative to their concentration in the blood that an active process is inevitable. The liver cells exhibit a certain maximum capacity for secreting various of the bile constituents, comparable to the tubular maximum of the kidney tubules for certain of the constituents of the urine. For example, there is a maximum rate of secretion of Bromsulphalein into the bile beyond which, an increase in the dose, or in the rate of infusion into the blood, no longer alters the secretion rate. Similar phenomena have been observed for sodium dehydrocholate, bilirubin, and certain dyes. The same cells are involved in the secretion of different organic compounds, as is indicated by the fact that the secretion of some of these by the liver cells limits the rate of secretion of certain others. For example, if the liver is actively secreting Bromsulphalein, its capacity to secrete bilirubin is limited, and if it is actively secreting bilirubin at a rate near its maximum capacity, it is unable to secrete bile salts at their normal maximal rate. This indicates that there is competition within the individual liver cells among the various substances that are secreted into the bile.

It has been possible to observe, in suitable preparations, the path taken by certain of the substances that are secreted into the bile. For example, fluorescein can be seen to appear first in the parenchymal cells of the liver, then secreted into the bile canaliculi, and then transported down the bile ducts. Similar observations are possible by different methods using radioactive isotopes. Thus it appears that all the constituents of the bile, both organic and inorganic are normally secreted by the liver cells and, with the possible exception of the inorganic salts, by a process which involves the expenditure of energy.

FUNCTIONS OF BILE IN DIGESTION

Only the salts of the bile acids are useful in digestion. The other constituents of bile are present as excretory products (with the exception of the inorganic salts which probably reach the bile by diffusion and are neither secreted nor excreted). The bile salts in the intestine aid in digestion and absorption of fat largely because of their surface tension-lowering properties and their ability to form chemical compounds with fatty acids, thus increasing their solubility. The ability of bile salts to reduce the surface tension of water aids in emulsification of fats and increases the activity of pancreatic lipase. Fats, being insoluble in water, present special difficulties to the digestive apparatus, since digestion is a hydrolytic process and the digestive enzymes are dissolved in water. Special means are necessary in order to bring the fat particles into contact with lipase, which is dispersed in the aqueous phase. This can be accomplished by any one of several wetting agents. Bile, being a natural detergent, accomplishes this purpose in the living body.

The fatty acids that are liberated by hydrolysis of triglyceride fat form soluble soaps in an alkaline medium, but the intestinal contents are usually not sufficiently alkaline to maintain any considerable quantity of fatty acids in solution in this way. After liberation from the glycerol molecule, the free fatty acids are said to combine with bile salts (Verzar and McDougall). It is believed that these soluble compounds can penetrate the epithelial cells of the intestine and thus facilitate absorption of fatty acids. Absorption of fats will be discussed in greater detail in the next chapter.

The idea put forward by Mellanby that bile acts as a stimulus for release of secretin from the intestinal mucosa, and in this way brings about secretion of pancreatic juice, has been proved to be erroneous. In certain circumstances bile may facilitate the release of secretin into the blood but this is not an important part of the secretin mechanism (Thomas and Crider, 1943). Bile in the intestine has a tendency to stimulate peristalsis and is often credited with having a mild laxative action. This action would probably be manifest only in a condition in which there was a pathological deficiency of bile in the intestine.

Jaundice

DEFINITION AND CLASSIFICATION

When bile pigment is present in an excessive amount in the blood (hyperbilirubinemia) it diffuses from the capillaries; the skin, mucous membranes and conjunctivas then become stained a pale yellow tint. However, the pigment is not merely dissolved in the tissue fluids, but appears to be bound in some way to the tissues. This discoloration is called *jaundice* or *icterus*. The bilirubin appears in the urine and sweat but does not pass into the saliva or milk, nor, as a rule, into the cerebrospinal fluid.[1] Jaundice may be due to the production of bile pigment in excess of the amount with which the excretory power of the liver can cope, or it may result from the failure of a damaged liver to excrete the bilirubin produced in normal amounts. Jaundice may therefore be divided into two main groups corresponding to the mode of its production: the *hemolytic* and the *hepatic*. The former results from increased production of bile pigment from hemoglobin, and the latter from depressed or suppressed excretion of pigment by the liver. In the hepatic form the retention of pigment may be due to: (a) obstruction of the bile passages, (b) damage of the liver cells by toxic agents or infections, or (c) a deficiency in the ability of the hepatic cell to conjugate and/or excrete bilirubin. Jaundice is also classified into obstructive and nonobstructive, the latter being subdivided into hemolytic, on the one hand, and toxic or infective on the other. These principal varieties of jaundice are tabulated below.

Hepatic
{
1. Hemolytic jaundice } Non-obstructive
2. Toxic, or infective jaundice }
3. Obstructive jaundice
}

A third classification proposed by Rich has come into use, based upon whether bile pigment has been taken up by the liver cells and then returned to the blood, or has been rejected by the cells (due to hepatic dysfunction or to an excess of pigment), and thus retained in the circulation. The first-mentioned type is called *regurgitation jaundice*; it includes obstructive jaundice, and

---

[1] Its appearance in the cerebrospinal fluid is not uncommon in children.

jaundice due to damage of liver cells and of the walls of the biliary canaliculi, which permits whole bile to "regurgitate" into the circulation.

In the *second* form, called *retention jaundice*, either excessive amounts of bile pigment are produced (hemolytic jaundice), part of which is not taken up by the hepatic parenchyma and is retained in the circulation; or the function of the hepatic cells is so depressed that a large part of the circulating bilirubin, even though not produced in excess, fails to be excreted.

Hemolytic (Retention) Jaundice

It has been mentioned that a small amount of bile pigment (0.2 to 0.8 mg. per cent) is present in normal human serum and that any condition which increases red cell destruction also increases the formation of bile pigment. However, the functional reserve of the liver is so great that it is very doubtful whether overproduction of bile pigment ever taxes the excretory capacity of an undamaged liver to the limit. But when the hepatic reserve is reduced as a result of disease, and hemolysis is excessive, the normal balance between the production and the excretion of pigment cannot be maintained; retention occurs and the bilirubin concentration of the unconjugated type increases in the blood above the normal limits. *Hemolytic agents* of all sorts, such as the toxins of certain infections, septicemia, etc., and various chemical poisons may induce icterus (ch. 28) of this type. It also occurs to some degree in such states as *pernicious anemia, malaria*, etc., in which blood destruction is a pronounced feature. It may be produced in animals by the injection of such hemolytic poisons as toluylenediamine and arseniuretted hydrogen. The disease known as *acholuric jaundice*, which tends to run in families and is associated with splenic enlargement and increased fragility of the red cells (p. 544), is of this type. Jaundice in the newborn, *icterus neonatorum (benign)*, frequently occurs as a slight transient staining of the skin. It is perfectly innocent and indeed may be considered physiological. It does not appear until a day or two after birth and lasts for five or six days.

Obstructive (Regurgitation) Jaundice

Obstructive jaundice results from blockage of the hepatic or common bile duct by: (a) a gallstone or parasites within its lumen, (b) compression of the duct by a tumor (e.g., in head of pancreas) or occlusion of its opening into the duodenum, or (c) congenital obliteration of the ducts (a fatal form of icterus neonatorum).

In complete biliary obstruction the stools are clay-colored; urobilinogen (p. 1145) is absent from the feces and urobilin is absent from the urine. In this type of jaundice, bile pigment is believed to pass into the liver cells, where albumin is split off and the pigment combined with glycuronic acid to form bilirubin glycuronide. The latter, after its discharge into the biliary canaliculi is returned—"regurgitated"—into the blood as a result of the rutpure or, in parenchymatous liver disease, disintegration of the canalicular walls.

McMaster and Rous (1921) found, for example, that when obstructive jaundice was induced in dogs, the ducts, if occluded for long, became filled with a fluid free from pigment and bile salts—the so-called "white bile" (p. 1161). According to the observers, the colorless fluid is not bile but is a simple seromucoid material secreted by the membrane lining the ducts.

The excretory mechanism of the liver has been shown by McMaster and Rous to possess a very large reserve since, in the dog, jaundice does not develop until from 90 to 95 per cent of the excretory ducts have been occluded.

Toxic and Infective Jaundice—Liver Damage

Liver damage and consequent depression of the secretory functions of the liver may be produced by: (a) various *poisons*, e.g., arsphenamine, phosphorus, chloroform, etc.; (b) *acute and chronic liver diseases*, e.g., infectious hepatitis, homologous serum jaundice, acute yellow atrophy, cirrhosis, inflammation of the bile passages (catarrhal jaundice, suppurative cholangitis); (c) *toxins* of various pathogenic bacteria; or (d) engorgement of the hepatic vessels as a result of *cardiac failure*. It has been pointed out by Meakins that, in the latter condition, the edema or ascitic fluid does not contain bilirubin and the skin over edematous regions is not stained. There is no explanation for this fact.

Jaundice Due to Lack of Glucuronyl Transferase

Mention has already been made of the Gunn rat, which has a congenital absence of glucuronyl transferase in the liver. Shortly after birth, such rats demonstrate jaundice due to high serum levels of unconjugated bilirubin. In these animals, no conjugated bilirubin appears in the bile although their liver cells are capable of excreting conjugated bilirubin.

Crigler and Najjar (1952) first described a similar type of non-hemolytic acholuric jaundice developing in infants shortly after birth. These infants' jaundice was found to be due to high levels of unconjugated bilirubin in the serum.

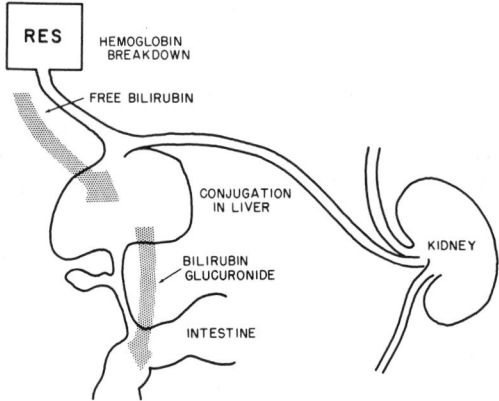

FIG. 59.3. Normal bilirubin metabolism. (Redrawn from Schmid, 1957.)

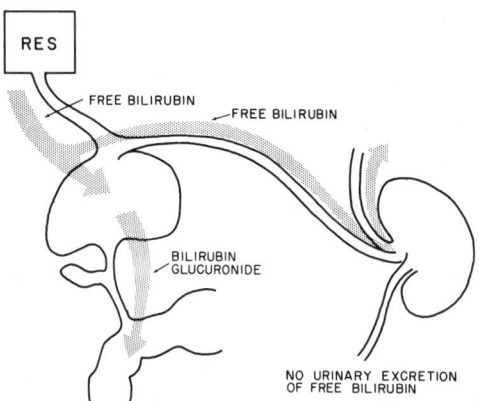

FIG. 59.4. Bilirubin metabolism in hemolytic jaundice (retention jaundice). (Redrawn from Schmid, 1957.)

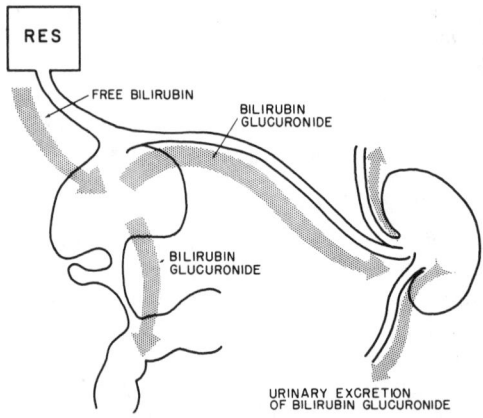

FIG. 59.5. Bilirubin metabolism in hepatogenous jaundice (regurgitation jaundice). (Redrawn from Schmid, 1957.)

Kernicterus is a severe cerebral form of icterus neonatorium in which degenerating changes in the subthalamus and lenticular nuclei usually develop. An absence of glucuronyl transferase in the liver tissue of these infants was demonstrated. Although rare, a congenital absence of the conjugating enzyme, glucuronyl transferase, may be a cause of jaundice in man, as was previously shown to be the case in the Gunn rat.

In the so-called *physiological jaundice* that develops in most full-term infants between the second and seventh days of life, there is no evidence of hemolysis and the jaundice is of the acholuric type. In newborn humans, a deficiency of glucuronyl transferase activity has been demonstrated. The activity of adult liver is not reached until about the tenth day of life. These observations suggest that physiological jaundice of the newborn is related to a delay in the development of the glucuronide conjugating system. In premature infants, the deficiency in glucuronyl transferase activity may lead to severe jaundice and kernicterus.

The pathways taken by the bile pigments normally, and in retention and regurgitation are illustrated in figs. 59.3–59.5 (from Schmid, 1957).

THE FEATURES IN DIFFERENT TYPES OF JAUNDICE COMPARED
(SEE TABLE 59.2)

In obstructive jaundice, and in jaundice resulting from liver damage, the staining of the skin, mucous membranes and urine with bilirubin tends to be much more pronounced than in the hemolytic type. Except for a short time after the duct has been obstructed, urobilin is absent from the urine and urobilinogen is absent from the feces (p. 1145). The plasma alkaline phosphatase shows a pronounced increase in obstructive jaundice, a smaller rise in parenchymatous liver disease, but little or no change in the hemolytic type. In obstructive jaundice, the effects (e.g., *bradycardia, itching of the skin (pruritus)*) referable to the retention of biliary constituents other than pigment may be evident. The cardiac slowing has been attributed to the action of the bile salts, although proof is lacking. Since the bile acids are conjugated in the liver, it is not to be expected that their concentration in the blood will be raised in a purely hemolytic type of jaundice; this is found to be the case. On this account, the latter type is sometimes spoken of as "dissociated jaundice." In severe liver damage bile acids may be absent from the blood, although the hyperbilirubinemia is pronounced. In other

TABLE 59.2

Differences in types of jaundice

	Types of Jaundice		
	Parenchymatous liver damage	Hemolytic	Obstructive (complete)
Serum bilirubin................	Moderate increase	Slight or moderate increase	Great increase
Urinary bilirubin..............	Moderate increase	Little or no change	Great increase
Urobilinogen in urine..........	Great increase	Moderate increase	Absent
Biluribin and urobilinogen (stercobilin) in feces.........	Moderate increase	Great increase	Absent
Albumin:globulin ratio.........	Greatly reduced or reversed	Little change	Little change
Van den Bergh test............	Delayed direct or biphasic	Indirect	Direct
Plasma alkaline phosphatase...	Little change	Little change	Great increase
Thymol turbidity cephalin flocculation and galactose tolerance tests....................	Positive	Negative	Negative
Jaundice......................	Moderate or slight	Moderate or slight	Pronounced, with pruritus

instances of relatively mild degrees of hepatic insufficiency, a converse type of "dissociated jaundice," namely, increased concentration of bile acids in the blood without icterus, is sometimes seen.

The bleeding tendency in obstructive jaundice is a serious hazard should a patient be required to undergo a surgical operation. Only within recent years, as a result of the work of Roderick, of Quick and his associates, and of Dam and Glavind, has the cause of the prolonged coagulation time been discovered. It is due to prothrombin deficiency, which is the result, in turn, of a virtual lack of vitamin K (p. 1442), for when bile is absent from the intestine the vitamin is not absorbed in adequate amounts. The oral administration of vitamin K with bile salts corrects the hemorrhagic tendency. Possibly an additional, though minor, factor in the lengthened coagulation time is the retention in the blood of certain organic sulfur-containing compounds (e.g., cysteine and taurine) possessing anticoagulant properties (Carr and Foote, 1934). Jaundice due to liver damage is also sometimes associated with a prolonged bleeding time, which appears to be due to the incapacity of the liver to manufacture adequate amounts of prothrombin, even though there is no lack of vitamin K in the diet or any failure in its absorption. The cause of the pruritis in obstructive jaundice is unknown. Rowntree and associates found that, though a high concentration of bile acids in the blood was frequently associated with pruritis, this symptom may occur with a normal bile-acid concentration or be absent when the latter is high.

In obstructive jaundice, with complete stoppage of the bile flow, urobilinogen is absent from the urine and feces, but bilirubin excretion in the urine is pronounced. In hemolytic jaundice the reverse is true; urobilinogen is excreted in the urine and feces in excess, but little bilirubin appears in the urine (table 59.2). In parenchymatous liver disease, the albumin per globulin ratio is reduced and may be reversed due to an increase in the β- and γ-globulin fractions, the albumin concentration often being reduced as well. In the other types of jaundice, the ratio shows little change from the normal, although there may be some reduction in the total protein concentration. Certain observations relevant to the foregoing discussion are given in table 59.2.

JAUNDICE USUALLY DUE TO A COMBINATION OF CAUSES

It should be pointed out that, in any given case of jaundice, two or all three causative factors may, and frequently do, coexist. Blood destruction alone, according to Rich, is not capable of producing jaundice except perhaps in rare instances when the hemolytic process is of extreme degree. In pernicious anemia, for example, there is an associated hepatic insufficiency, and even in the ordinary icterus of the newborn the immaturity of hepatic function is claimed to be a factor; also, many hemolytic substances are liver poisons as well. In obstructive jaundice the liver cells suffer damage from pressure, and the retention of bile salts probably induces a certain amount of hemolysis. Furthermore, in many inflammatory conditions of the liver or bile ducts an obstructive element (due to plugging of the intrahepatic ducts by the so-called bile-thrombi) exists in conjunction with the hepatic damage. In the jaundice of cardiac diseases, the hepatic engorgement produces obstruction of the finer bile capillaries as well as injury to the liver cells through anoxia. The occurrence of infarcts in the lung is also a factor in some cases; bilirubin production is increased through the breakdown of red cells in the infarcted areas.

Clinical Tests of Jaundice

THE VAN DEN BERGH REACTION. This test, a modification of Ehrlich's diazo reaction, is employed for the detection of bile pigment in blood serum. There are two main types of the reaction: the *direct* and the *indirect*. The direct reaction occurs without the addition of alcohol, which is essential for the indirect reaction.

The reagents used in the test are:

Solution A:
    Suphanilic acid...................... 0.1 g.
    Concentrated HCl................. 1.5 ml.
    Water up to......................100 ml.
Solution B:
    Sodium nitrite..................... 0.5 g.
    Water........................... 100 ml.

To perform the test, 10 ml. of solution *A* and 0.3 ml. of Solution *B* are freshly mixed. This mixture is used as the reagent in both forms of the test.

The *direct reaction* is that which follows the addition of 1 ml. of the reagent to 1 ml. of serum. It may occur in one of three forms: (a) *immediate* or *prompt*, a violet color due to the formation of diazobilirubin develops in from 10 to 30 sec. (b) *delayed reaction*, no change appears until several min. (5 to 15 or more) elapse, then a reddish color develops which gradually deepens to violet. (c) *biphasic*, a red color appears as promptly as in (a) but takes a variable but longer time than in (b) to change to violet.

The *indirect reaction* is carried out as follows: 1 ml. of serum is mixed with 2 ml. of 95 per cent alcohol. After shaking and centrifuging, to 1 ml. of the supernatant fluid, 0.25 ml. of the reagent mixture and 0.5 ml. of alcohol are added. A reddish-violet color develops almost immediately.

Normal bile and the serum in obstructive jaundice give the prompt direct reaction. Normal serum, the serum in hemolytic jaundice, and the bilirubin formed in old blood extravasations into the connective tissues, serous cavities, etc., give the indirect reaction and occasionally a delayed direct reaction. The sera in types of jaundice due to liver damage, e.g., hepatitis, give a direct reaction—(usually of the delayed or biphasic type); all sera which give the direct reaction also give the indirect, but the reverse does not hold. The qualitative van den Bergh reaction, as a means of distinguishing between the different types of jaundice, is regarded today with less favor than formerly.

THE QUANTITATIVE VAN DEN BERGH. The indirect reaction used as the basis for the *quantitative* estimation of bilirubin in all types of sera is of much more value. The serum, after the color reaction has developed, is compared in a colorimeter with a standard solution made by dissolving 2.161 g. of anhydrous cobaltous sulfate in 100 ml. of distilled water. The color of this standard corresponds to that developed by 1 unit of bilirubin. A *unit* is defined by van den Bergh as 1 part of bilirubin in 200,000 parts of serum. Normal serum contains from 0.4 to 1.5 unit (i.e., bilirubin is present in a dilution of 1 part in from 500,000 to 100,000 parts of serum, or from 0.2 to 1.0 mg. per 100 ml.). In the quantitative estimation of bilirubin in sera showing the direct reaction, the method has been rendered more accurate by the modification of Thannhauser and Anderson. This consists of first adding 0.5 ml. of the reagent to 1 ml. of the serum, and a minute or two later 2.5 ml. of alcohol and 1 ml. of a saturated solution of ammonium sulphate. By adding the diazoreagent before the alcohol, the loss of bilirubin which results from its being carried down with the albuminous precipitate is avoided. When the alcohol is added later, the diazobilirubin compound is not thrown down but remains in the supernatant fluid.

The quantitative van den Bergh reaction is of value in the detection of latent jaundice (i.e., a hyperbilirubinemia which has not reached the level at which jaundice appears), and in recording the progress of a case of manifest jaundice.

The difference between the direct and indirect van den Bergh reactions is due to the difference in the state of bilirubin in hemolytic and obstructive jaundice. Bilirubin that has passed through the liver cell and has been conjugated with glycuronic acid is soluble in water, and is able to react at once with the reagents used in the direct test without addition of alcohol. Consequently, bilirubin that has been secreted and reabsorbed, as in obstructive jaundice, gives the direct test. Circulating bilirubin that has not passed through the liver cell is insoluble except as a compound with some blood protein. It has to be set free and made soluble by addition of alcohol to the reagent before it will give the test.

The icteric index. The bile pigment concentration may also be estimated by comparing the color of the serum with that of a standard solution. A sample of blood is allowed to clot; after centrifuging, 5 ml. of serum are pipetted off and the color of the sample compared in a colorimeter with a 1:10,000 solution of potassium bichromate. The colorimeter is set at 15 mm. for the standard solution. This number is divided by the number on the serum scale when the color of the serum and of the standard solution match. The result is called the *icteric index.* Thus, if the reading of the serum scale is 3, the icteric index is 5. The test is invalidated by the presence in the serum of other coloring matter, e.g., carotenoids.

Tests of Liver Function

Besides the secretory and excretory functions dealt with in this section, the liver plays an important role in many other physiological processes. For the reader's convenience a list of these with page references follows.

An Enumeration of Hepatic Functions

(a) Storage of vitamin B_{12} (ch. 30).

(b) Fibrinogen production (ch. 22).

(c) Prothrombin production (ch. 33).

(d) Heparin production (ch. 33).

(e) Iron and copper storage (ch. 30).

(f) Blood volume regulation (ch. 24).

(g) Protein metabolism (chs. 64 and 65).

(h) Carbohydrate metabolism (ch. 67).

(i) Fat metabolism (ch. 68).

(j) Heat production (ch. 70).

(k) Formation of vitamin A from carotene (ch. 71).

(l) Liberation of a depressor principle (ch. 49). The hepatic circulation is dealt with in ch. 47.

Several of the specific functions of the liver have been utilized as tests for an investigation of the functional capacity of the liver as a whole,

i.e., as a means of detecting the presence of hepatic damage and, in some instances, of gauging the extent to which such damage has occurred, and to distinguish between different types of jaundice. Some of these tests will be very briefly described, the accounts being confined in the main to the general principles upon which the tests are based.

Tests Based Upon the Excretory Functions of the Liver

The quantitative van den Bergh reaction has been described (p. 1154). Since the excretion of bilirubin is an essential hepatic function, a determination of the quantity of circulating bilirubin is a valuable means of estimating the extent of liver damage associated with jaundice—provided the hyperbilirubinemia is not the result of biliary obstruction or of blood destruction.

The estimation of the quantity of *urobilinogen* excreted in the urine has also been employed as a test of liver function. Increased blood destruction, as in pernicious anemia, will also cause urobilinogenuria quite apart from liver damage, but it is usually much less pronounced than that due to parenchymatous liver disease. Also, infection of the biliary passages may increase the urobilinogen output out of all proportion to the reduction of liver function.

Other tests based upon the excretory function of the liver are the *Bromsulphalein, bilirubin,* and *rose Bengal* tests. In each of these tests, the respective material is injected intravenously and the rate of excretion is estimated from the quantity retained in the serum after the lapse of a specified time; the concentration of the material in the serum is determined colorimetrically. These three substances are excreted almost entirely by the liver, and no significant amounts are taken up by the reticuloendothelial cells. In normal persons, less than 5 per cent of Bromsulphalein (5 mg. per kg. of body weight injected) is retained after 45 min., or of bilirubin (1 mg. per kg. of body weight injected) is observed at the end of 4 hr. In the case of rose Bengal (10 ml. of 1 per cent solution injected without regard to subject's weight), 50 per cent or more disappears from the serum within 8 min. after the injection. These tests, like the van den Bergh test, will of course be of no value if obstruction of the bile ducts exists; obviously, whether damaged or not the liver cannot then excrete the injected substances. Colorimetric difficulties also render the dye tests inapplicable in the presence of hyperbilirubinemia from whatever cause. The bilirubin injection test is employed only in the absence of jaundice, for if the liver's power to excrete the endogenous bilirubin is depressed it is a foregone conclusion that it will show a corresponding incapacity to excrete the injected pigment. In the absence of jaundice, however, the bilirubin injection test is one of the most reliable means of estimating the degree of liver damage. Determination of the serum *alkaline phosphatase level* is one of the most sensitive tests of liver function (ch. 77).

TESTS BASED UPON THE METABOLIC FUNCTIONS OF THE LIVER

The Galactose and Levulose (Fructose) Tolerance Tests

In the *levulose tolerance* test, the blood sugar curve is determined after the ingestion of from 40 to 50 g. of pure levulose dissolved in 250 ml. of water. The dose of sugar is varied according to the subject's weight. The test is performed in the morning after a 12-hour fast. The blood sugar level is first determined before the ingestion of the sugar, and then every half hour for 2 hours thereafter. The liver converts levulose to glycogen, the greater the quantity of sugar so converted, the less pronounced will be the rise in the blood sugar. In the absence of hepatic disease, ingestion of 40 g. or so of the sugar causes a maximum rise of the blood sugar curve of 30 mg. per cent or less above the fasting level (when this is between 80 and 100 mg. per 100 ml.) within 1 hr. The curve returns to within 10 mg. per cent of the fasting level within 2 hr. Definite hepatic injury is indicated by a rise in the blood sugar of over 30 mg. per cent when the fasting level is between 80 and 100 mg. per cent, and a rise of 35 mg. per cent, and of 40 mg. per cent when the fasting levels are from 70 to 80 and from 60 to 70 mg. per cent, respectively. Failure of the curve to return to within 15 mg. per cent of the fasting level after 2 hr., regardless of the height of the curve, is also definitely abnormal.

A similar test may be made using galactose. At the end of a 12-hr. fast the blood sugar level is determined, and 40 g. of galactose given in 400 ml. of water. The blood galactose level is then estimated at half-hour intervals for 2 hr. Normally, the maximum value is reached in 1 hr. and does not rise to more than 63 mg. per 100 ml. and falls to 0 by the end of the 2 hr. Normally, by the end of the fifth hour the total urinary

excretion is less than 2.5 g. Higher values than these in blood and urine are found in hepatic insufficiency (Peters and Van Slyke, 1946).

Tests based upon the function of the liver to deaminate the amino acids with the production of urea or upon its detoxicating function have also been devised. Although in the dog hippuric acid is synthesized (from glycine and benzoic acid) only in the kidney, in the rabbit, and in man, this function is performed to an important extent by the liver as well. In carrying out this test, 6 g. of sodium benzoate are given orally and urinary excretion of hippuric acid is measured during the next 4 hr. Normally, over 3 g. of hippuric acid (expressed as benzoic acid) will be excreted in the urine. Quick (1936), who originated the oral hippuric acid test, later introduced an intravenous modification (1939) in which 1.77 g. of sodium benzoate is injected and urinary excretion is measured over a 1-hr. period. Normally, at least 0.7 g. of hippuric acid should be excreted in the 1-hr. period. In both the oral and intravenous tests, the patient must have adequate renal function to excrete the hippuric acid. A urea clearance test is frequently done simultaneously, to ensure that renal function is adequate. The determination of the *prothrombin time* (ch. 33) is also employed as a liver function test. In damage of the liver, the prothrombin time is prolonged.

TESTS BASED UPON THE PROTEIN CONSTITUTION OF THE PLASMA

When damage to the hepatic parenchyma exists, the albumin:globulin ratio of the plasma is reduced. This is due to an absolute increase in the β- and γ-globulin fractions and usually, to an absolute reduction in the albumin fraction as well. The tests to be described are based upon the rise in the globulin fractions and the reduction in albumin, for the latter fraction tends to protect the globulin from the action of the reagent and thus to inhibit the reaction. The higher the serum globulin and the lower the albumin, the more pronounced the reaction will be. The tests to be described cannot be correlated specifically with any given liver function and are, therefore, largely empirical. The first test of this type to be introduced is known as the *Taka-Ara* test, after its originators. In the presence of an excess of globulin a reagent composed of sodium carbonate, mercuric chloride and acid fuchsin, when added to the abnormal serum, causes precipitation of the mercuric chloride. A similar test is the *colloidal gold* test of Gray. But the most commonly used and the most satisfactory tests of this group are the *thymol turbidity* test of Maclagen and the *cephalin-cholesterol flocculation test* of Hanger. In the former, 3 ml. of the thymol reagent[2] are added to 0.05 ml. of serum and the degree of turbidity is measured after ½–1 hr. in a spectrophotometer at a wave length of 650 mμ. The turbidity is believed to be due to the precipitation of a globulin-thymol-phospholipid complex. The cephalin-cholesterol flocculation test consists of adding an emulsion of cephalin (100 mg. from sheep's brain) and cholesterol (300 mg.) to the serum and allowing the mixture to stand for 24 to 48 hr. Normal serum remains clear, whereas the serum from a patient with parenchymatous liver disease (inflammatory or degenerative) shows flocculation.

Several investigators have studied the reliability of the different liver function tests by comparing the results obtained with the histological findings in biopsy samples of hepatic tissue. Sherlock obtains a cylinder of hepatic tissue by the use of a needle 1 mm. in caliber and provided with a trocar. The liver is punctured through the skin under local anesthesia. She found the most useful and reliable tests to be: determinations of serum bilirubin, serum alkaline phosphatase, and the albumin:globulin ratio. In experiments upon dogs in which the liver was damaged by carbon tetrachloride, Drill and Ivy (1944) found that the number of hepatic functions affected increased with the severity of the liver damage. The excretion of Bromsulphalein was the first to become depressed. Serum alkaline phosphatase showed a rise about the same time or slightly later. Next in order of sensitivity was the test for the prothrombin time. The galactose tolerance test was the least sensitive of the four tests employed. From these results Drill and Ivy suggest that the *association* of hepatic functions rather than their *dissociation* (i.e., the singling out of one function or another by liver damage) should receive emphasis.

It is to be remembered that the foregoing are purely functional tests, and that a negative result does not necessarily indicate the absence of liver injury. On the contrary, liver disease may exist without its condition being revealed by any of these means. This is obvious from the observations of McMaster and Rous and of Mann and

[2] This consists of: 1.38 g. barbitone; 1.03 g. sodium barbitone; 3 g. thymol; 500 ml. doubly distilled water.

his associates upon the reserve function of the liver. The first mentioned observers showed that, in the dog, 95 per cent of the excretory function could be abolished before jaundice appeared. Mann and his associates found that the liver tissue could be reduced by 80 per cent or more without a fall in urea production occurring.

The Gall Bladder and Bile Ducts

ANATOMY

The human gall bladder has a capacity of about 50 ml. Its wall is composed of a thin layer of muscle fibers and fibroelastic tissue, with a lining of mucous membrane. The muscle fibers are sparse, and loosely interlaced with one another and with the strands of fibroelastic tissue. The mucosa is surmounted by a layer of columnar epithelium.

The *cystic duct*, through which the bile enters and later leaves the viscus, is tortuous, or S-shaped, and shows spiral folds of mucosa—the *valves of Heister*—within its lumen. These so-called valves do not have a valve-like action, for they offer little resistance to the passage of bile in either direction, nor do they seem to prevent a too rapid flow of bile as some have supposed. They develop late in phylogenetic history, apparently being associated with the erect posture, and they are found only in primates. The folds are formed in the embryo by the twisting or winding of the duct during development. Their function, as suggested by Keith and supported by Lichtenstein and Ivy (1937), is to stiffen the wall of the duct and so prevent its kinking.

The *common bile duct*, formed by the union of the hepatic and cystic ducts, passes very obliquely through the muscular wall of the duodenum and joins with the pancreatic duct to form the *ampulla of Vater* (fig. 59.6). The latter opens into the duodenum through an orifice situated at the summit of a small papilla about 3½ in. below the pylorus. The ampulla of Vater is surrounded, near its outlet into the duodenum, by a ring of muscle fibers—the *sphincter of Oddi*. Boyden (1937) has studied the circular fibers surrounding the common bile duct at its duodenal end (i.e., the smooth muscle usually referred to as the sphincter of Oddi) and distinguishes three sets of fibers: (a) *sphincter choledochus* (or *Boyden's sphincter*), fibers which surround the duct between its penetration of the duodenal wall and the point where it is joined by the pancreatic duct; (b) fibers encircling the pancreatic duct

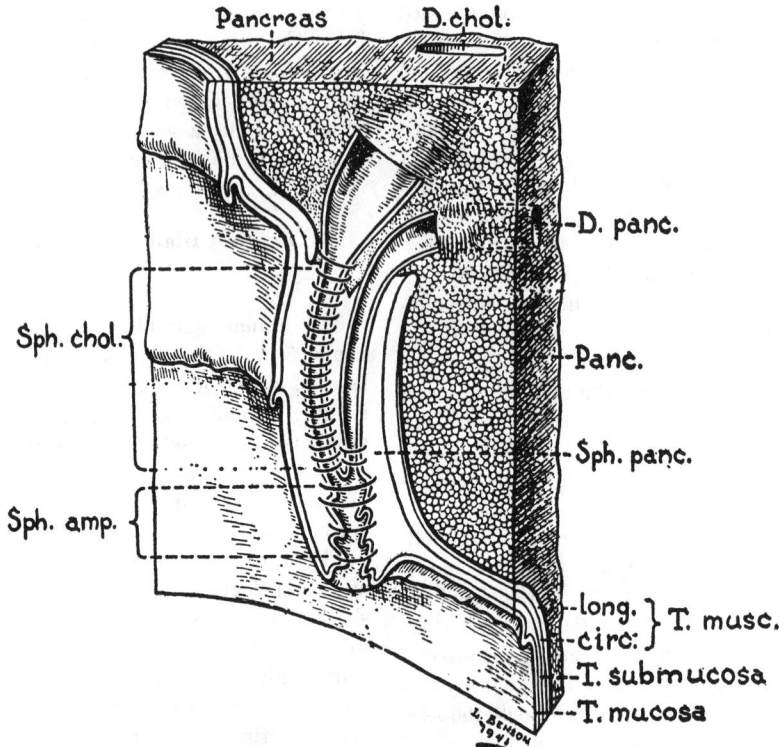

Fig. 59.6. Showing the smooth muscle surrounding the duodenal end of the common bile duct. (After Boyden, slightly modified.) D. chol., *common bile duct*; D. panc., *pancreatic duct*; Sph. chol., *sphincter choledochus (Boyden's sphincter)*; Sph. amp., *sphincter ampullae*; Sph. panc., *sphincter pancreaticus* surrounding the pancreatic duct; T. musc., T. submucosa and T. mucosa, *coats of the duodenal wall*.

where it opens into the ampulla; and (c) those which surround the ampulla itself. These latter are present in only about one-sixth of human subjects. When in spasm they may block the ampullary portion of the common bile duct, and permit bile to pass into the pancreatic duct or pancreatic juice to ascend the common bile duct. The mucosa of the common duct is devoid of the usual mucous glands, but contains special branched tubular glands lined with tall columnar cells. These glands furnish a thin fluid which dilutes the bile.

Though it possesses important functions the gall bladder is not indispensable, since it can be removed with impunity. After such an operation, however, the larger bile ducts undergo dilation, which may, in part, compensate for the removal of the viscus. The gall bladder is absent in some animals whose habits and digestive processes are not apparently essentially different from those of animals that possess one. It is absent in the horse, deer and rat but present in cattle, sheep, dogs, cats and mice. It is present in fish, amphibia,

reptiles and birds, but is absent from orders lower than these.

Fine Structure of the Gall Bladder Mucosa

The mucous membrane of the gall bladder of various animals and man has been studied in detail by light microscopy. However, only recently has the fine structure of the gall bladder mucosa of man been studied by electron microscopy. The mucous membrane of the gall bladder of man is composed of three distinct types of cells that have been designated "ordinary epithelial cells," "pencil cells," and "basal cells." The most common type of cell is the ordinary epithelial cell, which is arranged as a single layer of tall columnar epithelium. The so-called "pencil cell" is rarely seen but appears to be a compressed ordinary epithelial cell. Like the ordinary epithelial cell, it extends from the basement membrane to the lumen of the gall bladder. The third type of cell, the so-called "basal cell," is scattered randomly throughout the mucous membrane, occupying a position adjacent to the basement membrane. The basal cells do not extend to the luminal surface of the mucous membrane.

Electron microscopy reveals that the columnar epithelium of the gall bladder has many characteristics of an active absorbing membrane (Evett et al., 1964). The luminal surface of the epithelial cells is composed of a microvillus border. The plasma membrane of the microvilli is continuous with that of the intervillus surface and the lateral cell walls of the epithelial cell. At the luminal junction of adjacent epithelial cells, the plasma membrane forms "terminal bars" which are thought to prevent intraluminal material from gaining entrance into the intercellular spaces. The lateral walls of adjacent cells are interlocked into each other by folds in plasma membranes. The basal wall of the ordinary epithelial cell rests on the basement membrane and is straight.

The cytoplasm and organelles of the epithelial cells are stratified in a manner similar to that observed in other cells which participate actively in secretory or absorptive functions. Just below the microvillus border, there is a small cuticular zone that is clear, due to the absence of mitochrondria or granules. Immediately beneath this is the subcuticular or dark zone which extends over a third of the cell's height. It is in this zone that many mitochondria, vesicles, granules, and a dense endoplasmic reticulum are observed. Beneath the subcuticular or dark zone is observed the Golgi apparatus, which appears to be quite similar to that observed in other secreting or absorbing cells. The nucleus is large and rounded and occupies the lower third of the cell. It possesses no features to distinguish it from nuclei of other cells.

The pencil cell, like the ordinary epithelial cell, extends from the basement membrane to the lumen. It possesses microvilli and terminal bars, and has a stratification of cytoplasmic organelles similar to that of the ordinary epithelial cell. The basal wall of the pencil cells has papillary projections of cytoplasm which extend deep into the basement membrane. The function of the pencil cell is unknown.

The nucleus and cytoplasm of the basal cells are darker than those of the adjacent ordinary epithelial cells. The plasma membrane of the cell is relatively straight. The cytoplasm of these cells is more simply organized than is that of the other two cells previously described. Small infrequent mitochondria and the endoplasmic reticulum are randomly distributed throughout the cytoplasm. Only rarely are Golgi membranes

or vesicles observed. The function of the basal cell is not known.

CONTRACTIONS OF THE GALL BLADDER AND COMMON BILE DUCT

The gall bladder shows spontaneous *rhythmical contractions* which occur at the rate of 2 to 6 per min. (in the dog), and also a *tonic contraction* which lasts from 5 to 30 min. or more. The rhythmical contractions (in the dog) are capable of producing a pressure change of 250 to 300 mm. of water, which is about the maximal pressure at which bile can be secreted by the liver (fig. 59.7). Rhythmical contractions of the common bile duct have been demonstrated also in animals.

FUNCTIONS OF THE GALL BLADDER

Concentration and Storage of Bile— Secretion of Mucus

Gall bladder bile may have ten times more total solids than bile collected from the hepatic duct may have. Water and inorganic salts are absorbed through the lymphatics and blood vessels of the gall bladder wall. The composition of the absorbed fluid is virtually that of physiological saline. Bile pigments, bile salts, and cholesterol are not absorbed to any appreciable degree under normal circumstances.

It is undecided whether cholesterol is excreted by the normal gall bladder mucosa, although Elman and Taussig (1931) present evidence for such a process. In this connection, it may be mentioned that a pronounced diffuse deposition of a cholesterol ester in the connective tissue of the human gall bladder, ranging from 35 to 60 per cent of its dry weight, is seen as a pathological condition. The tissue of the vesicle is stiff and greatly thickened as a result of its impregnation with lipid material. The disturbances leading to this condition, which is spoken of as *cholesterosis of the gall bladder* or, from the appearance of the

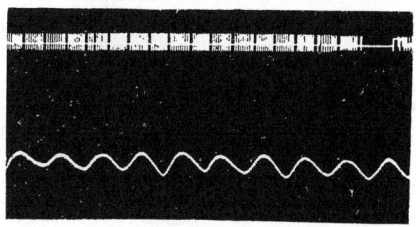

FIG. 59.7. Examples of normal gall bladder contractions. Time marker, 1 second. (After Taylor and Wilson).

mucosa, as the "strawberry gall bladder," are unknown. The existence of this condition cannot, however, be used as evidence for the secretion of cholesterol by the gall bladder mucosa under physiological conditions (see Elman and Graham, 1932).

We owe the greater part of our knowledge of the absorptive powers of the gall bladder to the work of Hammarsten, Rous and McMaster, and more recently that of Diamond (1962). By means of a cannula placed in the bile duct, Rous and McMaster collected the bile as it came from the liver and compared its composition with the bile in the gall bladder. The bilirubin percentages of the respective fluids were used as a measure of the degree of concentration that had been effected in the bile during its stay in the gall bladder. The bladder bile was found to be darker, thicker and more "syrupy" than the bile collected from the ducts. It contained from 3.1 to 10.8 times more bilirubin than the liver bile. Absorption occurred with remarkable rapidity in some instances. In one experiment about 50 ml. of bile which entered the gall bladder was reduced to less than 5 ml. in about 22 hr. In experiments involving the drainage of the gall bladder through a cannula inserted into its fundus, it has been shown that the mere passage of bile through the organ causes a nearly five-fold concentration. Inflammation of the gall bladder reduces or abolishes its concentrating power.

Diamond (1962) has shown, in a series of beautifully designed experiments, that the gall bladders of fish and rabbit *in vitro* absorb sodium chloride and water in isotonic proportions. The differences in composition between hepatic and gall bladder bile result secondarily from this

TABLE 59.3

Composition of canine hepatitis and gall bladder bile (mM)

	Hepatic Bile	Gallbladder Bile
Na$^+$	174	220–340
K$^+$	6.6	6–10
Cl$^-$	55–107	1–10
HCO$_3$	34–65	0–17
Bile acids	28–42	290–340
Ca^{2+}	6	25–32
Mg^{2+}	3.6	—

After Diamond, J. Physiol., 1962, **161**, 443. From analyses by Ravdin, Johnston, Riegel and Wright (1932). Reinhold and Wilson (1934), Wheeler and Ramos, (1960).

transport process across the gall bladder mucosa. Sodium and chloride are absorbed in 1:1 proportions and water movement is coupled to the salt movement. The differences in composition of hepatic bile and gall bladder bile of the dog are listed in table 59.3.

Using the gall bladder of a fresh water fish, the roach, Diamond has studied its absorptive functions *in vitro*. After the gall bladder is removed from the fish, the cystic duct is cannulated and the gall bladder is filled with a solution to be studied. The cannula and gall bladder are then suspended in a beaker containing a bathing solution. As a measure of absorption, the cannula and gall bladder are measured at 5 to 10 min. intervals. Figure 59.8 shows the results of such an experiment when Ringer's solution was used to fill the gall bladder and also for the bathing solution in the beaker. It was found that absorption occurred at a steady rate with the removal of approximately 38 mg. per hr. of the Ringer's solution in the gall bladder. After 3½ hr., iodoacetate, a metabolic poison, was added to the solution in the beaker. Absorption was promptly inhibited, as shown by no further loss of weight of the preparation, and so indicates that the absorptive process is metabolically dependent.

Unlike most membranes that actively transport sodium or chloride, no potential difference is observed across the gall bladder mucosa during active absorption. The "saline pump" is thus electrically neutral, due to the fact that for each sodium ion transported, one chloride ion is also transported. The limiting factor of the salt transport system appears to be the chloride concentration remaining in the gall bladder bile.

It will be recalled that bile is in osmotic equilibrium with plasma. The osmotic equilibrium exists even though the total electrolyte composition of bile may be as high as 600 mEq/l. This discrepancy in the total electrolyte composition and the osmolality of bile is observed in both common duct bile as well as in gall bladder bile, but it is much more marked in gall bladder bile that has been concentrated. The explanation of this apparent discrepancy is found in the fact that bile salt exists as aggregates or micelles that are osmotically inactive. As bile is concentrated, the formation of these macromolecular complexes (Juniper, 1964) reduced the osmotic effect of bile acid as well as the electrolytes in the bile, thus maintaining osmolality.

The gall bladder mucosa also adds to the viscosity of the bile by the *secretion* of a thick mucinous material. Little or none of this material

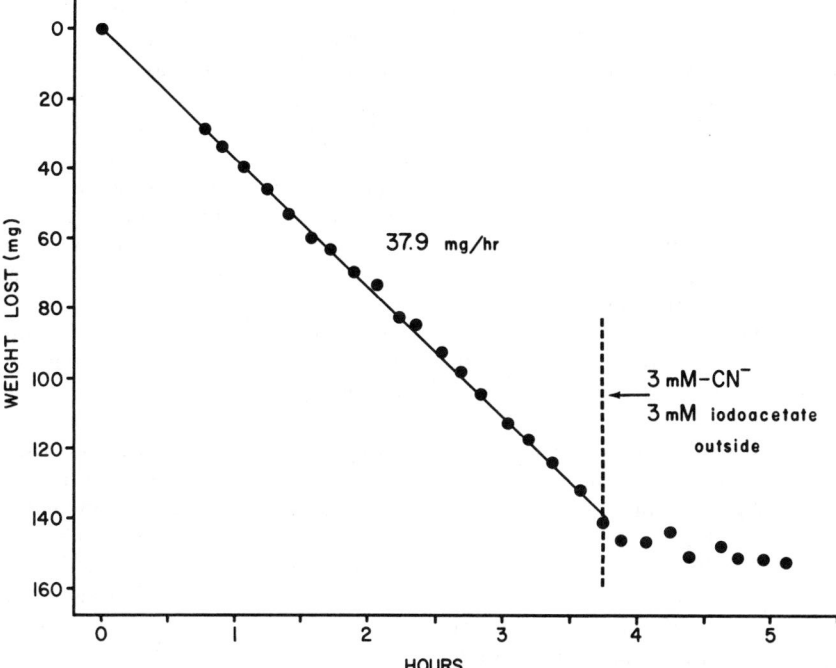

Fig. 59.8. Demonstrating absorption in the isolated gall bladder. Both sides of the gall bladder were initially bathed in Ringer's solution. Absorption from the gall bladder was determined by noting the decrease in weight of the preparation which averaged 37.9 milligrams per hour. At 3 hours and 48 minutes, NaCN and iodoacetic acid were added which blocked absorption as shown by no further decrease in weight. (Redrawn from Diamond, 1962).

is furnished by the bile ducts, nor were the latter observed to have any concentrating power, but were found, on the contrary, to dilute the bile with a thin watery fluid.

If the ducts are obstructed by ligation and the gall bladder is tied off, after some days a clear, colorless fluid is found to have collected within the ducts. This fluid, the so-called "white bile," is not uncommonly seen during an operation upon an obstructed bile duct associated with a functionless gall bladder. The "white bile," under these circumstances, is furnished solely by the mucosa of the ducts. It contains no pigment, bile salts, or cholesterol, and bears almost no resemblance to bile. The secretion of the latter has been suppressed by the rise in pressure (to 300 mm. or so of water) within the ligated duct system.

If the gall bladder is healthy, and left in communication with the obstructed system, the sequence of events is entirely different. Biliary stasis then causes thick, *greenish bile* to collect in the ducts and bladder as a result of the latter's concentrating activity, and of the mucinous material which it secretes. After a lapse of weeks the imprisoned bile develops an almost tarry consistency. The functions of the ducts and of the bladder are, therefore, antagonistic, the former tending to dilute, the latter to concentrate, the biliary fluid. The diluting effect is at first overbalanced by the concentrating action of the gall bladder, and when this remains in communication with the duct system, the net result is marked thickening of the bile. There is, however, a tendency for the activity of the ducts to overcome that of the gall bladder with time. The biliary constituents disappear, and ultimately the contents of the system are entirely replaced by the thin simple secretion of the ducts and mucinous material from the bladder known as hydrops (Rous and McMaster).

Another type of "white bile" is sometimes produced. In dogs, a clear colorless fluid is secreted by the liver cells when their true secretion is suppressed by some severe liver injury, such as that induced by the administration of chloroform (Drury and Rous). "White bile" of this type is sometimes seen in man as a result of hepatic disease.

Other functions of the gall bladder, subsidiary to its concentrating power, are the *reduction in the alkalinity* of the bile and the *equalization of pres-*

sure within the biliary duct system. Without the ability to absorb fluid and reduce the bulk of the bile, its power to equalize pressure would be negligible. It is to be remembered that the amount of bile secreted in 24 hr. is about twenty times or so greater than could be contained in the gall bladder. The loss of its action in equalizing the pressure within the duct system is probably a factor leading to the dilation of the bile ducts, which so frequently follows removal of the gall bladder (cholecystectomy). After this operation, the flow of bile into the intestine is nearly continuous at first, but, later, the adaptation of the ducts permits intermittent discharge.

The importance of the gall bladder in the control of pressure within the biliary ducts is apparent from the results of the experiments of Mann and Bollman. They found that after ligation of the common duct in dogs, a rise in the bilirubin concentration of the blood did not occur until 24 to 36 hr. had elapsed, and jaundice did not appear for 2 days. If, on the other hand, the gall bladder was removed at the time that the duct was ligated, jaundice was fully developed within 24 hr. due, presumably, to the rise in duct pressure and the "regurgitation" of bile into the blood.

Menguy and associates (1958) have made measurements of biliary and pancreatic ductal pressures and the resistance of the sphincter of Oddi in dogs, under various conditions. In intact dogs, the average biliary pressure was found to be 71 mm. of water. When pressures were simultaneously measured in the pancreatic ducts, the pancreatic intraductal pressure was always greater than the pressure in the common bile duct. After cholecystectomy, the pressure in the common bile duct was increased to an average of 111 mm. of water. This increased biliary pressure sometimes exceeded that measured in the pancreatic ducts. It was also noted that the biliary pressure was much less stable after cholecystectomy. The effects of a meal varied, according to whether or not the gall bladder was present. In intact animals, a meal always caused a moderate rise in pressure due to contraction of the gall bladder. In cholecystectomized animals, the already high fasting biliary pressure usually dropped after a meal. The resistance of the sphincter of Oddi was markedly diminished after feeding. Pilocarpine caused an abrupt rise in biliary ductal pressures due to contraction of the gall bladder. This increase in biliary pressure was not observed in animals recently fed, or in cholecystectomized dogs. In intact dogs, atropine

had little effect on biliary intraductal pressure, but in cholecystectomized animals an increase in intraductal pressure was observed. This was found to be due to an increase in the resistance of the biliary sphincter. When epinephrine was administered continuously by injection into the vein, a marked rise in biliary intraductal pressure was observed in cholecystectomized animals, due to an increase in the resistance of the biliary sphincter and an associated complete absence of duodenal motility. Relaxation of the sphincter after administration of epinephrine was discontinued coincided with resumption of normal duodenal peristalsis.

In dogs, cholecystectomy causes some impairment of liver function for at least 70 days following the operation, as shown by the serum phosphatase test. In man, the excretion of Bromsulphalein is reduced for a short time after this operation, presumably until the ducts can function vicariously for the gall bladder.

Filling and Evacuation of the Gall Bladder

The bile, as it leaves the liver, flows into the hepatic duct and then into the common bile duct. Its entrance into the duodenum is blocked during fasting by the tonic contraction of the sphincter muscle (sphincter choledochus) at the duodenal end of the duct. As the bile accumulates within the duct, its pressure rises, and reaching a height of 50 to 70 mm. of water, forces its way along the cystic duct into the gall bladder. During fasting, therefore, the viscus becomes gradually distended with retained bile.

The nature of the force by which the gall bladder is evacuated has been a question of some debate. As the wall of the gall bladder is relatively thin, and its muscle fibers so sparse, it seemed unlikely that it could exert the pressure required to discharge its contents—especially since the gall bladder is evacuated with considerable difficulty by manual compression. Intra-abdominal pressure, "milking" action exerted by the duodenal movements, and simple leaking into the duodenum as a result of relaxation of the sphincter of Oddi have been variously suggested as possible factors. It has, however, been proved quite definitely as a result of evidence derived from several modes of investigation that the contractions of the gall bladder itself, despite the apparent muscular weakness of its walls, are responsible for the expulsion of its contents. The times of emptying of the gall bladder are related to gastric digestion. During fasting, it remains distended with bile, although the sphincter guarding the common duct is relaxed, plainly indicating that the viscus is competent to retain the bile without the aid of the sphincter of Oddi

That changes in intra-abdominal pressure are not responsible for its emptying was shown by Mann and Higgins, working with guinea pigs, whose gall bladders can be readily mobilized. The abdomen was opened under local anesthesia, the gall bladder exposed and drawn outside the abdominal wound, which was then sutured around the cystic duct. The vesicle was observed to contract and expel its contents in response to food placed in the duodenum. It was also shown that in fish, which of course have no diaphragm and in which, apparently, the intra-abdominal pressure remains constant, intermittent evacuations occurred. In dogs, the influence of the sphincter was removed by suturing a catheter into the common duct; the abdomen was left open in order to minimize the effects of intra-abdominal pressure. The gall bladder remained distended; only during the digestion of a meal did it discharge its contents.

The role of the sphincter of Oddi in maintaining intraductal biliary pressure and filling of the gall bladder in man has been studied by Lempke and associates (1963). These investigators measured biliary ductal pressure, sphincteric resistance, and filling of the gall bladder in 12 patients who were subjected to sphincterotomy (surgical section of the sphincter). In addition, similar measurements were made on 3 patients subjected to gastrectomy. In all of the patients, a short limbed T-tube was placed in the common bile duct and brought to the outside through a stab wound in the abdomen. A radiopaque medium was infused into the biliary system through the T-tube and at the same time, biliary pressures were measured. In the patients who had had sphincterotomy, it was found that the gall bladder began to fill when a pressure of 14 cm. of water was reached. As the infusion continued, and the

intraductal pressure increased, the radiopaque material was observed to flow into the duodenum when the intraductal pressure reached 20 cm. of water, thus the sphincteric resistance was 20 cm. of water. In the control subjects, or those who had had gastrectomy but not sphincterotomy, the gall bladder began to fill when the intraductal pressure was 16 cm. of water, but the dye did not enter the duodenum until an intraductal pressure of 26 cm. of water was reached. These findings discount the belief that sphincterotomy abolishes gall bladder function by reducing the resistance of the biliary sphincter sufficiently to prevent the gall bladder from filling. As a matter of fact, in the patients who had sphincterotomy, biliary sphincter resistance had usually returned to normal within two weeks.

When the walls of the gall bladder contract, bile is discharged along the cystic and common ducts into the duodenum. The sphincter (or sphincters) guarding the lower end of the common bile duct normally can withstand a pressure of 100 or 200 mm. of water, but the pressure developed by the contractions of the gall bladder in dogs was shown by Mann and his associates to amount to over 250 mm. of water. Moreover, it is probable that relaxation of the sphincter occurs as part of a coordinated mechanism when the bladder wall contracts, and that the passage of bile through the sphincter is not simply a matter of the latter "giving way" before the biliary pressure created by the gall bladder contractions. The duodenal muscle surrounding the oblique intramural portion of the common bile duct is capable, when contracted, of offering a resistance of over 750 mm. of water. Since this is much higher than the pressure which contractions of the gall bladder can exert, the flow of bile is completely blocked during contractions of the duodenal muscle, but during the latter's relaxation the compression of the duct is relieved (fig. 59.9). Therefore, during the evacuation of the gall bladder and during active duodenal move-

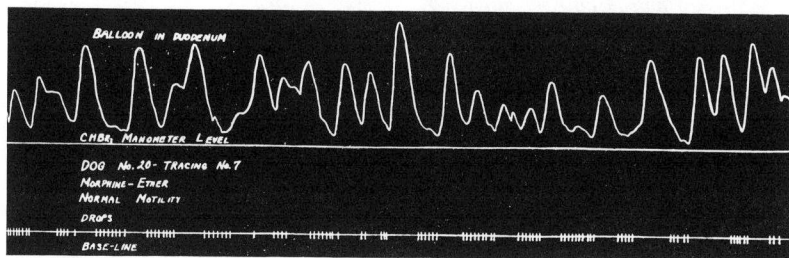

Fig. 59.9. This figure shows the relation between duodenal contractions and flow of bile (indicated in drops near bottom of figure) from the common duct into the duodenum (after Lueth).

ments, the bile may be observed to enter the duodenum in squirts. This is not due to the "milking" action of the peristaltic movements of the bowel but is the result of the alternate blockage and release of the duct; the bowel movements are incapable of causing any flow of bile when the gall bladder is not contracting.

The most effective stimulus for the discharge of bile is fatty food, particularly egg yolk, cream or olive oil. It appears that some degree of digestion of the fat must occur before evacuation results. The effect of fat upon the gall bladder was shown definitely by Boyden. He found that during a period of fasting the gall bladder in the cat was distended with bile, and its walls so stretched that they were reduced to about one-fifteenth of their thickness in the collapsed state. It emptied slowly after a meal, being collapsed, or nearly so, in 1¾–2 hr. The effect of meat upon the discharge of bile is much less than that of fat. Pure protein, such as egg white, and carbohydrate food are almost without effect. These findings have been amply confirmed by several observers. Whitaker (1926), for example, observed changes in the contour of the gall bladder after filling it with iodized oil and examining it radioscopically. The human gall bladder, when rendered opaque to the X-rays by the administration of tetraiodophenolphthalein, can also be seen to discharge its contents in response to a meal of fat. Its contractions have also been observed frequently during operations. The products of fat digestion, hydrochloric acid of a strength comparable to that in the chyme, or magnesium sulphate when placed in the duodenum, cause evacuation of the gall bladder and relaxation of the sphincter of Oddi. On the other hand, bile salts injected intravenously cause relaxation of the gall bladder. Liquid petrolatum introduced into the duodenum is without effect.

The emptying time of the gall bladder is said to be prolonged in duodenal ulcer, during pregnancy, and in pernicious anemia (Boyden).

The Mechanism Controlling Evacuation of the Gall Bladder

NERVOUS. It has been mentioned that relaxation of the sphincter of Oddi probably occurs as the gall bladder contracts. A coordinated action of this nature points to a nervous mechanism. The latter may depend upon intrinsic nervous plexuses in the walls of the biliary passages. The gall bladder contractions initiated by the stimulus of a meal might similarly be due to short reflexes through the intrinsic plexuses of the stomach

or duodenum and biliary tract. Nervous mechanisms are also indicated by the following observations. Electrical stimulation of the stomach and duodenum in animals is followed by contractions of the gall bladder. Contractions are occasionally induced by psychic influences, e.g., the smell or taste of food. The gall bladder also responds to experimental excitation of the vagus or sympathetic nerves. Experiments attempting to demonstrate the precise actions of the extrinsic nerves upon the gall bladder movements have, however, given very conflicting evidence. Several observers have obtained weak motor effects from both vagal and sympathetic stimulation. A motor action of the latter is also indicated by the fact that adrenaline is excitatory.

The results of the experiments of Johnson and Boyden, however, seem clear cut. Sectioning the right vagus nerve of the cat retarded emptying of the gall bladder, apparently as a result of the interruption of motor fibers to the gall bladder and of inhibitory fibers to the sphincter of Oddi. The left vagus was found to carry motor fibers to the gall bladder, but apparently does not contain inhibitory fibers for the sphincter. Reflex effects upon the movements of the gall bladder may be initiated from other abdominal viscera. Stimulation of the cecum, for example, causes inhibition of the movements. This reflex is abolished after sectioning the splanchnic nerves, or excision of the celiac ganglion. In the cat, Boyden has demonstrated an inhibitory effect upon gall bladder motility by electrical stimulation of the duodenum with tied-in electrodes. But in a similar human experiment (an electrode being passed into the duodenum through a Rehfuss tube), an inhibitory effect could not be demonstrated. From this, and from the fact that the rate of gall bladder emptying is little altered in subjects of double vagotomy, Boyden concludes that, in man, nervous control of the gall bladder is of little importance as compared with hormonal control.

HORMONAL. Even in animals, nervous mechanisms are not essential to gall bladder activity. This is evident from the fact that the reaction to the introduction of fat into the duodenum occurs after severing all nervous connections between the biliary and gastrointestinal tracts and between the former and the central nervous system. That gall bladder contractions can occur under such circumstances suggests a hormonal or humoral mechanism. Boyden found that the blood of an animal (taken at the height of digestion) injected into a fasting animal causes the evacuation of the bile; blood from a starved animal has no such effect.

Ivy obtained an acid extract from the mucosa of the upper part of the intestine which caused contraction of the gall bladder when injected intravenously into animals. The injection of acid alone has no effect, nor will fat or its derivatives excite contractions of the gall bladder when administered intravenously. Acid and other substances which are excitatory when placed in the duodenum or when fed apparently act by causing the production or liberation of a hormone in, or from, the intestinal mucosa. The active principle is related to secretin but it is quite distinct from this hormone, for it does not cause pancreatic secretion, and secretin does not cause gall bladder contractions. In crossed-circulation experiments, the introduction of acid into the duodenum of one animal caused contractions of the gall bladder of the other. Ivy and Oldberg named this hormone "cholecystokinin." As little as 0.2 mg. of the solid material prepared from a potent extract causes definite contractions of the gall bladder. It is free from histamine and other vasodilator substances. Its effect has been demonstrated upon man. The transfusion of blood from a human subject digesting egg yolk has been found to cause evacuation of the gall bladder of the recipient. No effect was observed with blood from a fasting donor.

The actions of drugs upon the motility of the gall bladder. Adrenaline, pitressin, histamine and mecholyl stimulate the smooth muscle of the gall bladder, whereas morphine, ergotamine and atropine are inhibitory.

CHOLECYSTOGRAPHY

Graham and Cole showed, in 1924, that if the chlorine radical of a dye such as tetrachlorphenolphthalein (which is excreted selectively by the liver) is replaced by iodine or bromine, the compound, after concentration in the gall bladder, is opaque to the X-rays. Sodium tetraiodophenolphthalein or the corresponding bromine compound (sodium tetrabromphenolphthalein) is given intravenously or by mouth in a special coated capsule. After a fasting period of about 14 hr., a radiogram is taken. The normal gall bladder at this time shows a well-defined shadow. The gall bladder is then stimulated to contract by means of a meal containing egg yolk and cream, and a second radiogram taken 5 hr. later, when the normal organ should be found practically empty. The depth of the shadow after dye administration depends directly upon the concentrating power of the gall bladder. For this reason, a diseased gall bladder may throw only a faint shadow or none at all.

Gallstones (especially those of a high cholesterol content) which are relatively transparent to the X-rays show up against the gall bladder shadow. Gallstones containing more than 0.5 per cent of calcium are visible without the aid of an opaque dye.

DISEASES OF THE GALL BLADDER AND BILE DUCTS

Among the common diseases of the gall bladder are: *inflammation (cholecystitis), gallstones (cholelithiasis)* and *new growths*. The factors involved in the formation of gallstones will be considered in detail later.

In the absence of inflammation, stones in the gall bladder give rise, as a rule, to no definite symptoms, but in their passage along the ducts severe pain *(biliary colic)* may be experienced as a result of the spasmodic contractions of the gall bladder and consequent distension of the duct walls. Vomiting may occur as a reflex phenomenon. In the dog, pain is produced when the gall bladder is distended by a pressure of 540 mm. of water. This is a much higher pressure than the contractions of the gall bladder can create. Pain is produced, however, by distending the *ducts* with a pressure of 270 mm. of water, just about the maximal pressure which the gall bladder contractions can produce. The cause of the expulsion of the stone from the gall bladder is not altogether clear. Although contractions of the gall bladder have been observed to cause movements of stones within its cavity, and even to force a stone into the cystic duct, gall bladder contractions do not, in the majority of instances, offer satisfactory explanation for the expulsion of the stone. According to some, inflammation and distension of the gall bladder are important factors leading to the passage of the stone into the cystic duct.

Biliary Dyskinesia

It is now generally recognized that biliary colic may occur in the absence of stone, inflammation or of any anatomical abnormality, such as kinking of the cystic duct, which would hinder the expulsion of bile from the gall bladder. In such instances, the colic has a functional origin, being due to the gall bladder contracting against a sphincter of Oddi in a state of spasm. Normally, as already mentioned, the sphincter relaxes when the gall bladder contracts. In biliary dyskinesia, the nervous mechanisms upon which this reciprocal action depends are apparently disordered. It has also been claimed that a sphincterlike action may be exerted at the junction of the cystic duct with the gall bladder, and that spasm of this ring of muscle during contraction of the gall bladder may give rise to biliary colic. Also, sudden distention with saline of the common bile duct of conscious patients causes pain resembling that of biliary colic. The pain is felt in the upper right quadrant of the abdomen and in the interscapular or the right scapular region. Nausea and vomiting may occur. The pain impulses travel by splanchnic fibers and enter the cord by the posterior nerve roots from the fourth to the ninth thoracic segments, inclusive.

Biliary Symptoms after Cholecystectomy

Unfortunately, a significant number of patients who have cholecystectomy continue to complain of similar or identical symptoms to what they had prior to operation. This situation is most commonly seen in patients who have been subjected to cholecystectomy because of "chronic cholecystitis" or "non-functioning gall bladder." It is less commonly seen in those patients who have had cholecystectomy because of cholelithiasis. At re-operation, some of these patients will be found to have some injury to the biliary system as a result of the first operation, or a long cystic duct stump may be found. If these, or other conditions, are found that can be corrected surgically, the patient usually will be relieved. In many patients, however, no explanation for their symptoms is found at re-operation. It is well to remember that vague symptoms as "indigestion," excess "gas," flatus and belching, as well as "intolerance" to fatty foods are usually not due to some dysfunction or disease of the gall bladder or biliary system. Thus, when a patient continues to complain of symptoms identical to those experienced prior to his cholecystectomy, it is likely that the gall bladder was not the cause of the symptoms in the first place.

Gallstones—Cholelithiasis

On the basis of autopsy data, it has been estimated that approximately 15 per cent of Caucasians have gallstones. The incidence of gallstones increases with age; cholelithiasis is rare in children and below the age of 20 years, but after the fourth decade, the incidence of gallstones is 25 per cent and after the seventh decade, 50 per cent. Gallstones occur twice as commonly in women, and even in children who develop gallstones the ratio of females to males is 2:1. In children who have gallstones, the possibility of hemolytic anemia existing should be considered strongly. In both humans and animals, it has been observed that the incidence of gallstones in females is greatest in those who have borne offspring.

The presence of gallstones is usually considered to be indicative of a diseased gall bladder. The incidence of gallstones is higher in patients with diabetes, hemolytic anemia and cirrhosis of the liver. In patients with pancreatitis, approximately one-third will have cholelithiasis. Except when producing obstruction of the biliary ducts, gallstones cause few symptoms. Although the incidence of gallstones is extremely high (65 to 100 per cent in various series reported) in patients with carcinoma of the gall bladder, only 1 to 2 per cent of patients with gallstones develop carcinoma of the gall bladder.

Gallstones are composed of constituents of the bile which have been thrown out of solution. Cholesterol is present in greater or less amounts in the commoner varieties of gallstone. Some stones may be composed almost entirely of this substance. In other types of stone, bile pigment or calcium is an important or the predominant constituent. Gallstones, therefore, differ considerably in size, color and inner structure, according to the materials of which they are composed. They are classified according to their composition into *"pure" cholesterol, cholesterol-pigment-calcium, "pure" bilirubin, bilirubin-calcium* and *calcium carbonate* stones. The latter are very rare in man but not uncommon in cattle. The "pure" cholesterol stone contains from 90 to 98 per cent of cholesterol, the remainder being made up of calcium, bile pigments, protein, etc. The "pure" pigment and the bilirubin-calcium stones, on the other hand, contain varying amounts of cholesterol. The cholesterol-pigment-calcium stone is the commonest variety. Stones of this type are usually multiple and, as a result of pressure of one stone against another, show numerous facets upon their surfaces. They contain about 80 per cent of cholesterol, which is deposited in cream-colored layers alternating with darker, bilirubin-calcium laminas. The great majority of stones are formed in the gall bladder, but they also may form in the hepatic duct, or even in the smaller ducts within the liver.

The Formation of Gallstones

The mechanism of gallstone formation is not clearly understood but the following are recognized as being the most important factors to be considered: (a) *injury, especially of an infective nature* to the gall bladder wall, (b) *disturbance in cholesterol metabolism,* (c) *stasis* of the bile, and (d) *reaction of the bile.*

(a) INFECTION. Following the classical work of Naunyn, infection was looked upon as the main, if not the only, cause of gallstone formation. Naunyn maintained, and it is now current teaching, that the cholesterol of the bile was not dependent upon the cholesterol level of the blood and could not be altered by diet. He also claimed, however, that abnormalities of cholesterol metabolism played a minor role in the production of gallstones. The mucosa of the gall bladder, he believed, normally secreted cholesterol and calcium, and the secretory process was stimulated by any local inflammatory state. Experiments in which human cholesterol stones were shown to be dissolved after a time in the gall bladder of the dog under sterile conditions, but not if infection were present; the production of gallstones by injections of microorganisms into the circulation after injury to the gallbladder; and the frequent occurrence of cholelithiasis after infective conditions, notably typhoid fever, were all taken to indicate that infection was essential for the production of biliary calculi. The solvent action of the bile salts upon cholesterol was also held to support this view and to contradict the suggestion that this biliary constituent could be thrown out of solution in the absence of infection. It was argued that the bile, as it came from the liver, could never have so high a concentration of cholesterol that simple deposition could result, but that the cholesterol must be produced in excessive amounts by an inflamed gall bladder in order to be precipitated. Little was then known of the normal concentrating power of the gall bladder (see p. 1159).

Though not denying the importance of gall bladder injury and the production of cholesterol from the inflamed mucosa in many cases of cholelithiases, Aschoff and others have insisted that these conditions are not essential to the formation of calculi, and that certain types, especially the solitary cholesterol stone (see below), can arise in sterile bile and in the absence of any diseased condition of the lining membrane. This view is now generally accepted. Much of the

earlier work upon cholesterol metabolism to which Naunyn pinned his faith has been proved to be erroneous.

The multiple cholesterol-pigment-calcium stones are usually looked upon as typical infection stones. They are laminated on cross-section and usually have a framework of coagulated protein. These stones are often very numerous, sometimes numbered by hundreds, and an examination of their structure will indicate that they all have been formed at about the same time. According to Aschoff, the starting point of their formation is the deposition of pigment in the form of fine, rosette-like structures upon which coatings of cholesterol, pigment and calcium are subsequently laid. The inflammatory exudate is rich in protein material derived from the blood, as well as in cholesterol and calcium. The protein, it is pointed out, carries an electric charge of opposite sign to that held by the cholesterol, pigment and inorganic constituents of the bile. It is believed that, as a result of these physicochemical relations, the deposition of cholesterol combined in varying degree with the other biliary constituents is effected.

(b) "METABOLIC." The typical "metabolic" calculus is the large single stone of almost pure cholesterol—the *cholesterol solitaire.* This type of stone, according to Aschoff, is formed quite independently of infection or injury of any sort, and is due to the crystallization of cholesterol out of a bile surcharged with this material. The common, mixed stones (cholesterol-pigment-calcium) are also composed predominantly of cholesterol and probably, in many instances, are metabolic rather than infective in origin. In certain conditions, e.g., pregnancy, in which gallstones are prone to develop, the blood cholesterol has been said to be higher than normal (hypercholesterolemia) and there is evidence of a disturbance in cholesterol metabolism. But as a matter of fact, hypercholesterolemia, according to Gardner (Gardner and Gainsborough, 1930), is not common in pregnancy; the normal proportions of free cholesterol to cholesterol esters (cholesterol combined with fatty acids), are altered, the former being increased, the latter reduced. Abnormalities in cholesterol metabolism leading to such changes are probably of more importance in the production of gallstones than a rise in the total blood cholesterol. It has already been mentioned that a high blood cholesterol does not cause an increase in the cholesterol of the bile. Also, in certain forms of renal disease, and in myxedema in which hypercholesterolemia exists, there is little evidence that the latter leads to the production of gallstones. In other forms of renal disease the incidence of gallstones is higher than usual, yet hypercholesterolemia does not occur.

It has been mentioned that increasing the cholesterol of the diet does not raise the cholesterol concentration of the bile, so there is no logical reason, as pointed out by Gardner and Gainsborough, for excluding cholesterol-rich materials from the diets of those subject to cholelithiasis. Indeed, a high fat diet, by stimulating gall bladder contractions and so preventing undue concentration and stasis of bile, may exert a beneficial effect.

The ratio of cholesterol in bile to the bile salts is an important factor in the formation of gallstones. The cholesterol:bile acid ratio in normal bile is between 1:20 and 1:30. Since neither bile salts nor cholesterol are absorbed under normal circumstances from the gall bladder, this ratio holds for both liver and gall bladder bile. According to Andrews, deposition of cholesterol occurs when the ratio falls to 1:13. He believes that when infection is a factor, it plays its part in gallstone formation not so much through increasing cholesterol production as through reducing the bile salt concentration, for he claims that bile salts are absorbed through the inflamed gall bladder mucosa. Dolkart and associates attach more importance to the concentration of fatty acids in the bile than to the concentration of the bile salts in preventing the precipitation of cholesterol.

"Pure" pigment stones (they contain calcium and cholesterol as well) also occur apart from infection. They are small and dark and, although usually occurring in the gall bladder, may be found in the bile passages. Their origin is not clear, but since they often occur in conditions associated with an abnormally high bilirubin excretion, e.g., acholuric jaundice, they may be the result of the precipitation of bilirubin from a bile which contains excessive amounts of the pigment.

(c) STASIS OR SLOWING OF THE BILIARY FLOW. Stasis or slowing of the biliary flow within the bile passages may be responsible for the formation of small stones of pigment-calcium in these situations. When there is complete stasis, due to mechanical obstruction, the fluid in the larger bile passages contains none of the important biliary constituents. The so-called "white bile" fills the ducts and, in consequence, the formation

of calculi is not possible (p. 1167). Complete biliary stasis also appears to be a minor factor in the production of stones in the gall bladder.

(d) REACTION OF THE BILE. Until the work of Drury, Rous and McMaster this factor had received comparatively little attention. These observers caused gallstones composed, in varying proportions, of calcium carbonate, pigment and cholesterol, to be formed in the bile of dogs which had their gall bladders removed and their common ducts drained into a system of tubing. Encrustations of biliary constituents, as well as more or less discrete calculi, formed upon the walls of the tubing. These occurred under sterile conditions and in the absence of stasis. The deposits are claimed to result from the alkalinity of the liver bile. Normal bile of the dog, as it flows along the bile passages, was shown by Okada to be definitely alkaline whereas that of the gall bladder was acid. Rous and his associates found the liver bile of dogs to have a pH of 8.20 or more, while after its stay in the gall bladder its reaction became decidedly acid—pH 5.18 to 6.00. Bile from the human gall bladder, though less alkaline than liver bile, rarely has a pH below 7.0. One of the functions of the normal gall bladder (p. 1161), therefore, appears to be depression of the pH of liver bile. So long as this occurs in the usual manner, the calcium carbonate of the bile remains in solution. In an alkaline bile, such as is collected from the common duct in the absence of the gall bladder, the calcium carbonate is thrown down, and with it the pigment and cholesterol constituents, to be deposited upon the walls of the delivery tubing. These observations suggest, therefore, that in any condition which interferes with gall bladder function, e.g., infection, injury, or intermittent stasis, the usual acidification of the liver bile will not occur. Calcium carbonate will then undergo spontaneous precipitation and serve as a center, or centers, upon which the other biliary constituents become deposited.

Experimental Production of Gallstones

Relatively little experimental work has been done on the pathogenesis of cholelithiasis. As in man, gallstones are not infrequently found in animals who possess gall bladders. Small animals, which have been used as experimental models for inducing cholelithiasis in the laboratory, include the guinea pig (Okeg, 1942), the hamster (Dam and Christensen, 1952), and the mouse (Tepperman et al., 1964). To induce cholelithiasis experimentally, manipulation of the diet of the animal has been the method most commonly employed. For example, Okeg found that with a high cholesterol diet with added vitamin B, gallstones would develop in 80 per cent of guinea pigs. A high cholesterol diet in itself would not induce cholelithiasis. In both hamsters and mice, the ratio of cholic acid to cholesterol in the diet, and in the secreted bile, appears to be a critical factor. It has already been mentioned that in normal bile, the cholesterol:bile acid ratio is between 1:20 and 1:30. When this ratio falls to 1:13, deposition of cholesterol occurs. In mice, a high incidence of cholelithiasis can be induced by simply adding 1 per cent cholesterol and 0.5 per cent cholic acid to the animal's regular laboratory chow diet. On such a diet, the mice will begin to show stones within three to four weeks. Females tend to develop stones earlier than males. Tepperman and his associates (1964) have pointed out that the rate of bile flow is also important in the production of cholelithiasis in mice. They found that female mice had a significantly higher rate of bile production than did males, and that estrogen increased the rate of bile flow in the male while androgen decreased the rate in the female. This recalled the well-known relationship between pregnancy and gallstones.

In both hamsters and mice who have developed cholelithiasis due to the addition of cholesterol and cholic acid in the diet, the stones tend to disappear after several months on a normal diet (Caldwell et al., 1964). The spontaneous disappearance of gallstones in man has also been reported (Miller, 1956; Dworken, 1960). The factors involved in the dissolution of gallstones are not understood. The explanation for the disappearance of a few small stones might be that they are passed through the biliary system into the intestine. This is not the explanation for large stones, however. Although apparently very rare, gallstones can on occasion spontaneously disappear.

Further study of the various animal models for the production of cholelithiasis should yield information that will be helpful, not only in understanding the etiology of cholelithiasis in humans, but also in prevention and therapy after gallstones have developed.

REFERENCES

BERMAN, A. L., SNAPP, E., IVY, A. C., AND ATKINSON, A. J. On the regulation or homeostasis of the cholic acid output in biliary-duodenal fistula dogs. Am. J. Physiol., 1941, 131, 776.

BILLING, B. H., COLE, P. G., AND LATHE, G. H. The secretion of bilirubin as a diglucuronide giving the direct van den Bergh reaction. Biochem. J., 1957, 65, 774.

BLOCH, K., BERG, B. N., AND RITTENBERG, D. Biological conversion of cholesterol to cholic acid. J. Biol. Chem., 1943, 149, 511. Also 1943, 157, 601.

BOYDEN, E. A. Analysis of reaction of human gallbladder to food. Anat. Rec., 1928, 40, 147.

BOYDEN, E. A. Sphincter of Oddi in man and certain representative mammals. Surgery, 1937, 1, 25. Also 1941, 9, 443 and 10, 567.

BRAUER, R. W. Mechanisms of bile secretion. Gastroenterology, 1958, 34, 1021.

CALDWELL, F. T., LEVITSKY, K., AND ROSENBERG, B. Dietary induction and dissolution of gallstones in mice. J.A.M.A., 1964, 188, 437.

CARR, J. L. AND FOOTE, F. S. Progressive obstructive jaundice; changes in certain elements of blood and their relation to coagulation. Arch. Surg., 1934, 29, 277.

CRIGLER, J. F., JR. AND MAJJAR, V. A. Congenital familial non-hemolytic jaundice with kernicterus. Pediatrics, 1952, 10, 169.

DAM, H. AND CHRISTENSEN, F. Alimentary production of gallstones in hamsters. Acta. Path. Microbiol. Scand., 1952, 30, 236.

DAM, H. AND GLAVIND, J. Vitamin K in human pathology. Lancet, 1938, 1, 720.

DIAMOND, JARED M. The reabsorptive function of the gall bladder. J. Physiol., 1962, 161, 442.

DIAMOND, JARED M. The mechanism of solute transport by the gall bladder J. Physiol., 1962, 161, 474.

DIAMOND, JARED M. The mechanism of water transport by the gall bladder. J. Physiol., 1962, 161, 503.

DOLKART, R. E., JONES, K. K., AND BROWN, C. F. G. Chemical factors concerned in formation of gallstones. Arch. Int. Med., 1938, 62, 618.

DRILL, V. A. AND IVY, A. C. Comparative value of Bromsulphalein, serum phosphatase, prothrombin time, and intravenous galactose tolerance tests in detecting hepatic damage produced by carbon tetrachloride. J. Clin. Invest., 1944, 23, 209.

DRURY, D. R., ROUS, P. J., AND McMASTER, P. D. Some causes of gallstone formation; relation of reaction of bile to experimental cholelithiasis. J. Exper. Med., 1924, 39, 403.

DRURY, D. R. AND ROUS, P. J. Jaundice as an expression of physiological wastage of corpuscles. J. Exper. Med., 1925, 41, 601.

DWORKEN, H. J. Recent experiences with spontaneous disappearing gallstones. Gastroenterology, 1960, 38, 76.

ELIAS, H. A re-examination of the structure of the mammalian liver; parenchymal architecture. Am. J. Anat., 1949, 84, 311.

ELIAS, H. A re-examination of the structure of the mammalian liver; the hepatic lobule and its relation to the vascular and biliary system. Am. J. Anat., 1949, 85, 379.

ELIAS, H. Morphology of the liver, in Liver injury, Trans. 11th Conference, Macy Foundation, New York, 1953.

ELMAN, R. AND GRAHAM, E. A. Pathogenesis of

"strawberry" gall bladder (cholesterosis of gall bladder). Arch. Surg., 1932, **24**, 14.

ELMAN, R. AND MCMASTER, P. D. Studies on urobilin physiology and pathology. I. The quantitative determination of urobilin. J. Exper. Med., 1925, **41**, 503. II. Derivation of urobilin. J. Exper. Med., 1925, **41**, 513. III. Absorption of pigments of biliary derivation from the intestine. J. Exper. Med., 1925, **41**, 719. IV. Urobilin and the damaged liver. J. Exper. Med., 1925, **42**, 99. V. The relation between urobilin and conditions involving increased red cell destruction. J. Exper. Med., 1925, **42**, 619. VI. The relation of biliary infections to the genesis and excretion of urobilin. J. Exper. Med., 1926, **43**, 73.

ELMAN, R. AND TAUSSIG, J. B. Increase in cholesterol content of gall bladder bile following ligature of cystic duct. Proc. Soc. Exper. Bio. & Med., 1931, **28**, 1066, 1068, 1070.

ELMAN, R. AND TAUSSIG, J. B. Cholesterol function of the gall bladder. J. Exper. Med., 1931, **54**, 775.

EVETTS, R. D., HIGGINS, J. A., AND BROWN, A. L., JR. The fine structure of normal mucosa in human gall bladder. Gastroenterology, 1964, **47**, 49.

FRIEDMAN, M. H. F. Personal communication to the author. See Thomas, 1950, p. 96.

FRIEDMAN, M. H. F. AND SNAPE, W. J. Comparative effects of extracts of intestinal mucosa in stimulating the external secretion of pancreas and liver. Fed. Proc., 1945, **4**, 21.

GARDNER, J. A. AND GAINSBOROUGH, H. Blood cholesterol studies in biliary hepatic disease. Quart. J. Med., 1930, **23**, 465.

GROSSMAN, M. I., JANOWITZ, H. D., RALSTON, H., AND KIM, K. S. The effect of secretin on bile formation in man. Gastroenterology, 1949, **12**, 133.

HANGER, F. M. Serological differentiation of obstructive from hepatogenous jaundice by flocculation of cephalin-cholesterol emulsions. J. Clin. Invest., 1939, **18**, 261.

HIGGINS, G. M. AND MANN, F. C. Emptying of the gall bladder. Am. J. Physiol., 1926, **78**, 339.

IVY, A. C. Cholecystagogues, choleretics and cholepoietics. Gastroenterology, 1944, **3**, 54.

IVY, A. C. AND OLDBERG, E. Hormone mechanism for gall bladder contraction and evacuation. Am. J. Physiol., 1928, **86**, 599.

JOHNSON, F. E. Effect of sectioning various autonomic nerves upon rate of emptying of biliary tract in cat. Surg. Gynec. and Obst., 1943, **76**, 395.

Juniper, K. Chemical and ultracentrifugal studies on the macromolecular complex in normal bile of the human gall bladder. Am. J. Surg., 1964, **107**, 371.

KOCOUR, E. J. AND IVY, A. C. The effect of certain foods on bile volume output recorded in the dog by a quantitative method. Am. J. Physiol., 1937, **122**, 325.

LEMPKE, R. E., KING, R. D., AND KAISER, G. C. Hydrodynamics of gall bladder filling. J.A.M.A., 1963, **186**, 152.

LESTER, R. The intestinal phase of bile pigment excretion. Gastroenterology, 1964, **47**, 424.

LESTER, R. AND SCHMID, R. Intestinal absorption of bile pigments. I. The enterohepatic circulation of bilirubin in the rat. J. Clin. Invest., 1963, **42**, 736.

LESTER, R. AND SCHMID, R. Intestinal absorption of bile pigments. II. Bilirubin absorption in man. New Eng. J. Med., 1963, **269**, 178.

LESTER, R. AND SCHMID, R. Enterohepatic circulation of urobilinogen. Nature (London), 1964, **201**, 711.

LEUTH, H. C. Studies on flow of bile into duodenum and existence of sphincter of Oddi. Am. J. Physiol., 1931, **99**, 237.

LICHTENSTEIN, M. E. AND IVY, A. C. Function of "valves" of Heister. Surgery, 1937, **1**, 38.

MANN, F. C. The effects of complete and partial removal of the liver. Medicine, 1927, **6**, 419.

MANN, F. C., AND ASSOCIATES. The formation of bile pigment after total removal of the liver. Am. J. Physiol., 1924, **69**, 393. The site of formation of bilirubin. Am. J. Physiol., 1925, **74**, 497. The formation of bile pigment from hemoglobin. Am. J. Physiol., 1926, **76**, 306. Spectrophotometric determination of bilirubin. Am. J. Physiol., 1926, **76**, 577. The liver as a site of bilirubin formation. Am. J. Physiol., 1926, **77**, 219. An experimental study of reduced hepatic function. Am. J. Physiol., 1926, **77**, 179. An evaluation of the relative amounts of bilirubin formed in the liver, spleen, and bone marrow. Am. J. Physiol., 1926, **76**, 384. A method for making a satisfactory fistula at any level of the gastrointestinal tract. Ann. Surg., 1931, **93**, 794.

MANN, F. C. AND BOLLMAN, J. L. Relation of gall bladder to development of jaundice following obstruction of common bile duct. J. Lab. and Clin. Med., 1925, **10**, 540.

McMASTER, P. D. AND ROUS, P. The biliary obstruction required to produce jaundice. J. Exper. Med., 1921, **33**, 731.

MEAKINS, J. C. Distribution of jaundice in circulatory failure. J. Clin. Invest., 1927, **4**, 135.

MENGUY, R. B., HALLENBECK, G. A., BOLLMAN, J. L., AND GRINDLEY, J. H. Intraductal pressures and sphincteric resistance in canine pancreatic and biliary ducts after various stimuli. Surg. Gyn. Obst., 1958, **106**, 306.

MILLER, M. C. Spontaneous disappearance of gallstones. Gastroenterology, 1956, **31**, 588.

OKADA, S. On the reaction of bile. J. Physiol., 1915, **50**, 114.

OKEG, R. Proc. Soc. Exper. Biol. & Med., 1942, **51**, 349.

PEDREIAR, F. AND TEPPERMAN, J. Bile flow rate and cholesterol content in mice fed a gallstone-inducing diet. Am. J. Physiol., 1964, **206**, 635.

QUICK, A. J. Clinical value of the test for hippuric acid in cases of disease of the liver. Arch. Int. Med., 1936, **57**, 544.

QUICK, A. J. Intravenous modification of the hippuric acid test for liver function. Am. J. Digest. Dis., 1939, **6**, 716.

QUICK, A. J., STANLEY-BROWN, L. M., AND BAN-

CROFT, F. W. Study of coagulation defect in hemophilia and in jaundice. Am. J. M. Sc., 1935, **190**, 501.

RABINOWITCH, I. M. Arch. Int. Med., 1930, **46**, 1014.

RAVDIN, I. S., JOHNSTON, C. G., RIEGEL, C., AND WRIGHT, S. L. JR. Studies of gallbladder function. VII. The anion-cation content of hepatic and gall bladder bile. Am. J. Physiol., 1932, **100**, 317.

RAWSON, A. J. Human bile proteins. I. Proteins identified by antibody to human serum. Clin. Chem., 1962, **8**, 310.

REINHOLD, J. G. AND WILSON, D. W. The acid-base composition of hepatic bile. I. Amer. J. Physiol., 1934, **107**, 378.

RODERICK, L. M. Pathology of sweet clover disease in cattle. J. Am. Vet. M. A., 1929, **74**, 314.

ROUS, P. AND MCMASTER, P. D. Concerning activity of the gall bladder. J. Exper. Med., 1921, **34**, 47.

ROUS, P. AND MCMASTER, P. D. Physiological causes for the varied character of stasis bile. J. Exper. Med., 1921, **34**, 75.

ROWNTREE, L. G., GREENE, C. H., AND ALDRICH, M. Quantitative Pettenkofer values in blood with special reference to hepatic disease. J. Clin. Invest. 1927, **4**, 545.

RUSSELL, IAN S. AND BURNETT, W. The proteins of human bile. Gastroenterology, 1963, **45**, 730.

SCHAFFNER, F. Morphologic studies on bile secretion. Am. J. Digest. Dis., 1965, **10**, 99.

SCHMID, R. Direct reacting bilirubin, bilirubin glucuronide, in serum, bile, and urine. Science, 1956, **124**, 76.

SCHMID, R. Some aspects of bile pigment metabolism. Clinical Chemistry, 1957, **3**, 394.

SHERLOCK, S. P. V. Aspiration liver biopsy; technique and diagnostic applications. Lancet, 1945, II, 397. Also J. Path. & Bact., 1946, **58**, 523.

SMYTH, F. S. AND WHIPPLE, G. H. Bile pigment metabolism: etc. J. Biol. Chem., 1924, **59**, 623, 637, 647. See also WHIPPLE AND HOOPER, 1917.

TEPPERMAN, J., CALDWELL, F. T., AND TEPPERMAN, H. M. Induction of gallstones in mice by feeding a cholesterol-cholic acid containing diet. Am. J. Physiol., 1964, **206**, 628.

THOMAS, J. E. AND CRIDER, J. O. The effect of bile in the intestine on the secretion of pancreatic juice. Am. J. Physiol., 1943, **138**, 548.

VERSCHURE, J. C. M. Electro-chromograms of human bile. Clin. Chim. Acta., 1956, **1**, 38.

VIRTUE, R. W. AND DOSTER-VIRTUE, M. E. Continued studies on production of taurocholic acid in dog; cysteine, homocysteine, and thioglycolic acid. J. Biol. Chem., 1939, **127**, 431.

WHEELER, H. O. AND RAMOS, O. L. Determinants of the flow and composition of bile in the unanesthetized dog during constant infusions of sodium taurocholate. J. Clin. Invest., 1960. **39**, 161.

WHIPPLE, G. H. AND HOOPER, C. W. Icterus. A rapid change of hemoglobin to bile pigment in the circulation outside of the liver. J. Exper. Med., 1913, **17**, 612.

WHITAKER, L. R. The mechanism of the gall bladder. Am. J. Physiol., 1926, **78**, 411.

Monographs and Reviews

ASCHOFF, L. The origin of gallstones. Hoeber, New York, 1924.

DRABKIN, D. L. Metabolism of hemin chromoproteins. Physiol. Rev., 1951, **31**, 345.

GRAHAM, E. A., COLE, W. H., COPHER, G. H., AND MOORE, S. Diseases of the gall bladder and bile ducts. Lea and Febiger, Philadelphia, 1928.

IVY, A. C. Applied physiology of the gastrointestinal innervation. Bull. New York Acad. Sc., 1934, **10**, 643.

IVY, A. C. The physiology of the gall bladder. Physiol. Rev., 1934, **14**, 1.

MACLEAN, H. Modern views on digestion and gastric disease. Constable, London, 1928.

MANN, F. C. The functions of the gall bladder. Physiol. Rev., 1924, **4**, 251.

PETERS, J. P. AND VAN SLYKE, D. D. Quantitative clinical chemistry. Williams & Wilkins Co. Baltimore, 1946, Vol. I, p. 347.

RAINS, A. J. H. Researches concerning the formation of gallstones. Brit. Med. J., 1962, Sept. 15, 685.

RICH, A. R. The formation of bile pigment. Physiol. Rev., 1925, **5**, 182.

ROLLESTON, H. D. AND MCNEE, J. W. Diseases of the liver, gall bladder and bile ducts. Macmillan, London, 1929.

SCHMIDT, C. L. A. The extra-hepatic functions of bile. Physiol. Rev., 1927, **7**, 129.

SOBOTKA, H. The chemistry of the bile acids and related substances. Chem. Rev., 1934, **15**, 311. The physiological chemistry of bile. Williams & Wilkins Co., Baltimore, 1937.

TEPPERMAN, JAN. Experimental production of gallstones. Gastroenterology, 1965. **48**, 261.

VERZAR, F. AND MCDOUGALL, E. J. Absorption from the intestine. Longmans, Green and Co., London, 1936.

WAKIM, K. G. The physiology of the liver. Am. J. Med., 1954, **16**, 256.

WHIPPLE, G. H. The origin and significance of the constituents of the bile. Physiol. Rev., 1922, **2**, 40.

CHAPTER 60

Secretion and Absorption in the Intestine

The food substances in the gastric chyme are far from being ready for absorption. The products of peptic digestion of protein are still relatively large molecules containing many amino acids. Starch digestion is incomplete and fat digestion has barely begun. In the intestine, the enzymes of pancreatic juice carry the digestion of protein a step further but leave most of it still in the form of peptides, which need further digestion before being absorbed. Starch and dextrins are reduced to maltose and some glucose. Presumably, fat digestion is accomplished by pancreatic lipase but even this may be aided by lipase from the intestine. Final food preparation for absorption is accomplished by enzymes found within the lumen of the small bowel and within the epithelial cells of the mucosa lining the small bowel.

Secretions of the Small Intestines

The structure of the intestinal mucosa, as we shall learn in a later section, is particularly adapted to provide an extremely large surface area to the intestinal contents and thus enhance the process of absorption. This increase in surface area is accomplished by the *villi* of the mucosa, and the brush border (composed of *microvilli*) of the epithelial cells covering the villi. At the base of the villi are small tubular glands known as the *crypts of Lieberkühn*. It has long been taught that the "intestinal glands" secreted and that the villi absorbed. Many enzymes have been identified in the contents of the small bowel and it was assumed that they were the products of secretion by the intestinal glands. This secretion, known as the *succus entericus*, was supposed to complete the digestion of carbohydrates, proteins and fats, in order that the products of digestion could be absorbed by the villi. Recent evidence has cast considerable doubt on this concept of intestinal secretion and absorption. It now appears that the primary function of the "intestinal glands" is to provide for the constant replacement of epithelial cells lost from the tips of the villi. In addition, it is now known that carbohydrates, proteins, and fats, do not have to be completely

reduced, respectively, to monosaccharides, amino acids, and fatty acids, prior to absorption.

METHODS OF STUDY

The secretion of the intestine may be collected in anesthetized, operated animals by opening the abdomen and inserting a tube into the part of the intestine from which the secretion is to be collected. This method has the serious disadvantage that operative trauma and anesthetic drugs depress the secretory activity of the intestinal glands. The effects of anesthesia may be largely overcome by decerebrating or decapitating the animal under anesthesia and then allowing time for the anesthetic to be eliminated, as was done by Wright and his coworkers (1940). It is also advantageous to immerse the animal in physiological saline, which eliminates the irritant effects to the intestine of drying and exposure. The best results have been obtained by study of unanesthetized animals with surgically isolated loops of intestine. A loop is prepared by cutting through the intestine at two points, thus isolating a segment and re-establishing the continuity of the bowel by end-to-end anastomosis. To make a *Thiry* (1864) *loop* one end of the isolated segment is closed and the other end brought out through the abdominal wall to form a fistula. The preparation was modified in 1888 by Vella who brought both ends of the loop out through the abdominal wall; such a preparation is known as a *Thiry-Vella loop*. These loops maintain their mesenteric connections and retain as much of their innervation as reaches them through the mesentery, but are separated from the myenteric and submucous plexuses of the intestine above and below.

Intestinal loops without a nerve supply have been prepared by isolating a segment of intestine, as in the preparation of a Thiry loop, and implanting it under the skin of a mammary gland of a lactating female animal (Ivy et al., 1927). The reason for choosing a lactating female is that the subcutaneous tissue in the vicinity of the mammary glands in such an animal has a very abundant blood supply. At first the mesenteric pedicle is left intact, but after a time the local blood vessels grow into the intestine and provide it with a new blood supply. It is then possible to sever the mesenteric pedicle without causing degeneration of the intestinal loop. When this is done, a portion of intestine is obtained which is entirely deprived of nervous influences; such a preparation is used to detect hormonal influences on secretion.

In man, and in animals with a simple intestinal fistula, it is possible to collect intestinal secretion by means of a multilumen intestinal tube (Miller and Abbott, 1934). Two of the lumens of the tube are used to inflate balloons; a third lumen, having an opening between the balloons, can be used to collect the secretion that accumulates in this area. In these, as in all studies of intestinal secretion, it is important to remember that mechanical stimulation, and especially distention of the intestine, is a strong stimulus to secretion. Consequently, when the quantity of secretion is to be determined, or when quantitative differences in secretion obtained under different circumstances are sought, it is essential that mechanical stimulation of the mucosa be avoided. For example, a Thiry fistula into which a catheter has been inserted for collecting the secretion will produce a greater than normal amount of succus entericus.

THE INTESTINAL GLANDS

The mucous membrane of the small intestine is covered everywhere with minute projections (about 1 mm. in height and somewhat less in diameter) called intestinal villi. The villi are invested with a layer of columnar cells, of the type characteristic of the intestinal mucosa, set upon a basement membrane beneath which is a fine layer of a smooth muscle fibers continuous with the muscularis mucosae. In the center of each villus is a lymphatic vessel continuous with the lymph vessels of the mucous membrane. This lymphatic is somewhat enlarged into a small sinus lined with endothelium. In some of the larger villi there are several lymphatics. Between the epithelium and the central sinus is a network of blood vessels. Contraction of the smooth muscle of the villus causes a characteristic type of movement which will be described in ch. 61. Between the villi are the openings of the *intestinal glands*, or *crypts of Lieberkühn*, which are simple tubular glands. The crypts do not penetrate the muscularis mucosae. The epithelium covering the villi is of the same type as that lining the crypts, and consists of a single layer of columnar cells with certain specialized cells interspersed among them. The free end of each columnar cell, next to the lumen of the intestine, is provided with a specialized cuticular border, resembling the brush border of certain renal tubular cells. The brush border of the surface epithelial cells of the villi is composed of *microvilli* approximately 1 μ in length and about 0.1 μ in width. Zetterqvist (1956) has estimated that each columnar absorbing cell in the mouse jejunum possesses about 600 microvilli and that one square mm. of absorbing surface will contain 50,000,000 such structures.

Here and there among the columnar cells are goblet cells that secrete mucus and specialized cells that stain with silver, and are called *argentaffine* or enterochromaffin cells. Other cells with a large acidophile nucleus known as *Paneth* cells are also present. The argentaffine cells are of particular interest because they secrete serotonin, or at least synthesize its precursor, 5-hydroxytryptophane (Erspamer and Asero, 1952). The functions of serotonin in the body are not known, but it has many powerful pharmacologic actions, among which are stimulation of gastrointestinal motility and inhibition of gastric secretion (Olson and Gray, 1958).

In the bottoms of the crypts, many of the epithelial cells may be seen to be undergoing mitosis, and at the tips of the villi one can see that cells are being shed into the lumen of the intestine (Leblond and Stevens, 1948). Thus, there is going on in the intestinal mucous membrane a process of continuous replacement of the epithelial lining, new cells being produced in the bottoms of the crypts and the older cells being continuously shed at the tips of the villi. The rate of renewal of shed epithelial cells has been estimated by means of autoradiography using tritiated thymidine to label the DNA of the nuclei (Leblond and Walker, 1956). When tritiated thymidine is injected into an animal, it is rapidly incorporated in the cells of the crypts undergoing mitoses. The migration of the labeled cells up the villus can be observed by obtaining biopsies at various times after the injection, and exposing thin sections on a photographic emulsion. In man, the time required for this migration has been estimated as 3 days. Thus, every 3 days the lining of the small bowel is replaced due to the rapid turnover of epithelial cells. Crosby (1961) has estimated, on the basis of calculations of the epithelial cell mass of the small bowel of man, that about 250 g. of epithelial cells are shed into the lumen of the small bowel each day.

In the first part of the duodenum, in addition to the regular intestinal glands, are special mucous glands known as *Brunner's glands*. These are similar in structure to the pyloric glands of the stomach. They are made up of long tubules, which branch frequently and are often tortuous, and which penetrate the muscularis mucosae. Their ducts empty into the crypts of Lieberkühn. Brunner's glands are very numerous in the duodenum between the pylorus and the entrance of the bile and pancreatic ducts. Below this level, they are seen less frequently, and none are found beyond the duodeno-jejunal junction.

INTESTINAL SECRETION OR
SUCCUS ENTERICUS

The composition of the fluid secreted by the intestinal mucous membrane varies somewhat in different parts of the intestine. For example, in the duodenal area, due to the secretion of the mucous glands of Brunner, the secretion contains more mucus than is found elsewhere. In general, the secretion of the small intestine is a thin, colorless, or slightly straw-colored fluid, somewhat opalescent and containing flecks of mucus. On centrifuging and examining the sediment, it can be seen that the cloudy appearance of the juice is partly due to mucus and partly due to cellular debris, including some intact cells of the type characteristic of the intestinal mucous membrane (Florey et al., 1941). When collected from the duodenum only, the juice has a more glairy appearance and a heavier consistency, and evidently contains a greater proportion of mucus. The chemical composition of the juice consists of water, inorganic salts, and organic material. The inorganic salts are those commonly present in body fluids, except that the bicarbonate concentration is higher than it is in blood or interstitial fluid. The alkalinity on titration is said to vary between 0.02 and 0.67 per cent sodium bicarbonate equivalent. Various estimates of the pH of the intestinal secretion have been given, ranging from 6.3 to 9.0. The higher values undoubtedly are the result of loss of carbon dioxide from the juice. It is certainly an alkaline fluid and may probably have a true pH as high as 8.3.

Except in the duodenum, the quantity of fluid secreted by the small intestine is never very great, a few ml. per hr. being the usual amount that it is possible to obtain experimentally, even under conditions of stimulation. In the dog, pig, rabbit and goat, spontaneous secretion of the Brunner's glands, amounting to 0.5 to 2.0 ml./hr., has been demonstrated. Spontaneous secretion apparently does not occur in the cat. In dogs, where more extensive studies have been done, the response of the Brunner's glands to feeding results in only

3 to 4 ml./hr. It is difficult to determine with accuracy the amount actually secreted because of the tremendous absorptive capacity of the intestine. Many times more than the amount that it is possible to collect may be secreted and reabsorbed during an observation period. It is evident that the mucosa is capable, under some circumstances, of passing enormous amounts of fluid into the lumen of the intestine as shown by the great water loss that occurs through the intestine in pathologic states such as cholera, diarrhea, or intestinal obstruction.

The organic matter of the juice consists of mucus, enzymes and cellular debris. The source of the enzymes is unknown but it is assumed that they are produced by the columnar cells, although the argentaffine cells or the Paneth cells may be responsible for some of them. There is no evidence that the mucosa of the small bowel *secretes* enzymes in the sense that secretion occurs in the gastric mucosa or in the pancreas. The exfoliation of epithelial cells into the bowel lumen, and their subsequent dissolution, probably accounts for the presence of enzymes in the intraluminal contents of the small intestine. A really formidable array of enzymes have been reported as occurring in intestinal secretion. A pepsinlike protease (from the duodenum only), an amylase, a lipase, at least two peptidases, sucrase (invertase), maltase, lactase, enterokinase, alkaline phosphatase, nucleophosphatases, and nucleosidases have been described.

Protease. A weak proteolytic enzyme with properties similar to pepsin was described as occurring in the duodenal secretion by investigators of the Pavlov school (Salaskin, 1902). The similarity of the Brunner's glands to the pyloric glands, and the fact that the pyloric portion of the stomach secretes pepsin in small amounts, made this observation seem plausible. However, Wright and his associates (1940), who made the most thorough study of intestinal secretion, could find no protease in duodenal secretion.

Peptidases. One of the major functions of intestinal digestion is final reduction of the products of peptic and tryptic digestion to amino acids; this is accomplished by intestinal peptidases. The presence of peptidases has been reported by all investigators who have studied the problem. The ones usually described are: amino peptidase, which acts on the peptide linkages of terminal amino acids possessing a free amino group, and tripeptidases and dipeptidases which split tri- and dipeptides, respectively, into their constituent amino acids.

Lipase. Most investigators have reported finding a weak lipase action in intestinal secretion (Boldyreff, 1904, 1912).

Disaccharidases. The various disaccharidases: sucrase, lactase, and maltase, are present in succus entericus under all normal circumstances.

Enterokinase. Enterokinase, the enzyme which converts trypsinogen to trypsin (see Pancreatic Secretion), is present in the intestinal secretion under normal circumstances. However, Savich (1904) stated that, if pancreatic juice was excluded from the intestine, enterokinase gradually disappeared from the secretion, as it did also from an intestinal loop in which the pancreatic juice did not circulate. Waldschmidt-Leitz and Harteneck (1925) likewise concluded that pancreatic juice was necessary for liberation of enterokinase from the epithelial cells. Florey, Wright and Jennings (1941) considered that the evidence was insufficient in either case. The point is of considerable interest and merits further investigation.

The studies of Wright, Jennings, Florey and Lium in 1940 raised a question as to the source of the enzymes ordinarily found in intestinal secretion. They reported that when they took precautions to prevent injury to the mucous membrane while collecting the secretion, and then immediately centrifuged the collected secretion so as to remove cellular debris, only amylase and enterokinase were consistently present in the supernatant fluid. They consider that these enzymes, and possibly maltase, are secreted by the intestinal glands in the usual sense. The others, they believe, are intracellular enzymes which exist in the cells of the mucous membrane and appear in the juice only as a result of the shedding of these cells and their disintegration in the intestine. They point to the opinions of many physiologists that most of the digestion of peptides and disaccharides takes place in the epithelial cells while these substances are being absorbed. This is not, however, a necessary conclusion from the observed facts. The rapid rate of mitosis in the depths of the glands of Lieberkühn, and the continuous shedding of epithelial cells from the tips of the villi, may represent a special kind of holocrine secretory process by which endocellular enzymes are secreted into the intestinal juice, the secretory product being the entire epithelial cell with its contained enzymes. Under normal circumstances, the presence of active trypsin in the intestinal contents would seem to insure the rapid disintegration of these cells and liberation of their

contained enzymes into the intestinal secretion. In this connection it may be significant that enterokinase is secreted directly, and so insures that activation of trypsinogen does not depend on the disintegration of shed epithelial cells.

REGULATION OF INTESTINAL SECRETION

Control of Brunner's Gland Secretion

Secretion of Brunner's glands is controlled by nervous and humoral mechanisms which do not affect the other intestinal glands, or if they do so it is only to a slight extent. The secretion of Brunner's glands increases on stimulation of the vagus nerves or the administration of parasympathomimetic drugs such as pilocarpine and physostigmine; it is not augmented by stimulation of the sympathetic nerves (Florey and Harding, 1934). The amount of secretion is increased after meals (Blickenstaff et al., 1949), even in transplanted denervated pouches of the duodenum (Florey and Harding, 1935b). This proves that there is a humoral mechanism for regulating the secretion, in addition to whatever nervous mechanisms there may be. The nature of the humor has been the subject of some discussion and is still undetermined; Florey and Harding (1935a) were convinced that it was secretin. They were led to this conclusion by the fact that practically all stimuli which increase pancreatic secretion, including contact of hydrochloric acid with the duodenal mucous membrane, also increased the secretion of Brunner's glands. They also found that what they considered to be a highly purified secretin preparation stimulated duodenal secretion when given intravenously. Sonnenschein and his associates (1947) were unable to confirm the results with secretin. Using what they believed was a crystalline picrolonate of secretin, they observed little effect on Brunner's glands, although crude secretin caused an abundant secretion. Grossman (1950) has suggested that there is a special hormone for these glands which he proposed to call *"duocrinin."*

Functions of the duodenal secretion. Florey and Harding (1933) emphasized the protective function of the secretion of Brunner's glands and considered it an important factor in preventing duodenal ulceration. In addition, it may assist in emulsification and suspension of fat and other food particles. Since, like other intestinal secretions, it contains enterokinase it helps to activate the trypsinogen of pancreatic juice. Duodenal secretion is also said to contain "intrinsic factor" and, therefore, probably assists in absorption of vitamin B_{12}. The various hormones known to be produced by the duodenal mucosa are probably not secreted into the lumen of the intestine except incidentally, and in small quantities, and are not functional in this situation.

Control of Secretion of Succus Entericus

It has long been known that local chemical and mechanical stimuli can evoke secretion by the small bowel. The neural and humoral mechanisms regulating secretion by the small bowel are poorly understood. Except for "paralytic secretion," discussed below, there is little evidence that neural and humoral mechanisms normally play a significant role. Our lack of knowledge is due to the l;mitations of the methods that have been developed to study intestinal secretion.

Nervous regulation. It was demonstrated in Pavlov's laboratory that stimulation of the vagus nerve in animals in which the spinal cord has been severed in the neck caused a moderate secretion of intestinal juice from the duodenum, and also from the rest of the small intestine, after a latent period of from 1 to $1\frac{1}{2}$ hr. (Savich, 1917). Wright and his coworkers (1940) were able to obtain an increased secretion from the duodenum on stimulation of the vagus in decerebrated or decapitated animals, but were unable to obtain clear evidence that vagal stimulation caused secretion from the jejunum or ileum.

Stimulation of the sympathetic causes no secretion but cutting the nerves results in a marked increase in secretion. This *paralytic secretion*, as it is called, is increased by physostigmine and inhibited by atropine; it is therefore considered to be dependent upon some cholinergic mechanism in the intestine. In general, parasympathomimetic drugs increase the paralytic secretion and sympathomimetic drugs tend to inhibit it. From these observations we can conclude that secretion is augmented by a cholinergic mechanism and that this mechanism is antagonized by the sympathetic. Whether this antagonism is direct, or whether it is caused by contraction of the blood vessels remains uncertain. One interpretation of the paralytic secretion is that section of the sympathetic nerves results in dilation of the blood vessels of the intestine, and in this way greatly increases the blood flow. Such an increase in blood flow would provide a greater amount of fluid for secretion and, presumably, might produce the augmentation of secretion seen on section of the sympathetic nerves (Starling, 1906). Babkin (1950) has pointed out that

cutting the sympathetic nerves to the small intestine increases its motility, which undoubtedly has a massaging effect on the mucous membrane. In view of the fact that one of the most effective stimuli for intestinal secretion is mechanical stimulation of the mucosa, this factor alone may be sufficient to account for the increased secretion.

Humoral regulation. The most effective stimulus for secretion of succus entericus is local, mechanical, or chemical stimulation of the intestinal mucous membrane. Such stimuli are always present in the digesting intestine, due to the presence of chyme and the food particles which it contains. Feeding is not very effective in increasing the rate of intestinal secretion from an isolated intestinal loop, provided the nerve supply is intact, but if the sympathetic nerves have been severed, a noticeable increase in secretion takes place when the animal is fed. This indicates that some factor, either nervous or humoral, operates to increase the secretion during digestion. The early investigators were of the opinion that pancreatic secretion was an effective stimulus for intestinal secretion (Delenzenne and Frouin, 1904). This point of view was a result of experiments in which injections of secretin-containing preparations resulted in undoubted increases in secretion of intestinal juice. However, as more highly purified preparations of secretin became available, the influence on intestinal secretion became less, so that now it is doubtful whether secretin, as such, acts on the intestinal glands. On the other hand, intestinal extracts, from which secretin has been totally eliminated, remain potent stimuli for intestinal secretion. This subject has been investigated most fully by Nasset and his coworkers (1938) who have prepared an extract of the intestinal mucous membrane which is free from secretin, from vasodilator material, and from toxic substances, but which causes an increase in the secretion of a denervated jejunal loop when given intravenously.

Subcutaneous injection is less effective, but in large doses produces some secretion. The material is thought to contain a hormone which augments the intestinal secretion; it is called *"enterocrinin."* The fact that a hormonal mechanism is involved in normal intestinal secretion is best supported by the work of Nasset and his coworkers (1935) with denervated loops of intestine. Such loops secrete when acid and certain other substances are placed in the intact portions of the intestine, and also after meals.

Regulation of enzyme secretion. There is little published data on the control of secretion of organic compounds in the succus entericus. However, Nasset (1956) is of the opinion that the parasympathetic nerves control the output of enzymes from the intestinal glands, as they do the secretion of organic matter in saliva. He also suggests that crude enterocrinin may contain a specific hormone for the secretion of intestinal enzymes comparable to pancreozymin, which promotes secretion of pancreatic enzymes.

THE FUNCTION OF THE SUCCUS ENTERICUS

Enzymatic digestion of food, in all its phases, is a hydrolytic process; therefore, an abundance of water to serve as one of the reacting substances is essential. The succus entericus provides this water in the area in which the major part of digestion of food occurs. Water is also necessary to serve as a solvent and as a medium of suspension and transport for the solids which are dissolved or suspended in the chyme. The enzymes, either in the secretion or in the cells, complete the digestion of protein and carbohydrate by reducing the peptides which result from peptic and tryptic digestion to amino acids, and the disaccharides which result from amylolytic digestion of starch to glucose. Other disaccharides that may be present in the food are likewise digested, liberating their constituent monosaccharides. In fat digestion, the succus entericus serves as a source of water and as a medium for suspension and emulsification of the fat particles; it also provides a certain amount of lipase.

SECRETION OF THE COLON

The mucosa of the mammalian cecum and colon is in many respects similar to that of the small intestine; crypts are present but there are no villi. As in the small intestine, the cells at the bottoms of the crypts exhibit numerous mitoses, suggesting the continuous replacement of shed epithelial cells. Goblet cells are more numerous than in the small intestine, and the epithelial cells between the goblet cells differ among themselves, but in the majority of cases the protoplasm is clear and free from secretory granules. The secretion is scanty (Wright et al., 1938), as is to be expected from the fact that a major function of the large intestine is absorption of water. The decrease in volume of intestinal contents that occurs in this area indicates that secretion does not keep pace with absorption. Actually, it is usually not possible to collect any secretion from

a colonic fistula unless the mucous membrane is stimulated mechanically by insertion of a catheter or other instrument. Even with this stimulation only a few tenths of a cubic centimeter per hour can be collected. When anything can be collected, it consists of watery fluid with clumps of white mucus; often it is viscous and opalescent. The reaction is alkaline, due to sodium bicarbonate which may be present in concentrations as high as 80–90 mEq/l., according to deBeer et al. (1935). Of the solids, 0.63 per cent is organic, and the remainder is inorganic material.

The secretion of the cecum apparently contains enzymes corresponding to those found in the small intestine, with the exception of enterokinase which is not present. The secretion of enzymes becomes progressively less and ultimately disappears toward the distal colon. The large intestine has an extraordinary capacity to secrete mucus, and under certain circumstances may secrete a surprisingly large amount of the material. As elsewhere in the intestine, mucus is secreted in response to strong local stimulation or irritation, hence, mucus is likely to be secreted in unusual amount in the presence of bacterial infection or other causes of local irritation, such as irritant cathartics. The secretion is an active process involving utilization of oxygen; it is inhibited by perfusion of the intestine with cyanide.

Nervous Control of Colonic Secretion

Florey (1930) and Wright et al., (1938) found that stimulation of the nervus erigens caused the colon to secrete a clear mucoid fluid. In contrast to the practical absence of spontaneous secretion, stimulation produced as much as 55 ml. in one 8-hr. period from the distal half of the colon; the average rate was about 5 ml. per hr. Reflex secretion was observed on stimulation of the cut end of one nervus erigens, the other being intact; the reflex center was located in the lumbar spinal cord. Larson and Bargen (1933) observed secretion of mucus in an isolated segment of the colon at the time of defecation. It should be recalled that the nervus erigens supplies only the distal portion of the colon with parasympathetic fibers; the parasympathetic supply for the proximal colon comes from the vagi. Acetylcholine and pilocarpine increase colonic secretion, atropine inhibits it. Histamine has been reported to cause a slight increase in secretion. The secretion is reduced by anesthetics. Cutting the sympathetics does not produce paralytic secretion in the large intestine, but stimulation of the sympathetics diminishes the secretory response to stimulation of the nervus erigens.

The relationship of secretory function of the colon to the autonomic nerves has a bearing upon the occurrence of certain diseases of the colon in which there is excessive secretion of mucus, for example, *mucous colitis*. This is a condition in which excessive amounts of mucus appear in the stools, constituting, in some cases, tubular casts of the colon. This has often been considered a psychosomatic disease and has a close relationship to abnormal emotional states.

The Intestinal Mucosa as an Excretory Organ

The feces contain small amounts of fat, even during prolonged starvation, indicating that some fat is eliminated by way of the intestine. Probably a great deal more fat is excreted into the intestine than escapes in the feces, the majority being reabsorbed (Sperry and Bloor, 1924). It also has been claimed that the colon excretes calcium, phosphorus, iron and various heavy metals. Although this is probably true, it is not likely that the intestine constitutes an important avenue of excretion for these substances once they have been absorbed.

Although probably not normally an important organ of excretion, the intestinal mucous membrane, by virtue of its permeability to numerous diffusible substances, can be made to function as an organ of excretion. For example, if a double lumen tube is placed in the intestine with one opening high up and the other low down, and fluid is perfused through it so that it enters at a high level and escapes the lower tube after passing through the intestine, it will carry away diffusible substances from the blood. Use has been made of this mechanism in cases of renal failure in which nonprotein nitrogenous substances and other toxic waste products accumulate in the blood. Since any diffusible substance will tend to establish an equal concentration in the blood and the intestinal contents, any mechanism which continually replaces and removes the intestinal contents will remove these substances from the body; thus the intestine may be used as an "artificial kidney." One great difficulty with this procedure is that not only the toxic substances which it is desired to remove will be removed, but all the diffusible constituents of the blood are also removed in this manner. It is necessary, therefore, that the fluid used for perfusion should approximate the composition of the blood plasma with respect to all normal diffusible constituents insofar as possible. The normal excretory function of the intestine, has to do with the disposal of the residues remaining after completion of digestion and absorption in the small intestine. This is accomplished mainly in the large intestine, where the water and salts of the intestinal contents are recovered and the solid residues formed into feces (ch. 61).

The Absorptive Function of the Intestine

The mucous lining of the small intestine is one of the most remarkable organs of the body. It secretes a variety of hormones which help to regulate gastric secretion and motility, the secretion of the pancreas and of the intestine itself, and the movements of the gall bladder and the intestinal villi. This endocrine activity, which is mainly concentrated in the upper intestine, has led Nasset to characterize the duodenum as the "hypophysis of the abdomen." The same tissue which secretes hormones into the blood, forms an external secretion containing a variety of digestive enzymes at least as numerous as those found in the pancreatic juice. During absorption, the mucosal cells perform a variety of hydrolytic and synthetic operations upon the food substances passing through them, greatly modifying the character of the absorbed material. Even while producing their own secretions, the epithelial cells are transferring water and dissolved substances from the lumen of the intestine into the interstitial fluid to be taken up by the blood. This absorptive activity is highly selective and frequently involves the expenditure of considerable energy. Probably nowhere, except possibly in the liver, is so great a variety of functions performed by a single tissue.

The ultimate aim of digestion is absorption. Only after the products of digestion have passed through the epithelial lining of the digestive tract and entered the blood stream are they able to serve their purpose of providing nourishment for the tissue cells of the body. Absorption of such materials takes place almost entirely from the small intestine. Although the stomach is capable of absorbing small amounts of water and certain food substances, notably glucose, and some foreign substances such as alcohol, the absorption that occurs here is negligible, partly because the food is not digested sufficiently in the stomach to be readily absorbed, but mainly because the gastric mucous membrane is not adapted for absorption as is the small intestine membrane. A possible exception is iron, which may be absorbed in significant quantities from the stomach. Although absorption of food occurs mainly in the small intestine, water and salts are absorbed in significant amounts from the large intestine.

The mucous lining of the small intestine is admirably adapted to its absorptive function. The structure of the epithelium has been described in connection with the discussion of intestinal secretion. The intestinal villi will be referred to in the chapter on movements of the alimentary canal. It has been estimated that the presence of the villi results in an increase of seven- or eight-fold in the surface area of the mucous membrane of the intestine. The microvilli increase the surface area by another 20-fold.

Methods for Study of Intestinal Absorption

The methods described in the section on intestinal secretion are also available for the study of absorption. In acute experiments, one places the material, the absorption of which is to be studied, in an isolated loop of intestine and, after a measured time, removes it and observes the volumetric or chemical changes that have taken place. The Thiry or Thiry-Vella loop may be used in the same manner. In the case of substances that can be readily detected in the blood, the material can be placed in the intact intestine and its absorption estimated by the rate of its appearance in the circulating blood, in the portal blood, or in the intestinal lymph, if the experiment is of such a nature as to make these vessels available. In recent years, it has been possible through the use of food materials tagged with radioactive isotopes, to gain much information that could not have been obtained by the older methods.

In man, intestinal absorption can be studied by an intubation technique. A multi-lumen tube, or two or more separate small polyethylene tubes may be used. After localization in the desired segment of intestine, the material to be studied, along with a nonabsorbable reference "marker," is introduced through the lumen of the proximal tube at a constant rate. Sampling is done through one or more of the distal tubes, whose openings are a measured distance from the opening of the proximal tube used for introduction. The concentration of absorbable material recovered is compared to the concentration introduced and a correction is made for any change in volume as indicated by the change in concentration of the "marker." Polyethylene glycol (PEG) and phenol red are commonly used as "markers" for such studies.

The development of *in vitro* techniques for the study of excised segments of intestine has also greatly increased our knowledge in recent years. A variety of techniques for this purpose have been described by different authors; all depend upon maintaining the vitality of a portion of the intestine that has been removed from the body by keeping it in contact with oxygenated fluid of appropriate composition. The preparation can be arranged so that the fluid inside the intestine, which is in contact with the absorbing surface, can be kept separate from that on the outside, which is in contact with the serosal surface, and the changes in composition of the internal and external fluid are used to measure the degree of absorption by the mucosa. A small segment of intestine can also be turned inside out, as described by Wilson and Wiseman (1954), and is known as the everted sac method. The method has the advantage of collecting high concentrations of the absorbed material in the small volume contained inside the serosal lined sac. Studies of this sort are done chiefly on smaller animals such as rats, guinea pigs and hamsters, since their relatively thin intestines are more easily maintained in a viable condition in an artificial medium.

Absorption of Water

Much that has been published on the absorption of water from the intestine is of little value because, until recently, it has been impossible to distinguish between the water that was secreted into the intestine and water that left the intestine by absorption. Changes observed in the volume of water in the intestine did not represent total absorption of water but merely the difference between the volume of water secreted into the intestine and that absorbed. Since there is reason to believe that water moves freely through the intestinal mucosa, it is essential that we know how much water entered the intestine in a given time if we are to make an intelligent estimate of the amount leaving by way of absorption in the same time. It has been possible to get around this difficulty, and to determine accurately the amount of water leaving the intestine by absorption in a unit of time, by the use of heavy water. Water containing heavy hydrogen can be readily detected in the blood, also, the amount remaining in the intestine can be accurately measured. Since, in a short period of time the water secreted into the intestine will be normal water, the change in heavy water content represents water actually absorbed. Or if, as in experiments on human subjects, it is not possible to determine the amount of water remaining in the intestine, the amount of heavy water appearing in the blood can be used as an estimate of the water absorbed.

Scholer and Code (1954) studied absorption of water from the human stomach and small intestine using heavy water as a tracer. They found that when 50 g. of water were given, 2.5 per cent of this amount was absorbed per min., so long as it remained in the stomach. When the water was placed in the small intestine it was absorbed at about ten times that rate, 26.1 per cent of the dose being absorbed per min. If the water remained in the stomach, it required 34.2 min. to absorb 67 per cent of the administered amount; whereas in the intestine, this percentage was absorbed in 3.7 min. In the intestine, 95 per cent of the administered water was absorbed in ten min. In these experiments only absorption was measured, and the net volume change was not observed; hence, no account was taken of the water that might have been secreted into the stomach or intestine during this same period of time. One interesting fact brought out in these studies is the extremely rapid absorption of water from the intestine. Another is that there is an appreciable absorption of water from the stomach. The statement often seen in the literature, that water is not absorbed in appreciable amounts from the stomach, is based on the net change in volume and no account is taken of the concurrent secretion of fluid into the stomach. Considering net absorption only, that is the decrease in the volume of intestinal contents, it appears that water is absorbed more rapidly from the terminal ileum than from other parts of the small intestine. Most of what remains is absorbed from the large intestine.

The net absorption of fluids from the intestine is influenced by hydrostatic and osmotic pressures. Blickenstaff and others (1952) found that there was a significant difference in the rate of absorption of chloride and water at different levels of hydrostatic pressure. Between the extremes, there was an optimal pressure at which absorption was most rapid. He also noted that water was absorbed more rapidly from dilute, than from concentrated solutions. Absorption is accelerated by an increase in hydrostatic pressure, up to the point where the pressure begins to interfere with the blood supply to the intestinal mucous membrane. Nasset and Parry (1934) found that negative hydrostatic pressure tended

to accelerate the net flow of fluid into the intestine, whereas increasing the pressure favored net absorption provided the pressure exceeded 25 cm. of solution. Between 5 and 25 cm. there was no change. It has been suggested by Verzar and McDougall (1936) that absorption of water from the large intestine is largely dependent on the relatively high hydrostatic pressure which they say is maintained in this organ. Other things being equal, it has been found that, within physiological limits, the rate of absorption of water is directly proportional to the hydrostatic pressure in the intestine. Considering net absorption only, the rate of absorption of water decreases with increasing osmotic pressure of the intestinal contents, but this relationship is not linear. More water is absorbed from hypotonic than from isotonic solutions, and more from isotonic than from hypertonic solutions.

Absorption of Inorganic Salts

Of the inorganic salts that are presented to the intestine for absorption, the most important are sodium, potassium and calcium chlorides, and phosphate. Absorption of iron will be considered in ch. 29. The absorption of chlorides of sodium and potassium are always accompanied by absorption of water, and the more rapidly the water is absorbed, the more rapidly will the salts be absorbed. The salt concentration in the solution passing through the mucosa from the lumen of the intestine toward the blood, is not necessarily the same as that of the intestinal contents. From an isotonic solution in the intestine, the fluid absorbed tends to be hypertonic, so that as absorption progresses the fluid in the intestine becomes hypotonic due to loss of salt (Visscher et al., 1944). The salt concentration in the absorbed mixture is proportional to the concentration in the intestinal contents, but due to the osmotic effect of concentrated salt solutions on the net movement of water, less salt may be absorbed from a concentrated solution than from a dilute solution. Rabinovitch (1927) found that the greatest percentage absorption of water was from salt solutions ranging in concentration from 0.4 to 0.6 per cent, and that the absolute amount of salt absorbed increased with increasing concentration of salt up to 0.8 per cent. He also noted that water and chloride are absorbed more rapidly when potassium ions are present, and that absorption was accelerated even more by calcium ions in the solution. An interesting paradox is that atropine, which inhibits most intestinal functions, accelerates net water and salt absorption. This is due to the inhibitory effect of atropine on intestinal secretion.

Calcium salts, including the phosphate, are absorbed more readily from the upper intestine than from the ileum. A problem in calcium absorption is the relative insolubility of the commonly occurring calcium salts, such as the phosphate, in alkaline and neutral solutions; consequently, calcium is absorbed better from an acid medium than from an alkaline medium. This fact may explain the better absorption of calcium from the relatively acid upper intestine. It has been noted that the phosphates enter the intestine chiefly as phosphoproteins or phospholipids, which may not be readily digested in the upper intestine where the principal calcium absorption occurs; hence calcium and the phosphates may be absorbed in different regions of the intestine, avoiding the formation of insoluble calcium phosphates. Nevertheless, in the absence of normal hydrochloric acid secretion by the stomach, calcium absorption tends to be poor, so that achlorhydrics often suffer from a calcium deficiency.

Calcium is said to be absorbed more readily by individuals suffering from a calcium deficiency, indicating some control of calcium absorption by systemic factors. The presence of an excess of magnesium is said to interfere with calcium absorption, as does phytic acid (which occurs in cereal grains, and which may be responsible for the tendency of these grains to produce rickets when fed exclusively or in excess). The administration of vitamin D accelerates absorption of calcium from the lower ileum but not from other parts of the intestinal tract. Vitamin D counteracts the effect of phytic acid, when it is given in adequate amounts it offsets the tendency of cereal grains to cause rickets.

The Mechanism of Water and Salt Absorption

Considering the apparently free permeability of the intestinal mucous membrane to water and the simple inorganic salts, it is tempting to try to explain the absorption of these substances on the basis of simple diffusion or osmosis. As we have seen, the physical and chemical laws are operative in the transfer of water through the intestinal mucosa, but as our knowledge has increased, it has become increasingly evident that these principles are inadequate to explain all the observed phenomena. Ingraham and Visscher (1936, 1938) showed that, in the presence of a sulfate solution, sodium chloride was absorbed against a concentration gradient; that is, its absorption went on until the concentration in the intestine fell far below that in the interstitial fluid and in the blood. Likewise, the osmotic activity of the fluid in the intestine decreased in their experiments until it fell to as much as half an atmosphere below the osmotic pressure of the blood plasma, leaving no doubt that the absorption took place as the result of osmotic work by the intestinal epithelium. In a later study (1944), in which they used isotopic tracer techniques so that they could measure absorption and secretion separately and determine precisely the amount of water and salt absorbed, they were able to determine that the rate of movement of water from gut to blood (absorption) was often as much as 100 times as rapid as it would have been under the same circumstances if only the laws of diffusion and osmosis were operating. Likewise, the amount of salt moved in either direction was often found to be at variance with the amount determined by calculation on the basis of the laws of diffusion and osmosis. Studies on isolated preparations have given results with similar significance.

McHardy and Parsons (1957), studying intact animals, found that chloride was absorbed from solutions containing from 20 to 50 mEq/l. less than the blood plasma. Sodium was absorbed from isotonic solutions containing from 45 to 75 mEq/l. less sodium than the plasma. They noted a statistically linear relation between the total absorption of solutes and the absorption rate of water, indicating an interrelationship between the absorption of these two types of products, but they were unable to determine which was dependent on the other. In isolated preparations, Smyth and Taylor (1957) found that the transfer of water from the mucosal to the serosal side of excised rat small intestine was dependent upon the presence of glucose and oxygen in the medium and was affected by temperature. It was prevented by various metabolic inhibitors, indicating that the transfer was an active metabolic process. Others have found that the transfer of a salt solution from the mucosal to the serosal side failed in the absence of oxygen.

It is necessary to conclude that the absorption of both water and salts, although influenced by physicochemical forces, is for the most part an active process, dependent upon the metabolic activity of the mucosal cells of the intestine. Little is known of the chemical mechanisms involved but oxygen appears to be necessary. The possibility remains that only one of the

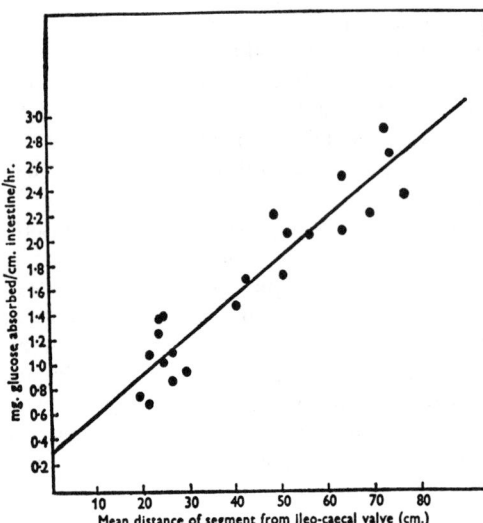

FIG. 60.1. Glucose absorption in surviving intestine. Relation between glucose disappearance from inner fluid and mean distance of segment from ileocecal valve in 1-hour experiments. From Fisher and Parsons, 1949. Courtesy of Cambridge University Press.

two substances, water and salt, is moved actively, since the movement of one would necessitate the transfer of the other in order to maintain osmotic equilibrium; thus, either water or salt may be absorbed actively and the other carried passively, but the evidence favors active transfer of salt. For example, in a salt-restricted diet, sodium practically disappears from the contents of the terminal ileum (Field, et al., 1955). This suggests a sodium conserving action of the upper intestine and strongly implies the selective absorption of sodium.

ABSORPTION OF CARBOHYDRATES

Monosaccharides are absorbed more readily by the intestinal mucous membrane. Some disaccharides are also absorbed, but the intestinal epithelium is, in general, impermeable to the polysaccharides. The important monosaccharides are glucose, fructose, and galactose. Glucose occurs as the final product of starch digestion, and as one of the two products of hydrolysis of sucrose and lactose. Fructose occurs as a product of sucrose digestion, and also in certain natural products such as some fruits and in honey. Galactose is one of the constituents of lactose. Other simple sugars such as mannose and pentoses are quantitatively unimportant. The three simple sugars, galactose, glucose, and fructose, are all actively absorbed from the small intestine, galactose more rapidly, and fructose less rapidly than glucose.

Absorption of Monosaccharides

The ability of the intestine to absorb glucose against a concentration gradient has been repeatedly demonstrated; i.e., glucose can be absorbed when the concentration of glucose in the intestinal contents is lower than the concentration in the blood. In an excised preparation, glucose passes from the mucosal to the serosal side, even when the concentration on the mucosal side of the preparation is lower than it is on the serosal side.

It is interesting to note that although the pentoses are more diffusible than the hexoses, the pentoses are absorbed at a much slower rate, proving again that the hexoses are actively absorbed. With most sugars, particularly those that are not actively absorbed, the rate of absorption increases with increasing concentration in the intestinal contents. With glucose and galactose, however, this is true only up to about a 5 per cent concentration, which for these sugars is approximately isotonic with the blood. Further increase in concentration of these sugars fails to increase or decrease their rate of absorption. Furthermore, if glucose and galactose are given simultaneously, each suppresses the absorption of the other (Cori, 1931) so that the total amount of sugar absorbed is not more than would be absorbed if only one of the sugars were present. These facts indicate that the mechanisms for active absorption can be saturated in a manner somewhat analogous to the tubular maximum for glucose in the renal tubules.

Glucose is absorbed much more rapidly from the upper than from the lower small intestine. Fisher and Parsons (1949) have shown that, in the rat, there is a linear gradient in the ability of the intestine to absorb glucose from the intestinal contents. The rate of absorption is directly proportional to the distance of the segment in question from the ileocecal valve (fig. 60.1).

Using various segments of hamster intestine, Crane and Mandelstam (1960) have shown that the midportion of the small intestine is the site for the most active rate of absorption of monosaccharides as glucose. Borgström and his associates in Sweden (1957) have studied the site of absorption of glucose and lactose in the small bowel of man. They used an intubation technique, with polyethyleneglycol as a nonabsorbable indicator substance. The subjects were fed a test meal containing 55 g. of glucose and 20 g. of lactose. Samples were then collected from various levels of the small bowel, and it was found that absorption began in the duodenum and was completed by the time the meal had reached a level about 100 cm. from the duodenum.

As to the specific site of absorption in the mucosa, Kinter (1961) using autoradiographic techniques, has shown that absorption of glucose occurs mostly in the upper third of the villus. Crane (1962) has presented evidence that the active transport of glucose actually occurs across the plasma membrane of the microvilli in the brush border.

Absorption of sugars is diminished in the presence of sodium chloride deficiency such as may occur in adrenal cortical insufficiency. This suggests that the neutral salts play a part in the active absorption of sugar. Absorption of sugars is accelerated in hyperthyroidism and depressed in hypothyroidism, in the latter case, administration of thyroxin improves absorption. Pantothenic acid, thyamine, and pyridoxine, members of the B vitamin group, are essential for normal sugar absorption.

For optimal absorption of glucose it is necessary that both sodium and potassium be present. The relationship of the absorption of glucose to sodium has been studied extensively, using isolated intestinal segments. If sodium is completely replaced by potassium, lithium, magnesium or manitol, active glucose transport ceases completely. In addition, if sodium transport is inhibited by cardiac glycosides, active glucose transport is also interfered with. It is now thought that mechanisms of glucose and sodium transport are closely coupled (Crane, Miller and Bihler, 1961) and dependent on one another. Whether the sodium "pump" and the glucose mechanism are the same for entry into the cell is not known, however, Bihler, Hawkins and Crane (1962) have suggested that two processes, both dependent on sodium, are involved in sugar transport: (1) an *entry* step that is sodium dependent but requires no energy, and (2) an *accumulation* step, also sodium dependent, but which requires energy to maintain a concentration gradient within the cell.

In addition to the specific dependence of glucose absorption and transport on the Na$^+$ ion, it is now known that there are specific structural requirements of the monosaccharide molecule for it to be actively transported. Our knowledge of the structural requirements for the active transport of monosaccharides has come mostly from the laboratories of Wilson and Crane, using the everted intestinal sac method developed by Wilson and Wiseman. The absorption of a great many naturally occurring and synthetic monosaccharides has now been studied in relation to the structural configuration of the molecule. To be actively transported, the following specific structural requirements of the monosaccharide molecule are known: (1) The hydroxyl (OH) group at carbon-2 must be present and have the same stereoconfiguration as exists in D-glucose. If the hydroxyl group at carbon-2 is replaced by H, as in 2-deoxyglucose; or if the H of the OH group is replaced by a methyl group, as in 2-O-methyl glucose; active transport does not occur. (2) A pyranose (6-membered) ring must be present, as in glucose and galactose. (3) One or more carbons must be attached to carbon-5. The structural requirements necessary for the active transport of monosaccharides are illustrated in fig. 60.2.

From the above, it can be reasoned that 5-carbon sugars such as xylose will not be actively transported. If a monosaccharide is a 7-carbon sugar, it may be actively transported if it has the specific structural requirements outlined above. The hydroxyl group at carbon-1,3,4, and 6 are not essential for active transport. Thus, phosphorylation which occurs at carbons-1 and -6 is not essential for active transport. In other words, monosaccharides with the necessary specific structural requirements can be actively transported in the absence of phosphorylation.

Absorption of Disaccharides

It has long been believed that disaccharides were hydrolyzed in the lumen of the small bowel by disaccharidases secreted by the small bowel into the "succus entericus." There is now much evidence that this is not the case, and that some disaccharides are absorbed and hydrolyzed *within* the epithelial cell by specific intracellular enzymes. Much of the evidence in support of intracellular hydrolysis of disaccharides has been due to the work of Miller and Crane (1961). These investigators incubated inverted segments of hamster small bowel in a sucrose solution, and found that glucose accumulated in the epithelium to a concentration 20 to 30 times that in incubating medium. This suggested that the sucrose was hydrolyzed after absorption, rather than before. In another experiment, maltose was used in the incubation medium but glucose oxidase was added also. A molecule of maltose results in two molecules of glucose on hydrolysis, but in the presence of glucose oxidase, the glucose would be oxidized and unavailable for absorption if hydrolysis occurred prior to absorption. Their findings were the same as when sucrose was used

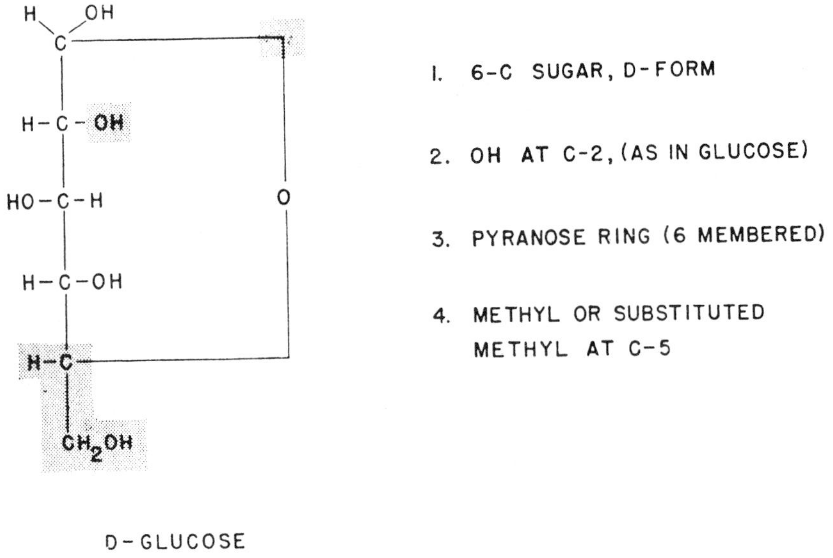

1. 6-C SUGAR, D-FORM

2. OH AT C-2, (AS IN GLUCOSE)

3. PYRANOSE RING (6 MEMBERED)

4. METHYL OR SUBSTITUTED
   METHYL AT C-5

D-GLUCOSE

FIG. 60.2. The minimal structural requirements for the active transport of monosaccharides by the intestine. From Isselbacher and Senior, 1964, Gastroenterology, **46**, 287.

TABLE 60.1

Specificity of disaccharidases isolated from human intestinal epithelium and their quantitative importance for hydrolysis of different disaccharides

Enzyme	Substrate	Total Activity against each Substrate
		%
Isomaltase = maltase	Isomaltose	100
Ia	Maltose	50
Invertase = maltase	Sucrose	100
Ib	Maltose	25
Maltase II	Maltose	15
Maltase III	Maltose	10
Trehalase	Trehalose	100
Lactase	Lactose	100
	Cellobiose	100

From Dahlqvist, Gastroenterology, 1962, **43**, 694.

in the incubation medium and glucose accumulated in the tissue, in spite of the fact that glucose oxidase was in the medium. Other experimental evidence provided by Miller and Crane in support of intracellular hydrolysis of disaccharides is their demonstration, by cell fractionation and enzymatic techniques, that practically all of the maltase and invertase activity of the small bowel mucosa can be found in the isolated brush border of the epithelial cells.

Within the past few years a new clinical entity has been described in patients who are unable to absorb certain disaccharides. The condition is now recognized as an *hereditary disaccharide intolerance* (Dahlqvist, 1962) and is due to the congenital absence of one or more of the disaccharidases normally found in the mucosa of the small bowel. When a patient with a congenital absence of a disaccharidase is fed the corresponding disaccharide he develops diarrhea, with watery stools of low pH, and containing large amounts of the disaccharide as well as lactic acid. Removing the specific disaccharide from the diet promptly causes the symptoms to disappear. Due to the inability to absorb certain disaccharides by these patients, a *disaccharide tolerance test* can be done to demonstrate the disorder. The test is similar to the oral glucose tolerance test, and consists of giving a loading dose of the disaccharide and observing whether or not a rise in the blood glucose level occurs. The interpretation of disaccharide tolerance tests must take into account the specificity of the various disaccharidases that have been identified in the small bowel mucosa of man. Dalhqvist (1962) has listed the specificity of various disaccharidases, as shown in table 60.1.

A congenital absence of lactase without intolerance to maltose or sucrose has been observed frequently. This condition is usually recognized in newborns and infants who are unable to tolerate milk. Sucrose and maltose intolerance are usually not recognized until later when these sugars are introduced into the diet. Combinations of sucrose and isomaltose intolerance have been recognized. From a study of table 61.1 it will be seen that four different maltases have been identified. Thus, maltose intolerance is extremely rare, as it requires the absence of all four of these enzymes. Such a patient would also be intolerant to isomaltose and sucrose.

ABSORPTION OF PROTEIN

It has been estimated that approximately 225 g. of protein may be absorbed per day by the small bowel of an adult man. The protein available for absorption in the small bowel has both an *exogenous* and *endogenous* origin. To maintain nitrogen balance, a 70 kg. man requires approximately 50 g. of dietary, or *exogenous*, protein per day. The source of *endogenous* protein absorbed by the small bowel is protein contained in the gastrointestinal secretions, and the protein in the desquamated epithelial cells from the lining of the gut. The protein of the secretions may amount to 150 g. per day, and that from desquamated cells 25 to 30 g. per day. Thus, the exogenous dietary protein is considerably diluted by the endogenous protein within the lumen of the small bowel.

Although some absorption of native protein and of intermediate products of protein digestion take place in the small intestine, the amount absorbed is insignificant from a nutritional standpoint. This will be discussed in more detail later. The greater part of protein in the food is reduced to amino acids before being absorbed. Protein absorption is, therefore, essentially amino acid absorption.

All available evidence indicates that amino acids are readily absorbed throughout the entire length of the small intestine. They are taken up about as rapidly as they are produced by the action of the digestive enzymes; consequently, only small amounts of amino acids can be found at any time in the intestinal contents. In fact, due to the dilution of exogenous protein previously mentioned, Nasset et al., (1955) have shown that feeding a dog a protein meal has little effect on the distribution of free amino acids in the intestinal contents that can be recovered from the lumen. Any excess of amino acids in the portal blood due to absorption disappears rapidly, so that it is difficult to trace the absorption of amino acids from the intestine by chemical means. Although all the amino acids are rapidly absorbed from the intestine, some are absorbed more rapidly than others. The following list is in the order of rapidity of absorption: glycine, alanine, cystine, glutamic

acid, valine, methionine, leucine, tryptophane, isoleucine, norleucine, and isovaline (Verzar and McDougall, 1936).

Mechanism of Amino Acid Absorption

Wiseman (1953) demonstrated that the levorotatory, or naturally occurring forms of alanine, phenylalanine, isoleucine, valine, methionine, and histidine are absorbed more rapidly than the dextrorotatory isomers, and that the levoforms could be transferred through the intestinal wall against a concentration gradient, whereas the dextro-forms tended to reach the same concentration on the two sides of the membrane (as did glutamic and aspartic acids). Eldsen and others (1950) found that if a racemic mixture of amino acids is introduced into the intestine, the levorotatory isomers were absorbed as much as six times faster than the dextro-isomers. These facts, and the fact that there are differences in the rate of absorption of amino acids that are not related to their diffusibility, as well as the rapid disappearance of amino acids from the intestine, all indicate that there is an efficient mechanism for the active absorption of many of the amino acids, and that their absorption does not depend upon diffusion and osmosis. This conclusion is further supported by the fact that amino acid absorption is inhibited by the absence of oxygen, and by several metabolic inhibitors such as dinitrophenol and desoxypyridoxine (Friedlander and Quastel, 1955). Phloridzin, which interferes with the active absorption of glucose, does not interfere with active absorption of amino acids. Nevertheless, amino acids are said to compete with sugars for the absorptive mechanism; that is, sugars are absorbed more slowly from a sugar-amino acid mixture than from a pure sugar solution (Cori, 1931).

The transport of neutral amino acids by the small bowel has been studied extensively in recent years by Wilson and others. It is now known that a number of neutral amino acids compete with each other for the same transport system through the cell membrane. The α-carbon of a neutral amino acid has four different groups attached to it: a carboxyl group, an amino group, a hydrogen ion, and a side-chain radical, usually referred to as R. An alteration in any of these groups attached to the α-carbon may interfere with the active transport of the amino acid. Thus, when the charge on the carboxyl group is removed by the formation of an ester or an alcohol, a compound is produced that is not actively transported by the small bowel. The removal of the charge of the amino group by acetylation, or by replacement of the amino group by a hydroxyl group, also results in an inactive compound. The α-hydrogen also has been shown to be essential for active transport to occur. Replacing the α-hydrogen by a methyl group reduces the rate of transport. A wide variety of side chains or radicals may be attached to the α-carbon and be actively transported. Thus, the carrier system for neutral amino acids is not selective in regard to the side chain, as long as the side chain does not contain a charge. If either a negative or positive charge is introduced into the side chain, active transport is interfered with.

The levo-forms of the basic amino acids, lysine, arginine, and ornithine, are also actively transported by the small intestine but at rates of only about one-tenth of that of most of the neutral amino acids. Like the neutral amino acids, the basic amino acids seem to share a common, but separate, transport system. Thus, any two of the above-mentioned basic amino acids will inhibit the transport of the remaining basic amino acid in the group. For some unknown reason, cystine, which is a neutral amino acid, appears to share the same transport system as the three basic amino acids.

As previously mentioned, the active transport of substances through the small bowel mucosa may involve a number of "steps." It has been demonstrated that during the process of absorption, amino acids accumulate in the mucosal cells and that their intracellular concentration may exceed that in the lumen. Thus, entry into the cell appears to be the active step. With accumulation within the cell, a favorable concentration gradient is created for diffusion out of the cell into the portal blood.

Transamination During Absorption

Most amino acids are not altered during transport through the epithelial cells lining the small bowel. However, it has been shown that glutamic acid and aspartic acid may undergo transamination with pyruvic acid so that alanine is produced and released into the portal blood. Thus, some amino acids are not necessarily delivered to the blood in the same form in which they are absorbed. In the case of glutamic and aspartic acids, it has been shown that if the absorption rate is slow, practically all the glutamic and aspartic acids undergo transamination to alanine; on the other hand, during rapid absorption, there is less transamination, and considerable

quantities of glutamic and aspartic acids appear in the blood (Neame and Wiseman, 1957). It has been suggested that in this way the intestinal mucosa can modify an amino acid mixture that is being absorbed from a particular meal, reducing the amount of amino acids that are in excess in the digesting mixture, and increasing the amount of those which are in short supply and so more nearly meet the needs of the organism for specific amino acids.

Absorption of Peptides, Proteoses, and Native Protein

Many of the intermediate products of protein digestion are soluble in water and some are diffusible. Thus, the question naturally arises as to whether peptides, proteoses, and peptones may be absorbed from the intestine without being reduced to amino acids. Peptone solutions certainly disappear from intestinal loops but this does not prove that the peptone is absorbed as such. It will be recalled that the peptidases of the intestinal secretion are believed to be intracellular enzymes, which are not actually secreted, but appear in the intestinal contents as a result of a breakdown of shed epithelial cells. It seems unlikely that peptides could get through the mucosal cell in any considerable quantity without being reduced to amino acids by the intracellular peptidases.

This same reasoning does not apply to native protein, however, which may have escaped digestion by the pepsin of gastric juice or the proteolytic enzymes of pancreatic juice for one reason or another. Except for traces of pepsin in the Brunner's gland secretion, there are no proteases in the intestinal secretion or in the mucosal cells which are known to attack native protein. Native proteins are absorbed by the small bowel by a process similar to phagocytosis known as *pinocytosis*. The absorption of native proteins by the process of pinocytosis has been demonstrated in the newborn of many mammalian species. The ability of the small bowel mucosa to absorb protein in this fashion disappears, however, from a few days to a few weeks after birth, depending upon the species. The mechanism is particularly valuable in those species that do not receive a passive immunity from the mother through the placenta. In these species, passive immunity is induced by the absorption of antibodies from the colostrum.

The adult mucosa, in all mammalian species studied, is very resistant to the absorption of native protein except in antigenic amounts.

Thus, it is not surprising to find that egg albumin and milk protein can sometimes be demonstrated in the blood by immunological methods after these proteins have been placed in the intestine. Absorption of native protein is not necessarily a result of a pathological condition of the intestinal mucosa, although the absorption may be greatly increased by an inflammatory condition. Gruskay and Cooke (1955) have found that after feeding 1 g. of crystalline egg albumin per kg. of body weight to normal children, they could detect, in the plasma of these children, between 0.45 and 7.3 µg. of egg albumin per ml. of plasma. In children recovering from diarrhea, the amount ranged from 4 to 53 µg. per ml. It seems likely that many cases of food allergy result from such absorption of native protein, either from a normal or from an inflamed intestine. Since the absorption is greater in inflammatory states, it appears that some caution is indicated in the feeding of patients suffering from enteritis.

ABSORPTION OF FAT

Dietary fat, consisting mainly of triglycerides, is insoluble in water and thus presents special problems for absorption by, and transport through, the intestinal epithelial cells. The complicated process of fat absorption is, even now, not fully understood. It is known that bile and pancreatic juice are important for normal fat absorption, yet appreciable amounts of fat can be absorbed from the intestine in the absence of both.

Although exclusion of bile from the intestine greatly reduces absorption of ordinary fat, if the fat is fed as an emulsion, ligation of the bile duct makes no significant difference in the amount of fat absorbed (Coffee et al., 1940). However, even with emulsified fat, removal of the pancreas seriously interferes with absorption (Wells et al., 1955). These observations suggest that bile is concerned in the emulsification rather than in the absorption of fat, and raises a question as to the role of the bile salts in absorption of fatty acids. The results with pancreatectomy may also suggest that hydrolysis of fat is more important than emulsification in determining total absorption.

Elaborate mechanisms exist in the intestine for splitting triglycerides into fatty acids and glycerol, and yet the fat that appears in the lymphatics after absorption is nearly all triglyceride fat, indicating that the products of fat digestion after absorption are reconstituted into neutral fat.

Theories of Fat Absorption

Efforts to explain fat absorption have been embodied in two main theories. The older, known as the *lipolytic theory*, was proposed by Pfluger in its original form, and was modified and supported by Verzar (Verzar and McDougall, 1936). The other, known as the *partition hypothesis*, was formulated by Frazer (1946). The similarities and differences between the lypolytic and partition theories of fat absorption are shown in fig. 60.3.

According to the lypolytic theory, all fat is hydrolyzed in the intestine to fatty acids and glycerol by the action of pancreatic, gastric and intestinal lipases. Prior to hydrolysis, the fat is emulsified by the action of bile and, after some hydrolysis has occurred, by soaps produced by the interaction of the liberated fatty acids with the alkali of the intestinal fluids. Since the upper duodenum is usually acid, and the ileum is only slightly alkaline, the fatty acids are insoluble in the intestine at the usual pH levels of the intestinal contents. They are made soluble, chiefly through the formation of complexes with the bile acids, glycocholic, and taurocholic acids. During absorption these complexes enter the mucosal cells, where the bile acids are split off and, for the most part, returned to the intestinal lumen. The fatty acids are recombined with glycerol to form triglycerides which are then transferred to the lymphatics. Somewhere in the process, either during absorption into the epithelial cells or during synthesis into triglycerides, phosphorylation takes place, the function of which is not clear but which is assumed to be essential to the process. Verzar leans toward the opinion that phosphorylation is essential to the resynthesis of triglycerides. According to this theory, although some fatty acid may be absorbed by way of the portal vein, the amount is negligible. No fat is absorbed directly as triglyceride.

Frazer (1946) has raised objections to the lipolytic hypothesis and presented one of his own which has come to be called the *partition hypothesis*. According to Frazer's view, bile and soap are not adequate emulsifying agents under the conditions found in the intestine, chiefly due to the acid reaction in the duodenum. However, emulsions can be formed in an acid medium, if in addition to bile, mono- and diglycerides are added to the mixture. These agents are produced by the hydrolytic action of lipases in the intestine, as steps in the process of hydrolysis of triglycerides. According to Frazer's view, the

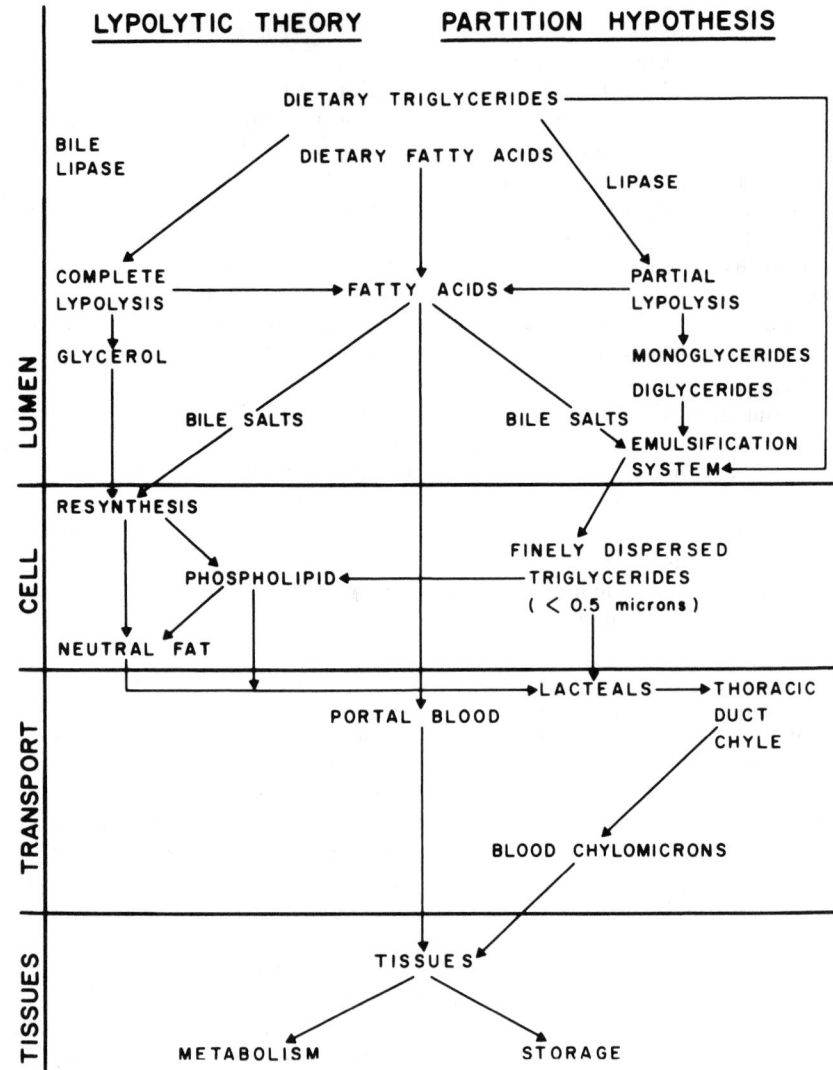

Fig. 60.3. Scheme showing similarities and differences between lipolytic and partition theories of fat absorption. From Turner, Am. J. Dig. Dis., 1958, 8, 594.

function of the lipases is mainly to form these compounds for the purpose of emulsifying the fat. Some free fatty acids are produced in the process and these are absorbed into the portal blood, after forming complexes with the bile acids as postulated by Verzar. According to Frazer, the important step in absorption is not lipolysis, but emulsification, and when the fat has been reduced to particles not exceeding 0.5 μ in diameter, they enter the epithelial cells as triglycerides and are directly transferred to the lymphatics. The small fat particles are known as *chylomicrons* and appear in the lymph and blood as such. Each chylomicron has a coating consisting of lipoprotein and phospholipid, and it may be that the phosphorylation is concerned with producing the necessary phospholipids for the formation of

chylomicrons. Resynthesis of fat in the epithelial cells is not a necessary part of the process of absorption according to this theory.

Present Concept of Triglyceride Absorption

Neither theory conforms to all the known facts but certain features of each have been well substantiated. Not all fat has to be reduced to free fatty acids and glycerol before it is absorbed. Ingested fat is rapidly, but incompletely, hydrolyzed in the upper small bowel by the action of pancreatic lipase in the presence of bile salts. Pancreatic lipase has a particular affinity for the outer [(alpha, alpha prime (α, α')] ester bonds of triglycerides producing free fatty acids and β-monoglyceride. Probably only 20 to 45 per cent of glycerides in the diet are completely hydrolyzed to free fatty acids and glycerol. Reiser and his co-workers (1952) fed animals triglyceride in which both the glycerol and fatty acids were labeled by means of appropriate isotopes. They found that only 25 to 45 per cent of the triglyceride was completely hydrolyzed. The remainder was hydrolyzed to monoglyceride and absorbed as such. Dawson and Isselbacher (1961) have also demonstrated that approximately 30 per cent of the fatty acids pass into the mucosal cells as glycerides.

The free fatty acids and monoglycerides which result from the hydrolysis of triglycerides by pancreatic lipase, combine with the conjugated bile salts present to form extremely small fat particles known as *micelles*. The micelles do not contain much tri- or di-glyceride or cholesterol. The diameter of the micelle particles varies from 40 to 200 Å. It is thought that fat in this form is presented to the epithelial surface for absorption. The exact mechanism whereby the fatty acids and monoglycerides penetrate the plasma membrane of the microvilli is not known. It is known, however, that the conjugated bile acids in the micellar dispersion are not absorbed in the upper small bowel at the site of the absorption of fatty acids and monoglycerides. The conjugated bile acids are turned back to the lumen of the gut and are re-used in the formation of new micelles.

During digestion of fat, there is synthesis as well as hydrolysis of glycerides in the intestinal lumen (Knoebel and Nasset, 1957); consequently, the triglycerides that are absorbed may have an entirely different arrangement of the fatty acids within the fat molecules than that which is fed. However, some of this redistribution probably takes place during resynthesis of triglyceride in the epithelial cells (Bergström and Borgström, 1956).

Resynthesis of fatty acids into triglycerides within the epithelial cells, as postulated by Verzar, has been abundantly confirmed by many investigators. For example, Bergström and others (1954) found that when free oleic acid labeled with C^{14} was fed, 63 per cent of the fed acid was recovered in the lymph as neutral fat. When triolein was fed, 65 per cent was recovered in the lymph. These authors also found that when fatty acids containing 10 or fewer carbon atoms were fed, they were absorbed by way of the portal blood, where they were transported mainly as free fatty acids. Longer-chain fatty acids were synthesized in the epithelial cells into triglycerides and were absorbed by way of the lymphatics. Kiyasu, Bloom and Chaikoff (1952)

also found that short-chain fatty acids were transported mainly by the portal pathway and long-chain saturated fatty acids by way of the lymph. Therefore, a sort of partition does occur in the intestine but it is not based on the degree of hydrolysis as proposed by Frazer.

It is now recognized that one of the major functions of the small bowel is the resynthesis of triglycerides from fatty acids and monoglycerides, and packaging them in the form of *chylomicrons*. The current state of knowledge regarding the intracellular resynthesis of triglycerides has been recently reviewed by Isselbacher and Senior (1964). The synthesis of triglyceride requires energy which is supplied in the form of adenosine triphosphate (ATP) from glycolysis or oxidative phosphorylation. In addition, magnesium ions and coenzyme A (CoA) are necessary. The fatty acids are first "activated" by the formation of a CoA derivative, which not only makes the fatty acids more reactive, but also water soluble. As a result of glucose breakdown, glycerophosphate is formed. The glycerophosphate combines with the activated fatty acids to form phosphataic acid, which after loss of its phosphate group becomes a diglyceride. The diglycerides are then esterified further to triglycerides, or converted to phospholipids. These events are shown diagrammatically in fig. 60.4. The direct esterification of absorbed monoglycerides to diglycerides has been suggested by Clark and Hübsher (1960). The process of forming triglycerides directly from monoglycerides has been referred to as a "monoglyceride shunt." Senior and Isselbacher (1962) have obtained evidence for the direct esterification of monoglycerides and have demonstrated the presence of a monoglyceride lipase within the epithelial cell. This lipase is distinct from pancreatic lipase and can split β-monoglycerides equally or even more readily than α-monoglycerides. It is relatively inert towards di- and triglycerides. Thus, if activated fatty acids are not available for combining with monoglycerides, the monoglycerides can be hydrolyzed into glycerol and a fatty acid.

The final step in the synthesis of triglycerides by the epithelial cells is the formation of chylomicrons for transport in the lymph. The chylomicrons are covered by a fine proteinaceous surface coating. The protein coating amounts to less than one per cent of the weight of the chylomicron. There is electron microscopic evidence that the chylomicrons are extruded from the lateral margins of the epithelial cells by a

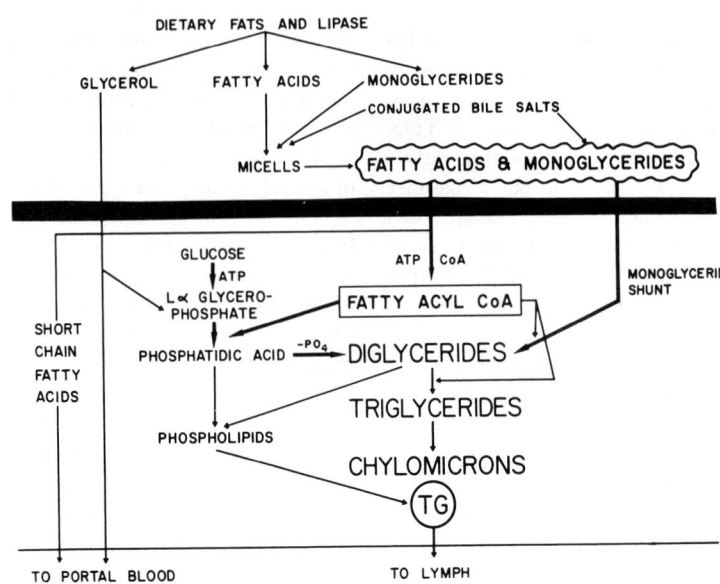

FIG. 60.4. The major biochemical pathways in the absorption and transport of fat by the intestine. From Isselbacher and Senior, Gastroenterology, 1964, **46**, 287.

process analogous to the pancreatic secretion of zymogen granules. The chylomicrons leave the epithelial cells at about the level of the nucleus, passing into the intercellular spaces. They eventually pass across the basement membrane and into the lymphatic vessels by passage between the endothelial cells.

Short-chained fatty acids absorbed by the epithelial cells are passed to the portal blood for transport to the liver. The fate of glycerol hydrolyzed in the lumen of gut during the process of digestion has been debated. From early isotope studies, Reiser and his co-workers (1952) concluded that glycerol released in the lumen of the gut during the process of digestion was not utilized in the resynthesis of triglycerides within the epithelial cells, but apparently took some other metabolic pathway. More recently, Saunders and Dawson (1962) have demonstrated that, if labeled glycerol is administered with a bile salt-fatty acid mixture, considerable incorporation of the label into lymph triglyceride glycerol occurs. Thus, apparently two sources of glycerol are available to the epithelial cell for the synthesis of triglycerides, that absorbed directly from the intestinal lumen and that available from the conversion of glucose to glycerophosphate.

Studies of the excised intestine of the rat (Smyth and Taylor, 1957) and of the golden hamster (Johnston, 1958) show that fatty acids are absorbed, or may be absorbed, by the intestinal mucous membrane against a concentration gradient and that this activity is prevented, or greatly reduced, in the absence of oxygen. There is also suppression of absorption by dinitrophenol and in the absence of glucose, but phloridzin has little effect. These observations indicate that fatty acids are absorbed by an active process which involves oxidation but not necessarily phosphorylation (the effect of phloridzin is somewhat equivocal; see Jervis, et al., 1956). Hogben (1960) has pointed out that the observed absorption of fatty acids against a concentration gradient may be due to differences in pH on each side of the membrane as a consequence of ion transport rather than some "active" process which is specific for fatty acids.

Site of Fat Absorption

It is commonly stated that fat absorption takes place most rapidly in the upper intestine, particularly in the duodenum and upper jejunum, but several recent studies have suggested that the ileum is the site of the major part of fat absorption. This may have something to do with the more alkaline reaction of this portion of the intestine. For example, Kremen and his co-workers (1954) found that, in dogs, the proximal 50 to 70 per cent of the small intestine could be removed with no apparent ill effects on food absorption, particularly fat absorption. However, if the distal 50 per cent were removed, there was a profound interference with fat absorption, associated with loss of weight; under these circumstances, from 80 to 90 per cent of the fat intake was lost in the feces. Benson and others (1956) also found that in rats that were sacrificed after a fat meal, the mucosa of the third-quarter of the intestine, as measured from the pylorus, contained a greater amount of fat apparently in processes of absorption, than did any other portion of the intestine. In similar experiments, Turner (1958) found that dogs sacrificed 3 hr. after a fat meal labeled with I^{131} triolein, demonstrated the highest residual radioactivity from the ampulla of Vater to the mid-jejunum. The experiments of Benson et al., and Turner, do not measure fat absorption directly but only residual radioactivity in the mucosa. However, fat is certainly absorbed from the upper intestine in appreciable quantities, as anyone who has opened the abdomen of an experimental animal that has recently eaten a fat meal will testify.

In man, Borgström and his associates (1957) have demonstrated that fat is absorbed mainly from the upper small bowel-duodenum and proximal jejunum. They fed a measured quantity of fat in a meal containing a nonabsorbable marker, polyethylene glycol, and sampled the intestinal contents at different levels. By comparing the concentration of intraluminal fat to the concentration of polyethylene glycol, they were able to calculate fat absorption at different levels of the small bowel and found that practically all of the fat had been absorbed by the time the meal had reached the distal jejunum.

Fat absorption is seriously impaired following bilateral adrenalectomy, due to the absence of cortical hormones. The role of the cortical hormones in fat absorption has not been clarified but it has been suggested that they play a part in the synthesis of triglycerides in the mucosal cells (Verzar). Another suggestion is that the loss of salt which follows adrenal cortical insufficiency is responsible for the poor fat absorption. This idea receives some support from the fact that fat absorption is improved in adrenalectomized animals by administration of sodium chloride solutions in adequate quantities.

Absorption of Cholesterol

Normally, about a half a gram of cholesterol is consumed each day in the diet. This dietary cholesterol is mixed with 2 to 3 g. of endogenous cholesterol within the lumen of the small bowel. The source of the endogenous cholesterol is the *bile* which may contain cholesterol in the amount of 1.5 to 2.5 g. per day, and from *desquamated epithelial cells* which may contain up to a half a gram of cholesterol per day. Thus, the small

bowel normally absorbs $2\frac{1}{2}$ to 3 g. of cholesterol per day. Only about one-fifth or one-sixth of this amount is represented by the dietary cholesterol. Borgström (1960) has demonstrated that cholesterol absorption in man occurs at higher rates in the upper small bowel than in the lower small bowel. He used a cholesterol labeled with radioactive carbon and determined its rate of disappearance from various levels of the small bowel. It has long been known that cholesterol absorption differs from fat absorption in a number of important respects. Only 40 to 60 per cent of dietary cholesterol is absorbed, as opposed to the absorption of 95 per cent of dietary fat. When radioactive cholesterol is administered as a single dose orally, and the radioactivity of the venous blood is determined, it is found that the peak radioactivity does not appear until 2 to 3 days later (Biggs, et al., 1952). When a similar study is done using radioactive fat, peak blood radioactivity is usually found 3 to 4 hr. after the oral dose. Although cholesterol probably enters the intestinal epithelium at a rate comparable to that of fat, once inside the cell, it is accumulated and released very slowly. This accounts for the delay in appearance of labeled cholesterol in the blood.

Bile is essential for cholesterol absorption, and pancreatic juice also plays an important role. If bile is diverted from the intestinal tract, cholesterol is not absorbed. (Siperstein et al., 1952). If pancreatic juice is diverted from the intestinal tract, the absorption of cholesterol is markedly reduced. Fats in the diet appear to stimulate cholesterol absorption. Vahouny (1958) found that optimal absorption of cholesterol occurred from a mixture of fatty acid, taurocholate, and cholesterol, in which the molar concentrations were in the ratios of 8, 4, and 1 respectively. Kim and Ivy (1952), in studying cholesterol absorption in rats, found that if the diet contained 24 parts of fat to one part of cholesterol, significant stimulation of cholesterol absorption occurred. They also found that fatty acids markedly stimulated the absorption of cholesterol. The stimulatory effect of triglycerides may be due to the fact that they provide a source of fatty acids, through the hydrolysis of fat by pancreatic lipase.

Most of the cholesterol in the diet is in the form of esters, but in the small bowel these esters are hydrolyzed by a cholesterol esterase present in pancreatic juice. Cholesterol esters are not absorbed as readily as free cholesterol. However, once absorbed, cholesterol is again esterified, and approximately two-thirds of the cholesterol appearing in the lymph is in the esterified form. Hellman and his colleagues (1960) have made some interesting observations in man, and found that when the thoracic duct was cannulated, and radioactive cholesterol was given by mouth, the dietary cholesterol was largely transported through the lymphatics after absorption, and the major portion was esterified during the absorptive process.

The exact mechanism by which cholesterol crosses the cell membrane barrier is not known, but as Wilson (1962) has pointed out, in our present state of knowledge it seems unnecessary to postulate any mechanism of entrance into the epithelial cell other than simple diffusion of cholesterol through solution in the lipid portion of the membrane. Once inside the cell, cholesterol is slowly esterified, then released for transport via the lymphatic to the thoracic duct.

Absorption of Vitamins

The *water soluble vitamins* are assumed to be freely absorbed by the intestinal mucosa, along with the other constituents of the foods in which they occur. It is generally believed that thiamin is less readily absorbed by older people than by young people in good health. This may be applicable also to some of the other vitamins and provides the basis for administration of vitamin supplements in the dietary of older people.

Absorption of *fat soluble vitamins*, particularly vitamins D and K, probably takes place under the same conditions as the absorption of fat. In any disease or dietary deficiency in which fat absorption is inadequate, the absorption of these vitamins is apt to be impaired. This is demonstrated by the deficient absorption of vitamin K in obstructive jaundice. A deficiency of this vitamin causes inadequate prothrombin production by the liver and a tendency to hemorrhage, hence jaundiced patients are apt to bleed on the operating table. This situation is remedied by the parenteral administration of vitamin K over a period of time, preoperatively, until the prothrombin level is normal. Absorption of vitamin E is also said to be impaired in the absence of bile.

Vitamin A is absorbed chiefly in the form of esters of the vitamin A alcohol with fatty acids. The esters are hydrolyzed in the intestinal lumen but are re-esterified in the epithelial cells. This mechanism parallels the one that is supposed to operate in the absorption of fat; it is not surprising, therefore, to find that the conditions that favor fat absorption also favor absorption of vitamin A. The presence of bile in the intestine apparently is necessary for the absorption of carotene, a precursor of vitamin A, but not for vitamin A itself. The absorption of the fat-soluble vitamins is adversely effected by the presence in the intestine of unabsorbable oil, such as mineral oil; it is therefore necessary to pay particular attention to the supply of these vitamins if mineral oil is to be administered in any considerable quantity over a period of time.

Absorption of vitamin B_{12}, which is essential for normal red-cell production, and perhaps for cell division in general, presents special problems. Although it is absorbed from the intestine, its absorption takes place only in the presence of a certain constituent of the gastric juice known, for want of a better name, as *intrinsic factor*. There may also be some intrinsic factor in duodenal secretion. This name comes down to us from the days when vitamin B_{12} itself was unknown (ch. 30).

The principle site of absorption of vitamin B_{12} in the rat has been found to be in the upper and midportion of the ileum. In man, however, evidence suggests that the lower ileum is the primary site of vitamin B_{12} absorption. Cooper and Castle (1960), as a result of studies with gastrectomized rats, have proposed that the mechanism of absorption of vitamin B_{12} consists of three phases. The first phase is a non-specie-related competitive binding of dietary B_{12} by intrinsic factor. The second phase consists of the absorption of the intrinsic factor bound B_{12} by the intestinal mucosa. This phase is dependent upon the presence of a divalent cation, preferentially calcium. The third phase is a species-related conversion of the Ca^{++} dependent bond and release of free vitamin B_{12} at the surface of, or within, the mucosal cell, possibly as a result of enzymatic action. The free B_{12} will then be accepted by an appropriate transport mechanism or will simply diffuse passively into the blood vessels of the intestine.

REFERENCES

Abbott, W. O. and Miller, T. G. Intubation studies of the human small intestine. J.A.M.A., 1936, **106**, 16.

Benson, J. A., Jr., Chandler, G. M., Vansteen-Huyse, F. E., and Gagnon, J. O. Studies concerning the site of fat absorption from the small intestine of the rat. Gastroenterology, 1956, **30**, 53.

Bergström, S., Blomstrand, R., and Borgström, B. Route of absorption and distribution of oleic acid and triolein. Biochem. J., 1954, **58**, 600. (See also Bergström and Borgström, Ann. Rev. Biochem., 1956, **25**, 177)

Biggs, M. W., Kritchevsky, D., Colman, D.,

GOFMAN, J. W., JONES, H. B., LINDGREN, F. T., HYDE, G., AND LYON, T. P. Observations on the fate of ingested cholesterol in man. Circulation, 1952, 6, 359.

BIHLER, I., HAWKINS, K. A., AND CRANE, R. K. Studies on the mechanism of intestinal absorption of sugars. VI. The specificity and other properties of Na ion-dependent entrance of sugars into intestinal tissue and under anaerobic conditions, *in vitro*. Biochim. Biophys. Acta, 1962, 59, 94.

BLICKENSTAFF, D. D., BACHMAN, D. M., STEINBERG, M. E., AND YOUMANS, W. B. Intestinal absorption of sodium chloride solutions as influenced by intraluminal pressure and concentration. Am. J. Physiol., 1952, 168, 303.

BLICKENSTAFF, D. D., GROSSMAN, M. I., AND IVY, A. C. Stimulating effect of fat and meat meals on duodenal secretion in the dog. Am. J. Physiol., 1949, 158, 122.

BOLDYREFF, W. N. (1904); Diss. St. Petersburg. (Cited by Babkin, 1927).

BOLDYREFF, W. N. Die Lipase des Darmsaftes und ihre Charakteristik. Hoppe Seyler's Ztschn. physiol. Chem., 1912, 50, 394. (Cited by Babkin, 1927).

BORGSTRÖM, B. Studies on intestinal cholesterol absorption in the human. J. Clin. Invest., 1960, 39, 809.

BORGSTRÖM, B., DAHLQVIST, A., LUNDH, G., AND SJOVALL, J. Studies of intestinal digestion and absorption in the human. J. Clin. Invest., 1957, 36, 1521.

BORGSTRÖM, B., LINDHE, B.-Å., AND WOLDAWER, A. Absorption and distribution of cholesterol-4-C14 in the rat. Proc. Soc. Exper. Biol. & Med., 1958, 99, 365.

CLARK, B. AND HÜBSCHER, G. Biosynthesis of glycerides in the mucosa of the small intestine. Nature, 1960, 185, 35.

COFFEE, R. J., MANN, F. C., AND BOLLMAN, J. L. The effect of exclusion of bile on the absorption of foodstuffs. Am. J. Digest. Dis., 1940, 7, 144.

COOPER, B. A. AND CASTLE, W. B. Sequential mechanisms in the enhanced absorption of vitamin B12 by intrinsic factor in the rat. J. Clin. Invest., 1960, 39, 199.

CRANE, R. K. Hypothesis for mechanism of intestinal active transport of sugars. Fed. Proc., 1962, 21, 891.

CRANE, R. K. AND MANDELSTAM, P. The active transport of sugars by various preparations of hamster intestine. Biochem. Biophys. Acta, 1960, 45, 460.

CRANE, R. K., MILLER, D., AND BIHLER, I. The restrictions on possible mechanisms of intestinal active transport of sugars, in Membrane Transport and Metabolism Symposium (ed. KLEINZELLER, A. AND KOTYK, A.) Prague, Publishing House of the Czechoslovak Academy of Science, 1961, pp. 439–449.

CROSBY, W. H. A concept of the pathogenesis of anemia applied to disorders of the intestinal mucosa. Am. J. Digest. Dis., 1961, 6, 492.

DAHLQVIST, A. Specificity of human intestinal disaccharidases and implications for hereditary disaccharide intolerance. J. Clin. Invest., 1962, 41, 463.

DAHLQVIST, A. The intestinal disaccharidases and disaccharide intolerance. Gastroenterology, 1962, 43, 694.

DAWSON, A. M. AND ISSELBACHER, K. J. Fat absorption. A.M.A. Arch. Int. Med., 1961, 107, 305.

DEBEER, E. J., JOHNSTON, C. G., AND WILSON, D. W. Composition of intestinal secretions. J. Biol. Chem., 1935, 108, 113.

DELENZENNE, C. AND FROUIN, A. La sécrétion physiologique du suc intestinal. Action l'acide chlorhydrique sur le sécrétion duodenale. Comp. rend. Soc. biol., 1904, 56, 319. (Cited by Babkin, 1950; see also Agren, 1934).

ELDSEN, S. R., GIBSON, Q. H., AND WISEMAN, G. Selective absorption of amino acids from the small intestine of the rat. J. Physiol., 1950, 11, 56.

ERSPAMER, V. AND ASERO, B. Identification of enteramine, the specific hormone of the enterochromaffin system as 5-hydroxytryptamine. Nature, London, 1952, 169, 800.

FIELD, H., JR., SERVELL, L., DAILEY, R. E., TROUT, E. C., AND BOYD, R. S. Electrolyte changes in ileal contents and in feces during restrictions of dietary sodium with and without the administration of cation exchange resins. Circulation, 1955, 12, 625.

FISHER, R. B. AND PARSONS, D. S. Glucose absorption from surviving rat small intestine. J. Physiol., 1949, 110, 281.

FLOREY, H. Secretion of mucus by the colon. Brit. J. Exper. Path., 1930, 11, 348.

FLOREY, H. W. AND HARDING, H. E. The functions of Brunner's glands and the pyloric end of the stomach. J. Path. and Bact., 1933, 37, 431.

FLOREY, H. W. AND HARDING, H. E. Further observations on the secretion of Brunner's glands. J. Path. and Bact., 1934, 39, 255.

FLOREY, H. W. AND HARDING, H. E. The nature of the hormone controlling Brunner's glands. Quart. J. Exper. Physiol., 1935a, 25, 329.

FLOREY, H. W. AND HARDING, H. E. Humoral control of secretion of Brunner's glands. Proc. Roy. Soc., London, ser. B., 1935b, 117, 68.

FRIEDLANDER, L. AND QUASTEL, H. H. Absorption of amino acids from isolated surviving intestine. Arch. Biochem., 1955, 56, 424.

GRUSKAY, F. L. AND COOKE, R. E. The gastrointestinal absorption of native protein in normal infants and in infants recovering from diarrhea. Pediatrics, 1955, 16, 763.

HELLMAN, L., FRAZELL, E. L., AND ROSENFELD, R. S. Direct measurement of cholesterol absorption via the thoracic duct in man. J. Clin. Invest., 1960, 39, 1288.

HOGBEN, C. A. M. The alimentary tract. Ann. Rev. Physiol., 1960, 22, 381.

INGRAHAM, R. C. AND VISSCHER, M. B. The production of chloride-free solutions by the action of the intestinal epithelium. Am. J. Physiol., 1936, 114, 667.

INGRAHAM, R. C. AND VISSCHER, R. B. Further studies on intestinal absorption with performance of osmotic work. Am. J. Physiol., 1938, 121, 77.

ISSELBACHER, K. J. AND SENIOR, J. R. The intestinal absorption of carbohydrate and fat. Gastroenterology, 1964, **46**, 287.

IVY, A. C., FARRELL, J. I., AND LUETH, H. C. Contributions to the physiology of the pancreas. III. A hormone for external pancreatic secretion. Am. J. Physiol., 1927, **82**, 27. (See also Nassett et al. 1935, and Florey and Harding, 1935a and b.)

JERVIS, E. L., JOHNSON, F. R., SCHEFF, M. F., AND SMYTH, D. H. The effect of phlorhizin on intestinal absorption and intestinal phosphatase. J. Physiol., 1956, **134**, 674.

JOHNSTON, J. M. An *in vitro* study of fatty acid absorption. J. Physiol., 1958, **134**, 675.

KIM, K. S. AND IVY, A. C. Factors influencing cholesterol absorption. Am. J. Physiol., 1952, **171**, 302.

KINTER, W. B. in Proc. 12th Ann. Conf. Nephrotic Syndrome (ed. by J. METCOFF). National Kidney Disease Foundation. New York, 1961, p. 59.

KIYASU, J. Y., BLOOM, B., AND CHAIKOFF, I. L. The portal transport of absorbed fatty acid. J. Biol. Chem., 1952, **199**, 415.

KNOEBEL, L. K. AND NASSET, E. S. The digestion and absorption of fat in dog and man. J. Nutrition, 1957, **61**, 405.

KREMEN, A. J., LINNER, J. H., AND NELSON, C. H. An experimental evaluation of the nutritional importance of proximal and distal small intestine. Ann. Surg., 1954, **140**, 439.

LARSON, L. M. AND BARGEN, J. A. Action of cathartics on isolated dog's colon. Arch. Surg., 1933, **27**, 1120.

LEBLOND, C. P. AND STEVENS, C. E. The constant renewal of the intestinal epithelium in the albino rat. Anat. Rec., 1948, **100**, 357.

McHARDY, G. J. R. AND PARSONS, D. R. The absorption of water and salt from the small intestine of the rat. Quart. J. Exper. Physiol., 1957, **42**, 33.

MILLER, D. AND CRANE, R. K. The digestive function of the epithelium of the small intestine. I. An intracellular locus of disaccharide and sugar phosphate ester hydrolysis. Biochim. Biophys. Acta, 1961, **52**, 281.

MILLER, D. AND CRANE, R. K. The digestive function of the epithelium of the small intestine. II. Localization of disaccharide hydrolysis in the isolated brush border portion of intestinal epithelial cells. Biochim. Biophys. Acta, 1961, **52**, 293.

MILLER, T. G. AND ABBOTT, W. O. Intestinal intubation: a practical technique. Am. J. M. Sc., 1934, **187**, 595. (See also Abbott and Miller, 1936).

NASSET, E. S. Enterocrinin, a hormone which excites the glands of the small intestine. Am. J. Physiol., 1938, **121**, 481. (See also Schiffrin and Nasset, 1939.)

NASSET, E. S. AND PARRY, A. A. Passage of fluid and certain dissolved substances through the intestinal mucosa as influenced by changes in hydrostatic pressure. Am. J. Physiol., 1934, **109**, 615.

NASSET, E. S., PIERCE, H. B., AND MURLIN, J. R. Proof of a humoral control of intestinal secretion. Am. J. Physiol., 1935, **111**, 145.

NASSET, E. S., SCHWARTZ, P., AND WEISS, H. V. The digestion of proteins *in vivo*. J. Nutrition, 1955, **56**, 83.

NEAME, K. D. AND WISEMAN, G. The transamination of glutamic and aspartic acids during absorption by the small intestine in the dog *in vivo*. J. Physiol., 1957, **135**, 442. (See also J. Physiol., **124**, 414).

OLSON, T. E. AND GRAY, S. J. Serotonin and gastroenterology. Am. J. Gastroenterology, 1958 **29**, 280.

RABINOVITCH, J. Factors influencing absorption of water and chlorides from the intestine. Am. J. Physiol., 1927, **82**, 279.

REISER, R., BRYSON, M. J., CARR, M. J., AND KNIFEN, K. A. The intestinal absorption of triglycerides. J. Biol. Chem., 1952, **194**, 131.

SALASKIN, S. S. Über das Vorkommen des Peptons bzw. albumosenspaltenden Ferments (Erepsin von Conheim) in reinen. Darmsaft vom Hunde. Hoppe Seyler's Ztschr. f. Physiol. Chem., 1902, **35**, 419 (Cited by FLOREY et al. 1941). (See also Kutscher and Seeman, 1902).

SAUNDERS, D. R. AND DAWSON, A. M. Studies on the metabolism of glycerol by the small intestine *in vitro* and *in vivo*. Biochem. J., 1962, **82**, 477.

SAVICH, V. V. The secretion of intestinal juice. Thesis, 1904. St. Petersburg. (Cited by BABKIN, 1950).

SAVICH, V. V. AND SOCHENSTVENSKY, N. A. L'influence du nerf vague sur la sécrétion de l'intestin. Comp. rend. Soc. biol., 1917, **80**, 508 (Cited by BABKIN, 1927).

SCHOLER, J. F. AND CODE, C. F. Rate of absorption of water from stomach and small bowel of human beings. Gastroenterology, 1954, **27**, 568.

SENIOR, J. R. AND ISSELBACHER, K. J. Direct esterification of monoglycerides with palmityl coenzyme A by intestinal epithelial subcellular fractions. J. Biol. Chem., 1962, **237**, 1545.

SIPERSTEIN, M. D., CHAIKOFF, I. L. AND RAINHARDT, W. O. C^{14} cholesterol. 5. Obligatory function of bile in intestinal absorption of cholesterol. J. Biol. Chem., 1952, **198**, 111.

SMYTH, D. H. AND TAYLOR, C. B. Transfer of water and solutes by an *in vitro* intestinal preparation. J. Physiol., 1957, **136**, 632.

SONNENSCHEIN, R. R., GROSSMAN, M. I., AND IVY, A. C. The humoral regulation of Brunner's glands. Acta med. scandinav., 1947, **28** (supp. 196), 296.

SPERRY, W. M. AND BLOOR, W. R. Fat excretion; quantitative relations of fecal lipoids. J. Biol. Chem., 1924, **60**, 261.

THIRY, L. Eine neue Methode den Dünndarm zu isoleiren. Sitzungsber, Akad. Wiss. Wien., Math.-Naturw. Kl., Vol. 1 (S. 77), 1864, p. 50. (Cited by BABKIN, 1927).

TURNER, D. A. The absorption, transport, and deposition of fat. Application of a new method for the determination of I^{131} lipid activity in dogs and man. I. Am. J. Digest. Dis., 1958, **3**, 495.

VAHOUNY, G. V. Quantitative effect of bile salt and fatty acid on cholesterol absorption. Am. J. Physiol., 1958, **193**, 41.

VELLA, L. Untersuch. Naturl. Mensch. Tiere.

1888, **13,** 40 & 432. (Cited by Florey et al., 1941).

Visscher, M. B., Fetcher, E. S., Jr., Carr, C. W., Gregor, H. P., Bushey, M. S., and Barker, D. E. Isotope tracer studies on movement of water and ions between intestinal lumen and blood. Am. J. Physiol., 1944, **142,** 550.

Waldschmidt-Leitz, E. and Harteneck, A. Zur Kenntnis der spontanen Activierung des Tryspins. Hoppe Seyler's Ztschr. Physiol. Chem., 1925, **149,** 221.

Wells, M. H., Shingleton, W. W., and Sanders, A. P. Absorption in dogs following exclusion of bile and pancreatic juice using I^{131} labeled fat. Proc. Soc. Exper. Biol. & Med., 1955, **90,** 717.

Wilson, T. H. and Wiseman, G. The use of sacs of everted small intestine for the study of the transference of substances from the mucosal to the serosal surface. J. Physiol., 1954, **123,** 116.

Wiseman, G. Active sterochemically selective absorption of amino acids from rat small intestine. J. Physiol., 1951, **114,** 7. (See also J. Physiol. 1953, **120,** 63.)

Wright, R. D., Florey, H. W., and Jennings, M. A. The secretion of the colon of the cat. Quart. J. Exper. Physiol., 1938, **28,** 207.

Wright, R. D., Jennings, M. A., Florey, H. W., and Lium, R. The influence of nerves and drugs on secretion by the small intestine and an investigation of the enzymes in intestinal juice. Quart. J. Exper. Physiol., 1940, **30,** 73.

Zetterqvist, H. The ultrastructural organization of the columnal absorbing cells of the mouse jejunum. Stockholm, Karolinska Institute, Aktiebolaget Godvil, 1956.

Monographs and Reviews

Babkin, B. P. Die Sekretorische Tatigkeir der Verdauungsdrüsen. Handbuch der normalen und pathologischen Physiologie 3, 589. Springer-Verlag, Berlin, 1927.

Babkin, B. P. Secretory mechanism of the digestive glands. Paul B. Hoeber, New York, 1950.

Bergström, S. and Borgström. B. Metabolism of lipids; under "Digestion and absorption." Annual Rev. Biochem., 1956, **25,** 177.

Cantarow, A. and Shepartz, B. Biochemistry. p. 384, W. B. Saunders Company, Philadelphia, 1954.

Cori, C. F. Mammalian carbohydrate metabolism. Physiol. Rev., 1931, **11,** 143.

Florey, H. W., Wright, R. D., and Jennings, M. A. The secretions of the intestine. Physiol. Rev., 1941, **21,** 36.

Frazer, A. C. The absorption of triglyceride fat from the intestine. Physiol. Rev., 1946, **26,** 103.

Granick, S. Ferritin, its properties and significance for iron metabolism. Chem. Rev., 1946, **38,** 379.

Granick, S. Structure and physiological functions of ferritin. Physiol. Rev., 1951, **31,** 489.

Grossman, M. I. Gastrointestinal hormones. Physiol. Rev., 1950, **30,** 33.

Leblond, C. P. and Walker, B. E. Renewal of cell populations. Physiol. Rev., 1956, **36,** 255.

Nasset, E. S. in Bard's Medical Physiology, 10th ed., p. 532, C. V. Mosby Co., St. Louis, 1956.

Sheehy, T. W. and Floch, M. H. The small intestine; its functions and disease. Hoeber Medical Division, Harper and Row, New York, 1964.

Starling, E. H. Recent advances in the physiology of digestion. A. Constable Company, London, 1906. (Cited by Babkin, 1950.)

Verzar, F. and McDougall, E. Absorption from the intestine. Longmans, Green and Company, London, New York, 1936.

Wilson, T. H. Intestinal absorption. W. B. Saunders Company, Philadelphia, 1962.

CHAPTER 61

Movements of the Alimentary Canal

From a clinical standpoint, disturbances of motility of the alimentary canal account for more symptoms of gastroenterologic disorders than alterations in absorptive or secretory mechanisms. Gastrointestinal motility is frequently disturbed by disease of the digestive tract. In fact, most of the major diseases of the digestive tract are manifested by a disturbance of motor activity. Dysphagia, vomiting, retching, crampy abdominal pain, diarrhea, and constipation are examples of symptoms produced by altered motility.

The development of new methods within recent years for studying motor activity in the intact man has provided new knowledge of motor activity in health and disease, as well as an opportunity to study the effects of drugs on motor functions. Techniques for the accurate and continuous recording of gastrointestinal intraluminal pressure and the development of cinefluoroscopy are two important methods frequently used to study motor activity.

Methods for recording intraluminal pressure usually employ small, open-tipped catheters that are water-filled and connected externally to a sensitive pressure transducer. The signal from the pressure transducer may be displayed on an oscilloscope, recorded after amplification by various direct writing recorders, or it may be used to energize a sensitive string galvanometer and a photographic record obtained. The recording of intraluminal pressure has been of particular value in studying esophageal motility.

Cinefluoroscopic equipment is now available which makes it possible to observe the transport of opaque material through the alimentary canal for prolonged periods without exposing the patient or the operator to excessive levels of radiation. In addition, it is possible to display the intensified fluoroscopic image on a closed circuit television system and simultaneously record the image on movie film.

Mastication

The first mechanical process to which the food is subjected in its progress through the alimentary tract is mastication, or chewing, which serves to break down the food particles into smaller masses, to enable the saliva to lubricate and moisten dry food, and to distribute the salivary constituents throughout the food mass. The decrease in the size of the food particles is accomplished by the action of the teeth through the movements of the lower jaw. The moistening is accomplished by the addition of saliva to the food and lubrication is due to the mucus secreted by the salivary glands. Starch digestion in the mouth by the salivary amylase is unimportant but the presence of food in the mouth gives rise to stimuli which serve to initiate reflexes that are important in the later stages of digestion. This relationship has been discussed in connection with the reflex phase of gastric secretion (ch. 57).

The importance of mastication as a health measure has been the subject of considerable discussion, much of it speculative. The experiments of Erik Becker (1927) are among the few efforts to obtain scientific information on the subject. He undertook to determine the completeness of digestion and absorption of protein, fat, carbohydrate and minerals in a patient by studying the losses of these various substances in the stool. He studied his patient during a period of time when her teeth were in very poor condition and not satisfactory for chewing, then again after her teeth had been removed and before she had been fitted with a prosthesis, and finally after she had been fitted with a good set of false teeth which enabled her to chew satisfactorily. There were no significant differences in the three sets of data. For example, when the patient had no teeth she lost in her stool, 15.2 per cent of the ingested protein, 5.2 per cent of the ingested fat, 4.2 per cent of the ingested carbohydrate, and 25.9 per cent of the ingested minerals. After being fitted with false teeth, the corresponding figures were 16.0 per cent for protein, 5.4 per cent for fat, 5.2 per cent for carbohydrate, and 25.9 per cent for minerals. The total calories lost were 6 per cent with no teeth and 6.7 per cent after being fitted with teeth. These experiments are open to the criticism that no observations had been made when the patient had a good set of natural teeth. These might have given better results.

The movements of the lower jaw in chewing are brought about by the muscles of mastication, which include the masseter, the temporal muscles, and the internal and external pterygoid muscles; all of which receive their nerve supply from the mandibular division of the trigeminal nerve. The buccinator muscle, which may also be considered a muscle of mastication, is supplied by the facial nerve. Through the action of the jaw muscle, the mandible may be moved in any one of several directions. Simple closing of the mouth, as in biting or crushing food, is accomplished by the combined action of the masseter, temporal and internal pterygoid muscles. Opening the mouth is accomplished by the action of the relatively weak digastric and myloid muscles and is aided by gravity. The grinding movements of the molar teeth are accomplished by a rotational movement of the jaw, resulting from contraction of the pterygoid muscles of one side. Contraction of the right pterygoid muscles, causes protrusion of the right half of the mandible, whereas the left half remains relatively stationary. This results in a rotational movement with the lower teeth on one side sliding over the upper teeth of the same side. The jaw is returned to midposition and then rotated to the opposite side by contraction of the left pterygoid muscles. This kind of chewing is accomplished by the alternate contraction of the right and left pterygoid muscles. When all four pterygoid muscles contract, protrusion of the jaw results. Retraction of the jaw is accomplished by contraction of the posterior fibers of the temporal muscles and the geinohyoid muscles.

Apparently, the force of the bite is limited by the sensitivity of the peridental membrane and not necessarily by the power of the muscles of mastication. In the human, the molars have been observed to exert a pressure in excess of 270 pounds (122+ kg.) (Black, 1895). The pressure exerted by the incisor teeth is necessarily less, due to the lesser mechanical advantage in this location. According to Howell and Manly (1948), pressure exerted by the incisors ranges from 11 to 25 kg. These authors found a force of 29 to 90 kg. for the molars. A dog, when chewing bones, may exert a force as great as 165 kg. (Trisca, 1924).

Chewing may be carried on voluntarily but for the most part it is a reflex act. The dual nature of the nervous mechanism is indicated by the fact that chewing movements may be elicited by electrical stimulation of appropriate areas of the cerebral cortex (Ferrier, 1886; Magoun and

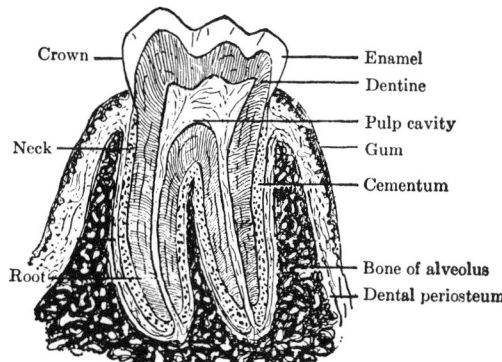

FIG. 61.1. Section through a molar tooth.

others, 1933), as well as by sensory stimulation of the mouth in decerebrate animals (Sherrington 1917; Bazett and Penfield, 1922). Magnus (1945) reports that there is a center in the medulla which mediates rhythmic movements of the jaw in response to stimulation of receptors in the mouth, but that this center is dominated by a thalamocortical center which is responsible for the finer regulation of the movements. Efficient chewing is accomplished only when the higher centers are functioning.

THE FORM AND STRUCTURE OF THE TEETH

A tooth consists of a *crown*, a *neck*, and a *root*. The crown is the part projecting beyond the gum; the root fits into the socket or *alveolus* of the jaw bone. The neck is the junction between crown and root, and normally, lies just below the gum. Three kinds of tissue, *enamel*, *dentine*, and *cementum*, compose the hard portion of the tooth. The cavity occupying the center is filled with a soft substance, the *pulp*, which is composed of connective tissue fibers and a gelatinous matrix where the nerves and blood vessels are embedded (fig. 61.1).

The enamel, which is of epithelial origin, is a white, translucent, very hard material—the hardest in the body. It is composed of calcium salts (95 per cent) in the form of apatite crystals (ch. 77), with from 3 to 5 per cent of organic material. Its structure consists of thin prisms or rods running through its entire depth, perpendicular to, and resting on, the dentin; the prisms are cemented together by protein material, or a material containing protein. The dentine surrounds the pulp cavity except at the apex of the root, where the nerves and vessels enter; it resembles bone chemically and structurally, but is harder, and contains numerous canaliculi (the *dentinal tubules*) which radiate from the pulp cavity. In the pulp lying against the dentine are large elongated cells with a radial and epithelium-like arrangement; they are called *odontoblasts* and send fine processes (fibers of Tomes) into the overlying dentinal tubules. The cementum surrounds the root outside the dentine; it is a bony material, but lacks Haversian canals, except in old age. It is penetrated by bundles of coarse fibers (Sharpey's fibers) derived from the *periodontal membrane;* this membrane lines the alveolus, for which it serves as periosteum, and acts as a close bond between the cementum and the bone. Bone cells are embedded in the cementum near the apex of the root. The viability of the cementum is dependent upon the integrity of the periodontal membrane; it undergoes necrosis when the latter is destroyed.

Like bone, tooth structure is in a continuous state of flux; minerals, calcium and phosphorus being continually removed and replaced.

Dental Decay, or Dental Caries

Calcium salts, which constitute such a large proportion of dental tissue, are soluble in acid; an increase in the acidity of the saliva was thought, therefore, to favor decalcification of the teeth, and in this way prepare them for the inroads of micro-organisms. But the saliva is normally slightly acid, and any significant increase in its acidity has not resulted in caries (Geis).

Bacterial decomposition of carbohydrate food with the production of lactic acid, especially in regions where food is likely to collect, such as in crevices between the teeth and at the margin between the tooth and gum, has long been recognized as an important element in tooth decay. Sugar, especially if highly refined, is undoubtedly potent in increasing susceptibility to the disease. Sugar has been shown to facilitate the penetration of the H-ion into the enamel.

Another local factor which has been suggested as predisposing to caries is the mucin content of the saliva. A juice rich in mucin flows less freely, and as a result of its high viscosity is less likely to penetrate into, and flush out, the smaller crevices where micro-organisms lurk and flourish upon food debris. Mucin may also encourage decay by forming a tenacious coating upon a sheltered surface of the tooth and thus serve to protect underlying bacteria from the action of the saliva.

The investigations of Pincus suggest that decalcification of the teeth by acid is of less importance than an attack upon the organic substance of the enamel by proteolytic bacteria.

Such a process had been suggested earlier by Hines. Pincus claims that digestion of the protein material permits the enamel prisms to fall apart, and this occurs apparently without a preliminary production of acid. Sulfuric acid liberated by the hydrolysis of chondroitin sulfate, according to Pincus, causes decalcification of the enamel, secondarily. Atkinson and Matthews agree that the primary point of attack is upon the organic matrix of the enamel, but that decalcification of both enamel and dentine is produced by the liberation of aspartic and glutamic acids. They found some 18 amino acids present in normal dentine, including aspartic and glutamic acids. These two amino acids were found in the free state in carious dentine, but not in healthy dentine. The brown discoloration of carious teeth is due to a melanin which is thought to be formed by the oxidation of tyrosine by proteolytic bacteria.

The researches of M. Mellanby on the teeth of dogs suggest that, in some cases at least, the structure of the teeth themselves, as in maldevelopment or an inherently poor tooth structure, or in dietary deficiencies (especially of vitamin D), may play a part in the occurrence of the disease. Contrary to the general belief, caries in wild animals is not uncommon. It starts, with few exceptions, in the dentine or cementum of the root, where this has become bare, and not in the enamel. The decay is most likely to occur in situations where food tends to pack and stagnate. In both domestic animals and animals in captivity, caries is much commoner, and the first signs of decay appear in the enamel, as in man. A survey of some 280 wild animals belonging to 60 different species was made by Sprawson, and the tooth enamel compared with that in human teeth. The structure of the animal enamel was found to be less dense, less fully calcified, and, on the average, of poorer quality than that of human enamel, a finding which, taken in conjunction with the less common occurrence of caries in wild animals, suggests a dietary factor in the production of the disease in man.

The beneficial effects of small amounts of fluorine upon tooth structure have received much of attention since Dean and his associates pointed out the low incidence of caries in districts where there was evidence of high concentrations (over 1 part per million) of fluorine in the drinking water. Excessively high concentrations of fluorine in the drinking water cause mottling of the enamel. Fluorine has also been shown to inhibit acid production by the *Lactobacillus acidophilus,* and in a concentration of 0.5 to 1 part per million, to be protective against dental caries. Another possible action of fluoride is to reduce the solubility of the enamel by acid. Stannous fluoride is more effective as a preventive than the sodium salt. From the dental examination of some 7,000 children in over 20 American cities it was found that the incidence of caries was inversely related to the concentration of fluorine in the drinking water. Mottling of the enamel does not occur in concentrations below 1 part in a million.

A curious condition known as *dermeus*, occurring in domestic animals and man, is seen in North Africa, and is attributed to a high concentration of calcium fluoride in the drinking water. It is characterizied by dystrophy of the second dentition. Kilborn has also reported the endemic occurrence of a severe arthritis and spondylitis in a region of Southwest China, which apparently is induced by the drinking of water rich in fluoride.

It is quite evident that the problem of dental caries is not a simple one. Several factors are involved in their production and much work must be done before the details of their actions are known and the relative value of each can be appraised. But from the point of view of prevention the most valuable measures are the curtailment of sugar in the diet and the addition of fluoride to the drinking water in those communities in which the latter has a low concentration of this element.

Deglutition

Magendie (1838) described the act of swallowing as occurring in three stages which he described as follows: "For the better understanding of the subject we shall divide deglutition into three stages. In the first the aliments pass from the mouth into the pharynx; in the second they pass over the opening of the glottis and nasal fossae and arrive at the esophagus; in the third they pass through this canal into the stomach." It is convenient to refer to Magendie's first stage as the oral stage, the second stage as the pharyngeal stage, and the third as the esophageal stage.

At the pharyngoesophageal and the esophagogastric junctions there are sphincteric mechanisms that normally seal off the lumen of the esophagus from the pharynx and the stomach. With deglutition these sphincters relax and permit the swallowed material to enter and leave the esophagus. The stages of deglutition and the function of the esophageal sphincters will be described in

detail after a consideration of the swallowing reflex and swallowing center.

The Swallowing Reflex

The first stage of swallowing, like chewing, may be initiated voluntarily but is normally a reflex action. The second and third stages of swallowing are entirely involuntary. If one wishes to swallow when the mouth is free of food or foreign material, a little saliva is passed backwards by the tongue and thus serves as a mechanical stimulus for the initiation of the second and third phases of the act which are purely reflex. If the mouth is kept perfectly free of saliva, deglutition becomes impossible.

Like chewing, swallowing may be produced by stimulation of appropriate areas of the cerebral cortex (Miller, 1919; Rioch and Brenner, 1938) or by stimulation of local receptors, even in the decerebrate preparations (Ferrier, 1886; Bazett and Penfield, 1922). The receptors for initiation of the swallowing reflex are situated in the vicinity of the entrance to the oral pharynx in all animals but are distributed somewhat differently in different species.

The most sensitive area for initiating swallowing in a rabbit is the membrane of the soft palate above the tonsils. Receptors are also located on the upper surface of the epiglottis and the posterior wall of the oral pharynx below the soft palate. In this animal, the soft palate is innervated by the second division of the trigeminal nerve and the pharyngeal wall by the glossopharyngeal; the epiglottis is supplied by the superior laryngeal nerve. In the dog, the posterior pharyngeal wall, the dorsal surface and the base of the epiglottis, and the soft palate contain receptors for the swallowing reflex. Cutting the second division of the trigeminal nerve eliminates the reflex from the upper part of the pharynx and the soft palate. The posterior pharyngeal wall is innervated by the glossopharyngeal. The superior laryngeal contains afferent fibers for the swallowing reflex in the dog but is said not to be stimulated by food that takes the usual pathway (Kahn, 1903). In cats, the distribution of receptors and afferent nerves is similar to that in the dog. In monkeys, the upper part of the palatine arch, near the tonsils, is the most sensitive area. This region is innervated by the trigeminal nerve. Less sensitive areas are the soft palate and the postpharyngeal wall. Reflexes may also be obtained in the monkey from the false vocal chords and the base of the epiglottis (Kahn, 1903).

In man, the receptors for the swallowing reflex are distributed in a ringlike fashion around the entrance to the oral pharynx and are found in the mucous membrane covering the anterior and posterior pillars of the fauces, the tonsils, the soft palate, the base of the tongue and the posterior pharyngeal wall. According to Pommerenke (1928), the most sensitive areas in the human are in the vicinity of the anterior and posterior pillars of the fauces and the tonsils.

The Swallowing Center

Coordination of the numerous somatic and visceral muscles involved in the act of swallowing is controlled by a group of neurons in the floor of the fourth ventricle known as the swallowing center, first described by Markwald in 1889. He found that destruction of the brain substance above and somewhat lateral to the alae cinereae of the medulla eliminates the swallowing reflex while leaving respiration intact. Destruction of the alae cinereae stops respiration but does not interfere with swallowing. Thus, the swallowing center is closely associated with, although distinct from, the respiratory center. This fact is of considerable clinical interest, because in diseases of the medulla, such as bulbar polio or brain tumor, difficulty in swallowing often precedes respiratory failure and is therefore an ominous sign in such conditions.

Innervation of the Muscles of Deglutition

The efferent nerve fibers involved in the act of swallowing are chiefly in the hypoglossal, glossopharyngeal and vagus nerves. The hypoglossal and glossopharyngeal nerves are chiefly concerned with the buccopharyngeal stage; the vagus, with the esophageal stage of swallowing. The vagus nerves supply the striped muscle of the esophagus with motor fibers, hence, one of the more serious consequences of cutting the vagi above the origin of the main esophageal branches is interference with swallowing. The striped muscle of the esophagus is permanently paralyzed after a high vagotomy (e.g., in the neck), but the smooth muscle of the lower third shows some degree of recovery; peristalsis in this portion may return and swallowing may again become possible (Cannon, 1907). In animals such as the dog and rabbit, in which the entire esophagus is made up of striped muscle, high vagotomy results in permanent inability to swallow. Paralysis of the esophagus, with the resultant accumulation of food and liquid in the esophagus and pharynx, and associated with the loss of the sensory innervation of the larynx, results in the aspiration of food and liquids into the lungs; the animal either suffocates or dies of aspiration pneumonia. Aspiration pneumonia is the most common cause of death after a high vagotomy in dogs.

The fact that peristalsis, at least in the striped muscle portion of the esophagus, is coordinated outside of the esophagus itself, within the central nervous system, was demonstrated in experiments by Mosso in 1876. He made a transverse section through the esophagus of the dog and placed a small wooden ball in the part below the cut. The animal was then stimulated to swallow; one or two seconds after contraction of the pharyngeal muscles, the peristaltic wave began to traverse the esophagus. The wave did not stop at the point of the incision but in due time appeared below and carried the ball into the stomach. These observations were later confirmed by Meltzer in 1899. Meltzer observed that if he used ether anesthesia he obtained results similar to those of Mosso. However, if the animal was narcotized with morphine alone, the peristaltic wave did not progress beyond the transverse incision. Likewise, it stopped at a longitudinal incision which permitted the contents of the esophagus to escape. Evidently, under these circumstances, local reflexes initiated by the contact of food with the mucosa of the esophagus were essential to the normal progress of peristalsis. Meltzer concluded that peristalsis in the striped muscle portion of the esophagus is coordinated in the central nervous system, but is aided by local reflexes arising within the esophagus.

Consideration of the manner of ending of the motor nerves to the esophagus will aid us in understanding this situation. The striped muscle is directly innervated by the vagus nerves, the fibers ending on the muscle cells without the intervention of any local ganglion cells. In the smooth muscle portion, however, there is an extensive local plexus including nerve cells and their branches similar to the myenteric plexus in other parts of the gastrointestinal tract. In this part the vagus fibers do not go to muscle cells but end on nerve cells within the esophageal plexus. It is true that a less dense plexus extends into the striped muscle portion but this is perhaps concerned with secretion of fluid by the esophageal mucous membrane rather than with contraction of the muscle. As we have already noticed, the local nerve plexus is capable of coordinating peristalsis in the smooth muscle portion of the esophagus, even in the absence of the extrinsic nerves.

THE FIRST OR ORAL STAGE OF SWALLOWING

The first stage of deglutition consists of passage of material through the oral cavity into the pharynx. This stage of swallowing is initiated voluntarily. With solid food, the act is usually preceded by mastication. The movements of the tongue against the hard palate and the cheeks help to form a bolus by moistening and mixing the material with saliva, thus softening and lubricating the bolus for passage through the pharynx and the esophagus. After this intraoral preparation, the bolus is maneuvered to a position on the postero-dorsal surface of the tongue. Bosam (1957) has described this as the "preparatory position," as he has observed that the bolus is always maneuvered to a constant position on the surface of the tongue.

With the bolus in the preparatory position, swallowing is initiated. The front portion of the tongue is retracted and depressed; the hyoid is elevated slightly; mastication ceases; respiration is inhibited reflexly; and the back portion of the tongue is elevated and retracted against the hard palate. This latter action of the tongue is produced principally by the myelohyoid, styloglossus and hypoglossus muscles, which force the bolus into the pharynx. Intraoral pressures recorded during swallowing have demonstrated that in the anterior part of the mouth near the incisor teeth, negative pressure changes as great as minus 300 cm. of water may occur (Miyakawa et al., 1957). In the posterior part of the oral cavity, positive pressure changes occur due to the forceful contraction of the tongue against the hard and soft palates. Positive pressures as great as 100 cm. of water are not uncommonly recorded in the posterior part of the oral cavity during swallowing (Hightower, 1958).

Hegner (1936) has described "pure swallowing" and distinguishes it from "mastication swallowing." He made his observations with a laryngoscope and noted that food swallowed during mastication passes from the mouth into the pharynx with very little muscular effort and goes down the side on which it is being chewed. In pure swallowing, with conscious effort, it may pass down on both sides, but usually also in this case, down the accustomed side; this is most often the right side. The lack of muscular effort in the first stage distinguishes mastication swallowing from pure swallowing.

Disturbances of the first stage of swallowing may be caused by a number of conditions. Any painful inflammatory process involving the mouth or tongue may make swallowing difficult. Neoplasms of the tongue or pharyngeal strictures may obstruct the passage of the bolus into the pharynx. Paralysis of the tongue can interfere markedly with swallowing. Congenital anomalies of the lips, tongue, and palate are commonly associated with difficulty in initiating the act of swallowing.

THE SECOND OR PHARYNGEAL STAGE OF SWALLOWING

The contact of material from the mouth with the pharyngeal and peripharyngeal structures initiate reflexes that complete the second and third stages of deglutition. These sensitive areas have already been described in the section dealing with the swallowing reflex. Cocainization of these structures inhibit the swallowing reflexes. The swallowing act, once initiated, is dominant over other functions occurring in this area. Thus, respiration and speech are interrupted by the second stage of the swallowing act. The complexity of the act, and the high degree of integration necessary, is appreciated when one recalls the timed sequence of events in this stage of deglutition and that the second stage is completed in less than one second.

Understanding of the second stage of swallowing will be easier if we keep in mind the fact that the alimentary tract crosses the respiratory tract in the region of the pharynx, so the swallowing movements have to serve two quite different functions: one, to propel the food through the pharynx and into the esophagus; and the other, to protect the airway, both above and below, from the possible entrance of food particles. Although the propulsive and protective mechanisms operate simultaneously it is simpler to describe them separately.

When the bolus reaches the base of the tongue, its movement is accelerated by a rapid downward and backward movement of the tongue which takes place at the same time as the forward movement of the larynx. With the entrance of the bolus into the larynx, contraction of the superior pharyngeal constrictor occurs, initiating a rapid pharyngeal peristaltic wave which moves down the pharynx, propelling the bolus in front of it. The walls and structures of the hypopharynx are elevated to engulf the oncoming bolus. The cricopharyngeus muscle, which has kept the esophagus closed until now, relaxes as the bolus approaches and allows it to enter the upper esophagus. The peristaltic contraction continues into the esophagus to become the primary esophageal peristaltic contraction.

As a result of the combined forces acting on it, the bolus moves with such speed that it is often projected deep into the esophagus. Rushmer and Hendron (1951) using cinefluoroscopy to study pharyngeal transport, observed that a bolus approached the pharynx with the velocity of 9 ft. per sec., passing through the pharynx, it attained a velocity of $19\frac{1}{2}$ ft., 24 ft., and $28\frac{1}{2}$ ft. per sec. in successive frames, then slowed to 12 ft. per sec., and finally to 5 ft. per sec. as it passed into the esophagus. These data were obtained with the subject in a horizontal position; in the erect position, the bolus moved even faster.

We must now consider how the airway is protected while the food is passing the pharyngeal crossroads. It will be recalled that there are four possible outlets from the oral pharynx through which food may be expelled. These are: back into the mouth, up into the nasopharynx, forward into the larynx, and downward into the esophagus. The swallowing reflex has to be so coordinated that the food takes only one of these possible paths, namely that into the esophagus. Return into the mouth is prevented by the position of the tongue against the roof of the mouth and the high pressure developed in this area. Passage into the nasopharynx is normally prevented by the combined action of the tensor veli palatini and the levator veli palatini muscles which together stiffen the soft palate and cause it to press against the posterior pharyngeal wall. It thus forms a protective partition between the oral pharynx and the nasopharynx. If these muscles are paralyzed or if there should be a defect in the soft palate, food enters the nasopharynx and swallowing becomes extremely difficult or impossible. An important factor in preventing entrance of food into the respiratory tract during swallowing, is the inhibition of respiration which occurs during the second stage of swallowing (Magendie, 1838).

The exact mechanism by which the larynx is protected during the passage of the bolus has been the subject of much study and controversy. It seems clear from the various descriptions that are available, that the laryngeal opening is closed during the act of swallowing by the approximation of both the true and the false vocal chords. In addition, the epiglottis serves to divert the oncoming bolus to one side or the other of the larynx. Only when liquid is being swallowed in considerable volume does the swallowed material cascade over the end of the epiglottis. In any case,

it usually prevents the passing material from coming directly in contact with the upper surface of the larynx. The position of the epiglottis at the moment of the passage of the bolus has been the subject of considerable argument; however, most observers agree that it is carried into a horizontal position by the backward movement of the tongue and the forward movement of the larynx. This same combination of movements results in the larynx being drawn up under the base of the tongue where it is completely out of the way of the oncoming bolus.

Many authors prefer to combine the first and second stages into a buccopharyngeal stage. The buccopharyngeal stage has been described by Pancoast, Pendergrass and Schaeffer (1940) as occurring in four phases: first, filling of the mouth and movement of the base of the tongue backward toward the postpharyngeal wall; second, as the bolus begins to move backward from the mouth, the base of the tongue comes against the postpharyngeal wall and the epiglottis goes backward and downward. Simultaneously, the larynx rises and the arytenoid cartilages come in contact with the under surface of the epiglottis, so that the tongue, epiglottis and arytenoids form a single homogeneous x-ray shadow. The meeting of these three structures closes the air passage to the larynx. Third, the bolus enters the laryngeal pharynx and immediately passes down into the esophagus. Fourth, the structures return to the resting position.

Disturbances of the second stage of swallowing are not unusual. Acute pharyngitis is probably the most common cause of painful dysphagia of the second stage of swallowing. Tonsillitis is another example of an inflammatory process that may interfere with the second stage of deglutition. Pharyngeal paralysis is usually indicative of serious neurologic disease and dysphagia developing in poliomyelitis, syringomyelia, multiple sclerosis, or after a cerebrovascular hemorrhage points to bulbar involvement. In these patients, it may be impossible for the soft palate to be elevated, thus allowing liquids to be regurgitated through the nose. The pharyngeal constrictions may be unable to initiate the peristaltic contraction which empties the contents of the pharynx into the esophagus. Cranial nerve (glossopharyngeal) neuritis also may result in pharyngeal paralysis. Diphtheria is sometimes followed by palative and pharyngeal paralysis.

Mobility of the larynx is essential to the second stage of deglutition. Any disease process that prevents the larynx from ascending to lie beneath

PHARYNGO-ESOPHAGEAL JUNCTION

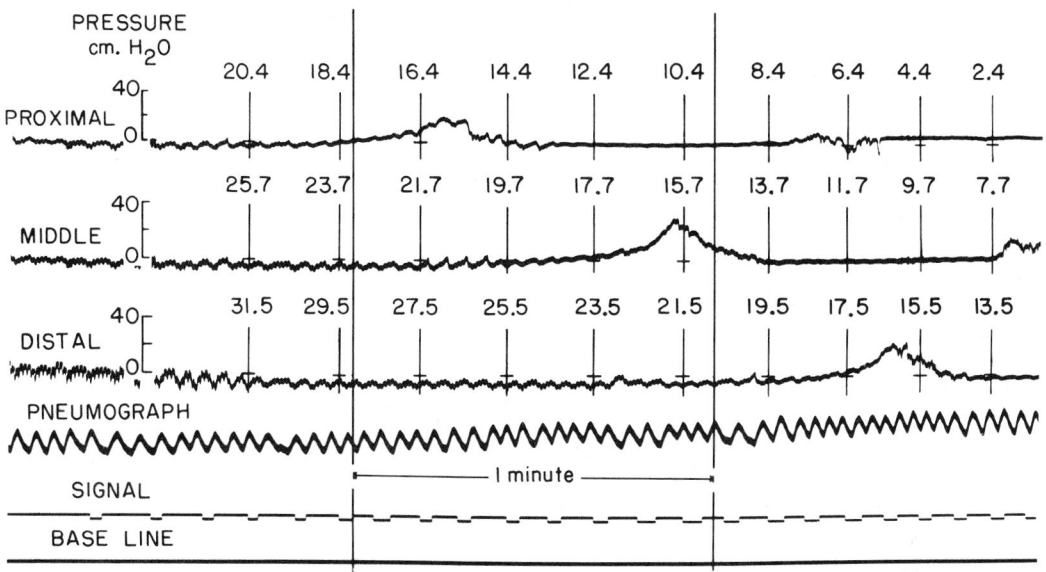

FIG. 61.2 Demonstration of the zone of high pressure at the pharyngoesophageal junction. The catheters were placed in the esophagus and slowly withdrawn through the upper esophageal sphincter while recording pressure continuously. Each centimeter of withdrawal is indicated by the signal and the vertical lines indicate the distance in centimeters from the incisor teeth to the tip of each catheter. This "pull through" technique clearly demonstrates the negative basal pressure in the esophagus and the zone of high pressure extending from 14 to 17 cm. in the upper esophageal sphincter. (From Hightower, Am. J. Digest. Dis., 1958, 3: 562.)

the base of the tongue causes marked dysphagia. Neoplasms, such as carcinoma of the larynx and thyroid, and infectious conditions such as tuberculosis and syphilis, may result in fixation of the larynx; thus making swallowing extremely difficult.

THE THIRD OR ESOPHAGEAL STAGE OF SWALLOWING

It has already been mentioned that at the junction of the esophagus with the pharynx above, and with the stomach below, there exist physiological sphincteric mechanisms that effectively maintain and separate the slightly negative intraluminal pressure of the esophagus from the positive pressures of the pharynx and stomach. Except during deglutition, these esophageal sphincters are normally closed and prevent the aspiration of air from above, or gastric juice from below, into the esophagus. They respond to deglutition by first relaxing and then contracting in a sequential manner with the primary peristaltic wave as it passes over these junctional zones. In describing the third stage of deglutition, the motor activity of the esophageal sphincters will be considered separate from that of the body of the esophagus.

The Upper Esophageal Sphincter

The pharyngoesophageal junction is characterized by a short zone of high-resting intraluminal pressure in the region of the inferior pharyngeal constrictor or cricopharyngeus muscle at the level of the cricoid cartilage (Fyke and Code, 1955). The circular muscle fibers in this area remain in a stage of tonic contraction, producing this zone of high-resting intraluminal pressure, and effectively separating the pharyngeal and esophageal luminae. The zone of high pressure is approximately 4 cm. in length and usually is located between 15 and 20 cm. from the incisor teeth. The basal-resting pressure in the high pressure zone varies from 20 to 30 cm. of water above atmospheric pressure (fig. 61.2).

When intraluminal pressures are recorded from the upper esophageal sphincter during deglutition, the pattern of pressure change is distinctly different from that recorded from the pharynx or upper esophagus (fig. 61.3). Immediately after the onset of deglutition, usually within 0.5 seconds, a brief increase in the high-resting pressure first occurs, but this lasts only a few tenths of a second, to be followed by a marked decrease in pressure below the resting basal pressure, and usually negative in comparison with atmospheric

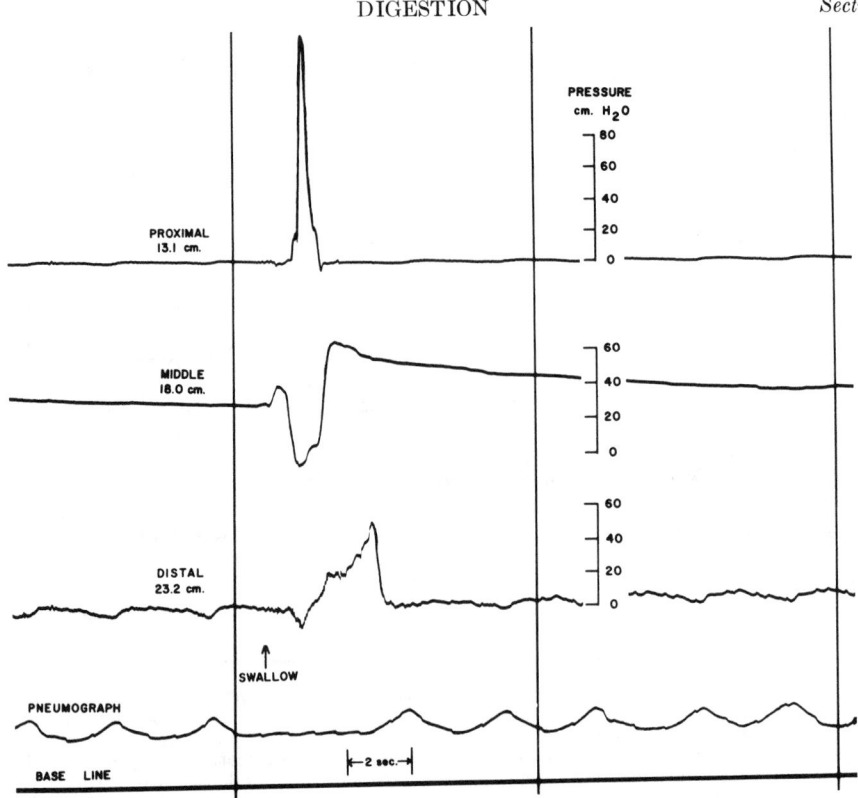

FIG. 61.3 Pressure changes in the upper esophageal sphincter during deglutition. The proximal catheter is recording pressure from the lower pharynx, the middle one from the sphincteric area, and the distal one from the upper esophagus. The sequential appearance of peak pressures in each complex, from above downward, indicates the passage of the peristaltic contraction from the pharynx over the pharyngoesophageal junction into the upper esophagus. (From Hightower, Am. J. Digest. Dis., 1958, 3: 362.)

pressure. The decrease in pressure in the pharyngoesophageal junction occurs almost simultaneously with the increase in pressure in the pharynx produced by the peristaltic wave resulting from the contraction of the superior and middle pharnygeal constrictors. These events markedly increase the pressure gradient from the pharynx across the upper esophageal sphincter. With the arrival of the swallowed bolus at the pharyngoesophageal junction, the previously relaxed fibers of the upper sphincter contract and propagate the peristaltic contraction and pressure gradient into the upper esophagus.

The small initial positive pressure wave observed in the pharyngoesophageal junction with deglutition may be due to an increase in the tonic contraction of circular fibers of the cricopharyngeus muscle, or it may be related to the elevation of the larynx and increased tension in this area. The duration of the negative component of the junctional pressure pattern of deglutition is usually 0.7 to 1.0 sec., after which time the pressure has returned to the previous basal level. The pressure continues upward, however, and a

positive pressure wave, forming the third component of the pattern, is observed. This positive pressure wave represents a continuation of the pharyngeal peristalsis through the pharyngoesophageal junction. The maximum pressure produced by this wave is usually 70 to 90 cm. of water above atmospheric pressure. The pressure within the junctional zone then returns to its previous basal level within 3 to 4 sec.

Motility of the Body of the Esophagus

Primary peristaltic contractions, previously described as originating in the pharynx and passing over the pharyngoesophageal junction, continue into the esophagus, sweeping the bolus onward and maintaining the pressure gradient. The primary peristaltic contraction, as observed fluoroscopically, has been described in considerable detail by Templeton (1944). The pressure pattern produced by the primary peristaltic contraction of the esophagus also has been well characterized by a number of investigators (Butin, et al., 1953; Sanchez, et al., 1953; Texter, et al., 1957). The pressure pattern consists of an

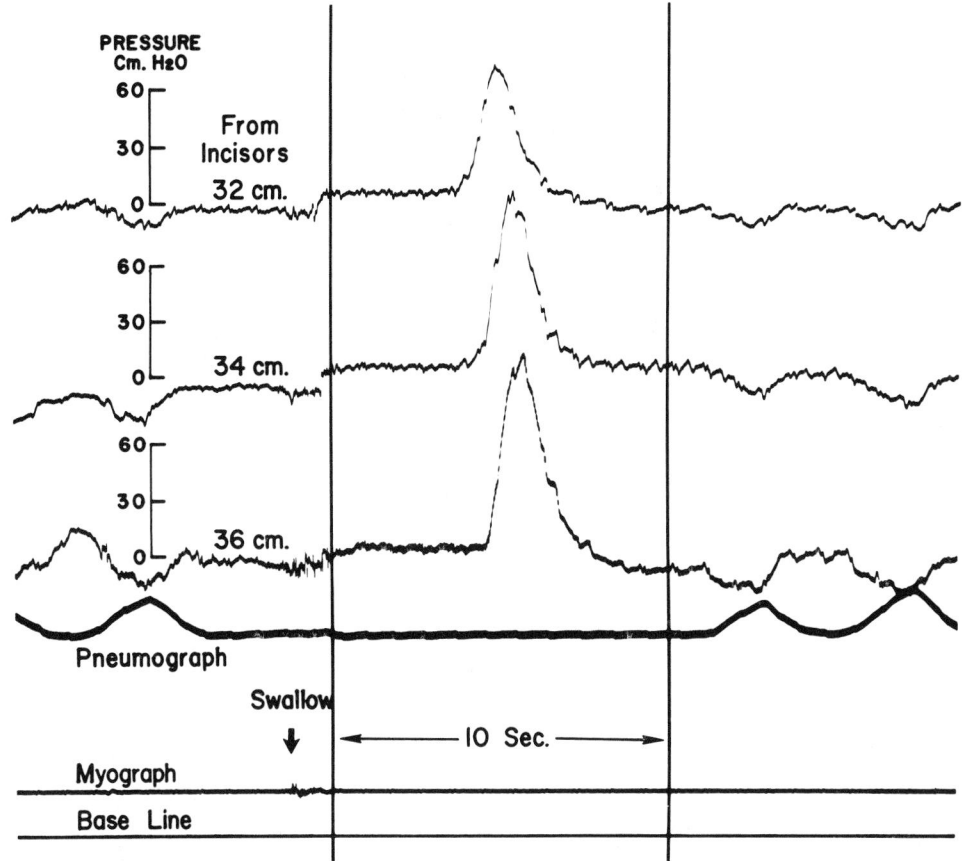

Fig. 61.4 Normal deglutition pressure complexes recorded from the lower esophagus. See text for detailed description. The pneumograph is recording respiration and note that respiration was voluntarily stopped at end-expiration a few seconds prior to deglutition. The myograph records the action potentials of the accessory muscles of deglutition in the neck and indicate the precise onset of swallowing.

initial negative wave followed by three positive pressure components (fig. 61.4). The initial negative component is of brief duration and occurs immediately after the onset of deglutition. It is observed more frequently in the upper than in the lower esophagus, and is thought to be due to the sudden stretching of the closed esophagus by elevation of the larynx. The negative component is followed by an abrupt increase in pressure of 10 to 15 cm. of water. The third component consists of a slowly increasing positive pressure change or else a plateau of positive pressure is maintained. The fourth, and most prominent, component of the deglutition pressure pattern, is a large, simple, monophasic positive pressure wave that rises rapidly to a peak pressure and declines with equal speed. The abrupt rise in intraluminal pressure following the initial negative component has been attributed to the sudden injection of the bolus or liquid into the esophagus, as it is observed to occur simul-

taneously at different levels of the esophagus. The gradual increasing or plateau of pressure is related to the approaching peristaltic contraction. Its duration and time is directly proportional to the depth of the recording catheter in the esophagus. The large monophasic positive pressure wave that terminates the complex is recorded as the peristaltic contraction passes over the open tip of the catheter.

Secondary peristaltic contractions are also observed in the esophagus. These contractions arise locally in the esophagus as a result of distention, and once initiated, progress down the esophagus in a manner similar to the primary peristaltic contraction. Secondary peristaltic contractions produce a pressure wave similar to the final pressure wave of the deglutition pressure pattern. It is a simple monophasic positive pressure wave that rises rapidly to a peak then returns promptly to the baseline. Secondary waves are usually of less amplitude than primary waves.

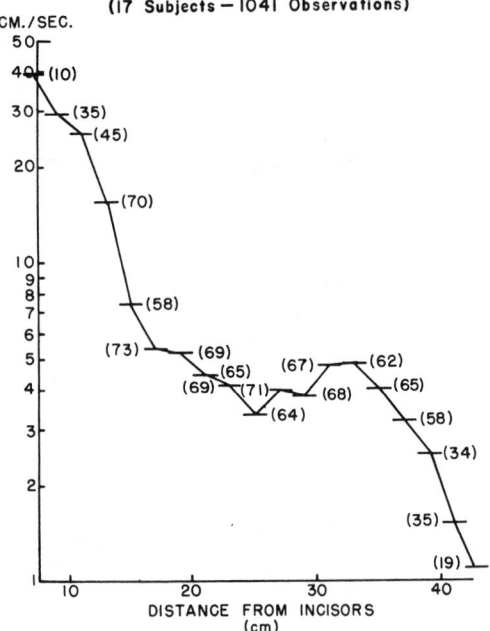

RATE OF PHARYNGEAL AND ESOPHAGEAL PERISTALSIS
(17 Subjects — 1041 Observations)

CM./SEC.

DISTANCE FROM INCISORS
(cm)

Fig. 61.5 The rate of propagation of primary peristaltic contractions in the pharynx and esophagus as determined in 17 healthy adults, The number of observations at each level is indicated in parenthesis. The short horizontal line indicates the distance over which the groups of observations were made.

In the normal esophagus, secondary peristaltic contractions may be caused by local distention by fluid or a solid bolus. If the primary wave is unable to propel the swallowed material, secondary contractions originate and complete the transport of the substance.

Tertiary esophageal contractions also have been observed in the esophagus. These contractions occur irregularly and locally, and are observed most frequently in the lower esophagus. They are not peristaltic. Their function is not known. Roentgenologically, they may produce a varied picture with a serrated or beaded appearance, or like multiple diverticula-like pockets. The roentgenologic picture of tertiary contractions has been referred to as "curling" and the "corkscrew esophagus." Lerche (1950) has suggested that contraction of the spiral muscular coat of the lower esophagus accounts for these teritary contractions.

There is considerable difference in the rate of progress of food through the esophagus in different animals and man in different positions; for example, in the goose, food takes from 9 to 12 sec. to reach the stomach, but in the dog, it takes

only 4 to 5 sec. (Cannon and Moser, 1898). Food moves more rapidly in the upper two-thirds of the esophagus than in the lower two-thirds. This is in accordance with the difference in the rate of contraction of striated and smooth muscles. In man, food takes longer to reach the stomach in the horizontal position than in the vertical position; this difference is especially pronounced if liquids are swallowed. Hurst in 1907, and Schreiber in 1915, studied swallowing in the human in the inverted position. Their observations indicated that gravity is an important factor in the progress of food through the esophagus. However, it is obvious that in animals such as the goose and the horse, which normally drink with the head down, peristalsis is capable of moving liquids against gravity.

In man, the rate of propagation of the primary peristaltic contraction has been determined with the subjects in the horizontal position (Hightower and Salem, 1958). The time required for the primary esophageal peristaltic contraction to traverse the entire esophagus is from 8 to 12 sec. As the peristaltic wave descends the esophagus, its rate of propagation becomes progressively slower. It has been found that the rate of propagation of a primary contraction is quite rapid in the pharynx and upper esophagus. Soon after it is initiated, it is traveling at a rate of approximately 50 cm. per sec. The rate rapidly decreases, however, as shown in fig. 61.5. When the peristaltic wave has traveled to a level 25 to 30 cm. from the incisor teeth, its speed has decreased to about only 3 cm. per sec. For some unknown reason, the rate then increases slightly as the contraction ring approaches the esophagogastric junction. After reaching the esophagogastric junction, the rate markedly decreases again until it is moving at less than 1 cm. per sec.

In the upright position, liquids travel through the esophagus at a speed that greatly exceeds the rate of propagation of the primary peristaltic wave. This rapid transport is considered to be due to the propelling force created by the contraction of the pharyngeal constrictors during the second stage of deglutition, as well as by the action of gravity upon the swallowed liquid. In the pharynx, near the end of the second stage of deglutition, pharyngeal pressure is mounting due to contraction of the pharyngeal constrictors and when the cricopharyngeus muscle suddenly relaxes and opens the upper end of the esophagus, which has a negative intraluminal pressure, the liquid is then more or less squirted into the lumen of the esophagus. In the upright position, the rapid passage of liquid through the esophagus requires only a second or two. Fluoroscopy demonstrates that swallowed liquids usually are arrested at the lower end of the esophagus and await the arrival of the peristaltic contraction before they are admitted into the stomach. At times, however, when a series of swallows occurs rapidly, as when drinking a glass of water, the liquid may pass on through the esophagogastric junction with little pause and enter the stomach within a second or two after drinking has begun.

The Lower Esophageal Sphincter

Probably no other area of the alimentary canal has caused more confusion and diverse opinion than the terminal few centimeters of the esophagus. Only within the past few years have anatomists, physiologists, radiologists, and endoscopists been able to reach some common agreement and understanding of the structure and function of the esophagogastric junction. It was Lerche's classic studies correlating anatomic and radiologic observations that stimulated reinvestigation of this area. Sanchez, Kramer and Ingelfinger (1953) demonstrated that the distal 2 to 5 cm. of the esophagus has a characteristic motor function. They found that the characteristic deglutition pressure pattern observed in the upper esophagus was not propagated into the vestibule. In addition, these same authors later demonstrated that the body of the esophagus and the vestibule react inversely to cholinergic and anticholinergic stimulation (1954).

Fyke, Code and Schlegel (1956) explored the esophagogastric junction of normal persons with a miniature pressure transducer and found a zone of high pressure similar to that encountered at the pharyngoesophageal junction. The high pressure zone extended from about 1 to 2 cm. below the hiatus of the diaphragm to 1 to 2 cm. above the hiatus. The mean resting maximum pressures in this region, expressed as centimeters of water above the pressure in the fundus of the stomach, were 10.7 at the end of expiration, and 3.5 at the end of inspiration.

As the peristaltic contraction approaches the lower esophagus, the deglutition pressure complex changes slightly as it reaches the slightly dilated or bulbar portion of the terminal part of the body of the esophagus known as the ampulla. The complex is more prolonged due to the slowing of the rate of propagation of the peristaltic contraction, and the large positive pressure wave terminating the complex tends to decrease in amplitude.

With deglutition, the high basal pressure that exists in the esophagogastric junction decreases to form a slow negative wave of 7 to 10 sec. duration. This decrease in pressure occurs while pressure is increasing in the lower esophagus; thus greatly extending the pressure gradient from the lower esophagus to the esophagogastric junction. The slow decline in pressure is followed by an equally slow increase to form a smooth negative pressure wave. This is continued into a similar slow positive pressure wave which appears to occur in sequence with the peristaltic pressure wave of the lower esophagus. The high pressure zone of the esophagogastric junction extends slightly above and below the diaphragmatic hiatus, and pressure changes due to deglutition are similar in each part but are of less magnitude when recorded from the segment below the diaphragm than from that part located just above the diaphragm.

The lower esophageal sphincter thus relaxes reflexly, as does the cricopharyngeus muscle at the pharyngoesophageal junction, allowing esophageal contents to be emptied into the sphincteric area by the progressing high pressure gradient between the lower esophagus and the sphincter segment. The sphincter then contracts slowly, with higher pressures in the part of the segment above the diaphragm than in that below. This provides for emptying of the sphincteric segment into the stomach. The motor function of the lower esophageal sphincter is distinct and separate from that of the body of the esophagus; however, the relaxation and contraction of this sphincteric segment in sequence with the advancing peristaltic contraction permits esophageal emptying into the stomach.

Disturbances of Esophageal Motility

Many diseases may alter the normal motor activity of the esophagus. Disturbances of esophageal motility usually result in dysphagia, or difficulty in swallowing. The dysphagia may, or may not, be associated with pain. Some of the more common causes of dysphagia, as observed clinically, will be discussed briefly.

Diffuse spasm of the esophagus produces dysphagia as a result of disturbed normal motor mechanisms. Dysphagia due to diffuse spasm characteristically occurs intermittently and is associated with pain. In this disorder, the esophageal musculature appears to be hypersensitive to the stimuli produced by deglutition and also by local distention. Following deglutition, long segments of the esophagus may go into a marked spasm, which produces severe substernal pain.

The pain may extend up into the neck, the jaw, or into the arms. Pain of esophageal origin is frequently confused clinically with that of pain of cardiac origin.

When esophageal intraluminal pressures are measured in patients who have diffuse spasm of the esophagus, deglutition may result in a marked distortion of the normal deglutition pattern. In these patients, intraluminal pressure may exceed 300 cm. of water pressure due to the spasm. In addition, the pressure complex may be markedly prolonged as well as increased in amplitude. The pressure pattern may be the same over a considerable length of the esophagus and the exaggerated response may occur repetitively; that is, one swallow may result in three or more such abnormal contractions. This type of motor response does not produce a pressure gradient from above downwards and transport does not occur. The abnormal pressure tracings are most frequently observed in the lower esophagus, but they can also be recorded from the upper esophagus. Both the upper and lower esophageal sphincters appear to respond normally to deglutition. The diffuse spasms are localized in the body of the esophagus between the two sphincters.

The etiology of diffuse spasm is unknown, but it is frequently observed in patients who have associated gastrointestinal diseases such as peptic ulcer, cholelithiasis, pancreatitis, and it is seen most frequently in association with hiatal hernia.

Achalasia results in a progressive dysphagia. The dysphagia results from an inability of the lower esophageal sphincter to relax reflexly in response to deglutition. In this disorder, the primary peristaltic contractions originate in the pharynx in a normal manner, but when they have reached a level of the upper esophagus, they become ineffective, weak, and finally fade away. Secondary contractions often occur due to the local distention by retained foods and secretions, but once initiated, these contractions move purposelessly up and down the esophagus for a short distance, then they too disappear. Without normal propagation of peristaltic contractions, little intraluminal pressure gradient is created and esophageal transport is markedly retarded. As the normal motor function progressively fails, the retention of solid foods, liquids, and secretions occur, and this leads to marked dilatation and elongation of the esophagus.

For many years, this condition was referred to as "cardiospasm," for it was thought that the lower esophageal sphincter was in spasm and that this accounted for the obstruction at the distal end of the esophagus. Hurst (1927) recommended the term "achalasia" in preference to cardiospasm. It was his opinion that achalasia was due to a degeneration of the myenteric plexus of the esophagus, as demonstrated by Rake (1927), and not to hypertrophy or spasm of the cardiac sphincter. Numerous investigators have since demonstrated a marked degeneration of Auerbach's plexus, especially in the lower parts of the esophagus in patients with achalasia. The cause of the degeneration of the myenteric plexus is unknown. The unusual sensitivity of the esophagus in patients with achalasia to mecholyl, supports the pathological findings that achalasia is due to a disorder of the intrinsic nerve plexuses. When mecholyl is administered subcutaneously in small doses of only one or two mg., the esophagus responds by going into marked spasm (Kramer and Ingelfinger, 1951; Hightower, et al., 1954). The response to mecholyl has been used as a diagnostic test in establishing the diagnosis of achalasia.

Scleroderma is an example of a systemic disease that may produce dysphagia by interference with the third stage of deglutition. The primary disorder of esophageal motility is the defective propagation of the primary peristaltic contraction due to a myogenic failure. Also, there is rather marked loss of muscular tone in the esophageal wall. As in achalasia, scleroderma involves most of the esophagus, and is not confined to any particular segment, although changes are usually more evident in the lower esophagus.

The primary peristaltic contraction originates normally in the pharynx and passes on into the esophagus, but the contraction fades out usually in the upper levels of the esophagus. Few deglutition pressure complexes reach the lower esophagus and those that do are usually at low amplitude. The esophagogastric junction is also involved in this disease, with a loss of the normal high pressure zone. With the loss of the pressure barrier between the esophagus and the stomach, gastroesophageal reflux is a common finding. Mecholyl does not increase esophageal intraluminal pressure in patients with scleroderma, as is observed in patients with achalasia.

Hiatus hernia is a very common disorder that may produce dysphagia due to the anatomical alterations of the normal esophagogastric junction. In these patients, the esophagogastric junction is displaced upward out of the diaphragmatic hiatus into the chest. When the esophagogastric junction is displaced into the chest, the high pressure zone is decreased and reflux from the herniated portion of the stomach above the diaphragm into the esophagus is a common finding. Some degree of peptic esophagitis is not at all uncommon and this probably accounts for the increased irritability and spontaneous contractions frequently observed in pressure records of the esophagus in patients with hiatal hernia.

Chalasia is a term applied to a relaxed esophagogastric junction; the esophagogastric junction is not displaced out of the diaphragmatic hiatus as in hiatal hernia, but there is a decreased high pressure zone within the lower esophageal sphincter. This permits frequent gastroesophageal reflux. This condition is usually seen in infants but it may occur in adults. Apparently, the lower esophageal sphincter does not remain tonically closed as occurs normally. Detection of gastroesophageal reflux in chalasia, and in patients with hiatal hernia, is best accomplished by measuring intraluminal pH by means of a small glass electrode attached to a thin flexible lead. A pH of 4.0 or lower recorded at a level of 4 to 5 cm. above the esophagogastric junction is evidence of gastroesophageal reflux.

Obstruction of the esophagus due to *neoplasm* or *stricture* is a common cause of dysphagia. In the case of neoplasms, dysphagia develops slowly but becomes progressively worse. Difficulty is usually first noticed with solid foods, and later with liquids. The patient will complain that foods "stick" or "hang-up" in the esophagus, and usually he can point to a site that indicates the level of the lesion. Strictures of the esophagus in children are frequently due to drinking caustic solutions carelessly left within their reach. Fortunately, lye stricture of the esophagus is becoming less frequent and is probably due to the development of modern detergents.

HEARTBURN AND BELCHING

"Heartburn is a painful sensation located retrosternally in the midline between the xiphoid process and the manubrium. Its duration is variable, but it always has a moving quality. It may radiate to the upper abdomen, to the lateral portion of the anterior chest wall, to the jaws, and even into the arms but the major component of this distress is in the midline and the pain is wave-like" (Tuttle, Rufin and Bettarello, 1961). Heartburn is frequently experienced by patients with hiatal hernia and occurs during the second half of pregnancy in approximately 50 per cent of cases.

"*Heartburn*" is ascribed by Alvarez to the stimulation of the mucosa of the upper part of the esophagus by acid fluid regurgitated from the stomach. Payne and Poulton suggest that a tonic spasm of the esophagus set up by the acid stimulus is responsible for the sensation. Jones and Richardson produced it in normal persons by distention of the lower third of the esophagus. The introduction of acid, cold water, or gastric contents, into this part of the esophagus also caused the burning sensation. It is generally agreed that the sensation does not originate within the stomach itself.

Tuttle, Bettarello and Grossman (1961) measured intraesophageal pH in patients who complained of heartburn not associated with belching, and found that the heartubrn was associated with a drop in pH to below 4.0 in the lower esophagus. There was no evidence of disturbed esophageal motility when heartburn was induced by instilling hydrochloric acid into the stomach of patients who had gastroesophageal reflux. Siegal and Hendrix, on the other hand, found pain and abnormal esophageal motility to occur at the same time when they perfused acid into the esophagus of patients with esophagitis. It is apparent that the cause of "heartburn" is still not completely understood. In a patient with esophagitis, the instillation of a number of noxious substances into the esophagus may cause the distress. Gastroesophageal reflux of acid gastric juice, with a drop in esophageal intraluminal pH to below 4.0, can be associated with heartburn. Abnormal esophageal motility may or may not be associated with heartburn.

Belching. The tendency, after a meal, for small amounts of gas to be expelled from the stomach into the esophagus and mouth is experienced by most normal persons. The repeated belching of gas is, however, abnormal. The gas in these instances is not, as a rule, produced by digestive or fermentative processes in the stomach, it is simply air which has been previously swallowed (aerophagy), and it has the composition of atmospheric air. The greater part of the swallowed air does not enter the stomach but is held in the lower part of the esophagus until a sufficient volume has collected to give the subject a certain satisfaction when it is belched. The condition is seen in the nervous type of subject, or in one who has some gastric discomfort; he resorts to the air swallowing trick in an effort to gain relief. The intragastric pressure is not increased above the normal, apparently, in subjects who have the sensation of "gas on the stomach" and the pressure is not lowered after gas has been belched.

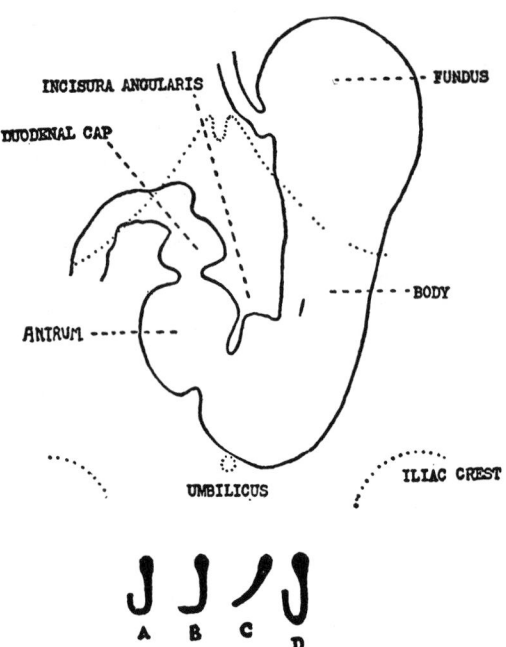

INCISURA ANGULARIS

DUODENAL CAP

ANTRUM

FUNDUS

BODY

UMBILICUS   ILIAC CREST

J J / J
A   B   C   D

FIG. 61.6. Diagram showing the position and subdivisions of the stomach. A, B and C represent J, reversed L and steer horn types of stomach, respectively. D, stomach of the J-shaped type with the greater curvature lying well below the level of the umbilicus. Antrum is also known as the vestibule.

In a recent study of the mechanism of belching (McNally, Kelley and Ingelfinger, 1964), radiological and pressure recordings were made during the distention of the human stomach with air. Pressures were recorded from both the esophagus and the stomach. As the stomach was slowly distended with air there was an initial increase in intragastric pressure of 2 to 6 mm. of Hg, but no further increase occurred, even when up to 1600 ml. of air was introduced, indicating that both gastric and intra-abdominal cavities relax receptively in response to increased gastric volume. Within 3 min. after the stomach had been distended with air, they observed that sudden equalizations of gastric and esophageal pressures took place at inconstant and intermittent intervals in their subjects. Cineradiography showed that the sudden equalization of gastric and esophageal pressures was associated with escape of air from the stomach into the esophagus. Usually, within 6 to 10 sec., a secondary esophageal peristaltic wave occurred, returned the refluxed air to the stomach, and reestablished the esophagogastric barrier. The reflux of air from the stomach into the esophagus was not associated with any discomfort, noise, or

belching and the authors referred to this as "simple reflux."

Pressure changes associated with belching were different from those observed during simple reflux. When belching occurred, a simultaneous pressure spike was recorded from the stomach and the esophagus in all subjects. In four subjects, in whom intracolonic pressures also were measured, similar pressure spikes were observed. In 87 per cent of the recorded belches, the pressure spike and the associated belching were superimposed on the pattern of simple reflux. After the belch, the intraesophageal pressure remained elevated, and identical with intragastric pressure for 6 to 10 sec., until secondary esophageal peristalsis emptied the esophagus and returned esophageal and gastric pressure to their control level.

Gastric Motility

Before attempting to describe the movements of the stomach it is desirable to define the anatomical terms that will be used (fig. 61.6). The stomach as a whole consists of a *fundus*, *body*, and a *pyloric portion* (antrum). The fundus is that portion of the stomach which, in the human in the upright position, lies above a horizontal plane passing through the esophageal opening. The body of the stomach (corpus ventriculi) extends from the fundus to the *incisura angularis* on the lesser curvature, and to a corresponding notch on the greater curvature. The incisura is a conspicuous notch on the lesser curvature, which serves not only to separate the anatomical divisions of the stomach, but also marks the position of a band of smooth muscle which has a higher degree of tonus than most of the remainder of the gastric muscle and causes a narrowing of the gastric lumen at this point. The pyloric portion (pars pylorica) extends from the incisura angularis in the lesser curvature, and the corresponding notch on the greater curvature, to the junction of the stomach with the duodenum. The pyloric portion differs from the remainder of the stomach in having much heavier musculature.

The cardia is simply the esophageal orifice, that is, the opening between the esophagus and the stomach. Properly speaking it refers to no anatomical structure; neverless the term is often used to refer to the entire region of the stomach surrounding the cardia and in that sense it includes the mucous membrane and muscle in the immediate vicinity of the orifice. The cardia is surrounded by a sphincter muscle known as the cardiac sphincter. This sphincter, although it appears thicker and heavier than the adjacent muscle when in the contracted state, is difficult to see in the dead stomach. The pylorus is the opening between the stomach and duodenum and, like the cardia, refers to no anatomical structure. However, the term is often used to designate the pyloric portion of the stomach. Likewise, the pyloric sphincter is sometimes referred to as the pylorus. These usages are incorrect and often give rise to misunderstandings. The lumen of the pyloric portion may be divided into an antrum and a pyloric canal. The separation between these two portions is marked by a sulcus intermedius when this is present. The portion to the right of the sulcus is known as the pyloric canal, and the portion to the left as the pyloric antrum. The antrum is not a structure but a space; nevertheless, the entire pyloric portion is often called the antrum in clinical literature.

THE PERIODIC ACTIVITY OF THE EMPTY STOMACH

The smooth muscle of the stomach is seldom completely inactive, but its activity increases during gastric digestion and periodically when the stomach is empty. The activity of the empty stomach was first observed by Schirokich (1901), whose observations were extended by Tscheschkow (1902), and later by Boldyreff (1904), all working in Pavlov's laboratory in St. Petersburg. Boldyreff, in particular, noted periodic activity of other organs of digestion including the small intestine and pancreas. The contractions of the empty stomach were further studied by Cannon and Washburn at Harvard in 1912. These authors recognized the relation between the contractions and the sensation of hunger and proposed for them the name *hunger contractions*. Later, hunger contractions were studied and described in detail by Carlson (1916) and his coworkers at the University of Chicago.

Hunger contractions are peristaltic waves superimposed on contractions of the gastric smooth muscle as a whole. In contrast to digestive peristalsis, which is evident chiefly in the distal part of the corpus and pyloric portion of the stomach, the hunger waves travel the entire length of the stomach.

Types of Hunger Contractions

Carlson recognized three types of hunger contractions.

Type I occurs when the tone of the stomach is feeble. It consists of single contractions superim-

posed on a low tone level. The tonus of the stomach does not rise between contractions and there is always an interval of time between the end of one contraction and the beginning of the next. Each contraction lasts for about 20 sec. and the interval between contractions is from $\frac{1}{2}$ sec. to 3 or 4 sec. When recorded by means of a small balloon in the antrum, Type I contractions produce a pressure change of approximately 5 cm. of water (Hightower and Code, 1950). They occur in both rhythmic and nonrhythmic patterns. When present rhythmically and recorded from the antrum, their rate is constant at 3 per min. Carlson referred to this as the "20-second rhythm." It is felt that the Type I waves of the stomach represent a "mixing" type of motor activity. One gets the impression from balloon-kymographic records, and also from fluoroscopic observations, that this type of motor activity represents a kneading of the gastric contents.

Type II hunger contractions occur when the tonus of the stomach is strong. There may be no intervening pause between the contractions and each lasts for 20 sec. Type II contractions may occur also in a nonrhythmic pattern, and when they do their duration is more variable, ranging from 12 to 25 sec. Pressure changes produced by these contractions usually range from 10 to 50 cm. of water, although at times pressures of 100 cm. of water are observed. Type II gastric contractions represent peristalsis. In the antrum, this type of motor activity creates the pressure gradient that effects gastric evacuation into the duodenum.

Type III gastric contractions have been described as an "incomplete tetanus." They are usually observed at the end of a period of gastric motor activity and are followed by a period of quiescence. They occur rarely in man and seldom make up more than one per cent of the activity observed in motility records. The Type III contraction is recorded as an increase in basal pressure lasting 1 to 5 min., with rhythmic Type II contractions superimposed upon the increase in basal pressure. From a functional standpoint, it is thought that this type of motor activity represents a change in tonus or decrease in diameter of the lumen. The increase in the basal pressure observed during a Type III contraction is usually less than 10 to 15 cm. of water.

When recorded from man, after an overnight fast, antral gastric motility records show that some type of activity is present approximately 40 per cent of the time and this activity is broken

TYPES OF WAVES OBSERVED IN THE GASTRIC ANTRUM OF HUMANS

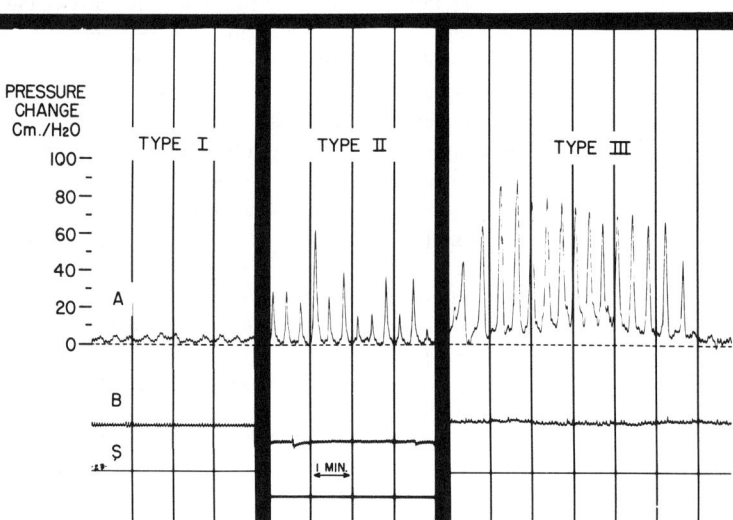

FIG. 61.7 Types of antral motility recorded from normal human being. Note that the rhythmic rate of Type I and Type II waves is identical at 3 per minute. The Type III complex consists of a rise in basal pressure on which is superimposed rhythmic Type II waves. (From Code, Hightower and Morlock, Am. J. Med., 1952, 13: 328.

down as follows: Type I contractions about 25 per cent, Type II about 15 per cent, and Type III 1 per cent during the period of observation. Examples of the three types of gastric contractions are illustrated in fig. 61.7.

Carlson noted that hunger contractions are apt to begin soon after the stomach has emptied. In the beginning they tend to be Type I and the hunger periods at first are of short duration. As the fast continues the hunger periods become longer and the rest periods shorter and eventually the contractions become Type II in character. Type III contractions are seen in animals after prolonged fasts; they rarely occur in humans as previously mentioned. Hunger contractions are more vigorous in young persons than in older persons, and the sensations associated with the contractions vary a great deal in different people. In some people they are definitely painful, whereas others are conscious merely of a vague feeling of emptiness, which is exaggerated during the contraction phase, but is apt to be more or less continuously present.

Associated with severe hunger contractions are certain systemic effects which are of interest in explaining the discomfort and the inefficiency that is associated with severe hunger. There is for example, an increased excitability of the reflex centers of the central nervous system which can be demonstrated by studying the knee-jerk. At the same time, there is general restlessness and increased movements in those animals that are governed by instinct; this doubtless has to do with the search for food. There is an increase in heart rate during the actual contractions and an increase in the salivary flow. The latter is evident during strong contractions only. There is apt to be a feeling of weakness and a general indisposition to make any vigorous effort, mental or physical. Along with the sensation of emptiness, which is referred to the epigastrium, there is often headache. The headache of hunger is peculiar in that it is relieved at once on taking food; it is probably reflex in origin. Finally, there is apt to be a sensation of nausea with severe hunger. As pointed out by Ivy and his associates in 1925, this latter effect is probably due to contractions of the duodenum. The duodenum and upper jejunum usually participate in hunger contractions.

Hunger contractions are inhibited by taking food. The presence of almost any substance in the stomach is sufficient to inhibit the contractions for a time; food in the mouth or in the intestine is also effective. Strangely enough, hunger contractions cease on the presentation of food even though the food is not eaten.

Hunger Contractions and Appetite

Although the sensation of hunger is associated with changes in the viscera which can be easily demonstrated by physical means, this is not true of appetite. Appetite is largely due to anticipation

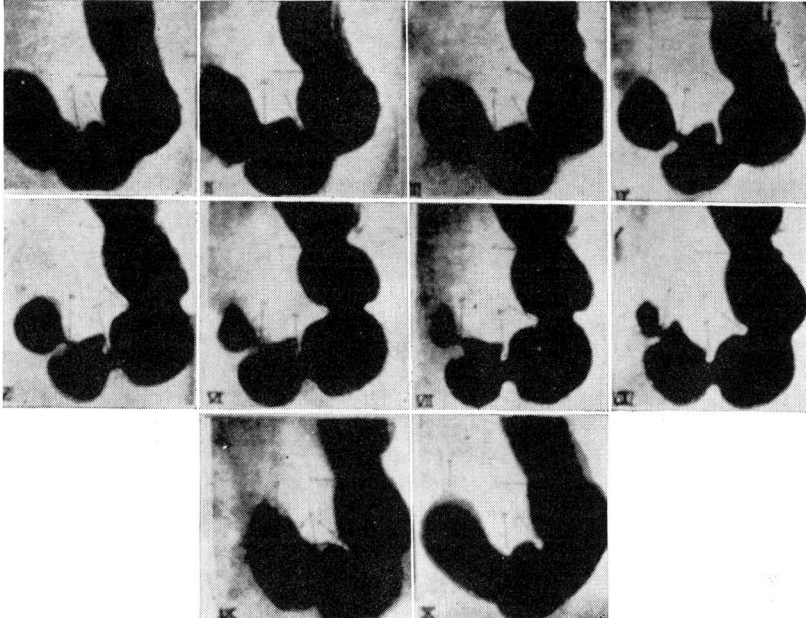

Fig. 61.8. Serial X-ray photographs of human stomach taken at 2-second intervals during digestion (From Cole.)

of the pleasure of eating. Although it is frequently associated with hunger, it is not necessarily so. One may have his hunger completely satisfied and still have an appetite for palatable food. Likewise, one may be hungry but because the food presented is distasteful, or the surroundings disagreeable, he may suffer from loss of appetite. Extreme hunger may, of itself, reduce appetite through producing a sensation of nausea. This subject is discussed more fully in ch. 62.

DIGESTIVE PERISTALSIS

As soon as food is taken, the hunger contractions cease, and after a variable period of time, they are replaced by digestive peristalsis. The outstanding characteristic of this type of gastric peristalsis is the constancy of its rhythm. When the stomach contains food, peristaltic waves occur regularly, at a frequency of about 3 per min. in the human, 4 per min. in the dog, and about 5 per min. in the cat. Each wave beings as a slight circular constriction of some part of the body of the stomach or corpus ventriculi (Cannon, 1898, 1911b). The exact point of origin varies with conditions, one of which is the amount of food in the stomach. The contraction appears in the x-ray silhouette as a slight indentation on the greater and lesser curvatures which travels toward the pylorus, becoming deeper meanwhile, until it finally ends with a contraction of the

pyloric sphincter (Wheelon and Thomas, 1920, 1921). Not all gastric waves reach the pylorus in this manner. Some appear to terminate at the incisura angularis (Hofmeister and Schutz, 1886), or they may end at some point on the pyloric portion, most frequently in the region of the pyloric canal. When this happens, the portion of the stomach beyond the point of termination of the wave appears to contract concentrically, expelling its contents either into the duodenum or back into the proximal portion of the stomach.

The difference between waves that go all the way to the pylorus and those that appear to stop short, may be explained by assuming that all waves progress peristaltically until they become deep enough to obliterate the gastric lumen. This would cause a sudden rise in pressure in the space beyond, and might act as a stimulus, causing the muscle surrounding this space to contract. It is probably significant that the antral muscle shows a greater tendency to contract in response to the stimulus of stretching, than do the other gastric muscles (Gellhorn and Budde, 1923).

A peristaltic wave takes one minute, more or less, to travel from its point of origin to the pylorus. Since there are three waves per min., the stomach will usually be occupied by three waves at one time, or by four or more if the origin is near the fundus (fig. 61.8). If the origin is low, only one or two may be seen. Cole recognized this fact, and spoke of one-, two-, three-, or four-cycle stomachs, depending on the number of waves that were visible at one time.

During digestion, the body and fundus of the stomach, which serve the reservoir function primarily, behave quite differently from the pyloric portion (which serves mainly the function of mechanical digestion and propulsion). The muscle of the body and fundus are relatively thin and participate to only a moderate extent in visible peristalsis. It is this portion of the stomach the undergoes the greatest changes in size and shape, accommodating itself through changes in tonus to the volume of its contents.

The Tonus of the Stomach

Tonus is a word that has a variety of meanings and is difficult to define precisely; nevertheless, there are certain characteristics of smooth muscle for which no other name is available. Tonus, as applied to smooth muscle, refers to the relation between the length of the muscle and the tension which it maintains; thus, it may mean either the tension in the muscle when maintained at constant length, or the length which the muscle assumes under constant tension. This is another way of saying that a change in the tonus of a muscle constitutes a change in its elastic properties. In the digesting stomach, the length of the muscle fibers is determined largely by the volume of the gastric contents. In these circumstances, changes in tonus express themselves primarily in terms of tension, and are indicated by the pressure within the stomach. If the stomach is empty, changes in tonus will express themselves by changes in the length of the muscle fibers, and this becomes manifest through changes in the shape of the stomach. The shape of the human stomach is subject to wide variations. Some of the shapes which it may assume are illustrated in fig. 61.6. The shape of the stomach is also influenced by the volume of its contents and by the posture. In the reclining position it tends to assume a more nearly transverse position, whereas in the upright position the midportion of the stomach has a tendency to descend, producing more of a J shape.

The tonus of the gastric muscle, in so far as it is inversely related to the average volume capacity of the stomach, must increase progressively as the stomach empties during digestion, otherwise the intragastric pressure would fall to a level too low to maintain emptying. Whether this necessary gain in tonus takes place by continuous gradual shortening of the fibers, as postulated by

Cannon (1911b), or in a stepwise manner as proposed by Cole (1911, 1917), is still uncertain. Cole described what he called "systole" and "diastole" of the stomach. These are contractions and relaxations, respectively, of the entire gastric musculature, occurring approximately once every 20 sec. in man. During each systole the peristaltic waves increase in force, as is indicated by deeper indentations on the greater and lesser curvatures in the x-ray silhouette. Decrease in the vigor of peristalsis is associated with the phase of diastole. If Cole's description is correct, the problem of gain in tone becomes merely a matter of a slightly lessened relaxation after each successive systole, the resulting decrease in volume corresponding to the volume of material expelled from the stomach.

The tonus of the gastric muscle and the peristaltic movements are closely related; anything that decreases gastric tonus depresses peristalsis, and any increase in tone is apt to be associated with an increase in the vigor of the peristaltic waves. For example, if the vagus nerves are cut, the stomach becomes hypotonic and propulsive peristaltic waves cease. After several weeks or months, the tonus is partially restored and with it, peristaltic activity. The apparent dependence of peristalsis on tonus suggested to Cannon (1911a) the thought that rhythmic peristalsis arises in muscle fibers that are under a certain optimal degree of tension, depending on the relationship between the volume of the gastric contents and the tonus of the muscle. Since systole and diastole of the stomach, as described by Cole, occur approximately once every 20 sec., which is also the interval between peristaltic waves, it may be that each peristaltic wave is initiated by an increase in the tone of the entire gastric muscle.

As already pointed out, the tonus of the stomach increases progressively during a prolonged fast, and eventually the stomach becomes tubular in shape. When food is taken, the stomach begins to relax progressively with each swallow, so that the intragastric pressure does not rise during the act of eating; this is the receptive relaxation of the stomach referred to earlier in this chapter. Once the stomach is filled, the tonus begins to recover, and after it reaches a certain level digestive peristalsis makes its appearance.

The Relation Between Hunger Contractions and Digestive Peristalsis

Hunger contractions and digestive peristalsis have been described as though they were entirely separate and distinct types of activity. This is largely the result of their having been investigated by different authors under different experimental conditions. In the pyloric portion at least, one cannot distinguish between a hunger contraction, and a peristaltic wave such as might occur during digestion. The contractions of the entire stomach that are seen during the hunger periods, are very similar to the systoles and diastoles described by Cole (1911) as occurring when the stomach was filled with a barium mixture. It is not unlikely that such real differences as there are between hunger contractions and digestive peristalsis are due merely to the different conditions under which they occur, and that they really represent the operation of a single motor mechanism.

Coordination of antrum, pyloric sphincter and duodenum. The fact that there is a relationship between duodenal motility and the gastric peristaltic cycle was first noted by Joseph and Meltzer. In a study on rabbits, they observed that "during each contraction of the pyloric part of the stomach, the duodenum stops its rhythmic activity and loses tone, only to resume both again as soon as the contraction of the stomach passes off." They remarked that the phenomenon resembles the relaxation of the stomach which occurs during the act of swallowing. Later, Wheelon and Thomas (1922) and Thomas and Crider noted a similar relationship in dogs. As interpreted by Thomas and Crider (1935), a typical gastroduodenal cycle is as follows: The gastric peristaltic wave approaches the pylorus and the tone and the rhythmic activity of the first part of the duodenum are progressively inhibited, reaching their lowest point just before the gastric wave reaches the pylorus. As the gastric wave ends in a contraction of the pyloric sphincter, the duodenum resumes its tone and rhythmic activity. The contraction of the sphincter is, therefore, accompanied by a contraction of the duodenum. Since the rhythmic contractions of the pyloric sphincter coincide with contractions of the duodenal cap, they are probably concerned primarily with control of regurgitation of duodenal contents into the stomach.

The Gastroduodenal Pressure Cycle

Numerous efforts have been made to measure pressures in the stomach and intestine, but the methods used were so inadequate that the observations contributed little to an understanding of gastric function. About 1940, Brody, Werle, Meschan and Quigley devised methods for the precise determination of intraluminal pressures in the gastrointestinal tract. They utilized modern precision manometers connected to small open tubes or tubes ending in small, metal-shielded balloons. The open ends of the tubes, or the end that was fitted with balloons, were placed in the areas from which pressures were to be recorded. The experimental animals were unanesthetized dogs provided with appropriate fistulas. Ordinarily the receiving ends of the pressure tubes were placed just above and just below the pylorus, hence, intragastric pressures were recorded from the terminal antrum, and duodenal pressures from the duodenal bulb. In some of their studies, graphic methods were combined with x-ray and fluoroscopic observations. This method yielded, in addition to pressure measurements, significant information regarding gastric and duodenal motility, pyloric sphincter activity, and the passage of contents through the pylorus. Brody and Quigley and their associates extended the study to human subjects.

When the stomach is at rest (peristalsis absent), or in the intervals between gastric peristaltic waves, the antral and duodenal (bulbar) pressures are low, being slightly above or below atmospheric levels. These pressures are referred to as basal pressures. Basal pressure in the antrum is 1 to 2 cm. of fluid above the basal pressure in the duodenum. Taking food increases basal pressure in both the antrum and the duodenum, but the pressure rise is greater in the antrum, hence the pressure difference between the antrum and the duodenum is increased. When a peristaltic wave approaches the pylorus, the antral pressure increases, usually to between 15 and 30 cm. of water, followed by an increase in bulbar pressure. However, the bulbar pressure rises more rapidly than the antral pressure, so that the two reach their peaks simultaneously, after which they both fall again to basal levels. This cycle is repeated, with only quantitative variations, with each gastric cycle. By other means it was established that contraction of the pyloric sphincter usually begins near the start of the rise in bulbar pressure but outlasts the increase in bulbar pressure.

In the fluoroscopic studies, passage of gastric contents through the pylorus could be seen to begin as the antral wave approached the pylorus but before the elevation in antral pressure could be detected. Evacuation continued through the early part of the rise in antral pressure but ceased some time during the succeeding rise in bulbar pressure (and the sphincteric contraction). Consequently, the time during which gastric contents

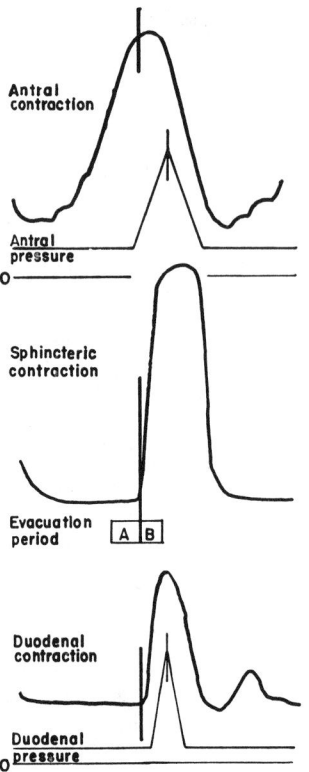

FIG. 61.9. Composite diagram showing the successive contractions of the pars pylorica ("antrum"), pyloric sphincter, and duodenum during a single gastric cycle and the associated intraluminal pressure changes. Evacuation periods A and B are also shown. The contraction curves are traced from a kymographic balloon water-manometer record. The pressure curves are approximate copies of the curves published by Quigley *et al.*, 1950. Vertical lines mark simultaneous points.

could be seen passing into the duodenum could be divided into two distinct but continuous phases: one, during which only basal pressures served as a driving force and resistance at the pylorus was low (designated evacuation period "A"), and another during which the antral pressure substantially exceeded the duodenal pressure and the pyloric resistance was rising (called evacuation period "B") (Quigley, 1943, 1944).

Figure 61.9 is an attempt to correlate the gastroduodenal pressure cycle with the motility cycle described in the preceding section. The antral pressure rise is seen to be related to the terminal phase of the antral contraction. The bulbar pressure rise is clearly a result of the contraction phase of the duodenal cycle. Both are closely related in time to the contraction of the sphincter muscle. By way of explanation let us assume that a strong antral wave is approaching

the pylorus. Presumably it obliterates the gastric lumen at some point, and would put pressure on the contents of the terminal antrum if they were not free to escape by way of the pylorus. However, they do escape at first (evacuation period "A"), hence no pressure rise is evidenced. Presently, as the wave approaches the sphincter, the contraction of that muscle begins, the pyloric lumen narrows, resistance increases, and the trapped contents of the terminal antrum are put under pressure, which is recorded as the antral pressure rise. At first the pressure is sufficient to overcome the increasing resistance at the pylorus (evacuation period "B"), but the rapidly contracting sphincter soon closes the pylorus and puts an end to this cycle of evacuation. It is not to be inferred that the stomach always empties in the manner described. Liquids have been observed to leave the stomach without any rhythmic changes in intragastric pressure or any evidence of gastric peristalsis (Thomas, 1957; Shay and Gershon-Cohen, 1934).

GASTRIC FILLING AND EMPTYING

It is possible to determine how solid or semisolid food arranges itself within the stomach of an animal by marking successive portions of the food with dyes or pigments so that they can be identified later. After the stomach is filled, the animal is killed, and the stomach removed and frozen, or otherwise fixed, and sectioned. In this way it has been found that the first food eaten lies against the greater curvature in the body and fundus of the stomach. Successive layers lie progressively nearer the lesser curvature until the last portion eaten is near the upper end of the lesser curvature in the vicinity of the cardiac orifice. Liquids, on the other hand, tend to remain near the lesser curvature of the stomach and to flow toward the pylorus along a V-shaped groove formed by the muscle in this region. This is the so-called *magenstrasse* which is evident in some animals, but less so in the human. In any case, if a large volume of liquid is swallowed, it flows around the food mass and tends to be distributed over the entire interior of the stomach between the food mass and the stomach wall.

A relatively small part of the energy expended by the gastric muscle is utilized in propelling food from the stomach into the intestine through the pyloric orifice. The vigor of the gastric muscular contraction is such that if it were all utilized in propulsion the stomach would empty itself within a very few minutes. By far the greater part of the work is utilized in mechanical digestion, serving to macerate the food particles and break them up into small fragments. This work is done largely by the pyloric portion, which in some ways resembles in function the gizzard of birds. The powerful contractions of the pyloric muscle drive the food against the pylorus. All but the small part that escapes into the duodenum is forced back through a narrow orifice, formed by the contraction wave, into the body of the stomach. It is this manipulation of the food mass which results in its being broken down and mechanically digested in the pyloric portion of the stomach.

The rate at which food leaves the stomach is determined by a variety of factors, among which are the total volume of the gastric contents, and the consistency, chemical composition, pH, and osmolar concentration of the food. Hunt and his co-workers (1951) have shown that for any individual, and for any type of meal, the amount evacuated in a unit of time is a function of the volume of the gastric contents. The effect of consistency on the rate of emptying is best seen by comparing the emptying of liquids with the emptying of solids. Inert liquids, which neither stimulate the stomach chemically nor osmotically, leave the stomach rapidly. Water, for example, begins to leave the stomach almost as soon as it is swallowed. Solids, on the other hand, are not normally evacuated from the stomach until they are reduced to a fluid or semifluid consistency. Undigested solids are not normally allowed to pass the pyloric sphincter but are returned to the body of the stomach (Cannon, 1911b).

The influence of the chemical composition of the food on emptying is shown by the relative rate of emptying of the three major foodstuffs. Cannon (1904) showed that for meals of a given size, a meal consisting mainly of carbohydrate left the stomach more rapidly than one consisting mainly of protein or fat, and that a protein meal left more rapidly than a fat meal. Fat, especially if eaten in large quantities, remains in the stomach for a very long time. It is not unusual to find food in a dog's stomach as long as 24 hours after a meal consisting largely of fat meat.

The osmolar concentration of the gastric contents has a profound effect upon the rate of gastric emptying. One of the earliest facts to be determined with respect to gastric emptying was that physiological saline leaves the stomach faster than does salt solutions of either greater or lesser concentration. More recently, Hunt

(1956) has shown that in human subjects, adding salt to water hastened emptying of the water from the stomach, up to a concentration of about 100 mEq/l. Above 150 mEq/l. the emptying was delayed. In this way he showed that making the gastric contents either hypertonic or hypotonic with respect to the blood caused a delay in emptying. This is an important factor in the slow emptying of sugar solutions although, as will be pointed out later, sugar slows gastric emptying in another way.

The effect of acid on gastric emptying has been the subject of considerable study and extensive speculation. It is well known that strongly acid solutions leave the stomach slowly, and that the rate of emptying of such solutions can be accelerated by neutralizing the acid. For example, in some experiments by Crider and Thomas (1937), 300 ml. of physiological saline left the stomach of a dog in an average time of 17 min., whereas it took 42 min. for the stomach to dispose of an equal amount of N/20 hydrochloric acid. However, it does not necessarily follow that hydrochloric acid plays an important part in regulating gastric emptying under ordinary circumstances. The acidity of the gastric and intestinal contents is usually not great enough during digestion to affect gastric emptying materially. For example, a pH of 3.0 in the duodenum is necessary in order to influence the rate of emptying of the stomach but the intestinal contents usually have a pH that is well above this level, pH values of 4.0 to 6.0 being most common. Nevertheless, the inhibitory effect of acid on gastric emptying has an important function in protecting the duodenal mucous membrane against excess acidity.

Regulation of Gastric Emptying

At least two mechanisms are available for regulating the rate at which the gastric contents pass into the duodenum. One is the powerful sphincter muscle that surrounds the pyloric orifice at the junction of the stomach and duodenum. Strong contraction of the pyloric sphincter could, if maintained, effectively prevent the passage of the gastric contents through the pyloric orifice. The other mechanism has to do with the control of gastric motor activities. In the early days of physiology it was taken for granted that gastric emptying was controlled entirely by the pyloric sphincter. This was the result of reasoning from structure to function; there was no other apparent use for the powerful sphincter muscle so strategically situated between the stomach and duodenum. However, a closer scrutiny of the function of the pyloric portion of the stomach reveals that a sphincter muscle is necessary at this point to enable the pyloric muscle to carry out its function of comminution and maceration of the food mass. It is also important to have a sphincter to serve as a valve which will prevent excessive regurgitation of duodenal contents into the stomach.

Another fact which has contributed to the concept of pyloric control of gastric emptying is the existence of a powerful pyloric reflex. This reflex is elicited by mechanical or chemical stimulation of the duodenum and results in contraction of the pyloric sphincter muscle. One of the stimuli which is capable of eliciting a pyloric reflex is relatively strong hydrochloric acid in the duodenum. This, along with other observations made in connection with his classical studies of gastric motility, led Cannon (1907) to propose his theory of the acid control of the pyloric sphincter. He assumed that the pylorus remains closed and thus prevents emptying of the stomach until the gastric contents become acid in reaction. As soon as the secretion of hydrochloric acid in the stomach is sufficient to acidify the gastric contents in the pyloric portion, the pylorus opens and allows some of the chyme to escape into the duodenum. The acid chyme in the duodenum then elicits a pyloric reflex and causes the pylorus to close, and to remain closed, until such time as the duodenal contents are neutralized. This attractive theory failed to take into account that gastric emptying proceeds normally in persons who secrete no hydrochloric acid, that there is no failure of regulation of gastric emptying when the pyloric sphincter area has been removed surgically, and that the acidity of the duodenal contents necessary to close the pylorus is far in excess of that which normally occurs in the duodenum. Thomas et al. (1934) found that even when the pyloric sphincter does contract in response to duodenal irritation, the contraction is of brief duration and is followed by relaxation to below the previous tone level.

If the pyloric sphincter were to act as a regulator of gastric emptying, it would be necessary for the sphincter muscle and the muscle of the remainder of the stomach to be reciprocally innervated, that is, that the innervation would have to be so arranged that when the sphincter is contracting, the stomach would relax, and vice versa. The true situation is quite the contrary; stimuli which cause contraction of the

gastric muscle also increase the tone and activity of the pyloric sphincter, whereas those which cause relaxation of the sphincter also cause relaxation of the gastric musculature (Thomas and Wheelon, 1922).

It has been shown that the major factors regulating gastric emptying are still effective, even though the pyloric sphincter is mechanically prevented from contracting by placing an open tube in the pyloric orifice (Crider and Thomas, 1937). In these circumstances, the differences in the rate of emptying of acid, saline, alcohol and olive oil are in no way modified by maintaining the pylorus in an open condition, except that the emptying time for alcohol and fat are somewhat prolonged. Evidently the reason for this is that duodenal contents regurgitate freely into the stomach when these two substances are being emptied through an open pylorus.

The enterogastric reflex. As soon as it became apparent that the characteristic response of the pyloric sphincter to acid in the duodenum was not contraction, although this sometimes occurs, but prolonged and persistent relaxation, and that this relaxation is associated with loss of tonus and relaxation of the remainder of the gastric muscle, it was evident that the acid control of the pyloric sphincter could not be a major factor in the regulation of gastric emptying. A more adequate explanation was found in the diminution of gastric peristalsis and gastric tone, with the consequent decrease in intragastric pressure, which follows duodenal stimulation. As long as the pressure in the stomach is below that in the duodenum, emptying cannot occur. Further study revealed that, not only acid, but many other constituents of the gastric chyme (such as products of protein digestion (Thomas and Crider, 1939), products of starch digestion (Quigley and Phelps, 1934), fats and fatty acids) all cause inhibition of the gastric muscle when present in the duodenum. None of these substances, with the exception of hydrochloric acid, causes even momentary contraction of the pyloric sphincter. Mechanical distention of the intestine by means of saline also has a moderate inhibitory effect on gastric motility. However, this particular method of stimulation also causes sustained contraction of the pyloric sphincter; hence, the inhibitory effect on the gastric muscle is probably of little consequence in regulating emptying in response to mechanical stimulation. Thomas, Crider and Mogan (1934) found that the inhibitory effect of many chemical substances disappears after the vagus nerves have been cut. They concluded that the inhibitory effect of these substances is caused by a reflex involving the vagus nerves and proposed that it be designated the *enterogastric reflex*.

Enterogastrone. The inhibitory effect of fat on gastric motility has been known for many years and was recognized by Cannon, who exempted the delayed emptying due to fat from his acid control theory. Fat exerts its effect in the absence of any available nerve supply (Farrell and Ivy, 1926). Kosaka and Lim (1930, 1933), and Quigley, Zettleman and Ivy (1934) showed that fat inhibition is caused by a hormone which Lim (1933) called *enterogastrone*. This hormone is released from the intestinal mucous membrane by fat or fatty acids and some other substances in the duodenum. While circulating in the blood, it is carried to the stomach, where it has an inhibitory effect on the gastric muscle. The fact that it also inhibits gastric secretion was mentioned in ch. 57. Quigley and Phelps (1934) were also able to demonstrate inhibition of the denervated stomach by carbohydrate substances when they were present in the intestine. It is assumed that carbohydrates also release enterogastrone or some closely related substance. In experiments on vagotomized animals, Thomas and Crider (1934) noted, in dogs, that hydrochloric acid continued to exert some slight influence on gastric motility after the vagus and splanchnic nerves were cut. They concluded that a hormonal mechanism, as well as a nervous mechanism, was probably involved in the action of hydrochloric acid. Schapiro and Woodward (1955) have found that acid in the intestine inhibits gastric motility in human subjects equally well, whether or not the vagi are intact.

In summary, we can visualize the events following a meal approximately as follows: Gastric emptying begins as soon as any part of the gastric contents become fluid enough to pass through the pylorus. Once started, it proceeds rhythmically, a small amount being evacuated about every 20 sec. in man. Regulation of emptying begins as soon as the evacuated material has accumulated in the intestine to the point where any one of the numerous stimuli to the intestine associated with the chyme reaches threshold value. These stimuli are comprised in the chemical constituents of the chyme and to some extent in its volume. The chemical stimuli include the following, listed in the order of inhibitory potency in the concentrations in which they are usually encountered: fats, fatty acids, proteoses, peptones, amino acids, sugars

and other products of starch digestion, and hydrogen ions; also effective are osmotically active substances and non-specific irritants. The effect of these stimuli is to decrease the tone and peristaltic activity of the stomach, thus reducing the pressure gradient which develops with each gastric cycle and which is responsible for the passage of fluid through the pylorus. With the more powerful inhibitors, e.g., fat, the gradient may be reversed, and duodenal contents will then be regurgitated into the stomach. The inhibitory effect is exerted through a reflex involving the vagus nerves (*the enterogastric reflex*) or through a hormone (*enterogastrone*) released into the blood from the intestinal mucous membrane, or both. Products of protein digestion, and acid and nonspecific irritants act mainly through enterogastrone. However, there may be a reflex element in the effect of the latter group, and there is undoubtedly a hormonal component in the effect of hydrochloric acid. The pyloric sphincter plays a part by preventing regurgitation of the duodenal contents into the stomach; it also contracts rhythmically in such a way that it apparently limits the volume evacuated at each cycle but as yet there is no evidence that this function is utilized in regulating the over-all rate of gastric emptying.

ABNORMAL GASTRIC MOTILITY

Either hyper- or hypomotility of the stomach may be seen clinically. In the absence of specific diseases involving these conditions, such changes are most often psychogenic and result from acute or chronic emotional disturbances. Acute emotional upsets are usually associated with relaxation of the gastric muscle due to increased activity of the thoracolumbar sympathetic nerves and the adrenal medulla. Hypermotility is said to occur more frequently in prolonged or chronic emotional states involving resentment or prolonged anger. Hyperperistalsis is seen in pyloric obstruction. In this situation, it is partially due to the absence of inhibitory reflexes from the duodenum (the enterogastric reflex) and, probably, partially due to continued stimulation by retained gastric contents. Excessive belching, heartburn (pyrosis), regurgitation of food, hiccuping and other types of gastric distress are probably traceable to some abnormality in the movements of the stomach but the relationships have not been well defined.

In 12 patients with active duodenal ulcer, and no evidence of pyloric obstruction, total gastric motility was essentially the same as that observed in normal individuals (Hightower and Gambill, 1953). A qualitative difference was noted, however, in that the incidence of Type II contractions was increased with a corresponding decrease in Type I contractions.

Hypotonus, or general loss of tonus in gastric muscle, is likely to be associated with the deterioration of all body function seen in asthenic states. Hypertonus is supposed to be associated with a condition called *vagotonia*. Vagotonia, if it exists, is a form of hyperactivity of the parasympathetic innervation of the viscera, but the condition has never been well defined clinically. Cardiospasm and pylorospasm are conditions in which these sphincter muscles are supposed to be in a state of sustained contraction. Doubtless such abnormalities can occur but probably much less frequently than they are diagnosed. Cardiospasm, for example, could be easily confused with loss of power in the esophageal muscle or absence of esophageal peristalsis; likewise, pylorospasm is often diagnosed when the true condition is failure of the gastric peristaltic mechanism to develop adequate gastric pressure, e.g., following the operation of vagotomy. In such instances, the pylorus is usually less contracted than normally; a closed pylorus being due to failure of the gastric muscle to develop sufficient power to force the gastric contents past even a relaxed pyloric sphincter. True pylorospasm occurs as a congenital condition in infants who suffer from hypertrophy of the pyloric muscle. More accurately, the term pyloric stenosis, or hypertrophic pyloric stenosis, should be applied to this condition. Pylorospasm rarely occurs in adults but when present it is associated with irritative lesions in the region of the pylorus, either of the duodenum or pyloric portion of the stomach.

VOMITING

Vomiting is a reflex which serves to relieve the upper gastrointestinal tract of its contents. This may occur either because the contents are irritating, or because the organs themselves, or the nerves that supply them, are more irritable than normal. In either case, there is an unusual degree of stimulation of some part of the tract. The most sensitive area is the first portion of the duodenum (Luckhardt, Phillips and Carlson, 1919), but adequate stimulation of other parts of the intestine, or of the stomach, can induce the reflex. Even mild mechanical stimulation of the pharynx or fauces is effective in most people. Inflammation or mechanical disturbances in the intestine (appendicitis, obstruction, or strangulation) may induce violent emesis. Vomiting may be induced by abnormal stimulation of sensory receptors in organs outside the gastrointestinal tract, such as the uterus, kidneys, heart or semicircular canals. Effective stimuli may also enter by way of the eyes, nose or mouth in the form of nauseating sights, odors, or tastes; these give rise to what is called psychic vomiting. It is not unusual for a soldier to vomit on going into battle, or at some time during the battle experience; some people vomit at the sight of blood.

Vomiting that is induced by irritation of organs other than those of the gastrointestinal tract is sometimes referred to as "reflex" vomiting. This is an incorrect distinction however, since nearly all vomiting is reflex in origin. Even psychic vomiting is probably the result of conditioned reflexes.

Vomiting may be induced by certain types of motion such as seasickness, air sickness and car sickness, or the nausea that some people experience when in a swing. This is probably the result of unusual stimulation of the equilibratory sense organs of the labyrinth.

The Vomiting Center

The vomiting center lies in the dorsal part of the lateral reticular formation of the medulla oblongata, close to (and to some extent including) the tractus solitaris. It lies in close relation to (but is quite distinct from) the respiratory centers. It is one of a constellation of visceral centers in this situation which includes salivatory nuclei, defecation, and vasomotor centers, as well as the vestibular nuclei. These form a relationship consistent with the physiological reactions (salivation, vasomotor, respiratory, etc.) associated with the vomiting act. The *efferent* fibers are contained chiefly in the phrenics, the vagi, and the sympathetics; but fibers are also conveyed by spinal nerves to the abdominal muscles and by cranial nerves to the muscles of the pharynx, palate, etc. The *afferent* impulses reach the center along a multitude of routes, the chief being the vagal and sympathetic fibers of the stomach and abdominal viscera.

"Central" vomiting. Vomiting may occur as a result of direct stimulation of the vomiting center in the medulla. Certain substances, such as *apomorphine, ipecac (or emetine),* and *picrotoxine,* when administered intravenously, cause

vomiting through a specific action upon the center. These substances induce vomiting in animals when applied directly to the center. Typical vomiting efforts (retching) follow the injection of apomorphine after removal of the stomach and intestines. The experiments of Wang and Borison point to a chemoreceptor "trigger" mechanism in the ala cinerea which, through its connection with the vomiting center itself, induces vomiting when stimulated by these emetics. These investigators found copper sulfate acted as an emetic, both peripherally, through the gastrointestinal tract, and centrally. A lesion in the ala cinerea abolished only the central action.

The central vomiting caused by traumatic stimulation of the center due to head injuries, increased intracranial pressure, brain tumor, or meningeal irritation is most important clinically. This type of vomiting is characterized by the great force with which the vomitus is ejected ("projectile vomiting"). There is also a minimum of nausea and a relative absence of participation of the voluntary muscles.

The persistence of pernicious *vomiting of pregnancy* is probably due to increased excitability of the center resulting from some metabolic disturbance. According to Harding, the important factors in its production are carbohydrate starvation and dehydration with ketosis. Ordinary morning sickness is looked upon as a minor form of this condition, and differing from pernicious vomiting only in degree. As a result of the demands of the fetus, liver glycogen is low during pregnancy. After the fast of the night, the reserves of carbohydrate are further reduced; a mild ketosis results which leads to nausea and vomiting. The distaste for food brought about by hindering the replenishment of the carbohydrate stores aggravates the ketosis. Thus, morning sickness merges insensibly into the pernicious type of vomiting. A neurotic element is also frequently a potent influence in the development and persistence of the condition. The obvious corrective measures are high carbohydrate feeding, the free administration of fluids, injections of glucose if necessary, mild sedatives, and rest and quiet.

The Vomiting Movements

Vomiting or emesis usually begins with nausea, which is characterized by the secretion of excessive quantities of saliva containing a large amount of mucus, and certain well known dis-

agreeable sensations. In the dog it has been possible to analyze by graphic methods the sequence of events in vomiting. The first muscular movement is a strong, sustained contraction of the upper small intestine. Next, the pyloric sphincter contracts; then the pyloric portion of the stomach contracts. These changes all take place during the period of nausea, and result in emptying the contents of the upper jejunum, duodenum, and pyloric portion of the stomach into the fundus and body of the stomach, which are relaxed and dilated. After this has occurred, the voluntary muscles come into play, and at the same time the lower esophageal sphincter, esophagus, and upper esophageal sphincter relax. Following an inspiratory movement, the glottis is closed and the abdominal muscles contract in a characteristic jerky manner (retching), compressing the stomach between the contracted diaphragm and the abdominal organs. The resulting pressure on the gastric contents causes their evacuation through the relaxed esophagus.

The precise sequence described above is probably not always followed and the mechanism may differ somewhat in different animals. For example, Cannon (1911b) gives the following graphic account of the act of vomiting in a cat as observed by means of x-rays:

The upper part of the stomach showed complete inhibition of its tone and appeared as a perfectly flaccid bag; the cardia relaxed. There then followed several deep peristaltic contractions which, commencing about the middle of the body of the organ, swept downward toward the incisura angularis where they came to a standstill forming a sharp ring of constriction. From this point a weaker wave continued to the pylorus. Finally, a very deep, strong contraction at the incisura appeared to almost divide the stomach in two, the upper part of the stomach and the cardia meanwhile remaining quite relaxed. A sharp contraction of the diaphragm and abdominal muscles then followed and ejected the gastric contents through the open cardia into the esophagus. The stomach played a more or less passive part in the process, its evacuation being effected by the strong compression to which it was subjected by the sharp descent of the diaphragm and the contraction of the abdominal muscles. Antiperistalsis was observed only once and then the wave did not proceed beyond the antrum. The deep contraction at the incisura offered an effectual barrier to the passage of stomach contents in a downward direction. Similar movements have been described in man.

Definite antiperistaltic waves in the stomach

TABLE 61.1

Drugs	Afferent Autonomic Fibers Acted upon	Organs Containing Susceptible Fibers
Mercuric chloride	Sympathetic and vagus	Stomach
Tartar emetic	Vagus	Stomach, duodenum and heart
Digitalis	Sympathetic and vagus	Heart
Pilocarpine	Sympathetic and vagus	Heart

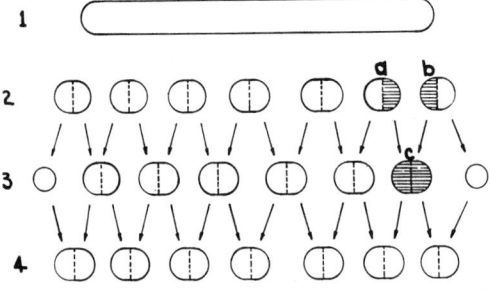

FIG. 61.10. Diagram representing the process of rhythmic segmentation. Lines 1, 2, 3, 4, indicate the sequence of appearances in a single loop. The dot lines represent the regions of division. The arrows show the relation of the particles (eg., a and b) to the segments they subsequently form (c). (After Cannon, 1911.)

are rarely seen although violent churning movements may occur.[1] In certain types of vomiting, e.g., intestinal obstruction, or in persistent vomiting from other causes, antiperistalsis arises in the small intestine and sweeps material into the stomach, or there may be a strong contraction of the duodenum which reverses the pressure gradient between the antrum and the duodenal bulb. Such movements of the duodenum occur sometime prior to the actual vomiting or at the same time; it accounts for the fact that a short time after the stomach has been thoroughly washed out, bile-stained fluid or fecal material may be vomited. According to Alvarez, reverse

[1] In certain lower forms, however, e.g., the fish and the frog, which of course have no diaphragm, vomiting is carried out by the activity of the stomach alone, antiperistaltic waves carrying the food through the cardia. This more primitive type of vomiting, i.e., where reverse peristalsis and relaxation of the cardia are the prominent features, occurs normally in infants. The excess fluid of an over-sized meal is regurgitated without the assistance, apparently, of the abdominal muscles or diaphragm; position, and external pressure upon the abdomen following the meal no doubt, also sometimes play a part.

peristalsis starting in the upper bowel is itself a potent cause of nausea and vomiting.

Relaxation of the cardia (lower esophageal sphincter) is an essential part of the vomiting act, for the stomach is subject to strong compression during coughing, defecation, etc., yet the gastric contents are not as a rule forced into the esophagus. The tone of the cardia is probably actually increased at these times. It has been mentioned that division of the vagi in animals causes the cardia to enter into a spastic state. Hatcher and Weiss found that if after such a procedure a vomiting reflex was initiated, mucus was expelled from the esophagus and the usual muscular movements were called into play, with the exception of relaxation of the cardia. That is, the animal retched but material was not expelled from the stomach. It is well known that with some persons vomiting is difficult, whereas in others little distress is experienced. Differences in the degree of tone of the cardia are probably responsible for these individual peculiarities (table 61.1).

During the ejection of the vomitus the esophagus is relaxed throughout; the glottis is closed, the respirations are inhibited, and the larynx and hyoid bone are drawn upward and forward and are held rigidly in this position. The throat is thus enlarged to allow free exit for the stomach contents, which are prevented from entering the nasopharynx by the elevation of the soft palate.

Small Bowel Motility

The major part of the smooth muscle of the small intestine is distributed in a thick, circular layer and a much thinner, longitudinal layer. The circular layer is responsible for most of the visible intestinal movements. The longitudinal layer undoubtedly participates in the movements, but the relation of its activity to that of the circular muscle has been described differently by different authors and is, therefore, somewhat uncertain. The outstanding characteristic of the muscle is its *rhythmicity*, which is manifest under appropriate conditions by alternate contractions and relaxations at a remarkably regular frequency.

RHYTHMIC SEGMENTING CONTRACTIONS

The more common type of rhythmic contractions occur at regularly spaced intervals along a section of the intestine, dividing it into short segments; also, they may occur singly, in pairs, or in a variety of other arrangements. The area involved in each segment may be less than 1 cm. or it may be several cm. long. In the cat, Cannon (1902) saw a certain type of rhythmic contraction in which a section of intestine was divided into short segments by rings of contractions occurring at regularly spaced intervals. When the contracted areas relaxed, the relaxed areas between them contracted, dividing each segment into halves. The two halves of adjacent segments joined together to form a new segment (fig. 61.10). Cannon described these contractions as *segmenting contractions* and that is the name most commonly applied to them at present.

The rhythmic nature of this activity reminded Ludwig (1861) of a pendulum, hence he applied the name "pendulum" movements to these contractions. Ludwig used the pendulum as a symbol of rhythm only, but some authors have attempted to apply the simile in the sense of the to-and-fro motion of a pendulum. Swaying movements of the intestinal coils are to be seen at times, as well as a to-and-fro motion of opaque masses within the intestine, as is seen with a fluoroscope. Alvarez (1940) described them as follows: "in the rabbit, and to a certain extent in other animals and in man, a local mixing of the intestinal contents with digestive juices, similar to that produced by the segmenting contractions is brought about by sway or 'pendular' movements. A segment of bowel is pulled first in one direction and then in the other. The wall apparently being drawn over its contents like a stocking over a foot. My impression from watching these movements in men and women who have taken a barium meal is that, in man, activity is more like a short pendular movement than a rhythmic segmentation." However, to identify these movements and these only as pendular movements is confusing, since the term as originally used and commonly applied is synonymous merely with rhythmic movement without regard to the effect of the activity on the intestinal coils or their content. If we exclude the swaying movements described by Alvarez, then the rhythmic segmenting contraction and the pendular movements are one and the same thing.

In a recent study of duodenal motility in man, using simultaneous cineradiographic and pressure measuring techniques, Friedman and his associates (1965) observed two types of segmenting contractions. One type consisted of a contraction localized in a segment less than 2 cm. in length which was most marked on the free or external border of the duodenum and was there-

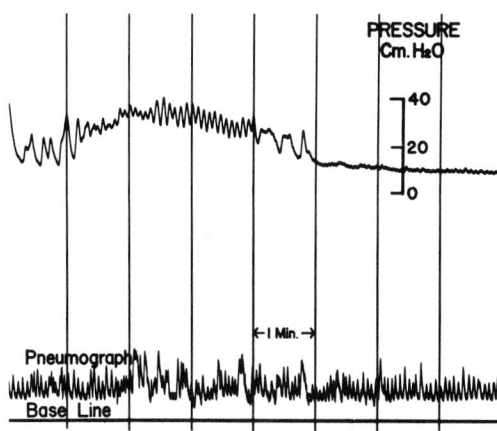

FIG. 61.11 Segmenting contractions recorded from the duodenum of man by means of balloon-kymographic system. Note that the rate of the rhythmic contractions (Type I waves) are 11 per minute. (From Hightower, in Disturbances of Gastrointestinal Motility, Chas. C Thomas, Springfield, Ill., 1959.)

fore *eccentric* in appearance. These eccentric contractions were observed to occur in two or three areas simultaneously or successively and were not followed in any sequential fashion by contractions in adjacent segments. These local eccentric contractions rarely succeeded in emptying the area of the duodenum completely and were not associated with any change in intraluminal pressure. From a visual point of view, they appeared to have a mixing function.

The other type of segmenting contraction observed in the duodenum was *concentric* and consisted of a local contraction involving a segment usually longer than 2 cm. and relatively uniform circumferentially. These concentric segmenting contractions were observed to empty the barium from the segment. Most of the barium leaving the segment was displaced distally, although a small amount was occasionally displaced proximally. As the segment relaxed, barium usually refilled the area, returning from both the proximal and distal adjacent segments. The concentric segmental contraction was associated with an intraluminal pressure change that produced a positive monophasic pressure wave on the pressure record.

The frequency of the rhythmic contractions varies with the species of animal and with the region of the intestine in which they occur. For example, in the rabbit the contractions occur at a frequency of about 20 per min. in the duodenum and about 10 per min. in the lower ileum. In the dog they occur at a frequency of about 18 per min. in the duodenum and 8 to 9 per min. in the

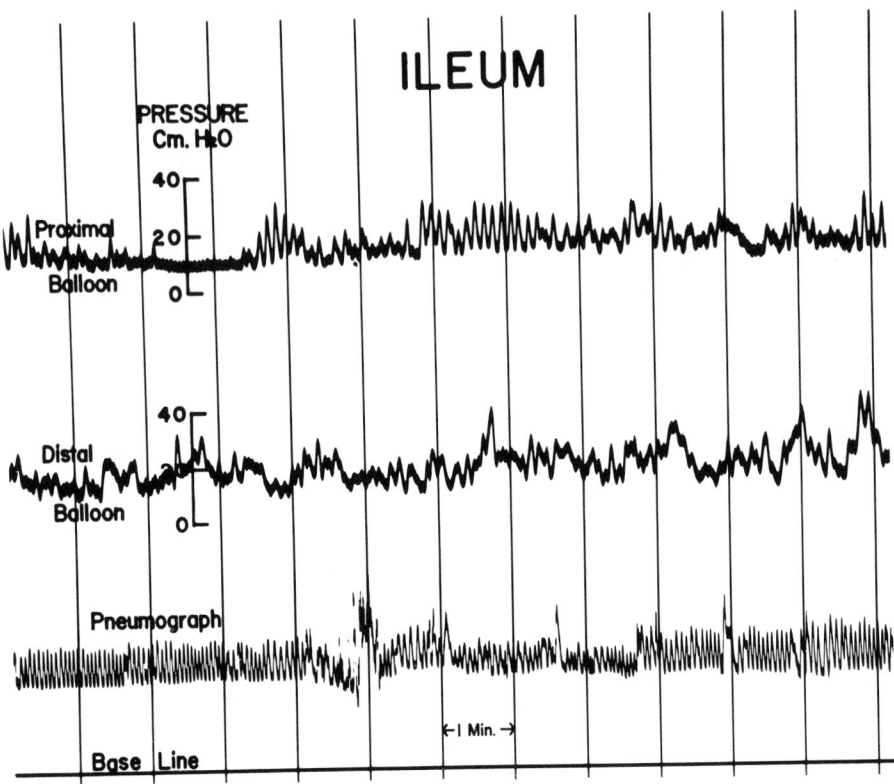

FIG. 61.12 Motility tracing obtained from lower ileum in a patient with an iliac stoma. A tandem system of balloons was used. The proximal balloon record shows short bursts of rhythmic segmentation with the rate of contractions being 8 per minute. (From Hightower, in Disturbances of Gastrointestinal Motility, Chas. C Thomas, Springfield, Ill., 1959.)

GRADIENT OF RHYTHMICITY
IN SMALL INTESTINE

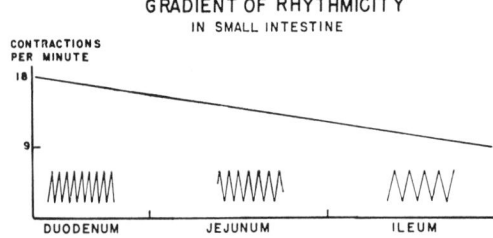

FIG. 61.13. Diagrammatic representation of the gradient of rhythmicity in the small intestine. The zig-zag lines are stylized representations of kymographic records of the contractions and relaxations of segments taken from the indicated levels of the intestine. The sloping line suggests a linear distribution of the gradient; however, there is no evidence that this is so.

lower ileum. In man, segmenting contractions occur at a rate of 11 per min. in the duodenum, and in the ileum their rate is 8 to 9 per min. (figs. 61.11 and 61.12). The frequency in other parts of the intestine is intermediate between these extremes, becoming less frequent as the distance from the pylorus increases. The frequency is surprisingly constant in any one area and is not affected by stimulation of the extrinsic nerves or by neurotropic drugs. In excised material the frequency varies with the temperature.

The variation in frequency at different levels of the intestine suggested to Alvarez and his pupils the idea that there is a gradient in the various physiological properties of the intestine, the activity being highest at the duodenal end and lowest at the ileal end of the small intestine. Among the properties for which a gradient has been established are rhythmicity, irritability, shortness of latent period, susceptibility to drugs, and others of less obvious importance (Alvarez and Hosoi, 1929). The most easily observed is the gradient of rhythmicity manifested by the variation in frequency of rhythmic contractions (fig. 61.13).

An interesting question with respect to the rhythmic contractions of the intestine is whether they originate in nervous or muscular tissue. All the available evidence indicates that the rhythmic contractions are *myogenic*. The problem has been studied by Magnus (1904), Gunn and Underhill (1914), Alvarez and Mahoney (1922) and numerous others. Using various methods of eliminating the influence of nerves upon the smooth muscle, each of these groups of investigators was able to demonstrate rhythmic activity in denervated intestinal muscle. Probably the most complete denervation was accomplished by

Gasser (1926) and van Esveld (1928), who made serial sections of their preparations and found a considerable number in which no nerve cells could be found. Such preparations, however, still respond to cholinergic and adrenergic drugs. When excised preparations of intestine are treated with high concentrations of nicotine (1 mg. per ml.), the response of the muscle to stimulation of the mesenteric nerves, and also the response to the autonomic drugs disappears; the autonomic receptors are apparently paralyzed by the nicotine. The smooth muscle, however, continues to contract rhythmically (Kuntz and Thomas, 1923). It should not be inferred from this that the rhythmic activity is uninfluenced by the intrinsic or extrinsic nerves. Although the frequency of the contractions is apparently not subject to nervous control, they can be made to increase or decrease in amplitude or to disappear altogether by stimulation of appropriate extrinsic nerves or by the application of drugs which mimic the action of the autonomic nerves.

Although the frequency of the rhythmic contractions is not influenced by ordinary nervous stimuli, it may be modified, or perhaps the contraction may even be initiated by stimuli of another sort. In 1949 Douglas reported that the frequency of rhythmic contractions in the dog's jejunum changed from about 18 per min. to 12 per min. if the jejunum was cut off from the duodenum. This observation suggests that the rhythm of the segmenting contraction is not determined locally but by conducted impulses, which are initiated at a higher level and which are conducted along the intestine in an aboral direction as a wave of excitation.

The function of the rhythmic contractions is evidently to agitate the intestinal contents. Such agitation facilitates several processes: it tends to increase the degree of subdivision of food particles, to mix the food with the intestinal secretions and other digestive fluids, and to change constantly the layers of fluid in contact with the mucosa, thus facilitating absorption. Changes in pressure brought about by these contractions may also be a factor in intestinal absorption.

The electrical studies of Ambache (1947), Bozler (1949), and Milton and Smith (1956) lend support to this view. These authors have described the electrical activity of the intestine as consisting of slow waves which are frequently, but not necessarily, associated with local muscular contractions, and rapid, spikelike waves which appear only when the muscle contracts. The slow waves have the same frequency as the rhythmic contractions, whether or not these are present, and (according to Milton and Smith) they are regularly conducted along the intestine in an aboral direction. In this connection it is interesting to recall that Bayliss and Starling (1899) saw shallow waves which travelled aborally over the intestine at regular intervals, and which seemed to initiate the rhythmic contractions in an area subject to local stimulation. These waves could have been caused by the regularly conducted impulses described by Milton and Smith.

Bass, Code and Lambert (1961) have studied the electrical activity of exteriorized loops of duodenum in trained dogs. Intraluminal pressures were recorded simultaneously to detect motor activity. They found, like others, that cyclical changes in the electrical potential of the duodenum occurred. This slow cyclical change was designated as the basic electrical rhythm (BER). In addition, irregular bursts of spike potentials were observed to be superimposed upon the BER. When recorded from one site the cyclical changes in the BER were observed to be identical with the maximal rate of rhythmic Type I contractions (18 per min.). When recorded from different levels of the duodenum the BER was observed to be propagated down the intestine at a rate of approximately 20 cm. per sec. The BER was recorded continuously, whether or not the intraluminal pressure catheter indicated the presence of motor activity.

Spike potentials were noted in about one-third of the cycles of the BER. They occurred in bursts of 1 to 3 spikes and were always located on the descending or negative slope of the slow potential change. When spike potentials occurred, they were uniformly associated with an increased pressure within the lumen of the gut. There was also an obvious correlation between the number and amplitude of the spikes and the magnitude of the increase in pressure in the gut, indicating a relationship between the number and amplitude of the spikes and the strength of the contractions occurring in the gut wall.

PERISTALSIS IN THE SMALL INTESTINE

Stimulation of the intestinal smooth muscle causes contractions which tend to travel from the stimulated point in both directions. However, under normal circumstances the progress of the contractions in an oral direction is quickly inhibited and the contractions disappear. The

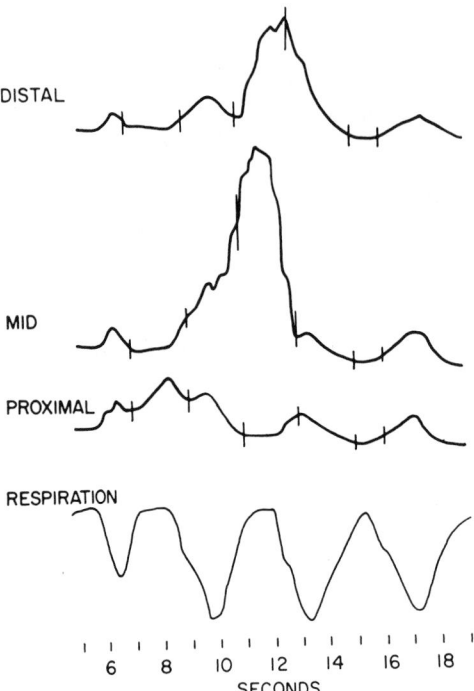

DISTAL

MID

PROXIMAL

RESPIRATION

```
6    8   10  12  14  16  18
            SECONDS
```

Fig. 61.14 Illustrating duodenal intraluminal pressure changes with peristalsis. The recording sites designated as proximal, mid, and distal are located at 2 cm. intervals. The short vertical lines indicate the frames of a cine sequence that were recorded simultaneously. This series of three monophasic contractions occurring in timed sequence was associated with the transport of barium in an aboral direction. In this patient, the peristaltic contraction traveled at about 1 cm. per sec. (From Friedman, et al., Gastroenterology, 1965, **49**: 37).

contractions which travel in an aboral direction tend to persist, so that the intestine may be said to be polarized in the sense that conducted contractions travel normally in only the aboral direction. Such aborally conducted contractions are commonly described as peristalsis. The term has been used to describe a variety of contractile phenomena which have only one thing in common, namely the direction of travel. The common conception of peristalsis as consisting of a wave of contraction progressing smoothly over otherwise relaxed intestine is erroneous. Usually the peristaltic movement is superimposed upon the rhythmic segmenting contractions in such a way that the two are present simultaneously. The peristaltic contraction makes itself manifest as a rise in the tone level of the intestinal muscle, without any interruption in the rhythm of the segmenting contractions; indeed, these are usually increased in amplitude at the peak of the wave. This has the effect of narrowing the lumen of

the intestine at the point at which the increase in tonus occurs and it may actually obliterate it. As this wave of contraction, or tonus, travels down the intestine, it tends to sweep the contents forward, or toward the distal end of the intestine. In another type of propulsive movement, rhythmic contractions, although retaining their character, recur at successively more aboral levels and thus appear to travel along the intestine as a wave of peristalsis. Ordinarily, peristaltic waves appear in the small intestine at irregular intervals and travel for varying distances (Bayliss and Starling); some travel only a few inches, others a few feet.

In the duodenum of man, Friedman et al. observed that some concentric segmenting contractions, instead of remaining localized in one area, would move distally over the duodenum into the jejunum. When these peristaltic contractions occurred, pressure waves were recorded in a sequential manner, from above downward, by the three intestinal catheters localized in the duodenum. The speed of the peristaltic contractions or stripping waves were about 1 cm. per sec. Figure 61.14 illustrates intraluminal pressure changes occurring in the duodenum with peristalsis.

Under the influence of especially strong stimuli such as irritant cathartics, a peristaltic wave may sweep over the entire length of the small intestine without interruption, or several such waves may occur in succession. Peristaltic waves of this character were described by van Braam Houckgeest in 1872; he called them "rollbewegungen" but they are usually described in the modern literature as *rush waves* or *peristaltic rush*, after the terminology proposed by Meltzer and Auer in 1907.

Whether the conditions that give rise to rhythmic contractions on the one hand or to peristaltic movements on the other, differ qualitatively or only quantitatively is not known. It is known that both mechanical and chemical stimuli are effective in promoting peristalsis, and that mild stimulation favors rhythmic activity. Doubtless, not only the nature and strength of the stimuli, but also the irritability of the intestinal neuromuscular mechanism play a significant part in determining the nature and location of the activity. The latter may be influenced by local and central reflexes and by circulating hormones and metabolites, as well as by the previous history of the muscle (e.g., by refractoriness or fatigue following a period of activity).

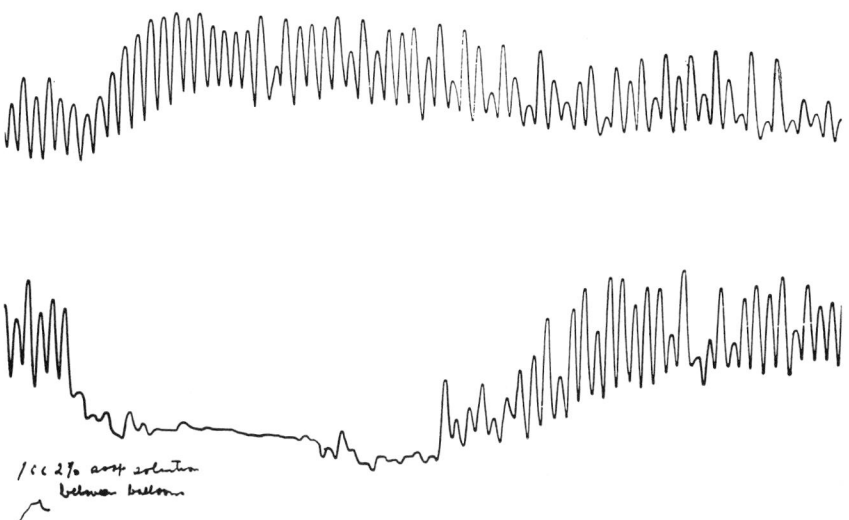

FIG. 61.15. Myenteric reflex in a dog's duodenum. Water manometer records from two balloons 5 cm. apart in the lower duodenum. Upper record is from the upper balloon. A stimulus consisting of 2 cc. of 2 per cent soap solution in the intestine between the balloons caused contraction above (over the upper balloon) and relaxation below (over the lower balloon) the stimulated point. (Thomas.)

The Law of the Intestine

The polarity of the intestine, that is the fact that peristaltic waves characteristically travel in one direction only, has been the subject of much interesting speculation but no satisfactory explanation has as yet been offered. Bayliss and Starling (1899, 1901), to whose classical studies we owe most of our basic knowledge of intestinal motility, observed that the response of the small intestine to local stimuli consists of a contraction of the smooth muscle above and relaxation below the stimulated area. "This," they said, "is the law of the intestine." Since the contraction wave and the preceding inhibition usually travel down the intestine in an aboral direction from the stimulated point, Bayliss and Starling thought that intestinal peristalsis might consist simply of a succession of responses to stimuli manifesting the law of the intestine. In their opinion, a particular mass might give rise to stimulation resulting in contraction above the stimulated point, with relaxation below, and this would cause the mass to move aborally. In its new position it would also act as a stimulus and again cause contraction of the muscle above and relaxation below, again being moved by this to a new, lower level. A succession of such responses could, according to them, constitute a peristaltic wave.

Cannon (1912) proposed that the reflex responsible for the law of the intestine be designated the myenteric reflex (fig. 61.15). The myenteric reflex disappears if the intestine is paralyzed by applying such drugs as nicotine or cocaine to the serosal surface. Presumably these drugs penetrate the longtitudinal muscle layer and paralyze the underlying nervous mechanism. Under these circumstances, the polarity of the intestine is also abolished, and contractions initiated by local stimulation travel equally well in the oral and aboral directions. Evidently, both the myenteric reflex and the polarity of the intestine are dependent upon the integrity of the myenteric plexus. Of course, this does not prove that intestinal polarity is due to the myenteric reflex. In fact, most observers have failed to find evidence of the occurrence of a myenteric reflex in ordinary peristalsis in the intestine. Although the rollbewegungen or rush waves are usually preceded by a phase of inhibition, the inhibitory phase has been difficult to demonstrate in spontaneous peristalsis of the intestine.

The Gradient Theory

Alvarez (1940) has proposed that the polarity of the intestine is related to the gradients of irritability, conductivity, rhythmicity, etc., that are known to exist, but he has failed to define the precise mechanism through which such gradients establish polarity. Some idea may be obtained from the study of the polarity of the heart muscle, where forward conduction is known to be related to the gradients of irritability mani-

POSSIBLE MECHANISM OF POLAR CONDUCTION

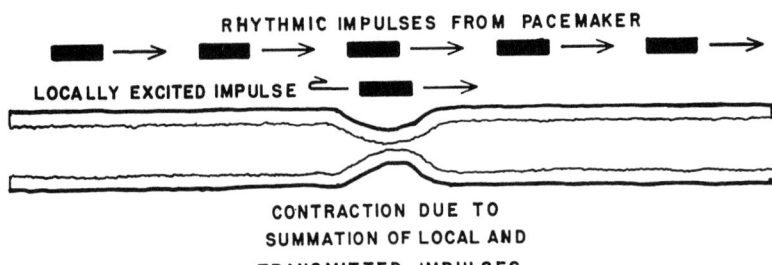

FIG. 61.16. Mechanism of polar conduction in the intestine suggested by physiological evidence for a pacemaker mechanism in the upper intestine. The block rectangles represent excitatory impulses; those in the upper row presumably arose in the pacemaker and are being conducted analward. A local excitory process cannot be conducted oralward because of the refractive phase following each conducted impulse from the pacemaker. (Thomas, 1955.)

fested by the several chambers of heart. In the heart, the gradients are significant only to the extent that they enable certain chambers always to initiate activity because of their higher degree of rhythmicity. In this situation the impulse always arises at the most irritable point, and because it has nowhere else to go, it travels in the direction of the less irritable chambers. A similar situation could exist in the intestine but up to the present time no pacemaker has been demonstrated anatomically. However, the slow electrical waves mentioned in a preceding paragraph may arise in such a pacemaker, for which there is as yet only physiological evidence. If such is the case, and if we may assume that in the intestine, as in the heart, each transmitted impulse is followed by a refractory phase, contraction waves travelling in an oral direction would be quickly extinguished by the refractoriness following the descending impulses. On the other hand, aborally travelling contractions would encounter no such difficulty (fig. 61.16).

THE INTESTINAL VILLI AND THE MUSCULARIS MUCOSAE

The absorbing surface of the small intestine is much greater than the serosal surface because of the superabundance of the mucosa which, under normal conditions, is thrown into circular folds called *plicae circulares*. A still greater increase in surface is provided by the *intestinal villi*. These are tit-like projections of the mucous membrane, about 1 mm. in length, which occur everywhere on the mucosal surface and which macroscopically resemble the pile on a piece of velvet. Our interest in these structures at this point has to do with the activity of the *muscularis mucosae*, which lies everywhere beneath the

mucous membrane, following each fold, and extending into each villus as a filament of smooth muscle fibers. In the fasting animal, the villi are inactive and lie flat on the mucosal surface when first exposed for study. Covering them with a liquid, such as a solution of sugar, salts, amino acids, weak alkalies, or even with distilled water, causes them to become active. In the fed animal activity of the villi can be observed without special stimulation. The activity is of two kinds: a lashing movement and a more or less rhythmical shortening and lengthening. It is generally believed that these movements accelerate the flow of blood and lymph and that they increase absorption, although King, Arnold and Church (1922) were unable to find evidence for any of these functions. More recent studies, especially those of von Kokas and von Ludany (1938), leave little doubt that efficient absorption of food stuffs from the intestine is dependent to some extent on the activity of the villi. The movements of the villi are partly under nervous control, being augmented by stimulation of the splanchnic but not the vagus nerves, and by sympathomimetric drugs. They are depressed by atropine and nicotine. Their activity is also increased by *villikinin*, one of the intestinal hormones.

No regular or consistent activity of the main sheet of muscle comprising the muscularis mucosae has been described, but it is believed to be active during digestion, and to be partly responsible for the various mucosal patterns seen in roentgenograms of the small intestine. One function of the muscularis mucosae has to do with protecting the intestine from penetration from within by sharp objects. It does this by forming deep pits or grooves in the mucosa at the point of contact with any sharp foreign body in the intestinal contents. The contracted muscle gives these depressions a firm base which is difficult to penetrate (Exner, 1902; King and Arnold, 1922).

DISTURBANCES OF SMALL BOWEL MOTILITY

Disturbances of small bowel motility are rare, except when due to infections or inflammatory conditions, and in these instances there is increased motor activity of the propulsive type usually associated with diarrhea. In some malabsorptive states, such as nontropical sprue, small bowel transit time may be slow. Abnormal motility patterns in the small intestine are seen in some nervous and endocrine disturbances and also in vitamin deficiency. Their significance, when they occur, is not always clear. Small bowel motility may be affected by intraluminal contents. Saline cathartics markedly increase small bowel transit time due to their hyperosmolarity. From a clinical standpoint, paralytic ileus and intestinal obstruction deserve further consideration.

Paralytic Ileus

Although the small intestine usually shows some degree of activity in the intact animal, a dramatic and presistent quiet ensues when the abdomen is opened. It is rare to see activity in the exposed intestine unless stimulating drugs are given or special measures adopted, such as cutting the splanchnic nerves, stimulating the vagi, or immersing the whole animal in warm physiological salt solutions. Abdominal surgery, particularly if its involves handling the intestine, is apt to be followed by a period of *ileus*, as the loss of motility is termed clinically. Peritoneal irritation from any cause, including bacterial peritonitis, may cause ileus. As a rule, recovery is prompt following removal of the cause but if the condition persists for some time it tends to be self perpetuating, due to the paralytic effect of the gaseous distention that usually develops. When this occurs, removal of the gas through an intestinal tube of the type described by Miller and Abbott (1934) may save the patient's life (fig. 61.17).

The cause of postoperative ileus was investigated by Cannon and Murphy (1906) and was found to be reflex inhibition of motility through reflexes from the irritated peritoneum in which the splanchnic nerves were an essential part of the reflex path. They found that cutting the

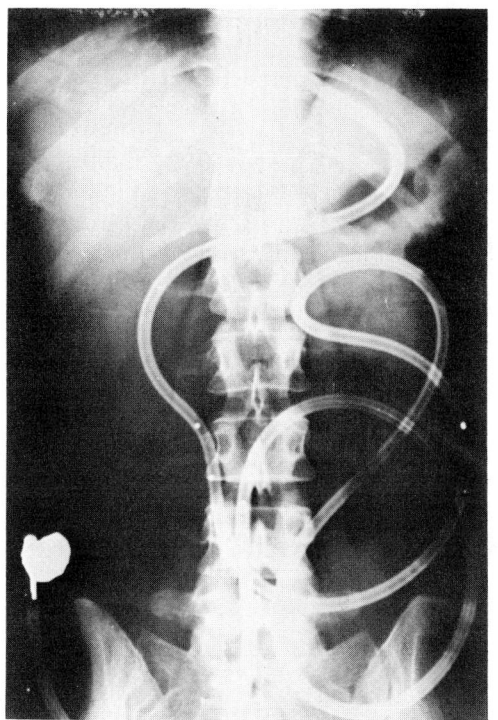

FIG. 61.17 X-ray of abdomen showing Miller-Abbott tube in the small intestine.

splanchnic nerves prevented the ileus. There was one exception to this finding; if the intestine itself was subjected to severe trauma, ileus ensued even with the splanchnics cut. Apparently, in this instance, the local nerve plexus serves as a pathway for the inhibitory reflexes. It has since been shown that intestinal paresis from a variety of causes (e.g., peritonitis) is relieved by spinal anesthesia, which is neurologically equivalent to splanchnic section.

Paralytic ileus may be produced in dogs by the injection of a solution of iodine into the peritoneal cavity. Markowitz and Campbell showed that the intestinal inhibition produced in this way could be abolished by spinal anesthesia, which apparently blocked inhibitory impulses reaching the bowel through the splanchnic nerves.

Intestinal Obstruction

Symptoms of intense severity result when the lumen of the small bowel is completely obstructed as a result of constriction by an adhesive band, kinking, twisting or pressure by new growth, intussusception, strangulation by a hernial ring, etc. The condition is ushered in by severe cramplike abdominal pain, vomiting and shock. If the condition is not relieved by operation, reverse peristalsis arises above the point of obstruction, intestinal contents pass into the stomach, and vomiting becomes fecal in character. Later, the bowel above the obstruction loses its tone, becoming dilated and filled with intestinal secretions and gas. The loss of fluid in the vomitus and the drainage of large quantities of fluid into the distended bowel leads to a *fall in blood chloride, alkalosis* and *dehydration*. Other blood changes are a rise in the *nonprotein nitrogen* and an *increase in the fibrinogen content*. The former is the result of tissue destruction combined with impairment of renal function. Great prostration occurs, ending in death.

Experimental obstruction. When the intestine of an animal is tied across, the symptoms which follow are chiefly weakness, prostration and vomiting. The animal shows little or no evidence that it is suffering pain. The higher in the intestinal tract the obstruction is made, the more severe are the symptoms, and the shorter is the duration of life after the operation. Following obstruction of the colon the animal may survive for some weeks, whereas after obstruction of the jejunum or duodenum it dies as a rule within five or six days.

The importance of distention as a factor in acute obstruction of the intestine is now generally recognized, and it has become the practice in suitable cases to decompress the bowel by suction-drainage through a tube passed from the mouth to the duodenum (Paine and Wangensteen) or, as in the method of Miller and Abbott, to insert a long, slender tube through the nose into the stomach and allow it to be carried to the level of the obstruction. The tube has a double lumen and is provided at its tip with a small balloon which can be moderately inflated after it has entered the duodenum. The balloon serves as a stimulus to peristalsis, which carries it and the tubing along the bowel to the point of obstruction (fig. 61.17).

The Ileocolic Valve (Valvula Coli)

This structure permits the passage of the contents of the small intestine at intervals into the cecum, but when competent, hinders the return of the material into the ileum. Its ability to do this depends, according to one view, not upon any mechanical valvelike device, but upon the contraction of the circular fibers of the gut which are thickened in this region to form a sphincter guard for the ileocecal orifice. But, although a sphincterlike thickening of the circular muscle fibers is found in this situation, most anatomists agree that the competency of the ileocolic valve is mainly, or at least partly, due to a valvelike construction. The ileum enters the cecum obliquely, and in doing so invaginates the cecal wall; this alone would tend toward a valvelike action. The valve proper is formed as follows: As the lower end of the ileum enters the cecum, the invaginated portion of the cecal wall forms two transverse folds or lips, one above the other on the cecal aspect of the ileocolic orifice. The lips fuse laterally to produce a fold on either side of the orifice (*the frenula coli*) which are continued around the interior of the cecum. As the cecum distends, the frenula are stretched and pulling upon the lips from either side, draw them firmly together. Thus the valve can withstand a high pressure in the cecum but yields to a low pressure from the ileal side. Materials introduced by enema may in some instances pass through the valve into the lower ileum. The ileocolic opening has been observed in man through a cecal fistula. It appears as an oval or round opening from 2 to 3 cm. in diameter situated in the center of a small papilla. When tightly closed, the valve was found to offer considerable resistance to the passage of the finger. While digestion was in progress, the papilla was observed to flush, its color altering from a pale pink to a vivid red. The orifice opened rhythmically at frequent intervals and allowed a jet of fluid to escape into the cecum. Emotional excitement or the swallowing of food increased the frequency of the ejections (*gastroileal reflex*). During fasting, nothing passed through for long periods, but in $\frac{1}{2}$ to 4 min. after food was taken into the mouth, fluid appeared in gushes of about 15 ml. every half minute or so.

Kelley (1965) has recently made pressure studies of the ileocolonic junctional zone in dogs. He prepared his animals by making ileal and colonic stomas and then measured pressures on either side of, and within, the ileocolonic junctional segment. When a water-filled catheter tip, for recording pressures, was withdrawn at 0.5 cm. intervals from the colon into the ileum of the fasted, conscious animal, a zone of high pressure was demonstrated at the ileocolonic junction. Mean pressures at the center of the junctional area were 20 cm. of water above ambient. The length of the high pressure zone was approximately 1 cm.

The functions of the ileocolic valve appear to be: (a) to prevent the contents of the ileum from passing into the cecum before the digestive processes have been completed, and (b) to serve as a barrier which prevents the bacteria-laden contents of the large bowel from contaminating the small intestine.

Large Bowel Motility

The colon receives the mixed residues remaining after completion of intestinal digestion and absorption. These consist of undigested or undigestible food residues, whatever remains of the digestive secretions including considerable quantities of water, and the fluid that has been swallowed or secreted and has escaped absorption in the small intestine. The colon extracts the water from this mixture and forms the indigestible residues into fecal masses which are later evacuated. The motor activities are appropriate to these functions. They may be divided into two classes: first, those that appear to be designed primarily to facilitate absorption; and second, those concerned principally with propulsion.

Mixing Movements of the Colon

Mixing movements of the colon have been studied in experimental animals and in man, although the human colon does not normally lend itself readily to experimental study. Barcroft and Steggerda (1932) studied the exteriorized cecum and proximal portion of the colon in dogs. In their experiments, the organ to be studied was brought out through an incision in the skin and after healing had taken place observations were made without anesthesia. They observed what they called kneading movements, antiperistalsis, and mass peristalsis. The kneading movements seemed to resemble segmenting contractions in the small intestine, except that they occurred at a slower rate and involved longer sections of the intestine. They appeared at intervals of about ½ min. Antiperistaltic waves appeared when the colon became distended, and they followed each other at a frequency of 5 to 7 per min. The "mass peristalsis" belongs to the second class of contractions and will be considered a little later.

Cannon (1902) studied the movements of the colon in cats by means of x-rays. He noted that the characteristic movement of the transverse and ascending portion was antiperistalsis. He described what he called mass contractions of the cecum and ascending colon, which forced material into the transverse colon, from which it was driven back by antiperistaltic waves. This is obviously a stirring and mixing function and is not concerned with the transport of material in the aboral direction.

Templeton and Lawson (1931) studied the movements of the colon in dogs, using multiple balloons and manometers. With these they were able to determine the extent of the contractions, if any, whether they progressed, and in what direction. They described three types of contractions which they designated as Type I, Type II and Type III. Type I movements were simple, rapid contractions and relaxations, frequently simultaneous over the three balloons but often confined to one balloon. These they considered to be stationary, rhythmic contractions. They are evidently analogous to the segmenting contractions in the small intestine. Type II are slower contractions, on which Type I movements were superimposed. Analysis indicated that these either swept analward, oralward, or remained stationary. They might start in one direction, become stationary, then move in the other direction. Antiperistaltic waves would be of this type but some were obviously peristaltic. Type II contractions are suggestive of the kneading movements described by Barcroft and Steggerda. Type III contractions were tone changes on which were superimposed Type II contractions. They were apt to be in opposite phase in the proximal and distal colon, and to increase in one region while decreasing in the other. These movements would result in a to-and-fro motion of the intestinal contents and are suggestive of Cannon's alternate mass contractions and antiperistaltic movements. Elliot and Barclay-Smith (1904) observed antiperistalsis in the colon of the dog, cat, rabbit and rat.

Todd (1930) observed slow peristaltic movements in the cecum of human subjects when it was being filled with barium from the ileum. He described these as follows: "As the ileal coils empty themselves, slow peristalsis taking place meanwhile, the outlines become better defined and the cecal peristaltic movement is plainly seen. The shadow of the cecum becomes denser as more contents are poured into it and slow massive movements occur, involving its entire outline. How they can drive the contents onward is altogether obscure but the dense barium shadow does progress upward." He also observed a "concertina-like" action of the transverse colon, which he attributed to contractions and relaxations of the teniae.

In the rabbit, and probably in other animals, there are contractions of the haustra (which are the bulgings of the wall of the colon between the

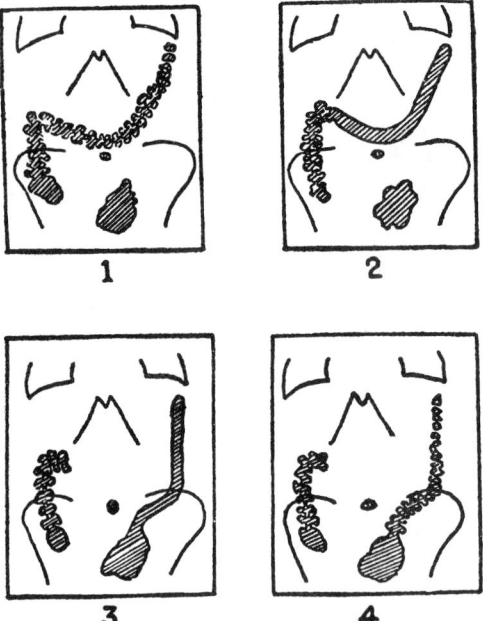

FIG. 61.18. Holzknecht's diagrams of the happenings during a mass movement of the large intestine. 1, distribution of the food before any change was noted; 2, the haustral segmentation in the transverse colon has disappeared; 3, the whole colon beyond the hepatic flexure passes on suddenly; 4, it is again a picture of "still life" a few seconds later and the haustral segmentation has returned. (After Barclay.)

teniae). Alvarez (1940) describes these contractions as resembling "those of the jointed curtains of two roll top desks facing one another. First one top is pulled down and then the other."

To summarize this rather confusing mass of data, it appears that the colon agitates its contents by means of: segmenting contractions similar to those seen in the small intestine; haustral contractions in which the colonic walls roll back and forth over the contents; kneading movements in which fairly large segments can contract while adjacent segments are relaxing to be followed by contraction and relaxation in reverse phase; and finally, by means of alternate peristalsis and antiperistalsis. It should be pointed out that these movements occur principally in the ascending and transverse colon where absorption of most of the water takes place. It is not to be inferred that each type of movement occurs in every species of animal. We can only be certain that they occur in those species in which they have been observed; for example, antiperistalsis has rarely been observed in the human colon. In spite of the variety of movements described, it is common to find no activity whatever

on x-ray examination of the human colon. Templeton and Lawson observed that, in spite of the presence of balloons in their animals, periods of activity in the colon alternated with periods of complete rest.

PROPULSIVE MOVEMENTS OF THE COLON

The second class of movement consists of those which propel the colonic contents analward and includes colonic peristalsis and mass movements. Peristalsis of the colon has been observed by a number of investigators, beginning with Bayliss and Starling in 1901. It does not differ materially from peristalsis in the small intestine, except perhaps in frequency of occurrence. It consists of a contraction wave preceded by relaxation (Auer and Kreuger, 1947) and its forward progress is dependent upon the integrity of the myenteric plexus. The movement proceeds with great power, particularly in the descending colon, due perhaps to the hard, dry character of the material to be moved. Auer speaks of seeing a hemostat with which the intestine was clamped, twisted apart by a peristaltic movement in the descending colon of the cat. Peristalsis is relatively rare in the human colon, except in association with mass movements or during the act of defecation (Todd, 1930).

Mass movements occur at relatively infrequent intervals and, in the past, generally have been confused with peristalsis; however, Code and his co-workers (1954) have pointed out that these movements, although their propulsive nature has not been questioned, are not true peristaltic waves since they involve simultaneous contractions of large segments of the colon. Holzknecht (1909) (fig. 61.18) was the first to describe these contractions and they were later studied in detail by Hurst (1907) and by Hertz (Hurst) and Newton (1913). The latter authors noted that they occur usually after a meal, or on any occasion when the stomach is being filled with food. They described the increase in colonic motor activity following a meal as the *gastrocolic reflex*. Hurst later observed that the terminal ileum also became hyperactive following meals and proposed that this phenomenon be called *"the gastro-ileac" reflex*. Douglas and Mann (1940) found that the entire small intestine manifests increased motility under these circumstances and that the excitation is transmitted along the intestine, and not by way of the central nervous system. In any case, not only mass movements but all motor activities of the colon are increased at this time. For example, in the experiment of Barcroft and Steggerda, kneading movements and antiperistalsis were increased in dogs after feeding. Hurst remarked that the taking of food is the most powerful of all stimuli to the motor activity of the colon in man. He found that the feces advanced considerably after each meal, much more progress having been made in one patient, for example, during the hours in which dinner was taken than in the previous 4 hr.

The mass movements of the colon serve to empty the contents of the proximal colon rapidly into the more distal portions. Frequently such movements are followed by a desire to defecate, and it is assumed that, on these occasions, the movement has been vigorous enough to carry fecal masses into the rectum. Since normally a desire to defecate does not follow every mass movement of the colon it must be assumed that, on some occasions, the forward movement of the colonic contents stops short of the rectum. People differ considerably with respect to their susceptibility to the gastrocolic or gastroileac reflex. Alvarez (1940) describes a patient in whom every mass movement resulted in defecation. He found that even the sight or smell or taste of food induced the gastrocolic reflex, so that in walking down the street it was necessary for him to avoid passing in front of restaurants if he wished to avoid trouble.

RECORDING OF COLONIC MOTILITY IN MAN

Four types of motility waves may be recorded with balloon or direct pressure measuring systems from the colon of man (Code, 1954; Hightower, 1959). When balloons are used to record colonic motility, they are usually water-filled, under low pressure, and small in size, with a length of approximately 5 cm. and a diameter of approximately 3 cm. Frequently, two or more such small balloons may be used in tandem to record colonic motility, being separated by 5 to 7 cm.

Type I waves are small, simple, monophasic, positive pressure waves of low amplitude and short duration, similar to the same type of wave occurring in other parts of the alimentary canal. The exact function of the Type I wave is not known but presumably it serves as a component of motor activity which contributes to mixing of the colonic contents. Type I waves usually have an amplitude of 5 to 10 cm. of water pressure and their duration varies from 5 to 10 sec. When occurring in a rhythmic pattern, the rate

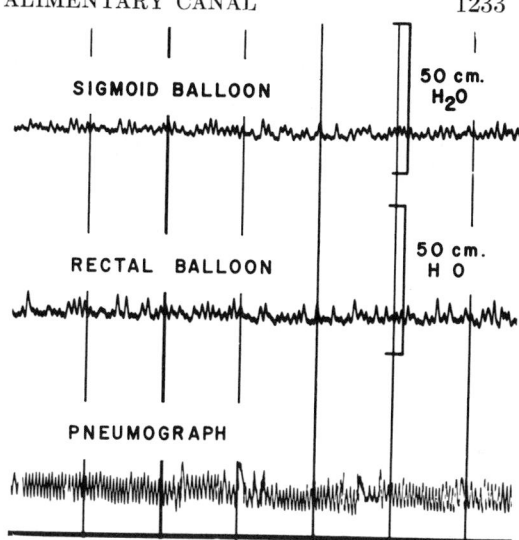

FIG. 61.19 Type I Waves. Record of sigmoidal and rectal motility obtained from a normal individual. Short bursts of rhythmical Type I waves are observed with a rate of 11 per minute. Distance between vertical lines is one minute; camera speed 0.4 mm. per second. (From Hightower, 1959.)

varies from about 8 to 12 per min, depending upon the site from which they are recorded.

Type II waves are similar to Type I. They are, however, of much greater amplitude and of longer duration. These waves are usually 25 to 30 sec. in duration and the amplitude usually varies from 15 to 40 cm. of water pressure. This type of activity accounts for the major portion of total colonic motility. They sometimes occur in rhythmical patterns with a rate of about 2 waves per min. The Type II waves are caused by the contractions in the large bowel which produce the haustra seen by radiologists. Type II waves represent, predominantly, a mixing type of motor activity, although they may contribute to some extent to propulsive motility.

Type III waves are of a complex pattern and consist of an increase in basal pressure or a change in tonus on which superimposed Type I or Type II waves, or both, appear. These waves usually last from 1 to 4 min. and the pressure change in baseline tonus is usually less than 10 cm. of water The exact function of the Type III wave is not clear but it probably is predominantly mixing in its action.

Type IV waves result from the "mass movement" activity of the colon. These waves are rarely recorded from a normal individual unless the recording is obtained shortly after or during the act of eating. These waves rarely occur in a rhythmical pattern, except in patients with

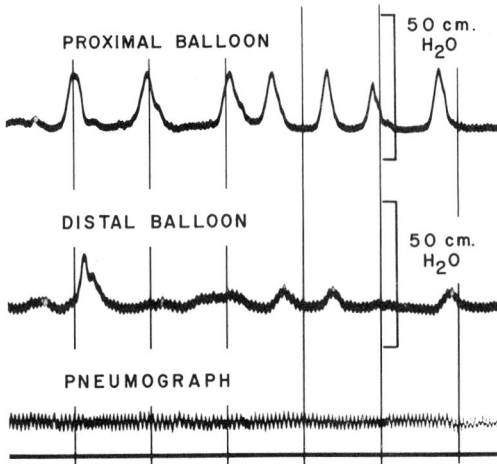

FIG. 61.20 Type II Waves. Record obtained from transverse colon in a patient with a colonic stoma showing Type II waves. The balloons are separated by a distance of 7 cm. Camera speed and time lines are the same as figure 61.19. (From Hightower, 1959.)

chronic ulcerative colitis, and then the rate is usually about 1 wave every 2 to 3 min. The amplitude of the Type IV wave may reach 80 to 100 cm. of water pressure. The duration of the wave is characteristically prolonged and lasts from 2 to 4 min. Their configuration is rather characteristic in that there is a fairly rapid increase in pressure at the beginning of the wave, the peak is reached, and then there is a rapid decline for 50 to 60 per cent of the elevation. The rate of decline changes and becomes much slower, producing a prolonged wave. See figs. 61.19 to 61.22 for types of colonic motility waves recorded in man.

In normal individuals who have fasted for 8 to 12 hr., some type of motor activity can be recorded from the colon for approximately 35 to 40 per cent of the period of observation. The predominant activity is the Type II wave and accounts for 90 to 95 per cent of the total activity. Type I waves usually occur during 1 to 2 per cent of the period of observation, and Type III waves, 2 to 4 per cent. Type IV waves are rarely observed normally and are present for less than 1 per cent of the period of observation.

Alterations of colonic and rectal motility. The effects of *emotions* on colonic motility has been extensively studied (Almy et al., 1947, 1949a, 1949b, 1950; Grace, Wolf and Wolff, 1948, 1950). Discussion of life situations which produce emotional conflict resulting in feelings of anger, anxiety, apprehension, resentment, hostility or guilt cause increased motor activity. However,

when fear, fright, or dejection is the predominant feeling of the subject, hypomotility has been reported. In patients with *chronic ulcerative colitis*, colonic motility records show rather characteristic differences from the normal. There is a marked increase in the incidence of Type IV waves, associated with propulsive action leading to the expulsion of fecal matter. Type I activity is also increased. There is a significant decrease in Type II activity and usually a complete lack of Type III waves. Thus, total motor activity is decreased in these patients, due mainly to the reduction in the mixing type of motor activity. At the same time, propulsive motility is increased.

The effects of drugs on colonic motility. Many drugs influence the motor activity of the colon. *Anticholinergic agents* of the quaternary amine type are potent inhibitors of colonic motility. *Parasympathomimetic agents,* such as neostigmine and methancholine, stimulate colonic motility. Neostigmine is particularly effective in producing a predominantly propulsive type of motor response. *Morphine* increases the amount of nonpropulsive motility and tends to eliminate propulsive activity. Morphine also markedly increases the tone of the large bowel. Most of the so-called *antispasmodic and spasmolytic agents,* when administered by mouth in the recommended therapeutic doses, have little or no effect on motility of the large bowel.

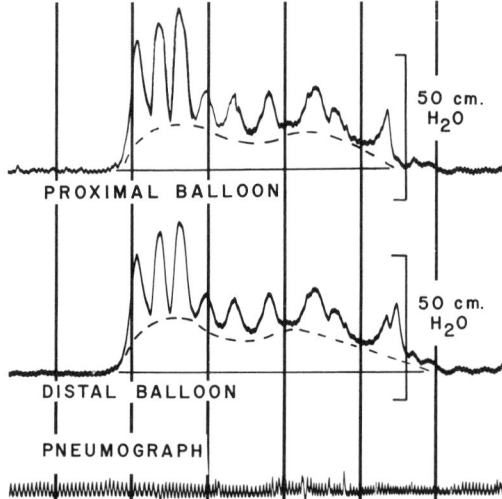

FIG. 61.21 Type III Waves. Record from descending colon via colonic stoma. Note rise in basal pressure with superimposed Type II waves. Both balloons are recording the Type III complex, indicating that a segment of colon at least 7 cm. in length is involved in the motility being recorded. Camera speed and time lines same as Figure 61.19. (From Hightower, 1959.)

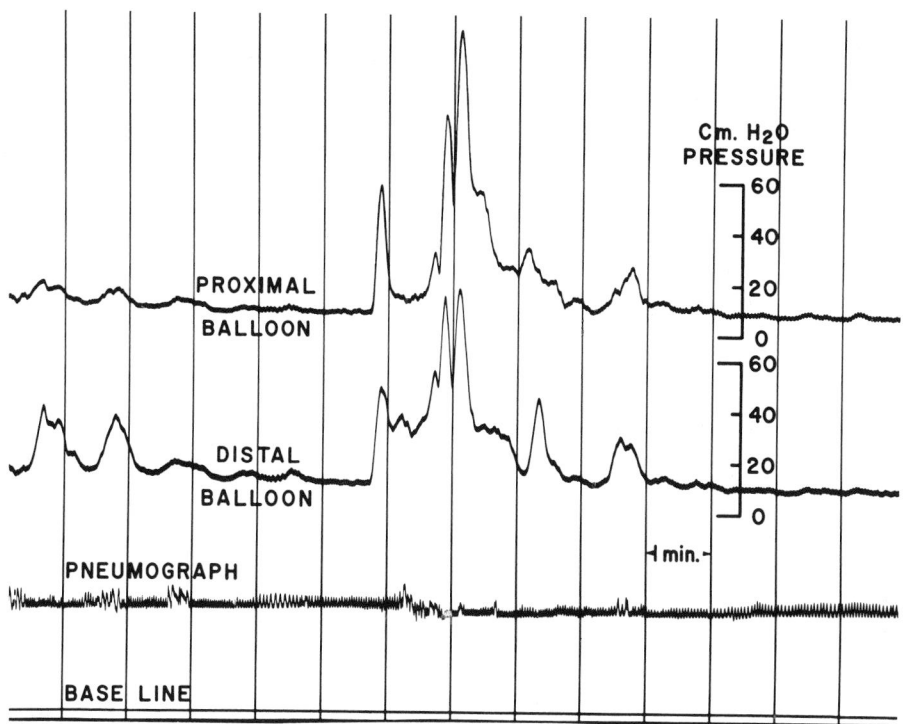

Fig. 61.22 Type IV Waves. This Type IV contraction was recorded from the sigmoid colon of a patient with chronic ulcerative colitis. Note that pressure exceeds 100 cm. water in the proximal balloon. Type II waves are observed at the left side of the tracings.

DEFECATION

As pointed out by Hurst (1909) the rectum is normally empty. The fecal masses driven forward by the mass movements of the colon are stored, not in the rectum, but in the sigmoid or pelvic colon. Fecal matter does not collect elsewhere if defecation is regular; however, if defecation is long deferred, the descending colon becomes filled when the pelvic colon can hold no more. The desire to defecate occurs when, as a result of a mass movement, some feces enter the rectum. An increase in rectal intraluminal pressure of 20 to 25 cm. of water will usually elicit the desire to defecate. While the usual stimulus is the taking of food, a glass of warm water, a cup of coffee, or smoking a cigar or cigarette may have the same effect. Many people find that a glass of cold orange juice, or lemon juice and water is an effective stimulus to the gastrocolic reflex. The desire to defecate may be induced by straining efforts, which may raise the abdominal pressure to as much as 200 mm. of mercury and force feces into the rectum.

When the rectum is filled with solids (feces), liquids or gas to an extent which raises the intraluminal pressure to 20 or 25 cm. of water,

the desire to empty the rectum is experienced. The receptors within the wall of the rectum are not only able to detect increases in pressure (pressorectors) but they can also, with a high degree of accuracy, differentiate whether the increase in pressure is due to feces, liquids or gas. The discriminating ability of these sensors is relied upon heavily by individuals who risk flatulating in a public place. In patients with infectious diarrhea or proctitis due to ulcerative colitis or other inflammatory conditions, the ability to discern the contents of the rectum is frequently lost, and these patients find the risk is too great to relieve themselves of an increase in rectal pressure which is suspected of being due to gas.

The act of defecation is, in the adult, preceded by a voluntary effort consisting of assumption of an appropriate posture, voluntary relaxation of the external anal sphincter, and usually, compression of the abdominal contents by means of straining efforts. These movements in turn probably give rise to stimuli which augment the visceral reflexes, although these originate primarily in the distended rectum. As a result of these reflexes, a mass contraction may involve the entire colon and the internal anal sphincter relaxes.

The mass contraction of the colon carries its contents into the pelvic colon, which in turn transfers them into the rectum, eventually to be evacuated by way of the anus; hence, the entire distal colon from the splenic flexure to the anus may be emptied at one time. A prominent mechanical feature of the final act of evacuation is contraction of the longitudinal muscle of the distal colon which is more pronounced in the rectum itself. The shortening of the distal colon tends to elevate the pelvic colon and obliterate the angle which it normally makes with the rectum. This straightening of the passage doubtless facilitates evacuation. Shortening of the rectum itself is an important factor in expelling the feces through the anal orifice.

The act of defecation provides another instance of a reflex that is under some degree of voluntary control. The voluntary regulation consists of the ability to inhibit the reflex under normal circumstances and to initiate it voluntarily, provided the necessary visceral stimulus (recent distention of the rectum) is present. Reflex centers for defecation have been located in the hypothalamus, in the lower lumbar and upper sacral segments of the spinal cord, and in the ganglionic plexus of the gut. The intrinsic intestinal plexus of the lower colon is able to take over the function of controlling defecation, even in animals in which the spinal cord has been destroyed. For this reason, in severe spinal injury the defecation reflex suffers less than does, for example, the reflex of micturition.

The Composition of the Feces

According to Cantarow and Schepartz (1954), adults on an average diet excrete from 75 to 170 g. of feces daily, about 25 to 30 per cent of which is made up of solids; the remainder is water. If the diet is rich in vegetables the quantity is greater, especially if the vegetables are eaten raw. Bacteria comprise about one-third of the dry weight of the feces under average conditions. The pH is 7.0 to 7.5. The feces contain those inorganic substances which are relatively insoluble at alkaline pH ranges such as calcium phosphate and oxalate, iron phosphate and similar compounds. The organic material is principally cellulose, protein and fats. About half the protein nitrogen of the feces if of bacterial origin; the remainder represents unabsorbed intestinal secretions and digested fluids, mucus, and desquamated epithelial cells from the mucosa. Only a small amount is actual food residue. Enzymes are also present but in very small quantities,

these are: pancreatic amylase and trypsin, nucleases, maltase, sucrase, lipase, and lysozyme. Fats comprise about 5 to 25 per cent of the feces under normal circumstances. They are greatly increased in conditions in which there is interference with pancreatic or biliary function. In the total absence of pancreatic juice from the intestine, as much as 90 per cent of the ingested fat may be excreted in the stools. Much of the fecal fat has undergone digestion, as indicated by the following average composition of fecal lipids: neutral fat, 7.3 per cent of dry weight of feces; free fatty acids, 5.6 per cent; and soaps, 4.6 per cent.

The color of the feces is due chiefly to bile pigments, stercobilin (*urobilin*), which is produced by reduction of bilirubin by the intestinal bacteria. The characteristic odor is due largely to indole and skatole, but is contributed to also by hydrogen sulfide and other odoriferous substances.

Gas in the Intestine

A variable amount of gas is always to be found in the small and large intestine, principally the latter. This consists of the respiratory gases: oxygen, carbon dioxide, nitrogen, methane, hydrogen, and small amounts of other gases including the rare atmospheric gases. The average composition according to Pogrund and Steggerda (1948) is as follows: carbon dioxide, 7.5 per cent; oxygen, 3.0 per cent; methane, hydrogen and other rare gases, 9.5 per cent; and nitrogen, 80 per cent. The source of the oxygen, nitrogen and carbon dioxide is swallowed air and diffusion from the blood. Bacterial fermentation and putrefaction of food residues in the intestine produce the methane and hydrogen. No matter what the composition of swallowed air may be, it quickly comes into equilibrium with the venous blood with respect to oxygen and carbon dioxide, and more slowly with respect to nitrogen; hence, the relative constancy of composition of intestinal gas with respect to these gases. The amount of putrefactive gas is much more variable. It is the rapid expansion of these gases that gives rise to intestinal cramps on ascending to high altitudes in an unpressurized plane. Some of this gas is absorbed into the blood and some escapes from the rectum as flatus. The amount in the intestine can be reduced by giving the subject pure oxygen to breathe. This reduces the partial pressure of nitrogen in the blood and thus favors diffusion of nitrogen from the intestine toward the circulating blood. Since nitrogen diffuses very slowly, it is necessary to continue the treatment over a long period of time in order to obtain any beneficial results. The same result could be obtained by using oxygen diluted with helium or other inert gas, as long as nitrogen is not present.

Abnormal Colonic Motility—Constipation

Abnormal motor activity in the colon is one of the most common conditions for which the physician may be consulted. The causes may be only local, or they may involve systemic disease. Psychic factors are important and it can be safely asserted that no other part of the gastrointestinal tract is so profoundly affected by emotional disturbances as is the large intestine. This statement is supported by lay observation as well as by clinical experience and experimental observations on suitable human subjects. It has been possible to demonstrate changes in tone, motility, or vascularity of the large intestine in response to experimentally induced emotional reactions. For example, in three children, four, nine and ten years old, studied by Friedman and Snape (1946), changes in color and motility were observed during emotional excitement; mild, painful stimuli or even the suggestion of pain or discussion of unpleasant experiences caused blanching of the mucous membrane; the sight or smell of appetizing food caused reddening. During eating, the mucous membrane was engorged, but it returned to normal after the meal. These changes of course indicate constriction (blanching) or dilation (reddening) of the blood vessels. In two adults studied by Grace, Wolf and Wolff (1948), experimentally induced anger, feelings of guilt, resentment, or hostility caused hyperfunctioning of the colon; there was increased lysozyme production and increased secretion of mucus; acute fear caused pallor and relaxation. Increased motor activity and blood flow were also observed in these subjects while they were eating a meal. During psychometric examination subjects also showed hyperfunction of the colon.

The most frequent manifestation of malfunction of the large intestine is constipation. For a discussion of the various causes and the treatment of this condition, appropriate clinical texts should be consulted. It may be mentioned here that one of the most frequent causes of chronic constipation is neglect of the call to stool. The desire to defecate is experienced whenever the pressure within the rectum is increased. An increase in the volume of the contents of the rectum of from 15 to 25 ml. has been shown to be sufficient to produce an urge. If the rectum is not emptied at such a time, the sensory mechanism becomes adapted to the pressure and the urge is no longer felt; it then requires a further increase in volume with a corresponding increase in pressure to produce a sensation. This will also pass if neglected and a still further increase in volume is required to arouse a sensation; finally the irritability of the rectum is so reduced that an urge is no longer induced. Usually the subject will then take a cathartic which further injures the sensory mechanism. Frequent repetition of this cycle results ultimately in dependence on cathartics. An important factor in the prevention or treatment of such a condition is the establishment of a conditioned reflex. Taking advantage of the gastrocolic reflex which follows a meal the subject selects a convenient time of day for going to stool, usually after breakfast. He then makes an effort to defecate at this time each day whether he gets the urge or not. In the beginning, mild laxatives may be necessary to facilitate the establishment of the reflex but once it is thoroughly established they can be omitted. Such a conditioned reflex can become so firmly established that one feels the desire to defecate at a particular time of day whether or not a meal has been eaten.

REFERENCES

ALMY, T. P. ET AL., Alterations in colonic function in man under stress. Gastroenterology, 1947, **8**, 616; 1949a, **12**, 424; 1949b, **12**, 437; 1950, **15**, 95.

ALVAREZ, W. C. The metabolic gradient underlying peristalsis. J.A.M.A. 1919, **73**, 1483. (Also series of papers by ALVAREZ and by ALVAREZ and STARKWEATHER in Am. J. Physiol, from 1915, Vol. 37 to 1919, Vol. **50**.)

ALVAREZ, W. C. AND HOSOI, K. A gradient of irritability in the small intestine. Am. J. Physiol., 1929, **89**, 182, 187; 1918, **45**, 342; 1918, **46**, 186; 1918, **47**, 293.

ALVAREZ, W. C. AND MAHONEY, L. J. The myogenic nature of the rhythmic contractions of the intestine. Am. J. Physiol., 1922, **59**, 421.

AMBECHE, N. Electrical activity of isolated mammalian intestine. J. Physiol., 1947, **106**, 139.

ATKINSON, H. F. AND MATTHEWS, E. Brit. Dent. J., 1949, **86**, 167.

AUER, J. AND KREUGER, H. Experimental study of antiperistaltic and peristaltic motor and inhibitory phenomena. Am. J. Physiol., 1947, **148**, 350.

BARCROFT, J. AND STEGGERDA, F. R. Observations on the proximal portion of the exteriorized colon. J. Physiol., 1932, **76**, 460.

BASS, P., CODE, C. F., AND LAMBERT, E. H. Motor and electrical activity of the duodenum. Am. J. Physiol., 1961, **287**, 201.

BAYLISS, W. M. AND STARLING, E. H. The movements and innervation of the small intestine. J. Physiol., 1899, **24**, 99.

BAYLISS, W. M. AND STARLING, D. H. The movements and innervation of the large intestine. J. Physiol., 1901, 26, 107.

BAZETT, H. C. AND PENFIELD, W. G. A study of the Sherrington decerebrate animal in the chronic as well as the acute condition. Brain, 1922, 45, 185.

BECKER, E. Zur Kenntnis der Bedeutung der zähne für die Ausnutzung des Nahrungsmittel im Verdauungsapparat bei normaler Sekretion der Magendrüsen. Skandinav. Arch. Physiol., 1927, 50, 283.

BLACK, G. V. An investigation of the physical characters of the human teeth in relation to their diseases and to practical dental operations together with the physical characters of filling materials. II. The force exerted in the closing of the jaws. Dental Cosmos, 1895, 37, 469.

BOLDYREFF, W. N. Die periodische Tätigkeit der Verdauungsapparates ausser der Verdauungszeit. Zentralbl. Physiol. 1904, 18, 489.

BOSAM, J. F. Deglutition: Pharyngeal stage. Physiol. Rev. 1957, 275, 37.

BOZLER, E. Reflex peristalsis of the intestine. Am. J. Physiol., 1949, 157, 338; 1945, 144, 693; 1942, 136, 543, 553; 1939, 127, 301; 1938, 124, 502.

BRODY, D. A., WERLE, J. M., MESCHAN, I., AND QUIGLEY, J. P. Intralumen pressures in the digestive tract, especially the pyloric region. Am. J. Physiol., 1940, 130, 791. (See also Gastroenterology, 1947, 9, 570; J. Lab. & Clin. Med., 1944, 29, 863; Med. Physics, 1950, 2, 280.)

BUTIN, J. W., ET AL. A study of esophageal pressure in normal persons and patients with achalasia. Gastroenterology, 1953, 23, 278.

CANNON, W. B. The movements of the stomach studied by means of the roentgen rays. Am. J. Physiol., 1898, 1, 359.

CANNON, W. B. The movements of the intestine studied by means of roentgen rays. Am. J. Physiol., 1902, 6, 251.

CANNON, W. B. The passage of different foodstuffs from the stomach and through the small intestine. Am. J. Physiol., 1904, 12, 387. (See also CANNON, 1911b.)

CANNON, W. B. Esophageal peristalsis after bilateral vagotomy. Am. J. Physiol., 1907, 19, 436.

CANNON, W. B. The acid control of the pylorus. Am. J. Physiol., 1907, 20, 283.

CANNON, W. B. The nature of gastric peristalsis. Am. J. Physiol., 1911a, 29, 250.

CANNON, W. B. Peristalsis, segmentation and the myenteric reflex. Am. J. Physiol., 1912, 30, 114.

CANNON, W. B. AND MOSER, A. The movements of food in the esophagus. Am. J. Physiol., 1898, 1, 435.

CANNON, W. B. AND MURPHY, F. T. The movements of the stomach and intestines in some surgical conditions. Ann. Surg., 1906, 43, 512.

CANNON, W. B. AND WASHBURN, A. L. An explanation of hunger. Am. J. Physiol., 1912, 29, 441.

CODE, C. F., WILKINSON, G. R., AND SAUER, W. G. Normal and some abnormal colonic motor patterns in man. Ann. N. Y. Acad. Sci., 1954, 58, 317.

COLE, L. G. Systole and diastole of the stomach. Arch. of the Roentgen Ray. 1911, 16, 242.

COLE, L. G. Motor phenomena of the stomach, pylorus and cap observed roentgenographically. Am. J. Physiol., 1917, 42, 618.

CRIDER, J. O. AND THOMAS, J. E. A study of gastric emptying with the pylorus open. Am. J. Digest. Dis & Nutr., 1937, 4, 295.

DEAN, H. T. AND ASSOCIATES. U. S. Pub. Health Rep., 1938, 53, 1443; 1941, 56, 365; 57, 1155.

DOUGLAS, D. M. AND MANN, F. C. The gastroileac reflex: Further experimental observations. Am. J. Digest. Dis., 1940, 7, 53.

ELLIOTT, T. R. AND BARCLAY-SMITH, E. Antiperistalsis and other muscular activities of the colon. J. Physiol., 1904, 31, 272.

EXNER, A. Wie schützt sich der Verdauungstract von Verletzungen durch spitze Fremdkörper. Arch. ges. Physiol., 1902, 89, 253.

FARRELL, J. I. AND IVY, A. C. Studies on the motility of the transplanted gastric pouch. Am. J. Physiol., 1926, 76, 227.

FRIEDMAN, E., WOLF, B. S., WAYE, J. D., AND JANOWITZ, H. D. Correlation of cineradiographic and intraluminal pressure changes in the human duodenum: An analysis of the functional significance of monophasic waves. Gastroenterology, 1965, 37, 49.

FRIEDMAN, M. H. F. AND SNAPE, W. J. Color changes in the mucosa of the colon of children as affected by food and psychic stimuli. Fed. Proc., 1946, 5 (part I), 30.

FYKE, F. E., JR. AND CODE, C. F. Resting and deglutition pressures in the pharyngoesophageal region. Gastroenterology, 1955, 24, 29.

FYKE, F. E., JR., CODE, C. F., AND SCHLEGEL, J. F. The gastroesophageal sphincter in healthy human beings. Gastroenterology, 1956, 135, 86.

GASSER, H. S. Plexus-free preparations of the small intestine; a study of their rhythmicity and their response to drugs. J. Pharm. & Exper. Therap., 1926, 27, 395.

GEIS, W. J. AND ASSOCIATES. J. Allied Dent. Soc., 1914, 9, 345.

GELLHORN, E. AND BUDDE, W. Beiträge zue Physiologie der Magenmuskulatur. Arch. ges. Physiol., 1923, 200, 604.

GRACE, WM. J., WOLF, S. G., AND WOLFF, H. G Influence of emotions and feeling states on the behavior of the human colon. Am. J. Physiol., 1948, 155, 439.

GUNN, J. A. AND UNDERHILL, S. W. F. Experiments on surviving mammalian intestine. Quart. J. Physiol., 1914, 8, 275.

HARDING, V. J. Nausea and vomiting in pregnancy. Lancet, 1921, 11, 327.

HATCHER, R. A. AND WEISS, S. Studies on vomiting. J. Pharmacol. & Exper. Therap., 1923, 22, 139.

HEGNER, K. Untersuchungen uber die Schluckstrasse. Arch. f. Ohren-Nasen-u. Kehlkopfheilk. ver Ztschr. Hals-, Nasen-u. Ohrenheilk., 1936, 140, 387.

HERTZ, A. F. AND NEWTON, A. The normal movements of the colon in man. J. Physiol., 1913, 47, 54, 57.

HIGHTOWER, N. C., JR. The physiology of symptoms (I) Swallowing and esophageal motility. Am. J. Digest. Dis., 1958, **3**, 562.

HIGHTOWER, N. C., JR. Motility of the alimentary canal of man, in *Disturbances in Gastrointestinal Motility*. Charles C Thomas, Springfield, Ill., 1959.

HIGHTOWER, N. C., JR. AND CODE, C. F. The quantitative analysis of antral gastric motility records in normal human beings, with a study of the effects of neostigmine. Proc. Staff Meet., Mayo Clinic, 1950, **25**, 697.

HIGHTOWER, N. C., JR. AND GAMBILL, E. E. The effects of banthine on pain and antral gastric motility in patients with duodenal ulcer. Gastroenterology 1953, **23**, 244.

HIGHTOWER, N. C., JR., OLSEN, A. M., AND MOERSCH, H. J. A comparison of the effects of acetyl-beta methyl-choline chloride (Mecholyl) on esophageal intraluminal pressure in normal persons and patients with cardiospasm. Gastroenterology, 1954, **26**, 592.

HIGHTOWER, N. C., JR. AND SALEM, M. E. The rate of pharyngeal and esophageal transport. J. Lab. Clin. Med., 1958, **52**, 820.

HOFMEISTER, F. AND SCHUTZ, E. Ueber die automatischen Bewegungen des Mangens. Arch. exper. Path. u. Pharmakol., 1886, **20**, 1.

HOLZKNECHT, G. Die normale Peristaltik des Kolon. München. med. Wchnschr., 1909, **56**, 3401.

HOUCKGEEST, vB. Undersuchungungen über Peristaltik des Mangens und Darmkanals. Arch. ges. Physiol., 1922, **59**, 97.

HOWELL, A. H. AND MANLY, R. S. An electronic strain gauge for measuring oral forces. J. Dent. Res., 1948, **27**, 705.

HUNT, J. N. Some properties of an alimentary osmoreceptor mechanism. J. Physiol., 1956, **132**, 267.

HUNT, J. N. AND SPURRELL, W. R. The pattern of emptying of the human stomach. J. Physiol., 1951, **113**, 157, 185.

HURST, A. F. The passage of food along the alimentary canal. Guy's Hosp. Rep., 1907, **61**, 389.

HURST, A. F. The treatment of achalasia of the cardia (so-called 'cardiospasm'). Lancet, 1927, **608**, 1.

INGELFINGER, F. J., KRAMER, P., AND SANCHEZ, G. C. The gastroesophageal vestibule, its normal function, and its role in cardiospasm and gastroesophageal reflux. Am. J. Med. Sci., 1954, **228**, 417.

JONES, C. M. AND RICHARDSON, W. Observations on the nature of "heartburn." J. Clin. Invest., 1926, **2**, 610 (proc).

JOSEPH, D. R. AND MELTZER, S. J. Inhibition of the duodenum coincident with the movements of the pyloric part of the stomach. Am. J. Physiol., 1910, **27** (Proc.) 1910, xxxi.

KAHN, R. H. Studien uber der Schluckreflex. I. Die sensible Innervation. Arch. f. Physiol. (Suppl. bd.), 386, 1903.

KELLEY, M. L., JR., GORDON, E. A., AND DeWEESE, J. A. Pressure studies of the ileocolonic junctional zone of dogs. Am. J. Physiol., 1965, **209**, 333.

KING, C. E., ARNOLD, L., AND CHURCH, J. G. The physiological role of the intestinal mucosal movements. Am. J. Physiol., 1922, **61**, 80.

VON KOKAS, E. AND VON LUDANY, G. Relation between villikinine and the absorption of glucose from the intestine. Quart. J. Exper. Physiol., 1938, **28**, 15. (See also Arch. ges. Physiol., 1933, **232**, 293.)

KOSAKA, T. AND LIM, R. K. S. Demonstration of a humoral agent in fat inhibition of gastric secretion. Proc. Soc. Exper. Biol. & Med., 1930, **27**, 890.

KOSAKA, T. AND LIM, R. K. S. On the mechanism of the inhibition of gastric motility by fat. An inhibitory agent from the intestinal mucosa. Chinese J. Physiol., 1933, **7**, 5.

KRAMER, P. AND INGELFINGER, F. J. Esophageal sensitivity to Mecholyl in cardiospasm. Gastroenterology, 1951, **19**, 242.

KUNTZ, A. On the occurrence of reflex arcs in the myenteric and submucous plexuses. Anat. Rec., 1922, **23**, 193.

KUNTZ, A. AND THOMAS, J. E. On the nature of the rhythmic contractions in the stomach and intestine. Proc. Soc. Exper. Biol. & Med., 1923, **20**, 256.

LERCHE, W. The esophagus and pharynx in action: A study of structure in relation to function. Charles C Thomas, Springfield, Ill., 1950.

LIM, R. K. S. Observations on the mechanism of the inhibition of gastric function by fat. Quart. J. Exper. Physiol., 1933, **23**, 263.

LUCKHARDT, A. B., PHILLIPS, H. T., AND CARLSON, A. J. Contributions to the physiology of the stomach. II. The control of the pylorus. Am. J. Physiol., 1919, **50**, 57.

MAGNUS, R. Die Beziehungen des Darmnervensystems zur automatischen Darmbewegung. Arch. ges. Physiol., 1904, **102**, 349.

MAGNUS, W. O. C. Uber die Zentren fur Lecken und Kawen. Monatschr. Psychiat. u. Neurol., 1945, **110**, 193.

MAGOUN, H. W., RANSON, S. W., AND FISHER, C. Corticifugal pathways for mastication, lapping and other motor functions in the cat. Arch. Neurol. & Psychiat., 1933, **30**, 292.

MARKOWITZ, J. AND CAMPBELL, W. R. The relief of experimental ileus by spinal anesthesia. Am. J. Physiol., 1927, **81**, 101.

MARKWALD, M. Uber die Ausbreitung der Erregung und Hemmung von Sckluckcentrum auf das Athemcentrum. Ztschr. Biol. New Series, 1889, **7**, 1.

McNALLY, E. F., KELLY, J. E., AND INGELFINGER, F. J. Mechanism of belching: Effects of gastric distention with air. Gastroenterology, 1964, **46**, 254.

MELTZER, S. J. On the causes of the orderly progress of the peristaltic movements in the esophagus. Am. J. Physiol., 1899, **2**, 266.

MELTZER, S. J. AND AUER, J. Peristaltic rush. Am. J. Physiol., 1907, **20**, 259.

MILLER, F. R. The cortical paths for mastication and deglutition. J. Physiol., 1919, **53**, 473.

MILLER, T. G. AND ABBOTT, W. O. Intestinal intubation, a practical technique. Am. J. M. Sci., 1934, **187**, 595.

MILTON, G. W. AND SMITH, A. W. M. The pace-making area of the duodenum. J. Physiol, 1956, **132**, 100. (See also Quart. J. Exper. Physiol., 1955, **40**, 79).

MIYAKAWA, K., KERSEY, J., AND VELA, A. R. Pressures in mouth and pharynx during sucking and swallowing. Fed. Proc., 1957, **89**, 16.

PAINE, J. R. AND WANGENSTEEN, O. H. The necessity for constant suction to inlying nasal tubes for effectual decompression or drainage of upper gastrointestinal tract. With comments upon drainage of other body cavities. Surg. Gynec. & Obst., 1933, **57**, 601.

PAYNE, W. W. AND POULTON, E. P. Visceral pain in the upper alimentary tract. Quart. J. Med., 1923, **17**, 53.

PINCUS, P. Caries: Attack on enamel protein in an alkaline medium. Brit. Dent. J., 1937, **63**, 511.

POGRUND, R. S. AND STEGERRDA, F. R. Influence of gaseous transfer between the colon and blood-stream on percentage gas composition of intestinal flatus in man. Am. J. Physiol., 1948, **153**, 475.

POMMERENKE, W. T. A study of sensory areas eliciting the swallowing reflex. Am. J. Physiol., 1928, **84**, 36.

QUIGLEY, J. P. A modern explanation of the gastric emptying mechanism. Am. J. Digest. Dis., 1943, **10**, 418.

QUIGLEY, J. P. AND BRODY, D. H. In Medical Physics (ed. GLASSER, O.), Chicago, Y. B. 1950, Vol. II, pp. 280–292.

QUIGLEY, J. P. AND BRODY, E. H. A physiologic and clinical consideration of the pressures developed in the digestive tract. Am. J. Med., 1952, 73.

QUIGLEY, J. P. AND PHELPS, K. R. The mechanism of gastric motor inhibition from ingested carbohydrate. Am. J. Physiol., 1934, **109**, 133.

QUIGLEY, J. P., ZETTLEMAN, H. J., AND IVY, A. C. Analysis of factors involved in gastric motor inhibition by fats. Am. J. Physiol., 1934, **108**, 643.

RAKE, G. W. Pathology of achalasia of the cardia. Guy's Hosp. Rep., 1927, **77**, 141.

RIOCH, D. M. AND BRENNER, C. Experiments on the corpus striatum and rhinencephalon. J. Compl. Neurol., 1938, **68**, 491.

RUSHMER, R. F. AND HENDRON, J. A. The act of deglutition. A cinefluoroscopic study. J. Appl. Physiol., 1951, **3**, 622.

SANCHEZ, G. C., KRAMER, P., AND INGELFINGER, F. J. Motor mechanisms of the esophagus, particularly of its distal portion. Gastro-enterology, 1953, **25**, 321.

SCHAPIRO, G. AND WOODWARD, E. R. Inhibition of gastric motility by acid in the duodenum. J. Appl. Physiol., 1955, **8**, 121.

SCHIROKICH, P. O. Prot. d. XI Kong, russ. Natur-forscher in Ärzte, 1901, **10**, 448 (Cited by B. P. BABKIN, 1928).

SCHREIBER, J. Über den bewegenden Einfluss der Schwerkraft beim Trinken in Awfrechten und Kopfstellung. Arch. Verdauungs-krankh. Stoff-wechselpathol. u. Diätetik, 1915, **21**, 1.

SHAY, H. AND GERSHON-COHEN, J. Experimental studies in gastric physiology in man. II. A study of pyloric control. The roles of acid and alkali. Surg. Gynec. & Obst., 1934, **58**, 935.

SHERRINGTON, C. S. Reflexes elicitable in the cat froR the pinna, vibissae and jaws. J. Physiol., 1917, **51**, 404.

SIEGEL, C. I. AND HENDRIX, T. R. The clinical value of esophageal motor studies. Postgrad. Med., 1961, **29**, 505.

TEMPLETON, R. D. AND LAWSON, H. Studies on the motor activity of the large intestine. I. Normal motility in the dog recorded by the tandem balloon method. Am. J. Physiol., 1931, **96**, 667.

TEXTER, E. C., JR., ET AL. Intraluminal pressures from the upper gastrointestinal tract: I. Correlation with motor activity in normal subjects and patients with esophageal disorder. Gastroenterology, 1957, **32**, 1013.

THOMAS, J. E., CRIDER, J. O., AND MOGAN, C. J. A study of reflexes involving the pyloric sphincter and antrum and their role in gastric evacuation. Am. J. Physiol., 1934, **108**, 683.

THOMAS, J. E., AND CRIDER, J. O. Rhythmic changes in duodenal motility associated with gastric peristalsis. Am. J. Physiol., 1935, **111**, 124.

THOMAS, J. E. AND CRIDER, J. O. Inhibition of gastric motility associated with the presence of products of protein hydrolysis in the upper small intestine. Am. J. Physiol., 1939, **126**, 28.

THOMAS, J. E. AND WHEELON, H. The nervous control of the pyloric sphincter. J. Lab. & Clin. Med., 1922, **7**, 375.

TRISKA, W. Experimentelle Studien uber die Beisskraft. Arch. ges. Physiol., 1924, **204**, 660.

TSCHESCHKOW, A. N. 1902. Diss. St. Petersburg. (Cited by B. P. BABKIN, 1928).

TUTTLE, S. G., BETTARELLO, A., AND GROSSMAN, M. I. Gastroestophageal regurgitation. J.A.M.A., 1961, **498**, 176.

TUTTLE, S. G., RUFIN, F., AND BETTARELLO, A. The physiology of heartburn. Ann. Int. Med., 1961, **292**, 55.

VAN ESVELD, L. W. Verhalten bon plexushaltigen und plexusfreien Darmmuskelpraparaten. Arch. exper. Path. u. Pharmakol., 1928, **134**, 347.

WHEELON, H. AND THOMAS, J. E. Observations on the motility of the antrum and the relation of the rhythmic activity of the antrum to that of the pyloric sphincter. J. Lab. & Clin. Med., 1920, **6**, 124.

WHEELON, H. AND THOMAS, J. E. Rhythmicity of the pyloric sphincter. Am. J. Physiol., 1921, **54**, 460.

WHEELON, H. AND THOMAS, J. E. Observations on the motility of the duodenum and the relation of duodenal activity to that of the pars pylorica. Am. J. Physiol., 1922, **59**, 72.

Monographs and Reviews

ALVAREZ, W. C. Intestinal autointoxication. Physiol. Rev., 1924, **4**, 352.

ALVAREZ, W. C. The mechanics of the digestive tract. Paul B. Hoeber, Inc. N. Y. 1928.

ALVAREZ, W. C. Nervous indigestion. Paul B. Hoeber, Inc. N. Y. 1931.

ALVAREZ, W. C. An introduction to gastroenterology, 3rd ed., Hoeber, N. Y. 1933.

ALVAREZ, W. C. An introduction to gastroenterology, 2nd ed., Hoeber, N. Y. 1940.

BABKIN, B. P. Die äussere Sekretion der Verdauungsdrüsen, Springer-Verlag, Berlin, 1928.

BARCLAY, A. E. The digestive tract. Cambridge University Press, 1933.

BAUMGARTNER, C. J. Survey of intestinal obstruction. Arch. Surg., 1947, 55, 607.

BORISON, H. L. AND WANG, S. C. The physiology and pharmacology of vomiting. Pharmacol. Rev., 1953, 5, 1953.

CANNON, W. B. The mechanical factors of digestion. Edward Arnold and Co., London, 1911b.

CARLSON, A. J. The control of hunger in health and disease. Univ. of Chicago Press, Chicago, 1916.

CANTAROW, A. AND SCHEPARTZ, B. Biochemistry, p. 276. W. B. Saunders Co., Philadelphia, 1954.

CODE, C. F., CREAMER, B., AND SCHLEGEL, J. F., ET AL. An atlas of esophageal motility in health and disease. Charles C Thomas, Springfield, Ill., 1958.

CODE, C. F. AND ASSOCIATES. Motility of the alimentary canal in man. Am. J. Med., 1952, 13, 75.

EVANS, C. L. The physiology of plain muscle. Physiol. Rev., 1926, 6, 358.

FERRIER, D. The functions of the brain. 2nd ed. p. 260. G. P. Putnam's Sons N. Y. 1886.

GARRY, R. C. The movements of the large intestine. Physiol. Rev., 1934, 14, 103.

GASK, G. E. AND ROSS, J. P. The surgery of the sympathetic nervous system. The Williams & Wilkins Co., Baltimore, 1934.

GOTTLIEB, B. Dental caries: its etiology, pathology, clinical aspects and prophylaxis. Lea and Febiger, Philadelphia, 1947.

GRACE, W. J., WOLF, S. AND WOLFF, G. G. The human colon: An experimental study based on direct observation of four fistulous subjects. N. Y., Hoeber, 1951.

HANDLER, P. AND PERLZWEIG, W. A. Detoxication mechanisms. Ann. Rev. Biochem., 1945, 16, 617.

HATCHER, R. A. The mechanism of vomiting. Physiol. Rev., 1924, 4, 479.

HERTER, C. A. Bacterial infections of the digestive tract. Macmillan, N. Y. 1907.

HURST, A. F. Constipation and allied intestinal disorders. H. Frowde, London, 1909.

HURST, A. F. The passage of food along the alimentary canal. Guy's Hosp. Rep., 61(46 of third series), 389.

INGELFINGER, F. J. Progress in gastroenterology: The esophagus, March 1961 to February 1963. 1963, 241, 45.

JONES, C. M. Digestive tract pain; diagnosis and treatment; experimental observations. The Macmillan Co., N. Y. 1938.

LANE, W. A. The operative treatment of chronic intestinal stasis. 4th ed. Oxford University Press, London, 1918.

LUDWIG, C. Lehrbuch der Physiologie des Menschen, vol. 2, page 615. Wintersche, Leipzig u. Heidelberg, 1861.

MAGENDIE, F. Precis elementaire de physiologie, Trans. by John Revere. (An elementary treatise on human physiology.) 5th ed. Harper and Bros., New York, 1838.

MAGGEE, H. E. The role of the small intestine in nutrition. Physiol. Rev., 1930, 10, 473.

McSWINEY, B. A. Innervation of the stomach. Physiol. Rev., 1931, 11, 478.

MELLANBY, M. The influence of diet on the structure of the teeth. Physiol. Rev., 1928, 8, 545.

METCHNIKOFF, E. The prolongation of life; optimistic studies. The English translation. Ed. by Chalmers Mitchell, W. Hinemann, London, 1907.

MOSSO. Moleschott's Untersuchungen, XI, 331, 1876 (Cited by Cannon and Moser 1898).

MURLIN, J. R. The emptying mechanism of the stomach. J. Nutrit. 1930, 2, 311.

NOBLE, R. L. Treatment of experimental motion sickness in humans. Canad. J. Res. Feb., 1946, p. 12. Motion sickness with special reference to air sickness. Practitioner, 1948, 160, 453.

PANCOAST, H. K., PENDERGRASS, E. P. AND SCHAEFFER, J. P. The head and neck in roentgen diagnosis, p. 797, Charles C Thomas, Springfield, Ill., 1940.

QUIGLEY, J. P. Medical Physics, p. 310. Year Book Publishers, Chicago, 1944.

TEMPLETON, F. E. X-Ray examination of the stomach. University of Chicago Press, Chicago, 1944.

THOMAS, J. E. Digestion and the nervous system. A review of the literature. Am. J. Digest. Dis., 1943, 6, 201.

THOMAS, J. E. Mechanics and regulation of gastric emptying. Physiol. Rev., 1957, 37, 453.

TODD, T. W. Behaviour patterns in the alimentary canal. The Williams & Wilkins Co., Baltimore, 1930.

TOVERUD, G. AND ASSOCIATES. A survey of the literature of dental caries. Pub. 225, Nat. Res. Council, Nat. Acad. Sc., Washington, 1952.

TYLER, D. B. AND BARD, P. Physiol. Rev., 1940, 29, 281.

VAN LIERE, E. J. The effect of anoxia on the alimentary tract. Physiol. Rev., 1941, 21, 307.

VERZAR, F. AND McDOUGALL, E. J. Absorption from the intestine. Longmans, Green & Co., London, 1936.

YOUMANS, W. B. Nervous and neurohumoral regulation of intestinal motility. Interscience Publishers, Inc., New York, 1949.

CHAPTER 62

Innervation and Visceral Sensations of the Gastrointestinal Tract

Innervation

The gastrointestinal tract receives an abundant nerve supply via the autonomic nerves. In addition, it contains within its walls an elaborate plexus of interconnected ganglia. This is usually described as consisting of two plexuses, the *myenteric plexus*, situated between the circular and longitudinal layers of the smooth muscle, and the *submucous plexus*, situated in the submucosa. Kuntz (1953) considers that this is an artificial division and that actually the plexuses function as a unit. Langley (1921) suggested that the enteric plexuses should be regarded as a separate subdivision of the autonomic nervous system and proposed that they be designated the "enteric nervous system." He wrote as follows: "This classification is, I think, advisable for the central connection of the enteric nerve cells is still uncertain and evidence has been obtained that they have automatic and reflex functions which other peripheral nerve cells do not possess. Functional evidence for reflex activity in the enteric nervous system has been available since the work of Bayliss and Starling." In 1922, Kuntz presented anatomical evidence of the existence of reflex arcs in the enteric plexuses. Understanding of the fact that the enteric plexuses constitute a complex and highly coordinated reflex mechanism is essential to an intelligent interpretation of the effects of the extrinsic nerves on intestinal smooth muscle.

Extrinsic Nerves

The autonomic nerves are classified as sympathetic and parasympathetic but it is more in keeping with modern thought to consider them as cholinergic or adrenergic, depending upon whether they liberate acetylcholine or an adrenalinelike substance at their final terminations on the muscles. In this sense, most parasympathetics are cholinergic and sympathetics are adrenergic, but there is considerable mixing, since cholinergic fibers have been demonstrated in considerable abundance in the sympathetics.

The parasympathetic nerve supply to the gastrointestinal smooth muscle comes mainly from the vagus (fig. 62.1); however, the pelvic nerves supply the distal portion of the colon (fig. 62.2). The parasympathetic fibers, whether vagus or pelvic in origin, do not end directly on the smooth muscle cells but end by making synapses with cells in the enteric plexuses. Therefore, as pointed out by Carlson (1922), they stand in relation to these plexuses as intercalated or internuncial fibers between reflex centers and not as ordinary motor nerve fibers. The function of such fibers in the central nervous system, and presumably in this situation also, is to increase or decrease the excitability of the reflex centers and not to initiate muscular activity directly.

The sympathetic supply to the stomach and small intestine is by way of the splanchnic nerves. The cecum, appendix, and ascending and transverse colon are supplied by nerves which arise from the superior mesenteric plexus. This plexus is a derivative of the aortic plexus through which it also receives vagus fibers from the celiac plexus. The lower part of the rectum is supplied by sympathetic fibers which arise from the upper and lower divisions of the hypogastric plexus (Kuntz, 1953). The preganglionic sympathetic fibers end in the celiac, superior or inferior mesenteric, or aortic ganglia. The fibers that reach the intestine, therefore, are postganglionic. They probably have no functional relation to the enteric plexuses, even though they traverse the enteric ganglia and are distributed along with the postganglionic enteric plexus fibers. Most of them are concerned with the vasomotor supply of the numerous blood vessels in the intestine but some go to the intestinal smooth muscle.

The Function of Extrinsic Nerves

The gastrointestinal tract is capable of carrying on its major functions after all the extrinsic nerves have been severed. This automaticity may be attributed partly to the local nervous mechanism and partly to the properties of the smooth muscle. Probably, the essentially rhythmic functions, such as gastric antral peristalsis and seg-

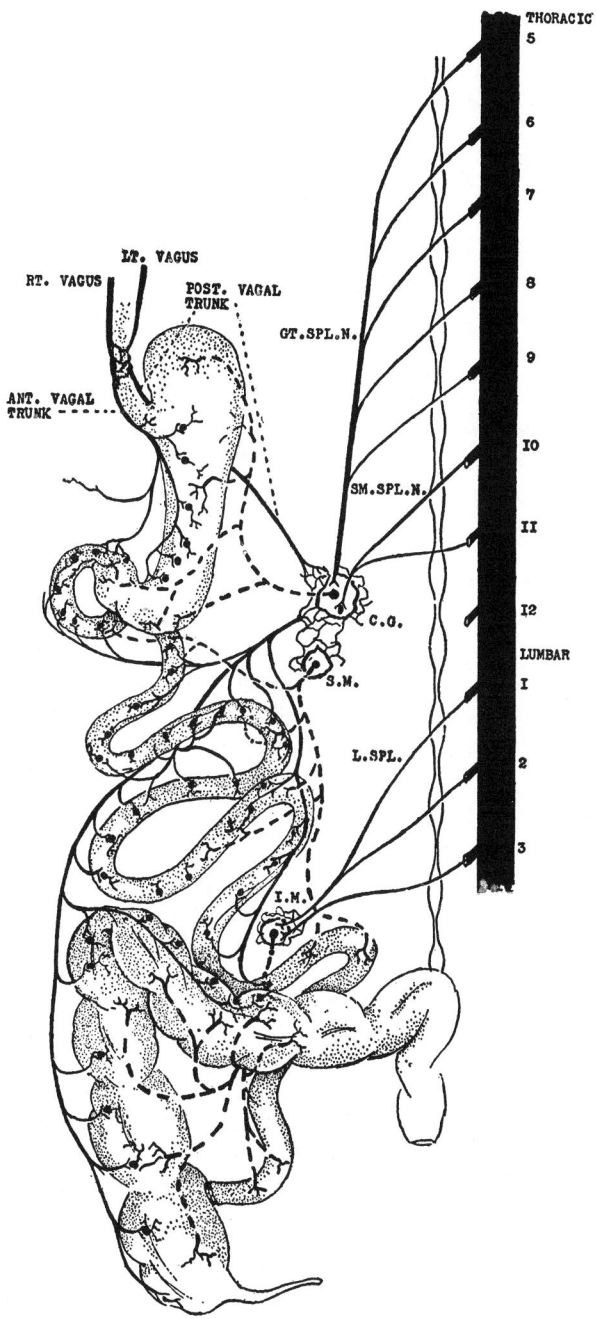

FIG. 62.1. Diagram of the innervation of the stomach, small intestine. and proximal part of the colon. GT.SPL.N , great splanchnic nerve; SM.SPL.N., small splanchnic nerve; L.SPL., least splanchnic nerve; C.G., celiac ganglion; S.M., superior mesenteric ganglion; I.M., inferior mesenteric ganglion. Continuous lines, vagal and sympathetic preganglionic fibers; broken lines, sympathetic postganglionic fibers ganglion cells and postganglionic fibers of vagus in gastrointestinal wall.

mentic contractions of the small and large intestine, are dependent upon the properties of the smooth muscle; whereas the more highly coordinated functions, such as forward peristalsis in the small intestine and mass movements in the colon, are dependent upon the functional integrity of the myenteric plexus. Both the neurogenic and myogenic functions are regulated

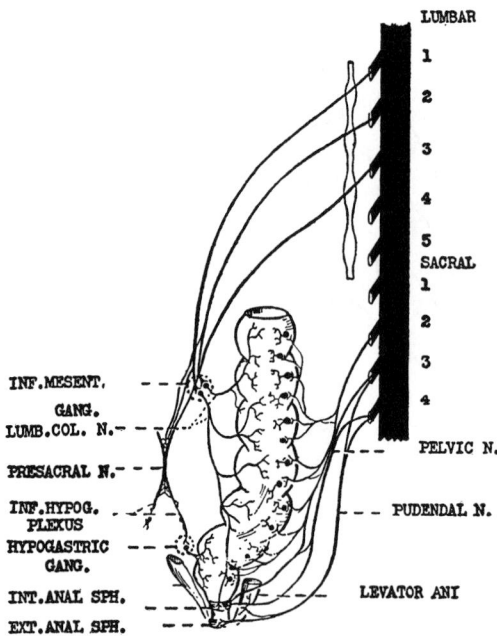

LUMBAR
1
2
3
4
5
SACRAL
1
2
3
4

INF.MESENT.
GANG.
LUMB.COL. N.
PRESACRAL N.
INF.HYPOG.
PLEXUS
HYPOGASTRIC
GANG.
INT.ANAL SPH.
EXT.ANAL SPH.

PELVIC N.
PUDENDAL N.
LEVATOR ANI

FIG. 62.2. Diagram of the innervation of the distal colon.

through central nervous system reflexes by way of the autonomic nerves.

The tone and peristaltic activity of the stomach are usually increased on stimulation of the vagus nerves. The statement that the vagus increases the activity of the muscle in the gastric wall while inhibiting the sphincters has been proved to be erroneous; when motor effects are observed in the muscle of the pyloric portion, for example, the pyloric sphincter responds in the same sense; thus the idea of a reciprocal innervation of the sphincters and the other muscle of the stomach is not borne out by the experimental facts (Thomas and Wheelon, 1922). There may be somewhat more justification for such a concept in regard to the relation between the esophagus and cardiac sphincter, but in order to demonstrate inhibition of the cardiac sphincter by vagus stimulation, Langley found it necessary to atropinize the animal first so as to paralyze the motor fibers.

The effect on the stomach of stimulating the splanchnic nerves is usually described as inhibitory but it is far from being invariably so. In simple acute experiments on anesthetized animals, increased motor activity is seen about as frequently as inhibition when the splanchnic nerves are stimulated; indeed, only motor responses are seen, unless care is taken to permit full recovery from the shock of the operation

and to avoid undue handling of the viscera while making the preparation. The fact is, as Carlson and his associates (1922) pointed out, that motor responses are more likely to be obtained when the muscle is in a state of relaxation, whereas inhibitory effects occur when the muscle is in a state of high tonus or vigorous activity. This rule applies to both vagus and sympathetic stimulation; nevertheless, with the muscle in a medium state of tonus, the vagi will more often produce excitatory effects while the splanchnics produce inhibitory effects. The reason for the preponderance of sympathetic motor effects in recently anesthetized, operated animals is that the stomach, in such circumstances, is always in a state of very low tone.

In the small intestine, the parasympathetic nerves are nearly always excitatory and the sympathetics nearly always inhibitory (fig. 62.3); however, the excitatory vagus effects, as mentioned previously, are usually preceded by a brief inhibition. In the upper portion of the small intestine, motor effects from stimulation of the sympathetic nerves are by no means uncommon. The tonus rule holds here also; motor effects are more apt to be observed in the relaxed intestine.

In the large intestine, stimulation of the parasympathetic innervation is reported to cause mainly increased activity, whereas stimulation of the sympathetic nerves gives results that are even more confusing than those obtained in the stomach. Some investigators report only inhibitory effects, others report only motor effects, whereas still others report inhibition of the walls of the viscera with contraction of the sphincters. There seems to be somewhat more basis for this last concept in the large intestine than is the case in the stomach. The sympathetic tends to cause retention of contents, for example, in the rectum, through contraction of the internal anal sphincter and relaxation of the rectal walls; the parasympathetics tend to promote evacuation of contents by causing relaxation of the sphincters and contraction and propulsive motility in the walls. Here also, muscle in high tonus tends to respond to nerve stimulation with relaxation, whereas muscle in low tonus tends to respond with contractions.

The effects of stimulating the autonomic nerves are confusing if one attempts to classify them simply as excitatory or inhibitory to the smooth muscle. It is much more understandable if we consider the fact that at least the parasympathetic nerves serve merely to increase or decrease the excitability of the local reflex mechanism.

Although it is true that stimulation of either vagus nerve generally increases the activity of the gastric and intestinal smooth muscle, inhibitory effects have been observed. Brief inhibition regularly precedes contraction in the small intestine following vagus stimulation (Bayliss and Starling, 1899); inhibitory effects are also seen occasionally in the stomach. The varying responses to parasympathetic stimulation may be interpreted as being due to the vagaries of the enteric reflex arcs which are subject to stimuli from many sources. The vagus impulses, being only one of these sources, could not be expected always to determine the response. The responses to sympathetic stimulation are undoubtedly influenced by changes in the blood supply brought about by the vasomotor fibers which always accompany the nerves to the intestinal smooth muscle, but mixed responses are obtained, even in excised, bloodless preparations, so we must assume the existence of fibers leading to both excitatory and inhibitory nerve endings.

Visceral Reflexes

While studying the effects of electrical stimulation of autonomic nerves, it is well to bear in mind the fact that nerves were not developed for the purpose of being artifically stimulated. Under normal circumstances, the autonomic nerves serve only reflex functions, and when aroused normally through their reflex connections they may produce effects quite different from those seen on electrical stimulation. Normal reflex stimulation is selective, exciting only those fibers which will promote the function subserved by the reflex, whereas ordinary electrical stimulation excites all the fibers without regard to their normal function.

Certain gastrointestinal reflexes involving the peripheral autonomic nerves have already been mentioned; among these are the receptive relaxation of the stomach, the enterogastric reflex, and the so-called gastrocolic reflex. These reflexes chiefly involve the parasympathetic nerves and are concerned with regulation of the normal functioning of the gastrointestinal smooth muscle. Other reflexes have been described which occur only under unusual circumstances, and generally involve the functioning of the sympathetic nerve supply. One of these is the *intestino-intestinal inhibitory reflex*. This consists of reflex inhibition of the whole intestinal tract as a result of distention of some one segment. The stomach may also be inhibited, but in this case we are dealing with a mechanism different from the enterogas-

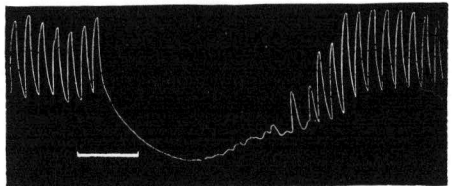

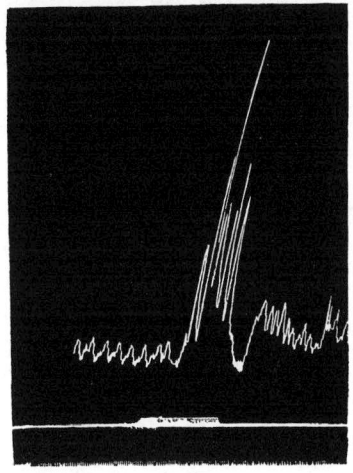

Fig. 62.3. Upper, shows the inhibitory effect of splanchnic stimulation upon the movements of the small intestine; the heavy white line indicates the time during which the stimulus was applied (after Starling). Lower, shows effect upon intestinal motility of stimulating vagus nerves. (After Thomas and Kuntz.)

tric reflex previously mentioned. The reflex is abolished or greatly diminished when the splanchnic nerves are cut, hence it involves discharge of impulses over the sympathetic nerves. It probably belongs in the category of responses to noxious stimuli which, generally throughout the body, tend to cause increased activity of the sympathetic nervous system, and to inhibit gastrointestinal motility. Other examples of reflex responses to noxious stimuli are: inhibition of the intestine due to irritation of the peritonium, distention of the gall bladder and bile ducts, overfilling of the bladder, or forcible stretching of the anal sphincters. All of these stimuli produce inhibition of the gastrointestinal smooth muscle through activation of adrenergic mechanisms, mainly the sympathetic nerves.

Visceral Sensations

The abdominal and thoracic viscera are insensitive to the several types of stimuli which readily arouse sensations in the skin and more superficial tissues of the body. The effects of the different varieties of stimulus, *thermal, chemical,*

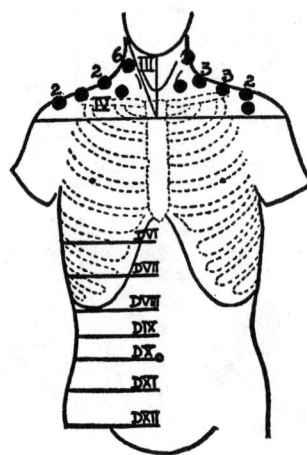

Fig. 62.4. Location of maximum points of referred neck pain from irritation of the diaphragm. The figures refer to the number of stimulations in each instance. They are all situated in the region supplied by the third and fourth spinal segments. (After Capps.)

tactile, and *pain*, have been investigated by a large number of observers.

TRUE AND REFERRED PAIN

Sensations of pain cannot be elicited from the viscera by the *usual means*. The intestine or the liver, the stomach or the heart may be cut, burned or pinched without arousing any immediate sensation. In the second stage of a colostomy operation, for example, the colon can be opened without pain being experienced by the patient. Harvey remarked upon the absence of sensation in the exposed heart of Viscount Montgomery.[1]

The insensibility of the alimentary tract to ordinary forms of stimulation commences in the lower or middle third of the eosphagus and extends as far as the commencement of the anal canal. How can these observations be reconciled with the well-known fact that pain is one of the commonest manifestations of visceral disease?

The whole subject of pain arising in, or referred from, the viscera is still highly controversial. No final answer can be given. The most that can be attempted is a summary of some of the more

[1] Harvey records, "I carried the young man to the King (Charles I) that His Majesty might with his own eyes behold this wonderful case; that, in a man alive and well, he might, without detriment to the individual, observe the movement of the heart, and with his proper hand even touch the ventricles as they contracted. And His Most Excellent Majesty, as well as myself, acknowledged that the heart was without the sense of touch; for the youth never knew when we touched his heart. . . ."

significant experimental results and clinical observations, and the opinions of those who have especially interested themselves in the subject.

Lennander considered that abdominal pain was always due to the stimulation of somatic nerve terminals in the parietal peritoneum or root of the mesentery; the bowel itself was supposed to be quite devoid of pain fibers. According to this view, therefore, pain localized within the organ itself and *true* visceral pain was an impossibility.

Ross's theory postulated that pain from the abdominal viscera was of two types: (a) *referred (somatic) pain*, and (b) *true visceral or splanchnic pain*, which was diffuse, and poorly localized, but felt in the viscus itself.

Mackenzie, as a result of his clinical observations, strongly supported Ross's idea of referred pain, but maintained that *all* visceral pain was of this nature, the viscera being quite insensitive to all forms of stimulation. In agreement with Lennander, he did not believe that the viscera contained pain fibers; true visceral pain, i.e., pain in the organ itself, was therefore never experienced.

Concepts of Ross and Mackenzie

When a viscus is diseased, pain or tenderness is frequently felt in the tissues approximately overlying it (abdominal or chest wall) or in some part quite remote from it. For example, pain is felt in the neck or shoulder (fig. 62.4) in conditions affecting the diaphragm, between the scapulas in gastric disease, in the region of the umbilicus in appendicitis, in the testis in renal colic and in the sternal region, or down the left arm in angina pectoris. Esophageal pain is frequently confused with that of cardiac origin, as it not only characteristically occurs substernally, but may extend into the neck, jaw, and even into the arms. When traction is made upon a coronary artery of a dog, the animal whines and indicates the location of the pain by limping on the left forepaw. In dextrocardia, anginal pain is felt in the right arm. Other examples are the pain in the perineum and tip of the penis caused by a stone in the region of the neck of the bladder, and the pain in the groin due to a stone in the ureter.

It will be recalled that a given spinal segment supplies a visceral area with autonomic nerve fibers (afferent and efferent) and also a well-delineated area of the skin (dermatone) with somatic nerves. The two types of structure linked in this way through the afferent nerves and the central nervous system may be some distance apart (e.g., diaphragm and shoulder) or be more closely related (e.g., area of abdominal wall and an underlying abdominal viscus). Mackenzie believed that afferent autonomic impulses arising in a diseased organ, although of themselves incapable of arousing any sensation, would upon entering the spinal cord set up an "irritable focus" with the result that cells accustomed to receive impulses from the corresponding somatic area were excited. Thus, the impulses from the viscera spread, or "irradiated," on to cells of the corresponding somatic center. New impulses originating in these cells travelled along the usual paths to higher perceptive centers (thalamus) which projected or referred the sensation to the somatic area, e.g., skin or muscle, from which it was accustomed to receive impulses. In this way, *spontaneous pain* in superficial structures remote from the diseased site was accounted for. Mackenzie spoke of these reactions as *viscerosensory "reflexes."* [2] *Tenderness* to touch, pressure or light pinching of the skin (hyperesthesia and hyperalgesia) was ascribed to the impulses (which ordinarily would be below the threshold for pain) arriving in the segment rendered hyperexcitable as a result of impulses received from the diseased organ. In the case of the abdominal viscera, Mackenzie claimed that the area of tenderness in the abdominal wall remained fixed, although the position of the diseased organ changed, thus indicating the referred nature of the pain. He explained the rigidity (hypertonus) of muscles overlying a diseased organ, the right rectus abdominis in acute appendicitis, for example, upon a similar basis. Afferent impulses of normal intensity arising in the muscle proprioceptors upon arriving at the spinal centers, which had been rendered hyperexcitable by the receipt of abnormal visceral impulses, resulted in a reflex increase in tonus of the corresponding muscles. The referred motor reaction he spoke of as a *visceromotor reflex* (see fig. 62.5).

The conception of referred pain was supported by the work of Head, who mapped out the segmental distribution of the cutaneous nerves responsible for hyperalgesia in diseased states, and showed that they came from the same segments as those which received autonomic fibers from the diseased organ.

In table 62.1 are given the segmental areas to which pain is referred in disease of various viscera (Head, 1894, 1896).

[2] This is obviously a most unsuitable term, for it is not a reflex in the ordinary accepted sense of that word.

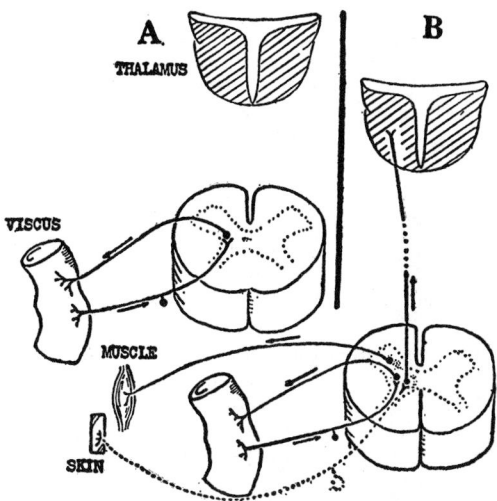

FIG. 62.5. Diagram to illustrate Mackenzie's theory of referred pain. A, representing normal conditions, a visceral reflex is shown. B, illustrates a visceromotor and a viscerosensory reflex. Impulses from a viscus are conceived as setting up an irritable focus in the cord which through the involvement of neighboring neurons increases the tone of muscles innervated by the same segment, and causes a discharge of impulses over the pathway for pain. The sensation is then projected in consciousness to the periphery, as indicated by the dotted line.

True Visceral (Splanchnic) Pain

True visceral pain, although denied by Mackenzie, exists. The pains of dysmenorrhea or childbirth, for example, or the pain of intestinal colic or an overdistended bladder, or the substernal pain of coronary occlusion, although diffuse, seem to arise within the organ itself, even when referred as well to a somatic structure, such as muscle or skin. Kinsella observed that, in conscious patients, pressure with the fingers upon an inflamed appendix caused pain centered in the viscus; a healthy appendix is insensitive. He and others have also shown that a chronic duodenal ulcer is also tender to direct contact. In transsection of the cord at the third thoracic vertebra in a patient (reported upon by Kinsella) in whom there was complete paralysis and anesthesia of the abdominal wall, intestinal pain was experienced which obviously could not be caused by reference to somatic nerves. Impulses in such cases must reach the central nervous system along intact visceral afferents. They apparently travel by sympathetic fibers which enter the cord above the level of the transection. It is unlikely that they are transmitted by the vagus.

Pain in a normal viscus may also result from disease in a distant organ through a visceromotor reflex. For example, painful contractions of the

TABLE 62.1*

Viscus	Spinal Segments
Lungs	1–7 dorsal, mostly 2–5 dorsal
Heart	3–5 cervical, 1–8 dorsal, predominantly on left side, sometimes bilateral
Esophagus	Mainly 5 dorsal, also 6, 7 and 8 dorsal
Breast	4 and 5 dorsal
Stomach	7, 8 and 9 dorsal, usually bilateral
Intestine	9–12 dorsal, bilateral or on left side only
Liver	8–10 dorsal on right side
Gall Bladder	Mostly 8 and 9 dorsal, also 5–7
Kidney	Mostly 10 dorsal, also 11 and 12 dorsal and 1 lumbar
Ureter	11 and 12 dorsal and 1 lumbar
Testis	10 dorsal
Epididymis	11 and 12 dorsal
Bladder	11 and 12 dorsal and 1 lumbar, also 3 and 4 sacral
Prostate	10 and 11 dorsal, also 1–3 and 5 sacral
Ovary	10 dorsal
Fallopian tubes	11 and 12 dorsal
Uterine cervix	11 and 12 dorsal and 1–4 sacral
Uterine body	10 dorsal to 1 lumbar

* From W. R. Brain, Diseases of the Nervous System, after Head.

small intestine may accompany disease of the appendix. A distinction should be drawn between pain of this nature and referred pain.

THE ADEQUATE STIMULUS FOR TRUE VISCERAL PAIN. The existence of true visceral pain is not incompatible with the statement made above, that the viscera are insensitive to the ordinary types of stimulus. From his investigations, Hurst concluded that the only adequate stimulus for visceral pain fibers is tension. Distention of a hollow viscus, e.g., stomach, intestine, gall bladder, etc., gives rise to pain, as a result of the stretch stimulus applied to the nerve terminals in its wall. The pain is roughly localized to the viscus itself, or referred. Under certain circumstances, chemical substances produced in an ischemic organ, as in angina pectoris or intermittent claudication, may stimulate nerve fibers subserving pain.

Although the question is by no means settled, it appears that *contraction* of the muscular wall of a hollow viscus such as the intestine does not cause pain unless the movement of the bowel makes traction upon the mesentery. Pain arises,

however, if the contraction causes distention of a neighboring portion of the wall, as may result when the contraction wave approaches a mechanical obstruction, a length of bowel in spasm, or a sphincter which fails to relax (*achalasia*). Poulton, for example, found that when a balloon was inserted into the lower part of the human esophagus, the approach of a peristaltic wave toward the obstruction caused pain, but during its passage over the esophageal wall in contact with the balloon no sensation was felt. Poulton ascribes the absence of pain during the passage of the contraction wave to the reduction in the diameter of the tube and the consequent release from stretch of the nerve endings lying between the muscle fibers. Pain was also relieved if the esophageal muscle relaxed to accommodate the balloon; that is, adjusted the length of its fibers to the distending force.

As further evidence for the effectiveness of distention in causing pain, the following observations may be cited. In animals, when an intestinal loop exposed under local anesthesia is stimulated to powerful contraction, there is no evidence of pain, whereas even moderate distention of the loop (as by inflating it with a balloon) is manifestly painful. Distention of the human appendix by the injection of fluids through an appendicostomy opening causes severe pain in the epigastrium or in the region of the umbilicus, and when the duodenum is distended by the injection of material through a duodenal tube, pain is felt on the right side. The pain impulses undoubtedly reach the central nervous system through the splanchnic nerves. Bentley and Smithwick distended the duodenum of patients whose splanchnics had been divided on one or both sides. After unilateral denervation, distention caused pain on the unoperated side only; no pain whatever was felt after bilateral splanchnic section.

Morley's Theory of Referred Pain

Morley contends that the referred pain of abdominal disease does *not involve visceral afferents* (as postulated by Mackenzie), but is due to the stimulation of *somatic* pain fibers in the parietal peritoneum or mesentery, the sensation being referred to the superficial area innervated from the same spinal segment. He expresses what he calls the *law of referred pain* in the following words: *Referred pain only arises from irritation of nerves which are sensitive to those stimuli that produce pain when applied to the surface of the body*, that is, by the stimulation of somatic sensory nerves. He believes that the somatic innervation of the peritoneum extends along the mesentery to within a short distance of its attachment to the bowel, and does not terminate, as has been generally supposed, near the root of the mesentery.[3] The mesentery or peritoneum is therefore sensitive to tearing, cutting, etc., whereas the organ itself, which contains only visceral afferents, is insensitive to these types of stimulus. In support of his views, Morley cites the pain in the shoulder associated with irritation of the peritoneal covering of the diaphragm. He points out that the diaphragm is innervated (through the phrenic) chiefly by the fourth cervical spinal segment and to a lesser extent by the third and fifth. None of these segments gives rise to autonomic fibers, but the third and fourth cervical nerves furnish somatic afferent fibers to the shoulder area in which the referred pain of diaphramatic disease is located. Morley explains muscular rigidity in a similar manner as the radiation of impulses over the motor nerves. He replaces Mackenzie's terms, viscerosensory and visceromotor reflexes, by *peritoneocutaneous radiation* and *peritoneomuscular reflex*, respectively. Morley also recognizes spontaneous, true (unreferred) visceral pain, resulting from an adequate stimulus—tension. The pain and tenderness that result from pressure upon an inflamed viscus (e.g., ulcer of the duodenum) through the abdominal wall, and which seems to arise in the organ itself, he ascribes, however, to the parietal peritoneum being brought into contact with the roughened surface of the lesion. As evidence that the sensation is not, in such instances, referred to the skin from the diseased structure, but is due to the stimulation of nerves in the parietal peritoneum, he states that: (a) the area of tenderness shifted with the movement of the viscus, and (b) direct pressure upon the inflamed organ when exposed by operation in a conscious patient (i.e., under local anesthesia) did not give rise to any sensation (fig. 62.6).

Morley has made out a case for the production of pain in some instances through a peritoneocu-

[3] Sheepan has made a study of the nerves of the mesentery and finds the following types of fiber: (a) Fibers ending in Pacinian corpuscles scattered throughout the mesentery. These are afferent sympathetic fibers which travel in the splanchnic nerves. (b) Free nonmyelinated fibers. These are afferent and efferent sympathetic fibers; their terminals are distributed to the serous covering of the bowel. They provide a medium for the transmission of true visceral pain. (c) Free myelinated fibers derived, presumably, from somatic nerves. These apparently do not extend as far as the serous covering of the bowel itself.

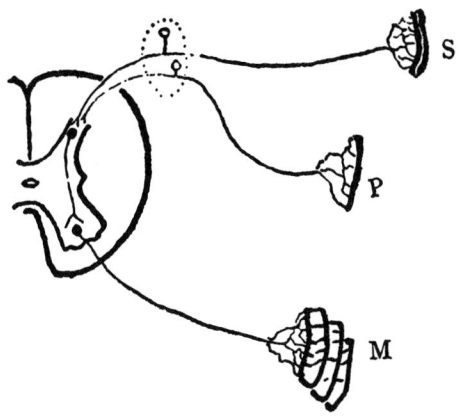

FIG. 62.6. Diagram to illustrate Morley's theory of peritoneocutaneous radiation and peritoneomuscular reflex; M, muscle; P, peritoneum; S, skin. After Morley, redrawn.

taneous reaction, and for pain and tenderness upon pressure resulting from the stimulation of somatic nerves in the parietal peritoneum. But his views cannot be accepted in their entirety. Others have reported that a duodenal ulcer is tender to direct touch, and there is no doubt that referred pain can be brought about through the mediation of either visceral or somatic nerves. Woollard and Carmichael, for example, have obtained evidence for the latter from experiments upon the human testis which, since it has migrated from the abdominal cavity and is enveloped by peritoneum, may be looked upon as an abdominal organ, so far as the question of referred pain is concerned. These observers found that after all the nerves to the testis except the autonomic fibers passing along the spermatic artery had been blocked by means of novocaine, no sensation was felt within the organ when it was compressed; but pain, referred to the tenth dorsal segment or lower abdomen and back, was experienced. The observation of Bentley and Smithwick, mentioned above, points in the same direction.

The Views of Lewis and Kelgren

Lewis and Kelgren postulate a common system of afferent nerves supplying deep somatic structures as well as the viscera. They maintain, with good reason, that since referred pain can follow the irritation of either visceral or somatic afferent nerves, there is no physiological justification for making a distinction between pain referred from a viscus and pain referred from the parieties, nor between the motor reactions (e.g., muscular rigidity) resulting from stimulation in either situation.

Although in the first instance visceral afferent fibers and in the second, somatic sensory nerves, are stimulated, the impulses in either case enter the spinal cord by the posterior nerve roots, and the nerve fibers which transmit them have their cell stations in the posterior root ganglia. There is no indication that they do not follow identical paths in the central nervous sytem. Thus, impulses from a viscus or a deep somatic structure cause a sensation which, in either case, is projected to a part remote from the part stimulated but which is innervated by the same spinal segment. The pains, whether referred from a viscus or from part of the soma, have common characteristics, being diffuse and poorly localized.

Lewis and Kelgren carried out experiments on a number of human subjects; their results are highly significant to the question of referred pain. Pain closely resembling in character the referred pain of visceral disease was induced by the injection of a small quantity (0.3 ml.) of hypertonic saline into an interspinous ligament. This induced pain was distributed in a manner strikingly similar to the pain of renal colic, namely, in the loin and in the inguinal and scrotal regions. The pain was accompanied by retraction of the testis. Injection into the ninth thoracic interspinous ligament caused pain in the back, in the region of the first lumbar spine, and over an area in front, extending from the ninth costal cartilage on the affected side to the umbilicus. Rigidity of the abdominal muscles and deep tenderness were associated with the pain. Stimulation of the eighth cervical ligament was followed by pain in the interscapular region, over the pectoralis major muscle, and down the inner side of the elbow and forearm, together with a sensation of constriction in the upper part of the chest on the stimulated side. Several subjects of angina pectoris were chosen for experiment and were asked to compare the pain which they experienced in an attack with that caused by stimulation of the seventh cervical or the first thoracic interspinous ligament. In all instances, the patients described the experimentally-induced pain as being identical in character with that caused by the disease, although it showed some minor differences in distribution.

Lewis and Kelgren also found that, in cats, mechanical stimulation (pinching) of the pancreas or of the mesentery in the duodenal loop caused motor reflexes from the abdominal muscles which resembled closely those caused by stimulation of the back muscles.

The Views of Pollock and Davis

Pollock and Davis stimulated the peritoneal surface of the diaphragm in dogs. The animals showed every sign of suffering pain, which was abolished by any one of the following procedures: section of the phrenic nerve; removal of the cervical sympathetic chains; severing the eighth cervical and the first, second and third thoracic anterior roots; transection of the cord at the seventh cervical segment; destroying the cord at the first and second dorsal segments; or section of the cervical posterior roots. Pollock and Davis conclude from these results that the pain impulses following stimulation of the diaphragm travel over the phrenic, enter the cord by the posterior cervical roots, descend the cord to the level of the eighth cervical and first, second and third thoracic segments. Connections are then made with cells in the lateral horn of gray matter (intermediolateral column), from which impulses pass by sympathetic preganglionic fibers to the cervical sympathetic chain, and then, by postganglionic fibers, "effectors in the skin, blood vessels, meninges and other structures, where by some vasomotor (?) or hormonal (?) process the sensory endings of the cerebrospinal system are stimulated and a sensory impulse travels over the ordinary cerebrospinal system, enters the spinal cord by the posterior roots and ascends to consciousness." The pain and cutaneous lesions of herpes zoster come to mind in this connection.

The diffuse character of deep pain, in contrast to the accurate localization of cutaneous stimulation, can be accounted for by: (a) the existence of relatively few afferent fibers in deep structures, (b) the lack of experience and training in the localization of sensations from the viscera, since they are normally felt very infrequently, and (c) by the fact that, when impressions from the internal organs do occur, their localization is not aided by sight as is the case in more superficial sensations. However, in experiments with intelligent subjects having some knowledge of anatomy, and in whom pain was evoked by inflating balloons inserted into hollow viscera, the subjects' sense of localization was much improved above the ordinary.

The Sensibility of the Alimentary Tract to Various Stimuli

Touch

The sensation of touch disappears at the lower end of the pharynx. This was shown by Hurst, who used an esophageal tube with a slit on one side through which the mucosa of the esophagus could be stimulated. Carlson, by means of a test-tube brush passed into the stomach, was unable to elicit the sensation of touch from the gastric mucosa. The rectum possesses no tactile sensibility but the anal canal is sensitive.

Thermal Sensibility

The esophagus is sensitive to extremes of heat and cold. The sensations of temperature that are felt when hot or cold materials enter the stomach have been thought by some to originate in the lower end of the esophagus, by others to arise in the skin of the epigastrium, either through thermal conduction or by reflex changes in the cutaneous blood vessels. Carlson has shown, however, that the gastric mucosa is sensitive to extreme temperature changes, i.e., protopathic thermal sensibility (below 13° C. or above 45° C.). It is the lower end of the esophagus, however, which is responsible for the greater part of the thermal sensation that is experienced when excessively hot or cold materials are swallowed. This is due to the greater sensitivity of the esophageal mucosa, as well as to the fact that the material is retained for an appreciable length of time above the cardia. The colon is insensitive to temperature changes, but even comparatively slight differences in temperature can be detected in the anal canal.

Chemicals

Chemicals, with the exception of alcohol, cause no sensation whatever when introduced into the stomach or intestinal canal. The mucosa is completely insensitive to acids; the introduction into the healthy stomach of a solution of 0.5% hydrochloric acid causes no pain or sensation of any kind. Alcohol stimulates the mucosa of the esophagus and stomach and causes a sensation of warmth. Peppermint and various condiments free from alcohol arouse no sensation. The pelvic colon and rectum show a similar sensitivity to alcohol but are insensitive to other chemicals. The anal canal is extremely sensitive, especially to alcohol and glycerine, both causing a burning sensation.

Nausea

Nausea usually precedes the act of vomiting but may occur alone. On the other hand, vomiting may occur without nausea, as in certain cerebral conditions. The sensation is felt in the back of the throat or pit of the stomach, and in its milder degrees is merely a "sinking" sensation in the epigastrium. It is frequently associated with vasomotor disturbances and sweating. Increased tension upon the walls of the stomach or duodenum is a potent cause of the sensation, and Poulton has shown that it is also induced by distention of the lower part of the esophagus. During the passage of a peristaltic wave which relieves the tension upon the nerve fibers in the esophageal walls, the sensation is relieved. Barclay showed, by radioscopy in the human subject, that nauseous odors caused the lower border of the stomach to descend an inch or two; evidently as a result of sudden relaxation of the abdominal muscles. This movement would tend to stretch the esophagus and gastric walls and so exert tension upon the nerve endings. The stimulus which induces nausea is, therefore, apparently the same as that which causes visceral pain, but of lower intensity. It is likely that the sensations experienced during changes in speed of an elevator are also the result of tension exerted upon the esophagus and gastric walls. This element is also probably a contributory factor in the production of seasickness, being brought into play by the pitch and roll of the ship.

The relief of nausea and vomiting by the application of counter-irritants to the epigastrium or over the sternum is probably due to either a reflex change in the tone of the gastric walls or to the reflex initiation of peristaltic contractions. The tension upon the nerve endings in the latter instance is taken up by the muscle fibers. Poulton observed, for example, that the sensations caused by a balloon in the esophagus were relieved by vigorous friction of the skin over the sternum; contraction of the esophagus in some cases, or adjustment of the postural tone of the esophageal wall in others, were observed to accompany the disappearance of the sensation.

Regulation of Food and Water Intake

The energy requirements of the body are met by the food that is consumed and absorbed. If an excess of food were consumed continually and there were no change in the energy expenditure there would be a consistent gain in weight. A shortage in the energy value of the food assimilated would result in a steady loss of weight. The fact that the average adult maintains a constant weight or gains or loses weight very slowly is sufficient evidence that a balance is usually maintained between the energy expended by the body and the energy content of the food that is assimilated. The precision of this adjustment can be appreciated when we realize that the addition of 500 mg. of dry food (less than one soda cracker) to each meal would cause an increase in weight over a 10-year-period of more than 10 pounds if there were no compensatory increase in energy expenditure. Of course some people do gain weight but it is believed that this is usually the result of some abnormality affecting the regulation of food intake.

The balance between food intake and energy output is maintained by regulating both the food intake and the output of energy. There is an immediate effect of the excess food through its specific dynamic action, which results in an increase in energy output. This however, is rarely sufficient to account for all the energy contained in the excess food eaten. If it were, there would never be a gain in weight. If an individual consumes a certain measured excess of food at each meal over a period of time he will gain weight steadily but the gain in weight will result in an increase in his basal metabolic rate which, if the excess food intake is not too great, will ultimately increase the metabolism to a point where the energy output will again equal the energy of the food, including the excess. In this way a new balance is established at a higher weight level. In addition, there is apparently another mechanism, less well understood, which, in some cases at least, balances the energy output against the food intake even when this is in excess. In experiments on dogs at the University of Illinois it was found that dogs which were maintaining a constant weight on the amount of food which they ate voluntarily could be given an excess over this amount, through a gastric fistula, amounting to 33 per cent of their voluntary food intake, without either diminishing their voluntary food intake or causing a gain in weight (Share et al., 1952). Evidently the animals had some means of metabolizing the excess food without increasing their total body mass. This suggests that there is some mechanism for adjusting the total body metabolism to the energy content of the food consumed, even though it is in excess of the need; however, we are concerned here with the other aspect of the adjustment of food consumption to energy output, that is, the regulation of food intake.

There are several methods to demonstrate the fact that food intake is regulated in some manner so as to equal the energy requirements of the animal. Healthy animals, when allowed all the food which they wish to eat, will consume only as much as is necessary to meet their energy requirements and to maintain their weight, or their normal growth if they have not already attained their adult weight. If the caloric value of the food is increased, the amount consumed will be diminished so as to maintain a normal intake of food calories. If, on the other hand, the caloric value of the food is decreased by dilution with inert material, the animal will usually consume more food, up to the limit of its capacity, in order to maintain an adequate caloric intake. This mechanism may be tricked by human devices into permitting an excess food intake, as in the experiments of Share and his co-workers described above, but usually it works very well. Adjustment of food intake to energy expenditure is illustrated in fig. 62.7.

HUNGER AND APPETITE

Since eating is a voluntary act, regulation of food intake must be accomplished through conscious sensations which indicate whether food is needed or if enough food has been consumed. The sensations which cause food to be eaten are described as hunger and appetite. These terms have never been precisely defined in the scientific sense, but in a general way we recognize that hunger is the sum of the sensations aroused by the physical need for food. Appetite, on the other hand, is a psychic or emotional desire to eat, and may or may not be associated with the need for food. Cessation of eating is also a voluntary act, and is induced by a conscious sensation called satiety when a sufficiency of food has been eaten. The mechanisms of hunger and satiety are probably inborn and dependent on the inherent organization of the nervous system. Appetite, on the other hand, is acquired, and is probably dependent upon pleasurable past experiences associated with eating. For example, an individual who is hungry will eat almost any wholesome food so long as it is reasonably palatable. When he has reached a state of satiety, however, he will eat only those foods which are particularly pleasing to him and with which he has had pleasant experiences in the past. Thus, because of hunger, one may eat a wholesome meal which is fully adequate for his needs and then, because of appetite, add to it a dessert which is entirely unnecessary so far as caloric requirements are concerned.

THE NEURAL REGULATION OF FOOD INTAKE

It has long been known that persons suffering from tumors of the hypophysis have a tendency to become obese; the condition is known as Frölich's syndrome. In 1940, Hetherington and Ranson showed that a similar condition could be produced

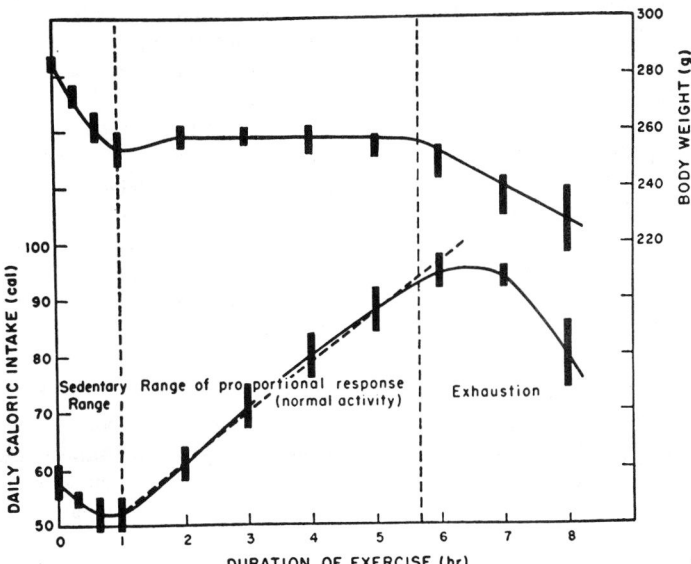

VOLUNTARY CALORIC INTAKE AND BODY WEIGHT AS FUNCTIONS OF EXERCISE IN NORMAL ANIMALS

Fig. 62.7. Illustrating the effect of exercise of various durations on caloric intake and body weight of exercised rats. Three ranges can be distinguished: sedentary, normal activity and exhaustion. (From Mayer, 1955. Courtesy of New York Academy of Science.)

in animals by injury to the hypothalamus in the vicinity of the hypophysis. Later, Brobeck and others (1943) showed that the obesity was caused by injury to the ventromedial hypothalamic nucleus situated in the tuber cinerium. If this area is destroyed in rats, cats or monkeys, instead of being satisfied with an amount of food appropriate to its caloric requirements, the animal continues to eat as long as it is able to swallow food or as long as food is available, with the result that it becomes excessively obese. A little later, Anand and Brobeck (1951) found that injuries to the lateral hypothalamic nuclei, just lateral to those involved in obesity, would cause the animal to stop eating altogether. Animals with such injuries absolutely refused food even though they starved to death. If an animal with a medial hypothalamic injury and consequent hyperphagia (habitual overeating) was subjected to an injury to the lateral hypothalamus, it not only recovered from its hyperphagia, but refused absolutely to eat anything. From these observations it was concluded that the nuclei in the lateral area of the hypothalamus contain a "feeding center," and that the medial hypothalamic nuclei contain a "satiety center." Since injury to the medial nuclei was effective only if the lateral nuclei were intact, it was concluded that the medial satiety center acted by inhibiting the lateral feeding center.

It is interesting to note that the areas of the

hypothalamus involved in the control of food intake have a much higher concentration of high energy phosphate compounds (adenosine triphosphate, creatine phosphate) in fasted animals than in animals recently fed; the increase in these compounds implies increased activity of these areas in hungry animals (Larsson, 1954). The medial hypothalamic areas, which are believed to inhibit the feeding centers in the lateral hypothalamus, exhibit increased electrical activity when drugs which reduce or abolish appetite, such as amphetamine, are given. It is believed that the increased electrical activity indicates stimulation of the medial nuclei and that these then inhibit the action of the feeding centers. It has been shown that electrical stimulation of the lateral hypothalamic nuclei by means of implanted electrodes produces hyperphagia (Brobeck et al., 1956) in rats, cats, mice, monkeys, goats and sheep. During the period of stimulation, the animals exhibit a compulsive desire to eat, and if food is available will eat as much as it is possible for them to swallow (Larsson, 1954).

The neural organization of the feeding centers in the rat have been investigated by Morgane (1961). He devised a clever experiment which required the animal to cross an electrical grill and press a lever to obtain food. After electrodes were implanted in various parts of the hypothalamus, stimulation of the far-lateral hypothalamus not

TABLE 62.2*

TABLE 62.2*

Classification of feeding reflexes on a basis of initial sensory stimulus (left side) or behavior pattern induced (right side)

Sensory Basis	Behavior Basis
Visual reflexes	Reflexes of attention
Olfactory reflexes	Reflexes of approach
Auditory reflexes	Reflexes of examination
Tactile reflexes	Reflexes of incorporation
Gustatory reflexes	Reflexes of rejection
Enteroceptive reflexes	

* From Brobeck, 1957.

only resulted in a feeding response in sated animals, but also motivated them to cross the electrical grill to obtain food. When the mid-lateral hypothalamus was stimulated, a feeding response was obtained, but the animals were not "motivated" to cross the electrical grill. Lesions were then placed in the medial fore-brain bundle, and it was found that a feeding response could still be obtained in sated animals by far-lateral hypothalamic stimulation but the animals would not cross the grill to obtain food. These results suggest that the medial fore-brain bundle is important in "hunger motivation," since overcoming a barrier to obtain food apparently depends upon the integrity of this bundle. When the medial fore-brain bundle was interrupted, basic feeding responses could still be obtained, but the animal would not "work" for his food. Morgane concluded that the feeding center in the rat probably is composed of both a basic feeding drive (mid-lateral hypothalamus) and a hunger drive (far-lateral hypothalamus) element, and that only the latter is depressed by the satiety mechanism.

Grossman (1960) has used an ingenious method of stimulating areas of the hypothalamus of the rat. He implanted a small double cannula into the lateral hypothalamus and was able to study the effects of stimulation of the "feeding area" by crystalline chemicals. Adrenergic agents, such as norepinephrine and epinephrine, caused satiated rats to eat, whereas cholinergic agents, such as acetylcholine or carbachol, caused the animals to drink large quantities of water. Thus, the feeding mechanism appears to be selectively activated by adrenergic stimulation, while the drinking mechanism responds selectively to cholinergic stimulation.

Brobeck (1957) has suggested that the areas of the hypothalamus which control food intake do so either by facilitating or inhibiting the reflex mechanisms involved in the acquisition and consumption of food; he calls these feeding reflexes. He classified these in two ways: (a) according to the sensory mechanism arousing the reflex, and (b) according to the nature of the response. The reflexes are listed in table 62.2. Probably the list could be extended if the mechanisms involved were better understood. The important point is that the hypothalamic centers do not control food intake directly, but do so by making more or less responsive to stimuli the lower brain centers which control the reflexes governing the acquisition, consumption and assimilation of food.

Peripheral Mechanisms

Consumption of food brings about consequences which induce satiety and stimulate the mechanisms that are inhibitory to the feeding reflexes; starvation, or the absence of food, brings about consequences which excite hunger and stimulate the feeding centers. In spite of extensive study, and even more widespread speculation, the peripheral mechanisms which contribute to hunger and satiety are still not fully understood. Among the possible operating devices we can recognize gastrointestinal mechanisms and metabolic mechanisms. The gastrointestinal mechanisms are mainly of a physical nature whereas the metabolic mechanisms are chemical. The physical mechanisms are presumed to act through stimulation of sensory nerve endings, whereas the chemical mechanisms are supposed to act on some hypothetical sensory device, either within the central nervous system or connected with it through afferent nerves, although this is by no means certain.

Among the gastrointestinal stimuli which tend to increase food intake and to cause a sensation of hunger are the so-called hunger contractions of the stomach and intestine (see Quigley, 1955). The fact that hunger contractions cause a sensation of hunger helps us little in the solution of our problem, for we still do not know what causes the hunger contractions. Beside mere emptiness of the stomach and intestine they are probably excited by something in the metabolic category. Emptiness is not the whole answer because, although the stomach may be completely empty a few hours after a meal, hunger contractions become more intense and more distressing the longer the fast is continued. However, they cease at once when food is taken and before any metabolic changes have taken place; therefore, whatever their cause, they can be completely inhibited by the presence of food in the stomach and intestine.

It is known that hunger contractions can be induced, or made more intense if already present, by inducing a state of hypoglycemia through administration of insulin (Quigley et al., 1929, 1930). This brings about stimulation of medullary centers, in which increased activity of the vagus centers is a prominent feature. If the vagus nerves are cut, insulin hypoglycemia does not stimulate hunger contractions (Quigley and Templeton, 1930); indeed it tends to inhibit them if they are already present. The hunger contractions induced by insulin evidently are due directly to an action of low blood sugar on the central nervous system. They can be inhibited by administration of glucose intravenously but the normally occurring changes in blood sugar level are in no way related to the presence or absence of gastric or intestinal hunger contractions (Quigley, 1955; Scott et al., 1938). Hyperglycemia may or may not inhibit hunger contractions; it obviously does not in diabetic subjects. In a majority of experiments on normal animals, hyperglycemia induced by injecting glucose intravenously does not inhibit gastric hunger motility. It has been shown by Stunkard and Wolff (1956) that, in those instances in which the hunger contractions were not inhibited by intravenous glucose, the injection of glucose did not cause a great rise in the arterial glucose concentration as compared to the venous glucose concentration. The arteriovenous glucose concentration difference is taken as an index of the rate of utilization of glucose by the tissues. On the other hand, in those instances in which there was inhibition of hunger contractions, there was an increase in arteriovenous glucose difference. Reference will be made to this fact a little later under the heading of "Metabolic Factors."

Undoubtedly, gastric hunger contractions contribute to the hunger state but they are by no means solely responsible for it. Enough human cases have been studied in which both splanchnic nerves were severed to establish the fact that this operation abolishes all sensation produced by contraction of the stomach during hunger. The contractions persist but they are no longer felt. However, individuals so operated upon do not experience any decrease in their desire for food and they have periods of hunger just as intense as before the splanchnic nerves were severed (Grossman and Stein, 1948). Cutting the vagus nerves abolishes the hunger contractions altogether for a time, but by no means abolishes the sensation of hunger. On the contrary, as judged by the amount of food consumed, the hunger sensation is intensified by vagotomy (Volkmann, 1844). We may conclude that the hunger sensation arises not only in the stomach and intestine but elsewhere in the body as well, and that the gastrointestinal component is dispensable.

Sensations arising in the gastrointestinal tract which diminish or abolish food intake are somewhat better understood. The act of eating will, in itself, diminish hunger and appetite. For example, if an animal is prepared with an esophagostomy so that food which is eaten passes through the mouth and pharynx and upper esophagus but does not enter the stomach, the animal will eat more food than would a normal animal, but feeding ceases eventually. If an animal is given a measured amount of food before its regular mealtime it will reduce the amount of its voluntary food intake proportionately. If the prefeeding is carried out through a gastric fistula instead of by mouth the reduction in voluntary food intake is much less pronounced, indicating that the decrease in food intake was not all due to distention of the stomach but partly to the oropharyngeal stimulation of eating.

Distention of the stomach alone inhibits hunger and appetite. For example, if an animal is given a portion of its food a few minutes before regular feeding time through a gastric fistula, and this practice is continued over a period of time, eventually the animal will come to reduce the size of its subsequent meal by an amount equal to the amount given through the gastric fistula, in other words, the total size of the meal will be maintained constant (Janowitz and Hollander, 1955). This adjustment does not occur immediately and is never very precise, but it does show that gastric distention with food tends to reduce hunger and appetite. Similarly, if the stomach is partly filled with inert materials, the size of the subsequent meal will be reduced. Inflation of a balloon in the stomach has the same effect (Janowitz and Grossman, 1949). That these effects are mechanical and not metabolic in nature is shown by the fact that, if the artificial feeding, instead of being given immediately before the regular meal, is given some 4 hours after, and time is allowed for it to be disposed of, the animal will eat a normal amount at the next regular meal, provided the artificial feeding was not too large. As much as one-third of the animal's regular food consumption can be given in this manner over a period of time without affecting his voluntary intake

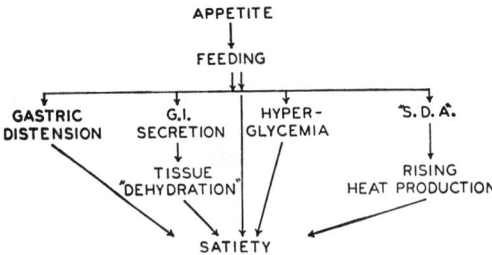

FIG. 62.8. Outline of mechanisms taking part in transition from appetite to satiety. (From Brobeck, 1957.)

(Share et al., 1952). The fact has already been referred to that animals so fed, although receiving 30 per cent or more in excess of their regular food intake, do not necessarily gain weight. The effect of gastric distention on hunger and appetite is doubtless due to the presence in the stomach of stretch receptors (Paintal, 1954) situated in the muscular walls and connected to afferent fibers of the vagus nerves; section of the vagi does away with the effects of gastric distention on appetite. Indeed, vagotomy produces a condition of hyperphagia comparable to that caused by lesions of the medial hypothalamic nuclei.

The effects of the gastrointestinal stimuli are largely confined to determining the size of an individual meal. They do not serve to regulate the overall balance between the energy intake represented by the food and the energy output represented by the total metabolism of the body. Presumably, metabolic factors are responsible for this type of regulation, but any discussion of such factors at the present time would be speculation. We know certainly only that some metabolic consequences of the assimilation of food are not effective as regulatory factors. It has been shown, for example, that changes in blood sugar, at least those that are not associated with changes in arteriovenous glucose difference, have no effect on voluntary food intake, nor do they influence hunger contractions—except those induced by insulin (Quigley and Hallaran, 1932). An increase in the amino acid concentration of the blood caused by intravenous injection of amino acids has no effect upon voluntary food intake in dogs. However, the slight increase in temperature which results from the presence of pyrogens in some intravenous solutions does definitely influence appetite, even though the rise in temperature is too small to be recognized clinically as a fever. This, and the fact that taking food causes a slight increase in temperature due to the specific dynamic action of the food, has suggested to Brobeck (1957) the possibility that the increase in body temperature caused by the specific dynamic action of the food may be a factor which limits food intake (fig. 62.8).

Mayer (1955) has suggested that food intake is controlled in some way through the metabolism of glucose—the so-called glucostatic hypothesis. Recognizing that hunger and appetite are not related to changes in blood sugar level, Mayer contends that they are governed by the utilization of carbohydrate food by the tissues: "According to the glucostatic theory the mechanism postulated for the short term regulation of energy intake rests on the concept that somewhere, possibly in the hypothalamic centers shown to be implicated in the regulation of food intake, perhaps peripherally as well, there are glucoreceptors sensitive to blood glucose in the measure that they can utilize it." In other words, when the tissues are utilizing glucose rapidly, thus establishing a high arteriovenous glucose difference, the glucoreceptors are stimulated, and through their central connections suppress hunger and appetite and inhibit food intake. On the other hand, when glucose is not available for tissue utilization, and the arteriovenous glucose difference tends toward zero, a state corresponding to tissue hunger exists; this is sensed in some way by the hypothalamic centers, which then facilitate the feeding reflexes.

Another theory suggests that the total energy stores of the body are maintained at a certain predetermined level by the balance between hunger and satiety. Whatever the mechanism may be, it is evident that metabolic factors are important and quite possibly play a determining role in the regulation of the balance between food intake and energy output in the body.

THIRST

The sensation of thirst is referred to the pharynx and is due to the stimulation of sensory nerve endings in this situation. Two theories have been advanced to explain the mechanism by which the sensation is aroused.

According to one view, thirst is due to the drying of the pharyngeal mucous membrane, the salivary glands being given a role in the regulation of the water balance of the body. When the water content of the body falls below a certain level, salivary secretion is depressed. The consequent drying of the mucous membrane of the throat then elicits the characteristic sensation. If such a view is correct, drying of the pharyngeal mucosa, from whatever cause, should cause thirst. Cannon, who provided the principal support for this theory, found, in studies upon himself, that after abstinence from fluids for a time the depression of salivary secretion which resulted was definitely associated with thirst. Atropine, which inhibits salivary secretion, also produced the typical sensation, and thirst aroused by the deprivation of water was relieved by the application of cocaine to the mucosa. Pilocarpine, or acid substances which stimulate the flow of saliva, also relieve thirst. In dogs, however, atropine and pilocarpine have no effect upon the water intake.

According to the other view, thirst is a sensation resulting from changes in blood composition, probably due to a rise in its osmotic pressure, which stimulates the afferent nerve endings or perhaps acts upon central nervous structures. Rowntree and his associates, for example, found that the thirst of diabetes insipidus was relieved neither by cocainization of the mucous membrane nor when salivation was induced by pilocarpine. The experiments of Gilman suggest that cellular dehydration, rather than a rise in osmotic pressure, is the prime factor in arousing thirst. Elevation of the osmotic pressure of the blood of dogs by the injection of a hypertonic salt solution, and the imbalance thus caused in the osmotic relationship between intra- and extracellular fluids, caused a much greater intake of water than an equivalent rise in osmotic pressure resulting from the administration of urea. After the injection of salt, sufficient water was drunk to reduce quickly the osmotic pressure of the blood. After injection of urea, to which the cells are readily permeable, and which did not disturb the osmotic relationships, the water intake was but little increased and the osmotic pressure of the blood remained elevated. In support of the view that a lowered water content of the cells is the true thirst stimulus, Gilman cites an experiment in which anhydremia was induced by the withdrawal of large quantities of extracellular electrolytes (e.g., NaCl) without the withdrawal of water. In such anhydremic animals, dehydration of the tissue cells does not occur, and although the oral mucous membranes are quite dry, there is no evidence of thirst and water is refused.

The two theories are not incompatible, as is indicated by the work of Holmes and Gregerson (1947), who found that, in human subjects, following the intravenous injection of 300 ml. of 5 per cent sodium chloride, although there was an increase in plasma volume there was a considerable decrease in salivary secretion associated with the sensation of thirst. This proves that the decrease in salivary secretion leading to a sensation of thirst may be caused by an increase in the osmotic pressure of the blood, and suggests that tissue dehydration may induce the sensation of thirst through the reduction in the flow of saliva.

The neural mechanisms for the regulation of water intake are similar to those for the regulation of food intake. Indeed, they are closely associated and have not as yet been clearly separated. Certain types of injuries to the lateral hypothalamus induce not only a cessation of food intake but also cessation of water intake. The animals die of dehydration unless given water by stomach tube (Greer, 1955; Morrison and Mayer, 1957). Greer found that stimulation of the dorsomedial nucleus in the cat caused violent drinking activity, thus there are probably centers in the hypothalamus for the regulation of water intake comparable to the feeding centers. Like the intake of food, the intake of water is influenced by gastric distention. Animals made thirsty by intravenous injection of hypertonic salt solution will usually drink an amount of water over a short period of time approximately equal to the amount necessary to dilute the injected salt to an isotonic concentration. If the stomach is distended by means of a water-filled balloon, the amount of water that is voluntarily drunk will be diminished and the replacement of the water deficit delayed. The vagi play a part in the regulation of water intake. Vagotomized animals not only eat more food but also drink more water than do normal animals. The food intake and the water intake are increased proportionately by vagotomy; they are decreased by sympathectomy (Towbin, 1955).

Excessive thirst also occurs in lesions of the anterior hypophysis, leading to diabetes insipidus. In this disease there is failure of production of the antidiuretic hormone of the anterior hypophysis, resulting in an excessive loss of water through the kidneys. In this case, thirst is probably secondary to dehydration.

REFERENCES

ANAND, B. K. AND BROBECK, J. R. Localization of a feeding center in the hypothalamus of the rat. Proc. Soc. Exper. Biol. & Med., 1951, 77, 323; Yale J. Biol. & Med., 1951, 24, 122.

BARCLAY, A. E. The normal stomach. Lancet, 1922, 2, 261.

BAYLISS, W. M. AND STARLING, E. H. The movements and innervation of the small intestine. J. Physiol., 1899, 24, 99.

BENTLEY, F. H. AND SMITHWICK, R. H. Visceral pain produced by balloon distention of the jejunum. Lancet, 1940, 2, 389.

BROBECK, J. R. Neural regulation of food intake. Ann. N. Y. Acad. Sci., 1955, 63, 44.

BROBECK, J. R., LARSSON, S., AND REYES, E. A study of the electrical activity of the hypothalamic feeding mechanism. J. Physiol., 1956, **132**, 358.

BROBECK, J. R., TEPPERMAN, J., AND LONG, C. N. H. Experimental hypothalamic hyperphagia in the albino rat. Yale J. Biol. & Med., 1943, **15**, 831.

CANNON, W. B. Proc. Roy. Soc., London, ser. B., 1917, **90**, 283.

CARLSON, A. J., BOYD, T. E., AND PEARCY, J. F. Studies on the visceral sensory nervous system. Arch. Int. Med., 1922, **30**, 409. Am. J. Physiol., **61**, 14.

CARLSON, A. J., AND HOELZEL, F. Alleged disappearance of hunger during starvation. Science, 1952, **115**, 526.

GILMAN, A. Relation between blood osmotic pressure, fluid distribution and voluntary water intake. Am. J. Physiol., 1937, **120**, 323.

GREER, M. A. Suggestive evidence of a primary drinking center in the hypothalamus. Proc. Soc. Exper. Biol. & Med., 1955, **89**, 59.

GREGERSON, M. L. AND CANNON, W. B. Studies on regulation of water intake; effect of extirpation of salivary glands on water intake of dogs while panting. Am. J. Physiol., 1932, **102**, 336.

GROSSMAN, M. I. Integration of current views on the regulation of hunger and appetite. Ann. N. Y. Acad. Sci., 1955, **63**, 76.

GROSSMAN, S. P. Eating and drinking elicited by direct adrenergic or cholinergic stimulation of hypothalamus. Science, 1960, **301**, 132.

HEAD, H. On disturbances of sensation with especial reference to the pain of visceral disease. Brain, 1893, **16**, 15; 1894, **17**, 339; 1896, **19**, 150.

HEATHERINGTON, A. W. AND RANSON, S. W. Hypothalamic lesions and adiposity in the rat. Anat. Rec., 1940, **78**, 149.

HOLLANDER, F. Introduction (to conference on hunger and appetite). Ann. N. Y. Acad. Sci., 1955, **63**, 3.

HOLMES, J. H. AND GREGERSON, M. I. Relation of salivary flow to the thirst produced in man by intravenous injection of salt solution. Am. J. Physiol., 1947, **151**, 252.

JANOWITZ, H. D. AND GROSSMAN, M. I. Some factors affecting food intake of normal dogs and dogs with esophagostomy and gastric fistula. Am. J. Physiol., 1949, **159**, 143.

JANOWITZ, H. D. AND HOLLANDER, F. The time factor in the adjustment of food intake to varied caloric requirements in the dog. A study of precision of appetite regulation. Ann. N. Y. Acad. Sci., 1955, **63**, 56.

KUNTZ, A. On the occurrence of reflex arcs in the myenteric and submucous plexuses. Anat. Rec., 1922, **23**, 193.

LARSSON, S. On the hypothalamic organization of the nervous mechanism regulating food intake. Acta physiol. scandinav. (suppl.)., 1954, **115**, 1.

LEWIS, T. AND KELLGREN, J. H. Observations relating to referred pain, visceromotor reflexes and other phenomena. Clin. Sc., 1939, **4**, 47.

MAYER, J. Regulation of energy intake and body weight. The glucostatic theory and the lipostatic hypothesis. Ann. N. Y. Acad. Sci., 1955, **63**, 15.

MAYER, J. The physiological basis of obesity and leanness. Nutrition Abstr. & Rev., 1955, **25**, 597, 871.

MONTGOMERY, M. F. Role of salivary glands in the thirst mechanism. Am. J. Physiol., 1931, **96**, 221; **98**, 35.

MORGANE, P. J. Distinct "feeding" and "hunger motivating" systems in the lateral hypothalamus of the rat. Science, 1961, **887**, 133.

MORRISON, S. D. AND MAYER, J. Adipsia and aphagia in rats after lateral subthalamic lesions. Am. J. Physiol., 1957, **191**, 248; **193**, 230.

PAINTAL, A. S. A study of gastric stretch receptors. J. Physiol., 1954, **126**, 255.

PAYNE, W. W. AND POULTON, E. P. Experiments on visceral sensation relation of pain to activity in human esophagus. J. Physiol., 1937, **63**, 217.

POLLOCK, L. J. AND DAVIS, L. Visceral and referred pain. Arch. Neurol. and Psychiat., 1935, **34**, 1041.

POULTON, E. P. Oliver-Sharpey lectures on experimental study of certain visceral sensations. Lancet, 1928, II, **12**, 1223; J. Physiol., 1927, **63**, 217.

QUIGLEY, J. P. The role of the digestive tract in regulating the ingestion of food. Ann. N. Y. Acad. Sci., 1955, **63**, 6.

QUIGLEY, J. P. AND HALLARAN, W. R. The independence of spontaneous gastrointestinal motility and blood sugar levels. Am. J. Physiol., 1932, **100**, 102.

QUIGLEY, J. P., JOHNSON, V., AND SOLOMON, E. I. Action of insulin on the motility of the gastrointestinal tract. I. Action on the stomach of normal and fasting man. Am. J. Physiol., 1929, **90**, 89.

QUIGLEY, J. P. AND SOLOMON, E. I. Action of insulin on the motility of the gastrointestinal tract. V. a. Action on the human duodenum; b. Action on the colon of dogs. Am. J. Physiol., 1930, **91**, 488.

QUIGLEY, J. P. AND TEMPLETON, R. D. Action of insulin on motility of the gastrointestinal tract. IV. Action on the stomach following double vagotomy. Am. J. Physiol., 1930, **91**, 482.

ROSS, J. On the segmental distribution of sensory disorders. Brain, 1887–1888, **10**, 333.

ROWNTREE, S. J., WEIR, J. F., AND LARSON, E. E. Studies in diabetes insipidus, water balance and water intoxication. Arch. Int. Med., 1922, **29**, 306.

RYLE, J. Visceral pain and referred pain. Lancet, 1926, **1**, 895.

SCOTT, W. W., SCOTT, C. C., AND LUCKHARDT, A. B. Observations on the blood sugar level before, during and after hunger periods in humans. Am. J. Physiol., 1938, **123**, 243.

SHARE, I., MARTYNIUK, E., AND GROSSMAN, M. I. Effect of prolonged intragastric feeding on oral food intake in dogs. Am. J. Physiol., 1952, **169**, 229.

SHEEPAN, D. Afferent nerve supply of mesentery and its significance in causation of abdominal pain. J. Anat., 1933, **67**, 233.

STUNKARD, A. J. AND WOLFF, H. G. Studies on the physiology of hunger, I. The effect of intravenous administration of glucose on gastric hunger contractions in man. J. Clin. Invest. 1956, **35**, 954.

THOMAS, J. E. AND WHEELON, H. The nervous

control of the pyloric sphincter. J. Lab. & Clin. Med., 1922, **7,** 375.

TOWBIN, E. J. Thirst and hunger behavior in normal dogs and the effects of vagotomy and sympathectomy. Am. J. Physiol., 1955, **182,** 377.

WOOLLARD, H. H. AND CARMICHAEL, E. A. Testis and referred pain. Brain, 1933, **56,** 293.

Monographs and Reviews

ADOLPH, E. F. AND ASSOCIATES. Man in the desert. Interscience Publishers, Inc., New York, 1947.

BARCLAY, A. E. The digestive tract. Cambridge University Press, London, 1933.

BROBECK, J. R. Neural basis of hunger, appetite and satiety. Gastroenterology, 1957, **32,** 169.

CANNON, W. B. Hunger and thirst. Murchison's handbook general experimental psychology. Clark Univ. Press, Worcester, Mass., 1934.

CARLSON, A. J. The control of hunger in health and disease. Chicago Univ. Press, Chicago, 1916.

HURST, A. F. The sensibility of the alimentary canal. Frowde, London, 1911.

JANOWITZ, H. D. Hunger and appetite. Am. J. Med., 1958, **25,** 327.

KINSELLA, V. J. The mechanism of abdominal pain. Australasian Medical Publishing Co., Sydney, Australia, 1948.

KUNTZ, A. The autonomic nervous system. 4th ed., Lea and Febiger, Philadelphia, 1953.

LANGLEY, J. N. The autonomic nervous system. Cambridge University Press, London, 1921.

LENNANDER, K. G. Observations on the sensibility of the abdominal cavity. Bale, London, 1903, (Quoted by Morley).

LEWIS, SIR T. Pain. The Macmillan Co., New York, 1942.

MACKENZIE, J. Symptoms and their interpretations. Shae & Sons, Ltd. London, 1920.

MAYER, J. Genetic, traumatic and environmental factors in etiology of obesity. Physiol. Rev., 1953, **33,** 472.

MORLEY, J. Abdominal pain. E. & S. Livingstone, Ltd., Edinburgh, 1931.

RYLE, J. A. Gastric functions in health and disease. Milford, London, 1926.

VOLKMANN, A. W. Wagner's Handworterbuch der Physiologie. 1844, **ii,** 585. (See also Holinger, Kelley and Ivy. Proc. Soc., Exper. Biol. & Med. 9132, **29,** 884.)

WOLF, A. V. Thirst. Charles C Thomas, Springfield, Ill., 1958.

VIII

METABOLISM AND NUTRITION

CHAPTER 63

Composition and Energy Content of Foods: General Metabolism

General Outline of the Function and Composition of Foods

Nutrition deals with the needs of the organism for sustenance. Nutrition concerns a complex aspect of living things (both plants and animals) that consists of the taking in and assimilation through chemical changes (metabolism) of material, whereby tissue is built up and energy liberated. There are three successive stages in the process, known as absorption, assimilation and excretion. In all animals, and certain plants, a stage known as digestion precedes the three stages named. In the more highly developed animals, digestion is preceded by mastication and deglutition, and excretion is effected by four routes, the processes being referred to as expiration, perspiration, urination and defecation. The essential feature in nutrition is the *intake* of the raw materials needed for the maintenance of life, but it overlaps victualling, food preparation and metabolism. The modern science of nutrition deals mainly with the requirements of the body, both in kind and amount, and the choice of foods to meet these needs.

The three chief functions of food are (1) to supply energy, (2) to form (or maintain) body tissue, and (3) to preserve a suitable internal environment so that the enzymes bringing about the metabolic reactions and the hormones regulating the processes may function properly.

Chemical methods for the analysis of foodstuffs, as they developed over the years, revealed that natural foods contain (besides water and the ash constituents) cellulose, lignins, galactosans, pentosans, starches, sugars, fats, waxes, sterols, carotenoids and other pigments, proteins, purines, pyrimidines, acids (such as oxalic, lactic, tartaric, citric, malic, benzoic, salicylic, quinic, and uric) and many other minor components, such as tannins, alkaloids and simpler bases, glucosides, and essential oils. Magendie (1783–1855) first tested the effects (in dogs) of feeding gelatin, sugar and butter alone and noted that animals cannot survive for long on such individual foodstuffs. Prout (1785–1850) in his notable book *Chemistry, Meteorology, and the Function of Digestion* (1834) developed the modern view that of the many components of nat-

ural foods, three kinds are essential in the diet, each possessing characteristic nutritive properties. Prout referred to them as the albuminous group (gelatin, cooked egg-white, cooked flesh being examples), the saccharine group (sugars and starches) and the oleaginous group; these are known today, of course, as the proteins, carbohydrates and the fats.

For many years (about 1860 to 1910) interest was focussed on the energy content of foods and the energy requirement of the body. The nitrogen (protein) requirement continued to receive much attention. Although chemists recognized that the methods for the analysis of foods were only approximate, and that carbohydrates were usually estimated by difference, so that the values always added to 100 per cent, the conclusion had been reached that minerals, proteins, carbohydrates and fats were the only nutrients required by man and animals. There seemed to be no room in the make-up of foods for any other ingredient of nutritive importance.

Besides the seven principal ash components (calcium, magnesium, sodium, potassium, phosphorus, sulfur and chlorine) at least seven other minerals, the so-called "trace elements" are today known to be essential for animals and man: iron, copper, manganese, zinc, cobalt, iodine and fluorine. The possible essentiality of aluminum, silicon, arsenic, boron, selenium and other elements has been suggested but not established.

Energy Content of Foodstuffs

There have been many tabulations showing the average chemical composition and energy values of the edible portion of common food materials. The values in these tables are based upon a number of assumptions that are commonly made by food chemists. A brief review of the techniques used and errors involved will illustrate the uncertainties inherent in many tabulations. In spite of these limitations, certain valuable generalizations about the nutritive worth of the commoner food materials have been reached.

The energy value of foods is measured in kilogram-calories or large Calories (spelled with a capital C). This is the amount of heat required to raise the temperature of a kilogram of water 1° (from 15 to 16°C.). The potential energy of a foodstuff can be estimated in three ways: (1) It may be determined *directly* by measuring the amount of heat generated when a weighed sample of the material is burned in a *bomb calorimeter* (see. p. 1273). (2) *Indirect calorimetry* involves measurement of the oxygen required to burn completely a sample of the foodstuff in the *oxy-calorimeter* (see p. 1273) and calculation of the energy content from the oxygen used. (3) As will be shown later, an approximation of the number of calories that a foodstuff will provide may be *calculated* from the chemical estimates of protein, fat and carbohydrate in it. "Physiological corrections" are then applied to allow for incomplete combustion and losses in the urine and feces.

Antoine Laurent Lavoisier (1743–1794), the founder of modern chemistry, first used the thermometer and balance in the study of metabolism.[1] His careful experiments and clear deductions explained the nature of oxidation, of combustion and of respiration and showed their similarities. He recognized that fuels and foods are composed of carbon, hydrogen and oxygen. Lavoisier showed that oxidation of these organic substances to carbon dioxide and water led to the production of characteristic amounts of heat.[2] Simultaneously,

---

[1] Graham Lusk has given an account of the scientific descent of the leading chemists who have devoted their lives to the nutritional aspects of physiology. Berthollet (1748–1822), who established the composition of ammonia and of hydrogen sulfide, and who showed (in 1786) that nitrogen is a constant constituent of animal tissues (a colleague of Lavoisier and instructor of Napoleon I in chemistry), bequeathed his sword to his favorite student, Gay-Lussac, originator of volumetric methods and formulator of the gas laws. Gay-Lussac (1778–1850) was the teacher of Liebig (1803–1873), the father of modern methods of organic analysis. Liebig, author of the first chemical text to deal extensively with agricultural matters and the composition of foods, tissues and excreta (*Animal Chemistry*, 1846) taught Carl von Voit (1831–1908). Under Voit's energetic leadership the Munich School became the outstanding centre of research in nutrition and metabolism (about 1860–1910). The conversion of carbohydrate to fat, and of part of the food protein to carbohydrate was demonstrated at Munich. Voit taught Rubner (1854–1932), Atwater (1844–1907), E. P. Cathcart (1877–1954) of Glasgow University, Graham Lusk (1866–1932) of Cornell University Medical College, New York, and others who were the authorities 30 to 50 years ago. They in turn taught and inspired many of the present leaders in nutrition.

[2] Lavoisier believed that the heat was produced through the oxidation of carbon and hydrogen in the *lungs*. Not until some years later was it shown that heat production was the result of the combustion of foodstuffs in the various tissues of the body.

---

in Britain, Crawford was making similar experiments on "animal heat" and combustion.

In 1842, half a century later, the English physicist, James Prestcott Joule (1818–1889) determined the mechanical equivalent of heat.[3] In the same year, the German physician-physicist Julius Robert von Mayer (1814–1878) published his revolutionary theory of heat together with his views on the conservation of energy. Mayer stated that the sum total of the energy in the universe remains constant but that any one form (mechanical, potential, thermal, chemical, electrical) may be converted into another. Several years later (1845) another German scientist, von Helmholtz (1821–1894) extended the application of the Law of Conservation of Energy and formulated it mathematically. It is interesting to know that at the time the contributions of both men were rejected by the leading German scientific journal!

Through the work of Voit, Pettenkofer and Rubner the Law of Conservation of Energy was shown to hold true in the animal body. Rubner established the heat value of carbohydrates, fat and protein when burned outside the body in a calorimeter (for operational details see p. 1273). He then fed the three types of foodstuffs separately to a dog in a calorimeter. Carbohydrate and fat produced the same amount of heat, within the limit of experimental error, whether combustion occurred within the body or outside it. The physiological heat value of protein, however, was found to be distinctly less than the bomb value. Carbohydrates and fats, after absorption, are fully oxidized to carbon dioxide and water in the body as well as in the bomb, but this is not so for protein. In the bomb calorimeter, proteins are burned completely to carbon dioxide, water and sulfuric acid; part of the nitrogen is converted to oxides of nitrogen and part occurs as free nitrogen. The body excretes in the urine urea and other nitrogenous compounds. These carry out some of the carbon, hydrogen and nitrogen before they are fully oxidized and thus some of the potential energy of the protein is lost. Only about three-quarters of the calories obtained from protein in the bomb are physiologically available because of the less complete oxidation in the body.

The calorie values (bomb) of different carbohydrates, fats and proteins are not identical, as may be seen in table 63.1. Animal proteins are often said to liberate slightly less energy per

---

[3] The unit of work, the erg = a force of 1 dyne acting through 1 cm. The joule is 10^7 ergs. The mechanical equivalent of heat is the quantity of energy which, when transformed into heat, is equivalent to unit quantity of heat: 1 calorie = 4.18 joules = 4.18 × 10^7 ergs.

TABLE 63.1

Energy content (by bomb calorimetry) of some fuels, foods and metabolic products

(Kilocalories per gram)

Hydrogen	34.2	Ethanol	7.13	Castor oil	8.85
Carbon		Glycerol	4.32	Cod liver oil	9.40
charcoal	8.09	Arabinose	3.74	Citric acid	2.47
diamond	7.87	Glucose	3.73	Malic acid	2.42
graphite	7.85	Fructose	3.76	Glycine	3.14
Methane (CH_4)	13.2	Galactose	3.73	Alanine	4.35
Ethane (C_2H_6)	12.3	Sucrose	3.95	Leucine	6.55
Ethylene (C_2H_4)	11.8	Lactose	3.96	Casein	5.85
Acetylene (C_2H_2)	12.0	Starch	4.12	Gelatin	5.30
Benzene (C_6H_6)	10.0	Acetaldehyde	6.34	Albumin	5.80
Petroleum	10.3	Acetic acid (C_2)	3.49	Dried muscle	5.40
Coal gas	10.7	*n*-Butyric acid (C_4)	5.96	Edestin	5.64
Anthracite coal	7.0–8.7	Palmitic acid (C_{16})	9.36	Gliadin	5.74
Wood		Stearic acid (C_{18})	9.54	Legumin	5.62
Pine	4.4	Oleic acid (C_{18})	9.41	Uric acid	2.74
Beech	4.2	Butter fat	9.30	Urea	2.53
Oak	4.0	Cottonseed oil	9.40	Creatinine	4.98
Methanol	5.33	Linseed oil	9.41		

gram than do plant proteins but this is an unsafe generalization (*cf.* table 63.1).

Rubner found the heats of combustion (Calories per gram) for glucose, lactose, sucrose and starch to be 3.69, 3.88, 3.96 and 4.12, respectively. He suggested 4.1 as the factor for the mixture of sugars plus starch in a mixed diet. Rubner adopted 9.3 as the mean factor for fat and 4.1 for the physiologically available energy from proteins. Atwater and Bryant proposed 4.0, 8.9 and 4.0, respectively. For practical purposes the simple factors 4, 9 and 4 are adequate.

UNCERTAINTIES IN ENERGY VALUES OF FOODS ESTIMATED FROM COMPOSITION. The main reasons for uncertainty about the correct energy value to assign to natural foodstuffs are (1) the difficulty of choosing a representative sample, (2) difficulties connected with accurate chemical analyses, (3) inconstancy of the moisture content of the samples, and (4) the difficulty of choosing appropriate factors (a) for conversion of nitrogen to protein and (b) for the energy available to the body from different foodstuffs. This latter point includes the uncertainties introduced by variations in digestibility. Each type of foodstuff raises special problems. These will be dealt with separately.[4]

CARBOHYDRATE. In the early days of food

[4] Specific dynamic action of foodstuffs, which will be discussed in the following section, is concerned with alterations in the basal metabolic rate induced by ingestion of foodstuffs and not with the intrinsic potential energy of the foods.

chemistry (and often today) carbohydrate was determined by difference, i.e., 100 − (moisture + ash + protein (N × 6.25) + fat). All the errors in the previous determinations, plus the undetermined matters in the food, are thus included with the carbohydrates. Only in recent years have efforts been made to determine individual carbohydrates.

The energy content of individual carbohydrates varies from 3.7 to almost 4.2 (table 63.1). The physiological availability varies from almost 100 per cent to zero. The energy of celluloses, although somewhat available to ruminants, is unavailable in man. Substances such as galactans, pentosans and hemicelluloses are poorly (if at all) utilized by man. The edible portions of most foods do not contain excessive amounts of indigestible carbohydrate but it is erroneous to conclude that all of the "carbohydrate" (as determined by difference) provides energy. Estimates of "crude fiber" are not given in older food tables. Sometimes no mention is made of whether a correction has been applied for indigestible carbohydrate. In a few cases, e.g., soyabean flour, only about 40 per cent of the carbohydrate is utilized by rats, and this probably represents the digestibility of these carbohydrates in man. The "average availability" figure of 97 per cent may be too high for mixed foods but is probably correct for mixed sugars and starches.

Organic acids occur in many foods, especially fruits; oxalic, malic and citric are the most widely found. Oxalic and tartaric are not utilized; malic and citric are completely oxidized in the body, giving 2.42 and 2.47 Calories per gram, respectively. In a few cases a large percentage of the total calories comes from acids, e.g., in lemon juice 62, grapefruit and squash 12, oranges and tomatoes 6, pineapple and cucumber 4, cabbage and carrot 2 to 3.

In general, the value 4.0 Calories per gram of carbohydrate is essentially correct if adjustment for crude fiber has been made. When pure sugars are added to a ration, their exact values can, of course, be used, although it is questionable whether one gains much in precision thereby. The reason for this pessimistic statement is that recent careful studies have shown that indigestible residues can interefere with the absorption of carbohydrates that would be completely utilized if fed separately. Thus other materials in the ration can play unpredictable roles in altering availability.

FATS. The fat content of foods is usually determined by extraction of the dried and powdered material with ether. Evaporation of the solvent leaves the "crude fat," which is conventionally weighed as such. It is sometimes grossly contaminated with nonlipid materials that have been taken out by the ether, e.g., pepper-corns contain 6.5 per cent of ether-soluble matter but only about 2 per cent of glycerides; ground ginger contains 3.3 per cent of "crude fat," only one-eighth of which is glyceride. For this reason the saponification procedure (Liebermann, 1898) and estimation of fatty acids has sometimes been used as a control. More often ether extraction gives low values, in some cases much too low: fat values found by ether extraction (Soxhlet) and by Liebermann's method on Horlick's malted milk are 1.2 and 8.6 grams per 100 grams, respectively; corresponding data for Kellogg's All-Bran are 1.0 and 4.5, for Grape-Nuts 0.4 and 3.0 and for whole wheat flour 0.6 and 2.1, respectively.

The energy value of most edible oils and fats lies in the range 9.2 to 9.4 Calories per gram. The availability in the 3 adult male subjects studied by Atwater and Bryant (1900) varied from 90 to 95 per cent, but it is unsafe to accept their mean value of 92 as being of universal applicability.

The main difficulty in deciding about energy values from dietary fat data in food tables concerns the decision as to what constitutes a representative sample of the food, especially of meat cuts. Because fat has a controlling influence on the energy content, small differences between the character of the sample eaten and that analyzed may introduce gross errors in the computation.

One large lean steak (200-gram portion, raw weight) of the following percentage composition: water 71, ash 1, protein 20 and fat 8 may be estimated to supply about 300 Calories; another steak of equal weight analyzing water 65, ash 1, protein 18 and fat 16 would supply more than 100 extra Calories (about 430), whereas a similar portion of a moderately fatty sirloin steak (28 to 32 per cent fat) would provide nearly 800 Calories if all the fat were consumed. Much is rendered out, however, some or all of which is left in the pan.

PROTEINS. Proteins differ in many ways from the other two foodstuffs. Proteins typically contain (besides carbon, hydrogen and oxygen) nitrogen, almost always sulfur and sometimes phosphorus. Heterogeneous substances varying in nitrogen content from about 12 per cent (in tendomucoid) to about 19 per cent (in silk fibroin), in molecular weight from about 12,000 to about 60,000,000 and in digestibility from 0 to 100 per cent are covered by the same name. Their nutritional value, which can be determined only by biological testing, varies just as greatly. Casein (15.8 per cent N) and egg albumin (15.5 per cent N) are high quality proteins, being well supplied with essential amino acids and readily digested. Zein and gelatin contain more nitrogen (16.1 and 18.0 per cent, respectively) but are incomplete, lacking certain essential amino acids, and although they are readily digested have low sustenance value when fed by themselves. Thus knowledge of protein *content* is of limited value in assessing foods until some biological tests have established the nutritional usefulness of the protein. Proteins that are useless for supporting growth may still be utilized (oxidized) to supply energy. It is wrong to think of proteins only as fuel, but it is equally wrong to think that they are not oxidizable if not used efficiently by the body for other purposes. Many proteins contain about 16 per cent of nitrogen. Food chemists therefore adopted the convention of using the factor 6.25 (i.e., 100/16) to convert *nitrogen found* in food to *protein content*. This factor has been used in preparing most food tables, although Rubner used 6.45 and Plimmer (1921) used 5.68 for nitrogen in plant products, 6.38 for dairy products and 6.25 for meats.

Use of the factor 6.25 is based on two assumptions. The first is that all proteins contain 16 per cent of nitrogen, but this is far from true. The second assumption, that all the nitrogen in food is present as protein, is also untrue. The amount of nitrogen present in simpler natural bases (choline, betaine, stachydrine, ·trimethylamine, creatine, etc.), purines, pyrimidines and other nitrogenous compounds is usually small, but in a few cases it is far from negligible.

For flesh, the factor 6.25 is reasonably correct. For milk proteins a factor of 6.38 is appropriate. The factor 5.83 is more correct for calculating the protein content of barley, oats, rye and whole wheat. For refined wheat flour the factor $5.70 \times N$ is recommended. The factor believed most appropriate for rice proteins is 5.95, for soyabeans is 5.71, peanuts and Brazil nuts 5.46, almonds 5.18 and other nuts and oil seeds 5.30. The factor 6.25 may still be applied to the nitrogen in foods where specific information is not available.

Besides uncertainty as to the actual *protein content* of foods, it must be remembered that different purified proteins on combustion release different amounts of energy. Further, there is considerable difference between proteins in their digestibility. Attempts to evaluate the *biological availability* of the energy of food proteins require two corrections (1) for loss in unabsorbed protein and (2) for further loss (from the portion digested and absorbed) in the urine of some potential energy in incompletely oxidized compounds such as urea.

Rubner determined the heat of combustion of urea and found it to be 2.52 Calories per gram or 5.4 Calories per gram of urea-nitrogen. He pointed out that the urine contains also creatinine, uric acid and other nitrogenous end-products capable of further oxidation. Attempts to estimate the physiologically available calories per gram of protein ingested were complicated by the finding that the heats of combustion of the organic substances excreted in the urine did not have a constant calorie value per gram of nitrogen. For example, the urine passed by a man eating a meat diet at one time and a potato diet at another gave 7.69 and 7.85 Calories per gram N, respectively, whereas the urine of a baby living on breast milk gave 12.1 Calories per gram N. Rubner also analyzed the feces of the man who acted as his experimental subject. The loss of energy in the nitrogenous substance amounted to 6.9 per cent of that of the ingested protein. Adding this value to that of 16.3 per cent lost in the urine he obtained a total calorie loss of about 23 per cent. Rubner therefore deducted 23 per cent from the bomb value for the heat of combustion of proteins.

A summary of our current knowledge of the composition and energy content of certain foodstuffs that are widely used is given in table 63.2.

Most of the data were taken from Agriculture Handbook No. 8 (Composition of Foods), issued by the U. S. Department of Agriculture (1950). The mineral content of certain foods is given in table 63.3.

MAIN FOOD GROUPS

1. Meats, fish, poultry, eggs. Protein-rich foods, also rich sources of certain vitamins of the B group. Eggs sometimes classed separately because of richness in vitamin A.

2. Legumes (dried peas and beans) and nuts. Protein-rich, but less costly; the proteins of these foods are of somewhat lower quality and vitamins in these products are less abundant.

3. Milk and milk products (other than butter). Economical sources of proteins of high quality, rich in calcium and riboflavin.

4. Grain products. Inexpensive sources of energy and of protein, although the latter are present in smaller amounts than in meats and milk products. If not too highly processed, good sources of iron and vitamins of the B group.

5. Green and yellow vegetables. Sources of vitamin A, minerals and certain other vitamins.

6. Tomatoes and citrus fruits. Rich sources of vitamin C.

7. Other vegetables and fruits. Sources of vitamins and minerals.

FOOD ADDITIVES AND RESIDUES

Foodstuffs available in modern markets are rarely free from foreign chemicals. Possibly over one hundred compounds not normally present in natural foods now find their way, accidentally or by intent, into the foodstuffs marketed in industrialized countries. Some are added to the food to increase shelf-life by decreasing spoilage or rancidity: antibiotics are added to refrigerated fish and poultry, antimycotics are used to prevent mold on cheese, fruits and bread. Other chemicals are added to prevent lumping, and some improve appearance. Vitamin C is used to prevent discoloration and flavor changes in frozen fruits and peeled potatoes. Besides these "additives" in foods many "residues" from other steps in their production may be present. Chemicals are used to increase the rate of growth of livestock or poultry or to improve the yield of vegetables. Pesticides, herbicides, antibiotics and even hormones used in earlier stages may appear in the food as purchased. Penicillin residues in milk (from treatment of mastitis in cows) have been known to produce allergic reactions in sensitive

TABLE 63.2

Composition and energy content of common foodstuffs

Foodstuff	Usual Serving	Food Energy	Composition of Foods, 100 Grams Edible Portion							
			Water	Protein	Fat	Carbohydrate		Ash	Calcium	Phosphorus
						Total	Fiber			
	gm.	Calories per 100 gm.	%	gm.	gm.	gm.	gm.	gm.	mg.	mg.
Bread										
White[a]	50[b]	275	34.7	8.5	3.2	51.8	0.2	1.8	79	92
Toasted	39[b]	313	25.5	9.7	3.7	59.0	0.2	2.1	90	105
Wholewheat	50[b]	240	36.6	9.3	2.6	49.0	1.5	2.5	96	263
Rye[c]	50[b]	244	35.3	9.1	1.2	52.4	0.4	2.0	72	147
Doughnut[d]	50	425	18.7	6.6	21.0	52.7	0.2	1.0	73	286
Candy										
Fondant	25	352	8.0	0	0	91.0	0	1.0	0	0
Fudge (plain)	25	411	5.0	1.7	11.3	81.3	0.3	0.7	48	67
Hard	25	383	1.0	0	0	99.0	0	0	0	0
Peanut brittle	25	441	2.0	8.3	15.5	72.8	0.8	1.3	38	124
Ginger root	25	340	12.0	0.3	0.2	87.1	0.7	0.4		
Candied peel	25	315	17.7	0.3	0.3	80.4	1.9	1.3		
Cereals										
Barley (pearled)		349	11.1	8.2	1.0	78.8	0.5	0.9	16	189
Cassava		345		1.6		84.6				
Corn meal (whole bolted)		362	12.0	9.0	3.4	74.5	1.0	1.1	6	(178)[e]
Corn (degermed and cooked)	200	50	87.7	1.1	0.2	10.7	0.1	0.3	1	14
Millet[f]		350	9–13	7–13	2.2±	73.0	2.0±	1–3		
Oatmeal (dry)		390	8.3	14.2	7.4	68.2	1.2	1.9	53	405
Oatmeal (cooked)	200	63	84.8	2.3	1.2	11.0	0.2	0.7	9	67
Rice (brown, raw)		360	12.0	7.5	1.7	77.7	0.6	1.1	39	303
Rice (milled, cooked)	160	119	70.5	2.5	0.1	26.2	0.1	0.7	8	45
Rye flour (light)		356	11.0	9.4	1.0	77.9	0.4	0.7	22	185
Rye flour (dark)		318	11.0	16.3	2.6	68.1	2.4	2.0	54	(536)[e]
Wheat flour (whole, from hard wheats)		333	12.0	13.3	2.0	71.0	2.3	1.7	41	372
Wheat flour (80% extraction)		365	12.0	12.0	1.3	74.1	0.5	0.65	24	191
Wheat germ	25	361	11.0	25.2	10.0	49.5	2.5	4.3	84	1096
Tapioca (dry)		360	12.6	0.6	0.2	86.4	0.1	0.2	12	12
Dairy products										
Butter	14[g]	716	15.5	0.6	81	0.4	0	2.5	20	16
Cheese (cheddar)	30	398	37.0	25.0	32.2	2.1	0	3.7	725	495
Cheese (cottage, from skim milk)	60	95	76.5	19.5	0.5	2.0	0	1.5	96	189

Most of the data are from U.S.D.A. Handbook No. 8 (1950), but the data for cassava are from U.S. D.A. 34.

[a] Four per cent nonfat milk solids.

[b] Two slices. Slices vary considerably in weight depending on the freshness: one slice fresh bread weighs about 23 to 28 grams.

[c] American rye bread (⅓ rye flour, ⅔ wheat flour).

[d] Cake type batter.

[e] Estimated value.

[f] Data for husked millet from Winton and Winton, 1932. It is a staple cereal in Central Africa, Southern China, in India and parts of Europe.

[g] Two patties.

TABLE 63.2—*Continued*

Foodstuff	Usual Serving	Food Energy	Composition of Foods 100 Grams Edible Portion							
			Water	Protein	Fat	Carbohydrate		Ash	Calcium	Phosphorus
						Total	Fiber			
	gm.	*Calories per 100 gm.*	%	*gm.*	*gm.*	*gm.*	*gm.*	*gm.*	*mg.*	*mg.*
Dairy Products— *Continued*										
Ice cream (plain).....	80[h]	207	62.1	4.0	12.5	20.6	0	0.8	123	99
Milk (cow, whole)....	250	68	87.0	3.5	3.9	4.9	0	0.7	118	93
Milk (cow, skim).....	250	36	90.5	3.5	0.1	5.1	0	0.8	123	97
Milk (dried, skim)....	10	362	3.5	35.6	1.0	52.0	0	7.9	1300	1030
Eggs (hen)										
Fresh (whole)........	50	162	74.0	12.8	11.5	0.7	0	1.0	54	210
Fresh (white)........	50		87.8	10.8	0	0.8	0	0.6	6	17
Fresh (yolk).........		361	49.4	16.3	31.9	0.7	0	1.7	147	586
Fresh (dried, whole)..	5	592	5.0	46.8	42.0	2.5	0	3.6	190	767
Fish										
Cod (raw)...........	150[i]	74	82.6	16.5	0.4	0	0	1.2	10	194
Halibut (raw)........		126	75.4	18.6	5.2	0	0	1.0	13	211
Halibut (broiled).....	120	182	64.2	26.2	7.8	0	0	1.9	14	267
Salmon (broiled)......	120	170	64.5	28.0	5.6	0.2	0	1.7		
Salmon (canned, sockeye)...............	90	173	67.2	20.2	9.6	0	0	3.0	259	344
Shell fish										
Crab (canned).......	90	104	77.2	16.9	2.9	1.3		1.7	45	182
Scallops (raw muscle).	140[i]	78	80.3	14.8	0.1	3.4	0	1.4	26	208
Fowl										
Chicken (raw, total edible)............	150[i]	200	66.0	20.2	12.6	0	0	1.0	14	200
Turkey (raw).........	150[i]	268	58.3	20.1	20.2	0	0	1.0	23	320
Fruits (raw)										
Apple................	150	58	84.1	0.3	0.4	14.9	1.0	0.3	6	10
Avocado.............	100	245	65.4	1.7	26.4	5.1	1.8	1.4	10	38
Banana..............	120	88	74.8	1.2	0.2	23.0	0.6	0.8	8	28
Cherries.............	150	61	83.0	1.1	0.5	14.8	0.3	0.6	18	20
Orange..............	150	45	87.2	0.9	0.2	11.2	0.6	0.5	33	23
Peach...............	120	46	86.9	0.5	0.1	12.0	0.6	0.5	8	22
Raspberries (red).....	90	57	84.1	1.2	0.4	13.8	4.7	0.5	40	37
Meat										
Bacon (raw).........		630	20.0	9.1	65.0	1.1	0	4.3	13	108
Bacon (fried)........	20	607	13.0	25.0	55.0	1.0	0	6.0	25	255
Beef (rib roast, cooked)	100	319	51.0	24.0	24.0	0	0	1.2	10	185
Beef (liver, fried).....	90	208	57.2	23.6	7.7	9.7	0	1.8	8	480
Lamb (leg roast, cooked)............	100	274	56.0	24.0	19.0	0	0	1.1	10	257
Pork (boiled ham)....	100	302	47.8	22.8	22.7	0	0	6.7	9	92
Nuts										
Almonds.............	20	600	4.7	18.6	54.1	19.6	2.7	3.0	254	475
Brazil...............	30	640	5.3	14.4	65.9	11.0	2.1	3.4	186	693
Peanuts (roasted).....	30	560	2.6	26.9	44.2	23.6	2.4	2.7	74	393
Walnuts.............	30	650	3.3	15.0	64.4	15.6	2.1	1.7	83	380

[h] Based on factory product containing 5 lb. of ice cream to the U. S. gallon.

[i] Weight after cooking will be less.

TABLE 63.2—*Continued*

Foodstuff	Usual Serving	Food Energy	Composition of Foods 100 Grams Edible Portion							
			Water	Protein	Fat	Carbohydrate		Ash	Calcium	Phosphorus
						Total	Fiber			
	gm.	*Calories per 100 gm.*	*%*	*gm.*	*gm.*	*gm.*	*gm.*	*gm.*	*mg.*	*mg.*
Vegetables										
Beans (green, cooked).	100	22	92.5	1.4	0.2	4.7	0.5	1.2	36	23
Beans (red kidney, cooked)	200	90	76.0	5.7	0.4	16.4	0.9	1.5	40	124
Beets (red, cooked)...	150	41	88.3	1.0	0.1	9.8	0.8	0.8	21	31
Cabbage (raw)	100	24	92.4	1.4	0.2	5.3	1.0	0.8	46	31
Carrots (raw)	100	42	88.2	1.2	0.3	9.3	1.1	1.0	39	37
Corn (sweet, cooked).	150	85	75.5	2.7	0.7	20.2		0.9	5	52
Kale (raw)	50	40	86.6	3.9	0.6	7.2	1.2	1.7	225	62
Potatoes (peeled, boiled)	140	83	77.8	2.0	0.1	19.1	0.4	1.0	11	56
Potatoes (French fried)	80	393	19.6	5.4	19.1	52.0	1.1	3.9	30	152
Sweet potatoes (boiled)	160	123	68.5	1.8	0.7	27.9	1.0	1.1	30	49
Tomatoes (raw)	150	20	94.1	1.0	0.3	4.0	0.6	0.6	11	27
Turnips (cooked)	150	27	92.3	0.8	0.2	6.0	1.2	0.7	40	34

consumers. Bacitracin, chlortetracycline, arsanilic acid, arsenosobenzene, 4-nitrophenylarsonic acid, nitrofurazone, phenothiazine, diethylstilbestrol and reserpine are examples of compounds added to animal feeds. Residues of these and of DDT, lead arsenate, parathion, dieldrin, 2,4-D, aminotriazole and similar compounds may sometimes reach hazardous levels.

Public health authorities in many countries are trying to establish sensitive methods for the detection of toxic residues and for the control of additives and residues in foods.

General Metabolism

The word metabolism has a broad meaning. It is the term employed to describe the chemical changes that occur within the tissues. The integration of these reactions leads (1) to growth, (2) to the production of the heat required to maintain body temperature, and (3) to supply the energy for other vital processes. It is convenient for teaching purposes to consider *energy metabolism*, which is concerned with the gross energy changes (heat production, muscular activity and energy for maintenance of vital functions), separately from *intermediary metabolism*, which is concerned with specific chemical reactions occurring in the body. This customary differentiation is, however, not a real one since energy changes are essential components of chemical reactions. Many metabolic reactions, especially those concerned with the breakdown of large molecules into simpler units, release energy; other reactions, especially those involving synthesis, absorb energy. The assimilative processes involved in the formation of new tissue are referred to as *anabolism*; the reactions concerned with tissue breakdown are referred to as *catabolism*.

Energy is required to maintain the body temperature, to support the automatic muscular movements of the heart, respiratory organs and gut and for the synthetic reactions that occur in the tissues (formation of protein, hormones and other complex metabolites). These activities, called *basal metabolism*, in an adult require about 500 Calories during an average 8-hour period of sleep or rest in bed. A similar energy expenditure continues during the waking hours (another 1000 Calories), giving a total basal expenditure of about 1500 Calories. A portion must be added for nonlabor activities (feeding, clothing, washing and amusing oneself); the energy required for these will vary considerably but probably averages about 500 Calories. The quota for the day's work varies from as low as 600 Calories (more frequently 800) for a sedentary student or clerk to possibly as much as 3600 Calories in a miner, woodcutter or athlete. Thus the total daily expenditure of energy of an average sedentary person weighing about 65 kg. would be about $1500 + 500 + 800 = 2800$ Calories. Total daily expenditures above 4400 Calories are uncommon.

Energy metabolism may be studied from several aspects: (a) the energy content (calorie value) of foods; (b) direct calorimetry; (c) the significance of the respiratory quotient (R.Q.), i.e., volume of carbon dioxide expired divided by the volume of oxygen consumed in the same period of time (CO_2/O_2); (d) indirect calorimetry; (e) basal metabolism; (f) energy cost (calorie requirement) of various types of activity; (g) the specific dynamic action (S.D.A.) of foods, i.e., the increased production of heat by the body as a result of a stimulus to metabolic activity caused by taking food.

HISTORICAL SURVEY

The first gas to be mentioned in the history of chemistry is one of great physiological importance, carbon dioxide. Van Helmont (1577–1644) corked up limestone with acid in a bottle and found that the pressure created by the substance being formed burst the bottle. He coined the word *gas*, derived from the Greek word *chaos*, to describe the wild motion of the particles responsible for the bursting force so generated. He called the product *gas sylvestre*. Joseph Black rediscovered and investigated carbon dioxide in 1754 and called it *fixed air*, Van Helmont's name *gas* having not yet been generally accepted.

In 1669 John Mayow (1641–1679) put a large glass globe over a mouse on a platform in a shallow dish of water. A perceptible contraction of the air occurred slowly and caused the level of the water to rise in the globe. A burning candle produced the same effect. A mouse introduced into a vessel with a burning lamp lived only about half as long as a mouse in the same vessel without a lamp. From these observations Mayow concluded that air is composed of two gases, one concerned in combustion and respiration (which he called *nitro-aerial spirit*, because it was apparently the same substance that is "fixed" in saltpeter, i.e., niter, and freed from it by heat), and a second gas incapable of supporting either combustion or respiration. Joseph Priestley (1733–1804) discovered several new gases (at that time called "airs") and established the existence of different airs, each with definite properties. In 1772 he made oxygen by heating niter (potassium nitrate) strongly, and observed that a mouse lived twice as long in the "new air" as in the same volume of common air. Priestley breathed the new air himself and fancied his "breast felt peculiarly light and easy for some

TABLE 63.3

Ash content of the edible portion of some common foods

(from Sherman)

	In 100 Grams Fresh Substance						
	Iron	Calcium	Magnesium	Sodium	Potassium	Phosphorus	Chlorine
	mg.	mg.	mg.	mg.	mg.	mg.	mg.
Beefsteak, lean.	3.0	11	22	65	333	204	76
Liver..........	12.0	8	22	91	296	373	101
Eggs...........	2.7	54	13	137	138	210	120
Milk, whole....	0.1	118	12	51	143	93	106
Cornmeal......	2.7	16	86		349	174	
Oatmeal.......	5.0	53	145	2	431	405	49
Rice, polished..	0.8	9	28	4	92	92	6
Wheat flour....	1.3	16	37	2	128	100	49
Wheat, entire grain........	5.7	54	147	12	430	374	49
Beans, lima, dried........	7.5	68	181		1727	381	31
Beans, string, fresh........	1.1	65	27	3	251	44	33
Cabbage.......	0.5	46	12	5	294	31	39
Corn, sweet....	5.0	9	38	1		120	14
Peas, dried.....	5.2	72	140	35	979	388	44
Potatoes.......	0.7	11	27	5	496	56	35
Spinach........	3.0	81	52	84	502	49	65
Turnips........	0.5	55	15	5	253	41	31
Apples.........	0.3	6	6	2	111	11	4
Raisins........	3.3	60	27	31	803	110	24

time afterwards"; he therefore recommended its use in medicine! Priestley wrote, "Who can tell but that, in time, this pure air may become a fashionable article in luxury. Hitherto only two mice and myself have had the privilege of breathing it." Today it is a common privilege.

A generation later Crawford placed a guinea pig in a water calorimeter and demonstrated a parallelism between the oxygen consumed and the heat generated by the animal. Approximately the same quantity of heat was produced by the animal as when the same amount of oxygen was used to burn carbon outside the body.

A few years later two French scientists, the chemist, Lavoisier (1743–1794), and the physicist, Laplace (1749–1827), performed a similar experiment but measured the carbon dioxide produced rather than the oxygen used. They placed a guinea pig in a closed chamber and showed that the same product of oxidation of carbon is formed in the body and eliminated from the lungs as is produced by the burning of a candle. They determined the quantity of carbon dioxide eliminated by the animal in a 10-hour period and found that it was the

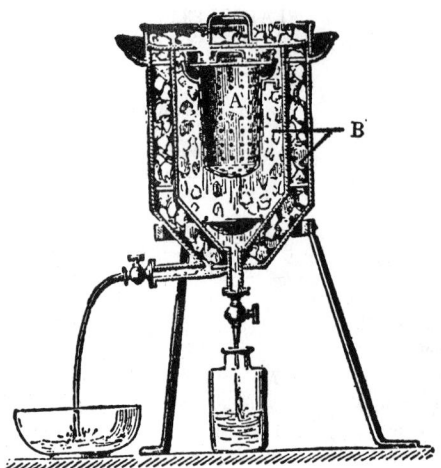

Fig. 63.1. Ice calorimeter of Lavoisier and Laplace. (After Luciani.) A, chamber for animal; B, two concentric chambers filled with ice.

same (12.1 grams) as that produced when 3.3 grams of pure carbon were burned in air. The guinea pig was next placed in a closed space, surrounded by ice (fig. 63.1) and the heat given out by the animal's body was calculated from the quantity of ice that was melted. A comparable amount of heat was generated when 3.3 grams of carbon were burned in the ice calorimeter. Lavoisier and Laplace concluded that the heat generated by the animal was produced by the combustion of 3.3 grams of the body's carbon. With this demonstration that animal heat is the result of the oxidation of carbon in the body, and establishment of a *parallelism between the amount of heat generated* in the animal's body *and the quantity of carbon dioxide eliminated,* the science of metabolism was begun.

Lavoisier believed that the oxidation of carbon and hydrogen occurs in the lungs. Heat production is now known to result from combustion of foodstuffs in the various tissues of the body.

J. von Liebig (1803–1873) established that it is not *carbon* and hydrogen that are burned by the tissues, but *carbohydrate* and *fat*. Liebig (1842) believed that oxygen is used in the metabolic combustion of these two foodstuffs but he thought that the breakdown of protein is of a different nature, being caused by muscular work. This belief, although unsupported by any experimental evidence, was generally accepted until Carl von Voit (1831–1908) showed conclusively in 1860 by experiments on dogs and man that the metabolism of protein is not affected by muscular work.

Metabolic balance studies originated with J. B. Boussingault (1802–1887). He compared the carbon, hydrogen, nitrogen and oxygen ingested by a dairy cow in its feed with the amounts of these elements excreted in the milk, urine and feces. The portions unaccounted for were considered to

have been used in respiration. Bidder and Carl Schmidt (1852) measured the protein intake and nitrogen excretion of adult dogs and cats and found that nearly all of the ingested nitrogen was eliminated in the urine and feces. Their findings were doubted until Voit (1857) measured the protein intake and nitrogen output of a dog for 58 days and recovered 99.7 per cent of the nitrogen in the excreta.

Regnault and Reiset in 1849 devised the first closed circuit apparatus for respiration experiments (to be described later) and in it measured the metabolism of poultry, swine, sheep and calves. They showed that the respiratory quotient (volume of carbon dioxide expired divided by the volume of oxygen consumed in the same time-period) is controlled by the nature of the foodstuffs being oxidized and does not depend on the species of animal used in the experiment. Pettenkoffer (1818–1901) constructed the first respiration chamber in which a man could live without discomfort for several days. He and Voit conducted many studies in it and established the fundamentals of energy metabolism. This aspect of metabolism received exhaustive study in the closing years of the last century by Rubner and his colleagues in Germany. Atwater (1844–1907), the outstanding American authority in this field, spent some time with Rubner; later, with the physicist, Rosa, he constructed the first human respiration calorimeter to be made on this side of the Atlantic and with F. G. Benedict and others perfected the study of energy metabolism.

Energy Content of Substances

As explained in the previous section, the *physiologically* available energy of the three major foodstuffs is generally taken as 9, 4 and 4 Calories per gram for fat, carbohydrate and protein, respectively.

The potential energy of a chemical compound or foodstuff is determined by measuring the amount of heat generated when the material is burned. The *bomb calorimeter* (fig. 63.2) employed for this purpose consists of a small, strong, platinum-lined steel vessel immersed in a can containing a known weight of water. This in turn is enclosed in an insulating outer container. A known weight of the dried foodstuff is placed in the bomb which is then filled with pure oxygen under pressure. The bomb is immersed in the water and the mixture is ignited electrically. A thermometer graduated in very small units, capable of being read to the nearest 0.001°C., is used. The amount of heat produced is calculated from the rise in temperature of the water, with appropriate corrections being made for the "water equivalent" of the bomb and calorimeter parts. The rise in temperature multiplied by the sum of the weight of the water (in kilograms) plus the "water equivalent" of the apparatus divided by the dry weight of the substance (in grams) gives in Calories the heat value of the material per gram.

THERMAL EQUIVALENTS. The heat production per liter of oxygen consumed varies from compound to compound (table 63.4) but the variation within groups of related compounds (e.g., carbohydrates) is smaller than between different groups of compounds (e.g., carbohydrates, fats and proteins). The thermal equivalent of the foodstuff is the number of calories liberated per liter of oxygen consumed or of carbon dioxide eliminated. The thermal equivalent of CO_2 varies much more than does that of O_2 (table 63.4). It is more usual, therefore, to estimate heat production from oxygen consumption rather than from carbon dioxide output. The thermal equivalent of oxygen when carbohydrate (mainly starch) is being burned is generally given as 5.04 and the corresponding value for fat is about 4.68. The thermal equivalent for protein varies; it has been given by Loewy as 4.683 and by Benedict and Fox as 4.60. For practical purposes an average value of about 4.5 Calories per liter of oxygen may be used for protein.

OXYCALORIMETER. Another type of apparatus used to determine the energy value of foodstuffs is the *oxycalorimeter* (fig. 63.3) devised by F. G. Benedict. Although less accurate than the bomb method, this procedure is useful for determining the energy value of actual meals. The sample is burned in a combustion chamber connected to a gas holder containing oxygen. The carbon dioxide is absorbed, permitting measurement of the *volume of oxygen used*. From the thermal equivalent of a liter of oxygen when used to burn the three primary foodstuffs (table 63.5), a value may be calculated for the heat available from the particular sample of food. This is an adaptation of the method of *indirect calorimetry* used in the clinic (see p. 1281).

Since the Calories liberated per liter of oxygen used in the combustion of foodstuffs in the oxycalorimeter vary only between 4.5 and 5.0, the use of a mean figure of 4.8 will result in values with an error no greater than 5 per cent of the true (bomb) value. If the foodstuff is predominantly of one type, choice of a more appropriate factor (e.g., 5.0 for a starchy food, or 4.5 for a

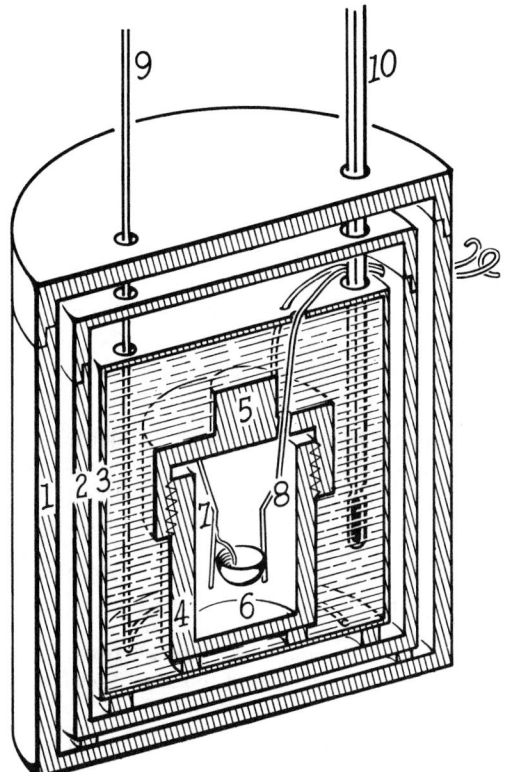

FIG. 63.2. The bomb calorimeter consists of three vessels (1, 2, 3) one inside the other. The outer vessels (1 and 2) are usually of a plastic composition and serve merely to provide insulating dead air-spaces. The innermost vessel (3) is of highly polished metal and contains a known weight of water in which the bomb (4) is immersed while the foodstuff is being burned. The top (5) of the bomb screws off to permit a known weight of dried foodstuff to be placed in the crucible (6). The top is replaced and through a valve oxygen under pressure of about 300 pounds per square inch is introduced. The foodstuff is ignited by means of electrical leads (7, 8). The water is mixed (stirrer, 9) and its rise in temperature is measured by the thermometer (10).

protein-rich one) gives a value very close to the true one.

In the body the calorie value of oxygen varies similarly between 4.5 and 5.0, depending upon the type and proportion of foodstuffs being oxidized. Because the respiratory quotient gives an indication of this ratio, it will be discussed next.

THE RESPIRATORY QUOTIENT

The ratio, vol. CO_2 expired : vol. O_2 used, is called the respiratory quotient or, briefly, the R.Q. Different relative amounts of carbon, hydrogen and oxygen are contained in the molecules of carbohydrates, fats and proteins. Therefore, different characteristic amounts of oxygen are

TABLE 63.4

Data required to calculate the R.Q. and thermal equivalents of typical food components

Substance	Mol. Wt.	Calories per		O₂ Used	CO₂ Formed	R.Q.	Thermal Equivalents	
		G.M.W.	gm.				Calories per liter O₂	Calories per liter CO₂
				l./gm.	*l./gm.*			
Galactose..............	180	670.7	3.73	0.746	0.746	1.00	4.99	4.99
Glucose...............	180	673.0	3.74	0.746	0.746	1.00	5.01	5.01
Fructose..............	180	675.6	3.75	0.746	0.746	1.00	5.03	5.03
Starch................	(162)	677.5	4.18	0.829	0.829	1.00	5.04	5.04
Sucrose...............	342	1349.6	3.95	0.787	0.787	1.00	5.02	5.02
Fucose[a].............	164	712.0	4.34	0.888	0.819	0.92	4.89	5.30
Desoxyribose..........	134			0.914	0.837	0.92		
Tributyrin............	302	1941.0	6.43	1.372	1.112	0.81	4.69	5.78
Tristearin............	891	8503.0	9.54	2.048	1.433	0.70	4.66	6.65
Triolein..............	885	8339.0	9.43	2.025	1.443	0.71	4.66	6.53
Glycine (bomb)........	75	234.5	3.12	0.672	0.597	0.88	4.64	5.23
Glycine (physiol.).....	75	158.7	2.12	0.448	0.448	1.00	4.73	4.73
Leucine (physiol.)[b]...	131	779.8	5.95	1.282	0.940	0.73	4.64	6.33
Muscle protein[c].......			4.23	0.981[d]	0.774[e]	0.79	4.32	5.43

[a] Fucose is an example of a desoxyhexose, $C_6H_{12}O_5$.

[b] Leucine—energy content (bomb)—855.6 Cal./mole.

　　"　　—physiological oxidation: $2 C_6H_{13}O_2N + 15 O_2 = CO(NH_2)_2 + 11 CO_2 + 11 H_2O$.

　　"　　—energy content (physiol.)/mole = $\dfrac{(2 \times 855.6) - 151.6}{2} = \dfrac{1559.6}{2} = 779.8$.

[c] Physiological value, calculated according to Loewy (as modified in text).

[d] It is customary to determine urinary N as a measure of protein metabolism. As shown in table 63.6, 1.00 gram of urinary N in the case of this particular protein arose from the catabolism of 100/16.28 = 6.14 grams protein requiring $6.14 \times 0.981 = 6.02$ liters of O_2 (STP) for its metabolism.

[e] Similarly CO_2 produced per gram of urinary N = $6.14 \times 0.774 = 4.75$ liters (STP).

required to oxidize the constituent carbon and hydrogen to carbon dioxide and water. In the case of proteins, part of the sulfur may be oxidized to sulfate, thus using up slightly more oxygen without any concomitant production of CO_2.

CARBOHYDRATE. The complete oxidation of glucose may be represented by the equation

$$C_6H_{12}O_6 + 6O_2 \longrightarrow 6CO_2 + 6H_2O \ldots\ldots(+ 673.0 \text{ Calories})$$
1 mol.　　6 mol.　　　6 mol. 6 mol.
180 gm.　　192 gm.　　264 gm. 108 gm.
6 × 22.4 liters　$\longrightarrow$　6 × 22.4 liters
(at S.T.P.)　　　　(at S.T.P.)

Since 1 gram molecular weight of any gas occupies 1 gram molecular volume (22.4 liters at standard temperature and pressure (S.T.P.)) it will be apparent that 180 grams of glucose require 134.4 liters of O_2 and that 1.00 gram would, therefore, require 0.746 liter, or approximately 0.75 liter. Similarly it may be calculated that 0.75 liter of CO_2 would be produced. Thus the R.Q. is 0.75/0.75 = 1.00. One may use the ratios of the number of Gram Molecular Volumes (G.M.V.) directly, as a chemist would do, R.Q. = 6/6 = 1.00.

For starches, the equation would be

$$(C_6H_{10}O_5)_n + 6n \ O_2 \rightarrow$$

$$6n \ CO_2 + 5n \ H_2O \ldots(+677.5 \text{ Calories})$$

$$R.Q. = \frac{6n \ G.M.V. \ CO_2}{6n \ G.M.V. \ O_2} = 1.00$$

FAT. The fats, being more highly reduced compounds than the carbohydrates, have a higher energy content. Because of their lower oxygen content, they require more oxygen per gram for their combustion. Equations for the complete oxidation of several fats are as follows:

$$2 \ C_3H_5O_3 \ (OC_4H_7)_3 + 37 \ O_2 \rightarrow$$
tributyrin (302)

$$30 \ CO_2 + 26 \ H_2O \ldots(+1941.1 \text{ Calories})$$

$$2 \ C_3H_5O_3 \ (OC_{18}H_{35})_3 + 163 \ O_2 \rightarrow 114 \ CO_2 + 110 \ H_2O$$
tristearin (891)

$$C_3H_5O_3 \ (OC_{18}H_{33})_3 + 80 \ O_2 \rightarrow 57 \ CO_2 + 52 \ H_2O$$
triolein (885)

tributyrin R.Q. $= \quad 30/37 \quad = 0.881$

tristearin R.Q. $= \quad 114/163 \quad = 0.699$

triolein R.Q. $= \quad 57/80 \quad = 0.713$

The mixed fats of the food, when burned in the body, are generally taken to have an R.Q. of 0.71.

PROTEIN. Amino acids are not oxidized completely in the body, as mentioned earlier. Approximate values for O_2 consumed and CO_2 produced may be calculated as follows. Assuming complete oxidation, glycine would react thus:

$$4 \, CH_2 \, (NH_2) \, COOH + 9 \, O_2 \rightarrow 8 \, CO_2 \\ + 10 \, H_2O + 2 \, N_2 \ldots (+ 4 \times 234.5 \text{ Calories}) \quad (1)$$

Such a reaction does not occur in the body, however; 40 per cent of this substance is excreted as urea. Assuming excretion of all the nitrogen of glycine in the form of urea, the equation for the partial oxidation would be

$$4 \, CH_2 \, (NH_2) \, COOH + 6 \, O_2 \rightarrow \\ 2 \, CO \, (NH_2)_2 + 6CO_2 + 6H_2O \quad (2)$$

One mole of urea, on combustion, liberates 151.6 Calories.

$$2 \, CO \, (NH_2)_2 + 3 \, O_2 \rightarrow 2CO_2 + \\ 4 \, H_2O + 2 \, N_2 \ldots (+ 2 \times 151.6 \text{ Calories}) \quad (3)$$

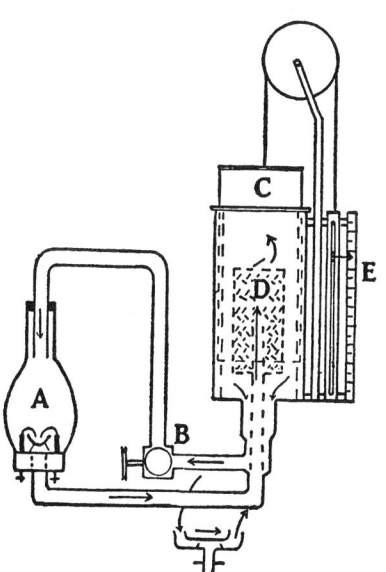

FIG. 63.3. Diagram of oxycalorimeter for determining energy values of foods, etc. (A) Combustion chamber, crucible and electrical connections. (B) Rotary blower. (C) Spirometer bell with oxygen in water seal. (D) Soda lime container. (E) Scale in millimeters for measuring the oxygen used. (F) Mouthpiece with valves for B.M.R. estimation (enlarged). Principle of the Benedict-Roth apparatus for determining B.M.R. is seen by replacing A and B by F. (After Cruickshank, E. & S. Livingstone, Ltd., Edinburgh.)

TABLE 63.5

"Metabolic constants" of fat, protein and carbohydrate

	Potential Energy		Oxygen Required[a]	CO_2 Produced[a]	R.Q.	Thermal Equivalent of O_2
	Bomb Calorimetry	Physiologically available				
	Cal./ gm.	Cal./ gm.	l./gm.[a]	l./gm.[a]		Cal./l.[a]
Fat.......	9.3	9.0	1.94[b]	1.39	0.71	4.74
Protein...	5.4	4.0	0.97	0.78	0.80	4.46
Carbohydrate...	4.1	4.0	0.83	0.83	1.00	5.05

[a] Gas measured at S.T.P.

[b] Depends on the fatty acid. For short-chain fatty acids this value is greater, e.g., for tributyrin, 2.41.

TABLE 63.6

Data used in calculation of R.Q. for oxidation of protein

(After Loewy)

All values are expressed in grams per 100 grams meat protein

Constituent	Constituent Ingested	Excreted in Urine and Feces	Portion Not Excreted
C	52.38	10.88	41.50
H	7.27	2.87	4.40
O	22.68	15.00	7.68
N	16.65	16.65[a]	
S	1.02[b]	1.02[c]	

[a] The bulk of this nitrogen (16.28 grams) was in the urine. Therefore 1.00 gram urinary N represents 6.14 grams meat protein.

[b] Present as sulfide (methionine) and disulfide (cystine).

[c] Present mainly as ethereal sulfate.

This energy does not become available to the organism because the urea is not oxidized in the body. Therefore the energy liberated in the physiological (partial) oxidation of glycine shown in the second equation is $(938.0 - 303.2) = 634.8$ Calories per 4 moles of glycine, or 158.7 Calories per mole (2.12 Calories per gram). Because of its relatively large oxygen content, glycine is an atypical amino acid. Corresponding calculations for leucine give the data shown in table 63.4.

A typical meat protein (according to Loewy) analyzed as shown in table 63.6 and the constituents contained in the urine and feces per 100 grams of ingested protein are shown in the third column.

The carbon and hydrogen unaccounted for in the excreta were presumably completely oxidized because none of the nitrogen was retained and therefore probably *all the protein was completely burned in the body.* The 7.68 grams of oxygen not excreted may be assumed to have oxidized an equivalent amount of hydrogen $(2/16 \times 7.68 = 0.96$ grams) to form what is sometimes called "intramolecular water," i.e., H_2O formed from H and O in the parent molecule. This would leave $4.40 - 0.96 = 3.44$ grams hydrogen and 41.50 grams carbon to be oxidized.

41.50 grams C require 110.6 grams O_2 and produce 152.2 grams CO_2

3.44 grams H require 27.5 grams O_2

Total CO_2 produced: 152.2 grams $\equiv$ 77.4 liters at S.T.P.

Total O_2 required: 138.1 grams $\equiv$ 96.7 liters at S.T.P.

Loewy's estimated R.Q. for this protein = 77.4/96.7 = 0.80.

Loewy made no allowance for oxygen used in the oxidation of sulfur. The chemistry of cystine was not well understood at that time and methionine was unknown, but it is odd that the conversion of organic sulfur to SO_3 was not considered. For simplicity we may use H_2S for writing the equation because the sulfur atoms of methionine and of cysteine are both at the same oxidation level as that in H_2S.

$$H_2S + 2 O_2 \rightarrow SO_3 + H_2O$$

32 grams S require 64 grams O_2 ($\equiv$ 44.8 liters at S.T.P.)

1.02 grams S require 2.04 grams O_2 ($\equiv$ 1.43 liters)

$\therefore$ Total O_2 used for this protein = 138.1 + 2.04 = 140.14 grams $\equiv$ 96.7 + 1.4 = 98.1 liters. Revised estimate for R.Q. of this protein:

$$77.4/98.1 = 0.79$$

The portion used for the oxidation of protein sulfur is small, probably always less than 1.5 per cent of the total oxygen requirement for protein; for practical purposes it may be neglected. Different proteins have different R.Q.'s, as do different fats and carbohydrates, but the values remain close to the commonly used figure of 0.80.

Because alcohol sometimes provides energy for man it may be of interest to note that the R.Q. of ethanol is 0.67.

The value of the respiratory quotient is taken as an indication of the *type* of food being metabolized. It gives no quantitative estimation of the metabolism. An R.Q. around unity is taken to indicate that the material being used is chiefly carbohydrate; one around 0.70 indicates that it is mainly fat.[5]

[5] Cathcart and Markowitz point out, however,

On an ordinary mixed diet the R.Q. is about 0.85 and in the postabsorptive state (p. 1286) about 0.82. In the formation of fat from carbohydrate, as in the fattening of farm animals, an oxygen-rich substance is being converted into one poor in oxygen. Oxygen is "liberated" in the conversion and less, in consequence, is taken in from the outside for general oxidative processes. The R.Q. may therefore rise above unity (up to 1.4). A very low quotient, as is seen in the hibernating animals, is supposed by some to indicate the reverse process, i.e., the conversion of fat to carbohydrate. In the hibernating marmot the R.Q. is between 0.6 and 0.7.

CALORIMETRIC MEASUREMENTS IN ANIMALS AND MAN

An animal's energy is derived from food, which is to the body what fuel is to a furnace or machine.[6] We have seen that the law of conservation of energy holds true for the animal body: in a healthy animal which is maintaining a constant weight the intake and output of energy are equal. The food undergoes combustion in the tissues, its carbon being oxidized to carbon dioxide, its hydrogen to water and its potential energy being converted into other forms of energy (mechanical, electrical, chemical and thermal). In a growing animal or in an animal during fattening the energy of the food is in part stored as newly formed tissue.

In the resting body all the energy liberated from the food ultimately appears as heat. It was for this reason that a heat unit was chosen as the most convenient one for measuring and expressing the energy exchanges of the body. This unit, the *large calorie* (Calorie or Cal.) is 1000 times the *small calorie* (calorie or cal.) used in physical measurements.

Calorimetry in man and animals involves two main types of procedure: (a) *direct*, the same in principle as that described above for the bomb

that probably too much reliance has been placed upon the value of the R.Q. as an unequivocal criterion of the type of foodstuff undergoing metabolism. The R.Q. in a given instance is undoubtedly a resultant of several different metabolic processes, syntheses and interconversions, as well as combustion.

[6] It may be well to remember that the analogy between *fuel for machines* and *food for men* (or animals) must not be pushed too far. Nutrition involves more than chemistry and physics. The available energy of a single foodstuff cannot be estimated without considering the adequacy of other factors in the diet, the effect of other factors on absorption (availability) and the level at which the nutrient is being fed.

calorimeter, and (b) *indirect*, in which the heat production is calculated from the respiratory exchanges. The latter is commonly used, the former rarely.

DIRECT CALORIMETRY. Respiration calorime-ters permit measurement of the gaseous exchange and simultaneous heat production. The apparatus (fig. 63.4) designed by Atwater and Rosa (1897) was of such technical perfection that when a known quantity of alcohol was burned in it the

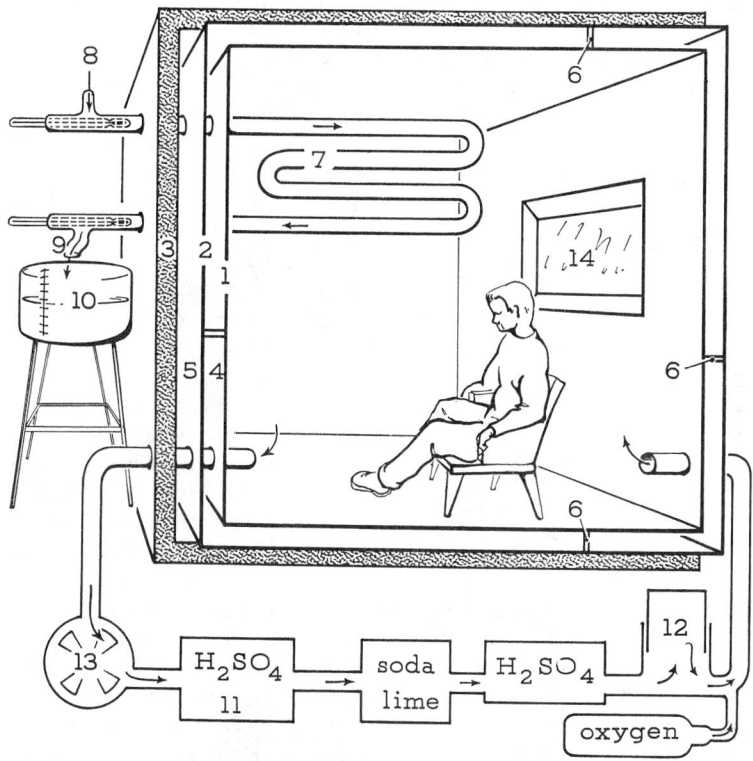

FIG. 63.4. The Atwater-Rosa-Benedict respiration calorimeter has two functional parts, one for measuring the heat production of the subject, the other for measuring the gaseous exchange. An air-tight copper box or small room (1), which is essentially a constant temperature, water-cooled calorimeter, is surrounded by a second copper box (2) and the whole is insulated by an outer layer of cork (3). This construction results in two insulating dead air-spaces (4, 5). Rosa placed thermocouples (6) in series between the two copper walls on the tops, sides and bottom to detect differences in temperature. When the inner and outer copper walls have the same temperature there can be no heat exchange between them. If the temperature of the outer wall increases it is quickly restored to that of the inner wall by a cooling current of water run through pipes (not shown) between the outer copper wall and the insulating wall. A fall in temperature of the outer wall is corrected by electrical warming of this interspace. The heat produced by the subject would cause the temperature of the chamber to rise unless the heat could be removed in some way. This is accomplished by allowing a current of cold water to flow through the copper tubes (7, suspended from the ceiling) at such a rate as to maintain a constant temperature in the chamber. Thermometers on the water intake (8) and outlet (9) give the temperature change; the volume of water which has passed through the cooling system is collected in a vessel (10) and weighed. The weight of water (in kilograms) multiplied by the temperature change in degrees Centigrade gives heat lost by radiation and conduction. To this must be added the latent heat present in the water vapor of the insensible perspiration and exhaled air (about one-quarter of the total heat produced by a man). The amount of this water is determined by weighing the first sulfuric acid absorber (11) before and after the experiment. The heat so carried out is calculated, knowing the latent heat of vaporization of water at 20°C. to be 0.585 Calories per gram.

The same apparatus can be used to determine the gaseous exchange of the subject. In principle, the procedure is as follows: air from the chamber is passed through the first sulfuric acid absorber to remove the water vapor, then through a moist soda lime absorber to remove carbon dioxide. A second sulfuric absorber takes up the moisture liberated from the soda lime. The gain in weight of the last pair of ab-sorbers equals the carbon dioxide produced by the subject. The oxygen used is determined by adding sufficient oxygen to a spirometer (12) to maintain a constant pressure in the system and by weighing the oxygen cylinder before and after the experiment. The circulation of the air in the system is maintained by a fan (13). A window (14) permits observation of the subject. Thermometers (not shown) record the temperature of the room and of the subject.

resulting carbon dioxide was recovered with an accuracy of 99.8 per cent and the heat to 99.9 per cent of the theoretical value.

The elaborate nature of the apparatus required for this method precludes its use, especially for the human subject, in any ordinary laboratory or clinic. There are indeed only a very few in existence.

The calorimeter consists of an insulated chamber large enough to accommodate an animal or a man. The heat conducted and radiated from the body is absorbed by water circulating in coils of copper pipes. The temperature of this water as

TABLE 63.7

Thermal equivalent of oxygen (Cal./liter) at different non-protein respiratory quotients

(After Zuntz and Schumberg, modified by Lusk*)

Nonprotein Respiratory Quotient	Calories per Liter O₂	Calories Derived from	
		Carbohydrate	Fat
		per cent	*per cent*
0.707	4.686	0	100
0.71	4.690	1.10	98.9
0.72	4.702	4.76	95.2
0.73	4.714	8.40	91.6
0.74	4.727	12.0	88.0
0.75	4.739	15.6	84.4
0.76	4.751	19.2	80.8
0.77	4.764	22.8	77.2
0.78	4.776	26.3	73.7
0.79	4.788	29.9	70.1
0.80	4.801	33.4	66.6
0.81	4.813	36.9	63.1
0.82	4.825	40.3	59.7
0.83	4.838	43.8	56.2
0.84	4.850	47.2	52.8
0.85	4.862	50.7	49.3
0.86	4.875	54.1	45.9
0.87	4.887	57.5	42.5
0.88	4.899	60.8	39.2
0.89	4.911	64.2	35.8
0.90	4.924	67.5	32.5
0.91	4.936	70.8	29.2
0.92	4.948	74.1	25.9
0.93	4.961	77.4	22.6
0.94	4.973	80.7	19.3
0.95	4.985	84.0	16.0
0.96	4.998	87.2	12.8
0.97	5.010	90.4	9.58
0.98	5.022	93.6	6.37
0.99	5.035	96.8	3.18
1.00	5.047	100.0	0

* This table has been further modified by Cathcart and Cuthbertson, see J. Physiol., 1931, **72,** 349.

it enters and leaves the chamber being known, and also its quantity, the heat production in Calories can be determined. To this must be added the energy carried out by the water vapor given off by the lungs and skin. This amounts to about one-quarter of the total heat production. (Further details about the apparatus and the calculations are given in the legend, fig. 63.4.) A calorimeter of this type is usually combined with apparatus for determining the heat production by indirect calorimetry as described below, the instrument being then referred to as a respiration calorimeter.

INDIRECT CALORIMETRY. The heat production of the body during a given period can be estimated using the thermal equivalents if one knows the quantity of oxygen consumed or of carbon dioxide produced during that time. As mentioned above, the estimate is more reliable when based upon oxygen consumption. Even so, the food mixture undergoing combustion, as indicated by the R.Q., must be taken into account. The heat or calorie values (thermal equivalent) of a liter of oxygen at different respiratory quotients are given in table 63.7, compiled by Zuntz and Schumberg (as modified by Lusk).

In table 63.7 the percentages of fat and carbohydrate undergoing combustion have been calculated for respiratory quotients ranging from 0.707 to 1.00. These so-called *nonprotein respiratory quotients* were obtained by determining the total oxygen consumption and carbon dioxide produced and then subtracting the volumes of these gases exchanged in the catabolism of protein. The quantity of protein undergoing catabolism is obtained from the urinary nitrogen, each gram of the latter being considered, by convention, equivalent to 6.25 grams of protein. In *precise* experiments upon heat production, the calories produced from the catabolism of protein as well as those derived from fat and carbohydrate would require determination. For example, a subject may be found to produce per hour 13.50 liters of carbon dioxide, consume 16.00 liters of oxygen and excrete 0.50 gram of nitrogen in the urine. According to Loewy's data, each gram of urinary nitrogen represents the production of 4.75 liters of carbon dioxide and the consumption of 6.02 liters of oxygen (table 63.4, footnote).

Therefore:

CO_2 produced by the subject in the catabolism of protein is $0.50 \times 4.75 = 2.38$ liters

O_2 consumed in the catabolism of protein is $0.50 \times 6.02 = 3.01$ liters

Then:

non-protein CO_2 production is $13.50 - 2.38 = 11.12$ liters

non-protein O_2 consumption is $16.00 - 3.01 = 12.99$ liters

the non-protein respiratory quotient is

$$11.12/12.99 = 0.86$$

It will be seen from table 63.7 that at this R.Q. the calorie equivalent of a liter of oxygen is 4.875. The heat produced by the combustion of non-protein materials is, therefore, $12.99 \times 4.875 = 63.3$ Calories of which 54.1 per cent is derived from carbohydrate and 45.9 per cent from fat.

The heat production due to protein is $3.01 \times 4.50 = 13.5$ Calories. As will be shown in the section on *Energy Balance* this may be estimated in another way: the calorie equivalent of each gram of urinary N is 26.4, so the heat production due to protein may also be obtained approximately by multiplying the figure for the urinary nitrogen (0.50) by $26.4 = 13.2$. The average value may be taken as 13.4 Calories.

The total heat production per hour is therefore $63.3 + 13.4 = 76.7$ Calories. Of this 34.2 Calories or 45 per cent are derived from carbohydrate, 29.1 Calories or 38 per cent from fat and 17 per cent from protein.

In ordinary determinations of the basal metabolic rate (p. 1286) urinary nitrogen is not measured and the foregoing calculations are not undertaken; only a slight error is involved if the R.Q. is assumed to be 0.82 and the heat production taken directly from table 63.7.

THE ISODYNAMIC LAW. It was demonstrated by Rubner that just as the production of heat by a stove may be maintained at a constant level by burning different types of fuel, so in the generation of animal heat the different foodstuffs may replace one another in the diet in accordance with their heat-producing values. The amounts shown of the following substances are isodynamic:

100 grams of fat × 9   = 900 Calories
225 grams of starch × 4   = 900 Calories
225 grams of protein × 4   = 900 Calories
128 grams of ethanol × 7   = 900 Calories

HEAT PRODUCTION IN RELATION TO SURFACE AREA. The heat produced by an individual at rest is proportional to the surface area of his body. Thus a fasting adult man and a starving dog, although the surface area of each and the *total* heat production were widely different, were shown by Rubner to give out in 24 hours closely similar amounts of heat *per square meter of body surface*, namely, 1134 and 1112 Calories, respectively. A small animal, e.g., a mouse, therefore, since its surface area is greater in proportion to its mass, and since it generates the same amount of heat per unit of body surface, must obviously generate more heat per unit of body weight than a larger animal. The heat is produced in the tissues (muscles, liver, etc.); consequently these, in the case of the smaller animal, must be the seat of a much more active metabolism (see table 63.8).

The shape of an object controls its surface area per unit weight. A sphere has the least surface area per unit of mass. The area of a cube is also relatively small; that of a thin sheet reaches the maximum. A few examples will illustrate the variation. A *sphere* (of material with density = 1) weighing 1000 gm. would have a radius of 6.20 cm. and a surface area of 484 sq. cm. A *cube* of the same weight would have an area of 600 sq. cm. An *elongated cylinder* (31.9 cm. by 6.32 cm. in diameter) would have a surface area of 694 sq. cm.; the same amount of material in the form of a *squat cylinder* (20 cm. diameter by 3.18 cm.) would have an area of 828. A rectangular block of the same weight (5 by 10 by 20 cm.) would have an area of 700 sq. cm.; a thick sheet (0.2 by 10 by 500) would have 10,204 and a thin sheet (0.01 by 200 by 500) would have approximately 200,000 sq. cm. Elliptical bodies with cylindrical appendages have a surface area per unit of weight

TABLE 63.8

Showing relation of heat production per kilogram and per square meter of body surface in animals of different sizes

	Weight	Calories	
		Per kilogram	Per square meter surface
	kg.		
Ox..............	391	19.1	1567
Pig.............	128.0	19.1	1078
Man............	64.3	32.1	1042
Dog............	15.2	51.5	1039
Goose*.........	3.5	66.7	967
Fowl*..........	2.0	71.0	947
Mouse..........	0.018	654.0	1188

* The relatively low figures for the heat production of birds shown in the last column are due to their bodies containing a high proportion of osseous tissue, which has an extremely low metabolism.

intermediate between that of a sphere and an elongated cylinder.

PHYSIOLOGICAL CONDITIONS WHICH STIMULATE METABOLISM. The heat production of the body is increased by (a) muscular work, (b) food, (c) a fall in environmental temperature, or (d) a rise in body temperature (fever). These influences will be considered later.

Indirect Calorimetry: Determination of the Heat Production from the Respiratory Exchanges

The results of indirect calorimetry agree within less than 1 per cent with those obtained by the direct method. Two forms of apparatus—the *closed-circuit* and the *open-circuit* or *air-current* types—are employed for indirect calorimetry. In the *closed-circuit* method the subject re-breathes the air contained in a closed system; the carbon dioxide eliminated by the subject is removed by soda-lime and weighed; a measured volume of oxygen is supplied to replenish that which has been absorbed. In the *open-circuit* type, the subject inspires room air and expires into some form of container: the entire volume of expired air is measured and a sample analyzed for its carbon dioxide and oxygen per-centages. Among the closed-circuit types of apparatus are those of Regnault and Reiset, and of Benedict and associates. The Douglas bag and Tissot methods are of the open-circuit type. In Haldane's method for small animals, although it is of the open-circuit or air-current type, the carbon dioxide is absorbed and weighed.

CLOSED-CIRCUIT METHODS. In the Regnault-Reiset type of apparatus, the air is circulated through a closed system of which a chamber, large enough to accommodate the subject, forms a part. Only a few institutions on this continent, such as the Russell Sage Institute in New York and the Nutrition Laboratory at Washington, possess an apparatus of this type (Atwater-Rosa) suitable for metabolic studies upon man. It is usually combined with an apparatus of the direct type. The construction of a closed circuit type of apparatus for laboratory animals is not, however, such a difficult matter (fig. 63.5). The air in the system is rebreathed repeatedly, carbon dioxide and water vapor being removed and oxygen supplied to replace that consumed. The quantity of carbon dioxide eliminated by the animal is given by the difference between the weights of the soda-lime container at the beginning and end of the experiment. Oxygen is

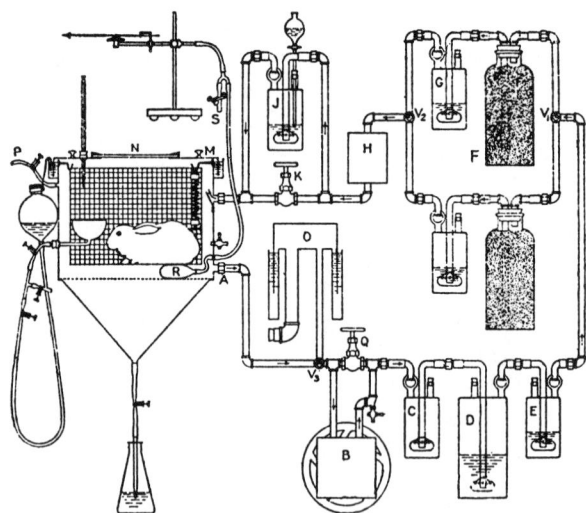

FIG. 63.5. Schematic outline of respiration apparatus for small animals. The air leaves the chamber at A and after passing through the rotary blower B, which keeps the ventilating current in motion, is forced through the glass vessel C, which serves as a safety trap. The air then passes through the bottles D and E containing sulphuric acid to remove the moisture. The air, now water-free, but containing the CO_2 produced by the animal and lacking the O_2 which the animal has consumed, passes into the 2-way valve V_1, where it may be deflected into the bottle F containing soda lime for the absorption of CO_2. The moisture gained from the soda lime is absorbed by sulphuric acid in bottle G. The air then passes through a second 2-way tap V_2 to H containing dry sodium bicarbonate which removes the traces of acid vapor taken up by the air in passing through bottle G. J is a glass vessel containing water which supplies sufficient moisture to the air for the comfort of the animal. K is a by-pass valve. The chamber is constructed of copper and has a cover with a water seal M. N is a glass plate through which the animal can be observed. O is a spirometer attached to the system on the intake side of the rotary blower B. (From F. G. Benedict.)

run into the system from a cylinder and measured by means of a gas meter or by weighing the cylinder at the beginning and end of the experiment. The air in the chamber is analyzed at the end of the observation in order to ensure that no change in its composition has occurred.

In other closed-circuit methods, such as the one described below, the subject is not enclosed within a chamber; he simply breathes in and out of the apparatus through a connecting tube.

Clinical types of closed-circuit apparatus. In the earlier clinical types the subject was connected by means of a mouthpiece and flexible tubing to the closed system and both carbon dioxide elimination and oxygen usage were determined. In the type most commonly used today—the Benedict-Roth apparatus (figs. 63.6 and 63.7)—the heat production is calculated from the oxygen consumption alone. In order to purify the air the carbon dioxide is absorbed by soda-lime but the amount of this gas eliminated is not measured. In determining the basal metabolism (p. 1286) the subject lies upon a couch and breathes in and out of the instrument through a mouthpiece and two wide-bore tubes (inspiratory and expiratory) provided with valves. The nose is clipped. The main part of the instrument consists of a bell-type spirometer. This is a hollow double-walled cylindrical vessel. In the narrow space between the two walls fits a second inverted hollow cylindrical vessel or bell. The bell is counterpoised so that it rides easily up or down in the annular space between the two walls.

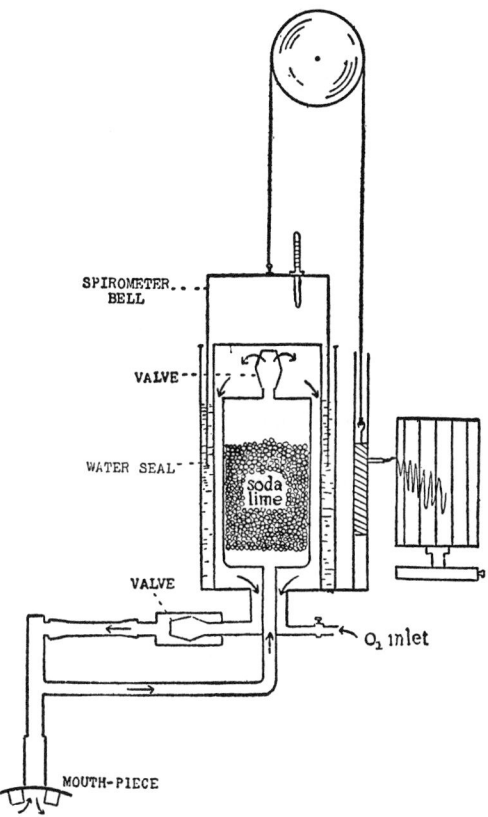

FIG. 63.7. Sectional view of Benedict-Roth closed-circuit respiration apparatus.

This space contains water which acts as a seal. At the commencement of the experiment, sufficient oxygen is admitted from an oxygen cylinder to raise a pointer on the spirometer bell to the zero mark upon an adjoined scale which has been calibrated to oxygen volumes. The breathing of the subject through the inspiratory and expiratory tubes keeps the air circulating freely through the system. As oxygen is consumed the spirometer falls and from the difference in the levels of the pointer at the beginning and end of the experiment the oxygen usage is calculated. The volume of oxygen used, dry and reduced to standard temperature and pressure, is then calculated. The heat production is found by reference to the table of respiratory quotients given on page 1278.

The R.Q. of the subject is not determined. The average R.Q. in the postabsorptive state (see p. 1286) (0.82) is assumed. It will be seen from table 63.7 that at this R.Q. the calorie equivalent of 1 liter of oxygen is 4.825.

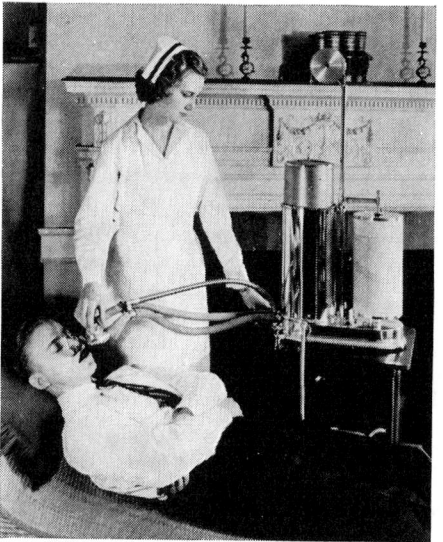

FIG. 63.6. Benedict-Roth apparatus (courtesy of Warren E. Collins, Inc., Boston).

OPEN-CIRCUIT OR AIR-CURRENT METHODS. In the *Haldane type* of calorimeter (which is suit-

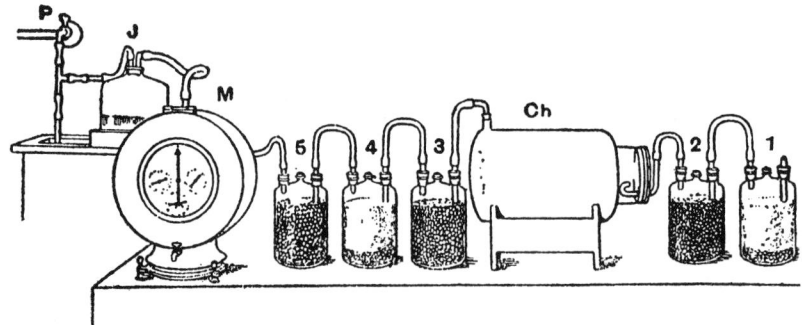

F͟IG͟. 63.8. Haldane's respiration apparatus. 1 and 4, soda lime; 2, 3 and 5, pumice stone soaked in sulphuric acid; Ch, animal chamber; M, meter. J is an inverted bell-jar standing in a trough of water; it serves to prevent sudden excess of negative pressure and to indicate the pressure actually employed. P, pump. (After Haldane.)

able only for small animals, mice, rats or rabbits) a current of air is drawn through the system (fig. 63.8). Carbon dioxide and water are removed from the air before it enters the chamber and again after its exit therefrom. The carbon dioxide absorber on the outgoing current of air is weighed at the commencement and end of the experiment as in the Regnault-Reiset method, in order to obtain the quantity of carbon dioxide eliminated. The system with the exception of the first pair of absorbers and including the animal is then weighed. Since only oxygen has entered this part of the system (the air being

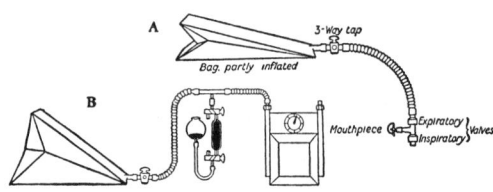

F͟IG͟. 63.9. Showing A, Douglas bag and tubing; B, Douglas bag with sampling bulb attached and gas meter for measuring the total volume of expired air (after Douglas and Priestley); C, subject equipped with Douglas bag apparatus during running or other types of muscular exercise. (After Hill.)

CO_2-free and dry) the gain in weight during the experiment gives the quantity of oxygen consumed by the animal.

The Douglas bag and Tissot methods (gasometric methods). In these methods the subject inspires *atmospheric* air and expires into a bag (Douglas method) or into a large bell-type spirometer (Tissot method). At the end of the experiment the total volume of expired air is measured and samples are analyzed for carbon dioxide and oxygen (figs. 63.9 and 63.10).

Gas analysis. The sample of expired air is drawn into the graduated burette of a Haldane gas analysis apparatus, saturated with water vapor and its volume measured (fig. 63.11). It is then passed back and forth through the bulb containing potassium hydroxide solution, which absorbs the carbon dioxide. It is then measured again. The difference between the two measurements gives the volume of carbon dioxide in the sample. Next, the oxygen is removed by passing the sample through a solution of potassium pyrogallate. The sample is measured a third time and the shrinkage in volume as shown by the difference between the second and third readings gives the quantity of oxygen absorbed. From the data so obtained the percentages of carbon dioxide and oxygen in the sample of air are calculated.

Calculation of results. The following illustrates the steps in an actual metabolism experiment, using the Douglas or Tissot method.

Period of observation 10 minutes, barometer 751.5 mm. Hg.

Volume of expired air as determined by passing the expired air, collected in a bag, through a meter (Douglas method) or as indicated by spirometer (Tissot method) = 70 liters.

Temperature of expired air (in meter or spirometer) 20°C.

The volume of the gases must be reduced to standard conditions, namely, to 760 mm. Hg pressure and to 273° absolute temperature (i.e., to 0°C.), and dry (i.e., the pressure of water vapor must be deducted from the barometer reading). The pressure of water vapor at 20°C. is 17.5 mm. So the corrected reading is;—

$$751.5 - 17.5 = 734.0 \text{ mm.}$$

The volume of the expired air at standard temperature and pressure (S.T.P.) and dry is therefore

$$70 \times \frac{734}{760} \times \frac{273}{273 + 20}$$

or

$70 \times 0.8993 = 62.95$ liters during the period of observation (10 minutes) or 6295 cc. per minute. In practice these detailed calculations are avoided by reference to table 63.9 which gives the required factor by which the observed volume is multiplied in order to reduce it to standard conditions and dry.

Result of gas analyses:

Expired air	Inspired air
CO_2 = 3.50 per cent	CO_2 = 0.04 per cent
O_2 = 16.90 per cent	O_2 = 20.93 per cent
N_2 = 79.60 per cent	N_2 = 79.03 per cent

Since the O_2 percentages in expired and inspired airs are 16.90 and 20.93, respectively, it might be

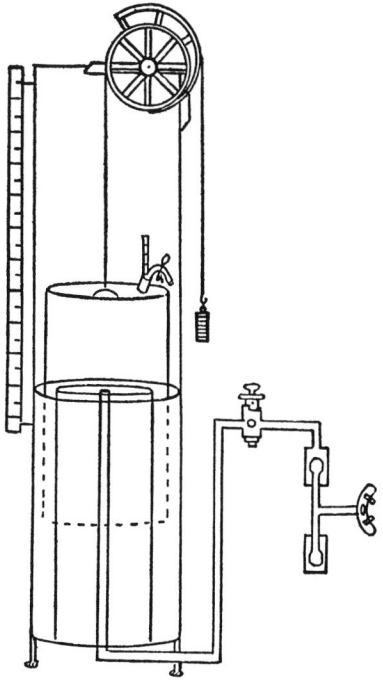

FIG. 63.10. Diagram of Tissot spirometer

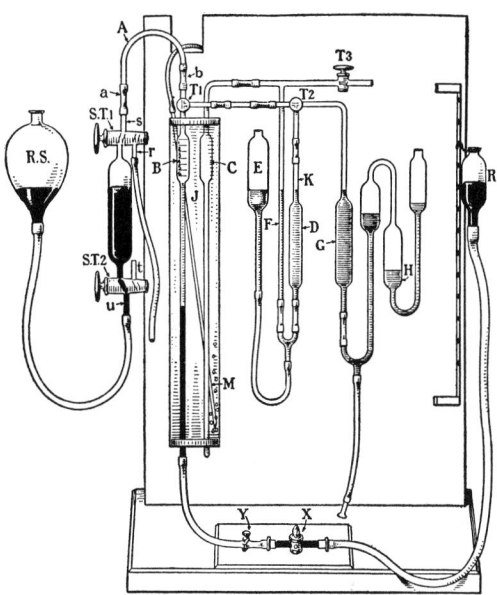

FIG. 63.11. Haldane gas analysis apparatus (small pattern) showing a gas sampler in position. A, glass tube connected to gas sampler; B, gas burette; C, control tube; D, caustic soda absorption pipette; E, caustic soda reservoir; F, caustic pressure tube; G, pyrogallol absorption pipette; H, caustic soda seal; J, waterjacket; M, aeration tube; R, mercury reservoir; X, one-way tap to control movements of mercury; Y, screw clip for fine adjustments of pressure in K after the tap X has been closed; R.S., mercury reservoir for gas sampler; S.T.1 and S.T.2, taps of gas sampler with double ports; r and t, side tubes by means of which, when S.T.1 or S.T.2 are placed in position, the "dead spaces" of these taps and of the tube A can be filled with mercury; a, rubber connection, any air bubble in A may be expelled here as described in text; F, pressure tube for control; K, pressure tube for burette. Note T3 is usually a three-way tap, placed at the junction of the vertical and horizontal tubes. (From Lamb, *An Introduction to Human Experimental Physiology*.)

thought that $20.93 - 16.90$ would give the percentage of O_2 absorbed. It will be noticed, however, that the percentage of N_2 is higher in the expired than in the inspired air. Nitrogen is inert insofar as respiration is concerned, being neither produced nor retained in the body, i.e., its absolute amount is not altered. Therefore, its greater proportion in the expired air can only mean that the volume of the inspired air (which of course was not measured) must have been greater than that of the *dry* expired air. So then, the volume of O_2 inspired must also have been greater than appeared from the analysis of the expired air. The cause of the discrepancy is that part of the absorbed oxygen has combined with hydrogen and in other ways, and so has not appeared as CO_2. The extent to which the O_2 in the inspired air exceeds that shown by the analysis of the expired air is proportional to the increased percentage of N_2 in the latter.

TABLE 63.9

Table for reduction to 0°C. and 760 mm. Hg and dry of 1 liter of air saturated with humidity, from 10° to 25°C., and 740 to 780 mm. (29.13 inches to 30.71 inches) of mercury

(Intermediate values may be obtained by interpolation)

Temperature	Barometer																					Temperature
	29.13 740	29.21 742	29.29 744	29.37 746	29.45 748	29.53 750	29.60 752	29.68 754	29.76 756	29.84 758	29.92 760	30.00 762	30.08 764	30.16 766	30.24 768	30.31 770	30.39 772	30.47 774	30.55 776	30.63 778	30.71 780	
10	927.7	930.2	932.6	935.1	937.6	940.4	942.9	945.4	947.9	950.5	953.0	955.6	958.0	960.6	963.1	965.7	968.3	970.8	973.3	975.9	978.4	10
11	923.6	926.1	928.5	931.0	933.5	936.3	938.8	941.3	943.8	946.4	948.9	951.5	953.9	956.5	959.0	961.6	964.1	966.6	969.1	971.9	974.2	11
12	919.5	921.8	924.2	926.7	929.3	931.8	934.3	936.8	939.4	942.0	944.4	947.0	949.4	951.9	954.4	957.0	959.5	962.0	964.5	967.1	969.6	12
13	915.4	918.0	920.4	922.9	925.4	928.0	930.4	932.9	935.5	938.1	940.5	943.1	945.5	948.1	950.6	953.1	955.6	958.1	960.6	963.2	965.7	13
14	911.3	913.9	916.3	918.8	921.3	923.8	926.2	928.8	931.3	933.9	936.2	938.9	941.3	943.8	946.3	948.8	951.3	953.8	956.3	958.8	961.3	14
15	907.1	909.7	912.1	914.6	917.1	919.6	922.0	924.5	927.1	929.7	932.0	934.6	937.0	939.5	942.0	944.4	947.0	949.6	952.0	954.5	957.0	15
16	902.9	905.5	907.9	910.4	912.9	915.4	917.8	920.3	922.8	925.4	927.8	930.4	932.8	935.2	937.7	940.1	942.6	945.2	947.6	950.1	952.6	16
17	898.7	901.3	903.7	906.2	908.7	911.1	913.5	916.0	918.5	921.1	923.5	926.0	928.5	930.9	933.4	935.8	938.3	940.9	943.3	945.8	948.3	17
18	894.5	897.1	899.5	902.0	904.5	906.8	909.2	911.8	914.2	916.8	919.2	921.7	924.2	926.6	929.1	931.5	933.9	936.5	938.9	941.4	943.9	18
19	890.2	892.7	895.1	897.6	900.1	902.5	904.9	907.4	909.9	912.5	914.8	917.2	919.7	922.2	924.7	927.1	929.5	932.0	934.4	936.9	939.4	19
20	885.9	888.4	890.8	893.3	895.8	898.1	900.5	902.9	905.3	907.7	910.4	912.8	915.2	917.7	920.2	922.6	925.0	927.5	930.3	932.5	935.0	20
21	881.8	884.3	886.7	889.2	891.7	894.0	896.4	898.9	901.3	903.9	906.2	908.6	911.1	913.5	916.0	918.4	920.8	923.3	925.7	928.2	930.7	21
22	877.1	879.5	881.9	884.4	886.9	889.0	891.4	894.1	896.6	899.2	901.4	903.8	906.3	908.7	911.2	913.6	916.0	918.4	920.9	923.4	926.0	22
23	872.6	875.0	877.4	879.9	882.4	884.7	887.1	889.5	892.0	894.6	896.9	899.2	901.7	904.1	906.6	909.0	911.4	913.8	916.3	918.8	921.3	23
24	868.1	870.6	873.0	875.5	878.0	880.1	882.5	885.0	887.5	890.1	892.3	894.6	897.1	899.5	902.0	904.4	906.8	909.2	911.6	914.0	916.5	24
25	863.5	865.9	868.3	870.8	873.3	875.7	878.1	880.5	882.9	885.5	887.9	890.1	892.6	895.0	897.4	899.8	902.1	904.5	906.9	909.3	911.7	25

TABLE 63.10

Volumes of oxygen in inspired air corresponding to 100 volumes of expired air with different percentages of nitrogen

Percentage Nitrogen in Expired Air	Volumes of Oxygen in Inspired Air	Percentage Nitrogen in Expired Air	Volumes of Oxygen in Inspired Air
78.5	20.80	79.6	21.09
78.6	20.83	79.7	21.12
78.7	20.85	79.8	21.14
78.8	20.88	79.9	21.17
78.9	20.91	80.0	21.20
79.0	20.93	80.1	21.22
79.1	20.96	80.2	21.25
79.2	20.99	80.3	21.28
79.3	21.01	80.4	21.30
79.4	21.04	80.5	21.33
79.5	21.07		

Instead of the inspired air having contained 20.93 volumes of O_2 for every 100 volumes of air expired, it must have contained

$$20.93 \times \frac{79.60}{79.03}, \text{ or } 0.265 \text{ (a constant factor)} \times 79.60$$

$$= 21.09 \text{ volumes.}$$

Therefore the O_2 absorption is

$$\frac{21.09 - 16.90}{100} \times 6295 = 264 \text{ cc. per minute.}$$

The calculation is abbreviated by the use of table 63.10.

The quantity of CO_2 produced may be calculated without correction since its percentage in the inspired air is negligible. Hence:

$$\frac{3.50 - 0.04}{100} \times 6295 = 218 \text{ cc. per minute.}$$

The respiratory quotient is therefore

$$\frac{\text{Vol. } CO_2 \text{ expired} = 218}{\text{Vol. } O_2 \text{ consumed} = 264} = 0.82$$

The calorie values of O_2 and CO_2 are given in, or can be calculated from, table 63.7, p. 1278. The heat production may be calculated from either of these values. For example, when the R.Q. is 0.82 the calorie value of 1000 cc. of O_2 is 4.825. Therefore, 264 cc. of O_2 represent a heat production of $4.825 \times (264/1000) = 1.27$ Cal. per minute or 76.20 Cal. per hour.

The Energy Balance

Rubner placed a full-grown dog in a calorimeter in which the heat production could be measured directly. He fed the animal measured

amounts of food for which the actual heat values had been calculated. The heat generated by the animal during the experiment, which extended in most cases over several days, when added to the heat equivalent of the excreta was found to agree, within about 1 per cent, with the calculated heat value of the ingested food. In other words, the energy intake and output balanced and the application to the body of the law of the conservation of energy was demonstrated (see table 63.11). Corresponding results were obtained by Atwater for man.

Rubner also demonstrated that the heat production of an animal as *calculated from the respiratory exchanges* (indirect calorimetry) agrees within 1 per cent with that *measured by direct calorimetry*, a brilliant confirmation of the conclusion arrived at by Lavoisier 100 years earlier.

Rubner fed 100 grams dried muscle powder (5.5 grams ash) with the following results:

Material balance	C	H	O	N
Content in protein fed (grams).......	50.50	7.60	20.97	15.40
Excreted in urine...	9.63	2.52	10.90	15.16
Excreted in feces...	1.67	0.25	0.54	0.24
Total in urine and feces...........	11.30	2.77	11.44	15.40
Balance for respiration..........	39.20	4.83	9.53	

Energy balance

In 100 grams muscle powder (bomb)..................... 534.50 Calories

Lost in excreta {urine... 112.94 Calories / feces.... 16.83

Total lost............. 129.77

Fuel value to body........ 404.73 Calories

TABLE 63.11*

Comparison of heat actually produced from metabolism of food with that calculated.

Food	Number of Days	Heat Calculated	Heat Directly Determined	Difference in Percentage
		Cal.	*Cal.*	
Starvation.....	5	1296.3	1305.2	+0.68
	2	1091.2	1056.6	−3.17
Fat............	5	1510.1	1495.3	−0.98
Meat and fat..	8	2492.4	2488.0	−0.17
	12	3985.4	3958.4	−0.68
Meat..........	6	2249.8	2276.9	+1.20
	7	4780.8	4769.3	−0.23

* From Rubner. (Ztschr. Biol., **30**, 73, 1894.)

(Energy lost per gram urine-N

$$= 112.9/15.16 = 7.45 \text{ Calories})$$

N in muscle protein

$$= 15.40 \times 100/94.5 = 16.3 \text{ per cent.}$$

Since the urinary N arises from the N in dietary protein it is obvious that 1 gram urinary N represents $100/16.3 = 6.14$ grams dietary protein absorbed by the body. Energy loss per gram urine-N ($\equiv 6.14$ grams protein) $\equiv 7.45$ Calories.

∴ Energy loss in urine per gram *protein* $\equiv 1.21$ Calories. Rubner even made corrections for the heat of imbibition of the protein and heat of solution of urea (2.69 and 1.99 Calories, respectively), to give a value of 400.05 as the number of Calories available from 100 grams of dried meat solids (94.5 grams of muscle protein). The physiologically available energy per gram of muscle protein is thus $400/94.5 = 4.23$ Calories.

It is sometimes useful to be able to estimate the energy obtained from dietary protein using the so-called calorie equivalent of each gram of urinary nitrogen. In Rubner's experiment 15.16 grams of urinary N were excreted when 400 Calories were liberated from the ingested protein. Thus each gram of urinary N corresponds to about 26.4 Calories retained by the body.

Atwater and his colleagues in America analyzed urines from 46 persons and measured the heat of combustion of the organic residue. For every gram of *nitrogen in the urine* they found unoxidized material sufficient to yield 7.9 Calories. This value is close to Rubner's estimate of 7.5. It represents about 1.25 Calories per gram of protein absorbed, *if the person is in nitrogen equilibrium.*

Although nitrogen in the urine can only arise from protein that has been absorbed, some writers have erroneously applied the correction to the protein *eaten*! Obviously, if digestibility is low or if the person or animal under study is retaining nitrogen for growth or losing nitrogen as a result of a wasting disease, different values would be obtained per gram of protein ingested. The use of the factor 1.25 Calories per gram of protein for the loss in the urine is hallowed by convention, although it is based on work done over 50 years ago with diets (the details of which are unknown today) fed to adult men. The effects of individual foodstuffs on males and females at different stages of growth should be determined, since the available energy doubtless varies considerably with age.

The Basal Metabolic Rate (B.M.R.)

This is the term applied to the heat production of a subject who, though awake, is as nearly as possible at complete *muscular* and *mental rest*, and is in the *postabsorptive* state (i.e., from 12 to 14 hours after a light meal when, it is assumed, the digestive processes are quiescent). The room temperature should be 20°C. For example, the prospective subject of a basal rate determination is directed to refrain from undue muscular exertion or fatiguing effort of any kind for 24 hours previously. A light meal with the minimum amount of protein is taken not later than 7 o'clock the night before the test which is undertaken at about 9 o'clock in the morning. For a period of 30 minutes or so before, as well as during the test the subject should be lying down comfortably in a room with subdued lighting.

The apparatus most commonly employed for the determination of the basal metabolic rate in the clinic is the instrument of Benedict and Roth (p. 1281). Tissot's method or the bag method of Douglas is also sometimes used.

Basal Metabolic Rate Standards

We have seen that the metabolism is proportional to the body's surface area rather than to its weight (p. 1279). Of two men of the same weight, one tall and lean and the other short and stout, the former will have a greater heat production. It is possible that this explains, in part at least, why a man of thin build often eats more than a stouter man of about the same weight. Since normal adults do not differ very greatly in size and shape, it may be stated as an approximation that the heat production of the human body is one Calorie per kilogram per hour. But for the reasons just given it is much more accurate to express the basal metabolism in terms of body surface. Thus, the average basal rate of normal men between the ages of 25 and 50 years is from 40 to 37 Calories per square meter of body surface per hour. This value is constant for all normal men whether they are tall, short, thin or stout, large or small. Knowing a subject's height and weight his surface area can be determined at a glance from the chart (fig. 63.12), or from table 63.12; or it may be calculated from the height-weight formula.[7] The average surface area for adults in Canada and the United States is about 1.6 square meters for women and 1.8 for men; the total basal heat

[7] The formula introduced by Meeh and modified by Du Bois and Du Bois is as follows:
$$A = W^{0.425} \times H^{0.725} \times 71.84 \text{ (a constant)},$$
where A = surface area in square centimeters, W = weight in kilograms, and H = height in centimeters.

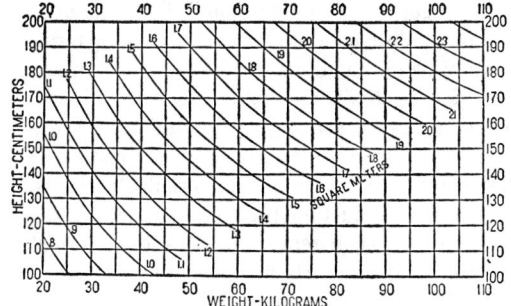

FIG. 63.12. Chart for determining surface area in man in square meters. (After Du Bois.) Example weight 60 kilograms, height 170 cm. = 1.70 sq. m.

production of the majority of normal adults ranges from 1400 to 1800 Calories per day.

The heat production per square meter of body surface is arrived at by dividing the value for the total heat production per hour of the subject, as determined by one or other of the methods already described, by the figure for the surface area. For example, a man 175 cm. tall weighing 75 kg. has a surface area of 1.91 sq. meters. His total heat production is, say, 76.20 Calories per hour. His heat production per square meter per hour is therefore

$$76.20/1.91 = 39.8 \text{ Calories}$$

Having obtained this figure it is customary to express the B.M.R. as normal or as a percentage above (+) or below (−) the normal. Thus, in the foregoing example the rate would be said to

be normal. If it were 30 Calories per square meter per hour it would be expressed as −25 per cent and if 50 Calories as +25 per cent. The age and sex must also be considered since 39.8 Calories per square meter, though normal for a full-grown man of 25 years or so, would be above normal for a woman of the same age and below normal for a child (see below).

Tanner has pointed out that more recent studies of "per-surface area" and "per kilo of body weight" ratios, so widely used in physiology (e.g., for expressing B.M.R.'s, oxygen consumption, cardiac output, glomerular filtration rate, drug dosage, etc.) are theoretically fallacious, being a special case of the condition known to statisticians as the spurious correlation of indices. Although the values often have practical utility, extrapolations based on these ratios have led to the invention of new (nonexistent) clinical syndromes.

CONDITIONS WHICH INFLUENCE THE BASAL METABOLIC RATE

A. Physiological

1. AGE AND SEX. The heat production per square meter of body surface diminishes progressively from infancy to old age, being about 50 Cal. per square meter per hour at the age of ten or twelve and about 32 Cal. at 90 years. The metabolism of the new-born is much lower (25 Cal.) than that of infants a few weeks older. Premature infants have a lower rate than those

TABLE 63.12

Relation of height and weight to surface area (After Du Bois)

Height in centimeters	Weight in Kilograms																
	25	30	35	40	45	50	55	60	65	70	75	80	85	90	95	100	105
200							1.84	1.91	1.97	2.03	2.09	2.15	2.21	2.26	2.31	2.36	2.41
195						1.73	1.80	1.87	1.93	1.99	2.05	2.11	2.17	2.22	2.27	2.32	2.37
190			1.56	1.63	1.70	1.77	1.84	1.90	1.96	2.02	2.08	2.13	2.18	2.23	2.28	2.33	
185			1.53	1.60	1.67	1.74	1.80	1.86	1.92	1.98	2.04	2.09	2.14	2.19	2.24	2.29	
180			1.49	1.57	1.64	1.71	1.77	1.83	1.89	1.95	2.00	2.05	2.10	2.15	2.20	2.25	
175	1.19	1.28	1.36	1.46	1.53		1.67	1.73	1.79	1.85	1.91	1.96	2.01	2.06	2.11	2.16	2.21
170	1.17	1.26	1.34	1.43	1.50	1.57	1.63	1.69	1.75	1.81	1.86	1.91	1.96	2.01	2.06	2.11	
165	1.14	1.23	1.31	1.40	1.47	1.54	1.60	1.66	1.72	1.78	1.83	1.88	1.93	1.98	2.03	2.07	
160	1.12	1.21	1.29	1.37	1.44	1.50	1.56	1.62	1.68	1.73	1.78	1.83	1.88	1.93	1.98		
155	1.09	1.18	1.26	1.33	1.40	1.46	1.52	1.58	1.64	1.69	1.74	1.79	1.84	1.89			
150	1.06	1.15	1.23	1.30	1.36	1.42	1.48	1.54	1.60	1.65	1.70	1.75	1.80				
145	1.03	1.12	1.20	1.27	1.33	1.39	1.45	1.51	1.56	1.61	1.66	1.71					
140	1.00	1.09	1.17	1.24	1.30	1.36	1.42	1.47	1.52	1.57							
135	0.97	1.06	1.14	1.20	1.26	1.32	1.38	1.43	1.48								
130	0.95	1.04	1.11	1.17	1.23	1.29	1.35	1.40									
125	0.93	1.01	1.08	1.14	1.20	1.26	1.31	1.36									
120	0.91	0.98	1.04	1.10	1.16	1.22	1.27										

TABLE 63.13

Basal and total metabolic rates of males and females
(From Cruickshank, compiled from Boothby
and associates)

Age	B.M.R. Calories per sq. Meter per Hour		Total Basal Metabolism in Calories per 24 Hours		Total Calories per Day	
	Males	Females	Males	Females	Males	Females
Birth	30	30	288	288	440	440
1	55	52	660	624	1000	1000
2	57	53	780	725	1200	1200
3	55	52	845	798	—	—
5	53	52	915	886	1600	1600
8	51.8	47.0	1143	993	2000	2000
11	47.2	45.2	1268	1193	2500	2500
12	46.8	43.3	1347	1267	—	—
13	46.5	42.0	1428	1330	—	—
14	46.4	41.5	1537	1391	3200	2800
15	46.0	40.0	1667	1420	—	—
16	45.7	38.8	1764	1434	3500	2600
18	43.2	37.5	1783	1440	3800	2500
20	41.6	36.3	1756	1437	3500	2400
25	40.3	36.0	1760	1442	3000	2400
40	38.0	35.0	1641	1344	3000	2400

born at full term. Females have a metabolic rate a little lower than that of males in the same age group. The relationship of heat production to age and sex is given in table 63.13.

2. RACE AND CLIMATE. Cramer and Lusk were both of the opinion that climate does not influence metabolism. In spite of suggestions by several workers that the B.M.R. of Eskimos is elevated and that that of persons in the tropics is lower than normal, more carefully controlled studies have shown that other explanations usually account for the findings. Seasonal fluctuations do occur which have contributed to the difficulty of drawing conclusions.

3. HABITS. Owing to the greater development of their muscular tissues athletes and laborers have in general a higher B.M.R. than persons leading a sedentary life.

4. PREGNANCY. The basal metabolic rate of the pregnant woman shows little change until the sixth or seventh month when the fetus causes an appreciable increase in the weight of the mother. The metabolism of the mother from this time to term is the sum of her own metabolism in the nonpregnant state and that of the fetus. It was found by Murlin and Carpenter, for example, that the metabolism of the new-born infant and the postpartum metabolism of the mother

added together practically equaled the metabolism of the pregnant state near the end of term. Boothby and Sandiford estimated the surface area of the fetus throughout gestation and concluded that the excess heat production of the pregnant state was derived from the fetus and the increased mass of the maternal structures, the energy production per unit of mass of the maternal organism remaining constant. Normal pregnancy, then, exerts little or no *specific* effect upon the basal metabolic rate.

5. DIET. The nature of the diet seems to have little influence upon the B.M.R., although in strict vegetarians it is said to be some 11 per cent lower than that of meat eaters.

6. VARIATIONS IN BAROMETRIC PRESSURES. A moderate reduction in oxygen pressure does not affect the metabolic rate, but a reduction in the latter occurs, which varies by from 5 to 25 per cent in different subjects, when the barometric pressure falls to half an atmosphere (O_2 pressure 75 mm. Hg). This is around the barometric pressure at which mountain sickness usually appears (ch. 54). Breathing excessively high tensions of oxygen does not raise the B.M.R. above the normal level. That is, the oxygen consumption cannot be raised simply by increasing the oxygen supply.

7. CHEMICAL SUBSTANCES. Caffeine, adrenaline, thyroid extract or thyroxine, benzedrine, and dinitrophenol raise the basal metabolic rate. Smoking a cigarette, especially if the smoke is inhaled, increases the metabolism of most subjects, the average increase being around 9 per cent.

B. Pathological

1. The B.M.R. is below normal in the following conditions:

Starvation and undernutrition (ch. 69).

Obesity due to pituitary or hypothalamic disorders (chs. 69 and 74).

Hypothyroidism (myxedema, ch. 75).

Addison's disease

Lipoid nephrosis

2. Conditions with a high B.M.R.:

Hyperthyroidism (exophthalmic goiter, ch. 75).

Fever (ch. 70). The basal rate is raised about 7 per cent for each degree (Fahrenheit) rise in temperature.

Diabetes insipidus (ch. 74).

Cardio-renal disease with dyspnea (+25 to +50 per cent).

Leukemia (+21 to +80 per cent).

Polycythemia (+10 to +40 per cent).

INFLUENCES WHICH RAISE THE METABOLISM
OF A NORMAL INDIVIDUAL ABOVE
THE BASAL LEVEL

We have already seen that the basal metabolism is defined as the heat production of a subject as nearly as possible at complete physical and mental rest, some hours after food and with the room temperature at about 20°C. These three factors—muscular exercise, the ingestion of food and environmental temperature—have a powerfully stimulating influence upon metabolism.

Muscular and mental effort. Even light muscular exertion, e.g., sitting, standing, dressing and undressing, sewing, etc., raises the metabolism by from 25 to 60 per cent above the basal level. Moderate exercise, such as walking, swimming, housework, light carpentry, etc., raises it from 100 to 200 per cent, and very hard work may increase it from 10 to 15 times over the basal level. Henderson and Haggard found that in three members of the Yale University boat crew, the total heat production during rest amounted to 1.65, 1.42 and 2.4 Calories per minute, respectively. The corresponding values during strenuous exercise on a rowing machine were 18.90, 21.83 and 29.37 Calories per minute. The extra energy expenditure caused by various occupations is shown in table 63.14. Mental effort, on the other hand, causes an almost negligible increase in metabolism. Benedict, for instance, after a series of experiments in which intense mental effort was expended in solving mathematical problems found an increase of only 3 or 4 per cent. He states, "The cloistered scholar at his books may be surprised to learn that the extra Calories needed for one hour of intense mental effort would be completely met by the eating of one oyster cracker or one-half of a salted peanut." The *basal* oxygen consumption of the brain however, is high, amounting to about 10 per cent of that of the entire body. *Strong emotion* may raise the metabolism from 5 to 10 per cent above the basal level.

During *sleep*, when the muscles are more completely relaxed than is possible during the waking day, the metabolism falls below the basal level. The reduction amounts to from 10 to 13 per cent. (Strictly speaking, the metabolism during restful sleep, since it is the physiological minimum, *is* the true basal level.) If sleep is disturbed and associated with muscular activity the metabolism may be as high as or even higher than

TABLE 63.14

Extra Calories of metabolism per hour attributable to occupation

(After Harrop)

	Extra Calories per Hour
Occupations of men:	
Tailor	44
Bookbinder	81
Shoemaker	90
Metal worker, filing and hammering	141
Painter of furniture	145
Carpenter making a table	164
Stonemason chiselling a tombstone	300
Man sawing wood	378
Occupations of women:	
Seamstress, needlework	6
Typist, 50 words per minute	24
Seamstress, using sewing machine	57
Bookbinder	63
Housemaid (moderate work)	81
Laundress (moderate work)	124
Housemaid (hard work)	157
Laundress (hard work)	214

the "resting level" conventionally referred to as the basal level.

The influence of *food* and of *environmental temperature* (p. 1309 and ch. 70) upon metabolism are dealt with elsewhere.

REFERENCES

BLOCK, R. J., AND BOLLING, D. The amino acid composition of proteins and foods, ed. 2. Charles C Thomas, Springfield, Ill., 1951.
JACOBS, M. B. The chemical analysis of foods and food products, ed. 2. Van Nostrand Co., Inc., New York, 1951.
MCCANCE, R. A., AND WIDDOWSON, E. M. The chemical composition of foods, ed. 2. Medical Research Council, London, Special Report Series, No. 235, 1946.
WATT, B. K., AND MERRILL, A. L. Composition of foods: raw, processed and prepared. United States Dept. Agriculture, Agriculture Handbook, No. 8, 1950.
WINTON, A. L., AND WINTON, K. B. The structure and composition of foods, Vol. I. John Wylie and Sons, Inc., New York, 1932.
Energy-yielding components of food and computation of calorie values. Food and Agricultural Organization Report, Washington, 1947.
Food composition tables: F.A.O. Nutritional studies. No. 3, Washington, 1949.
Food composition tables: Minerals and vitamins. F.A.O., No. 11, Rome, 1954.
Maize and maize diets: a nutritional survey. F.A.O. Nutritional studies, No. 9, Rome, 1953.
Symposium on the assessment of the energy value

of human and animal foods. Proc. Nutrition Soc., **14**, 130–160, 1955.

Symposium on additives and residues in human foods. Amer. J. Clin. Nutrition, 1961, **9**, 259.

Tables of food values recommended for use in Canada. Nutrition Div., Dept. Health and Welfare, Ottawa, 1951.

GENERAL METABOLISM

LUSK, G. The elements of the science of nutrition W. B. Saunders Co., Philadelphia, 1928.

McCOLLUM, E. V., ORENT-KEILES, E., AND DAY, H. G. The newer knowledge of nutrition, ed. 5. The Macmillan Co., New York, 1940.

McHENRY, E. W. Basic nutrition. Lippincott Co., Montreal, 1957.

McLESTER, J. S., AND DARBY, W. J. Nutrition and diet in health and disease, ed. 7. W. B. Saunders Co., Philadelphia, 1959.

PETERS, J. P., AND VAN SLYKE, D. D. Quantitative clinical chemistry, ed. 2, vol. I. The Williams & Wilkins Co., Baltimore, 1946.

SHERMAN, H. C. Chemistry of food and nutrition, ed. 8. The Macmillan Co., New York, 1952.

ENERGY METABOLISM

ATWATER, W. O., AND BENEDICT, F. G. Carnegie Inst. Washington, Pub. No. 42, 1905.

BENEDICT, F. G., AND COLLINS, W. E. Boston. Med. Surg. J., **183**, 449, 1920.

CATHCART, E. P. AND MARKOWITZ, J. J. Physiol., **63**, 309, 1927.

DOUGLAS, C. G. J. Physiol **42**, xvii, 1911.

HALDANE, J. J. Physiol., **13**, 419, 1892.

Monographs and Reviews

BOOTHBY, W. M. Basal metabolism. Physiol. Rev., **4**, 69, 1924.

DU BOIS, E. F. Basal metabolism in health and disease, ed. 3. Lea & Febiger, Philadelphia, 1936.

DU BOIS, E. F. Energy metabolism. Ann. Rev. Physiol., **16**, 125, 1954

KLEIBER, M. Body size and metabolic rate. Physiol. Rev., **27**, 511, 1947.

KROGH, A. The respiratory exchange of animals and man. Longmans, Green & Co., London, 1916.

PETT, L. B. A Canadian table of average weights. Canad. M. A. J., **72**, 12, 1955.

RICHARDSON, H. B. The respiratory quotient. Physiol. Rev., **9**, 61, 1929.

SWIFT, R. W., AND FRENCH, C. E. Energy metabolism and nutrition. Scarecrow Press, New Brunswick, N. J., 1954.

TANNER, J. M. Fallacy of per-weight and per-surface area standards and their relation to spurious correlation. J. Applied Physiol., **2**, 1, 1949.

Symposium on energy expenditure in man. Proc. Nutrition Soc., **15**, 72–93, 1956.

CHAPTER 64

Protein Metabolism

General Description and Classification of Proteins

Protein is a fundamental component of protoplasm and consequently forms a proportion of all living tissues—animal or vegetable; it is the predominant solid component of some tissues, e.g., muscle. It differs from the other foodstuffs—carbohydrates and fats—in containing (in addition to carbon, hydrogen and oxygen) nitrogen, sulfur and sometimes phosphorus. The molecules of certain proteins contain a prosthetic group, e.g., hemoglobin, glycoproteins, lecithoproteins, nucleoproteins, etc.

A classification and brief description of the various types of protein are given in table 64.1.

The Protein Molecule

The protein molecule is constructed of a number of units linked together. These units or "building stones" are called *amino acids*. They are separated when the protein molecule is hydrolyzed by boiling with acid or alkali, or by the action of the digestive enzymes (proteases). Some 25 different amino acids have been definitely identified as constituents of the protein molecule (see table 64.2). Some proteins contain nearly all of these in varying proportions; in others such as gelatin there are only 14 or 15 different kinds, some *essential* amino acids being missing, whereas such simple proteins as the protamines, sturine and salmine, contain only 3 and 4, respectively. The single amino acids have molecular weights ranging from 75 for glycine to over 200 for tyrosine and nearly 800 for thyroxine. The molecular weights of those proteins composed of large aggregations of amino acids are correspondingly great and extend over a very wide range. The molecular weight of egg albumin, for example, is 45,000, that of hemocyanin, over 6,000,000, and of tobacco mosaic virus, 40,000,000. Some basic proteins, protamines and histones, on the other hand, have molecular weights of about 2000 only.

Protein molecules also vary in shape. Studies of protein structure by means of X-ray diffraction photographs reveal that the molecules of some proteins, such as keratin, collagen and myosin—the so-called *fibrous proteins*—have an elongated fiberlike form, resulting, it is believed, from the extended arrangement of the polypeptide linkages of which the molecule is constructed (see below). When stretched such molecules become elongated still further but return to their previous length when released from the stretching force. The changes in length are described as being due to folding and unfolding of the polypeptide chains in a concertinalike fashion. Other proteins—the *globular proteins*—such as egg albumin and the serum proteins, are composed of molecules which are folded or arranged into a lattice pattern to form a compact structure of a more or less globular shape. Unfolding and the assumption of a permanent extended form is associated with denaturation. Proteins of approximately the same molecular weight may differ considerably in their molecular structure and for this reason may show differences in such physical properties as elasticity, osmotic pressure or viscosity. The fundamental structure of all proteins is believed by Astbury to be fibrous, but the intermolecular arrangement of the polypeptide chains varies widely between different types and in the same protein under different conditions. Thus a variety of patterns is produced.

The average elementary composition of the molecule of a protein such as albumin or globulin is as follows: C, 54 per cent; H, 7 per cent; N, 16 per cent; S, 1 per cent; O, 22 per cent.

The Amino Acids

The amino acids may be regarded as derivatives of the saturated fatty acid series in which the *alpha* hydrogen atom has been replaced by an amino (NH_2) group; in the case of proline and hydroxyproline, the substitution is by an imino

(NH) group. The simplest amino acid is amino-acetic (glycine or glycocoll)

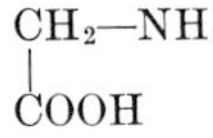

$$CH_2—NH_2$$
$$|$$
$$COOH$$

and the structure of the other amino acids, with the exception of proline and oxyproline, may be represented by the following type formula.

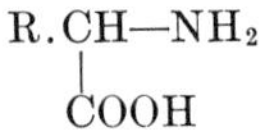

$$R.CH—NH_2$$
$$|$$
$$COOH$$

Amino acids therefore contain a basic (NH_2) group and an acid (COOH) group. R represents a chemical group which varies greatly in size and structure. In the synthesis of the protein molecule chains of amino acids are formed by the linkage of the basic group of one amino acid with the acid group of another and the liberation of a molecule of water. Thus

$$CH_3 \cdot CHNH_2CO[OH \ H]HN \cdot CH_2 \cdot COOH \rightleftharpoons CH_3 \cdot CHNH_2 \cdot CO—HN \cdot CH_2 \cdot COOH + H_2O$$

Alanine   Glycine   Alanylglycine

The junction, CO-NH, whereby amino acids become grouped together, is called the *peptide linkage*. The reverse process, namely, the separation of amino acids from one another is also effected at this link in the chain, a molecule of water first being taken up. This process is called *hydrolysis*.

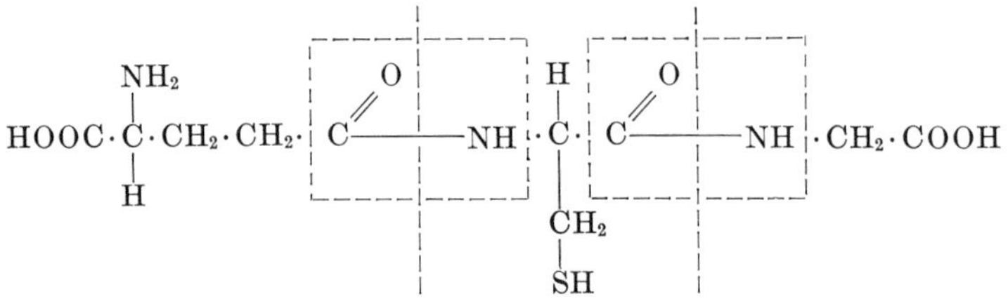

Upon hydrolysis by heating with acid the ring is broken, and in the case of glycine anhydride the dipeptide glycyl-glycine is formed.

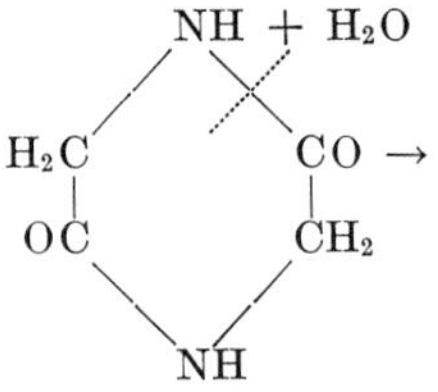

Diketopiperazine
(glycine anhydride)

$$CH_2—CO—NH—CH_2—COOH$$
$$|$$
$$NH_2$$

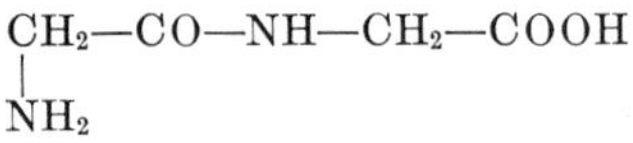

Glycyl-glycine

Terminal amino acids of peptide chains always have a free polar group. At one end a carboxyl group is found (e.g., in the glycine moiety of alanylglycine or of glutathione), at the other end an amino group (in the alanine moiety of alanylglycine, in the glutamic acid portion of glutathione). Diamino or dicarboxylic amino acids will also contribute further free amino or acid groups (as in the free carboxyl of the glutamyl radical of glutathione). By virtue of these it can act either

glutamyl- - - - - - - - - - - - - - - - - -cysteinyl- - - - - - - - - - - - -glycine
(Glutathione—a well known tripeptide)

Besides the chainlike combination of the amino acids in the protein molecule, a smaller proportion are believed to be united to form closed-ring compounds—*diketopiperazines* (*amino acid anhydrides*). The amino acids undergo dehydration and unite by their free amino and carboxyl groups to form the diketopiperazine ring. In the example shown below two glycine molecules join to produce glycine anhydride.

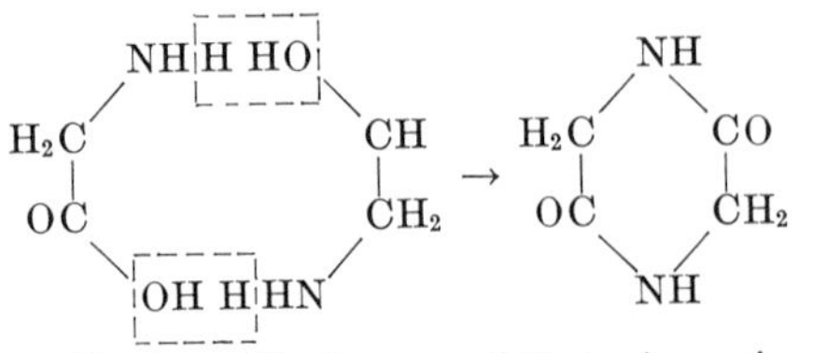

Glycine   Glycine   Diketopiperazine
(glycine anhydride)

as a weak base or as a weak acid. In acid solution it acts as a base yielding cations to form protein chloride, sulfate, etc. When a current passes through the solution the amino acid cation migrates to the cathode or positive pole.[1] In alkaline solution it behaves as an acid, forming anions to produce a proteinate of sodium, potassium etc., In an electric field the amino acid anion migrates to the anode. On account of these opposite reactions, depending upon the acidity or alkalinity of the solution, amino acids and the proteins which they compose are called *amphoteric electrolytes* or *ampholytes* (Gk. *amphō*, both). At a certain hydrogen ion concentration, which varies rather widely

[1] This migration in an electric field of cation and anions to the respective poles is called *electrophoresis* or *iontophoresis*.

TABLE 64.1

Class of Protein	Characteristics	Examples
	A. Simple proteins	
(1) Albumins	Soluble in water and coagulable by heat. Present in both animal and plant tissues	Serum albumin, egg albumin, lactalbumin and various vegetable albumins such as *leucosin* (in wheat, rye and barley), *legumelin* in lentils, soy beans, beans and peas and *phaselin* in kidney beans
(2) Globulins	Soluble in dilute saline solutions; insoluble in water. Animal globulins are coagulated by heat. Vegetable globulins imperfectly or not coagulated by heat	Serum globulin, fibrinogen (and *fibrin*) *vitellin* of egg yolk and vegetable globulins such as *excelsin* (Brazil nuts), *edestin* (hemp), *phaseolin* (kidney beans), *legumin* (peas and lentils) and *tuberin* (potatoes). A number of other vegetable globulins have been isolated and named
(3) Glutelins	Found only in plants. Insoluble in water, saline or alcohol, but soluble in very dilute alkali	Glutenin of wheat, *oryzenin* of rice and *glutelin* of maize
(4) Prolamines or gliadins	Found in cereals (except rice). Soluble in 70 to 90 per cent alcohol; insoluble in water. They contain a large proportion of proline and compounds giving rise to ammonia-nitrogen	Gliadin of wheat, *hordein* of barley and *zein* of maize
(5) Albuminoids or scleroproteins	Especially resistant to the usual reagents. They enter into the construction of protective and connective tissues, e.g., skin, tendons, ligments and bones	Keratin of hair, skin, bone, feathers, tortoise shell and eggshell, *elastin*, *collagen*, *ossein* and *gelatin* of tendons, ligaments, bone, etc.
(6) Histones	Soluble in water and precipitated by ammonia solution and by alkaloids. They contain a large percentage of diamino acids (p. 774)	Globin of hemoglobin, *thymus histone*; *scombron* and *gadus histone* in spermatozoa of mackerel and codfish respectively
(7) Protamines	Found in combination with nucleic acid in heads of fish spermatozoa. Constructed predominantly of diamino acids	Salmine and *sturine* in spermatozoa of salmon and sturgeon respectively

B. Conjugated proteins. Proteins whose molecule is combined with another nonprotein group

(1) Nucleoproteins	Nucleic acid in combination with a protein belonging usually to the class of histones or protamines. Found in cell nuclei	See ch. 47
(2) Chromoproteins	Protein in combination with a pigment (e. g., hematin) containing iron, copper or other metal	Hemoglobin, hemocyanin, etc.
(3) Glycoproteins	Proteins other than nucleoproteins in combination with a carbohydrate group	Mucin in salivary gastric and intestinal secretions; *ovomucoid* of egg white and *chondromucoid* of cartilage
(4) Lipoproteins	Proteins in combination with lipid	Present in plasma, milk, cell nuclei
(5) Phosphoproteins	Proteins other than nucleoproteins and lecithoproteins in combination with a phosphorus-containing group	Caseinogen (and casein), *vitellin* of egg yolk

TABLE 64.1—*Continued*

Class of Protein	Characteristics	Examples

C. *Derivatives of proteins—derived proteins.* These are produced by the action of acids, alkalis or proteolytic enzymes upon certain of the proteins listed above

Class of Protein	Characteristics	Examples
(a) *Primary derivatives*		
(1) *Proteans*	Insoluble products formed in the early stage of the action upon proteins of water, dilute acids and enzymes	
(2) *Metaproteins*	Formed in a later stage of the action of acid or alkali	*Acid* metaprotein, *alkali* metaprotein
(3) *Coagulated proteins*	Formed by the action of heat or of alcohol upon solutions of proteins	
(b) *Secondary derivatives*		
(1) *Proteoses*	Formed by the action of pepsin or trypsin upon proteins. They are soluble in water from which they are precipitated by saturation with ammonium sulfate. They are incoagulable by heat	*Albumose* from albumen, *globulose* from globulin, *caseose* from casein
(2) *Peptones*	These represent a further stage in action of proteolytic enzymes. They are soluble in water but are not precipitated from an aqueous solution by ammonium sulfate. They are not coagulated by heat	
(3) *Peptides, dipeptides, tripeptides* and *polypeptides*	Products formed in the final stages of proteolytic digestion	Glycyl-alanine, leucyl-glutamic acid, etc.

between different proteins, the amino acids are electrically neutral and protein behaves neither as an acid nor as a base. In an electric field no migration either to anode or cathode occurs. The pH at which this occurs is known as the *"isoelectric point"* though the effect rather than being restricted to a point extends over a pH range which with some proteins is considerable. *Isoelectric zone* is therefore a better term (table 64.3). Within the isoelectric zone the solubility of the protein is least; here it is readily precipitated by alcohol, neutral salts and other reagents. Some proteins are quite insoluble at the isoelectric point and precipitate spontaneously. According to the classical conception the electrical neutrality of protein at the isoelectric point was due to ionization of the amino acids being at a minimum or absent, as represented below in formula I. This view has

given place to the *Zwitterion theory*, which more readily explains the experimental findings.

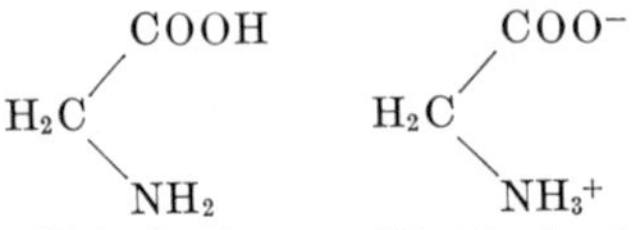

The "Zwitterion" theory. This postulates that the amino acids at the isoelectric point carry equal numbers of positive and negative charges and this accounts for their electrical neutrality. They are called *"zwitterions"* (Ger. *Zwitter*, hemaphrodite) or *dipolar ions* (see formula II above). Much experimental support has been gained for this theory since it was first proposed.

The behavior of an amino acid (glycine) in acid and in alkaline solution according to the two conceptions is illustrated below (on p. 1295). It will be seen that the end result on either side of the isoelectric point is the same according to either view. According, however, to the *Zwitter hypothesis* the ampholyte molecule gives off, at the isoelectric point, *equal numbers* of basic and acid ions, thus leaving ions—the so-called zwitterions—holding equal numbers of negative and positive charges (formula II). Many proteins, e.g., metaproteins, casein, etc., are almost insoluble at the isoelectric point—*isoelectric precipitation.*

Isoelectric glycine

I

$$H_2C \overset{\textstyle COOH}{\underset{\textstyle NH_2}{\big<}}$$

Unionized

II

$$H_2C \overset{\textstyle COO^-}{\underset{\textstyle NH_3^+}{\big<}}$$

"Zwitterion"

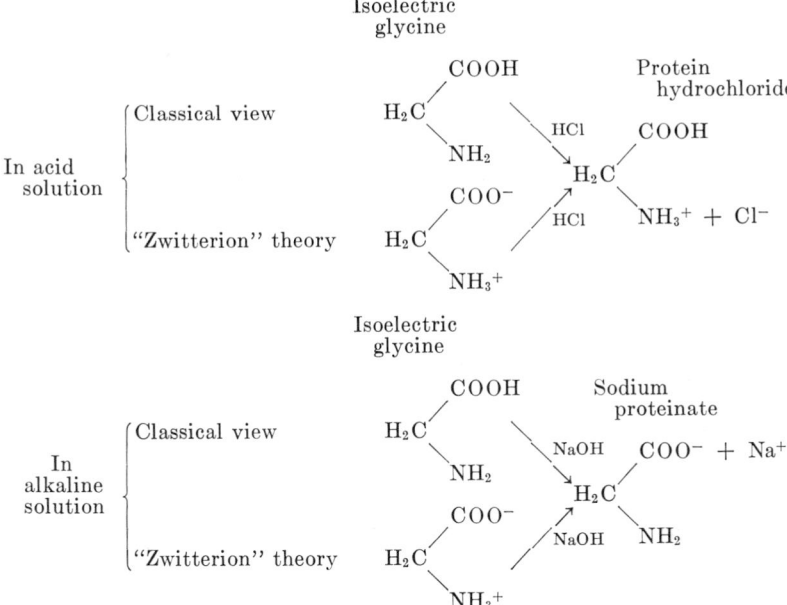

The Absorption of Protein

Under ordinary circumstances only negligible amounts of unchanged protein, or even such of its derivatives as proteoses, peptones and polypeptides, are absorbed into the blood from the alimentary tract. Generally speaking the protein molecule must first be hydrolyzed into its constituent amino acids. These are absorbed from the small intestine but not from the stomach to any significant extent. They enter the circulation mainly through the portal blood; much smaller amounts pass into the lymph (chyle) and hence into the thoracic duct.

Small quantities of certain proteins, e.g., raw egg white and blood serum, are sometimes absorbed from the intestine into the blood stream. They are excreted in the urine to a large extent unchanged. Such absorption which occurs more readily in young animals and children, should be regarded as a defect rather than as a physiological process. Nevertheless, experiments have shown that small quantities of protein introduced parenterally may be utilized by the tissues, and may even be capable of maintaining nitrogen equilibrium. It is, however, only for a short period and to a very limited extent that the body can utilize injected protein, for proteins are species specific and after a number of injections immunity is established to the foreign protein; an antibody known as a *precipitin* is formed which causes its precipitation. Furthermore, if a subsequent injection is given two weeks or so after a single injection or after the last of a series of such injections, a most serious toxic state—*anaphylaxis*—may ensue and

prove fatal. In the human subject such anaphylactic (or anaphylactoid) reactions may follow the second injection of a foreign protein, e.g., diptheria antitoxin (horse serum) or antitetanic serum. Skin rashes such as urticaria, erythema, eczema, giant edema, etc., or pain and swelling of the joints may occur. Collapse and death occasionally result. The sensitivity of some persons to certain proteins is also sometimes responsible for dietary idiosyncrasies. Certain foods such as shellfish, milk, strawberries, celery, etc., when ingested by persons sensitive to the proteins contained in these substances, result in cutaneous eruptions and sometimes localized edema. Minute amounts of the protein apparently enter the blood stream in an unchanged or partially digested state. Asthma, hay fever and other allergic conditions have been traced to foreign proteins (pollen, cat or horse hair, feathers, etc.) entering the body through the respiratory passages.

Homologous plasma protein, on the contrary, does not cause these effects and Whipple and his associates found that dogs could be maintained in nitrogen equilibrium (p. 1307) by the intravenous injection of plasma from other dogs as the sole source of protein.

A suitable assortment of amino acids, such as an hydrolysate of casein supplemented by cystine and tryptophane, injected intravenously, is capable of maintaining an animal in nitrogenous equilibrium. Animal gelatin or isinglass (fish gelatin) which differs from complete proteins in being nonantigenic, might be used for this purpose if supplemented by the missing amino acids.

The Fate of Amino Acids after Absorption

DEAMINATION. This term means the removal of amino groups from the amino acids. Less than 20 per cent of the amino acids absorbed into the portal blood pass through the liver unchanged into the general circulation. A very small proportion of these are excreted intact in the urine, some are deaminated by the kidney and the

TABLE 64.2

Classification of the amino acids

I. ALIPHATIC AMINO ACIDS

A. *Monoamino-monocarboxylic acids*

(1) Glycine (or glycocoll) $C_2H_5NO_2$, or amino-acetic acid

$$\begin{array}{c} CH_2\text{—}NH_2 \\ | \\ COOH \end{array}$$

(2) Alanine, $C_3H_7NO_2$, or α-amino-propionic acid

$$\begin{array}{c} CH_3 \cdot CH\text{—}NH_2 \\ | \\ COOH \end{array}$$

(3) Serine, $C_3H_7NO_3$, or α-amino-β-hydroxy propionic acid

$$\begin{array}{cc} CH_2 \cdot CH\text{—}NH_2 \\ | \quad\quad | \\ OH \quad COOH \end{array}$$

(4) Threonine, $C_4H_9NO_3$, or α-amino-β-hydroxy-*n*-butyric acid

$$\begin{array}{cc} CH_3CH \cdot CH\text{—}NH_2 \\ | \quad\quad | \\ OH \quad COOH \end{array}$$

(5) Valine, $C_5H_{11}NO_2$, or α-amino-isovaleric acid

$$\begin{array}{c} CH_3 \\ \diagdown \\ \quad\quad CH \cdot CH\text{—}NH_2 \\ \diagup \quad\quad | \\ CH_3 \quad\quad COOH \end{array}$$

(6) Norleucine, $C_6H_{13}NO_2$, or α-amino-*n*-caproic acid

$$\begin{array}{c} CH_3 \cdot CH_2 \cdot CH_2 \cdot CH_2 \cdot CH\text{—}NH_2 \\ | \\ COOH \end{array}$$

(7) Leucine, $C_6H_{13}NO_2$, or α-amino-isocaproic acid

$$\begin{array}{c} CH_3 \\ \diagdown \\ \quad\quad CH \cdot CH_2 \cdot CH\text{—}NH_2 \\ \diagup \quad\quad | \\ CH_3 \quad\quad COOH \end{array}$$

(8) Isoleucine, $C_6H_{13}NO_2$, or α-amino-β-ethyl-β-methyl-propionic acid

$$\begin{array}{c} CH_3 \\ \diagdown \\ \quad\quad CH \cdot CH\text{—}NH_2 \\ \diagup \quad\quad | \\ CH_3 \cdot CH_3 \quad\quad COOH \end{array}$$

Sulfur-containing monoamino-monocarboxylic acids

(9) Cystine, $C_6H_{12}N_2S_2O_4$, (or dicysteine) or di-(β-thio-α-amino-propionic) acid

$$\begin{array}{cc} CH_2\text{—}S\text{—}S\text{—}CH_2 \\ | \quad\quad\quad\quad | \\ CH\text{—}NH_2 \quad CH\text{—}NH_2 \\ | \quad\quad\quad\quad | \\ COOH \quad\quad COOH \end{array}$$

(10) Methionine, $C_5H_{11}SNO_2$, or α-amino-γ-methyl-thiol-*n*-butyric acid

$$\begin{array}{c} CH_3 \cdot S \cdot CH_2 \cdot CH_2 \cdot CH\text{—}NH_2 \\ | \\ COOH \end{array}$$

B. *Monoamino-dicarboxylic acids*

(11) Aspartic acid, $C_4H_7NO_4$, or α-amino-succinic acid

$$\begin{array}{c} COOH \cdot CH_2 \cdot CH\text{—}NH_2 \\ | \\ COOH \end{array}$$

(12) Glutamic acid, $C_5H_9NO_4$, or α-amino-glutaric acid

$$\begin{array}{c} COOH \cdot CH_2CH_2CH\text{—}NH_2 \\ | \\ COOH \end{array}$$

(13) Hydroxyglutamic acid, $C_5H_9NO_5$, or α-amino-β-hydroxy-glutaric acid

$$\begin{array}{c} COOH \cdot CH_2CHOH \cdot CH\text{—}NH_2 \\ | \\ COOH \end{array}$$

C. *Diamino-monocarboxylic acids*

(14) Arginine, $C_6H_{14}N_4O_2$, or α-amino-δ-guanidine-*n*-valeric acid

$$\begin{array}{c} NH_2 \\ | \\ HN\text{=}C\text{—}NH \cdot CH_2 \cdot CH_2 \cdot CH_2 \cdot CH\text{—}NH_2 \\ | \\ COOH \end{array}$$

(15) Lysine, $C_6H_{14}N_2O_2$, or α-ϵ-diamino-caproic acid

$$\begin{array}{c} NH_2 \\ | \\ CH_2 \cdot CH_2 \cdot CH_2 \cdot CH_2 \cdot CH\text{—}NH_2 \\ | \\ COOH \end{array}$$

TABLE 64.2—*Continued*

II. Aromatic Amino Acids

(16) Phenylalanine, $C_9H_{11}NO_2$, or α-amino-β-phenyl-propionic acid

$$
\begin{array}{c}
\text{H}\quad\text{H}\\
\text{C}=\!\!=\text{C}\\
\text{HC}\diagup\qquad\diagdown\text{C}-\text{CH}_2\cdot\text{CH}-\text{NH}_2\\
\diagdown\text{C}-\text{C}\diagup\qquad\quad|\\
\text{H}\quad\text{H}\qquad\qquad\text{COOH}
\end{array}
$$

(17) Tyrosine, $C_9H_{11}NO_3$, or α-amino-β-parahydroxy-phenyl-propionic acid

$$
\begin{array}{c}
\text{H}\quad\text{H}\\
\text{C}=\!\!=\text{C}\\
\text{HO}-\text{C}\diagup\qquad\diagdown\text{C}-\text{CH}_2\cdot\text{CH}-\text{NH}_2\\
\diagdown\text{C}-\text{C}\diagup\qquad\quad|\\
\text{H}\quad\text{H}\qquad\qquad\text{COOH}
\end{array}
$$

III. Heterocyclic Amino Acids

(18) Tryptophane, $C_{11}H_{12}N_2O_2$, or α-amino-β-indole-propionic acid

$$
\begin{array}{c}
\text{H}\\
\text{C}\\
\text{HC}\diagup\quad\text{C}\text{------}\text{C}-\text{CH}_2-\text{CH}-\text{NH}_2\\
\text{HC}\diagdown\quad\text{C}\qquad\text{CH}\qquad\quad|\\
\text{C}\quad\text{N}\qquad\qquad\text{COOH}\\
\text{H}\quad\text{H}
\end{array}
$$

Indole nucleus

(19) Histidine, $C_6H_9N_3O_2$, or α-amino-β-imidazol-propionic acid

$$
\begin{array}{c}
\text{CH}=\!\!=\text{C}\cdot\text{CH}_2\cdot\text{CH}-\text{NH}\\
||\qquad\qquad\qquad\\
\text{NH}\quad\text{N}\qquad\qquad|\\
\diagdown\text{CH}\qquad\qquad\text{COOH}
\end{array}
$$

Imidazole ring

(20) Proline, $C_5H_9NO_2$, or pyrrolidine-α-carboxylic acid

$$
\begin{array}{c}
\text{CH}_2\text{------}\text{CH}_2\\
|\qquad\qquad|\\
\text{CH}_2\quad\text{CH}-\text{COOH}\\
\diagdown\text{NH}\diagup
\end{array}
$$

Pyrrole nucleus

(21) Hydroxyproline (oxyproline), $C_5H_9NO_3$, or γ-hydroxy-pyrrolidine-α-carboxylic acid

$$
\begin{array}{c}
\text{HO}-\text{CH}\text{------}\text{CH}_2\\
|\qquad\qquad|\\
\text{CH}_2\quad\text{CH}-\text{COOH}\\
\diagdown\text{NH}\diagup
\end{array}
$$

Thyroxine (ch. 76), 3-5-*diiodotyrosine* or iodogorgoic acid, *citrulline* (α-*amino-δ-carbamido-n-valeric acid*) and *ornithine*(α,δ-*diamino-valeric acid*), and several others, would have to be added to complete the list of naturally occurring amino acids.

nitrogen excreted as ammonia; others are utilized without alteration by the tissues. The greater part of the amino acids reaching the liver are there retained and deaminated. The ammonia which is split off combines with carbon dioxide to form urea as described on page 1302. The deaminated remainder, i.e., the keto acid residue of the amino acid molecule may either undergo oxidation, and thus furnish energy to the body, or be transformed into glucose. The glucose may be burned or be stored as glycogen, or again it may be transformed into fat. Not all amino acids, however, are sugar or glycogen formers. Those which play the chief role in this respect are *glycine, alanine, aspartic, glutamic* and *hydroxyglutamic acids, serine, cystine, hydroxyproline* and *proline*. With the exception of *hydroxyproline* and *proline* these are all straight chain amino acids with less than six carbon atoms. *Arginine, valine,* and *threonine* form sugar to a limited extent,

TABLE 64.3

Approximate isoelectric points of some amino acids

Amino Acid	Approximate Isoelectric Points, pH
Glycine	6.1
Alanine	6.1
Valine	6.0
Leucine	6.0
Glutamic acid	3.2
Aspartic acid	3.0
Arginine	10.5
Lysine	9.6
Histidine	7.4
Phenylalanine	5.4
Tyrosine	5.4

whereas, *leucine, isoleucine, lysine, methionine, tryptophane, histidine, tyrosine* and *phenylalanine* are not glycogenic (see table 64.4). The quantity of amino acids present in 100 grams of protein is

TABLE 64.4

Classification of amino acids according to their glycogenic or ketogenic properties

Glycogenic	Ketogenic	Neither Glycogenic nor Ketogenic
Glycine	Leucine	Norleucine
Alanine	Isoleucine	Methionine
Serine	Phenylalanine	Lysine
Threonine	Tyrosine	Tryptophane
Cysteine		Histidine
Aspartic acid		
Valine		
Glutamic acid		
Arginine		
Ornithine		
Proline		
Hydroxyproline		

sufficient to form some 58 grams of glucose.[2] A depancreatized or phloridzinized dog, for instance, or the subject of severe diabetes, although upon a carbohydrate-free diet, continues to excrete large quantities of glucose. Also, the normal animal during prolonged starvation maintains its blood sugar at practically the normal level, which suggests that body protein is undergoing conversion to glucose. When protein is fed after a

[2] Since different proteins contain varying amounts of sugar-forming amino acids, this is an average figure. It was arrived at by calculation from the proportion of glucose (dextrose) to nitrogen in the urine—the so-called G:N (or D:N) ratio—in phloridzinized dogs fed exclusively upon protein or during a period of starvation. Lusk found the G:N ratio under such circumstances to be 3.65:1. The nitrogen of the urine is derived, of course, almost entirely from protein. The urinary glucose of an animal under the influence of phloridzin and whose glycogen stores have been exhausted is also assumed to be derived exclusively from protein. Now each gram of urinary nitrogen represents catabolism of 6.25 grams of protein. Therefore with a G:N ratio of 3.65:1 every 3.65 grams of glucose excreted indicates the conversion of 6.25 grams of protein. Thus,

$$(3.65/6.25) \times 100 = 58 \text{ per cent}$$

In diabetic (depancreatized) animals during starvation or upon a protein diet the G:N ratios obtained by different observers vary widely. Minkowiski's figure of 2.8:1 is most usually quoted (this would indicate the conversion of 45 per cent of protein to sugar). Macleod and his associates, however, have obtained ratios in depancreatized dogs after the withdrawal of insulin as high as 6:1 in some experiments, and less than 2:1 in others. The ratio did not show a constant value, either in different animals or in the same animal at different times. They have seriously questioned the reliability of the G:N ratio as an index of the extent of the protein to glucose conversion, and consider that protein is not the only source of the urinary glucose.

period of starvation, glycogen accumulates in the liver.

The conversion of protein to glucose is called gluconeogenesis and is an important process even in normal animals. It occurs almost entirely in the liver as Mann and Magath demonstrated when they showed that hypoglycemia following hepatectomy was not affected by the intravenous injection of glycine. That gluconeogenesis is a major metabolic process is evident from the fact that a depancreatized or phloridzinized dog, or an animal with severe diabetes, continues to excrete large quantities of glucose even when fed a carbohydrate-free diet. When the normal animal is starved for a prolonged period, gluconeogenesis permits it to maintain the blood sugar at a concentration which is only slightly below that normally found, and is responsible for the rapid accumulation of glycogen in the liver when the period of starvation is terminated by feeding protein. It is also an important homeostatic mechanism in normal animals fed a mixed diet. When the quantities of carbohydrate and fat consumed do not fulfil the caloric requirements of the animal, the deficit may be offset by converting more of the dietary protein to sugar. The transformation of protein to carbohydrate is accelerated by steroidal hormones from the adrenal cortex, and their secretion is in turn regulated by adrenocorticotrophin which is secreted by the anterior lobe of the pituitary gland. The adrenal steroids apparently act by reducing the uptake of amino acids by the muscle and other peripheral tissues, thereby leaving more of these metabolites available for deamination and other processes carried on in the liver.

Although deamination is a function of the kidney and other tissues as well, its main site is the liver. In the dog it appears to be carried on exclusively by hepatic tissue. Mann and his colleagues found no evidence in dogs of extrahepatic deamination. The injection of amino acids into the blood stream of a normal dog caused a rapid rise in the amino acid concentration of the blood and increased amino acid excretion in the urine. The level in the blood returned to normal in about two hours. *About 25 per cent of the injected amino acid nitrogen appeared in the urine as urea.* After hepatectomy, the urea concentration of the solid tissues, blood and urine fell, whereas the concentration of amino acids rose; amino acids injected into the blood stream were *completely recovered* unchanged, about a third from the urine and the remainder from the muscles. There was no sign of deamination or of urea synthesis.

Deamination is generally believed to be an oxidative process brought about by various enzymes in liver, kidney, and to some extent in other tissues. Oxidation of the *a*-carbon atom, i.e., the carbon atom to which the NH_2 group is attached, first occurs with the production of an *α-imino acid*. This involves the transference of two hydrogen atoms to a hydrogen acceptor through the action of *d-amino-oxidase, glycine oxidase*, or of *l-glutamic dehydrogenase*:

$$\underset{\substack{| \\ \text{COOH}}}{\overset{\substack{\text{R} \\ |}}{CHNH_2}} \rightarrow \underset{\substack{| \\ \text{COOH}}}{\overset{\substack{\text{R} \\ |}}{C}}=NH \ + \ 2H \xrightarrow[\text{acceptor}]{\text{to hydrogen}}$$

α-amino-acid α-imino-acid

The imino acid then undergoes spontaneous hydrolysis to form an *α-keto acid*:

$$\underset{\substack{| \\ \text{COOH}}}{\overset{\substack{\text{R} \\ |}}{C}}=NH \ + \ H_2O \ \rightarrow \ \underset{\substack{| \\ \text{COOH}}}{\overset{\substack{\text{R} \\ |}}{C}}O \quad + \ NH_3$$

α-imino acid   α-keto acid

TRANSAMINATION. An important reaction occurring in the metabolism of protein is the interconversion of amino acids by transference of the amino group from an α-amino acid to an α-keto acid. The change is catalyzed by an enzyme *transaminase*.

The reaction is reversible and occurs according to the equation:

$$R^1 \cdot CH(NH_2) \cdot COOH + R^2 \cdot CO \cdot COOH \leftrightarrows$$

$$R^1 \cdot CO \cdot COOH + R^2 CH(NH_2) COOH.$$

Transamination was first suggested as a possibility by Needham and later demonstrated in pigeon breast muscle by Braunstein and Kritzmann. They found that when *l*-glutamic acid and pyruvic acid were incubated with chopped liver or muscle α-ketoglutaric acid and alanine were produced, the amino group of the glutamic acid being transferred to pyruvic acid:

COOH   COOH
| |
CH_2 CH_3 CH_2 CH_3
| | | |
CH_2 + CO → CH_2 + $CH \cdot NH_2$
| | | |
$CH \cdot NH_2$ COOH C=O COOH
| |
COOH   COOH

1-glutamic pyruvic α-ketoglutaric alanine
acid   acid acid (some-
            times incor-
            rectly called
            α-ketoglutamic
            acid)

According to these investigators the majority of the amino acids (lysine is an exception) can take part in transamination reactions, their NH_2 groups being transferred to other amino acids or to various keto acids. Glutamic acid is especially active in this respect. Transamination occurs not only in liver and muscle but has been demonstrated in a number of other tissues and appears to be a function of tissues in general. Krebs observed that glycolysis in brain and retina was inhibited by glutamic acid, an effect which has since been shown to be due to the conversion of pyruvic acid to alanine through the transference of amino groups from the glutamic acid. Since transamination is a rapid process and concerned chiefly with those compounds, which play key roles in intermediary metabolism, Cohen suggests that it represents a "shuttle" mechanism in tissue respiration "whereby certain key protein and carbohydrate intermediates are rapidly interconverted." The demonstration of transamination affords further evidence for the highly dynamic character of protein metabolism. Amino groups are being continually exchanged between nitrogenous and non-nitrogenous compounds, and amino acids thereby synthesized. When an amino acid into which isotopic nitrogen (N^{15}) has been incorporated is fed and the tissues of the animal are analyzed a large number of amino acids are found to contain the isotope. Even ammonium citrate containing N^{15} fed to rats upon a low protein diet, is utilized for amino acid synthesis. Aspartic acid, histidine, arginine, glutamic acid and proline, isolated from the animals' bodies, were found to contain the isotope.

TRANSMETHYLATION. Although it has long been known that certain compounds when fed are excreted by the kidney in methylated form, e.g., pyridine as N-methyl pyridine, the mechanism involved in the transference of the methyl group from one compound to another has been discovered comparatively recently by du Vigneaud and his associates. Homocystine can be converted in the body to methionine by the addition of a methyl group. The methyl group is furnished by choline or betaine. An animal fed upon a diet lacking in methionine, but containing homocystine fails to grow; growth is resumed upon the addition of choline or betaine; the essential amino acid methionine being thus formed. The transference of the methyl groups from methionine or choline to glycocyamine with the formation of creatine is described on page 1304. Methionine, choline and betaine are, therefore, spoken of as transmethylating agents. The conversion of nicotinic acid to trigonelline may be another example of trans-methylation, although it may be due, in part, to direct methylation. The methyl group is not improbably derived from methionine.

Transamidation. This is the transference of an amidine group NH_2 as from arginine to glycine

$$C = NH$$

to form glycocyamine (p. 1305).

The Synthesis of Amino Acids

That the body tissues, given the necessary amino acids, can link them together and so synthesize protein is, of course, unquestioned. The extent to which the amino acids themselves can be synthesized has been a more difficult question to decide. That synthesis of amino acids does occur is clearly indicated by the fact that only a limited number (10) of amino acids found in animal tissue are essential constituents of the diet. Undoubtedly the body is able to synthesize glycine—the simplest amino acid. For example, milk proteins contain no more than 0.1 to 0.3 per cent of glycine, yet from 100 grams of the former the suckling animal can build up 78 grams of tissue protein containing 2.5 grams of glycine (Magnus-Levy). Also, the liver and kidney detoxicate benzoic acid by combining it with glycine to form hippuric acid which is excreted in the urine. When large quantities of benzoic acid are fed, the glycine in the excreted hippuric acid is greater in amount than that which could have been supplied preformed from body tissue. Analogous experiments with the detoxication of phenylacetic acid to phenylacetyl glutamine indicate that glutamic acid can also be synthesized. The mode by which synthesis of the amino acids takes place is obscure. The formation of amino acids by the transference of amino groups to non-nitrogenous compounds, e.g., pyruvic acid formed in the breakdown of carbohydrate, or even the utilization of ammonia, fed in the form of ammonium salts, has been mentioned. The ammonia probably unites with a keto acid to form an aminated hydroxy acid which by reduction yields an amino acid.

$$R \cdot CH_2CO \cdot COOH + NH_3 \rightarrow$$
keto acid

$$R \cdot CH_2COHNH_2COOH \rightarrow$$
hydroxyamino-acid

$$R \cdot CH_2CHNH_2 \cdot COOH + H_2O$$
amino acid

Embden found that alanine was formed by the surviving liver perfused with blood to which the ammonium salt of pyruvic acid had been added. Phenylalanine and tyrosine were also formed when the liver was perfused with the ammonium salts of the corresponding keto acids. Even the addition of ammonium chloride to the fluid perfusing a glycogen-rich liver resulted in the production of alanine. The latter also followed perfusion with ammonium lactate. Furthermore, it was shown by Knoop that when γ-phenyl-α-keto-butyric acid was administered to dogs the corresponding amino acid appeared in the urine, whereas the experiments of Cox and Rose and of Sherwin and their associates indicate that histidine, an essential amino acid, can be formed in the body when imidazole pyruvic acid or imidazole lactic acid is fed. The synthesis of arginine has also been demonstrated by Rose and his colleagues.

To sum up: it is established that glycine can be synthesized from precursors already present in the body. The same may also be said for glutamic and aspartic acids alanine and arginine. The perfusion experiments just mentioned suggest that alanine may be synthesized from the derivatives of carbohydrate metabolism plus the ammonia which would otherwise be excreted as urea. Some amino acids, such as tryptophane, lysine, methionine, threonine and several others (see table 65.2) cannot be formed in the body and are referred to as essential (indispensable) amino acids (see ch. 65). If, however, the special groups are supplied, as in the form of the keto acid or hydroxy acid, the corresponding amino acid can in some instances be formed.

Protein Synthesis

The synthesis of protein from free amino acids requires energy; the latter is derived from the oxidation of carbohydrate and fat. The energy liberated during oxidative catabolism is not contributed directly to the reactions involved in protein formation but is first used to synthesize adenosine-triphosphate (ATP) which acts as an intermediate source of energy (see Carbohydrate Metabolism). Thus, in conditions such as diabetes mellitus, where carbohydrate and fat utilization are severely impaired, peptide synthesis is also impaired. Protein formation is also reduced by substances such as dinitrophenol, which interfere with ATP synthesis and allow the energy liberated from oxidative reactions to be dissipated as heat.

The mechanisms responsible for the formation of peptide bonds and the factors which guide the selection of amino acids so that they may be linked together in the specific sequence that characterizes a particular protein, have only recently been understood. Borsook, with amazing perspicuity, proposed in 1944 that three steps are involved in the formation of the protein molecule. The first step consists of activation of the carboxyl group of an amino acid. In the second step, the activated amino acid is transported to a template or mold which aligns them in the specific sequence characteristic of the protein to be synthesized. During the third stage, the activated carboxyl groups combine with the amino groups of the adjacent molecules to form peptide bonds. The newly formed molecule then peels off the template to yield a new protein molecule. Elucidation of the basic mechanisms responsible for protein synthesis has occurred only within the past few years from the skillful and ingenious studies of a relatively small number of investigators. Their findings have shown that Borsook's concepts were, in general, correct. The main steps involved in the biosynthesis of protein are briefly outlined below.

1. The templates, or genes, which ultimately control the formation of specific proteins are, in themselves, segments of deoxyribonucleic acid molecules (DNA) which are located in the cell nucleus.

2. The DNA template is not directly involved in the formation of polypeptides. Ribonucleotides in the nucleus are polymerized through the action of an enzyme called ribonucleic acid (RNA) polymerase, to form an RNA molecule, which is patterned directly from the DNA strands, and which carries the information required for the synthesis of a specific protein.

3. This secondary template is termed messenger-RNA, since it leaves the nucleus and enters particulate bodies (microsomes) in the cytoplasm. It then becomes attached to structures within the microsomes called ribosomes. Messenger RNA then directs the synthesis of protein, utilizing the microsomal apparatus.

4. Free amino acids in the cytoplasm are enzymatically coupled to ATP. This reaction yields free phosphate and "activated" amino acids which are actually aminoacyl adenylates.

5. The activated amino acids then become attached to relatively small molecules of RNA dissolved in the cytoplasm. This second kind of RNA is termed soluble-RNA (s.-RNA) or transfer-RNA, since it transfers the amino acids to a specific location on the strand of messenger RNA attached to the ribosomes. A different transfer RNA appears to exist for each amino acid.

6. When all the amino acids are aligned on the messenger RNA in a specific sequence, they are linked together by the enzymatic formation of peptide bonds. The polypeptide or protein produced in this manner is then released from the matrix of the ribosomal (messenger) RNA.

The Classical as Opposed to the Modern View of Protein Metabolism

The classical view of protein metabolism was proposed originally by Folin. He believed that the creatinine and neutral sulfur excreted in urine were derived from the wear and tear of the body tissues and the amounts of these substances in the urine were taken as indices of endogenous protein metabolism. The urea, on the other hand, was believed to be derived solely from the catabolism of dietary or exogenous protein. Since creatinine represents a very small amount of the total urinary nitrogen and remains constant in amount, it was concluded that the tissue proteins were relatively inert and that only minute amounts of the dietary amino acids were needed to replace the protein lost from body tissues. This concept was challenged in 1935 by Borsook and Keighley who, on the basis of much indirect evidence, suggested that endogenous protein metabolism was a very active process and that a large proportion of the dietary amino acids were utilized by various tissues. Direct substantiation of this concept was obtained by Schoenheimer and his associates through the use of isotopically labelled compounds. Schoenheimer fed rats leucine and glycine labelled with N^{15}. If, as Folin believed, the body proteins were inert, nearly all of the label from the amino acids should have been recovered from the urine. However, only a fraction of the isotopic nitrogen was found in the urine whereas the remainder was found incorporated into the body tissues. It appears, therefore, that the body proteins are in a constant state of turnover, they are continually being broken down and replaced by new protein synthesized from dietary amino acids. Subsequent work indicates that the replacement of protein is rapid in plasma, liver, kidney and intestinal tract, and comparatively slow in hemoglobin, muscle and skin.

The rapid turnover of amino acids in various tissues has been considered by some to be due to the degradation and resynthesis of the intracellular proteins. Cohn and Monod have expressed reservations concerning this belief. They point out that what has been interpreted as evidence of intracellular turnover of protein may represent a turnover of whole cells, that is to say, the rate at which cells, not just the protein within them, are destroyed and replaced. It appears then that protein turnover may be due to both intracellular degradation and resynthesis and to replacement of whole cells.

Protein Storage—Labile Protein

In the latter half of the 19th century Voit observed that when dogs were starved, or fed a diet free of protein the nitrogen excretion fell rapidly for 5 or 6 days and then became relatively constant. The larger amounts of nitrogen excreted during the first few days were believed by Rubner to arise from unorganized storage protein that was utilized to fill a metabolic need for nitrogen

$$\begin{matrix} \text{NH}_2 \\ | \\ \text{HN}{=}\text{C} \\ | \\ \text{NH}\cdot(\text{CH}_2)_3\cdot\text{CHNH}_2\cdot\text{COOH} \end{matrix} \quad + \text{ H}_2\text{O} \rightarrow$$

Arginine

during times of protein deprivation. Research during the intervening years has failed to reveal a depot or special form of protein that functions exclusively as a reserve supply. However, the body tissues, particularly those of liver thymus, prostate, seminal vesicles, alimentary tract, pancreas, spleen and kidneys, do contain labile proteins that can be drawn upon when the need arises. These organs lose their labile protein rapidly. This process seems to account for the rapid fall and subsequent stabilization of urinary nitrogen excretion that occurs during the first few days of starvation. Some of the protein mobilized is utilized for the synthesis of other body proteins. This phenomenon is well illustrated by the experimental findings of Madden and Whipple. When severe hypo-proteinemia was produced by repeated plasmapheresis, a normal dog resynthesized 40 to 60 per cent of its plasma proteins while fasting. This, however, is not the only function of the protein. A large proportion is converted into carbohydrate, which is subsequently used to provide the energy required for vital processes. It appears then that the body tissues, particularly those of the viscera, do contain labile proteins, the supply of which, however, is quickly exhausted. The temporary loss of this protein does no permanent damage to the organ involved; there is no reason to believe that it differs chemically or functionally from the proteins that normally constitute the donor cell.

The End Products of Protein—Metabolism, Urea

The great proportion of the nitrogen released by the catabolism of the amino acids appears in the urine of man, mammals, amphibia and elasmobranch fish as urea. In birds and reptiles, on the other hand, the chief end product of protein breakdown is *uric acid*. In man and other mammals the latter is derived from the metabolism of the purines (ch. 66). Urea is formed directly (i.e., without preliminary deamination), from *arginine*, which is hydrolyzed by the action of an enzyme—*arginase*—into *urea* and *ornithine*. Arginase is present in the liver of mammals but not in that of birds and reptiles. The reaction may be represented thus

$$\begin{matrix} \text{NH}_2 \\ \diagup \\ \text{O}{=}\text{C} \\ \diagdown \\ \text{NH}_2 \end{matrix} \quad + \text{ NH}_2\cdot(\text{CH}_2)_3\cdot\text{CHNH}_2\cdot\text{COOH}$$

Urea   Ornithine

This important mechanism has been thought to account for the greater proportion of the urea formed in the body. When ornithine was incubated with slices of liver in the presence of ammonia and carbonic acid, large amounts of urea were formed. It is supposed that the ornithine combines with the ammonia and carbonic acid to form arginine which in turn is hydrolyzed by arginase into urea and ornithine. Thus arginine serves as an intermediary in the production of urea from the ammonia supplied by other amino acids. The ornithine liberated by the decomposition of arginine is used over again. Ornithine thus acts after the manner of a catalyst to facilitate urea production.

According to Krebs and Henseleit, the formation of arginine from ornithine occurs in two steps. (1) The formation of the amino acid *citrulline* by the addition of a molecule each of ammonia and carbon dioxide to ornithine.

$$\begin{matrix} \text{NH}_2 \\ | \\ \text{O}{=}\text{C} \\ | \\ \text{NH}\cdot\text{CH}_2\cdot\text{CH}_2\cdot\text{CH}_2\cdot\text{CHNH}_2\cdot\text{COOH} \end{matrix}$$

Citrulline

(2) The addition of a second molecule of ammonia to citrulline with the production of arginine. Therefore, the production of urea from ammonia and carbonic acid may be represented thus:

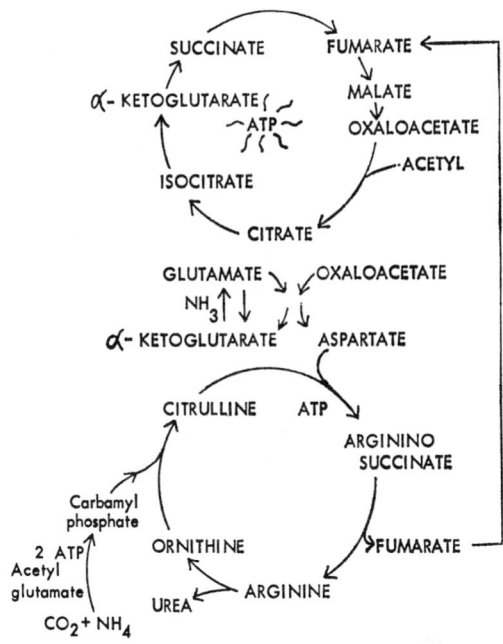

The ornithine cycle

Although the ornithine cycle may not be the only mechanism involved in the production of urea, it is undoubtedly the only pathway by which significant amounts of urea can be produced. Some of its details have been clarified by the work of several investigators (Cohen and Hayano, Borsook and Dubnoff, and Ratner and associates). Cohen and Hayano reported that for the production of arginine from citrulline glutamic acid rather than ammonia appeared to be the nitrogen donor, and that Mg ions, adenosinetriphosphate (ATP) and oxygen are required for the reaction. The transfer of the NH_2 group, it has been suggested, is effected by transamination and the simultaneous loss of two H atoms (transamination). The citrulline-arginine conversion occurs only in the presence of oxygen. Glutamate also acts as an acceptor of CO_2 and NH_3 in the synthesis of citrulline from ornithine, in the first stage of the ornithine cycle. Aspartic acid is, however, according to the researches of Ratner and her colleagues, the specific nitrogen donor in the conversion of citrulline to arginine, which occurs anaerobically in the presence of Mg ions and ATP. Fumaric acid is also formed in this reaction, but undergoes oxidation to oxalacetic acid. Through this latter reaction the tricarboxylic and ornithine cycles are interlocked. The following scheme is given by Ratner.

Urea is decomposed into NH_3 and CO_2 by the action of urease. This enzyme is found in leguminous plants, especially in soy bean, and in relatively high concentration in the gastric mucosa (ch. 58). Urease is employed in the determination of urea (from ammonia evolved) in urine and in other body fluids and in tissues.

THE EXCRETION OF UREA AND ITS DISTRIBUTION IN THE BODY. On an ordinary mixed diet from 80 to 90 per cent of the urinary nitrogen is urea-

nitrogen. The absolute amount of urea-nitrogen excreted daily is usually from 9 to 13 grams (20 to 30 grams of urea). Minimal amounts are also excreted in the sweat (ch. 70), salivary, intestinal and mammary secretions. The urea-nitrogen varies with the protein content of the diet. Upon a low protein diet the output may be as low as 2 grams and on a diet rich in protein it may be over 25 grams. The value of urea-nitrogen is therefore taken as an index of the magnitude of the catabolism of food protein (exogenous metabolism, see table, p. 1306).

The blood contains from 8 to 15 mg. of urea-nitrogen (18 to 35 mg. urea) per 100 cc. Urea is readily diffusible and is found in about the same concentration in the various tissues and other fluids, e.g., lymph, bile, cerebrospinal fluid and pancreatic juice, as in blood. The kidney, however, is an exception since it contains some 150 to 200 mg. of urea per 100 grams of tissue. We have already seen that the urinary ammonia is formed from glutamine and amino acids in the kidney and not from urea (ch. 79).

THE SITE OF UREA PRODUCTION. It has long been known that the liver is an important site of urea formation. Perfusion of the liver with amino acids or their addition to sliced liver tissue leads to the production of urea. Urea is very widely distributed throughout nature, being a constituent of the body fluids of the lowest forms of animal life. It is also found in plants. For this reason its formation in animals might be thought to be a function common to all tissues. But the experiments of Mann and his associates in hepatectomized dogs, points to the liver as being the main if not the sole site of urea production. After complete removal of the liver the formation of urea ceased, so that its concentration in the blood and urine fell progressively. If the kidneys as well as the liver were excised there was no accumulation of urea in the blood although the amino acid concentration rose. Also, after the injection of glycine or alanine into the hepatectomized animal, in contrast to the result obtained in the normal animal, the concentration of the injected amino acid rose in the blood and urine, and there was no evidence of urea production. That these results in dogs apply to man is indicated by the observation of Rabinowitch. He has reported that in a case of extensive damage to kidneys and liver (acute yellow atrophy) the excretion of urine was almost suppressed yet the blood was urea-free. The appearance of leucine and tyrosine in the urine which occurs in acute yellow atrophy of the liver may also be ascribed to the failure of deamination of these amino acids. Nevertheless, although the liver undoubtedly plays the predominant role in the production of urea, certain other tissues may under certain circumstances share to some degree in its formation. Graham and associates found, for example, that the active mammary gland produces not inconsiderable amounts.

Creatine and Creatinine

Creatine ($C_4H_9N_3O_2$) (methyl guanido-acetic acid or methyl-glycocyamine)

$$HN=C\begin{array}{l} \diagup NH_2 \\ \diagdown N(CH_3)\cdot CH_2\cdot COOH \end{array}$$

may be looked upon as a derivative of glycine, of guanidine or of guanido-acetic acid. It is also related to arginine. It is readily converted by acid *in vitro* to creatinine.

Creatinine, $C_4H_7N_3O$ (methyl glycocyamidine) is the anhydride of creatine. Its molecular constitution is shown by the following formula:

$$HN=C\begin{array}{l} \diagup NH\text{------}C=O \\ \diagdown N(CH_3)\cdot CH_2 \end{array}$$

Distribution of creatine and creatinine. There are about 120 grams of *creatine* contained in the adult human body. Of this 98 per cent is con-

tained in the muscles and 1.5 per cent in the nervous system. The remaining 0.5 per cent is distributed throughout the other organs of the body; of these, the testes contain it in highest concentration. The skeletal and cardiac muscles and the gravid uterus are a great deal richer in creatine than the smooth muscle of the gastrointestinal tract and elsewhere. About 80 per cent of the creatine in muscle is combined with phosphoric acid as *phosphocreatine* (ch. 51). Of the striated muscles, the rapidly contracting, pale type contain more than the slowly contracting red variety. In the muscle of invertebrates creatine is replaced by arginine.

Creatinine is present in muscle in much smaller amounts. One hundred grams of skeletal muscle, for example, contain 300 to 500 mg. of creatine and only 10 mg. of creatinine. The creatine of whole blood amounts to from 3.5 to 5.0 mg. and the creatinine to about 2.5 mg. per 100 cc. By far the greater part, if not all, of the creatine is contained in the corpuscles. The creatinine is about equally distributed between cells and plasma.

Excretion of creatine and creatinine. Creatine is normally absent from the urine of men, but is present in the urine of male and female children up to the age of puberty and frequently in the urine of women. The significance of these sex differences is not evident. In nonpregnant women the *creatinuria* is intermittent but is not related to menstruation. During pregnancy creatine is present continuously in the urine. This may be related to high creatine content of the uterus. For two or three weeks after childbirth the quantity excreted is even higher than during pregnancy. Reduction in the muscular mass of the uterus (involution) may account in part for the high output during the puerperium, but that uterine involution is not the chief cause is shown by the fact that it occurs although Caesarian section and removal of the uterus have been performed. Creatine also appears in the urine of either sex under the following conditions; *high protein diet, starvation, carbohydrate deprivation, diabetes, wasting diseases* and *fevers, exophthalmic goiter* and in certain *muscular dystrophies.* The creatinuria in all of these conditions except the last is probably due to an increase in the normal catabolism of muscular tissue, the liberation of creatine occurring more rapidly than its conversion to creatinine. Protein food, for example, has a stimulating effect upon metabolism (p. 1309), whereas in wasting diseases, fevers, etc., tissue breakdown is accelerated. Carbohydrate deprivation probably acts indirectly in that its sparing effect upon protein catabolism is absent. In the muscular dystrophies, e.g., *myasthenia gravis, progressive muscular atrophy, amyotonia congenita, anterior poliomyelitis*, etc., the urinary creatine is probably derived from the degenerating muscle fibers; the muscles also appear to be defective in their power to store creatine. The creatinuria of normal children has received no satisfactory explanation; it is said to be due to an increased production of creatine, induced in some way by the growth impulse, and also probably to a low capacity for creatine storage of the undeveloped muscles. Another possibility is that children have a relatively low power to convert creatine to creatinine (Hunter).

The origin of creatine and creatinine. Creatinine is undoubtedly derived from creatine but there has been much uncertainty concerning the latter's origin. One or other of the substances to which its chemical formula suggests a relationship, e.g., guanidine, glycine or arginine, has been considered as a possible precursor. The opportunity afforded by the creatinuria of muscular dystrophies has been taken advantage of by Brand and his colleagues in the investigation of this question. Various amino acids and other guanido compounds were fed to patients suffering from such disorders; ingested glycine, or gelatin which is rich in this amino acid, causes a pronounced rise (40 per cent) in the creatine excretion of these patients but not of normal persons. The proportion of ingested creatine which is retained is also much less than the normal (*creatine tolerance test*). Arginine and glycocyamine (guanidoacetic acid) were also effective. Feeding benzoic acid, which drew upon the body's glycine store for detoxication purposes caused a decrease in the creatine excretion. The importance of glycine in creatine synthesis is emphasized by the observation of Almquist and Mecchi that glycine, which is an indispensable amino acid for chicks, can be replaced in the diet of this species by creatine. These results pointed to arginine, guanidoacetic acid, and especially glycine as precursors of creatine.

The subject of creatine synthesis has been clarified recently through a number of experiments in which isotopes were used as markers to identify the particular substance under investigation after it had been absorbed. The administration of isotopic glycine (i.e., heavy nitrogen, N^{15}, incorporated in the glycine molecule) was shown by Bloch and Schoenheimer to give rise to creatine with a high concentration of the nitrogen isotope. Of all the other amino acids investigated by this method, arginine alone was found to be a primary precursor of creatine. The isotope N^{15} was incorporated into the amidine part (NH_2—C=NH) of the arginine molecule. When the isotopic arginine was fed, the creatine isolated from the tissues of the animal was found to contain the isotope in this part of its molecule. The researches of du Vigneaud, and of Borsook and Dubnoff, show clearly that the methyl group of creatine is furnished by methionine. The former worker prepared methionine in which the three hydrogen atoms of the S-methyl group were present as the isotope H^2 (deuterium). When this was fed and the creatine of the animals' bodies determined, the isotope concentration indicated that nearly 70 per cent of the methyl groups of the creatine molecule had been derived from methionine. Borsook and Dubnoff incubated liver slices with guanidoacetic acid (glycocyamine) which they found was slowly converted to creatine, the conversion being hastened by the addition of methionine. Glycocyamine is apparently an intermediary in the synthesis of creatine in the body; when the isotopic form of this compound is fed isotopic creatine is formed. The conclusions to be drawn from these experiments are that arginine, glycine and methionine enter into the synthesis of creatine but that other amino acids do not serve as precursors. The first reaction, it appears, is between the amidine part of arginine and glycine with the formation of glycocyamine. The guanidoacetic acid then undergoes methylation by the transference of the methyl group from methionine. Thus:

Glycine   Amidine group of arginine

$$NH_2 \qquad\qquad NH_2$$
$$| \qquad\qquad\qquad |$$
$$CH_2COOH \ + \ —C\text{=}NH \ \rightarrow$$

Glycocyamine   Creatine

$$
\begin{array}{ccc}
NH_2 & & NH_2 \\
| & & | \\
C—NH & & C\text{=}NH \\
\cdots\cdots|\cdots\cdots & +\ CH_3\ \rightarrow & | \\
NH & \text{from} & NCH_3 \\
| & \text{methionine} & | \\
CH_2COOH & & \rightarrow CH_2COOH
\end{array}
$$

The site of creatine production is not known definitely but it is probably in the muscles. These also in all probability are the site of creatine-creatinine transformation (by dehydration). Mann and Magath found that removal of the liver was without effect upon creatinine production. The creatine which gives rise to urinary creatinine is derived very largely from the phosphocreatine of muscle.

Creatine is not, as was held by some authorities

TABLE 64.5

Effect of dietary protein on composition of urine

(After Folin)

	Nitrogen-Rich Diet	Nitrogen-Poor Diet
Volume of urine..	1170 cc.	385 cc.
Total nitrogen....	16.8 grams	3.60 grams
Urea nitrogen....	14.70 grams = 87.5%	2.20 grams = 61.7%
Ammonia nitrogen	0.49 gram = 0.3%	0.42 gram = 11.3%
Uric acid nitrogen	0.18 gram = 1.1%	0.09 gram = 2.5%
Creatinine nitrogen............	0.58 gram = 3.6%	0.60 gram = 17.2%
Undetermined nitrogen.........	0.85 gram = 4.9%	0.27 gram = 7.3%
Total sulfur.......	3.64 grams	0.76 gram
Inorganic SO_3....	3.27 grams = 90.0%	0.46 gram = 60.5%
Ethereal SO_3.....	0.19 gram = 5.2%	0.10 gram = 13.2%
Neutral S........	0.18 gram = 4.8%	0.20 gram = 26.3%

in the past, simply a waste product of protein metabolism like urea. If, for example, a large dose of creatine is fed the greater part or the whole is retained in the body.[3] Creatinine, on the other hand is purely a waste product. Up to 80 per cent or more of an amount fed can be recovered unchanged in the urine. The investigations of recent years into the chemistry of muscular contraction have revealed the essential importance of creatine (as phosphocreatine) in the contractile process (ch. 51).

CREATININE EXCRETION AS AN INDEX OF MUSCLE METABOLISM

The daily output of creatinine in the urine is constant for the individual, amounting to from 1.5 to 2.0 grams for men and from 0.8 to 1.5 grams for women. This corresponds to about 2 per cent

[3] In the experiments of Benedict and Osterberg over half a gram of creatine hydrate was fed daily to dogs for a period of several weeks. In the first week none of the administered creatin was excreted, either as such or as creatinine. During subsequent weeks when the "creatine reservoirs" had apparently become filled a large part was excreted unchanged. A rise in the creatinine output also occurred, indicating the transformation of creatine to creatinine. Nevertheless, of some 33 grams of creatine administered over the entire period of 70 days about 20 grams were retained. Retention of ingested creatine is also demonstrable in man.

of the creatine of the body. Unlike the excretion of urea, which is derived largely from exogenous sources, the creatinine output is practically independent of the protein level of the food. This is evident from table 64.5. The creatinine excretion is therefore considered to be an index of the magnitude of the metabolism of the tissues and especially of muscle. The daily output of creatinine is extraordinarily constant for the individual; it is not influenced by ordinary exercise or by the urine volume. The creatinine coefficient—

$$\frac{\text{milligrams creatinine}^4 \text{ excreted per day}}{\text{body weight in kilograms}}$$

is from 20 to 26 for the majority of normal men and from 14 to 22 for women. Its value depends upon the muscular development of the individual; the sex variation being due presumably to the different relative amounts of fatty and muscular tissues of male and female bodies. Athletic women for this reason have a coefficient as high as or higher than a man of obese build and poor muscular development.

THE METABOLISM OF SULFUR

Sulfur enters the body mainly as a constituent of the amino acids *cystine* and *methionine*. Food also contains inorganic sulfates, small amounts of sulfur in the form of sulfolipids (sulfatides) in certain glycoproteins (mucoitin-sulfuric acid and chondroitin-sulfuric acid) and in organic sulfides, isothiocyanates, and sulfonium compounds. Sulfur in inorganic form cannot be used in the construction of body protein. Practically speaking, the body is dependent for its sulfur supplies upon the two sulfur-containing amino acids mentioned above.

THE DISTRIBUTION OF SULFUR IN THE BODY

Sulfur is contained in the ordinary tissue proteins; in hair, horn, feathers, etc.; in mucin, as mucoitin-sulfuric acid and chondroitin-sulfuric acid; in certain glycoproteins of tendons, vitreous humor, cornea and connective tissues; in glutathione and insulin; in the taurocholic acid of bile; as solfocyanate in saliva; in ergothionine, a compound found in red corpuscles; in certain pigments (melanins, urochrome), and in nervous tissue as sulfolipoids. Inorganic sulfates are contained in the body fluids generally.

The loss of sulfur from the body occurs in the shedding of hair, nails, etc., in the bile, saliva and

[4] Or creatine + creatinine, when creatinuria exists.

gastrointestinal secretions. The great bulk of the sulfur loss, however, occurs through the kidneys.

The history of sulfur in the body. The sulfur liberated in the catabolism of dietary protein is largely converted to inorganic sulfates. A part of the inorganic sulfate derived from this and other sources becomes conjugated in the liver with substances produced in the intestine by the bacterial decomposition of protein to form *ethereal sulfates.* The latter are excreted in the urine. The products of bacterial action, among which are phenol derived from phenylalanine and tyrosine, and indole and skatole from tryptophane, possess toxic properties. Their excretion as ethereal sulfates constitutes a detoxicating mechanism. When the detoxicating function of the liver is depressed as a result of hepatic disease, some of these toxic substances are excreted by the kidney in abnormal amounts in the free state.

Urinary sulfur. The total urinary sulfur is made up of the following:

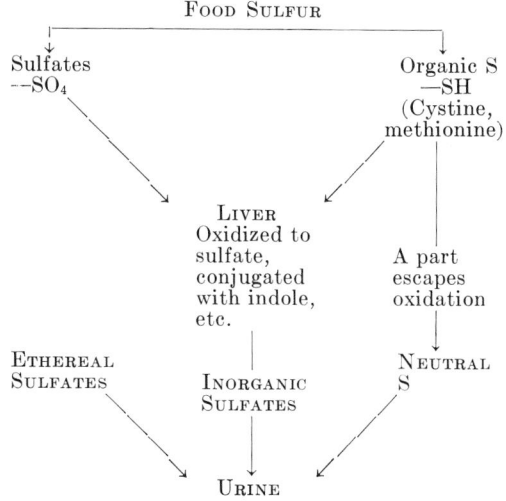

FOOD SULFUR

(1) Inorganic sulfur (85 to 90 per cent). Compounds of sulfuric acid with Na, K, Ca and NH₃.

(2) Ethereal sulfate sulfur (6 to 8 per cent), e.g., potassium and sodium salts of indoxyl sulfuric acid. The former is known as indican.

(3) Neutral sulfur (4 to 6 per cent) e.g., sulfur-containing amino acids, urochrome, thiosulfates, thiocyanates, taurocholic and oxyproteic acids.

The quantities of inorganic and ethereal sulfates in the urine vary with the protein level of the diet, and run more or less parallel with the nitrogen excretion; the neutral sulfur is influenced to a less degree. For this reason the two former partitions of the urinary sulfur were considered by Folin to represent food (exogenous)

sulfur while the neutral sulfur was taken to be derived mainly from body protein (endogenous sulfur). On a diet of meat or during prolonged starvation the ratio of sulfur to nitrogen in the urine is about 1 to 14, i.e., for every gram of sulfur there are approximately 14 grams of nitrogen. This is approximately the S:N ratio found in muscular tissue. A graphic summary of sulfur metabolism is shown above.

As a result of the excessive production and absorption of putrefactive products the excretion of ethereal sulfates is increased in acute intestinal obstruction. They are also increased in carcinoma of the liver. Chronic constipation, however, exerts little or no influence upon the excretion of these substances.

The excretion of neutral sulfur is increased in the rare metabolic anomaly known as *cystinuria* and in cases of *melanotic sarcoma*, when an abnormal sulfur-containing pigment appears in the urine.

The nonprotein sulfur of blood. The sulfur of blood, other than that present as a constituent of protein, amounts to from 3 to 5 mg. per 100 cc. The concentrations of the three forms are given in table 64.6.

AMMONIA (SEE PAGE 1693)

NITROGEN BALANCES

The difference between the nitrogen taken in the food and that excreted in the feces and urine is spoken of as the nitrogen balance (that lost in the hair, sweat, saliva, etc., is negligible). On an ordinary diet, the amounts of nitrogen excreted daily in the feces and urine, respectively, average 1.5 and 13 grams. The nitrogen of the feces is in part unabsorbed nitrogen of the food and in part nitrogen excreted through the intestinal wall.

TABLE 64.6

Concentrations of different forms of sulfur in whole blood and serum

(After Denis)

	Whole Blood	Serum
	per 100 cc. mg.	*per 100 cc.* mg.
Inorganic sulfur..............	0.1–1.1	0.5–1.1
Ethereal sulfate sulfur.......	0.1–1.0	0.1–1.0
Neutral sulfur....	2.2–4.5	1.7–3.5

The inorganic sulfur of blood is elevated in *renal insufficiency, intestinal obstruction* and *leukemia*.

TABLE 64.7

Example of adjustment of nitrogen balance to increased intake

Day	Nitrogen in Food	Nitrogen in Feces	Nitrogen "Absorbed"	Nitrogen in Urine	Nitrogen Balance
	grams	*grams*	*grams*	*grams*	*grams*
1	14.40	0.70	13.70	13.60	+0.10
2	14.40	0.70	13.70	13.80	−0.10
3	14.40	0.70	13.70	13.60	+0.10
4	20.96	0.82	20.14	16.80	+3.34
5	20.96	0.82	20.14	18.20	+1.94
6	20.96	0.82	20.14	19.50	+0.64
7	20.96	0.82	20.14	20.00	+0.14

* Modified from H. C. Sherman, Chemistry of Food and Nutrition, 4th edition.

When the intake and output are equal, the body is said to be in *nitrogen equilibrium.* When the intake exceeds the output the body is in *positive nitrogen balance*—nitrogen is being retained. If the reverse is the case, i.e., the output exceeds the intake, the balance is said to be *negative*—the body is losing nitrogen. When the nitrogen of the food is increased a greater quantity for a time thereafter is retained, but the body soon becomes adjusted to the higher intake and gradually a balance is re-established (table 64.7).

The healthy adult requires protein to replace the inevitable loss of tissue protein. When given a sufficient amount of protein to repair this so-called "wear and tear" his output and intake of nitrogen will balance, i.e., he will be in nitrogen equilibrium. If his diet contains protein in excess of this amount the nitrogen not employed for repair is excreted and nitrogen equilibrium maintained. In starvation or on a low protein intake, or on a diet which lacks certain essential amino acids, the individual continues to excrete nitrogen derived from the dissolution of his own protoplasma, and so goes into negative balance. In children, in adults recovering from wasting diseases or undergoing muscular training, and in pregnant women, the body, if the protein intake is liberal, does not excrete as much nitrogen as it received. Nitrogen is retained for the manufacture of new tissue. The daily excretion of nitrogen of a man of average weight upon a nitrogen-free diet amounts to from 0.75 to 3 grams. It might be thought that nitrogen equilibrium could be re-established by simply feeding this quantity of protein nitrogen. It is found however that a considerably larger quantity is necessary. Part of the reason for this is that the amino acids are re-

quired by the body in different proportions from those present in the food protein. In order that the body shall obtain a sufficient quantity of suitable amino acids for the replacement of its own protoplasm and for the manufacture of various secretions and other essential materials, a relatively large assortment must be available from which it can choose. Those not required are discarded. For this reason, equilibrium can be established upon a smaller quantity of animal protein, such as beef muscle which contains amino acids more nearly in the same proportions as those in human body protein, rather than upon vegetable proteins. The wastage of nitrogen is less in the former instance. If the only protein in the food is one entirely lacking in certain essential amino acids (lysine, threonine, etc.) the loss of nitrogen resulting from the breakdown of such amino acids in the body's protoplasm cannot be replaced. A negative balance results no matter how much of the inferior protein has been fed (see ch. 65).

The quantity of protein required to establish nitrogen equilibrium depends very greatly upon the content of the diet in the other two food principles—fats and carbohydrates. It is impossible, for example, to establish nitrogen equilibrium in man upon an exclusively protein diet; the excretion of nitrogen always exceeds the intake even though the individual ingests protein to his full capacity. The reason for this is that man cannot consume and digest sufficient amounts of protein to satisfy his energy requirements. Under such circumstances he draws upon his stores of carbohydrates and fats, but after these have been exhausted the protein elements of his tissues are disrupted. The non-nitrogenous portions of the amino acid molecules are burned to make up the calorie deficiency, and, as a consequence, quantities of nitrogen derived from food and body protein are excreted. It has been calculated that the human subject would have to consume, daily, some 8 pounds of meat—practically an impossible feat for a civilized man—in order to furnish the necessary energy and maintain the body in nitrogen equilibrium. On the contrary, a carnivorous animal such as the dog which possesses a large capacity for the digestion of protein food[5] thrives

[5] The daily energy requirement of man is, say, 3000 Calories. Eight pounds of meat (3600 grams approximately) which is 20 per cent protein, has a caloric value of $(20/100) \times 3600 \times 4.1 = 2900$. The energy expenditure of an average-sized dog, on the other hand, is around 600 Calories. It can consume in less than a minute 2 pounds (900 grams) of meat, yielding more than 700 Calories.

upon a diet composed entirely of lean meat. The Eskimos are also capable—according to Krogh—of consuming relatively enormous quantities of meat. On a mixed diet, as we shall see immediately, nitrogen equilibrium can be established on a very low protein intake.

Protein Sparers

Carbohydrates and fats are called *protein sparers* since their presence in the diet relieves tissue protein of the necessity of furnishing energy. The protection of body protein by carbohydrate has been shown clearly by numerous experiments. The following experiment performed by Lusk upon himself may be cited in illustration of this important principle. After a period during which a mixed diet had been fed and a small positive nitrogen balance established, 350 grams of carbohydrate were withdrawn from the diet. The nitrogen excretion increased from 19.84 to 27.00 grams daily, the balance becoming negative. Also, the nitrogen excretion in the urine in starvation is nearly three times greater than that upon a diet, nitrogen-free, but of adequate energy value (i.e., one composed exclusively of fat and carbohydrate). The nonprotein food has reduced the breakdown of tissue protein.

The nitrogen excretion on such a protein-sparing diet is therefore an index of the inevitable disintegration of body protoplasm which occurs under ordinary physiological conditions. For this reason it was called, by Rubner, the "wear and tear" quota of protein metabolism (see p. 1302). One of the lowest values reported for nitrogen excretion is that of Boothby and Sandiford, namely, 1.74 grams daily (0.024 gram per kg. of body weight).

Carbohydrate exerts a specific sparing action quite apart from the fact that it furnishes energy and so relieves protein of the necessity of performing this duty, for the sparing effect exhibited by a given quantity of carbohydrate cannot be brought about by an amount of fat possessing double the caloric value. Carbohydrate when fed alone has a marked sparing action, whereas fat alone has little or no protein-sparing effect and a positive nitrogen balance cannot be established in man on a diet composed entirely of fat and protein. Nor will fat by itself, when given after a period of fasting, reduce the nitrogen excretion below that during the fast. Indeed, it actually increases the output of nitrogen. A diet whose calories, up to 50 per cent or more, are derived from fat and the remainder from carbohydrate has, however, as great a protein-sparing action as one whose calories are derived from carbohydrate alone. Lactic and pyruvic acids, products of carbohydrate metabolism, are also protein-sparers to some extent. The sparing effect of carbohydrates can be demonstrated in the well nourished animal as well as during starvation. When dogs in nitrogen equilibrium are given extra glucose, nitrogen is retained but the balance is re-established when the administration of glucose is stopped (Larson and Chaikoff).

The difference between the sparing actions of fat and carbohydrate is not easily explained. According to one view (Landergren) the specific sparing effect of carbohydrate depends upon the fact that glucose is vitally essential to the body and must be constantly supplied whatever the cost. If it is not available from outside sources or from the glycogen stores, tissue protein is broken down to yield materials from which it may be synthesized.

Another more probable explanation of the peculiar sparing action of carbohydrate is, that it is used in the synthesis of the amino acids which are incorporated into body proteins. According to this view the nitrogen resulting from the breakdown of tissue protein during fasting (or from tissue and food protein when the diet consists exclusively of protein and fat) is largely or entirely excreted. If, on the other hand, certain intermediary products of carbohydrate metabolism are available, e.g., pyruvic acid, etc., it is possible for amino acids to be resynthesized. That is, nitrogen which would otherwise be wasted is retained.

The Specific Dynamic Action of Food

When a subject in the basal state ingests food, an increase is observed in the rate of heat production. This increase above the BMR due to ingestion of food is known as the specific dynamic action (SDA) or the calorigenic effect of food. The amount of extra heat produced and the length of time during which the heat production is above basal depends upon the kind and amount of food ingested. The heat production commences to rise within an hour after the food has been eaten, attains a maximum in about the third hour and is maintained above the basal level for several hours. The greatest specific dynamic action is exerted by protein food. When protein is fed alone to a fasting animal, in an amount possessing a heat value equivalent to the animal's estimated basal metabolism, the heat production is raised 30 per cent or more above the basal level. Carbo-

TABLE 64.8

The results of an experiment of Rapport's which illustrates the utilization of the "waste heat" of the specific dynamic action of fat and glucose in exercise

Heat production at rest and in exercise and recovery

	Rest-ing (per hour)	Devia-tion from (A)	Excess in Ex-ercise and Re-covery (per kg. of Work)*	Devia-tion from (A)
	calo-ries	*per cent*	*calories*	*per cent*
A. In the postabsorp-tive state........	12.7		2.40	
B. After ingestion of fat...............	15.2	+19.7	2.54	+ 5.8
C. After ingestion of glucose...........	15.4	+21.3	0.38	−0.8
D. After ingestion of meat:				
100 grams..........	16.2	+27.6	3.38	+40.8
200 grams..........	17.8	+40.1	3.48	+45.0

* Based on ½-hour period after beginning of exercise.

hydrate causes a rise of about 6 per cent and fat of 4 per cent. That is to say, when a quantity of protein, carbohydrate or fat possessing an energy value of 100 Calories is fed separately to an animal whose basal metabolism is 100 Calories daily, its actual heat production will be 130, 106 or 104 Calories, respectively. The extra heat is generated by the combustion of body substance, so if loss of weight is to be prevented such an animal must be supplied with slightly more than 130 Calories if his diet is protein; or if carbohydrates and fats are also consumed extra allowances must be made for the amounts of these substances which have been included.

To take a theoretical case in illustration; if a man with a basal metabolism of 1500 Calories were kept on a 1500-Calorie diet, his body weight would decline until the total heat production (basal + SDA) would just equal the energy value of the food; from there on, the body weight, and total metabolism would remain steady at the new levels. But if the energy value of the food were again reduced to the point where it just balanced the basal metabolism (no allowance being made for SDA) a further weight loss and diminution in basal metabolism would occur, and should the adjustment of food to basal heat production be

carried out repeatedly, the body tissues would be gradually consumed, as long as the subject survived, in order to furnish the extra heat caused by SDA. In planning a diet, therefore, an extra caloric allowance must be made for the SDA of the food itself (ch. 73).

The extra heat resulting from protein food cannot be employed for the production of mechanical or other forms of energy. It is waste heat and is simply added to heat produced by the muscular exertion. A diet very rich in protein is therefore unsuited to heavy muscular work. The SDA of protein is an important factor, however, in the regulation of body temperature (ch. 70). With fat and carbohydrate the case is different, for the extra heat is harnessed in the performance of work. When exercise is undertaken upon either of these substances the heat due to their specific dynamic action is almost abolished, the extra energy being incorporated in the energy exchanges of the exercise (table 64.8).

When new tissue is being formed, i.e., when the nitrogen balance is positive, protein does not exert its usual specific dynamic action. Nor does it occur in a fever, such as typhoid, when there is great destruction of tissue protein. The ingested food then merely replaces or spares the tissue protein.

THE CAUSE OF THE SPECIFIC DYNAMIC ACTION

Several explanations for the phenomenon have been offered. It is certainly not due to digestive processes, i.e., to the contractions of smooth muscle of the alimentary canal or to the work entailed in the secretion of the digestive juices. This is proved by the following facts. Bones given to a dog, or agar agar, saline cathartics, water or meat extracts (which stimulate powerfully the gastric secretion) given to man, have no effect upon the heat production. Also, as already mentioned protein has no SDA when new tissue is being laid down. On the other hand, the injection of certain amino acids into the blood stream is followed by a specific dynamic effect.

The cause of the SDA is still imperfectly understood. It is generally accepted that the extra heat produced by protein food is associated with the metabolism of the amino acids. They exert in some way a stimulating effect upon the tissue cells, raising their heat production to a high level, i.e., the oxidation of the cells' own fuel material is increased; the rate of other metabolic processes within the cells is raised. The extra heat is not due to the amino acids themselves being utilized as fuel nor to a stimulating action upon the tissue cells of these materials in the unchanged state. It is in the intermediary reactions of the amino acids that the specific dynamic action of protein should be sought—e.g., in the deamination process. Borsook and Winegarden conclude from their studies that the SDA of protein results from the metabolism (deamination and urea production) and the excretion of nitrogen; an increased excretion of nitrogen accompanies the greater heat production. According to Borsook an increase of from 7 to 10 Calories of extra heat are produced for each gram of extra nitrogen excreted. The remainder of the extra heat produced is a more variable and usually a larger fraction of the total; it is attributed to the metabolism of the carbon part of the protein molecule. There is a considerable body of evidence for the view that the deamination of the amino acids with the formation of urea contributes very considerably to the specific dynamic action of protein. Lundsgaard found, for example, that although the administration of sodium acetate or sodium lactate was followed by only a slight increase in heat production, ammonium acetate or ammonium lactate caused a pronounced rise; even ammonium chloride caused a well marked increase in heat production.

The reactions responsible for the SDA of protein are apparently situated in the liver and not in the tissue cells generally, since Wilhelmj, Bollman and Mann were unable to obtain any effect in hepatectomized dogs following the injection of amino acids. Dock also found that after the administration of casein to rats the oxygen consumption of the hindquarters (muscular tissue) was 8 per cent greater than in the corresponding tissues of a control group, whereas the oxygen consumption of the abdominal viscera was 141 per cent greater.

The specific dynamic action of carbohydrate is thought to represent the energy liberated in excess of that required for the conversion of glucose to glycogen. After a fast which depletes the glycogen stores, ingested glucose is oxidized in negligible amounts, yet it causes a pronounced specific dynamic action (Dann and Chambers).

The specific dynamic action of fat is ascribed to the increased concentration of fat in the tissue fluids and, as a consequence, to its more rapid oxidation ("plethora theory" of Lusk).

The glands of internal secretion appear to have no direct influence upon the SDA of protein; the usual effect has been observed in a cretin with a basal metabolic rate 20 per cent below normal and it is not altered in hyperthyroidism. Thyroidectomy in animals is said, however, to reduce the SDA of carbohydrate and fat. Cushing and Fulton found the SDA of protein within the normal range in a number of cases of pituitary disease (hypopituitarism and acromegaly). Gaebler found it of normal value in hypophysectomized animals. In undernutrition the SDA of all foods is increased.

It is, according to some observers, diminished in simple obesity (ch. 69).

The SDA of carbohydrate and protein or of carbohydrate and fat is less than the sum of the values of each when fed separately. There is only a slight discrepancy, however, between the values for protein and fat, fed together or separately.

REFERENCES

ALMQUIST, H. J. AND MECCHI, E. J. Biol. Chem., 1940, **135**, 355.

BACH, S. J. Biol. Rev., 1945, **20**, 158.

BENEDICT, S. R., AND OSTERBERG, E. J. Biol. Chem., 1923, **56**, 229.

BLOCH, K. AND SCHOENHEIMER, R. J. Biol. Chem., 1940, **133**, 633.

BOLLMAN, J. L., MANN, F. C. AND MAGATH, T. B. Am. J. Physiol., 1924, **69**, 371; 1926, **78**, 258; 1930, **92**, 92.

BOOTHBY, W. M. Arch. Int. Med., 1934, **53**, 39.

BORSOOK, H. AND DUBNOFF, J. W. J. Biol. Chem., 1940, **132**, 559.

BORSOOK, H. AND KEIGHLEY, G. L. Proc. Roy. Soc., London, ser. B, 1935, **118**, 488.

BORSOOK, H. AND WINEGARDEN, H. M. Proc. Nat. Acad. Sc., 1931, **17**, 31. Ibid., p. 75.

BORSOOK, H. AND DUBNOFF, J. W. J. Biol. Chem., 1941, **141**, 717.

BORSOOK, H. AND DUBNOFF, J. W. J. Biol. Chem., 1947, **169**, 247.

BRAND, E. AND ASSOCIATES. Am. J. Physiol., 1929, **90**, 296 (Proc.). J. Biol. Chem., 1930, **87**, ix; 1932, **92**, lix. J. A. M. A., 1933, **101**, 1047.

BRAUNSTEIN, A. E. AND KRITZMANN, M. G. Enzymologia, 1937, **2**, 129.

CHAMBERS, W. H. AND LUSK, G. J. Biol. Chem., 1930, **85**, 611.

COHEN, P. P. Fed. Proc., 1942, **1**, 273.

COHEN, P. P. AND HAYANO, M. J. Biol. Chem., 1948, **166**, 239, 251; 1948, **172**, 405.

COHN, M., Enzymes: Units of biological structure and function. Edited by O. H. Gaebler. Academic Press, Inc., New York, 1956.

COX, G. J. AND ROSE, W. C. J. Biol. Chem., 1926, **68**, 781.

CUSHING, H. AND FULTON, M. N. Arch. Int. Med., 1932, **50**, 649.

DANN, M. AND CHAMBERS, W. H. J. Biol. Chem., 1930, **89**, 675.

DENIS, W. AND ASSOCIATES. J. Biol. Chem., 1921, **49**, 311. Arch. Int. Med., 1928, **41**, 385.

DOCK, W. Am. J. Physiol., 1931, **97**, 117.

DU VIGNEAUD, V. AND ASSOCIATES. J. Biol. Chem., 1939, **131**, 57.

EMBDEN, G. AND SCHMITZ, E. Biochem Ztschr., 1910, **29**, 423.

Enzymes: Units of biological structure and function. Edited by O. H. Gaebler, Academic Press, Inc., New York, 1956.

FOLIN, O. Am. J. Physiol., 1905, **13**, 45, 66, 117.

GAEBLER, O. H. J. Biol. Chem., 1929, **81**, 41.

GORNALL, A. G. AND HUNTER, A. Biochem. J., 1941, **35**, 650.

GRAHAM, W. R., HOUCHIN, O. B. AND TURNER, C. W. J. Biol. Chem., 1937, **120**, 29.

HANDLER, P., Brookhaven Symposia in biol., 1952, **5**, 99.

HOLT, J. E. AND ASSOCIATES. Bull. Johns Hopkins Hosp., 1944, **74**, 308.

HOUSSAY, B. A. AND BIASOTTI, A. J. Physiol., 1932, **77**, 81. Endocrinology, 1931, **15**, 511.

JONES, M. E., SPECTOR, L., AND LIPMANN, F. J. Am. Chem. Soc., 1955, **77**, 819.

KNOOP, F. Ztschr. physiol. Chem., 1910, **67**, 489; 1925, **146**, 267.

KREBS, H. A. Biochem. J., 1935, **29**, 1951.

KREBS, H. A. AND HENSELEIT, K. Ztschr. physiol. Chem., 1932, **210**, 33.

LARSON, P. S. AND CHAIKOFF, I. L. J. Nutrition, 1937, **13**, 287.

LEUTHARDT, F. Ztschr. physiol. Chem., 1938, **252**, 238.

LUNDSGAARD, E. Skandinav. Arch. Physiol., 1931, **62**, 223. Ibid., p. 243.

MACLEOD, J. J. R. The fuel of life. Princeton University Press, Princeton, N. J., 1928.

MANN, F. C. AND ASSOCIATES. Am. J. Physiol., 1928, **87**, 497.

MARSHALL, R. O., HALL, L. M., AND COHEN, P. P. Biochem. et biophys. Acta, 1955, **17**, 279.

MARTIN, G. J. Proc. Soc. Exper. Biol. & Med., 1944, **55**, 182.

NEEDHAM, D. M. Biochem. J., 1930, **24**, 208.

RABINOWITCH, I. M. J. Biol. Chem., 1929, **83**, 333.

RAPPORT, D. AND BEARD, H. H. J. Biol. Chem., 1927, **73**, 299.

RATNER, S. Fed. Proc., 1949, **8**, 603.

RATNER, S., AND PETRACK, B. J. Biol. Chem., 1953, **200**, 175.

REICHARD, P. AND HANSHOFF, G. Acta. Chem. Scand., 1956, **10**, 548.

ROSE, W. C. AND BUNNEY, W. E. J. Biol. Chem., 128, **76**, 521.

ROSE, W. C. AND SCULL, C. W. J. Biol. Chem., 1930, **89**, 109.

SADOU, D. P. Missouri Agric. Exper. Station, Res. Bull., 1947, **108**, 1.

SCHOENHEIMER, R. AND ASSOCIATES. J. Biol. Chem., 1942, **144**, 541.

SHERWIN, C. P. AND HARROW, B. J. Biol. Chem., 1926, **70**, 683.

TROWELL, O. A. J. Physiol., 1941, **100**, 432.

DU VIGNEAUD, V. Harvey Lectures, 1942—1943; Biol. Symposia, 1941, **5**, 234.

WALKER, M. B. Lancet, 1934, **1**, 1200; 1935, **1**, 448.

Monographs and Reviews

BEARD, H. H. Ann. Rev. Biochem., 1941, **10**, 246.

BORSOOK, H. Biol. Rev., 1936, **11**, 147.

BORSOOK, H. Chemical pathways of metabolism. Edited by D. Greenberg. Academic Press, Inc., New York, 1954, **2**, 211.

CATHCART, E. P. The physiology of protein metabolism. Longmans Green & Co., London, 1921.

DAKIN, H. D. Oxidations and reductions in the animal body. Longmanns Green & Co., London, 1922.

DU VIGNEAUD, V. AND DYER. Ann. Rev. Biochem. 1936, **5**, 159.

HUNTER, A. Physiol. Rev., 1922, **2**, 586. Creatine and creatinine. Longmans, Green & Co., London, 1928.

KOTAKI, Y. Ann. Rev. Biochem., 1934, **3**, 193.

LEWIS, H. B. Physiol. Rev., 1924, **4**, 394.

LUSK, G. The elements of the science of nutrition. W. B. Saunders Company, Philadelphia, 1906.

LUSK, G. Medicine, 1922, **1**, 311. J. Nutrition, 1930, **3**, 519.

MANN, F. C. Medicine, 1927, **6**, 419.

MITCHELL, H. H. AND HAMILTON, T. S. The biochemistry of the amino acids. Chemical Catalog Co., New York, 1929.

OSBORNE, F. B. The vegetable proteins. Longmans, Green & Co., London, 1924.

PETERS, J. P. AND VAN SLYKE, D. D. Quantitative clinical chemistry. Vol. I. The Williams & Wilkins Co., Baltimore, 1931.

PLIMMER, R. H. A. The chemical constitution of the proteins. Longmans, Green & Co., London, 1917.

RAPPORT, D. Physiol. Rev., 1930, **10**, 349.

RATNER, S. Urea synthesis and metabolism of arginine and citrulline. Advances in Enzymol., 1954, **15**, 319.

SCHOENHEIMER, R. AND RITTENBERG, D. Physiol. Rev., 1940, **20**, 218.

SHERMAN, H. C. The chemistry of food and nutrition. Macmillan, New York, 1933.

J. Cell. & Comp. Physiol. 1956. Suppl. 1.

Symposium on amino acid metabolism. Edited by D. McElroy and B. Glass. Johns Hopkins Press, Baltimore, 1955.

WILHELMJ, C. M. Physiol. Rev., 1935, **15**, 202.

CHAPTER 65

Protein Metabolism—Continued

The Nutritional Value of Various Proteins

Over the years techniques for the biological evaluation of proteins in foods have become more sophisticated, the four main procedures being based upon: (1) growth, (2) nitrogen balance, (3) tissue regeneration, and (4) estimation of the essential amino acid composition of the isolated protein or natural foodstuff. Digestibility is the first factor to consider because amino acids cannot be utilized unless they are absorbed. The second factor is the suitability of the constituent amino acids for the construction of tissue protein.

1. THE DIGESTIBILITY OF PROTEINS. The digestibility of a particular protein is expressed as a percentage of the food nitrogen which has been absorbed. This percentage value is referred to as the *coefficient of digestibility*. For example, if the food contains 10 g. of nitrogen and it is found that 9.5 g. have been absorbed, the digestibility is 95 per cent. Although by far the greater part of the nitrogen arising from the catabolism of amino acids within the body is excreted in the urine, a small fraction is eliminated through the secretions of the digestive glands and intestinal mucosa. This, the so-called *metabolic nitrogen*, is estimated from the nitrogen of the feces upon a nitrogen-free diet. In a man it amounts to from 0.5 to 1.5 g. daily, varying in amount with the bulk (roughage) of the diet. In order to determine the proportion of a given protein which has undergone digestion and absorption, the total nitrogen content of the ingested protein is estimated assuming that 6.25 g. of protein equals 1 g. of nitrogen, and from this value the nitrogen of the feces less that for the metabolic nitrogen is subtracted. Thus:

absorbed N = food N − (fecal N − metabolic N)

Proteins of animal origin have the highest digestibility (95 to 100 per cent) with the wastage in digestion only 5 per cent or less. The digestibility of the proteins of nuts and fruits is low, that of the proteins of legumes and of potatoes is good (around 80 per cent) (see table 65.1), and that of wheat proteins is from 90 to 100 per cent, approaching that for animal proteins.

2. THE SUITABILITY OF A GIVEN PROTEIN FOR

THE SYNTHESIS OF BODY PROTEIN. This depends upon the amino acid constitution of the protein. It is obvious that the greater the proportion of amino acids in the dietary protein which can serve for the construction of tissue protein, the greater will be its potential nutritive value. In other words, the more closely the amino acid assortment in the food protein resembles that in body protein the less of the former need be furnished. A smaller proportion of the amino acids will then be discarded, their nitrogen eventually being excreted in the urine, i.e., less of the food protein will be wasted.

Growth was the first method tried for comparing the nutritional value of proteins and today it is still perhaps the most extensively used procedure.

Methods employed for estimating the nutritive values of proteins. Osborne and Mendel, employing rats, added a known amount of the protein to be tested to a diet free from protein, but believed to be adequate in other respects (i.e., one possessing the necessary energy value, minerals, and the vitamins then known). They expressed the nutritive value of the protein as the weight, in grams, gained by the animals per gram of protein fed, in the case of young rats (value for growth), or in the case of adult rats, the smallest quantity of the fed protein in grams, per gram of rat per week, necessary to maintain a constant body weight (value for maintenance). McCollum and associates also employed rats, feeding a basal diet of first class quality in all respects except that it lacked protein. The percentage of any protein required to be added to the food mixture in order to promote normal nutrition gave an index of its nutritive value. The general state of nutrition of the animals, as indicated by rate of growth, fertility, care of young and longevity, was noted over a period corresponding to two-thirds or more of their life span. On this basis, proteins were classed as "excellent" "good" or "poor." An excellent or first class protein is one which "will support nearly optimum nutrition over periods approximating two-thirds or more of the normal life span of the rat when fed in amount corresponding to 9 per cent in the food mixture." Thus in rats about 9 per cent appeared to be the minimal level for a protein of the highest nutritive value. Inferior proteins must be fed at higher levels. In other

TABLE 65.1

Protein values of foods for maintenance and growth:
Level of protein feeding, 8 to 10 per cent

(After Mitchell and Hamilton)

Food	Water Content[a]	Protein Content[a] on Fresh Basis	Quality of Protein — Digestibility	Quality of Protein — Biological value	Metabolic Protein in Feces on Fresh Food Basis	Protein Value of Food on Fresh Basis
	per cent	*per cent*	*per cent*	*per cent*	*per cent*	*per cent*
Whole egg[c]..	73.2	13.2	100	94	0.4	12.0
Milk........	87.0	3.3	100	85	0.2	2.6
Egg white[c]..	86.2	12.3	100	83	0.2	10.0
Beef liver...	71.2	20.4	90	77	0.4	14.9
Beef kidney.	76.7	16.6	99	77	0.3	12.3
Beef heart...	62.6	16.0	100	74	0.5	11.3
Beef round..	70.0	21.3	96	69	0.4	13.7
Pork ham...	60.0	25.0	100	74	0.6	17.9
Veal[d]........	73.4	20.7	100	62	0.4	12.4
Rolled oats..	7.7	16.7	90	65	1.3	9.8
Whole wheat.	11.4	13.8	91	67	1.3	7.1
White flour..	12.8	10.8	100	52	1.3	4.3
Whole corn..	10.3	7.5	95	60	1.3	3.0
Potato......	78.3	3.2	78	67	0.3	0.8
Navy beans[c].	12.6	22.5	76	38	1.3	4.2

[a] Average analyses taken, as far as possible, from Bulletin 28 (revised), Office of Experiment Stations, U. S. Dept. of Agriculture.

[b] The metabolic nitrogen in the feces is assumed to equal 0.23 gram per 100 grams of dry matter of food. See Bulletin National Research Council, 1926, xi, part 1, no. 55, p. 23.

[c] Cooked.

[d] The cut tested was not recorded. It proved to be very fibrous. Analysis for shoulder cut assumed.

species the protein requirement may be greater. In all species the requirement is considerably higher during the growing period than for maintenance in adult life.

The ratio of the grams of body weight gained (in a specified time) to the grams of protein consumed is often called the protein efficiency ratio (P.E.R.). Carefully conducted studies in a number of laboratories indicate that protein efficiency ratios relate well to estimates of nutritive quality made by other methods of evaluating proteins. In 1959 Chapman, Castello and Campbell described a standardized method for determining P.E.R. values to give more reproducible results. The relative values of several food proteins are shown below in descending order.

> Fish muscle, beef muscle
> Beef liver and kidney
> Egg (whole)

Milk
Soya bean
Oats (rolled)
Wheat (whole)

A food may contain a first class protein in small amounts or a poor protein in larger amounts. In some foods the protein is both poor in quality and low in amount whereas in others both the quantity and quality of the protein are high. The *protein value* of a food must take both these factors into account.

In order to know the value of a food as a source of protein the "biological value" must be considered as well as the quantity present (nitrogen $\times$ 6.25). The biological value of a protein is defined as

$$\frac{\text{Dietary N retained}}{\text{Dietary N absorbed}} \times 100.$$

This ratio, also referred to as *net protein utilization* (N.P.U.), can be represented algebraically as

$$\text{N.P.U.} = N_I - \frac{(N_U + N_F)}{N_I} \times 100$$

where N_I represents nitrogen intake, N_U and N_F urinary and fecal excretion of nitrogen.

The following data, from Mitchell, illustrate the calculation of biological value of a protein.

A rat receiving a diet containing about 4 per cent of protein, ingested daily 56.9 mg. of nitrogen and excreted 27.6 mg. of nitrogen in the feces. Of the latter 21.7 mg. constituted metabolic nitrogen (p. 791). The unabsorbed nitrogen was therefore only (27.6 − 21.7 =) 5.9 mg., and the absorbed nitrogen (56.9 − 5.9 =) 51.0 mg. The daily urinary nitrogen was 48.6 mg. Of this, 37.7 was derived from the body tissues (estimated from urinary nitrogen on a nitrogen-free diet (p. 785). The total urinary nitrogen less this value for the endogenous nitrogen must represent the quantity of absorbed nitrogen which was excreted, that is, (48.6 − 37.7 =) 10.9 mg. is the quantity of absorbed nitrogen which had been wasted in metabolism. The absorbed nitrogen, as just stated, amounted to 51.0. So, (51.0 − 10.9 =) 40.1 mg. were retained in the body. The biological value of the dietary protein was therefore ((40.1/51.1) × 100 =) 79 per cent.

Nitrogen balance (N_B), the difference between dietary nitrogen intake and nitrogen excreted, is another useful tool in the evaluation of the nutritive value of proteins. It is expressed algebraically as $N_B = N_I - (N_U + N_F)$. When the nitrogen intake (N_I) just equals the nitrogen excretion ($N_U + N_F$) the animal is said to be in equilibrium. When N_I is greater than ($N_U + N_F$) the animal is retaining nitrogen and is said to be in positive balance; if the nitrogen excreted exceeds the intake, the body is losing nitrogen and is said to be in negative balance. A number of factors may alter nitrogen balance. In order that none of the protein shall be burned for energy purposes, its level in the diet is kept low, i.e., there should be no excess over that required for growth or maintenance. Calorie intake affects protein utilization. The calorie intake for optimal nitrogen retention varies with age, being relatively high in weanlings and falling to a value that is characteristic of the adult of the species. Deficiencies of one or more essential amino acids, or any other form of malnutrition, will modify the nitrogen balance. Also, in some pathological states the animal as whole may be in nitrogen equilibrium or even positive balance, and yet be losing nitrogen from one or more tissues. Further, the possibility must be kept in mind that adaptive changes do occur during nitrogen balance studies and that these will complicate the interpretation of the findings.

When due attention is paid to the factors mentioned above their disturbing effects may be kept to a minimum and protein may be evaluated by comparing the amount of nitrogen needed to maintain equilibrium. This method is called the *determination of protein minima.* Protein minima of several common proteins for a normal dog with full protein stores were estimated to be (g. N/day/kg. body weight): egg white 0.17, whole egg 0.22, beef 0.25, casein 0.27, peanut flour 0.35, wheat gluten 0.44. The influence of nutritional status is shown by the finding that in a group of protein-depleted dogs the values were approximately: egg white 0.06, whole egg 0.065, casein 0.083 and wheat gluten 0.10.

The rat-repletion method (sometimes called

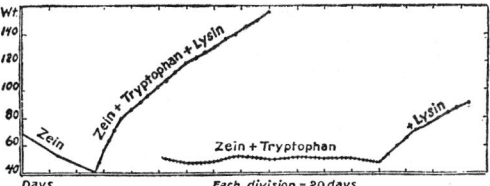

FIG. 65.1 Shows the indispensability of lysine for growth. (After Mendel.)

tissue regeneration method) of determining the nutritive quality of proteins is considered by many to be the most rapid and useful. This newer procedure, developed during the period 1944 to 1950 and since widely used, depends upon first depleting the protein stores of an adult animal (usually until it has lost 25% of the initial body weight). Good correlation is obtained between gain in weight during repletion and regeneration of blood, liver or carcass proteins. Thus rate of recovery of weight was shown to provide a good measure of nutritive value.

The value of a protein in nutrition depends primarily upon its amino acid constitution. Block and Mitchell have shown a very close correlation between the biological value of a protein and its amino acid content. Thus, by the hydrolysis of a protein and determination of its amino acid composition, an estimate of its nutritive value can be made. Although animal proteins are usually superior to those of plant origin, no generalization is possible. In table 65.2 the amino acid percentages in the proteins of liver and of soy bean are compared.

THE ESSENTIAL IMPORTANCE OF CERTAIN AMINO ACIDS FOR GROWTH AND MAINTENANCE

In 1907 Willcock and Hopkins found that when young mice were fed upon a diet which contained zein (a protein of maize) as its sole protein, growth was arrested and the animals died in about 17 days. Zein is almost completely free from tryptophane. Yet, the addition of this amino acid to the diet was not capable of promoting growth, and the survival period of the animals was extended to only 33 days. The addition of tyrosine was without effect since zein already contains this amino acid in adequate amounts. Later it was shown by Osborne and Mendel that when lysine, which is also absent from this protein was added to the zein diet together with tryptophane, the animals grew normally and remained in good health (fig. 65.1). Lysine added alone was of no more benefit than tryptophane alone. Osborne and Mendel determined the essentiality of individual amino

TABLE 65.2

(From data of Block and Mitchell)

Approximate amino acid content of liver and of soy bean compared

(Calculated to 16.0 grams of nitrogen)

Amino Acid	Liver	Soy Bean
	grams	*grams*
Arginine	6.6	7.1
Histidine	3.1	2.3
Lysine	6.7	5.8
Tyrosine	4.6	4.1
Tryptophane	1.4	1.2
Phenylalanine	6.1	5.7
Cystine	1.4	1.9
Methionine	3.2	2.0
Threonine	4.8	4.0
Leucine	8.4	6.6
Isoleucine	5.6	4.7
Valine	6.2	4.2

acids by feeding purified proteins known to be deficient in specific constituents and observing changes in weight during the test period. The classical studies of W. C. Rose and his colleagues during the 1930's, which revealed a new essential amino acid (threonine), were based upon feeding a mixture of purified amino acids, in the ratio found in casein, omitting a single amino acid at a time.

Gelatin, like zein, is an incomplete protein. It lacks tyrosine and tryptophane and is very deficient in cystine. A diet which contains gelatin as its sole protein will not permit growth nor even maintain nitrogen equilibrium in an adult animal. When, however, the lacking amino acids are added to the gelatin diet its defects are corrected.

Casein. Methionine (3%) is the limiting essential amino acid in casein, with threonine the second one; glycine and cystine are almost absent. When casein is fed in sufficient quantity—about 18 per cent of the diet—normal growth results (fig. 65.2). Similar growth can be achieved with smaller casein intake if a supplement of cystine is added to provide adequate organic sulfur.

Edestin (a protein in hemp seed) is relatively poor in lysine as is also *gliadin* (of wheat) whereas *phaseolin* (of navy bean) is deficient in cystine and tryptophane. If these, or other incomplete proteins, are supplemented by adding to the diet the amino acids in which they are deficient, growth is supported. Also when the amino acid deficiency is not too great, growth can be promoted by increasing the percentage of the incomplete protein in the diet (see table 65.3).

An essential or indispensable amino acid has been defined by Rose as one that cannot be synthesized by the animal organism out of the materials ordinarily available, at a speed commensurate with the demands for normal growth and which must therefore be supplied in the diet.

Of the 25 amino acids which have been identified as constituting protein material, 10 are indispensable for normal growth. They are as follows.

Arginine	Methionine
Histidine	Phenylalanine
Isoleucine	Threonine
Leucine	Tryptophane
Lysine	Valine

In early studies it was found that when casein

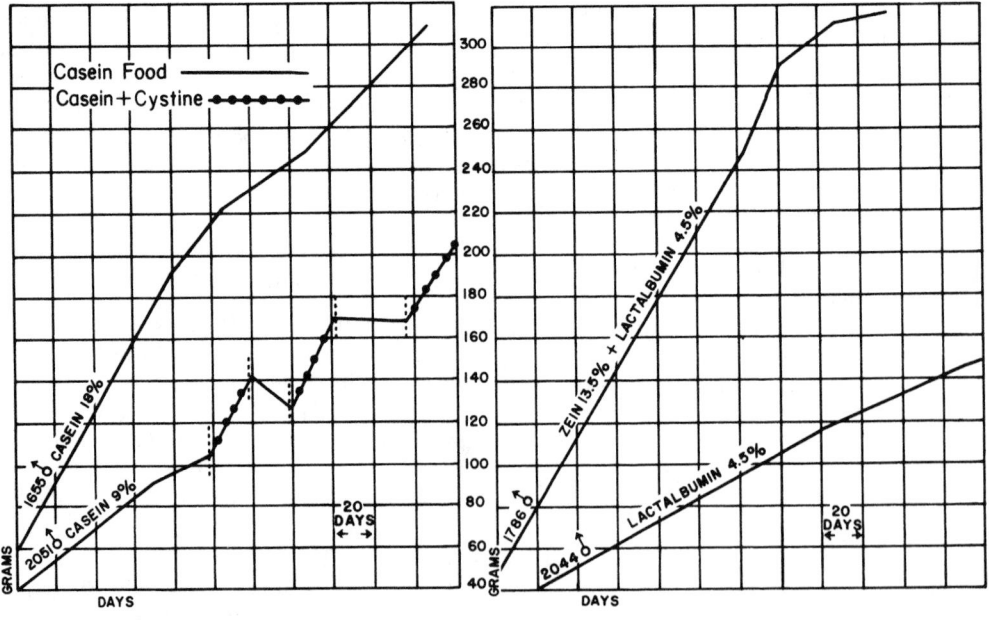

FIG. 65.2. *Chart on left* shows satisfactory growth of rat when 18 per cent of casein was present in the diet as the sole protein. With a smaller amount of casein—9 per cent—much less rapid growth ensued. That the insufficiency of the smaller amount of casein is essentially due to its relative deficiency in cystine is shown by the marked accelerating influence upon growth brought about by the addition of this amino acid to the food containing 9 per cent of casein and the prompt retardation of growth which resulted from the withdrawal of cystine from the diet. *Chart on right* shows the favorable effect upon growth of supplementing a protein (zein), incapable of maintaining animals when it is the sole protein furnished in the diet, with a more "perfect" protein (lactalbumin). The proportion of the lactalbumin used—4.5 per cent—was of itself insufficient for full growth. It evidently furnished the amino acid groups which were lacking in zein. (After Mendel.)

TABLE 65.3[a]

The amino acid content of a number of proteins, grams per cent

Amino Acid	Gelatin	Casein	Lactal-bumin	Egg Albumin	Gliadin	Zein	Edistin
Glycine	25.5	0.4	0.4	0.0	0.0	0.0	3.8
Alanine	8.7	1.8	2.4	2.2	2.0	9.8	3.6
Valine	0.0	7.9	3.3	2.5	3.3	1.9	
Leucine-isoleucine	7.1	9.7	14.0	10.7	6.6	25.0	20.9
Aspartic acid	3.4	4.1	9.3	6.2	0.8	1.8	10.2
Glutamic acid	5.8	21.8	12.9	13.3	43.7	31.3	19.2
Hydroxyglutamic acid	0.0	10.5	10.0		2.4	2.5	
Serine	0.4	0.5	1.8		0.1	1.0	0.3
Proline	9.5	8.0	3.8	3.6	13.2	9.0	4.1
Hydroxyproline	14.1	0.2				0.0	2.0
Phenylalanine	1.4	3.9	1.2	5.1	2.3	7.6	3.1
Tyrosine	0.01	6.5	1.9	4.0	3.1	5.9	4.5
Cystine	0.17	0.3	4.0	0.9	2.4	0.8	1.0
Arginine	9.1	5.2	3.0	6.0	3.2	1.8	15.8
Histidine	0.9	2.6	1.5	2.3	2.1	1.2	2.1
Lysine	5.9	7.6	8.4	3.8	0.6	0.0	2.2
Tryptophane	0.0	2.2	2.7	1.3	0.8	0.17	1.5
Total	92.4	94.8	81.9	63.2	91.8	103.4	96.6

[a] Modified from Mitchell and Hamilton, The Biochemistry of the Amino Acids, Am. Chem. Soc. Monograph Series No. 48, p. 191.

was the sole protein of the diet, growth did not occur unless it was fed in relatively large amounts or in smaller amounts supplemented with *cystine*. This observation led for many years to the belief that cystine is indispensable. The other sulfur-containing amino acid, *methionine*, had not yet been discovered and the mistaken conclusion resulted from the fact that cystine can substitute *in part* for methionine; cystine itself is not essential, for it can be *completely* replaced in the diet by methionine[1] which can be converted to cystine in the body. Proof that tissue cystine can be formed from dietary methionine was obtained by Tarver and Schmidt who fed animals methionine containing the radioactive isotope of sulfur (S^{35}) and later isolated isotopic cystine from their tissues. Cystine is a constituent of plasma protein and unless it or methionine is furnished in adequate amounts in the diet hypoproteinemia results. Cystine is also an essential component of keratin, the protein of hair, feathers, nails, horn, etc. *Arginine* can be synthesized in the body but not in adequate amounts for normal growth; it is

[1] To make this point clear we may use an illustration the case of a typesetter who has lost a number of dies for, say, the letter A. He can continue to set type so long as his supply of A letters lasts, but when this is exhausted his work must cease though there is still a large number of other letters. His typesetting is limited by his supply of A letters.

therefore an essential constituent of the diet of young animals. *Tyrosine* can be formed from phenylalanine. In rats deprived of *valine* grave nutritional defects develop which have been the subject of studies of Epstein and Rose. The animals become very sensitive to touch and show severe muscular incoordination, (e.g., staggering gait and circus movements) together with loss of appetite, emaciation and eventually death.

The amino acid requirements for building new tissue (growth) are more exacting than those for repair (maintenance), i.e., for the maintenance of nitrogen equilibrium in the adult and the prevention of a loss of weight. Some amino acids which are essential for the growing animal can be dispensed with in the adult. Arginine, for example, is not required in the diet of the adult dog, and in the adult rat nitrogen equilibrium can be maintained upon a diet lacking in this amino acid, but, as just mentioned, it is not synthesized rapidly enough to promote maximal growth. Even of the amino acids essential for maintenance the level in the diet need not be as high for maintenance as for growth. Adult man can be maintained in nitrogen equilibrium upon eight amino acids, histidine being dispensable.

The utilization of a protein deficient in one or other amino acid is limited by that deficiency. For example, if edestin, which is poor in lysine, is

TABLE 65.4[a]

Character of proteins in some common foods

Food Materials	Chief Kinds of Protein Present	Complete or Incomplete
Almonds...	Excelsin	Complete
Cheese...	Casein	Complete (low in cystine)
	Lactalbumin	Complete
	Glutelin	Complete
Corn.....	Zein	Incomplete (lacks lysine and tryptophane, low in cystine)
Eggs.....	Ovalbumin	Complete
	Ovovitellin	Complete
Gelatin....	Gelatin	Incomplete (lacks tryptophane and tyrosine; only a trace of cystine, high in lysine)
Lean meat	Albumin	Complete
	Myosin	Complete
Milk.....	Casein	Complete (low in cystine)
	Lactalbumin	Complete
Navy beans	Phaseolin	Incomplete (low in cystine)
Peas......	Legumin	Incomplete (low in cystine)
Soy beans	Glycinin	Complete
	Legumelin	Incomplete
Wheat....	Gliadin	Incomplete (lacks lysine)
	Glutenin	Complete

[a] From M. S. Rose, *Foundations of Nutrition.*

the sole protein of the diet, the other amino acids of which it is composed are utilized only in certain proportions limited by the lysine content. A large part of the remainder is discarded. Similarly the utilization of casein is limited by its cystine plus methionine content. Now if lysine is added to the diet of which edestin is the sole protein, or cystine or methionine is added to the casein diet, the other amino acids in these proteins can be utilized and built into body tissue. Lysine is essential for maintenance as well as for growth, but for the former, relatively small quantities are required. Gliadin (of wheat), which contains less than 1 per cent lysine, is inadequate for growth even though fed in large quantities but is suitable as the sole source of protein in an adult. Zein, on the other hand, which is entirely lacking in lysine and contains little tryptophane is inadequate for

either growth or maintenance. Serum albumin is deficient in tryptophane and isoleucine; it will not promote growth in young rats and will scarcely maintain body weight. The proteins of several common foods are given in table 65.4.

Most of the work relating to the indispensability of the various amino acids has been carried out upon rats. The amino acid requirements of adult man have been investigated by Holt and his colleagues and by Rose and his coworkers. Their results, in general, accord with those of animal experiments. Methionine, as the sole source of sulfur-containing amino acids, was found to be capable of maintaining nitrogen equilibrium. The nitrogen balance could not be maintained upon a diet completely lacking in *lysine*, whereas *histidine* and *arginine* proved to be dispensable. Others have found, however, that while nitrogen equilibrium can be maintained in men on a diet lacking in histidine, loss of weight occurred. *Tryptophane* was found to be indispensable, the subjects developing negative nitrogen balances within a few days after having been placed upon a diet lacking in this amino acid; nor could nitrogen equilibrium be maintained when *valine, threonine, leucine, isoleucine* or *phenylalanine* was lacking from the diet. *Lysine* and *methionine* were also found to be indispensable, but as mentioned above, adults can be maintained in nitrogen equilibrium in the absence of histidine.

Rose and his collaborators using synthetic diets have attempted to determine quantitatively the amino acid requirements of man. The diets used supplied from 6.7 to 7.1 grams of nitrogen per day and contained in addition to essential amino acids, glycine and urea. The latter two compounds served as a source of nitrogen for the synthesis of the dispensable amino acids. The amount of a given amino acid in the diet was decreased until the nitrogen balance of the subject became negative. The diet was then supplemented with the amino acid until nitrogen equilibrium was reestablished. The amino acid requirements of man determined by Rose in this manner are shown in table 65.5.

It seems that, generally speaking, the several amino acids which have been found indispensable for rats are also essential dietary constituents for other mammals, including man. There are, however, certain minor species differences, the growing mouse, for example, can dispense with arginine in the diet, since, apparently, it can synthesize this amino acid in greater amounts than can the rat. *Glycine* which is required especially for the manufacture of collagenous tissue and of protoporphyrin (ch. 27) can be synthesized by the body and, therefore, is not an essential constituent of the diet in mammals. It is indispensable, however, for the growth of chicks, although it can be replaced in this species by creatine. The chick, also unlike the rat, has no ability to synthesize arginine. The essential or nonessential nature of a particular amino acid, as well as the species differences, may possibly depend upon bacterial synthesis in the intestine; the bacterial synthesis of amino acids and even of protein is known to occur in the intestinal tract of ruminants. It has been found by Martin, for example, that rats fed a diet containing all the essential amino acids and the known vitamins fail to grow if succinylsulfathiazole, a bacteriostatic drug, is added to the food.

The most suitable proteins for growth are those of animal origin and especially those which nature has provided for the nourishment of the growing animal, namely,

lactalbumin (of milk)   *ovovitellin* (of hen's egg)
ovalbumin (of hen's egg)

These support growth when given at a level of about 9 or 10 per cent in the diet. Next in order of their biological value come,

     proteins of meat   *glutelin* (maize)
     glutenin (wheat)   *glycinin* (soy bean)
     casein (milk)

These support growth if given in sufficiently high concentration in the diet. Casein, for instance, is required to be given at a level of 18 per cent for growth and 10 to 12 per cent for maintenance. A comparison of the value for growth of several proteins, when given in the same percentage in the diet, is shown in figure 65.3.

The following vegetable proteins are incapable of supporting growth but are suitable for maintenance:

     gliadin (wheat or rye)
     legumin (pea)
     legumelin (soy bean)
     phaseolin (kidney bean)
     hordein (barley)

The following incomplete proteins are unsuitable for either growth or maintenance:

     zein
     gelatin

The biological values of the protein mixtures in the various foods are shown in table 65.1, p. 1314, from which it is seen that the values are in descending order as follows: eggs, milk, meats, whole wheat and potato, rolled oats, corn, white flour and beans. The nutritional value of ordinary meat

TABLE 65.5

Amino acid requirements of adult man

Amino Acid	Range of Requirements Observed	Proposed Tentative Minimum	"Safe Intake"
	grams per day	grams per day	grams per day
L-Isoleucine	0.65–0.70	0.70	1.40
L-Leucine	0.50–1.10	1.10	2.20
L-Lysine	0.40–0.80	0.80	1.60
DL-Methionine[a]	0.80–1.10	1.10	2.20
L-Phenylalanine[b]	0.80–1.10	1.10	2.20
L-Threonine	0.30–0.50	0.50	1.00
L-Tryptophan	0.15–0.25	0.25	0.50
L-Valine	0.40–0.80	0.80	1.60

[a] L-Cystine may replace up to 80 to 89 per cent of the minimal methionine needs. D-Methionine is fully as active as L-methionine.

[b] L-Tyrosine may replace up to 70 to 75 per cent of the minimal phenylalanine requirement.

varies largely with the cut—a tough fibrous meat, i.e., one with a high proportion of collagen and elastin has a low coefficient of digestibility and a low biological value. The biological value of some samples of very fibrous beef, for instance, may be little higher than that of white flour.

THE SUPPLEMENTARY RELATIONS AMONG PROTEINS

It does not necessarily follow that because a certain protein is inadequate for growth or even for maintenance that it is worthless in nutrition. It is evident from what has been said in the preceding paragraphs that an incomplete protein can be utilized if its shortcomings in one or more of the essential amino acids are made good by the addition to the diet of some other protein, rich in the elements which the first one lacked. Zein, for instance, fed in any quantity, is inadequate for either growth or maintenance. Lactalbumin at a level of less than 8 or 9 per cent is incapable of promoting normal growth. Yet normal growth and nutrition are supported by a diet containing 13.5 per cent zein and 4.5 per cent lactalbumin (fig. 65.2). The proportions of tryptophane and cystine and probably also of lysine are higher in lactalbumin than in body protein. Therefore, the excess of these amino acids in lactalbumin, instead of being wasted, combines with the amino acids of zein (which otherwise would be discarded) to form tissue protein.

In a similar manner the amino acids of gelatin are utilized if supplemented by a protein rich in tryptophane and cystine. Even two incomplete

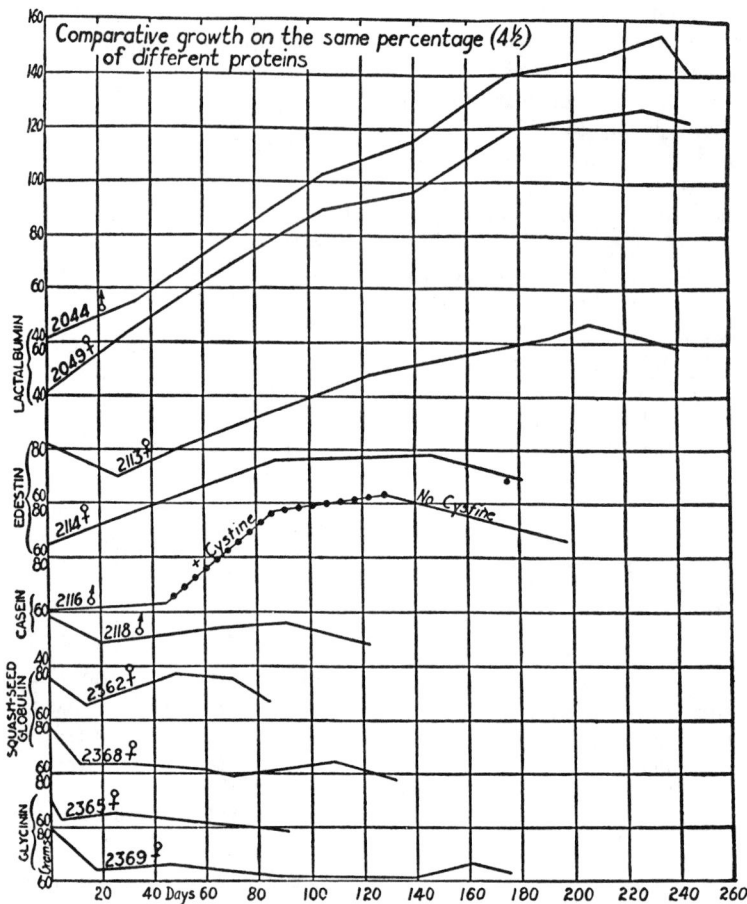

FIG. 65.3. Comparison of growth on diets containing approximately the same percentage (4.5 per cent) of different proteins, namely, lactalbumin, edestin, casein, globulin (squash seed) and glycinin (soy bean). (After Lusk.)

TABLE 65.6

Comparison of maximum protein utilization and relevant data

| Protein | C_{Pz} | Estimated NPUm | | FAO data (1957) | |
		Linear	Semi-log	Chemical protein score	Biological value (rat growth)
Egg.............	62	82	100 (108)	100	87–97
Fish flour......	58	78	97	70	75
Casein.........	59	67	75	80	69
Soy protein (isolated)....	73	60	82	73	75
Wheat gluten...	84	32	39	40	40

proteins, if one contains an abundance of the amino acids which the other lacks, supplement one another. So, the biological value of two proteins given together may be much greater than the sum of their values when fed alone. Proteins which lack the same amino acid (e.g., casein and phaesolin which are deficient in cystine) cannot of course supplement one another. The supplementary relations of proteins is evident in the chief natural foods: these all contain two or more proteins (see table 65.4). For example, in milk, the deficiency of casein in cystine and methionine is made good by the reltively high percentage of these amino acids in the other milk proteins. Also, though gliadin of wheat will not support growth, wheat itself will. The lysine-poor gliadin is supplemented by the other wheat protein, glutenin, which is rich in lysine. Maize contains, besides zein, the supplementary protein glutelin. These facts, obviously, are of fundamental importance in dietetics, especially in the economy of agricultural feeding. Cheaper foods can be fed and good nutrition promoted if due consideration be given to the supplementary relations of their contained proteins. Gelatin rich in lysine improves the nutritional value of wheat and oats, both relatively poor in this amino acid. There is also a pronounced supplementary relation between the proteins of milk and those of oats and wheat.

The *non-essential amino acids* must not be considered unimportant constituents of the diet. While they can be synthesized from the essential amino acids, metabolism proceeds more efficiently when all amino acids are provided so that fewer synthetic reactions need to be performed in the body. Recent studies have shown that non-amino N (e.g. urea added to the diet) can be used to a considerable extent for biosynthesis of some of these acids.

In 1961 Miller and Payne advanced a predictive scheme which they believed would make it possible to forecast the biological value of the protein components of foods from a knowledge of their amino acid composition. They pointed out that *net protein utilization* depends on both the quality of the protein and on the percentage of dietary calories derived from protein, which we may represent as C_P. With increasing C_P, N.P.U. decreases linearly. They believed that the rate of decrease is characteristic of each protein and assumed that all proteins have zero utilization for growth at a common extreme value which we may call C_{Pz} and which they estimated at about 54%. They noted that all proteins have a maximum value (which we will represent by NPUm) for net protein utilization which is reached at a certain low (maintenance) level of dietary protein (C_{Pm}), and that generally NPUm $\times$ C_{Pm} = 400. This maximum value for net protein utilization (NPUm) appears in practice to be effectively the same as *protein score* based on chemical analyses for essential amino acids, as calculated by Mitchell and Block, Flodin and others (see F.A.O. *Nutritional Studies. Protein requirements*. No. 16, Rome, 1957).

A recent careful re-examination of the influence of the quality and quantity of protein in the diet on net protein utilization (by Morrison, Sabry, Gridgeman and Campbell) showed that C_{Pz} is not constant, but is a variable which is related to protein quality. They found C_{Pz} values of five well-studied proteins to be as shown in Table 65.6. They depicted the relationship between N.P.U. and percentage of dietary calories supplied by protein (C_P) on both linear and semi-log plots. Their values for NPUm from the two sets of curves and the good agreement with both the chemical *protein score* and *biological values* by rat growth studies are shown in the table.

REFERENCES

BLOCK, R. J. AND MITCHELL, H. H. Nutrition Abstr. & Rev., 1946, **16**, 249.

BOOTHBY, W. M., SANDIFORD, I., SANDIFORD, K. AND SLOSSE, J. Trans. Assoc. Am. Physicians, 1925, **40**, 195.

CANNON, P. R., STEFFEE, C. H., FRAZIER, L. J., ROWLEY, D. A., AND STEPTO, R. C.: Fed. Proc., 1947, **6**, 390.

CHAPMAN, D. G., CASTILLO, R., AND CAMPBELL, J. A. Can. J. Biochem. Physiol., 1959, **37**, 679.

DANN, W. J. AND DARBY, W. J. Physiol. Rev., 1945, **25**, 326.

GEIGER, E. AND GEIGER, L. E. J. Nutrition, 1948, **36**, 813.

HENDERSON, R. AND HARRIS, R. S. Fed. Proc., 1949, **8**, 385.

HOLT, L. E. Fed. Proc., 1942, **1**, 117.

HOLT, L. E. AND NAJJAR, V. A. Fed. Proc., 1942, **1**, 117.

MADDEN, S. C. AND ASSOCIATES. J. Exper. Med., 1939, **69**, 721.

McCOLLUM, E. V. AND DAVIS, M. J. Biol. Chem., 1915, **20**, 415.

McCOLLUM, E. V., SIMMONDS, N. AND PARSONS, H. T. J. Biol. Chem., 1919, **37**, 155; 1921, **47**, 111, 175, 207, 235.

MILLER, D. S. AND PAYNE, P. R. Brit. J. Nutr. 1961, **15**, 11.

MORRISON, A. B., SABRY, Z. I., GRIDGEMAN, N. T., AND CAMPBELL, J. A. Can. J. Biochem. Physiol., 1963, **41**, 275.

OSBORNE, T. B. AND MENDEL, L. B. Series of papers in Journal of Biological Chemistry from 1912, Vol. 12, to 1920, Vol. 41.

ROSE, W. C. AND ASSOCIATES. J. Biol. Chem., 1924, **61**, 747; 1928, **76**, 521; 1930, **89**, 109; 1931, **94**, 155, 167, 173.

ROSE, W. C.: Fed. Proc., 1949, **8**, 546.

ROSE, W. C., WIXOM, R. L., LOCKHART, H. B., AND LAMBERT, G. F.: J. Biol. Chem., 1955, **217**, 987.

WILLCOCK, E. G. AND HOPKINS, F. G. J. Physiol., 1906, **35**, 88.

Monographs and Reviews

ALLISON, J. B. Biological evaluation of proteins. Physiol. Rev., 1955, **35**, 664.

F. A. O. Nutrition Studies. Protein requirements. No. 16. Rome, 1957.

FLODIN, N. W. Amino acids and proteins. Their place in human nutrition problems. J. Agric. Food Chem., 1953, **1**, 222.

McCOLLUM, E. V. AND SIMMONDS, N. The newer knowledge of nutrition. The Macmillan Company, New York, 1925.

MENDEL, L. B. Harvey Lectures, 1914–1915, **10**, 101.

MENDEL, L. B. Nutrition: the chemistry of life. Yale University Press, 1923.

MITCHELL, H. H. Physiol. Rev., 1924, **4**, 424.

MITCHELL, H. H. AND HAMILTON, T. S. The biochemistry of the amino acids. Chemical Catalog Co., New York, 1929.

ROSE, W. C. Harvey Lectures, 1934–1935, **30**, 49. Physiol. Rev., 1938, **18**, 109.

CHAPTER 66

The Metabolism of the Purine and Pyrimidine Bases

One class of conjugated proteins—the *nucleoproteins*—are compounds of simple basic proteins, *protamines* and *histones*, with *nucleic acid*. When a nucleoprotein is hydrolyzed, the protein is split off leaving nucleic acid. The nucleic acids are composed of: (a) phosphoric acid, (b) a pentose and (c) a nitrogenous group—a purine or pyrimidine.

A mononucleotide, the fundamental unit of the complex nucleic acid molecule may, therefore, be represented thus:

*phosphoric acid—pentose—purine or
pyrimidine base.*

The pentose part of the mononucleotide may be either 2-*d*-desoxyribose or *d*-ribose and the resulting compounds are referred to respectively as desoxyribonucleic acid (DNA) and ribonucleic acid (RNA). Desoxyribonucleic acid is a polymer molecule in the form of a double-stranded helix containing many thousands of subunits, genetic information is coded in sequences of these subunits or bases. The four bases contained in DNA are adenine, guanine, cytosine and thymine.

A typical mammalian cell has the capacity for making many thousands of different proteins. The flow of information in a cell begins with the pairing of bases found in the double helix of DNA. Three modes of information transfer occur. The first is *duplication*, which provides exact copies of the DNA molecule for transmission from one generation of cells to the next. The second mode of transfer is *transcription*, in which DNA is transcribed into ribonucleic acid (RNA) which, like DNA, has four code units or bases. Three are the same as those found in DNA, adenine, guanine and cytosine; the fourth is uracil which takes the place of thymine. One form of RNA known as "*messenger RNA*," a single strand polymer containing hundreds of subunits, carries the actual program for protein synthesis. This variety constitutes only about 5 per cent of all the RNA in the cells and is usually unstable, so must be continuously resynthesized. The third mode of information transfer converts the information from the four-element (base) language of "messenger RNA" to the twenty-element (amino acid) language of proteins. This step utilizes short, single stranded polymers, containing about 70 subunits or bases and conveys specific amino acids to the site of protein synthesis. Each amino acid has its own type of "*transfer*" or "*soluble*" RNA. The actual synthesis of proteins is carried out with the aid of *ribosomes*, globular cytoplasmic structures consisting of 40 per cent protein and 60 per cent RNA, which collaborate with "messenger" RNA to link together amino acids delivered by "transfer" RNA to create proteins. Transfer and ribosomal RNA make up about 95 per cent of the RNA found in a cell and are extremely stable.

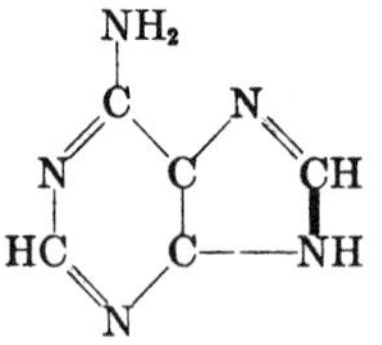

Adenine

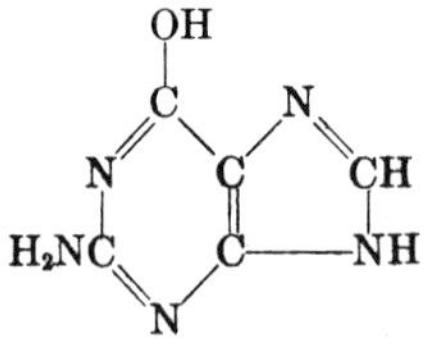

Guanine

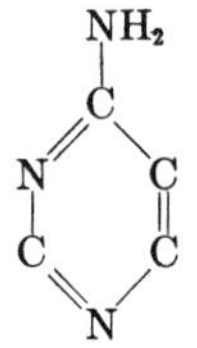

Cytosine
Bases present in DNA and RNA

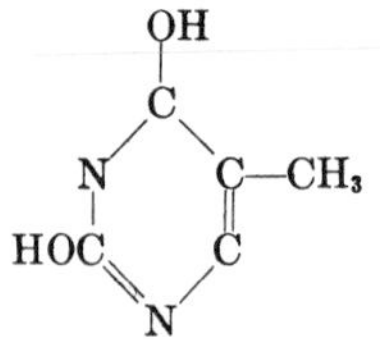

Thymine
Base present
only in DNA

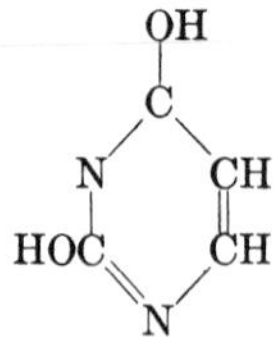

Uracil
Base present
only in RNA

When a purine or pyrimidine is linked to a sugar residue or pentose the resulting compound is called a *nucleoside*. If the sugar is also phosphorylated, a *nucleotide* results.

Pyrimidines have a simple 6-membered ring structure containing two N atoms; the major pyrimidines found in nucleotides and nucleic acids are cytosine, uracil and thymine. *Purines* are derived from 2-ringed structures each containing two N atoms; a 6-membered pyrimidine ring and a 5-membered imidazole ring. The purine bases are adenine and guanine. Pyrimidines combine with sugar residues at their 3-N position, purines combine with sugar residues at their 9-nitrogen position.

insoluble in water it can be evacuated in a semi-solid state. However, if the ureotelic human who excretes 15 g. of urinary nitrogen a day as urea (32 g. urea) were obliged to eliminate the same quantity of nitrogen as uric acid, he would be required to excrete 50 g. of uric acid daily. Under normal circumstances this would be an impossibility because of clogging of the renal tubular excretory system and ureters (normal excretion is less than 1 g. of uric acid per day). The great bulk of excess ammonia is converted to carbamyl

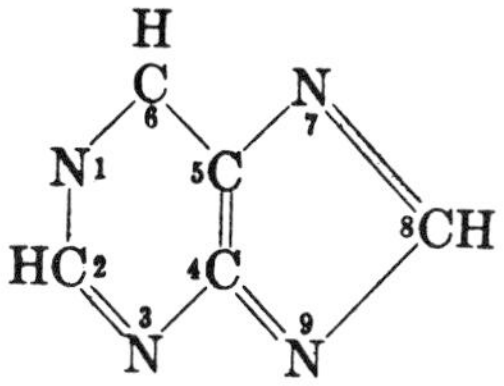

Adenine = 6 amino-purine
Guanine = 2 amino-6 hydroxypurine
Uric acid = 2:6.8-trihydroxypurine

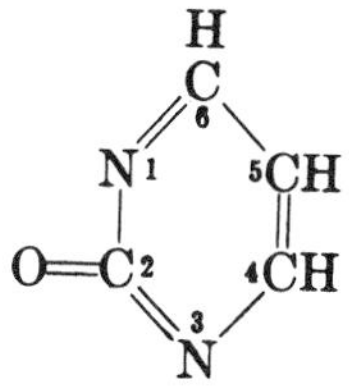

Purine nucleus

Cytosine = 6-amino-2-hydroxypyrimidine
Uracil   = 2:6-dihydroxypyrimidine
Thymine = 5-methyluracil

Pyrimidine nucleus

As the phylogenetic scale is ascended, there is a successive loss of degradative enzymes (urease, allantoicase, allantoinase, uricase, xanthine oxidase), and so to maintain nitrogen balance, ammonia derived from the breakdown of nucleic acids is handled and eliminated in various ways representing maximum adaptation to the environment. In creatures which live in an aqueous medium, ammonia and carbon dioxide may be eliminated directly into the surrounding water (marine and fresh water invertebrates, fresh water teleosts, lungfish and aquatic forms of amphibia and reptiles). Bacteria and crustacea are also ammonotelic. Marine teleosts and elasmobranchs which require a high concentration of urea in their plasma in order to remain hypertonic in relation to the surrounding sea water, excrete urea as their chief means of nitrogen disposal. Some fish lacking allantoicase excrete allantoic acid predominantly. Mammals other than man, apes, the Dalmatian dog, and certain insects, eliminate excess nitrogen as uric acid (uricotelic). This is ideal in an environment in which water is at a premium; since uric acid is so

phosphate and thence to urea. Some ammonia is converted to glutamine and to uric acid in the liver. In xanthinuria, an inborn error of metabolism in man in which there is a deficiency of xanthine oxidase, xanthine and hypoxanthine are excreted predominantly. In leeches and fresh water mussels, hypoxanthine is also excreted because of a deficiency of xanthine oxidase. In spiders, and to some extent in pigs and fish-eating birds, guanase is deficient and so degradation of purines does not proceed beyond the stage of guanine.

Uric acid is not the only end-product of purine metabolism in man. Small quantities of precursors totalling approximately 30 mg./day, have been recovered from urine. As well, an appreciable portion of the uric acid formed daily (approximately 30 per cent in normal man) is excreted into the gastrointestinal tract where it is degraded by uricolytic bacteria to CO_2 and ammonia. In patients with renal insufficiency, this extra-renal elimination of uric acid may be a major route of disposal.

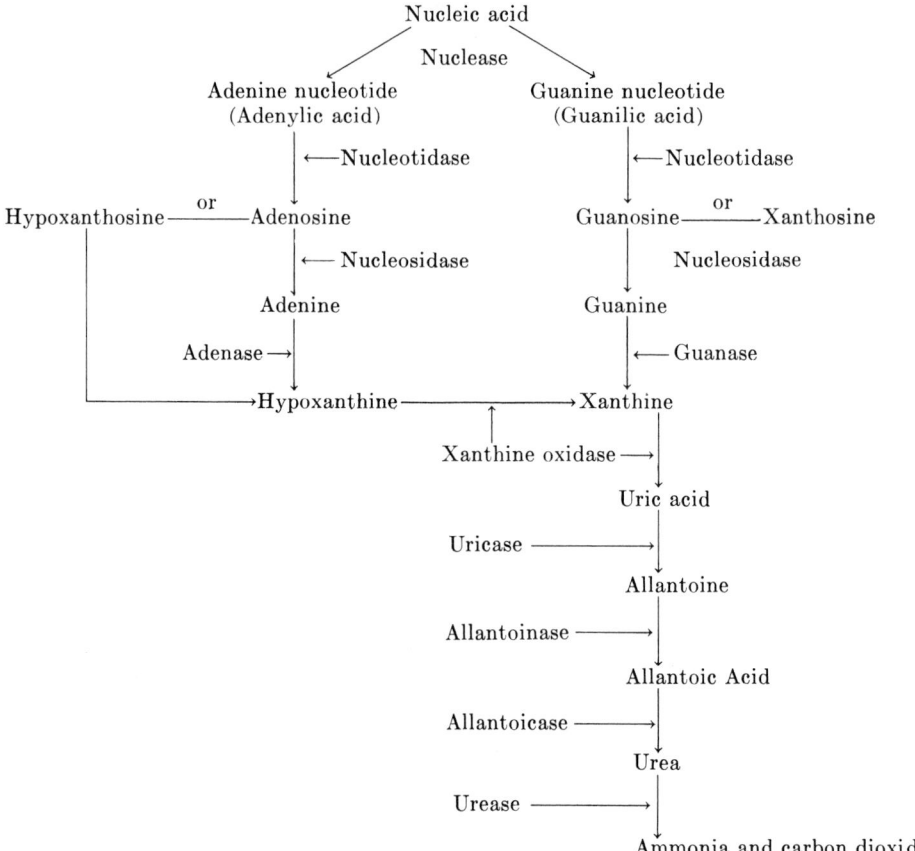

The major steps in the degradation of purines

Little is known concerning the fate of pyrimidines in man. In animals they are for the most part completely oxidized, the nitrogen being excreted mainly as urea. The urine contains pyrimidines in insignificant quantities. A rare disorder of pyrimidine metabolism has been described, consisting of increased urinary excretion of orotic acid, megaloblastic anaemia, leukopenia and retarded growth.

BIOSYNTHESIS OF PYRIMIDINES

The ring atoms of the pyrimidines are each derived from a specific source. This leads to uracil ribose phosphate from which the other pyrimidines are derived.

BIOSYNTHESIS OF PURINES

In man, uric acid is derived from two main sources; a portion is formed from the degradation of body purines (endogenous) and from the purines taken in the diet (exogenous); a second and substantial portion is derived from *de novo* purine biosynthesis. After an ordinary meal, containing purines, there is an appreciable increase in urinary excretion of uric acid although there may be no significant rise in serum uric acid. Following the ingestion of large amounts of purines, e.g. 4 g. RNA per day added to the diet, there may be an increase of 2 to 3 mg. per cent in serum urate and a 50 per cent increase in uric acid excretion. However, on a diet devoid

The methyl group of thymine is derived from methionine.

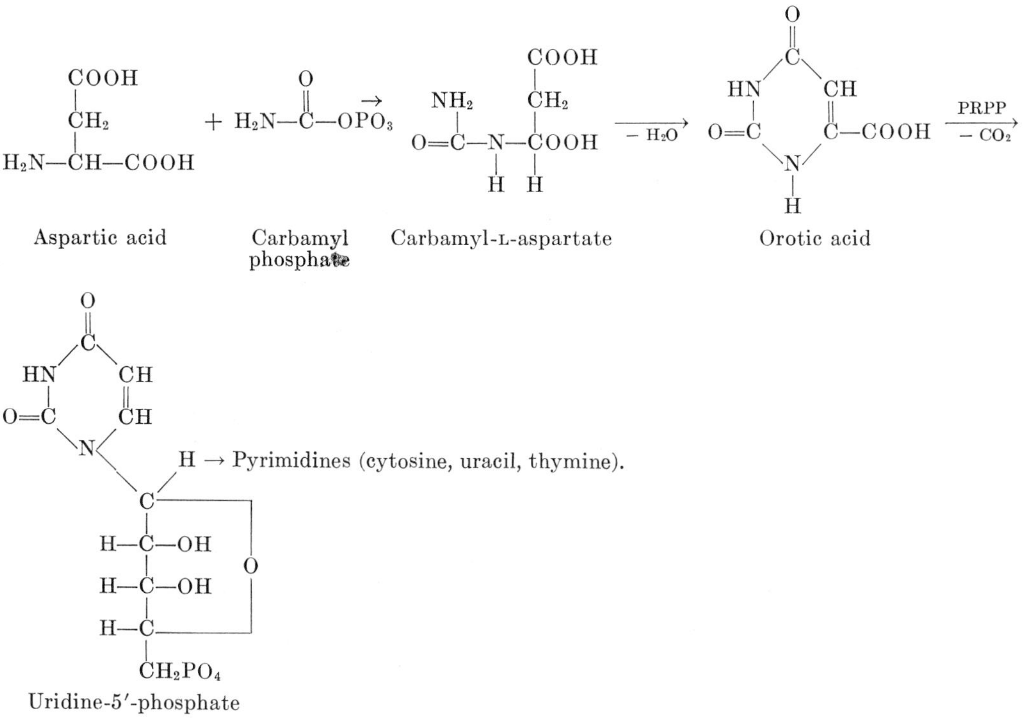

Aspartic acid　　Carbamyl phosphate　　Carbamyl-L-aspartate　　Orotic acid

H → Pyrimidines (cytosine, uracil, thymine).

Uridine-5′-phosphate

Pyrimidine synthesis

of purines, comprised exclusively of milk, the young mammal forms and excretes uric acid or allantoin, and at the same time manufactures nucleic acid for normal cell growth. That synthesis also occurs in the adult was shown by Benedict, who maintained a Dalmatian dog on a purine-free diet for nearly a year, during which time the animal excreted 100 g. of uric acid. This had not been obtained from body tissue since the animal maintained a constant weight.

Uric acid serves no biochemical function in the body other than being an end product of purine metabolism. The purines adenine and guanine serve as building blocks for nucleic acids and as important participants in a wide variety of biochemical reactions. These purines originate either from dietary sources or from *de novo*

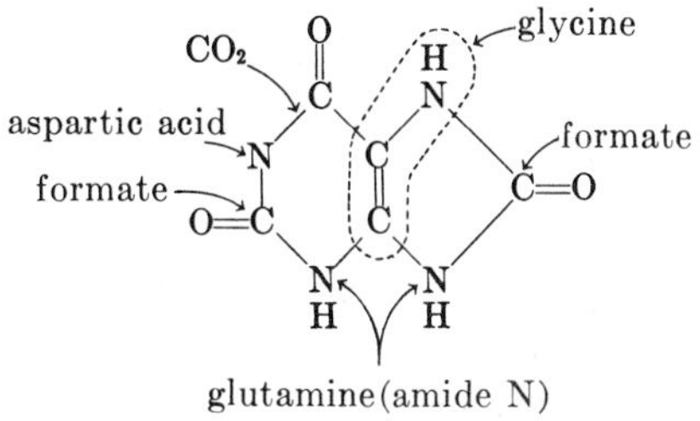

glutamine(amide N)

biosynthesis. Those formed in excess, or from tissue catabolism, undergo irreversible oxidation to uric acid.

In the *de novo* synthesis of uric acid, the purine ring is assembled stepwise in a complex series of enzymatic reactions from the precursors glutamine, glycine, aspartic acid, formyl derivatives of tetrahydrofolic acid and carbon dioxide.

The initial step involves the reaction of glutamine and phosphoribosyl pyrophosphate to yield phosphoribosylamine, the amide nitrogen of glutamine contributing N-9 to the evolving purine structure. The second step is the formation of glycinamide ribonucleotide by the interaction of phosphoribosyl amine, ATP and glycine, the latter contributing C-4, C-5 and N-7. Transformylation next occurs, contributing C-8, the beta carbon of serine being the purine source of "formyl." Amidization with N-3, derived from the amide nitrogen of glutamine, next takes place, bicarbonate then donating C-6 to the evolving structure. Aspartic acid donates N-1 and then the beta carbon of serine through formylation by N^{10} formyl-tetrahydrofolic acid donates C-2 to complete the synthesis of inosinic acid or hypoxanthine ribotide from which adenylic and guanylic acids are derived. The

Pathway for the biosynthesis of purines

latter two may then be incorporated into polynucleotides or other metabolically active purine compounds. A "shunt pathway" exists however for the direct degradation to uric acid via hypoxanthine and xanthine. This shunt pathway exists as an "overflow bypass for the elimination of surplus inosinic acid and other ribonucleotides generated in excess of biologic needs" (Gutman).

Gout

Gout comprises a group of metabolic disorders characterized by an increased concentration of uric acid (sodium urate) in the serum. When clinically active it is manifested by recurrent attacks of acute arthritis which develop over a period of hours and subside spontaneously, if no treatment is given, over a period of days or weeks. The pain may be excruciating and is usually accompanied by signs of acute inflammation, heat, swelling, redness and characteristically by overlying skin sensitivity. The disease afflicts predominantly (95%) the human adult male and although it may occur in either sex, it is rare in infancy, prepubertal males and premenopausal females. The incidence rises with age and although it commonly presents in the fourth decade it may occur initially as late as the eighth decade or even later.

The hallmark of the disease is hyperuricemia. Although the upper limit for serum urate concentration, based on a population survey, was 7.0 mg. % (uricase enzymatic method), for practical purposes values above 6 mg. % (enzymatic or colorimetric methods) are regarded as elevated. In females and prepubertal males the serum uric acid is 0.5 mg. %–1 mg. % lower. In normal infants the serum uric acid is considerably lower—values of 1.3 mg. % to 1.7 mg. % being reported.

The pKa of uric acid is 5.75 and therefore it is almost completely dissociated at the pH of plasma. It circulates as the monovalent ion and, therefore, tophaceous deposits of gout which occur in articular and periarticular structures, cartilage, synovial membrane, bursae, ligaments and tendons, as well as in subcutaneous tissues, exist as the monosodium urate monohydrate salt. At the pH of acid urine it is largely undissociated and is excreted predominantly as uric acid. Negligible amounts are bound to serum proteins. Recent studies have confirmed the observations that uric acid readily tends to form supersaturated solutions. Serum with a urate concentration of 6.4 mg. % is saturated, but values as high as 40 mg. %–60 mg. % have been reported in patients with lymphomas.

Uric acid is unevenly distributed in biologic fluids, but concentrations approximating serum levels have been documented in joint fluids, pleural and pericardial effusions. The concentration of urate in spinal fluid has been found to be very low (0.37 mg. % with a simultaneous serum value of 4.52 mg. %). Low or nondetectable concentrations of uric acid have been reported in sweat, and although low concentrations have been reported in saliva, well-documented cases of uric acid calculus of the parotid gland have been reported.

A number of factors determine size of the body pool of urate, including the level of ingested dietary purine, the rate of breakdown of tissue nucleic acids, *de novo* purine synthesis, renal excretion and intestinal uricolysis. The amount of uric acid in the body may be calculated following the intravenous administration of isotopically-labelled uric acid (N^{15}, C^{14}). By determining the rate at which the isotope content of urinary uric acid is diluted each day, the quantity of unlabelled uric acid introduced by biosynthesis into the body's miscible pool can then be determined. In the normal adult male the average miscible pool of uric acid is approximately 1200 mg., with a range of 866 to 1587 mg. Nontophaceous gouty patients may have a two- to fourfold increase in miscible pool, while in tophaceous gouty subjects there may be an increase of fifteen to thirty times the normal.

Studies of the incorporation of isotopically labelled precursors into uric acid have suggested that in approximately 30%–60% of patients with gout, there is an overproduction of uric acid presumably due to excessive synthesis via the "shunt pathway," which bypasses the normal incorporation of glycine into tissue nucleic acids. It has also been suggested that among gouty subjects who overproduce uric acid, there might be a defect in the feedback control of purine biosynthesis. This might be expected to act on the first irreversible step of purine biosynthesis, which is the enzymatic reaction of glutamine with 5-phosphoribosyl-1-pyrophosphate (PRPP) to form 5-phosphoribosylamine. Evidence for this has been advanced by Gutman and Yü who have suggested an abnormality of glutamine utilization for the renal production of ammonia (?glutaminase deficiency) in acid urine, allowing excess glutamine to be recycled to contribute to excess production of uric acid. This suggested metabolic defect, which results in a more acid urine by the reduction in urinary ammonia, as well as the increased production and renal excretion of uric acid, contributes to the high incidence of uric acid stones in patients with gout (10–20 per cent), an incidence approximately 1000 times greater than in the general population.

Normal man excretes uric acid by a three-phase process involving complete filtration of the plasma urate at the glomerulus, complete reabsorption probably at the proximal tubular level and then tubular secretion of approximately 5%–10% of the filtered urate load. The filtered urate load which averages 6.7 ± 1.4 mg. per min., does not approach the tubular maximum for reabsorption of urate, which has been estimated at 15 mg. per min. per 1.73 sq. m. of body surface area. On a low purine diet, man excretes 420 ± 80 mg. of uric acid daily in the urine (0.49 ± 0.16 mg./min.) with a uric acid clearance of 8.7 ± 2.5 ml. per min. In most patients with gout the glomerular filtration rate remains within normal limits. However, because of the raised serum concentration, the filtered urate load is much higher than in the normal, 10.1 ± 2.8 mg. per min. The excretion of uric acid does not parallel this increased filtered load (0.66 ± 0.24 mg./min.), yielding a somewhat lower clearance than in the normal (7.5 ± 2.4 ml./min.). The significance of these observations have not been generally agreed upon. Whether the discrepancy implies an increase in tubular reabsorption of urate or a failure of tubular secretion, or both, in patients with gout, is as yet unclear.

Factors responsible for the pathogenesis of the acute attack are currently being elucidated. The initial reaction would appear to be a precipitation of crystals of monosodium urate in the tissues or joint fluid, although the local tissue factors responsible for this are not known. An inflammatory reaction to the crystals develops with an influx of polymorphonuclear leucocytes. Vasoactive peptides have been implicated in the mediation of this response. The crystals are phagocytosed by the leucocytes, with an increase in their metabolic activity, an increase in local lactate production and a consequent fall in local pH which leads to further sodium urate crystallization. The therapeutic action of colchicine in terminating the acute attack of gouty arthritis, specific for this malady, is believed to be related to its ability to reduce phagocytosis, thereby decreasing lactic acid production by leukocytes, and stopping the self-propagating inflammatory reaction.

Other conditions may also be associated with hyperuricemia and, occasionally, with tophaceous deposition. These include: (1) conditions in which an *increased turnover of nucleoproteins* prevail, as in the myeloproliferative disorders polycythemia rubra vera, granulocytic leukemias and psoriasis (2) conditions in which there is an *increased production of uric acid*, as in glycogen storage disease. Because of the deficiency in the enzyme glucose-6-phosphatase, there is a shunting of glucose to phosphoribosyl pyrophosphate, which is the component required for the first stage of de novo purine biosynthesis. A rare syndrome consisting of mental retardation and self mutilation in association with overproduction of uric acid has also been described. (3) Conditions in which there is a *decreased excretion of uric acid*. Prolonged administration of diuretics of the benzothiazine family, salicylates in low doses, pyrazinamide (antituberculous agent) and other substances, may interfere with the tubular secre-

tion of uric acid. Starvation and the ketosis of diabetes also lead to hyperuricemia, because of the inhibitory effect on tubular secretion of uric acid of the ketone body B-hydroxy butyric acid. Chronic nephritis is commonly associated with hyperuricemia, but surprisingly little clinical gout is seen presumably because of the increased extra renal excretion of uric acid via the gut or because of the decreased inflammatory response noted in patients with chronic nephritis. Toxemia of pregnancy may also be associated with hyperuricemia, but the cause of this has not been definitely established although lacticacidosis has been suggested.

REFERENCES

HARPER, H. A. Review of Physiological Chemistry, Chapts. 4, 15, 16, Lange, Los Altos. 1965.

RICH, A. Polyribosomes, Scientific American, 1963, **209**, 6.

GUTMAN, A. B. Significance of the renal clearance of uric acid in normal and gouty man. Am. J. Med., 1964, **37**, 833.

WYNGAARDEN, J. B. The overproduction of uric acid in primary gout. Arth. & Rheum., 1965, **8**, 5 (Pt. I), 648.

SORENSON, L. B. Role of the intestinal tract in elimination of uric acid. Arth. & Rheum., 1965, **8**, 5 (Pt. I), 694.

McCARTY, D. J. The inflammatory reaction to microcrystalline sodium urate. Arth. & Rheum., 1965, **8**, 5 (Pt. I), 726.

OGRYZLO, M. A. Hyperuricemia induced by high fat diets and starvation. Arth. & Rheum., 1965, **8**, 5 (Pt. I), 799.

KRAKOFF, I. H. Studies of uric acid biosynthesis in the chronic leukemias, 1965. Arth. & Rheum., 1965, **8**, 5 (Pt. I), 772.

MONOGRAPHS

DAVIDSON, J. N. The biochemistry of the Nucleic Acids. 5th Ed. Methuen, London, 1965.

GUTMAN, A. B., ed. Proceedings of conference on gout and purine metabolism. Arth. & Rheum., 1965, **8**, 5 (Pt. I).

GUTMAN, A. B. AND YÜ, T. F. Uric acid metabolism in normal man and in primary gout. New Eng. J. Med., 1965, **273**, 252, 313.

TALBOTT, J. H. Gout. 2nd ed. Grune & Stratton. New York/London, 1964.

SEEGMILLER, J. E., LASTER, L., AND HOWELL, R. R. Biochemistry of uric acid and its relationship to gout. New Eng. J. Med., 1963, **268**, 712, 764, 821.

WYNGAARDEN, J. B. Gout. The Metabolic Basis of Inherited Disease. Edited by Stanbury, J. B., Wyngaarden, J. B., and Frederickson, D. S. 2nd ed. McGraw-Hill. New York, 1965.

CHAPTER 67

Carbohydrate Metabolism and Insulin

Carbohydrate Metabolism

THE IMPORTANCE OF CARBOHYDRATES

The carbohydrates of the body are important substances in metabolism. One carbohydrate, glucose, serves as an indispensable energy supply for brain tissue in which there is little carbohydrate stored. In the mammary gland, glucose may be converted to galactose and this may combine with another molecule of glucose to give lactose or milk sugar. Glucose can be oxidized—providing energy for muscular contraction, the activity of glands and so on. Under anaerobic conditions it may undergo glycolysis providing energy for muscle at a time when other sources of energy are not well utilized. The metabolism of glucose is important in ATP production since 38 mols of ATP (net) are formed in the oxidation of one mol of glucose or 2 (net) by glycolysis to lactic acid. ATP is essential for many metabolic processes, and for maintaining the normal relation of intracellular and extracellular electrolytes. Reduced nicotinamide adenine dinucleotide phosphate (NADPH, i.e. TPNH) generation in reactions in the pentose-phosphate pathway is important in fat synthesis. Excess glucose is converted to fats or to glycogen and many of the chemical changes in cells involve glucose or its derivatives. Glucuronic acid and acetyl derivatives of glucose are important in detoxifying actions in the liver.

CARBOHYDRATES OF THE BODY

Glucose appears in the body both free, and in combination with other substances such as phosphoric acid. Carbohydrates occur in mucopolysaccharides, for example heparin and hyaluronic acid, and are frequently combined with protein as in mucoproteins. Pentoses occur in combined forms as nucleotides. Carbohydrates may also be linked with fatty substances, as in the cerebrosides.

The sugars of the body can be grouped as monosaccharides, oligosaccharides and polysaccharides. The most important monosaccharide in the body is glucose. The important polysaccharide is glycogen.

GLYCOGEN

Glycogen is a polysaccharide composed of glucose units. It is widely distributed in the animal body but the largest bulk occurs in the muscles and the liver. The glycogens are a series of branched polysaccharides, the differences being chiefly in the degree of branching and in the length of the so-called inner and outer chains. The Meyer model for glycogen with regular rebranching (fig. 67.1) is space limited. If this molecule is more or less spherical, the limiting radius is 180 Å units and the molecular weight is $4\text{--}10 \times 10^6$.

Glycogen is resistant to alkaline hydrolysis. The glycogen products obtained by heating with strong alkali or with trichloracetic acid or with hot water are of different molecular weights and when cold water and differential centrifugation are used to isolate glycogen from guinea-pig liver (Lazarow) its molecular weight is many times higher than that obtained by other procedures. With the more drastic procedures there is probably some degradation during isolation.

Glycogen Synthesis

Glycogen is synthesized through the action of specific enzymes. In vitro, phosphorylase can be involved in both the synthesis and degradation of glycogen since its action is readily reversible. In vivo, the activation of phosphorylase by epinephrine, glucagon or a high sodium concentration, does not lead to glycogenesis but always results in glycogenolysis. In the muscles of patients with McArdle's disease, phosphorylase is not detectable and yet the amount of glycogen is normal or above. Thus it would seem that some enzyme other than phosphorylase is involved in its synthesis. In the developing chicken embryo the enzyme glycogen synthetase appears before phosphorylase and is associated with the appearance of glycogen. In the body, glycogen synthesis seems to occur usually by a different pathway than glycogenolysis. Incubation of uridine diphosphate glucose (UDPG) with liver extracts gives UDP and a transfer of glucose to glycogen. The enzyme, UDP glucose-glycogen glucosyltransferase or glycogen-synthetase is

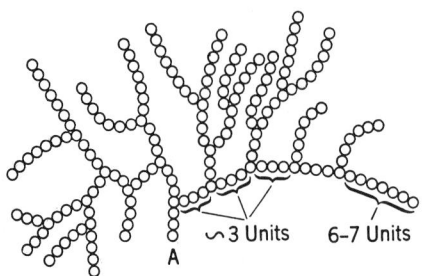

Fig. 67.1. Meyer model for the structure of glycogen. *A*, aldehydic end. ○, glucose units. (Meyer, 1943.)

involved in this transfer of glucose from UDP-glucose to glycogen, the action occurring along with that of the branching enzyme (fig. 67.2) to form the branched glycogen molecule. Glycogen synthetase and phosphorylase are similar in many respects but while the phosphorylase reaction is easily reversible, the equilibrium of the synthetase reaction is displaced in favour of glycogen synthesis. An increase in the concentration of glucose-6-phosphate has an activating effect on glycogen-synthetase and it seems likely that the concentration of glucose-6-phosphate has an important regulating influence on glycogen synthesis in vivo. There are two forms of glycogen synthetase, one acting independently of glucose-6-phosphate, (the independent or I form) and the other dependent on glucose-6-phosphate for its activity (the dependent or D form). When

glycogen synthetase is phosphorylated, the less active D form results.

It is also found that glycogen has some control over its own synthesis in muscle at least, since when tissue glycogen levels are low, glycogen synthetase D (the less active form), is converted to the more active I form and when tissue glycogen levels are high the reverse occurs.

The UDP glycosides are important not only in glycogen synthesis but, since they act as carriers of active sugar, also in the synthesis of oligosaccharides, mucopolysaccharides, glycolipids, uronic acids, glucuronides and a number of other substances. Alternative pathways to glycogen have been described but the one by way of UDPGlucose seems to be the important one in vivo.

Glycogen Breakdown

As indicated before, phosphorylase is involved in the breakdown of glycogen. Phosphorylase "a" (the active form) is converted by a tissue enzyme (phosphorylase phosphatase) into phosphorylase "b" (an inactive form). The less active phosphorylase "b" can be changed to the active phosphorylase "a" by a phosphorylase "b" kinase which exists in inactive form but whose action is enhanced by ATP in the presence of Mg^{++}. This activation of the phosphokinase is accompanied by the transfer of the terminal phosphate of the ATP to the kinase and this

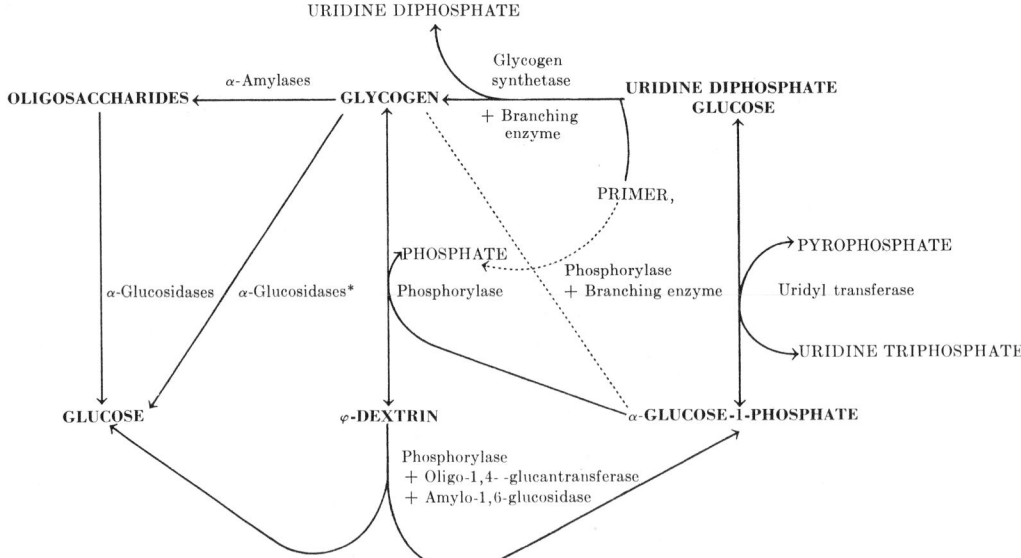

Fig. 67.2. Glycogen metabolism in rabbit muscle as agreed on by participants in Ciba Foundation Symposium on Glycogen (1964). Broken lines indicate possible though not major significance *in vivo*.

occurs more rapidly in the presence of cyclic 3'5'-adenosine monophosphate (AMP). Glucagon and epinephrine enhance glycogen breakdown through 3'5'-AMP.

While glycogenolysis in muscle can be regulated by the activity of phosphorylase, the study of glycogen breakdown in intact mice and in the perfused rat heart indicates that this breakdown is not always related to the fraction of phosphorylase in the "a" form. Anoxia produces a more rapid disappearance of glycogen than does glucagon although glucagon administration yields a higher fraction of phosphorylase "a." It would appear that the activity of phosphorylase "b" is inhibited by ATP but that inorganic P and AMP can enhance the activity of phosphorylase "b" itself. In anoxia, the activity of phosphorylase "b" is enhanced. Anoxia may increase the intracellular levels of inorganic phosphate and thus enhance glycogenolysis. It may also increase the activity of phosphorylase by increas-

ing the levels of 3'5' AMP and may dispose of hexose monophosphate more rapidly because of increased phosphofructokinase activity. It is suggested that changes in the concentration of nucleotides, glucose-6-phosphate and inorganic phosphate in the cell are important in the control of glycogenolysis, and probably just as important as the shift between the "b" and "a" forms of phosphorylase (Morgan and Parmeggiani).

Glycogen is broken down to glucose-6-phosphate in liver and muscle. In liver, the enzyme glucose-6-phosphatase causes the breakdown of glucose-6-phosphate yielding glucose. In muscle, the enzyme glucose-6-phosphatase is absent and hence glucose cannot be formed. In muscle, glycogen is broken down to pyruvate. Under conditions of adequate oxygen supply this will be oxidized largely to carbon dioxide and water, and under anaerobic conditions will form lactate. These pathways are shown in simplified form in fig. 67.3.

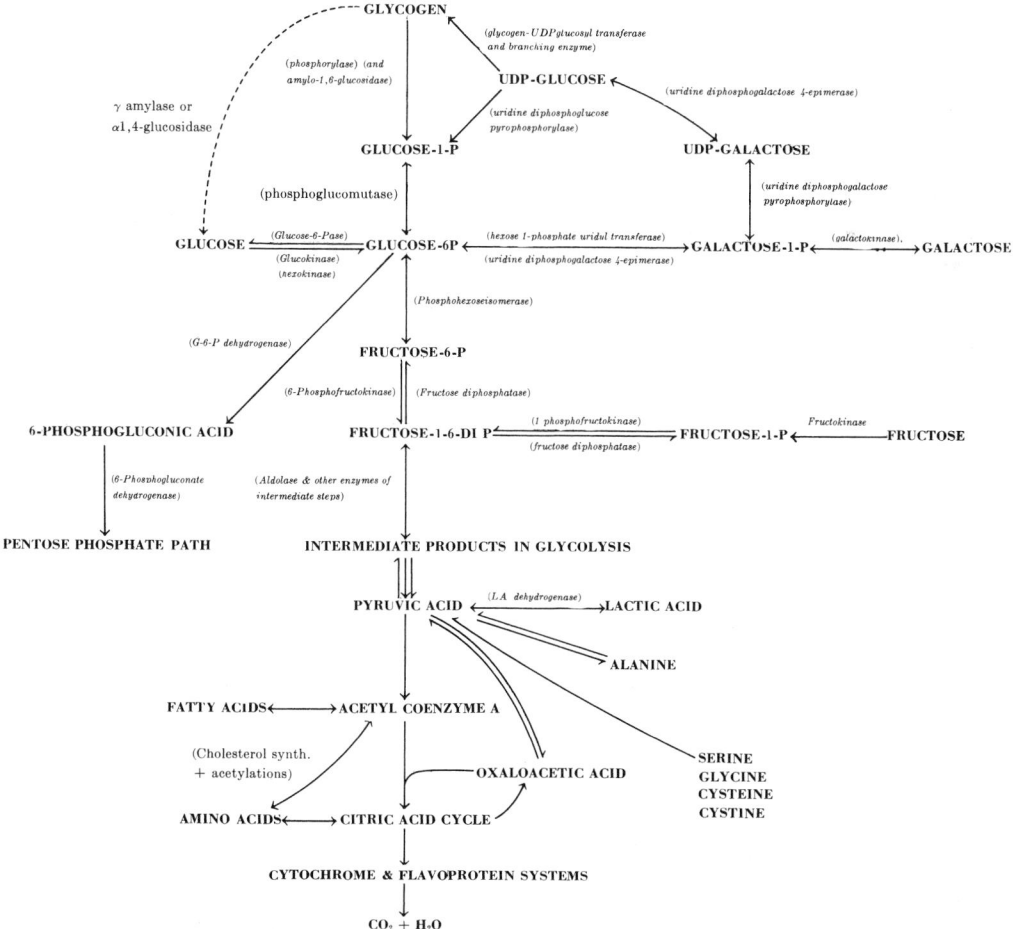

Fig. 67.3. Simplified scheme for carbohydrate breakdown and synthesis. P = phosphate.

Insulin and Glycogen Synthesis

The effect of insulin in promoting the synthesis of glycogen would appear to be due, in part at least, to the activation of glycogen synthetase. It was mentioned previously that phosphorylation of glycogen synthetase yielded the less active D form, but the phosphorylation of phosphorylase yields an active form of that enzyme. It has been suggested that a common phosphokinase might then influence both phosphorylase and glycogen synthetase in opposite directions, the activation of one being associated with inactivation of the other. 3'5'-AMP enhances phosphorylase activity as does also ATP but it decreases the activity of glycogen synthetase by increasing the I to D conversion. The directive effect of insulin then is apparently due to the activation of glycogen synthetase, increasing the I at the expense of the D. In addition, the glucose-6-phosphate is increased. Glycogen synthesis in muscle can be stimulated by insulin as seen above, or by increasing the concentration of glucose in the surrounding medium.

Disturbances in Glycogen Metabolism

Defects in the enzymes involved in the synthesis or degradation of glycogen may lead to disturbances of glycogen metabolism and to glycogen storage disease. While in some glycogen storage diseases the pathological effects are similar, the enzyme defects may differ. There is likely a genetic involvement in these defects but if so, this control is not understood as yet.

The glycogen storage diseases have been classified according to their enzyme defects. This classification is shown in table 67.1.

In type I, or Von Gierke's disease, there is a deficiency of glucose-6-phosphatase. The breakdown of glycogen is blocked but glycogenesis still occurs. Glycogen is not converted to glucose nor are *d*-galactose and *d*-fructose, and an accumulation of glucose-6-phosphate may enhance glycogen synthesis. Glycogen of normal structure

TABLE 67.1

Glycogen storage diseases

(From R. Schmid, Ciba Foundation Symposium on control of glycogen metabolism)

Cori type	Eponyms	Enzyme defect	Glycogen structure	Organs involved	Clinical manifestations
I	von Gierke's disease	Glucose 6-phosphatase	Normal	Liver, kidney	Hepatomegaly; hypoglycaemia, acidosis, ketonuria
II	Pompe's disease	Acid maltase (suggested)	Normal	Generalized	Cardiomegaly; cardiorespiratory failure and death
III	Cori's, Forbes's disease; limit dextrinosis	Amylo-1,6-glucosidase (debrancher)	Abnormal; short outer branches	Liver, heart, muscle	Hepatomegaly; moderate hypoglycaemia, acidosis
IV	Andersen's disease	Amylo-(1,4 → 1,6)-transglucosidase (brancher)	Abnormal; few branch points	Liver, heart, muscle, erythrocytes, others	Cirrhosis of the liver; progressive hepatic failure and death
V	McArdle's disease	Muscle phosphorylase	Normal	Muscle	Muscle cramps on exercise
VI	Hers's disease	Liver phosphorylase (suggested)	Normal	Liver, leucocytes	Hepatomegaly; moderate hypoglycaemia and mild acidosis

is deposited in the liver and kidneys, causing them to enlarge. Because of the difficulty in glucose formation, fasting hypoglycaemia is marked and acidosis is present.

In type II, or Pompe's disease, there is enlargement of the heart, and high muscle glycogen of normal structure (up to 12%) with muscular weakness and hypotonia. The blood sugar may respond normally to epinephrine and to glucagon and the blood lipids and lactate may be normal. The major enzyme defect is an absence of 1-4 glucosidase activity in liver and skeletal muscle.

In type III, a polysaccharide is found with a structure different from glycogen but similar to limit dextrin. Amylo-1-6-glucosidase activity is absent from the tissue and transferase activity may be defective.

Type IV also has present a polysaccharide different from glycogen, amylopectin, which may possibly result from a deficiency of branching enzyme. Patients with type IV disease have enlarged livers and spleens, and cirrhosis of the liver.

In type V, or McArdle's disease, muscle is affected. The exercise tolerance is greatly reduced and exercise, or epinephrine, fails to cause a normal elevation of blood lactate even though the level of blood sugar may rise. As noted previously, the enzymes of the UDPG pathway are present but phosphorylase activity is absent. Despite this, there is not as large a glycogen accumulation as in some of the other forms of glycogen storage disease.

Type VI disease involves the liver. There may be no marked known enzyme deficiency, though some show a moderate reduction in the phosphorylase of liver and in glucose-6-phosphatase activity.

In addition to these types of disturbances where glycogen is present in excess, there has been reported a *glycogen storage deficiency disease* due to a deficiency of glycogen synthetase. In this condition the stores of glycogen in the liver are low, and are quickly exhausted. Though the tolerance for glucose is reduced, the blood sugar levels fall readily during fasting and increased epinephrine secretion is not stimulated by the hypoglycaemia.

The Formation of Glucose

The important sugar of the body is glucose. It can be formed in the body by the breakdown of glycogen or by the conversion of other substances to glucose. Glucose may be obtained from the conversion of other monosaccharides or from deaminated amino acids, hence from protein and from the glycerol portion of fat. While labelled carbon in fatty acids can be incorporated into glucose in mammalian tissue, yet no net gain in carbohydrate can be obtained from fat. Amino acids and fatty acids can both yield acetyl-coenzyme A (acetyl-CoA) which condenses with oxalo-acetate to yield citrate and enters the tricarboxylic acid cycle (citric acid cycle) and may subsequently be oxidized. The pyruvate to acetyl-CoA step is essentially irreversible. However, oxaloacetate may go to pyruvate and thence to glucose or glycogen.

The Regulation of Blood Glucose Levels

The free glucose in the body, of which the extracellular glucose forms a major part, is in a dynamic state, constantly undergoing turnover, i.e. it is constantly being added to and constantly being removed. The glucose production rates (primarily hepatic) and the glucose utilization rates determine the amount of available glucose at any moment and the glucose concentration in the blood is an index of this. These rates depend on a number of factors. The magnitudes of these can be calculated in animals and in man by the use of different tracer dilution techniques, such as the method of *successive measured injections of tracer* (SMIT) (Wrenshall and Hetenyi).

The amount of glucose in the body undergoing turnover is usually referred to as the *glucose "pool"* and all tissues including the liver continuously remove glucose from it. Under basal conditions, the rate of release (rate of appearance) of glucose and the rate of removal (rate of disappearance) of glucose are usually identical, so the pool does not change with time. It is in the *dynamic steady state*. If the rate of appearance does not equal the rate of disappearance, the pool is not in a dynamic steady state. Deviations from the dynamic steady state are usually reflected in changes in the plasma glucose level, although changes in the pool are not necessarily of the same relative magnitude (percentage) as changes in the blood sugar level.

If the pool has been previously labelled by the injection of glucose tagged with C^{14}, the continuous addition of ordinary C^{12}-glucose from the liver or any other source will cause a continuous fall in the ratio of C^{14}-glucose to C^{12}-glucose in the "pool." This ratio of C^{14}-labelled to C^{12}-glucose (more exactly defined as the ratio of C^{14} to all C atoms in a mass of glucose) is referred to as the *specific activity* of glucose. If the amount of specific activity of the *injected* tracer-glucose is known, analysis of the decrease in the specific activity of plasma glucose with respect to time makes possible the calculation of the size of the "pool" and the rate of appearance of glucose into the "pool," at the time of the injection of the tracer. Repetitions of the injection of the labelled-glucose permit repeated calculations of the rate of appearance, and also the calculation of the change in the size of the "pool" with respect to time. This latter is necessary for the calculation of the rate of disappearance, which is the difference between the rate of appearance and the rate of change of the size of the "pool."

Method SMIT does not rely on assumptions concerning the constancy or anatomical interpretation of the "apparent distribution volume of glucose" or "glucose space" usually defined as the ratio of "pool" to the plasma glucose level. $(V = N/C)$.

The assumptions involved in the calculations are: (a) the C^{14}-glucose is handled by the organism in the same way as C^{12}-glucose; (b) the C^{14} label is firmly attached to the glucose molecule; (c) the specific activity of glucose in the plasma is a continuous function of time; (d) the injected tracer-glucose is intermixed uniformly with the "pool." The method SMIT has been validated against direct measurements in eviscerated and normal dogs.

Other tracer dilution techniques used to calculate the "pool size" and the rates of appearance and disappearance of glucose employ the constant infusion of labelled tracer glucose (Stetten, et al., Steele, et al.). While in this way it may be possible to register rapid changes in the rate of appearance, such methods have been shown to be dependent on more assumptions than method SMIT.

COMPARTMENTAL ANALYSIS. Under some circumstances, after the intravenous injection of the tracer, the specific activity *vs.* time curve of the traced material in the plasma takes a course analogous to one expected in systems consisting of more than one compartment characterized by different lengths of time necessary for the intermixing with the injected tracer. This analogy led to the hypothesis that glucose in the body is distributed into two compartments, one requiring a short and the other a very long time to achieve uniform intermixing with the injected tracer. It has been shown, however, that even if this were the case, any change in the inflow into or changes of the size of the second glucose compartment would scarcely, if at all, affect the first compartment (deBodo et al.). It has to be emphasized

that rates of appearance and disappearance of glucose into and from a "pool" of which plasma glucose forms a part, can be calculated without reference to compartments. In mice, however, there is some evidence for a second "compartment" into which glucose can be taken up, transformed to some non-glucose substance, and after re-synthesis, returned as glucose into the circulation (N. Baker).

ENTRANCE OF GLUCOSE INTO BLOOD. Glucose may enter the blood as a consequence of the breakdown of glycogen to glucose-6-phosphate and its subsequent change to glucose through the action of glucose-6-phosphatase. This takes place in the liver, and to a minor extent, in kidney and intestine, though not in muscle as has been mentioned. Glucose may also be newly formed from other substances (gluconeogenesis) as noted above. The liver glycogen may be considered as an emergency supply of carbohydrate which is available while the process of gluconeogenesis is improving. In the average man, approximately 100 grams of glycogen are present in the liver and this would only supply the demands for sugar for some five hours if gluconeogenesis were to cease. The rate of glycogen breakdown is affected by epinephrine and by glucagon, and the rate of gluconeogenesis by the internal secretions of the anterior pituitary gland, the adrenal cortex, and the thyroid and the pancreas, as will be discussed later. An important part of this homeostatic mechanism for the regulation of blood sugar appears to be the level of blood sugar itself (Soskin and Levine). Under experimental conditions in which variation in the rate of secretion of insulin is impossible, i.e., in the depancreatized dog given insulin at a constant rate, indirect evidence indicates that the administration of dextrose decreases the rate of output of sugar by the liver. Similarly in human subjects it has been shown by the method of successive tracer injections that a rise in blood sugar level decreases the rate of appearance of glucose in plasma. This effect was also obtained in mildly diabetic patients but not in ketotic ones (Forbath and Hetenyi). The insulin content of the blood may help to determine at what level of blood sugar gluconeogenesis in the liver will be inhibited. In the chronic absence of insulin glucose output by the liver is not inhibited.

THE ABSORPTION OF GLUCOSE FROM THE GUT. Glucose may enter the blood by absorption from the gastro-intestinal tract. Very little sugar is absorbed from the stomach but when the glucose concentrations reach 15% or higher there may be some absorption. This absorption is accompanied by the entrance of fluid into the stomach and the concentrated solutions are thus diluted. The glucose solution may be hypertonic in the duodenum but in the middle or lower jejunum or ileum the solutions have, as a rule, become isotonic. In the human, the absorption rate in the duodenum is 6–20 g. glucose/hour, and while the absorption rate is the jejunum may be as great or greater than this, usually a high percentage of the glucose has been absorbed before reaching this point. The maximal absorption rate per unit of body weight per hour (absorption coefficient) has not been measured for the human but has for the rat, and amounts to about 0.85 g. glucose/kg./hr. When there is hypertonic glucose in the stomach it becomes distended and emptying is delayed. Thus a stronger glucose solution will be delivered from the stomach to the small intestine more slowly and this will tend to offset any effect of a more rapid absorption resulting from the higher concentration of the sugar. In this way there is some equalization of absorption of sugar solutions of different concentrations. Using isolated perfused guinea-pig intestine, the absorption rate is found to increase with increasing glucose concentrations up to a maximum. In the rat, the rates of absorption of different monosaccharides are not the same, that of galactose being greater than that of glucose > fructose > mannose > xylose > arabinose. Some sugars are absorbed by passive diffusion. In isolated gut preparations these sugars show similar rates of transport from the inner to outer surfaces of the gut and from the outer to inner surfaces. The actively absorbed sugars have a much higher rate of transport from the inner to outer surface. Glucose and galactose are actively absorbed and this absorption can occur against a concentration gradient. Oxygen lack and metabolic poisons reduce their absorption and there is competition for transport between these two sugars, the addition of galactose reducing the absorption of glucose and vice versa. The actively transported sugars are hexoses having a *d*-pyranose ring structure and a hydroxyl group at carbon 2. This free hydroxyl group is essential, and when changed leads to altered transport. Sodium must be present in the gut for the best absorption of glucose.

In its transport, glucose enters the cells of the mucosa, a process apparently not enhanced by insulin. About 10% of the absorbed glucose is oxidized but glycolysis also occurs with the production of lactate. The lactate concentration on the serosal side of the gut thus may be high. The glucose that is oxidized or changed to lactate must be phosphorylated but phosphorylation does not seem to be essential for absorption, since only a relatively small fraction of the transported glucose goes through glucose-6-phosphate. Fructose may be absorbed by passive diffusion, or may be changed to glucose in the mucosa, or may undergo glycolysis and appear as lactate. There are species differences in the effect, a high proportion of the fructose absorbed being recoverable as lactate in the rat and a high percentage as glucose in the guinea pig, while in humans a high proportion seems to be recoverable as fructose.

THE FATE OF ABSORBED OR INJECTED GLUCOSE. The absorbed glucose is carried by blood to the liver where it may be stored as glycogen; or it may pass through the liver and be taken to other tissues where it may be: (1) diluted in extravascular fluid, (2) broken down by glycolysis and oxidation, (3) stored as glycogen, (4) stored as fat, (5) combined with other substances, or (6) excreted by the kidneys.

GLUCOSE TRANSPORT. The mode of entrance of glucose into cells differs for different types of cells. Some show active transport, requiring energy for movement of glucose against a concentration gradient, others do not. Some have a transport system sensitive to insulin, but not requiring additional energy. There is evidence for a sugar transport system influenced by insulin in skeletal muscle, heart muscle and adipose tissue but no specific sugar transport system seems to be present in liver.

The entrance of glucose into muscle cells is facilitated by insulin. The theory of Levine that insulin acts on glucose transport into the cell was based on findings using non-utilizable sugars and the assumption was that the response of glucose to insulin was similar. Several points of evidence support an effect of insulin on transport into the cell. The distribution of sugar into extracellular fluid is rapid in comparison with its rate of entry into muscle. The sugar transport is characterized by stereospecificity and different sugars can compete for transport. The transport systems can be saturated, suggesting a limited supply of a particular carrier. The sugar can enter without being phosphorylated. This transport is not energy-requiring and hence not an active process, yet there may be counterflow or uphill transport involving transport against a gradient when there is competitive inhibition (Morgan, Regen and Park).

It is of interest that, while anoxia accelerates

glucose transport in heart muscle, the insulin effect on transport is still obtained despite anoxia. Foa found that in the early chick embryo (5 days) there is no evidence for a special transport mechanism for glucose, yet insulin can influence lipogenesis even though it does not affect glucose entry. While this would support a metabolic effect of insulin independent of an effect on transport in the early chick embryo, dePocas found evidence for a relation between glucose entrance and glucose oxidation in the rat. When the blood glucose levels were elevated to 3 or 4 times normal, alloxan-diabetic rats showed approximately normal rates of glucose uptake and the ratio of the rate of oxidation of glucose to the rate of uptake of glucose was close to normal also. This was interpreted as indicating that with lack of insulin the pattern of intracellular regulation of glucose oxidation was not greatly altered. As in the normal animal, this seemed to be a function of the rate of uptake of glucose.

Randle and Smith suggest that insulin removes some factor inhibiting the uptake of glucose and in this way facilitates glucose entry. Krahl postulates that a decompartmentation within the cell, facilitating diffusion into the intracellular space may be a factor of importance. It has been suggested too that insulin may alter the configuration of lipoproteins at the cell surface, thus permitting more ready entry of glucose. While insulin has an action on the transport of glucose that seems to be exerted on the membrane of the cell and many theories have been proposed, we are forced to conclude that as yet the mechanism of this effect is not known.

Once glucose is within the cell it is then phosphorylated to form glucose-6-phosphate. In liver, this occurs through the activity of a specific kinase; and in muscle, through the action of a non-specific hexokinase. When glucose-6-phosphate is formed, it then may go by one pathway to glycogen, undergo glycolysis or be oxidized via the Embden-Meyerhof or Pentose Phosphate paths (fig. 67.3). In adipose tissue, fatty acids may be formed. The formation of fat from acetyl-CoA derived from glucose and certain amino acids is an important reaction. (It is of interest that this fat formed from carbohydrate is relatively high in saturated fatty acids.)

The balance between processes involving uptake of glucose by tissues, or supply of glucose by the liver through gluconeogenesis or glycogenolysis, will depend on the balance of hormones at that time and this in turn apparently influences the enzyme activities of tissues. Marked changes in enzyme activities have been noted in diabetic animals, and after the administration of insulin and adrenal hormones. We have already seen how insulin may influence glycogen synthesis by effects on the activity of glycogen synthetase. It has been reported that, in diabetes, enzymes concerned with the synthesis of glycogen, fatty acids and protein tend to be reduced in concentration or in activity whereas those involved in gluconeogenesis tend to be increased (Krahl). Adrenocortical hormones act as inducers of gluconeogenic enzymes whereas insulin blocks this enzyme synthesis (Weber). In liver there is a unique glucokinase involved in the phosphorylation of glucose, which is apparently induced by insulin. The activity of this enzyme seems to be adjusted to the level of portal blood sugar and is not inhibited by an increase in glucose-6-phosphate. This glucokinase of liver is greatly reduced in the diabetic and in starvation. The reappearance of its activity after insulin can be hindered by agents inhibiting protein synthesis (Sols).

REMOVAL OF GLUCOSE BY THE KIDNEYS. Glucose may be removed from blood by way of the kidneys. This will occur when the glucose level in blood is high or when the renal reabsorption of glucose is reduced. Glucose passes readily through the glomeruli. Normally it is reabsorbed in the proximal tubules and does not appear in the urine except in trace amounts. This reabsorption is an active process and there is a limit to the rate at which absorption can occur. When the amount of glucose delivered to the tubules is great enough to exceed the transport maximum (TmG) for the tubules, the excess glucose will be excreted in the urine. Phlorizin inhibits the tubular reabsorption of glucose and leads to glucosuria.

Glucosuria may result from any factors that sufficiently increase plasma glucose levels or reduce the ability of the renal tubules to reabsorb glucose. (For a detailed discussion of the renal handling of glucose refer to the chapter on Urine Formation, ch. 79)

ROLE OF THE LIVER IN THE REGULATION OF THE BLOOD SUGAR LEVEL. The liver is very important in the regulation of blood sugar. Following hepatectomy the blood sugar level falls. This is understandable since the liver is the only important source of glucose in the body. The glucostatic function of liver is indicated by the fact that when the blood sugar level falls, the liver starts putting out sugar and when the blood sugar level rises, as has been noted previously, the glucose output by the liver is reduced. The blood sugar level at which this output or uptake of sugar occurs seems to be influenced by the levels of certain circulating hormones. However, the details of the hormonal influence are not entirely clear. When *insulin* is given to intact animals, the fall in the concentration of free glucose in liver cell water will be less than in the plasma, therefore the apparent glucose space (ratio of tissue glucose concentration/extracellular glucose concentration) of liver is increased. This increase in apparent glucose space with insulin does not occur until the blood sugar level has fallen to a certain point. It is felt that, because the glucose uptake by muscle and adipose tissue is enhanced, the blood sugar level falls and glucose formation by liver is increased. By tracer-dilution techniques, an increased rate of glucose production in insulin-induced hypoglycaemia has been found by several investigators. Hyperglycaemia due to a glucose load reduces the glucose output by liver. Insulin enhances this inhibitory effect of hyperglycaemia on glucose output. However, when hyperglycaemia is produced by an acute insulin deficiency as a consequence of neutralizing insulin with antibody, the glucose output by liver is increased but can be returned to normal by giving insulin. There is no question, that, when insulin lack persists for a longer period, glucose output by liver is increased. This may be related to changes in the level of enzyme activities in the liver cells. It would seem that when the blood sugar levels fall below normal values, insulin has little influence on glucose output by liver apart from its effect through the lowering of blood sugar. However, when the blood sugar level stays at, or rises above, normal values, the presence or absence of insulin can influence glucose output by liver; its presence inhibiting and its absence enhancing this output.

Other hormones affecting glucose output by the liver are glucagon and epinephrine, both of which, as mentioned previously, enhance glycogen breakdown through an increase in 3'5'-AMP and an activation of phosphorylase. Prolonged treatment with certain steroid hormones of the adrenal cortex also enhances glucose output by the liver through stimulation of gluconeogenesis. Paradoxically, the infusion of a water soluble adrenal steroid decreases hepatic glucose production in both normal and diabetic dogs (Madison; Ninomiya, et al.). Administration of certain pituitary hormones can also stimulate gluconeogenesis and increase hepatic glucose output. There also may

be some interactions between hormones in their effects on liver, the presence or absence of insulin modifying certain effects of other hormones.

When the blood sugar level tends to fall, several compensatory responses are initiated, resulting in increased hepatic glucose output. First, there is a direct effect on liver leading to glycogen breakdown and glucose formation. Second, there is stimulation of the secretion of glucagon which enhances glycogen breakdown to glucose by liver. Third, the secretion of epinephrine is stimulated, epinephrine also enhancing glucose formation from glycogen in liver. This effect on epinephrine secretion seems to be centrally mediated, probably through the hypothalamus, and may be important in ensuring an adequate supply of glucose to the brain. Fourth, the secretion of glucocorticoids by the adrenal cortex is stimulated, with consequent new formation of glucose, coupled with a reduced peripheral utilization of carbohydrate. Increased formation of free fatty acids from depot fat under the influence of epinephrine, adrenal steroids, and certain pituitary hormones may also reduce the utilization of glucose by muscle and hence assist in maintaining the blood sugar level.

When the blood sugar level tends to rise, this rise is compensated first, by a direct effect on liver and muscle, increasing the uptake of glucose and second, by a stimulation of insulin secretion through a direct action of glucose on islet cells; the insulin would then enhance the uptake of glucose by liver, muscle and adipose tissue and encourage the formation of glycogen and of fat. It also seems possible that there may be an indirect stimulation of insulin secretion through an influence of the elevated blood sugar on a parasympathetic centre in the hypothalamus or brain stem. The evidence for this is not convincing and its influence cannot be fundamental, since the blood sugar levels can be regulated well even when the pancreas is denervated. The major changes under these circumstances are that the levels return more slowly to normal values after glucose hyperglycaemia or insulin hypoglycaemia.

The formation or breakdown of glycogen in liver may also be influenced by nervous factors. Claude Bernard, in 1855, showed that puncture (*piqure*) of the fourth ventricle produced hyperglycaemia within an hour and a persistent glucosuria lasting for several days. Glucosuria may result from hypothalamic lesions, apparently through stimulation of the sympathetic division of the autonomic nervous system, the effect being carried out through the splanchnic nerves to the liver. There are centres also in pons and mid-brain and possibly at other levels of the brain stem. In addition to this direct nervous effect on liver, there will be indirect effects through stimulation of the secretion of epinephrine by the adrenal medulla. It is possible, too, that other effects might be obtained through an influence on the pituitary gland mediated through the hypothalamus.

GLUCOSE TOLERANCE

When glucose is given by mouth, it is absorbed from the gut and its level in blood rises. Too small amounts may not produce a maximum hyperglycaemia. Too large amounts may prolong absorption. For man, the oral glucose tolerance test involves the giving by mouth of 100 g. of glucose, or 1.7 g. glucose/kg. ideal body weight based on age and height. The blood sugar levels are measured, in the fasting individual, before, and at intervals after the glucose administration for 3 hours. Normally the level rises from an initial value of 60–90 mg% (under 100 mg. %) to a peak value of less than 160 mg. % and returns again to under 110 mg. % within a two-hour period. In the diabetic patient, the fasting blood sugar level itself is usually elevated, and following glucose administration the blood sugar rises to higher values and falls more slowly, remaining elevated in the second-hour samples.

The tolerance for glucose will depend upon a number of factors. One of the important influences is the dietary history prior to the test. If the individual has been fasting for a period of time or on a high fat–low carbohydrate diet, then the curve will be high and prolonged, i.e. the tolerance for glucose will be reduced. It is essential therefore to have the individual who is going to be tested fed some standard diet, containing adequate carbohydrate, for a period of 3–5 days prior to the test. It is well to note, too, that successive doses of carbohydrate enhance the tolerance for glucose (Staub-Traugott phenomenon). This forms the basis for the two-dose tolerance test.

The oral glucose tolerance test also may be influenced by certain hormones that affect the absorption of carbohydrate from the gut. One of these is the hormone of the thyroid gland. After thyroidectomy, or in hypothyroid individuals, absorption of glucose from the gut is reduced and the glucose tolerance curve is flat whereas in hyperthyroid individuals the absorption from the gut is enhanced and the blood sugar levels rise to higher values than in normal controls. Hypophysectomy also reduces the absorption of glucose but this can be restored by thyroid administration. Adrenalectomy may affect the absorption of glucose from the gut but this can be brought back to normal by restoring electrolytes and particularly the sodium of the gut.

The administration of cortisone prior to the glucose tolerance test may affect the glucose tolerance adversely. The effect is more pronounced in ill than in healthy subjects (Engel). The cortisone-glucose tolerance test has been used in an attempt to determine a tendency for the development of diabetes before clinical diabetes is established ("prediabetes") (Fajans & Conn).

When the glucose load is given intravenously, instead of by mouth, the blood sugar rises very rapidly to its high level and then declines. Different amounts of glucose and different durations of injections have been used in these tests. If 25 g. are injected over 3–4 min. and blood samples obtained at regular intervals for 60–90 min. it is possible, from the percentage decrease of the glucose concentration in plasma (K) to obtain an index of glucose utilization. The intravenous glucose tolerance test gets away from any effects of changes in absorption of glucose but it is claimed that the rate of removal of glucose absorbed from the gut is greater than that for glucose injected intravenously and hence that the oral test is more physiological.

Pancreatic Diabetes

REMOVAL OF THE PANCREAS

When the pancreas is completely removed from a dog or cat, a characteristic syndrome rapidly develops (Von Mehring and Minkowski, 1889). When a diet including the known essentials is provided, the animals may live indefinitely if adequate amounts of insulin are administered. The animals recover rapidly from the operation and appear to be normal, but the diabetic state quickly supervenes when insulin is discontinued. The sugar content of the blood begins to rise within a very short time, depending on the size of the last dose of insulin, and increases from normal levels to 0.20–0.40 per cent or higher within 24 hrs. The urine gives a positive test for sugar when the blood sugar rises above approximately 0.16 per cent, since under these conditions, the renal transport maximum for glucose is exceeded (ch. 79). The excretion of nitrogen is increased and this may be taken to indicate protein breakdown or decreased protein formation. In the fasting diabetic the blood sugar and sugar excretion are maintained at high levels. The sugar is apparently formed in the liver chiefly from deaminated amino acids obtained from body protein. The blood sugar of the diabetic falls rapidly after hepatectomy. The amino acid contents of the blood and urine are increased. The loss of protein contributes to the decrease in body weight. The neutral fat content of the blood increases, due probably to the increased rate of mobilization of depot fat, and there is also a rise in cholesterol esters, phospholipid and free fatty acids.

The enhanced breakdown of fat in the depancreatized animal is indicated by the accumulation of ketone bodies in the blood and by the excretion of excessive amounts in the urine. The ketosis in a fat dog is greater than in a lean, but this species is characterized by its efficiency in metabolizing fats, without ketosis. The loss of body fat is rapid but the ketosis may be so severe, even in this species, that the animal dies in coma before the fat reserves are depleted. It has been proposed that, in diabetes, free fatty acids shift the metabolism of acetyl CoA toward increased formation of acetoacetate by changing the redox status of the liver through fatty acid oxidation and by inhibition of enzymes by activated fatty acids (Wieland). The production of acetoacetate thus becomes greater than its utilization and ketosis and ketonuria ensue.

Beta-hydroxy-butyric and acetoacetic acids and others derived from tissue breakdown may produce an acidosis. In acidosis the respiratory centre is stimulated and "air hunger" and coma are evident. The mechanism of coma production in diabetes is not completely known. In uncontrolled human diabetes the important problem is severe metabolic ketosis but there may sometimes be disturbances of hydrogen-ion equilibrium through excess lactic acid and hyperosmolar, non-ketotic diabetic coma may occur. In the latter, the plasma ketones may show little change and cellular dehydration is responsible for the disturbance of consciousness (Nabarro).

The depancreatized animal can still metabolize carbohydrate and at the high blood sugar levels of the diabetic this utilization may be normal. However at normal blood sugar levels the utilization is reduced. There is also evidence for increased new formation of glucose (gluconeogenesis) from other substances, chiefly protein. Calculation of rates of production and utilization of glucose based on rates of appearance and disappearance using labelled glucose show that the basal rate of glucose production is high as

compared to normal dogs (Hetenyi, Wrenshall and Best). Similarly, in diabetic patients, a higher than normal glucose output was calculated by Reichard, et al. The injection of insulin leads to a quick increase in the rate of glucose utilization (Henderson, Wrenshall, and Odense). Conversely, the sudden removal of insulin supply by blocking the circulation to a pancreatic remnant leads to a rapid decrease in the rate of utilization of glucose (Wrenshall, Vranic, Cowan, and Rappaport).

The respiratory quotient of the depancreatized animal not receiving insulin assumes the low level of 0.69 to 0.73 and is not usually raised when sugar is given.

The glycogen content of the muscles of a depancreatized animal may be reduced below the normal level, but appreciable amounts remain. There is no diminution of heart muscle glycogen and, indeed, convincing evidence of an increase has been obtained. Liver glycogen falls to very low levels. This is probably responsible for the fact that insulin injection in the depancreatized dog does not lead to an increase in the rate of appearance of glucose. A slight increase in both muscle and liver glycogen can be produced by giving large amounts of sugar without exogenous insulin.

Whereas the glucose utilization of the normal heart is low, that of the diabetic animal is even less when the blood sugar concentrations are the same. Lactate, however, is used almost as well by the diabetic as by the normal heart and fatty acids are also well utilized (Evans). The rate of usage of glucose but not of lactate by the diabetic heart is increased when insulin is supplied.

The excretion of phosphorus is increased in the depancreatized animal but the administration of sugar or epinephrine does not cause the prompt fall in the organic phosphate of the blood which is observed in normal animals.

The diabetic animal is very susceptible to infections but it is not established that this is due to the raised sugar content of the tissues. Some diabetic patients have a decreased ability to form antibodies. This defect appears to be more closely related to hypoproteinaemia than to hyperglycaemia. Pathological conditions are observed with considerable frequency in the eyes of diabetic animals.

Although there is considerable variation in the length of life of the depancreatized dog or cat, most animals fed on a mixed diet do not live for more than two or three weeks without insulin. Under certain conditions dogs may survive for seven weeks. It is established, however, that when the anterior pituitary is also removed, the animal (dog) may live for at least nine months and exhibit only a mild form of diabetes. Severe diabetes produced under these conditions by administration of the diabetogenic substances of the anterior pituitary is alleviated by insulin. As mentioned previously, the activities of enzymes concerned with the synthesis of glycogen, fatty acids and protein tend to be reduced in diabetes but those concerned with gluconeogenesis are increased. This effect of the absence of insulin on the enzyme composition of cells, and the effect of insulin on the induction of some enzymes and in inhibiting the effect of adrenal hormones on the induction of certain others, must be of great importance in determining the concentration of enzyme activities in the cell and hence in determining its metabolic activity.

Pathogenesis of Diabetes

Randle suggests that the imparied tolerance for glucose and reduced sensitivity to insulin in diabetic subjects may be the result of increased levels of free fatty acids (FFA). When an emulsion of fat was infused there was a rise in plasma FFA and the tolerance for glucose was impaired. In vitro, adding fatty acids to the medium decreased the effect of insulin on glucose transport, reduced the rate of phosphorylation of glucose, the rate of glycolysis, and the oxidation of pyruvate. When FFA are present they seem to be used preferentially by muscle and the utilization of glucose is reduced. In the intact animal this would lead to increased blood sugar levels and hence to a stimulation of insulin secretion. This insulin in turn would reduce FFA formation and help to restore carbohydrate utilization.

Various types of insulin antagonism have been described. One associated with plasma albumin, known as the synalbumin insulin antagonist has received considerable attention recently. This antagonism seems to be more pronounced in plasma albumin from diabetic patients. Vallance-Owen suggests that the separated B-chain of insulin and the synalbumin antagonist are identical. He postulates that the B-chain impedes the uptake of glucose by cells by competing with insulin for receptor sites. Other insulin antagonists have been reported but will not be dealt with here.

Moloney and Wright have produced diabetes by the use of insulin antibodies. Immunological reactions to an altered insulin have been postulated by some as the responsible factor in diabetes

production and in the genesis of some vascular complications.

Certain hormones can produce a persistent experimental diabetes in susceptible animals of some species but there is little clear evidence for the overactivity of diabetogenic hormones in well-established diabetes in man. It was found by Pfeiffer that in certain obese female "prediabetics" the fasting levels of growth hormone were elevated and there was an inversion of the diurnal rhythm of ACTH secretion. The combination of the elevated GH and altered circadian rhythm of ACTH secretion, while insufficient singly, together might be responsible for some diabetic changes.

Since the condition of diabetes may be relieved by injecting insulin it is reasonable to consider that it is a condition in which there is a relative lack of insulin. In human diabetes, beginning in childhood, the condition is not unlike that in experimental animals, there being a reduction in β-cells, a low insulin content of pancreas and, one presumes, an absolute lack of insulin—which is borne out by the insulin studies in the pancreas and in blood. However, in certain diabetics whose diabetes begins later in life, there may still be a considerable amount of normal islet tissue in the pancreas, and the insulin concentration in the pancreas may be within the normal range. Nevertheless, since the individual is diabetic there must be a relative lack of insulin. If this relative lack is due to an increased utilization or destruction of insulin, i.e. increased insulin removal, then this should increase insulin requirements and there should be some evidence of sustained stimulation of the islets and signs of islet degeneration or islet growth.

Since, in some of the maturity-onset diabetics, evidence for this is lacking, the conclusion can be drawn that if insulin requirements are excessive they are not being met by normal compensatory responses. An increase in insulin antagonists or diminished effectiveness of insulin because of elevated FFA should stimulate the islets. It would appear that compensatory stimulation of the islets is less than adequate. This does not seem to be due to a primary reduction in insulin synthesis, otherwise the insulin content of the pancreas should be low. For some reason, not yet clear, at normal blood sugar levels the stimulation of insulin secretion is not adequate. Some have postulated that the insulin that is secreted is altered in character and less effective. However pancreatic extracts from these subjects still have good biological activity. It is reasonable to conclude, then, that persistent diabetes is fundamentally a disorder in compensation by the islets and that the basic defect is in the ability of the beta cells of the islets to supply adequate amounts of insulin under ordinary conditions of stimulation. Why this is so has yet to be determined.

Vascular Changes in Diabetes

In the human, there may be vascular complications of diabetes, particularly in the eyes and in the kidneys. Diabetic microangiopathy often may be present early in clinical diabetes but there is usually a latent period before the vascular changes become evident. The relation between the occurrence of vascular changes and the degree of diabetic control is still not clear. That insulin deficiency may play a part in the vascular lesions of diabetes is supported by the finding that the uptake of UC^{14}-labelled glucose and lactate production by aortae from diabetic rabbits is less than in those from non-diabetic ones (Winegrad).

It has been proposed (Blumenthal) that autoimmune phenomena involving as antigen a changed endogenous insulin might account for the angiopathy in maturity-onset diabetics. Rabbits immunized with an insulin-adjuvant mixture and challenged with small amounts of insulin showed a number of lesions of small blood vessels similar to those found in diabetics.

The Antidiabetic Hormone—Insulin

The name insuline was suggested by de Meyer in 1909 for the hypothetical internal secretion of the pancreas, the search for which had been stimulated by von Mehring and Minkowski's findings (1889). Although Zuelzer and Scott obtained very suggestive results, which in some cases were probably due to the presence of insulin, Banting and Best (working in Macleod's laboratory) (1922), were the first to obtain a preparation containing the antidiabetic hormone in a form which consistently alleviated all signs of diabetes in completely depancreatized dogs (fig. 67.4).

Source of Insulin

In the mammalian organism, the pancreas appears to be the only organ to manufacture insulin or to store it in more than minute amounts. Only a small part of the pancreas is involved, namely, the islets of Langerhans. These are small masses of specialized tissue scattered throughout the pancreas and making up about 1% of the gland.

The islets of Langerhans are composed of two major cell types: the β- and α-cells with principal subtypes C, D and X (fig. 67.5). A number of other subdivisions have been described but it is

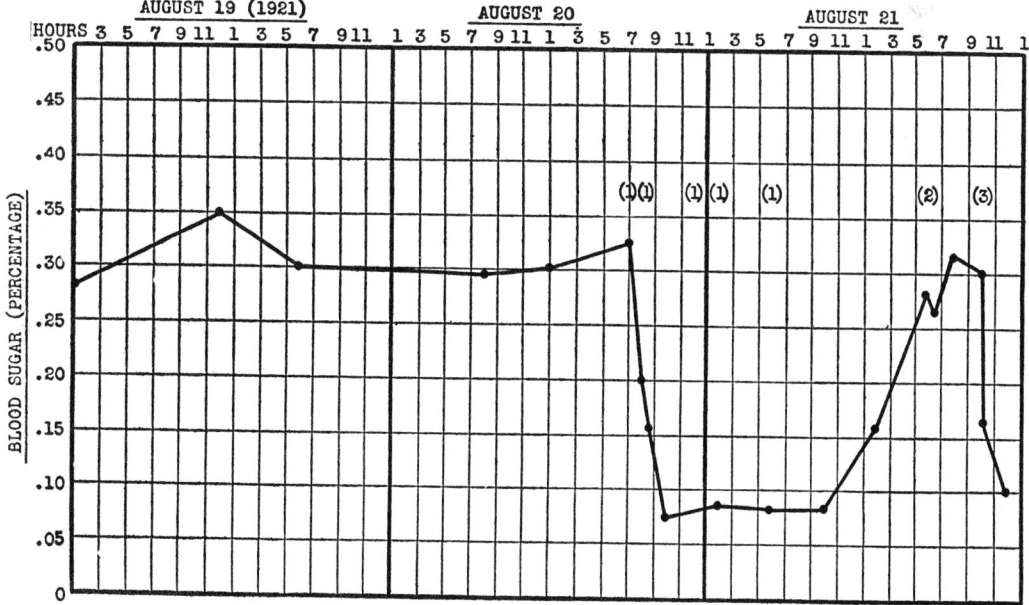

Fig. 67.4. Effect of insulin on the blood sugar curve of a depancreatized dog (redrawn from Banting and Best). (1) Injection of extract of degenerated pancreas; (2) extract after incubation with pancreatic juice; (3) extract incubated without pancreatic juice. Blood sugars by Myers-Bailey modification of Lewis-Benedict method.

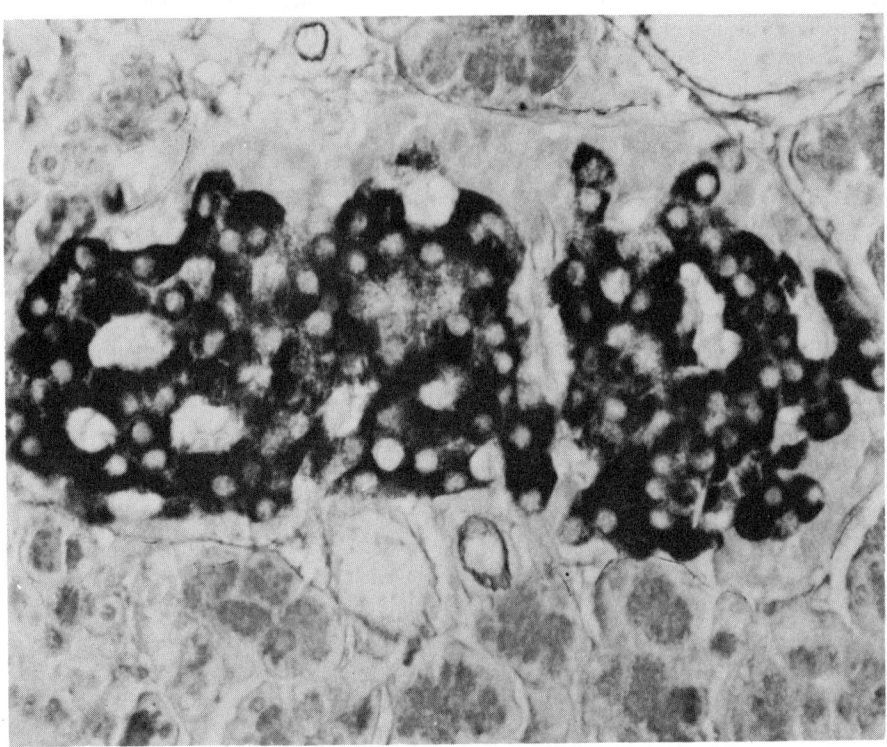

FIG. 67.5. Islets of Langerhans, of the rat pancreas, showing dark-staining β-cells.

questionable if they do represent distinct types. So far, only two hormones have been isolated from the islets, *insulin*, which is produced by β-cells and, *glucagon*, apparently a product of the α-cells. Insulin has been extracted from micro-dissected islets.

The β-cells of the islets of Langerhans synthesize, store, and secrete insulin and normally increase in number when the secretion of existing cells becomes inadequate. Evidence for changes in function can be obtained by changes in the histological appearance of the β-cells, changes in the insulin content of the pancreas, and changes in the insulin levels in blood. When the activity of β-cells is high, an increase in nuclear size, and in the prominence and complexity of the Golgi apparatus, and reduction in the granulation become evident. If the stimulation is continued and hyperglycaemia persists, there may be infiltration of β-cells with glycogen and hydropic changes. Continued stimulation also leads to an increase in the number of β-cells and thus, in some species, the potentiality for function is improved by increasing the amount of islet tissue. The changes in granulation of the β-cells and in

the insulin content of the gland are dependent upon the relationship between the synthesis and secretion of insulin. A reduction in granulation may occur when secretion is increased to a greater extent than synthesis, but it may also occur when synthesis is depressed to a greater degree than secretion. Reduction in granulation thus can occur either with stimulation or with depression of islet function. Figure 67.6 shows an electron micrograph of a portion of a β-cell. The electron-dense granules are evident. Species differences in the appearance of the β-granules may reflect the species differences in the insulin itself (p. 1348). There is little doubt that these granules contain stored insulin since the insulin content of the islet is related to the extent of this granulation and insulin has been extracted from separated islet granules. The pregranular synthesis of insulin probably is completed in the ribosomes which can be seen on the surface of the endoplasmic reticulum. Insulin then goes to the site of granule formation in the region of the Golgi bodies. When the granules are formed and secretion is to occur, the granules move to the capillary end of the cell, fuse with the plasma membrane

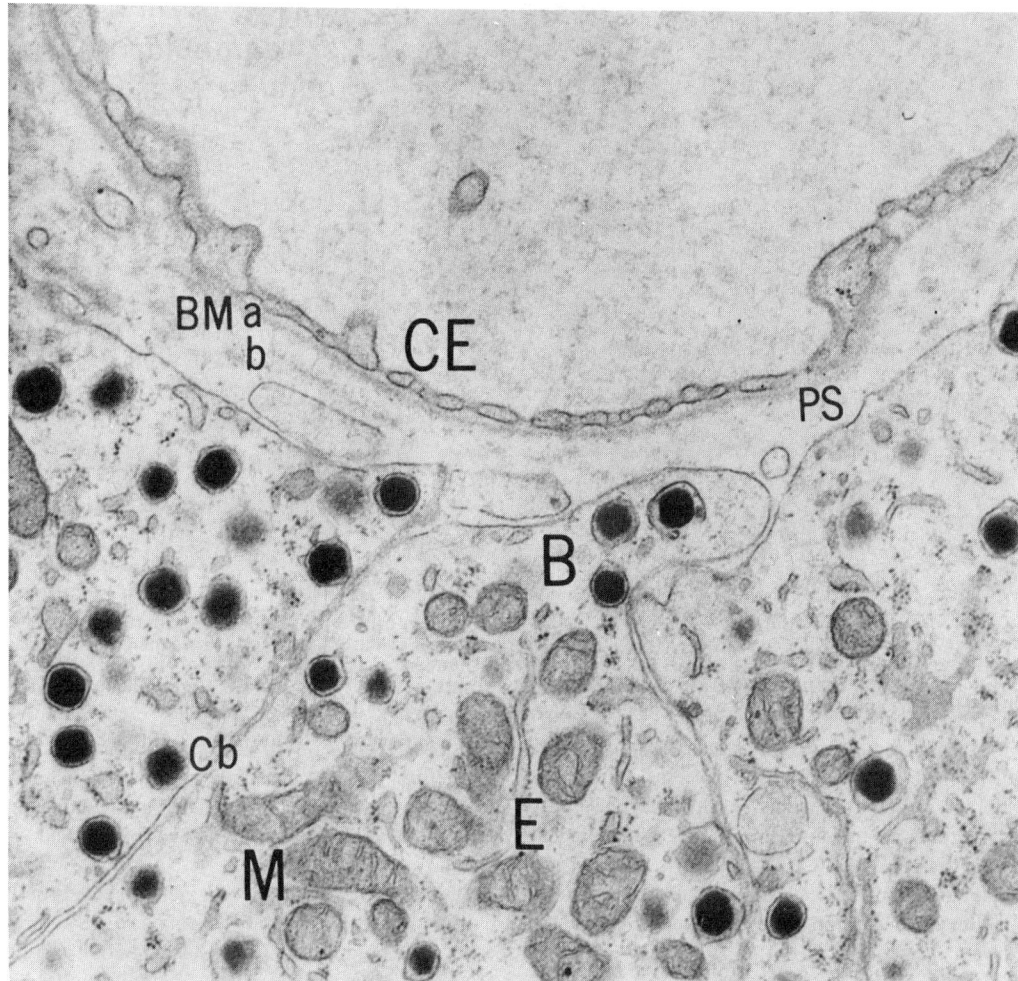

FIG. 67.6. Portions of three beta cells bordering a capillary. CE = capillary endothelium. BMa = basement membrane of the capillary. b = basement membrane of the beta cell PS = pericapillary space B = beta cell granules E = endothelial reticulum M = mitochondria Cb = boundary between two cells showing the plasma membranes. Ribosomes are seen as small dots throughout the cytoplasm. Magnification about 25,000 ×. (Photo through the courtesy of Dr. John Logothetopoulos.)

and are extruded. Other possibilities that must be considered in insulin secretion are shown in fig. 67.7. The insulin is secreted into the pericapillary space and from there passes through the capillary membrane into the capillary.

The secretion of insulin is stimulated by an elevation in the level of blood glucose. This may be achieved by the intravenous administration of glucose and direct stimulation of islet cells since it may be evident in the isolated perfused pancreas. Also, using pancreatic tissue in vitro, Bouman found that the presence of growth hormone enhanced the stimulating effect of a given level of glucose. However, it has been reported that injection of glucose into the portal vein in amounts not sufficient to raise the arterial blood sugar level stimulated the secretion of insulin (Goetz, Maney, and Greenberg) whereas fructose injection did not have this effect. The possibility must thus be entertained that there may be some receptor sites in portal vein or liver which are responsive to certain specific sugars and that some mechanism in addition to the direct stimulation of beta cells with glucose might be of importance.

Indirect evidence from studies of the insulin content of pancreas and islet growth suggest that the secretion of insulin by islet cells can be stimulated by glucose administration, by the administration of crude pituitary extracts, growth hormone, adrenal and gonadal steroids,

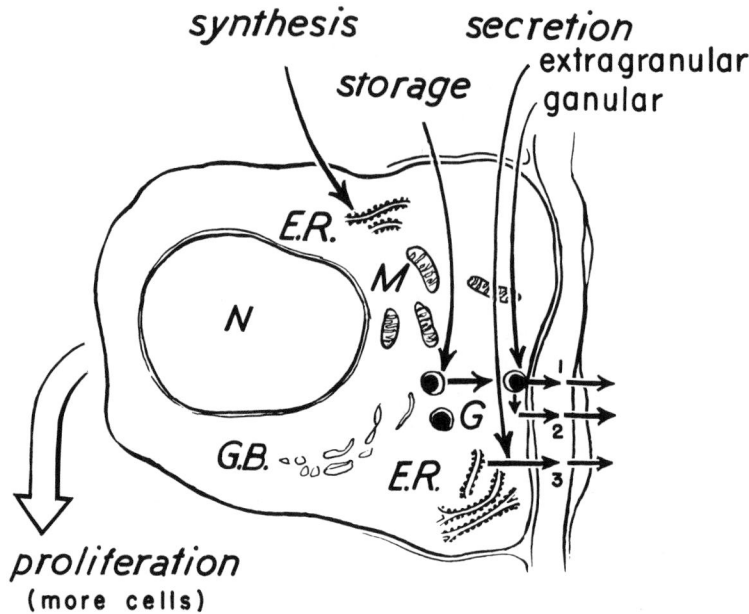

Fig. 67.7. The functions of β-cells are to synthesize, store, and secrete insulin; and to increase in number when necessary. Secretion is considered to be by: (1) granule extrusion, but other possibilities are (2) granular material may become more soluble and then leave, (3) some insulin may go directly from the synthetic site to the cell surface without passing through a storage form. E. R. = endoplasmic reticulum with ribosomes on its surface; G. B. = Golgi bodies; M = Mitochondria; N = Nucleus; G = Granule.

thyroid hormone, sulphonylureas, and by insulin antibodies, and that insulin secretion can be depressed by starvation, by low carbohydrate intake, and by insulin administration in sufficient quantities.

More direct evidence can now be obtained from studies of the insulin levels in blood.

The Insulin of Blood

Many attempts have been made to find reliable means for measuring the insulin levels in blood. The different assay procedures that have been used can be divided into bioassay methods and immunochemical assays. The bioassay procedures in turn are divided into those performed in vivo and those carried out in vitro. In the *in vivo* bioassays the reduction in glucose level in blood or the incidence of convulsions in response to standard and unknown insulin solutions is measured and compared in rats or mice made sensitive to insulin by hypophysectomy or adrenalectomy, or both, and sometimes, in addition made diabetic with alloxan.

The *in vitro* bioassay procedures can be divided into methods employing the diaphragm of rat or mouse, those using the fat pad of the rat and those employing other tissues of the rat, such as the mammary gland. In the methods using mouse or rat diaphragm, changes in glucose uptake or glycogen synthesis or the incorporation of labelled amino acids into protein are taken as measures of

the insulin effect. With the epididymal fat pad procedure, glucose uptake, glycogen synthesis, CO_2 formation from glucose-1-C^{14} and fat formation from labelled glucose have been used to measure the insulin effect.

It is possible to set up these assays as statistically valid procedures but this is not always done and while more than one dose of the insulin standard is used, very often there is only one dose of the unknown. Used in this way the results can be erroneous, and for satisfactory results a 4-point parallel slope assay should be carried out, though under some circumstances this cannot be undertaken.

The immunochemical assay procedures depend on the combination of insulin with insulin-antibody and the fact that I^{131}-labelled insulin and unlabelled insulin can compete for antibody. The more unlabelled insulin present, the less labelled insulin combines with antibody. This combined insulin-insulin-antibody is then separated either by electrophoresis or chromatography or by the precipitation of the insulin-antibody complex by an anti-globulin antibody. The radioactivity of the separated, combined insulin-insulin-antibody is measured and from comparison with the effects of known amounts of standard insulin the potency of the unknown can be determined.

The bioassays depend upon some activity of insulin on tissues and the general criticism is that the activity of insulin may be confused with the activity of other agents or materials. Hence one of the first things that should be known is the specificity of the test. The immunoassay procedures are felt to be specific for insulin but there is some question as to whether or not they measure all the insulin present. Any satisfactory method must be specific for insulin, must be precise enough for whatever use is to be made of it, and any effect of interfering factors should be known.

Not only have a variety of methods been used for assay, but also there have been differences in the way the blood serum has been prepared for assay. When untreated serum or plasma from fasted animals or man is tested, values in the neighbourhood of 0–150 microunits are found with the immunoassay procedures and the mouse hemidiaphragm assay. Dilution has been reported to increase the activity of plasma insulin with some of the testing procedures. When serum is treated with acid-alcohol and dialyzed in the cold (Davidson and Haist) or extracted with acid-alcohol (Moloney, Hagedorn, Baird, and Bornstein) or dialyzed against tap water after electrophoretic separation (Lyngsøe), values in the milliunit range have been found for samples from fasting human subjects and for serum of dogs and rats using bioassay procedures. However, this increased insulin activity is not usually demonstrable with immunoassay procedures.

The work that has been done makes it evident that there is a large amount of insulin activity normally present in blood that is not directly measurable in untreated serum but that can be made evident by treatment of serum with acidified alcohol or certain other procedures. The level of insulin activity in untreated serum is highest in that obtained from pancreatic venous blood in which it also forms a much higher percentage of the treated-serum insulin activity.

The level of insulin in blood, like the level of glucose, is a dynamic one, depending upon the balance between the secretion of insulin into the blood by β-beta cells of the islets of Langerhans and its removal from blood. Any change in level means there is a disproportion between the entrance of insulin into and its removal from blood, but not much is known concerning these removal mechanisms or how they are controlled or altered.

Since insulin is formed and secreted by the β-cells of the pancreatic islets, one would expect that, if blood insulin is being measured, the removal of the pancreas would cause the insulin of blood to disappear. One of the serious criticisms

of the epididymal fat-pad assay as usually carried out, is that, after pancreatectomy, the insulin-like activity of blood measured by this assay does not fall to zero. When the insulin potency is measured by the mouse hemidiaphragm or rat hemidiaphragm procedure using either glucose uptake or glycogen synthesis as criteria of the effect, then it is found that, following pancreatectomy, the insulin activity of the blood serum falls so low that the estimated values do not differ significantly from zero.

One important influence on blood insulin level is that produced by an increase in the level of blood glucose. After the administration of glucose, the blood insulin level rises in rat, dog and man. Using bioassay procedures both the activity in untreated serum and the activity in treated serum increased.

The insulin activity in untreated serum from the pancreatic vein is related to blood sugar level (Metz), and in the isolated perfused pancreas, when the glucose levels in the perfusate fell below 45–50 mg. %, the secretion of insulin was not detectable (Grodsky and Bennett). d-Mannoheptulose is reported to prevent the stimulating effect of glucose on insulin secretion (Coore and Randle). After glucose administration, changes in the degree of granulation of the β-cells and in the insulin content of the pancreas have also been observed, but unless the blood sugar levels are kept very high over a period of time, degranulation of the β-cells and reduction in insulin content are not great. The insulin content and granulation are probably maintained because insulin synthesis is stimulated along with secretion when the glucose levels are increased.

In the rat, when a continuous intravenous injection of sufficient amounts of glucose is given, the blood sugar will first be elevated. This presumably stimulates insulin secretion and the blood-sugar levels return rather quickly toward normal (Haist). With continuous glucose infusion in some species, the number of functioning β-cells increases, the synthetic process becomes better able to keep up with secretion and the granulation and insulin content of the islet cells return toward normal. When the proliferation of β-cells is not adequate, degranulation becomes prominent, the cells may become infiltrated with glycogen, and hydropic changes may become evident. It is possible that an increase in glucose supply to islets may be important for insulin synthesis. At all events, the incorporation of labelled glucose into insulin or acid-alcohol-soluble protein in islet tissue increases with the glucose concentration of the medium. Also, when the β-cells have been depleted of granules, regranulation is assisted by increasing the carbohydrate in the diet.

The secretion of insulin can be stimulated also by the sulfonylurea compound, tolbutamide (p. 1363). This stimulation occurs despite a reduction in blood sugar level, and, unlike glucose, the stimulation is not blocked by mannoheptulose. After tolbutamide administration insulin activities in pancreatic, portal and peripheral blood sera were increased. Compared to the effect of glucose the response was not great and of relatively brief duration. There is the possibility, as yet not confirmed, that tolbutamide stimulates the secretion of already formed insulin without having much influence on synthesis whereas glucose presumably affects both. Further evidence of an islet-stimulating effect of tolbutamide is found in the fact that islet growth can be stimulated by its prolonged administration.

A number of other factors will stimulate the secretion of insulin. Growth hormone, adrenal and gonadal steroids and glucagon have this effect but these factors all produce hyperglycaemia and the hyperglycaemia itself may be a stimulating influence, though not necessarily the sole one. The resulting changes are very much like those produced by glucose. Under certain circumstances, insulin secretion may be stimulated by the amino acid *l*-leucine.

Two conditions, starvation and the injection of large amounts of insulin, will depress islet activity. There are some species differences in the observable effects. In the rat, starvation produces a large fall in the insulin content of the pancreas whereas in the guinea-pig it does not. In the rat, too, injections of large amounts of insulin tremendously reduces the granulation of the β-cells but this effect was not observed in the rabbit. These findings emphasize the fact that granulation and insulin content may remain unchanged as long as the synthesis and secretion of insulin remain balanced, even though changes in function do occur.

There is considerable interest in the levels of insulin in the blood of diabetic patients. In general, the insulin activity of acid-alcohol-treated serum from severely diabetic patients is low or absent, and in untreated serum is absent if the patient received no insulin prior to the time of sampling. In mild diabetics the insulin activity of treated and untreated plasma is found to be within the normal range. Indeed, some have amounts of insulin above normal levels, and in

certain maturity-onset diabetics the insulin levels of untreated serum rise higher than in normal subjects after the administration of glucose. In such patients the insulin activity of acid-alcohol treated serum is usually within the normal range. Once the diabetic or the normal individual has received injections of insulin, the levels of insulin in blood become high, presumably because of the development of antibodies to the injected insulin and the retention of some injected insulin combined with antibody in the blood. Under these conditions the measurements of the insulin levels of blood have little meaning.

CHEMISTRY OF INSULIN

Insulin was first isolated in crystalline form by J. J. Abel in 1926. In 1934, D. A. Scott showed that it could be readily crystallized as the zinc salt and that the crystals, prepared according to Abel, contained zinc. Nickel, calcium and cobalt also aid in effecting crystallization of insulin preparations. There is about 0.5 per cent of metal in the crystals. The "salts" of the insulin protein may appear in various forms—the zinc compound usually as twin plate-like rhombohedra.

When insulin is in solution, its molecular weight is affected by its concentration, pH, protein concentration, and the presence of other ions. In more dilute solutions, the molecular weight of insulin appears to become smaller. Minimal values of about 6,000 have been obtained in acid or alkaline solutions. This corresponds well with what is calculated from Sanger's formula (5734) and is assumed to be the molecular weight of the monomer. A dimer structure of 12,000 m.w. has been proposed by Lindley and Rollett, and is often referred to as the monomer presumably because some investigators did not find molecular weights less than 12,000 by sedimentation, light-scattering or osmotic methods. Values in the neighbourhood of 24,000, 36,000 and 48,000 have been obtained through the association of the 12,000 m.w. units. With pH around neutrality the minimal molecular weight is 24,000.

Chemical analysis indicated that the insulin molecule is built up entirely of amino acids. Insulin is richer in the amino acids leucine, glutamic acid, and cystine, than most other proteins; methionine, tryptophane and hydroxyproline, which are common in many proteins, are absent from the insulin molecule.

Sanger applied methods he had developed for determining the sequence of amino acids in

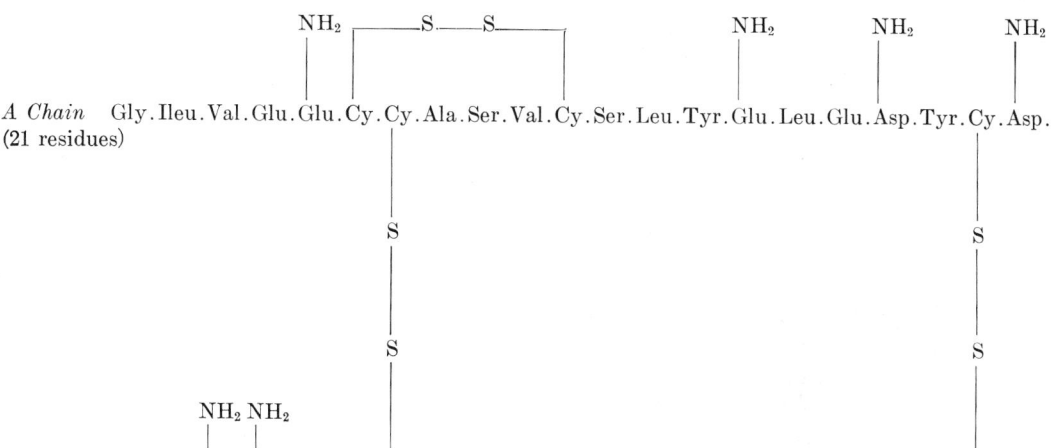

A Chain   Gly.Ileu.Val.Glu.Glu.Cy.Cy.Ala.Ser.Val.Cy.Ser.Leu.Tyr.Glu.Leu.Glu.Asp.Tyr.Cy.Asp.
(21 residues)

B Chain   Phe.Val.Asp.Glu.His.Leu.Cy.Gly.Ser.His.Leu.Val.Glu.Ala.Leu.Tyr.Leu.Val.Cy.Gly.
(30 residues)   [Glu.Ar.Gly.Phe.Phe.Tyr.Thr.Pro.Lys.Ala.

FIG. 67.8. The structure of beef insulin. (Sanger, F., Thompson, E. O. P. and Kitai, R., Biochem. J., **59**, 509, 1955.)

polypeptide chains to the study of insulin and showed that it was a protein made up of two components, an A or glycyl chain composed of 21 amino acids linked to a B or phenylalanine chain of 30 amino acids, by two disulphide linkages (fig. 67.8). The A chain itself contains a disulphide linkage. The disulphide bonds were broken by oxidation, the chains were separated, the amino acid sequences determined, and the arrangement of the disulphide bridges established. There are species differences in the amino acid chains (table 67.2) though the biological activity of these different insulins is similar. Highly purified A and B chains are devoid of insulin-like activity, but when a mixture of the A and B chains are treated with thiol-2-mercapto-ethanol, recombination with definite insulin activity is obtained (Dixon, Wardlaw, and Wilson). A better yield is obtained when an enzyme, insulin-glutathione transhydrogenase is used for the recombination of the two chains (Katzen, et al). The reconstituted insulin has characteristic biological activity, and is neutralized by specific insulin antibodies. The product has been recrystallized and found to have the same crystal form as beef insulin (Du Yu-Cang, et al). More recently the A and B chains themselves have been synthesized and the two synthetic chains subsequently combined to yield insulin activity (Katsoyannis, Zahn). It is probable that a specific enzyme is involved in insulin synthesis in the beta cell. It is felt that glutathione-insulin-transhydrogenase is probably associated with insulin degradation and that there may be a different enzyme for its synthesis. Lazarow and others have studied

TABLE 67.2

Species differences in the insulin molecule

Species	Amino Acids of Disulphide Ring of A Chain	C-Terminal Residue of B Chain
Cattle	Ala.Ser.Val.	Alanine
Sheep	Ala.Gly.Val.	Alanine
Horse	Thr.Gly.Ileu.	Alanine
Pig	Thr.Ser.Ileu.	Alanine
Whale	Thr.Ser.Ileu.	Alanine
Rabbit	Thr.Ser.Ileu.	Serine
Human	Thr.Ser.Ileu.	Threonine

the synthesis of insulin in the beta cells of the islets. In many respects this is comparable to the synthesis of proteins elsewhere. It is felt that amino acids enter the cell, are activated by an enzyme system requiring ATP, go with soluble RNA and then to the RNA of ribosomes where they are joined together in proper sequence. The A and B chains may be synthesized separately and may then be combined by the oxidation of the sulphydryl groups, forming disulphide bonds, under the influence of a specific enzyme (fig. 67.9). There is evidence that insulin is synthesized in the microsomes. Its transfer to the granule follows.

Slightly acidified insulin has been kept for long periods, but in dilute alkali insulin is relatively unstable. Attempts have been made to find what parts of the insulin molecule are essential for its biological activity. Information has been obtained by treatment of insulin with reagents specific for one type of group, by removal of parts of the molecule by enzymic

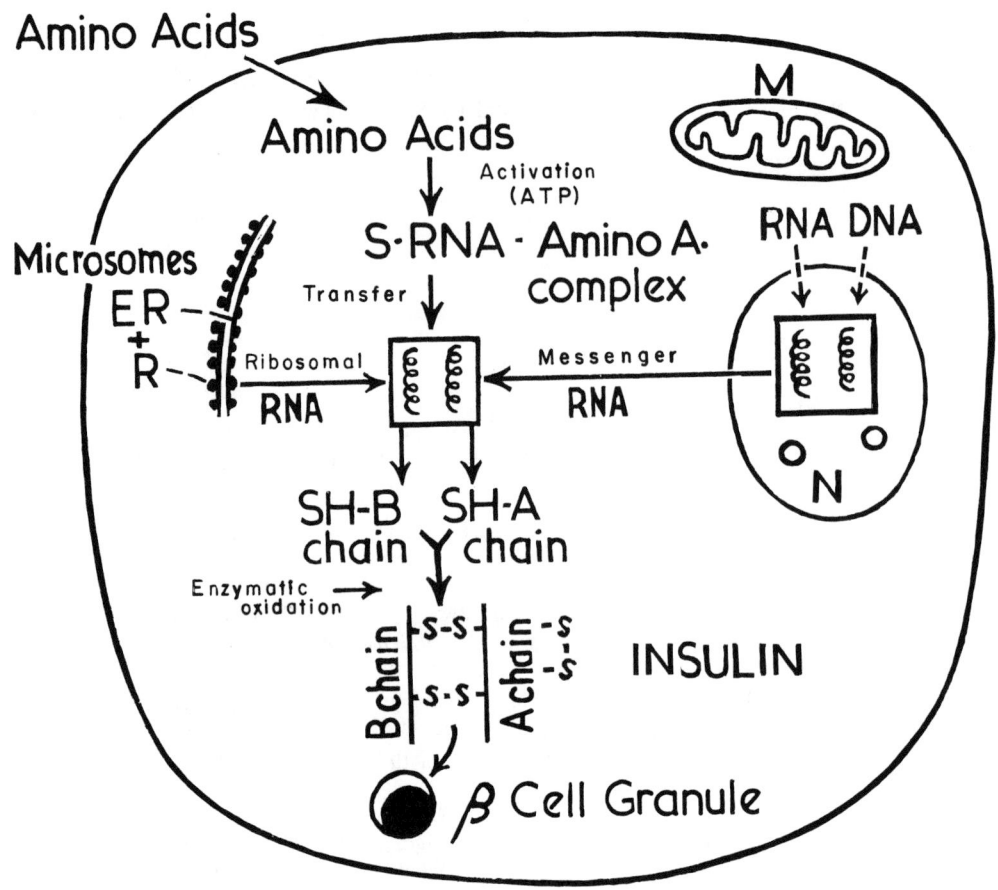

Fig. 67.9. Diagrammatic representation of insulin formation in the β-cell (after Lazarow).

hydrolysis and by noting differences in structure of insulins from different species. It is found that disulphide bridges, free carboxyl groups and phenolic hydroxyl groups are essential for its action. Blocking free amino groups and removal of the C-terminal alanine group does not lead to loss of activity whereas removal of the C-terminal asparagine group does. Removal of a heptapeptide (Gly.Phe.Phe.Tyr.Thr.Pro.Lys.) leaves an insulin residue with a reduced activity. Insulins from different species show differences in the three amino acids of the disulphide ring of the A chain, hence these are not likely to be important in determining biological activity. The B chains are identical in all species except in the C-terminal group; which in most species is alanine, in the rabbit is serine, and in man is threonine.

STANDARDIZATION OF INSULIN

Zinc insulin crystals from different sources (man, cattle, hog, sheep, bison, fish) have similar potencies. The fourth international standard, a preparation of zinc insulin crystals, contains 24 units per mg. There are two well established methods of assaying the potency of an insulin preparation. The lowering of blood sugar in fasting rabbits and the production of convulsions in fasting mice are both satisfactory effects of insulin for the comparison of unknown and standard products. The new international yardstick of insulin is free of glucagon.

IMMUNOLOGICAL EFFECTS OF INSULIN

Several reports have indicated that serum from certain insulin-resistant human subjects was able to reduce the hypoglycaemic action of insulin and the evidence supported the idea that the insulin resistance in these subjects was due to the neutralization of injected insulin in an antigen-antibody reaction. Moloney and his associates showed that insulin has the characteristics of a true, though weak, antigen. When crystalline ox or pig insulin is injected into the mouse, guinea-pig, rabbit, sheep or horse, a resistance to injected insulin can be induced but since these animals do not become diabetic, it would seem the antibody is effective against the injected insulin but not against the endogenous insulin. However, the antibodies in the sera of these animals neutralize the extracted pancreatic insulin of all species except the guinea-pig. It would appear that either the serum insulin is different from the pancreatic insulin or that the immunological specificity of the insulin of a particular species is altered by the extraction procedure. While anti-insulin sera from horse, sheep and guinea-pig reduces the hypoglycaemic action of injected insulin, only the guinea-pig anti-insulin serum produces a transient hyperglycaemia when injected alone into rats, indicating that it is neutralizing endogenous insulin. It also has been shown to induce transient hyperglycaemia in the rabbit, cat, dog, sheep, pig and cow. The differences in effectiveness of guinea-pig anti-sera and those of other species may be due to differences in avidity, i.e. the tendency for the insulin-antibody complex to dissociate.

In the mouse, injections of anti-ox insulin antibody prepared in the guinea-pig, produces a fatal diabetes, due to the neutralization of endogenous insulin. Large amounts of antibody must be used for this effect and the dose repeated frequently. Histological studies after injections into the rat of guinea-pig anti-ox insulin serum show that the beta cells of the pancreatic islets are extensively degranulated. In general, the effects of injections of potent guinea-pig anti-ox insulin sera are similar to the effects of pancreatectomy.

In studies on hybrid insulins, i.e. insulin in which the A chain from one species has been combined with the B chain from another, it was found that the ox A-cod B hybrid was neutralized by anti-ox insulin serum but not by anti-cod insulin serum, whereas with cod A-ox B hybrid, the reverse was true. The explanation seems to be that the antigenic site lies usually on the A chain. The insulin from a low order teleost fish, the bowfin, is neutralized by both anti-cod and anti-ox insulin sera, suggesting that the bowfin may have two antibody-combining sites (Wilson).

GENERAL EFFECTS OF INSULIN ON THE DIABETIC ORGANISM

It is well established that insulin restores to the depancreatized animal its ability to utilize sugars and fats in a normal manner. The excessive breakdown of protein is prevented. The ketosis rapidly disappears. Glycogen is deposited in large amounts in the liver. Muscle glycogen may be increased. The respiratory quotient rises when sugar is made available, or in fact when insulin alone is administered. Animals recover their ability to deal with infective agents. In brief, a well-treated depancreatized animal is difficult to distinguish from a normal one. There has been the difficulty, of course, that in the animal without a pancreas relatively large amounts of insulin are made available (by subcutaneous or intravenous injection) while in the intact animal small or large amounts are presumably liberated from the pancreas as the need arises. Adult depancreatized dogs on an adequate diet including the enzymes of the external secretion of pancreas have been maintained in good condition for more than six years (Macleod; Hédon; Bliss; Fisher; Wrenshall).

THE MECHANISM OF ACTION OF INSULIN

Insulin is an anabolic hormone. It is important in those metabolic activities concerned with the storage of food materials in muscle, liver and adipose tissue. Injections of insulin lower the glucose, inorganic phosphate, and amino acid concentrations of extracellular fluid in vivo or of the medium in vitro.

GLYCOGEN STORAGE. Small amounts of glycogen may be deposited in the muscles and liver of the depancreatized dog when no insulin is given but the administration of insulin produces a dramatic increase in the rate of deposition in both these tissues. In the normal animal one of the most clear cut effects of insulin is the increase in the rate of glycogen deposition in muscle. It is obvious that insulin also promotes glycogen storage in the liver of the diabetic animal and this situation should not be confused with the results of adding more insulin to an already normal supply. In the normal adult animal there may be an actual loss of glycogen from the liver when extra insulin is administered. This is probably due to the accelerated glycogen deposition in muscle and to the increased rate at which fat is formed and sugar oxidized. These latter processes would decrease the amount of sugar available for storage as glycogen in the liver. Madison reported that if the dose of insulin was small in dogs with porto-caval shunts, there was a reduction in glucose output by liver when insulin was given, but when the dose of insulin was large and produced hypoglycaemia, the glucose output was not reduced. Others found no reduction in glucose output by liver after insulin (Shoemaker, Mahler, et al.).

The action of insulin can be demonstrated well in eviscerated and in isolated perfused preparations such as the hind limbs of the cat or dog. Glucose must be supplied. Very great use has been made of the finding by Gemmill in 1940 that the rat diaphragm in vitro takes up more sugar and forms more glycogen when insulin is added. As little as 0.1 unit of insulin per kg. will double the diaphragmatic glycogen in the fasting adrenodemedullated rat. The isolated rat diaphragm does not respond to insulin with an increased use of oxygen but insulin can stimulate oxygen consumption in intact, normal frog muscle in vitro.

There is an increase in the glycogen of heart after removal of insulin from the body (Cruickshank). The renal tubules exhibit a deposition of glycogen in the diabetic state which may be related to the increase in sugar which they are attempting to reabsorb. The β-cells in the islands of the pancreas show glycogen infiltration in the diabetic organism. The effect of insulin on glycogen synthesis has been dealt with on p. 1329.

Insulin decreases the glucose-6-phosphatase activity in liver (takes 12 hours). The glucose-6-phosphatase activity of liver can be decreased also by the continuous infusion of glucose, the evidence suggesting that this is due to a stimulation of insulin secretion by the glucose.

ON FAT METABOLISM. In the depancreatized animal, insulin decreases the lipemia and cholesterolemia and prevents the deposition of the large amounts of excess fat which accumulate in the liver in the untreated animal. The level of the ketone bodies in the blood is restored to normal.

The fact that insulin increases the formation of fat has been obvious ever since the first emaciated dog or diabetic patient demonstrated a fine pad of adipose tissue, made as a result of treatment with the hormone. This effect was not perceptible in short term experiments without the aid of tracers and the disappearance of sugar was usually attributed to oxidation or perhaps in part to decreased gluconeogenesis. Using the technique of isotopic tracers, Stetten has calculated that in the well nourished rat only about 3 per cent of the glucose ingested each day is converted to glycogen, while 30 per cent is used to make fatty acids. In the absence of insulin the diabetic animal exhibits a much lower level of lipogenesis, as well as of glycogenesis.

In 1948 Bloch and Kramer were the first to demonstrate an in vitro effect of insulin on fat formation. Liver slices incubated in the presence of pyruvate and labelled acetate showed incorporation of the label into fatty acids and this process was enhanced by prior administration of insulin. This work has been strongly supported and extended by Gurin with Brady and Lukens and by Chaikoff and his group. Thus we learn that insulin has widespread effects on fat formation and mobilization. It promotes lipogenesis from glucose and acetate in the liver and in many extrahepatic tissues. It prevents the loss of depot fat and the accumulation of fatty deposits in the liver. It suppresses ketosis by inhibiting the formation of ketone bodies. It is probable that these different effects of insulin are closely interrelated and that they are all linked with its action on the oxidation of glucose. The effect of insulin on the unesterified fatty acids of the blood plasma is discussed under fat metabolism (ch. 68).

ON PROTEIN METABOLISM. The early work on insulin in Toronto demonstrated that insulin reduced the elevated nitrogen excretion characteristic of the diabetic state. In 1926 Janney and Shapiro noted a fall in blood urea and nonprotein nitrogen of normal human subjects given insulin and other investigators found a fall in blood amino acids in animals and man. In a classical study Mirsky showed that insulin decreased the rate of protein catabolism in the nephrectomized dog. Chaikoff and Forker in extension of F. N. Allan's original findings established a linear relation between insulin dose and nitrogen retention in depancreatized dogs. The evidence obtained by Forker, by Lotspeich, and by Sinex, MacMullen and Hastings indicates that insulin encourages the incorporation of labelled amino acids into protein. Krahl has reported the incorporation of C^{14} labelled glycine into glutathione and into protein in liver slices. This process is greatly reduced in diabetes but is restored to normal by insulin. The evidence suggests that insulin stimulates peptide synthesis rather than inhibiting breakdown. Sinex and associates, Krahl, and Manchester and Young have provided evidence that the incorporation of amino acids into the protein of isolated rat diaphragm is augmented by insulin in the absence of glucose in the medium. These findings suggest that this action of insulin is largely independent of a stimulation of glucose transport. An effect of insulin on the *net* synthesis of protein in vitro has not been well shown.

The literature records that Mirsky, Young, Gaebler, Lotspeich, Frame and Russell, and Lukens in distinct investigations have agreed that the presence of insulin is essential for the protein anabolic effect of the pituitary growth hormone, somatotropin. There is now direct evidence that an increased secretion of insulin occurs in response to somatotropin in several species of normal animals. Somatotropin has little anabolic effect in the complete absence of insulin and recent work has shown that insulin can stimulate nitrogen retention, bone growth, fat formation, etc., in the complete absence of somatotropin (Salter and Best). Normal growth undoubtedly requires the coordinated action of somatotropin, insulin and the other hormones.

ON OXIDATION OF SUGAR. The interpretation of most of the early work on this subject was confused by the lack of a suitably labelled glucose. In 1949 Villee and Hastings found that insulin increased the oxidation of glucose as judged by the rate of appearance of the carbon label in the CO_2 formed by the isolated rat diaphragm. Similar results have been secured by Sacks and Sinex who found that insulin increased the turnover of isotopic phosphorus in various phosphorus compounds, the deposition of C^{14}-labelled glucose as glycogen, and the oxidation of glucose. Feller, Chaikoff and associates, using C^{14}-glucose have established that the rate of utilization was reduced to half the normal value in dogs by removal of insulin and restored completely by giving the hormone. As mentioned previously, dePocas found, that in diabetic rats when the rate of uptake of glucose was restored by elevating blood sugar levels, the rate of oxidation of glucose was normal. Using C^{14}-labelled glucose in eviscerated rabbits Wick, Drury, Bancroft, and MacKay were able to distinguish between the glucose oxidized and the total amount which disappeared. When insulin was given there was a delayed, but large, increase in the labelled carbon of the expired air and therefore in the amount of glucose oxidized. The rest of the labelled carbon was found in glycogen, fatty acids, proteins, and in nonglucose water-soluble compounds.

ON CELL PERMEABILITY (see previous discussion on p. 1336.)

ON PHOSPHATE AND POTASSIUM. Insulin produces a dramatic fall in the inorganic phosphate of blood plasma (Harrop). Ingestion of glucose or injection of adrenaline has the same effect but not in the absence of the pancreas. Levine, Loube and Weisberg (1949) have shown that the intravenous administration of fructose to untreated depancreatized dogs consistently produces a fall in blood inorganic phosphate. The change in phosphate is apparently a consequence of the rapid entry of hexoses into cells. Insulin is necessary

for the entry of glucose but not of fructose. After insulin there may be a rise in the hexose monophosphate of muscle. This is an indirect effect apparently due to adrenaline liberation and a stimulation by it of phosphorylase action on glycogen and the formation of the first breakdown product, glucose-1-phosphate. Insulin does not significantly change the amount of adenosine triphosphate (ATP), phosphocreatine, or inorganic phosphate in muscle. There may be a rise in the ATP fraction of liver. The rate of turnover or regeneration of these phosphate compounds is increased by insulin and this is probably an index of the increased rate of phosphorylation of sugar which is, as we have seen, an indispensable preliminary step in its metabolism. The free energy for this change is made available by the conversion of ATP to adenosine diphosphate (ADP) plus a high energy phosphate grouping. This phosphorylation of glucose then permits glucose to enter the metabolic pathways in the cell. New molecules of ATP are provided as a result of subsequent steps in the breakdown of glucose.

Various changes in the concentration of the metallic constituents of the blood have been reported after insulin injection. These, and particularly that in the concentration of potassium, suggest a fundamental relationship between electrolyte and carbohydrate metabolism. The decrease in blood sugar produced by insulin is accompanied by a simultaneous fall in potassium. Though insulin induces the accumulation of potassium ions in the muscle of frog and mammal this seems to occur independently of any effect on glucose transport.

OTHER EFFECTS OF INSULIN

It is now well established that the administration of insulin lowers the insulin content of the pancreas in animals of certain species. Furthermore it protects the islet cells against the degenerative changes which occur after the removal of a large part of the pancreas. Similarly the degenerative changes in the islets and the loss of insulin content produced by the administration of the diabetogenic substance of the anterior pituitary gland are prevented if insulin is supplied. If, after the diabetic state has been produced in partially depancreatized cats by administration of diabetogenic preparations, insulin is given in adequate amounts, the diabetes may disappear. Thus insulin under these experimental conditions can both prevent and cure diabetes (Haist, Campbell and Best; Lukens and Dohan).

INTERFERENCE WITH THE ACTION OF INSULIN

Insulin antagonists may be agents which counteract effects of insulin or which combine with insulin and inactivate it or which modify its activity or degrade it. Growth hormone, adrenal steroids, and thyroid hormone can produce effects which run counter to those of insulin and hence lead to a reduced action of insulin. Insulin antagonism can result from the action of antibodies which combine with insulin and take it out of effective action (see previously). There are other factors in serum also that have antagonistic effects.

Bornstein and Park found that serum from alloxan-diabetic rats inhibited the uptake of glucose by rat diaphragm in vitro. This inhibitory effect was abolished by removal of the pituitary or adrenals and was restored by growth hormone and cortisone. This factor seemed to be associated with the B_1 lipoprotein fraction of serum and was inactivated by freezing and thawing. Vallance-Owen and Lukens observed an insulin antagonism in plasma from diabetic cats which was not abolished by freezing and thawing but which did require the presence of adrenal and pituitary factors. Vallance-Owen also found that, in the plasma of diabetic patients requiring insulin treatment, there was an antagonist associated with the albumin fraction. The antagonist can be separated from human albumin and inhibits the effect of insulin on glucose uptake by rat diaphragm. This synalbumin insulin antagonist is sufficiently similar to the B-chain of insulin to suggest that they are identical. Vallance-Owen postulates that the B-chain competes with insulin for receptor sites and thus interferes with glucose uptake by the cell.

The phosphorylation of glucose in intact rat diaphragm or rat heart muscle is under inhibition depending on a pituitary factor related to growth hormone (Kipnis and Cori, 1959; Park and Morgan, 1960). Insulin can counteract inhibition, e.g., the inhibition of muscle hexokinase by lipoproteins containing phosphatides.

In tissues there are also enzymes which result in insulin breakdown. Both reductive and proteolytic effects have been described. The term insulinase was first applied to this activity. This activity in liver was found in a fraction of the ultracentrifuged homogenate after removal of mitochondria, microsomes and nuclei. The fraction contained heat-labile and heat-stable portions, the heat-labile factor being responsible for the greater part of the insulin-degrading activity.

Such insulin-degrading activity of liver was reduced by fasting and restored by a diet high in carbohydrate. Removal of the pituitary or thyroid gland reduced its activity.

By extraction of beef liver powder and subsequent purification, Tomizawa and Halsey were able to isolate a highly purified enzyme which promoted the degradation of insulin. This was subsequently shown by Katzen and Stetten to catalyse the reduction of the disulphide bonds of insulin by reduced glutathione. Certain other substrates, oxytocin and vasopressin, were similarly affected. No hydrolysis of peptide bonds of insulin was detected. Because of its action, the enzyme was called glutathione-insulin-transhydrogenase. Two activities obtained in extracts of rat liver thus seem to be involved.

(1) $NADPH + GSSG + H^+ \rightarrow 2\,GSH + NADP^+$

glutathione reductase

(2) $Insulin + 2\,GSH \rightarrow reduced\ insulin + GSSG$

glutathione insulin transhydrogenase

The phenylalanyl (B) chain, a product of reaction (2), inhibits the glutathione reductase of reaction (1) and hence inhibits the regeneration of GSH. Further, reaction (1) consumes NADPH, which is generated chiefly in the oxidation of glucose-6-phosphate by reactions which are insulin dependent in certain tissues. These two facts suggest ways in which the extent of insulin breakdown may be regulated. Half the circulating insulin is broken down in about 40 minutes in man, according to Berson, Yalow, Bauman, Rothschild and Newerly. Izzo, using less highly iodinated insulin, found that 95% of a single dose was cleared in 8 minutes. As yet there is no good evidence, however, that changes in the activity of insulin-degrading enzymes play a significant part in the cause of diabetes.

REACTION OF TISSUES. Since insulin acts on the cells of the liver and muscles, factors which influence these tissues, acidosis for example, may modify insulin action. Furthermore, since the liver is so largely responsible for the regulation of blood sugar, influences affecting this organ may cause a change in sugar content quite apart from the action of insulin. A change in the acid-base equilibrium of the body toward the acid side renders injected insulin less effective, a change toward the alkaline makes insulin more effective.

PRODUCTS OF INFECTION. The toxic products elaborated by many microörganisms may interfere with the action of insulin. There is experimental evidence (1) that the insulin content of pancreas is decreased in certain severe infections but this does not necessarily indicate a decreased rate of liberation of the hormone, (2) that the suprarenal and thyroid glands are stimulated to release more of their internal secretions,[1] (3) that the synthesis of glycogen from lactic acid in the liver is inhibited and (4) it now appears that normally liver glycogen is changed to glucose by phosphorylase and glucose-6-phosphatase. Amylase, which splits glycogen to dextrins, maltose and finally to glucose, does not have access to the liver cells. When certain toxins are administered, however, amylase activity can be demonstrated and this abnormal route of glycogen breakdown provides another mechanism by which the products of infection make the organism resistant to the action of insulin.

ANESTHETICS. All anesthetics interfere somewhat with the action of insulin. More or less asphyxia is produced by all general anesthetics. In asphyxia (1) adrenaline is liberated and (2) acid products tend to accumulate. Chloralose and amytal cause relatively little disturbance of carbohydrate metabolism.

INSULIN REQUIREMENT AND ADMINISTRATION

Interesting studies have been made of the insulin requirements of depancreatized dogs under different conditions. Thus the blood sugar has been kept at a normal level by simultaneous and continuous intravenous injection of insulin and glucose solutions. The insulin required was between 0.06 and 0.4 units per kg. per hour, while the corresponding requirement of glucose was 0.2 and 0.6 gm. per kg. per hour. The higher values for insulin and glucose were those required by unanesthetized dogs; the others by anesthetized dogs. In another study the amount of insulin necessary to keep the blood sugar at a normal value in depancreatized dogs under basal conditions was between 0.005 and 0.035 units per kg. per hour, with an average value of 0.017 units per kg. per hour. The duration of action of insulin is not proportional to the size of the dose injected but is a simple function of the logarithm of the dose; i.e., insulin is inactivated in the body at a rate proportional to the amount in the body at the time. Thus if 1 unit lasts four hours, 10 units would last eight hours. Studies on the rate of

[1] The first effects of the products of infection may be to excite liver tissue to increased gluconeogenesis and discharge of glucose. Later the liver cells may be damaged so that less glucose is produced.

disappearance of free antibody suggest that insulin can be released by the pancreas at the rate of 25 milliunits per kg./min. in the intact rat (Wright). It is established that the completely depancreatized human subject may require less insulin than many "spontaneous" diabetics. Similarly, the alloxan-diabetic dog may require more insulin than the depancreatized.

Insulin may be administered effectively by the subcutaneous or intravenous route. Some absorption may be obtained by inunction or by application to the sublingual or other mucous surfaces. Rectal administration is ineffective. Studies continue to be made on the problem of the oral administration of insulin. Efforts have been made to combine it with various materials, dyes, phenolic substances, tannic acid, etc. which might protect the protein molecule from destruction by the intestinal enzymes. The difficulties involved are obvious, and it is therefore not surprising that, while some success has attended these efforts in the laboratory, no satisfactory application to the treatment of diabetic patients has yet been made.

MODIFIED INSULIN

One of the most obvious difficulties in the use of regular insulin in clinical diabetes is its transient and sometimes too violent action. This difficulty has been much more frequently encountered since the highly purified preparations of insulin have been made available. The cruder products were absorbed more slowly. While a great many attempts have been made to prolong the action of insulin, the first important success was obtained by Hagedorn, Jensen, Krarup and Wodstrup. These investigators showed that a compound of insulin with any one of several protamines exerts a slower and more prolonged anti-diabetic effect than regular insulin. This was shown by Beecher and Krogh to be due to the much slower absorption of the insulin combined with protamine than of the regular preparations of this substance.

Completely depancreatized dogs may be maintained sugar free, while receiving a very liberal diet, on one dose of protamine insulin daily without the development of any hypoglycemic reactions (Kerr and Best).

Scott and Fisher demonstrated that protamine insulin is greatly improved by the addition of a small amount of zinc. The resulting product, protamine zinc insulin, exerts a more prolonged hypoglycemic action and forms a much more stable suspension than protamine insulin.

Various other forms of modified insulin have

been prepared and tested clinically. Histone insulin and globin insulin are examples. Protamine zinc insulin has been prepared in crystalline form (Hagedorn) and free insulin is stable when added to this compound. Crystalline zinc insulin preparations, without protamine or added protein exerting a prolonged action, have been made available by Hallas-Møller and associates.

Moloney, Aprile and Wilson modified insulin chemically by sulphating it with sulphuric acid. This sulphated insulin exhibited decreased antigenicity in guinea-pigs, was not neutralized readily by anti-serum against ox insulin, and reacted poorly with the latter antiserum also in agar immunodiffusion, complement fixation and haemagglutination tests. A number of insulin-resistant diabetic patients were controlled with this insulin at much lower doses than when standard insulin was used. The sulphated insulin is insoluble at pH 3, and has a molecular weight of 5,700 at pH 8. The sulphated insulin retains biological activity but its immunological responses are greatly altered. This is of importance in the treatment of certain insulin-resistant diabetics, as indicated, but it also is of interest in relation to the possibility that changes in the endogenous insulin molecule may alter its neutralizability and hence may affect its measurement by immunochemical assay procedures.

Hypoglycaemia

Under certain circumstances hypoglycaemia may be produced by excessive utilization of glucose (prolonged very violent muscular exercise and insulin injection). Infusions of insulin lead to a reduction in blood sugar level and the rate of glucose production is increased in normal and adrenalectomized but not in depancreatized dogs (Hetenyi and Wrenshall). It seems necessary to conclude that insulin hypoglycaemia is due to an increase in the rate of removal of glucose by tissues and that the increased glucose production by liver is secondary to the reduced blood sugar level, the compensation being incomplete.

Interference with the formation of sugar in the liver is a frequent important factor in the production of hypoglycaemia. Factors which diminish sugar production are: (1) abnormalities of liver cells, (2) decreased hepatic gluconeogenesis resulting from diminished output of the anterior pituitary, thyroid, or adrenal secretions, (3) an inhibiting action of insulin on gluconeogenesis.

A great variety of experimental and clinical conditions may cause hypoglycaemia, e.g., phosphorus or hydrazine poisoning, yellow fever, acute yellow atrophy, and the bacterial infections. These act by interfering with liver function. When the normal liver is completely removed, profound hypoglycaemia occurs promptly. Approximately 80 per cent of the normal liver must be removed before hypoglycaemia is produced. The relative importance of the three glands of internal secretion mentioned may vary in different species. Removal of the thyroid increases the sensitivity of an animal to insulin and the same is true of the adrenal medulla, but hypoglycaemia is not produced. When the anterior pituitary is extirpated, however, there may be profound hypoglycaemia unless the animal is well fed. In some species removal of the whole adrenal gland causes hypoglycaemia and this is, at least partially, corrected by the administration of cortical extract. Clinically, certain cases of Simmond's disease (diminished anterior pituitary secretion) and of Addison's disease (involvement of adrenal cortex) may exhibit hypoglycaemia.

Another important cause of hypoglycaemia is *hyperinsulinism*. This term should be reserved for conditions in which it is established that there is liberation of excessive amounts of insulin from the pancreas. This has been the case in numerous instances in which the removal of a tumor of islet cells has corrected the hypoglycaemia. Correction of the condition by removal of a large part of the pancreas does not prove that the cause was liberation of abnormal amounts of insulin, since decreasing the amount of insulin may merely compensate for the first abnormality. The insulin levels in blood are not always elevated in patients with hyperinsulinism.

Signs and Symptoms

The signs of hypoglycaemia were first adequately described by Mann and his collaborators. The low blood sugars were produced in dogs by removal of the liver. The description of this condition enabled the Toronto investigators to recognize that the effects of large doses of insulin were the same as those due to hypoglycaemia produced by other means. The signs and symptoms vary in the different species. The first signs in the rabbit are hyperexcitability and desire for food. The excitability becomes greater, and mild and then severe convulsions are exhibited. The head is retracted and the hind limbs extended in the intervals between convulsive seizures. Coma is frequent. The animals may exhibit rigor mortis immediately after death.

The signs in dogs are quite similar. Mice, in some instances, may become comatose without exhibiting convulsions. Cold blooded animals do not show any signs until many hours or even days after insulin injections. The signs and symptoms in man have been extensively studied in the laboratory and clinic. The initial symptoms may be hunger or a feeling of nervousness—a sense of impending danger. A little later there may be profuse perspiration, alternate pallor and flushing of the face, vertigo and diplopia. The blood sugar at this stage is 0.06 to 0.04 per cent but the level varies greatly in different individuals. Most hypoglycemic reactions proceed no further than this. In very severe cases there may be delirium, convulsions, and death. The true blood sugar may decrease until only nonsugar-reducing power remains.

Sakel's insulin-shock treatment for schizophrenia has focussed attention on the metabolism of brain and the effects of prolonged hypoglycemia. Brain tissue utilizes carbohydrate almost exclusively. Hypoglycemia interferes with the supply and produces much the same condition as O_2 deficiency. The electrical activity of the cerebral cortex is depressed in hypoglycemia and restored to normal by the administration of glucose. The reduction in the oxidative metabolism of brain is undoubtedly responsible for this and other changes.

Cerebral damage, which may be permanent, has been observed in both animals and man as a result of prolonged hypoglycemia.

Alleviation of Hypoglycemia

The intravenous administration of glucose is the most effective method of alleviating hypoglycemia. The prompt recovery of almost moribund animals provides one of physiology's most fascinating demonstrations. Mannose is almost as useful as glucose, and fructose also occupies a preferential position. Galactose and maltose have a slight but transient effect. Injections of lactose and pentoses are not effective. Glycogen and glycerol have been shown to exert some beneficial action. The effect of these substances in hypoglycemia is probably largely dependent on the rapidity with which they are transformed into glucose in the liver. In liver, galactose and fructose may reach the same metabolic pathway as glucose (fig. 67.3). Fructose may be converted to glucose in muscle but there is a possibility that it may be utilized directly (Griffiths and Waters). The usefulness of other carbohydrates in relieving hypoglycaemia would depend chiefly on the ease of their conversion into glucose. Adrenaline may be used to alleviate hypoglycaemia but glucose is more efficacious and safe. Liberation of adrenaline is, however, one of the physiological mechanisms by which hypoglycaemia is corrected and the secretion of glucagon also appears to be involved.

The Insulin Content of the Pancreas under Different Conditions

The insulin content of the pancreas has been determined in various animal species. Insulin is extracted from minced pancreases with acid alcohol at low pH. Certain contaminating material is removed and the active material is precipitated. This is then redissolved and estimated by the mouse method of assay or other assay procedures. In the dog, the insulin content of the free splenic end of the pancreas is greatest, that of the attached duodenal portion has an intermediate value, while that of the free duodenal end is lowest, the values being about 4, 3, and 2 units per g., respectively. In partially depancreatized dogs, provided sufficient pancreas is left to prevent the onset of diabetes, the insulin content does not differ from that of the corresponding part in a normal dog, nor are

TABLE 67.3

Factors depressing islet growth

1. Restriction of caloric intake.
   Restriction of carbohydrate intake.
2. Administration of large amounts of insulin.
3. Removal of the pituitary gland.

Factors increasing islet growth

	Intact	Hypox
1. High carbohydrate intake.		
2. Continuous injection of glucose.	+	−
3. Injections of anterior pituitary extract.	+	+
4. Injections of growth hormone preparations.	+	+
5. Injections of ACTH.	+	+
6. Injections of cortisone.	+	+
7. Thyroid administration.	+	+
8. Estradiol benzoate.	+	†
9. Diethylstilbestrol.	+	†
10. Progesterone.	+	†
11. Testosterone.	*	†

From R. E. Haist.
* Not significant.
† Not done.

any degenerative changes in the β-cells noted. If diabetes supervenes, hydropic degeneration of these cells is observed, and the insulin content of the remnant of pancreas falls to extremely low values. The daily injection into dogs of diabetogenic extracts from the anterior lobe of the pituitary gland produces a prompt and profound decrease in the insulin content of the pancreas (in seven days to 0.2 units per gram). If the injections are stopped at this stage, the insulin content is restored to normal within four days. If the administration is continued the insulin is reduced to negligible amounts and ultimately a point will be reached when no recovery will occur. Simultaneous administration of insulin prevents or greatly modifies the fall in the insulin stores. This fact strongly suggests that the β-cells are permanently damaged by the extract through overwork and that the simultaneous administration of insulin relieves the cells of some of this excessive demand for the hormone.

Starvation (seven days) or a diet rich in fat produces a decrease in the insulin content of the rat's pancreas to about half the normal value, which is about $2\frac{1}{2}$ units per rat. (It should be noted however that a similar reduction is not obtained in the guinea-pig.) The fasted rats have their insulin stores speedily restored to normal (in six days) when they are returned to a balanced diet; carbohydrate alone effects a partial restoration. Daily injection of insulin into rats causes an even more marked decrease in the insulin content of the pancreas than does starvation (Haist and Best). Massive doses of insulin over prolonged periods may produce atrophic changes in the pancreatic islets of partially depancreatized dogs which survive the treatment (Mirsky).

The injection of anterior pituitary extracts in certain strains of rats increases the islet volume and the insulin content of pancreas (Young, Richardson and Marks). In other strains there is no increase in insulin content.

The factors which affect the volume (growth) of the β-cells of the pancreas are given in table 67.2. Stilbestrol may exert a diabetogenic effect in force-fed normal and partially depancreatized rats, and under these conditions Ingle has been able to demonstrate diabetogenic effects of all the estrogens. Under more physiological conditions Houssay, Foglia, Martinez and their colleagues have demonstrated that the estrogenic substances decrease the incidence of diabetes in partially depancreatized rats—presumably by stimulation of the β-cells in the pancreatic remnant.

The effect of age on the insulin content of the pancreas has been studied in the cow. In fetal calves under 5 months the concentration was 34 units per gram; in calves 6 to 8 weeks old, 10 units per gram; in heifers 2 years old, 5 units per gram; in cows over 9 years, 2 units per gram. Pregnant cows 7 years old and older showed no change from the normal insulin content of about 2 units per gram (Scott and Fisher). In Wistar rats the total insulin content of the pancreas increases with age.

Pancreases obtained from nondiabetic persons at autopsy have an average insulin content of about 2 units per gram. This is probably somewhat lower than the true value. Pancreatic tissues from diabetic persons show wide variations. The pancreas from diabetic children contains very little insulin. Pancreas from diabetic adults contains on the average some 40 per cent of the normal amount of insulin (Wrenshall). The insulin content of a tumor of islet tissue surgically removed from a patient suffering from hyperinsulinism may be as high as 214 units per gram, though this is not a consistent finding and much lower insulin concentrations have been noted. The insulin content of the pancreas represents a balance between the rate of production of the hormone in the islets and the rate of liberation. There is good reason to believe that under certain conditions the rate of liberation is proportional to the content. Under other circumstances this is probably not true. The conclusion has been drawn from some of these results, combined with histological studies, and in some instances by blood insulin studies, that the function of islet cells is reduced after administration of insulin, by starvation, and by a high fat diet and that less insulin is excreted by the pancreas than under normal conditions. Partial pancreatectomy, sufficiently extensive to result in diabetes, or administration of diabetogenic extracts or of pituitary growth hormone causes (1) marked stimulation of the islets and (2) subsequent degenerative changes and loss of insulin.[2]

The Use of Insulin in Nondiabetic Conditions

Favorable results have been claimed for the use of insulin in a very great variety of nondiabetic conditions. It has been used in pernicious anemia, in acute infectious diseases, in eclampsia, in pernicious vomiting of pregnancy, and in hepatitis—to mention only a few. While it is

[2] For references to work on insulin content of pancreas, see Haist, 1944 and Wrenshall, 1952.

conceivable that insulin might be of slight benefit in some of these conditions, it would appear that equally satisfactory results can be secured by the administration of glucose alone. It is a clinical fact that the administration of glucose produces favorable results in a variety of hepatic abnormalities. A high glycogen content appears to protect the liver cells from damage and inhibition of gluconeogenesis produced by both insulin and glucose may also play a role.

Insulin can now be considered, however, an established adjuvant in the treatment of certain cases in which lack of appetite prevents the ingestion of adequate amounts of food. The physiological basis for this use of insulin in these non-diabetic individuals rests very largely upon the increase in hunger and appetite which may be caused by the administration of sufficient material to produce a definite but not too marked hypoglycemia. In 1924 Bulatao and Carlson reported that production of hypoglycemia in experimental animals by the subcutaneous injection of insulin was uniformly accompanied by hypertonus and hypermotility of the stomach. The gastric tonicity and motility increase as the hypoglycemia deepens until complete tetanus is reached, which persists until the dog exhibits hypoglycemic convulsions or until sugar is given. The effect of sugar is immediate, but if a large dose of insulin has been given the hyperactivity of the stomach returns as soon as the blood sugar falls again. The first record of the increase in gastric peristalsis in the human individual after insulin administration was that of Dickson and Wilson, 1924.

It is known that insulin does not exert its effect on gastric motility and secretion after section of the vagus nerves. This means that either insulin acts centrally by stimulating the vagus, or that the continued elaboration of acetylcholine, which we now know is an essential part of the mechanism by which the vagus exerts its action, provides a foundation upon which the peripheral effects of insulin may be superimposed.

Insulin augments also, to some extent, peristalic movement in the duodenum and in the colon, but the effect is not as marked as in the case of the stomach. It will be remembered that one of the early symptoms observed in experimental animals and also in human subjects after the administration of insulin is an increase in hunger. In animals an attempt to consume material of little nutritive value which under ordinary conditions they would not attempt to eat is often observed. It would appear, therefore, that the clinician is able to take advantage of this situation by providing nutritious food for his hungry patient. The increase in weight observed in both animals and patients when appropriate doses of insulin are given for prolonged periods is due to increased deposition of fat, and to a lesser extent to increased deposition of carbohydrate and protein. The increase in weight is not attributable to unphysiological retention of water.

Influence of Other Endocrine Glands on Carbohydrate Metabolism

THE ADRENALS

The glucosuria produced by epinephrine was first noted by Blum. The intravenous route of administration gives the greatest rise of blood sugar but subcutaneous, intramuscular or intraperitoneal injections are effective. The immediate rise in the sugar of the blood is due to breakdown of liver glycogen to glucose. There may be a considerable decrease in the amount of liver glycogen. Epinephrine also mobilizes muscle glycogen (Cori) but here the immediate product is lactic acid and not glucose. A part of the lactic acid is carried by the blood to the liver where it is converted to glycogen, which in turn furnishes the blood with glucose. Muscle glycogen is therefore available indirectly to replenish blood glucose. When lactic acid from the muscles has been changed in appreciable amounts to glycogen in the liver the amount of glycogen in this organ may be increased over the normal level. Epinephrine therefore in moderate dosage, first causes a decrease and then an increase in liver glycogen. Very large doses over prolonged periods may lower both muscle and liver glycogen. The nervous control of epinephrine secretion will be discussed in chapter 76, and the manner in which thoracic autonomic impulses may affect blood sugar through its liberation will be appreciated. Epinephrine does not accelerate sugar formation from other substances in the liver. Diabetes has not been produced by the continued administration of epinephrine.

Insulin and epinephrine are not chemical antagonists but possess opposing physiological actions. Epinephrine accelerates the breakdown of both liver and muscle glycogen through $3'5'$-AMP (see discussion on page 1331) but the lactic acid made from muscle glycogen may lead to an actual increase in hepatic glycogen. Insulin promotes the formation of glycogen in both tissues, but the increase in muscle glycogen may be at the expense of sugar, which would have formed liver glycogen. When the blood sugar is lowered to about 0.06 per cent by insulin, an increased rate of liberation of epinephrine may be detected (Cannon; Houssay, Armin and Grant).

Epinephrine may lead to the secretion of adrenocorticotropic hormone (ACTH) in animals (Vogt; Long and Fry). Thus adrenaline, a substance released in an emergency, causes a prompt hyperglycaemia and may at the same time set in motion other changes (e.g. liberation of ACTH) which stimulate gluconeogenesis and thus provide for the continuation of the blood sugar rise. On the other hand, a meal high in carbohydrate given to fasted rats causes a reduction in the cholesterol content of the adrenal cortex (liberation of cortical hormone) which is coincident with a rise in liver glycogen (Abelin).

THE ADRENAL CORTEX AND CARBOHYDRATE METABOLISM

After double adrenalectomy in some species (cat and rat), the carbohydrate reserves of the liver and muscles are depleted and there may be definite hypoglycaemia (Britton and Silvette). These workers showed that the hypoglycaemic condition may be corrected when the cortical hormone and glucose are provided but not when the latter alone is given. They reported that the administration of extracts of the cortex elevated the carbohydrate stores of adrenalectomized animals well beyond the normal limits. Insulin and glucose did not increase glycogen deposition in the adrenalectomized animal unless cortical extract was supplied (Britton) but it is possible that this effect might occur if the animals were supplied with a diet adequately low in potassium and high in sodium. Long and his collaborators greatly extended the earlier experiments of Britton and Silvette and found rather remarkable increases in liver glycogen in fasted or fed normal animals when extracts of the adrenal cortex were administered. Muscle glycogen was not affected by the cortical material in these experiments but may be increased when adequate amounts of sugar are supplied.

After Houssay's demonstration that removal of the pituitary gland attenuates the severe diabetes resulting from total pancreatectomy in the toad and dog, Long and Lukens showed that a similar change could be produced by adrenalectomy in the depancreatized cat or dog. It has been shown by Lukens and Dohan that the diabetes of adrenalectomized-depancreatized animals and also that of hypophysectomized-depancreatized

animals can be increased in severity by the injection of cortical extracts.

Long, Katzin and Fry have shown that the rat, partially depancreatized by the method of Shapiro and Pincus, is an excellent preparation for the demonstration of the role of the adrenal cortex in carbohydrate metabolism. Adrenalectomy attenuates the diabetes which may be observed in these animals. The grafting of cortical tissue may restore the glucosuria to the extent which has been observed before adrenalectomy.

Injections of ACTH, Cortisol, cortisone and corticosterone can lead to glucose excretion in force-fed rats but not all adrenal steroids are diabetogenic. This activity depends on their chemical structure, the 11-oxysteroids being diabetogenic whereas deoxycorticosterone is not. The effectiveness in producing diabetes is increased by the presence of a hydroxyl group at the 17 position. In man, Cortisol has more effective diabetogenic action than cortisone, which is greater than corticosterone or 11-dehydrocorticosterone. Prednisone and Prednisolone have a potent action and fluorine-containing steroids are especially effective. There are species differences in the diabetogenic responses to these steroids, the effect being easily elicited in the guinea pig and rabbit. In the rat, forcefeeding is necessary, and in the dog and cat it is difficult to show the diabetogenic action unless part of the pancreas has been removed, or a very potent steroid used. While diabetogenic effects have been observed in man it should be emphasized that diabetes does not often result from steroid therapy, even when this is prolonged. Glucosuria is more prominent, however, since these steroids have an influence on the reabsorption of glucose in the renal tubules. When diabetes does occur it is usually mild, resistant to insulin, and temporary, with a glucosuria that is more than one would expect from the height of the blood sugar or the nitrogen loss. The evidence, while somewhat conflicting, indicates that, if enough of a potent steroid is used in a susceptible species, then the utilization of carbohydrate is reduced by the administration of adrenal steroids. Since these steroids stimulate the production of free fatty acids and ketones from adipose tissue they can, by making these products available, block glucose uptake by muscle and interfere with the stimulating effect of insulin on glucose uptake and hence affect carbohydrate utilization. It is interesting that, after repeated injections of adrenal steroids, there may be an improvement in the tolerance for carbohydrate and diminished diabetogenic effects. This adaptation seems to result from a stimulating effect on the islets of Langerhans. With continued stimulation the islet mass increases and the ability to make and secrete insulin improves. If the islet compensation is good the diabetogenic effect is less apparent.

Some but not all of the abnormalities of carbohydrate metabolism in adrenalectomized animals are apparently due to the disturbance in sodium and potassium metabolism. Thus the delayed absorption of sugar and fat and the failure to store glycogen from glucose can be favorably affected by appropriate salt treatment. On the other hand the sharp fall in carbohydrate levels in fasting adrenalectomized animals and the amelioration of diabetes in partially depancreatized rats by adrenalectomy are not corrected by feeding salt but are by the administration of suitable cortical materials.

THE PITUITARY AND CARBOHYDRATE METABOLISM

It has been appreciated for many years that abnormalities in carbohydrate metabolism may be associated with acromegaly of long standing or with the presence of various pituitary tumors. In 1911 Cushing observed that "pituitary deficiency" may be accompanied by an increased carbohydrate tolerance.

Interest has been focussed on the anterior lobe of the pituitary by the brilliant researches of Houssay and his collaborators and of other investigators. The main points established in Houssay's laboratory are as follows: (a) Removal of the anterior lobe of the pituitary increases the sensitivity to insulin of the normal animal and diminishes the intensity of diabetes in the depancreatized animal. (b) Injections of preparations from the anterior pituitary into normal or hypophysectomized animals diminish their sensitivity to insulin and increase the severity of the diabetic state in hypophysectomized-depancreatized (Houssay) animals. (c) The administration of a suitable extract of the anterior pituitary can induce a diabetic condition. This point was independently established by the reports of Evans and his colleagues and of Baumann and Marine.

The effects of pancreatectomy and hypophysectomy are contrasted in the following summary, and the condition of the animal from which the pancreas and the pituitary have both been removed is briefly described.

Pancreatectomy (Dog)	*Hypophysectomy (Dog)*
Hyperglycemia	Low blood sugar, hypo-
Polyuria	glycemic convulsions
Glycosuria	during fasting
Ketonuria	
Azoturia	
Insulin necessary for survival	Greatly increased sensitivity to insulin
Metabolic rate normal or slightly raised	Low metabolic rate
Decreased ability to utilize carbohydrate	Carbohydrate furnishes increased proportion of fuel
Decreased ability to form glycogen fat and protein	Rapid disappearance of liver and muscle glycogen due to utilization of carbohydrate and decreased gluconeogenesis.[3]

Pancreatectomy and Hypophysectomy

Animals survive without insulin. Polyuria, glucosuria, ketonuria, azoturia slight or absent. Administered carbohydrate partially or completely retained, i.e., carbohydrate utilization much better than in depancreatized dog. Metabolic rate low. Glycogen deposition.

PERMANENT DIABETES. The anterior pituitary gland contains a number of substances which affect carbohydrate metabolism in a variety of ways. These will now be considered briefly. Evans, Meyer, Simpson and Reichert in 1932 demonstrated the production of a prolonged diabetes in normal intact animals by anterior pituitary extract, F. G. Young, 1938, was however, the first to produce a permanent diabetes comparable in intensity to that resulting from complete pancreatectomy, by injection of extracts of the anterior lobe of the pituitary. He has found, in a very large number of dogs, that he is able consistently to produce a permanent state of diabetes by the daily injection, either intraperitoneally or subcutaneously, of a preparation of anterior lobe material. The permanent state of diabetes may be produced after as few as eleven daily injections but more are usually required. The diabetogenic activity, that is, the active material which will produce permanent diabetes in dogs, is associated with the globulin and pseudoglobulin fraction of the pituitary extract. Young's work was confirmed by Campbell and Best and by Dohan and Lukens and many others. Degenerative lesions of the islet cells of the

---

[3] For direct evidence of this effect see Crandall and Cherry.

pancreas were first noted in these permanently diabetic animals by Richardson and Young. Signs of proliferative changes in the islet cells in the early stages of the injections were found by these workers and by Ham and Haist who also observed proliferative changes in the acinar and duct cells of the pancreas. The diabetogenic extract produced proliferative changes in various other glandular tissues in the body. Campbell, Haist and Best noted that the diabetic state produced by the pituitary extract was not intensified by complete removal of the pancreas and secondly, that the insulin content of pancreas was reduced to a negligible quantity. This latter point has been discussed elsewhere.

It would appear that the main effect of the substance or substances which produced the permanent diabetes is exerted upon the islets of Langerhans. These cells are apparently first stimulated and then destroyed by the repeated injections of the active material.

The permanent diabetes produced by the above procedures differs from that caused by pancreatectomy, in that the animals may live for long periods without the administration of insulin. In some cases, however, insulin is required. Starvation or a diet very rich in fat causes a marked diminution in the intensity of diabetes in the permanently diabetic animal.

The production of permanent diabetes by the diabetogenic substance of the anterior pituitary can be prevented by the simultaneous administration of large doses of insulin (Haist, Campbell and Best). The islet cells are protected from profound degenerative changes, the insulin content of the pancreas remains at a moderately high level, and the state of permanent diabetes is not induced. Lukens and Dohan have shown that permanent diabetes produced in partially depancreatized cats by administration of the diabetogenic substance of the anterior pituitary gland can be cured by the use of insulin, by a reduction in the caloric value of the diet or by an increase in its fat content. Recovery from early diabetes has followed a reduction in the diet only when the diabetes was very mild but treatment with insulin produced recovery at this stage regardless of the severity of the disease. If treatment were delayed until after the Islets of Langerhans had become atrophic, no recovery was possible.

It is to be noted that in the prevention and cure of this experimental diabetes, the level of the blood sugar is probably one of the most important factors which determined the direction in which

the islet lesions will progress. This interpretation is supported by all the results which Young; Haist, Campbell and Best; and Lukens and Dohan have obtained and is in line with the earlier studies of F. M. Allen, Copp and Barclay, and others. The rise of blood sugar in itself may constitute an adequate stimulus for the production of the extensive changes in the islet cells and the diabetogenic factor may operate through other mechanisms as well to produce the islet changes.

Highly purified growth hormone has been shown to be diabetogenic, i.e., to produce permanent diabetes in cats (Cotes, Reid and Young, 1949) and in dogs (Campbell, Davidson, Snair and Lei, 1950). It would appear that this is the main diabetogenic component of anterior pituitary extracts but the cortical hormone liberated by ACTH and the thyroid product by the thyroid stimulating hormone must also play their part, as described elsewhere. Growth hormone stimulates growth in young dogs and does not produce diabetes until the animals have matured (Young). If a part of the rat's pancreas is removed, but not enough to cause diabetes, this condition may be produced by large doses of growth hormone, thyroxin or cortisone (Houssay). The rat is very resistant to these diabetogenic influences, perhaps in part because of its ability to make more insulin when needed. In the intact rat, however, on a high carbohydrate diet, growth hormone and ACTH (given together) regularly produce hyperglycemia and glucosuria (Engel).

Russell and Wilhelmi (1950) showed that purified growth hormone is able to prevent loss of glycogen from skeletal muscle and from diaphragm and to restore heart glycogen to the normal fasting level in hypophysectomized rats.

The permanent diabetes produced by growth hormone is due to destruction of the β-cells of the pancreas, but growth hormone inhibits peripheral utilization of carbohydrate. It raises the blood sugar and intensifies the diabetes of completely depancreatized animals. ACTH, by liberating adrenal cortical steroids greatly increases gluconeogenesis and probably also inhibits peripheral utilization of glucose. Cortisone under certain conditions also stimulates the islets and thus may modify the diabetic state. The action of growth hormone or cortisone in decreasing peripheral utilization of sugar raises the blood sugar and this is undoubtedly part of the mechanism by which the β-cells are stimulated and destroyed. However, Bouman has shown a direct stimulating effect of growth hormone on insulin secretion by pancreas in vitro. When insulin is absent the phosphorylating action of muscle is decreased. This can be corrected by removal of the pituitary gland and accentuated by injections of growth hormone. Hypophysectomy enhances the effect of insulin on glucose transport whereas growth hormone diminishes its effect. Growth hormone inhibits fat formation, stimulates fat breakdown, increases free fatty acids (FFA) and ketones and results in a resistance to insulin. The effect of FFA on carbohydrate utilization has been discussed previously (p. 1340). Growth hormone effects are not the same in all tissues. In muscle, GH administration for 4–5 days depressed the utilization of glucose and responsiveness to insulin, whereas in adipose tissue the oxidation of glucose was increased and insulin responsiveness was not changed. In human subjects, growth hormone administration increased plasma FFA levels after an initial fall but did not change the glucose and insulin levels. It did, however, reduce glucose turnover and impair the tolerance for carbohydrate (Kipnis). The lipolytic effects of growth hormone would seem to be important in its diabetogenic actions. The intracellular concentrations of FFA may be important and it should be borne in mind that these may change out of proportion to the changes in plasma levels.

The anterior pituitary gland also affects carbohydrate metabolism through the thyrotropic and probably also the gonadotropic hormones. Removal of the adrenal cortex, thyroid or gonads produces histological changes in the anterior pituitary indicative of overactivity, i.e., of attempts to stimulate the missing target organs.

Modification of pituitary function by stalk section or irradiation with heavy particles (Yttrium-90) has been used in the treatment of diabetic retinopathy. Such treatment does not influence the vascular complications outside the eye and it is too early yet to conclude whether the improvement noted in some cases is due to the specific therapy or to better-controlled general care.

The Thyroid and Carbohydrate Metabolism

The aggravation of diabetes in man by hyperthyroidism and its amelioration by removal of the thyroid establishes a link between this gland and carbohydrate metabolism. It is surprising that very little influence on the diabetes of depancreatized animals can be demonstrated by thyroidectomy. This may be due in part to incomplete removal of thyroid tissue. When very extensive atrophy of the thyroid is produced by hypophysectomy in dogs, the blood sugar and a normal level of urinary nitrogen can be maintained for long periods during fasting if thyroxin is supplied. Without it hypoglycemia may soon terminate the experiment. Thus it appears that the thyroid may play a role in the effect of the anterior pituitary on carbohydrate metabolism. The slight effect of thyroxin administration on the intensity of pancreatic diabetes in some animals still requires explanation but Houssay, Foglia and their colleagues have shown that in thyroidectomized rats 95 per cent of the pancreas can be removed without causing glucosuria. The administration of thyroid preparations to such animals may result in the development of permanent diabetes (metathyroid diabetes). In some partially depancreatized dogs permanent diabetes could also be induced by large doses of thyroid material.

The administration of thyroid substance or of thyroxin to normal animals has no immediate effect on blood sugar but a loss of liver glycogen may be demonstrated within six hours. There is also apparently a rise in the protein content of liver due perhaps to mobilization from peripheral tissues. Increased gluconeogenesis from protein can be readily demonstrated when thyroid substance is fed. An increase in the d-amino-acid oxidase activity of liver has been reported.

In clinical hyperthyroidism a mild hyperglycemia and glucosuria may be present. A comparable condition may be produced in animals by administration of thyroid material. At this stage liver glycogen is easily mobilizable (the actual amount present may be less than normal) and adrenaline elicits more hyperglycemia and insulin less hypoglycemia than normally.

When thyroid feeding is continued there is a profound decrease in liver, muscle and heart glycogen. In this second stage the animals are resistant to adrenaline and extremely susceptible to insulin. They may exhibit spontaneous hypoglycemia or develop it as a secondary result of a small injection of dextrose. This latter effect may be due to the liberation of insulin, the action of which is not buffered by liver glycogen.

Thus the effect of the thyroid on carbohydrate metabolism may result from: (1) increased oxidation of carbohydrate in tissues generally, (2) an increased rate of hepatic gluconeogenesis, and (3) changes in the sensitivity to epinephrine.

Glucagon

Kimball and Murlin were the first to suggest that the initial transient rise in blood sugar in normal animals which received the solution of crude insulin intravenously was due to a separate substance. They introduced the name "glucagon" which was adopted by Bürger (1929) who, with his colleagues, has been responsible for most of the early studies of the properties of this material. Bürger demonstrated that glucagon could be separated from insulin and that the hyperglycemia was accompanied by a fall in liver glycogen. Adrenalectomy did not eliminate this effect. Shipley and Humel (1945) showed that crude insulin preparations accelerated glycogen breakdown in liver slices. Sutherland and Cori (1948) obtained evidence that this glycogenolysis was due to glucagon and that this substance activated the phosphorylase system. Staub, Sinn and Behrens (1953) obtained glucagon in crystalline form as a polypeptide differing significantly from insulin in amino acid content. Bromer, Sinn, Staub and Behrens have shown that glucagon is a single polypeptide chain containing 29 amino acid residues. There are many converging paths of evidence which suggest that this substance is made in the α-cells of the pancreatic islets. The best evidence is that of Logothetopoulos who observed that after prolonged administration of large amounts of glucagon, the α-cells of the pancreatic islets became atrophic and lost their specific granules.

It has been found that glucagon through 3′5′-AMP production, in addition to stimulating hepatic glycogenolysis also reduces pyruvate formation in the liver. It greatly increases the catabolism of amino acids as indicated by the fall in their concentration in blood and the rise in urea production and in nitrogen excretion. The deaminated residues of the amino acids are presumably synthesized into glucose. Thus the hepatic glycogenolysis and gluconeogenesis may both contribute to the hyperglycaemic action of glucagon. The overproduction of glucose under experimental conditions can be of sufficient magnitude to produce a diabetic-like state in many animal species including man. While a permanent diabetes has not been produced, nevertheless one that persisted for 18–63 days after the cessation of injections has been observed (Logothetopoulos). The significance of glucagon, if any, in the pathogenesis of human diabetes remains obscure (Izzo, 1957; Elrick, 1958). In man, glucagon stimulates ketone body produc-

tion and reduces creatine excretion (Ezrin, Salter and Best, 1958). Glucagon injections reduce the levels of fatty acids and of cholesterol in plasma.

The metabolic rate of rats treated with glucagon may show a 50 per cent rise within an hour. Glucagon also affects certain aspects of gastrointestinal function. It has been reported to decrease gastric motility and acidity and the flow of pancreatic juice (Stunkard, et al. 1955; Robinson, et al. 1957; Necheles, et al. 1957).

From cross-circulation experiments in dogs, it appeared that glucagon was secreted by the pancreas when the blood sugar levels fell (Foa). Recently a highly specific and sensitive radioimmunoassay method for glucagon estimation has been developed by Unger and his associates. Using this, it was found that, when blood glucose levels fell, glucagon secretion rose; and that when blood glucose levels rose, the glucagon secretion was suppressed. Starvation increased glucagon levels in peripheral blood and this increase persisted even during the hyperglycaemia in the immediate post-starvation period (Unger and Eisentreut).

Undernutrition and Carbohydrate Metabolism

In 1873 Lehmann and in 1877 Claude Bernard noted a glucosuria in fasting animals after the administration of carbohydrate, and in 1890, Hofmeister, who made the first quantitative studies, named the condition "hunger diabetes." Utilization of carbohydrates is at a maximum in animals which have been fed on diets rich in these substances. After periods of fasting or of fat feeding, there is a definite impairment of glucose utilization which may easily be detected by the results of a glucose tolerance test. The feeding of an exclusively fat diet produces effects on glucose utilization indistinguishable from those of complete starvation. Proteins exert an effect intermediate between that of sugar and fat, i.e., some impairment of glucose utilization is produced by an exclusively protein diet. Diets adequate in other respects but providing a low caloric intake cause little disturbance in carbohydrate utilization. The administration to animals or human subjects exhibiting hunger diabetes of a diet containing glucose causes a prompt improvement in carbohydrate tolerance.

The mechanisms of production and alleviation of the defect in carbohydrate utilization produced by fasting are not as yet completely elucidated. It would appear from the findings of Chambers,

Cori and others that oxidation of glucose in the tissues is interfered with to a much greater extent than is glycogen formation. It has been established that the administration of insulin effects a partial restoration of carbohydrate utilization (Cori and Cori; Dann and Chambers). This finding suggests that insulin liberation may be depressed in hunger diabetes. Himsworth feels that a change in sensitivity to insulin is involved rather than a diminution of pancreatic output. On the other hand, the observation by Haist, Ridout and Best shows that the insulin content of the pancreas of rats may be reduced to nearly half the normal value by starvation or by fat feeding. This finding in conjunction with others supports the view that insulin liberation may be decreased. The recent report of Oyama that starvation reduces the insulin level in plasma in the rat, supports this view. The effect of starvation on enzyme induction in cells, hence on the enzyme concentrations in cells, may be of great importance in these effects. For example, liver glucokinase activity is greatly reduced in starvation; whereas hepatic phosphorylase and glucose-6-phosphatase activities are enhanced. Indeed at least some of the enzyme changes are similar to those following pancreatectomy. The finding that insulin does not rapidly restore the carbohydrate to erance of fasted animals to normal would suggest some change such as this, that requires time for its restoration.

Alloxan Diabetes

This type of experimental diabetes was first produced by Dunn, Sheehan and McLetchie (1943) who showed that alloxan has a selective necrosing action on the Islets of Langerhans. In 1937 Jacobs had noted the effect of alloxan in rabbits—an initial hyperglycemia and a subsequent hypoglycemia. No histological studies were made and Jacobs postulated an insulinlike action of alloxan. It has now been shown that the hypoglycemia can be obtained if alloxan is given immediately after the pancreas has been removed. Hence, it cannot be ascribed to damaged islets with excess release of insulin and probably is a consequence of some change in liver function. The diabetic state is caused by a failure of islet cells to produce insulin. The diabetic action of alloxan has been demonstrated in the rabbit, rat, cat, monkey and dog. Unsuccessful attempts have been made to destroy the abnormally active islet cells in advanced cases of hyperinsulinism in man by the administration of alloxan. Lesions in the liver and kidney, less marked than those produced in the islets, are seen in some species after the injection of this chemical.

The Oral Hypoglycemic Agents

In 1918, Watanabe noted that guanidin poisoning was accompanied by hypoglycemia. In 1926, Frank, Nothman and Wagner found a derivative of guanidin which produced a lowering of blood sugar, and which they felt was not as toxic as guanidin. This material was synthalin, a decamethylene guanidin. Very soon, however, clinicians noted disturbing side reactions, primarily in the gastrointestinal tract, and in 1929 Karr reported fatty degeneration and necrosis of the livers of patients receiving this material. The use of synthalin was followed by that of a great variety of oral preparations: Glukhorment, Anticoman, etc. These were various mixtures of guanidin derivatives. Eventually they all proved to be dangerously toxic for human use. In 1942, Janbon and co-workers accidentally observed that a new sulfonamide, para-aminobenzene-sulfamido-isopropyl-thiodiazol, a drug that was originally synthesized by von Kemmel and Kimmig, produced severe hypoglycemia in patients who had been treated for typhoid fever. Loubatières investigated the mode of action of this drug in animal experiments and suggested that it stimulated the Islands of Langerhans. Clinical application of this substance was not made, however, until December 1955, and in the meantime a group of German workers carried out experimental and clinical studies with another sulfonamide, N_1-sulfanilyl-N_2-N-butyl-carbamide (BZ-55). This drug soon became widely used for oral treatment of obese elderly diabetics. Prolonged experiments in animals, however, revealed disturbing bleeding tendencies (Sirek et al., 1957) as well as hepatic damage (Schambye, 1957). Almost at the same time another sulfonylurea derivative was made available, the N-(4-methyl-benzene-sulfonyl)-N-butyl-urea (D860 or tolbutamide). This substance has now been widely used in the obese elderly non-ketotic type of diabetics, and the incidence of disturbing side effects in man has remained negligible. However, only a proportion of apparently suitable subjects respond satisfactorily. Some of these might be controlled by dietary changes alone. Tolerance to the drug may develop after a period of years. In the absence of exogenous insulin, there must be functioning β-cells of the pancreatic islets if tolbutamide is to have a hypoglycaemic effect. Tolbutamide fails to produce hypoglycaemia in depancreatized or alloxan-diabetic animals not receiving insulin. After doses of tolbutamide there may be decreased granulation of the β-cells and decreased insulin content of the pancreas, and, if the administration is prolonged, an increase in islet volume. Other evidence that tolbutamide stimulates the islets is found in the changes in serum insulin levels in the pancreatic vein after its administration (see section on blood insulin). The time relations between the blood insulin and blood glucose responses make it seem likely that changes in liver function under the influence of the drug are also important in relation to its hypoglycaemic action. A second sulphonylurea, chlorpropamide, has also been used. It has a more potent hypoglycaemic effect but has not been as extensively studied as tolbutamide.

In addition to these sulfonylureas, which do not act in the absence of the pancreas, derivatives of guanide have also been tried. Phenethylbiguanide (DBI) has been reported to be effective in certain cases of juvenile diabetes. It is less dependent on the pancreas and hypoglycaemic effects may be observed in insulin-deficient diabetics. It inhibits oxidative phosphorylation leading to a condition of tissue anoxia. This increases glucose uptake by muscle, enhances lactic acid formation and decreases hepatic gluconeogenesis. Gastro-intestinal side-effects make the drug difficult to use.

Various new sulfonylurea derivatives are now in the stage of experimental or clinical trial.

REFERENCES

ABEL, J. J., GEILING, E. M. K., ROUILLER, C. A., BELL, F. K., AND WINTERSTEINER, O. J. Pharmacol. & Exper. Therap., 1927, **31**, 65.

ALLEN, F. M. J. Metabolic Res., 1922, **1**, 75.

ARMIN, J., CUNNINGHAM, N. F., GRANT, R. T., LLOYD, M. K., AND WRIGHT, P. H. J. Physiol., 1961, **157**, 64.

ARMIN, J. AND GRANT, R. T. J. Physiol., 1959, **149**, 228.

BAIRD, C. W. AND BORNSTEIN, J. Lancet, 1957, **i**, 1111.

BAKER, N. AND HUEBOTTER, R. Fed. Proc., 1963, **22**, 357.

BANTING, F. G. AND BEST, C. H. J. Lab. Clin. Med., 1922, **7**, 251.

BERNARD, C. Compt. rend. Soc. Biol., 1849, **1**, 14.

BERSON, S. A., YALOW, R. S., BAUMAN, A., ROTHSCHILD, M. A., AND NEWERLY, K., J. Clin. Investig., 1956, **35**, 170.

BLUM, F. Deutsches Arch. klin. Med., 1901, **71**, 146.

BLUMENTHAL, H. G., GOLDBERG, S., AND BERNS, A. W. "On the Nature and Treatment of Diabetes," Chap. 27. (Ed. B. S. LEIBEL AND G. A. WRENSHALL) Excerpta Medica Foundation, Amsterdam, 1965.

BORNSTEIN, J. Diabetes, 1953, **2**, 23.

BORNSTEIN, J. AND PARK, C. R. J. Biol. Chem., 1953, **205**, 503.

BRITTON, S. W. AND SILVETTE, H. Am. J. Physiol., 1932, **100**, 693.

BROMER, W. W., SINN, L. Y., STAUB, A., AND BEHRENS, O. K. Diabetes, 1957, **6**, 234.

BÜRGER, M. Ztschr. ges. inn. Med., 1947, **2**, 311.

CAMPBELL, J. AND BEST, C. H. Lancet, 1938, **1**, 1444.

CANNON, W. B., SHOHL, A. T., AND WRIGHT, W. S. Am. J. Physiol. 1911, **29**, 280.

CONN, J. W., LOUIS, L. H., AND JOHNSTON, M. W. Proc. Am. Diabetes, A., 1948, **8**, 213.

COORE, H. G., RANDLE, P. J., SIMON, E., KRAICER, P. F., AND SHELESNYAK, M. C. Nature, 1963, **197**, 1264.

CORI, G. T. AND CORI, C. F. J. Biol. Chem., 1927, **72**, 615.

CRANDALL, L. A. AND CHERRY, I. S. Am. J. Physiol., 1939, **125**, 658.

CRANDALL, L. A. AND LIPSCOMB, A. Am. J. Physiol., 1947, **148**, 312.

DAVIDSON, J. K. AND HAIST, R. E. Lancet, 1963, **ii**, 656.

deBODO, R. C., STEELE, R., ALTSZULER, N., DUNN, A., AND BISHOP, S. J. Recent Prog. Horm. Res., 1963, **19**, 445.

DeMAYER, J. Arch. Fisiol. 1909, **7**, 96.

DEPOCAS, F. Am. J. Physiol., 1964, **206**, 119.

DIXON, G. H. "On the Nature and Treatment of Diabetes," Chap. 6. (Ed. B. S. LEIBEL AND G. A. WRENSHALL) Excerpta Medica Foundation, Amsterdam, 1965.

DIXON, G. H. AND WARDLAW, A. C. Nature, 1960, **188**, 721.

DOHAN, F. C. AND LUKENS, F. D. W. Am. J. Physiol., 1939, **125**, 188.

DU YU-CANG, ZHANG YU-SHANG, LU ZI-XIAN, AND TSOU CHEN-LU. Sci. Sinica (Peking), 1961, **10**, 84.

DUNN, J. S., SHEEHAN, H. L., AND McLETCHIE, N. G. B. Lancet, 1943, **1**, 484.

ELRICK, H., RACHIELE, F. J., AND HLAD, C. J. Diabetes, 1958, **7**, 129.

ENGEL, F. L. Shock & Circulatory Homeostasis. Second Conf., 1952, Josiah Macy Jr. Foundation, p. 26.

EVANS, J. R. Circulation Res., 1964, **15**, Suppl. II, 96.

EVANS, H. M., MEYER, K., SIMPSON, M. E., AND REICHERT, F. L. Proc. Soc. Exper. Biol. Med., 1932, **29**, 857.

EZRIN, C., SALTER, J. M. OGRYZLO, M. A., AND BEST, C. H. Canad. M. A. J., 1958, **78**, 96.

FAJANS, S. S. AND CONN, J. W. Diabetes, 1954, **3**, 296.

FOA, P. P. Chicago Med. School Quart. 1953, **14**, 145.

FOA, P. P. Action of insulin on chick embryo heart, Fed. Am. Biol. Soc., Symposium, 1965.

FORBATH, N. AND HETENYI, G. Excerpta Medica Int. Cong. Series. #74, 1964, p. 125.

GEMMILL, C. L. Bull. Johns Hopkins Hosp., 1941, **68**, 329.

GOETZ, F. C., MANEY, J., AND GREENBERG, B. Z. Excerpta Med. Int. Cong. Series, #74, 1964, p. 135.

GRIFFITHS, J. P. AND WATERS, E. T. Am. J. Physiol., 1936, **117**, 134.

GRIFFITHS, M. J. Biol. Chem., 1948, **172**, 853.

GRODSKI, G. M. AND BENNETT, L. L. Proc. Soc. Exp. Biol. Med., 1963, **114**, 796.

GUIDOTTI, G., KANAMEISHI, D., AND FOA, P. P. Am. J. Physiol., 1961, **201**, 863.

HAGEDORN, H. C., JENSEN, B. N., KRARUP, N. B., AND WODSTRUP, I. J.A.M.A. 1936, **106**, 177.

HAIST, R. E. Ann. N.Y. Acad. Sci., 1959, **82**, 266.

HAIST, R. E. "On the Nature and Treatment of Diabetes," Chap. 2. (Ed. B. S. LEIBEL AND G. A. WRENSHALL) Excerpta Medica Foundation, Amsterdam, 1965.

HAIST, R. E., CAMPBELL, J., AND BEST, C. H. New England J. Med., 1940, **223**, 607.

HALLAS-MØLLER, K., JERSILD, M., PETERSEN, K., AND SCHLICHTKRULL, J. J.A.M.A., 1952, **150**, 1667.

HAM, A. W. AND HAIST, R. E. Am. J. Pathol., 1941, **17**, 787.

HARFENIST, E. J. AND CRAIG, L. C. J. Am. Chem. Soc., 1952, **74**, 3087.

HARTROFT, W. S. AND WRENSHALL, G. A. Diabetes, 1955, **4**, 1.

HÉDON, E. J. Physiol. Path. gen., 1927, **25**, 1.

HENDERSON, M. J., WRENSHALL, G. A., AND ODENSE, P. Can. J. Biochem. Physiol., 1955, **33**, 926.

HETENYI, G., WRENSHALL, G. A., AND BEST, C. H. Diabetes, 1961, **10**, 304.

HETENYI, G. AND WRENSHALL, G. A. Excerpta Medica, Int. Congress Series ≠48, Leiden, 1962.

HOFMEISTER, F. Arch. exper. Path. u. Pharmakol., 1889, **25**, 240.

HOUSSAY, B. A. Endocrinology, 1944, **35**, 158.

HOUSSAY, B. A. AND BIASOTTI, A. Rev. Soc. Argent. Biol., 1930, **6**, 8.

HOUSSAY, B. A., FOGLIA, V. G., SMYTH, F. S., RIETTI, C. T., AND HOUSSAY, A. B. J. Exper. Med., 1942, **75**, 547.

HOUSSAY, B. A. AND POTICK, D. Compt. rend. Soc. biol., 1929, **101**, 940.

INGLE, D. J., BEARY, D. F., AND PURMALIS, A. Proc. Soc. Exper. Biol. Med., 1954, **85**, 432.

IZZO, J. L., RONCONE, A. AND PALIANI, M. A. Fed. Proc., 1957, **16**, 200.

IZZO, J. L., RONCONE, A., IZZO, M. J., AND BALE, W. F., Fed. Proc., 1964, **23**, 460.

JACOBS, H. R. Proc. Soc. Exper. Biol. Med., 1937, **37**, 407.

KATZEN, H. M. AND STETTEN, D., Diabetes, 1962, **11**, 271.

KATZEN, H. M., TIETZE, F., AND STETTEN, D. J. Biol. Chem., 1963, **235**, 1006.

KATSOYANNIS, P. G., TOMETSKO, A., AND FUKUDA, K., J. Am. Chem. Soc., 1963, **85**, 2863.

KATSOYANNIS, P. G., FUKUDA, A., TOMETSKO, A., SUZUKI, K., AND TILAK, M. J. Am. Chem. Soc., 1964, **86**, 930.

KIPNIS, D. M. "On the Nature and Treatment of Diabetes," Chap. 18. (Ed. B. S. LEIBEL AND G. A. WRENSHALL) Excerpta Medica Foundation, Amsterdam, 1965.

KIPNIS, D. M. AND CORI, C. F. J. Biol. Chem., 1959, **234**, 171.

KRAHL, M. E. Ann. New York Acad. Sc., 1951, **54**, 694.

KRAHL, M. E. The Action of Insulin on Cells. Academic Press, N.Y. & London, 1961.

KRAHL, M. E., PENHOS, J. C., AND KRAEMER, A. "On the Nature and Treatment of Diabetes," Chap. 7. (Ed. B. S. LEIBEL AND G. A. WRENSHALL) Excerpta Medica Foundation, Amsterdam, 1965.

LAZAROW, A. Anat. Rec., 1942, **84**, 31.

LAZAROW, A. "On the Nature and Treatment of Diabetes," Chap. 3. (Ed. B. S. LEIBEL AND G. A. WRENSHALL) Excerpta Medica Foundation, Amsterdam, 1965.

LECOCQ, F. R., MEBANE, D., AND MADISON, L. L. J. Clin. Investig., 1964, **43**, 237.

LEHMANN, W. L. Arch. exper. Path. u. Pharmakol., 1874, **2**, 463.

LEVINE, R. "On the Nature and Treatment of Diabetes," Chap. 17. (Ed. B. S. LEIBEL AND G. A. WRENSHALL) Excerpta Medica Foundation, Amsterdam, 1965.

LEVINE, R. AND GOLDSTEIN, M. S. Rec. Prog. Hormone Research, 1955, **11**, 343.

LINDLEY, H. AND ROLLETT, J. S. Biochim. et. Biophys. Acta., 1955, **18**, 183.

LOGOTHETOPOULOS, J., SHARMA, B. B., SALTER, J. M., AND BEST, C. H. Diabetes, 1960, **9**, 756.

LONG, C. N. H., KATZIN, B., AND FRY, E. G. Endocrinology, 1940, **26**, 309.

LONG, C. N. H. AND LUKENS, F. D. W. J. Exper. Med., 1936, **63**, 465.

LUKENS, F. D. W. AND DOHAN, F. C. Endocrinology, 1938, **22**, 51.

LUKENS, F. D. W. AND DOHAN, F. C. Endocrinology, 1942, **30**, 175.

LYNGSØE, J. Acta med. scand., 1963, **174**, 589.

VON MEHRING, J. AND MINKOWSKI, O. Arch. Exper. Path. u. Pharmakol., 1889, **26**, 371.

MEYER, K. H. Advanc. Enzymol., 1943, **3**, 109.

MEIENHOFA, J., SCHNABEL, E., BREMER, H., BRINKHOFF, O., ZABEL, R., SRCKA, W., KLOSTERMAYER, H., BRANDENBURG, D., OKUDA, T., AND ZAHN, H., Z. fur Naturforschung, 1963, **18b**, 1120.

METZ, R. DIABETES, 1960, **9**, 89.

METZ, R. AND SALTER, J. M. Nature, 1962, **196**, 1094.

MIRSKY, I. A. AND BROH-KAHN, R. H. Arch. Biochem., 1949, **20**, 1.

MOLONEY, P. J. Ciba Colloquia on Endocrinology, London. Immunoassay of Hormones, 1962, **14**, 169.

MOLONEY, P. J. AND COVAL, M. Biochem. J., 1955, **59**, 179.

MOLONEY, P. J. AND GOLDSMITH, L., Can. J. Biochem. Physiol., 1957, **35**, 79.

MOLONEY, P. J., APRILE, M. A., AND WILSON, S. J. New Drugs, 1964, **4**, 258.

MORGAN, H. E. AND PARMEGGIANI, A. Control of Glycogen Metabolism. Ciba Foundation Symposium (1964). (Ed. W. J. WHELAN AND M. P. CAMERON). J & A. Churchill Ltd., London. P. 254.

MORGAN, H. E., REGEN, D. M., AND PARK, C. R. J. Biol. Chem., 1964, **239**, 369.

NABARRO, J. D. N. "On the Nature and Treatment of Diabetes," Chap. 40. (Ed. B. S. LEIBEL AND G. A. WRENSHALL) Excerpta Medica Foundation, Amsterdam, 1965.

NECHELES, H. Am. J. Physiol., 1957, **191,** 595.

NINOMIYA, R., FORBATH, N. F., AND HETENYI, G. Diabetes (in press) 1965.

ONCLEY, J. L., ELLENBOGEN, E., GITLIN, D., AND GURD, F. R. N., J. Phys. Chem., 1952, **56,** 85.

OYAMA, J., THOMAS, J. A., AND GRANT, R. L. Diabetes, 1963, **12,** 332.

PARK, C. R. AND MORGAN, H. E. Diabetes, 1960, **9,** 250.

PFEIFFER, E. F. "On the Nature and Treatment of Diabetes," Chap. 26. (Ed. B. S. LEIBEL AND G. A. WRENSHALL) Excerpta Medica Foundation, Amsterdam, 1965.

RANDLE, P. "On the Nature and Treatment of Diabetes," Chap. 25. (Ed. B. S. LEIBEL AND G. A. WRENSHALL) Excerpta Medica Foundation, Amsterdam, 1965.

RANDLE, P. J. AND SMITH, G. H. Biochem. J., 1958, **70,** 490, 501.

RANDLE, P. J. AND TAYLOR, K. W. Hormones in blood (Chap. II, p. 11) (Ed. C. H. CRAG AND A. L. BACHARACH). Academic Press, Lond. and N.Y. 1961.

REICHARD, G. A., JACOBS, A. G., KIMBEL, P., HOCHELLA, N. J., AND WEINHOUSE, S., J. Applied Physiol, 1961, **16,** 789.

RICHARDSON, K. C. AND YOUNG, F. G. J. Physiol., 1937, **91,** 352.

RICHARDSON, K. C. AND YOUNG, F. G. Lancet, 1938, **1,** 1098.

ROBINSON, R. M., HARRIS, K., HLAD, C. J., AND EISEMAN, B. Proc. Soc. Exper. Biol. Med., 1957, **96,** 518.

SANGER, F. Brit. Med. Bull., 1960, **16,** 183.

SANGER, F. Bull. Soc. chim. biol., 1955, **37,** 23.

SANGER, F. AND TUPPY, H. Biochem. J., 1951, **49,** 463.

SANGER, F. AND THOMPSON, E. O. P. Biochem. J., 1953, **53,** 353.

SALTER, J. M., DAVIDSON, I. W. F., AND BEST, C. H. Diabetes, 1957, **6,** 248.

SALTER, J. M., EZRIN, C., LAIDLAW, J. C., AND GORNALL, A. G. Metabolism, 1960, **9,** 753.

SCHMID, R. Control of Glycogen Metabolism. Ciba Foundation Symposium (1964) (Ed. W. J. WHELAN AND M. P. CAMERON). J. & A. Churchill Ltd., London. P. 306.

SCOTT, D. A. Biochem. J., 1934, **28,** 1592.

SCOTT, D. A. AND FISHER, A. M. J. Pharmacol. & Exper. Therap., 1936, **58,** 781.

SOLS, A. "On the Nature and Treatment of Diabetes," Chap. 9. (Ed. B. S. LEIBEL AND G. A. WRENSHALL) Excerpta Medica Foundation, Amsterdam, 1965.

SOSKIN, S. AND LEVINE, R. Carbohydrate Metabolism. University of Chicago Press, 1946.

STEELE, R., WALL, J. S., DEBODO, R. C., AND ALTSZULER, N. Am. J. Physiol., 1956, **187,** 15.

STETTEN, DEW. Bull. New York Acad. Med., 1953, **29,** 446.

STETTEN, JR., D. W., WELT, I. D., INGLE, D. J., AND MORLEY, E. H. J. Biol. Chem., 1951, **132,** 817.

STUNKARD, A. J., VAN ITALLIE, T. B., AND REISS, B. B. Proc. Soc. Exper. Biol. Med., 1955, **89,** 258.

SUTHERLAND, E. W. AND CORI, C. F. J. Biol. Chem., 1948, **172,** 737.

TOMIZAWA, H. H. AND HALSEY, Y. D. J. Biol. Chem., 1959, **234,** 307.

UNGER, R. H. AND EISENTREUT, A. M. "On the Nature and Treatment of Diabetes," Chap. 19. (Ed. B. S. LEIBEL AND G. A. WRENSHALL) Excerpta Medica Foundation, Amsterdam, 1965.

UNGER, R. H., EISENTREUT, A. M., McCALL, M. S., AND MADISON, L. L. J. Clin. Investig., 1961, **40,** 1280.

VALLANCE-OWEN, J. "On the Nature and Treatment of Diabetes," Chap. 23. (Ed. B. S. LEIBEL AND G. A. WRENSHALL) Excerpta Medica Foundation, Amsterdam, 1965.

WEBER, G. "On the Nature and Treatment of Diabetes," Discussion following Chap. 10. (Ed. B. S. LEIBEL AND G. A. WRENSHALL) Excerpta Medical Foundation, Amsterdam, 1965.

WEITZE, M. AND HAGEDORN, H. C. In Experimental Diabetes, p. 279 (Ed. J. F. DELEFRASNAYE AND G. H. SMITH). Blackwell, Oxford, 1954.

WICK, A. N., DRURY, D. R., BANCROFT, R. W., AND MACKAY, E. M. J. Biol. Chem., 1951, **188,** 241.

WIELAND, O. "On the Nature and Treatment of Diabetes," Chap. 39. (Ed. B. S. LEIBEL AND G. A. WRENSHALL) Excerpta Medical Foundation, Amsterdam, 1965.

WILSON, S. "On the Nature and Treatment of Diabetes," Discussion after Chap. 6. (Ed. B. S. LEIBEL AND G. A. WRENSHALL) Excerpta Medica Foundation, Amsterdam, 1965.

WILSON, S. AND DIXON, G. H. Nature, 1961, **191,** 876.

WILSON, S., DIXON, G. H., AND WARDLAW, A. C. Biochim. Biophys. Acta, 1962, **62,** 483.

WINEGRAD, A. I., YALCIN, S., AND MULCAHY, P. D., "On the Nature and Treatment of Diabetes," Chap. 31, (Ed. B. S. LEIBEL AND G. A. WRENSHALL) Excerpta Medica Foundation, Amsterdam, 1965.

WRIGHT, P. H. "On the Nature and Treatment of Diabetes," Chap. 24. (Ed. B. S. LEIBEL AND G. A. WRENSHALL) Excerpta Medica Foundation, Amsterdam, 1965.

WRENSHALL, G. A. AND HETENYI, G. Metabolism, 1959, **8,** 531.

WRENSHALL, G. A. AND HETENYI, G. Diabetes, 1962, **11,** 236.

WRENSHALL, G. A., VRANIC, M., COWAN, J. S., AND RAPPAPORT, A. M. Excerpta Med. Int. Cong. Series, #74, 1964, p. 141.

YOUNG, F. G. Lancet, 1936, **1,** 237; 297. Ibid., 1937, **2,** 372.

Monographs and Reviews

DEBODO, R. C. AND ALTSZULER, N. Insulin hypersensitivity and physiological insulin antagonists. Physiol. Rev., 1958, **38,** 389.

CHAMBERS, W. H. Undernutrition and carbohydrate metabolism. Physiological Rev., 1938, **18,** 248.

Ciba Foundation Symposium. Control of glycogen metabolism. (Ed. W. J. WHELAN AND M. P. CAMERON) J. & A. Churchill, London, 1964.

CORI, C. F. Phosphorylation of glycogen and glucose. Biol. Symposia, 1941, **5,** 131.

FIELD, J. B. Factors concerned with insulin synthesis and release, Metabolism, 1964, **13,** 407.

Fourth International Standard for Insulin. D. R. BANGHAM AND M. V. MUSSETT. Bull. World Health Org., 1959, **20,** 1209.

HAIST, R. E. Factors affecting the insulin content of pancreas. Physiol. Rev., 1944, **24,** 409.

HAIST, R. E. Effects of Steroids on the Pancreas in Methods in Hormone Research, (chap. 8) vol. 4, 1965, Academic Press, N. Y. and London.

HOUSSAY, B. A. AND BIASOTTI, A. The hypophysis, carbohydrate metabolism and diabetes. Endocrinology, 1931, **15, 511.**

Insulin; British Medical Bulletin, 1960, **16** ≉3, British Council, London.

KRAHL, M. E. The action of insulin on cells. Academic Press, New York & London, 1961.

On the Nature and Treatment of Diabetes (Ed. B. S. LEIBEL AND G. A. WRENSHALL) Fifth Congress Internat. Diab. Fed. 1964, Excerpta Medica, Amsterdam, 1965.

RANDLE, P. J. AND TAYLOR, K. W. Insulin, Chap. 11, in Hormones in Blood (Ed. C. H. GRAY AND A. L. BACHARACH). Academic Press, N. Y. and London.

SAKEL, M. Neue Behandlungsmethode der Schizophrenie. Perles, Wien., 1935.

CHAPTER 68

Fat Metabolism

Types of Lipids Occurring in the Body

Lipids are substances that can be extracted from tissues by solvents such as hydrocarbons, halogenated hydrocarbons, certain alcohols (methyl, ethyl and isopropyl alcohols), acetone, ethyl ether, etc., or combinations of these. The complete extraction of lipid presents difficulties, because some of them are more or less tightly bound to tissue proteins. Polar solvents are more effective than nonpolar in disrupting the bonds in lipoprotein complexes. Hot alcohol or a mixture of ether and alcohol extract almost all fatty substances. The oily residue obtained after removal of the solvents is a complex mixture of crude lipids. Lipids that have been isolated in purified form from such residues are now briefly described; the simplified structures are shown in fig. 68.1.

FATTY ACIDS. The fatty acids of tissues have carbon atoms in straight-chain (normal) arrangement, with a terminal carboxyl group. Fatty acids with branched chains (methyl side-groups) occur in certain bacteria, particularly mycobacteria, and in the preen gland of the duck and the goose, but have only recently been detected, in very small amounts, in human fat (Lederer, Hirsch). Long-chain fatty acids, with 12 to 18 carbon atoms in the molecule are commonest, although lower and higher are also present. The lipids of milk, for example, contain fatty acids of lower molecular weight, from butyric acid (C4) up. The number of carbon atoms in the long-chain medium-chain and short-chain fatty acids are considered to be 12 and over, 8–10 and 4–6 respectively. Naturally-occurring long-chain fatty acids in mammalian tissues have mainly an even number of carbon atoms; only minor amounts of these with an odd-number of carbon atoms have recently been found in adipose tissue (Hirsch).

In fatty acids the chains of carbon atoms may be fully saturated with hydrogen atoms, or contain 1 to 6 unsaturated linkages (double bonds). The unsaturated fatty acids are more liquid, i.e., have lower melting points, and are more readily oxidized by chemical means than the corresponding saturated fatty acids. The long chains of carbon atoms impart paraffin-like properties, e.g.

insolubility in water, solubility in organic solvents and in other lipids, and low electrical and thermal conductivity. The polar carboxyl groups impart hydrophylic properties, and react with hydroxyl groups of glycerol and cholesterol to form esters, or with amino groups to form fatty acid amides, as in sphingomyelins.

The fatty acids of tissues and body fluids are present predominantly in triglycerides; very much smaller amounts occur in phospholipids and still less in sterol esters.

Nonesterified fatty acids occur in adipose tissue, particularly during lipid mobilization, and are always found in blood plasma, in amounts related to physiological conditions. The non-esterified fatty acids (NEFA) in plasma, also referred to as unesterified fatty acids (UFA) or free fatty acids (FFA), are bound to albumin, in which form they are water soluble.

The following convention provides a convenient method of designating fatty acids. The carbon atoms are numbered from that bearing the carboxyl group (C1). An even simpler notation, in which the number of carbon atoms in the molecule, and the number of unsaturated linkages (—CH=CH—) are given, separated by a colon, is shown in table 68.1.

GLYCERIDES. Triglycerides (neutral fats or fats) are compounds of one molecule of glycerol united by ester bonds to three molecules of fatty acids. A great variety of triglycerides are possible, depending on the fatty acids present. The natural triglycerides are usually mixed, i.e. different component fatty acids are present. In the fat of human adipose tissue, 24 long-chain fatty acids have been identified, but only 6 of these account for 91 per cent of the total; in decreasing amount they are oleic, palmitic, linoleic, stearic, palmitoleic and myristic acids (table 68.1).

Diglycerides and monoglycerides also occur in small amounts, e.g., in adipose tissue and intestinal mucosa. These are transitional stages in the formation and degradation of triglycerides and phospholipids. In diglycerides, the fatty acids occur in the 2 and 3 positions of the glycerol, and in monoglycerides in the 2 position. These configurations are attributed to steric specificity of enzymes.

Fatty acids:

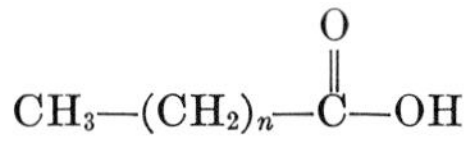

$$CH_3—(CH_2)_n—\overset{\overset{\displaystyle O}{\|}}{C}—OH$$

In long chain fatty acids, n is an even number, commonly 10 to 18. There may be unsaturated linkages in the chain.

Glycerides:

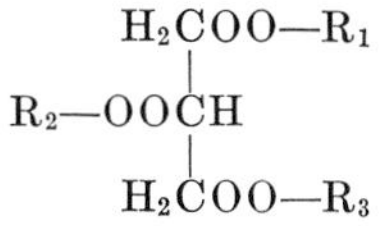

$H_2COO—R_1$	H_2COH	H_2COH
$R_2—OOCH$	$R_2—OOCH$	$R_2—OOCH$
$H_2COO—R_3$	$H_2COO—R_3$	H_2COH
Triglycerides	*Diglycerides*	*Monoglycerides*

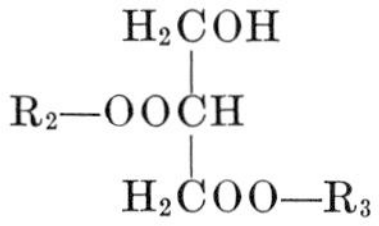

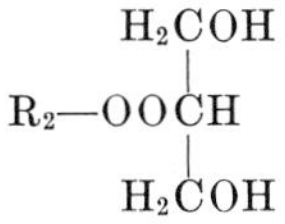

R— represents the fatty acid chain from C2 to the end.

Glycerophosphatides:

Phosphatidic acids:

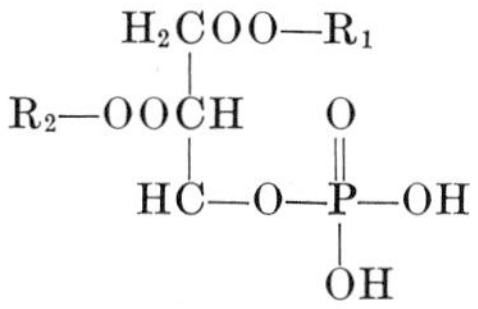

$$
\begin{array}{l}
H_2COO—R_1 \\
R_2—OOCH \quad\;\; O \\
\quad HC—O—\overset{\overset{\displaystyle O}{\|}}{P}—OH \\
\qquad\qquad OH
\end{array}
$$

Phosphatidyl esters:

$$
\begin{array}{l}
H_2COO—R_1 \\
R_2—OOCH \quad\;\; O \\
\quad HC—O—\overset{\overset{\displaystyle O}{\|}}{P}—OH \\
\qquad\qquad O—R_3
\end{array}
$$

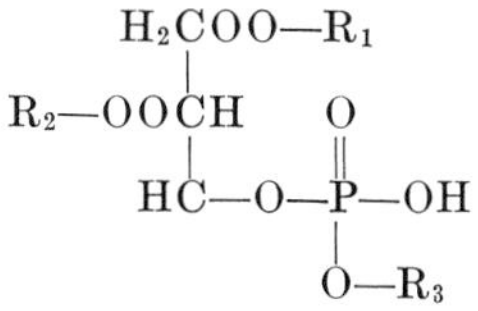

R_1 and R_2 represent fatty acid chains from C2 to the end.

Phosphatidyl esters	$—O—R_3$ group
Phosphatidylcholine	Choline: $—OCH_2CH_2\overset{\overset{\displaystyle OH}{\|}}{N}(CH_3)_3$
Phosphatidylethanolamine	Ethanolamine: $—OCH_2CH_2NH_2$
Phosphatidylserine	Serine: $—OCH_2CHNH_2COOH$
Phosphatidylinositol	Myoinositol: $—OCH(CHOH)_5$

Acetal phosphatides or *plasmalogens:*

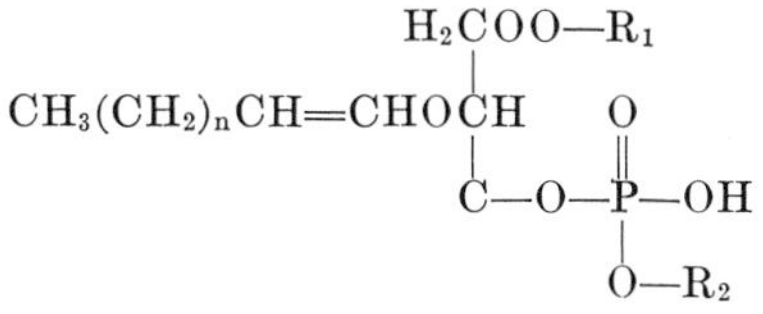

$$
\begin{array}{l}
\qquad\qquad\qquad H_2COO—R_1 \\
CH_3(CH_2)_nCH=CHOCH \qquad O \\
\qquad\qquad\qquad \overset{\overset{\displaystyle O}{\|}}{C}—O—P—OH \\
\qquad\qquad\qquad\qquad\quad O—R_2
\end{array}
$$

The $—O—R_2$ group is either ethanolamine, choline or serine.

Sphingomyelins: (See p. 1371).
Cerebrosides:

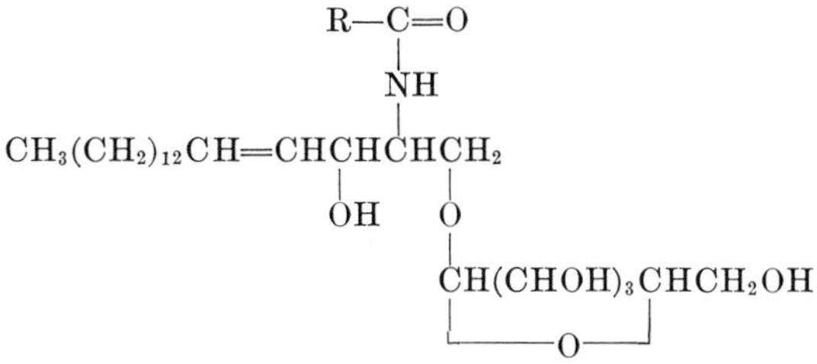

$$
\begin{array}{l}
\qquad\qquad R—C=O \\
\qquad\qquad\;\; NH \\
CH_3(CH_2)_{12}CH=CHCHCHCH_2 \\
\qquad\qquad\quad OH \quad\; O \\
\qquad\qquad\qquad\qquad CH(CHOH)_3CHCH_2OH \\
\qquad\qquad\qquad\qquad\;\; \rule{}{}—O—
\end{array}
$$

Cerebroside	*Component fatty acid* $(R—\overset{|}{C}=O)$
Kerasin	Lignoceric: $CH_3(CH_2)_{22}\overset{|}{C}=O$
Phrenosin	Cerebronic: $CH_3(CH_2)_{21}CHOH\overset{|}{C}=O$
Nervone	Nervonic: $CH_3(CH_2)_7CH=CH(CH_2)_{13}\overset{|}{C}=O$
Oxynervone	Oxynervonic: $CH_3(CH_2)_7CH=CH(CH_2)_{12}CHOH\overset{|}{C}=O$

FIG. 68.1. Type structures of lipids occurring in mammalian tissues

TABLE 68.1

*Fatty acid composition of human adipose tissue**

Fatty Acid†	Carbon Atoms: Double Bonds	Per Cent of Total Fatty Acids
Lauric	12:0	0.9
Myristic	14:0	3.5
Palmitic	16:0	19.0
Palmitoleic	16:1	5.1
Stearic	18:0	6.2
Oleic	18:1	43.1
Linoleic	18:2	13.9
		91.7

* Modified from J. Hirsch, in *Adipose Tissue as an Organ*, Ed. L. W. Kinsell, Springfield, Illinois, C. C. Thomas, 1962, p. 79.

† Only those fatty acids that constitute over 0.9 per cent of the total amount are listed.

PHOSPHOLIPIDS. Many combined or conjugated lipids have the common property of containing a phosphate radicle, and are collectively known as *phospholipids*. They include the glycerophosphatides and the sphingomyelins.

GLYCEROPHOSPHATIDES. The glycerophosphatides consist of α-glycerophosphoric acid esterified with fatty acids. A nitrogenous base or a carbohydrate is usually esterified with the phosphoric acid moiety. They include the phosphatidic acids, phosphatidylcholines, phosphatidylethanolamines, phosphatidylserines, phosphatidylinositols and the acetal phosphatides.

PHOSPHATIDIC ACIDS. The least complex of the glycerophosphatides are the phosphatidic acids in which two fatty acid molecules are attached in positions 2 and 3 (or β- and α-) of the glycerol portion. The phosphatidic acids are present in very low concentrations in tissue lipids. They are intermediates in the formation of other, more complex, phospholipids, and of triglycerides. They are rapidly utilized and do not accumulate. A precursor of phosphatidic acids in tissues is L-α-glycerophosphate, which is derived from glucose-6-phosphate by glycolysis. In the liver, intestinal mucosa, and apparently in brain, it is produced also by conjugation of glycerol and phosphate in a reaction catalysed by glycerokinase.

The designation of lecithins and "cephalins" as derivatives of phosphatidic acids is in accord both with their chemical constitutions and with their modes of biosynthesis.

PHOSPHATIDYLCHOLINES or LECITHINS (from the Greek equivalent of egg yolk), were first recognized as components of brain and egg yolk lipids. They are compounds in which the phosphoric acid group of phosphatidic acid is bound to choline. In lecithins, the fatty acids are often more unsaturated than in the triglycerides of the same tissue, but not always so. Pure synthetic lecithins identical in every respect with the natural substances have been made by Baer and his associates. Their work indicates that the naturally-occurring lecithins are of the L-α type.

PHOSPHATIDYLETHANOLAMINES and PHOSPHATIDYLSERINES are compounds in which the hydroxyl groups of ethanolamine ($CH_2NH_2CH_2OH$) and of serine ($CH_2OHCHNH_2COOH$), respectively, are bound to the phosphoric acid radicle of phosphatidic acid. Long ago, during the separation of lipids from brain, with alcohol, a sparingly soluble fraction was designated "cephalin". It was believed to be phosphatidylethanolamine. In 1942 however, Folch found that the "cephalin fraction" contains at least two other phospholipids, phosphatidylserine and phosphatidylinositol. The term cephalin is no longer specific for phosphatidylethanolamine.

Phosphatidylcholines, phosphatidylethanolamines and phosphatidylserines are widely distributed in nature, being found in all active or soft tissues, and in the body fluids. Lecithins are quantitatively the most important of these substances (table 68.2).

PHOSPHOINOSITIDES are compounds in which myoinositol is esterified at position 1 with the phosphate group of the phosphatidic acid. PHOSPHATIDYLINOSITOL, sometimes referred to as monophosphoinositide, is the most widely dis-

TABLE 68.2

*The lecithin, cephalin, and sphingomyelin content of normal human organs**

Organ	Lecithin†	Cephalin†	Sphingomyelin†
Brain‡	4.81	20.42	5.66
Lung	3.85	2.00	1.45
Spleen	3.54	4.16	0.86
Kidney	5.10	3.26	0.72
Liver	4.81	4.62	0.38
Heart	4.47	2.06	0.34

* From Thannhauser et al. (J. Biol. Chem., **129**, 717, 1939).

† The values representing mg. per 100 mg. of dried organ.

‡ Including both white and grey matter.

tributed of these inositides. It is found in brain, cardiac and skeletal muscle, visceral organs, the thyroid and adrenal glands, and in the plasma, erythrocytes and leucocytes of the blood. It may account for 2–8% of the total lipid phosphorus.

DIPHOSPHOINOSITIDES and TRIPHOSPHOINOSITIDES are derivatives of phosphotidylinositol, containing phosphate radicles combined to the hydroxyl group of the myoinositol at C4, and at C4 and 5, respectively. Originally thought to be present in nervous tissue only, they have recently been found, in small amounts, in adrenal glands. These compounds have been reviewed by Hawthorne.

PLASMALOGENS (acetal phosphatides), which give a positive reaction for aldehydes, are closely related to phosphatidyl esters. Plasmalogens contain a fatty acid in ester linkage and a second long-chain component in an unsaturated vinyl-ether linkage. The aldehydes corresponding to palmitic and stearic acids have been isolated from plasmalogens of brain. Plasmalogens containing ethanolamine predominate in nature, but those with serine or choline have also been found.

Plasmalogens are widely distributed in animal tissues. The myelin of brain and nerve contains relatively large amounts. They are also present in heart and skeletal muscle and in semen. Their functional roles are unknown.

SPHINGOMYELINS contain two bases, choline and sphingosine, a fatty acid and phosphoric acid. The sphingosine, or a related base, is bound by amide linkage to the fatty acid, and by ester linkage to phosphorylcholine. In sphingomyelins from brain, the fatty acids found are stearic, lignoceric $(CH_3(CH_2)_{22}COOH)$ or nervonic $(CH_3(CH_2)_7CH=CH(CH_2)_{13}COOH)$ acids; in those from lung and spleen, the fatty acids may be palmitic or lignoceric.

CEREBROSIDES (glycolipids) consist of a nitrogenous base (sphingosine or dihydrosphingosine), a long-chain-fatty acid of the type found in sphingomyelins, and a hexose. Cerebrosides occur in brain, adrenal gland, kidney, spleen, liver, leucocytes, thymus, lung, retina, egg yolk and fish sperm. In Gaucher's disease they occur in relatively large amounts in spleen and liver. The sugar in the cerebrosides of brain is galactose.

OTHER COMPLEX LIPIDS. Recent studies of phospholipid fractions from invertebrates and other less explored organisms have disclosed the occurrence of minor amounts of glycerophosphatides containing a variety of bases and, even

TABLE 68.3

Whole-body composition in normal subjects

Mean values of body components as per cent of body weight

	Men				Women		
	Age, Years						
	20	25	30	55	25	30	55
Fat.............	10	14	16	23	23	25	32
Water..........	65	62	60	55	55	54	49
Solids, non-fat..	25	24	24	22	22	21	19

more interesting, analogs in which glycerophosphonic acid replaces glycerophosphoric acid.

Lipids in Tissues[1]

Studies of whole body composition of normal subjects have provided the representative values for fat, water and non-fat solids shown in table 68.3. The mean fat content in man rises from 10% in the age-group of 20 years to 23% at 55 years. In women, the fat content of the body is generally higher, by about 15 per cent, than in men at corresponding ages. Similar trends in body fat with age and sex occur in laboratory animals.

The concept of a gross division of body lipid into two major types, has persisted. Terroine emphasized that on prolonged fasting most of the body lipid disappeared, yet a small, relatively constant fraction remained bound in tissues. That which was utilized, the variable element, is rich in neutral fat. That remaining, the constant element, is rich in phospholipids and cholesterol.

Experiments in which tritium-labeled water was administered to rats indicate that a rather large proportion of the total phospholipid of the body is relatively inert, with a biological half-life of 220 days, as compared to 20 days for the metabolically-active component. Presumably the long-lived component is part of the cell structure. In more recent studies, the lean body mass is estimated to contain about 2% of lipid; this

[1] The following abbreviations are used: CoA or CoASH, coenzyme A; ATP, adenosine triphosphate; ADP, adenosine diphosphate; AMP, adenosine monophosphate; Pi, inorganic phosphate, PPi, inorganic pyrophosphate; DPN, diphosphopyridine nucleotide; DPNH, reduced diphosphopyridine nucleotide; TPN, triphosphopyridine nucleotide; TPNH, reduced triphosphopyridine nucleotide; HMG, B-hydroxy-B-methyl glutaric acid; FAD, flavin-adenine-dinucleotide.

portion is considered essential for the structural integrity and for the metabolic activities of cells. Body water bears a close relation to non-fat solids, the water being 69–72% of lean body mass. With accumulation of fat, the proportion of water in the whole body decreases.

In well nourished animals, the typical adipose tissue cell is distended by a huge oil droplet or vacuole, and the cell structure is stretched to a thin layer surrounding it. The droplet contains over 90% of triglycerides. Much smaller intracellular lipid droplets stainable by fat-soluble dyes are frequently seen in liver, kidney and muscle cells. In the liver, fat droplets may increase greatly in size and number under certain conditions; they may be arranged in the liver lobules in a characteristic pattern. When the accumulation of lipid is due to mobilization of fat from body stores, the arrangement of the droplets in the liver cells is initially periportal; when it is due to dietary deficiency of lipotropic factors the arrangement initially is centrolobular. With excessive accumulation, the lipid droplets are densely and uniformly distributed throughout the lobules.

Lipid cannot be detected in normal liver tissue by ordinary staining methods, although it is present to the extent of 5–7 per cent. It is bound to tissue proteins in non-stainable forms. This lipid is composed of triglycerides 45–50 per cent; phospholipids, 45–50 per cent; and cholesterol less than 0.4 per cent. Hepatic phospholipids consist of about 40 per cent of phosphatidylcholines, 25 per cent of phosphatidylethanolamines and the remainder composed of phosphatidylserines, phosphatidylinositols and sphingomyelins in almost equal proportions. The phospholipids extracted from kidney and heart muscle are similar.

When cell components are separated and collected by the technique of differential centrifugation into nuclear, mitochondrial, microsomal and cytoplasmic (supernatant) fractions, each of these fractions is found to contain considerable quantities of lipid. The mitochondria and microsomes of rat liver are rich in lipid (25–50 per cent of dry weight), of which 50–60 per cent is phosphatide. In each of these cell fractions about one-half of the phosphatides is lecithin, 20–40 per cent is phosphatidylethanolamine, and small amounts of phosphatides containing serine, inositol and sphingosine are present. The supernatant (cytoplasmic) fraction contains less total lipid, which has a higher proportion of triglyceride and less phosphatide than does the lipid of the

particulate fractions. Fractionation of kidney and heart tissue yields similar results. According to Davson and Danielli, cell membranes are composed of a double layer of lipid molecules, covered on both surfaces with protein layers.

Functions of Lipids

NUTRITIVE. Certain unsaturated fatty acids are required in the diet for growth and maintenance. These essential fatty acids include linoleic (18:2) and arachidonic (20:4) acids. Vitamins A, D, E and K have solubilities similar to lipids and are absorbed with lipids. Fats are important in improving the palatability of foods, and have a high satiety value.

LIPID TRANSPORT AND EXCHANGE. For transport in blood and lymph, and for the exchanges between blood and tissues, it is apparent that lipid must be in special forms. The triglycerides are carried in chylomicrons and lipoproteins. It appears that phospholipids and cholesterol are required for this transport function, since they are also present in these carriers.

CELL STRUCTURE AND ACTIVITIES. Lipids are integral components of cell structures, as mentioned above. There is much further evidence (see References) that lipoprotein complexes are of fundamental importance in cellular activities. Processes in which phosphatides are involved include: enzymatic activities of mitochondria, protein synthesis, the formation of external secretions, and the transport of water, ions and other substances through cell membranes.

LUNG ELASTICITY. A lipid-protein complex in the membrane of the lung alveoli is required for the maintenance of normal elasticity of the lung (Clements). The lipoprotein complex (surfactant) lowers the surface tension, and plays a critical role in determining the tension of the alveolar wall. Lecithin is a major component of the complex, which is essential in prevention of certain types of atelectasis and pulmonary edema. It may be pointed out that all the lipid which enters the blood, from the intestine, from the liver, and from adipose tissue, first passes through the pulmonary circulation before entering the systemic arterial vessels. The synthesis of lipid (triglycerides and lecithins) by lung tissue *in vitro* has been demonstrated.

MECHANICAL, THERMAL AND ELECTRICAL INSULATION. In certain regions of the body adipose tissue protects against mechanical pressure and shock, e.g., in the buttocks, soles of the feet, palmar surfaces of the hands, orbit of the eye, and the perirenal tissues. In certain marine

TABLE 68.4

Lipids of feces in man on an unregulated diet

Feces, total weight, grams per day: 100–200
dry substance, grams per day: 23–32

Lipids	Per Cent of Dry Substance	
	Mean	Range
Total fat....................	18	7–28
Neutral fat.................	7	2–12
Fatty acids, free............	6	1–10
Fatty acids, soaps..........	5	1–11

From F. S. Fowweather, Brit. J. Exper. Path., 1926, **7**, 15.

mammals, such as the seal, a thick layer of subcutaneous fat tissue surrounding the deeper tissues may serve as thermal insulation for the body (Hart). The myelin sheath surrounding nerve fibers appears to provide protection against mechanical shock and pressure. The myelin sheath, through its low electrical conductivity, appears to increase the threshold for excitation of nerve trunks, and is involved in saltatory conduction in nerve.

ENERGY STORAGE. The body is capable of storing large amounts of fat, chiefly in adipose tissue which is specialized for this function. Triglycerides are stored in an almost water-free state in the large intracellular droplets of adipose tissue, providing the utmost concentration of potential energy and economy of space. On oxidation in the body, fat yields 9 Calories per g., compared to 4 for each of protein and carbohydrate. The release of lipid from the fat depots is controlled by chemical, neural and hormonal factors, so that homeostasis is maintained under diverse conditions and body states.

METABOLIC. Through oxidation in the tissues, lipids yield metabolites which are utilized in interconversion of substances. The energy released by oxidative processes appears in the forms of heat, muscular contraction, glandular secretion, electrical variations, etc. Energy is utilized also in the synthesis of compounds.

The brown fat tissue that is prominent in rodents, appears to have a special function in providing heat at the body core, during periods of deprivation of food or hibernation. The heat may be produced by lipolysis of triglycerides, with reesterification of fatty acids and oxidation of fatty acids. The location of the brown fat tissue favors the transfer of the heat to the central nervous system and the heart.

BLOOD COAGULATION. The phosphatides of blood platelets are involved in the production of thromboplastin activity in the early stages of blood clotting.

Digestion and Absorption

Since fats and fatty acids are only slightly soluble in water, the explanation of their absorption presents special difficulties. It is estimated that normally over 95 per cent of the fat in the diet is absorbed. The fat in feces is a mixture of unhydrolysed fat and fatty acids. In man this is usually less than 5 g. per day (table 68.4). The continued excretion of fat when the diet is practically devoid of it indicates that fat is normally excreted by the intestine. The fat of the feces represents, therefore, unabsorbed dietary fat, together with fat that is excreted (that present in cellular debris from the intestine and produced by intestinal flora). Fat absorption is usually complete in 4 to 5 hr. after the ingestion of a meal containing an ordinary amount of fat, about 30 g. The relatively long time required for absorption of fats, as compared to protein and carbohydrate, is due to the slower rates of digestion and absorption processes. Fats also decrease the tonus and motility of the stomach and intestine and inhibit gastric secretion. Absorption of fat, which promotes the flow of bile, occurs in the intestine, the rate being higher in the upper jejunum than in the ileum. Little or no absorption occurs in the colon. Following the ingestion of a meal containing fat, the absorption of lipid can be seen when the abdomen is opened; in the regions of absorption the intestine appears lighter in color due to the fat contained in the wall, while the lacteals or lymph vessels in the mesentery appear white and opaque, due to the cream-like contents.

Pancreatic juice and bile are required for adequate digestion and absorption of fat. The main pancreatic duct and the common bile duct meet at the ampulla of Vater and their juices enter the duodenum through a common orifice. When this orifice is transplanted lower down in the intestine, the absorption of fat begins below this point, not above. On exclusion of bile from the intestine, the fat content of the stools is increased. If pancreatic juice is excluded, the stools are a clay color due to the high content (50–60 per cent) of fat, which is largely unhydrolysed. On exclusion of both secretions from the intestine, the fat content of the stools may reach 80–90 per cent.

Emulsification of fat in the lumen of the intestine is a complex phenomenon in which the lipids and other substances of the chyme interact with the digestive secretions (pancreatic juice, intestinal juice and bile) in an aqueous medium. The process is aided by the churning action produced by the intestinal movements and the body temperature. In the digestion of fat, pancreatic lipase is the principal enzyme. The chief products of digestion are fatty acids and monoglycerides. Frazer found, in model systems *in vitro*, that the combination of unsaturated fatty acid, monoglyceride and bile salt was the only one that was highly effective in emulsifying triglycerides. The monoglycerides and fatty acids lower the oil-water interfacial tension, to produce a stable suspension of fine oil droplets, and the bile salts provide a charge on the particles. Lipolysis by pancreatic lipase provides fatty acids and monoglycerides, and the bile provides the third component, bile salts. This system promotes the emulsification of the remaining glycerides. Frazer suggested that lipolysis was not complete in the intestine; mono-, di- and even triglycerides appear to be absorbed along with fatty acids. This hypothesis of restricted lipolysis in the intestine has subsequently been confirmed. By use of isotope-labeled lipids it has been shown that 25–50% of dietary glycerides are absorbed before complete hydrolysis. However, Frazer's "partition theory"; absorption of triglycerides as a fine emulsion, with their transport by way of the lymphatic vessels, and transport of absorbed fatty acids by the blood stream through the portal vein directly to the liver, has been disproved.

Hofmann and Borgström have emphasized that ordinary emulsification is not sufficient for lipid absorption, and that a further physical-chemical process of subdivision of the oil droplets into micelles is required. Typical emulsions with particles 0.3–1 μ in diameter are opaque, or scatter light strongly; the polar groups of these oil droplets are concentrated at the oil-water interface. On addition of pancreatic lipase to a triglyceride emulsion in the presence of conjugated bile salts, the emulsion clears, indicating a marked reduction in particle size. The resulting micelles (association colloids) are small molecular aggregates, probably spherical, 3–10 mμ in diameter (about double the length of the paraffin chain of fatty acids), having a fluid interior of hydrocarbon or non-polar parts of molecules, with polar groups orientated at the surface. For micelle formation, molecules that contain both a polar and non-polar region, such as soaps and

conjugated bile salts (glycocholic and taurocholic acids) are required, these being termed amphipathic substances. When their concentration in an emulsion exceeds a certain critical level (the critical micellar concentration or CMC) they associate into micelles. Amphiphilic substances (free fatty acids, lecithin and monoglycerides) have such a low solubility in water that they themselves do not form micelles, but, with soaps, form mixed micelles. The combination of amphipath above its CMC and amphiphile is most effective in formation of micelles. Solubilization of neutral fat or other non-polar compounds by micelle formation is also aided by salts in solution in the aqueous phase. Thus, by increasing the dispersion of lipids in the aqueous medium of the intestinal lumen, they are brought to a physical-chemical state which permits the absorption of fatty acids and monoglycerides, with lesser amounts of diglycerides and triglycerides. Absorption of fat begins in the upper jejunum. Cholesterol and bile acids, in the rat and guinea pig, are absorbed mainly in the lower part of the ileum. It is not yet clear whether complete micelles as such, i.e., aggregates of lipid moieties with bile salts, enter the mucosa; or whether fatty acids and monoglycerides are released from the micelles to enter the mucosal cells. Low polarity cholesterol and hydrocarbons, both are absorbed to a lesser extent than triglycerides when fed together. The partition of cholesterol between oil droplets of emulsions and micelles will be in favour of the oil, thus delaying its absorption.

Within the mucosal cells, fatty acids and monoglycerides are esterified to glycerides and, to a lesser extent, to phospholipids. Fatty acids are "activated" by combination with the coenzyme of acetylation (CoA) to form acyl-CoA thioesters by the enzyme fatty acid thiokinase. The energy required for the formation of these high-energy products is derived from adenosine triphosphate (ATP). These fatty acid CoA compounds are utilized in the formation of triglycerides by two major metabolic routes. The first involves phosphorylation, by reaction with L-α-glycerophosphate, the subsequent reactions yielding successively monoglyceride phosphate, diglyceride phosphates (phosphatidic acids), diglycerides, and finally triglycerides (fig. 68.2). The glycerophosphate utilized in these reactions is produced by glycolysis from glucose, and also by phosphorylation of glycerol by ATP (glycerokinase enzyme). By the other route, termed the direct pathway, fatty acid CoA compounds react di-

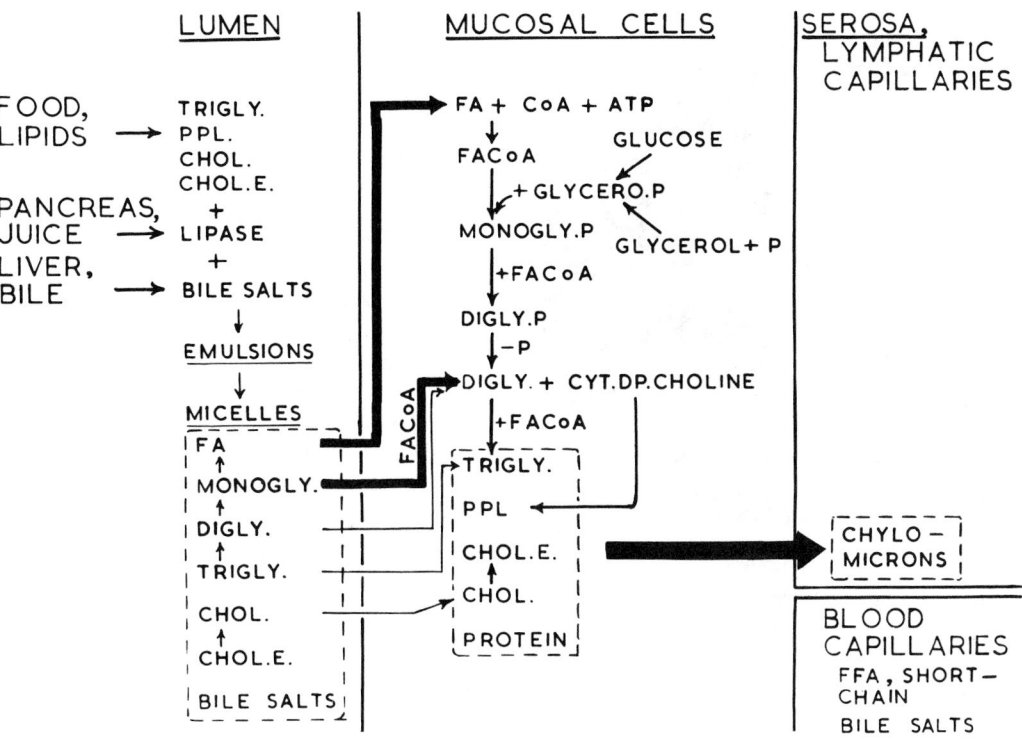

Fig. 68.2. Schematic outline of fat absorption in the intestine, showing passage through the intestinal wall, indications of enzymatic processes in the mucosal cells, and transfer to lymph and to blood. Modified from K. J. Isselbacher, Federation Proc., 1965, 24, 16. Abbreviations are: Trigly., triglycerides; Digly., diglycerides; Monogly., monoglycerides; PPL, phospholipids; Chol., cholesterol; Chol. E., cholesterol esters; FA, fatty acids; CoA, coenzyme A; ATP, adenosine triphosphate; P, phosphate; and Cyt.DP choline, cytidine diphosphate choline.

rectly with monoglycerides to form successively diglycerides and triglycerides. When C^{14}-labeled stearic acid is ingested, it is incorporated, in 5 to 60 min., in about equal proportions into the phospholipids and glycerides of the mucosal cells of the intestine. This indicates that phospholipid formation is also important in lipid absorption (Ragharan et al.). Hydrolysis of monoglycerides to fatty acids and glycerol has also been demonstrated within the mucosal cells. These free fatty acids entering a metabolic pool will presumably be available for reesterification. Triglycerides of medium-chain fatty acids can enter the mucosa with relative ease. In the mucosal cells, conditions appear to favor hydrolysis of these triglycerides. In contrast to the long-chain fatty acids, those of low molecular weight (C_6, C_8, C_{10}) are mainly not esterified, but are transferred to the blood directly and are carried to the liver via the portal blood stream, where they are presumably metabolized or converted to long-chain fatty acids.

A defect in esterification of fatty acids in adrenalectomized animals is indicated, because the extent of fat absorption is reduced and the amount of unesterified fatty acids in the intestinal

mucosa following oral administration of fat is increased. The sub-normal activity of a microsomal fraction from the intestinal mucosa of adrenalectomized animals in the esterification of fatty acids supports this explanation. The defect in fat absorption is corrected, and the enzymatic activity of the mucosa is restored, by the administration of hydrocortisone, but not by the administration of saline alone.

Different modes of absorption of the medium-chain fatty acids mentioned above are also suggested by the effects of adrenalectomy which, in the rat, depresses the absorption of fats containing long-chain fatty acids, but does not appreciably alter that of the triglycerides of butyric acid (C4), caproic acid (C6) and caprylic acid (C8). However, the rates of absorption of caprylic and capric (C10) acids, when fed as the free acids, are slower after adrenalectomy.

TRANSPORT OF LIPID FROM THE INTESTINE

The particles containing absorbed esterified lipids accumulate in the spaces of the endoplasmic reticulum of the mucosal cells. They pass into the intercellular spaces and to the central lymph

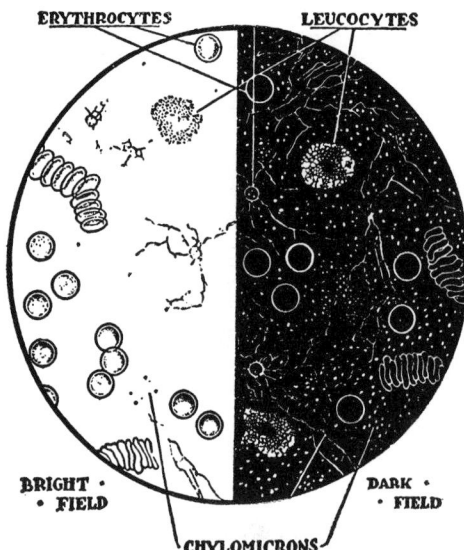

ERYTHROCYTES　　　　LEUCOCYTES

BRIGHT ·
· FIELD

DARK ·
· FIELD

CHYLOMICRONS

FIG. 68.3. Shows chylomicrons in blood (After Gage.)

vessels of the villi; hence to the lacteals (lymph vessels) of the mesentery, to the cisterna chyli, and through the thoracic duct to the subclavian vein at its junction with the left internal jugular vein, where the lymph stream mingles with the venous blood stream. Following a meal rich in fat, the lymph becomes white and opaque, resembling cream, due to the presence of chylomicrons which are fat-laden particles up to 1 μ in diameter. This also causes, usually after about 2–3 hours, milkiness (lactescence) in the blood plasma; this is termed alimentary lipemia (Fig. 68.3).

Chylomicrons are aggregates of triglycerides, with much lesser amounts of phospholipids (6–10 per cent), cholesterol and cholesterol esters and a small, but essential amount of protein or peptide (2 per cent). There are a great many lipid-protein substances in lymph and blood. Since there appears to be an almost infinite gradation in molecular size and in composition of the lipid, the classification of these substances is on the basis of physical properties, such as density, sedimentation or flotation rates and molecular size, and on chemical composition, particularly of the lipid moiety. Thus the great aggregates, the chylomicrons, grade into the β-lipoproteins, and these into the α-lipoproteins. The preferential mode of removal of lipid from the intestine to the lacteals is as lipoprotein.

The relatively minor amounts of lipid removed directly from the intestine by the blood stream,

appear to be in the forms of lipoproteins and of free fatty acids. The transfer of free fatty acids from the intestine by the blood, as fatty acid-albumin complexes, is probably a similar process to the transfer of free fatty acids from adipose tissue.

DISTURBANCES IN FAT ABSORPTION

Deficient pancreatic secretion with insufficient supply of lipase and alkali, as in cystic fibrosis of the pancreas, results in defective absorption of fat, and enhanced excretion of fat (steatorrhea). The feces may contain more unhydrolysed lipid than normal, but not always, due to the action of the intestinal flora in splitting fats. The accompanying defective digestion and absorption of protein tends to aggravate the condition, leading to a malabsorption syndrome. Decreased secretion of bile also leads to defective absorption of lipid; deficiency of bile salts reduces micelle formation and lipase activation.

In celiac disease and in nontropical sprue, the stools are frequent, voluminous, offensive and contain large amounts of fat. There is usually sufficient pancreatic lipase and bile secretion; the defect appears to be in the intestinal mucosa. The cells of the intestinal mucosa do not produce peptidases in amounts adequate for protein digestion and absorption. In celiac disease, the proteins of wheat or rye are particularly injurious. Even when wheat protein is predigested with pepsin and trypsin it does not lose its disastrous effect in celiac disease and sprue patients, but if it is predigested with an extract of pig intestinal mucosa, the harmful effect disappears. Any excess of protein in the diet, even in the absence of gluten, may also be injurious in these diseases. Defective protein digestion, accumulation of peptides in the intestine, increased activity of putrefactive bacteria, irritation of the mucosa and absorption of toxic products, are associated with the defective absorption of lipid and steatorrhea.

In chronic malabsorption of lipid, the possibility must be kept in mind that deficiencies of the fat-soluble vitamins A, D, E and K may be induced. Since fatty acids tend to bind calcium and magnesium, deficiency of these minerals may occur in chronic malabsorption of lipid.

The protein vehicle of chylomicrons and of lipoproteins appears to be synthesized by the intestinal cells. According to Isselbacher, deficient protein synthesis, induced experimentally by agents such as puromycin, acetoxycycloheximide or ethionine, causes the mucosa to become filled with fat, blood triglyceride and β-lipoprotein levels fall, and fail to increase after a fat load. Thus, these effects appear to be due to deficient synthesis of the protein moiety of lipoproteins, (not to deficiency in lipid absorption or esterification in the mucosa) leading to decreased transfer of lipid from the intestine. The importance of synthesis and metabolism of lipoproteins in the intestinal absorption of lipids is shown in a relatively rare genetic disorder known as β-lipoprotein deficiency. In this disease, the problem appears to be inadequate transfer of lipid from the intestine, probably associated with deficient synthesis of the protein vehicle. Patients with this disorder exhibit impaired absorption of fat, accumulation of lipid in large intracellular droplets in the intestinal mucosa cells, increased excretion of fat in stools, and low blood lipid levels. There is involvement of the central nervous system leading to muscular weakness and uncoordinated movements, changes in the retina (retinitis pigmentosa) leading to impaired vision and blindness, and irregularly-shaped erythrocytes.

Origins of Lipid in the Body

Lipids in the body are derived by: (1) intestinal absorption and uptake by tissues, (2) modification of fatty acid structure, with the production of related fatty acids, and (3) synthesis from carbohydrate and protein.

Absorbed Lipids

Fatty acids and monoglycerides, the forms in which lipids are chiefly absorbed, are the most important dietary determinants of the composition of the triglycerides that occur in the tissues. Interposed between absorption from the intestinal lumen and the triglycerides of tissues are three stages at which triglyceride composition can be modified. These are: (1) in the intestinal mucosa, where esterification is predominant, (2) in the plasma, where some degree of hydrolysis of chylomicron-lipid by lipoprotein lipase can occur, and (3) during the uptake of lipid by tissues, e.g., on perfusion of C^{14}-labeled chylomicrons through adipose tissue, about two-thirds of the triglycerides taken up were hydrolysed, the remainder were retained without hydrolysis in the fat cells (Rodbell and Scow).

The chemical structures of the dietary fatty acids would, therefore, be expected to influence the kind of fatty acids found in the tissues. It is well known in animal husbandry that diet influences the depot fat, e.g., swine fed starchy cereals develop a hard fat, whereas peanut-fed swine develop a liquid lard. In early investigations, it was found that feeding mutton fat, high in saturated fatty acids, tended to produce a harder type of fat in the dog. Diets containing a high proportion of fish oils, which are high in unsaturated fatty acids, produced a more liquid fat in the tissues of cats. When lipids that contain fatty acids labeled with deuterium or iodine are fed, the labeled fatty acids appear in the lipids of the body. The extent of this dietary influence on body fat is dependent on conditions. In patients maintained by formula diets in metabolic equilibrium, the rate of entry of dietary linoleate (not synthesized in the body) into adipose tissue was very slow, but in patients gaining weight the rate was much higher (Hirsch).

The stored lipids resemble the fat typical of the species more closely than that of dietary lipids, however, because the tissues can convert long-chain fatty acids to other fatty acids of the same series, and they also can synthesize fat.

Interconversion of Fatty Acids

Schoenheimer and Rittenberg demonstrated the interconversion of fatty acids by tissues. Palmitic acid (16:0) labeled with deuterium was fed to rats; after eight days the body lipid contained about half the isotope ingested, distributed in palmitic, lauric (12:0), myristic (14:0), stearic (18:0), palmitoleic (16:1) and oleic (18:1) acids. Thus, addition or removal of a two-carbon unit and desaturation occurred. On feeding oleic acid, saturation was also demonstrated, since the stearic acid of the tissues was labeled.

The fact that essential fatty acids (e.g., linoleic (18:2) and arachidonic (20:4) acids) are necessary in the diet for normal growth and maintenance, indicates that they cannot be produced in the body in adequate amount, i.e., that there are limitations in the interconversions of fatty acids. Linoleic acid is converted in the body to arachidonic acid and related fatty acids, i.e. to a certain "family" of unsaturated fatty acids. Recent studies (Holman) have shown that oleic acid is further desaturated to a different family of unsaturated fatty acids, and that linolenic acid (18:3) appears to yield a third family of polyunsaturated fatty acids in the body. These families of unsaturated fatty acids are apparently not interconvertible. There is evidence of competition between the fatty acids of these families

Enzymatic Synthesis of Long-Chain Fatty Acids

The soluble enzyme systems are extractable from the cell cytoplasm of mammalian and avian liver, mammary gland, adipose tissue, yeasts, bacteria, insects and plants.

Step 1. Formation of malonyl CoA from acetyl CoA and bicarbonate:

$$CH_3COSCoA + CO_2 + ATP \xrightarrow[\text{(biotin-bound)} + Mn^{++}]{\text{Acetyl CoA carboxylase}} HOOCCH_2COSCoA + ADP + Pi$$

Step 2. Conversion of malonyl CoA to palmitic acid:

$$CH_3COSCoA + 7 HOOCHCH_2COSCoA + 14 TPNH + 14 H^+ \xrightarrow{\text{Enzyme } R_{2a}}$$

$$CH_3(CH_2)_{14}COOH + 14 TPN^+ + 7 CO_2 + 8 CoASH + 6 H_2O$$

The carbons 1 to 14 of palmitic acid are derived from malonyl CoA, and 15 and 16 from acetyl CoA.

Fig. 68.4. From S. J. Wakil and R. Bressler, Metabolism, 1962, **11**, 742.

for conversion in the tissues, e.g., the feeding of large amounts of linolenic acid inhibits the conversion of linoleic acid to other members of its family of acids, and conversely.

Synthesis of Fat

The formation of body fat from carbohydrate in the diet was established by the classical work of Liebig (1852) and Lawes and Gilbert (1859). The latter investigators found, in growing pigs given a high-carbohydrate ration, that the gain in body fat carbon was greatly in excess of the carbon of the protein and fat ingested, consequently most of the fat must have been synthesized from carbohydrate. Many tissues have been shown, both *in vivo* and *in vitro*, to incorporate carbon atoms (C^{14}) of glucose, and of intermediates of carbohydrate metabolism (e.g., pyruvate and acetate) into lipids. Synthesis of fatty acids occurs in adipose tissue, liver, kidney, mammary gland, adrenal gland and other tissues. The formation of body fat from protein has also been demonstrated. Deamination of amino acids occurs chiefly in the liver; the resulting ketoacids may be used in the synthesis of lipid.

An enzyme system that synthesizes long-chain fatty acids is found in cell-free extracts of liver and adipose tissue and is probably present in other tissues also (Wakil). It is contained in the cytoplasmic (supernatant) fraction separated from homogenates of tissue. In this enzyme system, acetyl CoA, bicarbonate, ATP and TPNH are utilized in reactions catalyzed by two separate enzymes to produce free palmitic acid (fig. 68.4). In the first of these steps, a biotin-bound enzyme (acetyl CoA carboxylase) catalyzes the reaction of acetyl CoA with bicarbonate to form malonyl CoA. ATP is utilized as a source of energy in the reaction, and magnesium ions are required. This first intermediate in the syn-

thesis of long-chain fatty acids, malonyl CoA, was isolated and identified by Wakil. Addition of di- and tricarboxylic acids to the reaction mixture stimulated the formation of malonyl CoA; isocitrate gave the highest stimulation. Avidin, a biotin-binding protein of egg white, inhibited the carboxylase activity of the enzyme.

In the second step, another enzyme, designated R_2a, catalyzes the reaction of malonyl CoA with acetyl CoA, in the presence of TPNH, to produce chiefly palmitic acid. In this reaction, CO_2 is released (the same carbon that was fixed in Reaction 1), and a linkage of two-carbon units occurs. Carbon atoms 1 to 14 of the palmitic acid are derived from malonyl CoA, and carbon atoms 15 and 16 are provided by acetyl CoA. Free palmitic acid is produced. Possibly the initial product is palmityl CoA, which is rapidly converted by a deacylating enzyme to the free acid. It appears that this is the chief enzyme system involved in the synthesis of fatty acids in the body. The palmitate synthesized appears to be converted, in part, to related fatty acids by other enzymes.

Enzymatic reactions involved in the synthesis of triglycerides and phospholipids have been elucidated by Kennedy and others, and are shown schematically in fig. 68.5. The first step is the activation of the long-chain fatty acids, by reaction with CoA, which is catalyzed by fatty acid thiokinase, to form the acetyl CoA derivatives. The energy required for the formation of this high energy compound is derived from ATP. The fatty acid CoA compounds react with L-α-glycerophosphate to form phosphatidic acids. These are dephosphorylated by a phosphatase to form D-1,2-diglycerides. Triglycerides are formed by the reaction of diglycerides with fatty acid CoA compounds. The enzymes necessary for these reactions are present in liver and other

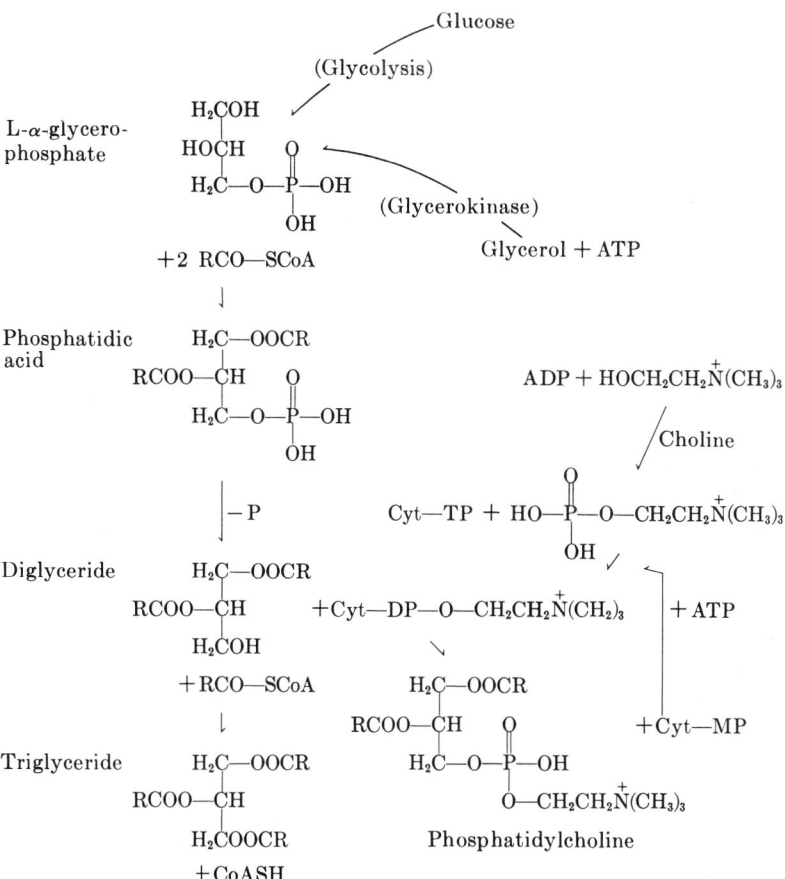

Fig. 68.5. Enzymatic synthesis of phospholipids and triglycerides. From E. P. Kennedy, Federation Proc., 1957, **16**, 847. The abbreviations are: RCO-SCoA, acetyl CoA derivatives of long-chain fatty acids; ATP, adenosine triphosphate; CoASH, coenzyme A; Cyt.MP, cytidine monophosphate; Cyt.TP, cytidine triphosphate; Cyt.DP choline, cytidine diphosphate choline.

tissues. Preparations of microsomes of the intestinal mucosa also catalyze the condensation of monoglycerides with acyl CoA compounds to form triglycerides. The glycerophosphate utilized in these reactions is derived in the tissues from carbohydrate, by glycolysis. Enzymes of the intestinal mucosa and liver have the special property of producing glycerophosphate by the direct phosphorylation of glycerol.

The enzymatic synthesis of lecithins and other phospholipids has been described by Kennedy. Choline is phosphorylated at the expense of ATP. The phosphorylcholine reacts with cytidine triphosphate to form cytidine diphosphate choline (fig. 68.6). This coenzyme-form of choline yields phosphorylcholine, in a reaction with diglycerides, to form phosphatidylcholines (lecithins). The cytidine monophosphate produced in this reaction can be converted to cytidine

triphosphate at the expense of ATP, thus completing a cycle. At each turn of the cycle, one mole of phosphorylcholine is converted to the coenzyme form, and subsequently by the phosphorylcholine-diglyceride transferase reaction to lecithin. The synthesis of phosphatidylethanolamines has also been achieved by a comparable sequence of enzyme-catalyzed reactions, whereby cytidine diphosphate ethanolamine reacts with diglycerides to form phosphatidylethanolamines. There is evidence also for the synthesis of sphingomyelins by reactions of a sphingosine derivative with cytidine diphosphate choline.

Fatty Acid Utilization

Even when substantial amounts of dietary fat are absorbed, the carbon of the fat is practically completely recovered in the carbon dioxide exhaled, indicating that under ordinary metabolic

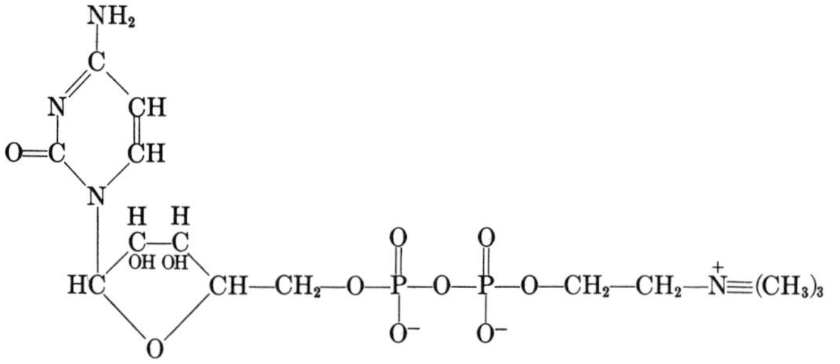

Fig. 68.6. Cytidine diphosphate choline.

conditions, fatty acids are completely oxidized to carbon dioxide and water. The yield of energy in the body is the same as during combustion in the bomb calorimeter, 9 Calories per g. In the oxidation of fat, or of long-chain fatty acids, the value of the respiratory quotient, i.e., the volume of carbon dioxide produced/volume of oxygen utilized, is about 0.70, while for carbohydrate and protein the values are, respectively, 1.0 and about 0.80. Under conditions such as fasting, and in insulin deficiency (in which an increased proportion of fat is utilized) the R.Q. is reduced.

Much of the knowledge of fat oxidation has been derived from studies of the ketone bodies, acetoacetic acid, β-hydroxybutyric acid and acetone, which are chiefly derived from the oxidation of fatty acids. They are normally present in low concentrations in blood (1 to 3 mg. total ketones per 100 ml.), and only about 0.3 gram is excreted daily.

Precursors of Ketone Bodies

Under conditions in which the utilization of fat is increased, such as fasting, ingestion of high-fat diets, and diabetes mellitus in man, and of pancreatectomy and phlorhizin diabetes in animals, the concentration of ketone bodies in blood is elevated, and substantial amounts are excreted. The administration of the ethyl esters of even-numbered saturated fatty acids, from C_4 to C_{18}, by stomach tube to fasting rats induces ketonuria (Deuel); ethyl oleate is also ketogenic (Deuel). The perfused liver, and liver slices *in vitro*, also oxidize even-numbered fatty acids, with the production of acetoacetate. The incorporation of isotopic carbon of fatty acids into acetoacetate produced by tissue *in vitro* has also been demonstrated.

Under unusual metabolic conditions, it has been shown that certain amino acids are ketogenic. Ketoacids produced by the deamination or transamination of amino acids may be con-

verted, depending upon their chemical structure and physiological conditions in the tissues, either to ketone bodies or to carbohydrate (glycogen or glucose). The former amino acids are said to be ketogenic, the latter are glucogenic or antiketogenic. A few amino acids are neither. The effects of different amino acids have been tested by administration to diabetic patients or to fasting phlorhizinized dogs, by perfusion through the liver or by incubation with liver slices. The amino acids found to be ketogenic by such means are leucine, isoleucine, phenylalanine and tyrosine. The glucogenic amino acids (giving rise to extra excretion of glucose) are glycine, alanine, serine, cysteine, cystine, aspartic acid, glutamic acid, valine, arginine, proline, hydroxyproline and ornithine. In some early studies, it was indeed proposed that ketone bodies originate chiefly from the metabolism of proteins, but the idea was soon abandoned. In the fasting phlorhizinized dog, about 60 g. of glucose are excreted in the urine for every 100 g. of body protein metabolized. Thus, the average dietary protein yields an array of amino acids whose metabolic effect is potentially, and chiefly, glucogenic rather than ketogenic.

In the fasting animal, pyruvate is glucogenic and antiketogenic; in the diabetic patient and in the phlorhizinized dog, it gives rise to extra glucose in the urine. Pyruvate is a product of carbohydrate metabolism or it is derived from certain amino acids on deamination. When metabolized under special conditions, however, it may yield ketone bodies, e.g., when it is added to the fluid perfusing the glycogen-poor liver of the dog, or to the medium bathing liver slices *in vitro* in the presence of malonate, or to a liver cell homogenate. Only the α- and β-carbons of pyruvate are incorporated into acetoacetate by the liver homogenate. This indicates that pyruvate is decarboxylated, and that the 2-carbon moiety forms acetyl CoA. The liver has been

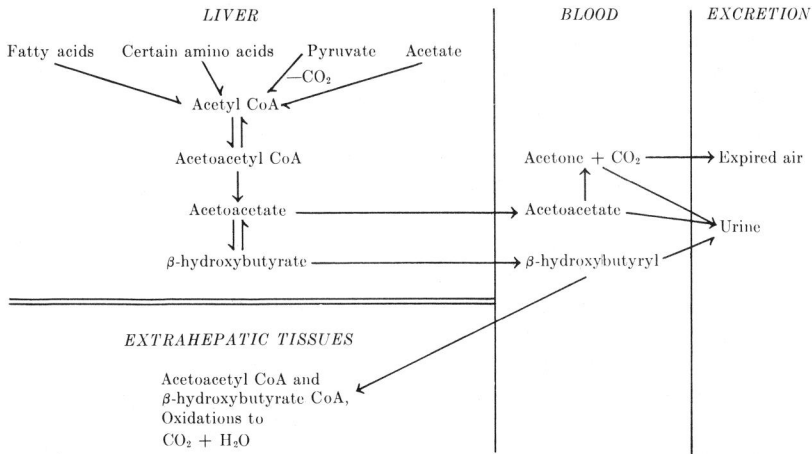

FIG. 68.7. Outline of the interconversion and metabolism of the ketone bodies.

shown to utilize acetate for the production of acetoacetate.

SITE OF PRODUCTION OF KETONE BODIES

The liver is the sole organ that adds ketone bodies in significant amounts to the circulation. Results of diverse experimental procedures have provided evidence for this: (1) the amounts of ketone bodies produced on perfusion of the liver and other organs with fluids containing various substrates, (2) ketone body production by liver slices *in vitro*, (3) differences in ketone body concentrations in blood entering and leaving the liver, (4) the rapid decline in ketone body concentration following hepatectomy and (5) suppression of ketone body excretion by the Eck fistula.

Acetoacetate and β-hydroxybutyrate are endproducts of fat metabolism in the liver; they are not further oxidized in this organ to an appreciable extent. When the rate of addition of ketone bodies to the blood by the liver exceeds the rate of removal by the extrahepatic tissues, the concentration in the blood rises. The interconversions of ketone bodies and their transfer and utilization by extrahepatic tissues are outlined in fig. 68.7. As ketone bodies accumulate in blood and tissues, the proportion of β-hydroxybutyrate to acetoacetate rises. In liver, kidney and other tissues, a DPN⁺-dependent dehydrogenase enzyme associated with the mitochondria catalyzes the interconversion of these acids:

$$CH_3CHOHCH_2COOH + DPN^+ \rightleftharpoons$$
$$CH_3COCH_2COOH + DPNH + H^+$$

The kidney, heart, skeletal muscle and other organs rapidly take up and utilize fatty acids from the FFA fraction of the blood. Isotopic carbon of the fatty acids removed from the blood is found in the tissue lipids and in the carbon dioxide produced. Although the extrahepatic organs utilize lipid, their production of ketone bodies, estimated by arterial-venous differences, is small and inconstant (Himwich). These organs usually remove ketone bodies from the blood and oxidize them to carbon dioxide. In the metabolism of acetate-C^{14} by kidney slices *in vitro*, Medes, Floyd and Weinhouse found, however, by an isotope-dilution technique (addition of excess unlabeled acetoacetate to the medium) that labeled acetoacetate was produced in amounts that accounted for about 44 per cent of the acetate utilized. The result suggests that, in the oxidation of acetate and of fatty acids that yield a 2-carbon fragment during oxidation, acetoacetate or its immediate precursor, acetoacetyl CoA are produced by these organs. The route of fatty acid oxidation in these organs thus appears to be similar to that in the liver. In the extrahepatic tissues, acetoacetate or acetoacetyl CoA are rapidly utilized, and so do not accumulate and do not enter the blood.

Knoop (1904) demonstrated that fatty acids are oxidized in the body at alternate carbon atoms, and suggested that acetic acid molecules, and a terminal 4-carbon keto-acid, acetoacetic acid, are thereby produced. It was later shown *in vivo* and *in vitro* that oxidation of 1 mole of long-chain fatty acid could yield up to 4 moles of acetoacetate. MacKay proposed that pairs of 2-carbon moieties produced by beta oxidation of fatty acids condensed to form acetoacetate. This

β-oxidation-acetic acid condensation hypothesis was found to fit rather well the results of many experiments employing labeled substrates. Thus Weinhouse, Medes and Floyd found that oxidation of octanoate-1-C^{14} by liver slices resulted in the production of acetoacetate with the isotope distributed approximately equally between carbon atoms 1 and 3. This could only have resulted from random condensation of pairs of 2-carbon moieties arising from β-oxidation of the fatty acid. Subsequent studies have shown that, when carboxyl-labeled fatty acids are utilized, the ratio of the label in the carbonyl : carboxyl carbon varies in a regular manner with chain length, rising from about 0.3 for butyrate to 0.8 for octanoate, and to 1.0 for higher fatty acids. These inequalities have been explained by Lynen, Green, Wakil and others.

Role of Coenzyme A

Recent knowledge of lipid metabolism rests on the discovery of the *coenzyme of acetylation* by Lipmann and his colleagues. They found that a cofactor was required for acetylation of aromatic amines, succeeded in isolating it from liver, and identified pantothenic acid as a component. The factor is known also as *coenzyme A* or CoA. The components of the molecule are: adenine-phos-phoribose - phosphate - phosphate - pantothenic acid-mercaptoethanolamine (fig. 68.8). The SH is the functional group, combining with acyl substances, having the carboxyl group (RCOOH) to form thioesters (RCO—S—CoA). In recognition of this linkage, the factor is designated CoASH by Lynen. Acyl CoA compounds of many fatty acids and other organic acids are produced in tissues. This linkage is a high-energy bond, and is formed at the expense of ATP. The acids are said to be *activated* by combination with CoA, since it is in this form that the fatty acids and their products are oxidized.

Lynen and his colleagues isolated a substance from yeast which performed acetylation without the consumption of ATP, and demonstrated that the substance was acetyl-SCoA. It soon developed that this was, indeed, the long-sought, active two-carbon moiety, or active acetate, involved in the synthesis and the degradation of fatty acids, and that it was utilized also in other processes.

Fatty acid oxidation is a function of mitochondria. The enzymes have been prepared in soluble form and isolated. The mechanism by which fatty acids are oxidized is known as the β-oxidation cycle. There are five steps in the cycle:

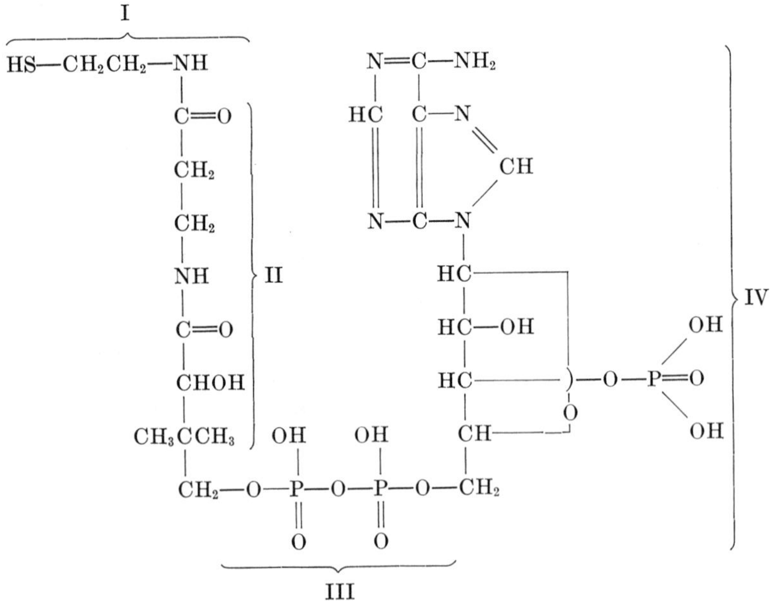

Coenzyme A

Fig. 68.8.

1. Esterification of the fatty acid to a thiol ester of CoA:

$$R \cdot CH_2CH_2COOH + CoASH + ATP$$

$\downarrow$ fatty acid thiokinase

$$R \cdot CH_2CH_2 \cdot CO \cdot SCoA + PPi + AMP$$

2. α-β-dehydrogenation of the CoA ester of the fatty acid:

$$R \cdot CH_2CH_2 \cdot CO \cdot SCoA + FAD$$

$\downarrow$ acyldehydrogenase

$$R \cdot CH{=}CH \cdot CO \cdot SCoA + FADH_2$$

3. Addition of water at the double bond:

$$R \cdot CH{=}CH \cdot CO \cdot SCoA + H_2O$$

$\downarrow$ enoylhydrase

$$R \cdot CHOHCH_2 \cdot CO \cdot SCoA$$

4. Oxidation of the β-hydroxyacyl CoA ester to the corresponding β-ketoacyl CoA derivative:

$$R \cdot CHOHCH_2 \cdot CO \cdot SCoA + DPN^+$$

$\downarrow$ β-hydroxyacyl dehydrogenase

$$R \cdot COCH_2 \cdot CO \cdot SCoA + DPNH + H^+$$

5. Thiolysis by CoASH of the β-ketoacyl CoA ester to acetyl CoA and a new fatty acyl CoA ester:

$$R \cdot COCH_2 \cdot CO \cdot SCoA + COASH$$

$\downarrow$ Thiolase

$$R \cdot CO \cdot SCoA + CH_3CO \cdot SCoA$$

The net result of these five steps is the elimination of a two-carbon moiety in the form of acetyl CoA, and the formation of an acyl CoA that is two carbons shorter than the initial. The cycle is repeated until the pairs of carbon atoms in the fatty acid chain are converted to acetyl CoA.

Further oxidation of long-chain fatty acids occurs by way of the tricarboxylic acid cycle. Acetyl CoA condenses with oxalacetate to form citrate. In this reaction, catalyzed by the condensing enzyme, CoA is liberated for recycling. The acetyl carbons are then oxidized in the Kreb's cycle to carbon dioxide and water. The energy released in this oxidation is utilized, to over 50 per cent, in the esterification of inorganic phosphate by conversion of ADP to ATP. The tricarboxylic acid cycle enzymes are contained chiefly in the mitochondria.

METABOLISM OF ACETYL CoA

Acetyl CoA is utilized in cells in various ways: (1) oxidation by the tricarboxylic acid cycle, described above, (2) fatty acid synthesis, by the malonyl CoA pathway, (3) interconversion of fatty acids, by increasing chain length, (4) acetylations, of choline (in nerve), of aromatic amines, etc., (5) formation of acetoacetyl CoA, (6) synthesis of cholesterol, and (7) synthesis of steroid hormones. Thus, acetyl CoA can be regarded as a focal point in metabolism; a common high-energy substance, produced by the metabolism of fatty acids, amino acids and pyruvate from carbohydrate, and utilized in many ways (fig. 68.9).

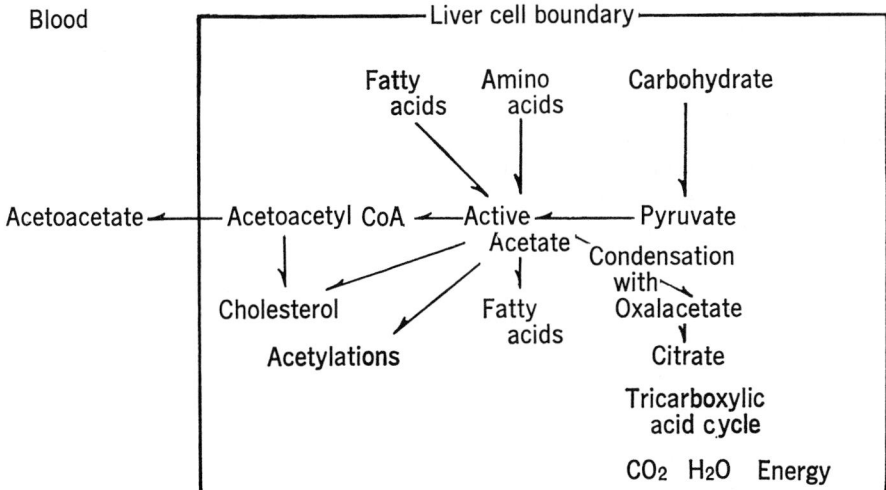

Fig. 68.9. Outline of the routes of formation and of utilization of active acetate (acetyl coenzyme A) by liver cells.

Liver Metabolism

We shall now return to the metabolism of the liver cell. In the production of ketone bodies, acetoacetyl CoA is the precursor. It is produced by the condensation of two acetyl CoA molecules, with liberation of CoASH. Two mechanisms have been proposed to account for the production of free acetoacetic acid from acetoacetyl CoA. One route is direct deacylation, by acetoacetyl CoA deacylase, to CoASH plus acetoacetate, proposed by Stern. The other, shown by Lynen and his colleagues, occurs in two steps: first, condensation of acetoacetyl CoA and acetyl CoA to form β-hydroxy- β-methyl-glutaryl CoA (HMG CoA) and CoASH. Cleavage of this compound yields acetyl CoA and free acetoacetate. The relative importance of these alternative routes in ketone body production by the liver is being debated. HMGCoA is on the path to the synthesis of mevalonic acid, which is an intermediate in the synthesis of cholesterol (fig. 68.14). It is interesting that acetoacetate and cholesterol, both produced by the liver, should have this common precursor.

The distinctive capability of the liver to produce acetoacetate is related to: (1) its ability to accumulate lipids from which the ketone bodies arise, (2) high rate of production of acetyl CoA and of acetoacetyl CoA, (3) high acetoacetyl CoA-deacylase activity, and (4) low activity in formation of acetoacetyl CoA from acetoacetate at the expense of succinyl CoA.

It has long been known that carbohydrate has an antiketogenic effect; in the normal subject when fasting or consuming a high-fat diet, and in combination with insulin in the diabetic subject. The addition of acids of the tricarboxylic acid cycle to preparations from liver tissue *in vitro*, accelerate the oxidation of fatty acids to CO_2, and reduce the production of acetoacetate. The acids that give rise to oxalacetate, e.g. fumarate and succinate, are particularly effective (Lehninger). These "sparkers" of fatty acid oxidation may act by production of oxalacetate, or by promotion of the condensation of acetyl CoA and oxalacetate, or by production of ATP for activation of the fatty acids. Their effect is to "prime" the fatty acid oxidation cycle, which then continues to recycle. These observations explain the antiketogenic action of carbohydrate, since these acids of the tricarboxylic acid cycle are produced by oxidation of carbohydrate.

The active acetate generated in liver cells is utilized in several alternative processes. The relative rates of utilization through the various pathways must be determined by the inherent characteristics of the cells, and by the chemical, hormonal and nervous influences acting upon them. Acetoacetate is only one of the possible products of fatty acid oxidation in the liver, and under most conditions the quantities produced are relatively small.

Intracellular Enzymatic Processes

Electron microscopy of tissue secretions reveals that the cell cytoplasm is traversed by a complex interconnecting system of tubules and vesicles, termed the *endoplasmic reticulum*. The membrane forming the wall of this tubular network, which contains ribonucleic acid (RNA), gives a basophilic staining reaction to dyes. The outer (cytoplasmic) surface of the membrane may be rough or smooth. The rough surface is caused by attached particles, 10–15 mμ diameter, known as Palade granules or *ribosomes*. These granules, which are also found distributed in the cytoplasm, are rich in RNA. The membrane of the endoplasmic reticulum appears to be continuous with the cell membrane, so that the content of the tubules and vesicles of the endoplasmic reticulum is in direct communication with the extracellular fluid. The endoplasmic reticulum also appears to enfold the nucleus, and to form the outer of the two nuclear membranes. Thus, the fluid in the space between the outer and inner nuclear membranes is continuous with that in the tubules and cavities of the reticulum. The nuclear envelope is also penetrated by pores, giving direct access from the nucleoplasm to the cytoplasm. Many specialized membranes of the cell, such as those surrounding the nucleus, the Golgi spaces, the plasma (outer) membrane, and the various secretory and storage vesicles, therefore appear to be parts of one endoplasmic reticulum system. The membranes divide the cell into two compartments: one inside, containing the cytoplasm, mitochondria, ribosomes and various cellular inclusions, and a space outside, containing excretory or secretory or pinocytotic material, and also the nucleus enclosed in its inner membrane.

The *mitochondria* are organized bodies within the cytoplasm. They vary greatly in size from tissue to tissue, from 200 to 500 mμ in diameter, and from 300 up to 5000 mμ in length. The inner membrane is folded into *cristae*, which protrude into the chamber of the mitochondrion.

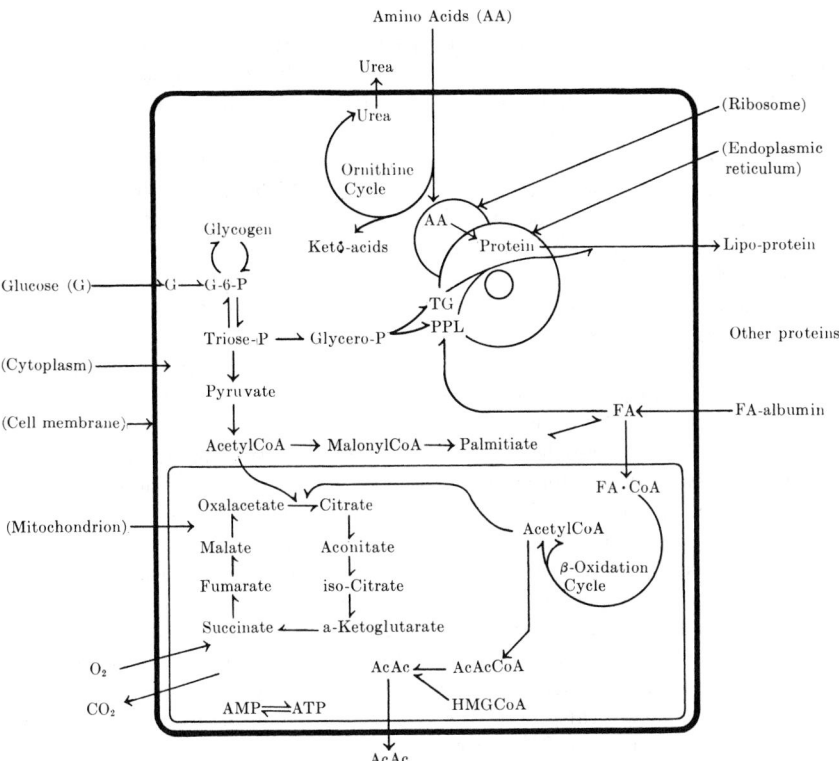

FIG. 68.10. Schematic representation of lipid metabolism, and related processes of carbohydrate and of amino acid metabolism, in a parenchymal cell of the liver. The drawing in only roughly indicative of the structures, in order to simplify. The nucleus and ribosomal particles in the cytoplasm are omitted, and the endoplasmic reticulum is indicated by a cross-section of a single tubule. The major sites of enzymatic activities are shown. Abbreviations are: AA, amino acids; FA, long-chain fatty acids; AcAc, acetoacetic acid; HMGCoA, hydroxymethylglutaric acid-CoA; AMP, adenosine monophosphate; ATP, adenosine triphosphate; LP, lipoproteins; PPL, phospholipids; TG, triglycerides; P, phosphate.

By techniques of fragmentation of cells, and differential centrifugation, cell components have been separated into nuclear, mitochondrial, microsomal and cytoplasmic fractions. The microsomes of tissue homogenates are chiefly fragments of the endoplasmic reticulum. It can be appreciated readily that it is difficult to obtain good separation of these fractions, and to minimize the transfer of components of one fraction to another. Despite these difficulties and uncertainties, a picture of the activities of cell components is emerging.

The distribution of the enzymatic activities involved in the metabolism of lipid, and the associated processes of carbohydrate and amino acid metabolism in the parenchymal cell of the liver, are indicated schematically in fig. 68.10. The cytoplasmic fraction contains the enzymatic activities associated with the Embden-Meyerhof cycle and the pentose phosphate cycle, whereby glucose-6-phosphate is converted to triosephosphates, to glycerophosphate and to pyruvate.

This fraction also contains the enzymatic activities for the synthesis of glycogen and for its conversion to glucose. The enzyme system for the synthesis of palmitate from acetyl CoA derived from pyruvate is contained chiefly in this fraction. These activities are, therefore, represented as occurring in the cytoplasm of the cell. The enzyme that produces glucose from glucose-6-phosphate, a phosphatase, is associated, however, with microsomes.

Although some of the individual enzymatic activities of the tricarboxylic acid cycle are found in the cell cytoplasm, all of these enzymes are concentrated chiefly in the mitochondria. The mitochondria also contain the enzymes of: (1) the cytochrome oxidases or electron transport system, (2) oxidative phosphorylation, (3) activation of fatty acids, by formation of their acyl CoA derivatives, (4) the fatty acid oxidation cycle, (5) acetoacetyl CoA production, (6) acetoacetate production, (7) interconversion of acetoacetate and β-hydroxy-butyrate, and (8) interconversion of fatty acids by lengthening or reducing chain-length.

The mitochondria have been likened to a "power house." Here the oxidative reactions that yield the major amounts of energy occur, with the transport of oxygen through the cytochromes and coenzyme Q (ubiquinone), and the production of carbon dioxide and water. Here also occurs oxidative phosphorylation, whereby the energy released by oxidation is transferred by means of ATP and other coenzymes, to specific reactions requiring high chemical energy input. The ATP generated by oxidative phosphorylation is also made available for reactions in other parts of the cell. Examples of such endergonic reactions are: activation of fatty acids by formation of acetyl CoA compounds, phosphorylation of glucose, fatty acid synthesis from CoA, cholesterol synthesis and phospholipid synthesis.

The endoplasmic reticulum with attached ribosomes appears to be the final site of synthesis of cellular protein, and of those proteins that are secreted. The processes of protein synthesis, and of the ornithine cycle, are not indicated in relation to cell components in this diagram. The microsomes also possess enzyme activities for activation of fatty acids (fatty acid kinase), for production of phosphatidic acids, and for synthesis of triglycerides and of phospholipids. In cholesterol synthesis, the precursor, hydroxymethylglutarate, is produced by mitochondrial fractions, but the subsequent steps can be effected by microsomal and cytoplasmic fractions. In view of this association of protein synthesis, esterification of fatty acids, and cholesterol synthesis, lipoprotein synthesis is represented as a microsomal function.

Blood Plasma Lipids

The chylomicrons, ranging in diameter from about 0.2 to 1 μ are the largest lipid-bearing particles in blood plasma. The β-lipoproteins, α-lipoproteins and free fatty acid-albumin complexes follow in order of decreasing size. All lipid in plasma, whether esterified or non-esterified, is associated with protein in some form of binding. In the chylomicrons, the proportion of lipid to protein is very high, and this proportion decreases as the particle size of the lipoproteins decreases.

Chylomicrons and lipoproteins present a graded series, or spectrum of particles of different sizes. As it is not feasible to isolate and characterize single entities, the particles are classified, between certain convenient but arbitrary limits, according to their physical properties, such as particle size, density, electrophoretic mobility, and solubility. The particles may also be classified by their chemical properties, such as the proportion of total lipid to protein, the proportions of the constituent lipids and the nature of the protein carrier (Putnam, Gurd).

The most widely used procedure for the separation of lipoprotein types is by flotation in fluid mediums of known density under high gravitational fields in the ultracentrifuge. The density of each lipoprotein reflects the densities of the components of which it is composed, lipids being of lower density (0.92–1.06) than peptides (1.35). The rate of flotation of lipoprotein in a medium of higher density, or of sedimentation in a medium of lower density, is determined by the difference in density between particle and the medium, and the mass, and the shape of the particle. For ultracentrifugal analysis, the density is usually adjusted to 1.063 at 26° C. The low density β-lipoproteins rise at various rates under high centrifugal force, while the higher density α-lipoproteins settle.

The characteristics of the lipoproteins and chylomicrons in sera from normal male subjects, determined by such methods, and by analysis of the lipoprotein fractions, are shown in table 68.5. The β-lipoproteins have larger particle size, lower density, higher proportion of total lipid to protein, lesser solubility, higher optical density in serum, and in the lipid fraction, a higher proportion of triglycerides to phospholipids and cholesterol than α-lipoproteins. In a single β-lipoprotein particle, there may be 1000–2000 lipid molecules per molecule of protein, so that only certain of the lipid molecules may be in direct contact with protein. The nature of the binding or attractive forces between lipid and protein are not fully understood. In the smaller, soluble lipoproteins, the binding forces may be stronger and more specific than in the larger aggregates. The chylomicrons are considered to have a central oil droplet surrounded by a film of protein oriented at the oil-water interface.

Following the absorption of a meal rich in fat (2–3 hours after ingestion), the serum may appear opalescent, or even milky and opaque due to chylomicrons and β-lipoproteins poured into the blood by the lymph stream from the intestine. An index of the degree of this alimentary lipemia can be obtained from the optical density of the plasma or serum, or the number of particles

TABLE 68.5

Characteristics and composition of major lipoproteins of human plasma

	Chylomicrons	Lipoproteins			
Densities, g/ml		0.98	1.035	1.09	1.14
Approx. S_f class	>400	~10–400	~3–9		
Concentration in plasma, mg./ml	100–250	130–200	210–400	50–130	290–400
Components	**Per Cent**				
Peptide	2	9	21	33	57
Triglyceride	83	50	10	8	5
Phospholipid	7	18	22	29	21
Cholesterol, free	2	7	8	7	3
Cholesterol, ester	6	15	38	23	14

From F. R. N. Gurd, in *Lipide Chemistry*, D. J. Hanahan. New York, John Wiley and Sons, 1960 p. 260.

estimated by counting under the microscope with dark-field illumination. On centrifuging the plasma or serum, a creamy layer collects at the top of the tube, due to the low density of the lipid, leaving a clear layer of serum beneath. In about 4 hours the opalescence of the serum usually disappears, yet, on analysis, a substantial amount of lipid remains in soluble form (table 68.6). The clearing is associated with decrease in the concentration of lipid, disappearance of chylomicrons, and change in the type of lipoprotein present, i.e. from the β-lipoproteins to the more soluble α-lipoproteins.

The protein associated with the lipid in serum functions as a vehicle: as a dispersing agent for the larger lipoproteins and a solubilizing agent for the smaller particles. Protein appears to be necessary for the transfer of the lipids from cells of origin to the blood or lymph, and also for the transfer from plasma to cells (see also fat absorption and lipotropic factors). It appears that, in the uptake of the esterified lipids, the protein vehicle remains behind in the circulation.

Esterified lipids secreted by the intestinal mucosa and the liver are added to the blood. The liver is the chief site of production of plasma lipoprotein. It is also an important organ in the uptake of lipoprotein (see the section on *the liver and fat metabolism*). Lipids in chylomicrons and lipoproteins are rapidly taken up from the blood plasma by many other tissues, including adipose tissue, skeletal muscle and the heart. The C^{14}-labeled lipids taken up by these cells are metabolized, as shown by the production of labeled carbon dioxide (Fredrickson and Gordon).

TABLE 68.6

Lipid components of plasma in the fasting state (mean values in mg. per 100 ml.) After Boyd.

	Man	Rat	Rabbit	Cockerel
Total lipid	530	230	243	520
Total fatty acid	316	152	169	361
Neutral fat	142	85	105	225
Phospholipid	165	83	78	155
Total cholesterol	152	52	45	100
Free cholesterol	46	21	22	34
Cholesteryl esters*	178	52	39	111

* Bound cholesterol × 1.68.

According to Albrink, the uptake of lipid by tissues is promoted by active carbohydrate metabolism, and is therefore dependent on adequate supplies of carbohydrate and insulin.

When lactescent samples of serum, or particularly of plasma containing heparin as anticoagulant, are allowed to stand at room temperature, they may become translucent, without any change in total lipid concentration. This "clearing reaction" occurs rapidly in the circulating blood on intravenous injection of heparin. The clearing is associated with increase in free fatty acids and glycerol, and change of the large β-lipoprotein particles to smaller and more soluble α-lipoprotein particles. The reaction is catalyzed by an enzyme termed *lipoprotein lipase*. Heparin promotes the activity of the enzyme, and may act as an albumin-bound cofactor in the reaction. It has been suggested that lipoprotein lipase is released from capillary walls, and that it may be a factor in the uptake of esterified lipids by tissues (Korn).

The outstanding physiological importance of the free fatty acids associated with plasma albumin (found by Kendall and by Cohn and his colleagues) was not appreciated until the discoveries of Dole and of Gordon, reported simultaneously in 1956. The free fatty acids (FFA) of the blood, known also as the non-esterified fatty acids (NEFA), or unesterified fatty acids (UFA), are bound to albumin in varying proportion. The site of production of FFA is the adipose tissue cell. By a process of lipolysis, triglycerides stored in the intracellular lipid droplets are hydrolyzed to free fatty acids and glycerol, which pass through the cell and other barriers to enter the blood stream. There the fatty acids combine with albumin to form the FFA, and the glycerol remains in the free state. The composition of the serum FFA will be determined by the composition of the mixture of fatty acids released by adipose tissue, and by that of the fatty acids taken up by active tissues.

The affinity of albumin for fatty acids is quite specific. Albumin has, per mole, about 7 sites of high affinity for long-chain fatty acids, 2 of these being especially strong, and about 20 other sites of indifferent affinity. When bound to albumin, the fatty acids are soluble in water.

In the well-fed subject, and most experimental animals, the concentrations of FFA are usually 0.5 to 0.8 mEq/l. of serum, which is about 5 per cent of the total lipid. The concentrations rise under the following conditions: fasting, diabetes mellitus, hyperthyroidism, emotional disturbance, administration of norepinephrine, epinephrine, adrenocorticotrophic hormone and growth hormone. Elevation of serum FFA, due to accelerated release of FFA from the triglycerides of adipose tissue cells, is caused chiefly by increased lipolysis. An opposing factor, diminishing FFA release, is adequate carbohydrate metabolism due to the action of insulin and carbohydrate. The operation of these factors will be discussed under *adipose tissue metabolism* and *lipid mobilization*.

Adipose Tissue Metabolism

Knowledge of the metabolism, and the important functional roles of adipose tissue as an organ, has greatly expanded during the past decade, as witnessed by the publication: "Adipose Tissue", Section V, "Handbook of Physiology," American Physiological Society, 1965. When adipose tissue is incubated *in vitro* it is responsive to substrates and hormones added to the medium. Much of the information on the metabolism of adipose tissue is derived from *in vitro* studies, but due caution must be exercised in relating the results obtained to the activities *in situ*. It is recognized that free fatty acids in adipose tissue may be attached to different carriers than they are in plasma. The free fatty acids in both situations are termed FFA, however.

UPTAKE OF LIPID. Adipose tissue extracts lipid from the chylomicrons and lipoproteins. The low-density lipoproteins appear to be the most important source; they increase in the blood during periods of plethora. Lipoprotein lipase, situated on, or in, the endothelium of the capillaries in adipose tissue, may be involved in the uptake. Chylomicrons in which triglycerides are labeled with C^{14} are taken up by perfused adipose tissue; about one-third of the triglycerides enter the tissue without prior hydrolysis, while two-thirds are hydrolysed (Rodbell and Scow).

Free fatty acids labeled with C^{14} are also taken up by adipose tissue *in vitro*, and are chiefly esterified to triglycerides. A small amount of the fatty acid taken up is oxidized to carbon dioxide, more in the tissue of fasted than of fed rats. The uptake of fatty acids, and their incorporation into triglycerides, is increased by glucose and insulin *in vitro*. It appears that the uptake of FFA by adipose tissue *in situ* is not quantitatively important. In most conditions which increase FFA concentrations in the blood, e.g. fasting and diabetes, there is increased lipolysis of triglycerides, increased FFA concentration in adipose tissue, net release of FFA from the tissue, and decreased fatty acid synthesis.

GLUCOSE UPTAKE AND METABOLISM. Adipose tissue, both *in vivo* and *in vitro*, takes up glucose, which is phosphorylated to glucose-6-phosphate. This is probably a one-way process in adipose tissue, since glucose-6-phosphatase activity could not be detected in it. Within the tissue, glucose is utilized in various ways including: (1) formation of glycogen, (2) glycolysis via the Embden-Meyerhof pathway and, also (3) by the pentose cycle, (4) production of glycerophosphate, (5) synthesis of fatty acids by a process similar to that revealed by Wakil in liver, and (6) oxidation by the tricarboxylic acid cycle. Cahill and his colleagues suggest that the pentose cycle is probably important as a means of generating TPNH, which is required for the enzymatic synthesis of fatty acids. The production of α-glycerophosphate is important, as it is required for the esterification of fatty acids (arising from lipolysis, uptake or synthesis) to triglycerides. For esterification, activation of the fatty acids to their acyl CoA forms is required. Oxidation of glucose is important also in fatty acid synthesis and esterification, since both of these processes require energy, supplied by ATP. Presumably, the palmitic acid produced by synthesis via the malonyl CoA path is converted in part to other fatty acids, to give the mixed triglycerides characteristic of adipose tissue. Labeled glucose administered to mice is incorporated into adipose tissue triglycerides at rates which led Favarger to conclude that adipose tissue is quantitatively the most important of the body organs in lipid synthesis.

EFFECTS OF INSULIN. *In vitro* studies of adipose tissue from fasted rats, and from diabetic rats, have shown that glucose uptake, fatty acid synthesis and glucose oxidation are much less than in that from normal fed rats. Administration of insulin to the diabetic animals restores these activities to normal. Insulin stimulates, in adipose tissue, the uptake of glucose, the synthesis of fatty acids from glucose, the oxidation of glucose to carbon dioxide, the production of glycerophosphate, and the esterification of fatty acids. Insulin also appears to activate the pentose cycle to a greater extent than the Embden-Meyerhof pathway. Adipose tissue *in vitro*, is remarkably sensitive to insulin, showing measurable responses to concentrations of the hormone that are normally present in blood. Adipose tissue *in vitro* is used in the assay of insulin-like activity in the blood.

RELEASE OF FREE FATTY ACIDS. In adipose tissue, lipolysis of triglycerides occurs, with the production of glycerol and FFA. The production of mono- and diglycerides in adipose tissue, in which the rate of lipolysis is high, has also been observed. Glycerol is not utilized in adipose tissue, and passes into the blood, or into the fluid bathing the tissue *in vitro*. The amount of glycerol produced is an index of lipolysis. The FFA are reesterified to triglycerides in adipose tissue or pass through the tissue membranes to the blood plasma, and are carried as free fatty acid-albumin complexes. These processes of breakdown and reformation of triglycerides appear to be continuous in adipose tissue, but are greatly influenced by many factors.

CONTROL OF ADIPOSE TISSUE METABOLISM. Under conditions that increase the mobilization of lipid in animals, including fasting, diabetes and the administration of pituitary adipokinetic hormones (ACTH, TSH and growth hormone) and of catecholamines, the amounts of FFA in adipose tissue and in the plasma increase markedly, and the glycerol levels also rise. When adipose tissue from these animals is incubated *in vitro*, the rate of release of FFA to the medium, and the accumulation of FFA in the tissue, are greater than in tissue from normal fed animals. Lipolysis in isolated adipose tissue is directly stimulated by the addition of ACTH, TSH, norepinephrine, epinephrine and glucagon, as is indicated by increased amounts of FFA and glycerol in the tissue, and in the medium in which it is incubated. The catecholamines and ACTH increase lipolysis and reesterification simultaneously, with the rate of lipolysis predominating. Growth hormone is much less active in stimulating lipolysis in adipose tissue *in vitro*. When it is injected in animals, it causes a transient decrease in plasma FFA, within 2 hours, followed by a rise above normal.

A fat-mobilizing (adipokinetic) factor, a peptide, occurs in the urine of fasting subjects and experimental animals. It also increases lipolysis in adipose tissue *in vitro*, resembling ACTH in its effects. Its absence from hypophysectomized animals indicates that it may be of pituitary origin, but it differs in chemical characteristics from ACTH.

Insulin causes an immediate decrease in plasma FFA in normal subjects, and in diabetic patients the effect is especially pronounced. It is due to reduction in the rate of release of FFA from adipose tissue. Insulin acts directly on adipose tissue, causing reduction in the rate of release of FFA by the tissue *in vitro*. The effect is enhanced by the addition of glucose. Insulin evidently reduces FFA in the tissue, and the medium, by increasing the rate of reesterification of FFA, through its effects on carbohydrate metabolism. There are indications that it may also inhibit lipolysis (Ball).

Plasma albumin, in addition to its function as an acceptor protein for the transport of FFA in the blood, is necessary for the release of FFA from adipose tissue. Other proteins, not of plasma origin, are ineffective in promoting release. The observation that, in patients with hypoalbuminemia, the rise in plasma FFA in response to the injection of epinephrine is less than in the normal patient, supports other evidence that albumin levels influence fat mobilization (Bogdonoff).

An influence of sympathetic nerves on fat mobilization is indicated by the observations that, in denervated adipose tissue, the loss of lipid in fat mobilization is reduced, and that adrenergic blocking agents inhibit the release of

FFA from adipose tissue (Schotz and Page). Thus, it is obvious, that a number of factors influence the activities of adipose tissue.

The Liver and Fat Metabolism

The importance of the liver in various aspects of fat metabolism has been described above. The roles of the organ in the body will now be outlined.

UPTAKE OF FREE FATTY ACIDS. The liver rapidly assimilates FFA from the blood plasma, as shown by the incorporation of isotopic FFA into glycerides and phospholipids of the organ. The rate of uptake is correlated with the concentration of FFA in plasma. Under conditions that increase plasma FFA due to mobilization of lipid from the depots, lipid may accumulate in the liver, indicating that its rate of uptake of FFA is high as compared to other organs.

FATTY ACID SYNTHESIS. The liver is an important site for the synthesis of fatty acids from glucose, pyruvate, acetate and other precursors. The malonyl CoA pathway for synthesis of palmitate, described above, appears to be the chief route. The fatty acids synthesized are found in the glycerides and phospholipids.

SYNTHESIS OF TRIGLYCERIDES AND PHOSPHOLIPIDS. FFA taken up by the liver are rapidly incorporated into glycerides and phospholipids, indicating that esterification processes in the organ are highly active. Labeled FFA taken up appear in a few minutes, first in the glycerides of the microsome fraction of liver cells, then in the mitochondrial fraction, then they may accumulate in intracellular droplets (Stein and Shapiro).

The rate of turnover of phospholipids, estimated by the intravenous administration of isotopic phosphate, is high in the liver in comparison to other organs. The rates of incorporation of N^{15}-labeled choline, and of C^{14}-labeled fatty acids into phospholipids, are also relatively high in the liver. High rates of turnover, under the experimental conditions, indicate that the rate of phospholipid synthesis is high and, in the steady state, is balanced by equally high rates of removal (by transformation within the organ or transfer from the organ). The liver is also an important site of cholesterol synthesis.

LIPOPROTEIN SYNTHESIS AND SECRETION. On the administration of P^{32}-labeled sodium phosphate to dogs, the isotope appears in the phospholipids of the blood plasma (Chaikoff). Also, shortly after intravenous administration of C^{14}-labeled free fatty acids (Borgström and

others), both the glycerides and phospholipids of the plasma become labeled. These and other studies have shown that the liver is the chief organ involved in the production of the esterified blood lipids, since the labeling of the plasma lipid was greatly diminished by obstruction of blood supply to the liver or by hepatectomy. Because these lipids are present as lipoproteins in plasma, it follows that the liver is the principal organ for the production of lipoproteins in the postabsorptive state. Further investigations have shown that lipoprotein particles are released by the perfused liver, and by liver slices. It has also been found that, under these conditions, labeled amino acids are incorporated, at relatively high rates, into the protein component of lipoprotein. Thus, the liver synthesizes the lipid and the protein parts of lipoprotein, and secretes lipoprotein into the blood. When labeled fatty acids are administered, the glycerides of the plasma are labeled first and to the greatest extent, followed in order by phospholipids and cholesterol esters. The liver tends to produce low-density lipoproteins at higher rates than it produces high-density lipoproteins.

UPTAKE OF ESTERIFIED LIPID. Labeled phospholipids administered intravenously in dogs are removed rapidly from the plasma by the liver (Chaikoff and colleagues). The rate of removal is greatly reduced by hepatectomy. This combination of release and of uptake of esterified lipid indicates that the liver is of great importance in regulation of plasma lipids. Lipoproteins also appear to pass from the plasma through the liver sinusoids to the lymph, without appreciable alteration, this being a "recycling" process (Morris and Robinson). The esterified lipids of plasma appear to be taken up and utilized at slower rates by the liver than the FFA (Felts and Mayes). The various oxidative processes in the liver involving lipids, and their relations to carbohydrate and amino acid metabolism, are described above.

The liver of the normal animal contains 4 to 8 per cent of total lipid. The average percentage composition of hepatic lipids is roughly, glycerides 45–55, phospholipids about 50, free cholesterol 3 and cholesterol esters 1. Histological and chemical evidence indicate that this lipid is largely bound to tissue proteins. When lipid accumulates in the liver, as a result of dietary deficiency of lipotropic factors, it appears in intracellular droplets, the triglycerides and cholesterol esters increase, but the phospholipids and free cholesterol remain remarkably constant per unit weight of dry fat-free solid. The amount of fat in the liver at any time depends on the following factors: (1) the rates of uptake of lipid as free fatty acids and as esterified fatty acids, (2) the rates of synthesis of lipid from carbohydrates and amino acids, (3) the rate of release of esterified fatty acids as lipoproteins, and (4) the rate of utilization of lipid. In the steady state, i.e. when the amount of lipid remains unchanged, the rate of gain (sum of 1 and 2), is balanced by the rate of loss (sum of 3 and 4), i.e. rate of gain − rate of loss = 0. Increases in the amount of lipid in the liver result from an increase in (1) or (2) or from a decrease in (3) or (4), or a combination of these effects. Some factors that cause accumulation of lipid in the liver are mentioned elsewhere in this chapter. Other conditions that have this effect are: (1) environmental changes—reduced atmospheric pressure, e.g., at high altitudes or elevated temperatures, (2) poisoning by phosphorus, chloroform and other chlorinated compounds, benzol, ketene, phloridzin, or bacterial toxins, and (3) pernicious anemia, yellow fever, and toxemia of pregnancy.

Functional Relations between Organs

Schoenheimer and Rittenberg, using deuterium as a label of fatty acids, demonstrated that the lipids of the body are constantly in a state of flux, i.e. lipid molecules disappear and are replaced by others. The lipids of the tissues may remain fairly constant in amount and kind from day to day, and over longer periods, under ordinary conditions of nutrition and activity. In this *steady state*, the rate of loss or utilization is equalled by the rate of gain or replacement. This lipid homeostasis is achieved by the operation of controlling factors of neural, hormonal and chemical nature. Under other conditions, lipid may be lost or gained by the body or by individual organs. By studying the rates of loss or gain of lipid when experimental conditions are altered, it is possible to obtain information on the nature of this control. Shifts of lipid caused by various conditions are shown schematically in fig. 68.11.

The situation of homeostasis at the end of absorption is represented in fig. 68.11,a. A small amount of glyceride may still be entering the blood from the intestine via the lymph of the thoracic duct, due to absorption of endogenous lipid and the last residue of dietary fat. The liver maintains secretion of lipoprotein. The recycling of lipoprotein-lipid from the blood through the liver is indicated. The adipose tissue and other

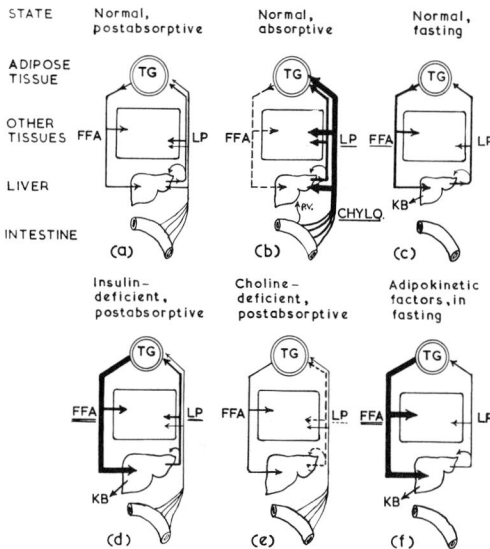

Fig. 68.11. Schematic representation of lipid transfers between organs in various body states and conditions. The organs arranged from the top down are: adipose tissue, "other" tissues, liver and intestine. Transfers of esterified lipids in chylomicrons (chylo.) and lipoproteins (LP) are indicated on the right, and of free fatty acids (FFA) on the left side. Other abbreviations are: TG, triglycerides; KB, ketone bodies; and P.V., portal vein. Increased lipid transfer is indicated by thick lines, and decreased transfer by dotted lines, as compared to the rates in the normal, postabsorptive state.

tissues take up lipoprotein-lipid which may be utilized or deposited. The adipose tissue produces FFA from the stored triglycerides. The FFA of the plasma are taken up by the liver and other tissues, are esterified and stored or oxidized. The system is *open*, in the sense that energy escapes, and the adipose tissue is the source of the lipid utilized.

During absorption (b) the dietary lipids are transported as chylomicrons through lymph to the venous blood. The clearing factor activity decreases the size of these lipid-bearing particles, and promotes their uptake by the tissues. The liver appears to be particularly active in the uptake of chylomicron lipid; after a meal rich in fat the lipid content of the liver may increase. Adipose tissue and other organs also take up chylomicron lipid and lipoprotein lipid secreted by the liver. The metabolism of the carbohydrates and amino acids also absorbed promotes lipid uptake, regulates fatty acid oxidation in the liver by inhibiting ketone body production, and in adipose tissue promotes lipid synthesis and suppresses FFA production.

Mobilization of lipid from body fat depots occurs during a fast. In the initial phase of fasting, the reserves of glycogen are rapidly depleted. In the second phase, endogenous lipid provides about four-fifths of the energy utilized in man, and protein the remainder. In the third phase, after depletion of the utilizable lipid, amino acids are utilized.

A characteristic pattern of alterations in lipid metabolism can be recognized in lipid mobilization, although there are considerable differences between species in the degrees of change. Loss of adipose tissue lipid by the fasting animal indicates utilization of depot fat. Increased rates of lipolysis of triglyceride in adipose tissue and of release of FFA cause a rise in FFA concentration in the blood. The rates of uptake of FFA by other active tissues must increase, due to the preponderant utilization of lipid as a source of energy. The rate of uptake of FFA by the liver, and probably by other tissues also is related to the concentration of these substances in the blood. In certain animals, e.g. the mouse, guinea pig and rabbit, lipid accumulates in the liver during a fast coincidently with the loss of depot lipid. In primates, including man, and to a lesser extent in the dog and rodents, ketonemia and ketonuria develop. The rise in blood ketone bodies is associated with increased production of these substances by the liver. Ketone body utilization by extrahepatic tissues increases in the dog during a fast. The alterations in serum lipids are variable; it has been reported that when previously well-nourished dogs are fasted the serum lipids increase, but in other experiments reduction has been observed under these conditions. The maintenance of lipoprotein levels in serum indicates that these substances are being continuously secreted by the liver and utilized by the tissues. The interaction of adipose tissue and liver roles in the fasting animal thus provides a "mixed diet" of free and esterified fatty acids for the active tissues. The lipid-mobilizing factor may appear in the urine of man and animals during starvation.

Certain fractions of the anterior pituitary gland intensify the mobilization of lipid in fasting animals (rats, mice and guinea pigs). Triglycerides are the chief form of lipid involved in this mobilization from the depots and deposition in the liver. This activity is possessed by the growth, adrenocorticotrophic and thyrotrophic hormones, and possibly more specific hormones of the adenohypophysis, and by the fat-mobilizing factor of urine, fig. 68.11(f). Treatment of fasting animals with these factors causes: (1) over-all increase in utilization of fat in the body, with depletion of fat reserves, (2) increase in serum FFA, associated with accelerated release of FFA from adipose tissue, (3) rapid and massive accumulation of fat in the liver, due to deposition of fat from the depots, (4) ketonemia and ketonuria, and (5) increased retention of nitrogen and glycogen in the liver. The protein- and glycogen-sparing effects of anterior pituitary extract in fasting animals appears to be due to increased utilization of lipid. Liver tissue of pituitary-treated rats produces acetoacetate, and utilizes oxygen *in vitro* at greatly increased rates. These effects on liver metabolism are due to increased concentration of substrate (lipid) and to stimulation of the oxidative activity of liver tissue.

Lipid mobilization, as indicated by increase in liver lipid, is inhibited by *adrenalectomy*. However, administration of ACTH to adrenalectomized rats produces some increase in blood ketone body concentration (Engel). The adipose tissue of adrenalectomized rats release FFA *in vitro* in response to ACTH at a much lesser rate than that of normal animals. Adrenal corticoids usually have little or no significant fat-mobilizing effect in animals, although Jeanrenaud and Renold observed that corticosterone and cortisol increased FFA release by rat adipose tissue *in vitro*. From these and other results, two effects of adrenal cortical activity on lipid mobilization have been postulated, one, a "permissive effect", enabling the tissues to respond to fat-mobilizing factors, the other, a direct lipolytic effect. In favor of the permissive function, is the observation of Shafrir and Steinberg that epinephrine does not increase serum FFA in adrenalectomized dogs, but that the response can be restored by prior treatment with cortisone. Thyroidectomy causes inhibition and loss of response to adipokinetic factors, and thyroid treatment restores the response.

Deficiency or absence of insulin. In diabetes mellitus and in experimental diabetes in depancreatized dogs, a number of characteristic changes are observed, fig. 68.11(d): (1) wastage of body tissues (depletion of carbohydrate, fat and protein reserves), (2) increased rate of release of FFA from adipose tissue, (3) marked increase in serum FFA concentrations, (4) rapid and massive accumulation of lipid in the liver, with increase in the size and friability of the organ (lipid also accumulates, but to a lesser extent, in the kidney and heart), (5) great increase in ketone bodies in blood and in the amounts excreted in the urine, and (6) inhibition of glucose utilization and lipid synthesis. Thus, deficiency of insulin causes mobilization of lipid in overwhelming amounts from adipose tissues, deposition and accumulation of lipid in liver and kidney, and increases utilization of lipid. In diabetes mellitus the plasma lipoproteins, particularly the low-density types, are greatly increased. In the postabsorptive state, the serum is normally clear, but in the uncontrolled diabetic it is usually lactescent. Even in well-controlled diabetic patients, the serum lipoprotein concentrations are usually above normal (Dole). It appears that hyperlipidemia in diabetes may be due to both increased production and to decreased uptake of lipoprotein.

The administration of insulin prevents or reverses all these alterations found in experimental diabetes and in diabetes mellitus. The evidence available is in agreement with the suggestion of Winegrad and Renold that "adipose tissue is a major anatomical site of insulin action."

The pituitary and adrenal glands may be involved in producing these effects of insulin deficiency. The ketosis and accumulation of fat in the liver of the depancreatized dog, and the extent of the glycosuria, are diminished by hypophysectomy (Houssay and Biasotti). Similar effects are produced in depancreatized animals by adrenalectomy (Long and Lukens).

In the diabetes induced in dogs during the daily administration of growth hormone, there occurs a massive accumulation of lipid in the liver, with enlargement and increased friability of the organ. The serum FFA concentration rises rapidly, then ketonemia and serum lipoprotein rise occurs.

In *deficiency of lipotropic factors*, there occurs an early fall in serum phospholipid, which appears to be associated with a decreased rate of production of lipoprotein by the liver, leading to accumulation of fat in the organ, fig. 68.11(e).

Ketosis

The physiological significance of the ketone bodies is not yet clear. Under ordinary conditions their contribution to total metabolism appears to be small or insignificant. In dogs, during 2 to 5 days of fasting, Crandall *et al.* estimate that the amounts of ketone bodies produced by the liver would account for variable proportions of the total heat production, ranging from 17 to 50%. It has been suggested that the liver may provide, by this means, a readily-usable substrate for oxidation by extrahepatic tissues when supplies of carbohydrate are deficient (MacKay). The FFA and ketone bodies are raised concurrently in blood, but their relative rates of uptake and oxidation under such conditions are not known. In view of the adverse effects of ketosis, it is also possible to regard the ketone bodies as metabolites produced under conditions of metabolic stress, involving increased fatty acid oxidation during deficient carbohydrate oxidation. In the high concentrations which they reach in fasting, etc., these products of incomplete metabolism of fatty acids are injurious.

Ketosis (accumulation of ketone bodies in the blood, and excretion of unusually large quantities) in man, may be induced by fasting and by high intake of fat. It occurs in diabetes mellitus, fevers, toxemia of pregnancy and certain forms of glycogen-storage disease. Ketosis can be produced experimentally by: fasting, the oral administration of fatty acid esters, high-fat diets in pregnant rats, fasting in pregnant guinea pigs, pancreatectomy and other means of producing insulin-deficiency, the injection of phlorhizin in fasting animals, and the administration of anterior pituitary extracts or hormones, including growth hormone and ACTH. In ruminants, ketosis may occur during pregnancy and lactation. This condition is associated with low blood sugar levels, and underfeeding.

Other factors that influence the occurrence and intensity of ketosis are: *species* (ketosis due to fasting is most marked in man and apes), *age* (ketosis is induced more rapidly in children than in adults during a fast; a similar effect of age is found in experimental animals), *sex* (in women, fasting ketosis is more intense than in men; a similar sex difference in the rat is abolished by ovariectomy).

Metabolic adaptation to high fat diets appears to occur in man with prolonged intake of such diets. In the Eskimo, the consumption of food high in fat and protein is not associated with ketosis. In subjects whose diet was voluntarily limited to meats and fat, a chronic ketonemia occurred, but diminished after several months. Carbohydrates have a marked effect in diminishing or preventing ketosis. The antiketogenic effect of carbohydrate has been demonstrated in subjects who are fasting or whose diet is high in fat. Protein also has an antiketogenic effect, much less than that of carbohydrate.

HORMONAL FACTORS. Pancreatectomy results in ketosis, as well as hyperglycemia (von Mering and Minkowski, 1889). Insulin prevents ketosis in depancreatized dogs (Banting, Best and their colleagues, 1922). Following pancreatectomy in the rat, a rise in blood sugar is first observed; within 2 hours blood ketone bodies also increase. The administration of insulin in the diabetic animal causes a prompt fall in blood sugar and FFA, and shortly thereafter a marked decrease in ketone bodies. In diabetes mellitus, it is possible to prevent ketosis and to maintain blood ketone bodies at normal level by the well-controlled administration of insulin and proper regimen. Inadequate insulin dosage results in hyperglycemia and ketonemia. Administration of insulin with carbohydrate, together with other measures, has a profound effect in restoring metabolism toward normal in patients with diabetic ketosis.

Hypophysectomy prevents ketosis and greatly diminishes accumulation of fat in the liver in the depancreatized dog (Houssay). The same effects are produced by adrenalectomy in the depancreatized animal (Long and Lukens). These effects are evidently related to reduced mobilization of FFA from adipose tissue. In the fasting animal, the administration of certain fat-mobilizing anterior pituitary extracts, growth hormone, ACTH and thyroid-stimulating hormone induce ketonemia, which can be maintained, with ketonuria, by repeated injections. The ketogenic effects of growth hormone and ACTH may be diminished by adrenalectomy in the rat, but not eliminated (Engel).

An imbalance between the rate of ketone body released by the liver and the rate of utilization by other tissues results in ketosis. Perfusion of the liver, studies on liver slices, and measurement of the arterial-venous differences in ketone body concentrations across the liver, show that overproduction of ketone bodies occurs in the fasting state after pancreatectomy, and following the administration of anterior pituitary extract and growth hormone. In the depancreatized dog, hepatectomy results in rapid disappearance of ketone bodies from the blood. While ketosis is usually due to overproduction of ketone bodies by the liver, in the severely diabetic state, underutilization may also be a factor.

Acetoacetic and β-hydroxybutyric acids are nonvolatile and moderately strong acids. In ketosis, the plasma bicarbonate concentration may fall from the normal range of 26–32 mEq/l. to 20–10 mEq/l., due to binding of base by these acids. These acids are excreted by the kidney, and tend to carry base out of the body with them. Renal compensation involves the excretion of an acid urine, so that the acids are excreted partly in the free form. The formation of ammonia by the kidney spares an equivalent amount of base that would be bound to the acids. In diabetic acidosis, the urine volume is high, which tends to deplete body water and base. The loss of base, water, nitrogen, and energy in ketosis, leads to acidosis and dehydration. Diabetic coma is a critical emergency that must be treated promptly if the patient is to be rescued. The high concentrations of ketone bodies in the blood (100 to 300 mg. per 100 ml.) and tissues, probably contribute to the severe metabolic upset to an important degree.

The Lipotropic Factors

Choline and its dietary precursors, betaine and methionine, are in the rations of animals so as to prevent the accumulation of excessive amounts of fat in the liver (fig. 68.12). Choline, a quaternary ammonium base:

$$(CH_3)_3N\!\!-\!\!CH_2\cdot CH_2OH,$$
$$\underset{\textstyle OH}{|}$$

occurs widely distributed in nature although it is rarely found in the free condition in more than traces. It was first isolated (from bile) by Strecker in 1849 and has long been known as a constituent of lecithin and sphingomyelin. Lean meats (muscle) contain about 100 mg. choline per 100 grams of fresh meat. Kidney contains 200 to 300 mg., brain 350 to 450 mg., liver from 450 to 600 mg., fish muscle 50 to 80 mg., whole eggs 350 to 700 mg.; egg yolk about 1400 to 1700 mg., whole wheat 50 to 100 mg., wheat germ 350 to 400 mg., oats, barley, rye, corn and rice contain about 60 to 100 mg., yeast (brewer's dried) 240 to 360 mg. per 100 g. Vegetables, as a group, are low in choline and fruits are very low. Edible fats, as obtained commercially, are almost free from choline.

The other naturally occurring substances which possess lipotropic activity are betaine (the internally neutralized acid formed by oxidizing the primary alcohol group of choline), methionine and β-propiothetin. They have been shown to possess labile methyl groups and it is believed that they possess lipotropic activity by acting as precursors of choline. Vitamin B_{12} and folic acid, which are important in hematopoiesis, are also able under some conditions to produce a lipotropic effect. The relations between these two substances in lipotropic phenomena are not yet clearly understood but vitamin B_{12} appears to be concerned in the biosynthesis of

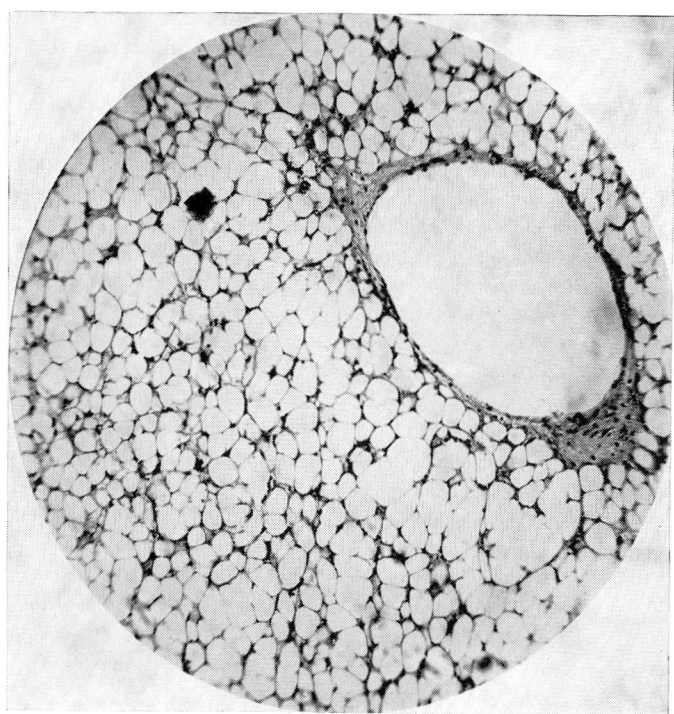

FIG. 68.12 Section from liver of depancreatized dog fed a diet low in choline. Ether-soluble material over 60 per cent of wet weight. ×200. (From Best, Huntsman and Young.)

labile methyl groups and folic acid in transmethylation reactions or in the synthesis of some other part of the choline molecule. Inositol exerts a limited lipotropic effect in fat-free diets but this effect is minimized when any fat is in the food. The crude pancreatic extract which has been referred to as "lipocaic" was at one time thought to possess some unique lipotropic influence since it was believed to be free from choline. While it may contain only traces of free choline, its content of bound choline sometimes makes it one of the richest known sources of this base. Methionine and vitamin B$_{12}$ are also present in this extract, and if proteolytic enzymes are present they may make methionine available from the dietary protein (Fig. 68.12).

In 1924 Allan, Bowie, Macleod and Robinson in Toronto, and Fisher in Chicago, noted that large fatty livers developed in depancreatized dogs maintained for a long time with insulin. Inclusion of raw beef pancreas in the diet prevented this fatty change. Hershey and Soskin noted a similar protective effect with crude egg lecithin. In 1932 Best, Hershey and Huntsman found that they could produce fatty livers in rats by dietary means in about three weeks, as contrasted with a period of more than six months required in the depancreatized dog. With this more rapid method of investigation, they quickly identified choline as the active constituent in the lecithin molecule. Betaine was found to exert a similar effect. It was soon discovered that casein and certain other proteins possess lipotropic activity. This activity of protein was largely accounted for in 1937, when Tucker and Eckstein discovered the lipotropic property of methionine. It exerts a lipotropic effect by transferring its methyl group to ethanolamine, thus effecting the biosynthesis of choline (du Vigneaud). When choline, betaine or methionine labelled in the methyl group with deuterium were fed singly to rats, the choline of tissue phospholipids, the methionine of tissue proteins and urinary creatinine were all found to contain labelled methyl groups. The enzymatic process involved is known as transmethylation and the particular groups concerned are said to be labile methyl groups. Not all methyl groups are labile; a distinction must be made between the processes of *de*methylation and *trans*methylation since *de*methylation does not necessarily give rise to a labile methyl group (e.g., sarcosine).

The original view, that the animal body is unable to synthesize methyl groups, had to be modified when it was found that rats could survive and grow slowly under certain dietary conditions on rations devoid of any preformed methyl groups (Bennett, Medes and Toennies). Later, the importance of vitamin B_{12} and of folic acid in the biosynthesis of methyl groups and in the metabolism of the "one carbon fragment" became apparent.

A labile methyl group is not necessary for lipotropic action. Tracer studies have indicated that the methyl groups of choline are not labile and *only become so after oxidation* to betaine. It had been recognized previously that arsenocholine (Welch), triethylcholine (Channon, McArthur), and sulfocholine (du Vigneaud) which contain *no labile methyl groups* exert a lipotropic effect. When fed, they are incorporated into liver phospholipids as the intact molecule. These observations suggest that the lipotropic action of choline is exerted by the intact molecule and not by virtue of its methyl groups. Dietary components with labile methyl groups exert their lipotropic effect by favoring biosynthesis of choline.

The physiological test for a labile methyl group is to feed the compound containing the methyl group to a rat being fed a synthetic diet complete in every sense, except that methionine is replaced by homocystine. If growth occurs, which can only happen when methionine is formed, transfer (or synthesis) of methyl groups must have taken place.

When the lipotropic factors[2] are not available in the diet, large amounts of fat accumulate in the liver. In young animals hemorrhagic lesions are seen in the kidneys and other tissues (Griffith and Wade), and these may produce death. The antilipotropic factor cholesterol aggravates the liver and kidney changes while choline, betaine and methionine prevent their development. When young rats are subjected for only five days to a diet deficient in choline and its

[2] The term lipotropic was originally used to describe the action of choline which prevented the deposition of, or accelerated the rate of removal of fat from the liver. It now has a somewhat broader meaning and is used to describe the action of choline and its precursors methionine and betaine on fat deposition in liver and kidney. Only those effects of methionine and betaine which are exerted through formation of choline are included in the term "lipotropic." Substances such as cholesterol which cause a deposition of liver fat are referred to as antilipotropic and hypothetical diets free of lipotropic factors may be described as alipotropic. Cystine, under certain dietary conditions increases the deposition of liver fat and the incidence of hemorrhagic kidneys. This is apparently related to an improvement in the diet; the resulting increased food intake stimulates growth and creates an additional need for the lipotropic factors.

precursors, and are then returned to a full normal diet, a malignant hypertension of renal origin develops, four or five months later, in a considerable proportion of the animals (Hartroft and Best).

In the depancreatized dog, choline has been shown to be one of the active components of beef pancreas which as previously stated prevents the development of fatty livers. The protein of pancreas through its methionine content will presumably also exert a lipotropic effect. Furthermore, the pancreatic enzymes will help to liberate choline and methionine from the phospholipids and protein of the diet. There are thus three pathways by which the minced pancreas, the study of which initiated these investigations, may have contributed the lipotropic agents.

The mechanism by which choline exerts its lipotropic action has not yet been elucidated. Choline stimulates the oxidation of fatty acids by liver slices under certain conditions (Artom), but this effect does not account satisfactorily for lipotropic phenomena.

Recent work suggests that choline deficiency in animals results in defective transport of fatty acids from the liver. Choline deficiency in the rat produces, within 1 day, a marked fall in plasma phospholipids, which is corrected by restoring choline to the diet. Production of fatty liver in the rat by hypolipotropic diets is associated with decreased secretion of triglycerides by the perfused liver (Haines, Mookerjea and others). Thus accumulation of lipid in the liver in choline deficiency appears to be due, at least in part, to diminished rate of transfer from the liver.

Cirrhosis

Prolonged exposure to certain toxic chemicals, infective agents or to dietary deficiencies which cause fatty livers, may lead eventually to excessive production of fibrous connective tissue in the liver. The liver parenchyma appears to be "strangled" by the bands of connective tissue. The shrunken, distorted liver that results is usually of a peculiar orange-to-brownish color. It is this aspect which Laennec featured in the name *cirrhosis*. The pathogenesis of cirrhosis in rats due to deficiency of choline in the diet was studied by Hartroft and others. Intracellular lipid droplets appear in the central zone of the liver lobule at an early stage of fat accumulation. This change extends outwards to involve all cells, as the lipid droplets increase in number and size. With excessive distension by fat, cells are ruptured and atrophy. The lipid droplets may coalesce to form large extracellular droplets. The stroma is replaced by fibrous connective tissue. By repetition and extension of this process, the fibrous scars extend throughout the liver, including areas around large portal veins. The lesion can be prevented or, in its early stages, cured, by the addition of choline or its precursors to the diet. *Kwashiorkor* is a deficiency disease in infants and children, that is pandemic in many parts of the world. It is primarily caused by severe protein malnutrition. The liver is enlarged and fatty, and later may become cirrhotic. Lipotropic factors have not been found effective in treatment. Excellent results have been obtained by the provision of good protein, e.g., skim milk. The provision of protein supplements from plant sources such as leguminous seeds, oil seeds, nuts, palm kernels and leaf proteins is being studied and shows promise (Scrimshaw).

Alcoholic cirrhosis is often possibly of dietary rather than toxic origin. Excessive consumption of alcohol supplies sufficient calories to reduce seriously the intake of protective foods that would provide the proteins, vitamins and minerals necessary for maintenance. The toxic effects of alcohol in large doses in various tissues cannot be doubted, however.

Cholesterol

Chemical Nature

Cholesterol is a white, waxy, solid found associated with fats, but is chemically different from them. The carbon ring structure characteristic of sterols is that of the 17-carbon cyclopentanophenanthrene (fig. 68.13). Cholesterol, the principal sterol of animal tissues, has a hydroxyl group at C_3, an unsaturated bond at C_5-C_6, two methyl groups at C_{10} and C_{13}, and an 8-carbon paraffin side-chain attached to C_{17}. Cholesterol occurs both free, and combined with fatty acids by ester linkage at the hydroxyl group. Cholesterol in ester form is often referred to as

"bound." Cholesterol esters are normally rich (40 to 50 per cent of the total) in linoleic acid.

Steroids closely related to cholesterol, and accompanying it in tissues, include: 7-dehydrocholesterol, which occurs in skin and can be converted by ultraviolet radiation to vitamin D_3, dihydrocholesterol, the bile acids, hormones of the adrenal cortex and of the sex glands.

Distribution

Cholesterol is found in all tissues and fluids of the body. The free cholesterol content of a particular tissue is characteristic, and normally remains relatively constant; the esters vary in amount between tissues, and with changes in dietary, hormonal and other factors. The brain and suprarenal glands are richest in cholesterol. In the former, almost all is in the free form, and in the latter, about 90 per cent is in the form of esters. In the corpuscles of human blood it is chiefly in the free state, but in plasma only about one-third is free (table 68.7). In most other tissues there is more free than bound cholesterol. The average total cholesterol contents of normal tissues of the rabbit and man are shown in table 68.7.

Absorption, Transport and Excretion

Cholesterol of the diet is contained chiefly in milk and milk products, eggs and meats. The dietary intake varies considerably, depending on the kinds of food. Keys and his colleagues estimate this to be 2 to 3 g. weekly. In a continuing study of the relationship of diet to heart and vascular disease, residents of Framingham, Massachusetts, 30 to 59 years of age, are being routinely examined. Estimates of mean daily intakes for men were 3160 Calories and 700 mg. of cholesterol, and for women were 2140 Calories and 490 mg. of cholesterol. About 40% of the total calories were derived from fat, of which 72 per cent and 69 per cent, respectively, were from animal sources (Kagan *et al.* 1962).

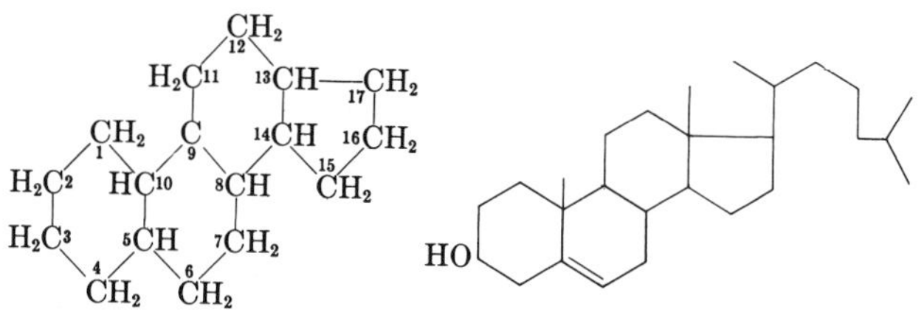

cyclopentanophenanthrene:
$C_{17}H_{28}$

Cholesterol: $C_{27}H_{42}O$

Fig. 68.13

TABLE 68.7

Total cholesterol content of normal tissues
(per cent of fresh tissue)

	Rabbit*	Man†
Adrenals	7.3	4.74
Brain	1.8	1.93
Skin		0.93
Kidney	0.44	0.33
Spleen	0.38	0.36
Lung	0.38	
Liver	0.29	0.32
Adipose tissue (subcut.)		0.24
Hair		0.17
Blood (whole)	0.08	0.17
Plasma	0.06	0.23
Corpuscles	0.12	0.12
Heart		0.14
Muscle	0.06	0.07

The tissues of a man weighing 70 kg. may be calculated to contain slightly over 100 grams of total cholesterol: about 30 grams in adipose tissue, 25 grams in brain, 20 grams in muscle, slightly over 5 grams in whole blood, 5 grams in liver; because of their small size adrenals account for only about 0.5 gram.

* After Chamberlain.

† After Cook.

Cholesterol also enters the duodenum as a constituent of bile. This cholesterol secreted by the liver cells is entirely in the free form. About 700–1200 ml. of bile are secreted by the liver daily, containing 0.9 to 1.8 g. of cholesterol per liter. The amount of cholesterol excreted in the bile, i.e., 1 to 2 g. daily, exceeds the dietary intake under usual conditions. This is due to both synthesis of cholesterol in the body and to recycling of cholesterol by reabsorption and reexcretion. Cholesterol is also added to the chyme by the intestinal mucosa. The production of cholesterol in the intestine by synthesis appears to be quantitatively important.

A considerable part of the cholesterol from these three sources is absorbed from the lumen of the intestine. Part of the cholesterol in the intestine is degraded by microbial action to other sterols. The feces in man contain about 0.3 to 1 g. of sterols daily, chiefly in the forms of cholesterol, coprostanol and cholestanol.

Cholesterol esters are hydrolyzed before absorption. The free cholesterol absorbed is partly esterified by the mucosal cells and is transferred, as a component of the chylomicrons, through the lymph to the venous blood stream. Free and ester forms of cholesterol are present in lymph chylomicrons in about equal proportions. The absorption of sterols is selective. Many other sterols, including plant sterols closely related to cholesterol, pass through the gut without being absorbed.

SYNTHESIS

The entire carbon skeleton of cholesterol can be synthesized in the animal body from acetate. The conversion of deuterioacetate, in mice and rats, to deuteriocholesterol was shown by Bloch and Rittenberg in 1942. A concept of the pathways of synthesis has emerged from many investigations, notably those of Cornforth and Popjak. Intermediate substances, and the distribution of labeled methyl- and carboxyl-carbon atoms of acetate in the cholesterol synthesized, are shown in fig. 68.14. Steps in the synthesis of cholesterol are still being investigated. Squalene constitutes over 50 per cent of the liver lipids of certain sharks; it occurs also in mammalian liver, but only in low concentrations. The rate of turnover of squalene is very rapid, and its conversion, by liver tissue, to lanosterol and cholesterol has been shown.

The liver is particularly active in cholesterol synthesis. The perfused liver and liver slices can synthesize it from acetate and intermediate steps are effected by liver homogenates. In hepatectomized rats, cholesterol synthesis was found to occur in the small intestine, kidney, testis and skin. The process also occurs in slices of the adrenal cortex, and brain of newborn rats. Although many tissues have this capacity, the liver and intestinal mucosa make the greatest amounts.

METABOLISM

The liver converts cholesterol to bile acids, and secretes these, as conjugates with taurine and glycine, into the bile. The direct metabolic relationship between cholesterol, a C27-compound and bile acids (C24) was shown conclusively by Bloch and his colleagues in 1943. After the intravenous administration of randomly-deuterated cholesterol to a dog with drainage of bile from the gall bladder through a transplanted ureter to the urinary bladder (cholecystonephrostomy), the cholic acid isolated from the urine had the same isotope concentration as the cholesterol injected. It was calculated that at least two-thirds of the excreted cholic acid had arisen from the cholesterol injected. Cholic acid originates from cholesterol by removal of the three terminal carbon atoms of the

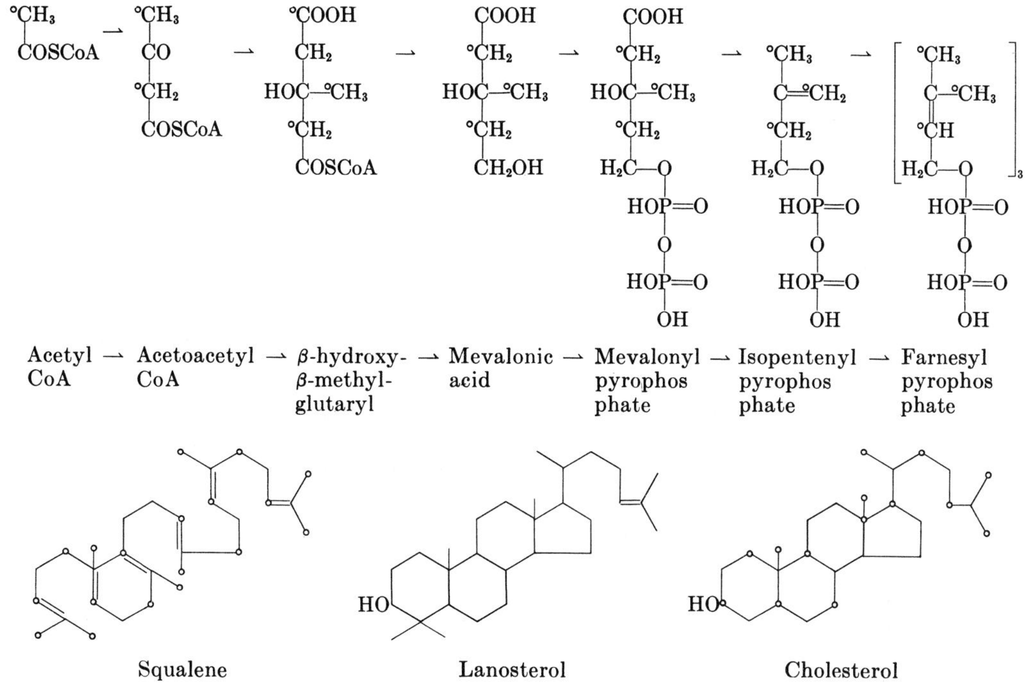

FIG. 68.14. A postulated sequence of reactions in the biosynthesis of cholesterol. The methyl carbon of C^{14}-labeled acetate is indicated in the acetate utilized, the intermediate products and in the cholesterol formed. See Cornforth, J. W., J. Lipid Res., 1959, 1, 3.

side chain, numbers 25, 26 and 27 (Zabin and Barker). The sterol nucleus of cholesterol is resistant to oxidation in the body, but the side chain can be partially oxidized (Chaikoff and his colleagues). Cholesterol labeled with C^{14} at position 4, in the ring structure, and at position 26, in the side chain, was administered. As much as 31 per cent of the side-chain carbon was excreted as carbon dioxide within 1 day, but the carbon of the ring was eliminated only in the feces; none appeared in the expired air.

The "primary" bile acids produced by the liver cells in man are chiefly cholic acid and chenodeoxycholic acid (Bergström), fig. 68.15. The extent of this conversion is important. It has been estimated that 90 per cent of a dose of isotopic cholesterol administered to the rat was excreted in the form of bile acids, and 10 per cent as free cholesterol. The liver, from this and other evidence, appears to be the chief organ for the conversion and excretion of cholesterol.

The bile salts, as mentioned earlier, are highly important in the absorption of lipid from the intestine; they are themselves reabsorbed, but mainly by a different route: in the blood, via the portal vein to hepatic blood vessels. Bile salts are extracted from the blood by the liver and are re-excreted in bile. Bile acid molecules appear to go through this enterohepatic circula-tion cycle on the average 5 to 10 times before being excreted with the feces.

The bile salts are hydrolysed and degraded by microorganisms in the intestine to deoxycholic acid, lithocholic acid and a series of other acids. Alterations in the steroid ring appear to render the products less absorbable. This action of the intestinal flora increases bile salt excretion, possibly by increasing the rate of removal from the body. The metabolism and recirculation of cholesterol and bile acids, with estimates of pool sizes and the daily balances in man, is shown in fig. 68.16 (Bergström).

The conversion of cholesterol in perfused adrenal glands to adrenal cortical hormones, and to other steroids of unknown physiological activity, has been demonstrated. Cholesterol is also utilized in the synthesis of steroid hormones by the testis, and by the ovary and placenta. These modes of utilization of cholesterol are, of course, of great physiological importance, but the amounts involved are insignificant in relation to total cholesterol turnover in the body. Cholesterol and derivatives of it are excreted by the skin. The extent of this process is not known; it probably represents an unimportant fraction of the cholesterol balance in man.

In summary, the liver and intestine are of great importance in cholesterol metabolism: both or-

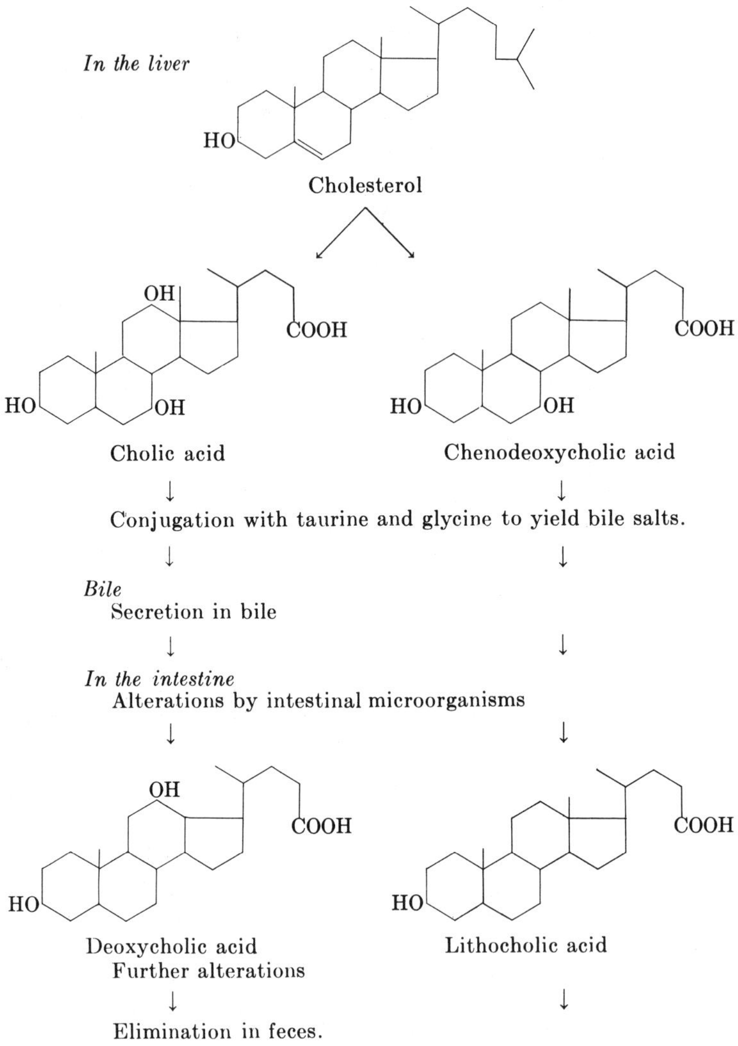

FIG. 68.15. Formation and excretion of the bile acids in man. After S. Bergström, Federation Proc., 1962, **21**, 28.

gans make substantial contributions to total body cholesterol by synthesis, and both secrete cholesterol in lipid-protein aggregates into the blood stream; the intestines are active in this respect during lipid absorption. Cholesterol is excreted by the intestinal mucosa and by the liver cells via the bile. The major route for excretion of cholesterol is by its conversion to bile acids in the liver. Control of cholesterol and bile acid production by the liver is largely effected by reabsorption of cholesterol and bile acids through the enterohepatic cycle. The intestinal bacteria modify reabsorption of cholesterol and bile salts. The intestine is the major route for the elimination of steroids.

Factors Influencing Cholesterol Metabolism

(1) BILE SALTS. The recycling of bile acids depresses the production of these acids and of cholesterol by the liver. When bile is removed through a bile duct fistula in man, a considerable increase in bile formation occurs. In the rat, with drainage of bile through a fistula, the production of bile acids, from the second day, is raised more than ten-fold, and can be brought back to normal by the continuous injection of bile salt into the lower end of the bile duct. Conversely, in the rat, an increase in the amount of bile acids absorbed from the intestine diminishes both the synthesis of cholesterol and its oxidation to bile acids in the liver, and causes a

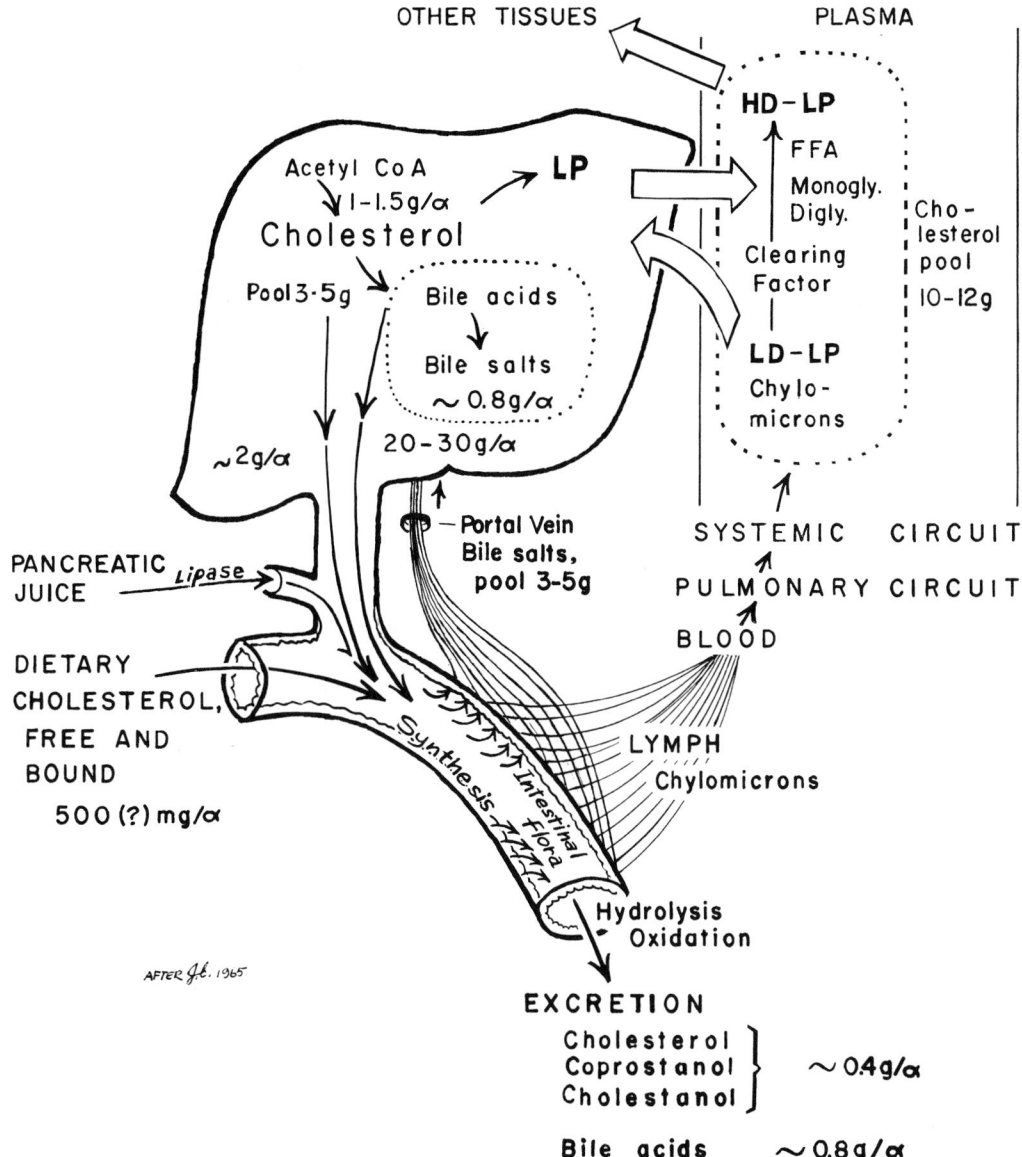

FIG. 68.16. Schematic representation of the metabolism of cholesterol. After S. Bergström, Federation Proc., 1962, **21**, 28. Abbreviations are: FFA, free fatty acids; HD-LP, high-density lipoproteins; LD-LP, low-density lipoproteins; Digly., diglycerides; and Monogly., monoglycerides.

rise in serum cholesterol. Obstruction of the common bile duct results in hypercholesterolemia.

The feeding of resins that bind bile acids and so prevent their reabsorption, causes lowering of blood cholesterol in human subjects and experimental animals (Tennent *et al.*). The resins eliminated in the feces increase fecal excretion of bile acids; the blood bile acid concentration may be reduced. When given in larger doses, the resins may increase excretion of dietary

triglycerides, i.e., may decrease lipid absorption. The action of the resins may be to stimulate the liver to increase the rate of oxidation of cholesterol, with resulting decrease in circulating cholesterol (van Itallie).

The effect of the intestinal microorganisms is apparently to increase bile salt production. In the normal rat, fed a tracer dose of C^{14}-labeled cholic acid, half the isotope was excreted in 2–3 days, but in rats treated with a non-absorbable chemotherapeutic drug, this interval was extended to 8–10 days. It is suggested that, by converting the bile acids to less absorbable forms, the bacteria may reduce reabsorption, thus maintaining production in the liver.

(2) HORMONES. In the hypothyroid rat, the rate of excretion of bile acids through a bile duct fistula (10 mg./day) is much less than in the fistulated normal rat (70 mg./day). Hypothyroidism in man is associated with raised serum cholesterol. Oestrogen administration tends to lower serum cholesterol. In rats given oestrogen, liver cholesterol is increased. It has been suggested that there may, therefore, be withdrawal of cholesterol from serum to liver under the influence of the female sex hormones. Cortisone in the rabbit increases serum lipid and cholesterol levels.

(3) DIETARY INFLUENCES. The effect of dietary cholesterol on serum cholesterol levels has been a subject of controversy. In man, the intake of large amounts of cholesterol has limited effect on serum cholesterol. Addition of cholesterol to the diet of a dog increased cholesterol levels considerably in plasma and bile, and slightly in liver and intestinal mucosa. At the same time, the hepatic synthesis of cholesterol from C^{14}-acetate was much decreased (Gould). In the rabbit, dietary cholesterol causes fatty liver, increases serum cholesterol levels, and precipitates the formation of atheromatous deposits in the aorta. The feeding of large amounts of cholesterol, 1% of the diet, to rats, results in accumulation of cholesterol esters in the liver, with slight or no effect on serum cholesterol. In the rat, removal of absorbed lipids by means of a cannula in the thoracic lymph duct increases many-fold, within an hour, the synthesis of cholesterol from acetate in the liver. Thus dietary cholesterol, under experimental conditions, suppresses cholesterol synthesis; in some animals it raises serum cholesterol.

Animal fats, which tend to be consumed in large amounts in affluent societies, are suspected of raising serum cholesterol and contributing to the increasing incidence of cardiovascular disease. Animal fats contain cholesterol, but the nature of their fatty acids is currently thought by some investigators to be more important. Extensive replacement of these by polyunsaturated fatty acids in the diet, fed either as triglycerides, e.g., in corn oil and safflower seed oil, or experimentally as ethyl esters, usually lowers serum cholesterol, especially in patients with chronic hypercholesterolemia. The relationships between dietary fat, serum cholesterol, and cardiovascular disease are complex and as yet unresolved.

Atherosclerosis

The characteristic, but not the earliest, lesion of an atherosclerotic artery is the cholesterol-rich plaque which forms on the wall, and may in time almost occlude the lumen. Prolonged hypercholesterolemia and atherosclerosis are related in some way. The evidence linking high cholesterol concentrations in serum with coronary heart disease is strong on a statistical basis, but the efficiency of the values for diagnosis and prognosis in individuals is low. Kinsell regards the upper limit of "normal" total cholesterol in plasma (fasting) as 180 mg. per 100 ml., others consider 200 mg. per 100 ml. to be a reference point. The total lipids, in the so-called giant molecules of low density lipoproteins, are also suspected of being related to the lesion.

The local accumulation of lipid in the lesion may arise: (1) from increased deposition of plasma lipid, (2) an increased production of lipid in the tissue, or (3) defective utilization of lipid by the tissue. It is also possible that a primary defect in the tissue may lead to atheroma by one or more of these processes. The relative importance or even relevance of these possibilities in the development of the lesion is not yet established.

Many factors in addition to the above are associated with development of cardiovascular disease; important among these are advancing age, sex (higher incidence in males), high arterial blood pressure, excessive intake of calories, obesity, diminished exercise, cigarette smoking, electrocardiographic abnormalities, decreased vital capacity and diabetes mellitus.

Serum cholesterol levels can be reduced in man in three ways: (a) by limiting calorie intake, (b) by reducing the intake of animal fats (Keys), and (c) by increasing the intake of polyunsaturated fatty acids (Kinsell, Sinclair, Bronte-Stewart, Ahrens and others). The sterol fractions of vegetable oils (containing sitosterol) also reduce serum cholesterol levels in subjects on formula diets (Beveridge). The possible role of dietary protein and carbohydrates in atherosclerosis is currently being investigated.

For further discussion of diseases characterized by evidence of abnormal lipid metabolism the reader may refer to Stanbury, Wyngaarden and Fredrickson.

REFERENCES

ALLAN, F. N., BOWIE, D. J., MacLEOD, J. J. R., AND ROBINSON, W. L. Brit. J. Exper. Path., 1924, 5, 75.

BENNETT, M. A., MEDES, G., AND TOENNIES, G. Growth, 1944, 8, 59.

BEST, C. H., AND CAMPBELL, J. J. Physiol., 1936, 86, 190.

BEST, C. H., HERSHEY, J. M., AND HUNTSMAN, M. E. J. Physiol., 1932, 75, 56.

CHAIKOFF, I. L. AND SOSKIN, S. Am. J. Physiol., 1928, 87, 58.

DuVIGNEAUD, V., CHANDLER, J. P., MOYER, A. W., AND KEPPEL, D. M. J. Biol. Chem., 1939, 131, 57.

EMBDEN, G. AND KALBERLAH, F. Beitr. Chem. Physiol. Path., 1906, 8, 121.

ENTENMAN, C., CHAIKOFF, I. L., AND ZILVERSMIT, D. B. J. Biol. Chem., 1946, 166, 15.

FISHER, N. F. Am. J. Physiol., 1924, 67, 634.

GOLDMAN, D. S., CHAIKOFF, I. L., REINHARDT, W. O., ENTENMAN, C., AND DAUBEN, W. G. J. Biol. Chem., 1950, 184, 727.

HAINES, D. S. M. AND MOOKERJEA, S. Canad. J. Biochem., 1965, 43, 507.

HART, J. S. AND IRVING, L. Canad. J. Zool., 1959, 37, 447.

HARTROFT, W. S. AND BEST, C. H. Brit. Med. J., 1949, 1, 423.

HERSHEY, J. M. AND SOSKIN, S. Am. J. Physiol., 1931, 98, 74.

KEYS, A., ANDERSON, J. T., MICKELSEN, O., ADELSON, S. F., AND FIDANZA, F. J. Nutr., 1956, 59, 39.

KNOOP, F. Beitr. chem. Physiol. Path., 1904, 6, 150.

LEHNINGER, A. L. J. Biol. Chem., 1946, 164, 291.

LYNEN, F., HENNING, U., BUBLITZ, C., SÖRBO, B., AND KRÖPLIN-RUEFF, L. Biochem. Zeits., 1958, 330, 269.

McARTHUR, C. S., LUCAS, C. C., AND BEST, C. H. Biochem. J., 1947, 41, 612.

von MERING, J. AND MINKOWSKI, O. Arch. exper. Path. u. Pharmakol., 1889, 26, 371.

RAGHARAN, S. S., JUREJA, H. S., MURTHY, S. K., AND GANGULY, J. Nature, 1965, 206, 189.

RODBELL, M. AND SCOW, R. O. Am. J. Physiol., 1965, 208, 106.

SCHOTZ, M. C. AND PAGE, I. H. J. Lipid Res., 1960, 1, 466.

SHAFRIR, E. AND STEINBERG, D. J. Clin. Invest., 1960, 39, 310.

STETTEN, D. W. JR. AND SALCEDO, J. J. Biol. Chem., 1944, 156, 27.

TASKER, R. R. Canad. J. Biochem. Physiol., 1955, 33, 361.

TUCKER, H. F. AND ECKSTEIN, H. C. J. Biol. Chem., 1937, 121, 479.

WEINHOUSE, S., MEDES, G., AND FLOYD, N. F. J. Biol. Chem., 1944, 155, 143.

WEINMAN, E. O., CHAIKOFF, I. L., ENTENMAN, C., AND DAUBEN, W. G. J. Biol. Chem., 1950, 187, 643.

WELCH, A. D. AND LANDAU, R. L. J. Biol. Chem., 1942, 144, 581.

Monographs and Reviews

ARTOM, C. Role of choline in the hepatic oxidation of fat. Am. J. Clin. Nutr., 1958, 6, 221.

BAER, E. The synthesis of phospholipids, *in* Progress in Chemistry of Fats and Other Lipids, 1963, 6, 31.

BERGSTRÖM, S. Metabolism of bile acids. Fed. Proc., 1962, 21, 28.

BLOCH, K., Ed. Lipide Metabolism, John Wiley and Sons, N. Y., 1960.

BRONTE-STEWART, B. Lipids and atherosclerosis. Fed. Proc., 1961, 20, 127.

CAMPBELL, J. Hyperlipidemia with ketoacidosis. Metabolism, 1962, 11, 762.

CAMPBELL, J. AND BEST, C. H. Physiologic aspects of ketogenesis. Metabolism, 1956, 5, 95.

CLEMENTS, J. A. Surface phenomena in relation to pulmonary function. The Physiologist, 1962, 5, 11.

DEUEL, H. J., JR. The Lipids, vol. 1. Chemistry, 1951; vol. II. Biochemistry; Digestion, Absorption, Transport, and Storage, 1955; vol. III. Biochemistry; Biosynthesis, Oxidation, Metabolism, and Nutritional Value, 1957, N. Y., Interscience Publishers.

DuVIGNEAUD, V. A Trail of Research in Sulfur Chemistry and Metabolism in Related Fields. Cornell Univ. Press, Ithaca, N. Y., 1952.

FAVARGER, P. The liver and lipid metabolism *in* The Liver, Morphology, Biochemistry, Physiology, vol. 1. (CH. ROUILLER, ed.), N. Y., Academic Press, 1963, p. 549.

FRAZER, A. C. Role of lipids in normal metabolism. Fed. Proc., 1961, 20, suppl. 7, 146.

FREDRICKSON, D. S. AND GORDON, R. S., JR. Transport of fatty acids. Physiol. Rev., 1958, 38, 585.

GIBSON, D. M. Fatty acid biosynthesis, *in* Progress in Chemistry of Fats and Other Lipids, 1963, 6, 117.

GOULD, R. G. Lipid metabolism and atherosclerosis. Am. J. Med., 1951, 11, 209.

GREEN, D. E. Fatty acid oxidation, *in* Progress in Chemistry of Fats and Other Lipids, 1963, 6, 87.

HANAHAN, D. J., GURD, F. R. N., AND ZABIN, I. Lipide Chemistry, John Wiley and Sons, N. Y., 1960.

HAWTHORNE, J. N. The biochemistry of the inositol lipids. Vitamins and Hormones, 1964, 22, 57.

HOFMANN, A. F. AND BORGSTRÖM, B. Physicochemical state of lipids in intestinal content during their digestion and absorption. Fed. Proc., 1962, 21, 43.

HOGEBOOM, G. H. Separation and properties of cell components. Fed. Proc., 1951, 10, 640.

HOLMAN, R. T. Nutritional and metabolic interrelationships between fatty acids. Fed. Proc., 1964, 23, 1062.

HOLMAN, R. T., LUNDBERG, W. O., AND MALKIN, T. Progress in Chemistry of Fats and Other Lipids, 1963, 6, Pergamon Press, N. Y.

ISSELBACHER, K. J. Metabolism and transport of

lipid by intestinal mucosa. Fed. Proc., 1965, **24,** 16.

KAGAN, A., DAWBER, T. R., KANNEL, W. B., AND REVOTSKIE, N. The Framingham study: a prospective study of coronary heart disease. Fed. Proc., 1962, **21,** 52.

KAMER, J. H. VAN DE AND WEIJERS, H. A. Malabsorption syndrome. Fed. Proc., 1961, **20,** 335.

KENNEDY, E. Biosynthesis of the phospholipids. Fed. Proc., 1957, **16,** 847.

KINSELL, L. W. Adipose Tissue as an Organ, Charles C Thomas, Springfield, Illinois, 1962.

KLENK, K. Plasmalogens, *in* Progress in Chemistry of Fats and Other Lipids, 1963, **6,** 1.

LEDERER, E. The origin and function of some methyl groups in branched-chain fatty acids, plant sterols and quinones. Biochem. J., 1964, **93,** 449.

LYNEN, F. Functional group of coenzyme A and its metabolic relations, especially in the fatty acid cycle. Fed. Proc., 1953, **12,** 683.

MACKAY, E. M. The significance of ketosis. J. Clin. Endocrin., 1943, **3,** 101.

PRATTLE, R. E. Surface lining of lung alveoli. Physiol. Rev., 1965, **45,** 48.

RENOLD, A. E. AND CAHILL, G. F. (eds.) Adipose Tissue, Handbook of Physiology, Section V, American Physiological Society, Washington, D. C., 1965.

ROSSITER, R. J. AND STRICKLAND, K. P. The metabolism and function of the phosphatides, *in* Lipide Metabolism (Ed., K. BLOCH). John Wiley and Sons, N. Y., 1960, p. 69.

ROUILLER, CH. (ed.) The Liver, Morphology, Biochemistry and Physiology, vol. I, Academic Press, N. Y., 1963.

SCHOENHEIMER, R. The Dynamic State of Body Constituents. Harvard Univ. Press. Cambridge, Mass. 1942.

SCRIMSHAW, N. S. AND BRESSANI, R. Vegetable protein mixtures for human consumption. Fed. Proc., 1961, **20,** 80.

SIEKEVITZ, P. Protoplasm: endoplasmic reticulum and microsomes and their properties. Ann. Rev. Physiol., 1963, **75,** 15.

STANBURY, J. B., WYNGAARDEN, J. B., AND FREDRICKSON, D. S. The Metabolic Basis of Inherited Disease. The Blakiston Division, McGraw-Hill Book Co., N. Y., 1960.

Symposium on Chemistry and Functions of Coenzyme A. Fed. Proc., 1953, **12,** 673.

Symposium on Molecular basis of membrane structure and function. Sixth Internat. Cong. of Biochem. Section VIII, Cellular Organization, 1964, p. 603.

Symposium on cytochemistry. Fed. Proc., 1951, **10,** 629.

TENNENT, D. M., HASHIM, S. A., AND VAN ITALLIE, T. B., Bile-acid sequestrants and lipid metabolism. Fed. Proc., 1962, **21,** 77.

VAUGHAN, M. The metabolism of adipose tissue *in vitro.* J. Lipid Res., 1961, **2,** 293.

WAKIL, S. J. AND BRESSLER, R. Fatty acid metabolism and ketone body formation. Metabolism, 1962, **11,** 742.

CHAPTER 69

The Metabolism in Starvation, Semistarvation and Obesity

Starvation

The metabolic changes in starved animals and man were investigated extensively several generations ago. Studies of a number of professional fasters have been reported. Among the most famous of these are Succi, whose metabolism was studied by Luciani and others, Cette, investigated by Munk and Zuntz, Levanzin by Benedict and Beauté by Cathcart. One of the longest of such fasts upon record is that of Merlatte of Paris which lasted for 50 days. A dog has been starved for 117 days. By the end of this time it had lost 63 per cent of its weight, but was fairly active. Succi on the 40th day of his fast had lost about 25 per cent of his weight. The length of time a man could survive would depend largely upon his physical condition (fat stores, etc.) at the commencement of the fast, but it would probably not exceed 9 or 10 weeks in any event. Terrence MacSwiney, Mayor of Cork, after his arrest during the Irish troubles in 1920, went upon a hunger strike which lasted 74 days; it was terminated by his death in coma. Keys and his associates question to what extent the response of professional fasters can be accepted as typical of the general population, especially the emotional and behavioural adjustments. After World War II, thousands of persons were found on the verge of death from starvation in concentration camps and enabled studies to be made of advanced and terminal stages of starvation. The well-controlled Minnesota experiment, started in 1944, with 36 volunteers subjected to prolonged semi-starvation, provided valuable fundamental data and information useful in the rehabilitation of famine victims.

Starvation induces a number of metabolic changes, some occurring within a few days. A progressive fall in basal metabolic rate, body temperature, pulse rate and blood pressure occurs; ketosis develops and some retention of salt and water occurs. Table 69.1 shows typical changes during fasting.

An animal deprived of food derives energy first from the combustion of its own carbohydrate stores (glycogen). Next, the fat reserves mainly are drawn upon and finally, after these have been exhausted, tissue protein is broken down, the fatty acid part of the molecule is burned while the nitrogen is excreted in the urine mainly as urea.

During starvation the loss of weight is not distributed evenly throughout the body, some organs and tissues losing a much greater proportion of their weight than others (fig. 69.1). During the first few days the subcutaneous tissues and other fat depots bear the brunt of the effect of the fast. Large quantities of extracellular water are also lost at this time. Later, dissolution of muscular tissue occurs, as indicated by the N:S ratio of the urine (about 14:1). The water lost during this period is derived mainly from intracellular sources. Later, dissolution of protoplasmic structure occurs. The central nervous system, even in prolonged starvation, loses only about 5 per cent of its weight (as estimated from normal standards), whereas the muscles lose about 35 per cent or more. The weight losses of muscular tissue, liver, gastrointestinal tract and spleen run approximately parallel with that of the body as a whole. The muscle fibers are reduced in size, and many are destroyed. Contrary to general belief, the percentile weight loss of the heart is only a little less than that of the skeletal muscles. The kidney loses only 20 per cent or less of its weight, and the gonads, adrenals and thyroid only from 2 to 8 per cent. Some of the small weight losses reported, e.g., of the central nervous system, may be due to the replacement of solid substance by fluid (see fig. 69.1).[1]

NITROGEN EXCRETION. *The total output of nitrogen* in the urine falls for the first day or two of the fast when the body is subsisting chiefly upon its carbohydrate supplies. The length of this period varies, of course, with the size of the carbohydrate stores at the commencement of the fast. A steady rise in nitrogen excretion follows, and usually reaches a maximum about the third or

[1] There does not appear to be any definite level of emaciation, that is, of weight loss of the body as a whole as a percentage of the normal body weight, at which death is inevitable. Recoveries with judicious feeding and transfusions of plasma have been recorded after losses of body weight up to 50 or even 60 per cent of the normal weight.

TABLE 69.1

Subject L. Height, 170.7 cm. Only distilled water was taken during this fast

(Abridged, after Benedict)

	Day of Fasting			
	1st	11th	21st	31st
Body weight, kg	59.60	53.88	50.49	47.39
Rectal temperature at 7 a.m.		36.54	36.04	35.96
Pulse-rate, morning, awake	74	61	59	60
Urine:				
Total solids, grams	43.51	42.05	31.88	27.07
Total N	7.10	10.25	7.93	6.94
Urea N	5.68	7.66	5.54	4.84
Ammonia N	0.41	1.58	1.57	1.24
Uric acid N	0.112	0.116	0.112	0.122
Creatinine + Creatine N	0.48	0.49	0.38	0.32
Chlorine	3.77	0.36	0.18	0.13
P_2O_5	1.66	1.95	1.60	1.32
$N:P_2O_5$ ratio	4.28	5.26	4.96	5.26
S	0.46	0.62	0.51	0.49
N:S ratio	15.4	16.5	15.5	14.2
β-oxybutyric acid		1.4	5.0	4.5
Ca	0.217	0.220	0.237	0.138
Mg	0.046	0.072	0.053	0.052
K	1.630	1.006	0.644	0.606
Na	2.070	0.100	0.066	0.053
Loss of flesh calculated from N loss	213	308	238	208
R.Q., night	0.78	0.72	0.73	0.72
Calories, indirect, 24 hours' complete rest	1441	1193	1032	1072*
Calories per square meter (DuBois), 24 hours	843	732	653	701†

* Previous day = 1025.

† Previous day = 661.

fourth day, but from then on it shows a progressive decline and may reach a value of less than 6 grams per day. The nitrogen excreted during the earlier part of the fast is apparently derived largely from the mobilization of "reserve protein" (p. 1302). The *urea nitrogen* excretion at first rises, then falls; its percentage of the total nitrogen excretion also diminishes. The *ammonia* excretion rises. The *creatinine* output shows a steady decline but this is largely compensated for by the appearance of creatine (p. 1305) so that the creatinine + creatine excretion remains fairly constant. As a result of some experiments of Voit many years ago, it is very often stated that a pronounced rise in nitrogen excretion occurs shortly before death from starvation, which is attributed to an accelerated breakdown of tissue protein. But this so-called *premortal rise* in nitrogen excretion is a very inconstant phenomenon, and of very doubtful significance, for death very often occurs in starved animals in its absence. The total quantity of body protein catabolized may be deter-

mined by calculation from the total nitrogen excretion on the assumption that tissue protein contains 16 per cent of nitrogen and that practically all the nitrogen derived from the breakdown of body protein appears in the urine. That is, each gram of urinary nitrogen represents the deamination of 6.25 grams of protein, so the quantity of protein broken down is calculated by multiplying the figure for the nitrogen excretion by 6.25. On this basis the average daily loss of body protein of an average sized man during starvation is about 50 grams or about 0.4 per cent of the total amount in his body. For a few days following the termination of a prolonged fast the nitrogen excretion shows a pronounced fall—nitrogen is retained for the reconstruction of tissue protein.[2]

[2] The loss of protein varies widely among different organs and tissues. Addis and his colleagues found that in rats fasted for 7 days the several tissues contributed to the total protein loss in the following proportions, muscles and skin 62 per cent, liver 16 per cent, alimentary tract, spleen and pan-

MINERAL METABOLISM. The urinary excretion of *phosphorus* and *sulfur* shows an initial rise, and then a gradual decline, thus showing a curve which roughly parallels that of the total nitrogen excretion. Toward the latter part of the fast the N:P and N:S ratios are around 5.3:1 and 14:1 respectively. The excretion of P in relation to N is greater than one would expect were it all derived from the soft tissues; the same is true for Ca, which indicates that the skeleton contributes to the quantities of these minerals in the urine. The calcium excretion above that which the soft tissues can account for is much greater (10 times) than that of phosphorus, from which it is deduced that calcium carbonate rather than calcium phosphate is liberated from the bones. The ratio of N to S is a little higher than that of the bulk of the soft tissues, which suggests that the sulfur-containing amino-acids are conserved or excreted in only minimal amounts.

The urinary excretion of *chloride, sodium, potassium* and *magnesium* is reduced from the beginning of the fast. This is to be expected since the intake of minerals is restricted to that provided by the water which is drunk. The concentrations of these minerals in the blood shows little change, but the sodium bicarbonate is reduced when ketosis supervenes.

KETOSIS. The increase in urinary ammonia is a result of the production of excessive amounts of acid metabolites, especially β-hydroxybutyric and acetoacetic acids. The latter are formed as a result of the carbohydrate deprivation, and the consequent excess combustion of fat. Succi toward the end of his fast excreted, daily, from 7 to 13 grams of acetone bodies. In a fasting female subject reported by Folin and Denis the acidosis was extreme, some 18 grams of β-hydroxybutyric acid being excreted upon the fourth day of the fast. Fasting ketosis is much more pronounced in women than in men. This sex difference is not related to the usually greater adipose tissue of females, for a very lean woman excretes larger amounts of ketone bodies than does a man of overweight. Nor, generally speaking, is ketosis during fasting greater in an overweight person than in one of normal weight.

CARBOHYDRATE METABOLISM. Even in the later

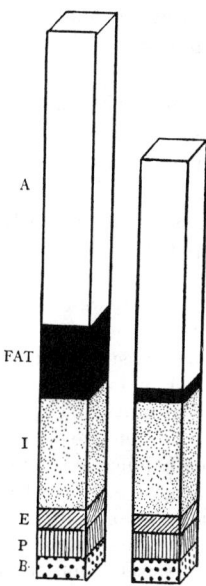

FIG. 69.1. The weights of the major compartments of the body of young men in normal nutrition, on left; after 24 weeks of semi-starvation, on right; A, active tissue (total body weight less the other indicated compartments); B, bone mineral; E, erythrocytes; I, interstitial fluid, (thiocyanate space less plasma volume), from Keys and associates, the Biology of Human Starvation, University of Minnesota Press, redrawn and modified.

stages of the fast glycogen is found in the liver, and the blood sugar is little depressed. Sugar is apparently synthesized from protein. In the earlier stages there may be a temporary hypoglycemia.

Semistarvation, Undernutrition[3]

Prolonged use of a diet providing energy considerably below the requirement, as during famine, war blockade, extreme poverty, disease (e.g., stricture of the esophagus or pylorus) or improper feeding of infants, will cause not only loss of weight, but nutritional deficiencies involving better quality proteins, vitamins and essential minerals. A man who performs heavy work upon a diet which is adequate only for a sedentary worker will suffer from undernutrition. As a consequence, the incidence of specific deficiency disorders, e.g., stunting, xerophthalmia, rickets, osteomalacia, scurvy, etc., is also high when the calorie value of the diet is markedly lowered.

creas 14 per cent, blood 6 per cent, kidneys 1 per cent, heart 0.5 per cent and the remaining organs 0.5 per cent. Or put in percentages of the protein contents of individual normal organs; the brain loses about 4 per cent of its protein; the muscles, skin and bones about 8 per cent; the heart 18 per cent; the kidneys 20 per cent; the gastrointestinal tract 28 per cent; and the liver 40 per cent.

[3] Comprehensive reports of studies on undernutrition have been published within recent years, e.g., *Malnutrition and Starvation in the Western Netherlands*; Netherlands Government 1944–1945; and the two volume monograph by Ancel Keys and his associates, *The Biology of Human Starvation*, Univ. of Minnesota Press, 1950.

These special aspects of undernutrition are dealt with in other chapters.

Pronounced instances of undernutrition and emaciation are met with most commonly in anorexia nervosa, pituitary cachexia, the later stages of malignant disease, and in prolonged and severe infections.

The following is a summary of the main effects of severe undernutrition.

(1) Reduction in body weight—emaciation. The body attempts to make up the calorie deficiency by burning its own tissues. The loss of weight is due chiefly to loss of fat, but also in severe instances to a loss of protein. The nitrogen balance is negative. In children growth is retarded. The positive nitrogen balance is smaller than normal, it may even be negative. In the less severe grades of undernutrition in children the growth impulse continues to cause an increase in height of the skeleton but the muscles and the breadth of the body are poorly developed.

(2) The loss of internal fat which normally serves to support the organs—stomach, kidneys, uterus, etc.—against the effect of gravity, results in their displacement (visceroptosis). The lost body fat is partially replaced by water.

(3) Edema develops in some cases (see ch. 25).

(4) Reduction in basal metabolic rate. The total basal metabolism, i.e., the heat production as related to surface area, is, as one would expect owing to the reduction in the mass of active tissue, diminished in semistarvation, but the metabolism per unit (kilogram) of body weight is reduced as well. The total metabolism is diminished by nearly 40 per cent, and the heat production per unit of body weight by nearly 20 per cent. The cause of the reduction per kilogram has not been fully explained, but it can be accounted for in part by the decline in cardiac work (by about 50 per cent), the lowered tone of the skeletal muscles, and the subnormal body temperature, which would tend to slow the rate of all chemical reactions in the tissues. The subject is abnormally sensitive to cold, due to the fact that the skin vessels are constricted in an attempt to reduce the dissipation of heat through radiation and convection (ch. 70). The skin temperature upon which our thermal sensations depend is therefore lowered. The specific dynamic response to food may be increased.

(5) The subject is readily fatigued, and shows a lack of a zest for physical exertion. Work is performed with the same expenditure of energy as normally, so, though energy is economized in the carrying on of the vital processes as shown by the reduced B.M.R. and cold skin, no economy is effected in the execution of muscular work.

(6) Susceptibility to infections: "Fever and plague dog the footsteps of famine." This is an old adage, but with the exception of tuberculosis (in which resistance is definitely lowered) and certain specific effects of vitamin deficiencies there is really little evidence that undernutrition increases the susceptibility to infection.

It is natural to suppose that the production of γ-globulin which is so closely associated with immune bodies would be depressed by undernutrition, especially if involving severe protein deficiency. The investigations of Cannon and his colleagues have gone far to show that this, indeed, does occur. In the Minnesota experiment the concentration of γ-globulin in the plasma of the subjects was moderately reduced, but this was not accompanied by any apparent increase in susceptibility to infections; the semistarved subjects of the experiment had slightly fewer colds over a comparable period than the controls. On the other hand, there is a considerable body of evidence to support the conception that undernutrition actually reduces the susceptibility to certain infections. It has been reported, for example, by McCay that underfed rats were surprisingly free from the usual laboratory infections; others have concluded from their experiments and observations of naturally occurring disease, that well nourished animals are more susceptible to infection than are undernourished ones. When a severe infection is established, however, the undernourished animal is at a disadvantage, and is more likely to succumb.

It is recognized that some noninfectious conditions such as hypertension, neoplastic diseases, and diabetes are benefited by undernutrition. In animals, very severe undernutrition definitely inhibits tumor growth, but whether less severe calorie deficiency has such an effect in man is uncertain. The evidence for the incidence of hypertension being reduced is mainly statistical.

(7) Psychological changes. Mental apathy, moral deterioration, depression, tendency toward introversion and other changes in personality, and lowered intellectual capacity are common effects. "The brain is in some sort of custody of the stomach and relief of malnutrition gives relief of mental dullness" (Roger Bacon). An unresponsive, complaining and uncooperative attitude in semistarved persons of Western Europe receiving relief after World War II was very frequently observed. Drummond remarked upon this and stated that it disappeared completely when the food intake was raised above 1500 to 1800 Calories per day.

Obesity

The usual cause of overweight is excess of body fat but it may also result from abnormal retention of water, unusual muscular development or, rarely, from large tumors. Obesity may be defined as abnormally high body weight due to an excessive accumulation of fat. Its prevalence in North America is increasing and is accompanied by increased morbidity and mortality from several degenerative diseases. Obesity displays its adverse effects in the increased incidence of coronary heart disease, high blood pressure, arteriosclerosis, strokes, kidney disease, diabetes and diseases of the digestive system (especially the liver and gall bladder). It is estimated that in the United States in 1964 there were more than 15 million overweight persons. Thus obesity, reaching almost epidemic proportions in our affluent society, is becoming an urgent public health problem (table 69.2).[4]

Although strictly speaking obesity is not a disease, but rather a sign-syndrome, it is justifiably receiving intensive study similar to that previously applied only to serious diseases. Genetic, metabolic, emotional and sociological factors have been implicated. Statistical evidence suggests that a genetic element is concerned in simple obesity. Mayer and others have shown that genetic factors may influence body weight and may cause obesity. The hereditary obesity of a strain of yellow mice is well known. A Mendelian dominant gene carries the characters for yellowness and obesity; nonyellow mice of the same litter are not obese. The basal metabolic rate of the obese animals is said to be reduced and the body temperature subnormal; a hereditary hypothalamic origin of the obesity has been suggested. Another form of obesity in mice which is accompanied by hyperglycemia has been described. The food consumption of these animals is much greater than nonobese controls.

The suggestion (Astwood) that genetic constitution is the chief determining factor seems, however, to be an oversimplification. Mayer cited data showing that children of normal parents have a 9 percent chance of being obese; with one parent obese the probability rises sharply to 50 percent and when both parents are obese the probability is 73 percent. Such findings suggest a genetic "predisposition." The effect could however, be largely environmental, since the kind and amount of food eaten and the social situation of the children and parents would be similar. More convincing clinical evidence for a genetic influence in man has been reported.

[4] For many years the height-weight tables used in North America were based on data collected from insured persons during the periods 1885–1900 and 1909–1927. The new tables (1959) show that men are about 5 pounds *heavier* than formerly; in contrast, women under 40 are about 3 pounds lighter. Among men 20% or more overweight, the excess mortality (*above* "Standard Risk") is currently as follows: for heart disease 43%, cerebral hemorrhage 53%, diabetes 133%, diseases of the digestive system (gall stones, cirrhosis, etc.) 68%.

TABLE 69.2

Comparison of average actual weights and desirable weights

Height	Current Average Weights*			Desirable Weights†		
	Age groups			According to frame structure, at ages 25 and over		
	20–24	30–39	50–59	Small	Medium	Large
Men						
5′4″	136	145	149	118–126	124–126	132–148
6″	142	153	157	124–133	130–143	138–156
8″	149	161	166	132–141	138–152	147–166
10″	157	170	175	140–150	146–160	155–174
6′0″	166	179	185	148–158	154–170	164–184
2″	174	188	194	156–167	162–180	173–194
4″	181	199	205	164–175	172–190	182–204
Women						
5′0″	108	120	130	96–104	101–113	109–125
2″	115	126	136	102–110	107–119	115–131
4″	121	132	144	108–116	113–126	121–138
6″	129	139	152	114–123	120–135	129–146
8″	136	146	160	122–131	128–143	137–154
10″	144	154	169	130–140	136–151	145–163
6′0″	154	164	180	138–148	144–159	153–173

* Build and Blood Pressure Study (1959). Weights in pounds; height with shoes (men 1″ heel, women 2″ heel); wearing indoor clothing.

† Computed by Metropolitan Life Insurance Co. (Statistical Bulletin, 1960). Since longevity is probably the best single criterion of the "correct" weight this has been used to construct the table.

Gordon observed three very obese young women, children of obese parents, adopted in early childhood into foster homes where husband and wife were slim. These obese women had, for most of their lives, eaten at a table that produced slimness in others. They protested that they ate but little food and Gordon confirmed this in metabolic studies.

Numerous studies have strengthened the belief that basic thermodynamic efficiency may vary appreciably from individual to individual. Although the basal metabolic rate per unit of body surface is normal in simple obesity, several definite metabolic defects have been discovered in obese individuals. Abnormally high fasting levels of free (non-esterified) fatty acids (FFA) in the plasma and a decreased responsiveness to lipolytic stimuli have been observed in obese humans and obese experimental animals. Whether

TABLE 69.3

Influence of overweight on mortality

Pounds Overweight	Increase in Death Rate in Persons Aged 45 to 50*	% Overweight	Excess Mortality†	
			Men	Women
10	8			
20	18			
30	28	10	13	9
40	45			
50	56			
60	67	20	25	21
70	81			
90	116	30	42	30

* After Newburgh (1944).

† Build and Blood Pressure Study (1959).

these changes are the cause of obesity, or a result, is not yet clear. These recently found metabolic abnormalities in obesity are receiving active study.

Jacobs, an endocrinologist, has pointed out that hereditary obesity is not congenital. Only the predisposition to obesity is inherited; ultimate obesity is acquired by over-eating. *Obesity is invariably caused by a greater intake of calories in food than is expended in heat production and work.* It is now obvious that overnutrition has detrimental effects on the body and constitutes malnutrition, just as does undernutrition.

Most young people and many mature ones possess an appetite-regulating mechanism (for which Jolliffe has coined the word *appestat*) which adjusts, automatically and very accurately, the intake of food calories to the energy expenditure. An appetite for an amount of food in excess of that required for maintenance of normal weight is called *bulimia*. The "appestat" is located in the hypothalamus. It may be damaged by encephalitis, tumors or by surgical or other means, causing bulimia, leading to obesity. While some forms of obesity are definitely due to a hypothalamic lesion or to several other rare organic conditions (e.g. atrophy of the pituitary, lowered B.M.R., abnormally low blood sugar associated with pancreatic tumors) that cause bulimia, these conditions occur too infrequently to account for the prevalence of obesity in our population.

Carefully conducted investigations, repeatedly confirmed, have established that: (1) obese persons and animals have no defect in *basal* metabolism that can account for their excessive accumulation of fat; (2) the obese exhibit no metabolic defect that permits them to perform work more efficiently (i.e. on less energy) than normal persons. (Actually, the obese have a lessened mechanical efficiency and require a greater expenditure of energy than normal persons to perform the same amount of work); (3) The obese have no defect in specific dynamic action; (4) they absorb no more calories from their food than do normal people; and (5) they have no disorder of the endocrine glands that will account, without bulimia, for their overweight.

Defects of the endocrine glands can affect appetite and can alter the *distribution*[5] of fat, but cannot alter the fact that obesity arises only when more food calories are eaten than are required for the energy expended by the body.

The basic problem in obesity is usually to discover the reason for the increased appetite.[6] Many clinicians working with obese patients feel that emotional factors are the primary cause in a significant proportion of cases. The psychological responses to the stresses of life often lead to increased intake of food (and drink) and decreased activity (physical and social); both changes favor an increase in weight. Emotional and sociological aspects will not be discussed here.

THE "COST" OF OBESITY. (See table 69.3.) (1) Owing to the increased weight, muscular exertion places a greater load upon the heart and circulatory system. The incidence of arterial hypertension is relatively high in persons who are overweight. (2) Dissipation of heat by conduction and radiation (ch. 70) is reduced through the heat-insulating effect of the mantle of subcutaneous fat. Sweating is in consequence more profuse. (3) Diabetes is more common in the obese than in persons of normal weight. Joslin refers to diabetes as "the fat man's folly," and to obesity as "the open door to diabetes." Reducing the weight of an obese diabetic has been found to diminish the sugar excretion by as much as 75 per cent. (4) Persons who are grossly obese are said to be less resistant to infections and poorer surgical risks than those of normal weight. (5) The incidence of gallstones is relatively high in the obese according to Baumann; 88 per cent of persons with

[5] Removal of ovaries before puberty leads to a masculine distribution of fat, castration of the male before or after puberty leads to a feminine distribution. Cushing's syndrome (p. 1522), results in a redistribution of fat from the limbs to the face and trunk; Frölich's syndrome (p. 1525) may lead to extreme obesity of trunk and upper limbs yet the hands and feet are small and shapely.

[6] Anand has reviewed knowledge about the nervous regulation of food intake (Physiol. Rev., 1961, **41,** 677).

gallstones are overweight. (6) *Life expectancy.* Insurance statistics show that overweight after the age of 35 years is associated with a death rate much higher than that of lean persons or of those of normal weight, a fact which has been pithily expressed in the phrase, "the longer the belt the shorter the life."

GENERAL PRINCIPLES IN THE TREATMENT OF OBESITY. The basis of treatment should be, as already indicated, (a) reduction in the calorie intake and (b) increase in the energy expenditure through moderate exercise. The dietary restrictions should not be extreme and should be made gradually. The extent to which the calorie intake should be reduced will depend upon the degree of obesity and the amount of exercise prescribed, but it should never be pushed to the point where the protein of the subject's tissues is drawn upon for energy purposes; nitrogen equilibrium should be maintained. Above all things a properly balanced diet should be devised and an adequate supply of vitamins and minerals provided. When the obesity is pronounced (body weight 25 per cent or more above normal), weight reduction is brought about by placing the subject upon a diet possessing a caloric value 40 or even 60 per cent below his energy requirement; he is thus forced to consume his own fat. The calorie value of human adipose tissue is about 3500 Calories per pound.[7] The total requirement of the average obese subject is around 2500 Calories per day. A reduction in the energy intake by 40 per cent of the requirement, that is, to 1500 Calories, will therefore entail a weight loss of nearly a third of a pound per day. The subject is kept upon the restricted diet until the desired weight has been reached; his calorie intake is then adjusted to his requirement (see ch. 73).

The failure of an overweight person to lose weight promptly after having been placed upon a "reducing" diet has been a mystifying observation which appeared to refute the conclusion that obesity is due simply to a balance of energy intake over energy output. But the original weight is maintained for only two or three weeks, and is due to the retention of water which replaces the tissue broken down for energy purposes. At the end of this period water excretion increases above the normal and the weight falls rapidly (Fig. 69.2).

Ideally, the reducing diet should form the basis for dietary re-education so that proper eating habits will continue after the desired loss of weight has been attained (Jolliffe). A slow but

[7] Pure human fat has a caloric value of approximately 9.5 Cal. per gram. 3500 Cal. per pound here given is the value after allowance has been made for connective tissue and water content.

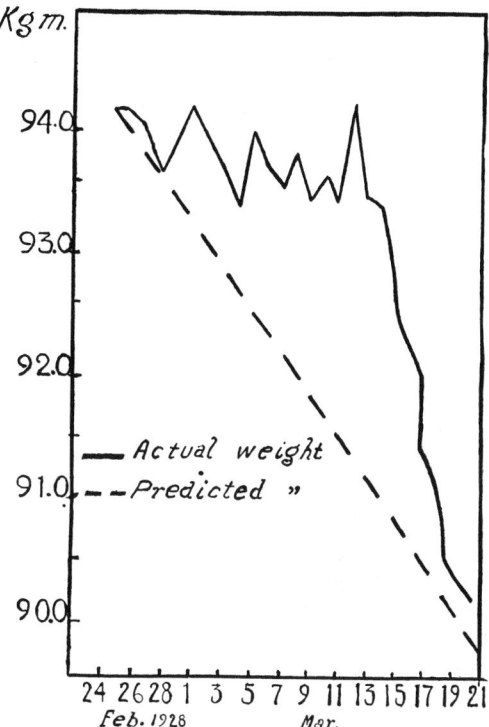

FIG. 69.2. Showing the delay in the loss of weight on a reducing diet owing to the retention of the water. (After Newburgh, modified.) This subject lost as much weight in 6 days (March 12 to 18) as it was predicted would be lost in about three weeks as a result of the destruction of body tissue and without water retention.

steady loss of weight is much to be preferred to drastic procedures because it permits the patient's "appestat" to become adjusted to a lower level of energy intake. Jolliffe points out that periodic "cheating" while on a reducing diet not only interferes with the steady weight loss but tends to recondition the "appestat" at a higher level than is desired. As mentioned above the reducing diet should contain sufficient high quality protein to prevent breakdown of vital body tissues: about 1 gram for each kilogram of *ideal* body weight (table 69.2) is the smallest amount that will provide sufficient essential amino acids over a prolonged reducing regimen. Restriction of the more concentrated forms of food is particularly desirable, according to many authorities, but this is questioned by the proponents of the high-fat reducing regimens (see below). Sugar in the form of sweetening for beverages, in jams, honey or chocolates is a highly concentrated food. By curtailing its consumption a large reduction in the calorie value of the diet can be effected without the disadvantages attending the reduction of some of the other foods. Bulky foods, e.g., green vegetables and salads of low calorie value but satisfying to the appetite may be substituted. Undue restriction of the water intake is sometimes practiced but this measure appears to be of no benefit and may be a detriment to health. Alcohol has a high calorie value and is therefore, except in minimal amounts, excluded from the diet.

Thyroid extract is sometimes employed to raise the metabolic rate and so reduce the obesity. The hormone is clearly indicated as a means of raising a low metabolic rate to normal, otherwise its use is not to be advocated except in exceptional cases and only when the subject's basal metabolic rate can be followed by frequent determinations. *Dinitrophenol* is another agent which raises the metabolic rate and has been employed in the treatment of obesity. It is a dangerous drug unless given under the strictest supervision. Cataract has been reported following its use; liver injury may also result.

While the above well established facts continue to be the basis of the treatment of obesity some new ones are struggling for acceptance. Dramatic weight loss on a high fat diet was described by William Banting, the excessively fat and prosperous undertaker who made the Duke of Wellington's coffin, in a famous pamphlet published at his own expense in 1864. Although his facts were clear they failed to fit accepted theories and were therefore not accorded the study they warranted. Clinical studies in New York about 20 years ago (Donaldson) belatedly confirmed the findings and showed that Banting was no charlatan. In 1956 Kekwick and Pawan described careful metabolic studies of obese patients fed a variety of diets. They confirmed the well accepted view that the rate of weight loss is proportional to deficiency in calorie intake, when the proportions of fat, carbohydrate and protein are kept constant at each level of calorie restriction. However, at a constant energy intake (say 1000 Calories), the *rate of weight loss varied greatly on diets of different composition*, being most rapid with high-fat diets. They showed that obese patients whose weight

was maintained (or increased) on 2000 Calories of the usual mixed diets lost weight when the intake was raised to 2600 Calories *provided mainly in the form of fat and protein*. Thus the refractive obese patient appears to suffer from some defect in dealing with carbohydrate which leads to an unnatural conversion of it to fat and to storage of the fat. Avoidance of too much dietary carbohydrate reduces this tendency. A striking resistance to ketosis is found in the obese. The treatment of obesity is still in a dynamic state and the use of high fat diets deserves further study.

REFERENCES

Monographs and Reviews

BENEDICT, F. G. A study of prolonged fasting. Carnegie Inst., Washington, Pub. 203, 1915.

BERRYMAN, G. H. Metabolism, 1954, 3, 544.

Build and Blood Pressure Study. 1959. Vol. I. Chicago Soc. of Actuaries, 1959.

CANNON, P. R. Sc. Monthly 1943, 56, 5. Food and the War. *In* Medicine and the War, ed. by W. H. Taliaferro, pp. 23–39. University of Chicago Press, Chicago, 1944.

CONN, J. W. Physiol. Rev., 1944, 24, 31.

GOLDNER, M. G. (ed.) Symposium on obesity. Metabolism, 1957, 6, 404.

HALPERN, S. L. (ed.) Symposium on obesity. *In:* Medical Clinics of North America, 1964, 48, pp. 1283–1405.

JOLLIFFE, N. Reduce and stay reduced on the prudent diet. 3rd ed. Simon and Schuster, New York, 1963.

KEKWICK, A. AND PAWAN, G. L. S. Lancet, 1956, 2, 155.

KEYS, A., BROZEK, J., HENSCHEL, A., MICKELSEN, O. AND TAYLOR, H. L. The biology of human starvation, vols. I and II. University of Minnesota Press, Minneapolis, 1950.

LUSK, G. Physiol. Rev., 1921, 1, 523.

MACKARNESS, R. Eat fat and grow slim. The Harvill Press, London, 1958.

MAYER, J. Physiological and nutritional aspects of obesity. Borden's Rev. Nutrition Res., 1958, 19, 35.

METROPOLITAN LIFE INS. Co. Overweight: its prevention and significance. Statistical Bulletin, 1960.

NEWBURGH, L. H. Physiol. Rev., 1944, 24, 18.

TEPPERMAN, J. Perspectives Biol. Med., 1958, 1, 293.

CHAPTER 70

The Body Temperature

The normal body temperature, recorded from the mouth, is usually given as 98.6°F. (37.0°C.). The rectal temperature averages ⁶⁄₁₀ of a degree F. higher than this and the axillary temperature at least 1 degree F. lower. No absolute figure can be given, for there is a wide variation between individuals. The oral temperatures of a large group of normal persons range from 96.6° to 100.0°F. (35.8° to 37.8°C.), the average being around 98.4°F. (36.9°C.). Ivy, in a study of nearly 300 medical students, obtained a mean oral temperature of 98.1°F. (36.7°C). Variations in the body temperature also occur in the same individual throughout the day—a difference of 2.0 or even 3.0°F. occurring between the maximum in the late afternoon or early evening, and the minimum between 3 and 5 o'clock in the morning. In night workers the times of the maximal and minimal temperatures may be reversed. The temperature of the internal organs is higher by several degrees than the temperature of the skin. The temperature of the liver, for example, is about 100°F. (37.8°C.), whereas that of the skin covered with clothes is from 85° to 93°F. (29.5° to 33.9°C.). The temperature of the bare skin varies widely, of course, with the environmental temperature. The influence of the latter upon the temperature of the covered skin will depend upon the heat-insulating properties of the clothing, air movement (breeze, wind), atmospheric moisture, etc. Strenuous muscular exercise causes a temporary rise in body temperature of 1.0° to 4.0°F. or more; a temperature of over 104°F. (40.0°C.) during exercise has been reported (L. Hill).

The heat-regulating mechanisms are not fully developed at birth. The body temperature of the newborn child, although in general the same as that of the adult, tends to be irregular and unstable. Spontaneous variations of from 1 to 2°F. are common during the first year. Excitement or other strong emotion, even in older children, may raise the temperature by as much as 2°F.

The Regulation of Body Temperature

The almost unchanging body temperature of warm-blooded animals, living under a variety of environmental conditions, indicates a remarkably efficient thermostatic control and regulating system. The temperature of a warm-blooded (homoiothermic) animal remains practically unchanged although the surrounding temperature may vary between 0°F. or less and 100°F. or upwards. On the contrary, the body temperature of a cold-blooded (poikilothermic) animal such as the frog, turtle, etc., is practically that of its environment (fig. 70.1).

Heat is continuously being produced within the body by metabolic activity, the rate of heat production being minimal during sleep and increased by muscular activity. In order to maintain a constant temperature, the rate of heat loss must be adjusted to equal the rate of heat production. This process is complicated by the varying environmental temperatures. A high ambient temperature reduces the rate of heat loss. A low temperature may increase the rate of heat loss to such an extent that metabolism must be increased by means of shivering to maintain the balance. With environmental temperatures in excess of the body temperature, or if heat is being produced rapidly by muscular activity, the evaporation of sweat is necessary to dispose of the excess heat. Shivering and sweating are "emergency" measures. Throughout the range of moderate temperatures the rate of heat loss can be regulated by varying the rate of blood flow through the skin. Heat is produced mainly in the deeper structures (muscles and viscera), which are insulated from the environment by subcutaneous fat and skin. The heat is transported by the blood which is warmed in the deep central structures and cooled at the body surface. Although the temperature of the skin may vary widely, the central or "core" temperature is maintained homeostatically within a very narrow range. The body absorbs heat radiated from surrounding objects with temperatures higher than its own, and from direct or reflected sunshine, a stove or an open fire. Heat is also gained by the ingestion of hot food. Heat production is the result of chemical reactions and was therefore called the "chemical" regulation of body temperature by Rubner. Heat loss is dependent upon physical (and physiological) factors—"physical" regulation. These terms are redundant and an oversimplification, since the chemical and physical cannot be separated.

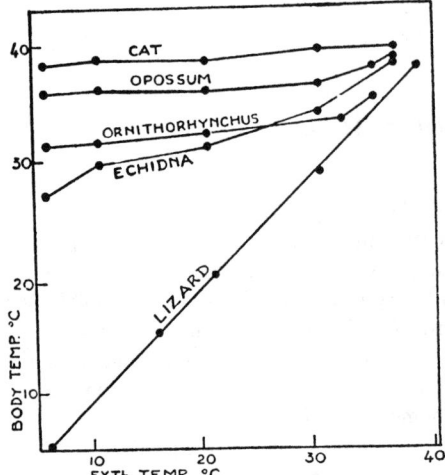

FIG. 70.1. Variation of body temperature of different types of animals by sojourn for two hours in an environment of 5° to 35°C. (After Martin.)

Under basal conditions, when no external work is being done, all the metabolic energy ultimately appears as heat. If this heat were not lost to the body, the body temperature would rise. The basal metabolic rate usually produces heat amounting to about one Calorie per kilogram of body weight per hour. Since the body is composed chiefly of water, it has a specific heat of a little less than one, so the body temperature would rise about 1°C. per hour if no heat were lost.

With strenuous physical exertion more than three-quarters of the increased metabolism appears as heat within the body; the remainder appears as external work. Fever increases the metabolic rate; the average increase being 13 per cent to each degree C. rise (7.2 per cent per degree F.). This change in metabolism corresponds to a temperature coefficient (Q_{10}) of between 2.0 and 3.0. The temperature coefficients of the various metabolic reactions are not, however, identical, consequently, a rise in temperature causes a disturbance in the metabolic pattern of the body. The resulting disorganization of function in the brain is made evident by the delirium induced by high fever and the mental confusion accompanying hypothermia.

The body's heat-regulating mechanism is supposed to be in abeyance below an internal temperature of 75°F., because the activity of the underlying nervous structures is suppressed. The body then gains or loses heat like an inanimate object. The lower lethal temperature for the human is about 79.5°F. (26°C.), although lower temperatures have been induced with survival during therapeutic hypothermia. Death is due to cardiac failure. The upper lethal limit is not clearly defined; cases are recorded to have recovered after attaining a rectal temperature of 110.8°F. (43.5° C.). Probably the average upper limit is about 110°F. (43°C.) (See DuBois).

HEAT LOSS

Although the body temperature is in excess of the ambient temperature in temperate climates, the constant production of heat by metabolism necessitates a constant dissipation of heat. It is only under exceptional circumstances that in such climates the excess heat of the environment must be counteracted in addition to the normal metabolic heat. In cold weather where more heat is lost than can be balanced by that of the resting metabolism extra heat is produced by increased muscular activity—increased tension of muscles, shivering, "goose flesh," and shaking. Throughout the range of moderate temperatures, i.e., within the comfort zone, neither shivering nor sweating occurs even while the body is at rest. Heat is lost from the body mainly at the skin surface, although some is lost through the respiratory passages where air comes in contact with the body.

Heat is lost from the body through: (a) radiation, conduction and convection from the skin; (b) warming and humidifying inspired air; (c) evaporation of sweat and insensible perspiration; (d) urine and feces.

Of these various routes only (a) and (c) are directly under physiological control. The temperature of the skin determines the rate of heat loss from the body surface. The heat lost in warming and moistening the inspired air, and the rate of evaporation through the skin (insensible perspiration) will depend upon the temperature and humidity of the ambient air. It is only indirectly, by creating a "local climate" by means of clothing or air conditioned dwellings, that these avenues of heat loss can be regulated.

Under the ordinary conditions of every day life over 95 per cent of the total heat loss occurs through (a), (b) and (c). The heat lost in raising the temperature of the inspired air to body temperature (c) will, of course, vary with the air temperature, but at ordinary room temperatures it does not amount to more than 2 or 3 per cent of the total. Air is a very poor conductor, so terrestrial animals conduction plays a very minor role except under special circumstances, as when the body is in contact with a cool object, cold ground or immersed in water. Radiation is responsible for about 50 per cent of the total heat loss and convection for about 15 per cent (see table below). The heat lost in the urine and feces accounts for only 2 per cent, or less, of the total heat loss.

The total quantity of heat lost in 24 hours must, of course, just equal the amount produced; otherwise the body temperature would rise or fall. The heat production of an average man doing light work is about 3000 Calories. The proportions of this which are dissipated through the various channels at ordinary room temperature are given in the following table, in approximate figures.

	Calories	Per cent
(a) Radiation, convection and conduction...............	1950	65
(b) Evaporation of water from skin and lungs, and liberation of CO_2..............	900	30
(c) Warming inspired air........	90	3
(d) Urine and feces (i.e., heat of these excreta over that of the food and water)........	60	2
Total daily heat loss.............	3000	100

RADIATION AND CONVECTION AND THEIR VARIATION BY PHYSIOLOGICAL FACTORS

The rate of cooling of any warm object varies with the temperature of the air and of colder objects in contact with or near it. When a large temperature difference exists between the two, the warm object loses heat rapidly through radiation, convection and conduction. The rate of heat loss, however, becomes gradually less as the temperature of the object approaches that of the environment. The dead human body behaves in a manner similar to that of any inanimate object, taking from 10 to 20 hours on an average to reach the temperature of its surroundings. In the living body, on the other hand, factors operate to encourage or minimize heat loss, respectively, when the environmental temperature is high or low, or corresponding changes in the body's heat production occur.

The factors involved in heat conservation or heat loss are dependent to a large extent upon reactions of the autonomic nervous system. The following are the principal adjustments which take place in the blood-vascular system. (a) *Redistribution of blood*. The subcutaneous tissue acts as an insulating layer. The insulating quality of this layer can be altered by varying the blood flow through it. By the redistribution of blood the temperature of the skin may be adjusted to any temperature from about 15°C. (59°F.) up to

the central body temperature. At a room (ambient) temperature of 34°C. (93°F.) the quantity of blood circulating through the skin may, according to DuBois, amount to 12 per cent of the cardiac output. Scott, Bazett and Mackie found that the blood flow through the fingers would increase from 1 cc. per minute per 100 grams of tissue in a cool environment to 80 or 90 cc. per minute upon exposure to heat. These changes may be initiated in one or all of four ways, a change in temperature of the blood supplying the nervous centers; reflexly through centers in the brain and cord in response to changes in skin temperature (stimulation of hot or cold spots, p. 52); through local axon reflexes, and finally through responses of the vessels to direct stimulation by changes in external temperature. (b) *Variations in blood volume* (see p. 500). A rise in temperature causes an increase in blood volume; the blood is diluted by fluid drawn into the circulation from the tissues, chiefly the skin, muscles and liver. Blood is expelled from the spleen (p. 535). It has been found that an unacclimatized man is capable of increasing the total circulating blood volume by about 10 per cent in 2 or 4 hours on exposure to heat of sufficient severity to cause a diffuse cutaneous vasodilatation. The increased blood volume is chiefly in the plasma although additional cells may be added from the spleen. The initial increase of the blood is brought about by dilution with water drawn from the other cells, so that the hematocrit drops a little and the plasma protein concentration decreases. Associated with the decreased osmotic pressure of the plasma protein a mild edema of the ankles is frequently observed in unacclimatized persons suddenly exposed to heat. The body can manufacture the proteins rapidly so that after two or three days exposure to heat the blood osmotic pressure has been restored and the edema will disappear. At low temperatures the blood volume is reduced, the blood becoming more concentrated as shown by an increase in the percentage of blood solids. The sudden return to a cool environment causes a rapid decrease of blood volume associated with a marked diuresis. This is frequently seen in moving from the tropical plains in India to the temperate hill stations (Powell, personal comment). (c) *Increased circulation rate*. The increased cardiac output ensures a rapid blood flow through the dilated cutaneous vessels.

As already stated, half of the total heat loss is brought about through radiation. The human skin (of whatever color) within the range of the infrared to which it is usually exposed, is an almost perfect "black body radiator." That is to say, it radiates nearly all infrared rays[1] (up to 1 or 2 per cent) or absorbs to the same extent such rays as fall upon it (Hardy and Muschenheim).

The skin and the subcutaneous tissues when the vessels are constricted are a little more efficient as insulating material than a layer of cork of the same thickness (DuBois). The subcutaneous layer varies considerably in thickness in different persons and is thicker in women than in men. This accounts for the greater ability of women than of men to withstand cold.

The radiating surface of the standing human body[2] is only about 85 per cent of the total surface area, for apposed surfaces, e.g., axillae, inner surfaces of the thighs and upper arms, do not lose heat to the environment by radiation. It is for this reason that one huddles in the cold and spreads out one's limbs in the heat. Adolph has shown that the nude man, sitting in the sun, absorbs on an average 143 Calories per hour by radiation. This is reduced by clothing. Molnar *et al.* found that clothing by reflecting radiation can diminish the absorption of heat from the sun and sky by about 60 Calories per hour. On the other hand, clothing will reduce heat loss by radiation since the external surface of the clothing has a lower temperature than the skin and consequently radiates less heat. The main factor influencing heat loss through radiation is the temperature of surrounding objects relative to that of the skin. The body, for example, radiates heat to a block of ice but absorbs heat from a hot stove or radiator. It should be remembered that the air intervening between the body and the source of heat is not heated by radiant energy, but only by convection. Another factor, though a very minor one, is the humidity of the atmosphere. Air with a high water vapor content is more opaque to radiant heat than dry air. Heat lost through radiation is therefore slightly reduced when the relative humidity is high.

CONVECTION. The rate of movement of warm air from the neighborhood of a heated object varies, of course, with the temperature of the atmosphere. The clothed body has a layer of warm moist air in contact with the skin which tends to become trapped in this situation and in the spaces of the clothing. In the absence of a temperature difference between it and the external air or of some movement to cause mixing, this air will remain practically stagnant and little or

no heat is lost through convection. However, when the atmosphere is cooler, convection currents are set up which mix the air lying against the skin with fresh air. Convection is essentially dependent upon the relative densities of air at different temperatures, the warmer and lighter air rising, the cooler air falling. Dry air is denser than air possessing a high content of water vapor. One would expect therefore that changes in the humidity of the atmosphere should alter the heat lost by convection, but as a matter of fact, the relative humidity of the external air has little effect upon heat loss through convection. Probably the most important factor influencing heat loss by convection is air movement, the loss increasing with the square of the wind velocity up to 60 miles per hour; a wind velocity beyond this exerts little or no further effect.

EVAPORATION OF WATER

It is obvious that the nearer the temperature of the environment comes to that of the blood the smaller will be the amount of heat which can be lost by radiation and convection. At an air temperature of about 98.6°F. (37°C.) heat loss by these means must cease. At higher air temperatures than this the body, would actually gain heat if no other means of cooling were available. Large quantities of heat are lost to the body through the secretion and evaporation of sweat and the exhalation of water vapor, expired air being 95 per cent saturated with moisture. Its temperature can for this reason, be maintained constant when the atmosphere (dry) has a temperature about 150°F. (65°C.) above that of the blood. The heat absorbed in the evaporation of 1 cc. of water amounts to 0.58 Calorie. Even at ordinary room temperatures, when there is no obvious perspiration, the heat lost through evaporation from the lungs and skin amounts to about 17 Calories per hour. About two-thirds of this is from insensible perspiration through the skin, the remainder from the lungs. Newburgh and his associates have found that people, living in a cool environment performing only the routines of life, lost heat by the insensible evaporation of water from the skin and lungs, equivalent to about 24 per cent of the metabolic rate; the absolute amount depending upon the metabolic rate. At higher temperatures the increase in the proportion of heat lost by evaporation of water as compared with that lost by radiation and convection is shown in figure 70.2. It will be seen that evaporation plays little part in heat regulation until the air temperature reaches between

---

[1] The wave length of the infrared rays emitted by skin at usual temperature (34°C.) is 9440 mμ.
[2] This has been called the *profile area.*

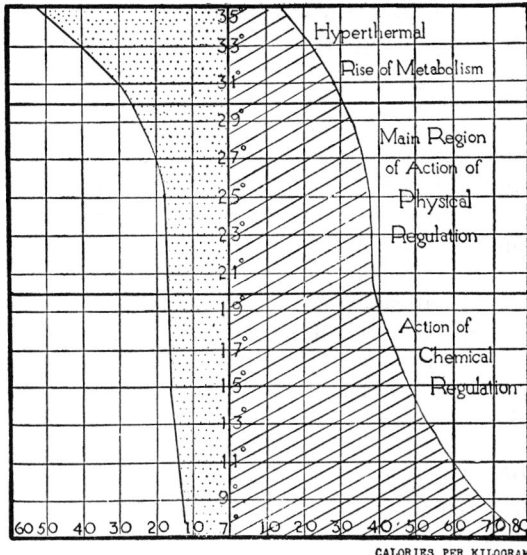

FIG. 70.2. Rubner's chart showing the manner of heat loss in the dog at different room temperatures. Stippled area, heat loss in calories through evaporation of water; cross-hatched area, heat loss in calories through radiation and convection. The distance between opposite points on the curved boundary lines represents the total heat production at a particular temperature. (Redrawn and slightly modified from Lusk.)

28° and 30°C. (82° to 84.5°F.), the heat loss by this means remaining nearly constant below this level but increasing rapidly above it. At a temperature above 35°C. evaporation accounts for all or nearly all the heat lost.

It is to be remembered that evaporation from the body surface occurs quite independently of sweat secretion, for the skin is not entirely impervious to water; fluid extravasated from the cutaneous capillaries seeps into the epidermis. There is a continuous diffusion through the epidermis from the moist deep layers to the dry skin surface. The evaporation of this water that diffuses through the skin has been called insensible perspiration. The speed by which water diffuses through the skin is determined by the diffusion gradient and is greatest in dry atmospheres when the water vapor pressure of the air is low and the skin dries rapidly. It has been shown in persons in whom sweat glands were absent from birth that some 18 grams of water per square meter of body surface may be lost hourly by evaporation. This is about the same as that of a normal man under ordinary conditions, and represents a total daily heat loss of about 450 Calories for a body of average size (surface area 1.8 square meters), which is not far from the normal. At high temperatures, or even during mild exercise, however, a person without sweat glands is at a great disadvantage; his body temperature will rise.

The respirations are increased by a rise in air temperature or by a greater heat production; the heat loss through warming the inspired air and the vaporization of water from the lungs, and the liberation of CO_2, is thereby increased. Hyperpnea (panting) is the chief means possessed by the dog (in which functioning sweat glands are largely confined to the footpads) for increasing the vaporization of water and combating a rise in body temperature.

The rate of evaporation of water is influenced inversely by the degree to which the atmosphere is already saturated with moisture, i.e., by its relative humidity.[3] Sweat which is not evaporated but simply drips from the skin, of course does not increase heat loss. For this reason the sweating mechanism for the elimination of heat is badly crippled when the relative humidity is high.[4] We are all familiar with the insufferable heat of a hot humid day, and the comparative comfort when

[3] It is dependent essentially upon the difference in the vapor pressure at the skin and of the surrounding air.

[4] The relative humidity is defined as the ratio of the weight of water vapor contained in a given volume of air to the weight which the same volume of air would contain when saturated. The quantity of water vapor which air can hold when saturated increases with the temperature. The relative humidity is expressed as a percentage. Thus, if a sample of air at a certain temperature contains 20 per cent of the water vapor which it is possible for it to contain at that temperature, it is 20 per cent saturated, and so has a relative humidity of 20 per cent.

the air is simply hot and dry. A man can maintain a normal temperature in an atmosphere of from 240° to 260°F. (a temperature that will grill a beefsteak) provided the air is perfectly dry; his ability to sweat profusely is sustained by large draughts of water, and evaporation is facilitated by stripping the greater part of the body's surface. On the other hand, a damp atmosphere with a temperature of 120°F. causes the body temperature to rise rapidly, and cannot be endured for more than a few minutes. Evaporation and consequently heat loss by this means is greatly hastened by air movement. The layer of air nearly saturated with water vapor lying next the skin is thus replaced by drier air.

SWEATING

Sweat is a weak solution of sodium chloride in water together with urea and small quantities of potassium and lactic acid. It has a specific gravity of from 1.002 to 1.003. Its pH as reported by different observers varies from 4.2 to 7.5. The percentage of sodium chloride varies between 0.2 and 0.5. Muscular exercise increases the salt concentration, which is also higher in sweat secreted by clothed than by naked skin. The quantity of nonprotein nitrogen ordinarily excreted in the sweat, per day, is according to Benedict, 0.071 gram; on the other hand, if the sweating is copious from 0.5 to 1.0 gram may be eliminated per hour. The actual concentration of nitrogen in the sweat falls, however, when sweating becomes profuse, whereas the concentrations of sodium chloride and potassium rise. However, when acclimatization has been established the percentage of salt diminishes. About 3 grams of salt daily are required after acclimatization to maintain the salt balance. Nevertheless, even after acclimatization, if strenuous work is performed for a long period in a high temperature, and large quantities of water are drunk, depletion of the body's supplies of chloride and a lowered concentration of this element in blood and tissue fluids occurs, producing severe cramps in the muscles of the limbs and abdominal wall (heat or stoker's cramps; see p. 1423).

THE CONTROL OF SWEAT SECRETION. The sweat glands, which number over two and a half million in a man living in temperate climates, are cholinergic yet under the control of the sympathetic nervous system. These glands are, however, anomalous in their responses to sympathetic and parasympathetic drugs, in that they are stimulated by muscarine, pilocarpine and acetylcholine, and inhibited by atropine (ch. 11). According to

Coon and Rothman, the action of acetylcholine is twofold—stimulation of the glands directly through a muscarinelike action and through the initiation of axon reflexes (nicotinelike action). In man and most animals, they are not excited by adrenaline nor paralyzed by ergotoxine. The usual stimulus to sweat secretion is a rise in blood temperature which exerts its effect in two ways— directly upon the nervous centers, which is of more importance, and reflexly by stimulation of heat receptors in the skin. The sweat response to a rise in temperature is abolished by sectioning the nerves to a part and is therefore not due to direct stimulation of the glands. That a rise in temperature of the centers alone will induce the secretion of sweat has been shown by heating the hypothalamus in the cat (whose sweat glands are confined to the paw pads); sweating then occurs although the paws themselves remain cold. The centers may also be stimulated in man by the injection of pituitrin into the lateral ventricle. In the initial stages of muscular exercise sweating is apparently initiated by the discharge of impulses from the motor cortex. It occurs before there is any change in rectal temperature. Later on, the effect of a rise in body temperature comes into play. In a man (indoor clothing) at rest, visible sweating usually commences at an air temperature between 27° and 32°C. (80 and 90°F.). Sweating may be induced by the experimental stimulation of regions of the diencephalon (hypothalamus, p. 156). Spinal centers for segmental control of sweating exist, for peripheral sweating occurs in quadraplegic patients who have complete transverse cervical cord lesions. Such patients have lost temperature control to a large extent, for neither adequate sweating, shivering nor changes in cutaneous blood flow can occur for the regulation of body temperature. Destruction of the sympathetic nerve supply to a part completely abolishes the sweating response to a rise in temperature. The sweat glands, however, still respond to pilocarpine and acetylcholine. The former drug, which has been employed in the past for the purpose of demarcating areas deprived of their sympathetic supply, is of no diagnostic value, for it acts peripherally, i.e., directly upon the gland cells. Sweating is not dependent upon the circulation for it occurs after occlusion of the vessels and can even be induced by stimulation of the nerves in an amputated limb. Although usually associated with cutaneous vasodilation it may occur with constricted vessels—"cold sweat." This is usually the result of psychic influences, e.g., nervousness, fear, fatigue or mental work. The sweating occurs most noticeably in these instances on the forehead, the palms of the hands, and the soles of the feet, which do not, as a rule give a pronounced response to heat. In many persons, reflex sweating, confined to the face and neck, is induced by eating spicy or appetizing food (gustatory sweating), or sometimes sweating over a remote part, e.g., the knee, occurs. Faradic stimulation of the human skin over the forearm induces local sweating due apparently to direct stimulation of the glands, for it occurs after section and degeneration of the nerve supply.

The few observations that have been made upon the secretion pressure of sweat indicate that it is high, 250 mm. of mercury or more. Sweat is therefore a true secretion and not simply a filtrate. The secretion rate may be enormous, amounting to a liter or more per hour, and may be increased some 80 times over the normal by immersing the body in a bath at 108°F. At ordinary room temperatures the sweat evaporates as quickly as formed, so that there is no apparent secretion.

HEAT PRODUCTION

The several factors which stimulate the chemical processes of the body and so increase the heat production have been dealt with in chapter 44. An account of the manner in which chemical and physical factors interact to maintain a constant body temperature remains to be given.

A low environmental temperature is a potent influence in stimulating heat production. At air temperatures below about 28°C. (82.4°F.) the body (nude) loses heat rapidly. Within the temperature range between 28° and 31°C. (87.8°F.), the naked male body is able quite easily to maintain the balance between heat loss and heat production. There is neither sweating nor shivering and a male subject feels comfortable. This range of temperature is therefore called the "comfort zone." For reasons given below the comfort zone is broader (27° to 33°C. or 80.6°F. to 91.4°F.) for women. The external temperature (about 23°C. or 73.4°F.) below which heat production must be increased in order to maintain a normal body temperature is sometimes called the "critical temperature."

Below the critical temperature heat loss by radiation and convection increases progressively with falling air temperature, but heat loss by vaporization shows little change. The naked body at a temperature below the comfort level (28°C. or 82.4°F.) loses more heat than it can produce in the basal state, and at about 23°C. (73.4°F.) shivering occurs. Heat production is thus increased in

an effort to raise the body temperature to the normal level. In the human, heat production is not increased until the onset of shivering and in nude men under basal conditions the metabolism remains constant within the range of air temperature from 35° to 23°C. (96° to 73.4°F.). It has been shown by Hardy and DuBois that this is not true for women. They show a reduced heat production of from 14 to 20 per cent at temperatures between 30° and 32°C. (86° and 89°F.). Also, owing to the greater insulation afforded by the thicker layer of subcutaneous fat the heat loss of the female body in a cold environment is some 10 per cent less than that of men. Thus women have the more efficient thermoregulating mechanism, being better able to maintain the heat balance at lower temperatures without shivering, and also to be more comfortable at higher temperatures.

The critical temperature and the temperature of comfort will vary of course with the amount and nature of the clothing. The cooling effect of water by conduction is some 20 times greater than that of air—a cold bath at 4°C. (40°F.) increasing the heat production some 5 times above the basal level.[5] Few men can survive for long in very cold water, below 4°C. (approximately 40°F.) which is about the winter temperature of the sea in temperate latitudes. Heat production becomes depressed after immersion for 20 minutes or so, and the body temperature falls. In an experiment in Germany during the last war, one man survived a temperature of 5.5°C. (42°F.) for three hours. His body temperature was then 25.2°C. (77.3°F.).

It will be seen from figure 70.3 that heat loss increases both above and below the critical temperature. At the lower temperatures heat is lost mainly by radiation and convection, at the higher temperatures mainly by vaporization. It will also be noticed that at the lower temperatures the skin temperatures follow a straight line, but that the curve commences to flatten out at around 30°C. (87°F.). This is attributed to dilation of the cutaneous vessels and the flooding of the skin with blood.

The muscular tissues (particularly of the extremities) and the liver, wherein numerous chemical reactions are carried out, are the main sources of the body's heat. The rise in metabolism which results from a fall in atmospheric temperature is effected through an increase in activity of the

---

[5] In cold-blooded animals the metabolism as measured by the carbon dioxide output falls with the environmental temperature.

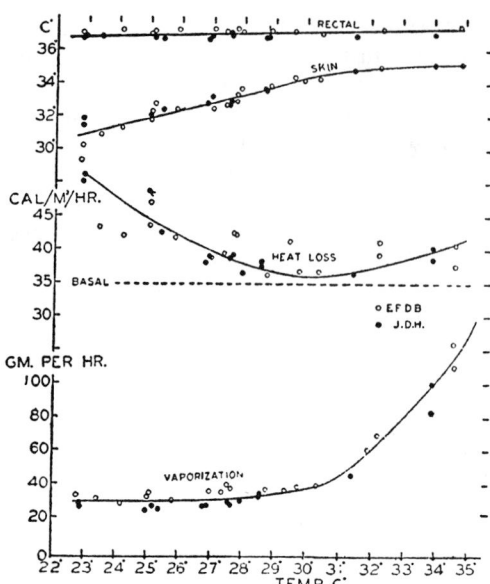

FIG. 70.3. Showing effect of a rising air temperature on rectal and skin temperatures, heat loss, and vaporization. (Modified from DuBois.)

skeletal muscles and in some instances by fine involuntary contractions, e.g., shivering and chattering of the teeth and increased muscular tension. By these means the heat production may be increased approximately three times over the resting level. Contractions of the smooth muscle of the skin, giving rise to "goose flesh" also contribute heat. In some mammals and in birds, the contraction of the cutaneous muscles also curtails heat loss through ruffling of the hair or feathers. In man, too, the smooth muscle of the skin may, when stimulated by cold, cause erection of the fine hair on the body surface; the effect however is rudimentary and without value. After the skeletal muscles are paralyzed by curare, an animal loses the power to maintain a normal body temperature in a cold environment. Its ability to dissipate heat is, however, intact so that it can resist high air temperatures. Isolation of the muscles from control by section of the cord in the lower cervical region (C6) also abolishes the extra heat production. This operation divides as well the vasoconstrictor nerves which travel through the cervical cord to the sympathetic outflow in the thoracic region. A redistribution of blood is not possible, and the body temperature will fall if the animal is exposed to a low air temperature. The rise in body temperature in strenuous muscular effort is apparently due, not to any failure of the heat-dissipating mechanisms, but because heat is produced more rapidly than it can be dissipated.

Food, especially protein through its specific dynamic action, is an important factor in the regulation of body temperature. At high environmental temperatures the specific dynamic action of food increases the heat production and adds an extra burden upon the heat loss mechanisms. For this reason a low protein diet is more suitable in hot weather. At very low atmospheric temperatures, on the contrary, the specific dynamic effect of food is almost completely masked, since it simply replaces the environmental effect (cold) upon heat production. That is to say, the neuromuscular mechanisms called into play to increase heat production at low temperature are less necessary since the food itself raises the level of metabolism. Protein food in cold climates is therefore a valuable aid to the regulation of body temperature.

The effect of protein ingestion upon the heat production of a dog at different temperatures is shown in table 70.1 (Lusk).

STORAGE OF HEAT. The body has a large specific heat (about 0.85), so that a rise in the temperature of a 70-kg. man of 1°C. may increase the stored heat by about 60 Calories, or 2 per cent of the average daily heat production. A considerable storage of heat may occur in strenuous muscular exercise (140 Calories or so in a 100-yard sprint), and, until the heat-dissipating mechanisms become fully effective, the body temperature may rise 2°C. or more. A rise in rectal temperature may also occur in a robust person after a cold plunge. The cold water causes, through vasoconstriction, diminished heat dissipation and through involuntary muscular action increased heat production. The body temperature may rise for a few minutes. After the first effect of the plunge the vessels are released from spasm, the stored heat is eliminated, the surface of the body glows and a feeling of comfortable warmth is experienced. This constitutes the "healthy reaction" of a cold shower. A comparable drop in rectal tem-

TABLE 70.1

Atmospheric Temperature	Heat Production in Calories per Kilogram of Body Weight		
	Starved	550 grams of meat fed	Increase
°C			
4.2	128	133	4
14.5	101	111	9
22.1	71	101	43
30.7	62	117	89

perature has been observed on suddenly passing from a temperate to a hot environment, or on entering a hot bath.

HEAT REGULATING CENTERS

Section of the neuraxis through the midbrain at the level of the superior colliculi, or at any level posterior to this and anterior to the lower cervical cord, renders an animal poikilothermic (fig. 70.4). Section of the cord in the upper thoracic region, i.e., above the level of the outflow of the greater part of the sympathetic fibers causes a gross disturbance in the temperature regulation. The muscles of the head, neck and forelimbs remain in communication with the brain, so that shivering in these parts will prevent a fall in body temperature. On the other hand, the hypothalamus has lost control over the temperature regulation of ⅔ of the skin surface; and no sweat is produced for temperature regulation below the segmental level of the lesion. Consequently, the body temperature tends to rise in warm environments, and may fall in cool environments, for the excess heat from shivering of the arms may be lost from the lower parts of the body. The effect of section through the brain stem indicates that the main center or centers controlling heat regulation must lie anterior to the superior colliculi. Removal of the cerebral cortex, thalamus or corpus striatum does not destroy the controlling mechanisms so long as the hypothalamus remains intact. Destruction of this region alone, however, was found by Keller and Hare to abolish the ability to maintain a normal body temperature upon exposure to cold. The heat-dissipating mechanisms remained intact and were, in fact, released from restraint by the hypothalamic lesion, as evidenced by pronounced panting, vasodilation, and sweating of the toe pads (of cats).

The thermoregulatory centers have been located more precisely by Ranson and his associates. From the results of their experiments upon cats and monkeys they place the centers controlling heat loss (sweating and panting) in the preoptic and supraoptic regions between the anterior commissure and the optic chiasma. Heating this area causes sweating and panting or rapid breathing and a fall in body temperature. Destructive lesions in this location are followed by hyperthermia when the animal is exposed to a degree of heat that would cause little effect upon the body temperature of a normal animal. Sweating or panting does not occur though the temperature rises to over 41°C (106°F.). Such lesions have little effect upon the animal's ability to resist

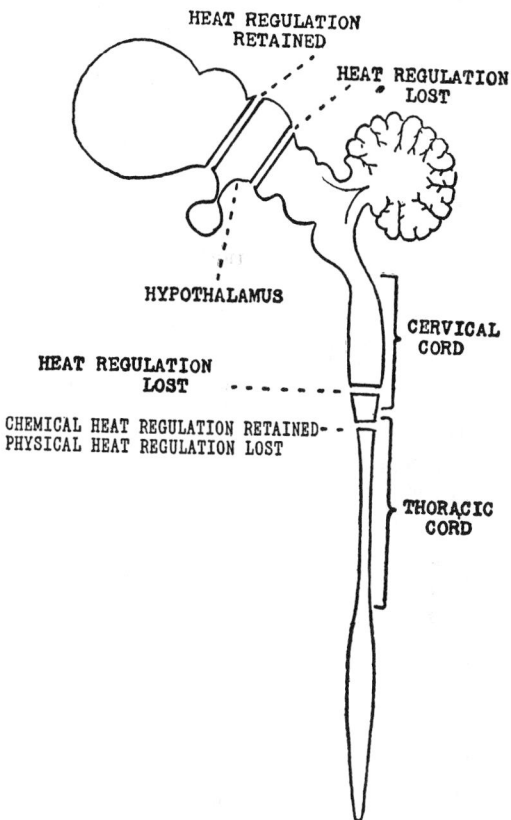

FIG. 70.4. Diagram to illustrate the nervous control of the heat-regulating mechanisms. (Modified from Martin.)

cold. The centers controlling heat production and heat conservation, i.e., the mechanism whereby an animal is enabled to maintain a normal body temperature when exposed to cold, is situated, according to these investigators, in the caudal part of the lateral hypothalamus; it appears to be identical with the sympathetic center. The existence of a center for shivering (heat production) in the hypothalamus is suggested by the fact that under certain circumstances shivering in animals is accompanied by some of the manifestations of "sham rage" (Barcroft and Izquierdo). That the posterior part of the hypothalamus contains the main shivering center is indicated by the experimental results of Kellar and his associates and of Ranson and his colleagues who found that, in cats, shivering was abolished by a destructive lesion in this location. The efferent pathway for shivering is unknown, but an observation upon a patient in whom both spinothalamic tracts had been sectioned and who did not shiver when the legs were immersed in cold water, suggests that the impulses descend the cord by these paths. The impulses are not transmitted by sympathetic nerves, since shivering occurs in sympathectomized parts. Shivering is reduced or abolished by certain drugs, especially calcium chloride and aminopyrine which most probably act upon the shivering center.

From observations of patients with intracranial lesions involving the base of the brain, it seems most likely that in man the centers are situated as described by Ranson and his associates for animals. Lesions in the supraoptic region are sometimes associated with hyperthermia; hypothermia, on the other hand, may accompany lesions involving the posterior part of the hypothalamus.

The main heat-regulating centers are apparently influenced in two ways—reflexly from the skin and by the temperature of the blood flowing through them.

The posterior hypothalamic center apparently exerts its controlling influence upon temperature through the transmission of sympathetic impulses to the cutaneous vessels, sweat glands and pilomotor muscles; removal of the sympathetic renders an animal unduly susceptible to cold (ch. 12).

The Endocrines in Thermoregulation

The thyroid and adrenals also play their roles, probably important ones, in the regulation of body temperature. The calorigenic effects of the secretions of these glands are well known (ch. 75 and 76). Cannon observed that exposure to cold caused an increase in the rate of the denervated heart. It has also been reported that the serum taken from an animal exposed to cold raises the metabolism of a second animal into which it has been injected. If the first animal has been thyroidectomized, the effect upon the metabolism of the second is not observed. The adrenal secretion exerts a calorigenic effect which is immediate and of short duration. Its liberation follows short periods of exposure to cold. But owing to the delayed action of the thyroid hormone, and the persistence of its effects, it does not seem possible that the thyroid could play any part in increasing heat production unless the cold stimulus were continued over a long period. Rats exposed over a period of weeks to low temperatures (7.8° to 12.2°C. or 46° to 52°F.) show thyroid hyperplasia and a rise in metabolic rate of as much as 16 per cent which was not reached, however, until the lapse of from 2 to 4 weeks. Thyroidectomized rats, on the contrary, show little rise in metabolic rate under the same condi-

tions. The experiments of Uotila point to the pituitary as being responsible (influenced through the hypothalamus) for the thyroid response to cold, for hypophysectomy causes thyroid atrophy as usual, though the animals are exposed to a low temperature for long periods. It may be mentioned in this connection that the temperature tends to be subnormal in supradrenalectomized or thyroidectomized animals, in Addison's disease, and in cretinism.

Disturbances of Heat Regulation (Other Than Fever)

Since the body temperature represents the balance struck between heat production and heat loss, an alteration in the value of one of these factors in relation to the other obviously will be followed by a change in body temperature.

Temporary rises in temperature will occur in health as a result of hot baths, which prevent heat loss through convection, radiation and the evaporation of sweat, as well as by actually adding heat to the body; or during violent muscular exercise which increases heat production. Since the metabolic rate can be increased easily and rapidly to several times the basal level, a fall in the temperature of a normal person is much more difficult to produce than a rise.

The heat regulating mechanisms are depressed by anesthetics, hypnosis and by general bodily fatigue. During sleep the heat regulating mechanisms continue to function though somewhat sluggishly. The body temperature falls a little, reaching a minimum between 3 and 5 a.m.

There are four separate syndromes which result from exposure to excessive heat. These are: *Heat exhaustion, dehydration exhaustion, heat cramps* and *heat stroke.* Although each of these syndromes is encountered in a pure form, there is frequently an overlap of the syndromes and difficulty in distinguishing between them.

HEAT EXHAUSTION. Upon sudden exposure to a high temperature there is a dilation of the peripheral vessels greatly increasing the vascular space. The heart rate and cardiac output increase and the blood pressure may fall a little. If, in addition, physical work is performed, the heart may not be able to maintain the blood pressure and the condition known as "heat exhaustion" ensues. The patient is confused, fatigued to exhaustion and feels hot. The skin is moist and sweating may be profuse. The pulse is rapid, the blood pressure low. The patient feels extremely uncomfortable and may be mildly dyspneic. The symptoms are indicative of cardiac insufficiency. The patient may collapse and loose consciousness. He is very uncomfortable and dyspneic lying flat, and is more comfortable with his head and shoulders propped up (orthopnoea). The condition responds rapidly to rest and fluids by mouth.

DEHYDRATION EXHAUSTION. Although heat exhaustion may occur any time after exposure to heat, it usually occurs when unusual physical demands are made upon an unacclimatized subject. Dehydration exhaustion, however, occurs after longer exposure to heat, if the fluid loss is not replaced. In a hot environment with extensive sweating the blood volume is reduced, this reduction in the blood volume associated with the larger vascular space again produces cardiac insufficiency and exhaustion to collapse. As dehydration progresses the heart rate rises and exertion becomes progressively more difficult. Ultimately even standing becomes an intolerable strain. This exhaustion occurs when the body has lost about 5 per cent of its weight. The patient may suddenly collapse unconscious with an extremely rapid heart rate. General discomfort and extreme fatigue are the main symptoms, just before collapse. Dehydration exhaustion responds to rest, restoration of body fluids and cooling of the body. Again, orthopnoea may be a prominent feature. Water may be administered by mouth or intravenously. The intravenous fluid provides a rapid recovery, but fluid by mouth is satisfactory. Death from dehydration exhaustion occurs suddenly with little warning, and may be proceeded for some hours by extensive edema of the legs, indicating the cardiac origin of the syndrome (see Rawicz).

HEAT CRAMPS. If the sodium chloride content of the body is decreased, as will occur with sweating and a low salt intake, exertion will induce severe painful muscle contractures. After exertion these painful cramps will continue until the salt balance is restored. The administration of sodium chloride, either by mouth or parenterally, will rapidly cure the cramps. In order to maintain the salt balance under desert conditions, 2 grams of salt should be provided for each hour of exercise and ½ gram for each hour of rest. This averages about 24 grams per day.

HEAT STROKE. This is a rare condition compared with heat exhaustion. It is characterized by a rising temperature with a dry skin. The patient, apparently well, may suddenly become unconscious. The rectal temperature is high 41° to 43°C. (106° to 110°F.). There appears to be a complete breakdown of the heat regulating mechanisms. Unless the temperature is promptly reduced, there may be permanent damage to the nervous system. Heat stroke often terminates in death. The pathogenesis of heat stroke is obscure, its onset usually occurs with exertion, which may be quite mild. It is probable that heat stroke requires an inter-current infection, the toxins from which disturb the heat regulating centre in the hypothalamus.

SUN STROKE is a term applied to those cases of heat stroke that occur during exposure to tropical sun. Powerful sunshine itself, however, will not cause sunstroke provided heat dissipation is adequate to keep pace with heat production, i.e., when the air is dry and cool and strenuous exercise is not undertaken.

The frequent occurrence of heat exhaustion and heat stroke among British troops serving in the tropics during the nineteenth century was probably due to lack of understanding of the mechanisms of heat regulation, and the use of quite unsuitable uniforms. The use of toupees and spinal pads is quite unnecessary if proper clothing and adequate water are provided.

Fever—Pyrexia

There are 5 types of fever. (1) *Infectious fever*, e.g., sepsis, typhoid, pneumonia, etc. (2) *Surgical fever* which arises after an extensive aseptic operation and is apparently due to toxic substances liberated by the injured tissues. (3) *Neurogenic fever* from injuries to nervous centers, especially lesions in the neighborhood of the third ventricle, internal capsule, medulla or upper part of spinal cord. (4) *Fever of dehydration* due to a reduction of blood water (anhydremia, p. 496). This is particularly likely to occur in young children. (5) *Fever produced by drugs and other chemical substances.*

Body temperatures as high as 45°C. (113°F.) have occasionally been reported, but survival with a hyperpyrexia above 44.5°C. (112°F.) is rare. In the great majority (over 95 per cent) of fevers, from whatever cause, the temperature does not exceed 41°C. (106°F.). Temperatures higher than 41.6°C. (107°F.) become harmful or dangerous from the high temperature itself. The infrequency of temperatures above 41°C. (106°F.) suggests that some safety thermostatic mechanism comes into operation around this level.

Intravenous injections of concentrated solutions of glucose or salt induce fever by causing anhydremia (p. 496). Drastic cathartics, by drawing water from the blood into the bowel, may cause fever in a similar manner. Caffeine and cocaine in large doses induce fever by increasing muscular activity (greater heat production) and by causing blood concentration (reduced heat loss). Hemoglobin solutions when injected into the blood stream exert a pyretic action; the hemolysis resulting from the intravenous injection of distilled water acts similarly. The manner in which the fever is produced is unknown. β-Tetrahydronaphthylamine injected subcutaneously raises the temperature by its action upon the central and peripheral sympathetic mechanisms, causing cutaneous vasoconstriction and consequently a greater conservation of heat. It also, through its action upon the muscles, causes increased heat production. The adrenal medulla is also probably stimulated by this drug and the outpouring of adrenaline may be an added factor in the temperature rise. Ergotoxine causes a rise in temperature in some animals (cat), presumably through a direct action upon the heat centers. Dinitrophenol, a drug sometimes used in the treatment of obesity, and injections of foreign protein also raise the body temperature. Dinitrophenol acts by stimulating oxidative processes in the tissues. Adrenaline and thyroxine in large doses may also, through their stimulating effect upon the metabolism, cause a rise in temperature.

INFECTIOUS FEVERS

At the onset of an acute infectious fever the heat regulating center brings into action the mechanisms to conserve heat. It is as if the "thermostat" had been set to a higher level. This is brought about by the action of the bacterial toxins on the heat regulating centers in the hypothalamus. There is a redistribution of the blood flow, with constriction of the skin vessels, producing a cold, pale or slightly cyanotic skin. This reduces the heat loss by radiation and conduction. Since the normal comfortable feeling of warmth depends upon stimuli from temperature sensory endings in the skin and subcutaneous tissues, there is a feeling of cold. This is known as a *chill*. If this heat conserved by the redistribution of the blood flow does not raise the internal temperature fast enough, shivering and the other reactions of a normal person exposed to severe cold, occur. Such violent shivering at the onset of a fever is known as a *rigor*. The involuntary contractions produce heat, which with the constricted

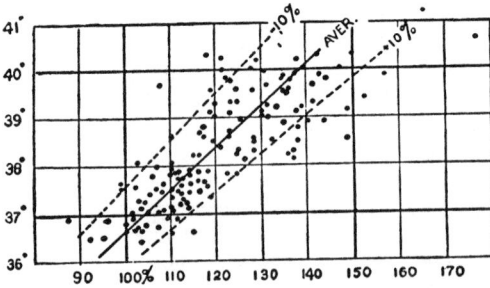

FIG. 70.5. Relationship between basal metabolism and body temperature in fever. Results in six different fevers grouped in one chart. The continued line shows the average metabolism, the interrupted lines the metabolism 10 per cent above and 10 per cent below the average respectively. (After DuBois.)

skin vessels causes a rapid rise in the internal temperature. The chills and rigors occur as the body temperature rises. When the "new setting of the thermostat" has been reached, and the fever is at its height, an unstable state occurs. Usually the skin is flushed, hot and dry but sweating or chills may supervene rapidly. At the elevated body temperature the *basal metabolism* is elevated 7 per cent for every °F. rise. The effect of fever on the basal metabolic rate is shown in figure 70.5.

DuBois, in an experiment upon a normal man and a malarial fever patient, demonstrated the reduced heat elimination which occurs during the chill. The normal subject imitated as closely as possible for a period of 34 minutes the shivering of the patient and thereby increased his heat production by nearly 200 per cent. Most of the extra heat was eliminated as it was produced, the body temperature showing only a slight rise. In the malarial patient, on the contrary, in whom the heat production during the chill was increased to about the same degree, all the extra heat was retained. The heat retention caused a rise of 2°C. in body temperature. After the chill the heat elimination rose and the temperature fell.

The "continued" fever, which usually follows the initial chill of an infectious disease, or which develops in other instances without this preliminary, is due essentially to the raised threshold for heat loss. There is, of course, increased heat production but this is mainly secondary—the velocity of the oxidative processes of the tissues being increased by the rise in temperature induced by the diminished heat elimination. That the latter, rather than increased heat production, is the principal factor in the elevated temperature is indicated by the fact that in fever a temperature of 104°F. (40°C.) is accompanied by an increased heat production of only about 35 per cent, whereas in health the heat production must be increased several fold (as in muscular exercise) in order to raise the body temperature even transiently to this extent. Also, the metabolism may be raised 40 per cent or so in an animal by protein feeding (see specific dynamic action, p. 1310) without the occurrence of a temperature rise. Furthermore, the increased metabolism in ordinary fevers occurs simultaneously with the temperature rise. If the latter were the result rather than the cause of the former, it should be possible to demonstrate by indirect calorimetry a period of increased metabolism preceding the rise in temperature; this, however, does not occur.

When the infection has been overcome, the "thermostat" setting is returned to normal. This may occur rapidly as in malaria or the resolution by *crisis* in pneumonia, or gradually as in the resolution by *lysis*. In either case the body must dissipate the excess heat. The skin is flushed, warm and moist. In the crisis there will be profuse sweating. When the temperature regains its proper level, the normal heat regulating mechanisms again come into play.

SPECIAL METABOLISM IN FEVER

Water and salt. At the onset of a high fever there occurs a retention of chloride which apparently is deposited in the tissues, the chloride concentration of the blood being normal or below normal. The urinary chlorides in most fevers are greatly reduced. During the course of the fever there is a pronounced reduction in urine volume. The vaporization of water from the skin is increased owing to the high temperature, and from the lungs for the same reason, but to a more important extent, as a result of the more rapid breathing.

At the termination of the fever the retained water and chloride are eliminated by diuresis and sweating. Chloride retention is especially pronounced in pneumonia.

Protein. The excretion of nitrogen in the urine is greatly increased in most infectious fevers. This is furnished by body protein, the protein minimum, i.e., the "wear and tear" quota of protein metabolism (p. 1308), being much higher than normal. In very severe infections from 300 to 400 grams of body protein may be destroyed daily. It has been found impossible to maintain the fever patient in nitrogen equilibrium (p. 1307) by giving liberal allowances of protein combined with supplies of carbohydrate which under ordinary circumstances would be considered quite adequate for energy purposes. It has, therefore, been held that the toxins of the disease were responsible for the protein destruction, the so-called "toxic destruction" of protein. It has been shown, however, by Schaffer and Coleman that if a diet be given possessing a caloric value 50 to 110 per cent in excess of the patient's requirements, as actually determined by calorimetry, and containing a liberal supply of protein (160 to 200 grams), nitrogen equilibrum can be established. The high protein catabolism which has been observed in fever patients on the usual diet is therefore thought to have been due in large measure to the fact that the caloric intake was far below the requirements, which owing to the higher metabolism in fever are considerably greater than has been supposed. In other words, a fever patient upon a diet which has been considered adequate in the past is actually in a half-starved state, and is, in consequence, forced to consume his own tissues.

Nevertheless, even on a high caloric diet composed of carbohydrate and a small quantity of fat, the nitrogen excretion still remains well above that of a normal person. Moreover, a protein allowance equivalent to that of a healthy man, together with carbohydrate somewhat more than sufficient to cover the calculated caloric requirements of the febrile state, will not maintain nitrogen equilibrium. As just mentioned, the caloric allowance must in some instances be double the heat production of the patient. It therefore appears that the toxic process itself must be responsible in part for the increase in protein metabolism. Creatinine, uric acid, purine bases and phosphates also appear in the urine in increased amounts—further evidence of a destruction of body protein. The manner in which the "toxic" effect is produced is not known. It does not seem to be due merely to the high temperature, for raising the temperature of a normal person to 40°C. (104°F.) by immersion in a hot bath does not increase the nitrogen excretion significantly. In fevers with much destruction of body protein the specific dynamic action of food is absent.

It must be apparent from the foregoing remarks that in order to reduce the waste of body tissue in fever a liberal diet should be given, provided such is not contraindicated by some special feature of the disease. The old adage "feed a fever" holds true. Since the very high protein diet required for the establishment of nitrogen equilibrium in the fever patient has its disadvantages, one must usually be satisfied with reducing the waste of body protein rather than aiming to abolish it. Special attention, therefore, is directed toward furnishing an abundance of protein-sparing food (p. 1309), namely carbohydrate, and thus avoiding excessive quantities of protein. The more abundant diet causes a negligible increase in heat production and no elevation of the temperature.

Fats and carbohydrates. The metabolism of body fat or carbohydrate shows no definite abnormality in fever. In patients upon a low food intake body fat and glycogen are utilized as fuel. Acidosis results from the excess combustion of fat only if the available carbohydrate is inadequate in amount.

The Action of Antipyretic Drugs
(Fever-Reducing)

A list of chemical substances which are capable of inducing a rise in body temperature has been given on page 1288. Other drugs, e.g., antipyrine, acetylsalicylic acid (aspirin), salicylates, quinine, etc., although they exert little effect upon the normal temperature, lower the temperature in fever by increasing heat elimination. According to Barbour they bring about this effect through drawing water from the tissues into the vessels and thus increasing the volume of fluid in the body's heat-radiating system. They seem to exert little effect upon heat production. The effect upon the blood volume is possibly brought about indirectly. All these substances raise the blood sugar; the greater sugar concentration may then through osmotic forces attract water into the vascular system.

Morphine and general anesthesia depress cerebral activity, including the regulation of body temperature. During some stages of anesthesia sweating may occur which further disorganizes the regulation of body temperature. The anesthetic reduces metabolic activity, hence less heat is produced. The temperature of an anesthetized patient is liable to shift, either up or down, depending upon the room temperature, and the coverings. Under the drapes in an operating room body temperature frequently rises, but if left uncovered in a cool room the temperature will fall.

Alcohol causes cutaneous vasodilation. This hastens heat loss, for the skin is warm and often moist. The warm skin gives a sensation of warmth, hence the belief that alcohol will warm a person who is suffering from cold. In fact, it increases heat loss and may cause a lowering of body temperature.

THE VALUE OF FEVER. Fever is frequently the herald of serious disease; nevertheless, unless of high degree and on this account endangers the functions of vital tissues, it should not be looked upon as a reaction detrimental in itself. On the contrary, there is every indication that its occurrence is an important aid to the body in its combat with the disease. It is well known, for example, that in infections that overwhelm the patient the fever reaction is depressed. But the role played by fever in the defensive process is unknown. It has been suggested that antibodies can be elaborated in adequate amounts only at higher temperatures.

In support of the belief that moderate fever is not injurious in itself but is actually beneficial the following observations upon animals may be cited. (a) The body temperature of rabbits has been maintained by the application of external heat at a level of over 40.5°C. (105°F.) for weeks at a time without ill effects. (b) In animals infected with certain microorganisms the disease runs a milder course when the temperature is is raised (to 40°C. or 104°F.) artificially. High temperature is thought to be favorable for the elaboration of antibodies. (c) It has been reported that with moderate overheating the formation of various antibodies is increased, but at higher temperatures the process, apparently, is depressed. (d) The immunity of fowl to the ordinary pyogenic infections is ascribed to their higher body temperature which is inimical to the growth of pus-forming bacteria. (e) Fevers induced artificially by means of foreign proteins or injections of malarial blood are used as therapeutic agents in arthritis and in chronic nervous disease due to the pathogen of syphilis (Treponema pallidum). Short wave diathermy has been employed with success in the treatment of certain infections—the high temperature produced in the tissue exerting a lethal action upon the microorganisms. (f) In the past it has been common practice to reduce fever (above 40°C. to 104°F.) by cold bathing, but it was found that the patients did not do well and the practice, except in an extremely high fever which is dangerous in itself, has been abandoned.

REFRIGERATION—HYPOTHERMIA. The lowering of the body temperature occurs when the rate of cooling exceeds the rate of the heat production. This can occur with inadequate clothing in freezing weather, but will occur much more rapidly in water. As the temperature of the tissues fall, their metabolic rate falls, the oxygen needs are reduced and the circulation can be interrupted for a much longer time without damage. For these reasons hypothermia is induced artificially to protect the brain during operations on the heart and great vessels, or upon intracranial vessels. The patient is given a sedative, and a drug such as chlorpromazine to inhibit shivering. Under minimal anesthesia the patient is placed in ice water. The rectal temperature will fall to 30°C. (86°F) in 1½ to 2 hours. Respiratory and heart rates fall; the blood pressure is reduced a little to about 90/70. Urine production is decreased.

REFERENCES

BARBOUR, H. G. AND PRINCE, A. L. J. Pharmacol. & Exper. Therap., 1914, **6**, 1.

BARCROFT, J. AND IZQUIERDE, J. J. J. Physiol., 1931, **71**, 364.

BURTON, A. C. Proc. Fed. Am. Soc. Exp. Biol., 1946, **5**, 344.

COON, J. M. AND ROTHMAN, S. J. Pharmacol. & Exper. Therap., 1941, **73**, 1.

DuBois, E. F. J.A.M.A., 1921, **77**, 352.

HARDY, J. D. AND DuBois, E. F. Nat. Acad. Sci., 1940, **26**, 389.

HARDY, J. D. AND MUSCHENHEIM, C. J. Clin. Invest., 1934, **13**, 817; 1936, **15**, 1.

KELLER, A. D. J. Neurophysiol., 1938, **1**, 543.

KELLER, A. D. AND HARE, W. K. Proc. Soc. Exper. Biol. & Med., 1931, **29**, 1067. Ibid., p. 1069.

KUNO, Y. Lancet, 1930, **2**, 912.

MARTIN, C. Lancet 1930, **2**, 561, 617, 673.

MOLNAR, G. W., TOWBIN, E. J., GOSSELIN, R. E., BROWN, A. A. H. AND ADOLPH, E. J. Am. J. Hyg. 1946, **44**, 411.

NEWBURGH, L. H., JOHNSTON, M. W., LASHMET, F. H. AND SHELDON, J. M. J. Nutrition, 1937, **13**, 203.

RANSON, S. W. and associates. J. Neurophysiol., 1939, **2**, 61.

RAWICZ, S. The long walk. Constable, London, 1956, p. 165.

SCOTT, J. C., BAZETT, H. C. AND MACKIE, G. C. Am. J. Physiol., 1940, **129**, 102.

SHAFFER, F. A. AND SWIFT, R. W. J. Nutrition, 1932, **5**, 227.

SWIFT, R. W. J. Nutrition, 1932, **5**, 227.

Monographs and Reviews

ADOLPH, E. F. Am. J. Physiol., 1938, **123**, 486.

BARBOUR, H. G. Physiol. Rev., 1921, **1**, 295.

BAZETT, H. C. Physiol. Rev., 1927, **7**, 531.

DEIGHTON, T. Physiol. Rev., 1933, **13**, 427.

COLEMAN, W. Arch. Int. Med., 1909, **4**, 538. J.A.M.A., 190, **53**, 1145. Ibid., 1912, **59**, 363.

DILL, D. B., EDWARDS, H. T., BAUER, P. S. AND Levenson, E. J. Arbeitsphysiologie, 1931, **4**, 508.

DuBOIS, E. Basal metabolism in health and disease. Lea & Febiger, Philadelphia, 1936. p. 432. Metabolism in fever and certain infections. In Barker's Endocrinology and Metabolism, 1922, **4**, 95. Heat loss from human body. Bull. New York Acad. Med., 1939, **15**, 143; Fever and the regulation of body temperature. Charles C Thomas, Springfield, Ill., 1948.

HILL, L. AND CAMPBELL, A. Health and Environment. Arnold, London. 1925.

KUNO, Y. The physiology of human perspiration. Churchill, Lond., 1934.

LUSK, G. The elements of the science of nutrition. Saunders, Philadelphia, 1906.

RANSON, S. W. A. Res. Nerv. & Ment. Dis., Proc., 1940, **20**, 342.

SUNDSTROEM, E. S. Physiol. Rev., 1927, **7**, 320.

CHAPTER 71

The Vitamins

Historical Introduction

The increasing understanding of metabolic processes has revealed that some of the enzymes catalyzing vital reactions need, as cofactors, minute traces of organic compounds. These cannot be made by the body and, therefore, must be supplied in the food. These compounds, now known as vitamins, posed many a complex riddle for nutritionists and biochemists. The student is referred to textbooks of biochemistry for details of the structure and properties of the vitamins. The present discussion will review their discovery, occurrence and principal functions.

Vitamins have been defined briefly as organic compounds required in minute amounts for normal health. Expanding knowledge of the metabolic roles of the vitamins makes it increasingly difficult to formulate a definition that is concise and yet complete. They occur in natural foods (either as the vitamin itself, or as a precursor) and are neither oxidized to supply energy nor used to build tissue structures.

Some 20-odd growth factors for animals have now been identified, but only about 15 (or fewer) seem to be required by man. For historical reasons they are usually classified and referred to as fat-soluble vitamins (A, D, E and K) and water-soluble ones (B complex and C). More than a dozen components have now been isolated and identified in the water-soluble group: thiamine, riboflavin, nicotinamide, pyridoxine, pantothenic acid, para-amino benzoic acid, choline, inositol, biotin, lipoic acid, folic acid, folinic acid and cyanocobalamin; ascorbic acid (vitamin C) and certain flavanoids (vitamin P) are in this same category.

Sir Frederick Gowland Hopkins (1861–1947) of Cambridge University in England is generally credited with the first experimental proof that accessory food factors are necessary to supplement the five well known dietary essentials: water, minerals, protein, carbohydrate and fat. Many years earlier several clinical and experimental studies had pointed clearly in the same direction but the publication in 1912 of Hopkins' findings aroused a world-wide interest in this new field. At about the same time Stepp in Germany was reaching similar conclusions.

HISTORICAL REVIEW. DEVELOPMENT OF THE VITAMIN CONCEPT

A brief review of the discovery of the vitamins will serve to acquaint the student with the nature and seriousness of deficiency diseases that were in former times the mysterious cause of millions of deaths. It will also show how the vitamin concept had its origins.

SCURVY. Scurvy is said to have afflicted the Crusaders. During the 1400's and 1500's it was apparently one of the more prevalent diseases in Europe. It attacked with particular virulence the inmates of besieged garrisons and sailors on long voyages. Vasco da Gama reported the death by scurvy of 100 sailors out of the crew of 160 men, and Jacques Cartier, obliged to winter in Canada in 1535, lost one-quarter of his men and the remainder were severely ill with the disease. Strangely enough, in view of its prevalence in Europe, Cartier wrote that " . . . the disease was wholly unknown to us." From the Indians, Cartier learned the curative value of a decoction of the leaves and bark of twigs of the *"annedda"* tree, apparently the cedar, arbor vitae.

Admiral Sir Richard Hawkins mentioned in 1593 that within his own personal experience 10,000 seamen had died of scurvy, and he reported that the juice of oranges and lemons was able to cure the disease. As early as 1601 the ships of the East India Company had adopted the regular use of oranges and lemons to prevent scurvy, apparently upon the recommendation of the English privateer, Sir James Lancaster.

In 1720 a physician to the Austrian army, Kramer by name, had written of scurvy and reported that a supply of green vegetables, or of oranges, lemons or limes could cure this dreadful disease without other help. Captain Lind of the British navy wrote a celebrated *Treatise on Scurvy* in 1753 in which he reported experiments on sailors which proved beyond doubt that "salads, summer fruits, etc." would prevent the disease and that the severest cases could be so cured within six days.

BERIBERI. Three other diseases, beriberi, pellagra and rickets, are now known to be of dietary origin. The patient suffering from *beriberi* first notices numbness in his legs. Later pain develops in the calf muscles. Exhaustion, emaciation and paralysis, with increased heart rate and enlarged right heart, lead to death from heart failure. One of the most characteristic features, clinically, is peripheral neuritis. Nearly 80 years ago, Admiral

Takaki, Director-General of the Medical Service of the Japanese navy, had convinced himself that beriberi, which sometimes crippled up to 50 per cent of the sailors on long voyages, was due to some fault in the diet. He arranged in 1882 to have the usual diet (largely of polished rice) on a Japanese training ship augmented with meat, fish and other protein-rich items. The improvement in the health of the sailors was so dramatic that the diet throughout the Japanese navy was similarly enriched and beriberi vanished. But in other parts of the world thousands continued to die from the disease which was still commonly believed to be due to poor sanitation, to contaminated rice or to a microbe.

In 1890 Eijkman (1858–1930), a medical investigator in the Dutch East Indies, accidentally made an observation which led him to discover an analogous disease in chickens. Birds fed milled (polished) rice developed polyneuritis and other signs resembling those of patients with beriberi. If they were fed unmilled rice, or if the bran was restored to their ration, the birds recovered. Eijkman soon showed that the curative principle could be extracted from the bran with water or alcohol and that it was dialyzable.

Eijkman thought that he had discovered a pharmacological antidote against the "toxin" or "microbe" in polished rice, but his colleague, Grijns, suggested in 1901 that beriberi was caused by a *lack* of some substance essential to the metabolism of the nervous system.

THE "VITAMINE" CONCEPT. Attempts to isolate the protective or curative principle from rice bran followed the adoption of Grijn's deficiency theory. Dr. Casimir Funk, of the Lister Institute in London, was among those who were more successful in their efforts to isolate Eijkman's anti-beriberi substance. When he thought he had it in pure form, Funk proposed for the substance a name which has since become famous. At the suggestion of Dr. Max Nierenstein the term *vitamine* was applied because the compound, he thought, was an *amine* that appeared to be essential to life.

Funk was also the originator of the "vitamine theory." He suggested in 1912 that there were four different vitamines: his antiberiberi vitamine, an antiscurvy vitamine, and probably also antirickets and antipellagra vitamines. Funk was led to this conclusion by a careful study of the pertinent medical and experimental literature. Some clinical observations pointing in this direction have already been described. Several other medical and earlier experimental studies will now be mentioned.

In 1888 Lunin, a student with Professor Bunge at Basle, had reported that mice could not survive on synthetic diets composed of purified proteins, fats and carbohydrates, plus mineral salts and water. Thus Lunin provided proof over 70 years

ago that the known components of natural foods are unable to support life, and he drew the logical conclusion that natural foodstuffs (such as milk) must contain small quantities of unknown substances indispensable for normal nutrition. In the next 20 years many other workers confirmed the inability of the known dietary components to support growth.

In 1905 a Dutch physiologist, Pekelharing, published the results of experiments actually done some years earlier which showed that a very small amount of whole milk added to an artificial food mixture (i.e., made from purified chemicals) was able to transform the mixture to a nutritious food. Pekelharing wrote " . . . there is still an unknown substance in milk, which, even in very small quantities, is of paramount importance to nutrition." Similar experiments by Hopkins, published in English in 1912, and Funk's vitamine theory published in the same year, finally drew the attention of physiologists and chemists throughout the world to new fields of knowledge—clinically, to a group of affections that came to be recognized as *deficiency diseases*, and chemically, to a class of substances of great potency that would prevent and cure such diseases.

ARE GROWTH FACTORS AND "VITAMINES" THE SAME? For a period there was confusion as to whether only one or more than one factor was needed for growth, and whether the growth factor(s) were the same as the vitamine(s) that cured beriberi and scurvy. In 1915 E. V. McCollum and Margaret Davis showed that there are two *growth* factors at least: *fat-soluble A* found in butter and in egg-yolk but not in all fats (e.g., lard and olive oil lack it); *water-soluble B* found in the watery part of milk, in watery or alcoholic extracts of egg-yolk, in whole wheat or whole rice, but not in polished rice. It was soon found that the water-soluble B growth factor could cure polyneuritis in birds, indicating the presence of Funk's antiberiberi vitamine in the water-soluble B factor. Some workers were therefore tempted to assume that the growth factors and Funk's curative vitamines are one and the same.

Over the years, as one after another of the protective compounds was isolated from foodstuffs, and its chemical nature established, it was found that many were not amines. McCollum and Kennedy (1916) had pointed out that the word vitamine connoted a vital function, but that such a property had not been demonstrated for the growth factors. They, therefore, rejected Funk's term and proposed fat-soluble A and water-soluble B. However, the terminology was cumbersome, and Funk's designation had much popular appeal. In 1920 J. C. Drummond (1891–1952) proposed that the final *e* be dropped to avoid the indication of amine character and that these interesting substances (until fully characterized chemically) be provisionally called vitamin A, B, C, etc.

After McCollum and Davis proved that for the satisfactory growth of rats at least two different factors are required, the question arose as to how many growth factors there were and whether these were really the same as Funk's vitamines.

A few years earlier, Holst and Frölich in Norway, while trying to induce beriberi by feeding purified diets to guinea pigs, had produced instead a condition which they recognized as scurvy. Further work showed, as Funk had suggested, that the specific substance capable of curing scurvy differed from fat-soluble A and water-soluble B. Hence it was called vitamin C.

RICKETS. The number of recognized accessory food factors increased to four when the studies of Sir Edward Mellanby (1884–1956) in England and of McCollum and of Sherman and their associates in the United States showed that so-called fat-soluble A was not a unit substance but a complex of at least two factors. Mellanby was seeking the cause and cure of *rickets*, a bone disease known for at least 300 years to afflict especially children living in crowded industrial cities in the northern temperate zone (see also p. 1439). Across the Channel A. Trousseau, in 1865, had described cod-liver oil as the perfect cure for rickets. Almost 30 years earlier another Frenchman, Jules Guerin, convinced that rickets is caused by faulty diet, had proved his point by producing the disease experimentally in puppies. In France and the Baltic countries the virtues of cod-liver oil were quickly recognized. But in England and many other countries rickets continued to deform and cripple thousands of children each year because medical teaching favored lack of lime salts, infection, hypothyroidism or confinement and lack of exercise as causes. The situation was very confused when in 1890 an English physician, T. A. Palm, made a thorough study of a widely held belief that exposure to sunlight prevents rickets and could even cure the disease in children. His data showed that rickets is common in cloudy regions and rather rare wherever sunshine is abundant. In 1919 Huldschinsky, in Berlin, had the idea of using artificial sunlight (ultraviolet rays) and was successful in curing rickets by so-called actinotherapy. Mellanby at Cambridge (1919, 1921) showed that cod-liver oil and other animal fats (e.g., butter and fat of egg yolk) that were known to contain the fat-soluble A of McCollum and Davis protected puppies against rickets. This observation provided experimental proof that a dietary factor is concerned in rickets, and Mellanby at first assumed that it was fat-soluble A. In 1921 McCollum and associates showed that certain foods (e.g., carrots and green vegetables) failed to prevent rickets although they are rich in vitamin A activity. Further, it was soon found, both in Britain and the

United States that the treatment of cod-liver oil with a stream of hot air to destroy vitamin A did not eliminate the rickets-preventing effect. The two factors must therefore differ. Since 1923 the antirachitic factor has been called vitamin D.

In 1924 two Americans, Hess, a physician, and Steenbock, a biochemist, independently made a surprising discovery; rickets could be prevented by irradiating the food of the animal with ultraviolet light just as well as by treating the animal itself. The solution to this puzzle proved to be, of course, that in both cases an inert precursor was converted by the ultraviolet light to the biologically active substance, vitamin D.

PELLAGRA. Meanwhile, evidence had been accumulating that water-soluble B was not a single factor but probably a complex mixture. Beriberi is practically unknown in Europe and America but in parts of the United States, in Egypt, Italy, Rumania and other countries where Indian corn (maize) is eaten, largely to the exclusion of other foods, another disease, *pellagra*, was very common. Between 1910 and 1930 pellagra, sometimes called the corn-eaters' disease, was extremely prevalent in the southern regions of the United States. The skin in this disease becomes bronzed and thickened, especially where exposed to sunlight, the tongue is swollen and glossy and mental troubles develop, which progress to dementia in the last stages. It was referred to as the disease of the "three D's"—*dermatitis, diarrhea* and *dementia*, and although at first its cause was unknown, it came in time to be associated with the use of a diet known as the "three M's"—*maize-meal, molasses* and *meat* (salt pork). Dr. Joseph Goldberger (1874–1929) was put in charge of a study of pellagra sponsored by the United States Public Health Service to determine whether it was caused by an infective agent, a chemical toxin, an amino acid deficiency or lack of a pellagra-preventing factor (the P-P factor). Goldberger's associates eliminated the possibility of an infective agent and showed that most foods rich in 'vitamin B' would prevent and cure pellagra. Lack of a suitable experimental animal delayed progress until it was found that dogs fed a certain purified diet developed a sore mouth, called "black tongue," resembling the oral lesions so characteristic of human pellagra. In 1926 Smith and Hendrick showed that the water-soluble growth factor B, (which seemed to be the same as the beriberi-preventing substance of Funk), contained two different substances, one destroyed by heat, and one heat-stable. The latter was soon found to cure pellagra. Goldberger called it the P-P factor but many Americans referred to it as vitamin G, in honor of Goldberger. The antineuritic factor they continued to call vitamin B. In Britain the antineuritic factor was referred to as vitamin B_1 and the antipellagra factor as vitamin B_2. The latter

TABLE 71.1

The vitamins

Original Name	Currently Accepted Name	Alternative and Obsolete Names	Effect of Deficiency*	Human Daily Requirement†
Fat soluble A	Vitamin A_1	Axerophthol, Biosterol, Ophthalamin, Anti-infective vitamin	Keratinization of epithelial structures; night blindness	5000 IU
	Vitamin A_2 (Carotene)	(Provitamin A)		(7500 IU)
Vitamin D	Vitamin D_2	Calciferol, irradiated ergosterol, ergocalciferol	Rickets, osteomalacia	(400 IU)
	Vitamin D_3	Cholecalciferol, activated 7-dehydrocholesterol Antirachitic vitamin		
	Vitamin E	Alpha-tocopherol, fertility vitamin, anti-sterility vitamin	Sterility, muscular dystrophy	Unknown
	Vitamin K	Methylnaphthoquinone, menadione, antihemorrhagic factor, prothrombin factor	Bleeding	Unknown
	Lipoic acid	Thioctic acid, pyruvate oxidation factor, protogen	Growth failure (microorganisms)	Unknown
Water soluble B	Thiamine	Vitamin B_1 Aneurin Oryzamin Torulin	Beriberi; polyneuritis	1.8 mg.
B_2 or G (later found to be a mixture of vitamins)	Riboflavin	Vitamin B_2 Vitamin G, lactoflavin Ovoflavin	Loss of appetite and weight; unspecific lesions; corneal vascularization; (cheilosis, dermatitis)	1.8 mg.
	Nicotinic acid Nicotinamide	Niacin (USA) Niacinamide (USA), PP factor	Pellagra	1.8 mg.
Vitamin B_6	Vitamin B_6 Three active related compounds	Pyridoxine Pyridoxal Pyridoxamine Adermin, yeast eluate factor	Dermatitis in rats; microcytic anemia in dogs; convulsions in infants (?)	2.0 mg. (?)
	Pantothenic acid	Antidermatitis factor, liver filtrate factor	Dermatitis in chicks; spastic gait in pigs	Unknown
	Biotin	Bios II, Bios IIB, vitamin H, factor W, coenzyme R.	Dermatitis; gastrointestinal symptoms, lassitude	Unknown 300 μg. (?)
	p-Aminobenzoic acid	Anti-gray hair factor, bacterial growth factor P, PABA or PAB	Graying of hair	Unknown
	Folic acid	Pteroylglutamic acid (PGA), vitamin M, factor U, vitamin Bc.	Macrocytic anemia	0.5 mg.
	Folinic acid	Citrovorum factor (CF), Leucovorin		

TABLE 71.1—*continued*

Original Name	Currently Accepted Name	Alternative and Obsolete Names	Effect of Deficiency*	Human Daily Requirement†
	Vitamin B_{12}	Cyanocobalamin, animal protein factor (APF)	Macrocytic anemia	1.2 μg.
	Choline		Fatty livers, (cirrhosis)	Unknown
	Inositol	Inosite, meso-inositol, muscle sugar	Alopecia	Unknown
	Lipothiamide	(see lipoic acid)		
Vitamin C	Ascorbic acid	Hexuronic acid, antiskorbutin	Scurvy	75 mg.

* Only the main effects can be shown here. See text for further details and for species concerned.

† The concept of *exact* nutrient requirements suggested by a single figure in a table is misleading. Great variation is encountered for a number of reasons: (1) biological variation, (2) effects of age, sex and environmental factors, (3) effects of dietary composition, e.g. the nicotinic acid requirement is influenced by the tryptophane content of the diet.

term became internationally accepted. Later the B_2 fraction was shown to consist of a number of vitamins.

This historical introduction would not be complete without mention being made of other accessory food factors that have subsequently been discovered as the techniques of preparing "purified diets" have been perfected. The isolation of vitamins A, B_1, B_2, C and D in pure form, their chemical identification and eventual availability in crystalline form made possible the recognition of other growth factors: choline, nicotinic acid, pyridoxine, pantothenic acid, biotin, inositol, folic acid, folinic acid, vitamin B_{12}, lipoic acid, vitamin E, vitamin K and other substances required specifically by certain organisms (see table 71.1).

It should be emphasized that not all organisms, not even all mammals, have the same nutritional requirements. Man, monkeys and guinea pigs require vitamin C; but rats, dogs and many other species are able to manufacture this vitamin. These varying nutritional requirements of different species have led to a great deal of confusion in past experimental studies. Now that the situation is recognized much fruitless work can be avoided by finding which species are suitable for a particular study and using only appropriate test organisms. In the confused period (1930–1940) during which fractionation of the vitamin B complex was being conducted in many laboratories, other vitamins were described whose existence has never been established. Some of the accepted vitamins have not yet been shown to be essential for man, and in some cases they are so ubiquitous that a deficiency is unlikely to arise. Choline, inositol, *p*-amino-benzoic acid, lipoic acid and possibly biotin, belong in this category.

Fat-Soluble Vitamins

VITAMIN A

In 1914 Osborne and Mendel noted that some fats (butter and egg yolk fat) when added to a purified diet caused good growth while other fats (lard and oil of almonds) did not. The eyes of rats fed these latter fats for long periods became red and sore and eventually purulent. The condition was quickly cured by butter fat and cod-liver oil. In 1915 McCollum and Davis announced similar findings and proposed the term "fat-soluble A." By 1919 Steenbock had shown that carotene isolated from carrots is active (although xanthophyll is not) and had suggested that the vitamin A activity of foods is related to the yellow pigments they contain. It was puzzling to find that fractions rich in vitamin A from animal sources were often practically colorless. Today, we understand the reasons for what was then a baffling mystery.

Chemistry and Occurrence

Vitamin A can be isolated only from animal tissues, but vitamin A *activity* is found in plants as well. This is due to the occurrence in many yellow-colored and green plant tissues of one or more precursors called provitamins, the most important of which is β-carotene, an orange-yellow-colored hydrocarbon, $C_{40}H_{56}$. Vitamin A_1 (generally called vitamin A) is an unsaturated alcohol, $C_{20}H_{29}OH$ (see Table 71.2).

Attention is drawn to the presence of 5 double bonds, one in the ring, because *cis-trans* isomerism can, and does, occur around the double bonds in the side-chain. Vitamin A is all *trans-*

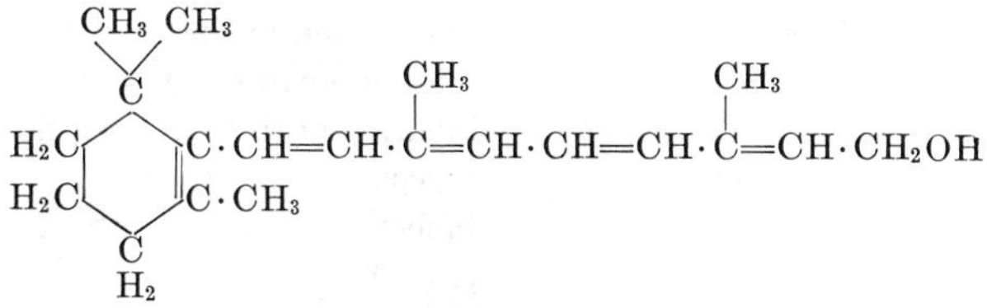

Vitamin A₁

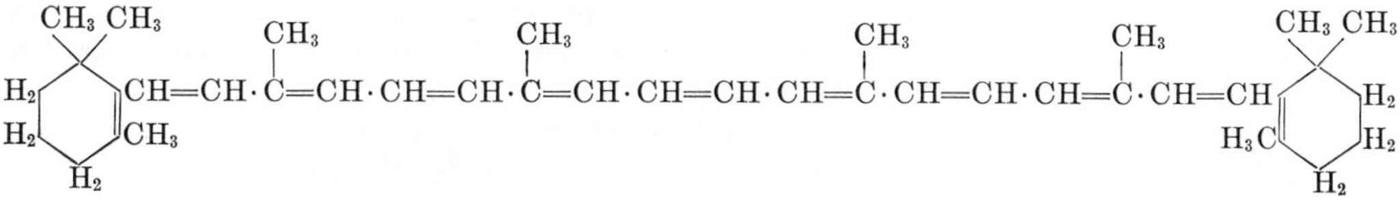

$$CH_3\ CH_3$$

Vitamin A₁

$$\beta\text{-Carotene}$$

β-Carotene

isomer. In many species of animals it is formed in the body (probably in the intestinal tract) by an imperfectly understood hydrolytic and oxidative scission of the provitamins. Some animals (the carnivores) are apparently unable to effect this cleavage and must therefore obtain vitamin A from the flesh of their prey.

The actual vitamin itself is found in animal tissues, especially the liver, and in butter, cream and egg yolk. Vitamin A in the blood plasma is mainly free, that in the liver is mainly present as esters. The richest and most important natural sources are the oils from the livers of salt-water fish (cod and especially halibut). A number of isomers are known. Vitamin A₂, possessing one more double bond in the ring, is found in the liver oils of fresh-water fish. Its biopotency is about 30 to 40 per cent of that of the all *trans* vitamin A₁. All natural samples of vitamin A₁ and even synthetic vitamin A₁ have been found to contain a stereoisomer, neovitamin A, in which the configuration around the C_{7-8} double bond is believed to be *cis*. It constitutes from 30 to 55 per cent of most commercial samples of vitamin A. Its potency is about 85 per cent of the all *trans* vitamin A. Synthetic vitamin A is on the market in the U.S.A. at a remarkably low price—in 1958 at about 25 cents per million units.

CAROTENE. In Canada and the United States carotene is the principal nutritional source (and also the cheapest) of vitamin A. There are several slightly different forms of carotene. β-Carotene is by far the most important; in many kinds of plants it is the only carotene present in appreciable amount. Other carotenes and crypto-xanthin, which may be present in minor quantities, also can function as provitamin A. The other carotenes display, on a weight basis, only one-half or less of the vitamin A activity of β-carotene. This was formerly explained by the

TABLE 71.2

Comparison of vitamin A and carotene

Vitamin A ($C_{20}H_{30}O$)	β-Carotene ($C_{40}H_{56}$)
Stored by animals (conversion of carotene in some animals).	Synthesized by plants
Almost colorless	Reddish-yellow
Absorption band at 325 to 328 mμ	No absorption band at 326 mμ
Vivid blue color with antimony trichloride (maximal absorption at 620 mμ)	Greenish blue color with antimony trichloride (maximal absorption at 590 mμ)
Vitamin A₂ plus SbCl₃ gives maximal absorption at 696 mμ.	

symmetrical nature of the β-carotene molecule. Oxidative-hydrolytic cleavage at the central double bond theoretically could give rise to 2 molecules of vitamin A; other carotenes with the characteristic ring (an essential part of the vitamin A molecule) on only one end of the hydrocarbon chain could give rise to only one such structure per molecule. Recent more careful biological assays indicate that β-carotene itself appears to give rise to only one molecule of vitamin A. The reason for the lesser activity of the other carotenes must be in the lower efficiency of their biological conversion.

Carotene *injections* are relatively ineffective in correcting vitamin A deficiency. Large amounts of the injected carotene may be stored in the liver *while deficiency of vitamin A is present*. When carotene is given orally, vitamin A appears in the liver. These and other observations have led to the belief that the conversion of carotene to vitamin A occurs in the intestinal mucosa during absorption. There are great differences in the extent to which this change occurs. Some animals have white body fat (e.g., sheep, goats, pigs and rats) because carotenoids are almost completely absent from their tissues. In these species the conversion is virtually complete. In humans, however, and in hens, cattle and many other animals, considerable amounts of carotenoid pigments are absorbed without conversion to vitamin A. Dairy cattle convert part of the carotene of the fodder (alfalfa is a particularly rich source) into colorless vitamin A. The latter, as well as unchanged carotene, is secreted in the milk. It is thus evident that a pale-colored milk may have a vitamin A content equal to or higher than one that is more richly colored by carotene.

Clinical and experimental observations have shown a relationship between the activity of the thyroid gland and the availability of dietary sources of vitamin A. The earlier belief that thyroxine favored the conversion of carotene to vitamin A has been modified as the data are more consistent with a stimulating effect of the thyroid hormone (and an inhibitory effect of thiouracil, a drug which depresses thyroid activity) on the intestinal absorption of carotene.

Effects of Deficiency

Deficiency of vitamin A may be caused by (a) inadequate amounts in the diet, (b) defective

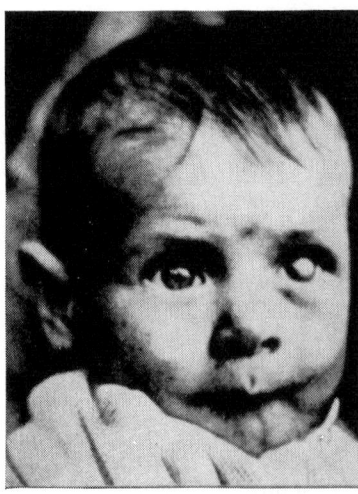

FIG. 71.1. Illustrates a baby which had suffered from an attack of ophthalmia of dietary origin, and was cured by administration of fat-soluble A as butter and cod-liver oil. The disease had, however, progressed so far that the sight of the left eye was destroyed and the right eye damaged. (After Bloch, from McCollum and Simmonds, *The Newer Knowledge of Nutrition*.)

absorption, (c) inadequate conversion of the provitamin (carotene) to vitamin A, or to a combination of these. Absorption of the vitamin, and especially of carotene, is favored by the simultaneous uptake of fat. This relationship is of importance when the diet consists largely of vegetables, for these provide carotene but often in a medium low in fat. Absorption of vitamin A or its precursor is impaired in diseases (such as sprue and celiac disease) where fat absorption is defective. The chief function of vitamin A appears to be the maintenance of epithelial tissues, but the method by which it operates has not yet been discovered.

Lack of vitamin A causes (1) failure of growth in the young (2) severe damage to the rods and cones of the retina, resulting in night blindness,[1] (3) redness and drying of the eye (xerophthalmia) with consequent softening or destruction of the cornea (keratomalacia), (4) drying and altered structure (xerosis and metaplasia) of epithelial tissues, such as papular eruptions and drying of the skin due to changes in hair follicles, atrophy of sebaceous and sweat glands, (5) secondary infections[2] due to the epithelial abnormalities, (6) swelling of the gums (gingival hypertrophy), (7) overgrowth of bones, especially those of the cranium and vertebral column which may compress or pinch off nerves in their passage through the foramina, (8) stones in the kidney (renal calculi), (9) degeneration of nervous tissue, (10) failure in reproductive function (Fig. 71.1).

The effect of vitamin A in curing night blindness has been explained in part by the discovery of a close chemical relationship between vitamin A and two compounds, rhodopsin and retinene, that have been isolated from dark-adapted eyes. Rhodopsin, (ch. 13) is a protein conjugate with a vitamin A derivative.

Units and Requirement of Vitamin A

Vitamin A activity is usually expressed in terms of international units (IU). The unit has had a constant magnitude but it has been expressed or defined in different ways. The original standard

[1] Vitamin A deficiency is not the only cause of night blindness. Even when deficiency of vitamin A is the cause there is no proof that defects in regeneration of rhodopsin account fully for the night blindness. Degenerative changes may have occurred in the visual receptors or optical neurons.

[2] The former term, "anti-infective vitamin," is inappropriate and even misleading. Vitamin A does not improve immunological responses nor has it been beneficial in the treatment of infections. By its action in *maintaining* the epithelial tissues, infection is resisted.

of reference for vitamin A activity, adopted in 1931, was 1 µg. of crystalline (mixed) carotenes. This was replaced in 1934 by 0.6 µg. of pure, crystalline β-carotene. In 1949 the reference standard became 0.344 µg. of pure vitamin A acetate (equivalent to 0.300 µg. of vitamin A alcohol). For vegetable products, the carotene standard of 1934 has been retained.

The careful biological comparisons upon which these standards are based have shown that one C_{40} molecule of carotene gives rise to but one *biologically available* C_{20} molecule of vitamin A. A number of factors (e.g., differential absorption, efficiency of conversion) affect the comparison.

The vitamin A requirements of certain species of animals are fairly well established but in man the picture is complicated by dietary variability (i.e., intake of other vitamins) in different regions, differences in activity, etc. Actual data on human requirements are meager. The Food and Nutrition Board of the National Research Council (U.S.A.) recommends (1964) a minimal intake of 5000 IU (from mixed sources) per day for a 70-kg. man. An ordinary mixed diet in North America provides about one-third of the total vitamin A activity as preformed vitamin and two-thirds in the form of carotene. Because carotene is often less efficiently absorbed than is vitamin A, it is usual to recommend higher unitage when vegetable sources provide the bulk of the dietary supply of vitamin A activity than when the principal sources are liver, milk, butter, cod-liver oil or pharmaceutical concentrates of vitamin A. A study at Sheffield under the auspices of the British Medical Research Council led to the recommendation of 2500 units of vitamin A as such, or an intake of 7500 units per day for adults, when carotene was the only source. In 1950 the Canadian Council on Nutrition reviewed the available data and decided that vitamin A requirements are proportional to body weight. Their latest publication (1964) recommends 50 to 55 IU per kg. for adults. They point out that the average Canadian diet provides 1 IU of carotene with each IU of vitamin A and that about one-third of the ingested carotene is available for conversion to vitamin A.

Although the evidence for an increased requirement during pregnancy and lactation is questionable, it is customary to recommend during the third trimester of pregnancy 6000 units of vitamin A per day and 8000 units per day during lactation (Table 73.2).

SOURCES OF VITAMIN A. As mentioned earlier, vitamin A occurs only in the animal kingdom, but several provitamins (principally β-carotene) occur in vegetables and fruits. Vitamin A activity is most reliably assayed biologically, but this method of assay is time-consuming and costly. Values found by chemical or physical methods, especially for carotene, may give quite an erroneous impression of the vitamin available, because inefficient absorption and conversion may limit the amounts reaching the tissues (see table 71.3).

HYPERVITAMINOSIS A (TOXICITY). Vitamin A given in excessive amounts causes toxic reactions. Adults who ingested 300 to 500 grams of polar bear liver became severely ill. Headache, vomiting, diarrhea and giddiness appeared promptly. About a week later desquamation of the skin and some loss of hair occurred. The intake may have been about seven million IU since the vitamin A content of polar bear liver may be as high as 18000 IU per gram. Numerous instances of poisoning have been described in infants and children given excessive dosage of vitamin A in the form

TABLE 71.3

Vitamin A activity of various fresh liver oils and foods

	International Units Vitamin A*	
	per gram	per serving
Fish liver oils		
Cod	2,000	
Halibut	87,000	
Ling cod	175,000	
Sword fish	250,000	
Liver, beef (cooked, 2 oz.)		30,000
Carrots (cooked, 1 cup)		18,000
Squash (winter, cooked, 1 cup)		12,700
Sweet potatoes (baked, one medium)		11,400
Kale (1 cup)		9,200
Tomato (cooked, 1 cup)		2,500
Egg (boiled, one medium)		550
Milk (cow, whole, 1 cup)		390
Butter (1 pattie, 7 grams)		230
Margarine (1 pattie, 7 grams)		230

* The values shown are average. The variation is often considerable, sometimes up to fourfold (and in the case of the fish oils even more) depending upon the season of collection, etc. Both vitamin A and carotene are susceptible to oxidative breakdown, especially when heated. Losses during food processing (dehydration and canning) are minimized when the latter are conducted in a vacuum.

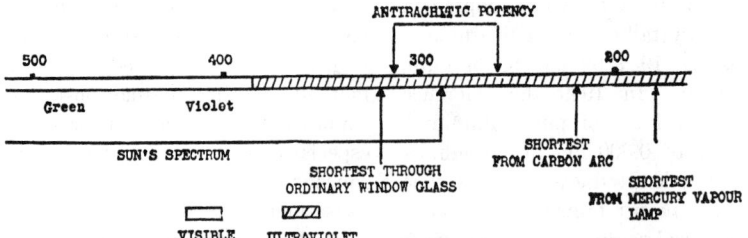

Fig. 71.2. Scheme of wave lengths of spectrum, showing the range of those possessing antirachitic properties. Figures refer to millimicrons. The hatched area indicates the ultraviolet part of the spectrum. (Redrawn and modified from Blunt and Cowan.)

of fish liver oil concentrates. Scaly dermatitis, patchy loss of hair, fissured lips, skeletal pain, irritability and anorexia were common to all these patients. The insidious onset of the symptoms and prompt response to cessation of overdosage are characteristic. Permanent sequelae are unusual. More cases of vitamin A overdosage than of deficiency have been reported in the medical journals in recent years. The condition has been studied in a human volunteer. Nothing is known of the biological properties of vitamin A that will account for these reactions.

Vitamin D

The curative value of cod liver oil in the treatment of rickets had been noted as early as 1782. Largely due to the efforts of Huldschinsky in Berlin and of Harriet Chick in Britain and in Vienna the curative effect of sunlight (and artificial sunlight, produced by mercury vapor lamps) on rickets was established (1919). The discovery by Hess and by Steenbock in the United States (1924) that irradiation of some foods generates protective substances led to reconciliation of the cod-liver oil and the actinotherapy schools of thought. It is now known that animals and man, under the influence of ultraviolet light (from the sun or elsewhere), can manufacture the antirachitic vitamin from steroid secretions on the surface of the skin (fig. 71.2). Ready-made vitamin D is obtained from certain foods, particularly dairy products.

CHEMISTRY. The term "vitamin D" refers to several chemically related compounds (steroids) that possess the property of preventing or curing rickets. They differ in the potency with which they are effective in different species. The provitamins of the D group are sterols whose molecules undergo slight rearrangement of structure under the influence of ultraviolet light. The naturally occurring antirachitic vitamin, now called D_3, arises upon irradiation by the sun of 7-dehydrocholesterol which is present in the oily secretions of the skin. Animals may lick it off the

fur, but in man absorption is through the skin. The plant sterol, ergosterol, when irradiated, gives rise to vitamin D_2. The synthetic product is known as *calciferol* or *viosterol*. In both cases the complex ring system of the sterol nucleus is broken by opening of the B-ring between carbon atoms 9 and 10. The products, no longer sterols in the strict sense, are referred to as steroids. Toxic by-products are formed by other rearrangements during artificial irradiation of sterols and these must be removed, or conditions must be arranged to minimize their formation. Ergosterol and vitamin D_2 have similar structural formulas to those of vitamin D_3 and its provitamin, but with a double bond between carbon atoms 22 and 23 of the side chain and an extra methyl group on C-24. Vitamins D_2 and D_3 have equal antirachitic potency in the rat and in man, but in chicks the

Ergosterol ($C_{28}H_{43}OH$)

Calciferol—Vitamin D_2
(viosterol)

7-Dehydrocholesterol

Activated 7-dehydrocholesterol—Vitamin D₃

synthetic product (D₂, calciferol, made from ergosterol) is much less active. There is no vitamin D₁.

Vitamin D is soluble in fats and fat solvents. It is considerably more stable to oxidation than is vitamin A.

Effects of Deficiency

When vitamin D is inadequate, the calcification of bone is defective. The resulting clinical condition is called rickets in children or osteomalacia in adults (figs. 71.3 and 71.4). In rickets the intestinal absorption of calcium is reduced; the renal clearance of phosphate is usually elevated. Aminoaciduria occurs as a result of a lowered renal threshold rather than to an increased concentration of amino acids in the blood.

Early signs of vitamin D inadequacy are an increased elimination of phosphate in the urine (elevated renal clearance), a fall in the concentration of inorganic phosphate in the plasma, and an elevation of alkaline phosphatase activity in the blood (reflecting increased osteoblastic activity in the bones). In vitamin D deficiency formation of cartilage continues but no longer in an orderly way; bone formation becomes irregular and calcification may stop entirely.

DEFECTIVE CALCIFICATION OF THE GROWING BONE AND COMPENSATORY HYPERTROPHY OF THE

EPIPHYSEAL CARTILAGES ARE CHARACTERISTIC PATHOLOGICAL CHANGES. The band of cartilage at the end of growing long bones may become up to ten times wider than normal, leading to the typical X-ray picture (fig. 71.5). The cartilage expands at the ends of the long bones, especially the distal end of the radius; enlargement of the costochondral junctions leads to a series of small swellings on the thorax commonly referred to as a *rachitic rosary* (beading of ribs). Defective ossification causes the typical deformities (knock knees, bow legs, spinal curvature (*scoliosis*), malformations of the chest and pelvis, and soft, depressible areas in the parietal bones (*craniotabes*).

Animal experiments have confirmed clinical experience that the effects of a diet lacking vitamin D are greatly altered by the composition of the ration: the ratio of calcium to phosphorus is important. Some animals (e.g., rats) do not develop rickets unless this ratio is grossly abnormal. In children (and puppies) the disease develops when vitamin D is inadequate, even without serious disturbance in this ratio. Imbalance increases the susceptibility. Experience suggests that the ideal ratio of Ca:P in the diet is about 1:1, and that the calcium intake of children 3 to 13 years of age should be about 1 gram per day. In man, dietary ratios of Ca:P within the limits 2:1 to 1:2 appear to give optimal utilization of both elements.

Increasing the proportion of cereal in the diet, especially of oatmeal, has been found to have an aggravating effect on the tendency to develop rickets. Much of the phosphorus in cereals is present as *phytin* (the calcium magnesium salt of the hexaphosphoric ester of inositol), which is very poorly absorbed; phytin combines with dietary calcium in the intestine and renders it unavailable. The customary use of milk with porridge provides extra calcium needed under these conditions.

Vitamin D favors the absorption of calcium from the intestine; the coincident improvement in tubular reabsorption of phosphate by the kidney may be a secondary effect of the improvement in calcium metabolism. Vitamin D, at least in excessive dosage, mobilizes calcium from the bones; it is possible therefore, that it may have the same action in physiological concentrations. The parathyroid hormone also affects calcium metabolism; this is discussed elsewhere.

Vitamin D is also concerned in the development and maturation of normal teeth. In the absence of vitamin D the structure of the teeth is defective and predisposes to the development of

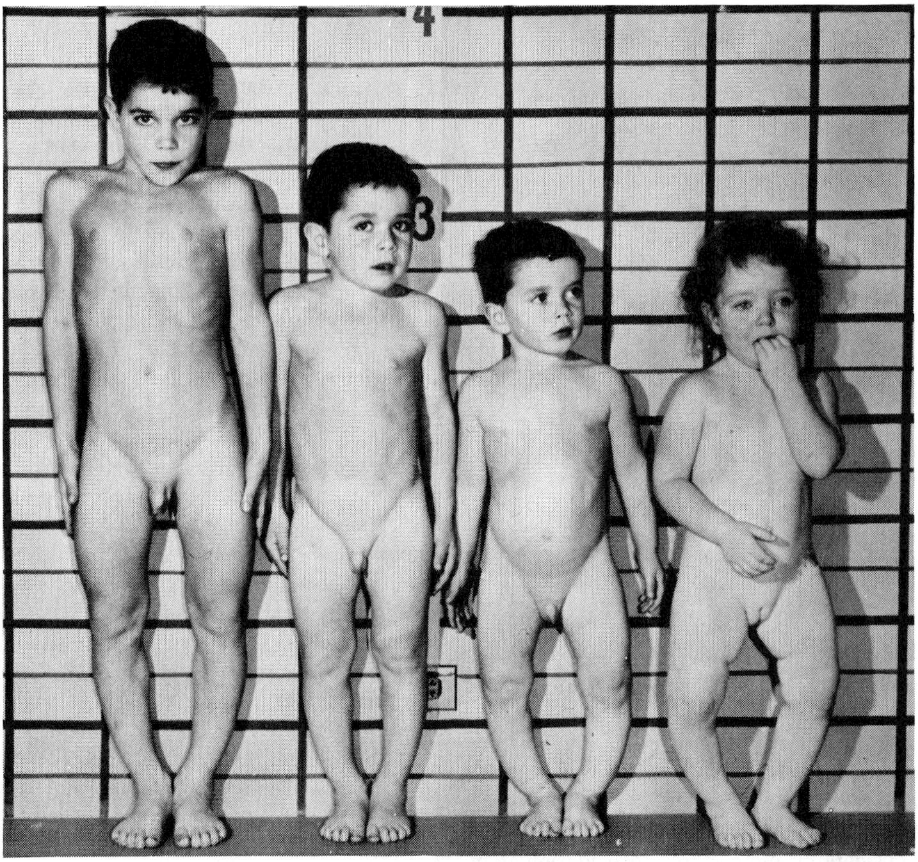

FIG. 71.3. Late effects of rickets in a family with hereditary refractoriness to vitamin D (three brothers and a first cousin). (Kindness of Dr. D. Fraser and the Hospital for Sick Children, Toronto, Canada.)

FIG. 71.4. A rickety dog. The animal was brought up on a diet deficient in the anti-rachitic vitamin D. (After E. Mellanby.)

dental caries, not by a direct action, but indirectly, by maintaining or improving the quality of these structures.

SOURCES. Foods containing vitamin D are few in number (table 71.4). They all come from the

dental caries. Vitamin D can prevent or arrest animal kingdom. Fish come first, notably the flesh of those fish that contain much body oil, e.g., salmon, herring and sardine.

The vitamin D content of dairy products varies greatly depending upon the diet of the cows and hens and on their exposure to sunlight. Natural milk has very little of this vitamin. Today milk is often fortified with vitamin D either by direct addition of the vitamin or by irradiation of the milk. There is some evidence that vitamin D supplied in milk is more readily absorbed, or at least has greater protective effect, than when supplied as an oily concentrate. Different fish liver oils vary tremendously in vitamin D content; oils from different species of tuna contain on the average from 38,000 to 45,000 IU per gram, halibut 1200, cod 100, dog fish 3, sturgeon 0. In any one species, there is considerable seasonal variation in the liver oils. Fish liver oils (especially cod, halibut, tunny), while not natural articles of diet, are important commercial sources of natural vitamin D, i.e., D_3. Because of the relative stability of vitamin D, losses during preparation and storage of foods are usually small.

It is an unfortunate fact that most natural foods are low in vitamin D content. Man should, therefore, endeavor to obtain as much sunlight as possible, so that by the natural irradiation of the sterols in or on the skin an adequate supply of vitamin D may be maintained. In northern regions the short days and low angle of the sun during winter months may not provide enough ultraviolet light to form adequate vitamin D for a rapidly growing child (fig. 71.6). If sunlight is filtered through smoke and dust, its effectiveness is reduced still further, and in industrial areas the antirachitic effect may be almost obliterated. This explains the former high incidence of rickets in large cities where industry was concentrated. Cod or other fish liver oils or commercial concentrates of vitamin D may be taken with advantage especially by children during winter months.

STANDARDS AND REQUIREMENTS. The present international standard for vitamin D, adopted by the World Health Organization in 1949, is pure vitamin D_3. The international unit is defined as the vitamin D activity of 0.025 μg. of the standard.

The dietary requirement depends upon the amount of exposure to sunlight. Adults in a sunny climate may not need any vitamin D in their food. Pediatricians recommend that infants be started on supplementary vitamin D about 2 weeks after birth. Cod-liver oil, oleum percomorphum or vitamin D concentrates containing 400 to 500 units in a few drops are commonly used. Some workers suggest doses of 1000 to 3000 units per day to allow for defective absorption. However, the minimal toxic overdose does not appear to be far from the optimum curative dose. L. J. Harris in Great Britain gives the daily *preventive* dose as 500 to 1500 IU, the curative dose as 1000 to 3000 and the toxic overdose as anything over 10,000 IU. Where more sunshine is encountered, these values would be somewhat lower. *American and Canadian authorities suggest that children may require up to 400 IU per day.* The same intake (400 IU) is recommended during the last trimester of pregnancy and for nursing mothers during lactation.

HYPERVITAMINOSIS D (TOXICITY). Excessive intake of vitamin D in experimental animals or in man is deleterious. The first signs of toxicity are digestive disorders (vomiting and diarrhea) with loss of appetite and considerable loss of weight. Kidney damage finally results in death. Excessive doses of vitamin D cause hypercalcemia and calcification of the joints and soft tissues, especially the kidneys, large and medium sized arteries, heart, lungs, bronchi, pancreas and parathyroid gland. What has been described as early retention of calcium followed by decalcification of the skeleton may represent a translocation of the mineral to abnormal sites.

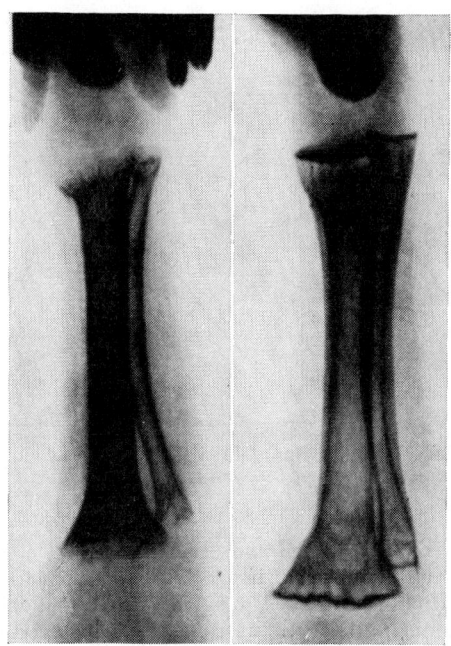

FIG. 71.5. *Left*, rickety bone, tibia of child 1$\frac{4}{12}$ years of age. *Right*, same bone after the child had received daily doses of cod-liver oil for a period of 14 days. (After H. A. Harris.)

TABLE 71.4

Vitamin D in common foods

Food	I.U. per 100 Grams
Cow's milk (raw)......	0.3 to 4
Butter................	8 to 100
Margarine (vitamins added)...............	200 to 300
Egg yolk..............	150 to 500
Liver (ox).............	40 to 50
Herring (fresh)........	800
Cod liver oil...........	2000 to 30,000
Halibut liver oil.......	20,000 to 400,000
Tuna liver oil.........	2,000,000 to 6,000,000

VITAMIN E (TOCOPHEROL)

During the early 1920's several groups of investigators became aware that rats required a fat-soluble substance for normal reproduction. Mattill and Conklin observed that rats reared on a diet of whole milk are usually sterile. Evans and Bishop found that addition of wheat germ, alfalfa or lettuce to a diet of casein, starch and lard (con-

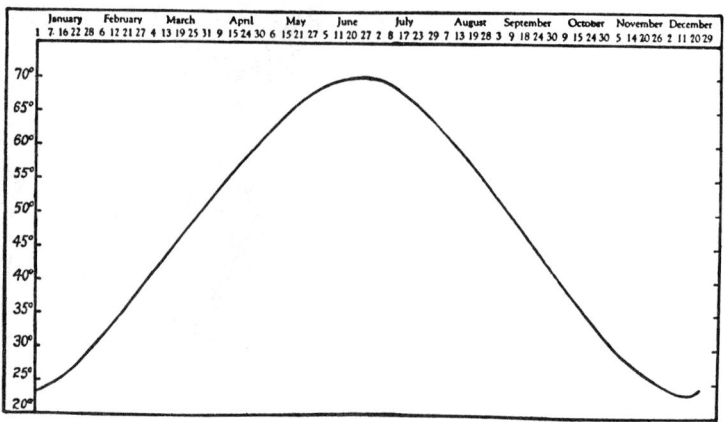

Fig. 71.6. Maximum daily altitude of the sun throughout the year at the latitude of Toronto. (From Tisdall and Brown.)

taining cod liver oil and other known vitamins) corrected its sterility-inducing effects. The active principle was referred to as the fertility vitamin or antisterility factor until Sure (1924) suggested that it be called vitamin E. Parallelism was noted between vitamin E activity and antioxidant (antirancidity) properties, suggesting a significant relationship. However, as fractionation progressed, the biological and antioxidant activities did not always have the same ratio to each other in different concentrates.

CHEMISTRY. A material possessing the characteristic biological activity was isolated in 1936 from the unsaponifiable fraction of wheat germ oil; it proved to be a mixture of three closely related compounds. A fourth member with similar characteristics was later found and recently (1955) two more have been recognized. All are viscous oils. Vitamin E activity resides to varying degrees in each of them, and all exhibit antioxidant properties, also to varying degrees, thus explaining the earlier discrepancies and confusion. The compounds are known collectively as tocopherols (from *tokos*: childbirth, *pheros*: to bear, and the chemical suffix-*ol*, signifying an alcohol). The most active of these, biologically, is α-tocopherol, $C_{29}H_{50}O_2$:

The β- and γ-tocopherols ($C_{28}H_{48}O_2$) each contain one less methyl group and δ-tocopherol ($C_{27}H_{46}O_2$) has still one less. These differences in methylation of the tocol nucleus affect profoundly the biological activity and other properties. The reported preponderance of the α-form in American wheat germ oils and of the β-isomer in European wheat oils is interesting but unexplained.

RELATIVE POTENCY OF THE VITAMERS (VITAMIN ISOMERS). The physiological activity of the α, β, γ and δ-isomers, by rat assay, varies considerably. The relative potencies have been reported to be approximately 100:40:8 (or less): 1, respectively; some workers believe the β and γ isomers to be more nearly equal in biological activity. For the cure of muscular dystrophy in rabbits the potencies of natural α, β and γ-tocopherols are in the ratio of 100:30:20. The biopotency of the esters is equal to that of the free alcohols, or even slightly greater, because the esters are not auto-oxidizable.

Wheat germ oil (containing mainly α- and β-tocopherols), cottonseed oil (α- and γ-forms in about equal amounts), corn oil (largely γ-tocopherol) and soybean oil (α, γ- and δ-forms) are the main sources of the natural tocopherols. These oils contain from 0.1 to 0.3 per cent of total tocopherols. Today much of the vitamin E available

Vitamin E, α-Tocopherol ($C_{29}H_{50}O_2$)

α-Tocopherol
(5, 7, 8-trimethyltocol)

β-Tocopherol
(5, 8-dimethyltocol)

γ-Tocopherol
(7, 8-dimethyltocol)

δ-Tocopherol
(8-methyltocol)

commercially is not the natural d-α-tocopherol, but a synthetic dl-α-tocopheryl acetate.

By definition, synthetic α-tocopheryl acetate has been assigned a biological potency of 1000 IU per gram. Pure d-α-tocopheryl acetate has the highest potency of any vitamin E product, with 1,360 IU per gram. Other products have the following activity, d-α-tocopherol 920 IU, dl-α tocopherol 680 IU per gram.

Effects of Deficiency

The relatively large amounts of vitamin E found stored in all tissues examined (from animals and man) suggest that it possesses an important metabolic role. However, no characteristic biochemical disturbances attributable to lack of vitamin E are known. One property of probable significance is the antioxidative effect of the tocopherols. It has been shown that the vitamin A requirement is partly dependent on the vitamin E content of the diet. The sparing effect of the natural vitamin E on vitamin A is not shared by the synthetic ester, dl-α-tocopheryl acetate, and hence it appears to be concerned with the antioxidant properties of the free tocopherols.

Deprivation of vitamin E in the rat leads to changes in the reproductive organs. In the female a mild deficiency may disturb the estrous cycle, a further deficiency leads to resorption of the fetuses about eight or ten days after normal conception. Prolonged deficiency in the female leads to loss of ability to conceive. Restoration of vitamin E to the ration permits pregnancies to proceed normally once more, i.e., in females the changes are reversible. In the male rat, prolonged deficiency of vitamin E leads to atrophy of the testes and to irreversible changes in the germinal epithelium, with complete sterility.

A common finding in rats, guinea pigs and rabbits is the development of degenerative changes in the muscles, leading to actual paralysis (nutritional muscular dystrophy). Both sexes and all age groups appear equally susceptible to this effect of vitamin E deficiency.

A characteristic pigment, called *ceroid*, probably formed by autoxidation of unsaturated lipids, is often found in the muscles, sex glands and liver cells of rats fed E-deficient diets.

Necrosis and *fibrosis* of the *heart muscle* have also been reported in experimental animals kept for long periods on rations deficient in vitamin E. In chicks, vitamin E deficiency leads to *embryonic mortality* (due to disintegration of blood vessels), to the appearance of large patches of subcutaneous edema on the breast, abdomen, neck and legs (*exudative diathesis*), and a nutritional *encephalomalacia* characterized by motor incoordination, head retraction, stupor and death.

Experiments in rats and rabbits have shown that animals given adequate vitamin E survived hypoxia (reduced atmospheric pressure) much better than E-deficient ones. They also survived exposure to a high oxygen tension (98 per cent oxygen at 5 atmospheres pressure) much better. The way in which vitamin E protects against changes in oxygen tension is not known.

Although man apparently requires vitamin E, much less is known about the role of this vitamin in human nutrition. Beneficial results have been reported from its use in habitual abortion, muscular dystrophies, peripheral vascular disorders (indolent ulcers, early gangrene of the extremities, thrombophlebitis), heart diseases and the menopause. These claims have been denied or minimized by other clinical investigators. Many contend that it has never been established that the conditions seen in humans (superficially resembling those observed in animals) are due to lack of vitamin E. The literature is decidedly controversial. The high dosage levels of vitamin E often advocated in clinical medicine seem unreasonable. On the basis of animal studies of storage and utilization of fat-soluble vitamins, including E, the possibility seems remote that adults ever suffer from avitaminosis E. Moore (1956) has pointed out that in man the concentration, by weight, of vitamin E in the plasma normally exceeds by about thirty-fold that of vitamin A.

In early life the stores of vitamin E may be much less, but even in the case of infants some of the evidence for a beneficial therapeutic effect of vitamin E is unconvincing. There is evidence, however, that the sensitivity to hemolysis of the red cells of newborn and premature infants can be reduced by giving tocopherol.

SOURCES. Vitamins E occur so ubiquitously, being found in essentially every article of diet, that consumption of a normal mixed ration provides enough to keep the body stores well supplied. Unmilled cereals, vegetable oils and eggs are the richest sources. The average daily intake of *d*-α-tocopherol by an adult man has been estimated to be 14 to 19 mg. Part of this is oxidized in the intestine to quinones and part is excreted in the feces. Possibly only one-third of the intake, or about 5 to 7 mg. per day, are actually absorbed. Nothing definite is known about the human requirement.

Vitamin E is stored in all tissues. Adipose tissue is the major storage site. Hypervitaminosis E has been studied in several species but no toxic effects have been observed even when massive doses have been administered over a prolonged period.

VITAMIN K

(See also ch. 33)

Between 1929 and 1935 several reports appeared of a hemorrhagic condition in chickens raised on purified diets consisting of cereals plus yeast. The disease, due to defective blood clotting, was seemingly of dietary origin. In 1935 Dam proposed the name vitamin K (*Koagulation*) for the protective nutritional factor which his experiments, confirmed by Almquist and Stokstad, had shown to be present in the fat-soluble fraction of green leaves.

meal product proved to have 10 more carbon atoms in a longer side chain and was called vitamin K_2 to distinguish it from the alfalfa product, $C_{31}H_{46}O_2$, which was called K_1.

CHEMISTRY. A number of compounds possessing vitamin K activity are known, all being derivatives of 2-methyl-1,4-naphthoquinone, i.e., all active compounds appear to possess the general formula:

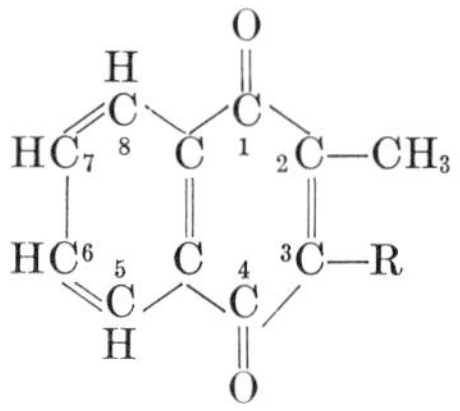

Synthetic 2-methyl-1,4-naphthoquinone, (R=H) sometimes called *menadione* and sometimes vitamin K_3, is readily prepared in pure, crystalline form, and apparently possesses all the physiological properties of the natural vitamin. Natural

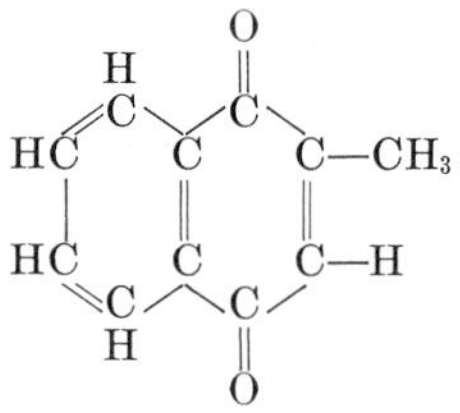

Menadione
(Vitamin K_3).

vitamin K_1 differs from menadione by having at position 3 a phytyl side chain C_{20}, with 1 double bond) and vitamin K_2 has a difarnesol substituent (C_{30}, with 6 double bonds).

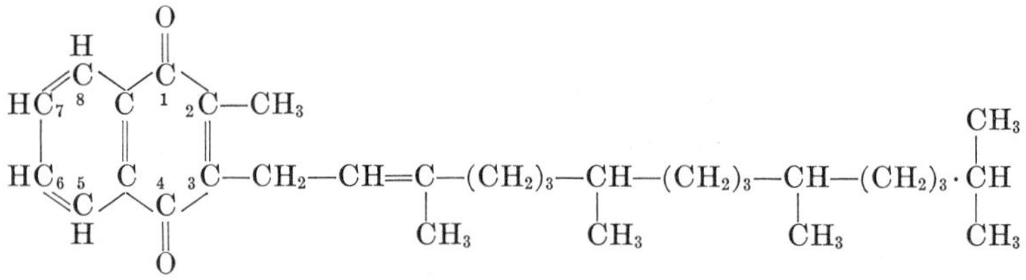

Vitamin K_1 (2-methyl-3-phytyl-1,4-naphthoquinone) $C_{31}H_{46}O_2$

There was no direct relationship of coagulation factor with the chlorophyll, carotene or xanthophyll content of the leaves. When the activity was shown to be in the nonsaponifiable nonsterol fraction it was obviously different from any previously known fat-soluble vitamin. In 1939, two groups accomplished the isolation, Dam and Karrer and their colleagues from alfalfa, Doisy and his associates from both alfalfa and fishmeal. The fish-

The structure of vitamin K was elucidated fairly rapidly, after its isolation, because of similarities in chemical and physical properties to *phthiocol*. This substance had been isolated from tubercle bacilli six years earlier by Anderson and his colleagues, and its structure proven by synthesis to be 2-methyl-3-hydroxy-1,4-naphthoquinone:

$$\text{Phthiocol}$$

When phthiocol was tested in vitamin K-deficient chicks it proved to be active and was thus the first form of vitamin K to be identified.

It had been noted during the isolation that fishmeal improved as a source of the factor when putrefaction set in. Many bacteria, including those in the flora of the human and animal intestine, have since been shown able to synthesize vitamin K_2. Treatment of animals or patients with sulfonamides or certain antibiotics reduces, and may even abolish intestinal synthesis of vitamin K_2. Natural sources of vitamin K_1 include green-leaf vegetables (e.g., kale, cabbage, spinach) and tomatoes.

Effects of Deficiency

In chicks, where the deficiency was first observed, the prolongation of clotting time may result in internal bleeding; in severely deficient birds even minor injury (such as pulling out a pin feather) may cause death from hemorrhage. Other poultry (geese, ducks, turkeys) develop the deficiency as readily as chickens, but in mammals it is much more difficult to produce. Later it appeared that this difference is due to a constant supply of vitamin K_2 being manufactured by bacteria in the intestine.

In vitamin K deficiency the disturbance in blood coagulation is caused by the combined reduction in prothrombin and a number of other factors in the blood. Because these proteins are made mainly in the liver, their levels in the plasma may be dangerously low in patients with liver damage, in spite of an adequate intake of vitamin K in the diet.

Vitamin K cannot *substitute* for prothrombin; but it is necessary for the formation of prothrombin in the liver. It is also important to point out that vitamin K is of no value in other hemorrhagic conditions not due to lowered prothrombin levels (e.g., hemophilia). Vitamin K is of clinical value especially in four conditions: (1) to control bleeding that may occur following operations in patients with obstructive jaundice; (2) in the hemorrhagic diathesis of new-born infants; (3) in conditioned vitamin K deficiency due to failure of absorption from (or production in) the intestine; (4) to counteract overdosage with synthetic anticoagulants such as Dicumarol, cyclocumarol, phenylindanedione, and accidental poisoning with Warfarin (a coumarin-type rat poison).

Vitamin K being fat-soluble, is absorbed from the gut, like other lipids and fat-soluble vitamins, only in the presence of bile salts. The water soluble analogs, however, do not require bile for their absorption.

In obstructive jaundice, bile salts being excluded from the intestine, vitamin K, either of dietary origin or produced by intestinal bacteria, is not absorbed in adequate amount. This would explain the prolonged prothrombin-time and tendency to bleeding in these patients. The bleeding sometimes seen in new-born infants may be due to failure of placental transfer of vitamin K, to inadequate intake of the vitamin by the mother, to delay in the development of the intestinal flora to make vitamin K, or to a combination of these defects.

Disturbances in blood coagulation due to lowered prothrombin (except those caused by liver disease) are promptly corrected (3 to 6 hours) orally or by injections of vitamin K_1 (oily emulsion) or the synthetic analogs of vitamin K. The usual therapeutic dose is 1 to 5 mg. per day. Other forms that have been used clinically include phytylmenadione oxide, menadione sodium bisulfite and Synkavite (2-methyl-1,4-naphtho-*hydroquinone* diphosphoric ester). Regardless of the route of administration a lag of several hours occurs before any change in the clotting response is perceptible.

Synthetic phytylmenadione, i.e., vitamin K_1, is commercially available but expensive. The weight of evidence is that the natural vitamin or synthetic K_1 is more effective than menadione in correcting the effects of overdosage with anticoagulant dicoumarins. It has been suggested that the effect of dicoumarol is an example of reversible inhibition by an antimetabolite. Woolley doubts that it acts this way since the dicoumarol-vitamin K antagonism differs in several ways from the characteristic competition between analogs. Whatever the process by which it acts, dicoumarol(3,3'-methylene-bis-(4-hydroxycoumarin)), when administered by mouth to man or animals causes a marked lowering of the plasma prothrombin level with consequent lengthening of the clotting time. It is used clinically to control thrombus formation (see ch. 33).

TOXICITY OF VITAMIN K. Before dicoumarol came into clinical use, vitamin K and its analogues were given in small doses of a few milligrams per day. Larger doses, of several hundred milligrams per day, are now given to counteract overdosage with synthetic dicoumarins used as anticoagulants. Patients given 150 to 600 mg. daily of water-soluble synthetic vitamin K analogues intravenously have complained of nausea and of more severe reactions. Some deaths of infants have been attributed to overdosage with a water-soluble analogue. The naturally occurring phytyl compound is not toxic when fed or injected in relatively massive amounts.

Sublethal doses of menadione derivatives (but not of phytyl-menadione) have induced anemia in rats, rabbits and dogs. Occasionally polycythemia has been observed in the same animals. In the mouse, the LD_{50} of menadione (orally) has been reported as 500, 620, 800 and 840 mg. per kg., by different workers; in rabbits it is 250 mg. per kg.

LIPOIC ACID. Lipoic acid, formerly known as protogen and as pyruvate oxidation factor, is a fat-soluble material which is an essential growth factor for certain bacteria and protozoa. It was isolated in 1951 from yeast and liver. Five different forms, with differing activities, have been described: a bound form, a water-soluble complex, and three fat-soluble varieties. All are derivatives of an acid containing eight carbon atoms and two sulfur atoms. Because of this it is also known as thioctic acid:

$$HOOC \cdot CH_2 \cdot CH_2 \cdot CH_2 \cdot CH_2 \cdot CH \cdot CH_2 \cdot CH_2$$
$$\underset{S \text{———} S}{}$$

Lipoic acid or its amide appears to function as a further cofactor sometimes necessary, along with thiamine pyrophosphoric ester (TPP), in the decarboxylation reactions (involving pyruvic and ketoglutaric acids) discussed briefly under *thiamine* and more fully under *carbohydrate metabolism*. The active agent, lipothiamide pyrophosphoric ester, is referred to briefly as LTPP.

CHAPTER 72

The Vitamins (Continued)

Water-Soluble Vitamins

VITAMIN B COMPLEX

Lack of vitamin B leads to loss of appetite with consequent loss of weight (fig. 72.1). Early fractionation studies of "growth factors" in aqueous extracts of yeast, liver and other animal and plant tissues revealed that an antineuritic substance (vitamin B_1 = aneurin = thiamine) could be separated from a pellagra-preventing (P-P) factor. Later, other growth factors were found in various fractions. Different names were applied in different laboratories so that a study of the literature of several decades ago may prove baffling to modern readers. Some of the synonyms are shown in table 71.1. Twelve substances are grouped together because of their close association in tissues and because for a long time their separation proved most difficult: *thiamine, riboflavin, nicotinic acid, pyridoxine, pantothenic acid, biotin, para-aminobenzoic acid, folic acid, folinic acid, cyanocobalamin, choline,* and *inositol.* All have been isolated in pure form, and most of them have been synthesized in the laboratory.

THIAMINE

ISOLATION, IDENTIFICATION AND SYNTHESIS. The contributions of Takaki, Eijkman, Grijns, Hopkins and Funk have already been mentioned. McCollum and Davis (1915) had found that young rats grew poorly on a purified diet containing dextrin as the carbohydrate, but that growth improved when lactose was used. The growth-stimulating principle was destroyed by heating the lactose, and it could be leached away from the milk-sugar with alcohol. The substance responsible for growth-stimulation was called "water-soluble B" by McCollum. Yeast was soon found to be an excellent source of this factor. In 1920 Emmett and Luros provided evidence for the dual nature of water-soluble B when they found that autoclaved yeast no longer contained Funk's antiberiberi substance but that it still promoted the growth of rats fed certain purified diets.[1] In 1926 the heat-sensitive antiberiberi-substance, vitamin

[1] Growth promotion was less, due to loss of Funk's factor, but the factor remaining, designated B_2 (now known as riboflavin), stimulated growth considerably.

B_1 (in those days often called the antineuritic factor) was isolated in Holland by Jansen and Donath. They proposed the name *aneurin.* The synthesis was accomplished in 1936 by R. R. Williams and his colleagues in the United States.[2]

Water-soluble growth factor(s)

VITAMIN B

Heat treatment

Heat labile component
VITAMIN B_1

Thiamine

Heat stable component
VITAMIN B_2

Adsorption on fuller's earth

Filter

Adsorbate
Factor 1 (Pyridoxine) Riboflavin, nicotinamide, etc.

Elute with baryta

Eluate factor
Factor 1 (Pyridoxine) Riboflavin, nicotinamide, etc.

Treat with heavy metal salt

Filtrate factor
Factor 2 (Pantothenic acid), etc.

Filtrate
Pyridoxine

Precipitate
Riboflavin
Insoluble in acetone, chloroform, ether and benzene.

Nicotinamide
Soluble in acetone, chloroform, ethanol, butanol, somewhat soluble in ether and benzene. Distills in very high vacuum.

[2] Papers of fundamental importance appeared from other laboratories within a few days of each other, as has frequently happened with studies of

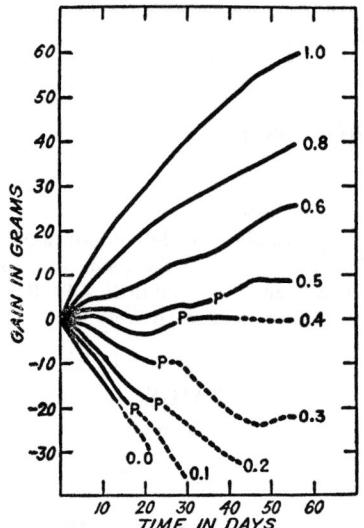

FIG. 72.1. Average weight gain curves of rats on vitamin B-free diet plus daily supplement of ground whole wheat of 0.1, 0.2, 0.3, 0.4, 0.5, 0.6, 0.8 and 1.0 grams. Negative controls (marked 0.0) received basal diet only. P, point where, on the average, chronic symptoms of polyneuritis appeared. Lines broken from the points at which some individuals died. (After Chase, from Sherman and Smith, *The Vitamins*.)

The presence of a sulfur atom and primary amino group led Williams to propose the name *thiamine*, which is now the term in general use.

CHEMISTRY OF THIAMINE (VITAMIN B₁). Thiamine contains two ring systems, the pyrimidine and thiazole, joined by a methylene bridge. It possesses a strongly basic quaternary nitrogen atom and hence forms chlorides and other salts

nitrates, picrates and other salts have been prepared. The naturally occurring vitamin is thiamine chloride hydrochloride although it is commonly referred to merely as thiamine. Today it is produced synthetically on a large scale and is available commercially at surprisingly low cost.

Thiamine is readily soluble in water and rather insoluble in most organic solvents. Its aqueous solution is strongly acid, due to the hydrochloric acid dissociated from the amino group. In acid solution (including acid foods) thiamine is reasonably stable even when heated, but is unstable on the alkaline side. At pH 3.5 boiling causes little destruction. At higher temperatures (autoclaving at 120°, for example) thiamine (in yeast) is stable for short periods, but after 2 to 3 hours most of it is destroyed. Riboflavin (vitamin B₂) is much more stable under these conditions. Near neutrality (pH 5 to 7) thiamine is much less stable to heat, and in alkaline foods it is rapidly destroyed by heating. Farrer measured the percentage loss on boiling thiamine at 100° for 1 hour in solutions of pH 3, 4, 5, 6, 7, 8 and 9 as 16, 20, 40, 53, 68, 100 and 100, respectively. Later he found that the buffer used was important: phosphate confers considerable protection and pyrophosphate even more. Storage on the alkaline side even at room temperature should be avoided. Thiamine is readily destroyed by an enzyme found in certain foods as well as by atmospheric oxygen. *Thiaminase* has been found in some raw fish (herring, carp), raw clams, shrimps and mussels and in certain plants (bracken ferns). Its occurrence was discovered following a study of the paralyses and convulsions seen in foxes and in cats fed rations containing large amounts of raw fish.

Thiamine is believed to act in the metabolic

$$N{=}C{-}NH_2HCl$$

Pyrimidine ring   Methylene bridge   Thiazole ring

Thiamine (Vitamin B₁)
($C_{12}H_{18}N_4OSCl_2$)

that dissolve in water and ionize freely; it also possesses a primary amino nitrogen which can form salts such as the hydrochloride. Sulphates,

other vitamins. Assignment of priority is difficult. Todd and Bergel in England, Windaus in Germany, and Makino and Imai in Japan made important contributions. Andersag and Westphal of the I.G. Farbenindustrie may have been the first to accomplish the synthesis but the company policy with respect to patent protection delayed publication of their work until 1937.

systems of the body as the ester, thiamine pyrophosphate (TPP). This molecule, known as *cocarboxylase*, is the coenzyme or prosthetic group of the enzyme decarboxylase which decarboxylates α-keto acids, especially pyruvic, in the body. Subsequent studies have shown that most, if not all, vitamins act as coenzymes to facilitate some essential step in intermediate metabolism.

Thiamine Deficiency

The effects of thiamine deficiency have already been mentioned—beriberi in humans, and polyneuritis in chickens, pigeons, rats, mice, dogs and other species. Two types of beriberi are seen in Japan, Southern China, India, the Philippine islands, Dutch East Indies and other places where the staple is polished rice: (1) the wet type, with edema, (2) the dry type, without edema. Multiple peripheral neuritis and muscular atrophy are characteristic in both. Weakening of the muscles accounts for the cardiovascular and gastrointestinal defects (enlarged right heart, peripheral vasodilatation, indigestion, gastric atony, severe constipation). Anorexia (loss of appetite) leads to loss of weight and general debility; tenderness of the feet and legs, lameness, ataxia, paralysis, inflammation of the ocular nerve and heart failure are usual sequelae.

In experimental animals the first signs of thiamine deficiency are loss of appetite, arrested growth, reduced motility of the gastrointestinal tract, and marked slowing of the heart. An extreme degree of bradycardia is seen in rats fed rations deficient in vitamin B_1. In man the opposite effect is produced, i.e., tachycardia.

Thiamine is necessary for the utilization of pyruvic acid, i.e., for the final stages of carbohydrate metabolism. The debility and tissue degeneration in thiamine deficiency are probably due to decreased ability to use carbohydrate. The central nervous system derives its energy mainly from carbohydrate, and this doubtless explains the lesions in the central and peripheral nerves.

Function of Thiamine

R. A. Peters at Oxford noted that lactic and pyruvic acids accumulated in the brains of thiamine-deficient pigeons and described the principal effect of vitamin B_1 deficiency as a "biochemical lesion" in which carbohydrate metabolism is impaired by the failure to convert

$$CH_3CO \cdot COOH + \tfrac{1}{2}O_2 \rightarrow CH_3 \cdot COOH + CO_2 \quad (1)$$

pyruvate to acetate. The original view that a simple oxidative decarboxylation occurs has had to be modified. A series of decarboxylating enzymes, all with thiamine pyrophosphate (TPP) as coenzyme, are concerned with the decarboxylation of α-ketonic acids. More recent work suggests that (under some conditions, at least) lipoic acid is combined with TPP to form a more complex cofactor (lipothiamide) for the oxidation or dismutation of pyruvic acid. The discoveries leading to this view will be indicated briefly.

In 1929 Evans and Lepkovsky had demonstrated that the vitamin B_1 requirement decreases when the fat content of the diet is increased. Although this effect has been described as a thiamine-sparing action of dietary fat, it now appears more accurate to say that the thiamine requirement increases as the proportion of dietary carbohydrate increases.

In 1936 Platt and Lu showed that the blood of patients with beriberi contained pyruvic acid and other ketone bodies and that these increased on exertion. Seven years earlier Kinnersley and Peters had found more lactic acid in the brains of pigeons lacking vitamin B_1 than in normal brains, and in 1934 Westenbrink had claimed that either lactic acid or pyruvic acid was the toxic metabolite responsible for at least some of the conditions seen in vitamin B_1 deficiency.

In a paper of fundamental significance Peters (1936) reported that the brains of pigeons deficient in vitamin B_1 had a much lower oxygen uptake (measured on slices in Ringer phosphate solution) than did normal brains, when glucose was supplied as energy source. The same result was obtained when sodium pyruvate or lactate was provided as substrate. Addition of vitamin B_1 raised the oxygen uptake to normal in all three cases. The reaction proved to be not only highly specific for vitamin B_1 but extremely sensitive. Peters described it as the *catatorulin effect* and used it as the basis of a method for determining thiamine. The simultaneous accumulation of lactic acid was puzzling until Sherman and Elvehjem showed that the accumulating pyruvic acid inhibits the enzyme lactic dehydrogenase. Thiamine facilitates removal of pyruvate and permits the normal metabolism of lactic acid.

Actually, as was suggested earlier, thiamine itself is not the catalyst. Westenbrink and Pollak observed a ten-minute delay, after adding thiamine to a polyneuritic brain preparation, before oxygen uptake began. About the same time Lohmann and Schuster isolated from yeast the pyrophosphoric ester of thiamine, and Weil-Malherbe showed that the vitamin could be transformed into this ester (i.e., into cocarboxylase) by the action of adenosine triphosphate (ATP). Lipmann suggested, in 1937, that added thiamine must first be converted to the pyrophosphoric ester which then acts as the coenzyme (cocarboxylase) of a system catalyzing the liberation of CO_2 from pyruvic acid. Neither thiamine nor its monophosphoric ester has any coenzyme activity.

UNITS AND REQUIREMENTS. The International Unit of vitamin B_1 adopted by the Health Organization of the League of Nations was 3 μg., i.e., 3 one-millionths of a gram, of thiamine chloride hydrochloride. Today values are almost invariably given in μg. or mg.

Estimates of human requirements for thiamine are usually expressed in relation to the total daily calorie intake, values ranging from 0.17 to 1.0 mg. per 1000 Cal. having been advocated. In 1953, after consideration of the available data the United States Food and Nutrition Board recommended that the minimum requirement for adults be 0.23 mg. for each 1000 Cal. This value may be compared with those found in a dietary survey by E. G. Young among Canadian families on rather low incomes: 0.20 mg. for men, 0.19 mg. for women and 0.22 mg. per 1000 Calories for children. No evidence of thiamine deficiency could be detected clinically in this group. It is interesting to recall that many years ago Williams and Spies (1938) had suggested a thiamine intake of 0.18 mg. per 1000 Cal. when fat provided 40 per cent of the total calorie intake, and an increase to 0.3 mg. per 1000 Cal. when the diet was essentially free from fat. The Canadian Council on Nutrition (1964) with this effect of fat in mind, recommends 0.3 mg. per 1000 Cal. since fats are costly items in the diet, and persons on low incomes will not consume as much fat as their more affluent countrymen.

Some workers in England, the United States and elsewhere are not satisfied that this dosage (0.75 mg. per 2500 Cal.) is adequate. The latest recommendations of the United States Food and Nutrition Board (1964) are shown in Table 73.2. No single figure can ever be given as the ideal value because the requirement varies with the composition of the diet as well as with the individual. A constant supply is necessary because the body is unable to store thiamine to any great extent.

These recommendations are generous and are possibly somewhat above the average requirement. They are easily met by the thiamine content of the foodstuffs commonly used in Canada and the United States, and a slight excess can do no harm. On the other hand, there is no evidence that an intake of thiamine in excess of the requirement affords any extra benefits.

TOXICITY. Tremendous doses of thiamine can be lethal. The acute fatal doses (mg. per kg.) by the *intravenous* route for mouse, rat, rabbit and dog were found to be 125, 250, 300 and 350 mg., respectively. The lethal dose by *subcutaneous* injection was about six times as great and *orally* about *forty* times these values. The toxic signs observed in dogs were: marked but transitory vasodilation with consequent fall in blood pressure, bradycardia and death (due to respiratory arrest). In man, sensitivity to excessive dosage with thiamine (especially when injected) has been observed: nervousness, tremors, tachycardia,

sweating, herpes zoster and even anaphylactic shock.

Mills has suggested (1941) that because parenteral injection of even moderate doses of thiamine may sometimes lead to anaphylactic reactions this route should never be used. Untoward reactions to oral administration of reasonable doses are virtually unknown.

SOURCES. Thiamine is widely distributed in natural foods of both plant and animal origin. Until man attempted to improve upon nature by refining his food, beriberi was apparently unknown. Plants synthesize thiamine which is found in roots, stems, leaves, flowers, fruits and seeds, e.g., average values (μg. per 100 gram edible portion) in beets 200, carrots 180, turnips 65, onions 120, asparagus 160, watercress 180, lettuce 270 and cauliflower 120 to 330. Peas and beans are rich sources, as are whole cereal grains. Nuts are also good sources of thiamine (Table 72.1).

There tends to be more thiamine in the mature dry seed than in other parts of the plant. *Unmilled* cereal grains are richer in thiamine than the highest recommended dietary allowance (i.e., 0.5 mg. per 1000 Cal.) since whole wheat averages better than 1.0 mg. per 1000 Cal. Whole rice and rye may average somewhat lower than this but whole oats may sometimes contain more thiamine per 1000 Cal. than does wheat. The bulk of the thiamine in cereal grains resides in the germ which is removed in conventional milling processes. The refined white wheat flour, polished rice or corn meal (hominy) will keep much better in storage than the unmilled grains, but the unfortunate penalty paid for this "improvement" is that the bulk of the thiamine has been eliminated. In some regions, thiamine (synthetic) is now added to the milled products, with or without other nutrients. Such fortification of white flour and polished rice is technically and legally referred to as *enrichment*.

Dried yeast is the richest of all known sources, containing from 1800 to 36,000 μg. (usually about 10,000 μg.) per 100 grams. Among foods of animal origin lean pork is the richest source of thiamine (500 to 1500 μg. per 100 grams); other meats contain much less (e.g., beef 80 to 300 μg.). Ox liver contains 350 to 450 μg. per 100 grams. Milk contains relatively little thiamine, eggs somewhat more. Oatmeal is a good and cheap source, one serving supplying more thiamine than 2 cups of milk or 5 average boiled eggs. To illustrate that it is relatively easy for Americans and Canadians to obtain a liberal supply of thiamine the following tabulation (after McHenry) shows the thiamine contribution made by average servings of a few foods commonly used in North America:

1 orange.	0.12 mg.
1 serving oatmeal.	0.22 mg.
3 cups milk.	0.27 mg.
4 slices enriched bread.	0.24 mg.
1 serving roast beef.	0.05 mg.
1 boiled potato.	0.14 mg.
1 serving carrots.	0.04 mg.
1 serving cabbage.	0.06 mg.
Total.	1.14 mg.

RIBOFLAVIN

As early as 1917 Emmett and McKim noted that two growth factors exist in the water-soluble extract of rice polishings, one (later called vitamin B_1) that cures rat polyneuritis and another, more heat stable, that produces weight gains under specific dietary conditions (see Fractionation scheme on p. 1445). Emmett and Luros (1920) found the same two factors in yeast. The dual nature of water-soluble B was also shown by Smith and Hendrick (1926).

Goldberger and Lillie (1926), in the course of their study of pellagra, produced a deficiency disease in rats characterized by ocular changes (conjunctivitis, corneal vascularization and eventually corneal opacity), and bilaterally symmetrical loss of hair. The factor that prevented these lesions was heat stable and was called the "P-P" (pellagra preventive) factor by Goldberger although his admirers called it vitamin G and in Britain it was called vitamin B_2. Meanwhile, other workers, using different dietary conditions were reporting different lesions (including a dermatitis, so-called "rat pellagra") cured by a heat stable factor. Finally it became clear that several different factors, all more stable to heat than vitamin B_1, were involved. The discovery that canine black-tongue could be induced by diets similar to those producing rat pellagra seemed an indication of progress, but in due course, it appeared that neither lesion was caused by lack of vitamin B_2. Birch, György and Harris (1935) differentiated the anti-black-tongue and P-P factor from vitamin B_2 (riboflavin) and the dermatitis factor (vitamin B_6). In 1936 Dann reported that riboflavin did not cure human pellagra, and in 1937 Sebrell and his colleagues confirmed that it did not cure canine black-tongue. It was thus obvious by 1937, that vitamin B_2 (riboflavin) had no direct connection with pellagra although its absence from the ration may complicate the pellagrous condition. Thus the term vitamin B_2, *initially intended to designate the factor that cures pellagra*, came in the end to be applied to riboflavin, the rat growth factor that is responsible also for preventing characteristic ocular lesions.

CHEMISTRY. Elucidation of the chemical nature of vitamin B_2 was rather rapid because at the time

TABLE 72.1

Typical vitamin content of some common foods

Food	A	Thia-mine	Ribo-flavin	Nico-tinic Acid	Ascor-bic Acid
	IU/100 grams	*mg. per 100 grams*			
Cereals					
Corn, maize, meal bolted. .	440	0.30	0.08	1.9	0
Rice					
Brown, raw. .	0	0.32	0.05	4.6	0
White, milled. . . .	0	0.07	0.03	1.6	0
Wheat, whole. .	0	0.55	0.12	4.3	0
Flour (80%). .	0	0.26	0.07	2.0	0
Germ.	0	2.05	0.80	4.6	0
Dairy products					
Butter.	3,300	trace	0.01	0.1	0
Cheese, ched-dar.	1,400	0.02	0.42	trace	0
Eggs, whole. . . .	1,140	0.10	0.29	0.1	0
Milk, cow, whole.	160	0.04	0.17	0.1	1
Fish, flesh					
Cod, raw.	0	0.06	0.09	2.2	2
Halibut, raw.	440	0.07	0.06	9.2	
Salmon, sock-eye, canned.	230	0.04	0.16	7.3	0
Fruit					
Apples.	90	0.04	0.03	0.2	5
Apricots.	2,790	0.03	0.05	0.8	7
Bananas.	430	0.04	0.05	0.7	10
Orange juice . . .	190	0.08	0.03	0.2	49
Peaches.	880	0.02	0.05	0.9	8
Plums.	350	0.06	0.04	0.5	5
Fowl					
Chicken.	0	0.08	0.16	10.2	0
Meat					
Beef, lean.	0	0.08	0.17	4.7	0
Kidney.	1,150	0.37	2.55	6.4	13
Liver.	43,900	0.26	3.33	13.7	31
Pork, medium. .	0	0.58	0.14	3.1	0
Kidney.	130	0.58	1.74	9.8	13
Liver.	14,200	0.40	2.98	16.7	23
Nuts					
Almonds.	0	0.25	0.67	4.6	trace
Peanuts, roasted.	0	0.30	0.13	16.2	0
Vegetables					
Beans, dried . . .	0	0.67	0.23	2.2	2
Cabbage.	80	0.06	0.05	0.3	50
Carrots.	12,000	0.06	0.06	0.5	
Kale.	7,540	0.10	0.26	2.0	115
Potatoes.	20	0.11	0.04	1.2	17
Spinach.	9,420	0.11	0.20	0.6	59
Tomatoes.	1,100	0.06	0.04	0.5	23

TABLE 72.1—*Continued*

Food	A	Thia-mine	Ribo-flavin	Nico-tinic Acid	Ascor-bic Acid
	IU/100 grams	*mg. per 100 grams*			
Yeast, compressed Baker's........	0	0.45	2.07	28.2	0

Values for pyridoxine, pantothenic acid, biotin and folic acid are not given, as many data now in the literature are known to be unreliable.

Taken from United States Department of Agriculture Handbook No. 8, 1950.

(1925–1933) a number of workers were studying fluorescent pigments isolated from sources as varied as egg yolk, dandelion flowers, grass, milk, liver, kidney, muscle and retinae. Names indicating the source were applied (*ovoflavin* to the substance from eggs, *verdoflavin* from grass, *lactoflavin* from milk, etc.), but subsequently many of these substances proved to be identical. Kuhn, György and Wagner-Jauregg (1933) isolated from egg white an orange-yellow compound with an intense yellowish-green fluorescence which, at doses of 100 µg. per day, stimulated the growth of rats on a purified diet. A similar growth-promoting fluorescent substance was isolated from whey (Booher, 1933). Kuhn suggested that these pigments might be related to the "yellow enzyme" isolated from yeast by Warburg and Christian in the preceding year. This yellow respiratory ferment was separated by Theorell (1934, 1935) into a protein fraction and a small molecule (the pigment, flavin), neither of which alone possessed enzymic activity. The identity of this flavin with the yellow pigments from various sources was soon shown and its structure was established by synthesis (accomplished almost simultaneously by two groups in 1935—Kuhn and his colleagues at Heidelberg and Karrer and co-workers in Switzerland). When the yellow compound, $C_{17}H_{20}N_4O_6$, was shown to contain the pentose sugar, ribose, attached to a dimethyl derivative of isoalloxazine, the name *riboflavin* was suggested.

Ribose

Riboflavin ($C_{12}H_{20}N_4O_6$)

Riboflavin crystallizes from dilute acetic acid, alcohol or pyridine in fine orange-yellow needles. It is only slightly soluble in water (about 12 mg. per 100 ml. at 25°) and is insoluble in ether, chloroform and benzene. Compounds such as urea, propylene glycol and sodium desoxycholate increase the solubility of riboflavin in water. It is relatively stable under ordinary cooking conditions but it is less stable to bright sunlight than many other vitamins.

The enzymes containing riboflavin are called flavoproteins. These enzymes accept hydrogen atoms from specific substrates, thus oxidizing them; the hydrogen is then passed on to other molecules. Alternate reduction and oxidation of the enzyme accomplishes oxidation of one and then reduction of a different component of the metabolic cycle.

The first of these prosthetic groups to be identified was the "riboflavin mononucleotide" of Warburg and Christian's "yellow enzyme" (which Theorell had split by dialysis into the protein carrier (apoenzyme) and the yellow coenzyme). The nature of the latter was established by Kuhn and Rudy (1936) as riboflavin-5'-phosphoric acid. It is the coenzyme for three different systems: Warburg's yellow enzyme, for *cytochrome c reductase* and for L-amino acid oxidase. A second active form of riboflavin (coenzyme) is riboflavin adenine dinucleotide, in which a complex of adenine-ribose-phosphoric acid is attached to the riboflavin phosphate to give a large complex molecule with a central pyrophosphate linkage. This compound acts as coenzyme for many systems, including xanthine oxidase, fumaric hydrogenase, the Schardinger enzyme aldehyde oxidase, glycine oxidase, D-amino acid oxidase, diaphorase, histaminase and other diamino-oxidases, etc.

Riboflavin Deficiency

The role of riboflavin in human nutrition is still somewhat controversial. As in animal studies, the lesions affect the eyes and skin. In rats, failure of growth is followed by dermatitis, loss of hair, cataract, some nerve degeneration and reproductive defects (cessation of estrous cycles, atrophy of testes). The early studies in man were complicated by the presence (unsuspected, of course) of other dietary deficiencies. One of the earliest reports of artificial riboflavin deficiency in man (Sebrell and Butler, 1938) revealed (1) fissures developing in the lips and at the corners of the mouth (cheilosis), (2) a sore tongue (inflamed and smooth) simulating the glossitis of pernicious anemia, (3) a seborrheic dermatitis affecting especially the face (ears, nose, forehead). (4) Sydenstricker has described a vascularization of the cornea due to lack of riboflavin (fig. 72.2). The cornea does not normally contain blood vessels, but when the diet lacks sufficient riboflavin for prolonged periods, capillary loops extend into the cornea, the eye becomes itchy, light sensitive (photophobia), vision is poor in dim light, and in time the corneal vascularization may lead to severe interstitial keratitis. These observations have been confirmed in a number of clinical centers and in several species of animals. Other workers have failed to induce corneal vascularization in subjects kept for some months on a diet very low in riboflavin. Several factors (some not yet understood) may be concerned. Corneal changes of this nature, when present, are not specific signs of riboflavin deficiency. Some patients with such lesions have responded to supplements of riboflavin; many have not. Whereas the cheilosis and glossitis often respond to riboflavin alone, sometimes nicotinic acid and other members of the vitamin B complex are required to effect improvement.

The absence of more profound and specific effects of riboflavin deficiency in man is curious because riboflavin is in the prosthetic group of so many enzyme systems catalyzing important transformations.

RIBOFLAVIN REQUIREMENT. There is no International Unit for riboflavin. The quantities of this (and of most other vitamins available in crystalline form) are now stated on a weight basis.

The riboflavin requirement of man, like that of most of the vitamins, is not known, although there is general agreement that the minimal intake for maintenance of health lies between 0.5 and 3 mg. per day. A common method of expression is to relate it to the energy intake. This is done because riboflavin is concerned in the oxidative processes going on in practically all cells and its loss and replacement quota might reasonably be expected to be proportional to the energy production. Several lengthy clinical studies indicate that about 0.3 mg. per 1000 Cal. of food are adequate. The Canadian Council on Nutrition (1964) recommend 0.5 mg. riboflavin per 1000 Cal. For an average man consuming food to give 3000 Cal. per day this would be 1.5 mg. riboflavin.

The United States Food and Nutrition Board (1953) decided that the riboflavin requirement is *not* related to energy intake or muscular activity. They recommend that the riboflavin allowance be calculated in terms of the recommended protein intake (although the evidence relating riboflavin need to protein metabolism is sketchy). Their latest recommendations,

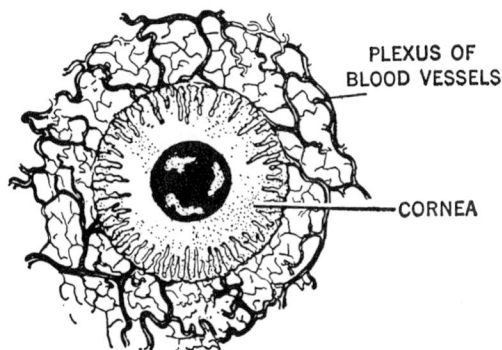

Fig. 72.2. Showing engorgement of the limbic plexus and vascularization of the cornea in riboflavin deficiency. Note the loops of vessels of the limbic plexus penetrating more than half way to the pupil. White areas are corneal opacities.

shown in table 73.2, are not significantly different from the Canadian.

SOURCES OF RIBOFLAVIN. All cells seem to require riboflavin. It is one of the most widely distributed vitamins. The richest known edible sources are some highly pigmented crustaceans (dorsal muscles of some crabs contain from 2.4 to above 20 mg. per 100 grams). Other good sources are liver (0.1 to 4.4 mg. per 100 grams), kidney, heart, muscle (meat, fish, fowl), egg white, milk and growing leafy vegetables.

Cow's milk usually contains between 0.1 and 0.15 mg. per 100 ml. and pasteurization (143 to 145° for 30 minutes) has a negligible effect. Irradiation of milk to increase its content of vitamin D does not reduce the riboflavin content but prolonged exposure to sunlight does. Milk is the chief source of dietary riboflavin (3 cups per day provide about 1.2 mg.). Cheese, eggs, meats and vegetables in the diet usually fail to satisfy the riboflavin requirement: unless some milk is consumed a deficiency may occur.

Riboflavin can now be produced more cheaply by fermentation than by chemical synthesis. Exceptional yields are obtained from the molds *Eremothecium ashbyii* or *Asbya gossypii*, in submerged culture with continuous aeration and agitation; yields up to 600 mg. per liter in 4 days have been reported from commercial producers.

TOXICITY. The low solubility in water may be responsible for the low toxicity of riboflavin. Oral doses of 2 grams per kg. to dogs and 10 grams per kg. to rats produced no signs of toxicity. Mice given 5000 times the therapeutic dose, intraperitoneally, suffered no ill effects. In rats the LD_{50}[3] for riboflavin (intraperitoneally) is

[3] This means the dosage at which 50 per cent of a population (or large representative sample) would be killed.

560 mg. per kg. Death occurred in 2 to 5 days due to kidney concretions; cytological changes were also noted in the pituitary, adrenals, pancreas and heart.

NICOTINAMIDE AND NICOTINIC ACID (P-P FACTOR)

Nicotinic acid and its amide have similar physiological activities, but it is in the form of nicotinamide that the vitamin is found in its natural, active combinations. Both compounds prevent pellagra. Nicotinamide functions as an essential unit of several different coenzymes that act as prosthetic groups for a variety of enzymes. Coenzyme I (also known as cozymase, codehydrogenase, and diphosphopyridine nucleotide, DPN) contains, besides nicotinamide, one molecule of adenine, two molecules of ribose and two molecules of phosphoric acid. Coenzyme II, previously known as the coferment of Warburg's yellow enzyme is a triphosphoric ester, the third phosphate group being attached to carbon atom 2 of the ribose joined to adenine; it is now more commonly referred to as triphosphopyridine nucleotide or TPN.

CHEMISTRY AND FUNCTION OF NICOTINAMIDE. Nicotinic acid was first obtained by Huber in 1867, by the oxidation of the alkaloid nicotine. Its presence in biological material was first shown almost simultaneously by Suzuki and associates (1912) who obtained it from rice bran during attempts to isolate the antiberiberi substance and by Funk (1911, 1913) who identified it as a component of his "vitamin" fraction from yeast. Both observed its inability to cure beriberi and set it aside as of no interest. Neither suspected that they had in hand the cure for another equally devastating deficiency disease but that 25 years would elapse before this was realized. In 1926 Vickery again isolated it from yeast and commented that "it has so far not been found in any other materials than rice polishings and yeast." Its nutritional importance remained unknown.

Nicotinic acid, $C_6H_5O_2N$, is a white crystalline substance that is only moderately soluble in water (about 1 per cent) but which is readily soluble upon the addition of alkali or acid, due to salt formation with the carboxyl group or basic nitrogen atom, respectively. The amide is more soluble in water. It is stable to heat in neutral solution but is converted to nicotinic acid by acid or alkali.

In the United States nicotinic acid is known as *niacin*. This name was coined to make the distinction between the vitamin and the alkaloid (nicotine) clear to the public lest they get the mistaken idea that "enriched" foods are being poisoned by the addition of the tobacco alkaloid. The terms niacin and niacinamide are official in the United States. In the present discussion the universally accepted names will be used.

Nicotinic acid, its ethyl ester, nicotinic acid N-methyl amide, β-picoline and several related compounds display vitamin activity, presumably being readily converted to nicotinamide in the animal body.

In 1934 Warburg and Christian found nicotinamide in coenzyme II, which they showed accomplishes hydrogen transport in cells, and a year later von Euler and his colleagues found it in coenzyme I, which is necessary for the fermentation of carbohydrate. Thus by an unusual inversion of the ordinary sequence of events in the vitamin field, the biological significance of nicotinamide was understood before its specific nutritional importance was realized. It was not until 1937 that Smith and others demonstrated its therapeutic value in pellagra.

The prosthetic groups containing nicotinamide (coenzyme I or DPN and coenzyme II or TPN) are unique in that they appear to be loosely bound to the protein part of the enzyme system, i.e., they are mobile coenzymes. About 40 reactions are known to be catalyzed by either one or both of these coenzymes. For example, DPN is specific for 3-phosphoglyceraldehyde dehydrogenase, TPN is specific for isocitric dehydrogenase, yet either can function with glutamic dehydrogenase. DPN occurs in all animal and plant cells in which carbohydrates are metabolized. It effects the conversion of glucose to gluconic acid, of α-glycerophosphoric acid into phosphoglyceric acid, and of ethanol into acetaldehyde. It also effects the dismutation of aldehyde into alcohol and acid, of β-hydroxybutyric acid into acetoacetic, of lactic acid into pyruvic acid and of malic into oxaloacetic acid. The list of reactions catalyzed by DPN in the presence of specific apoenzymes, i.e., different protein carriers, could be greatly extended. A different list, with some common items, could be made for metabolic reactions catalyzed by TPN.

Nicotinamide Deficiency

Deficiency of nicotinamide in man leads to serious consequences. Lack of it has led to the most serious of the deficiency diseases encoun-

Nicotinic acid
(Niacin)
Pyridine-3-carboxylic
acid

Nicotinic acid amide
(Nicotinic amide,
nicotinamide,
niacinamide).

tered in North America—*pellagra*. Between 1907 and 1937 the disease was endemic in the southern United States. The name is of Italian origin (*pelle agra* means rough skin). The disease is known to have occurred in Spain before it was first described by an Italian physician in 1771. In the past century pellagra was endemic in parts of Egypt, Rumania and France. The skin, especially the areas exposed to sunlight (face, neck, hands, sometimes the feet), becomes bronzed, resembling sunburn, and later thickened. The tongue is swollen, glossy and "beefy." The disease follows a terrible and inevitable course from mild psychic disturbances through dementia to death.

That pellagra is undoubtedly of dietary origin was made clear by Goldberger and his associates in 1915. The consumption of maize was recognized to be a prominent feature, but some workers suspected the presence of a toxic principle or bacterium in the corn. In view of the relationship between dietary tryptophan and nicotinic acid, established in the early 1950's, it is interesting to recall that Goldberger suspected that an *amino acid deficiency* as well as a vitamin deficiency was involved in the etiology of pellagra.

Liver and a commercial extract of liver proved to be strongly curative and fractionation studies were initiated in a number of laboratories. The use of experimental animals in the search for the curative agent for pellagra led to bewildering and often contradictory results that were difficult to interpret. As mentioned earlier, canine black-tongue is readily produced when young dogs are maintained on the Goldberger diet; a dermatitis produced in rats by a similar maize diet was called "rat pellagra" and later a dermatitis of dietary origin in chickens was called "chick pellagra." In the end it turned out that the work with rats and chicks was irrelevant to the disease in man. The lesions in both species were cured by extracts of autoclaved yeast and of liver that cured black-tongue in dogs and pellagra in man, but the appellation "pellagra" was unfortunate and unwarranted in both cases. In 1934 György showed that these dermal lesions of rats are prevented by vitamin B₆ (pyridoxine), and five years later Jukes showed that the chick lesions are cured by pantothenic acid.

Eventually it became clear that the foodstuffs and liver fractions that cured black-tongue in dogs also cured pellagra in man. About this time Knight, in London, and others found that nicotinamide is a growth factor for bacteria. In

1937 Elvehjem, Madden, Strong and Woolley isolated nicotinamide from a fraction of liver extract with marked antiblack-tongue activity and showed that it, and nicotinic acid, were highly curative. The beneficial effect of nicotinic acid in pellagrous patients was soon established, and a new era dawned in the treatment of pellagra.

NICOTINIC ACID-TRYPTOPHAN RELATIONSHIP. A new aspect of the puzzling pellagra problem was exposed when Krehl and his colleagues in Elvehjem's group found, in 1945, that extra tryptophan could substitute for nicotinic acid in purified diets of rats: addition of either 1 mg. nicotinic acid or 50 mg. L-tryptophan per 100 grams of diet restored growth to the normal rate. This discovery was an outstanding event in nutritional research for, as a rule, vitamins of the B complex cannot be formed by the tissues of higher animals. Later work showed that nicotinic acid can be synthesized from tryptophan with variable efficiency in many species (rat, pig, dog, horse, chick, turkey, and others) provided that other B vitamins (pyridoxine, riboflavin and thiamine) are adequate. This discovery explained several curious paradoxes: (1) although wheat and rice are essentially as low in nicotinamide content as is maize, pellagra is far more prevalent among maize eaters (maize is much lower in tryptophan content); (2) milk and milk products are among the most valuable pellagra-preventing foodstuffs and yet they are known to be low in nicotinamide (the milk proteins are, however, very good sources of tryptophan). The reason for the special susceptibility of maize eaters to develop pellagra was at last understood, and also why rats (with good synthetic powers) failed to develop lesions and even thrived on diets that were deficient for monkeys and pigs.

REQUIREMENTS AND SOURCES. Since dietary tryptophan can to some extent supply the tissues with nicotinamide, and since many other factors are now known to affect the requirement, exact information on the human requirements is not available. In 1941 the Food and Nutrition Board of the National Research Council (United States) estimated the nicotinic acid requirement of adults to vary from 23 mg. per day for a very active man to 12 mg. for a sedentary woman. Current recommendations (1964) are somewhat lower, 15 to 19 mg. for men, 13 to 14 for women and up to 20 during lactation. The Canadian recommendation (1964) is 3 mg. per 1000 Calories.

Both nicotinamide itself and nicotinic acid may be present in foods. Animal tissues usually contain a larger proportion in the form of the amide; plant tissues often have more present as nicotinic acid. For practical purposes the ratios in which they occur are unimportant as they possess equal biological activity. Fish and meat are good sources; kidneys are richer than corresponding muscle, and liver is richer still. The richest edible and readily available source is yeast. Baker's yeast contains 7 to 12 mg. and dried brewers' yeast from 30 to 90 mg. per 100 grams. Nuts are richer than legumes, and these, in turn, contain more nicotinic acid than do most vegetables and cereals. Fruits are poor sources (Table 72.1).

Nicotinic acid tablets (50 mg.) are sold by pharmaceutical suppliers. The acid has a marked pharmacological effect, a pronounced but transient vasodilator action. An oral dose of about 20 mg. causes flushing and tingling of the skin, fall of blood pressure and dizziness that may be alarming to patients not warned to expect these effects. Nicotinamide does not have this action. Both compounds are relatively nontoxic, the ratio of therapeutic dose to toxic dose being at least 1:1000. The toxicity of nicotinic acid is lower than that of nicotinamide, the LD_{50}[3] for rats being 4 to 7 grams per kg. and 1.5 to 1.7 per kg., respectively. As much as 5.4 grams of nicotinic acid per day has been given orally to man without harmful effect.

PYRIDOXINE (VITAMIN B₆) AND ITS AMINE AND ALDEHYDE

In the previous section it was mentioned that when rats were fed a purified diet deficient in vitamin B_2 they developed a dermatitis which Goldberger believed to be analogous to that seen in pellagrins. It was thought that cure of this condition in rats could be used as a test for the P-P factor. In Britain, where the lesion was called rat acrodynia, Birch, György and Harris (1935) found that it was cured not by nicotinic acid (the P-P factor) or vitamin B_2 (riboflavin) but by a factor to which György assigned the name vitamin B_6. György's substance was adsorbed from yeast extract onto charcoal, from which it could be eluted. It was found to be adsorbed also onto fuller's earth from which it could be eluted with baryta solution. Hence, it came to be called the *eluate factor*, or Factor 1. Meanwhile, in the United States a "chick dermatitis" factor was being investigated. Because it was not adsorbed on fuller's earth, the chick factor came to be called the *filtrate factor* or Factor 2. The use of different sources (yeast, liver, rice bran), of different adsorbents

and of different test animals led to considerable confusion during this period. The fractionation scheme (p. 1445) indicates the prominent characteristics that assisted in the fractionation and influenced interim naming of the components of the vitamin B complex.

In 1938 the isolation of vitamin B_6 in crystalline form was announced from five laboratories: (1) György and (2) Kuhn and Wendt obtained it from yeast, (3) Lepkovsky, (4) Keresztesy and Stevens and (5) Ichiba and Michi isolated pyridoxine from rice bran extract; later a sixth laboratory reported a different method of isolation from rice bran (Matukawa, 1940). It is interesting to note that some years earlier, in 1932, Ohdake had isolated from rice polishings a nitrogenous compound with the same empirical formula, $C_8H_{11}O_3N \cdot HCl$. No biological activity was attributed to it, and only later was it shown by Wiardi (1938) to be identical with vitamin B_6.

CHEMISTRY. The constitution of vitamin B_6 was established in 1938 by Kuhn and Wendt in Germany, who proposed the name "adermin." An independent synthesis by Harris and Folkers in the United States in 1939 confirmed the structure. György and Eckardt (1939) proposed the name "pyridoxine" which is now the one generally accepted.

In 1942 Snell and his associates studied the growth-promoting effects of pyridoxine on different microorganisms. Marked discrepancies were found when three different assay procedures (chemical, animal and microbiological) were used to measure the vitamin B_6 potencies of extracts of tissues. Out of these studies came the finding of two new substances closely related to pyridoxine, one in which the $-CH_2OH$ on carbon 4 is oxidized to an aldehyde, the other in which the same $-CH_2OH$ group is altered to $-CH_2NH_2$. These compounds are now called pyridoxal and pyridoxamine, respectively. All three have essentially equal growth effects in rats. However, in the case of some lactic acid bacteria, the aldehyde and amine have a growth-promoting

Pyridoxine (2-methyl-3-hydroxy-4, 5-di-[hydroxy-methyl] pyridine ($C_8H_{11}O_3N$))

Pyridoxal   *Pyridoxamine*   *Pyridoxalphosphate*

activity several thousand times that of pyridoxine.

Pyridoxal is the biologically active compound. Its phosphoric ester is the coenzyme concerned in the decarboxylation of certain amino acids. Transaminases, racemases and several other types of enzymes concerned with amino acid metabolism appear to contain pyridoxal phosphate as coenzyme.

In mammals, pyridoxine and pyridoxamine are converted to pyridoxal. Foods contain varying proportions of the three compounds. Since all three have equal growth-promoting effects in rats, the activity is usually expressed as "milligrams of vitamin B_6."

Pyridoxine Deficiency

Effects of pyridoxine deficiency have been seen in all species of animals studied, but these signs vary considerably. Rats lose their appetite, fail to maintain their weight, sometimes develop a typical dermatitis with swelling and edema (acrodynia); after prolonged deficiency loss of muscle tone develops and convulsions occur. In dogs a microcytic hypochromic anemia is regarded as a characteristic feature of vitamin B_6 deficiency. Turkeys develop hyperexcitability and convulsions without anemia, ducklings develop anemia without convulsions or paralysis. Chicks exhibit various convulsive movements; pigs, like rats, may have epileptiform fits, and they develop a microcytic anemia.

Observations *in vitro* have tended to implicate vitamin B_6 in protein metabolism, but systematic attempts to explore this in animals have given ambiguous results. One observation that should be mentioned is the similarity in the dermatitis produced in rats by essential fatty acid deficiency and vitamin B_6 deficiency. Witten and Holman suggest that vitamin B_6 is concerned in the conversion of linoleic and linolenic acids to arachidonic acid, which they regard as the essential fatty acid.

In man the effects of pyridoxine deficiency are less definite. Attempts to produce vitamin B_6 deficiency in human subjects have not been very successful. After a subject had been fed for a 55-day test-period on a diet devoid of vitamin B_6, Hawkins and Barsky found no marked alterations in the blood picture or biochemical findings. Nitrogen equilibrium was maintained, indicating no serious abnormality in protein metabolism. The test period may have been too short to bring on the deficiency state. Holt and associates fed a diet deficient in vitamin B_6 to two infants: one developed convulsions, the other hypo-

chromic anemia. These limited observations made little impression and were practically overlooked. Then in 1951 an epidemic of convulsions among babies fed a commercial liquid formula occurred in the United States. A dry powder preparation made from the same formula in the same plant did not induce convulsions. The cause was traced to excessive destruction of vitamin B_6 in the sterilization of the liquid preparation. Addition of extra pyridoxine to the liquid formula eliminated the trouble.

Vilter and his associates produced vitamin B_6 deficiency in patients by giving a pyridoxine analogue, desoxypyridoxine, which appears to have antivitamin effects. Some of the patients developed skin lesions and various other effects were noted that could be cured by giving pyridoxine. It is now generally accepted that vitamin B_6 is essential for man.

For the most part, the therapeutic use of vitamin B_6 has been empirical. It has been of no value in the treatment of the anemias. Muscular weakness has not responded and various types of nervous disorders and convulsive seizures have not been cured. The nausea and vomiting of pregnancy as well as that following X-ray treatments were claimed to respond to 10 to 20 mg. doses three or four times daily, but there have been more failures than successes; where benefit was noted it may have been largely psychogenic. Pyridoxine has been reported to be of value in cheilosis and post-adolescent *acne vulgaris*.

Requirements, Sources and Toxicity

The pyridoxine requirements of man are not known. A figure of 1.5 to 2 mg. per day has been suggested, based on animal studies, but it is only a guess. The vitamin occurs in the tissues of plants and animals, often combined in protein complexes.

The richest natural sources of pyridoxine are those foods known to be good sources of the other members of the B complex; yeast, rice polishings, meats, liver, egg yolk, whole grains and germs of various cereal grains. Celery, lettuce and green peppers are excellent vegetable sources. No natural antagonist is known. The synthetic antagonist, desoxypyridoxine, is phosphorylated in the body, and as phosphoric ester competes with pyridoxine phosphate for the apoenzyme.

Pyridoxine has very low toxicity, doses up to 1 gram per kg. being tolerated without obvious effect by rats, rabbits and dogs. In rats the LD_{50} orally is 5.5 grams per kg., by subcutaneous injection 3.7 grams per kg. and intravenously 657 mg.

per kg. Tonic convulsions precede death in mice and rats. Daily doses larger than 1 gram per kg. in rats, rabbits and dogs caused impaired coordination within two or three days, progressing to severe tonic convulsions and death in the stage of paralysis (Unna, 1940).

PANTOTHENIC ACID

In 1901 the Belgian scientist, Wildiers, recognized that yeast requires, for optimal growth, a special factor in addition to the known nutrients. He called it *bios* and attempted to isolate it. Professor Lash Miller in Toronto with G. H. W. Lucas and others, separated bios into several components—bios I (later identified by Eastcott as meso-inositol) and bios II. The latter was soon shown to be a mixture. The component called bios IIa (later found to be pantothenic acid) was shown by Miller to contain β-alanine, which in itself is sufficient for some yeasts.

In 1938 R. J. Williams and associates isolated from liver an acidic substance that had a marked effect on the growth of yeast. Because it is found widely distributed in plant and animal tissues Williams suggested the name pantothenic acid (meaning from everywhere). In the same year Woolley and others in Elvehjem's laboratory isolated the chick pellagra factor (filtrate factor) and believed it to be identical with pantothenic acid. Within a few months this was confirmed by Jukes, and about a year later Williams and Major at the Merck laboratories established the structure by synthesis.

CHEMISTRY

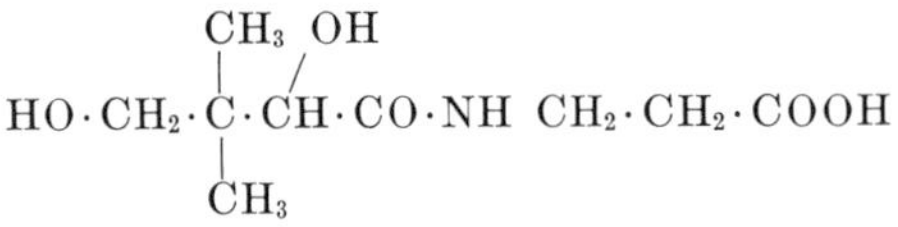

$$\underset{\text{Pantothenic Acid}}{HO \cdot CH_2 \cdot \overset{\overset{\displaystyle CH_3}{|}}{\underset{\underset{\displaystyle CH_3}{|}}{C}} \cdot \overset{\overset{\displaystyle OH}{/}}{CH} \cdot CO \cdot NH \; CH_2 \cdot CH_2 \cdot COOH}$$

This condensation product between pantoic acid (α,γ-dihydroxy-β,β-dimethylbutyric acid) and β-alanine is a yellow, viscous oil, soluble in water, and labile to acid, alkali and heat. The sodium and calcium salts, which are soluble in water and crystalline, are considerably more stable.

ACETYL-COENZYME A (ACETYL-COA). A specific functional role for pantothenic acid was soon discovered. In 1942 a stimulatory effect of pantothenic acid upon pyruvic oxidation had been observed in *Proteus morgani*. Then in 1946 Lipmann, while studying the acetylation of sulfanilamide by liver, found that a new coenzyme was involved which could not be replaced by any of the coenzymes known at the time. Also in 1946, Feldberg and Mann in England and Nachmansohn and Behrman in the United States found that a new stable cofactor is necessary for the acetylation of

choline. These and other observations on acetylating systems led to the isolation of a new cofactor, called coenzyme A (A for acetylation), and to the finding of pantothenic acid in it. The presence of 1 mole of adenosine, 3 moles of phosphoric acid and 1 atom of sulfur per mole of pantothenic acid was soon shown, and the following structure was finally established by Hoagland and Novelli (1954):

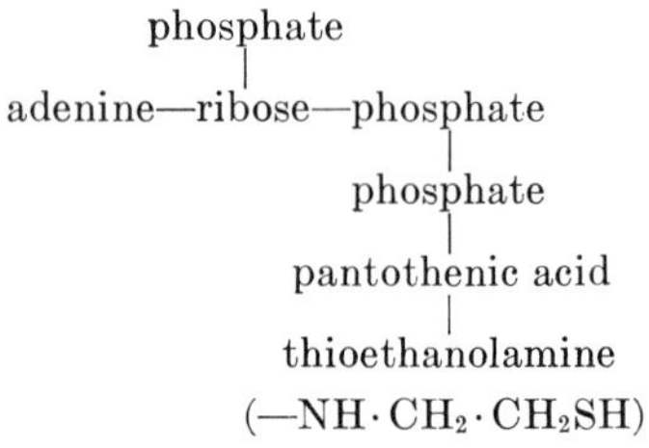

phosphate

|

adenine—ribose—phosphate

|

phosphate

|

pantothenic acid

|

thioethanolamine

$(-NH \cdot CH_2 \cdot CH_2SH)$

Coenzyme A

Coenzyme A acts as an acetyl carrier. It is shown elsewhere that carbohydrate (via pyruvate) and fat (via acetoacetate) give rise in the body to a metabolically active fragment containing two carbon atoms. The work of Lynen and Reichert in Germany, and of many others, culminated in proof that the "active two-carbon fragment" or "active acetate" is attached to the —SH group.

Pantothenic Acid Deficiency

All species of animals tested (e.g., rat, mouse, dog, fox, monkey, pig, chick and others) require pantothenic acid. The effects of deficiency vary considerably from species to species. Deficiency of this vitamin in the rat results in failure of growth, achromotrichia (graying of the hair) in black or brown strains, adrenal necrosis, hemorrhagic lesions, "bloody whiskers" (porphyrin-caked), "spectacled eyes" (circumocular loss of hair) and a sticky exudate on the lids, dermatitis, a spastic gait, and, sporadically in some animals, anemia and leucopenia. In chicks, dermatitis (mouth and eyelids chiefly, feet slightly), poor feathering, poor growth with weight loss are seen, followed by incoordination, paralysis and death. Turkeys, ducks and pigeons react similarly to lack of pantothenic acid. In dogs, irritability develops and sudden prostration occurs; respiration and heart beat become rapid and convulsions lead to death.

In man, until recently, no definite pathological lesions due to deficiency of pantothenic acid had been described. Perhaps the abundance of pantothenic acid in most foodstuffs accounts for this. There is no evidence to support extravagant claims that graying or loss of hair in man is due to lack of pantothenic acid. One condition has come to light, "burning feet syndrome," that may be due to lack of pantothenic acid. This syndrome was observed in prisoner-of-war camps in Japan and Burma and is common in parts of India. It does not respond to thiamine, riboflavin or nicotinic acid, singly or together. Gopalan has reported striking improvement following daily injections of 20 to 40 mg. calcium pantothenate.

REQUIREMENTS, SOURCES AND TOXICITY. No data on human requirements for pantothenic acid are available. The average intake on different dietary regimens has been estimated. Average (American) diets probably provide between 3 and 12 mg. daily, with a mean value about 9 mg. The highest excretion on normal diets was 5.3 mg. per 24 hours. Liver, kidney, egg yolk and fresh vegetables are the best dietary sources of pantothenic acid. Yeast and royal jelly are also good sources. Milk, meat, grains, fruits and nuts are fair to good; corn and rice are relatively poor sources.

The pantothenic acid in foods is reasonably stable for periods of storage, up to one year, under proper conditions, e.g., eggs and meat in cold storage, cereal grains, intact or ground, at room temperature. Usual cooking procedures and dehydration do not cause appreciable loss, but holding products at high temperatures for long periods (100 to 150° for 2 to 6 days) destroys much of their pantothenic acid.

Little is known concerning the pharmacology of pantothenic acid. Its toxicity is very low. The LD$_{50}$, orally, for mice is 10 grams per kg. of body weight, but rats given the same dosage survive without showing any signs of toxicity. Monkeys weighing 4 to 5 kg., fed 1.0 gram daily over a period of 6 months, showed no abnormality. Doses of 100 mg. have been given to man, intravenously, without toxic reactions; doses of from 10 to 20 grams given orally occasionally produced diarrhea, and, in a few patients, edema.

BIOTIN

The essentiality of biotin for man seems proven but whether it ever poses a problem in practical human nutrition is questionable. Biotin deficiency has been produced experimentally in human volunteers. Several spontaneous occurrences have been reported, but because biotin occurs so widely distributed in Nature (in wheat and most other seeds, in animal organs, in yeast, etc.) endemic deficiency is unknown.

The complex nature of Wildier's bios was suggested in 1922 by Fulmer and Nelson. By 1924 Lash Miller in Toronto had separated bios into three fractions, all of which were essential for *Saccharomyces cerevisiae*. The identities of bios I and of bios IIa (thought to be β-alanine but later found to be pantothenic acid) have already been mentioned. The third factor, bios IIb, later given the name biotin, proved to be identical with vitamin H, a factor that cures the strange condition known as 'egg white injury'.

Skin lesions, loss of hair, progressive emaciation, nervous manifestations and death followed the feeding of diets containing a large proportion of raw or commercially dried egg white (Bateman, 1916; confirmed by others). Two women workers have contributed much to this field. M. A. Boas-Fixsen in 1927 observed that liver and yeast contain a "protective factor X," and that *cooked* egg white is not toxic. In 1933 Helen T. Parsons and E. Kelly reported that small supplements of liver, yeast or egg yolk to the diet neutralized the toxic effect of the uncooked egg white. The toxicity of raw egg white can be eliminated by digestion with pepsin or with hydrochloric acid as well as by adequate treatment with heat. Attempts to isolate vitamin H (a name chosen by György for this vitamin because of its ability to alleviate the peculiar skin lesions; H for *Haut* = skin, in German) from liver and yeast progressed slowly because the animal assays were laborious and not very sensitive. Identification of biotin (the potent growth factor for yeast, isolated from egg yolk by Kögl and Tönnis) with the curative factor (vitamin H) was made by György, Melville, Burk and duVigneaud in 1940. Its structure was published by du Vigneaud in 1942, and its synthesis was accomplished in 1943 by Harris and his colleagues.

CHEMISTRY, SOURCES AND REQUIREMENTS. Biotin, $C_{10}H_{16}O_3N_2S$, is an acid, sparingly soluble in cold water and dilute acids, but freely soluble in hot water and in dilute alkali. It is practically insoluble in organic solvents.

Biotin ($C_{10}H_{16}O_3N_2S$)

A number of homologues (compounds with side-chains of different length) and analogues (with oxygen replacing sulfur) have been prepared, some of which can substitute for biotin and some of which are inhibitory. Oxybiotin can cure biotin deficiency in rats and chicks, but larger doses than of biotin are required. Desthiobiotin stimu-lates the growth of yeast (*Saccharomyces cere-visiae*) in a biotin-free medium; in contrast, it acts as an antimetabolite with *Lactobacillus casei*, blocking the utilization of biotin. The most potent inhibitors are biotin sulfone and DL-homo-biotin (with five methylene groups (CH_2) in the side chain).

Biotin occurs in natural products mainly in bound forms. One of these, biocytin, is a peptide with L-lysine. Biocytin, like biotin, is water-soluble and dialyzable, yet tissue biotin is not dialyzable until after treatment with acid (pH 3) or dilute sodium hydroxide. The binding is per-haps a peptide linkage since pepsin frees biotin. For the physiologist and nutritionist one of the most interesting bound forms of biotin is its combination with *avidin*, a special protein com-ponent of egg white. Avidin, so named because of its avidity for biotin, by forming an insoluble compound with biotin is responsible for the toxic effect known as "egg white injury." Avidin is denatured by heat and thereby inactivated. Biotin bound to avidin is not released by treat-ment with acid or the combined action of trypsin, pancreatin and papain. Biotin bound to avidin passes through the alimentary tract unchanged. Avidin has been found only in egg white (eggs of hens, turkeys, geese and ducks) and in the egg jelly of frogs. It appears to be a secretion from the mucosa of the oviduct.

The attempts to isolate biotin-containing co-enzymes have not been successful although a number of enzymatic processes have been dis-covered in which biotin appears to play a part directly or indirectly. There is some evidence that biotin-coenzymes are concerned in decar-boxylation and in carbon dioxide fixation as well as in the deamination of aspartic acid, serine and threonine.

The biotin requirement of many microorganisms is known, but that of man and higher animals is less certain. An intake of 150 to 300 μg. per day has been suggested for man. Such figures can at best be called a guess. Balance studies in man have shown a urinary excretion greater than the intake in some cases, and the fecal output is often greatly in excess of the intake. This suggests that in man synthesis by intestinal bacteria may provide more biotin than does the food.

p-AMINOBENZOIC ACID (PABA)

In 1935 a new red dye with spectacular proper-ties was described by Domagk. It could kill hemo-lytic streptococci in mice although it lacked this property *in vitro*. Tréfouël and his associates in France studied a series of related azo dyes and noted that all the ones displaying this property possess a sulfonamide group in the para position to the nitrogen linkage. Following this lead, para-aminobenzene-sulfonamide was tested and found to be highly active both *in vivo* and *in vitro*. Dis-covery of the potent antibacterial activity of sulf-anilamide was not only a milestone in medicine, causing a tremendous new interest in chemother-apy, but led to a new concept in metabolism, viz. of antimetabolites. Woods (1940) fractionated an antisulfanilamide fraction of yeast extract and obtained a material (with many of the properties of PABA) that neutralized the antibacterial ac-tion of sulfanilamide. When he tested PABA and found that it did, indeed, nullify the antistrepto-coccal activity of sulfanilamide he suggested that the action of the latter was the result of its com-peting with PABA for an enzyme controlling meta-bolic reactions, essential for bacterial growth. Later Rubbo and Gillespie (1940) isolated pure PABA from yeast and showed that 1 mole of PABA could antagonize 23,000 moles of sulfa-nilamide. Fildes (1940) expressed Wood's theory in more general terms by suggesting that PABA is an *essential metabolite*, although not necessarily a growth factor, for organisms inhibited by sulf-anilamide. Ansbacher (1941) believed that PABA is a vitamin necessary for the growth of chicks and that it acts as an anti-gray hair factor in the rat. There is no evidence to support the claim that PABA prevents or cures the graying of hu-man hair. The modern view is that PABA should not be considered a vitamin since its essentiality is confined to microorganisms; it is not required in the diet of animals.

CHEMISTRY

$$NH_2 \cdot HCl$$

$$HCl \cdot H_2N \langle \rangle N = N \langle \rangle SO_2NH_2$$

Prontosil (Domagk's red dye)

$$H_2N \langle \rangle COOH \qquad H_2N \langle \rangle SO_2NH_2$$

p-aminobenzoic acid   Sulfanilamide

PABA is a white, crystalline solid that is readily soluble in alcohol and ether and slightly soluble in water. It occurs widely distributed throughout the plant and animal kingdom. It is found both free and in combined forms. One of the better known conjugates is folic acid. Thus the view expressed by Fildes, that PABA is an essential *metabolite*, even though it may not be a *dietary* essential, has been substantiated.

PABA is relatively nontoxic in either single

pteridine derivative   p-aminobenzoic acid

pteroyl—   glutamic acid

"Liver *L. casei* factor" = pteroylglutamic acid = folic acid

doses or on prolonged administration. The acute LD_{50} for mice, rats and dogs (oral administration) is about 3, 6 and 1 to 2 grams per kg., respectively. Large doses (20 to 30 grams per day) have been administered to patients with louse-borne rickettsial diseases (typhus and Rocky Mountain spotted fever) without serious pathological changes being caused by the drug.

FOLIC ACID (PTEROYLGLUTAMIC ACID, PGA)

(See also ch. 30)

Five different fields of work merged in the discovery of folic acid. Some groups were fractionating liver extracts in the search for a cure for pernicious anemia, others were looking for vitamin M (needed by monkeys) and still others were trying to isolate vitamin Bc, a factor needed to prevent hyperchromic macrocytic anemia in chicks. Meanwhile microbiologists had found that certain bacteria, e.g., *Lactobacillus casei* ε and *Streptococcus fecalis* R (formerly called *S. lactis* R) would not grow on a mixture of salts, sugars, amino acids and known vitamins, but that addition of extracts of leaves, liver or yeast would initiate growth. Thus one of these latter groups of workers was searching for the *L. casei factor* and another for the *S. lactis* R factor. A feature common to the isolation of all these agents (i.e., the several factors comprising the folic acid complex) is that all

to the name folic acid (Mitchell, Snell and Williams, 1941, 1944) from *folium*, a leaf.

Concentrates from different sources displayed variable potency when tested in different species. For a short period the nature and relationships of these several closely related growth factors were uncertain.

"Fermentation L. casei factor" was found to contain *three* glutamic acid residues and *"yeast vitamin Bc conjugate"* contains *seven* such residues.

Pteroylglutamic acid produces partial and sometimes even complete remission of pernicious anemia, and certain other macrocytic anemias, in man. Although folic acid promotes regeneration of red blood cells it is unable to control the degeneration of the spinal cord that occurs in pernicious anemia. In some cases treatment with folic acid hastens the degeneration. Thus early hopes that folic acid would prove to be the antipernicious anemia factor of liver were dashed.

Meanwhile the nutritional requirements of *Leuconostoc citrovorum* were being studied by Sauberlich and Baumann (1948) and isolation of another unknown factor, the so-called *citrovorum factor* (CF), also referred to as *leucovorin*, was attempted. A relationship to pteroyl-glutamic acid was soon discovered. The structure of this new growth factor, now referred to as *folinic acid*, is:

Folinic acid
(5-formyl-5,6,7,8 tetrahydropteroyl-glutamic acid)

tors comprising the folic acid complex) is that all are adsorbed on charcoal and eluted, more or less quantitatively, by dilute ammonia. Hence the term *norit eluate factor* was also applied to the material, before it was isolated and identified.

The isolation of an active agent from spinach, and its wide-spread occurrence in green leaves, led

It is probable that in many biochemical systems, folic acid is not active as such, but that it must be converted to folinic acid which is (or is closely related to) the citrovorum factor (CF) which seems to be the functional form of the compound or is closely related to a more labile intermediate (transformylating coenzyme).

Effects of Deficiency

The pteroylglutamates are necessary for monkeys, chicks, turkeys, dogs, foxes, mink, guineapigs and for rats treated with sulfa drugs (see ch. 30). An experimental deficiency of folic acid has not been produced in man so it is not possible to state with assurance that man requires it. On the other hand, the proven value of folic acid in sprue and the pernicious anemia of pregnancy, and in megaloblastic anemia in infants, nutritional macrocytic anemia and related megaloblastic anemias makes it likely that it will prove to be essential in man when the proper test has been made.

Function of Folic Acid

The primary biochemical role of folic acid appears to be concerned with the incorporation of a one-carbon unit into a variety of essential metabolites: purines, pyrimidines and certain amino acids. The labile one-carbon unit has been referred to as "active formate" or "active formaldehyde." Formate precursors include the methyl groups of choline, methionine, sarcosine and dimethylglycine, the beta carbon of serine, the methylene carbon of glycine, and histidine and acetone. Active formate or active formaldehyde appear to be compounds with tetrahydrofolic acid that aid in the transfer of one-carbon units, i.e., that act as transformylating coenzymes.

Although folic acid and vitamin B_{12} have been shown to play a role in lipotropic phenomena, the details of the picture are obscure. The lipotropic effect is clear cut in rats fed certain diets; on other diets these vitamins may produce no alteration in liver fat or they may even exert an antilipotropic effect. Neither folic acid nor vitamin B_{12} is necessary for *transmethylation*. Folic acid is needed for transformylation reactions and vitamin B_{12} seems to be concerned in the reduction of formate via formaldehyde to biologically labile methyl.

The folic acid antagonists *aminopterin (4-amino-pteroylglutamic acid)* and *A-methopterin (4-amino-10-methyl-pteroylglutamic acid)* inhibit the incorporation of radioactive carbon from formate into the nucleic acid purines. These and other folic acid antagonists have been used therapeutically in attempts to control leukemia in man. Remissions have been induced that are more frequent and of longer duration than those common to the natural course of the disease, but no cures have been reported.

SOURCES AND TOXICITY. Substances with folic acid activity, as measured by microbiological assay, are widely distributed in nature. Most of the activity is present in 'bound forms' (conjugates). Liver has the highest activity; vegetables and many fruits are rich sources; nuts, dried beans and peas are good sources. Folic acid is synthesized by intestinal bacteria. The extent to which this occurs affects the dietary requirement.

Pteroylglutamic acid has very low acute and chronic toxicity.

VITAMIN B_{12} : CYANOCOBALAMIN

Antipernicious Anemia Factor; Animal Protein Factor (APF)

(See also ch. 30)

Several papers appeared during the period 1934 to 1946 indicating that an active substance, different from other known dietary factors, improved the hatchability of hen's eggs and increased the growth rate and survival time of chicks fed cereal rations free from animal protein. Because the factor (or a related substance) was found in products as diverse as liver, animal flesh, fish meals, condensed fish solubles, chicken droppings and cow-dung, but not in plant materials, it was called the "animal protein factor," or APF. In 1946 Cary and associates described a new factor, X, necessary for the growth of rats. It occurred in crude casein but could be leached out by suitable treatment. Factor X appeared to be the same as, or closely related to, the animal protein factor.

In 1948, Mary Shorb reported that a certain bacterium, *Lactobacillus lactis* Dorner, could be used to test for and assay the rat growth vitamin, APF. Later work of Shorb, Folkers and others suggested that this new factor, which they named vitamin B_{12} , was identical with the long-sought for antipernicious anemia principle. The final stages of the isolation of vitamin B_{12} were greatly accelerated by using this bacterial assay method, which in a few hours gave answers that by animal tests had taken weeks, and months by the tedious and costly clinical tests.

CHEMISTRY. Vitamin B_{12} is a red crystalline substance (mol. wt. about 1350) which contains a metal-porphyrin nucleus similar to that of heme or chlorophyll, but with cobalt (4.5 per cent) as the metal. It has the most complex structure of any vitamin known. The base dimethylbenzimidazole (which also occurs in riboflavin) was identified fairly early; later it was shown to be linked to ribose phosphate; a 2-aminopropanol unit, later shown to be Dg-1-amino-2-propanol, and a cyanide ion were also identified. The short name cobalamin was proposed for the active material.

A search for other and possibly richer sources of vitamin B_{12} led to the discovery that it occurs in many animal products but that plant materials show no measurable activity. It now seems that neither animals nor higher plants can make vitamin B_{12}. Certain nonphotosynthetic organisms serve as the primary source. It was from the fermentation broth of a strain of *Streptomyces griseus* that the workers in the United States isolated crystalline vitamin B_{12}.

Fermentation broths from other organisms provided several closely related compounds with equal activity in the treatment of pernicious anemia. They are related coordination compounds of cobalt in which the CN^- ion is replaced by a hydroxyl group or water molecule. The three compounds are, therefore, called cyanocobalamin (B_{12}), hydroxocobalamin ($B_{12}b$) and aquacobalamin, respectively. Analogous compounds are known in which "unnatural" nucleotide bases have been introduced by biosynthetic means, or in which halogens, thiocyanate or nitrite ions have replaced the cyanide ion.

Seven years were required to elucidate the arrangement of the recognized fragments in the antipernicious anemia vitamin. It is of great scientific interest that a new "tool" was used with outstanding success in solving this problem.

The structure of the formidably large and complex vitamin B_{12} molecule was deduced largely from crystallographic evidence supplied by X-ray reflections (Hodgkin *et al.*). Using automatic computers, a series of calculations of successive degrees of approximation to the correct electron density distribution provided a solution to the chemical structure of the nucleotide-free hexacarboxylic acid ($C_{46}H_{60}O_{13}N_6CoCl\cdot 2H_2O$) that was obtained from vitamin B_{12} by alkaline hydrolysis. Elucidation of the structure of such a molecule from X-ray data represents a great triumph for crystallography. This information, in conjunction with the chemical evidence accumulated during the seven years, enabled Todd and Smith and their associates to propose the formula $C_{63}H_{90}O_{14}N_{14}PCo$ and the probable structure:

VITAMIN B_{12}
(Taken from Nature, **176**, 329, 1955.)

OCCURRENCE. Accurate figures for the occurrence of vitamin B_{12} were not easily obtained; microbiological assays, animal tests and clinical trials frequently gave inconsistent data. Many values in the earlier literature are therefore suspect. Plant materials show no measurable activity; animal tissues and secretions usually show some, but extremely variable, potency. Extracts of human livers and of livers of 26 species of mammals and 3 species of fish were active in pernicious anemia. Estimates of the amount of vitamin B_{12} in various foodstuffs (μg. per 100 grams) are: mammalian muscle (horsemeat, beef, pork, mutton) 1 to 5; different organs showed considerable variability (beef kidney and liver 15 to 20); egg yolk, 1 to 3; milk, traces; cheese, milk powder and crude casein, 1 to 3. Concentrates of cobalt-containing pigments from cow-dung and from certain mould cultures are inactive in pernicious anemia but become active after digestion with gastric mucosa or pancreatic enzymes.

Effects of Deficiency

The greatest interest in vitamin B_{12} concerns its effectiveness in the treatment of pernicious anemia. Doses as small as 1 to 3 μg. per day cure both the hematological and neurological defects.

Vitamin B_{12} is more effective in patients by injection than by mouth. Oral doses 30 to 60 times the effective parenteral dose may cause a slow response in some patients. Vitamin B_{12} has other physiological effects besides the stimulation of hematopoiesis. It promotes the growth of animals fed diets low in the animal protein factor, i.e., consisting mainly of protein from plant sources. There appears to be a relationship between B_{12} and thyroid activity but this needs further study.

In vitamin B_{12} deficiency, rats develop enlarged kidneys and elevated blood urea levels. Deficient chicks also show an elevated blood NPN. A nutritional edema preventable by vitamin B_{12} (and also by choline) has been described in dogs and rats. Vitamin B_{12}, in conjunction with folic acid, is concerned in the metabolism of the one-carbon fragment, including the biosynthesis of methyl groups. This vitamin is not involved in transmethylation reactions but it does seem to be concerned in the reduction of active formate (5-formyltetrahydrofolic acid) to active formaldehyde (5-hydroxymethyl-tetrahydrofolic acid) with ultimate formation of a biologically labile methyl group.

INOSITOL

Inositol has been known since 1850 when Scherer isolated it from muscle and called it "muscle sugar." It was shown by Maquenne in 1887 to be a hexahydroxycyclohexane. In 1928 Edna V. Eastcott first demonstrated its biological importance when she showed mesoinositol to be the growth factor for yeast called bios I. Although inositol is essential for the growth of yeasts and some other microorganisms, its role in mammalian nutrition is less clear.

In 1940 D. W. Woolley found inositol to be an essential dietary factor for a mammal—attempts to rear mice on a purified diet lacking it results in failure to grow and loss of hair. Production of alopecia in mice and rats fed diets lacking inositol has been confirmed by a number of workers. Inositol improves the growth rate of chicks, guinea-pigs and hamsters.

Inositol plays some role in fat metabolism although the mechanism is not known. In fat-free diets lacking choline it exerts a small but clear-cut lipotropic effect. It exerts a definite supplementary lipotropic action in diets containing choline. The presence of fat in the diet tends to block the lipotropic action of inositol. This fact and its inability to protect weanling rats from developing hemorrhagic kidney lesions when fed hypolipotropic diets shows that it is not a lipo-

tropic agent in the usually accepted sense. Many text books have misinterpreted the data on the lipotropism of inositol (see Best *et al.*, 1950, 1951). The so-called "lipotropic effect of inositol under conditions where choline is ineffective" is really a synergistic lipotropic effect of inositol in a ration already containing much more than a maximally effective dose of choline in the basal diet. More choline obviously could have no further effect. The failure to appreciate that the basal diet contained so much choline led to the erroneous belief that inositol possesses some unique lipotropic properties.

CHEMISTRY. Inositol, $C_6H_{12}O_6$, is a hexahydroxycyclohexane:

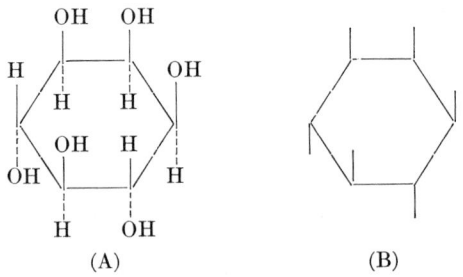

(A)　　　　　　　　　　　　　(B)

Formula A attempts to show the spatial arrangement of the hydrogen atoms and hydroxyl groups with respect to the plane in which the carbon atoms of the ring lie. Formula B is an abbreviated but very useful representation in which the short vertical lines represent the position of the hydroxyl groups. As the formula suggests, nine stereoisomers are possible. The isomer which is most frequently encountered in nature, and which is important in the nutrition of animals and some bacteria, was originally called "muscle sugar," but because it is optically inactive it has also been called *i*-inositol or *meso*-inositol. These names are inappropriate because there are six other optically inactive isomers. Lardy has suggested that these chemically incorrect and confusing terms be replaced by *myo*-inositol.

Inositol is present in combined forms in yeast and other microorganisms, in heart muscle, thyroid, kidney, spleen and testes.

REQUIREMENT AND SOURCES. No lesion due to lack of inositol is known in man and no role can be assigned to it in human nutrition or metabolism. No estimate can be made of the human requirement. Williams has estimated that the average mixed diet (2500 Cal.) provides about 1 gram of inositol.

Inositol occurs in leaves and seeds. It is found combined with phosphoric acid in esters (mono-, tri- and hexaphosphoric). The latter ester (phytic acid) occurs in cereals as a mixed calcium-magnesium salt called *phytin*. This compound immobilizes calcium in a nonavailable form and is the compound responsible for the rachitogenic effect of oatmeal. Inositol has been found in the phosphatides isolated from soya beans, brain and livers.

Choline and the Lipotropic Agents

Choline and the dietary components that serve as precursors are known as lipotropic agents (see ch. 68).

The word *lipotropic* was coined to describe *dietary* factors that prevent the accumulation of fat in the livers of experimental animals fed high-fat, low-protein diets. Later it was shown that no fat whatever in the food is needed to produce fatty livers, provided that the ration is made relatively low in lipotropic agents. The nutritional importance of choline was not discovered until 1932. Some workers doubt whether choline should be included with the other B vitamins. The amount required is large (5 to 30 mg. per day for a rat) compared with that of other recognized members of the B group whose requirement is often measured in micrograms; furthermore, choline is used for structural purposes in nervous tissue. Regardless of what we call it, choline has been found to be an essential growth factor for all species of animals tested.

In 1924 Allan *et al.* and Fisher noted independently that depancreatized dogs maintained with insulin developed large, fatty livers. Feeding raw pancreas prevented this. Several years later Hershey showed that commercial egg yolk lecithin also prevented the development of these fatty livers. In 1932 Best, Hershey and Huntsman identified choline as the protective agent. Betaine was soon found to possess similar activity.

The nature of the protein used in the preparation of rations low in lipotropic action affects the amount of fat deposited in the liver. The variable lipotropic effect of protein seemed to be explained when methionine was found to possess lipotropic properties. Choline, betaine and methionine are the three lipotropic agents found in common foodstuffs. Sulfur analogues of betaine

$$CH_3 \cdot S \cdot CH_2CH_2CH{-}COOH$$
$$NH_2$$
Methionine

occur in small amounts in some plants. These so-called *thetins* are strongly lipotropic, but their distribution is limited; and probably they play a negligible lipotropic role in normal diets.

Dietary choline is necessary for normal growth and continued health in species as varied as rats, mice, dogs, rabbits, chicks, turkeys, trout, cockroaches, and mosquito larvae. Fatty livers due to lack of choline have been observed in rats, mice, dogs, rabbits, hamsters, guinea-pigs, calves, pigs, monkeys and ducklings. (It should be kept in mind that fatty livers may develop from other causes, such as infections, toxic chemicals, hepatic anoxia or other deficiencies that interfere with hepatic function. Choline cannot prevent damage occurring from these conditions.) A prolonged lack of choline leads to the appearance of fibrotic changes in the liver, with the eventual development of cirrhosis. Choline deficiency leads to a number of other abnormalities. Bradycardia has been observed in choline deficient rats. Sure has shown that it is needed for normal lactation in the rat. Weanling rats, calves and pigs develop a hemorrhagic renal lesion that is often fatal, and rabbits develop a nonhemorrhagic renal lesion preventable by choline. Muscular weakness has been noted in rats and pigs, and muscular dystrophy in rabbits fed choline deficient rations. Baby chicks, turkey poults and ducklings fail to grow on diets poor in choline and develop perosis (a paralyzing slipped-tendon disease). Many other defects due to choline deficiency have been described but cannot be listed here.

Besides the well known accumulation of glycerides and concomitant increase of cholesteryl esters in the liver, several other biochemical changes are caused by lack of choline. The turnover of hepatic phospholipids increases when choline is removed from the diet. The prompt further increase in the turnover of liver phospholipid-P caused by feeding or injecting a single dose of choline is nonspecific, however, for a similar effect may be produced by methionine, cystine or ethanolamine. Plasma phospholipids of rats are decreased in choline deficiency and there is a marked reduction in the low-density lipoprotein fraction of the serum. As the liver damage in rats and dogs progresses to cirrhosis, with prolonged choline deficiency, the concentration of cholesteryl esters in the blood serum falls to very low levels.

Ascorbic Acid (Vitamin C)

As recounted earlier, scurvy in man has been known for centuries and the protective value of

CH₃ choline structure:

$$CH_3 \diagdown$$
$$CH_3{-}N{-}CH_2CH_2OH$$
$$CH_3 \diagup OH$$
Choline

$$CH_3 \diagdown$$
$$CH_3{-}N{-}CH_2C{=}O$$
$$CH_3 \diagup \quad {-}O{-}$$
Betaine

fresh vegetables and fruits (especially lemons and limes) was discovered, forgotten and rediscovered several times. When Holst and Frölich in 1907 found that guinea-pigs develop an analogous scorbutic state, progress in the isolation of the curative principle became possible. Zilva and associates in Britain, Szent-Györgyi (1928) in Hungary and Waugh and King (1932) in the United States made the major contributions to the isolation of the "hexuronic acid" with unusual reducing properties which was soon identified with vitamin C. The configuration was established in 1933 in Haworth's laboratory in England and within a few months the synthesis was achieved almost simultaneously by Reichstein and associates in Switzerland and by Haworth's group.

CHEMISTRY. Ascorbic acid, $C_6H_8O_6$, is an enediol of the lactone of L-gulonic acid:

Ascorbic acid   Dehydroascorbic acid

Vitamin C is a moderately strong acid (pK = 4.21) which is stable in the crystalline state but in solution is readily oxidized by atmospheric oxygen. The product of this reaction, dehydroascorbic acid, is also produced quantitatively when iodine or the dye 2,6-dichlorophenolindophenol acts upon vitamin C. These reagents are used for its determination. The dehydro compound is readily reduced to reform ascorbic acid. This property of easily reversible oxidation and reduction is bound up with its apparent function in the tissue, namely, transport of hydrogen.

Vitamin C is one of the few vitamins that occurs in nature as a single active compound, *viz.* L-ascorbic acid and its reversibly oxidized form (*cf.* vitamins A_1 and A_2, the several active carotenoid pigments, the several forms of vitamins D, E, K, etc.). Vitamin C has not been found in any coenzyme complex, nor has any "combined form" been isolated. It is one of the few water-soluble vitamins for which no acceptable microbiological method of assay has been found. Some fruits and vegetables, notably bananas and cauliflower, contain *ascorbic oxidase*, an enzyme which can cause rapid oxidative loss of vitamin C when the foodstuff is cut or crushed during preparation for the table.

Little was known until recently about the precursors of vitamin C, but now evidence points to the sequence of changes: D-glucose → D-glucurono-γ-lactone → L-gulono-γ-lactone → L-ascorbic acid. D-Galactose can also function as precursor by a corresponding series of changes via D-galacturonic acid and L-galactono-γ-lactone. The change from the D- to the L-series at the second step is remarkable, and it is thought that the few species requiring vitamin C do so because they lack the enzyme needed for this change.

Ascorbic Acid Deficiency

All species of animals studied have shown a need for ascorbic acid in their *metabolism*, but most species have the ability to meet this requirement by biosynthesis from carbohydrate precursors. The guinea-pig and primates (including man) are the only animals known to require vitamin C in the diet. Early studies were complicated by the failure to realize that this dietary peculiarity is limited to a few species. Once it was recognized that the guinea-pig is highly susceptible to lack of vitamin C, and that the resulting lesions are similar to those seen in man, experimental studies enabled the sequence of changes due to vitamin C deficiency to be elucidated.

An outstanding feature of vitamin C deficiency is the failure to deposit intercellular cement substances (collagen, osteoid and dentine). This explains the petechial hemorrhages and ecchymoses (related to fragility of the tissues), the pains in bones and joints, the weakened bones and badly formed teeth (in children) and loosened teeth in adults with scurvy. There is no correlation, however, between the intake of vitamin C and the incidence of human caries. Although the final lesions can be attributed to an impairment in the functioning of the formative cells, the underlying biochemical defect is still not known. The well known liability to infection, in both guinea-pigs and man, during vitamin C-deficiency suggests that the lowered resistance to infection may be due to impairment in the disease-resisting mechanisms.

Ascorbic acid has been shown, both *in vivo* and *in vitro*, to promote the oxidation of tyrosine and phenylalanine. Because other substances, without antiscorbutic activity, can also stimulate tyrosine oxidation, it is doubtful whether this interesting property of ascorbic acid accounts for its prevention of scurvy.

The finding that ascorbic acid is needed by the system concerned with the conversion of folic acid to *citrovorum factor* (folinic acid) may lead to a better understanding of the unclear relationship between scurvy and anemia.

REQUIREMENT. Improvements in food handling (collection, transportation, storage and processing) have largely eliminated scurvy. It is still occasionally seen, however, on this continent, in Britain and elsewhere among both infants and adults.

The amount of vitamin C needed to prevent scurvy, known as the "minimum protective dose," appears to be in the region of 10 mg. per day, as established by a carefully controlled experiment on adult volunteers at Sheffield, England (1948). However, the amount needed for abundant good health is not known. The uncertainty has led to considerable controversy. The Accessory Food Factors Subcommittee of the British Medical Research Council concluded that there is no evidence that intakes exceeding 30 mg. per day confer any extra benefit. This amount is recommended by the latest bulletin (1964) of the Canadian Council on Nutrition. Others contend that such evidence does exist. The Food and Nutrition Board of the National Research Council, United States (1964) recommends (but without sound experimental data to support the values) daily intakes of 70 mg. for adults, with 100 mg. during pregnancy and lactation. They suggest that infants should get 30 mg. and children get 40 to 80 mg. daily.

Harris and his colleagues in Britain attempted to assess the nutritional status of patients with respect to vitamin C by doing so-called loading or saturation tests which were supposed to reveal the extent of the reserves. Persons whose diets have been rich in vitamin C presumably have their tissues saturated with the vitamin; those with lower intakes are presumably in a lower state of saturation. In partial support of this concept, a lower urinary excretion of ascorbic acid is usually observed with lower intakes of vitamin C. This resting level of excretion did not provide a reliable measure of nutritional status, however. A better assessment was obtained by administering a large test dose of the pure vitamin each day, for a period, and measuring the excretion during each 24 hours.

If the previous diet had been adequate with respect to vitamin C, the tissues did appear to be relatively saturated with it because most of the extra vitamin C in the loading dose was excreted promptly in the urine. The number of days required to reach a high level of excretion was found to be related to the previous intake; with higher intakes (75 mg. or more per day) the peak followed the first dose; an intake of 30 mg. per day led to peak excretion after 1 or 2 days; patients ill with scurvy required dosing for 7 to 10 days to reach peak excretion values.

Similar loading or saturation tests have subsequently been used in studying the nutritional status of patients with respect to other vitamins. The significance of the findings has not always been clear. There is controversy over the value of some loading tests.

Attempts have been made to measure the vitamin C status of patients by determining the amount of ascorbic acid in their blood. In human blood plasma, ascorbic acid is normally found in the range 0.7 to 1.2 mg. per 100 ml.; values between 0.4 and 0.7 are believed to indicate a mild deficiency and below 0.4 mg. per 100 ml. a severe deficiency. There is some evidence that the ascorbic acid content of the white cells may have greater diagnostic value than that of the plasma.

DISTRIBUTION. Some fruits and vegetables are rich sources of vitamin C (currants, strawberries, citrus fruits, kale, parsley, spinach, tomatoes, cress and green peppers), while others provide a negligible amount (apples, cherries, pears, plums, lettuce, radish, celery, beets). Germinating grains and pulses contain vitamin C. Cow's milk has very little, 0 to 2 mg. per 100 ml. (calves do not need it). Human milk contains about 6 mg. per 100 ml. Foods devoid of ascorbic acid include yeast, eggs, meat, fish, nuts, cereals, bread, dried peas, beans and corn (maize). (See Table 72.1.)

SOME OTHER ACCESSORY FACTORS. In 1936 Szent-Györgyi and his colleagues noted that guinea pigs raised on scorbutic diets did not get as much protection from pure ascorbic acid as they did from an equivalent amount of vitamin C provided in natural food sources, such as citrus fruits and peppers. The difference was attributed to a new agent which Szent-Györgyi called vitamin P because it occurs in paprika and lemon peel and was believed to be concerned with capillary permeability and fragility. Other workers have been unable to confirm the role of vitamin P in capillary fragility but it does appear to improve utilization and/or storage of vitamin C. A number of pure compounds possess vitamin P activity. These are flavone glucosides: *rutin* (from tobacco and buckwheat), *hespiridin* and *eriodictin* (from lemon peel) and *esculin* (from horse chestnuts). The pure flavone glucosides are much less active than crude concentrates. Thus neither can properly be called vitamin P.

Joint stiffness has been observed in guinea pigs fed diets rich in milk (Wulzen and Bahrs). The condition has been confirmed in several laboratories. Extensive calcification of the joints, body wall and cavity occurs, and profound changes have been noted in the skull and teeth. Difficulties in assaying the protective principle have interfered with its isolation and identification. A number of steroids possess some antistiffness potency. The subject is still in an unsatisfactory state.

As an outgrowth of studies on rheumatic fever (Coburn, 1945, 1954), it was found that an active fraction from egg yolk will inhibit experimental anaphylactic arthritis in guinea pigs. Certain other lipid-rich materials were found to possess anti-inflammatory activity, e.g., peanut (arachis) oil and soybean lecithin. The active principle has been isolated from the latter source and identified as N-(2-hydroxyethyl)-palmitamide.

ANTIMETABOLITES AND ANTIVITAMINS

It has long been known that when a small alteration occurs in the molecular structure of a metabolite, some (and often all) of its activity is lost. In some cases the new compound may actually antagonize the biological action of the metabolite; it is then called an antimetabolite. About fifty years ago chemists found that enzyme action is often inhibited by substances whose molecular structure resembles that of the substrate. Innumerable examples have since come to light.[4] Kinetic studies have indicated that these effects are due to combination of the unnatural substance with the enzyme to form a more stable compound, thus blocking normal functioning of the enzyme. In some cases the union is so firm that the combination is classed as irreversible; in such a case the reaction is essentially a complete blocking, or poisoning, of the enzyme. In others, a large excess of the natural substrate can displace the unnatural substance from its union with the enzyme. This latter situation is spoken of as *competitive inhibition*. Antivitamins are compounds (antimetabo-

[4] Malonic acid, for example, is a competitive inhibitor of succinic dehydrogenase.

$$
\begin{array}{cc}
\text{COOH} & \text{COOH} \\
| & | \\
\text{CH}_2 & \text{CH}_2 \\
| & | \\
\text{COOH} & \text{CH}_2 \\
& | \\
& \text{COOH} \\
\text{Malonic acid} & \text{Succinic acid}
\end{array}
$$

lites) that antagonize the action of vitamins; they often function as competitive inhibitors of vital processes.

Antivitamin action was probably first observed in 1938 by Woolley, Strong, Madden and Elvehjem. Dogs suffering from nicotinic acid deficiency were given two analogous compounds, pyridine-3-sulfonic acid (II) and 3-acetylpyridine (III), to see whether these structures retained any protective properties. Surprisingly, the condition of the dogs was made worse.

$$
\begin{array}{ccc}
\overset{\displaystyle\text{COOH}}{\underset{\text{N}}{\bigcirc}} & \overset{\displaystyle\text{SO}_3\text{H}}{\underset{\text{N}}{\bigcirc}} & \overset{\displaystyle\text{COCH}_3}{\underset{\text{N}}{\bigcirc}} \\
\text{I} & \text{II} & \text{III}
\end{array}
$$

About two years later Woods showed that PABA neutralizes the antibacterial action of sulfanilamide, and he suggested that this effect is due to competitive inhibition of some essential metabolic reaction. Fildes (1940) suggested that a series of useful new chemotherapeutic agents might be produced by synthesizing compounds closely resembling vitamins or essential metabolites, but with some small structural change. Within a few months McIlwain showed that pyridine-3-sulfonic acid (II) does inhibit several bacteria that require nicotinic acid, and that growth was resumed when a large excess of nicotinic acid was added to the medium. Since that time a large number of "antivitamins" that work in bacterial cultures have been found. Only a few of these have been shown to exert their effects in animals. A few of these have powerful chemotherapeutic effects and are used in medical practice, e.g., p-aminosalicylic acid in tuberculosis, pyrimethamine in malaria and A-methopterin in leukemia.

Several better known examples of antivitamins will be mentioned. Pyrithiamine (thiamine with the thiazole ring replaced by pyridine) produces a characteristic thiamine deficiency in mice. Oxythiamine (in which the amino group of the pyrimidine ring is replaced by hydroxyl) also causes death, but without the signs of polyneuritis produced by the pyridine compound. Oxythiamine prevents the *formation* of cocarboxylase; its diphosphate prevents *utilization* of this coenzyme. Powerful antiriboflavin activity in mice is displayed by an analogue in which the pyrimidine ring is replaced by a 2:4-dinitrobenzene ring. Desoxypyridoxine (in which the —CH_2OH group on position 4 is replaced by CH_3) produces signs of pyridoxine deficiency in chicks, rats and man. Recent evidence suggests that the analogue is inactive until it is phosphorylated in the body; the resulting ester combines with the apoenzyme and prevents the normal union of pyridoxal phosphate with the protein(s) to form the amino acid decarboxylase(s). Methoxypyridoxine (in which the same

—CH$_2$OH group is changed to —CH$_2$OCH$_3$) is an antivitamin in chicks, but rats and mice are able to convert it to pyridoxine.

The antituberculosis drug, *isoniazid*, causes signs of pyridoxal deficiency in man, but not by competitive inhibition; the vitamin aldehyde reacts with the drug to form the inert isonicotinyl hydrazone of pyridoxal.

Pantoyltaurine, in which the carboxyl group of pantothenic acid is replaced by a sulfonic acid (SO$_3$H) group, displays competitive inhibition of the vitamin in a number of bacteria but is not inhibitory in animals. Although pyridine-3-sulfonic acid inhibits growth of some bacteria it does not produce nicotinamide deficiency in vertebrates. However, 3-acetylpyridine does compete in vertebrates, and either nicotinic acid or its amide can reverse the inhibition, but it is not an antivitamin for bacteria. A large number of antagonists of folic acid have been described; two of the more potent are 4-amino-pteroylglutamic acid, commonly called aminopterin, and A-methopterin (4-amino-N^{10}-methylpteroylglutamic acid). From the observation that substances containing the 2:4-diaminopyrimidine nucleus are antagonists of folic acid in certain microorganisms, but possess low toxicity for mammals, has come a powerful antimalarial drug, pyrimethamine = Daraprim. A whole family of hydroxycoumarins substituted in the 3-position display antivitamin K properties. Even salicyclic acid has anticoagulant action that is reversible by vitamin K.

The combination of avidin with biotin to form an inactive compound and the interference of phytin (in cereals) with the absorption of calcium, which indirectly affects the requirement for vitamin D, are examples of vitamin anagonists that do not act as competitive inhibitors.

An enzyme, thiaminase, occurs in several species of fresh and salt water fish and other marine creatures. When these lake- or sea-foods are fed raw to foxes or other animals a form of paralysis (Chastek) develops that can be cured by giving extra thiamine.

Antagonists of amino acids, purines, pyrimidines, of hormones and of other metabolites are known but cannot be discussed here. An interesting compound which blocks the citric acid cycle is fluoroacetic acid. It is accepted by cells as if it were acetic acid and appears to cause no damage until it becomes fluorocitric acid. Here it competes with citric acid and quickly causes death of the cell. Some plants, by concentrating fluorides from the soil (when an excess is present), become toxic to cattle; the seeds of ratsbane contain a poisonous fluorinated fatty acid which exerts its lethal effect in this way. Many of the insecticides and herbicides now available act by competitive inhibition of some vital function of the insect or plant being controlled. Woolley has published a book on anti-

metabolites and Albert has recently reviewed the subject.

REFERENCES

AXELROD, A. E. AND PRUZANSKY, J. Vitamins & Hormones, 1955, **13**, 1.

BEST, C. H , LUCAS, C. C. AND RIDOUT, J. H. Brit. M. Bull., 1956, **12**, 9.

COWARD, K. H. Biological standardization of the vitamins. Ed. 2, Baillière, Tindall & Cox, London, 1947.

DAY, P. L. Vitamins & Hormones, 1944, **2**, 71.

EDDY, W. H. AND DALLDORF, G. The avitaminoses. Williams & Wilkins, Baltimore, 1944.

FOLLIS, R. H. JR. The pathology of nutritional diseases. Charles C Thomas, Springfield, Ill., 1948.

GOODHART, R. S. Vitamin therapy today. Medical Clinics of North America. W. B. Saunders Company, Philadelphia, 1956, **40**, No. 5.

GYÖRGY, P. Vitamin methods. Ed. 2, Academic Press, Inc. New York, 1951.

HARRIS, L. J. Vitamins in theory and practice. Ed. 4, Cambridge University Press, 1955.

KON, S. K. AND PORTER, J. W. G. Vitamins & Hormones, 1954, **12**, 53.

MAPSON, L. W. Brit. M. Bull., 1956, **12**, 73.

McCOLLUM, E. V. Nutrition Rev., 1956, **14**, 257.

MICKELSEN, O. Vitamins & Hormones, 1956, **14**, 1.

MELLANBY, E. Nutrition and disease. The interaction of clinical and experimental work. Oliver & Boyd, Edinburgh, 1934.

PETT, L. B. Vitamins & Hormones, 1955, **13**, 214.

ROSENBERG, H. R. Chemistry and physiology of the vitamins. Interscience, New York, 1945.

SEBRELL, W. H. Harvey Lectures, 1943–44, **39**, 288.

SPIES, T. D. J. A. M. A., 1958, **167**, 675.

YOUNG, E. G. Canad. Bull. on Nutrition 1953, **3**, No. 1.

Bulletin. Canad. Council on Nutrition 1950, **2**, No. 1; 1964, **6**, No. 1.

Recommended Dietary Allowances. Nat. Acad. Sci., Nat. Res. Co. Washington, 1953, No. 302; 1958, No. 589; 1964, No. 1146.

Recent Research on Vitamins. Brit. M. Bull. 1956, **12**, 1.

The Vitamins (ed. by SEBRELL, W. H., JR. AND HARRIS, R. S.) Vols. I, II, III. Academic Press Inc., New York, 1954.

Vitamin A

HOPKINS, F. G. J. Physiol. 1912, **44**, 425.

McCOLLUM, E. V. AND DAVIS, M. J. Biol. Chem. 1913, **15**, 167. Ibid., 1914, **19**, 245.

OSBORNE, T. B. AND MENDEL, L. B. J. Biol. Chem. 1913, **15**, 311. Ibid., 1913–14, **16**, 423.

STEENBOCK, H. Science, 1919, **50**, 352.

Monographs and Reviews

COLLINS, F. D. Biol. Reviews of the Cambridge Phil. Soc. 1954, **29**, 453.

DOWLING, J. E. AND WALD, G. Proc. Nat. Acad. Sc. 1958, **44**, 648.

HARRIS, R. S., INHOFFEN, H. H., MASON, K. E., MATTSON, F. H., MILAS, N. A., POMMER, H.,

WALD, G. AND WOLBACH, S. B. The Vitamins. Vol. I. Ch. 1, 1954.

JEGHERS, H. AND MARRARO, H. Amer. J. Clin. Nutrition, 1958, **6**, 335.

LOWE, J. S. AND MORTON, R. A. Vitamins & Hormones, 1956, **14**, 97.

NIEMAN, C. AND OBLINK, H. J. K. Vitamins & Hormones, 1954, **12**, 691.

RUBIN, S. H. AND DE RITTER, E. Vitamins & Hormones, 1954, **12**, 102.

RUSHTON, W. A. H., CAMPBELL, F. W., HAGINS, W. A, AND BRINDLEY, G. S. Optica Acta, 1954, **1**, 183.

Symposium on vitamin A. Brit. J. Nutrition 1951, **5**, 94.

Vitamin D

HESS, A. F. AND WEINSTOCK, M. J. Biol. Chem. 1924, **62**, 301.

HULDSCHINSKY, K. Deutsche med. Wchnschr. 1919, **45**, 712.

MELLANBY, E. Brit. Med. Res. Council, Spec. Rep. No. 61, 1921. Ibid., No. 93, 1925.

STEENBOCK, H. AND BLACK, A. J. Biol. Chem. 1924, **61**, 405.

Monographs and Reviews

BILLS, C. E. Physiol. Rev., 1935, **15**, 1.

BILLS, C. E., HARRIS, R. S., JONES, J. J., KANOF, A. AND KRAMER, B. The Vitamins. Vol. II, Ch. 6, 1954.

FRASER, D. AND SALTER, R. B. Pediat. Clin. North America, 1958.

IRVING, J. T. Vitamins & Hormones, 1957, **15**, 292.

LAURENS, H. Physiol. Rev., 1928, **8**, 1.

MELLANBY, E. Physiol. Rev., 1928, **8**, 545.

NICOLAYSEN, R. AND EEG-LARSEN, N. Vitamins & Hormones, 1953, **11**, 29.

Vitamin E

EVANS, H. M. AND BISHOP, K. S. Science, 1922, **55**, 650.

MATTILL, H. A. AND CONKLIN, R. E. J. Biol. Chem. 1920, **44**, 137.

SURE, B. J. Biol. Chem. 1924, **58**, 693.

Monographs and Reviews

HARRIS, P. L., HARRIS, R. S., MASON, K. E. AND MATTILL, H. A. The Vitamins. Vol. III, Ch. 17, 1954.

HICKMAN, K. C. D. AND HARRIS, P. L. Advances in Enzymology, 1946, **6**, 469.

MOORE, T. Vitamin E. Brit. M. Bull. 1956, **12**, 44.

Biological Antioxidants. First to Fifth Conference. Josiah Macy, Jr., Foundation, New York, 1946–1950.

Vitamin K

ALMQUIST, H. J., HARRIS, R. S. AND OWEN, C. A. JR. The Vitamins, Vol. II, Ch. 9, 1954.

ALMQUIST, H. J. AND STOKSTAD, E. L. R. J. Biol. Chem., 1935, **111**, 105.

BUTT, H. R. AND SNELL, A. M. Vitamin K. Saunders, Philadelphia, 1941.

DAM, H. Biochem. J., 1935, **29**, 1273; Vitamins & Hormones, 1948, **6**, 28.

Lipoic Acid

REED, L. J. Physiol. Rev. 1953, **33**, 544.

Thiamine

ELVEHJEM, C. A. J. A. M. A., 1948, **138**, 960.

EMMETT, A. D. AND LUROS, G. O. J. Biol. Chem., 1920, **43**, 625.

EVANS, H. M. AND LEPKOVSKY, S. J. Biol. Chem., 1929, **83**, 269.

FARRER, K. T. H. Biochem. J., 1947, **41**, 167.

McCOLLUM, E. V. AND DAVIS, M. J. Biol. Chem., 1915, **20**, 641. Ibid, 1915, **23**, 231.

PLATT, B. S. AND LU, G. D. Biochem. J., 1939, **33**, 1525.

Monographs and Reviews

HARRIS, R. S., JANSEN, B. C. P., SEBRELL, W. H., JR., UNNA, K. R. AND WUEST, H. M. The Vitamins. Vol. III, Ch. 16, 1954.

REED, L. J. Physiol. Rev., 1953, **33**, 544.

Riboflavin

EMMETT, A. D. AND McKIM, L. H. J. Biol. Chem., 1917, **32**, 409.

SEBRELL, W. H. AND BUTLER, R. E. U. S. Pub. Health Rep., 1938, **53**, 2282. Ibid., 1939, **54**, 2121.

SYDENSTRICKER, V. P. Am. J. Pub. Health, 1941, **31**, 344.

Monographs and Reviews

BRO-RASMUSSEN, F. Nutrition Abstr. & Rev., 1958, **28**, 1, 369.

GYÖRGY, P. Nutrition Rev., 1954, **12**, 97.

HARRIS, R. S., HEGSTED, D. M., HORWITT, M. K., SNELL, E. E. AND WAGNER-JAUREGG, T. The Vitamins. Vol. III, Ch. 15, 1954.

SNELL, E. E. Physiol. Rev. 1953, **33**, 509.

Nicotinic Acid

ELVEHJEM, C. A., MADDEN, R. J., STRONG, F. M. AND WOOLLEY, D. W. J. Am. Chem. Soc., 1937, **59**, 1767.

GOLDBERGER, J., WARING, C. H. AND WILLETS, D. G. United States Pub. Health Rep., 1915, **30**, 3117, and subsequent articles by Goldberger and his associates up to 1927.

KREHL, W. A., TEPLEY, L. J., SARMA, P. S. AND ELVEHJEM, C. A. Science, 1945, **101**, 489.

Monographs and Reviews

HARRIS, R. S., HUNDLEY, J. M. AND SNELL, E. E. The Vitamins. Vol. II, Ch. 10, 1954.

SYDENSTRICKER, V. P. Amer. J. Clin. Nutrition, 1958, **6**, 409.

Pyridoxine

BIRCH, T. W., GYÖRGY, P. AND HARRIS, L. J. Biochem. J., 1935, **29**, 2830.

GYÖRGY, P. Amer. J. Clin. Nutrition, 1954, **2**, 44.

WITTEN, P. W. AND HOLMAN, R. T. Arch. Biochem. 1952, **41**, 266.

Monographs and Reviews

GYÖRGY, P., HARRIS, R. S., KEEVIL, C. E. JR., KERESZTESY, J. C., SHERMAN, H., SNELL, E. E.,

UMBREIT, W. W. AND UNNA, K. R. The Vitamins, Vol. III, Ch. 14, 1954.
SNELL, E. E. Vitamins & Hormones, 1958, **16**, 78.
WAYNE, L., WILL, J. J., FRIEDMAN, B. I., BECKER, L. S. AND VILTER, R. W. A. M. A. Arch. Int. Med., 1958, **101**, 143.

Pantothenic Acid

EASTCOTT, E. V. J. Phys. Chem., 1928, **32**, 1094.
FELDBERG, W. AND MANN, T. J. Physiol., 1946, **104**, 411.
HOAGLAND, M. B. AND NOVELLI, G. D. J. Biol. Chem., 1954, **207**, 767.
LUCAS, G. H. W. J. Phys. Chem., 1924, **28**, 1180.
WILDIERS, E. La Cellule, 1901, **18**, 313.

Monographs and Reviews

BRIGGS, G. M., DAFT, F. S., HARRIS, R. S., LEPKOVSKY, S., LIPMANN, F., RALLI, E. AND SNELL, E. E. The Vitamins, Vol. II, Ch. 11, 1954.
LIPMANN, F. Advances in Enzymology, 1946, **6**, 231.
NOVELLI, G. D. Physiol. Rev. 1953, **33**, 525.

Biotin

BATEMAN, W. G. J. Biol. Chem., 1916, **26**, 263.
BOAS, M. A. Biochem. J., 1927, **21**, 712.
GYÖRGY, P., MELVILLE, D. B., BURK, D. AND DU VIGNEAUD, V. Science, 1940, **91**, 243.
KÖGL, F. AND TÖNNIS, B. Z. Physiol. Chem., 1936, **242**, 43.
PARSONS, H. T. AND KELLY, E. J. Biol. Chem., 1933, **100**, 645.

Monographs and Reviews

GYÖRGY, P., HARRIS, R. S. AND SNELL, E. E. The Vitamins, Vol. I. Ch. 4, 1954.
HERTZ, R. Physiol. Rev., 1946, **26**, 479.
LICHSTEIN, H. C. Vitamins & Hormones, 1951, **9**, 27.

p-Aminobenzoic Acid

ANSBACHER, S. Science, 1941, **93**, 164.
FILDES, P. Lancet, 1940, **238**, 955.
RUBBO, S. D. AND GILLESPIE, J. M. Nature, 1940, **146**, 838.
WOODS, D. D. Brit. J. Exper. Path., 1940, **21**, 74.
YEOMANS, A., SNYDER, J. C., MURRAY, E. S., ZARAFONETIS, C. J. D. AND ECKE, R. S. J. A. M. A. 1944, **126**, 349.

Monographs and Reviews

HARRIS, R. S., SCOTT, C. C., TAVORMINA, P. A., WRIGHT, L. D. AND WUEST, H. M. The Vitamins, Vol. III, Ch. 12, 1954.

Folic Acid

BROCKMAN, J. A. JR., et al., J. Am. Chem. Soc., 1950, **72**, 4325.
MITCHELL, H. K., SNELL, E. E. AND WILLIAMS, R. J. J. Am. Chem. Soc. 1941, **63**, 2284; Ibid., 1944, **66**, 271.

Monographs and Reviews

BETHELL, F. H., HARRIS, R. S. AND STOKSTAD, E. L. R. in The Vitamins, Vol. III, Ch. 13, 1954.

DARBY, W. J. Vitamins & Hormones, 1947, **5**, 119.
PETERING, H. G. Physiol. Rev., 1952, **32**, 197.
TRUFANOV, A. V. Am. J. Clin. Nutrition, 1959, **7**, 302.
WELCH, A. D. Nutrition Rev., 1957, **15**, 33.

Vitamin B_{12} (Cyanocobalamin)

BONNETT, R., CANNON, J. R., JOHNSON, A. W., SUTHERLAND, I. AND TODD, A. R. Nature, 1955, **176**, 328.
HODGKIN, D. C., PICKWORTH, J. ROBERTSON, J. H., TRUEBLOOD, K. N., PRO'SEN, R. J. AND WHITE, J. G. Nature, 1955, **176**, 325.
MINOT, G. R. AND MURPHY, W. P. J. A. M. A., 1926, **87**, 470; Ibid., 1927, **89**, 759.
RICKES, E. L., BRINK, N. G., KONIUSZY, F. R., RUBIN, M. AND BIRD, H. R. J. Biol. Chem., 1946, **163**, 387.
SHORB, M. S. Science, 1948, **107**, 397.

Monographs and Reviews

BETHELL, F. H., FOLKERS, K. E., HARRIS, R. S., JUKES, T. H., WILLIAMS, W. L. AND WOLF, D. E. The Vitamins, Vol. I, Ch. 3, 1954.
UNGLEY, C. C. Vitamins & Hormones, 1955, **13**, 139.

Inositol

BEST, C. H., LUCAS, C. C., PATTERSON, J. M. AND RIDOUT, J. H. Biochem. J., 1951, **48**, 448. Ibid., 1951, **48**, 452.

(Note: In this article an unfortunate transposition of Figs. 1 and 3 was not detected in the galley proof. The curves over the caption "Fig. 3" on p. 456 represent data with fat-free diets and should be located on p. 454; the curves over caption Fig. 1 are from rats fed diets with 12% fat and should be on p. 456).

EASTCOTT, E. V. J. Phys. Chem. 1928, **32**, 1094.
GAVIN, G. AND MCHENRY, E. W. J. Biol. Chem., 1941, **39**, 485.
GAVIN, G., PATTERSON, J. M. AND MCHENRY, E. W. J. Biol. Chem., 1943, **148**, 275.
WOOLLEY, D. W. J. Biol. Chem., 1940, **136**, 113. Ibid., 1941, **139**, 29.

Monographs and Reviews

CHARGAFF, E., CUNHA, T. J., HARRIS, R. S., LARDY, H. A., LIVERMORE, A. H., MILHORAT, A. T., SNELL, E. E. AND WEIDLEIN, E. R. JR. The Vitamins, Vol. II, Ch. 8, 1954.

Choline

BEST, C. H., HERSHEY, J. M. AND HUNTSMAN, M. E. Am. J. Physiol., 1932, **101**. 7P.
CHANNON, H. J. AND WILKINSON, H. Biochem. J., 1935, **29**, 350.
HERSHEY, J. M. Am. J. Physiol., 1930, **93**, 657P.
TUCKER, H. F. AND ECKSTEIN, H. C. J. Biol. Chem., 1937, **121**, 479.

Monographs and Reviews

BEST, C. H. Proc. Roy. Soc., London. ser. B., 1956, **145**, 151.
BEST, C. H., GRIFFITH, W. H., HARRIS, R. S., HARTROFT, W. S., LUCAS, C. C. AND NYC, J. F. The Vitamins, Vol. II, Ch. 5, 1954.

DU VIGNEAUD, V. A trail of research. Cornell University Press, Ithaca, N. Y. 1952.
LUCAS, C. C. Am. J. Clin. Nutrition, 1958, **6,** 504.
OLSEN, R. A. Am. J. Clin. Nutrition, 1958, **6,** 197.

Ascorbic Acid

HOLST, A. AND FRÖLICH, T. J. Hyg., 1907, **7,** 634.
SZENT-GYÖRGYI, A. AND HAWORTH, W. N. Nature, 1933, **131,** 24.
WAUGH, W. A. AND KING, C. G. J. Biol. Chem., 1932, **97,** 325.
UHL, E. Am. J. Clin. Nutrition, 1958, **6,** 146.

Monographs and Reviews

HARRIS, R. S., MAPSON, L. W., OLLIVER, M., REID, M. E., SMITH, F. AND VILTER, R. W. The Vitamins, Vol. II, Ch. 2, 1954.
JACQUES CARTIER et "La grosse maladie," reprinted for XIX International Physiol. Congress, Montreal, Canada, 1953.
LIND, J. Treatise on Scurvy. London, 1757. Quoted from Med. Res. Coun. London. Sp. Report, No. 167, 1932.

Symposium on Vitamin C. Ann. N. Y. Acad. Sci., 1961, **92,** 1–332.

Accessory Food Factors

BENTSAITH, A., RUSZNYÁK, ST. AND SZENT-GYÖRGYI, A. Nature, 1936, **138,** 798.
COBURN, A. F. Am. J. Dis. Children, 1945, **70,** 339.
COBURN, A. F., GRAHAM, C. E. AND HANINGER, J. J. Exper. Med., 1954, **100,** 425.
KUEHL, F. A., JACOB, T. A., GANLEY, O. H., ORMOND, R. E. AND MEISINGER, M. A. P. J. Am. Chem. Soc., 1957, **79,** 5577.

Monographs and Reviews

CHELDELIN, V. B. The Vitamins, Vol. III, Ch. 18, 1954.

Antimetabolites and Antivitamins
Monographs and Reviews

ALBERT, A. Brit. M. Bull., 1956, **12,** 67.
WOOLLEY, D. W. Physiol. Rev., 1947, **27,** 308.
WOOLLEY, D. W. A study of antimetabolites. Chapman & Hall, London, 1952.

CHAPTER 73

Dietary Requirements

In planning a diet the following requirements must be taken into account:

1. The total calorie value.
2. The proportions of the different foodstuffs—carbohydrate, fats, and protein.
3. The mineral constituents.
4. The vitamin content.

In order that the body shall not be forced to consume its own tissues for fuel, the calorie value of the ingested food for 24 hours must balance the energy (work plus heat) output by the individual during the same period. The basal metabolic rate is obtained by direct determination (ch. 63) or by calculation from the subject's height and weight. The extra calorie allowances for two different grades of muscular activity are given below.

Sample Calculation of Calorie Requirement

The approximate basal metabolism of an average size man (20 to 40 years of age) may be calculated as follows: the energy output per square meter is 40 Calories per hour (p. 1286); the average surface area of 1.8 square meters corresponds to 72 Calories per hour. While the subject is asleep (8 hours) the metabolism is about 90 per cent of this value; during this period about 520 Calories are required. The basal requirement for 16 waking hours (16 × 72) is about another 1150 Calories. The hourly work increment of those in sedentary occupations varies from 20 Calories for writing to 45 for tailoring while in the more strenuous occupations it varies from 180 (heavy carpentry) to 380

| | Estimated daily Calorie requirement | |
	Clerk	Miner
Metabolism of sleep (8 hours)	520	520
Basal metabolism (16 hours)	1150	1150
Nonwork allowance (8 hours)	400	400
Work allowance (8 hours)	300	3040
Subtotal	2370	5110
10 per cent for specific dynamic action	240	510
Total	2610	5620

(mining, lumbering) or more. To the total so estimated, 10 per cent is added to cover the increased metabolism (specific dynamic action) due to the food itself.

For more precise calculation of the calorie requirements, other factors must be taken into account, e.g., the body weight and the temperature at which the work is performed. An allowance or a deduction of 3 per cent is made, respectively, for each 10 degrees F. rise or fall from the average temperature (70°F.). Thus, if the total metabolism as calculated above is 5620 Calories, but the temperature is 60°F., the diet is planned for a total energy expenditure of (5620 + 170) = 5790 Calories. In performing certain types of work, such as walking, ascending stairs, or any work which entails lifting the body or its heavier parts, the energy expenditure is more nearly proportional to the body weight raised to the power 0.7, than to the surface area.

The Relation of Age and Sex to the Calorie Requirement

Women have a somewhat lower basal metabolic rate than men, and, generally speaking, they expend less energy in muscular work; their food requirement is proportionately less, approximately 83 per cent of a man's or about 2000 to 3000 Calories per day. The calorie intake should be about 20 per cent greater during the latter part of pregnancy, and about 30 per cent greater during lactation than at ordinary times.

Children require, weight-for-weight, a greater food allowance than the average adult for three reasons: (a) Their basal metabolic rate is considerably higher, especially at the younger ages. (b) A proportion of the food material is utilized for building body tissue. (c) Children, as a rule, expend more energy in muscular activity than the average adult. For example, a boy of 16 years of age, of average physique and taking an active part in games, requires a daily energy intake equal to that of a man—from 3000 to 4000 Calories or from 50 to 70 Calories per kilogram of body weight per day (average adult requirement, 46 Calories per kilogram).

During the first 3 months of life the dietary requirement is about 120 Calories per kilogram. From 4 to 9 months the requirement falls to about 110, and during the ages 10 to 12 months it is about 100 Calories per kilogram. Since a child 1 year of age usually weighs about 9 to 11 kg., its dietary energy requirement is about 900 to 1100

TABLE 73.1

*Effect of age and sex on estimated
calorie requirements*

(Recommended daily allowances—F.A.O., 1957)*

Age group	Calories per Day		
	Male and Females	Males	Females
years			
1	1150		
2	1300		
3	1450		
4 to 6	1700		
7 to 9	2100		
10 to 12	2500		
13 to 15		3100	2600
16 to 19		3600	2400
20 to 30		3200	2300
31 to 40		3100	2250
41 to 50		3000	2150
51 to 60		2800	2000
61 to 70		2550	1800
Over 70		2200	1600

* Allowances are estimated for individuals engaged in moderate physical activity. They are excessive for those in sedentary occupations and low for laborers.

Calories. Data for other age groups are shown in table 73.1.

The Protein Allowance

A great deal of controversy has centered around the question of the protein requirement of the adult. Chittenden, some years ago, made a study of the subject in a series of experiments upon himself and groups of students, soldiers, and athletes. He showed that nitrogen equilibrium could be maintained upon a total daily intake of 25 grams or less of first-class protein.[1] Upon an ordinary mixed diet containing proteins of varying biological values, nitrogen equilibrium was established on an allowance of between 40 and 50 grams for a man of average weight (70 kg.). This is from 0.6 to 0.7 grams of protein per kilogram. Chittenden claimed that the larger protein intake recommended by previous observers (e.g., 120 grams by Voit) was unnecessary, if not actually deleterious to health. It was contended that the renal work entailed in the excretion of large quantities of

nitrogen was conducive to kidney disease. Many other ills were ascribed to the excessive consumption of protein. He also reduced the total energy intake to around 2000 Calories and stated that the more liberal diets were dictated by appetite rather than by physiological necessity. His subjects, he claimed, could carry out their usual activities just as well upon such a diet and enjoyed better health than they had previously upon their customary fare.

Since nitrogen equilibrium can be established upon a protein intake of around 40 grams per day, it *would* seem unnecessary to give more. The excess amount must obviously be catabolized to furnish energy, which can be furnished more economically by non-nitrogenous food[2] or be simply stored as carbohydrate or fat. The weak point in this argument is, as many critics of the low protein dietary have pointed out, that the ability of the body to adapt itself for a few months to a restricted protein intake is not proof that such constitutes the physiological optimum. It has also been pointed out that custom has dictated for persons in temperate climates a higher protein intake than Chittenden's standard. The daily protein intake per person in the United States is between 90 and 120 grams. Even the diets of the Japanese and of the hardier races of India, according to McCay, contain a greater quantity of protein than that recommended by Chittenden. Tribes in India who are accustomed to diets with the higher protein content are healthier and of better physique than those subsisting upon a more restricted protein intake. The value of a generous protein allowance is also illustrated by the report of Orr and Gilks concerning two African tribes who, though living side by side, eat quite different diets. The members of the meat-eating Masai tribe are some 5 inches taller and 50 pounds heavier than the vegetarian Akikuyu, and their muscular power is about 50 per cent greater. The Masai are comparatively free from disease, whereas bone deformities, dental caries, anemia, pulmonary diseases and tropical ulcer are prevalent among the Akikuyu. Arthritis, however, was found to be much more common among the Masai.

Protein probably plays an important part which is not revealed by short-term experiments

[1] The daily urinary excretion of N on a nitrogen-free diet but of adequate calorie value is around 3 grams. This represents the catabolism of 18.75 grams (3 × 6.25) of tissue protein.

[2] Calories furnished by protein are by far the most expensive. It has been calculated that 1,000,-000 Calories derived from cane sugar require for their production 0.15 acre, as compared with 17 acres necessary to produce the same amount of energy as represented by beef protein.

based upon the study of nitrogen balances. There are indications that physical fitness and resistance to disease are associated with the higher protein intakes. There is little evidence, on the other hand, that a high consumption of protein causes renal or other diseases. Thomas records that the Greenland Eskimos are almost exclusively carnivorous, consuming enormous quantities of meat (and up to 300 grams of fat per day); yet renal and cardiovascular disease is not common among them. The Arctic explorers Stefansson and Anderson showed no ill-effects, either upon blood pressure or renal function, after living for 12 months upon a diet composed entirely of meat (reported by Lieb). The effect of a high protein diet upon established renal disease is another matter.

It now appears that the true protein requirement for the average man lies about midway between the two extremes of Chittenden and the older observers. A generous allowance is from 70 to 100 grams (somewhat more than 1 gram per kilogram of body weight) and about 15 per cent less than this for women.

Because of the large differences in the nutritive value of individual proteins any quantitative statement on protein requirement must be related to specific proteins or types of protein. Milk, eggs, and meat have long been regarded as of excellent quality, and their superior value for human beings has been confirmed by research on infants and adults. The F.A.O. Committee on Protein Requirement (1957) decided to express requirements in terms of a *reference protein* which they defined as of "high nutritive value," citing the proteins of milk, eggs, and meat as examples. Later, from a study of human requirements for individual essential amino acids, a provisional *amino acid pattern* was put forward. Whereas neither milk nor egg proteins correspond precisely in composition with this "ideal" pattern, they are similar. It is assumed that a hypothetical protein containing amino acids in these ratios would be of high biological value, falling into the category of a reference protein.

The F.A.O. Committee, emphasizing the provisional nature of their recommendations, tentatively suggested 0.35 gram per kilogram of body weight as the average *minimum* requirement of adults for *high quality protein*. The requirement is greater in children and increases to a maximum in infancy. Unfortunately, the data are least reliable in this highly critical period of maximum rate of growth. Possibly it is as high as 2.3 grams per kilogram for suckling infants during the first few weeks, falling to about 1.5 by 6 months, to 1.0 gram per kilogram at about 3 years of age, and levels off between 0.6 and 0.7 grams per kilogram of body weight from 6 to 11 years. Just before puberty, a short-lived but acute spurt in growth occurs (in girls at 10 to 14 years, in boys at 13 to 16 years of age) during which the requirement for high quality protein is temporarily increased, being not lower than 0.8 gram per kilogram. Following this period the requirement falls slowly to the adult value of 0.35 gram per kilogram of body weight.

During pregnancy an additional 10 grams of high quality protein should be added per day to the value calculated using the adult factor (0.35), and during lactation the recommended daily increment is 30 grams. In many pathological states and during convalescence the protein requirement is increased, but it is impossible to give data of general applicability. Extremely heavy work (lumbering, mining, harvesting, and the like, without mechanical aids) causes an increase in muscle mass and a substantial increase in protein requirement.

The daily dietary allowances recommended by the Food and Nutrition Board of the National Research Council (U.S.A. 1963) (table 73.2) are somewhat higher for protein than those of the F.A.O.: 1 g. of average mixed protein per kg. of body weight (i.e., 70 g. for the average man or 58 g. for the average woman). These values appear to be generous.

The emphasis today is being placed on the dietary supply of essential amino acids and total utilizable nitrogen rather than on the protein content of a foodstuff or ration. Knowledge of the average requirement of human infants, children, and adults, for each of the essential amino acids is still fragmentary but is becoming increasingly available, largely from the laboratories of W. C., Rose, Ruth M. Leverton, L. E. Holt, Jr., H. H. Mitchell, Marian E. Swendseid, and M. S. Dunn, and their associates. Many others have made important contributions. Only eight amino acids appear to be essential in the diet to maintain nitrogen equilibrium in adults. Histidine is essential for the growing child. Tentative values are shown in table 73.3. Whereas the adequacy of the essential amino acids determines the nutritional quality of a protein, the pattern of the nonessential amino acids is important for several reasons: (a) tyrosine can spare phenylalanine, (b) cystine can spare methionine, and (c) unless an ample supply of nonessential amino acids (or other forms

TABLE 73.2

*Recommended dietary allowances (revised 1963) for normal activity in a temperate climate**

(Food and Nutrition Board, National Research Council of the U. S. A.)

	Calories	Protein	Calcium	Iron	Vitamin A†	Thiamin (B₁)	Ribo-flavin	Niacin (Nicotinic Acid)	Ascorbic Acid	Vitamin D
		grams	*grams*	*mg.*	*I.U.*	*mg.‡*	*mg.*	*mg.‡*	*mg.‡*	*I.U.*
Infants (under 1 yr.)	115/kg.	2.5/kg.	0.7	1/kg.	1500	0.4	0.6	6	30	400
Children										
1–3‖	1300	32	0.8	8	2000	0.5	0.8	9	40	400
3–6	1600	40	0.8	10	2500	0.6	1.0	11	50	400
6–9	2100	52	0.8	12	3500	0.8	1.3	14	60	400
Boys										
9–12	2400	60	1.1	15	4500	1.0	1.4	16	70	400
12–15	3000	75	1.4	15	5000	1.2	1.8	20	80	400
15–18	3400	85	1.4	15	5000	1.4	2.0	22	80	400
Girls										
9–12	2200	55	1.1	15	4500	0.9	1.3	15	80	400
12–15	2500	62	1.3	15	5000	1.0	1.5	17	80	400
15–18	2300	58	1.3	15	5000	0.9	1.3	15	70	400
Man (70 kg)										
Age 18–35	2900	70	0.8	10	5000	1.2	1.7	19	70	§
35–55	2600	70	0.8	10	5000	1.0	1.6	17	70	—
55–75	2200	70	0.8	10	5000	0.9	1.3	15	70	—
Woman (58 kg)										
Age 18–35	2100	58	0.8	15	5000	0.8	1.3	14	70	§
35–55	1900	58	0.8	15	5000	0.8	1.2	13	70	—
55–75	1600	58	0.8	10	5000	0.8	1.2	13	70	—
Pregnant	+200	+20	+0.5	+5	6000	1.0	1.5	16	100	400
Lactating	+1000	+40	+0.5	+5	8000	1.2	1.8	20	100	400

* Tentative goal toward which to aim in planning practical dietaries; can be met by a good diet of natural food. Such a diet will also provide other minerals and vitamins, the requirements for which are less well known.

† Requirements may be less if provided as vitamin A; greater if provided chiefly as the provitamin carotene.

‡ 1 mg. of thiamin equals 333 I.U.; 60 mg. dietary tryptophane represents 1 mg. niacin; 1 mg. of ascorbic acid equals 20 I.U.

§ Vitamin D is undoubtedly necessary for older children and adults. When not available from sunshine, it should be provided, probably up to the minimum amounts recommended for infants.

¶ Needs of infants increase from month to month. The amounts given are for approximately 6 to 8 months. The amounts of protein and calcium needed are less if derived from human milk.

‖ Allowances are based on needs for the middle year in each group (as 2, 5, 8, etc.) and for moderate activity.

Further Recommendations.

The requirement for *iodine* is small; probably about 0.002 to 0.004 mg. a day for each kilogram of body weight (about 0.15 to 0.30 mg. daily for the adult). This need is easily met by the regular use of iodized salt; its use is especially important in adolescence and pregnancy.

The requirement for *copper* for adults is in the neighborhood of 1.0 to 2.0 mg. a day. Infants and children require approximately 0.05 mg. per kilogram of body weight. The requirement for copper is approximately one-tenth of that for iron.

Fatty foods, because of their high energy content, are preferred by men performing heavy work, especially in cold climates. Not only do fats provide 9 Calories per gram, as compared with 4 for carbohydrates and protein, but fat-rich foodstuffs are much lower in water content than are carbohydrate-rich foods (e.g., butter contains only 15 per cent water, bread contains 35 to 40 per cent). Thus, on a bulk or weight basis, fatty foods are up to four times as rich in energy as those low in fat.

TABLE 73.3

Suggested average minimal requirements for essential amino acids

(milligrams per kilogram body weight) Taken from F.A.O. Bulletin, No. 16, 1957.)

| | Isoleucine | Leucine | Lysine | Phenylala-nine | Sulfur-containing Acids | | | Threonine | Trypto-phan | Valine |
					Methio-nine	Cystine	Total			
Infants*	90	?	90	90†	85	0	85	60	30	85
					65	Present	—			
Men	10.4	9.9	8.8	4.3†	1.5	11.6	13.1	6.5	2.9	8.8
				13.3‡	13.2	0	13.2			
Women	5.2	7.1	3.3	3.1†	4.7	0.5	5.2	3.5	2.1	9.2
					3.8	2.2	6.0			
					3.4	3.4	6.8			
					3.0	4.2	7.2			

* Infants display a considerable requirement for histidine during the first few months but this soon decreases. About 34 mg./kg. daily has been suggested as adequate for very young infants (Holt and Snyderman, 1961); human milk would provide this amount at an intake of about 155 ml./kg.

† Tyrosine present.

‡ Tyrosine absent.

of utilizable nitrogen) is provided, the need for essential amino acids will be increased because they will be used to make nonessential amino acids that are inadequately supplied by the ration.[3]

It must be remembered that if one diet is higher in protein content than another, it is not necessarily superior, since the biological value depends upon the completeness of the essential amino acids provided. In very few countries is it possible for the bulk of the population to live principally on foodstuffs containing high quality proteins. In many regions wheat, rye or millet, rice, potatoes, maize, pulses, or cassava provide the major proportion of the food eaten. None of these supplies all of the essential amino acids in proper ratio or in adequate amount. As was pointed out by Osborne and Mendel many years ago, certain combinations of these vegetable proteins may supplement each other with marked improvement of nutritive properties. For example, the maize protein (which is very poor in tryptophane and

[3] Measurement of "essential amino acid requirements" of adults fed simplified diets, and of "protein requirements" (supplied as individual sources, e.g. milk, egg, soybean or peanut) lead to apparent discrepancies of considerable magnitude. For example, the quantities of milk required to provide "adequate protein" contain two to five times the minimal essential amino acid requirements found by Rose and others in similar studies with young adults. The dietary conditions under which the tests are made appear to affect strongly the utilization of individual essential amino acids: a generally applicable figure for "minimal requirements" may not exist.

lysine), the navy bean protein (deficient in methionine and tryptophane) and sesame seed protein (deficient in lysine and valine) when combined in the ratio 40:30:30 offer a product that is much improved nutritionally.

The Indispensability of Fat

Since body fat can be derived from carbohydrate food, it might be thought that dietary fat could be dispensed with. However, this does not seem to be so. Fats provide fat-soluble vitamins and certain fatty acids (linoleic, linolenic, and arachidonic) that are essential for health which cannot be synthesized (at least not at an adequate rate) by the body. If purified fat-soluble vitamins and essential fatty acids are made available, there is no evidence that fats (glycerides) are essential components of the diet.

Although glycerides may not be dietary essentials, they increase palatability of the food and decrease the bulk necessary to provide adequate calories. Fat pork, beans, and peas are prominent items in the diet of Canadian lumbermen and construction workers. The daily energy expenditure of some of the former workers may run to 8000 Calories. Another advantage of fat is its superior "staying power." Its digestion and absorption are extended over a much longer period than those of carbohydrates. Hunger, "emptiness," and fatigue are experienced much sooner upon a diet high in carbohydrate than upon one containing a liberal allowance of fat. The actual efficiency of fat as a fuel for muscular work as shown by Krogh and Lindhard and by Murlin and Marsh is from 10 to 12 per cent less than that of carbohydrate. It is often recommended that children be given a larger proportion of fat in the diet (30 to 35 per cent of the calorie intake) than is suggested for adults, 20 to 25 per cent. Actually, very little, if any, information is available on the fat *requirement* of man. It appears that fat and carbohydrate can replace each other, within wide limits, as a source of energy.

Much has been written on the comparative nutritive value of different fats. Better growth of rats was reported when diets containing butterfat were fed than when corn, cottonseed, coconut, or soybean oils were used. Later it appeared that this superiority depended upon the nature of the carbohydrate in the diet. The subject has been controversial; if there are any differences they are small, except with respect to essential fatty acids.

The essential fatty acids are provided principally by plant oils, lard, egg-yolk fat, and butterfat. Highly unsaturated fatty acids are abundant in fish-liver oils, but they are of different structure from the animal oils and their value as essential fatty acids is doubtful.

In 1929, Mendel and his colleagues noted that the growth of rats on a fat-deficient ration is poor, and in the same year, Burr and Burr described a new deficiency disease (in rats) caused by the elimination of all fat from the diet. After about 3 months a scaly condition of the skin developed; later the tail became inflamed and swollen, and eventually the tip became necrotic. The feet also became swollen and sore. The hair fell out about the face, throat, and back, and sores often appeared on the body. Kidney lesions led to death. Later, Burr and his associates showed that very small amounts of either linoleic acid ($C_{18}H_{32}O_2$ with two double bonds) or linolenic ($C_{18}H_{30}O_2$ with three) produced beneficial effects in rats. More recently certain other polyunsaturated fatty acids (e.g., arachidonic, $C_{20}H_{32}O_2$, with four double bonds) have been found to possess similar activity, although the several members are not entirely equivalent in protective effect. Some restore growth and cure skin lesions, others only restore growth. Linoleic acid is the only *vegetable* acid that meets all the requirements of the animal for essential fatty acids. Arachidonic acid (found only in animal lipids) also restores growth and cures the skin defects. It appears to be from 2 to 6 times as effective as linoleic acid, depending on the methods of making the comparison. Probably arachidonic acid is the functional compound and

linoleic and linolenic acids are dietary precursors. It has been suggested that conversion (in the animal) of some of the dietary linoleic acid of plant origin to arachidonic acid explains the disappearance of all the signs of deficiency. Linolenic acid, in contrast, is converted principally to a six double-bonded acid which is unable to cure the skin lesions but which does stimulate growth and fat synthesis. The wide-spread occurrence in vegetable oils of glycerides containing linoleic acid (soybean oil 50 to 60 per cent, cottonseed oil 40 to 48 per cent, and corn oil 34 to 42 per cent,) and the presence in animal fats of arachidonic acid (lard 0.4 per cent, and butterfat, a trace) makes it unlikely that deficiency of essential fatty acids will occur in man or animals eating a good variety of natural foods.

Limited data are available to indicate the magnitude of the human requirement for linoleic or arachidonic acids. Some workers even doubt whether the essential fatty acids are of importance in the nutrition of adults. Infants do require linoleic acid; about 4 per cent of total calories should be provided as glycerides of linoleic acid. This amount is provided by breast milk. Babies kept for several months upon a diet very low in fat often develop a generalized eczema which is corrected when the fat of the diet is restored. During the period of low fat feeding, the iodine number of the serum lipids of these infants is depressed. (See Burr and associates.)

Discovery of a statistical correlation between the concentration of cholesterol esters in the blood serum and the incidence of cardiovascular disease led to the proposal that the incidence of atherosclerosis in adults is connected with the cholesterol content of the diet. More carefully controlled studies on patients, human volunteers, and animals revealed that dietary cholesterol has only a limited effect on the level of cholesterol esters in the serum. Epidemiological and experimental studies showed that the *fat* content of the diet is the dominant factor. Some workers believe that animal fats (especially butter) are more deleterious than vegetable oils. The effects of diet on the walls of the blood vessels and on blood-clotting are currently being studied with great vigor. A number of dietary factors appear to be involved in the enigma of atherosclerosis—the kind and amount of fat, cholesterol, protein, sulfur-containing amino acids, carbohydrate, choline, pyridoxine and possibly other vitamins, and magnesium; exercise (or lack of it) and energy balance are possibly contributing factors. Much experimental work is still necessary before proper dietary advice can be given on this subject. The preferential use of vegetable oils in cooking has been recommended. The data currently available do not warrant any drastic alteration in menus, such as *complete* elimination of eggs, bacon, and butter, as advised by some clinicians. Reduction of the intake of animal fat to minimal amounts providing palatability and variety may be desirable.

Mineral Constituents (See pp. 539, and 1592)

The minimal daily requirements of calcium, phosphorus and iron for the average adult (70 kg. in weight) are 0.8 g., 1.2 g., and 10–20 mg., respectively. In childhood and in pregnancy (especially in the later months) and in lactation the calcium requirement is higher than that given above (see table 73.2). In the later months of pregnancy, when from 20 to 30 grams of the mineral are being deposited in the fetus, daily allowance should be at least 1.3 grams; this intake should be continued during lactation. The best source of calcium for the growing child is milk, which contains about 1.3 grams per quart. Other dairy products, e.g., cheese and ice cream, are excellent sources of calcium. Cereals also are rich in calcium though much of it is not absorbed and retained; meat contains insignificant amounts of this element (see table 63.3) (p. 1271).

It is unnecessary, as a rule, to pay attention to the phosphorus content of the diet provided that the protein and calcium of the diet are adequate, for protein is relatively rich in phosphorus, and the latter is associated with calcium in milk, eggs, cereals, legumes, and several other foods.

The daily requirement of children for iron is, on a weight basis, higher than for adults; milk-fed infants, therefore, tend to develop anemia (ch. 50) after the fourth month or so unless given iron in inorganic form because milk is very poor in this element. Egg yolk, meat, liver and kidney, fruits, and nuts are the main sources of iron.

The basic elements, sodium, potassium, and magnesium, are derived chiefly from cereals, fruits, and vegetables. Sodium chloride is also added during cooking and at the table. The average daily intake is from 10 to 12 grams. Many preparations of table salt are also sources of iodine, since it has become the custom of the manufacturer to add minute quantities of potassium iodide to his product. The daily iodine requirement of adults is from 100 to 150 μg. Other ele-

TABLE 73.4

Per capita consumption of some major foods
(United States, 1949)

	Lb. per year
Dairy products (excluding butter)	429
Fats (including butter)	65
Eggs	46
Meats, poultry, fish	159
Potatoes (and sweet potatoes)	116
Grain products	173
Dry peas, beans and nuts	16
Citrus fruits and tomatoes	98
Leafy green and yellow vegetables	111
Other vegetables and fruits	235
Sugars and syrups	106

These foods provided average amounts of certain nutrients per day, estimated to be as follows:

Energy	3250 Calories
Protein	94 grams
Fat	141 grams
Carbohydrate	403 grams
Calcium	1.05 grams
Vitamin A	8500 I.U.

ments (trace elements), e.g., copper, cobalt (for erythropoiesis), fluorine (for tooth and bone structure), zinc (for the action of carbonic anhydrase and insulin), and manganese (for erythropoiesis and the action of phosphatase) are essential, but are present naturally in the diet in adequate amounts.

The dietary allowances recommended by the Food and Nutrition Board of the National Research Council, Washington, are given in table 73.2. The concept of *exact* nutrient requirements, as expressed in current recommendations (sometimes referred to as standards), must not be accepted too literally because the amount required varies with individuals and from day to day. Different races, with varying environmental situations and differing genetic make-up, have somewhat different requirements. Nutritional groups in many countries (e.g. Japan, India, Central America) are assessing the local requirements. The extent to which the "recommended allowances" represent "requirements" is variable.

THE PROPER PROPORTION OF THE THREE FOODSTUFFS IN AN ADULT DIET

From data given in table 73.4 one may calculate the proportions of the different nutrients consumed by the average American citizen to be as follows:

	Grams	Calories	Per cent of total Calories
Protein...........	94	376	12
Fat..............	141	1269	39
Carbohydrate......	403	1612	49
Total...........		3257	

There is no evidence that these calorie-ratios (approximately 10:40:50) are *proper*.[4] According to many authorities both the protein and fat intakes are greater than necessary. Stare and his associates, at the Harvard School of Public Health, found the protein requirement (for a 70 kg. man) to be met by 30 to 40 grams of mixed proteins (50 per cent from white bread), a range of values consistent with that found by Bricker, Mitchell, and Kinsman. Increasing the fat content of the diet can influence protein utilization, when both are fed at low levels, and there is other evidence that the nature of the nonprotein calories may affect the utilization of protein, i.e., different carbohydrates *are not strictly interchangeable*.

Present knowledge does not permit us to state with exactness the optimal amount of fat compatible with health, nor the *proper* proportions in which the three major foodstuffs should be consumed. Balanced nutrition should supply sufficient calories (mainly as carbohydrate and fat) but should avoid excess; it should provide minerals, vitamins, essential amino acids, and utilizable nitrogen in adequate amounts and in proper ratios to calorie intake and to each other.

REFERENCES

AAES-JØRGENSEN, E. Essential fatty acids. Physiol. Rev., 1961, **41**, 1.

[4] In 1962 protein accounted for 12%, fat 41% and carbohydrate 47% of the energy of food "as purchased" in the United States. The British Medical Association Committee on Nutrition recommended that 20 to 25 per cent of the calories should be provided as fat, with slightly larger proportions for very active persons (laborers, children, and adolescents).

BEATON, G. H. AND McHENRY, E. W. (eds.). Nutrition: a comprehensive treatise. Academic Press, New York, 1964.

BOURNE, G. H. AND KIDDER, G. W. (eds.). Biochemistry and physiology of nutrition. 2 vol. Academic Press, New York, 1953.

BURR, G. O. Fed. Proc., 1942, **1**, 224.

CHITTENDEN, R. H. Physiological economy in nutrition. Frederick A. Stokes Co., New York, 1907.

DAVIDSON, S., MEIKLEJOHN, A. P., AND PASSMORE, R. Human nutrition and dietetics. E. and S. Livingstone Ltd., Edinburgh and London, 1959.

DEUEL, H. J., JR. AND REISER, R. The physiology and biochemistry of the essential fatty acids. Vitamins and Hormones, 1955, **13**, 29.

HEGSTED, D. M., TRULSON, M. F., AND STARE, F. J. Role of wheat and wheat products in human nutrition. Physiol. Rev., 1954, **34**, 221.

HOLT, L. E. AND SNYDERMAN, S. E. J. A. M. A., 1961, **175**, 100.

McHENRY, E. W. Basic nutrition. J. B. Lippincott, Philadelphia and Montreal, 1957.

ROSE, W. C. Fed. Proc., 1949, **8**, 546.

SWANSON, P. P. Fed. Proc., 1951, **10**, 660.

A dietary standard for Canada. Canadian Bulletin on Nutrition, Vol. 6, No. 1, 1964.

Calorie requirements. F.A.O. Nutritional Studies, No. 15, Rome, 1957.

Energy-yielding components of food and computation of calorie values. FAO Report, Washington, 1947.

Present knowledge in nutrition, 2nd ed. The Nutrition Foundation, Inc., New York, 1956.

Protein requirement. F.A.O. Nutritional Studies, No. 16, Rome, 1957.

Recommended dietary allowances, 6 revised ed. Publication No. 1164, National Academy of Sciences, National Research Council, Washington, 1964.

Report of the Committee on Nutrition. Brit. Med. Assn. London, 1950.

Supplement for 1949 to Consumption of food in the United States, Miscellaneous Publication No. 691. Department of Agriculture, Washington, 1950.

Symposium on nutrition. Proceedings of the Borden Centennial, New York, April, 1958.

Symposium on nutrition. Fed. Proc., 1959, **18**, Suppl. 3, part II. 1–148.

Symposium on calorie balance in man. Proc. Nutrition Soc., 1961, **20**, 52–89.

IX

THE DUCTLESS GLANDS OR ENDOCRINES

Introduction —Ductless Glands or Endocrines

EVOLUTION. Two methods are used by the organism for transmitting messages from one organ to another. First, the nervous system forms an interconnecting mechanism by means of which rapid communication between different regions is established. And second, chemical substances called *hormones* are liberated into the blood from particular glands, and carried humorally to exert specific effects on distant structures. These latter act more slowly, and may have a more prolonged effect, than those messages sent by the nervous system. They are also of more ancient lineage, for it has been found that plants, in which no nervous system exists, use various hormones (auxins and others) to influence budding, growth, flowering, and possibly other functions. In the last 20 years much work has been devoted to the study of hormones in the invertebrates. Endocrine systems have been described in worms, crustaceans, insects, mollusks, and tunicates. Particular attention has been paid to the mechanisms controlling color changes in crustaceans and growth, differentiation, and moulting in insects. It is of special interest that in many of these forms the brain seems to play a dominant role as an organ of internal secretion. The process of elaboration of a hormone by the nervous system has received the term *neurosecretion*. Such a process in higher forms is discussed more fully below. The homology between higher invertebrate and lower vertebrate glands is, in many cases, uncertain.

HISTORY. The science of endocrinology began with the observations of Berthold in 1849, that removal of the testes in cocks resulted in changes in the birds so that they approached the build and behavior of the hen, and that these changes could be avoided by grafting the testes to the gut. The evidence was very strong then that the testes liberated some substance into the blood stream that was responsible for the masculine features and behavior of the normal cock. Claude Bernard is usually regarded as the originator of present views regarding internal secretion, though his discovery that the liver liberates glucose into the blood cannot now be included as an endocrine phenomenon. It was from clinical studies that modern views of endocrinology first became clarified. Semon (1883) suggested, and Horsley (1888) showed, that myxedema and cretinism were due to failure of thyroid secretion, and Murray (1891) reported the benefit accruing to a case of myxedema from administration of thyroid extract.

Later clinical studies suggested that various disease states might result from over secretion of endocrine glands (Greenfield, 1893, Graves' disease; Tamburini, 1894, and Benda, 1900, acromegaly). The physiological evidence on endocrine organs may be said to date from the classical studies of Oliver and Schäfer (1894) on the pressor principle of the adrenal medulla, Oliver and Schäfer (1895) and Dale (1909) on the pressor and oxytocic actions of posterior pituitary extracts, and Marshall and Jolly (1907, 1908) on the activity of ovarian transplants. Bayliss and Starling (1904) first established that a chemical substance could be secreted by one organ (in their case, secretin from the intestinal mucosa) and carried by the blood stream to exert a specific effect on distant structures. They also proposed the term 'hormone' (from ὁρμάω—I arouse to activity). Great impetus was given to the subject by the studies of H. M. Evans and his group on the effects of hypophysectomy and replacement therapy in the rat (P. E. Smith, 1927), on the estrous cycle and vaginal smear technique in the rat (Long and Evans, 1922), on vitamin E and its relation to reproductive phenomena (Evans and Scott, 1922), and on the purification of various anterior pituitary hormones.

STRUCTURE. In the vertebrates the following organs are now well established as endocrine glands: anterior pituitary (adenohypophysis), posterior pituitary (neurohypophysis), ovary, testis, thyroid, adrenal cortex, adrenal medulla, parathyroids, islets of Langerhans in the pancreas, and various parts of the intestinal mucosa.[1] All these organs have certain anatomical features in common. *First,* they are typical glands (except the neurohypophysis which belongs to a special class of neurosecretory organs) in that they are composed of masses of secretory cells arranged usually in columns or clumps. These cells may occasionally, as in the case of the thyroid, be arranged in alveoli or acini with their secretory product stored in the lumen. More commonly, however, the hormones or their parent substances are stored as granules in the cells. *Second,* although glandular in nature, no ducts are present. *Third,* since the blood stream functions as a "duct" and carries off the secretory products, they are all richly vascularized. And *fourth,* the

[1] It is possible that the pineal and thymus are endocrine glands, but little is known as to their function at the present time.

passage of the hormones into the vascular stream is facilitated by the replacement of thick collagenous connective tissue fibers by fine reticular fibers, and by the nature of the blood vessels which are thin-walled sinusoids.

CHEMISTRY. The hormones fall into several chemical groups. The pituitary hormones are proteins or polypeptides; the gonadal and adrenocortical hormones are steroids; whereas the thyroid and adrenomedullary hormones are composed of simpler and smaller molecules.

THE HORMONES AND THEIR FUNCTIONS. In order to study the endocrine glands in detail, it is advantageous to have a general picture of the system as a whole first.

The pituitary gland or hypophysis is connected to the base of the brain by the pituitary stalk. The *anterior pituitary gland* is usually thought to secrete six hormones. The names of these, their synonyms, and abbreviations (their site of action being given in parentheses) are as follows:

Anterior pituitary hormones
  A. Gonadotrophic hormones
    1. Follicle stimulating hormone, FSH (ovary and testis)
    2. Luteinizing hormone, LH, or interstial cell stimulating hormone, ICSH (ovary and testis)
    3. Luteotrophic hormone, LTH, or prolactin, or lactogenic hormone (ovary, in some species) and mammary glands)
  B. Thyrotrophic hormone, TSH (thyroid)
  C. Adrenocorticotrophic hormone, ACTH (adrenal cortex)
  D. Growth hormone, or somatotrophic hormone, STH (body tissues—stimulates growth))

From this outline it may be seen that the anterior pituitary has a wide field of action. In addition to exerting a major influence over body growth (growth hormone) and over milk secretion in mammary tissue (lactogenic hormone), its hormones are largely, if not solely, responsible for maintaining and regulating the functions of the thyroid, adrenal cortex, ovary, and testes. In the absence of the anterior pituitary these latter four glands undergo atrophy and a great diminution in activity.

The *thyroid gland* secretes thyroxine and small amounts of tri-iodothyronine; hormones which are responsible for maintaining oxidative processes in bodily tissues in general. The *adrenal cortex*, like the thyroid, has no specific target organ upon which its hormones act, but by means

of steroidal compounds it exerts a major influence over carbohydrate, protein, and electrolyte metabolism. The gonads also secrete steroidal hormones, estrogens and progesterone in the case of the *ovary*, and androgens in the case of the *testes*. They act both upon tissues in general (as may be seen from the changes produced under their influence at puberty), and upon specific target organs such as the breast, uterus, vagina, seminal vesicles, prostate, and penis.

The *posterior pituitary gland* secretes one or two hormones. Physiologically active polypeptides have been extracted from the gland and obtained in a highly purified state. They have also been synthesized. The *antidiuretic* or vasopressor hormone exerts a regulating action on the volume of urine, and amount of chloride, excreted by the kidney. In large doses this hormone has a pressor action, increases intestinal motility, and raises the blood sugar. The *oxytocic hormone* causes contraction of uterine muscle and of mammary tissue. It thus aids in the expulsion of the fetus from the uterus and of milk from the breast. The *adrenal medulla*, a gland in several ways comparable with the posterior pituitary, secretes adrenaline and noradrenaline in amounts which vary in proportion in different species and probably in different individuals within a species. These two hormones are secreted during times of emergency or stress. Under conditions of fright, rage, pain, and similar states, the adrenal medulla is activated. In general it may be said that its hormones tend to reinforce the action of the sympathetic nervous system and exert widespread effects, such as increasing the general blood pressure, dilating the vessels of skeletal and cardiac muscle, and raising the blood sugar, which equip the animal as a more efficient machine for "fight or flight."

The *parathyroid glands* secrete a hormone, often referred to as *parathormone*, which has an important influence over calcium and phosphorus metabolism.

REGULATION OF ENDOCRINE ACTIVITY—THE NEUROENDOCRINE HIERARCHY AND THE FEEDBACK MECHANISM. The adjustment of endocrine function to meet the varying needs of an organism in an unstable environment is clearly a matter of some importance, but it is only in the last few years that data has become available on this subject.

A few of the glands may be dealt with briefly at this point. The regulation of insulin secretion by the islet tissue of the pancreas is dealt with elsewhere (ch. 67). Little is known regarding the control of parathyroid function. It appears unlikely that the parathyroids are under the control of either a secretomotor innervation or of a trophic hormone from the pituitary. Available evidence indicates that their activity is directly affected by the blood concentration of calcium.

Figure 74.1 depicts various relationships involved in the control of the major part of the endocrine system. The function of two of the glands is dependent upon, and regulated by, a direct secretomotor nerve supply. The neurohypophysis is controlled by the supraopticohypophysial tract from the hypothalamus. This same part of the diencephalon also regulates adrenomedullary activity by means of nervous pathways descending in the brain stem and spinal cord, with outflows to the gland through the sympathetic chain and splanchnic nerves. It is of interest that the posterior pituitary and adrenal medulla are among the most rapidly reacting endocrine glands and that they are under the direct control of the nervous system with its well-known high speed of response.

There can be little doubt that various parts of the central nervous system (such as the reticular formation of the brain stem, the temporal lobes and amygdaloid nuclei, the frontal lobes, and other regions), acting through the hypothalamus, influence the secretory activity of the anterior pituitary which in turn controls the ovary, testis, thyroid, and adrenal cortex. The hypothalamo-hypophysial unit may, in general terms, be looked upon as a bottle-neck between the two great systems; the nervous and the endocrine. The neuroendocrine hierarchy, central nervous system, and hypothalamus → anterior pituitary → target glands, may be analyzed in terms of three "levels of activity."

1. Intrinsic or autonomic activity of the target glands. This is revealed in the hypophysectomized animal. In the absence of the pituitary the gonads show no sign of endocrine function, but the thyroid and adrenal cortex still secrete, though at a very low rate.

2. Intrinsic activity of the anterior pituitary. If the pituitary gland is disconnected from the hypothalamus, by section of the pituitary stalk and insertion of a plate between the cut ends, or by transplantation of the gland to a distant site in the body, it also shows some low level intrinsic activity. As far as can be seen with present tests, secretion of FSH and LH ceases, though LTH, TSH, and ACTH are still released into the blood at low rates. Thus, in the pituitary stalk-sectioned animal the ovaries appear totally inactive (except that any corpora lutea present at the time of

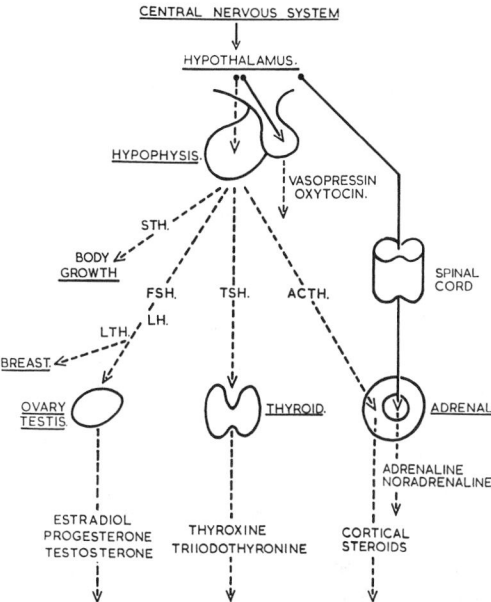

FIG. 74.1. The relationship between the nervous system and endocrine system. ——, nerve pathway; – – –, vascular pathway. Note that two glands, the adrenal medulla and neurohypophysis are regulated by a direct nerve supply whereas the activity of the other glands is controlled by humoral or hormonal agents carried in the blood stream.

operation may be maintained) whereas the thyroid and adrenal cortex show some function. The level of function in these latter two glands is greater than that seen in the hypophysectomized animal, since to the autonomous function of the target glands is added the autonomous release of TSH and ACTH by the anterior pituitary.

3. Normal activity. The full activity of the anterior pituitary-target gland system is only seen when the central nervous system maintains and regulates anterior pituitary function through intact connections between the hypothalamus and adenohypophysis. The connections concerned are the hypophysial portal vessels of the pituitary stalk.

The hypothalamus, then, occupies a key position in regard to the endocrine system. Not only does it regulate the activity of the adrenal medulla and neurohypophysis through direct nerve supplies to these glands, but through its influence over the anterior pituitary it also regulates the activities of the ovary, testis, thyroid, and adrenal cortex. The effects exerted by the central nervous system over these endocrine organs may be summarized as follows:

1. It maintains their function at a normal level. In the absence of neural control, the activity of

some glands ceases entirely (posterior pituitary gland) and in the others falls to low levels.

2. It is responsible for maintaining rhythmic activity, such as that of the ovary during normal sexual cycles.

3. It acts as an intermediary between the varying external environment and the endocrine system. Environmental stimuli, acting through the central nervous sytem, evoke changes in endocrine activity appropriate to the situation.

4. It possibly acts as part of the central mechanism involved in the "feed-back" action of the target gland hormones. The anterior pituitary and its target glands act in reciprocity. For example, if the blood concentration of thyroid hormone is increased, then by some central action the rate of secretion of TSH is reduced so that thyroid activity and the blood level of thyroid hormone is also reduced. If the blood concentration of thyroid hormone falls, the reverse situation is brought about. Similar reactions occur with changes in the blood concentration of gonadal or adrenal cortical hormones. It is uncertain whether alterations in the blood level of the target gland hormones elicit these changes in pituitary activity by exerting a direct action on anterior pituitary cells, or whether the hypothalamus is sensitive to changes in blood concentration of these hormones and in turn regulates anterior pituitary activity appropriately. This feed-back mechanism whereby the anterior pituitary and its target glands form a self-balancing system, probably acts to stabilize endocrine activity under basal resting conditions, rather than to regulate activity under conditions calling for increased or decreased function. This phenomenon becomes a matter of practical importance in considering transplantation of endocrine glands. Halsted, many years ago, pointed out that most endocrine transplants take more readily if a state of deficiency in the host exists for the particular gland concerned. This statement has been verified many times and has become known as *Halsted's Principle of Deficiency.* As an example of this principle, it may be said that ovarian transplants survive better in an ovariectomized animal than in a normal animal. This is probably because the ovariectomized animal has a higher level of circulating gonadotrophic hormone than has the normal.

In summary, then, it may be said that the main factor maintaining endocrine activity at a normal level and concerned with regulating this activity under varying environmental conditions is the influence exerted by the central nervous system. The feed-back mechanism probably operates as a stabilizing system whereby endocrine function is maintained at a preset level under constant conditions.

THE NATURE OF HORMONES AND THEIR TRANS-

PORT. The term *hormone* refers essentially to a chemical messenger in the blood stream. In the case of some glands the hormone has been identified in the venous blood from the gland or in the general systemic circulation, but in other cases data as to the nature of the hormone has been surmised from studies on material extractable from the gland itself. This latter approach may be fallacious. For example, it is known that the thyroid stores thyroglobulin, and that this substance is degraded before the hormone itself is liberated into the blood. Therefore, material extractable from a gland may represent a precursor of the hormone rather than the hormone itself. However, in the case of some glands, such as the anterior pituitary, the only information available is derived from studies of glandular extracts. Six purified and pharmacologically active extracts have been obtained from adenohypophysial tissue, and although it is convenient and customary to speak of these pituitary principles as separate hormones, there is no means of knowing whether the active materials obtained by rather drastic methods of extraction are actually secreted as separate entities by the living gland. It may be that the extraction products of the anterior lobe represent, as Riddle suggests, "hormone fragments" or as Collip expresses it, "chemically dissected" parts which represent prosthetic groups split off from a smaller number of larger hormone molecules. The only unequivocal test is the identification of the hormones, individually and separately, in pituitary venous blood. The position is further complicated by the fact that some hormones, such as thyroxine, become bound to plasma proteins during transport in the blood, and by the possibility, not yet established, that a hormone may need to be chemically changed in the tissues before it is able to exert its characteristic action.

CELLULAR ACTION AND EXCRETION OF HORMONES. It is not possible at the present time to state the precise nature of hormone action at a cellular level. Two general views are that hormones act at cell surfaces or boundaries to affect cellular excitability or metabolism, or that they form part of an enzyme system within the cell. It is too early to make a definite statement but studies such as those of Csapo, on the relationship between estrogens and the actomyosin content of uterine muscle and his finding that progesterone alters the balance of extracellular and intracellular sodium and potassium as well as the excitability of uterine muscle, may point the way to further elucidation of this difficult problem.

For detailed discussions of this topic the reviews of Hechter (1955) and Levine (1957) may be consulted.

The rate of inactivation or excretion of some hormones is very rapid. For example, ACTH is quickly lost from the blood (in seconds-minutes), as are the posterior pituitary and adrenomedullary hormones. Some information is available as to the tissues which inactivate and/or excrete certain of these substances. Thyrotrophic hormone appears to be inactivated by thyroid and lymphatic tissue. Estrogens are conjugated in the liver and excreted to some extent in the bile. Thyroxine is also partly excreted in the bile and feces. Many hormones appear to be partially degraded and excreted in the urine (some anterior pituitary and placental hormones, ovarian and adrenal cortical steroids).

HORMONES AND BEHAVIOR. Attention has been drawn above to the regulating effects the central nervous system exerts on endocrine function. The reciprocal picture also exists. It is clear that various hormones act on the central nervous system to determine the behavioral response of the organism to environmental stimuli. A simple example may be taken from the field of reproductive physiology. A female cat with a low blood concentration of estrogen reacts to the attentions of a male cat with signs of displeasure (spitting, striking with the forepaws) and avoidance, whereas a female cat with a high blood concentration of estrogen reacts with a complicated but stereotyped pattern of courtship and mating activities. In the clinical field, a striking difference in mental state is seen in the extreme nervousness and irritability of patients suffering from hyperthyroidism (Graves' disease) as compared with the mental apathy and sluggishness of cases of hypothyroidism (myxedema). Although it seems almost certain that these behavioral changes are brought about by a direct action of the hormones on the central nervous system, very little information is available as to what regions of the nervous system are affected by the different hormones, or indeed to what extent the hormones are able to cross the "blood-brain barrier."

METHODS OF STUDY. Studies on an endocrine organ fall into two groups; those necessary to demonstrate that a particular organ is a gland of internal secretion, and those dealing in detail with its regulation, hormones, and mode of action.

To establish that an organ is an endocrine gland, several or all of the following criteria should be fulfilled:

1. A typical syndrome is induced by its destruction by disease or experimental removal. The initial observations have, in many cases, been made on the human. Attention was first drawn to endocrine deficiencies resulting from castration, tubercular destruction of the adrenal glands, and removal of the thyroid, from observations on man.

2. Substitution therapy. The deficiency state induced by removal or destruction of the gland should be reparable by administration of suitable extracts of the gland or by grafting the removed gland into a distant site in the body. The preparation of a suitable extract may present many difficulties. In the case of the thyroid gland it was early shown that a simple glycerine extract of the sheep's gland was curative in cases of myxedema. However, the thyroid offered favorable circumstances for this demonstration in that it stores large quantities of active material which is effective when administered by mouth. Such is not the case for the other glands, for which delicate methods of chemical extraction may have to be developed before a suitable extract is obtained. The repair of a deficiency state by transplantation of an endocrine gland to a distant site in the body is a classical procedure in endocrine studies, and demonstrates that the organ concerned produces its effects by secretion into the blood stream, and also that its activity is dependent on some humoral agent carried in the general circulation. There is no evidence that the neurohypophysis or adrenal medulla has ever been transplanted and shown normal function. This is due to the fact that these glands are dependent on a nerve supply for normal function, and cannot be taken as evidence related to their mode of action. In transplantation studies attention must be paid to the source of the material. Tissue removed from and transplanted back into the same animal (*autotransplant*) has the best chance of 'taking' and remaining viable. Tissue removed from a donor animal and transplanted into a closely related member of the same species (*homotransplant*) often 'takes,' remains viable for a few weeks, and then undergoes lymphocytic infiltration and absorption. Tissue removed from a donor animal and grafted into a recipient of another species (*heterotransplant*) is usually absorbed within a few days. For this reason,

it is unlikely that endocrine transplantation will ever form a useful therapeutic procedure. The beneficial results occasionally claimed following the transplantation of animal material into human cases may in part be due to absorption of hormone stored in the transplanted material or to the psychological effects of the procedure.

3. Administration of large doses of a glandular extract should produce signs of overdosage and a state that is often comparable to disease states, in which a secreting tumor of an endocrine gland results in the discharge of excessive amounts of hormone into the circulation. For example, excessive dosage with thyroid or adrenocortical hormones in the human produces states similar in many ways to Graves' disease and Cushing's syndrome, respectively.

After an organ has become established as a gland of internal secretion the following major points require investigation:

1. The factors regulating the activity of the gland. A change in the external environmental conditions exerts a powerful influence on the activity of many endocrine glands. Thus, the gonads of many seasonal breeding forms are activated by increased periods of illumination; a fall in environmental temperature leads to increased function of the thyroid gland; stresses and conditions of emergency excite adrenal cortical and medullary activity, and so on. The physiological mechanisms by which such factors influence endocrine function still require further investigation. In order to study these factors it is advantageous to have a simple and quick measure of glandular activity. From the point of view of the organism as a whole, the most exact definition of such activity is, the amount of hormone secreted into the blood in unit time. In order to obtain this estimate it is necessary to know the rate of blood flow through the gland and the hormone content of the arterial blood entering, and the venous blood leaving, the organ. Ideally, it is desirable to be able to make such observations in the unanesthe-

tized animal. At the present time this is barely possible, so that indirect measures of glandular activity are generally used, such as observing the effect the hormone exerts on some process or target organ (e.g., vaginal epithelium in the case of the ovarian hormones, basal metabolic rate for the thyroid hormones), or observing the concentration of the hormone in the general systemic circulation, or the rate of excretion of the hormone or its degradation products in the urine.

2. The analysis of the biochemical processes occurring in the gland. Simple substances (glucose, amino acids, inorganic salts) are extracted by the gland from the blood, converted into more complex compounds (steroids, polypeptides) and secreted back into the blood. A rudimentary knowledge of the chemical changes involved has been obtained in some cases. Radioactive iodine has been a valuable tool in analyzing such processes in the thyroid, and the use of the artificially perfused gland with blood containing C^{14}-labeled substrates has aided materially in work on the adrenal cortex. In the case of other glands, such as the anterior and posterior pituitary, very little data exist. Such information may be of much practical use. In cases of hyperthyroidism it is possible to administer antithyroid compounds which block the organic binding of iodine by the gland and so prevent the secretion of excessive amounts of hormone.

3. The carriage and fate of hormones in the blood. Knowledge as to the carriage of hormones in the blood (i.e., whether as a complex with plasma proteins), the metabolic changes undergone in the tissues, and the processes of inactivation and excretion of the hormones are largely dependent on the development of reliable assay methods for the hormones in body fluids.

4. The mechanism of action of the hormones at an organ, cellular and organelle level. As mentioned above, very little knowledge has so far been obtained on this topic.

CHAPTER 74

The Pituitary Gland or Hypophysis Cerebri

Origin and Structure

The average weight of the human hypophysis is about 0.5 gram. It is slightly heavier in females, especially in those who have borne children, than in males. Its average dimensions are 10 mm. (sagittal) by 13 mm. (transverse) by 6 mm. (vertical). It lies within the small cavity formed by the *sella turcica* of the sphenoid bone which is closed above by a thin membrane, *diaphragma sellae*, except where it is pierced by the pituitary stalk. The stalk connects the pituitary gland below to the hypothalamus of the brain above.

The pituitary body consists of an anterior and posterior part readily separable along a natural line of cleavage, which represents the original, embryonic cavity of Rathke's pouch (see below). Until recently the two parts of the pituitary were generally referred to as the *anterior* and *posterior lobes*, and the stalk as the *infundibulum*. Though these terms are still used somewhat loosely, it is preferred, for more precise description of the hypophysis, to employ a nomenclature based upon the origins of its different parts. The pituitary has a dual origin in the embryo—from the ectoderm in the roof of the primitive mouth (stomodeum) just in front of the buccopharyngeal membrane as well as from the base of the brain. In the early embryo a pouch extends from the stomodeum to meet a corresponding hollow diverticulum prolonged downward from the floor of the third ventricle. The evagination from the primitive mouth is called *Rathke's pouch*. Through pressure upon its posterior wall by the downgrowth of nervous tissue, this wall of Rathke's pouch is approximated to the anterior wall and the cavity reduced to a cleft or (in the human) to a row of vesicles. The original stalklike connection of Rathke's pouch with the stomodeum, known as the *craniopharyngeal canal*, also becomes largely obliterated, though a remnant may remain as a "pharyngeal pituitary" (embedded in the mucosa on the dorsal wall of the pharynx) and other fragments may in later life give rise to tumors situated in the anterior wall of the sella turcica. The original cavity of the neural element of the pituitary disappears completely in man, so that the pituitary stalk becomes solid, though in some adult animals, such as the cat, this cavity persists and communicates with the third ventricle. It should be mentioned that bilateral diverticula of Rathke's pouch, the *lateral lobes*, climb upward to surround the upper end of the stalk and give rise to the pars tuberalis.

The part of the pituitary which originates from Rathke's pouch has a glandular structure and is, therefore, called the *adenohypophysis*. The portion developed from the brain is known as the *neurohypophysis*. Each division of the hypophysis is subdivided into three parts. Thus, the neurohypophysis consists of the expanded distal portion, the *infundibular process* or *neural lobe*, the nervous part of the stalk known as the *infundibular stem* or *neural stalk*, and the expanded upper end of the stalk, which is the *median eminence* of the tuber cinereum. It is important to realize that all three parts of the neurohypophysis are glandular and may liberate hormone into the blood stream. The tissue of the neural stalk and median eminence constitutes about 13 per cent of the total neurohypophysial tissue. The adenohypophysis consists of the *pars tuberalis* (a thin strip of tissue surrounding the median eminence and the upper part of the neural stalk), the *pars intermedia* (that portion posterior to the cleft and in contact with the neural lobe), and the *pars distalis* or anterior lobe (the major secretory part of the gland lying anterior to the cleft). The development and different parts of the gland are summarized in figure 74.2 and table 74.1.

The neural stalk, together with its sheath, the pars tuberalis, is known as the *hypophysial* or *pituitary stalk*.[2]

The *pars distalis* is richly vascular, showing numerous blood sinuses between cords of cells. The cells fall into two main groups; (a) *chromophobe* or *reserve* cells which possess no granules, stain lightly, and apparently do not secrete, and (b) chromophil cells which contain large numbers of granules which stain readily (they are believed to elaborate the secretions of the anterior lobe). On a basis of the character of the granules, the chromophil cells are grouped again into two varieties (a) *acidophil* (or α) cells, which stain more readily with acid dyes, and (b) *basophil* (or β) cells, which have a greater affinity for basic stains. The three types of cells (chromophobe and the two types of chromophil cell) are scattered indiscriminately throughout the pars distalis. The proportions found in man by Rasmussen, were around 50 per cent chromophobes, 35 per cent acidophils, and 15 per cent basophils. It now ap-

---

[2] The spelling "hypophysial" is correct. The alternative "hypophyseal" became current as the result of a misprint in one of Dr. Harvey Cushing's monographs.

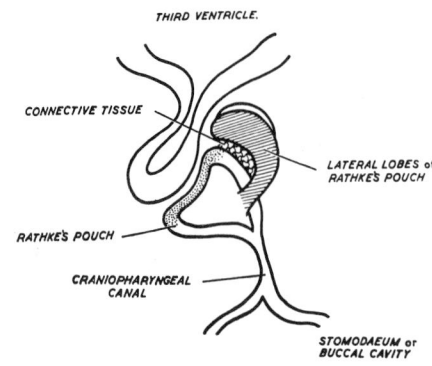

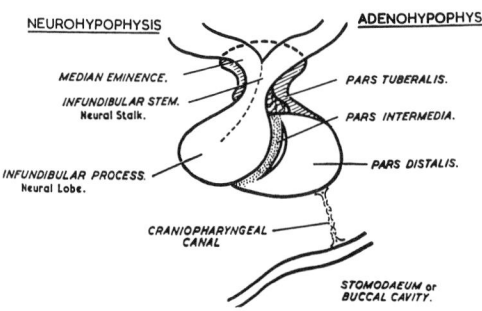

FIG. 74.2. The embryological development of the different parts of the pituitary. The neurohypophysis consists of three parts, the median eminence, infundibular stem, and infundibular process; and the adenohypophysis also of three parts, the pars tuberalis, pars intermedia, and pars distalis. In some forms (such as the whale and elephant) a thick connective tissue septum extends upward between the infundibular process and pars intermedia, to merge with the connective tissue wedge illustrated in the diagram. However, in all forms the pars tuberalis encircles the median eminence and forms the bed of a vascular path linking the median eminence and the pars distalis.

pears that the chromophobes represent mother cells and, by development, give rise to either acidophils or basophils. (Chromophobe cells may also represent "chromophil" cells in which a high level of secretory activity is present—so high that storage of hormone is absent.) Catchpole (1947) first stained glycoproteins in anterior pituitary basophil cells, using the periodic acid-Schiff

method (PAS). Since then, various subdivisions of the basophils have been distinguished in the anterior pituitary of the *rat*. This has been made possible by the fact that under special physiological conditions, variations occur in certain groups of the basophil cells. After castration, some basophils undergo enlargement and vacuolization, with displacement of the nucleus to one side of the cell ("signet ring" or "castration cells"). Other cell types described are "thyroidectomy cells" and "pregnancy cells". With such methods it is possible to define three groups of basophil cells in the rat pituitary: (1) "thyrotrophs"—polyhedral cells distributed throughout the interior of the gland, (2) "central gonadotrophs"—ovoid or spherical cells, contained in the centre of the gland and near the pars intermedia, which secrete luteinizing hormone, and (3) "peripheral gonadotrophs"—ovoid or spherical cells, contained in the periphery of the pars anterior on the inferior surface and at the anterior margin, which secrete follicle-stimulating hormone. The distribution of these basophils is represented in fig. 74.3. According to their staining reactions, and to the changes they show in the reproductive cycle, two classes of acidophil cells are distinguished: (1) "orangeophil" cells—which secrete growth hormone, and (2) "carminophil" cells—which secrete prolactin or the lactogenic hormone. Thus five out of the six anterior pituitary hormones may be ascribed to a certain cell type. It should be pointed out that owing to variations in staining properties of pituitary cells in different species, the above state-

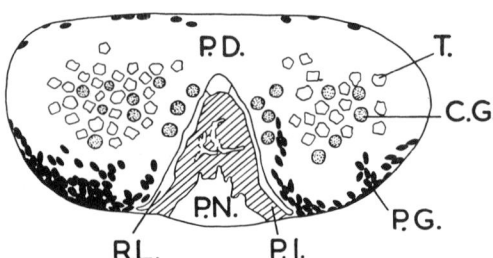

FIG. 74.3. Morphology of the hypophysis related to its function. From "Sex and Internal Secretions," edited by W. C. Young, chapter III, volume I.

TABLE 74.1

Origin	Primary Division	Subdivisions	
From primitive buccal cavity	Adenohypophysis	1. Pars distalis (anterior lobe) 2. Pars tuberalis 3. Pars intermedia	} (Posterior lobe)
From floor of third ventricle	Neurohypophysis	1. Infundibular process, neural lobe 2. Infundibular stem } Neural stalk 3. Median eminence	

ments can only be taken as a generalization. Which cell the adrenocorticotrophic hormone is secreted by, remains an intriguing problem. The *pars intermedia* is the least vascular part of the pituitary. In some forms (cat, rabbit) it forms a well marked, thick layer, but in the human it consists of only a few cells. It is common to find cysts of various sizes, containing a hyaline or colloid material, in the region of the pars intermedia. The *pars tuberalis* resembles the pars distalis in being constituted of cords of cells separated by blood sinuses. The cells, however, are nongranular.

The three parts of the neurohypophysis—the median eminence, infundibular stem, and process —are composed of similar tissue, which is different from that of the hypothalamus proper in vital staining properties, vascular supply, and cytology. Gross inspection of the region would lead one to draw the line of demarcation between the neurohypophysis and hypothalamus at the level of the infundibular stem, whereas it is in reality at a considerably higher level. This fact has important implications when considering various experimental findings concerning the neurohypophysis. The tissues of the neurohypophysis consist of (a) a profusion of unmyelinated nerve fibers, (b) fusiform cells with several processes and containing granules of a brown pigment in their cytoplasm (the *pituicytes* of Bucy), and (c) numerous blood vessels, neurological cells, mast cells, and hyaline bodies. The hyaline bodies are of historic interest, in that Herring (1908) put forward the view that the active material in the posterior lobe is derived from basophil cells of the pars intermedia migrating posteriorly into the neurohypophysis, and becoming transformed into hyaline masses. These hyaline masses, he supposed, were traveling up the pituitary stalk to be liberated into the cerebrospinal fluid in the third ventricle and there to exert their action on the nerve centers in the hypothalamus. This view was current for many years and had the support of such authorities as Harvey Cushing. However, it now seems clear that the neurohypophysis passes its secretion directly into the blood stream.

The extent to which the adenohypophysis makes contact with the neural lobe varies considerably. It may almost entirely surround the latter (cat), or in some forms (elephant, cetacea, armadillo) is separated from the neural lobe by a connective tissue septum. However, in all forms examined the pars tuberalis establishes contact with the neural stalk.

THE BLOOD SUPPLY OF THE HYPOPHYSIS (fig. 74.4). The vascular territory of the neural lobe is separated from that of the median eminence and adenohypophysis. It is supplied by posterior or inferior hypophysial arteries and drains by short veins into the surrounding venous sinuses.

FIG. 74.4. Diagram of a sagittal section through the pituitary gland (below) and hypothalamus (above) of a rabbit, showing the blood supply of the gland. The anterior and posterior hypophysial arteries (*a* and *b*) are derived from the internal carotid arteries. The arterial twigs (*c*) to the pars tuberalis and the primary plexus of the portal vessels in the median eminence are derived from the internal carotid and posterior communicating arteries. The venous drainage (*d*) passes to surrounding venous sinuses in the dura mater or in the basisphenoid bone. In many forms the arterial supply to the pars distalis (*a*) is reduced or appears to be absent. In these cases the portal vessels may form the sole blood supply to the anterior pituitary gland. (From Harris.)

The blood supply of the pars distalis may be compared with that of the liver in that it possesses a systemic arterial supply, a portal supply, and a venous drainage. The *venous drainage* is similar to that of the neural lobe in that it passes by short wide veins into adjacent venous sinuses. The *arterial supply* varies in different forms. The rabbit pituitary is supplied by a branch of one internal carotid, usually the left, arising and penetrating the gland at a level below the diaphragma sellae. However, Daniel and coworkers claim that the pars distalis of the human, and some other forms, lacks a direct arterial supply. The *portal supply* of the pars distalis was first described by Popa and Fielding (1930) in the human, and their anatomical findings confirmed by Wislocki and others in many lower forms. The general arrangement of the system is as follows. Small arterial twigs from the circle of Willis supply a vascular plexus situated in the pars tuberalis, which in turn supplies a multitude of capillary loops or tufts situated in the nervous tissue of the median eminence and infundibular stem. These capillaries are known as the *primary plexus of the hypophysial portal vessels.* They drain by means of large vascular trunks which pass down the pituitary stalk to distribute their blood into the sinusoids of the pars distalis. These vessels, therefore, start as capillaries in the median eminence and end as sinusoids in the pars distalis (fig. 74.5). Since the median eminence is part of the neurohypophysis, the entire extent of the portal vessels is contained within the hypophysis and they should be referred to as the *hypophysial portal vessels* and not as the hypothal-

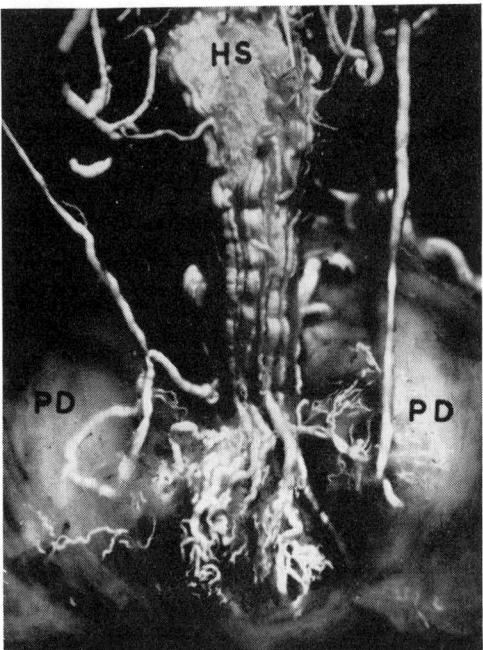

FIG. 74.5. Photograph of anterior aspect of pituitary stalk of man. The blood vessels have been injected with neoprene latex. Note the prominent trunks of the portal vessels. These vessels start as capillaries in the median eminence (*HS*) of the tuber cinereum and neural stalk and carry blood downward into the sinusoids of the anterior lobe (*PD*). (From Xuereb, Prichard, and Daniel.)

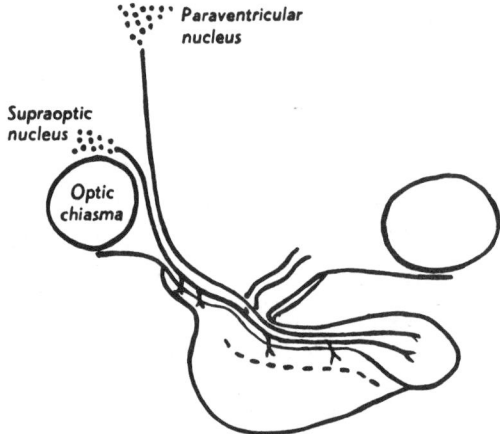

FIG. 74.6. Diagram of a sagittal section through the pituitary gland showing the large nerve tract, derived from the supraoptic and paraventricular nuclei and other nuclei of the hypothalamus, which innervates the neurohypophysis. A few nerve fibers penetrate into the pars intermedia. (From Harris.)

amo-hypophysial portal vessels. When it became apparent that these vessels might form an important part of the functional link between the central nervous system and the pars distalis of

the pituitary, and be involved in some neuro-humoral mechanism whereby the nervous system controls anterior pituitary activity, they were re-investigated in detail and the following significant points established: (a) They are present in all the major classes of vertebrates (Green, 1951), (b) the direction of blood flow in these portal vessels is from the median eminence down to the pituitary (this was observed by microscopic examination of the vessels in living amphibians, rats, mice, and dogs), and (c) after cutting the pituitary stalk they have marked powers of regeneration, so that investigations on the effects of pituitary stalk section must be carried out on animals in which a plate or some impervious barrier is placed between the stalk ends.

THE NERVE SUPPLY OF THE HYPOPHYSIS (fig. 74.6). The *adenohypophysis* receives a very scanty innervation, if any at all. From time to time it has been suggested that the pars distalis might be innervated from one or more of three sources: (a) by nerve fibers from the hypothalamo-hypophysial tract in the pituitary stalk, (b) by the carotid sympathetic plexus, and (c) by a parasympathetic innervation derived from the greater superficial petrosal nerves. However, the most careful histo-logical studies (Rasmussen, 1938; Green, 1951) have failed to reveal any innervation of the secretory cells. The scanty nerve fibers seen in the anterior lobe are (as seems to be the case with some other endocrine glands, such as the thyroid and adrenal cortex) in all probability vasomotor in nature. Such a view is supported by recent studies with the electron microscope.

The *neurohypophysis* is richly innervated by the *hypothalamo-hypophysial* tract from the hypothal-amus. These fibers originate in the supraoptic and paraventricular nuclei in the hypothalamus and probably from other, as yet undetermined, nuclei. The number of fibers in this tract has been esti-mated at 10,000 (rat), 50,000 (dog, monkey), and 100,000 (man). They are fine unmyelinated fibers; they may be stained with one of the silver impreg-nation methods or with the Gomori chrome-alum haematoxylin method. Their origin has been de-termined by microanatomical studies and by the fact that the supraoptic and paraventricular nuclei undergo retrograde degeneration, and lose some 90 per cent of their cells, if the nerve tract is cut above the median eminence. Their termina-tion is in close proximity to blood vessels in all three parts of the neurohypophysis. This has been clearly established by such studies as those of Bodian (1951) on the neurohypophysis of the opos-sum. In this animal a more orderly architecture prevails in the neural lobe than in most other ani-mals. In recent years great interest has centered around the neurosecretory potentialities of this nerve tract (see below).

The Physiology of the Adenohypophysis

The adenohypophysis is the master gland of the endocrine system. Many different types of effects have been identified with this part of the pituitary. Most of these actions can be produced by one of the six purified extracts that have been obtained from anterior lobe tissue. These extracts are, by common usage, referred to as hormones and are known as (a) the *growth* or *somatotrophic* hormone, (STH), (b) the *thyrotrophic* or *thyroid-stimulating* hormone (TSH), (c) the *adreno-corticotrophic* hormone (ACTH), (d) and (e) the *gonadotrophic* hormones (*follicle-stimulating* hormone (FSH), and *luteinizing* hormone (LH)), and (f) *prolactin* or *lactogenic* hormone (in some species also gonadotrophic, and known as *luteotrophic* hormone (LTH)).[3]

The effects of hypophysectomy. The results of early work on hypophysectomy were complicated by the fact that the operation involved a trans-temporal intracranial approach to the gland, with the risk of concurrent damage to the hypothalamus. It was at first thought that removal of the pituitary was fatal within a few days. The development of the parapharyngeal operation by P. E. Smith, in which hypothalamic injury is avoided, showed that hypophysectomized animals may survive for long periods, though their life span is ultimately shortened. In this operation the gland is removed through a trephine hole in the base of the skull. The diaphragma sellae remains intact, and the infundibular stem and median eminence (of the neurohypophysis) and the pars tuberalis (of the adenohypophysis) are left *in situ*. These remnants may be sufficient to prevent signs of neurohypophysial deficiency (see below) but important abnormalities result from the loss of anterior lobe hormones. These are (a) arrested growth, (b) atrophy of the gonads and, indirectly, of the accessory organs of sex, (c) suppression of milk secretion and involution of the mammary glands, (d) atrophy of the thyroid and adrenal

[3] The Third International Conference on the Standardization of Hormones has recommended that the suffix -*tropic* in the adjective qualifying the hormones of the anterior pituitary be replaced by -*trophic* (see Collip), and that the termination -*trophin* be used in forming the name of the hormone (e.g., thyrotrophin). The suffix -*tropic* is from the Greek *trépein* to turn, and in this sense has been used in such terms as heliotropic, geotropic, etc. The suffix -*trophic* is derived from the Greek word *trophein*, to nourish or nurture and is, therefore, more appropriate as an ending for those pituitary hormones which affect the development and growth of other endocrines. The -*tropic* ending is also accepted usage.

cortex, (e) lowered metabolic rate, (f) a tendency to hypoglycemia, and an increased sensitivity to insulin and reduction in liver and muscle glycogen, and (g) depression of spontaneous activity, and diminished resistance to infections and shock. With the advent of hypophysectomy as a therapeutic procedure for mammary carcinoma and other conditions, many of these effects have been observed in the human, though the position here is usually complicated by the necessary replacement therapy with thyroxine and cortisone.

It may be mentioned that in some fish and in amphibia the loss of the pars intermedia hormone (intermedin) results in a silvery, albino appearance. This is due to contraction of the melanophores of the skin. No deficit due to loss of this hormone is known in mammals.

The Growth or Somatotrophic Hormone (STH)

The first indication that the pituitary gland exerts an effect on body growth came from the observations that human cases of acromegaly and gigantism commonly have pituitary tumors, and that hypophysectomized dogs (Crowe, Cushing, and Homans, 1910), tadpoles (Smith, 1916; Allen, 1916), and rats (Smith, 1930) show reduced body growth. In 1921, Evans and Long showed that injection of an extract of ox pituitary resulted in gigantism in rats.

Purified preparations of growth hormone have been prepared from pituitaries of a variety of mammals. Such preparations have been reported to be free from other active contaminants and to behave as a homogenous substance to various physicochemical tests. The hormone is a protein with a molecular weight of 40,000–50,000 (beef, pig, sheep and whale) and 20,000–30,000 (monkey, man). Thus different proteins perform the same function in different species. Growth hormone is species-specific; only primate growth hormone is active in the human. It has been found recently that human growth hormone has lactogenic activity as well as growth-stimulating activity; in this respect it differs from the growth hormone found in lower forms.

The source of growth hormone appears to be the acidophil cells of the anterior pituitary. The evidence is that acromegaly and gigantism in man are associated with oversecreting tumors (adenomata) of this cell type, and that pituitaries of dwarf mice are lacking in acidophils.

The loss of growth hormone resulting from hypophysectomy results in two main deficits in the organism—a reduction in the rate of body growth (fig. 74.7) and disturbances in metabolism, especially of proteins and carbohydrates. Growth does not always cease in the hypophysectomized animal, but may continue at a greatly reduced rate, perhaps 50 per cent of the normal. The fact that in the absence of the pituitary, mitotic figures appear in the mammary glands of parturient rats, and that hypertrophy of the remaining kidney follows unilateral nephrectomy, also demonstrates that STH is not the sole factor controlling growth. Growth of the hypophysectomized animal is favored, at least transiently, by the provision of a nutritious diet, by insulin administration, or by androgen therapy. Further, hypophysectomy affects the growth of some tissues more than others. Thus rats hypophysectomized at 6 days of age die at about 75 days, since growth of the skull fails to keep pace with that of the brain. Removal of the pituitary results in a striking increase in sensitivity to insulin. In some animals, such as rabbits, this results in a certain mortality from hypoglycemia during the first few days after operation. If placed on a restricted diet, hypophysectomized rats show a greater loss of body weight and a greater loss of body protein, but less of fat, than the controls. The deposition of protein is clearly an essential part of growth processes. The fasted hypophysectomized animal rapidly develops hypoglycemia and shows abnormally low liver and muscle glycogen stores.

FIG. 74.7. Hypophysectomized puppy (right) and litter mate control (left) 3 months after removal of the hypophysis when 3 weeks old. (From Dandy and Rickert.)

The effect of anterior pituitary extracts on growth was first demonstrated by Evans and Long. These workers found that an alkaline or saline extract of the gland when given daily by intraperitoneal injection (but not by mouth) extended the growth period beyond the normal limit. Some of these animals finally attained a size larger, by 100 per cent or more, than that of their untreated litter mates (fig. 74.8). The effect was usually greater in the female. Gigantism, acromegaly (p. 1521), and splanchnomegaly have been produced in bulldogs by Putnam, Benedict, and Teel. Airedales, Boston terriers, and dachshunds have been shown by others to respond to such an extract (fig. 74.7). Administration of growth hormone to adult rats produces more uniform body growth than in adult dogs. This is because the epiphysial cartilages of rats do not fuse so that the limbs retain the potentiality of growth in length (cf. the effect of acidophil adenomata in the immature and adult human). The width of the epiphysial cartilage is reduced after hypophysectomy. Growth hormone exerts a specific stimulating effect upon such a cartilage. The cartilage cells become enlarged, active osteoblasts appear, the whole plate becomes thicker, and a zone of newly formed bony trabeculae develops. Studies with radioactive calcium show that the rate of deposition of calcium in the cartilage is accelerated by STH. As might be expected, the stimulus to growth is accompanied by an increase in the body stores of protein and a positive nitrogen balance. The extra nitrogen stored under the influence of growth hormone is deposited as protein, mainly in the muscles. Some muscles of the rat have shown an increase of nitrogen content of as much as 60 per cent under these conditions. These changes are initiated quickly. Within a few hours after administration of STH to a fasted animal, the concentration of free amino acids in the blood and tissues decreases. That this is due to protein anabolism is shown by the simultaneous decrease in urea formation and excretion.

The anterior pituitary gland is related to carbo-

FIG. 74.8. Litter mate female dachshunds 11½ months old. HY-26 injected with growth hormone for 35 weeks; HY-27 control. (From Evans and associates.)

hydrate metabolism in many ways. Houssay first showed that dogs made diabetic by pancreatectomy showed a marked amelioration of the diabetes if subjected to hypophysectomy. Such a preparation, known as the *Houssay dog*, may live for long periods without insulin. They are, however, in a state of unstable equilibrium and easily become diabetic or hypoglycemic if subjected to adverse conditions. These observations show the antagonistic influences the pituitary and pancreatic secretions exert over carbohydrate metabolism. This fact was again emphasized by the classical work of Young, who showed that administration of anterior pituitary extracts to adult dogs and cats for periods of several weeks might result in a permanent state of diabetes mellitus. Such animals show severe damage of the pancreatic islet tissue. This early study, performed with crude pituitary extracts, raised several questions; is the diabetogenic activity a property of a known pituitary hormone or not? and, why are immature dogs and cats, as well as adult animals of some other species such as the rat, resistant to the diabetogenic activity of pituitary extracts? With the advent of purified extracts it became clear that diabetogenic effects are associated with the growth hormone. Diabetogenic action can be demonstrated even with the most highly purified preparation and is apparently a property of the growth hormone molecule itself. In reply to the second question, it has been suggested that the variability of the diabetogenic activity of STH in the young as opposed to the adult dog, and in different species, is due to variation in the capacity of the pancreas to secrete insulin. Administration of growth hormone results in certain metabolic effects which elicit increased secretion of insulin. If the pancreatic response is adequate then protein deposition and growth ensues. In the adult dog and cat, however, the pancreatic response fails, "exhaustion atrophy" of the islet tissue occurs, and a state of diabetes supervenes. In this context it may be noted that rats, which are resistant to the diabetogenic action of pituitary extracts, may respond to such extracts in the fasting states with a hypoglycemia; hypertrophy of pancreatic tissue may also occur. Administration of ACTH or adrenal cortical steroids results, in some respects, in effects similar to those induced by growth hormone. Thus adrenal cortical hormones increase gluconeogenesis and reduce the rate of glucose oxidation. If given to the fasting hypophysectomized animal the danger of hypoglycemia is reduced. Further, the effect of adrenalectomy on the carbohydrate metabolism

of pancreatectomized animals may be very similar to that of hypophysectomy. Thus, in considering the overall relationship of the endocrine glands to carbohydrate metabolism, the pituitary gland, through its secretion of STH and ACTH, exerts opposing actions to those of insulin. ACTH acts through the intermediation of the adrenal cortex, although STH acts directly and not through the intermediation of other glands.

In the early days when only crude anterior pituitary extracts were available, a number of actions of these extracts were ascribed to specific "factors." These, and their actions, may be enumerated as follows: (a) *Hyperglycemic factor*, causes an immediate increase in blood sugar; (b) *hypoglycemic* or *pancreatrophic factor*, decreases blood sugar from stimulation of the islet tissue of the pancreas; (c) *glycotropic factor*, inhibits the action of small doses of insulin; (d) *glycostatic factor*, maintains the muscle glycogen of fasting, hypophysectomized animals; (e) *ketogenic factor*, increases the ketosis of a fasting state; and (f) *fat-mobilizing factor*, increases liver fat and the metabolism of fat, at the expense of depot fats. It is probable, though, that these actions are not due to "factors" separate from the usually accredited pituitary hormones, but may be attributed to the actions of either STH or ACTH, or both.

Growth hormone preparations derived from ox or pig tissue have been disappointing in their effects on the primate. It now seems very likely that growth hormone is species specific, since extracts of primate origin have been found capable of causing marked nitrogen retention and the typical changes in carbohydrate metabolism in primates, whereas bovine and porcine preparations are inert in this regard. The effect of primate growth hormone on growth was first demonstrated by Knobil and his colleagues, using the histological changes in the costochondral junction of hypophysectomized monkeys as a test object. Treatment of pituitary dwarfs with somatotrophin prepared from human glands has been found to result in increased body growth.

The bioassay of pituitary growth hormone is best performed on the hypophysectomized rat. The ability of the hormone to increase the body weight, or to increase the width of the tibial epiphysial cartilage, may be utilized. The tibial cartilage assay is a specific and sensitive test, and may detect as little as 5 μg. of an active extract. Immunological methods have recently been applied for the assay of growth hormone, especially in human serum. The tanned red cell

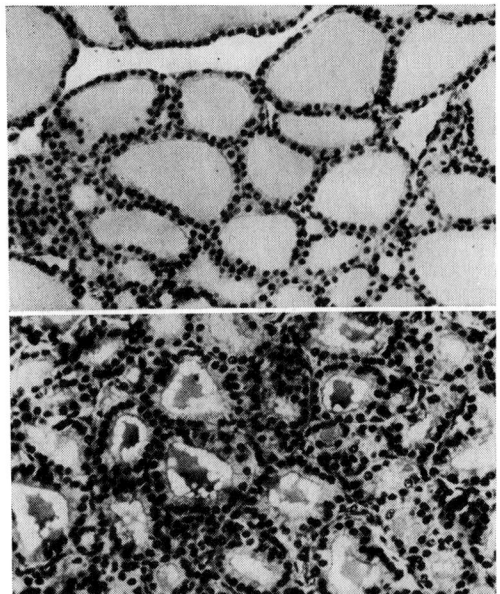

Fig. 74.9. Photomicrographs of sections through the thyroid gland of a normal dog (above) and a dog which had received seven daily injections of anterior pituitary extract containing thyrotrophin (below). (From Ham.)

hemagglutination inhibition test and radio immunological methods have given useful results, though they are hardly available for routine use.

The factors controlling secretion of STH are unknown. It is, indeed, debatable as to how actively this hormone is secreted in adult life. Young (1945) has suggested that growth hormone is secreted during conditions of starvation. This view is based on the fact that the metabolic pattern of an adult animal consuming a normal ration of food, but given anterior pituitary extract, is similar to that of a starving animal. Immunological assays have demonstrated a rise in serum growth hormone levels in man after insulin-induced hypoglycemia, fasting and muscular exercise. The data available suggests that secretion of STH is under hypothalamic control, since transplantation of the pituitary to a site remote from the sella turcica leads to marked retardation of body growth, and since hypothalamic lesions may be followed by signs of interference with growth and carbohydrate metabolism which may be rectified by administration of growth hormone.

The Thyrotrophic Hormone, Thyrotrophin, Thyroid Stimulating Hormone (TSH)

A functional relationship between the pituitary gland and thyroid was suspected during the last century after it had been found that thyroidectomy results in histological changes in the pars distalis. The effect of hypophysectomy in preventing metamorphosis of the tadpole was ascribed by Adler (1914) to the associated atrophy of the thyroid. Smith showed clearly that replacement therapy (pituitary implants) would repair the atrophic thyroid gland of the hypophysectomized rat. An acid extract of the anterior pituitary was then prepared (Loeb and Bassett; Aron) which was found to have thyroid stimulating properties on injection.

The cells of origin of TSH in the anterior pituitary are basophilic, and stain with the periodic acid-Schiff technique. They are centrally situated in the pars distalis of the rat and are angular and polyhedral in shape.

Several procedures are available for obtaining TSH in a highly purified state, though it has not yet been established that the preparations are entirely free from other pituitary hormones or that they are chemically homogenous. The data indicates that TSH is a protein with a molecular weight of about 28,000, and that the molecule probably contains a carbohydrate moiety. It is inactivated by proteolytic enzymes and must be administered by injection.

The thyrotrophic hormone exerts a powerful controlling influence over the activity of the thyroid gland, and has also been implicated as having a direct action in the development of exophthalmos in certain pathological states. The thyroid gland extracts iodide ions from the blood stream, combines these organically, and stores its hormonal activity as a protein known as thyroglobulin. From this protein, thyroxine and tri-iodothyronine are liberated into the blood stream to stimulate the metabolism of nearly every tissue in the body. Hypophysectomy does not abolish thyroid function completely, but greatly reduces it. In man, hypophysectomy results, within some weeks, in a condition of thyroid deficiency known as myxedema. The thyroidal changes resulting from removal of the pituitary may be summarized as follows: (a) Reduction in size, weight, and vascularization, (b) histological changes, notably a reduction in the height of the epithelial cells of the acini, and an increased amount of acinar colloid, (fig. 74.9) and (c) a reduction in all the chemical processes of iodine metabolism in the gland. The uptake of iodide ions from the blood, conveniently measured as a thyroid:serum (T:S) ratio (ch. 75) may be reduced in the rat from values of about a 100 to about 2. The organic binding of iodine in the gland and the liberation of iodine containing hormones from the gland are also markedly depressed by hypophysectomy. These changes are all reversible by the administration of an exogenous TSH extract. Not only may the state and function of the gland of the hypophysectomized animal be returned to normal, but injection of excessive doses of TSH result in a hyperplastic thyroid and signs of hyperthyroidism. The gland enlarges and becomes hypervascular. The acinar cells show hypertrophy and hyperplasia with a reversal in the polarity of the mitochondria and Golgi apparatus. The colloid undergoes a peripheral vacuolization, a change in its staining properties so that it appears basophilic instead of eosinophilic and becomes reduced in amount as the stored hormone is liberated into the blood in increased amounts. As the blood concentration of thyroid hormones rises, signs of thyrotoxicosis ensue. An increased metabolic rate, sweating, nervousness, tremor, and cardiac irregularities have been reported in the human. The above changes do not occur simultaneously after administration of TSH. Within half an hour of TSH injection there is, in the experimental animal, an increase of proteolytic enzyme in the follicles and an increased release of thyroidal hormone as detected by examination of thyroid vein blood. Some 8 hours or so later an increase in the rate of uptake of iodine from the blood occurs. The different time relationships of these processes are shown in figure 74.10. The enlargement of the gland and the signs of hyperthyroidism take longer to develop.

Thyrotrophic hormone acts directly on the thyroid gland and probably on intraorbital tissues. Patients with a diffuse enlargement of the thyroid gland and signs of thyrotoxicosis often show exophthalmos. This protrusion of the eyes is characterized by edema and a lymphocytic and fatty infiltration with fibrosis of the retrobulbar tissues. A similar state of the eyes has been produced in normal and thyroidectomized guinea pigs by injection of extracts rich in TSH, and on these grounds it has been suggested that in Graves' disease both the thyroidal disturbance and the exophthalmos are due to direct actions of TSH. Since in these cases blockage of thyroid activity by thyroid-inhibiting drugs, or thyroidectomy (procedures which increase TSH secretion in the normal animal) are often followed by an increase in the severity of the exophthalmos, and since administration of large doses of adrenal corticoids or pituitary stalk section (procedures

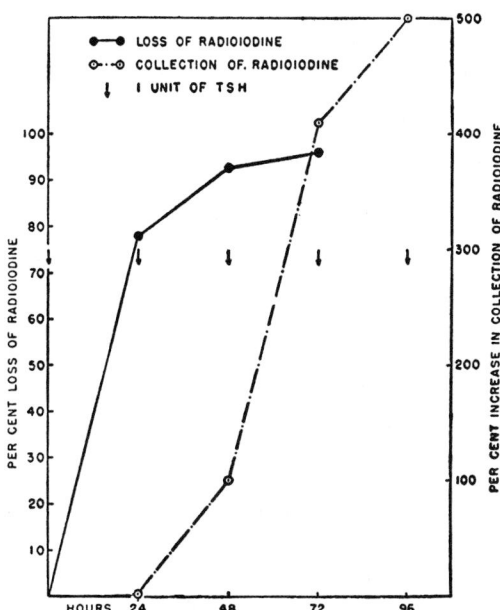

FIG. 74.10. Showing the percentile loss of radioiodine from and the delayed increase in radioiodine in the thyroid under influence of TSH. (From Rawson.)

which decrease the secretion of TSH in the normal animal) have been reported to decrease or abolish the exophthalmos, indirect support for this view is forthcoming. However, McCullagh, who has critically examined the evidence, points out that thyroidectomy or myxedema in previously normal subjects does not lead to the development of exophthalmos. A possible explanation of the pituitary relationship to exophthalmos comes from the work of Dobyns and his collaborators. It has previously been found that a marked exophthalmic state developed in Fundulus, the common Atlantic "minnow," following administration of small amounts of anterior pituitary extract. Using this animal as a test for exophthalmic producing substance (EPS), Dobyns found it possible to separate TSH and EPS in pituitary extracts by means of their different solubilities in trichloracetic acid. TSH was obtained free from EPS, although the EPS fraction still contained some TSH activity. The evidence is suggestive then that an exophthalmos producing principle is often, though not always, liberated in association with TSH. Recent work on the long active thyroid stimulator (LATS), a substance found in the blood of thyrotoxic and exophthalmic patients and which may not be of pituitary origin, raises the question of a causal relationship between LATS and exophthalmos.

Species differences exist in the quantity of TSH stored in the pituitary gland and in the sensitivity of the thyroid gland to a given dose of TSH. The anterior pituitary content of thyrotrophic hormone of several forms has been given, in ascending order, as follows: guinea pig, chick, cat, rabbit, man, ox, sheep, pig, dog, mouse, and rat. The guinea pig and chick thus have a low TSH content in their anterior pituitaries but more sensitive thyroids than the other forms. They are, therefore, animals of choice for assay of TSH preparations. On the other hand, the rat, which normally has a more active thyroid, is less sensitive to administration of TSH.

A refractory state to the action of TSH develops after repeated administration of thyrotrophic extracts obtained from a different species. This state has been shown by Collip and Anderson to be due to the formation of some inhibiting substance (antihormone; see p. 1510) which they found in the serum of the treated animals. The injection of bovine TSH into rabbits, for example, results in the production of antibodies to this TSH preparation. The rabbit antiserum can neutralize the biological activity of the bovine hormone. This again emphasizes the species-specificity of these protein hormones.

Many *assay methods* are available for measuring the TSH content of materials rich in thyrotrophic activity. Few of these methods however will detect or measure the amounts of TSH normally present in body fluids. The increase in weight of the thyroid gland in immature male guinea pigs, the increase in mean cell height of the thyroidal epithelium of few-day-old chicks, the increase in uptake of I^{131} by the thyroid glands of young rats (in which thyroidal activity has been depressed below normal by previous feeding with iodinated casein) and other criteria of thyrotrophic activity have been utilized as a basis for assay methods. The "stasis tadpole" method of D'Angelo is among the most sensitive. The starved tadpole develops thyroid atrophy and a consequent arrest of metamorphosis. Injection of TSH, in about 1:100th the amount detectable in the young guinea pig, produces histological changes in the thyroid gland. Other, recently published methods for which high degrees of sensitivity are claimed involve the release of radioactive hormone from the thyroid gland of the guinea pig or mouse (McKenzie assay), and the I^{131} turnover in the guinea pig thyroid cultured *in vitro*. The development of an immune-type assay method may solve many problems in the future. A method that would accurately determine TSH levels in body fluids would be of great value in the study of the factors determining the rate of TSH release in the normal

animal and might throw light on the etiology and changes occurring in hypo- and hyperthyroid states in man. It should be emphasized that the thyrotrophic activity of any given sample is best expressed in terms of the recently established (1955) International Unit (I.U.). The International Unit is approximately equal to the pre-existing national (USP) Unit and is defined as the activity of 13.5 mg. of an international standard powdered preparation.

TSH is rapidly inactivated and excreted from the body. Using the stasis tadpole technique D'Angelo calculated that only 3 per cent of an injected dose was present in the blood of a rat at the end of 1 hour, and 1 per cent at 5 hours. The fate of the hormone is uncertain. Since it disappears from the blood of thyroidectomized animals more slowly than intact animals, and since *in vitro* tests show that thyroid (and lymphatic and thymic) tissue inactivates thyrotrophin, it is possible that it is inactivated by its own target gland.

The regulation of the release of TSH from the anterior pituitary gland is influenced by two chief factors, (a) the blood concentration of thyroid hormone, and (b) nervous influences from the hypothalamus. As described earlier, the blood concentration of hormones from the pituitary target glands determines, within limits, the rate of secretion of the appropriate pituitary trophic hormone. Thus a rise in concentration of thyroid hormone in the blood depresses the secretion of TSH, and a fall in concentration increases TSH release. This homeostatic or feed-back mechanism may be illustrated in several ways. A fall in level of thyroid hormone in the blood may be brought about by administration of a goitrogenic drug (which blocks the synthesis of thyroid hormone in the gland). Under these conditions the thyroid becomes depleted of colloid, shows hypertrophy and goiter formation, and all the signs of thyrotrophic activation. Such does not occur if the drug is administered to the hypophysectomized animal, or to an animal receiving large doses of thyroxine. Dempsey and Astwood (1943) used these observations to study the rate of release of thyroid hormone at various environmental temperatures. Thiouracil-treated rats were exposed to temperatures of 1°, 25°, and 35°C., and the least amount of thyroxine to maintain a normal thyroid histology was estimated. It was found that the daily dose required was 9.5 μg. at 1°, 5.2 μg. at 25°, and 1.7 μg. at 35°C. These experiments demonstrate the amount of exogenous thyroxine required to maintain the pituitary-thyroid equilibrium under varying environmental conditions. The decreased secretion of TSH which follows a rise in blood level of thyroid hormone is shown by the thyroidal inhibition which follows administration of thyroxine to the normal animal. This has been clearly observed in the rabbit, in which the rate of release of radioactive hormone from the thyroid was studied. It was found that the release of thyroid hormone was inhibited within 2 hours by injection of thyroxine, and that a dose of about 15 μg. per day was required to suppress thyroid function. This amount of thyroxine then appears to be the equivalent of the daily secretion of the thyroid in this species.

The hypothalamus regulates the pituitary secretion of thyrotrophic hormone through a mechanism involving the hypophysial portal vessels of the pituitary stalk. If the pituitary stalk is cut, or if the pituitary gland is transplanted to a distant site in the body, the activity of the thyroid is decreased, and various environmental influences which previously modified thyroid function are now without effect. The hypothalamus appears to exert a tonic influence in maintaining the basal level of thyrotrophic secretion and, by means of nervous reflexes, to modify TSH release in accord with the requirements of the environment. Thus, stress stimuli of an emotional or nervous type which normally inhibit TSH release, and the stimulus of a cold environment which normally excites TSH release, no longer do so after the pituitary is disconnected from the central nervous system. The influence of the hypothalamus on TSH secretion or thyroid activity has recently been investigated with regard to the effects produced by localized hypothalamic lesions and electrical stimulation. It has been found that lesions in the anterior hypothalamus, in the region of the supraopticohypophysial tract result in reduced thyroid function, whereas stimulation of approximately the same site results in an increase in thyroid activity. Electrical stimulation of this area has also been shown to cause an increased blood level of TSH in rats and rabbits.

Two questions arise from the above discussion. First, whether the feed-back effects of thyroid hormone act through the intermediation of the hypothalamus, and second, whether feed-back or neural influences take priority in the normal animal. The evidence relating to the former problem is indeterminate. The effect of the blood level of thyroxine in regulating TSH output is still apparent in the pituitary stalk-cut, or pituitary transplanted animal. However hypothalamic lesions decrease the sensitivity of the animal to the goitrogenic action of propylthiouracil (Greer), or to the effects of hemithyroidectomy (Reichlin). It may be that the feed-back system operates at both a hypothalamic and pituitary level and that in the normal animal the hypothalamus forms the more sensitive receptor mechanism. The answer to the second question is more certain. Presently available evidence indicates that the feed-back system acts to stabilize thyroid function at a particular level and that the nervous system superimposes its action on this baseline. Thus, as Brown-Grant has shown, emotional stress in the rabbit is associated with a decrease in thyroid activity *at the same time* as there occurs a fall in thyroid hormone in the blood. Conversely Harris and Woods have found that electrical stimulation of the hypothalamus results in a marked and maintained increase in thyroid activity in spite of a rise of blood concentration of thyroid hormone.

The Adrenocorticotrophic Hormone (ACTH), Corticotrophin

Since the early work of Smith, it has become firmly established that the adrenal cortex is under the control of a hormone secreted by the anterior pituitary gland. Smith found that atrophy of the adrenal cortex occurred in the hypophysectomized rat and that repair took place under the influence of pituitary implants.

It is uncertain which cells of the anterior pituitary secrete ACTH. The observations of Cushing that a certain clinical entity characterized by adrenal cortical hypertrophy and overactivity was associated with a "basophil" adenoma of the pituitary led many workers to cite a basophil origin of this hormone. Recent studies of the human gland have indicated that under acute conditions of stress, in which it is known that ACTH is secreted in increased amounts, a basophil degranulation occurs with recovery under chronic conditions. However, other studies on the cytology of the rat pituitary, under a wide variety of experimental conditions, have not succeeded in establishing a correlation between ACTH secretion and any particular cell type.

Collip and his colleagues (1933) were the first to prepare an extract from the anterior pituitary which acted specifically upon the adrenal cortex. This extract was highly effective in restoring to normal the atrophied adrenal cortex of hypophysectomized animals. A protein with high corticotrophic activity was isolated by Li and his associates in 1942, and by Sayers and his colleagues in

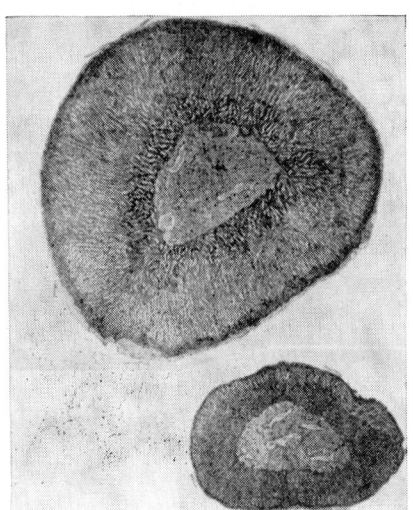

FIG. 74.11. Showing adrenal atrophy following hypophysectomy. Normal gland (above) and gland of hypophysectomized animal (below). (From P. Smith.)

1943. These extracts were found to have a molecular weight of around 20,000. The technique of Astwood and his colleagues, who employed oxycellulose to adsorb and purify adrenocorticotrophin, enables a large polypeptide (or small protein) to be extracted from these original preparations. This polypeptide retains all the physiological activity and is about 100 times as active as the starting protein extract. It has now been found that ACTH of pig, sheep, beef and human origin consists of a chain of 39 amino-acids. The first 24 amino-acids in the chain, starting from the NH₂-terminal end, are identical in all four species and there are only slight differences in the remaining sequences. It is in the first 24 amino-acids that the full biological activity of ACTH seems to reside. The first 13 amino-acids of ACTH show a similar sequence to that of MSH, which accounts for some melanocyte-

stimulating activity on the part of ACTH. ACTH is fairly resistant to pepsin but destroyed by trypsin. It is almost inactive when given by mouth. The most effective route of administration is by slow intravenous infusion. If injected subcutaneously or intramuscularly the effect of a given dose is increased if the extract is mixed with a diluent that slows absorption, such as beeswax and oil or gelatin.

The physiological activities of ACTH may be divided into those indirect functions which are dependent on stimulation of the target gland, and those direct activities which possibly occur in the absence of the adrenal cortex.

Adrenal activities. Hypophysectomy results in adrenal cortical atrophy, although the different zones of the cortex atrophy to different degrees. Greep and Deane emphasize that the zona glomerulosa of the rat remains well developed after hypophysectomy, and other workers have reported somewhat similar findings in the dog. Greep correlates this fact with the relatively intact electrolyte metabolism found in the hypophysectomized, but not adrenalectomized, animal and suggests that the zona glomerulosa is responsible for secreting aldosterone (see p. 1571) and that this function is largely free from pituitary control. It has recently been shown by *in vitro* methods that the outer zone of the adrenal cortex synthesizes aldosterone at a higher rate than other parts. The zona fasciculata shows marked thinning after hypophysectomy, loses much of its lipoid material and develops a characteristic sudanophobic zone. These changes are all reversible by administration of ACTH. The injection of ACTH into the hypophysectomized or normal animal, or the exposure of the normal animal to stressful or noxious stimuli (known to evoke ACTH discharge from the pituitary) results in the reverse changes. Thus administration of ACTH induces (a) increased size of the adrenal

Ser-Tyr-Ser-Met-Glu-His-Phe-Arg-Try-Gly-Lys-Pro-Val-Gly-Lys-Lys-Arg-Arg-Pro-Val-Lys-Val-Tyr--
1   2   3   4   5   6   7   8   9 10 11 12 13 14 15 16 17 18 19 20 21 22 23

Beef	Phe-Glu-Leu-Pro-Phe-Ala-	(NH₂)Glu-Ala-Ser-Asp-Glu-Ala-Glu-Gly-Asp-	Pro- - - - - -
	39 38 37 36 35 34	33 32 31 30 29 28 27 26 25	24
Pig	Phe-Glu-Leu-Pro-Phe-Ala-	(NH₂)Glu-Ala-Leu-Glu-Asp-Glu-Ala-Gly-Asp-	Pro- - - - - - -
	39 38 37 36 35 34	33 32 31 30 29 28 27 26 25	24
Sheep	Phe-Glu-Leu-Pro-Phe-Ala-	(NH₂)Glu-Ser-Ala-Glu-Asp-Asp-Glu-Gly-Ala-	Pro- - - - - -
	39 38 37 36 35 34	33 32 31 30 29 28 27 26 25	24

The structure of ACTH in three species. The amino-acid sequence in positions 1–23 are common. The amino-acids in positions 1–13 have common sequences with MSH (see p. 1513) and endow the hormone with MSH potency. Sequences 25–33 show the species variations in the molecule.

which may be detectable within a few hours, (b) a depletion of the ascorbic acid content of the adrenal within 15 to 30 minutes (the exact physiological significance of this response is unknown, but it forms the basis of an assay method for ACTH), (c) a fall in concentration of adrenal cholesterol and stainable lipoid (it is now known that cholesterol is a precursor of the adrenal steroids, so that the fall in adrenal cholesterol presumably reflects increased hormonal synthesis), and (d) an increased release of adrenal steroids as detected by assay of adrenal vein blood (this is a rapid response, occurring within a few minutes, and is associated with an increased blood flow through the gland). In general, it may be said that the adrenal cortex secretes three groups of steroids; glucocorticoids, mineralocorticoids, and androgenic steroids. It is of interest that administration of ACTH may affect the type of glucocorticoid secreted in a particular species. Thus the rabbit, which normally secretes corticosterone, releases predominantly hydrocortisone after chronic treatment with corticotrophin. There has been much discussion as to the control the pituitary exerts over aldosterone secretion. It seems established that aldosterone release is less dependent on pituitary adrenocorticotrophin than is the release of the glucocorticoids. Aldosterone output is reduced, but not to such a marked degree as that of the glucocorticoids by hypophysectomy in the dog or cat, and the effect of administration of ACTH on aldosterone secretion is reported as inconstant or small in comparison with the effect on glucocorticoid secretion. Little is known about the regulation of secretion of adrenal androgens. 17-ketosteroids have been found in the adrenal vein blood of the dog and man, but their physiological role is uncertain. In certain pathological states of virilism in young girls, the androgenic secretion of the adrenal cortex seems to be maintained by pituitary ACTH, since Wilkins has found that administration of cortisone (which inhibits ACTH release through the feed-back mechanism) may control the disease.

The quantitative aspects of ACTH control of glucocorticoid secretion has been studied most carefully in the dog. Hypophysectomy lowers the amount of 17-hydroxycorticosterone (F) in adrenal vein blood, whereas injection of a large intravenous dose of ACTH (20 to 40 units), or surgical trauma, raises the 17-hydroxycorticosterone secretion from a resting figure of about 7 μg. per kilogram per hour to about 50 μg. per kilogram per hour. It should be pointed out that under certain conditions the adrenal cortex is relatively resistant to the action of ACTH. The atrophic adrenal consequent to hypophysectomy, a hypopituitary state or to chronic blockade of ACTH release by cortisone, is insensitive to ACTH and may require several days of corticotrophin administration before normal sensitivity is regained. States of adrenal cortical deficiency may be encountered clinically if cortisone therapy is stopped too suddenly.

Certain extra-adrenal activities of ACTH have been described from time to time. It is now known that many of these were due to impurities in the extracts used. However ACTH does have melanophore-stimulating actions as an intrinsic property of its molecule. This is due to the fact that a certain amino acid sequence in the polypeptide chains is common to both β-corticotrophin and melanophore-stimulating hormone (MSH). The present known preparations of ACTH also seem to possess fat-mobilizing (adipokinetic) activity and ketogenic activity.

The physiological actions observed after administration of ACTH are very largely those mediated by the adrenal cortex, and chapter 76 may be consulted for an account of these. Minor differences in the effects observed after ACTH or hydrocortisone administration in the human have been reported. ACTH therapy is said to be followed by a greater degree of salt and water retention, and by a greater incidence of virilizing manifestations. These effects may be due to the stimulation of secretion of aldosterone and androgenic steroids, as well as of 17-hydroxycorticosterone, by ACTH.

The *assay* of ACTH is dependent on biological methods. These may be divided into those employing intact or hypophysectomized animals, although *in vitro* procedures have been newly proposed. It is probably inadvisable to rely upon methods using intact animals in view of the ease in which endogenous ACTH can be discharged by such trivial stress stimuli as those associated with handling or with injection. However, the use of animals in which the release of ACTH has been blocked with DOCA has been proposed as an alternative to hypophysectomy (Buttle and Hodges). The more important methods include: (a) *Ascorbic acid depletion test* (Sayers' test) in which the left adrenals of male rats (120 to 180 grams) are removed 24 hours after hypophysectomy. The hormone preparation is then given intravenously and the right adrenal removed 1 hour later. Both adrenals are analyzed for ascorbic acid and the response is calculated as the difference in ascorbic acid between the right and left glands. As little as 0.2 milliunits of the international standard can be detected by this method. (b) The *repair test:* in this case the quantity of ACTH required in a 4-day period to restore the normal histological appearance of the adrenal cortex of 28-day-old female rats hypophysectomized 14 days previously is determined. (c) The *maintenance test:* a unit of ACTH as defined by this test is the amount required over a period of 15 days to maintain the preoperative weight of hypophysectomized 40-day-old male rats. (d) *Corticosteroid release:* hypophysectomized dogs are maintained on ACTH until about 16 hours before the assay. For the assay the adrenal vein is cannulated, samples of adrenal vein blood are collected at intervals and the corticosteroid content determined by the Porter-Silber reaction. The effect of ACTH preparations may then be directly compared with a standard by means of the increase in corticosteroid output induced (Nelson and Hume). A similar assay using the hypophysectomized rat has recently been introduced. A log-dose relationship is obtained between 0.05–1.0 mU. ACTH. (e) *Release of corticosteroids in vitro:* rat adrenal glands are cut into pieces and the fragments incubated with ACTH preparations in a Warburg apparatus. The steroids released are extracted from the medium and assayed by chemical means. It has been suggested that since the results obtained by the adrenal weight method and the Sayers' method do not give parallel findings for some pituitary extracts that there are two corticotrophins, an "adrenal weight factor" and an "adrenal ascorbic acid depletion factor." The different results obtained by the two methods are perhaps more easily explained by the different routes of administration of the extracts used in the two assays. Amounts of ACTH should be expressed quantitatively in terms of the international standard. The International Standard powder of purified pig corticotrophin has an activity of 100 IU/mg. when given by subcutaneous injection.

The *inactivation* of ACTH occurs very rapidly in the body. It is not excreted in the urine though appreciable amounts of an administered dose may be recovered from kidney tissue. The half-life of the hormone in the blood of the rat is about 1 minute.

The regulation of the secretion of ACTH by the anterior pituitary has been intensively investigated since it became realized that release of the hormone at increased rates was one of the organism's defense reactions to stress or trauma, and that ACTH given in large pharmacological doses was of use in rheumatoid arthritis, in other so-called collagen diseases, and in various allergic disorders. As with most other pituitary trophic hormones the secretion of ACTH appears to be controlled by two main factors, the feed-back of its target gland hormones (the adrenal steroids) and by an influence from the central nervous system *via* the hypothalamus. In the following discussion two points should be borne in mind. First, the adrenal cortex of the *hypophysectomized* animal still secretes sufficient steroids (aldosterone especially) to maintain life under optimal conditions, and second, the pituitary gland removed from the influence of the central nervous system still secretes basal amounts of ACTH. Thus both the adrenal cortex and anterior pituitary possess some autonomous secretory activity and it is against this background that the factors regulating ACTH secretion have to be studied. It was at one time claimed that the feed-back mechanism of the adrenal cortical hormones was sufficient to regulate the output of ACTH under resting conditions and also under conditions of stress (starvation, cold exposure, infection, tissue damage, emotional excitement, etc.) in which corticotrophin secretion is greatly increased. It was argued that stressful stimuli increased the tissue utilization of adrenal cortical hormones, that the blood concentration of these hormones was thereby decreased, and that *via* the feed-back action the liberation of ACTH was augmented, leading to increased adrenal cortical activity. (There can be no doubt that an increased blood level of adrenal steroids tends to suppress ACTH release and *vice versa*). Arguments against this view are: the lack of evidence that noxious influences do in fact increase the tissue utilization of adrenal corticoids, and that if this mechanism holds true then it would seem impossible for the organism to maintain an increased blood concentration of adrenal steroids for any length of time. That this hypothesis does not represent the whole story was shown most convincingly by Sydnor and Sayers (1954). These workers developed a method for assaying the blood level of ACTH in rats. It was found that adrenalectomized rats had a higher level than that of normal rats (which was undetectable by the method) and that stress stimuli (ether anesthesia, scalding, bleeding) had a rapid and dramatic effect in increasing the blood ACTH concentration in both normal and adrenalectomized animals. It is clear that the stress stimuli could not have affected ACTH secretion by a feed-back action in the adrenalectomized rats. It is likely that the servo mechanism acts rather as a stabilizing system to maintain a constancy of adrenal cortical function at any set level. The most potent influence in maintaining the normal rate of ACTH secretion, and in increasing this rate under conditions of stress, appears to be derived from the hypothalamus. Reasons for this statement are as follows: (a) Separation of the pituitary from the hypothalamus by section of the pituitary stalk and the placement of a plate between the stalk ends, or by pituitary transplantation, results in adrenal cortical atrophy (though the ultimate size of the gland is somewhat greater than that of the hypophysectomized animal), (b) hypothalamic lesions have been found to result in a diminution of ACTH concentration in systemic blood, a diminution of 17-hydroxycorticosteroids in adrenal vein blood, a loss of the compensatory hypertrophy which follows unilateral adrenalectomy, and abolition of the adrenal cortical response to stress stimuli, (c) administration of morphine has been found to blockade the ACTH release evoked by such stress stimuli as injection of histamine or unilateral adrenalectomy (it seems likely that morphine exerts this effect by an action on the nervous system), and (d) electrical stimulation of the hypothalamus results in increased corticoids in adrenal vein blood and in signs of increased adrenal cortical activity (lymphopenia, eosinopenia, decreased adrenal ascorbic acid, and histological changes in the sudanophilic material of the adrenal cortex). The pathway by which the hypothalamus affects the activity of the pars distalis is a vascular one: the portal vessels of the pituitary stalk. The exact mechanism is unknown although evidence is accumulating that it involves the transmission of a humoral agent from the tuber cinereum to the anterior pituitary.

One corollary to the above discussion should be added. Stressful stimuli which involve tissue damage or metabolic disturbance still evoke ACTH discharge even when the pituitary gland is separated from the nervous system. On these grounds, Fortier originally divided stresses into two types: neural (emotional excitement, uncomfortable noise, pain, fright), acting on the anterior pituitary solely through the nervous system, and systemic (involving surgical trauma and changes in the composition of the circulating systemic blood), which can act directly on anterior pituitary cells without the mediation of the nervous system. In the intact animal the neural component probably plays a part in the response to both types of stimuli. As pointed out by Fortier, and later by Sayers, this distinction may involve not a difference of modality, but one of intensity, of the stresses used in the original experiments. Thus, a pituitary stalk cut animal may liberate enough "humoral transmitter" from the tuber

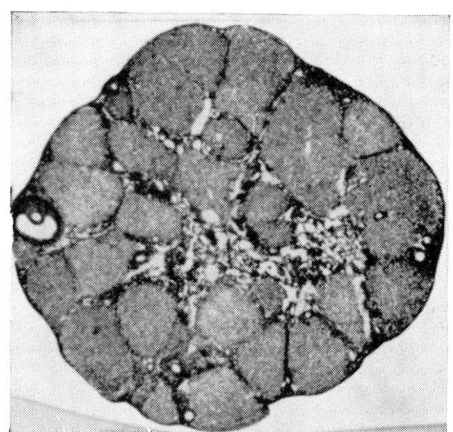

Fig. 74.12. Ovary of adult mouse injected with alkaline extract of anterior lobe of pituitary. Large numbers of corpora lutea are present, and few follicles. (From Parkes, *The Internal Secretions of the Ovary*, by permission of Longmans, Green & Co.)

cinereum, in response to a severe stress, to be carried around the general circulation to affect corticotrophin release by the pituitary gland.

Gonadotrophic Hormones, Gonadotrophins (Follicle-Stimulating Hormone, FSH; Luteinizing Hormone, LH, or Interstitial-Cell Stimulating Hormone, ICSH)

Several observations in the past have pointed to extraovarian factors as regulators of ovarian activity. After removal of one ovary the same number of follicles develop in the remaining ovary as in the original pair (law of follicular constancy). The fact that ovaries from immature animals grafted into the adult, or ovaries from adult animals grafted into the immature, behave according to the age of the recipient host, indicated that ovarian function was controlled humorally by some substance external to the ovary itself. This hypothetical substance was termed "generative ferment" by Heape, and "X substance" by other early workers. The gradual atrophy and suppression of sex functions which occurs with diseases of the anterior pituitary in man (acromegaly, Frohlich's syndrome) and the atrophy of the gonads after hypophysectomy in animals, indicated the pituitary as the source of this substance. A firm basis for this belief was established by the following observations: (a) Evans and his associates found that a crude saline extract of the anterior lobe caused luteinization of ovarian follicles (fig. 74.12), (b) Smith and Engle observed that when *fresh* mammalian anterior lobe tissue was implanted daily into imma-

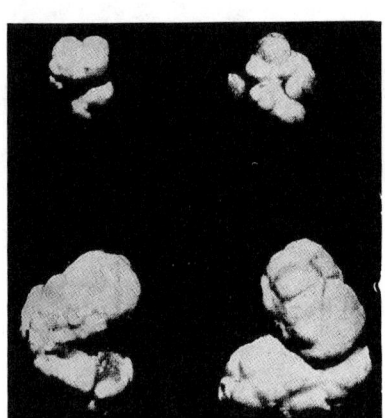

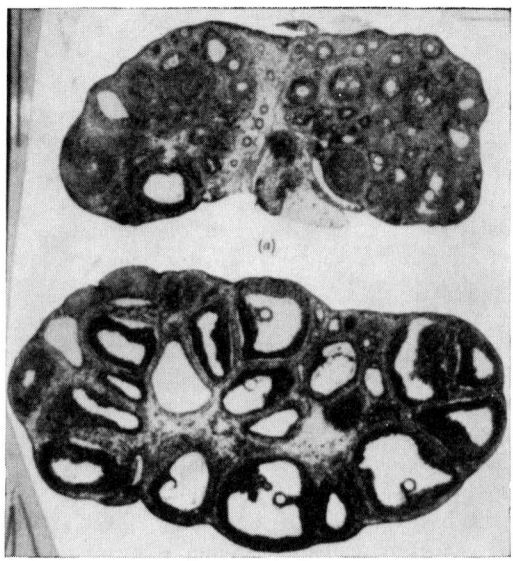

FIG. 74.13. Showing effect of anterior pituitary upon ovaries. On left (below), ovaries of rat after 12 implantations of fresh rat pituitary gland; (above) ovaries of litter mate control rat. (From Collip.) On right (below), follicular maturation induced in immature rat on 29th day by eight daily implantations of fresh pituitary gland; (above) ovary of litter mate control. (From Smith and Engle.)

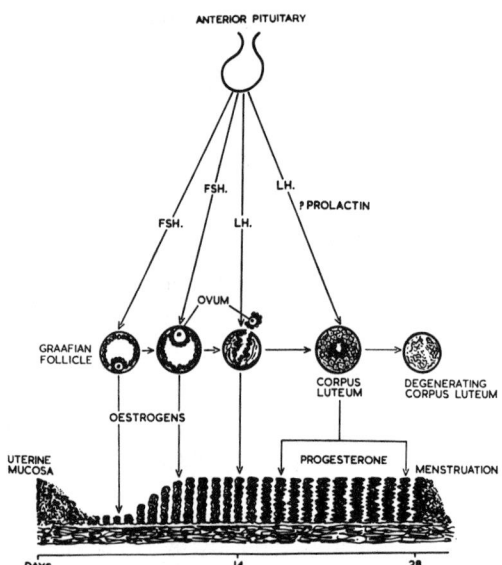

FIG. 74.14. Diagram summarizing the relationships of the anterior pituitary, ovary, and endometrium through the menstrual cycle.

ture female rats or mice, estrus was precipitated and ovulation followed. The ovaries and uterus showed enlargement to about 5 to 10 times normal size (fig. 74.13), the ovaries discharged an excessive number of ova (superovulation) and the solid vaginal canal (typical of the immature rat or mouse) developed a lumen. In immature male animals, the testes, seminal vesicles, and penis were stimulated to increased growth. Further,

the gonadal atrophy which followed hypophysectomy was prevented by anterior lobe implants, (c) Ascheim and Zondek first found that injection of the blood or urine of pregnant women into immature rats caused follicular development, ovulation, and luteinization. They termed this substance Prolan. It has since been found that Prolan originates in the chorion of the placenta (*human chorionic gonadotrophin*, HCG) and not in the pituitary and that its action is mainly luteinizing, and (d) the discovery that the urine of menopausal women, or of castrated men and women, contains a substance which stimulates the ovary. This substance is probably of pituitary origin and its main action is follicle-stimulating. It is now generally held that the pituitary secretes two, if not three, gonadotrophic hormones. The first is concerned with ripening of the ovarian follicles (FSH) or spermatogenesis, the second with ovulation, luteinization, and maintenance of the interstitial tissue of the gonads (LH or ICSH), and possibly a third that maintains luteal activity (*prolactin* or *luteotrophic hormone*, LTH).

A detailed account of the reproductive processes may be found in chapter 78. A summary of the events occurring during a sexual cycle is given in figure 74.14. As a basis for discussion it may be said that at the beginning of a sexual cycle, when the ovary and the uterus are in a resting phase, the pituitary liberates FSH. Under the influence of this hormone, follicles ripen in the ovary and estrogen secretion occurs. This in turn produces development of the uterus and other parts of the reproductive tract. At about the 14th day of the cycle in the human, release of LH occurs and under the continued action of LH and FSH, a ripe follicle ruptures, and a corpus luteum develops. This in turn secretes progesterone which results in secretory activity of the endometrium and characteristic changes in uterine muscle reactivity. In some forms luteal secretion is dependent upon prolactin release from the pituitary but this has not been established for primates. Thus the changes typical of the first, follicular, half of the sex cycle are regulated by FSH release from the pituitary and of the second, luteal, half of the cycle by LH (and possibly LTH release).

The origin of the gonadotrophic hormones in the anterior pituitary lies in the basophil cells (see p. 1487).

The chemical separation of pituitary extracts into two gonadotrophic fractions was first accomplished by Fevold, Hisaw, and Leonard in 1931. Since then several methods have been developed for obtaining either FSH or LH in a highly purified form. It is perhaps doubtful whether FSH has been obtained entirely free from LH. It is possible that some LH activity may be a property of the FSH molecule. It is also debatable whether the pituitary secretes one hormone with multiple gonadotrophic activities or two hormones with actions comparable to those of the present chemical extracts. FSH is a glycoprotein, rich in carbohydrate. Its hormonal activity is destroyed by ptyalin and takadiastase, so that its activity may be dependent on the integrity of the carbohydrate fraction of the molecule. It is not destroyed by trypsin, however, a fact which has been utilized in one method to separate it from LH. Purified preparations have been obtained from both sheep and swine pituitary tissue. It is of interest that the preparation derived from these two sources behave alike biologically but may differ chemically. The molecular weight of pig FSH has been given as 29,000. LH is also a glycoprotein but its biological activity is not destroyed by ptyalin. It has likewise been prepared in a purified state from sheep and swine pituitaries; the material obtained from the two sources showing different physicochemical and immunological properties. For example, pig LH has a molecular weight of about 100,000 and sheep LH about 40,000.

The physiological properties of FSH and LH extracts are best investigated in hypophysectomized animals using biologically pure preparations. This is even more important in the study

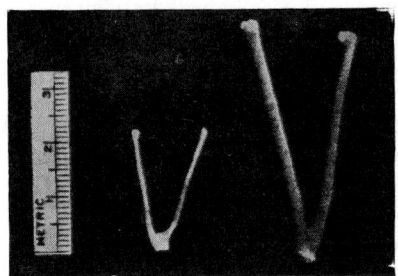

FIG. 74.15. Effect of hypophysectomy upon the uterus. On right, uterus of normal rat; on left, that of an hypophysectomized rat. (From van Dyke, *The Physiology and Pharmacology of the Pituitary Body*, by permission of the University of Chicago Press.)

of gonadotrophins than for the other pituitary hormones since the presence of small amounts of other endogenous or exogenous gonadotrophins in the circulation may alter the effects observed both quantitatively and qualitatively. The gonads of hypophysectomized animals show pronounced loss of size and weight. Primordial follicles are still present in the ovaries but do not develop to the stage of antra formation. No ovulation occurs and no corpora lutea are formed. In animals such as the rat, in which interstitial tissue is present in the ovary, this tissue shows obvious degenerative changes. The cells become smaller with dense pyknotic nuclei. Hormonal activity on the part of the ovary also ceases, as shown by the atrophy of the accessory reproductive organs (fig. 74.15). On administration of FSH preparations to such an hypophysectomized animal, follicles enlarge and ripen and a marked increase occurs in ovarian weight. Such administration, however, does not result in ovulation or corpora lutea formation, nor repair of the interstitial tissue or hormone secretion by the ovary. The reproductive tract, therefore, remains atrophic. Administration of purified LH to the hypophysectomized rat repairs the interstitial tissue of the ovary. Follicular growth does not occur and no sign of estrogen secretion is apparent in the uterus and vagina. If FSH and LH are administered together then follicular ripening, ovulation, and corpus luteum formation occurs. The optimum dosage of these hormones for ovulation is about (FSH:LH) 10:1. FSH and LH given together also result in estrogen secretion and development of the genital tract. However, the corpora lutea do not become functional and secretory in the rat unless prolactin (luteotrophic hormone) is also present. The synergism which exists between the action of FSH and LH when given together is clearly seen when the effect upon ovarian weight is studied. FSH given alone increases the weight of the ovary in the hypophysectomized rat; LH alone has little effect. FSH and LH given together result in a much greater increment in ovarian weight than would be expected from a simple summation of responses. This is known as the *augmentation effect* and must be allowed for when considering assay procedures for these hormones. In the hypophysectomized male rat, purified FSH results in development of the testicular tubules and spermatogenesis, but has no effect on the interstitial or Leydig cells. On the other hand, purified LH results in development of the interstitial cells and secretion of androgen. The androgenic activity in turn results in development of the seminiferous tubules and spermatogenesis, and also development of the accessory organs such as the seminal vesicles and ventral prostate. The stimulation of gametogenesis by LH in the male, through the androgenic secretion elicited, seems to have no equivalent in the female. It is, however, well established that androgens stimulate the seminiferous tubules directly in the rat.

Evidence has accumulated that administration of the gonadotrophins results in a reduction of ovarian and testicular cholesterol. It is likely that the cholesterol in these glands is a precursor of estrogens and androgens, and the condition may be compared with that existing in the adrenal cortex.

Substances with gonadotrophic activity may be extracted from blood and urine in various normal and pathological states. These gonadotrophic substances may be of pituitary or placental origin, but all appear to be glycoproteins.

1. Menopause or castration urinary gonadotrophin (CU). This substance was first found in the blood or urine of menopausal women, and later in the urine of both sexes after castration. It is probably of pituitary origin. Cessation of function, or removal, of the gonads results in release of the pituitary from the feed-back of gonadal hormones and an increased secretion of pituitary gonadotrophins. In support of this view is the fact that extracts of the pituitary of the castrate animal have similar physiological effects to CU, in that they are very largely folliclestimulating in nature.

2. Human chorionic gonadotrophin (HCG). In 1927, Aschheim and Zondek reported the presence of a gonadotrophic substance in the blood and urine of pregnant women. On injection of an extract of HCG into an immature mouse or rat, follicular development, ovulation, and luteinization occurs in the ovaries. However on injection into an hypophysectomized rat no follicular development occurs. Its actions are explainable on the grounds that HCG stimulates the animal's own pituitary to secrete FSH, while possessing LH-like activity itself (for further information see ch. 78).

3. Pregnant mare serum gonadotrophin (PMS). Cole and Hart (1930) first observed the presence of a powerful gonadotrophic substance in the blood of pregnant mares. It is thought to originate from cells in the endometrial cups of the placenta. On injection into hypophysectomized animals it exerts a predominantly follicle-stimulating effect. Unlike the other gonadotrophic substances it persists in the blood stream, after a single injection, for many days (see also ch. 78).

The *bioassay* of gonadotrophins is usually performed with reference to their follicle-stimulating or interstitial cell-stimulating activity. The augmentation effect must be borne in mind and may be circumvented when assaying FSH either by eliminating the action of LH (by using hypophysectomized animals and purified preparations of FSH), or by deliberately adding to the extract to be assayed amounts of an LH substance which produces maximum augmentation. Thus FSH activity may be assayed (a) by ascertaining the amount of material necessary to re-establish follicular growth in the *hypophysectomized* animal, or (b) by finding the least amount of the preparation that will double the ovarian weight of the *normal* immature animal when administered in combination with a substance having LH activity. LH activity, on the other hand, may be measured more satisfactorily, since a test is available for LH which is independent of the augmentation effect. The increase in weight of the ventral prostate of the hypophysectomized immature male rat gives an index of the amount of LH activity in an injected extract. A recently introduced procedure, the Parlow assay, is the most sensitive method for measuring LH. It depends on the ability of LH to reduce the ascorbic acid content of the corpora lutea of pseudopregnant rats. Immature rats are used and are made pseudopregnant by previous treatment with PMS and HCG.

The *inactivation* of pituitary gonadotrophic hormones in the blood stream proceeds more slowly than do some other anterior pituitary hormones, such as ACTH and TSH. Significant amounts of gonadotrophin may be detectable in the blood some 24 hours after administration of an extract. The measurement of the normal levels of gonadotrophic hormone in the blood is of questionable accuracy throughout the major part of the menstrual cycle. At the midpoint of the cycle, however, at about the time of ovulation, a rise of blood gonadotrophic activity undoubtedly occurs. There is evidence from *in vitro* studies that ovarian tissue inactivates gonadotrophin. Small amounts of these hormones are also excreted in the urine.

The regulation of anterior pituitary secretion of gonadotrophins has been studied in detail. Research in this field preceded investigation of the control of other anterior pituitary hormones since changes in gonadotrophin secretion could be easily inferred from study of the sexual cycles, and since in particular forms specific changes in the environment were found to be associated with alterations in the sexual rhythm. Thus growth of follicles and induction of estrus during periods of sexual quiescence, indicative of increased secretion of FSH, may be induced in birds (Rowan, 1926), ferrets (Bissonnette, 1932), and other forms by exposure to extra hours of daily illumination. Similarly, ovulation and the formation of corpora lutea, indicative of LH release, does not occur spontaneously in many birds, rabbits, cats, ferrets, and some other mammals, but requires the triggering stimulus of mating for its initiation. It is likely that these are examples of a general pattern of nervous control of the secretion of gonadotrophic hormones. A similar conclusion regarding a nervous influence may be drawn from clinical observations. The fear of pregnancy in unmarried girls, the change of occupation from day to night work, and emotional upsets of many types, such as those induced by aerial bombardment in World War II or by incarceration in a concentration camp, have all been found to be associated with loss of menstrual cycles.

The first clear-cut experimental data that gonadotrophin secretion from the anterior pituitary is dependent upon the nervous system came from experiments in which the pituitary stalk had been cut and a plate placed between the hypothalamus and pituitary, and others in which the hypophysis had been transplanted to a distant site in the body. It is now generally agreed that these procedures result in ovarian atrophy and cessation of hormonal secretion by the ovary. The reproductive tract thus undergoes atrophy. On the other hand, it has been found by Harris and Jacobsohn that if the pituitary gland is removed from the sella turcica, and anterior pituitary tissue placed not in a distant site but directly under the hypothalamus, the hypophysial portal vessels between the tuber cinereum and pars distalis regrow and normal reproductive functions are re-

gained. Everett and Nikitovitch-Winer have even found that if the pituitary gland of a female rat is transplanted under the kidney capsule a period of sexual quiescence and atrophy occurs, but if this same transplanted pituitary tissue is then replaced under the hypothalamus, apparently normal reproductive functions return. In these latter animals the portal vessels were again found to have reconnected the tuber cinereum and anterior pituitary tissue. For these and other reasons given below, it may be said that the hypothalamus maintains and regulates the secretion of gonadotrophins.

In order to analyze the hypothalamic mechanisms involved in more detail, experiments have been conducted in which localized lesions and stimulation have been made in the hypothalamus. Lesions of the hypothalamus have been found to result in (a) cessation of sexual cycles and atrophy of the reproductive organs (median eminence lesions), (b) abolition of sexual cycles with the intervention of prolonged periods of follicular development in the ovary and a state of constant estrus (lesions in the anterior, paraventricular region of the hypothalamus), (c) the induction of a state of sexual activity and development at a time of year when seasonally breeding animals (ferrets) would normally show atrophic organs and sexual quiescence (anterior hypothalamic lesions), and (d) the precocious development of puberty in immature animals (anterior hypothalamic lesions). This last observation is of clinical interest in that young boys and girls afflicted with hypothalamic tumors, especially those of congenital origin known as hamartomata, may show full development of physical and psychic sexual function when only a few years of age. It seems likely that FSH secretion is regulated by a predominantly inhibiting influence of the hypothalamus over the anterior pituitary, and that if this influence is removed by a hypothalamic lesion then signs of a release effect on FSH secretion are observed. It is noteworthy that no records are available of an increase in FSH release following electrical stimulation of the hypothalamus.

Stimulation of the hypothalamus has, however, been shown to evoke release of LH and ovulation in the rabbit. As mentioned above, this species does not ovulate spontaneously but normally requires the sensory stimuli, associated with the act of mating, to excite various nervous reflex paths and, thus, in turn LH secretion and follicular rupture. Adapting Sherrington's term for spinal reflexes to neuroendocrine reflexes, it may be said that the hypothalamus and pituitary stalk form the "final common path" for the latter. Thus, it seems likely that the electrical stimuli which result in ovulation when applied to the posterior tuber cinereum and median eminence are activating the terminal parts of the reflex paths which normally underlie the ovulation response. The mechanism involved in the cyclical release of LH in spontaneously ovulating forms also seems to involve the hypothalamus, since hypothalamic lesions have been found to block ovulation and to result in a state of continuous estrus in rats, and since such drugs as barbiturates, well known for their action on the central nervous system, may also block ovulation in these animals. Recent data also implicate other areas of the brain, such as the reticular activating system and amygdaloid nuclei, as participating in the control of LH release. It is likely that these areas act through their projections to the hypothalamus.

The timing of puberty, and the endocrine changes associated with it, also seem to be under central nervous control. In the early days of this century it was believed that an "ageing process" in ovarian tissue might determine the time of puberty. However, this is clearly not the case since ovaries from immature animals transplanted into ovariectomized adults, behave as adult organs. Also, pituitary tissue from newborn rats, transplanted under the hypothalamus of hypophysectomized adults, has also been found capable of maintaining normal adult function. Therefore, it may be said that puberty is not dependent on a maturation process in ovarian or anterior pituitary tissue. When these data are combined with those indicating that hypothalamic lesions, both in the human and the experimental animal, may be associated with *pubertas praecox* it is clear that the central nervous system is in some way related to pubertal development. One hypothesis, that at the moment harmonizes with the experimental data, is that the gonads from birth to puberty secrete gonadal hormones at a low rate, but at a rate sufficient to exert a restraining influence on anterior pituitary activity. This influence may be exerted through the hypothalamus, and in this case would be abolished by a lesion in this structure.

A problem in some ways allied with that of puberty concerns the sexual differentiation of the mechanisms regulating gonadotrophic secretion. The secretion of gonadotrophic hormones occurs in a cyclical fashion in the adult female, but in a more constant manner in the adult male. This may be illustrated by the fact that ovaries transplanted into castrated males show constant follicular development but absence of ovulation and corpus luteum formation. Pfeiffer in 1936, made an extensive study of the effects of gonadal transplants in immature rats on their subsequent sexual function. He concluded that the immature gonads secrete hormone at a sufficient rate between birth and puberty to impose a sexual differentiation upon the maturing pituitary gland, and that the pattern of gonadotrophic release in adult life is dependent upon this sexual maturation of the pituitary. His data indicated that basically the mechanism concerned is cyclic in function and that this is converted in the developing male animal to one that is acyclic. It is now clear, however, that the anterior pituitary gland remains functionally plastic. This can be seen most easily from the fact that pituitary tissue obtained from a male rat can, if transplanted under the hypothalamus of an hypophysectomized female rat, maintains female sexual cycles and pregnancy. Thus pituitary tissue itself retains a male and female bipotentiality. It seems clear, from the results of Pfeiffer and many later workers, that testosterone secretion by the developing testis of the foetal or neonatal animal exerts an important "organizational" or "inductive" action on the developing central nervous system. It is also becoming realized that this is only one facet of the whole process of sexual differentiation of the foetus. The presence of testis hormone induces, in both genetic male and female mammals, the development of a male genital tract and a male-type brain. The absence of testis hormone (in the normal female and after gonadectomy in both sexes) allows the development of a female genital tract and a female-type brain. A male- or female-type brain is understood to be one that regulates gonadotrophin secretion by the anterior pituitary according to the male or female pattern, and one that regulates the sexual behavior of the adult in a predominantly male or female pattern.

The blood level of the gonadal steroids is an important factor controlling gonadotrophin release in the normal adult. Administration of estrogens to the normal female results in atrophy of the ovaries through inhibition of gonadotrophin secretion. Removal of an ovary results in hypertrophy of the remaining gland. Therefore, it is very probable that a similar feedback effect of target gland hormone occurs in the case of the ovary as for the thyroid and adrenal cortex. Moore and Price (1932) first expressed the view that the cyclical nature of sexual cycles was due to a self-regulating reciprocity between the pituitary and the gonads, based on the feed-back action. Later evidence tends to the view that the gonadal hormones exert their effects on anterior pituitary secretion *via* the intermediation of the hypothalamus. In this case the gonadal hormones would exert an effect on some receptor mechanism in the central nervous system which would adjust pituitary activity accordingly. Such a view would be more in keeping with the finding that an anterior hypothalamic lesion may convert a female rat or guinea pig, showing normal cycles, to one in a state of constant estrus, and it would also explain the findings of Flerkó that small fragments of ovary transplanted into the hypothalamus near the paraventricular nuclei, but not in other regions, result in a diminution of uterine weights.

Prolactin, Lactogenic Hormone, Mammotrophic Hormone (MH) or Luteotrophic Hormone (LTH)

In 1928, Stricker and Grueter reported that injection of pituitary extract into a pseudopregnant rabbit before or after ovariectomy resulted in lactation. Within the next few years several groups of workers reported the isolation of a pituitary extract with lactogenic activity. Hypophysectomy prevents the onset of lactation, or results in abrupt cessation of an existing lactation. However, injection of a suitable anterior pituitary extract into hypophysectomized animals produces lactation. In 1931, Riddle and Braucher found that pituitary extracts caused development of the crop glands in pigeons. These glands consist of circumscribed areas of mucosa in the dorsal part of the crop, and are responsible for secreting "crop milk" which is regurgitated by either parent and utilized to feed the young. Riddle and his colleagues later showed that the crop gland effect in pigeons is probably due to the same hormones which cause lactation in mammals and suggested the term *prolactin.*

The cellular site of origin of prolactin is thought to be a type of acidophil cell in the anterior pituitary. The evidence for this is indirect, and is based on observations that the peripheral zone of the anterior lobe of the ox pituitary contains more prolactin and more acidophils than the central region, and that during the incubation period in pigeons, or lactation in mammals, the main cytological changes in the pituitary concern the α cells of the pars distalis. The cell has been identified electron-microscopically, and changes

in its ultrastructure correlated with its function during lactation.

Prolactin is a protein. A pure and potent preparation was first obtained by Lyons, and a crystalline preparation by White. Subsequent studies have been successful in obtaining pure preparations from sheep, cattle and human glands. The molecular weight is of the order 21,500–26,000. The ovine and bovine hormones are very similar; but the human preparation contains full growth hormone activity as well as lactogenic activity.

The physiological activities of prolactin are exerted upon the mammary gland, the pigeon crop sac and, in certain species, the corpus luteum. The effects produced by prolactin on the mammary gland form a difficult subject of study. Species differences and the simultaneous actions of other hormones on the gland must be carefully considered. This subject is dealt with in chapter 78, and it will, therefore, suffice to say here that the initiation of lactation (lactogenesis) and its maintenance are probably due to a complex of pituitary hormones centering around prolactin as an essential element. Lyons and coworkers recently stated " . . . in the Long-Evans rat, at least 5 of the 6 well-identified anterior pituitary hormones play important parts in mammogenesis and lactogenesis." The effect of prolactin on the crop sac of the male or female pigeon, on the other hand, is a specific and direct action of the lactogenic hormone. It thus forms a more suitable reaction in many ways for assay purposes. The stimulating effect prolactin exerts on the secretory activity of the corpus luteum of the rat was observed in 1941, and led to the synonym luteotrophic hormone (LTH) for prolactin. It would seem established now, that FSH and LH are responsible for ovulation and the *formation* of the corpus luteum during the normal estrous cycle in the rat. This corpus luteum, however, does not necessarily become functionally active and secrete progesterone. If sterile or fertile coitus occurs during estrus, this in some way triggers the release of LTH from the pituitary and so results in a functionally active luteal phase and an associated period of pseudopregnancy or pregnancy. However, since the original observations, little evidence has accumulated that prolactin exerts a luteotrophic action in other species, such as the rabbit, monkey, or man. Recent work, however, indicates that prolactin has an effect in prolonging the active life of the corpus luteum in the sheep and possibly ferret.

The assay of prolactin may be performed using the crop gland or mammary response. The increase in weight of the pigeon crop after intramuscular injection of the hormone, or histological changes in the crop mucosa after intradermal injection of the hormone immediately over the crop gland, are both used. It has been suggested that the increased uptake of radioactive phosphorus by the crop sac under the influence of prolactin may form the basis of a sensitive and objective assay method. In mammals the formation of milk in the mammary tissue of the estrogen-progesterone treated or pseudopregnant rabbit, following either systemic administration or injection into a lactiferous duct, may be employed. An international standard of prolactin is available. One I.U. is the activity contained in 0.1 mg. of the standard preparation.

Little is known regarding the *inactivation and excretion* of prolactin in the body. Some *in vitro* studies have indicated that prolactin is inactivated by the tissues of the mammary gland, ovary, and pigeon crop gland, that is by tissues of its three target organs.

Factors regulating the secretion of prolactin have been studied by observing the effect of different procedures on the activity of the mammary gland, or the corpora lutea of the rat. These indirect methods of assessing prolactin are necessary since the techniques for measuring prolactin in body fluids are not sensitive or accurate enough to allow direct measurement. In chapter 78 it is pointed out that there is suggestive evidence that the sensory stimuli associated with the act of suckling stimulate by various reflexes the pituitary secretion of prolactin, and, therefore, play an important part in maintaining milk secretion in the breast. Similar evidence relating to prolactin secretion is that the suckling may induce the development of functional luteal tissue in the rat. As mentioned above, corpora lutea are formed, but do not function, during the normal estrous cycle in this animal. If mating occurs, however, prolactin release is stimulated by reflex action, the corpora lutea become functional and the next estrus is delayed for the period of pregnancy or pseudopregnancy. During the period of pseudopregnancy, trauma to the endometrium results in the formation of a tumorlike mass in the uterus known as a deciduoma. Deciduoma formation only occurs in an endometrium under the influence of progesterone. Activation of corpora lutea with the development of a pseudopregnancy may be stimulated in the rat not only by sterile coitus but by experimental procedures such as

glass rod stimulation of the vagina, electrical stimulation of the uterine cervix, or massive electrical stimuli passed through the head. The stimulus of suckling produces a similar response. Selye and coworkers showed that the regular estrous cycles of rats and mice could be interrupted by supplying them with relays of litters obtained from other animals. Prolonged suckling in these animals resulted in pseudopregnancy and lactational development of the mammary gland. It seems clear that in this condition, known as suckling pseudopregnancy, the stimulus of suckling has evoked prolactin release. Coitus and suckling then are physiological stimuli which act by nervous reflex paths and the hypophysial portal vessels, to excite prolactin secretion. The nervous control of prolactin secretion by the hypothalamus differs from that of the other five anterior pituitary hormones, in so far as prolactin appears to be regulated by a mechanism which is inhibitory in its normal overall effect, whilst the others are regulated by an excitatory mechanism. Thus if neural control over the anterior pituitary is removed (as by effective pituitary stalk section, by transplantation of the pituitary, or possibly by administration of such drugs as chlorpromazine or reserpine) the rate of release of prolactin is increased and the release of the other hormones is decreased or abolished. This dual type of control of anterior pituitary function may be compared with that of the parasympathetic and sympathetic systems over cardiac function.

The Control of the Secretion of the Adenohypophysis

In discussing the individual hormones above, it has been emphasized that the secretory activity of the anterior pituitary is regulated by the following:

1. A feed-back of target gland hormones. It is uncertain whether this effect is due to a direct action on anterior pituitary cells or to an action on the nervous system which in turn modifies pituitary function. This mechanism serves as a homeostatic mechanism to maintain a *constant* level of hormones in the blood.

2. The central nervous system, acting through the hypothalamus and hypophysial portal vessels of the pituitary stalk. The hypothalamus acts to maintain anterior pituitary function at a *normal* level and to vary this level according to external stimuli and the needs of the organism. The liberation of gonadotrophic hormone by sex-

ual excitement in the rabbit (p. 1505) or by extra illumination in birds and many mammals, the release of adrenocorticotrophic hormone under states of emotional stress (p. 1505), and the secretion of thyrotrophic hormone upon exposure to cold, are outstanding examples of the relationship between the anterior pituitary and the nervous system. It is most probable that peripheral sensory stimuli activate nervous reflex paths which eventually converge into the hypothalamus. However, very few, if any, nerve fibers pass from the hypothalamus to the anterior pituitary. What then is the functional link between the hypothalamus and adenohypophysis? The vascular supply to the pars distalis (p. 1487) offers the basis for an explanation. The hypophysial portal vessels connect the median eminence of the tuber cinereum of the hypothalamus with the anterior pituitary gland, and the evidence is now convincing that these vessels mediate, in some way, the influence the nervous system exerts over the activity of the pars distalis.

The Functional Significance of the Hypophysial Portal Vessels

1. All vertebrates possess a system of vessels passing from the median eminence to the anterior lobe of the pituitary. From amphibians to man, these vessels are truly portal, in that they start as capillaries in, or in contact with, the median eminence, form vascular trunks which run down the pituitary stalk, and break up into the sinusoids of the anterior pituitary.

2. The direction of blood flow in these vessels is *from* the median eminence *to* the anterior pituitary.

3. The effects of pituitary stalk section are conditioned by the subsequent state of the portal vessels. If these vessels regenerate across the site of the cut, normal anterior pituitary function may be regained. If regeneration of the vessels is prevented by the placement of a plate between the stalk ends, then anterior pituitary function remains greatly reduced.

4. The effects of pituitary transplantation vary with the anatomical site of the transplant. If the pituitary gland is removed from the sella turcica and placed in the subarachnoid space below the hypothalamus, the tissue may become revascularized by an outgrowth of portal vessels from the tuber cinereum and normal anterior pituitary function regained. If the transplant is placed in a distant site in the body (muscle, anterior chamber of the eye, kidney), then only fragments of normal

anterior pituitary function are observed. However, if the tissue is transplanted a second time in the same animal, and placed in contact with the tuber cinereum, then normal anterior pituitary function may be regained.

5. Electrical stimulation of various sites in the hypothalamus has been found effective in causing discharge of luteinizing hormone, adrenocorticotrophic hormone, and thyrotrophic hormone from the anterior pituitary. On the other hand, if the electrode is placed directly in the adenohypophysis, similar electrical stimuli are ineffective in evoking hormonal release. This finding is compatible with the view that the activity of the gland is normally controlled by a humoral mechanism and not by a direct secretomotor nerve supply.

There can be no reasonable doubt that the functional activity of the adenohypophysis is dependent on its hypophysial portal blood supply. In some way these vessels transmit the influence the nervous system exerts over the activity of the gland. The mechanism involved is not yet clear. The most probable view is that various hypothalamic nerve tracts liberate some humoral substance(s) into the capillaries of the portal vessels in the median eminence, and that the humoral substance(s) is carried by these vessels to the pars distalis where it excites or inhibits the glandular cells. This idea of a neurohumoral mechanism regulating anterior pituitary activity finds indirect support from the present concepts regarding posterior pituitary function. It is now generally held that the posterior pituitary hormones are formed in the cells of the supraoptic and paraventricular hypothalamic nuclei (neurosecretion), are transported down the nerve fibers of the supraopticohypophysial tract in the pituitary stalk and liberated from the nerve terminals into the blood vessels of the neural lobe of the pituitary (see p. 1490). Such a mechanism is very closely analogous with that suggested for anterior pituitary control. Both suppose the formation of hormonal substances by hypothalamic neurones, and both suppose the liberation of these substances into blood vessels of the neurohypophysis, either into the primary plexus of the portal vessels in the median eminence, or into the capillaries of the infundibular process. It is of interest that the blood vessels of both these parts of the neurohypophysis have similar permeability properties (as judged by the diffusion of vital dyes and radioactive substance), which are different from those of the hypothalamic blood vessels. It should be mentioned here that the neurosecretory concept is, of course, not new. The existence of secretory neurones in the nervous system of invertebrates (insects, mollusks, worms, etc.) has been well established.

In the last few years the neurohumoral theory of anterior pituitary control has received direct support from the study of the properties of extracts of the median eminence. The median eminence is the region where the nerve fibers of the hypothalamus terminate in abundance (as seen with the electron microscope) on the endothelium of the primary plexus of the portal vessels. If neural control of anterior pituitary activity is dependent on the release of various humoral agents from these nerve terminals into the vessels, then extracts of the median eminence might be expected to contain substances active in exciting anterior pituitary secretion (in the same way that extracts of the neural or posterior lobe of the pituitary afford a rich source of the materials liberated from nerve terminals into the blood vessels in this structure). In summary of much recent work in this field it may be said that different substances may be obtained from median eminence tissue which excite (in the case of ACTH, LH, FSH, TSH and possibly STH) or inhibit (in the case of prolactin) the secretion of anterior pituitary hormones. These substances are generally becoming known as Releasing Factors (RF). Thus the factor active in exciting release of adrenocorticotrophic hormone (ACTH) is referred to as the corticotrophic-releasing factor (CRF). Similarly LRF refers to the luteinizing hormone; FRF to the follicle-stimulating hormone; TRF to thyrotrophic hormone; and GRF to growth hormone. The secretion of prolactin, regulated by an inhibitory substance, is referred to as PIF (prolactin-inhibiting factor). As far as the evidence goes, these factors appear to be polypeptides, with molecular weights in the same region as those of the posterior pituitary polypeptides. However, much work remains to be done in identifying the chemical structure of these substances, and in assessing their presence or absence in portal vessel blood.

SPECIES SPECIFICITY AND IMMUNOLOGICAL REACTIONS OF ANTERIOR PITUITARY HORMONES. Collip and his colleagues (1934) demonstrated that certain hormones, when injected, cause the formation of a substance in the serum of the treated animal which exerts a specific antagonism to, and may completely abolish the effect of, the injected hormone. They thought that the inhibitory principle was not an antibody in the ordinary sense, but was rather in the nature of an "antihormone." The difficulty in reaching a decision at that time was the fact that only impure preparations of protein hormones were available. During the last ten years, the development of immunochemical techniques, and the availability of purer extracts of hormones, have resulted in much information on the antibody reactions that may develop following injection of a protein hormone. As mentioned elsewhere in this chapter, the protein hormones of the anterior pituitary and the polypeptide hormones of the posterior pituitary vary in their chemical structure from species to species. For example, growth hormone obtained from ox and sheep has a molecular weight of about 46,000, an isoelectric point of about 6.8, and probably a branched-chain structure. Primate growth hormone, on the other hand, has a molecular weight of about 26,000, an acidic isoelectric point, and probably consists of a single peptide chain. It is then, perhaps, not surprising that ungulate protein hormones are not very active in primates, and that antibody reactions to a foreign protein may be set up by injection of such a hormone from one species into another. The lower molecular weight polypeptide hormones are generally poor or ineffective antigens, and little is known regarding the antigenicity of the posterior pituitary hormones.

The growth in knowledge of immunological responses to anterior pituitary hormones has opened the way to the development of assay procedures based on such responses. Although such assay methods promise much for the future, they are not yet in routine use.

The Physiology of the Neurohypophysis

An active extract of the pituitary was first obtained in 1894, by Oliver and Schäfer who described its effect in raising the blood pressure. Howell, 3 years later, showed that the posterior lobe alone contained the pressor principle. The extract has been used in medicine for many years under such commercial names as *Pituitrin, Infundin, Infundibulin,* etc., or as the official solutions of the British and United States pharmacopoeias (B.P. and U.S.P.).[4] Much of our knowledge regarding the pharmacological actions of posterior pituitary principles has been derived from work using crude *whole extract* of the posterior pituitary.

[4] The official solution of U.S.P. (XIII) *Posterior Pituitary Injection* is an aqueous solution of the principles of the posterior lobe of the pituitary of "healthy domesticated animals used as food by man." It has a specific activity (oxytocic, antidiuretic, or pressor) of 10 posterior pituitary units per cubic centimeter. A *Posterior Pituitary Unit* (B.P., U.S.P., or International) is the potency of 0.5 mg. of the Posterior Pituitary Reference Standard.

The single extract may be fractionated into *two extracts* which contain in a nearly pure form the vasopressor or antidiuretic hormone and the oxytocic hormone (marketed as *Pitressin* and *Pitocin*, respectively, see p. 1514). *Pitressin* and *Pitocin* have largely replaced *Pituitrin* in clinical use, and even more highly purified or synthetic compounds are being used for research purposes. However, an account of the actions of the whole posterior lobe extract will first be given.

The Actions of Whole Posterior Pituitary Extract

These fall into 8 main groups.

1. CIRCULATORY. The blood pressure is raised, the systemic arterioles and capillaries both undergoing constriction. Marked pallor of the skin results. An initial depressor effect, or a pressor succeeded by a depressor effect, may precede the main rise in blood pressure. Repeated injections invoke smaller and smaller pressor responses (tachyphylaxis) and may even result only in a depression of the blood pressure (inversion effect). This depressor effect is cardiac in origin as indicated below. Posterior lobe extract causes constriction of the coronary and pulmonary vessels but dilates the cerebral and renal vessels. The dilator effect upon the two last mentioned sets of vessels is a passive one being caused by the rise in systemic blood pressure. The heart is slowed by posterior lobe extracts if the vagus nerves are intact, the effect being a reflex result of the blood pressure rise, but increased cardiac rate occurs if the nerves have first been cut. Some dilatation of the heart and weakening of its beat occur in the dog, rabbit and, with large doses, in the cat. The coronary constriction and the weakening effect upon the cardiac muscle cause a reduced cardiac output and a fall in pressure in the pulmonary artery (dog and rabbit). These experimental results indicate that commercial extracts are of no value *clinically* as a means of strengthening the action of a failing heart but may actually exert a deleterious effect. The fall in blood pressure which follows repeated injections of posterior pituitary extract (inversion effect) is due, according to Melville and Stehl, to the weakening of the heart and is not of vascular origin. The portal venous pressure is reduced by posterior pituitary extract, as a result of constriction of the splanchnic vessels.

2. RESPIRATORY EFFECTS, e.g., increased rate of breathing, alternating at times with periods of apnea, are produced by the extract, but they are secondary to the effects on the circulation.

3. PLAIN MUSCLE, in general, is stimulated by whole posterior lobe extract. This action differs from the smooth muscle stimulating action of adrenaline in that it does not parallel the action of the sympathetic nerves; smooth muscle, receiving motor innervation from the parasympathetic, is excited as well. The muscular walls of the *intestine*, *gall-bladder*, *ureter* and *urinary bladder* (detrusor and trigone) are excited. Peristalsis in the human small intestine and to a less extent in the colon, is stimulated, but the tone is unaffected. Sometimes the smooth muscle of the bronchioles is stimulated, but this is due to contamination of the extract with histamine and is not specific.

4. UTERINE. The stimulating effect of posterior pituitary extract upon the isolated virgin guinea pig's uterus was demonstrated by Dale in 1909, and termed the *oxytocic effect*. It is used as a means of assaying the potency of pituitary extracts. Some highly purified preparations exert an oxytocic effect in a dilution of 1 part in 2,000,-000,000. The effect of these extracts upon the uterine muscle is antagonized by the hormone of the corpus luteum (see p. 1633). The oxytocic effect varies with the species, and, as a consequence of the interplay of other hormones, especially of the luteal hormone, with the phases of the sexual cycle (e.g., period of estrus, pregnant or nonpregnant state of the uterus). An interrelation between the actions of adrenaline and posterior pituitary extract is indicated by the fact that if the nonpregnant uterus of the cat is first treated with pituitary extract, adrenaline causes contraction instead of the usual relaxation (p. 1559). The human uterus is most sensitive at the end of pregnancy, and the extract is used as an obstetric aid to produce uterine contraction after the expulsion of the placenta and so to prevent or check postpartum hemorrhage.

5. MAMMARY. Lactation consists of two main processes. First, milk formation or secretion which is intimately related to the anterior pituitary gland (p. 1507), and second, a process known as milk ejection, which is controlled by the posterior pituitary gland. Ott and Scott in 1910, first showed that injection of posterior pituitary extract increased the amount of milk obtainable from the cannulated udder of the goat. This action of the extract, causing an active expression of the milk present in the lactating breast or udder, has been confirmed in many species including man. Much discussion centered at one time around the question of the contractile element concerned. In many forms plain muscle exists only around the larger ducts in the mammary gland,

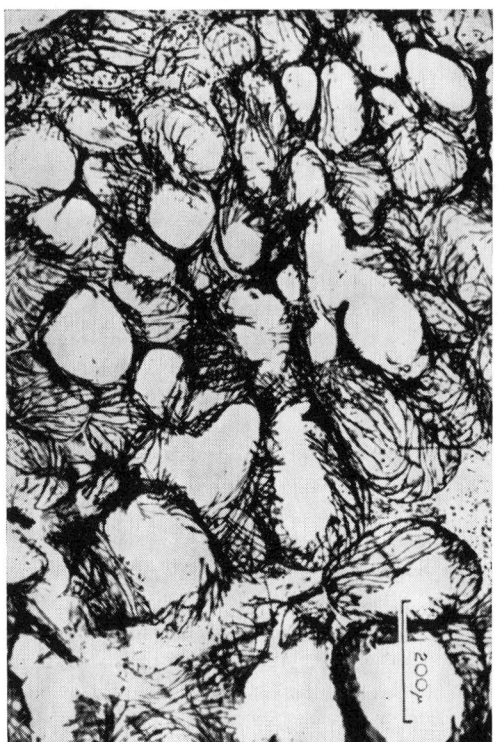

FIG. 74.16. Section of part of a lobule of the mammary gland of a goat, fixed in the distended state, showing the myoepithelial cells stained with silver. (From Richardson.)

and it was difficult to understand how milk contained in the alveoli could be expressed. The histological studies of Richardson have now established that a specialized contractile tissue, composed of *myoepithelial cells* (see fig. 74.16), is extensively distributed around the alveoli and ducts of the mammary gland, and there can now be little doubt that this is the effector element stimulated by posterior pituitary extract. In order to demonstrate the action of posterior pituitary extracts on the mammary gland it is necessary to cannulate the nipple or teat (to overcome the sphincter action of this structure). Very small doses of extracts (of the order of 0.001 unit) are then effective in exciting milk ejection.

6. KIDNEY (Antidiuretic hormone, ADH). The action of posterior pituitary extracts upon renal function was discovered by Magnus and Schäfer in 1901, but they described only a *diuretic* effect. The diuresis, however, is of brief duration and may be preceded by anuria due to ureteral spasm; this early diuretic action is due to the rise in general blood pressure, and the passive dilatation, thereby, of the afferent glomerular vessels. The important and specific renal effect is, however, an increase in the tubular reabsorption of water

and, as a consequence, a reduction in urinary flow. In anesthetized animals the specific antidiuretic action is absent; diuresis due to the vascular factors is the outstanding effect. Posterior lobe extract postpones for several hours the diuresis induced in normal animals by water drinking, and reduces the polyuria of diabetes insipidus. Associated with the antidiuretic effect is an increase in the percentage of sodium and chloride in the urine and, as a result of a reduction in the tubular reabsorption of these electrolytes, an increase in their total excretion (see also ch. 79).

The antidiuretic principle is an essential factor in the maintenance of the water balance of the body, being secreted when the need for water conservation arises. For example, the quantity of the hormone in the urine, which reflects presumably its concentration in the blood stream, is increased in dehydrated states but decreased in hydremia (Gilman and Goodman). In man, it is through a more active tubular reabsorption rather than by a reduction in the filtration rate through the glomerulus that the kidney plays its part in conserving water.

It is only in mammals and birds that posterior pituitary extract exerts any effect upon tubular reabsorption. And, as compared with mammals, the antidiuretic action of the extract in birds is feeble. Only these two classes secrete a hypertonic urine, and their nephrons alone possess a thin segment of Henle's loop. It is thought, therefore, that this part of the renal tubules is the site of action of the antidiuretic hormone (see also ch. 79). However, the hormone is not without effect upon the water exchange of amphibia and reptiles. Frogs, for example, immersed in water increase their body weight if injected with posterior pituitary extract (*Brunn effect*) as a result of the uptake of water through the skin; they also lose water readily in a dry environment if treated with the extract. This effect[5] is due to a principle in pituitary extracts other than ADH; it is closely associated with the oxytocic principle but does not seem to be identical with the latter. It is called the *water balance principle* and can be prepared from the pituitaries of mammals as well as from those of amphibians.

7. METABOLIC EFFECTS. Reduced tolerance for sugar, diminution in hepatic glycogen, hyperglycemia, glycosuria, and a fall in the basal metabolic rate follow the injection of posterior lobe extract. The effect of insulin is antagonized. That

[5] It is not seen in fish or reptiles, but in the latter the extract exerts a renal effect, but one different from that induced in mammals, namely, a reduction of the filtration rate.

is to say, the pancreatic hormone produces less effect upon the blood sugar and a greater amount is required to produce hypoglycemic convulsions if its administration has been preceded by an injection of posterior pituitary extract. This extract also causes an increase in liver fat. The effects on carbohydrate and fat metabolism are probably nonspecific, and, therefore, do not represent physiological actions.

8. MELANOCYTE STIMULATING ACTIVITY. The skins of many cold-blooded animals contain peculiar cells with branching processes and mobile pigment granules whose movement toward the periphery of the cell or toward the center is under hormonal influence. Such cells have been given the general name of *chromophores*. Those containing black pigment (melanin) are known as *melanophores*, and those with red or yellow pigment are called *erythrophores* or *xanthophores*, respectively.

Hogben and Winton showed that posterior pituitary extracts caused the pigment granules in the melanophores of the frog to become dispersed throughout the bodies and branching processes of these cells. This results in darkening of the skin. Thus, the injection of a small dose of posterior pituitary extract into a frog causes its skin to become almost coal black as a result of the melanophore reaction. On the other hand, after hypophysectomy, owing to the disappearance of the pituitary hormone from the circulation, the pigment granules gather near the center of the cells and the skin becomes pale. Hypophysectomized tadpoles have, instead of the usual dark brown or green color, a silvery appearance. The changes in color which certain amphibia, reptiles, and fish undergo in order to blend into the color of their surroundings is largely due to variations in the concentrations of the pituitary hormone in the blood or to the balance between the concentrations of the melanophore-expanding principle and adrenaline. Blinding a frog deprives it of its adaptive power.[6] Nervous impulses arising in the retina are believed, therefore, to govern the liberation of the melanocyte stimulating hormone (MSH). The *production* of melanin in the skin of

[6] The phenomenon of light influencing structure and function through the mediation of a retinohypophysial mechanism is not peculiar to cold-blooded animals. The work of a number of experimenters indicates that the well-known association of the seasonal periods with morphological changes (e.g., color and texture of hair or plumage) and with the sexual cycles of certain mammals and birds as well as with the migration of birds, is due, in part at least, to light acting upon the *anterior* pituitary through the medium of retinal impulses. Rowan, for example, was able to induce sexual ac-

the frog is said to be stimulated by this principle.

In most animals MSH principle is elaborated by the pars intermedia.[7] Cultures of tissue from the pars intermedia alone yield this principle, whereas, cultures of the neural part of the pituitary or of the anterior lobe do not. Nevertheless, the hormone finds its way into the neural part of the pituitary and unpurified extracts of the latter always contain it as a contaminant. But it is possible to prepare it free from antidiuretic, pressor, and oxytocic effects.

It now appears that there are two melanocyte-stimulating hormones, called α- and β-MSH. They are polypeptides. Pig β-MSH was found to contain eighteen amino-acids, and pig α-MSH, thirteen amino-acids. Their structure is as follows:

---

tivity in crows and canaries at any desired time of the year by varying the periods of their exposure to artificial light; it is also well known that the domestic fowl will lay regularly in winter if its period of exposure to light is lengthened by artificial means. Cognate experiments have been carried out upon mammals; ferrets, hedgehogs, and racoons. The seasonal onset of estrus in the ferret has been shown to be conditioned by the length of the day; and optic nerve section or hypophysectomy abolishes the phenonenon. The sexual cycles are abolished, of course, by hypophysectomy (lack of gonadotrophic hormone) but their periodicity in relation to the length of exposure to light is lost after optic nerve section alone. The extreme sensitivity to light of the pigeon with respect to the time of egg laying is extraordinary. The pigeon lays a pair of eggs in the morning, the second of the pair being laid, with the regularity of clock-work, half an hour after the first. Lengthening or shortening the period of exposure to light alters the duration of the interval between the laying of the first and second eggs of the pair.

[7] In those species such as the chicken, porpoise and whale which do not possess a pars intermedia, the melanophore-dispersing principle is found in extracts of the anterior lobe; none is present in the posterior lobe.

In 1958 Lerner and his coworkers succeeded in isolating, from mammalian pineal tissue, a substance which proved to be the most potent whitening agent of amphibian skin yet isolated. This pineal hormone, named melatonin by Lerner, is derived from 5-hydroxytryptamine (serotonin) by N-acetylation followed by O-methylation and the enzyme which catalyses this final step, hydroxyindole O-methyl transferase (HIOMT) has only been found in pineal tissue. It would now seem possible to revive the bihormonal theory and consider that colour change in amphibia is under the influence of the pineal and pituitary glands with, perhaps, some form of interaction between these two organs.

	1	2	3	4	5	6	7	8	9	10	11	12	13	14	15	16	17	18
Pig β-MSH	Asp-	Glu-	Gly-	Pro-	Tyr-	Lys-	Met-	Glu-	His-	Phe-	Arg-	Try-	Gly-	Ser-	Pro-	Pro-	Lys-	Asp

	1	2	3	4	5	6	7	8	9	10	11	12	13
Pig α-MSH	R-Ser-	Tyr-	Ser-	Met-	Glu-	His-	Phe-	Arg-	Try-	Gly-	Lys-	Pro-	Val

	1	2	3	4	5	6	7	8	9	10	11	12	13 14...39
Pig ACTH	Ser-	Tyr-	Ser-	Met-	Glu-	His-	Phe-	Arg-	Try-	Gly-	Lys-	Pro-	Val-Gly...

..........Phe

It may be seen that they contain amino-acid sequences in common with that of ACTH, which in all probability accounts for the MSH activity inherent in the ACTH molecule (see p. 1498). This fact may explain the occurrence of pigmentation in Addison's disease, when the atrophic adrenal cortex allows increased release of ACTH (feed-back action).

Whilst the functions of MSH in amphibians seem clear, it is speculative as to what its function is in mammals. Lerner and his colleagues have shown that daily injection of MSH in man, for 7–12 days, produces darkening of the skin. It may play a part in the skin reaction to sunlight. Also since melanocytes are derived embryologically from the neural crest, MSH may be related in some way to nervous function.

mainly oxytocin (oxytocic hormone). They are marketed commercially as *Pitocin* and *Pitressin*. These are white amorphous powders freely soluble in water. However, van Dyke and colleagues obtained a noncrystalline material of protein nature from posterior lobe extracts which, from electrophoretic, ultracentrifuge, and solubility studies, seems to be a pure substance free from contaminating material. It possesses oxytocic and pressor activities in the same ratios as in the crude extracts. A significant advance was made by du Vigneaud and his team. Taking advantage of such modern techniques as countercurrent distribution between immiscible solvents, chromatographic separation on paper, or starch columns, they obtained highly purified preparations of vasopressin and oxytocin from beef material and were able to establish the structural formulas of these compounds. These are as follows:

Structure of oxytocin and vasopressin (ox)

$$Cys^8.Tyr.Ileu.Glu(NH_2).Asp(NH_2).Cys.Pro.Leu.Gly(NH_2)$$

Oxytocin

$$Cys^8.Tyr.Phe.Glu(NH_2).Asp(NH_2).Cys.Pro.Arg.Gly(NH_2)$$

Vasopressin

Fractionation of the Posterior Lobe Extract. Oxytocin and Vasopressin

Considerable quantitites of histamine may be present in commercial pituitary extracts which have not been carefully purified; indeed it was believed for a time by some (Abel and associates) that the plain muscle stimulating and depressor effects were due simply to histamine. Abel also maintained that the other effects (pressor and antidiuretic) were due to a single hormone. The work of Dudley, and especially of Kamm and his associates has shown that the specific effects are not due to histamine, and that there are at least two distinct active principles in a posterior lobe extract. From the crude extract Kamm and his associates have isolated two relatively pure fractions, one containing mainly vasopressin (the vasopressor or antidiuretic hormone) and the other

Each hormone contains eight amino acids, six of which (aspartic acid, cystine, glutamic acid, glycine, proline, and tyrosine) are common to the two. The isoleucine and leucine in oxytocin are replaced by phenyl alanine and arginine. It is of interest that in hog vasopressin lysine replaces the arginine of beef vasopressin. The molecular weight of oxytocin is 1007 and of beef vasopressin is 1084. Both these compounds have been synthesized by du Vigneaud and his group and the synthetic compounds have been found to be identical with the natural products in biological and chemical tests.

The Hormones in Other Vertebrates

One of the fascinating recent developments in knowledge of the pituitary gland concerns the polypeptide hormones in the neurohypophysis of lower (submammalian) vertebrates, and the con-

---

[8] Position of free amino group.

TABLE 74.2

Oxytocin	Cys.	Tyr.	Ileu.	Glu.	Asp.	Cys.	Pro.	Leu.	Gly.	*
	1	2	3	4	5	6	7	8	9	

	8 Arg. oxy. (vasotocin)	8 Ileu. oxy. (Mesotocin)	Oxytocin	3-Phe-8-Arg. oxy. (Arg. vasopressin)	3-Phe-8-Lys. oxy. (Lys. vasopressin)
Mammals	—	—	X	X	X
Birds	X	—	X	—	—
Reptiles	X	—	X?	X?	—
Amphibians	X	X	—	—	—
Agnatha	X	—	—	—	—

* The amino-acids in positions 3 and 8 are the ones that are very largely involved in this polypeptide evolution.

struction of a tentative scheme of the biochemical evolution of these hormones.

Before describing this work, it is necessary to mention the nomenclature which is coming into general use for these polypeptides. The molecule of oxytocin is taken as the basis, the amino-acid sequences being numbered from left to right.

Cys.	Tyr.	Ileu.	Glu.	Asp.	Cys.	Pro.	Leu.	Gly.
1	2	3	4	5	6	7	8	9

Oxytocin

Thus arginine vasopressin is alternatively termed 3-Phe-8-Arg. oxytocin, and lysine vasopressin is 3-Phe-8-Lys. oxytocin. In referring to the hormones in lower vertebrates this terminology will be used.

Many years ago, Heller described a principle present in several nonmammalian pituitaries that differed in its activity from the known mammalian vasopressin and oxytocin. More recently, van Dyke and his associates investigated the polypeptides present in the neurohypophysis of the chicken. They found oxytocin was present, were unable to detect vasopressin, but in its place found a substance which they suggested might have the ring structure of oxytocin with the side-chain of arginine vasopressin. Using the present nomenclature, this is 8-arg. oxytocin. Curiously, du Vigneaud and his colleagues had already synthesized this polypeptide, and on testing its relative activities in a number of different assays they were found to match exactly those of the chicken principle. (du Vigneaud had already termed this substance *vasotocin* on the grounds

that part of its molecule was similar to vasopressin and part to oxytocin). Further work showed that this polypeptide, 8-arg. oxytocin, was widely distributed among the vertebrates, being present in all forms except mammals and elasmobranch fishes. It is the only neurohypophysial hormone present in the lowest vertebrate with a pituitary gland, i.e. the Agnatha.

Table 74.2 attempts to depict the evolution of neurohypophysial polypeptides in the main vertebrates. The parent molecule, 8-arg. oxytocin, persists from the agnatha, up through most fishes, the amphibians, reptiles and birds. It is absent in the mammals. In the amphibians (and possibly in some fishes, such as polypterus and protopterus) a second polypeptide is found, 8-Ileu. oxytocin (or *Mesotocin*) in which isoleucine replaces the arginine of 8-arg. oxytocin. [In elasmobranch fishes the hormones are unknown and are referred to simply as Elasmobranch Principles I and II. In teleosts a further polypeptide appears—4-Ser-8-Ileu. oxytocin—known also as Isotocin or Ichthyotocin]. Possibly, in the reptiles, oxytocin and 3-Phe-8-Arg. oxytocin are derived, by a change in one amino-acid respectively, from 8-Arg. oxytocin. In the Sauropsid reptiles, leading to the birds, the 3-Phe-8-Arg. oxytocin fails to develop or perhaps disappears, so that birds retain only 8-Arg. oxytocin and oxytocin. In the Therapsid reptiles, leading to the mammals, 8-Arg. oxytocin seems to disappear, leaving the mammals with oxytocin and 3-Phe-8-Arg. oxytocin (arginine vasopressin). In the Swinae (domestic pig, hippopotamus, wart hog and peccaries), 3-Phe-8-Arg. oxytocin is replaced by 3-Phe-8-Lys, oxytocin (lysine vasopressin).

It may be mentioned that many synthetic polypeptides, unknown in nature, have now been prepared with varying degrees of biological activity.

The Control and Function of the Neural Lobe

The preparation of highly purified and synthetic oxytocin and vasopressin has made possible the analysis of the physiological activities of whole posterior pituitary extract, described above, in terms of these two compounds. It seems clear that oxytocin is responsible for the action of pituitary extracts on uterine muscle and on the mammary gland, whereas vasopressin acts on the blood pressure and water excretion by the kidney. There are no good grounds for believing that the pressor and antidiuretic activities are due to two different substances. It is of interest that vasopressin has some slight oxytocic activity (uterine-stimulating and milk-ejecting activities) and oxytocin has slight pressor and antidiuretic actions. This is so even with the highly purified preparations and appears to be due to the similarity of molecular structure of these hormones.

The functional activity of the neurohypophysis is entirely dependent on its nerve supply from the hypothalamus. This innervation is described above (see p. 1489); it consists of a large number of unmyelinated fibers (100,000 in man) arising from the supraoptic and paraventricular hypothalamic nuclei, and possibly other nuclear groups. These fibers converge to the pituitary stalk and end in all three parts of the neurohypophysis; the median eminence, the infundibular stem, and the infundibular process. This latter point is of much significance when earlier studies are considered, for section of the pituitary stalk clearly does not denervate the whole neurohypophysis. The upper end of the stalk and the median eminence of the tuber cinereum, which constitute about 13 per cent of total neurohypophysial tissue, remain intact and innervated. The statement that neurohypophysial function is dependent on its nerve supply is based on the facts that, first, a lesion placed in the supraopticohypophysial tract in the hypothalamus results in loss of posterior pituitary activity, atrophy of all three parts of the gland, loss of extractable activity from the gland, and disappearance of neurones from the supraoptic and paraventricular nuclei. Second, electrical stimulation of the supraopticohypophysial tract results in rapid discharge of posterior pituitary hormone as shown by an increase in uterine activity, milk ejection, antidiuresis, increase in intestinal peristalsis, possibly

a slight increase in blood pressure, and an increased excretion of antidiuretic material in the urine.

The physiological actions of the neurohypophysis are suggested by the responses excited by injection of small doses of posterior pituitary extract; they are confirmed as potential activities of the gland when similar responses are observed to follow electrical stimulation of the supraopticohypophysial tract; they are established as physiological functions if they are abolished by denervation, or removal, of the entire neurohypophysis, and they occur after physiological stimuli such as suckling.

1. ANTIDIURETIC ACTION. Very small doses of posterior pituitary extract, or purified vasopressin, are effective in inhibiting a water diuresis. In the rabbit, about 0.1 to 1 milliunit is sufficient in this respect. Electrical stimulation of the supraopticohypophysial tract in the conscious animal, by the remote control method, is also effective in inhibiting a water diuresis. The magnitude of the antidiuretic response varies with the strength and duration of the stimulus and can be very closely matched, in both the effect on water and chloride excretion, by injection of an appropriate dose of vasopressin.

It has long been known that a lesion in the floor of the third ventricle may be followed by the clinical condition of *diabetes insipidus*, in which large volumes of hypotonic urine are excreted each day (see p. 1524). Ranson and his colleagues were able to produce a similar picture in cats and monkeys, by placing bilateral electrolytic lesions in the supraopticohypophysial tract in the hypothalamus. Their cats developed a permanent polyuria of 300 to 500 ml. of urine per day (normal urine output for the cat is about 100 ml. per day), which could be reduced to normal levels by replacement therapy with posterior pituitary extracts. After killing these animals they found that the greater number of nerve fibers in the neural lobe of the pituitary had disappeared, that the neurohypophysis was shrunken and hypercellular, and that extracts of these atrophic glands possessed greatly diminished pressor, antidiuretic, and oxytocic activity, though the melanophore activity was normal. This latter observation may be correlated with the normal pars intermedia found in these animals. Previous to this study it had been found by other workers that pituitary stalk section in the monkey did not lead to diabetes insipidus, though it did in the dog. On these grounds it was argued that denervation of the neural lobe was not essential to the onset of diabetes. However, Fisher and coworkers in a later study showed that stab wounds placed in the median eminence of the monkey resulted in a marked polyuria, and suggested that pituitary stalk section in this form left intact sufficient neurohypophysial tissue in the still innervated median eminence to prevent the onset of diabetes. It may be pointed out that animals deprived of the pars distalis, as well as the neurohypophysis, develop only a slight polyuria if any at all. The pars distalis exerts a general diuretic effect which is necessary for the development of a marked polyuria. This may be observed in human patients with an expanding lesion in the sella turcica. Destruction of the neurohypophysis results in diabetes insipidus, but further development of the lesion may destroy the pars distalis with amelioration of the diabetes.

The reflex release of antidiuretic hormone in response to physiological stimuli has been studied particularly by Verney and coworkers. Emotional excitement and the osmotic pressure of the blood are prominent factors in this category. Emotional stress produced in a variety of ways (exercise, loud noise, pain) was found to be associated with an antidiuresis of the same type as that following injection of posterior pituitary extract. Prior removal of the posterior lobe of the pituitary or section of the supraopticohypophysial tracts reduced the response to about 5 per cent of its previous magnitude. In early work, Verney formed the view that the diuresis which follows the drinking of water was due to inhibition of the posterior pituitary gland. If this inhibition was mediated by a reduced osmotic pressure of the blood, then injection or slow infusion of *hypertonic* sodium chloride, especially into the arterial supply of the hypothalamo-hypophysial region, would be expected to cause discharge of antidiuretic hormone. Such was found to be the case. For example, injection of 20 cc. of 0.343 M NaCl in 25 seconds into the carotid artery produced a marked inhibitory response on the course of a water diuresis. A similar injection made intravenously had little effect, and the response to the carotid injection was markedly reduced by previous removal of the neural lobe. It is likely that the sensitive osmoreceptors lie in or near to the supraoptic nuclei in the hypothalamus. By slow infusions of hypertonic solutions into the carotid artery, Verney showed that changes of only 1 per cent in the osmotic pressure of the blood are effective in exciting release of about 1 microunit per second of antidiuretic substance. Such changes in osmotic pressure are within the range of the

falls reported in water diuresis in man. The dog has been found to liberate about 1 to 5 milliunits of antidiuretic hormone per hour, and under the influence of an emotional stimulus discharges 5 to 10 milliunits of hormone. For further information see the review by Verney (1947).

2. PRESSOR ACTION. Much larger doses of vasopressin are required to elicit a pressor than an antidiuretic response. Electrical stimulation of the supraopticohypophysial tract in the conscious animal excites a slight increase in blood pressure of the same type as that following injection of vasopressin. However, the fact that hemorrhage and fainting appear to stimulate secretion of the vasopressor hormone supports the view that this hormone plays a physiological role in maintaining the blood pressure.

3. ACTION ON INTESTINAL PERISTALSIS. Again, large doses of vasopressor hormone are required to elicit an observable increase in intestinal peristalsis. However, electrical stimulation of the nerve supply to the neurohypophysis evokes a clear increase in peristalsis in the colon of the conscious rabbit. Although posterior pituitary extracts have long been used in man for the treatment of paralytic ileus, there is little evidence in the human that the posterior pituitary normally plays a physiological role in regulating intestinal motility. In this respect, Cushing's observation that patients with tumors that have destroyed the neurohypophysis are " . . . notably victimized by chronic constipation," is of interest.

4. HYPERGLYCEMIC ACTION. Both vasopressin and oxytocin cause hyperglycemia, but which one will have the greater effect depends largely on the species. In rabbits vasopressin has the greater hyperglycemic action, whereas in dogs oxytocin is more effective. The dose necessary to induce this effect is very large. No equivalent hyperglycemic action has been obtained by electrical stimulation of the neurohypophysis. It is unlikely that the posterior pituitary plays a physiological role in regulating the blood sugar.

5. OXYTOCIC ACTION ON THE UTERUS. The discovery of the oxytocic (swift birth) action of posterior pituitary extracts led, as it was bound to do, to the theory that the elaboration and discharge of a principle by the pituitary constituted an important factor in the birth mechanism. Such a view received tacit acceptance until it was found that many forms, including mice, rats, rabbits, guinea pigs, and others, delivered their young after hypophysectomy. However, Fisher and coworkers noted that six out of seven cats, suffering from diabetes insipidus consequent to hypo-

thalamic lesions, had serious difficulty in parturition. They suggested that the reports of successful delivery after hypophysectomy might be due to the fact that neurohypophysial tissue in the pituitary stalk and median eminence had been left intact by the operation. A further study by Fisher and his colleagues showed that slightly less than one-third of a number of guinea pigs, in which the neurohypophysis had been completely denervated by hypothalamic lesions, could undergo normal parturition. Similar, somewhat discordant, findings have been reported for human patients with diabetes insipidus. It seems then that in the absence of neurohypophysial function other factors may compensate and result in apparently normal parturition in a proportion of cases.

Electrical stimulation of the neurohypophysis or its nerve supply has been found to result in increased uterine contractions in postpartum and estrous rabbits. Haterius and Ferguson showed that electrical stimulation of the pituitary stalk in anesthetized rabbits, 2 to 8 hours after delivery, resulted in increased uterine activity. Ferguson later showed that this response was still obtained even if all the tissues of the neck were crushed except the carotid arteries, jugular veins, and a flap of skin. In a more recent study by Harris it was found that electrical stimulation of the supraopticohypophysial tract in the conscious, estrous rabbit evoked increased uterine activity. The magnitude of the response varied with the intensity and duration of the stimulus. The pattern of the uterine response could be matched more nearly by intravenous injection of an oxytocic extract than by an injection of whole posterior pituitary extract. Maximal stimulation was found to be equivalent to the injection of 200 to 500 milliunits of the oxytocic fraction. Cross (1958) has recently found that labor may be induced in anesthetized rabbits at term by injection of 50 to 200 milliunits of oxytocin or by electrical stimulation of the supraopticohypophysial tract. From his experiments Cross concludes that the secretion of oxytocin may well play a part in initiating labor and may be secreted during the course of labor under the influence of nervous reflexes initiated by distension of the uterine cervix, as first suggested by Ferguson. The studies of Caldeyro-Barcia and coworkers on the reactivity of the human uterus to synthetic oxytocin infused intravenously, lend indirect support to the views that the oxytocic hormone forms part of the mechanism controlling uterine activity during normal labor. Also in favor of this view is the observation of Gunther who noted milk ejection from the

nipple of a woman during parturition. The mammary expulsion of milk coincided with the labor pains, and afforded sound evidence of an increased concentration of oxytocin in the blood at these times.

The suggestion has been made that oxytocic hormone is released by a nervous reflex excited by the act of mating, and that the resultant increase in uterine motility normally plays a part in the transport of seminal fluid up the female reproductive tract. Data relating to this view may be summarized as follows.

1. The ascent of spermatozoa in the genital tract of many forms (rat, rabbit, guinea-pig, dog, sheep, and cow) occurs too rapidly to be accounted for in terms of sperm motility.

2. An increase in uterine activity has been found to follow mating or mechanical stimulation of the external genitalia or cervix of the uterus.

3. Evidence that oxytocin is released by the act of mating, or by manipulation of the vulva or cervix uteri is afforded by the milk ejection that has been observed to follow these stimuli.

4. Fitzpatrick and Hughes have observed an increase in oxytocic activity in jugular vein blood of cows consequent to manipulation of the uterus or cervix.

The evidence is suggestive that the oxytocic hormone normally plays a role in seminal transport, but further work involving assays of oxytocin before and after coitus and investigations of any disabilities in sperm transport in animals after disturbance or denervation of the neurohypophysis are required.

6. MILK EJECTING ACTION. As with the oxytocic effect on the uterus, milk ejection may be produced in the lactating mammary gland by administration of very small doses of oxytocin that seem within a physiological range. As recounted above, there has long been evidence that the transfer of milk from mother to suckling young involves an active squeezing out of milk from the mammary tissue by the maternal organism. Petersen was the first to suggest that reflex stimulation of posterior pituitary secretion was involved in the process. Definitive evidence that this is so came from experiments in sheep, goats, and rabbits in which it was demonstrated that electrical stimulation of the supraopticohypophysial tract results in milk ejection. Conversely, it was found that following denervation of the neurohypophysis by the placement of hypothalamic lesions in lactating rabbits, the young obtained only a small fraction of the normal quantity of milk. However, if the mother

animal was injected with oxytocin just prior to suckling, the milk obtained by her young approximated the normal amount. From this and other evidence there can be no doubt that the sensory stimuli associated with suckling, and probably conditioned stimuli as well, reflexly excite the neurohypophysis to discharge oxytocic hormone. This hormone in turn causes contraction of the specialized myoepithelial tissue in the mammary gland, so that a positive ejection of milk occurs.

There is much evidence that a similar mechanism occurs in the human. It is well known that embarrassment, worry, or fright at the time of nursing may inhibit the flow of milk to the baby. This inhibition may, however, be overcome by injection of oxytocin. Haeger and Jacobsohn have observed striking increases in milk yield to follow injection of oxytocin into women with poor lactational performance but with engorged and painful mammae. It is of interest that after a single injection of oxytocin lactation proceeded normally, without the need of further injections, in the majority of cases.

In summary it may be said that posterior pituitary hormones play a physiological role in regulating the excretion of water by the kidney, and the ejection of milk from the lactating mammary gland. In all probability the oxytocic activity is of importance in parturition, and may also be concerned with the transport of seminal fluid in the female reproductive tract. It is possible that neurohypophysial secretion is one of the factors regulating intestinal motility and in maintaining a falling blood pressure. The hypoglycemic action of posterior pituitary extracts is of pharmacological interest only.

The melanophore-expanding principle (present in posterior pituitary extracts but a secretion of the pars intermedia of the pituitary) plays an important role in lower forms (fishes, amphibians) in regulating the expansion of melanophores and erythrophores in response to retinal-nervous reflexes.

Assay of Posterior Pituitary Hormone

Assays of posterior pituitary hormones are performed with regard to their antidiuretic, vasopressor, or oxytocic activity. Since the vasopressor and oxytocic hormones have overlapping activities, no assay method is entirely specific, though suitable corrections may be made for the overlapping activity. For further details see the review by van Dyke and coworkers (1955).

1. *Antidiuretic assays.* The unknown and standard extract are administered to rats or dogs during a water diuresis, and the antidiuretic response

measured. Probably the method of choice involves the use of the trained dog, given water by stomach tube, and the extracts by intravenous injection. This is a specific and sensitive method, and will detect 0.25 milliunit of antidiuretic hormone.

2. *Vasopressor assays.* In the past assay of the pressor potency of pituitary hormone has frequently been performed on the dog or cat, but the anesthetized rat now seems the method of choice. The extracts are injected intravenously; about 4 milliunits of vasopressin produces a definite pressor response.

3. *Oxytocic activity.* The classical method involving the use of the isolated guinea pig uterus *in vitro* is suitable for assay of material of high potency. The depressor action of oxytocin on the blood pressure of the fowl has been widely used as the basis of an assay method but is relatively insensitive. Probably the most sensitive and reliable method is that devised by van Dyke and his colleagues in which the milk ejection response of a cannulated teat duct of an anesthetized rabbit is employed. The threshold dose is of the order 2 to 3 milliunits in this preparation.

The results of all assays should be expressed in terms of the international standard. One international unit is the antidiuretic, pressor or oxytocic activity present in 0.5 mg. of the international standard preparation.

THE FORMATION AND FATE OF NEUROHYPOPHYSIAL HORMONES. The fact that the neurohypophysis lacks glandular cells has long posed the problem as to the cellular site of formation of the hormones. For a long time it was believed that the cells of the pars intermedia migrated posteriorly into the neurohypophysis and liberated posterior pituitary hormones. That this is not so is shown by the facts that such forms, such as the porpoise and whale, in which the neural lobe is separated from all parts of the adenohypophysis by a thick connective tissue septum, show the usual activities of neural lobe extracts (except melanophore-expanding activity), and also that animals with an atrophic neurohypophysis due to an hypothalamic lesion show a loss of extractable activity although the pars intermedia appears normal. It was then suggested that certain rather specialized cells in the neurohypophysis (pituicytes of Bucy; or the parenchymatous glandular cells of Gersh) secreted neurohypophysial hormones. However, the data regarding the secretory nature of these cells were controversial, and the evidence that material rich in posterior pituitary activity could be extracted from the hypothalamus was difficult to explain since such cells do not exist in this region.

A view, which has received wide acceptance in the last 10 years, holds that the hypothalamo-neurohypophysial unit acts as a *neurosecretory mechanism*. E. and B. Scharrer have for many years investigated the possibility that neurons in the central nervous system secrete hormone into the blood stream. There was formerly more evidence to uphold this thesis in invertebrates than vertebrates, but in 1949, Bargmann demonstrated that the cells in the paraventricular and supraoptic nuclei, and their nerve fibers sweeping through the basal hypothalamus, pituitary stalk, and neural lobe, may be selectively stained by the Gomori-chrome-alum hematoxylin method. Striking histological pictures have been obtained in many forms in which cell groups and nerve tracts are deeply stained in contrast to surrounding neural structures. The general view is that the stainable material seen in these neurons is either neurohypophysial hormone or some carrier material closely linked with the hormone, and that it is found in the cell bodies in the hypothalamic nuclei and transported down the axons to be liberated into the blood vessels in three parts of the neurohypophysis. There are no reasons to doubt that these neurons function also as do other nerve cells, and that the rate of discharge of hormone from the nerve terminals into the vascular system is regulated by nervous impulses in the same nerve fibers. It is unlikely that the hormone can be discharged from any part of the neuron except the nerve terminals existing in the neurohypophysis, since lesions in the nerve tract above the median eminence uniformly result in diabetes insipidus and since the permeability properties of the blood vessels of the neurohypophysis are so markedly different from those of the hypothalamus proper. The evidence relating the stainable material to hormonal activity has been mainly concerned with the antidiuretic function. In different forms, and in the same form under different conditions of dehydration or exposure to stress, there is a correlation between the amount of stainable material and the content of vasopressor hormone. The relationship with oxytocin is less clear, since it has been established that there is very little oxytocic activity in extracts of hypothalamic tissue. It is possible that oxytocic hormone is formed during the transport of neurosecretory material into the neural lobe itself. The neurosecretory view of the origin of posterior pituitary hormones affords an obvious explanation for the lack of secretory cells in the neurohypophysis and for the presence of hormonally active material in hypothalamic extracts.

Although at one time it was thought that the hormones of the posterior pituitary passed up the pituitary stalk and into the third ventricle, it is now believed that they are secreted into the capillaries of the gland and into the venous system directly. The form in which the hormones are transported in the blood is unknown, but it is possible that they are secreted as polypeptides and become linked to the plasma protein. The hormonal activities of injected extracts disappear from the blood stream within a few minutes, and evidence exists that a major part of this inactivation occurs in the liver and kidneys (Heller, 1957). A further portion (about 25 per cent) of the activity of administered hormone, or of the hormone discharged from the neurohypophysis by electrical stimulation, appears in the urine; it is impossible to say though, whether this represents the unchanged hormone or a biologically active metabolite.

Disorders of the Pituitary in Man

Derangements of pituitary function may take the form of overactivity or of deficiency. In the former case tumors composed of functioning endocrine tissue are frequently the cause of the disorder; in the latter, atrophy or degeneration of the specific secreting cells, either primarily or as the result of mechanical pressure by tumors, may be responsible. A pituitary tumor of the anterior lobe may be composed of any of the cellular elements of the gland; *chromophobe, acidophil, or basophil* adenomas. Squamous-celled growths (craniopharyngeomas) may also arise from epithelial rests (remnants of Rathke's pouch) near the root of the infundibular stalk. As a result of the confined position of the pituitary within the sella turcica the entire gland is likely to suffer from pressure effects when one of its parts becomes enlarged. For this reason and on account of the proximity of other important structures, e.g., hypothalamus and optic chiasma, and the proclivity of tumors to invade or press upon neighboring structures, the manifestations of a pituitary tumor are not always referable simply to the part of the pituitary originally involved. Any function (growth, sex, water elimination, or the metabolism of carbohydrate or fat) presided over by the pituitary-hypothalamic mechanism may, therefore, be disturbed by a lesion in this region. Nevertheless, the site wherein the tumor arises and the nature of the cells of which it is composed do very often determine the predominant features of the condition, and certain fairly well defined groups of symptoms (syndromes) are recognized. To these may or may not be added symptoms referable to pressure upon, or to irritation or destruction of, nearby nervous structures.

The following is a short classification of pituitary diseases.

I. Anterior lobe
  A. Overactivity
    1. Acromegaly
    2. Gigantism
    3. Pituitary basophilism (Cushing's disease)
  B. Deficiency
    1. Dwarfism
    2. Pituitary cachexia (Simmond's disease)
    3. Acromicria
II. Posterior lobe deficiency or hypothalamic lesion
  A. Diabetes insipidus
III. Anterior lobe deficiency together with posterior lobe deficiency or hypothalmic lesion
  A. Dystrophia adiposo-genitalis (Frohlich)
    1. Infantile or juvenile type
    2. Adolescent or adult type

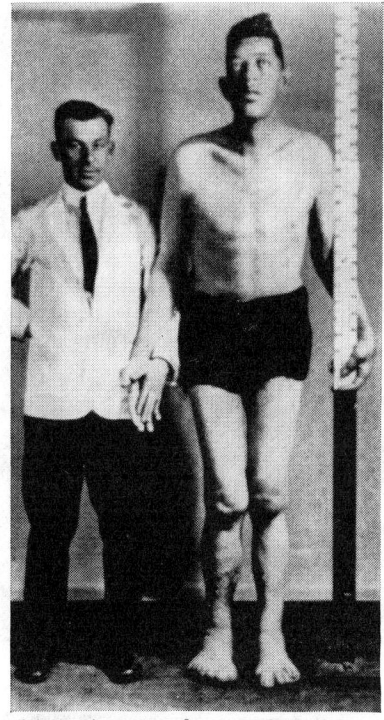

Fig. 74.17. Acromegaly, together with enlarged stature—acromegalic **gigantism**. (From Cushing and Davidoff.)

ACROMEGALY

This condition was first described by Pierre Marie in 1885. It is due to the excessive elaboration of the growth hormone during adult life, i.e., after the usual age of full skeletal growth (fig. 74.17). An adenomatous tumor of the anterior lobe composed of acidophil cells is responsible or the hypersecretion. The characteristic features of the condition are: (a) Overgrowth of the bones of the hands, feet, and face. Of the latter, the mandible, nasal bones, and supraorbital ridges are especially involved (fig. 74.18). The feet and hands are greatly increased in size, the latter being usually broadened and the fingers thickened; under the X-rays, the terminal phalanges appear tufted, thus resembling a wheat sheaf in shape.

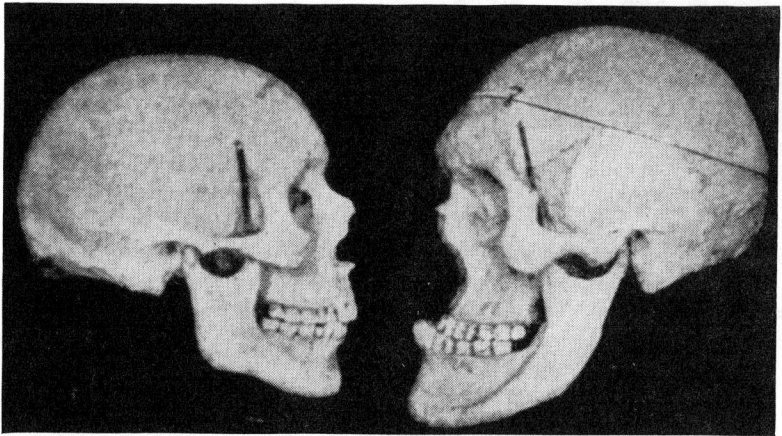

Fig. 74.18. Skulls of a normal person (left) and of an acromegalic (right). (From Cushing and Davidoff).

FIG. 74.19. Gigantism

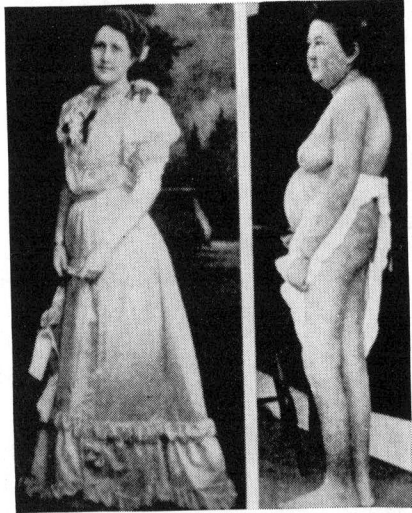

FIG. 74.20. On left, at 20 years of age; on right, 5 years later at height of the disease. (From Cushing and Turney.)

tion of gonadotrophins. In the earlier stages, however, there may be evidence of increased sexual function. (d) Enlargement of the viscera (splanchnomegaly). The tongue, lungs, thymus, heart, liver, and spleen are greatly enlarged. The thyroid, parathyroids, and adrenals may show hypertrophy or adenomatous growth. Hyperthyroidism may be present in the early stages. (e) Glycosuria and hyperglycemia are common, and a condition indistinguishable from diabetes of pancreatic origin may be present. The metabolic rate may be raised from 10 to 70 per cent; the specific dynamic action of protein is not altered (p. 1310).

GIGANTISM

Gigantism is due to a pituitary lesion of a similar nature to that responsible for acromegaly, but the condition arises in preadult life, i.e., before ossification is complete (fig. 74.19). A general overgrowth of the skeleton results and the production of persons of enormous stature, 7 or 8 feet or more in height. The limbs are usually disproportionately long. The viscera are not enlarged out of proportion to the frame unless, as is sometimes the case, the gigantism is accompanied by the characteristic features of acromegaly, as may occur after adolescence.

CUSHING'S DISEASE: CUSHING'S SYNDROME

This is a rare disease. Its main features are: (a) Obesity of the trunk (especially of the abdomen), face, and buttocks, but not of the limbs; these latter show some wasting (fig. 74.20). The fattening of face leads to rounding of the facial contours which obscures the bony structure, producing the so-called "moon face." There is, thus, a redistribution of body fat, which is mobilized from the limbs and deposited in the regions mentioned. The fatty deposits are frequently tense, tender, and painful. Purplish striae, due to distension, are present over the lower abdomen. (b) Polycythemia with cyanosis of the face, hands, and feet, pigmentation of the skin, and excessive growth of hair. Women may grow a mustache or a beard. (c) Loss of mineral from the bones, leading to osteoporosis, softening or brittleness. The softening often involves the dorsal vertebrae, and causes kyphosis, which with the deposition of fat in the interscapular region gives the appearance known as "buffalo neck." (d) Systolic hypertension. (e) Suppression of sexual functions. (f) Hyperglycemia and glycosuria and in some cases increased urinary excretion of nitrogen. (g) Atrophy of

Bowing of the spine (kyphosis) is common. The soft tissues of the nose, lips, forehead, and scalp are thickened, the latter being thrown into folds or wrinkles (bulldog scalp). There is a general overgrowth of body hair. (b) Atrophy of the gonads and suppression of the sexual function (amenorrhea in women, impotence in men). (c) Moderate increase in the urinary excretion of 17-ketosteroids and corticoids with reduced excre-

testes or ovaries, and hypertrophy of the adrenal cortex with signs of hypersecretion of its hormones. (h) Increased urinary excretion of 11-oxycorticosteroids, and often of 17-ketosteroids; high uric acid:creatinine ratio. (i) Eosinopenia, lymphopenia, low blood potassium, and retention of sodium chloride with increase of body fluids and a tendency to edema.

The disease as originally described by Harvey Cushing (1932) was associated with a basophil adenoma of the adenohypophysis.[9] It has since been found that the syndrome may arise either as a result of a pituitary tumor (excess ACTH production and stimulation of the adrenal cortex) or from primary hyperplasia or tumor of the adrenal cortex. The manifestations, it will have been observed, are in either case referable for the most part to excessive adrenocortical secretion. Sometimes Cushing's *disease* is restricted to cases associated with a pituitary tumor, and Cushing's *syndrome* applied to the condition due to primary adrenal tumor or hyperplasia.

DWARFISM

The arrested skeletal development which results from deficiency of the growth hormone of the anterior pituitary is spoken of as the *Lorain* type of infantilism (fig. 74.21). These dwarfs are usually, though not invariably, undeveloped sexually. They do not show deformity or, as a rule, mental inferiority, and are generally not unattractive in appearance. Sometimes, however, they are wizened and except for their diminutive stature appear older than their years (progeria). The condition may then be considered the counterpart of Simmond's disease, but commencing before puberty. The anterior lobe dwarf at adult age may be no more than 3 or 4 feet high. During infancy and childhood, the ossification centers, as observed by radioscopy, appear normal and dentition is not delayed. The relative proportions of the different parts of the skeleton are not far from normal though they tend toward those characteristic of childhood; the head being large relative to the body. Some encouraging results have been reported from the treatment of this type of dwarfism with anterior pituitary extracts of primate origin.

⁹ Susman found, however, that in the postmortem examination of a large number of pituitaries, small basophil adenomas were present in 3.1 per cent, though no sign of basophilism was observed during life. Crook also states that a basophil adenoma or a general increase in basophil cells is an inconstant finding in Cushing's syndrome, but that hyaline degeneration of these cells (with or without adenoma) is invariable.

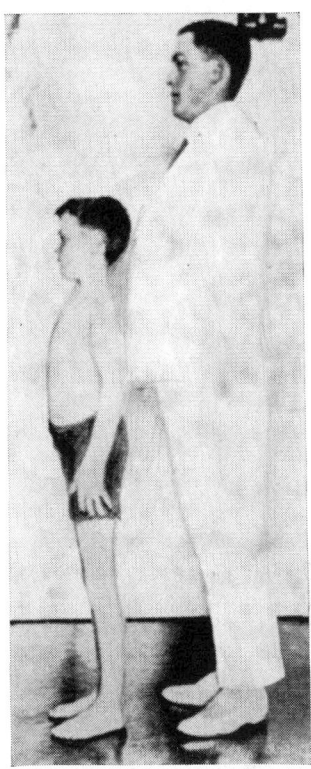

FIG. 74.21. Infantilism due to anterior lobar deficiency. Age 21 years. Man on right is 5 feet 7 inches tall. (From Lisser.)

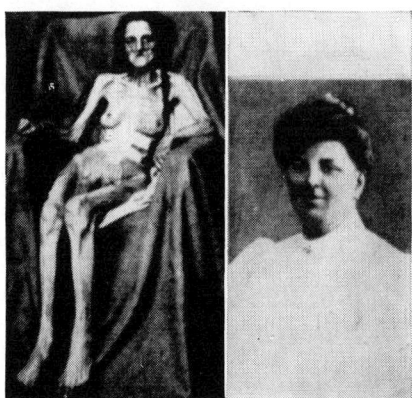

FIG. 74.22. Pituitary cachexia. On left, patient aged 42 years; on right, the same woman at the age of 34 years. (From Zondek, *Diseases of the Endocrine Glands*, by permission of Edward Arnold & Co., London.)

PITUITARY CACHEXIA (SIMMOND'S DISEASE)

This rare disease was first described by Simmonds of Hamburg. It is due to atrophy or degeneration of the anterior lobe. The main features of this disease form a picture which may best be described as that of a premature and rapidly developing senile decay (fig. 74.22). They are largely referable to severe depression of activity of the adrenal cortex and other target organs, e.g., gonads and thyroid, as a result of deficiency of the trophic hormones of the pituitary.

The characteristics of the disease are as follows: (a) *General appearance* (loss of axillary and pubic hair, hair of the head prematurely gray and sparse, loss of teeth, skin of face wrinkled and dry, smallness of hands and feet, and shrunken appearance of the facial features); (b) *anemia;* (c) *low metabolic rate* and *hypoglycemia;* (d) *amenorrhea or impotence;* (e) *mental deterioration, muscular weakness, death in coma;* (f) *atrophy of the gonads* and a general smallness of the internal organs (*splanchnomicria*); (g) *reduced urinary excretion of gonadotrophins, 11-oxycorticoids and 17-ketosteroids, and depression of protein bound iodine of the blood;* (h) *acute adrenal insufficiency may occur;* (i) *emaciation,* such as shown in fig. 74.22, may occur but is not common.

The disease most commonly follows childbirth in which there has been severe hemorrhage with peripheral circulatory collapse. It is likely that the hypophysial portal blood supply in some way becomes obstructed, thus accounting for the necrosis and fibrosis found on postmortem examination of the pituitary. Milder manifestations of the disease developing after childbirth have been described by Sheehan, which are now referred to as *Sheehan's syndrome.*

DIABETES INSIPIDUS (see also p. 1516 and ch. 79)

Diabetes insipidus is a condition in which large quantities of urine of very low specific gravity, 1.002 to 1.006, and low chloride content are excreted. In an ordinary case the daily output of urine is 4 or 5 liters, but daily amounts several times these figures have been reported. A corresponding increase in the fluid intake occurs and thirst is often intense. The condition frequently accompanies tumors of the pituitary or hypothalamic region, and is essentially due to lack of posterior pituitary hormone through damage to the hypothalamo-neurohypophysial unit. As described above (p. 1516), Fisher, Ingram, and Ranson were able to duplicate this state experimentally and showed that either damage to the neurohypophysis, or denervation of the neurohypophysis by means of a hypothalamic lesion, were equally effective in evoking this condition.

It will be recalled (ch. 79) that only about 15 per cent of the glomerular filtrate is reabsorbed by the nephron distal to the proximal convoluted tubule ("facultative" reabsorption) and upon this fraction alone is the action of the antidiuretic

hormone exerted; the reabsorption of water by the proximal tubule ("obligative" reabsorption) is not altered. Therefore, a limit is set to the increase in urine output even though ADH be completely absent. If, say, the glomerular filtrate amounts to 180 liters daily, at least 150 liters must be reabsorbed under all circumstances, leaving less than 30 liters as the maximum amount of urine which could be produced.

The failure of total hypophysectomy to produce diabetes insipidus is due to the loss of the anterior pituitary gland. This was first pointed out by von Hann from his findings at human autopsies, and confirmed by the experimental work of Richter. It seems that the anterior lobe, through its general metabolic effects, exerts a diuretic influence, and that in the absence of this action posterior pituitary deficiency is not revealed by the development of polyuria.

In diabetes insipidus the ingestion of large quantities of water of a temperature below that of the body necessitates readjustments in the heat regulating mechanisms. Vasoconstriction of the skin vessels occurs; the extremities are often cold and may be cyanotic, and the subject is very sensitive to cold. The vasoconstriction is apparently a compensatory measure for heat conservation. Shivering and a rise in the metabolic rate may also result; the food intake is then, as a consequence, increased.

Administration of posterior pituitary extract is the only available means for the control of diabetes insipidus and, as mentioned below, this is not successful in some cases. The whole extract (or the vasopressin fraction) may be given by injection or by means of pledgets of absorbent cotton soaked in the solution and inserted into the nose. The polyuria of nephritis is not influenced by this medication. Water intoxication may occur in diabetes insipidus if posterior pituitary extract is administered and the patient is requested to maintain the usual fluid intake. The urea clearances are normal as a rule.

The fundamental mechanisms concerned in the polyuria of diabetes insipidus appear to be allied in nature to those underlying the diuresis of water drinking in normal persons. But the thirst and the consequent excessive ingestion of water experienced by subjects of diabetes insipidus is not primary, as in the water diuresis of normal persons, but is secondary to the polyuria and the resulting tendency toward dehydration: the deprivation of water carried to the limit of endurance does not prevent the excretion of large quantities of water.

The results of Richter's work upon rats, in which diabetes insipidus was produced by partial hypophysectomy or a stab wound in the floor of the third ventricle, indicate that in the experimental condition polyuria is also primary. He states that polyuria preceded polydipsia and that animals deprived of water continued to excrete large quantities of urine.

About 10 per cent of cases, classed as diabetes insipidus, do not respond to postpituitary preparations, or do so very poorly. Such cases are congenital or show a familial tendency, and are thought to be due to an inherent defect of the renal tubules with respect to the renal absorption of water—a persistence, it would seem, of the infantile incapacity of the tubules to concentrate the urine.

Polyuria, simulating in some ways diabetes insipidus, occurs in *chronic nephritis* (ch. 80) and in *psychogenic polydipsia*. The polyuria in chronic nephritis is not corrected by pituitary extracts and in polydipsia thirst is *primary*; the urine volume is reduced and the specific gravity of the urine is raised by rigid deprivation of water; the polyuria is simply a normal diuretic response to water drinking.

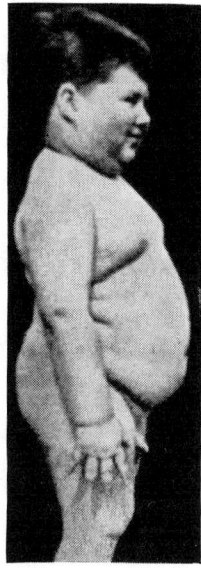

Fig. 74.23. Male aged 8 years. Hypopituitarism following whooping cough, with characteristic growth and sex defects and obesity; Fröhlich's syndrome. (From Gardiner-Hill.)

DYSTROPHIA ADIPOSO-GENITALIS

Dystrophia adiposo-genitalis, as its name suggests, is a condition in which obesity, sexual infantilism, and dwarfing (if the condition occurs during the growing period) are the essential features. It is due to a lesion of the anterior lobe of the pituitary, which accounts for the sexual immaturity and dwarfing, and of the hypothalamus. The experiments of Smith with hypophysectomized rats, and of other investigators, point to injury of the hypothalamus as being chiefly responsible for the obesity. Marked obesity is also a feature of certain hypothalamic disorders in man unassociated apparently with any disease of the pituitary itself. Dystrophia adiposo-genitalis appears in two forms according to the age at which it develops; the *infantile* or *prepubertal* and the *adolescent* or *adult*.

THE INFANTILE OR PREPUBERTAL TYPE, FROLICH'S SYNDROME (fig. 74.23). This type may occur in children of any age before puberty. It may be the result of an inherent defect of the pituitary, of atrophy of the secretory cells by pressure (e.g., by tumors), injury (e.g., a penetrating wound), or of some infectious disease. Polyuria and a high sugar tolerance are frequent accompaniments of the disease. The subjects are lethargic or somnolent and often of subnormal intelligence. They usually have voracious appetites and especially a craving for sweets. The "fat boy" of *Pickwick Papers* was undoubtedly an example of this condition. The younger the age of the child at which the disease commences the greater, obviously, will be the degree of stunting. When the dwarfing is of high grade, this combined with the obesity makes a very striking picture. These subjects are human counterparts of Smith's rats in which the pituitary was destroyed (and the hypothalamus presumably injured) by chromic acid injections. Since obesity and an *apparent* sexual infantilism may occur in normal adolescent boys, the diagnosis of Frohlich's syndrome in such cases should be applied only to those patients with proven hypothalamic damage.

THE ADOLESCENT OR ADULT TYPE. Male subjects of this condition are often effeminate in disposition and appearance. The excess fat has a feminine distribution, the adiposity being noticeable chiefly in the mammary region, buttocks, thighs, and over the mons veneris. The hair over the pubis and in the axillae is sparse or absent; the skin of the face and the body is smooth, soft, and hairless; the hips are broad. In female subjects the obesity is often extreme, a weight of 300 pounds being not very unusual (fig. 74.24). In both sexes the feet and hands are small and "pretty," the finger tips being slender and tapering with narrow pointed terminal phalanges. The extremities thus give a picture the reverse of that

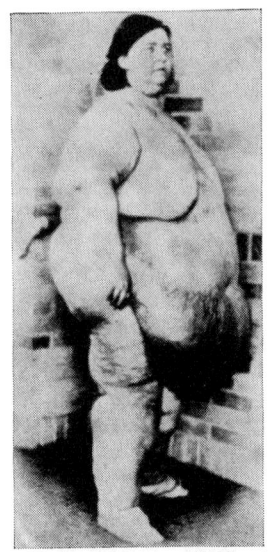

FIG. 74.24. Extreme case of obesity, due to pituitary or hypothalamic disease. (From Timme).

seen in acromegaly. The basal metabolic rate is often subnormal and sugar tolerance increased. Diabetes insipidus is a common, and narcolepsy (p. 160) an occasional, accompaniment.

REFERENCES

ALLEN, B. M. Anat. Rec., 1916, 11, 486.

ASCHHEIM, S. AND ZONDEK, B. Klin. Wschr., 1927, 6, 1322.

ASCHNER, B. Arch. ges. Physiol., 1912, 146, 1.

BAILEY, P. AND BREMER, F. Arch. Int. Med., 1921, 28, 773.

BAYLISS, W. M. AND STARLING, E. H. Proc. Roy. Soc. London, Series B, 1904, 73, 310.

BERTHOLD, A. A. Arch. Anat. Physiol. Berlin, 1849, 42.

BEST, C. H. AND CAMPBELL, J. J. Physiol., 1936, 86, 190.

BEST, C. H. AND CAMPBELL, J. Lancet, 1938, 1, 1444.

BISSONETTE, T. H. Proc. A. Res. Nerv. & Ment. Dis., 1936, 17, 361.

BISSONETTE, T. H. Wilson Bull., 1937, 49, 241.

BISSONETTE, T. H. Endocrinology, 1938, 22, 92.

BLACK, P. T., COLLIP, J. B. AND THOMSON, D. L. J. Physiol., 1934, 82, 385.

BLOUNT, R. F. Proc. Nat. Acad. Sc., 1930, 16, 222.

BODIAN, D. Bull. Johns Hopkins Hosp., 1951, 33, 354.

BURN, J. H. AND LING, H. W. Quart. J. Pharm. & Pharmacol., 1933, 6, 31.

BURN, J. P. J. Physiol., 1923, 57, 318.

COLLIP, J. B. Proc. Soc. Exper. Biol. & Med., 1933, 30, 544.

COLLIP, J. B. Tr. Am. A. Study Goiter, 1937.

COLLIP, J. B. Endocrinology, 1938, 23, 718.

COLLIP, J. B. Endocrinology, 1939, 25, 318.

COLLIP, J. B. AND ANDERSON, E. M. Lancet, 1934, 1, 76.

COLLIP, J. B. AND ASSOCIATES. Lancet, 1933, 2, 347.

CROOKE, A. C. J. Path. & Bact., 1935, 41, 339.

CROSS, B. A. J. Endocrinol., 1958, 16, 261.

CUSHING, H. AND DAVIDOFF, L. M. Rockefeller Institute for Medical Research, New York, Monograph No. 22, 1927.

CUSHING, H. AND GOETSCH, E. Am. J. Physiol., 1910, 27, 60.

DALE, H. H. Biochem. J., 1909, 4, 427.

DANDY, W. E. AND REICHERT, F. L. Bull. Johns Hopkins Hosp., 1938, 62, 122.

D'ANGELO, S. A. AND TRAUM, R. E. Ann. New York Acad. Sc., 1958, 72, 239.

DOBYNS, B. M. AND STEELMAN, S. L. Endocrinology, 1953, 52, 705.

DUDLEY, H. W. J. Pharmacol. & Exper. Therap., 1919, 14, 295.

VAN DYKE, H. B. AND ASSOCIATES. J. Pharmacol. & Exper. Therap., 1942, 74, 190.

EVANS, H. M. AND LONG, J. A. Anat. Rec., 1921, 21, 62 (Proc.).

EVANS, H. M., MEYER, K. AND SIMPSON, M. E. Mem. Univ. California, 1933, 11, 1.

FERGUSON, J. K. W. Am. J. Physiol., 1939, 126, 489.

FISHER, C., INGRAM, W. R. AND RANSON, S. W. Arch. Neurol. & Psychiat., 1935, 34, 124.

FISHER, C., INGRAM, W. R. AND RANSON, S. W. Anat. Rec., 1935, 63, 29.

FISHER, C., INGRAM, W. R. AND RANSON, S. W. Arch. Int. Med., 1936, 57, 1067.

FRIEDGOOD, H. B. Bull. Johns Hopkins Hosp., 1934, 54, 48.

GEILING, E. M. K. AND DeLAWDER, A. M. Bull. Johns Hopkins Hosp., 1932, 51, 1.

GEILING, E. M. K. AND DeLAWDER, A. M. Bull. Johns Hopkins Hosp., 1932, 51, 335.

GEILING, E. M. K. AND OLDHAM, F. K. Tr. Am. A. Physicians, 1937, 52, 132.

GILMAN, A. AND GOODMAN, L. J. Physiol., 1937, 90, 113.

GRATTAN, J. F. AND JENSEN, H. J. J. Biol. Chem., 1940, 135, 551.

GREEN, J. D. Am. J. Anat., 1951, 88, 225.

HALMI, N. S. Endocrinology, 1950, 47, 289.

HALMI, N. S. Endocrinology, 1952, 50, 140.

HAM, A. W. AND HAIST, R. E. Am. J. Path., 1941, 17, 787.

VON HANN, F. Frankfurt. Ztschr. Path., 1918, 21, 337.

HARRIS, G. W. Physiol. Rev., 1948, 28, 139.

HARRIS, G. W. J. Physiol., 1950, 111, 347.

HARRIS, G. W. Ciba Foundation Colloquia on Endocrinology, 1952, 4, 106.

HARRIS, G. W. AND JACOBSOHN, D. Proc. Roy. Soc. London, Series B, 1952, 139, 263.

HELLER, H. Biol. Rev., 1945, 20, 147.

HERRING, P. T. Quart. J. Exper. Physiol., 1908, 1, 121.

HIMSWORTH, H. P. AND SCOTT, D. B. M. J. Physiol., 1938, 91, 447.

HOGBEN, L. T. AND WINTON, F. R. Proc. Roy. Soc. London, Series B, 1922, 93, 318.

HOUSSAY, B. A. AND ASSOCIATES. Compt. rend. Soc. biol., 1922, 86, 115.

HOUSSAY, B. A. AND ASSOCIATES. Endocrinology, 1931, 15, 511.

HOUSSAY, B. A. AND ASSOCIATES. J. Physiol., 1932, 77, 81.

HOUSSAY, B. A. AND ASSOCIATES. Compt. rend. Soc. biol., 1932, 111, 479.

HOUSSAY. B. A. AND ASSOCIATES. Compt. rend. Soc. biol., 1933, 112, 497.

HOWELL, W. H. J. Exper. Med., 1898, 3, 245.

INGRAM, W. R. AND FISHER, C. Anat. Rec., 1936, 66, 271.

INGRAM, W. R. AND FISHER, C. Endocrinology, 1936, 20, 762.

KAMM, O. AND ASSOCIATES. J. Am. Chem. Soc., 1928, 50, 573 (I and II).

LI, C. H. AND ASSOCIATES. Science, 1942, 96, 450.

LI, C. H. AND ASSOCIATES. J. Biol. Chem., 1943, 149, 413.

LI, C. H. AND ASSOCIATES. Harvey Lectures, 1951.

LOEB, L. AND BASSETT, P. B. Proc. Soc. Exper. Biol. & Med., 1929, 26, 860.

MAGNUS, R. AND SCHÄFER, E. A. J. Physiol., 1901, 27, ix.

MARIE, P. Brain, 1889, 12, 59.

MARKS, H. P. J. Physiol., 1936, 87, 15P.

MARSHALL, F. H. A. AND JOLLY, W. A. Tr. Roy. Soc. Edinburgh, 1907, 45, 589.

MARSHALL, F. H. A. AND JOLLY, W. A. Quart. J. Exper. Physiol., 1908, 1, 115.

NIKITOVITCH-WINER, M. AND EVERETT, J. W. Endocrinology, 1958, 63, 916.

OLIVER, G. AND SCHÄFER, E. A. J. Physiol., 1895, 18, 277.

PFEIFFER, C. A. Am. J. Anat., 1936, 58, 195.

POPA, G. T. AND FIELDING, U. J. Anat., 1930, 65, 88.

POPA, G. T. AND FIELDING, U. J. Anat., 1933, 67, 227.

PURVES, H. D. AND GRIESBACH, W. E. Endocrinology, 1951, 49, 244, 427, 652.

PUTNAM, T. J., BENEDICT, E. B. AND TEEL, H. M. Am. J. Physiol., 1928, 84, 157.

PUTNAM, T. J., BENEDICT, E. B. AND TEEL, H. M. Arch. Surg., 1929, 18, 1708.

RASMUSSEN, A. Am. J. Path., 1929, 5, 263.

RASMUSSEN, A. Am. J. Path., 1933, 9, 459.

RAWSON, R. W. Ann. New York Acad. Sc., 1949, 50, 279.

REID, E. J. Endocrinol., 1952, 8, 50.

RICHARDSON, K. C. Proc. Roy. Soc. London, Series B, 1949, 136, 30.

RICHARDSON, K. C. AND YOUNG, F. G. J. Physiol., 1937, 91, 352.

RICHTER, C. P. Brain, 1930, 53, 76.

RICHTER, C. P. Am. J. Physiol., 1934, 110, 124.

RICHTER, C. P. Am. J. Physiol., 1935, 112, 481.

RIDDLE, O. Ohio J. Sc., 1937, 37, 446.

RIOCH, D. M., WISLOCKI, G. B. AND O'LEARY, J. L. Res. Publ. A. Nerv. & Ment. Dis., 1940, 20, 3.

ROWAN, W. M. Nature, 1925, 115, 494.

ROWAN, W. M. Nature, 1927, 119, 351.

ROWLANDS, I. W. AND PARKES, A. S. J. Physiol., 1936, 88, 305.

SHIPLEY, R. A. AND LONG, C. N. H. Biochem. J., 1938, 32, 2242.

SIMMONDS, M. Deutsche med. Wchnschr., 1914, 40, 322.

SMITH, P. E. Science, 1916, 44, 280.

SMITH, P. E. J. A. M. A., 1927, 88, 18.

SMITH, P. E. Am. J. Anat., 1930, 45, 205.

SYDNOR, K. L. Endocrinology, 1955, 56, 204.

SYDNOR, K. L. AND SAYERS, G. Endocrinology, 1954, 55, 621.

DU VIGNEAUD, V. AND ASSOCIATES. J. Am. Chem. Soc., 1953, 75, 4879, 4880.

WILKINS, L., BONGIOVANNI, A. M., CLAYTON, G. W., GRUMBACH, M. M. AND VAN WYCK, J. Ciba Foundation Colloquia on Endocrinology, 1955, 8, 460.

XUEREB, G. P., PRICHARD, M. M. L. AND DANIEL, P. M. Quart. J. Exper. Physiol., 1954, 39, 219.

YOUNG, F. G. Lancet, 1937, 2, 372.

YOUNG, F. G. Proc. Roy. Soc. Med., 1938, 31, 1305.

YOUNG, F. G. Biochem. J., 1945, 39, 515.

ZONDEK, B. J. A. M. A., 1935, 104, 537.

Monographs and Reviews

ABRAMOWITZ, A. A. AND ASSOCIATES. Endocrinology, 1944, 34, 103.

Advances in neuroendocrinology (ed. A. V. NALBANDOV), University of Illinois Press, Urbana, 1963.

BARGMANN, W. AND SCHARRER, E. Am. Scientist, 1951, 39, 255.

BROWN, J. H. U. AND BARKER, S. B. Basic endocrinology. Blackwell Scientific Publications, Oxford, 1962.

BURN, J. H., AND DALE, H. H. Medical Research Council, London, Special Report No. 69, 1922.

CUSHING, H. The pituitary body and its disorders. Lippincott, Philadelphia, 1912.

CUSHING, H. Papers relating to the pituitary body, hypothalamus and parasympathetic nervous system. Charles C Thomas, Springfield, Ill., 1932.

CUSHING, H. Harvey Lectures, 1932–1933, 28, 90.

VAN DYKE, H. B. The physiology and pharmacology of the pituitary body, Vols. I, II. University of Chicago Press, Chicago, 1936, 1939.

VAN DYKE, H. B. Bull. New York Acad. Med., 1953, 29, 24.

VAN DYKE, H. B., ADAMSONS, K. AND ENGEL, S. L. Recent Progr. Hormone Res., 1955, 11, 1.

EINHORN, J. Acta radiol., 1958, Suppl. 160.

EVANS, H. M., MEYER, K. AND SIMPSON, M. E. Mem. Univ. California, 1933, 11.

FARRELL, G. Physiol. Rev., 1958, 38, 709.

FITZPATRICK, R. J. *In* The neurohypophysis, edited by H. Heller. Butterworth Scientific Publications, London, 1957.

FISHER, C., INGRAM, W. R. AND RANSON, S. W. Diabetes insipidus. Edwards Brothers, Ann Arbor, Mich., 1938.

GEILING, E. M. K. Physiol. Rev., 1926, 6, 62.

GEILING, E. M. K. Harvey Lectures, 1941–1942, 37, 269.

GREER, M. A. Recent Progr. Hormone Res., 1957, 13, 67.

GUILLEMIN, R. Recent Prog. Hormone Res., 1964, 20, 89.

HAM, A. W. Histology, 2nd ed. Pitman Medical Publishing Co., London, 1953.

HANSTRÖM, B. *In* The neurohypophysis, edited by H. Heller. Butterworth Scientific Publications, London, 1957.

Harris, G. W. Neural control of the pituitary gland. Edward Arnold, London, 1955.

Harris, G. W. Proc. Roy. Soc. London, Series B, 1958, **149**, 336.

Hechter, O. Vitamins & Hormones, 1955, **13**, 245.

Heller, H. *In* The neurohypophysis, edited by H. Heller. Butterworth Scientific Publications, 1957.

Houssay, B. A. New England J. Med., 1936, **214**.

Houssay, B. A. Endocrinology, 1942, **30**, 884.

Levine, R. *In* Survey of biological progress, Vol. III, edited by B. Glass. Academic Press, New York, 1957.

McCann, S. M. and Ramirez, V. D. Recent Prog. Hormone Res., 1964, **20**, 131.

Pincus, G. and Thimann, K. V. (editors). The hormones, Vols. I, II, III. Academic Press, New York, 1948, 1950, 1955 (various reviews).

Purves, H. D. Ch. 3, Vol. I *in* Sex and internal secretions, (ed. W. C. Young), Baillière, Tindall & Cox, Ltd., London, 1961.

Rawles, R. E. Physiol. Rev., 1948, **28**, 383.

Rolleston, H. D. The endocrine organs in health and disease. Oxford, London, 1936.

Sawyer, W. H. Endocrinology, 1964, **75**, 981.

Sayers, G. and Brown, R. W. *In* Glandular physiology and therapy, 5th ed. Lippincott, Philadelphia, 1954.

Sayers, G., Redgate, E. S. and Royce, P. C. Ann. Rev. Physiol., 1958, **20**, 243.

Scharrer, E. and Scharrer, B. Recent Progr. Hormone Res., 1954, **10**, 183.

Severinghaus, A. Res. Publ. A. Res. Nerv. & Ment. Dis., 1936, **17**.

Severinghaus, A. E. Physiol. Rev., 1937, **17**, 556.

The pituitary gland, in 3 vols. (eds., G. W. Harris and B. T. Donovan), Butterworth Scientific Publications, London, 1966.

Verney, E. B. Proc. Roy. Soc. London, Series B, 1947, **135**, 25.

White, A. Physiol. Rev., 1946, **26**, 574.

Young, F. G. Recent Progr. Hormone Res., 1953, **8**, 471.

Zarrow, M. X., Yochim, J. M., and McCarthy, J. L. Experimental endocrinology. Academic Press, New York, 1964.

See also references in chapter 75.

The Thyroid Gland

Development, Histology, Blood, and Nerve Supply

Very early in its evolutionary history the thyroid had a digestive function. This is recalled in its embryonic development from a single median outgrowth of hypoblast derived from the ventral wall of the primitive pharynx at the level of the first visceral cleft. This extends downward and its lower end bifurcates and enlarges to form the isthmus and lateral lobes of the thyroid. Its upper end gives rise to the foramen caecum of the tongue. The intervening portion, the thyroglossal duct, normally disappears, but sometimes persists and may give rise to accessory thyroids or to the so-called thyroglossal cysts.

The thyroid tissue is composed of cuboidal epithelial cells arranged in a single layer around spaces roughly spherical in shape. These spaces, variously known as follicles, vesicles, acini, or alveoli, contain a homogenous gelatinous material, the colloid substance, which is the stored secretion of the gland. Connective tissue fibres support the alveolar walls and form septa which divide the gland into smaller masses. The cells lining the alveoli contain numerous mitochondria and a well-defined Golgi apparatus. Studies with the electron microscope have shown that the inner (luminal) borders of these cells possess microvilli, which are characteristic features of cells engaged in absorption or secretion. When the gland becomes active, the Golgi apparatus hypertrophies and droplets of colloid appear in its proximity. Other histological changes typical of increased activity in the thyroid are: increase in the epithelial cell height, increase in mitotic figures, decrease in amount of colloid in the follicles (with a tendency to become basophilic rather than acidophilic in staining properties), and an increase in vascularity. The maximal normal weight of the human thyroid is, according to Marine, from 20 to 35 g. or around 0.4 g. per kg. of body weight. The thyroid tissue of the early foetus consists of masses of epithelial cells showing little or no arrangement into follicles. The latter appear about the third month in the human but are small and contain little colloid.

Functional activity first appears in the foetal gland at about this time. Concentration of inorganic iodide is demonstrable before the appearance of colloid but organic binding (formation of iodinated amino acids) is not observed until colloid is demonstrable histologically in other species.

The blood supply comes from the superior and inferior thyroid arteries, chiefly the former. The blood flow is profuse, the blood passing with little resistance from the arterial to the venous side through a wide capillary bed. The flow amounts to from 3.5 to 6 ml. per g. of tissue per min., or about 5 l. per hr. for the whole gland in man. The gland is richly supplied with lymphatics which drain the lymph spaces surrounding the follicles and may play a minor part in the release of hormone from the gland.

The nerve supply of the thyroid is derived from the vagus and the sympathetic nerves. The sympathetic fibres leave the spinal cord between the second and fifth thoracic segments, and pass to cell stations in the superior and middle cervical ganglia, where they are relayed to the gland through the superior laryngeal nerves and along the blood vessels. It is probable that the thyroid nerves are purely vasomotor in function and influence the activity of the gland indirectly, if at all, by altering its blood supply. Control of thyroid activity is exerted mainly, if not exclusively, by the thyrotrophic hormone of the pituitary.

The Actions of Thyroid Hormone

Many of the actions of thyroid hormones in the human were first discovered when the clinical pictures of hyper- and hypothyroidism were recognized. The experimental investigation of the physiological effects exerted by the thyroid gland has likewise involved the study of hypothyroid states (produced by surgical thyroidectomy or goitrogen administration) and their repair, and hyperthyroid states (produced by administration of thyroxine or tri-iodothyronine). The qualitative effects produced by thyroxine and tri-iodothryonine are similar, but tri-iodothyronine acts more quickly, is usually the more po-

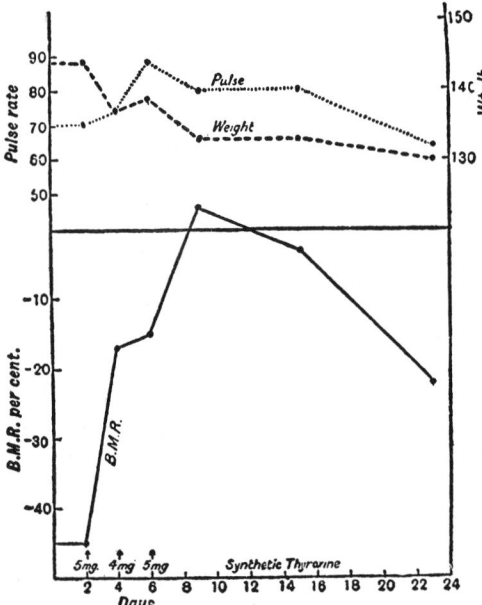

FIG. 75.1. The effect of thyroxine on a hypothyroid patient. (From Harington, 1933.)

tent of the two compounds, and has a shorter-lived action. These facts may be connected. Tata (1961) has suggested that the apparent greater response to T_3 may be because measurements were made soon after injection; if the total response (of the B.M.R. for instance) is measured, both intensity and duration of response being considered, the compounds are more nearly equipotent.

HEAT PRODUCTION: CALORIGENESIS. Magnus Levy, in 1895, first described the low oxygen consumption of patients with hypothyroidism and showed that thyroid feeding raised the basal metabolic rate in the human. The effect of a single administration of thyroxine upon the basal metabolic rate develops slowly but is prolonged (fig. 75.1); it commences after a lapse of 12 to 48 hr., reaches its maximum in 8 to 10 days, and may last for several weeks. In the athyroid human, the basal metabolic rate may be only one-half the normal value, whereas in severe thyrotoxicosis it may be double. To maintain a normal basal metabolic rate in hypothyroidism requires the daily administration of about 200 to 300 μg. of 1-thyroxine.

In vitro studies of the oxygen consumption of tissues taken from animals rendered hyper- or hypothyroid show that these tissues have an increased or decreased gaseous exchange respectively. Thus the calorigenic action of thyroid hormone is exerted directly upon the cells

rather than through the nervous system. It should be noted that, if thyroxine is added to the incubation medium containing tissue taken from a normal animal, no immediate calorigenic effect is observed. However, Barker has described effects obtained *in vitro* on the respiration of kidney slices stored at 0°C. and observed over several days.

Such obvious mental changes are observed in Graves' disease and hypothyroidism that thyroxine might be expected to exert a marked effect on cerebral metabolism. However, this does not seem to be the case, since the respiratory metabolism of tissue from the brains of rats rendered hyper- or hypothyroid is normal. In this respect, brain tissue behaves differently from many other tissues but the gonads, accessory reproductive organs, spleen, thymus, lymph nodes and lung have also been shown to be metabolically unresponsive to thyroid hormone. Similarly, the cerebral oxygen consumption of thyrotoxic patients is not increased, although oxygen and glucose consumption of the brain has been reported as low in hypothyroidism.

GROWTH AND DIFFERENTIATION. The earliest and clearest evidence that the thyroid is closely concerned with tissue differentiation came from the experiments of Gudernatsch in 1912. He showed that feeding thyroid tissue to frog tadpoles resulted in early metamorphosis and the production of small frogs. Later studies showed that thyroidectomized tadpoles fail to metamorphose, and developed into abnormally large larval forms (fig. 75.2). The human cretin, besides showing retardation of growth, shows marked

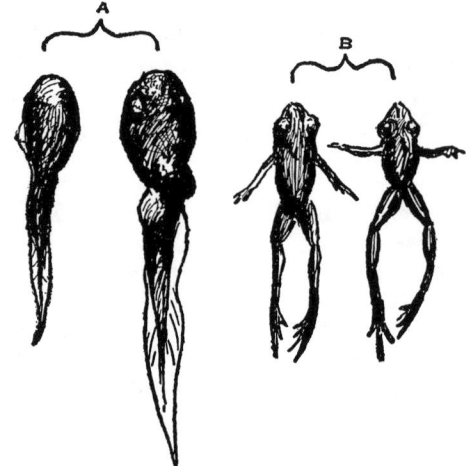

FIG. 75.2. The effect of removal of the thyroids upon the development of tadpoles. *A*, Thyroidless tadpoles; *B*, normal frogs of the same age as *A*. (From Allen, redrawn.)

failure in the maturation of the skeletal and other bodily systems. The growth process is influenced both by growth hormone (STH) from the anterior pituitary and by thyroid hormone (fig. 75.3), whereas the process of maturation and differentiation (formation of ossification centers in the epiphyses, eruption of primary and secondary dentition) is more solely influenced by the thyroid hormone. For example, hypophysectomized young rats treated with growth hormone show bony growth but abnormal development of epiphyses, whereas treatment of similar animals with thyroxine results in slight growth of the bones but marked stimulation of epiphysial development and bony maturation. The growth and development of the brain appears to be particularly dependent on the thyroid hormone. Experimental studies have shown that young animals rendered hypothyroid, surgically or with drugs, show impaired growth of the brain, decreased size of cortical neurones, a decreased density of the neuropile between the cortical neurones, and retarded myelination of cerebral nerve tracts.

METABOLIC PROCESSES. The increased basal metabolic rate typical of hyperthyroidism is associated with a normal fasting respiratory quotient. The ratio of the different foodstuffs metabolized remains within normal limits. Increased protein catabolism and an increased excretion of urinary nitrogen occurs in both hyper- and hypothyroidism. The administration of small doses of thyroxine to hypothyroid animals results in protein deposition. This may be correlated with the increased growth which occurs in young hypothyroid animals under therapy. Creatinuria is typical of the hyperthyroid state. An increased concentration of blood lipid and cholesterol occurs with thyroid deficiency, and has some diagnostic significance in suspected cases of hypothyroidism. An increased excretion of calcium, sometimes in association with osteoporosis, occurs in hyperthyroidism; this may, though rarely, result in bony fractures. In the absence of the thyroid hormone, the conversion of carotene to vitamin A is impaired, possibly through defective intestinal absorption of carotene. The occasional failure of night vision in cases of hypothyroidism may be thus explained.

Numerous hypotheses have been put forward to explain the mechanism of action of the thyroid hormones at the subcellular or molecular level, and there is a voluminous literature on the experimental aspect of the subject. No firm con-

FIG. 75.3. The effect of thyroxine deficiency in young mammals. Triplet kids. Center animal normal; right- and left-hand animals thyroidectomized at 20 days of age. Photograph taken 13 weeks after operation. (From Sutherland Simpson.)

clusions seems to have emerged; certainly no one single biochemical reaction has been identified as the crucial point at which thyroid hormone exerts its effects. Several comprehensive reviews may be consulted for further details (Hoch, 1962; Tapley and Hatfield, 1962; Wolff and Wolff, 1964).

The Thyroid in Poikilotherms

A typical thyroid gland is found in vertebrates as primitive as the adult Cyclostomes (the ammocoete larvae possess a digestive organ, the sub-pharyngeal gland, comparable to the endostyle of Amphioxus, which contains cells capable of accumulating inorganic iodine and forming thyroxine: at metamorphosis these cells form the thyroid gland of the adult). There is no evidence that thyroxine is concerned with the process of metamorphosis in Cyclostomes. In the adult a reciprocal relationship exists between the adenohypophysis and the thyroid and this is also true for the bony (Teleost) and cartilaginous (Elasmobranch) fishes. Despite the existence of mechanisms capable of regulating the blood level of thyroid hormone in these animals, little is known of its function. It does not have the metabolism-stimulating effect seen in the higher animals; it has been suggested that it may be concerned in some way with osmoregulation, a pressing problem for these aquatic creatures (Leloup and Fontaine, 1960).

In the Amphibia the role of the thyroid is much better understood. It plays a central role in the dramatic process of metamorphosis from an aquatic larval stage to an air-breathing adult. Inhibition of metamorphosis by removal of the thyroid or pituitary gland and its acceleration by the administration of thyroid extract were among the classic experiments of the early pioneer endocrinologists (fig. 75.2). More recent studies have been concerned with the demonstration of changes in thyroid activity during spontaneous metamorphosis and the details of the biochemical processes involved. The simultaneous stimulation of protein catabolism—(resorption of tail and gills) and protein anabolism—(growth of the limbs) has led to a renewed interest in the effects of thyroxine on nitrogen metabolism in mammals. Abnormalities of the metamorphic process in Amphibia have also provided some interesting new ideas as regards the mode of action of thyroid hormones. It has been known for many years that, in contrast to the Anura (frogs and toads), the tailed amphibia (Urodeles) may exhibit the phenomenon of neoteny—arrested development at the larval stage with gonadal maturation and reproduction at this stage. In the case of the *Axolotl* the neoteny is only apparent and if thyroid hormone is supplied in adequate amounts, metamorphosis occurs; other types, such as *Necturus*, cannot be induced to metamorphose even when exogenous hormone is administered in large quantities. A failure of the tissues' capacity to respond to thyroid hormone has been postulated for these perennibranchiate amphibia, and it has been shown that, in contrast to larvae capable of responding, their tissues are unable to deiodinate thyroxine.

The Nature of the Thyroid Hormones and the Role of Iodine

Although descriptions of goitres (clinically obvious enlargements of the thyroid gland) are known from Chinese sources as early as the second millenium B.C., and references are known for almost all periods since (except for the Dark Ages in Europe) (see Rolleston, 1936 and Trotter, 1964), the major contribution of clinical studies to the early stages of our understanding of the thyroid was the delineation of the effects of lack of some secretion from the gland in the growing animal and in the adult as discussed above. The stage was thus set for the experimental study of the physiological effects of the hormone. The beginnings of our biochemical knowledge of the hormone must be dated from the work of Baumann (1896), who demonstrated the presence in the thyroid of considerable quantities of the

halogen, iodine, an element first isolated by the French chemist, Courtois, in 1812, from the ash of burnt sea weed. Trotter comments that Baumann seems to have been surprised by his discovery; in the light of modern knowledge of the concentration and properties of heavy elements in animal tissues we too should be surprised. Gofman (1962) points out that for elements of atomic number (Z) greater than 20 (the element of atomic number 20 is calcium) the concentration in animal tissues falls rapidly. Only 4 elements of $Z720$ (Br, Fe, Cu, and Zn) have concentrations in plasma of the order of one part per million. That iodine (atomic number 53) should be present at a concentration as high as 0.5 parts per million in plasma, and in milligram quantities in the thyroid, is astonishing. The recognition of the part played by iodine deficiency in the causation of endemic goitre followed eventually, and in the laboratory, the work of Kendall and of Harington led to the isolation, characterization, and finally the synthesis of the biologically-active iodine-containing amino acid, thyroxine. This was long thought to be the unique hormonal product of the thyroid but in 1952, following earlier studies in Leblond's laboratory at McGill University, Gross and Pitt-Rivers in London and Roche, Michel and Lissitsky in Paris, reported the presence of a second biologically-active compound, $3,5,3'$-triiodothyronine, in the thyroid and in plasma. This compound has qualitatively the same actions as thyroxine and must be regarded as a second thyroid hormone.

Consideration of the iodine metabolism of the body is basic to an understanding of the physiology and pathology of the thyroid. It is fortunate that radioactive isotopes of this element have been widely available since 1945 to facilitate the study of this problem. The stable, naturally occurring isotope is ^{127}I (the superscript denotes the atomic weight of the isotope). Some twenty radio-active isotopes of iodine are known, with atomic weights from 119 to 139, and half-lives (the time taken for the number of unstable atoms originally present at zero time to fall to half this number) from 2.7 seconds (^{139}I) to 108 years (^{129}I). The first animal experiments involving radio-active isotopes of iodine were reported by Hertz in 1938 using ^{128}I with a half-life of 25 min. The most commonly used isotope now is ^{131}I, which has a convenient half-life of 8 days, and which emits a penetrating gamma radiation, thus enabling measurements to be made of the distribution and concentration of the isotope by external counting in the living animal or patient.

Beta radiation of moderate energy is also emitted, which allows liquid samples such as urine or blood to be counted with fair efficiency by means of relatively inexpensive Geiger counters, and also permits the preparation of autoradiographs of tissues containing the isotope with a moderate degree of resolution. Only two other isotopes have been much used for experimental purposes: ^{132}I (half-life, 2.4 hr) delivers a lower radiation dose to the thyroid than ^{131}I, and the short half-life may be an advantage when repeated tests at short intervals are required. The energy of the gamma radiation differs from that of ^{131}I, and the two isotopes can be measured separately, when present together, by means of the sophisticated counting apparatus (NaI crystal scintillation counter plus gamma ray spectrometer) now fairly generally available. In this way different phases of iodine metabolism may be studied simultaneously by the double isotope technique. The second isotope, ^{125}I, has the advantages of a 56-day half-life and a low energy radiation (X-rays plus Auger electrons) following decay by K capture. The low energy offers the possibility of much improved resolution, at the electron microscope level, in autoradiographic studies (Stein and Gross, 1964), and of reduced radiation induced decomposition for radio-iodine labeled compounds such as thyroxine, of high specific activity. Certain other isotopes may be particularly suitable, because of the properties of their radiation, for therapeutic use to destroy hyperactive or cancerous thyroid tissue (Goolden, 1964) and the use of the artificially produced halogen element, astatine or eka-iodine which, like iodine, is concentrated in the thyroid and emits a short range, heavily ionising alpha particle has also been suggested.

With this background the knowledge of the physiology and biochemistry of the thyroid obtained by isotope studies can be considered.

Uptake of Iodide by the Thyroid Gland

The thyroid gland was shown by Marine to have a remarkable affinity for iodine. Though constituting only about 0.05 per cent or so of the body weight, the gland contains about half the body's entire iodine content.

If a tracer dose of ^{131}I (2 to 4 μc.) is administered to an animal such as a rabbit, an immediate, slow, steady increase of ^{131}I in the thyroid gland follows, which reaches a peak after about 30 hr. The ^{131}I is taken up from the blood in the inorganic (iodide) form, converted into organic compounds and stored as thyro-globulin. If di-

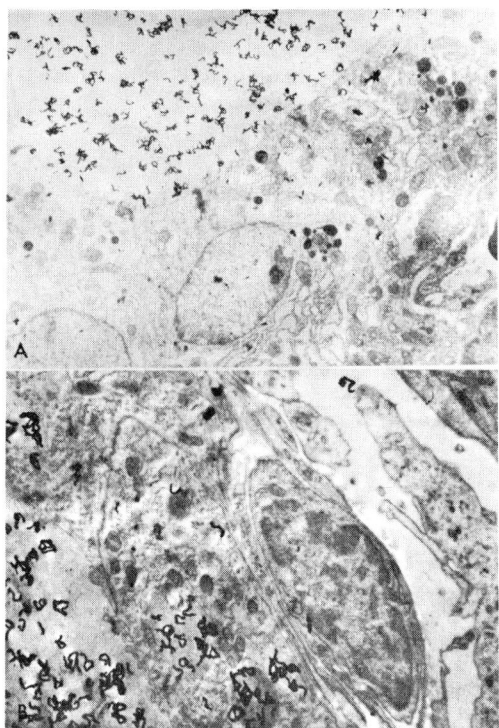

Fig. 75.4*A*. Mouse thyroid 25 min. after the injection of ^{125}I. Note distribution over grains mainly over the colloid at this early stage and the association of grains with the microvilli. *B*. Mouse thyroid 20 hr. after injection of ^{125}I. Note the grains over the colloid and that the intracellular activity is confined to the membrane-bound vacuoles (colloid droplets). These electron microscope autoradiographs are taken from Stein and Gross (1964) and reproduced through the courtesy of the authors and publishers.

iodotyrosine or thyroxine is injected instead, then the uptake of iodine by the thyroid is delayed, and occurs only after the organic compound is degraded and iodide released. The partial visualization of these processes has been made possible by the use of the radio-autographic technique. Radioiodine in contact with a photographic emulsion acts on it to give a dark mark; when the emulsion is spread upon a microscopic section of thyroid tissue which has taken up the isotope, the latter's position in relation to the histological structure can be observed (fig. 75.4). Leblond and Gross used this technique to investigate the site of ^{131}I in the thyroid at various time intervals after injection of the isotope into rats and guinea-pigs. It was found that, with animals on a high-iodine diet, the radioactivity in the thyroid was mostly present at the periphery of the follicles at 1 hr., and throughout the colloid at 24 hr. after injection. If the animals were placed on a low-iodine diet, or thyroid activity was increased by injection of thyrotrophin, the deposition of radioactivity in the colloid was much accelerated, since it was found there as early as 2 min. after injection. These results imply that the chemical conversion of iodide to thyroglobulin may occur very rapidly in the thyroid gland. Improved resolution obtained with ^{125}I, and electron microscopic autoradiography (Stein and Gross, 1964) has now shown that organically bound iodine is never found in the cells before it appears in the colloid. Gross suggests that iodination occurs in the colloid at the surface of the microvilli and that organically bound iodine in the cells represents colloid absorbed by pinocytosis and undergoing proteolysis intracellularly.

Biochemistry of Thyroid Hormone Formation

The autoradiographic evidence discussed above suggests that the various stages in hormone biosynthesis and release may occur successively intra-, extra-, and again intra-cellularly. Whatever their anatomical locus, the different stages have certainly been separated biochemically.

The first stage is the accumulation of inorganic iodide from the blood, in which it is present at the very low concentration of about 0.24 μg./100 ml. plasma in man. (These are indirectly determined values obtained by Wayne, Koutras and Alexander in Glasgow, Scotland. Published values for the United States have tended to be rather higher, around 0.5 μg./100 ml., perhaps because of the widespread domestic use of iodised salt. Canadian values are intermediate.) The accumulation is an active transport process: it occurs against a concentration and electrochemical gradient, is energy-dependent, can be saturated by an excess of iodide, and competitive inhibition by other anions can be demonstrated. The best known of these are the perchlorate (ClO_4') and thiocyanate (SCN') ions but a whole range of more exotic competing anions have been tested, such as monofluorosulfonate (SO_3F') and tetrafluoroborate (BF_4^-). The common factor for those competing anions, that are themselves also taken up by the thyroid, appears to be a single negative charge, a similar ionic volume to iodide, and a spherical or tetrahedral shape.

The ability to concentrate iodide has been shown to be a property of the thyroid epithelial cells. Isolated thyroid cells in tissue culture can accumulate iodide and, during embryonic development, iodide concentration can be demonstrated before colloid appears in the gland although later stages in biosynthesis (organic binding) are not seen before colloid formation has begun (cf. discussion of autoradiographic evidence given above). The kinetics of iodide transport have been studied intensively *in vivo* and *in vitro*, both for their theoretical interest and because iodide accumulation is a critical and may, under some circumstances, be a rate-limiting stage in hormone formation. The subject has been reviewed in detail by Halmi (1961, 1964) and Wolff (1964). The ability to carry out active transport of iodide is not peculiar to the thyroid; it has been detected in salivary gland, gastric mucosa, choroid plexus, ciliary body, skin, placenta, oviduct and mammary gland. The older work on this topic was reviewed by Brown-Grant in 1961. These extra-thyroidal mechanisms have certain features in common with the thyroidal mechanism: they are inhibited by the same anions, for instance, and examples are known where a genetically determined inborn error of metabolism, failure of the thyroid iodide transport mechanism was associated with failure of salivary gland and gastric transport mechanisms for iodide (Stanbury, 1963). So far as is known, only the thyroidal mechanism is influenced by the level of circulating thyrotrophic hormone. If the organic binding of iodine is blocked by the administration of certain drugs, such as propylthiouracil or mercaptoimidazole, the activity of the iodide transport mechanism may be assessed by measuring the equilibrium thyroid/serum concentration ratio for iodide (nearly always for radioactive ^{131}I-iodide) that is achieved. This T/S ratio is a useful index of the level of TSH stimulation in experimental investigations. The T/S ratio may be more than 100 in the stimulated gland of rats and mice. The T/S ratio in unblocked glands, i.e., where organic binding is going on, is difficult to measure and to interpret. Where binding is rapid, removal of transported iodide may proceed so quickly that the apparent T/S is reduced. A further complication in the use of ^{131}I in unblocked glands is the possible existence of a second iodide "pool," which is not in rapid equilibrium with plasma iodide, and which may represent iodide produced within the gland by deiodination of free iodotyrosines (see discussion of thyroidal dehalogenases).

The next stage in the biosynthesis of the hormone is the formation of iodinated amino acids. Under normal circumstances in man, and in most laboratory animals except the guinea-pig, this is a rapid process and the concentration of newly arrived inorganic iodide in the gland is therefore low. The process takes place in the colloid, probably at the surface of the microvilli of the thyroid epithelial cells at the cell-colloid interface. Although the presence of free iodine (I^2) in the thyroid has not been unequivocally demonstrated, it is thought, on chemical grounds that iodination involves the action of an enzyme, iodide peroxidase, in the presence of hydrogen peroxide, to oxidise iodide to iodine or to a hypothetical "active iodide," which may be either the iodinium (I^+) or the hypoiodite (IO^-) ion. This active iodide reacts with the tyrosyl residues of the protein chain of thyroglobulin, possibly under the influence of a distinct enzyme, tyrosine iodinase, to form the mono-substituted derivative, 3-monoiodotyrosine (MIT) (fig. 75.5). The source of the H_2O_2 in the intact gland is not known but it may be produced by flavine-linked enzymes. Evidence derived from a study of the specific activity of the different iodinated amino acids at different times after ^{131}I administration shows that MIT is the first product. Subsequently, further iodination leads to the formation of 3,5-diiodotyrosine (DIT) (fig. 75.5). Coupling of two iodinated tyrosines, with the loss of the alanine side chain, leads to the formation of iodothyronines, the tetraiodinated compound, thyroxine (T_4), being formed from the two DIT residues and the 3,5,3'-triiodothyronine from the coupling of one DIT and one MIT residue (fig. 75.5). The specific enzymes involved have not been identified. Theoretically, two other thyronines could be formed; 3,3'-diiodothyronine from 2 MIT residues and 3,3',5'-triiodothyronine. These compounds have, in fact, been detected in very small quantities in hydrolysates of thyroid tissue. They are both virtually devoid of biological activity. It is important to note that these reactions do not occur *in vivo* with the free amino acids but with constituent amino acids of the protein chain of the characteristic protein of the thyroid colloid, thyroglobulin. This may have an important bearing on the ease with which iodination of the tyrosyl residues occurs, and on the rate and extent of the coupling reaction and the type of iodothyronine formed. Further details of the process of thyroxine formation in the gland, and of the large amount of work on chemical and biochemical models studied *in vitro*, are given in the monograph by Pitt-Rivers and Tata.

The end result of the process of hormonogenesis is a store of hormone in the gland, in the molecules of thyroglobulin of the colloid. The amount of

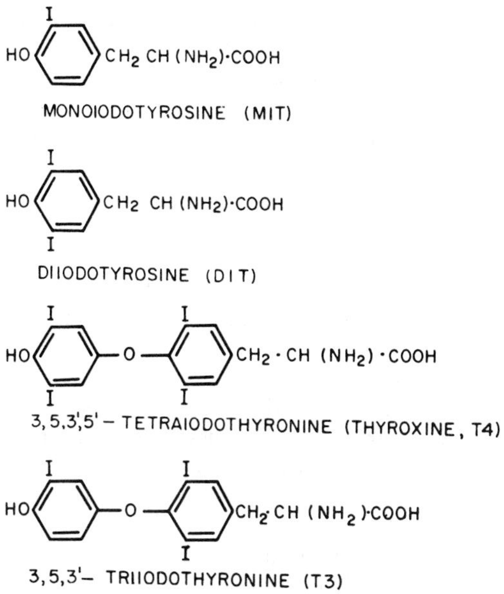

HO⟨⟩CH$_2$ CH (NH$_2$)·COOH

MONOIODOTYROSINE (MIT)

HO⟨⟩CH$_2$ CH (NH$_2$)·COOH

DIIODOTYROSINE (DIT)

HO⟨⟩—O—⟨⟩CH$_2$·CH (NH$_2$)·COOH

3,5,3',5' – TETRAIODOTHYRONINE (THYROXINE, T4)

HO⟨⟩—O—⟨⟩CH$_2$ CH (NH$_2$)·COOH

3,5,3'– TRIIODOTHYRONINE (T3)

FIG. 75.5. The chemical formulae of the iodinated amino-acids of biological importance.

hormone stored in this way, in relation to the daily hormone requirements, varies widely from species to species and with the availability of iodide in the diet. The rat thyroid generally contains but a few days supply, the human thyroid normally several weeks, and consequently the rate of turnover of thyroidal iodine is more rapid in the rat. When a single dose of radioiodide is administered, part of it is taken up by the thyroid and appears as iodinated amino acids in the colloid, and the rest is excreted, largely by the kidneys. The changes in thyroidal radio-content can be followed by external counting, the values being corrected for physical decay of the isotope. An initially rapid rise gradually slows, and after the time of peak content is reached, the amount of activity in the gland begins to decrease exponentially; this "release curve" gives an indirect estimate of the rate of secretion of hormone. Its slope is steep in the rat, where the store of hormone is small, and shallow in the human, where only a small percentage of the gland content of hormone need be released per day to supply the body's requirements. If the gland content of hormone remains constant, acute changes in the radio-iodine release curve provide a valuable experimental method for the study of variations in thyroid gland activity. Variations in the slope of the "release curve" or the biological "half-life" of thyroidal radio-iodine between animals, or groups of animals, cannot be used directly, or alone, to provide an estimate of the absolute level of activity, or of the secretion rate in terms of micrograms of hormone per day. Complex mathematical analysis may be needed to achieve this; a lucid account of the kinetics of iodine metabolism and their interpretation, with particular reference to man is, given in a classic review by Riggs (1952).

The underlying biochemical events in the release of hormone from the gland have been studied in detail. The hormones (T_3 and T_4) appear in the thyroid venous blood as "free" amino acids (that is they are no longer linked by covalent bonds in the protein chain of thyroglobulin). Some labelled iodide may also appear in the venous effluent, particularly if there is intense stimulation by TSH, even though ^{131}I was administered some days before and little labelled iodide can be detected in the gland itself at this time; iodotyrosines are not normally found in the thyroid venous blood. Studies *in vitro* have shown that the thyroid cells contain proteases and peptidases which liberate free amino acids from thyroglobulin. The process is probably largely intracellular in life, the small fragments of colloid appearing as colloid droplets initially at the apical pole of the thyroid cells, possibly by a process of pinocytosis. It has been suggested that the membranes surrounding these droplets may contain the enzymes concerned with the breakdown of protein. The free iodothyronines diffuse into the blood across the basal cell border. The free iodotyrosines do not normally appear in the blood because of the presence in thyroid cells of specific enzymes, the thyroid dehalogenases, which rapidly split off the iodine from free iodotyrosines but, unlike the dehalogenases of peripheral tissues discussed later, do not act upon the iodothyronines. Most of the iodide liberated is retained in the gland, re-entering the biosynthetic pathway along with iodide freshly accumulated from the blood. When deiodination is proceeding very rapidly, some iodide may escape and appear in the thyroid venous blood.

The stages in the synthesis and release of thyroid hormones are illustrated in fig. 75.6. The rate at which these processes occur is dependent upon the level of stimulation of the gland by the thyrotrophic hormone (TSH) of the anterior pituitary. After hypophysectomy, the thyroid is virtually functionless. Many attempts have been made to discover a single, critical, rate-limiting step at which TSH might exert its stimulatory effect on the overall process of synthesis and release. It appears, however, that although different phases of thyroid activity may respond at different rates to changes in TSH level (increased breakdown of thyroglobulin, seen histologically as the appearance of colloidal droplets within the cell and detected chemically by the appearance of T_3 and T_4 in the venous effluent is one of the earliest responses—about 30 minutes after TSH injection while the T/S ratio may not change for several hours) all aspects of thyroid gland activity are influenced by TSH and no single key response has been identified. Freinkel (1964) has presented a critical and detailed review of the as yet unsuccessful search for a "unifocal" site of TSH action and of the effects of TSH on the intermediary metabolism of the gland.

Goitrogenic Compounds

Under this general designation are included several classes of compounds which have in common the property of causing enlargement of the thyroid gland when administered to intact animals. This effect is due to interference with the synthesis of thyroid hormones, which leads to a fall in the level of circulating hormone, stimulation of pituitary TSH secretion, and hypertrophy and hyperplasia of the thyroid in an attempt to supply an adequate amount of hormone. The process is thus an example of compensatory hypertrophy. The goitrogenic compounds are important for several reasons. There may be administered deliberately to patients suffering from the effects of thyroid hyperfunction to control their disease. They may be drugs used in the treatment of other disorders which happen to possess unwanted anti-thyroid activity or naturally occurring compounds found in foodstuffs which, when eaten in large quantities, may cause goitres in animals or man. Finally, they have been widely used in investigations of the physiology and biochemistry of the thyroid. There appear to be two distinct ways in which these compounds act at the thyroid level and it is convenient to discuss them on this basis.

Interference with the Iodide Transport Mechanism

Concentration of inorganic iodide in the thyroid by an active transport mechanism is an essential step in thyroid hormone formation when the plasma iodide level is at its normal low value. Many monovalent anions will interfere with iodide transport as discussed earlier. Thiocyanate

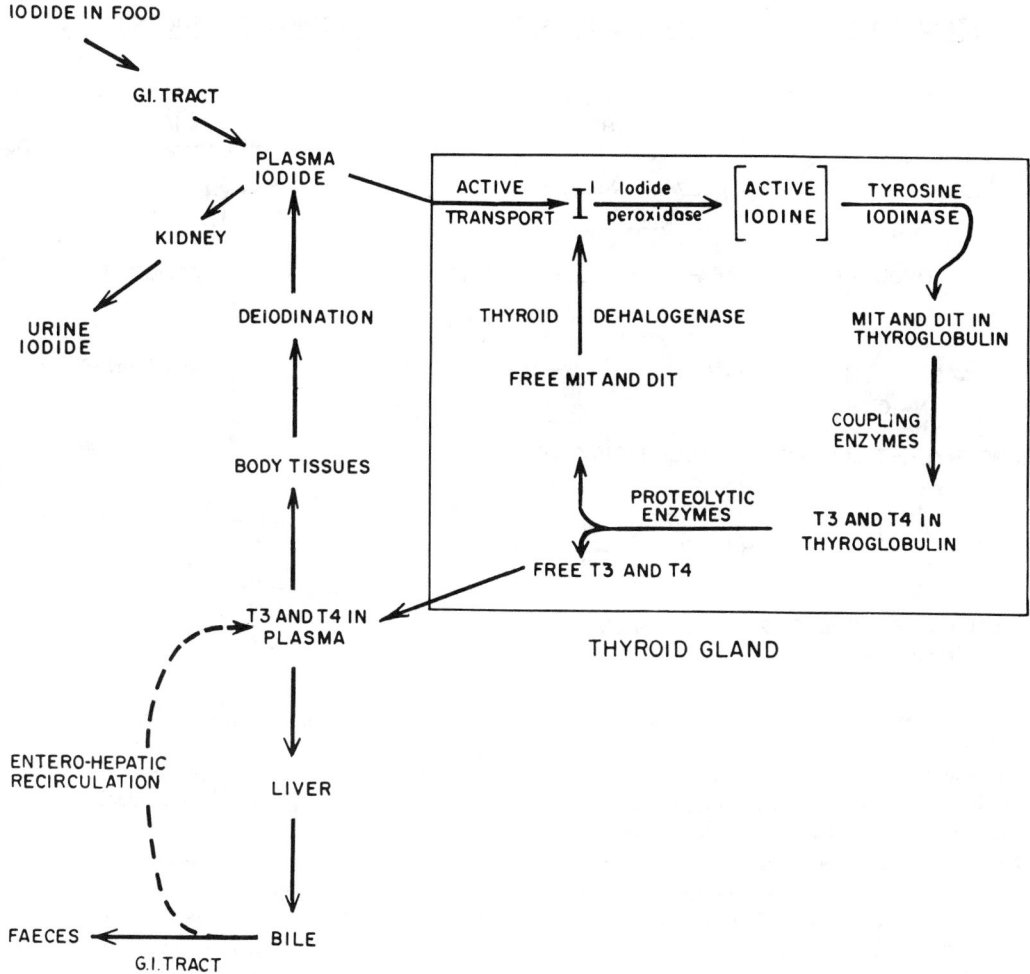

Fig. 75.6. Schematic representation of the processes involved in the synthesis, release and metabolism of the thyroid hormones.

(SCN⁻) was at one time used, without great success, in the treatment of hypertension and it was the incidental observation that some patients receiving this treatment developed goitres which first suggested that thiocyanate had anti-thyroid properties. The development of thiocyanate goitre can, of course, be suppressed or reversed by the administration of thyroid hormone. When the mode of action was determined, it was later shown that large doses of iodide, such that the gland receives an adequate supply of iodide (about 100 µg. per day in man) by passive diffusion from the blood, will also prevent goitre formation. Perchlorate (ClO_4^-) acts in the same way and 500 to 1,000 mg. of $KClO_4$ per day in three or four doses is a cheap and effective form of drug treatment for hyperthyroidism. So far as is known, thiocyanate, which may be formed by the breakdown of inactive mustard oil glycoside precursors, is the only naturally-occurring goitrogen of significance that acts via an effect on iodide transport. It is found in plants of the cabbage family.

Interference with Organic Binding of Iodine

Incidental observations in several laboratories in the United States about 1940 showed that many simple organic compounds such as thiourea or the sulphonamide drugs (then being intensively studied as chemotherapeutic agents in bacterial infections) were goitrogenic in large doses. This led to a deliberate search for similar compounds with enhanced anti-thyroid activity: Astwood (1945) reviewed the studies, in which his laboratory played a prominent part, that led to the discovery of clinically useful anti-thyroid drugs such as methyl- and propylthiouracil. These

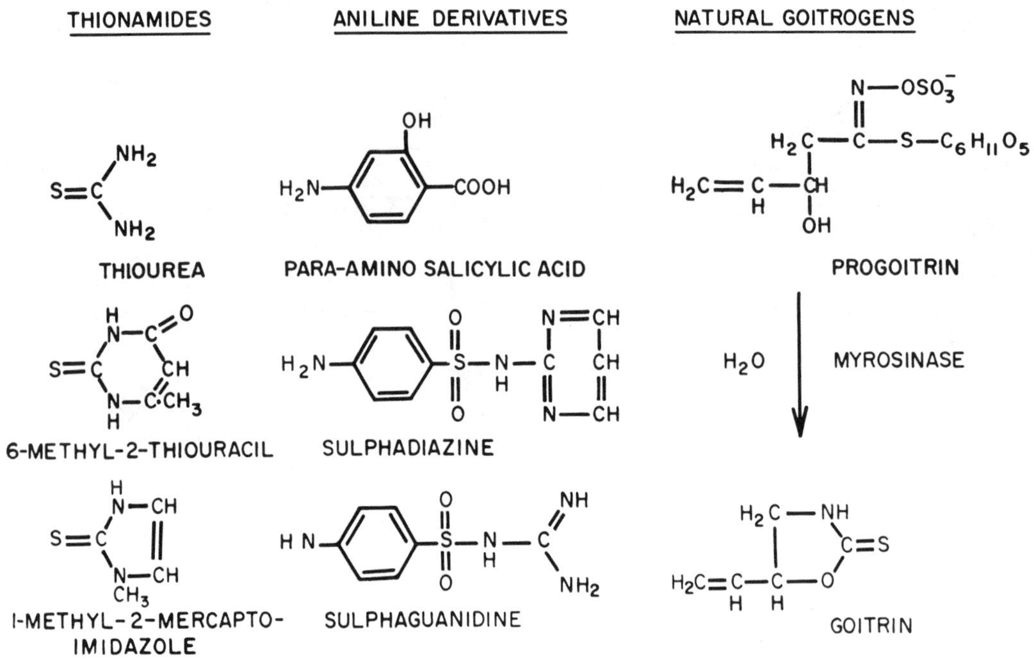

FIG. 75.7. The chemical formulae of some compounds with goitrogenic activity.

compounds act by interfering with the organic binding of iodine by the thyroid; goitre formation can be prevented by thyroid hormone administration but, because the block in biosynthesis occurs after the stage of iodide accumulation, supplying an excess of iodide does not overcome their effects. The supply of iodide may have a marginal effect on the response, however. A partial block of iodination, coupled with a relative or borderline dietary iodine deficiency, may lead to goitre formation when neither alone is sufficient. This may be of importance clinically, in areas of the world where a moderate iodine deficiency and ingestion of naturally occurring goitrogens of this type exist together.

The organic compounds which have these properties fall into several groups; many belong to the class of thionamides. Potent examples include thiourea and 2-thiouracil, together with its 4-methyl and 4-n-propyl derivatives which have been widely used to treat cases of hyperthyroidism, and the group of mercaptoimidazoles such as methimazole ("Mercazole" or "Tapazole") which is also used clinically. Many aniline derivatives also have goitrogenic properties, including several compounds used clinically, such as para-amino-salicylic acid, used in the treatment of tuberculosis, the sulphonamides, and Amphenone B. The sulphonylurea derivatives, such as "Tolbutamide," which are used

in the treatment of some types of diabetes mellitus, are also goitrogenic. The chemical structure of some of these compounds is shown in fig. 75.7. The best known of the naturally occurring goitrogenic agents acting by a block of organic binding is *goitrin*, which has been intensively studied by Greer (1964). It is found in the seeds of many plants of the cabbage family, and in the edible portion of many types of rutabaga and turnips, where it is present as an inactive glycoside precursor, pro-goitrin, from which it is released by enzymic hydrolysis carried out by bacteria in the gut.

The details of the mode of action of these compounds at the molecular level is not established. It has been suggested that some may act as competitors to tyrosine as a substrate for "active iodine," or that they may inhibit the peroxidase enzymes of the gland, or reduce "active iodine" before iodination of tyrosine can occur. None of these suggestions has received general acceptance. It was thought at one time that their action was solely on the initial process of iodination but more detailed studies, using graded doses of thiouracils, have shown that the coupling reaction is the most sensitive and the first to be inhibited, DIT formation the next most sensitive, and MIT formation the least sensitive. Even very large doses do not produce absolutely complete inhibition of MIT formation, though it is not certain that the minute quantities of MIT still formed in the presence of a high concentration of blocking agent are being produced by the normal biosynthetic pathway. MIT formation appears to be a rather less specific process than the other stages of thyroxine production: it may persist in abnormal thyroid tissue (tumours) which have lost the ability to carry out the other stages and has been observed in salivary and mammary glands and in the stomach under certain conditions.

It was thought at first that the thiouracil derivatives acted only on the thyroid gland but it was later shown that these compounds also interfered with the metabolic actions of exogenous thyroxine in thyroidectomized animals. A possible biochemical explanation for this finding has been provided by the demonstration that these compounds inhibit the deiodination of thyroxine and its analogues by the peripheral tissues, both in rats and in man. If the plasma level of thyroxine is raised, the absolute amount of T_4 deiodinated per day can be restored to normal; this may explain why, in order to prevent goitre formation in thiouracil treated animals or to restore the B.M.R. to normal, it is necessary to administer a dose of thyroxine sufficient to maintain a supranormal blood thyroxine level. Estimates of the thyroxine-secretion rate derived from goitre prevention assays in thiouracil-treated animals are probably overestimates for this reason. Perchlorate and methimazoles do not appear to have any effect on the peripheral metabolism of thyroxine. Some workers have taken these observations, like the studies on perennibranchiate amphibia discussed earlier, as further evidence that the peripheral deiodination of thyroxine is linked to the exertion of its hormonal effects on the tissues but this is by no means generally accepted.

The Distribution and Metabolism of the Thyroid Hormones

The thyroxine and triiodothyronine found in thyroid venous and peripheral blood are present in the plasma as "free" amino acids, in the sense that they are no longer joined by covalent bonds to any other molecule. They are, however, not freely dialysable from plasma and they are precipitated with the plasma proteins by agents such as trichloracetic acid. They exist, in fact, not "free" but bound by non-covalent linkages to certain specific carrier proteins of the plasma. The determination of the protein-bound iodine (PBI) of the plasma measures the level of hormonal iodine for this reason. The association with protein can be disrupted by extraction of the plasma with organic solvents such as *n*-butanol. Hence, the butanol extractable iodine (BEI) is also a measure of the hormonal iodine of the plasma. PBI values in euthyroid man are in the range of 4–8 μg./100 ml. of plasma, which is equivalent to a thyroxine concentration of about 6–12 μg./100 ml., a molar concentration of approximately 2×10^{-7}. The distribution of thyroxine between different plasma proteins has been studied by adding ^{131}I-labelled T_4 (of high specific activity so that the total thyroxine content is not significantly raised) to plasma and then carrying out an electrophoretic separation of the proteins on filter paper strips or on starch gel by standard methods. The distribution of the T_4 is determined by auto-radiography or by counting the strips and of the protein by suitable staining methods. At physiological T_4 levels in human plasma, 60% of the thyroxine is present in the inter α-globulin region between the α_1- and α_2-globulins; 30% migrates ahead of the albumin in the pre-albumin region and 10% is associated with the albumin. When the distribution of T_4 and of protein are compared, it is evident that the absolute protein concentration in the inter alpha and prealbumin areas is very low. The hormones are associated with proteins that are present in trace quantities only, and it follows, therefore, that their affinity for T_4 must be very high compared with that of albumin, which is present in gram quantities. It is now accepted that the two specific binding proteins of human plasma are the T_4-binding globulin (TBG), which is probably a glycoprotein, and the T_4-binding pre-albumin (TBPA). When increasing quantities of stable thyroxine are added to plasma, along with the labelled T_4, before electrophoresis, changes in the distribution between the different protein fractions are observed, T_4 being progressively displaced from TBG to TPA and then to albumin. Knowing the total concentration of T_4 in the plasma, and measuring the per cent in each area at increasing plasma levels, it is possible to show that the absolute amount in the TBG and TBPA areas reaches a characteristic maximal value; this represents the *capacity* of these proteins to bind T_4. The binding capacity of TBG is about 25 μg./100 ml. and of TBPA about 250 μg./100 ml. in normal human plasma. Because it is present in gram quantities, the binding capacity of the albumin fraction is virtually unmeasurable. The distribution of T_4 between the different fractions will be a function of their concentration and the respective association constants. In general terms, T_4 binding will follow the Law of Mass action:

$$[T_4] \quad \times \quad [TBP] \quad \underset{k_2}{\overset{k_1}{\rightleftharpoons}} \quad [TBP \cdot T_4]$$

Free thyroxine concentration	Concentration of unoccupied binding sites	Concentration of $T_4 \cdot TBP$ complex

Accurate prediction of the distribution between different proteins in a complex mixture such as plasma, and calculation of the expected equilibrium concentration of "free" (unbound) T_4 is difficult, because of uncertainties as to the concentration of the different proteins, the values of the association constants, and the possible existence of more than one class of binding sites with different properties on a single protein molecule. Despite the theoretical difficulties, Robbins and Rall in 1960 were able to calculate that, in human plasma, only about 0.05% of the total thyroxine would be present as "free" or unbound hormone. Methods based on gel filtration of sera (to which labelled T_4 has been added) on Sephadex columns (Lee, Henry and Golub, 1964) or the technically rather difficult measurement of the minute amount of labelled thyroxine in a dialysate of plasma (Oppenheimer and Surkes, 1964; and Sterling, 1964) have confirmed their prediction experimentally. At normal total plasma levels, the concentration of "free" hormone is about 5×10^{-11} molar.

It appears probable that the level of thyroid hormone stimulation of the tissues, the regulation of pituitary TSH secretion, and the rate of T_4 degradation are more closely related to the free, than to the total T_4 level of the plasma. It is interesting to consider the consequences of changes in the level of binding protein with this in mind. (The existence of different binding proteins is ignored in this discussion.) Assume that the level of TBP rises; more T_4 will be bound and the free T_4 level falls. The reduced rate of T_4 degradation, and the stimulation of pituitary TSH secretion leading to an increased release of T_4 from the thyroid, will result in a rise in total T_4 plasma level. Eventually, sufficient T_4 will be present to occupy the newly-available binding sites and the previous absolute level of free T_4 will be restored, though this will now represent a smaller per cent of the total plasma T_4 content. The patient will be euthyroid, degradation and thyroid secretion rates will be restored to their original values. The following changes will, however, have taken place; assuming the volume of distribution (the thyroxine space of

the body) to be unaltered, the higher total T_4 level in plasma means that the size of the extra-thyroidal organic iodine pool is increased. Free T_4 levels are unchanged and so absolute degradation rate (μg. T_4 degraded/day) is unaltered but this now represents a smaller proportion of the extra-thyroidal pool. Consequently, if the biological half-life of thyroxine is measured by injecting labelled T_4 and following its disappearance from the blood for several days, this will be found to be prolonged. When a fresh equilibrium is reached, following a rise in TBP level, the *status quo* is restored by a reduced fractional rate of turnover of an enlarged extra-thyroidal thyroxine pool. This is the situation seen when TBP (actually TBG levels) rise during pregnancy in primates or following the administration of oestrogens (whether the rise in pregnancy is directly related to the high level of oestrogen secretion in this condition is not established). An elevated TBG level has also been detected as a symptomless, genetically determined abnormality in a few families.

The opposite changes are seen when TBP levels fall, as may occur after the administration of certain synthetic steroids of the group known as anabolic steroids, or when levels are low because of an inherited abnormality. Reduced TBP levels mean that a normal free T_4 level will obtain at a lower total concentration. As TBP levels are actually decreasing, free T_4 will rise, the degradation rate will increase, and there will be a transient depression of TSH and hence of thyroidal secretion. At equilibrium, an increased fractional rate of turnover of a reduced extra-thyroidal pool (reflected in a lower total plasma T_4 level) will give a normal absolute degradation rate, and a normal free T_4 level means that the patient will be euthyroid and TSH and thyroid secretion will be normal. An effect similar to that of a reduced TBP level will result from the administration of compounds that compete with thyroxine and displace it from its binding sites on the carrier protein. Several examples of this type of action are already known; salicylates and related compounds have this effect, as does diphenylhydantoin (a drug used in the treatment of epilepsy) and di-nitro-phenol. There may be many others, including, perhaps, some drugs in common clinical use.

The great differences in the biological half-lives of T_3 and T_4, and in the rapidity and duration of their action after a single injection in many species of mammals, has been explained on the basis of a more rapid entry of T_3 into the peripheral tissues. This appears to be due largely to the fact that the affinity of the binding proteins for T_3 is much lower than their affinity for T_4. In man, T_3 is easily displaced from TBG by T_4 when both are present in the serum and TBPA does not appear to bind T_3 at all. The chicken and other birds have been reported not to possess a specific thyroxine-binding protein in their blood; both T_3 and T_4 are said to be bound mainly to albumin with roughly equal affinities and their half-lives in the chicken were found to be identical. When a partially purified human TBG preparation was injected, the half-life of T_4 but not of T_3 was prolonged. Although the presence of binding proteins may influence the half-life, particularly by affecting the rate of removal from the vascular compartment of the body, this is not the only factor involved. In the rabbit, for instance, the half-lives of T_3 and T_4 in the body are the same in contrast to the rat and man, where the half-life of T_3 is much shorter despite the fact that the rabbit has a binding protein in the plasma with a greater affinity for T_4 than for T_3.

The recognition of the importance of the protein-binding of T_4 in plasma has introduced a new factor into the consideration of many aspects of thyroid physiology; on first acquaintance the situation may appear to have become more complicated but in fact it has provided an ex-explanation for many previously puzzling anomalies. The raised PBI level in pregnancy, co-existing with a euthyroid state of the tissues, because the level of free T_4 is, in fact, unaltered, is one important example. Most of the work so far has been on man; it may be that when similar studies are undertaken in laboratory animals some of the experimentally-induced changes in thyroid activity, such as the depression produced by many types of non-specific "stress," will be found to be related to changes in binding proteins. Apart from the sources already cited, further discussion of the significance of protein binding can be found in the articles by Ingbar and Freinkel (1960); Tata (1964), and Brown-Grant (1966).

The metabolism of thyroid hormone, when it reaches the peripheral tissues, is fairly well understood; because most of the studies have been carried out with hormone labelled with radioactive iodine rather than with ^{14}C or ^3H in the aromatic rings or alanine side chain, the eventual fate of the rest of the molecule once the iodine atoms have been lost, has not been followed in detail although it is known that a

proportion of the carbon atoms appear as exhaled CO_2. However, as the deiodinated molecule is biologically inactive, this gap in our knowledge is not of great practical importance. Broadly, the hormone may be deiodinated, or the intact molecule or some conjugate may be excreted in the bile. Modification of the alanine side chain may precede either of these processes.

Deiodination

Many of the tissues of the body can deiodinate thyroxine and triiodothyronine and their derivatives. A specific enzyme, thyroxine dehalogenase, may be involved but the interpretation of many of the studies *in vitro* that have been claimed to demonstrate enzymatic deiodination is complicated by the fact that boiled tissues can also catalyse deiodination under certain conditions. Quantitatively, the skeletal muscle may be the most important site of deiodination, not because of a high activity per gram of tissue, but because it is a major fraction of the total body mass. It is probable that once deiodination has begun, all the iodine atoms are rapidly lost from the molecule. It is not now considered that any significant amount of T_3 is produced in the peripheral tissues by the mono-deiodination of T_4. The liberated iodine enters the general body pool and is shared between the thyroid and the kidney in the same way as iodide derived from the diet. Depending on the proportion of hormone deiodinated and the avidity of the thyroid for iodine, there will, therefore, be a variable degree of recirculation of iodide from degraded hormone.

Conjugation and Biliary Secretion

Biliary secretion of T_4 and T_3, either as the unchanged amino acid or as a β-glucuronide or sulphate conjugate at the phenolic hydroxyl position occurs in the liver; the excretion of conjugate may represent a detoxification mechanism. A proportion of the unchanged hormone may be reabsorbed from the intestine and undergo a further cycle of entero-hepatic recirculation; this process is probably not normally of great importance in man.

Modification of the Alanine Side Chain

Like other α-amino acids, T_3 and T_4 may be acted upon by enzymes which carry out oxidative deamination with the formation of the corresponding α-keto derivatives, the thyro-pyruvic acids. These are rather unstable, and oxidative decarboxylation to yield the acetic acid derivatives follows rapidly. These changes are most

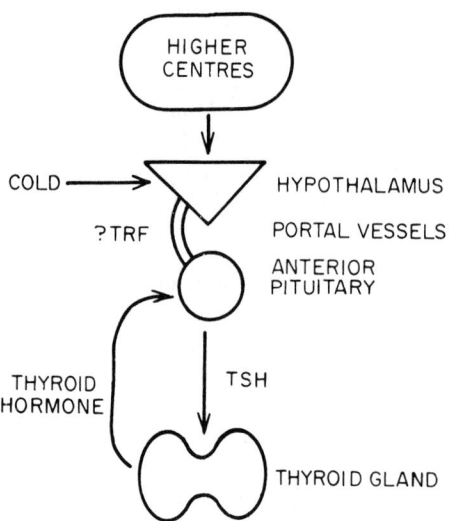

Fig. 75.8. Diagram to illustrate the inter-actions of the 'feed-back' and the neuro-humoral control mechanisms concerned in the regulation of TSH secretion.

prominent in the kidney, but the acetic acid derivatives have been found in many other tissues of the body. It was at one time thought that the acetic acid derivatives were the chemical form in which the hormones were active at the tissue level but this is no longer generally believed. The formation of the acetic acid derivatives is a minor metabolic pathway of no major physiological importance; these derivatives undergo deiodination and conjugation and biliary excretion like the parent amino acids do.

The fraction of the hormone metabolised by the two major pathways of deiodination and biliary excretion can be followed fairly easily by measuring the ^{131}I excreted in urine and in the feces after the injection of ^{131}I-labelled hormone. The proportions excreted by these two routes vary in different species and also with the amount of stable hormone administered. The laboratory rat is characterised by a predominance of the biliary-fecal pathway but this may be a reflection of the fact that most commercial rat cubes provide a very high residue diet. Variations in diet that alter the fecal bulk can have profound effect on the thyroxine metabolism of the rat. In man, the major excretion of iodine is in the urine, suggesting that deiodination is the most likely fate of a thyroxine molecule.

When an excess of hormone is administered, the proportion of the hormone excreted in the feces is increased—strikingly in the rat and

significantly in man. In both cases, it appears that when the blood level of hormone is raised, the rate of biliary clearance (ml. of plasma cleared of thyroxine per unit time) of thyroxine increases. Biliary clearance of T_3 is normally greater than that of T_4 but is not increased when large doses are given. It is suggested that the increased clearance of T_4 is due to a rise in the free hormone level in the blood as saturation of the binding capacity of TBG is approached. T_3 is not firmly bound, even at normal blood levels, so that the free T_3 level does not increase so markedly, even when large doses are administered. In support of this view, is the finding that the administration of drugs that are known to displace T_4 from its protein-binding sites will rapidly increase the biliary clearance rate of thyroxine in acute experiments. The increase in the rate of loss of T_4 in the bile when blood levels are raised may represent a relatively crude regulatory mechanism.

Regulation of the Thyroid Gland Activity

There is no evidence of any physiologically important regulating system for the thyroid gland other than variations in the level of the thyrotrophic hormone of the pituitary (TSH) to which it is exposed. If the pituitary is removed, thyroid activity falls to very low levels, and this low level of activity is not altered in response to variations in the body's needs for hormone. In contrast to the gonadal and adrenocortical hormones, large fluctuations in the plasma level of thyroid hormones do not normally occur; this implies that some reasonably efficient control system sensitive to variations in blood hormone level (or, more probably, the "free" hormone level) must exist. Such a negative "feedback" system exists in the form of a reciprocal relationship between the anterior pituitary and the thyroid and was recognised and elegantly described by Aron and his co-workers as early as 1931. The relationship is illustrated in fig. 75.8. In general terms, any procedure that reduces the blood level of thyroid hormone will result in an increase in the secretion of TSH, with consequent stimulation of the thyroid in an attempt to produce enough hormone to restore the blood level to normal. This sequence of events follows such experimental interventions as hemi-thyroidectomy, administration of anti-thyroid drugs, reduction of the iodide intake to inadequate levels, or an increased rate of metabolism of hormone such as occurs in animals during chronic exposure to cold. Conversely, raising the blood hormone level by the administration of thyroxine will result in a depression of TSH secretion, hypofunction and eventually atrophy of the thyroid. The "feedback" system is central to the regulation of TSH secretion; the site of action of thyroid hormones in bringing about these changes is thus of great interest. The evidence, derived from experiments in which hormone was injected directly into the pituitary by means of indwelling cannulae, and the study of responses to variations in blood hormone level after section of the pituitary stalk or transplantation of the gland, suggests that thyroxine can, and does, act directly at the pituitary level to regulate TSH secretion. It does not appear necessary to postulate an action on the hypothalamus in the present state of our knowledge but the possibility of a "thyroxine receptor" in the brain cannot be excluded. Although the CNS does not seem to be involved in the functioning of the "feedback" system, there is no doubt that a pituitary in normal vascular relationships to an intact hypothalamus is essential for certain thyroid responses to occur and probably also to maintain a normal basal level of activity. Lesions of the anterior hypothalamus, stalk-section, or transplantation of the gland, all result in a lowered basal level of activity, though some response to changes in blood hormone level can still be elicited. Further, electrical stimulation of the anterior basal hypothalamus in the region of the supraoptico-hypophyseal tract has been shown to increase thyroid activity via an increased release of TSH. The acute (1–2 hr.) increase in thyroid activity that normally follows the exposure of laboratory animals to a reduced environmental temperature is blocked by lesions of the anterior hypothalamus. Andersson (1964) has shown that local cooling of the anterior hypothalamus in goats causes TSH release and thyroid gland activation, and that warming of this same restricted area of the brain prevents the thyroid activation that normally follows cooling of the whole animal despite a fall in deep body temperature. These results indicate that some form of super-imposed neural drive must be included in our picture of the regulation of TSH secretion (fig. 75.8). The means by which the hypothalamus influences TSH secretion is most probably by the agency of a thyrotrophin releasing factor that reaches the pituitary in the portal vessels (see section on the *anterior pituitary gland*). Detailed discussions of the control of TSH secretion have been published by D'Angelo (1963) and Brown-Grant (1966).

Relationship with other Endocrine Glands

A complex relationship between the thyroid and the ovary, conceivably contributing in some way to the much higher incidence of thyroid disorders in women than in men, has been recognized since the original descriptions of the syndromes of hypo- and hyperthyroidism by Gull and Parry. The details of this relationship remain obscure. In the human, the best known interaction is the very common enlargement of the thyroid during pregnancy, with a demonstrable increase in the uptake of radio-iodine beginning as early as the third month. As discussed previously, the raised PBI observed is related to an increase in the thyroxine-binding of globulin level, the "free" T_4 content of the serum remaining within normal limits as does the absolute T_4 degradation rates, so that these changes, once established, do not explain the thyroid gland enlargement. It has recently been demonstrated by workers in Aberdeen, Scotland (a fishing port where the sea-food consumption and hence iodine intake is relatively high), that the renal clearance of iodide is doubled in pregnancy and that this leads to a marked fall in the plasma inorganic iodide level. Although the thyroid plasma clearance rate by the hyperactive gland is increased, absolute iodine uptake remains within normal limits (Aboul-Khair *et al.*, 1964). The thyromegaly of human pregnancy may be a response to a relative iodine deficiency of renal origin. The influence of the adrenal-cortex on the thyroid still presents many problems; it appears that gluco-corticoids in high dosage may depress some indices of thyroid gland activity in many species and that non-specific "stress" will also reduce thyroid activity, apparently independently of its effect in causing an increased secretion of glucocorticoids. The details of these changes are not well understood and there may be considerable species difference in the response. Ingbar and Freinkel (1956) have discussed this topic in detail.

The thyroid in turn, influences gonadal and adrenocortical functions. Extreme variations in thyroid activity, either hyper- or hypofunction, have an adverse effect on reproductive performance, especially in the female, but moderate degrees of thyroid dysfunction are compatible with normal sexual cycles and successful pregnancy and lactation. No specific mechanism for these effects is known. Hyperfunction of the thyroid is generally associated with adrenocortical hypertrophy and increased urinary secretion of corticosteroid metabolites and hypofunction, with some degree of adrenocortical atrophy and reduced urinary excretion. In both states, the *plasma* corticosteroid levels are essentially normal. It has been shown that these changes are associated with increased and decreased rates of turnover of corticosteroids, respectively, and that these in turn, are probably related to changes in the liver content of the enzymes concerned with corticosteroid metabolism which are influenced by the thyroid hormone levels. In hyperthyroidism the enzyme level is raised, the half-lives are reduced, and a higher rate of secretion is necessary to maintain a normal plasma concentration and *vice versa*.

A functionally important relationship between the adrenal medulla and sympathetic nervous system and the thyroid has been postulated in the past but is not now believed to be of significance in the physiological regulation of the thyroid gland's activity. Episodes of acute thyroid enlargement lasting minutes or a few hours are among the rarer but pathognomonic signs of a paroxysmal secretion of nor-adrenaline by a phaeochromocytoma of the adrenal medulla. A more recent field of study is the relationship between the actions of thyroxine (or T_3) and adrenaline on the peripheral tissues. It is possible that a better understanding of the mechanism of action of both hormones may emerge from these investigations. The review by Harrison (1964) covers most of the recent work.

Physiological Aspects of Thyroid Disease

Clinically obvious enlargements of the thyroid gland (goitre) was described many centuries ago. The recognition of syndromes associate with hyper- and hypofunction of the gland is more recent. Sir William Gull, a London physician, published in 1874 a description of "A cretinoid state supervening in adult life in women" [hypothyroidism in childhood (cretinism) had been recognised as a thyroid disorder about the middle of the nineteenth century]. The successful treatment of adult hypothyroidism by injection of sheep thyroid extract was reported by Murray in 1891, and in the next year Fox and MacKenzie simultaneously reported that oral administration was equally effective. Caleb Hillier Parry, a Welsh physician practising in England, described the clinical picture of hyperthyroidism in a paper published in 1825 and Robert Graves, an Irish physician, published, in 1835, a paper entitled

"A newly observed affection of the thyroid gland in females," describing the same condition. For reasons that are now obscure, the name of Graves' rather than Parry is attached to one form of hyperthyroidism. In continental Europe, the eponym Basedow's disease is favoured, doubtless to celebrate the publication of a precise description of the same syndrome by K. A. von Basedow in 1840. These and many other original papers describing endocrine disorders are reproduced in Major (1948).

Thyroid diseases may be classified in many different ways; as the main concern here is with the underlying disorder of function, this is the basis on which they are discussed.

Hyperthyroidism

An excessive supply of thyroid hormone to the peripheral tissues is the basis of this condition. Generally this arises from an overactivity of the gland but a similar state may sometimes result from the ingestion of exogenous hormone in large amounts. Clinically, a distinction is usually drawn between hyperthyroidism in young, adult patients, generally female, in whom there is a generalised enlargement of a previously apparently normal thyroid with obvious changes in the eyes—the classic Graves' disease (fig. 75.9); and hyperthyroidism, usually occurring in rather older patients, often with a history of many years of nodular enlargement of the thyroid without previous evidence of overactivity and in whom ocular changes are minimal or absent and the main deleterious effect of the excess of hormone is apparent in the cardiovascular system. Auricular fibrillation not responding to treatment with cardiac glycosides (digitalis or digoxin) or frank congestive heart failure may be the presenting symptoms. Such cases are described as "Toxic nodular goitre" or, where a single nodule appears to be hyperactive, as "toxic adenoma." The classical Graves' disease and "toxic adenoma" may be the two extremes of a continuous spectrum of disorders with a common aetiology, or the hyperthyroidism may be the result of quite distinct pathological processes. Neither possibility can be excluded, as at present the cause of any or all types of hyperthyroidism is unknown. The view that there may be an excessive secretion of TSH has been widely discussed, often coupled with the suggestion that some emotional disturbance may be the precipitating factor in the onset of the disease. A corollary of this view is that the regulation of TSH secretion by the level of circulating thyroid hormone must

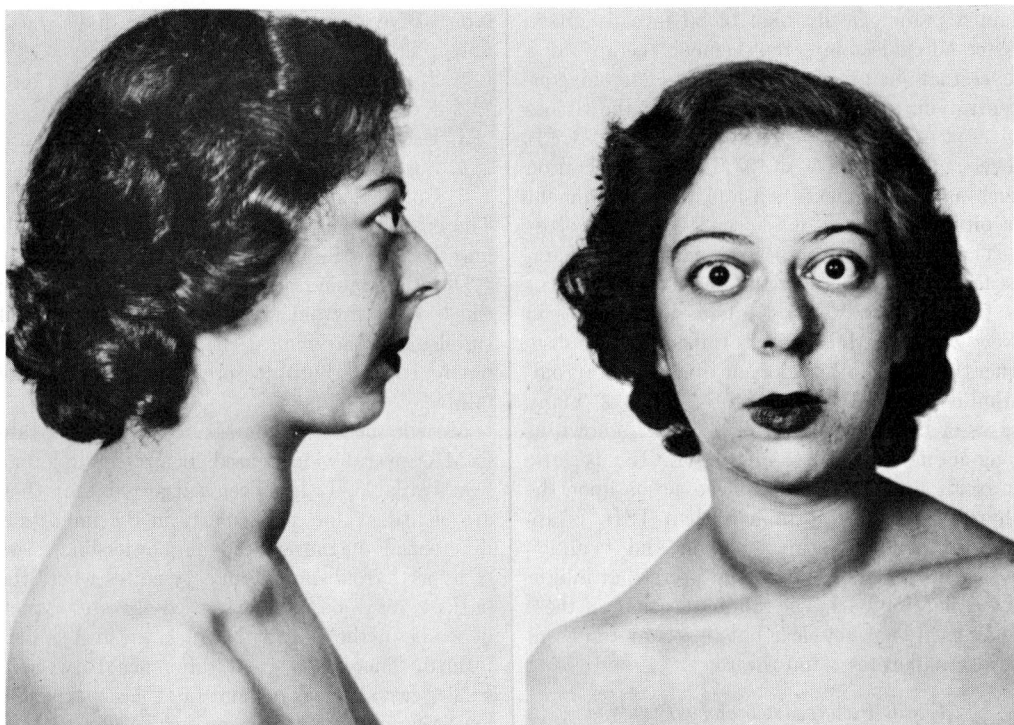

Fig. 75.9. Graves' disease in a young woman. Note the obvious generalised enlargement of the thyroid. Lid retraction, exophthalmos and supraorbital swelling are present. Photographs made available through the courtesy of Dr. A. W. Spence and the Department of Medical Illustration, St. Bartholemew's Hospital, London.

also be abnormal, in that secretion is not suppressed by the raised blood hormone level. There is remarkably little direct or indirect evidence to support this view. Assays of blood TSH levels, in so far as they are reliable, have failed to demonstrate any constant rise; the levels may even be subnormal in contrast to the findings in primary hypothyroidism (McKenzie, 1965). It has been argued that the rise in blood TSH level is too small to be detected by any assay method yet available and this is difficult to refute directly. However, if it is assumed that the essential change is a "resetting" of the feed-back mechanism to operate at a dangerously high, but controlled, blood thyroxine level, and involving undetectable but significant rises in TSH level, then additional large doses of exogenous thyroid hormone sufficient to sustain a raised blood level should depress TSH secretion and reduce the level of thyroid gland activity. This prediction has not been confirmed, and, indeed, the failure to depress thyroid gland activity by large doses of hormone in true cases of hyperthyroidism is the basis of a valuable test to distinguish between cases of mild hyperthyroidism and patients in whom thyroid gland

activity is at the upper limit of the normal range. Further, if the "resetting" hypothesis were correct, when the level of circulating hormone was reduced to normal by anti-thyroid drugs, one would expect a further increase of TSH secretion and rapid enlargement of the gland in an attempt to restore the previous raised value. In practice this only occurs when sub-normal levels of circulating hormone are produced, which suggests that the "feedback" mechanism is intact and normal and TSH secretion was suppressed while the disease was active. The contrast between hyperthyroidism and the form of Cushing's syndrome (hyperadrenocorticism) associated with bilateral enlargement of the adrenal cortex which appears to be a true disorder of the "feedback" control mechanism, is striking. The blood level of glucocorticoids is raised with the development of a characteristic clinical picture from the effects on the peripheral tissues. In the untreated state, blood ACTH levels are also high; these levels are not depressed when doses of exogenous corticosteroids are administered which are sufficient to maintain normal blood levels and suppress ACTH secretion in healthy individuals, but are reduced when sufficient steroid to maintain a pathologically high blood level is given. After adrenalectomy, replacement therapy at a level that maintains normal blood steroid concentrations and a eucorticoid state of the tissues is associated with persistently raised blood ACTH levels, and evidence of ACTH hypersecretion such as skin pigmentation and the development of pituitary tumours may occur.

The aetiology of hyperthyroidism is still uncertain. The most interesting recent development is the demonstration by Adams and Purves in New Zealand, McKenzie in Canada, and subsequently, many others, of an abnormal thyroid-stimulating substance in the serum of many cases of hyperthyroidism. This agent, known as long-acting thyroid stimulator (LATS) because it exerts a much more prolonged action upon the thyroid gland of test animals than TSH, is apparently not of pituitary origin, and its action is said not to be blocked by anti-sera that inhibit the actions of TSH. The full implications of these findings are not yet clear but they may represent a very important step forward.

Clinical Picture, Laboratory Tests and Treatment

Apart from the diffuse or nodular enlargement of the thyroid, the effects of an excess of hormone on many of the systems of the body are obvious in a typical case. Increased metabolism is manifested: (1) as an abnormal (or recently altered) tolerance of cold or intolerance of heat, (2) the inefficiency of the oxidative mechanisms as increased effort in completing a given amount of muscular work, (3) activation of the heat-loss mechanism as cutaneous vasodilatation and sweating (the hot, moist palms are characteristic), (4) as increased appetite, despite which weight loss may be severe, and (5) as an increase in the sleeping pulse rate. In older patients, effects on the heart, rather than general effects, may predominate. The nervous system is characteristically involved; tremor of the outstretched hands is common but not diagnostic. The behaviour tends to be impetuous and patients are often irritable; emotional lability is common. All these, of course, may be life-long characteristics; recent changes in these respects, of which an intelligent patient may be well aware, are of greater diagnostic significance. The eye signs (fig. 75.9) may be more or less prominent; rarely, they may become worse as the hyperthyroidism is brought under control (but this may be coincidence), or they may exist without hyperthyroidism ever having been present or developing

later. Five types of abnormality have been noted; Trotter (1962) lists them as:

1. Spasms of the upper eyelid (lid retraction).
2. External ophthalmoplegia.
3. Exophthalamos (proptosis of the eyeball).
4. Supra- and infra-orbital swelling.
5. Congestion and oedema of the eye.

The origin of the eye changes is obscure; details may be found in any clinical textbook.

Objective laboratory tests intended to measure the level of thyroid gland activity, confirm and supplement the clinical diagnosis; they should not replace it—both doctors and technicians are fallible.

Measurements of the basal metabolic rate (BMR) were widely used before radio-iodine was available. It has been suggested that they are of little value, particularly in the important differential diagnosis between border-line cases of hyperthyroidism and anxiety states where the patient may be unable to co-operate. Much depends on the care with which the test is performed. There is a great difference between a single casual measurement and accepting the lowest of four estimations on two successive days obtained from patients heavily sedated with barbiturates for the actual test (Wayne, 1960). In fact, the BMR is a rather unpleasant test to take, especially for a nervous patient, and is often omitted in favour of some form of radio-iodine test. Many tests have been devised, and much time and energy expended, in attempting to establish a marginal superiority of one form or the other. The short term (2–4 hr.) uptake by the gland, some form of cumulative measurement of renal excretion, or the conversion ratio (the proportion of total plasma radio-activity present as protein-bound ^{131}I 24 or 48 hours after administration), have all been widely used. The theoretical basis and limitations of such tests has been well described by Riggs (1952). Translation of isotope data to absolute iodine uptake measurements, by the indirect determination of the plasma inorganic iodide concentration, has been employed extensively by the Glasgow group (Wayne, Koutras and Alexander, 1964). The methods are not particularly demanding, judged by the standards of modern clinical pathology, and they add so much to the value of the results that they seem likely to be widely adopted in centres that undertake any considerable amount of diagnostic work. Any laboratory carrying out the radio-iodine tests can also perform the very valuable triiodothyronine suppression test. If the original test shows a value on the upper limit of the normal range and the diagnosis is still in doubt, T_3 (120 μg./day for 8 days) is given and the test repeated. Normal thyroid function is suppressed by about 80%; as discussed above, the activity of the hyperthyroid gland is essentially unchanged.

Estimation of the protein-bound iodine of the serum appears to be routine in the United States and is slowly becoming more common in the United Kingdom and in Europe. The red cell or resin triiodothyronine uptake test involves adding radio-active T_3 to the patient's blood or plasma *in vitro* and measuring the uptake of T_3 by the cells or resin after incubation. The theoretical basis of this test is that the uptake by cells or resin is proportional, other things being equal, to the "free" T_3 and inversely proportional to the bound T_3 of the plasma. This, in turn, is related to the number of unoccupied binding; and this, in turn, to the plasma T_4 level, assuming the level of binding protein to be normal. A high T_4 level results in a low concentration of unoccupied binding sites, little protein binding of T_3 and high uptake by red cells or resin. Clearly this is a remarkably indirect test of thyroid function; its popularity is difficult to explain except that it is easy to perform, after a fashion, although difficult to interpret in any precise terms.

Treatment of hyperthyroidism consists in reducing the activity of the thyroid gland in one of several ways:

1. *Surgical removal.* It is essential that the patient be euthyroid at the time of operation. This is now achieved by treatment with an anti-thyroid (goitrogenic) drug that blocks organic binding of iodine. Perchlorate is not used, as it is customary to give large doses of iodide for the 7 to 10 days preceding the operation, to reduce the vascularity of the gland and thus simplify the surgeon's task. The effect of perchlorate, it will be recalled, is to block active transport of iodide and the effect on hormone synthesis can be overcome by large doses of iodide. The preoperative iodide (whose mode of action is still not understood) would bring about an exacerbation of the disease in a patient controlled by perchlorate. It is general practice to remove about ⅞ths of the gland. The medical results are generally excellent; surgical complications include the possibility of damage to the recurrent laryngeal nerves.

2. *Destruction of the gland tissue by irradiation.* External irradiation of the thyroid is no longer practiced. Administration of a radio-active isotope achieves the desired effect by virtue of the radiation emitted by the radio-active atoms

collected in the thyroid when they disintegrate. In some clinics, the dose to be given is calculated by a complex formula involving gland size, per cent uptake of a tracer dose, estimated biological half-life in the gland, and the energy of the emitted radiation. Others proceed on the basis of past experience and clinical judgement (educated guess work). Initial dosage may range from 5 to 25 mc. (millicuries), in contrast to diagnostic use of 10 to 50 μc. (microcuries) (1 millicurie equals 1,000 microcuries). A quarter to a third of patients require a second dose to render them euthyroid, however the initial dose is estimated.

3. *Administration of anti-thyroid drugs.* Methyl- or propyl-thiouracil, methimimazole, and car-bimazole and perchlorate are the most widely used. Their mode of action has already been discussed. The minimal dose necessary to ameliorate the signs and symptoms is given for some months, after initial control has been established. When the disease enters a natural remission, therapy may be stopped but further attacks are not unknown.

The choice of treatment in a particular case is determined by many factors, including the experience of the medical practitioner looking after the case. Treatment A may theoretically be thought preferable to treatment B, but not if the doctor has wide experience of B and little of A. The indications and contra-indications are dealt with in textbooks of medicine. All three methods are effective in the majority of cases.

Compensated Hypothyroidism

This is the useful term employed by Trotter to describe the physiological state of patients with simple or non-toxic goitre. As discussed previously, if the supply of hormone from the gland is reduced for any reason, the pituitary secretion of TSH will increase, and hypertrophy and hyperplasia of the thyroid will follow in an attempt to compensate for the deficiency and provide an adequate amount of hormone. This is exactly the situation that exists in the endemic goitre areas of the world where the supply of iodine in the diet is inadequate. Virtually all the population have goitres but few are clinically hypothyroid, the enlarged, hyperactive gland being able, in most cases, to obtain enough iodine to provide sufficient hormone. Areas where specific goitrogens occur in the food provide another example of the same general phenomenon. Sporadic familial goitre, where a genetically determined deficiency of certain thyroid enzymes may impair the formation of hormone, is another example and is discussed in more detail under hypothyroidism. At one time it was considered necessary to discuss the gross and microscopic anatomical findings in cases of simple goitre in great detail, and to classify them into many subdivisions on this basis, but with a better understanding of the underlying mechanism it has become apparent that any originally diffusely enlarged hyperplastic gland may, if left untreated become a nodular goitre with local areas of excessive colloid accumulation. These changes are a late stage in a disease process that can be cured or arrested before they occur if the aetiology of the condition is understood.

Endemic goitre is essentially a response to iodine deficiency and has been eliminated in many areas of the world by the compulsory addition of iodide or iodate to cooking and table salt and by iodide supplements to school meals. This is essentially a public health problem on the national or international scale rather than the problem of the individual case. The practical and administrative difficulties of iodine prophylaxis are naturally greater in underdeveloped countries but are not insuperable if adequate funds are available to support the programme. The claims of a vocal minority to exercise their freedom to have goitre or dental caries rather than have "chemicals" added to their food or water may be an obstacle in more advanced countries. A detailed account of the findings in a cooperative study of a South American endemic goitre area is presented in the very interesting monograph by Stanbury et al. (1954). Identification and elimination of naturally occurring goitrogens from the diet may be a more difficult problem. Clements (1960) has described the studies on "milk goitre" in children in Tasmania, and elsewhere in Australia, due to feeding of stock on pastures where goitrogen-containing weeds abound. Numerically, this is a much less important problem than that of iodine-deficiency goitre.

Treatment of the individual case of simple goitre in nonendemic areas requires more detailed consideration. It is important to realise that compensatory hypertrophy, of whatever origin, can be reversed by thyroxine administration, at least in the early stages before nodule formation, and this type of treatment, which removes the stimulus to further growth, may be used. Radio-iodine or surgical removal have no place in the treatment of the moderately enlarged diffuse simple goitre. Removal or destruction of thyroid tissue without treatment of the underlying cause

may precipitate hypothyroidism or leave the patient with a rapidly regenerating remnant of thyroid tissue. Surgical removal of a goitre that is causing damage by pressure on neighbouring structures or mental distress may be appropriate; thyroxine treatment is used after the operation to discourage regeneration.

Hypothyroidism

The consequences of a lack of thyroid hormone in infants and adults were recognised in the nineteenth century and effective replacement therapy was available before 1900. Studies during the last ten or fifteen years have considerably advanced our understanding of the aetiology of the condition, both in infants and in adults. It is convenient to consider the disorder in terms of the age of onset; the major effects in the young are related to failure of normal development and, in the adult, to the depressed metabolism.

Onset in Infancy

Except for the rare cases where goitrogenic drugs administered to the mother are transmitted to the foetus *in utero*, or in the milk after birth, and the condition disappears when the drugs are withdrawn, hypothyroidism manifest at birth or in the first few months of life is a serious condition, calling for prompt and continued treatment if irreparable damage is to be avoided. The common clinical features are: failure to thrive, feeding difficulties, somnolence and often extreme constipation. Growth both in weight and in length is subnormal. The enlarged tongue is characteristic and may cause choking fits. Puffiness of the face and limbs may occur later (fig. 75.10). The end result, if treatment is not begun promptly, is also illustrated—a dwarf, retaining infantile bodily proportions, and with mental retardation varying from severe impairment to complete imbecility (fig. 75.11). At this stage, it is said, there is little to be achieved by thyroxine treatment except the conversion of an amiable, easily managed idiot to a difficult and aggressive one. Major brain growth occurs during the first year of post-natal life, and if effective treatment is not begun at this stage, permanent damage will result. A major anatomical finding in the brain, in experimental studies in rats rendered hypothyroid before or soon after birth, is the failure of growth of the dendritic processes of cortical nerve cells (Eayrs, 1964).

It was customary at one time to refer to all cases of hypothyroidism in infancy as cretins. This term was originally introduced towards the

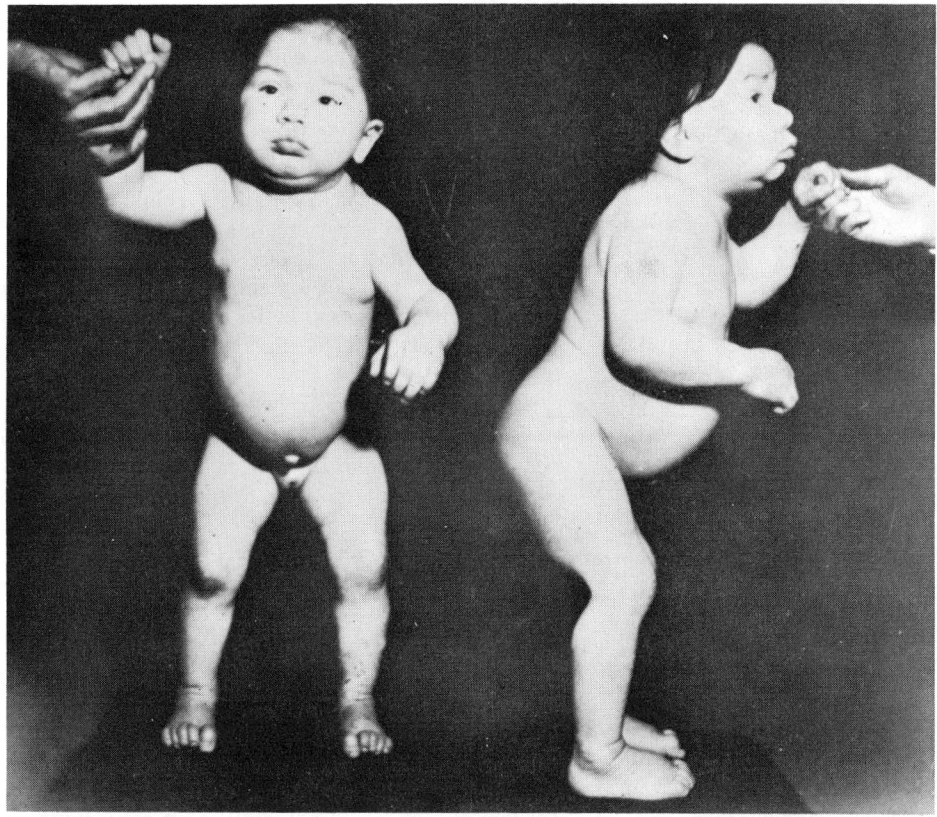

FIG. 75.10. The hypothyroid infant. Note the lethargic appearance, pot belly and poor posture·
Photographs through the courtesy of Dr. A. W. Franklin, St. Bartholemew's Hospital, London.

end of the eighteenth century to describe the mentally defective, often dwarfed, deaf and often deaf-mute individuals common in the mountainous endemic goitre areas of Europe and found later in other remote endemic goitre areas such as the Himalayas. Subsequently, when some of the same features were recognised in children in non-endemic areas, the name came to be applied to them also. It is difficult at this stage to decide how many of these cases in endemic goitre areas would now be thought to be due to hypothyroidism during foetal or neo-natal life and how many would be classified as idiots of some other type. Two puzzling features are the apparent occurrence of mental defectives of normal or near-normal stature and the very high incidence of deafness and deaf-mutism among cretins. Neither of these findings is characteristic of congenital hypothyroidism in non-endemic areas, and suggests that genetic factors may also be involved in endemic cretinism. The effects of iodine prophylaxis in reducing the incidence of cretinism may be coincidental; better communications to and from the remote mountain areas developed at the same time and greater oppor-

tunity for matings outside the previously isolated group may have been concerned in the reduction of the incidence of idiocy. The term cretin should probably be restricted to the type of case found in endemic goitre areas, and cases of congenital hypothyroidism occurring sporadically in non-endemic goitre areas should be described as such. This leaves open the question of genetic factors versus severe hypothyroidism during foetal life in the aetiology of endemic cretinism. The evidence that hypothyroidism *in utero* is of importance in man is not convincing; various experimental and clinical studies, including the problems of the possible transfer of maternal hormone to the foetus, are described by Osorio and Myant (1960) and by Myant (1964).

Two types of sporadic congenital hypothyroidism are recognised. In the first, the thyroid is absent, or present only as a small remnant, possibly as a lingual thyroid. In the second, an anatomically normal thyroid is present, or may even be enlarged, but is the site of a genetically determined enzyme defect—an inborn error of metabolism. This group of "familial sporadic goitrous cretins" has received much attention

Fig. 75.11. The end result of untreated hypo-thyroidism in infancy. This dwarf was aged 10 years at the time the photograph was taken. Such cases are rare today and the photograph is repro-duced from McCarrison, R. The aetiology of endemic goitre. Bale, London, 1913.

recently, and the precise stage in biosynthesis at which the enzyme defect, either relative or absolute, occurs has been determined. A general discussion of inborn errors of metabolism is given by Harris (1959) and detailed accounts of the thyroid abnormalities by McGirr (1960) and Stanbury (1963). The defect may be an absence of: (1) the iodide transport mechanism (not only from the thyroid but also from salivary gland, gastric mucosa and choroid plexus), (2) of the enzyme or enzymes responsible for the oxidation and organic binding of iodine (this defect may be associated with a type of perceptive deafness and the combination is known as Pendred's syndrome), (3) of the coupling enzymes, (4) of the thyroidal iodotyrosine dehalogenases, (5) of the enzymes concerned in thyroglobulin synthesis (an abnormal iodinated protein is present in the gland and may appear in the serum). The de-gree of interference with thyroid hormone syn-thesis varies, suggesting that the gene concerned is recessive; some members of the family may show hypothyroidism and goitre formation in infancy; in others it may not appear before puberty, and in others (possibly heterozygotes), there may be goitre but no hypothyroidism. These latter cases fall into the category of compensated hypothyroidism. Whereas the athyreotic type of disease is unlikely to affect more than one child in the family, the enzyme defects are likely to appear in the siblings, and if a positive diag-

nosis can be made in one child, the others can be examined for marginal degrees of hypothyroidism and treated promptly should the need arise.

Hypothyroidism in Childhood

Many of these cases are of the inherited enzyme defect type. Typically, the child fails to maintain the expected progress at school or is brought to the doctor because of failure of growth. After two years of age the prognosis, if there is delay in diagnosis, is better than in cases of early onset; most of the changes are reversible by treatment.

Hypothyroidism in the Adult

Primary and secondary hypothyroidism are recognised, the former of thyroid and the latter of pituitary origin. Hypothyroidism is rarely the sole or most prominent aspect of pituitary disease and the distinction is usually obvious on clinical grounds. In cases of doubtful origin, the effect of TSH administration on the ^{131}I uptake can be tested (see *laboratory tests*). Hypothyroidism in the adult may present in a variety of ways, and although the clinical picture of advanced hypo-thyroidism (fig. 75.12) is easily recognised, the diagnosis may be a difficult one. The onset is usually gradual: a progressive lethargy and dis-interest, slurred speech and often deafness, loss of appetite but a moderate increase in weight (due largely to water retention), and increasing intolerance to cold are typical. The appearance is characterised by a thickening of the skin of the lips and fingers and edema below the eyes and the hair is brittle and scanty. The colour is pale from the associated anemia, which may be resistant to treatment until the hypothyroidism is relieved. Apart from the lethargy, the mental changes may progress to the stage of psychosis; sometimes the hypothyroidism remains undiag-nosed and the patient is placed in a mental hospi-tal (Asher, 1949). Myxedema, the deposition of an excess of mucoprotein in the skin, usually occurs in the forearms and often in the legs and feet. Though this was originally described as a salient feature of the disease (myxoedema is often used as a synonym for adult hypothyroidism), it should be emphasized that in fact, gross changes in the limbs are present only in severe cases, and are not a necessary, or even very important, feature of hypothyroidism.

Primary hypothyroidism of adult onset, except for cases following the administration of goitro-genic drugs, thyroidectomy or destruction of the gland by radio-iodine, was generally given the noncommital name "spontaneous hypothy-

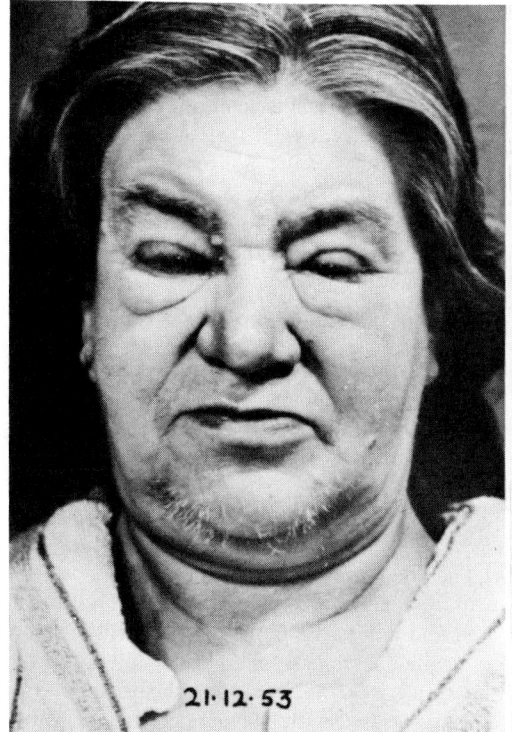 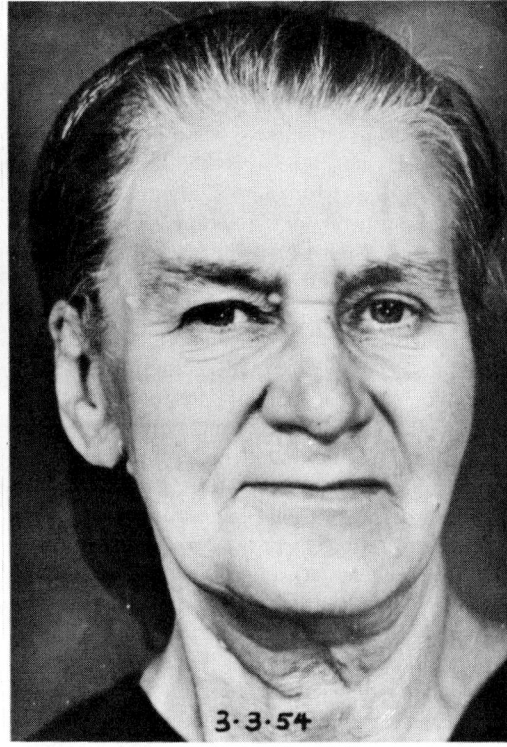

FIG. 75.12. Hypothyroidism before and after treatment with thyroid extract. The excess of facial hair before treatment is the result of a characteristic lack of interest in her personal appearance. Case of Dr. R. Asher, Central Middlesex Hospital, London, whose permission to publish these photographs is gratefully acknowledged.

roidism," since no definite cause for the failure of thyroid function could be found. Recent work suggests that many cases of "spontaneous hypo-thyroidism" may be the terminal stage of an unusual disease process known as auto-immunity. It is known that the body is capable of responding to the parenteral absorption of foreign proteins by manufacturing proteins which circulate in the blood and these antibodies react in a highly specific manner with the foreign proteins (antigens) that elicited their formation, both in the body and *in vitro*. The development of antibody to the toxin of the diphtheria bacillus, following the injection of inactivated toxin is a familiar example. The body does not normally possess or make antibodies against its own proteins; these, in some way, it recognises as "self." As discussed in the chapter on blood groups, an individual of Group B will not have anti-B antibodies in his serum, but will have anti-A antibodies, which will agglutinate Group A or Group AB cells. It now appears that in some circumstances, an individual may develop antibodies to certain proteins derived from his own thyroid gland, and that these antibodies, or some factor

closely related to them, may subsequently reach and damage his thyroid. This process of immunisation against the body's own protein (auto-immune disorder) was first recognised by Roitt and Doniach, at the Middlesex Hospital in London, in connection with an unusual form of chronic thyroiditis known as Hashimoto's disease or lymphadenoid goitre and now often referred to as auto-immune thyroiditis. Hashimoto described, in 1912, a number of cases of diffuse enlargement of the thyroid, of insidious onset, in middle-aged women, not associated with eye changes or evidence of hyperthyroidism. Histologically, the gland shows marked infiltration with lymphocytes and plasma cells, either collected in lymphoid follicles or scattered throughout the gland, and in some cases in the lumen, of thyroid follicles replacing the colloid. The epithelial cells appeared damaged in many areas, sometimes showing a peculiar eosinophilic staining reaction, while elsewhere, the epithelium showed signs of intense TSH stimulation. The evidence pointed to damage from some unknown cause, resulting in impairment of thyroid function, stimulation of TSH secretion, and growth of the gland in attempt to compensate. This is another example of compensated hypothyroidism and, as would be expected, thyroxine administration is successful in reducing the size of the gland. Roitt and Doniach showed that in more than 95% of such cases, relatively high titres of antibodies reacting with normal human thyroid tissue were present in the serum. Later studies showed the presence of precipitating antibodies to thyroglobulin and a complement-fixing antibody to some protein associated with the microsomal fraction of the thyroid epithelial cell. It was at first considered that the reaction of these antibodies with the patients thyroid might be responsible for the damage, but later a distinct cytotoxic factor was found in serum from cases of Hashimoto's disease which inhibited the growth of thyroid cells in tissue culture. This, too, may be an antibody. It is not certain whether the development of antibodies precedes and causes, or is a consequence of the damage to thyroid tissue, but it is established that the presence of circulating antibodies is associated with a high liability to eventual failure of thyroid function. Evidence of an auto-immune process in association with hyperfunction of the gland, or in compensated hypothyroidism, indicates the need for careful management of the case. It has been known for some years that cases of hyperthyroidism in which lymphocytic infiltration was observed in glands examined postoperatively were particularly liable to develop hypothyroidism later. It has now been shown that some hyperthyroid cases may have a high titre of precipitating- or complement-fixing antibody, and that these are cases with a high liability to hypothyroidism after treatment by thyroidectomy or radio-iodine. It seems that conservative treatment with antithyroid drugs is preferable for these cases if they are recognised in time. The type of auto-immune thyroiditis that approximates to Hashimoto's original description may also need careful handling. Clinical, mild hyperthyroidism may be present, and the results of radio-iodine tests may be in the hyperthyroid range; in particular the ^{131}I conversion ratio (ratio of PB ^{131}I to inorganic ^{131}I in the plasma 24 or 48 hours after administration) may be raised because of the presence of a reduced amount of hyperactive tissue and a small thyroidal iodine pool with a rapid turnover. The correct diagnosis is suggested by the normal or low PB ^{127}I level, and the presence of a high titre of circulating antibodies. The correct treatment is, of course, thyroxine administration. The ad-

ministration of ^{131}I or thyroidectomy will precipitate hypothyroidism. The liability to hypothyroidism has been emphasised, and it is striking that the highest incidence of serological evidence of autoimmunity, except for Hashimoto's disease itself, is in cases of non-goitrous hypothyroidism ("spontaneous" hypothyroidism) of adult onset. Some 60% of patients had high titres of antibody, and it is now thought that auto-immunity may have an aetiological role in the majority of such cases thus linking them with Hashimoto's thyroiditis. A better understanding of the origin of the disease may eventually make it possible to prevent its development, rather than simply to abolish the symptoms which is what the treatment available at the moment does.

LABORATORY TESTS AND TREATMENT OF HYPOTHYROIDISM

The determination of the plasma-protein-bound iodine level is of great value in both children and adults. Radio-iodine tests will give low or negligible values for thyroid uptake when the gland is atrophic or fibrotic or absent. In cases associated with enzyme defects and goitre, the pattern of uptake may take many forms, depending on the abnormality, and detailed biochemical investigations may be needed to determine the exact abnormality present. In children, determination of the bone age by X-rays of the limbs, is a valuable guide to both the degree of retardation of growth present and also as to the progress when replacement therapy is begun. In adults, measurement of the BMR (reduced), blood cholesterol (raised), and ECG (low voltage with depressed or inverted T waves), may provide additional confirmatory evidence. The distinction between primary hypothyroidism and changes secondary to pituitary disease is assisted by the fact that the ^{131}I uptake and other radio-iodine tests are improved by TSH administration in cases of pituitary origin.

Treatment is by thyroxine given by mouth; there is no advantage and, in the opinion of many clinicians, a positive disadvantage in giving either thyroid extract or tri-iodothyronine instead of thyroxine. It is usual to begin treatment with 50 μg. per day in children and old people, 100 μg. in young adults, increasing the dose as necessary. A usual adult maintenance dose is 200 to 300 μg. per day. Cautious initial treatment is especially indicated in adult cases with a long history, to avoid precipitating attacks of angina pectoris as the myocardium is one of the first tissues to respond. Dosage is adjusted to that which keeps the adult patient fit and happy rather than to obtain a particular BMR or PBI level. In children, a normal rate of growth is a good indication that treatment is adequate.

REFERENCES

ABOUL-KHAIR, S. A., CROOKS, J., TURNBULL, A. C., AND HYTTEN, F. E. Clin. Sci., 1964, **27**, 195.

ANDERSSON, B. Ciba Foundation Study Group, No. 18, 1964, p. 35, Churchill, London.

ARON, M., VAN CAULERT, C., AND STAHL, J. C.R. Soc. Biol., Paris, 1931, **107**, 64.

ASHER, R. Brit. Med. J., 1949, **ii, 555.**

ASTWOOD, E. B. HARVEY LECTURES, 1945, **40**, 195.

BASEDOWE, K. A. VON. Wschr. ges. Heilk., 1840, **14**, 197.

BAUMANN, C. Ztschr. physiol. Chem., 1896, **21**, 319.

BROWN-GRANT, K. Chapter 7, vol. 2 in The pituitary gland (ed., HARRIS, G. W. AND DONOVAN, B. T.) Butterworths, London, 1966.

CLEMENTS, F. W. Brit. Med. Bull., 1960, **16**, 133.

D'ANGELO, S. A. Chapter 6, *in* Advances in neuro-endocrinology (ed., NALBANDOV, A. V.), University of Illinois Press, Urbana, 1963.

EAYRS, J. T. Animal Behaviour, 1959, **7**, 1.

EAYRS, J. T. Ciba Foundation Study Group, No. 18, 1964, p. 60, Churchill, London.

Fox, E. L. Brit. Med. J., 1892, **ii**, 941.

FREINKEL, N. Chapter 7, *in* The thyroid (ed., PITT-RIVERS, R. AND TROTTER, W. R.). Butterworths, London, 1964.

GOFMAN, J. W. Advances in medical and biological physics, 1962, **8**, 1.

GOOLDEN, A. W. G. Chapter 15, *in* The thyroid (ed., PITT-RIVER, R. AND TROTTER, W. R.). Butterworths, London, 1964.

GRAVES, R. G. London Medical and Surgical J., 1835, **7**, 516.

GREER, M. A. Rect. Prog. Hormone. Res., 1962, **18**, 187.

GREER, M. A., KENDALL, J. W., AND SMITH, M. Chapter 14, *in* The thyroid (ed., PITT-RIVERS, R. AND TROTTER, W. R.), Butterworths, London, 1964.

GROSS, J. AND PITT-RIVERS, R. Lancet, 1952, **i,** 439.

GULL, W. Tr. Clin. Soc. London, 1874, **7**, 180.

GUDERNATSCH, J. F. Am. J. Anat., 1914, **15**, 431.

HALMI, N. S. Vitamins and Hormones, 1961, **19**, 133.

HALMI, N. S., Chapter 3. In The Thyroid, edited by Pitt-Rivers, R. & Trotter, W. R. Butterworths, London, 1964.

HARINGTON, C. R. AND BARGER, G. Biochem. J., 1927, **21**, 169.

HASHIMOTO, H. Arch. fur klin. chir., 1912, **97**, 219.

HERTZ, S., ROBERTS, A., AND EVANS, R. D. Proc. Soc. Exp. Biol., N.Y., 1938, **38**, 510.

INGBAR, S. H. AND FREINKEL, N. Chapter 15, *in* Hormones in human plasma (ed., ANTONIADES, H. N.). Little, Brown & Co., Boston, 1960.

KENDALL, E. C. J. Biol. Chem., 1919, **39**, 125.

LEBLOND, C. P. AND GROSS, J. Endocrinol., 1948, **43**, 306.

LEE, N. D., HENRY, R. J., AND GOLUB, O. J. J. Clin. Endocrinol., 1964, **24**, 486.

LELOUP, J. AND FONTAINE, M. Ann. N.Y. Acad. Sci., 1960, **86**, 316.

McGIRR, E. M. Brit. Med. Bull., 1960, **16**, 113.

MACKENZIE, M. W. G. Brit. Med. J., 1892, **ii**, 940.

MAGNUS-LEVY, A. Berliner Klin. Wchnschr., 1895, **32**, 650.

MURRAY, G. R. Brit. Med. J., 1891, **ii, 796.**

MYANT, N. B. Chapter 12, *in* The thyroid (ed., PITT-RIVERS, R. AND TROTTER, W. R.). Butterworths, London, 1964.

OPPENHEIMER, J. H. AND SURKS, M. I. J. Clin. Endocrinol., 1964, **24**, 785.

OSORIO, C. AND MYANT, N. B. Brit. Med. Bull., 1960, **16**, 159.

PARRY, C. H. 1825, reprinted in Major, R. M. (1948).

ROCHE, J., MICHEL, R., AND LISSITSKY, S. C.R. Acad. Sci., Paris, 1952, **234**, 1228.

ROITT, I. M. AND DONIACH, D. Brit. Med. Bull., 1960, **16**, 152.

ROITT, I. M., DONIACH, D., CAMPBELL, P. N., AND HUDSON, R. V. Lancet, 1956, **ii**, 820.

STANBURY, J. B. Rect Prog. Horm. Res., 1963, **19**, 547.

STEIN, O. AND GROSS, J. Endocrinol., 1964, **75**, 787.

STERLING, K. Mayo Clinic Proc., 1964, **39**, 586.

TATA, J. R. Memoirs Soc. for Endocrinol., 1961, **11**, 90.

TATA, J. R. Chapter 8, *in* The thyroid (ed., PITT-RIVERS, R. AND TROTTER, W. R.). Butterworths, London, 1964.

TROTTER, W. R. Chapter 1, *in* The thyroid (ed., PITT-RIVERS, R. AND TROTTER, W. R.). Butterworths, London, 1964.

WAYNE, E. J. Brit med. J., 1960, **i**, 1.

WOLFF, E. C. AND WOLFF, J. Chapter 11, *in* The thyroid (ed., PITT-RIVERS, R. AND TROTTER, W. R.). Butterworths, London, 1964.

Monographs and Reviews

Brit. Med. Bull., 1960, **16,** part 2, The thyroid gland.

BROWN-GRANT, K. Physiol. Rev., 1961, **41**, 189.

Ciba Foundation Study Group, Number 18, Brain-Thyroid Relationships, Churchill, London, 1964.

GORBMAN, A., AND BERN, H. A. A textbook of comparative endocrinology. John Wiley, London, 1964.

HARINGTON, C. A. The thyroid gland, its chemistry and biology. Oxford University Press, London, 1933.

HARRIS, H. Human biochemical genetics. Cambridge University Press, Cambridge, 1959.

HARRISON, T. S. Physiol. Rev., 1964, **44**, 161.

HOCH, F. L. Physiol. Rev., 1964, **42**, 605.

INGBAR, S. H. AND FREINKEL, N. Metabolism, 1956, **5**, 652.

McKENZIE, J. M. J. Clin. Endocrinol., 1965, **25**, 424.

MAJOR, R. M. Classic descriptions of disease. Blackwell, Oxford, 1948.

PITT-RIVERS, R. AND TATA, J. R. The thyroid hormones. Pergamon Press Ltd., London, 1959.

PITT-RIVERS, R. AND TROTTER, W. R. (eds.). The thyroid gland. Volumes 1 and 2. Butterworths, London, 1964.

RALL, J. E., ROBBINS, J. AND LEWALLEN, C. G. Chapter 3, p. 159, The thyroid, *in* The hormones, Vol. 5 (ed. PINCUS, G., THIMANN, K. V., AND ASTWOOD, E. B.), Academic Press. London, 1964.

RIGGS, D. S. Pharmacol. Rev., 1952, 4, 284.

ROBBINS, J. AND RALL, J. E. Physiol. Rev., 1960, 40, 415.

ROLLESTON, H. D. The endocrine organs in health and disease, with a historical review. Oxford University Press, London, 1936.

STANBURY, J. B., BROWNELL, G. L., RIGGS, D. S., PERINETTI, H., ITOIZ, J., AND DEL CASTILLO, E. B. Endemic goitre: the adaptation of man to iodine deficiency. Harvard University Press, Cambridge, (Mass.), 1954.

TAPLEY, D. F. AND HATFIELD, W. B. Vitamins and hormones, 1962, 20, 251.

TROTTER, W. R. Diseases of the thyroid. Blackwells, Oxford. 1962.

WAYNE, E. J., KOUTRAS, D. A., AND ALEXANDER, W. D. Clinical aspects of iodine metabolism. Blackwells, Oxford. 1964.

WERNER, S. C. (ed.) Thyrotrophin. Thomas, Springfield, 1963.

WERNER, S. C. (ed.) The thyroid. 2nd edition. Hoeber-Harper and Row, New York, 1962.

WOLFF, J. Physiol. Rev., 1964, 44, 45.

CHAPTER 76

The Adrenal (Suprarenal) Glands

DEVELOPMENT AND STRUCTURE

The mammalian adrenal gland, like the pituitary body and the thyroid-parathyroid apparatus, consists of two parts which, though closely associated anatomically, have separate origins and are structurally different. The central part of the gland is called the *medulla*: the outer enveloping rim of tissue is known as the *cortex*. In certain fishes (Elasmobranchs) the two parts are present but not combined as a single gland. Tissue corresponding to the mammalian medulla, for example, is found as a number of small discrete masses on either side of the spine in association with the sympathetic ganglia (*chromaffin tissue*), whereas an elongated structure lying between the kidneys (*inter-renal body*) corresponds to the adrenal cortex of mammals. In the amphibia and reptilia the two types of tissue have come together, but masses of cortical cells are intermingled with islets of medullary tissue and the two tissues are not segregated into a peripheral and a central zone, as in the mammalian adrenal.

In all animals the medullary tissue and the sympathetic ganglion cells have a common origin; they develop from primitive cell masses which have separated from the neural crest. Migrating from their sites of origin these masses of ectodermal cells undergo differentiation along two paths, some into sympathetic ganglion cells, others into *chromaffin tissue*. This latter term is derived from their reaction with chromic acid or its salts in which the cells are stained dark brown. Chromaffin or chromophil cells are also stained blue by ferric chloride and black by osmic acid. In the abdomen, on either side of the midline, a relatively large mass of chromaffin cells becomes enveloped by cortical tissue to constitute the adrenal medulla. Other smaller masses persist as accessory chromaffin tissue in association with the ganglia and plexuses of the sympathetic, and are called *paraganglia*. On the other hand, sympathetic ganglion cells may be found scattered among the cells of the adult adrenal medulla. The cortex is developed from mesoderm. It arises as a bud from the celomic epithelium covering the inner side of the fore part of the mesonephros. The celomic epithelium immediately behind this area gives rise to the germinal epithelium from which in turn the sex glands develop.

The medulla is composed of closely packed groups of polyhedral cells containing chromaffin granules which are looked upon as the mother substance of the medullary secretion. The cell groups are separated by blood sinuses which empty into a central vein. The cells of the cortex are arranged in three zones. These are, from without inward, the (1) *zona glomerulosa*, in which groups of cells are arranged in a circular or oval pattern, (2) *zona fasciculata*, in which the cells are arranged in columns, and (3) *zona reticularis*, which is composed of a network of cell cords (fig. 76.1). The cells of the cortex in a number of species contain fine lipid droplets which can be made apparent by a variety of histochemical or optical methods. Such lipid droplets appear to be associated with the secretion of the gland, but in some forms (e.g., the hamster, other hibernants and ruminants) these droplets are not visible microscopically.

The characteristic zonation of the adrenal cortex has led many workers to consider that the cells of the cortex originate at the periphery of the gland, in the zona glomerulosa just beneath the capsule or from the capsular cells. With increasing age the cells were believed to move inward, through, and as constituents of, the zona fasciculata to the zona reticularis where cellular death and absorption ensued. More recent opinion favors the view that the three zones of the cortex reflect differing functional activities, although it is well established that following an almost complete adrenalectomy a few zona glomerulosa cells are able to regenerate a new adrenal cortex with the normal zonation.

The adrenal gland of the human fetus is proportionally some 10 to 20 times larger by weight than that of the adult. Most of the gland is comprised of an enormously enlarged reticular (or fetal) zone which is destined to involute soon after birth. The function of the fetal zone is not clear; it may be developed under the influence of chorionic gonadotrophin.

A sex difference in the size and histological appearance of the adrenal cortex has been demonstrated in animals. The glands are larger in women than in men, a difference which is enhanced when the smaller female body is taken into account. In animals, the adrenals of the female are reduced to the size of the male glands under the influence of testosterone.

BLOOD AND NERVE SUPPLY. The adrenal is one of the most richly vascular organs in the body, receiving 6 to 7 cc. of blood per gram of tissue per minute. It is supplied by three small arteries which are derived, respectively, from the inferior phrenic

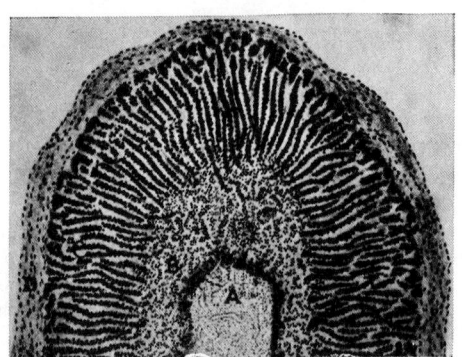

Fig. 76.1. Section of the human adrenal gland: *A*, medullary portion; *B*, zona reticularis; *C*, zona fasciculata; and *D*, capsule. The zona glomerulosa is situated just beneath the capsule. (From Maximow and Bloom.)

artery, the renal artery, and the aorta. These form rich plexuses in the cortex. The plexuses are continuous with the sinuses of the medulla which drain into the central vein of the latter. The right adrenal vein empties directly into the inferior vena cava, the left vein into the renal vein. The nerves are derived from the splanchnic nerves and the lumbar sympathetic chain, the fibers passing through a plexus (suprarenal) before entering the gland. These fibers are medullated and have no cell stations in their course. That is, they are entirely preganglionic, the medullary cell itself taking the place of the ganglion cell and postganglionic fiber; they differ thus from all other sympathetic pathways (see ch. 12).

The Adrenal Medulla

Thomas Addison's report in 1855 (p. 1576), and the experimental work of Brown-Séquard in 1856, gave the first hints concerning adrenal function. The last mentioned observer showed that complete removal of the glands from rabbits caused death. Not until many years later was it shown that the effects described by these pioneer investigators were due to loss of the adrenal *cortex*. The French physiologist Vulpian, working at about the same time as Addison and Brown-Séquard, discovered that the medulla, unlike any other tissue, was stained blue-green by ferric chloride and that the blood of the adrenal vein sometimes gave a similar reaction. The staining reaction, it is now known, is characteristic of the internal secretion of the medulla (adrenaline). In 1894, Oliver and Schäfer obtained an aqueous extract from the medulla which upon injection caused a pronounced rise in blood pressure.

An active principle present in the extract was obtained in pure form in 1901 by Takamine and by Aldrich. This substance has been given various names: adrenaline (or adrenin) and epinephrine; the first is most commonly used. More recently it has been established that the adrenal medulla contains a mixture of amines, and these may be released in different proportions in different circumstances. Three amines are now known, *adrenaline, noradrenaline* and *dopamine*. Since they are all derivatives of catechol they are termed catechol amines.

Adrenaline was first prepared synthetically by Stoltz (1904) and by Dakin (1905). Like noradrenaline, it is a secondary alcohol; the alcoholic group is attached to an asymmetric carbon atom. Both adrenaline and noradrenaline occur in nature in the levorotatory forms, which are many times more active than the dextrorotatory forms.

FORMATION OF CATECHOL AMINES

The catechol amines are formed in the adrenal medulla, from the amino-acids L-phenylalanine or L-tyrosine. Five changes are involved in the formation of adrenaline from phenylalanine:

$$\text{C}_6\text{H}_5\text{—CH}_2\cdot\text{CH}\cdot\text{NH}_2$$
$$|$$
$$\text{COOH}$$

Phenylalanine

↓

$$\text{HO—C}_6\text{H}_4\text{—CH}_2\cdot\text{CH}\cdot\text{NH}_2$$
$$|$$
$$\text{COOH}$$

Tyrosine

↓

$$\text{(HO)}_2\text{C}_6\text{H}_3\text{—CH}_2\cdot\text{CH}\cdot\text{NH}_2$$
$$|$$
$$\text{COOH}$$

Dihydroxyphenylalanine (dopa)

↓

$$\text{(HO)}_2\text{C}_6\text{H}_3\text{—CH}_2\cdot\text{CH}_2\cdot\text{NH}_2$$

Dopamine

↓

$$\text{(HO)}_2\text{C}_6\text{H}_3\text{—CH}\cdot\text{CH}_2\cdot\text{NH}_2$$
$$|$$
$$\text{OH}$$

Noradrenaline

↓

$$\text{(HO)}_2\text{C}_6\text{H}_3\text{—CH}\cdot\text{CH}_2\cdot\text{NH}\cdot\text{CH}_3$$
$$|$$
$$\text{OH}$$

Adrenaline

Evidence in favour of the pathway shown is derived from a variety of experiments. Using isotopically labelled precursors, phenylalanine, tyrosine or dopamine; radioactive noradrenaline or adrenaline have been isolated from the adrenals or from adrenal homogenates incubated in vitro. Moreover, a number of enzymes have been characterized which catalyse one or the other of the intermediate steps in the pathway of catechol amine formation. The first and the second step, the introduction of the two phenolic hydroxyl groups, is not restricted to the adrenal medulla, but occurs also in other tissues. The amino acid *dihydroxyphenylalanine*, usually called *dopa*, occurs in the adrenal medulla. It is decarboxylated by the enzyme dopa decarboxylase, which occurs in the adrenal medulla; the decarboxylation reaction gives rise to *dopamine*, the first of the three catechol amines. Dopamine is a substrate of the enzyme dopamine β-oxidase, which has also been found in the adrenal medulla; this enzyme gives rise to noradrenaline. Noradrenaline is N-methylated by an N-methyl transferase, an enzyme also present in the adrenal gland; this enzyme transfers the N-methyl group of methionine to noradrenaline to give adrenaline.

The enzymes involved in the formation of the catechol amines have also been demonstrated in other locations in which catechol amines have been found, e.g., in sympathetic ganglia and in the brain.

Inactivation of Adrenaline

It has long been known that adrenaline disappears rapidly after injection, due to uptake by the tissues, but it is only relatively recently that it has been recognised that the endings of adrenergic neurones are involved in the active uptake of the catechol amines. Ultimately, the fate of the amines is inactivation by enzyme action. The pathways of inactivation have only been established in recent years, after some of the urinary metabolites of the amines in human urine had been characterised. In 1957, Armstrong and McMillan discovered *vanillylmandelic acid (VMA)* in human urine. They suggested that this acid was derived from adrenaline and noradrenaline and they showed that, in patients suffering from a tumour of the chromaffin tissue (pheochromocytoma), the excretion of VMA was greatly increased. (Normally the daily output of VMA is about 2–8 mg.) This observation showed that two changes occur: the amines lose the amino (or methylamino) group, and the phenolic hydroxyl group in position 3 is methyl-

ated. The two enzymes involved are amine oxidase (or monoamine oxidase) and catechol-O-methyl transferase. That the three catechol amines are oxidised by amine oxidase, has been known since the 1930's; the action of catechol-O-methyl transferase on the amines was described by Axelrod in 1957, after the discovery of VMA.

The pathway of biological inactivation of adrenaline is shown in the following scheme. Adrenaline is attacked by both amine oxidase and catechol-O-methyl transferase, both enzymes which occur in many mammalian tissues. Amine oxidase removes the methylamino group and leads eventually to the formation of dihydroxymandelic acid, small amounts of which are excreted in human urine. This acid is a substrate of catechol-O-methyl transferase and it is converted to VMA. Adrenaline is also directly attacked by catechol-O-methyl transferase; the product formed in this reaction is known as metanephrine (similary, noradrenaline gives rise to normetanephrine). Metanephrine also occurs in small amounts in human urine, but most of it is further oxidised by amine oxidase and leads to the excretion of VMA. In other words, one and the same end product arises by two different pathways. It seems likely that, in the tissue fluids the primary reaction is O-methylation, but in many tissues, including the heart and the brain, amine oxidase seems to be the principal primary catalyst of inactivation.

In aqueous solution adrenaline is unstable; it is oxidised to give a pink compound (adrenochrome). In tissue fluids and blood, adrenaline is protected from this type of oxidation, and it is doubtful if adrenochrome appears as a normal metabolite of adrenaline in the body.

Actions of Adrenaline and Noradrenaline

Although Oliver and Schäfer discovered the pressor effect of an extract of adrenal medulla as long ago as 1894, not until nearly 50 years later was it discovered that the gland contained noradrenaline (arterenol, norepinephrine) as well as adrenaline. Noradrenaline is present in adrenergic nerve trunks, sympathetic ganglia and the hypothalamus, and brain stem, but absent in nerve free tissues such as placenta and bone marrow. Adrenaline and noradrenaline are present in the adult human adrenal medulla in the proportion of about 5 to 1, but the reverse proportion is obtained in children and very large amounts of noradrenaline (up to 90 per cent) may be found in some adrenal tumors (pheochromocytomas).

Scheme of Adrenaline Breakdown

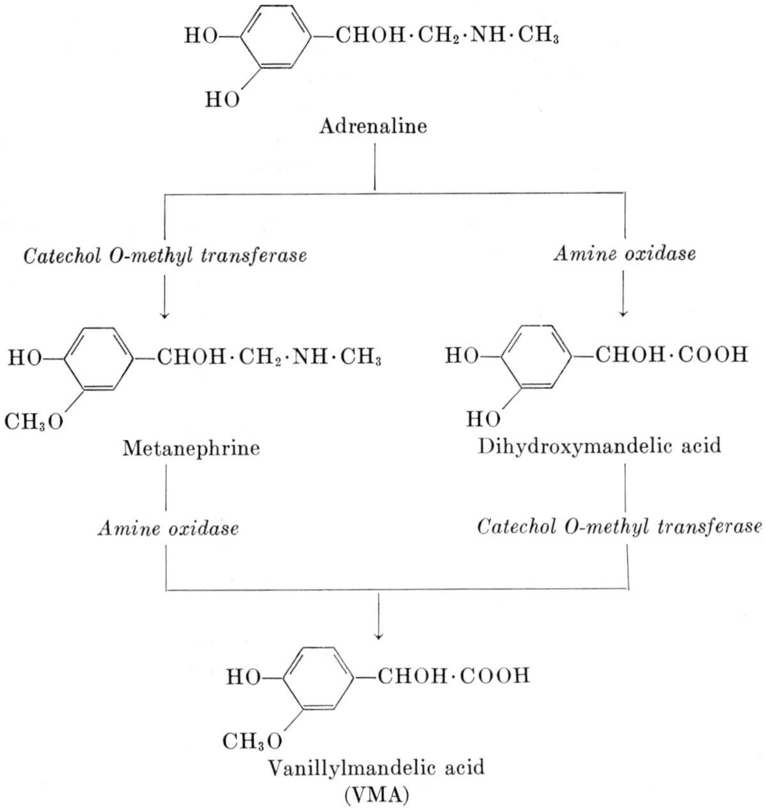

$$HO-\text{\textcircled{\hphantom{O}}}-CHOH \cdot CH_2 \cdot NH \cdot CH_3$$
$$HO$$

Adrenaline

Catechol O-methyl transferase | *Amine oxidase*

$$HO-\text{\textcircled{\hphantom{O}}}-CHOH \cdot CH_2 \cdot NH \cdot CH_3$$
$$CH_3O$$

Metanephrine

$$HO-\text{\textcircled{\hphantom{O}}}-CHOH \cdot COOH$$
$$HO$$

Dihydroxymandelic acid

Amine oxidase | *Catechol O-methyl transferase*

$$HO-\text{\textcircled{\hphantom{O}}}-CHOH \cdot COOH$$
$$CH_3O$$

Vanillylmandelic acid
(VMA)

In some tumors of the adrenal medulla, the so-called neuroblastomata, large amounts of dopamine have been found. Dopamine is also present in relatively large amounts in the basal ganglia particularly in the caudate nucleus.

It is probable, as noted earlier, that noradrenaline is the immediate precursor of adrenaline but in addition to its importance as precursor the substance has physiological functions of its own. In general it may be said that the main function of noradrenaline seems to be the normal control of the circulation, whereas adrenaline produces a variety of 'metabolic' effects useful in an emergency. Both agents act upon structures innervated by sympathetic nerve fibers and because of this are called (like certain other drugs) *sympathomimetic* (Barger and Dale).

1. VASCULAR EFFECTS. Adrenaline has a pronounced pressor action causing widespread vasoconstriction. But adrenaline is by no means a general vasoconstrictor. Its over-all effect upon the vascular system is to decrease rather than to increase the peripheral vascular resistance of the body as a whole. It constricts powerfully the arterioles and capillaries of the skin and the arterioles of the kidney, but, in small or moderate doses, dilates the vessels of the skeletal muscles and liver, and probably also of the coronary system. This vasodilator effect upon the muscles and liver overshadows the vasoconstrictor effects with a consequent decrease in the total peripheral resistance. The pronounced rise in blood pressure (fig. 76.2), a true adrenaline effect, is due mainly to its increasing the cardiac output. The rise in blood pressure is confined to the systolic phase, the diastolic phase showing no change or a fall, an expression either of the absence of any increase in, or a reduction of the total peripheral resistance (see table 76.1).

Noradrenaline is an over-all vasoconstrictor, causing an increase in the total peripheral resistance, and a hypertensive effect which is from 30 to 70 per cent greater than that of adrenaline. Noradrenaline constricts the cutaneous vessels, but to a lesser degree than adrenaline, the latter in man causing a much more pronounced pallor. Noradrenaline causes a reduction in blood flow through the brain of about 10 per cent, whereas adrenaline increases it by 20 per cent or so.

2. HEART. Adrenaline (U.S.P. epinephrine)

exerts a direct stimulating effect upon the myo-cardium; it increases the oxygen consumption of the heart and augments the cardiac output mainly by an increase in stroke volume, this being responsible for the rise in systolic pressure. These effects are apparently due to the action of adrenaline as such, for noradrenaline either has no effect upon the cardiac output or decreases it. Both drugs dilate the coronary vessels and increase the coronary flow. In animals with the vagus nerves intact, adrenaline slows the heart as a secondary effect of the hypertension (due to reflex inhibition—Marey's law) but causes cardiac acceleration after vagal section. In hearts protected from reflex inhibition by division of the vagus nerves or atropine, the force and rate of the heart are increased and conduction improved by both drugs. In man, adrenaline accelerates the heart whereas noradrenaline causes bradycardia. Adrenaline also appears to increase the susceptibility of the ventricular muscle to the development of extrasystoles, or even of ventricular fibrillation.

3. RESPIRATION. After a short initial period of

TABLE 76.1

Effects of adrenaline and noradrenaline on blood flow (ml. per min.)

(After Barcroft, modified)

	Before Adrenaline or Noradrenaline	During	
		Adrenaline	Noradrenaline
Liver	1500	3000	1500
Kidneys	1500	900	1200
Muscles	1000	2000	1000
Brain	750	900	675
Over-all	4750	6800	4375

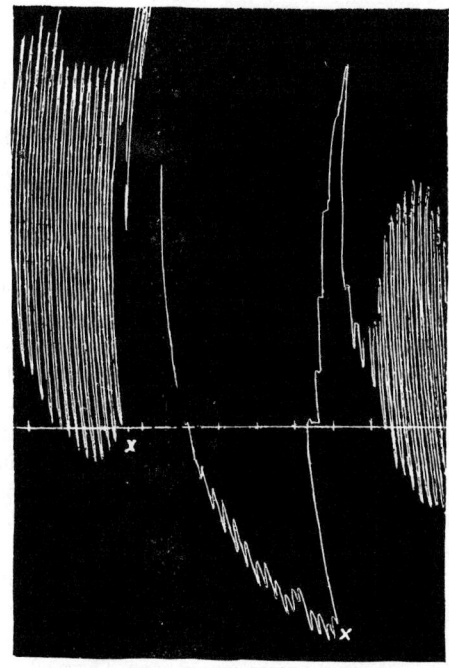

FIG. 76.3. Rabbit's intestine in Ringer's solution. At X, Ringer's solution plus adrenaline 1:100,000,000; at X', Ringer's solution substituted. Time 30 seconds. (From Hoskins.)

apnea the respirations are increased in rate and depth, both by adrenaline and noradrenaline. The apneic period is apparently secondary to the rise in blood pressure and is brought about through the carotid sinus mechanism.

4. SMOOTH MUSCLE. Adrenaline inhibits the muscle of the *stomach, intestine, bronchioles,* and *urinary bladder*. Both the tone and movements of the intestine are inhibited (fig. 76.3); the bronchioles are dilated. It excites the muscle of the *splenic capsule, ureter, trigone* and *sphincter of the bladder*, the *retractor penis*, and the *pyloric, ileo-colic,* and *internal anal sphincters*. The *uterus,*

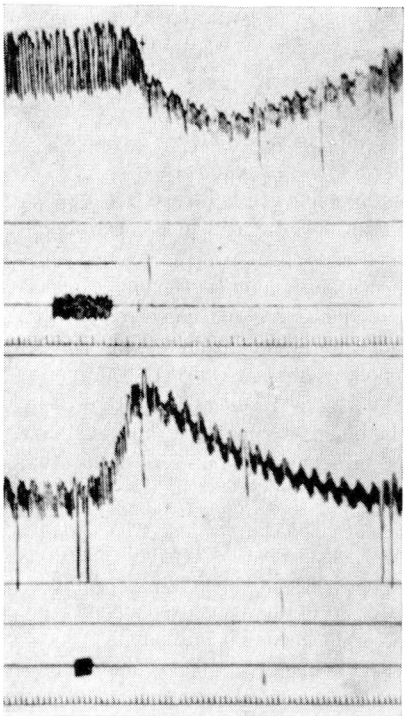

FIG. 76.2. Lower tracing shows the effect of intravenous injection of 0.02 mg. of adrenaline upon blood pressure. Upper tracing from the same animal shows the fall in pressure produced by the injection of 0.02 mg. of adrenaline following a previous dose of 0.4 mg. per kilogram of ergotamine tartrate. (From Geiling.)

whether pregnant or nonpregnant, is contracted in man and in many animals, but in the cat, rat, mouse, and guinea pig, the pregnant organ alone is contracted by adrenaline; the nonpregnant is relaxed. The contractions of the human uterus at term are often inhibited by adrenaline. Most of these effects are exhibited, though less strongly, by noradrenaline, with the exception of the excitation of the pregnant uterus of the cat upon which noradrenaline exerts a greater effect. As a result of the excitation of the radiating fibers of the *iris* (dilator pupillae) the pupil is dilated by adrenaline especially if the superior cervical ganglion has been previously excised. *Mueller's muscle* is stimulated and the eyeball protruded. Retraction of the *upper eyelid* is caused by the stimulation of its smooth muscle. The *nictitating membrane* of animals is retracted. Adrenaline also stimulates the *erectores pilae muscles* and other smooth muscle fibers in the skin. After denervation the sensitivity of some tissues to noradrenaline (e.g., the nictitating membrane of the cat) is greatly increased, whereas that to adrenaline is only slightly affected.

5. SKELETAL MUSCLE. Adrenaline postpones muscle fatigue and increases the tension developed in a twitch of skeletal muscle. It increases muscle tone, and may cause tremors or muscular twitching. The effects of noradrenaline upon muscle are much less pronounced. When the sympathetic supply to a muscle is excited during stimulation of the motor nerves, the contractions are increased. This effect is known as the *Orbeli phenomenon.*

6. CARBOHYDRATE METABOLISM. Adrenaline administered by injection causes hyperglycemia and glycosuria. It shows an antagonism to insulin; relieving hypoglycemic convulsions. These effects, which are also shown by noradrenaline, but to a lesser degree, are due to the mobilization of sugar from the liver whose glycogen stores are thus reduced. The hyperglycemic effect is, therefore, greatest in well fed animals with an abundant hepatic store of carbohydrate, and of course is not obtained in hepatectomized animals. The glycogen of the muscles is also reduced by adrenaline. On the other hand, there is evidence (Himsworth and Scott) that the rate of removal of glucose from the blood by the tissues is accelerated. When administered to animals after a prolonged fast or in other conditions which deplete the hepatic glycogen stores, adrenaline causes an *increase* in liver glycogen. The latter is due to the breakdown of muscle glycogen to lactic acid which, diffusing into the blood, is carried to the

liver where resynthesis to glycogen occurs. There is a fall in the inorganic phosphate of the blood due apparently to the phosphorylation of glycogen and the formation of glucose monophosphate. If the adrenaline administration is continued the liver glycogen is converted in turn to glucose which passes into the blood, causing hyperglycemia; it is subsequently reconverted to glycogen in the muscles (Cori). The cycle may be represented in the following scheme:

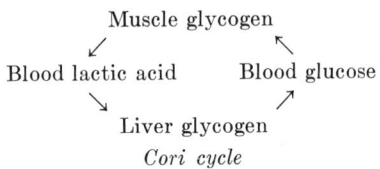

Cori cycle

Much work has been done to elucidate the mechanism of activation of phosphorylase by catechol amines. It has been shown that the activation of phosphorylase is due to the transformation of an inactive form of the enzyme to the active form. This reaction requires the presence of a cyclic form of adenosine monophosphate, 3'5'-AMP. The latter is formed from adenosine-triphosphate (ATP) by another enzyme, called adenyl cyclase, and it is in the latter reaction, the formation of the cyclic form of AMP from ATP, that adrenaline (and other catechol amines) acts as an activator. The mechanism of this activation is as yet unknown.

Noradrenaline exerts little effect upon the concentration of lactic acid in the peripheral blood (Bearn *et al.*).

7. ACTION ON ADIPOSE TISSUE. In recent years much evidence has accumulated to show that catechol amines mobilize fat from adipose tissue. The effect is mediated by the activation of a lipase, with the result that glycerol is released into the blood stream and a considerable amount of the fatty acids is also released, thus contributing to an increase in the free fatty acid level in the blood plasma.

This effect of the catechol amines is of interest, since it has been shown that the adipose tissue normally contains noradrenaline. The latter appears to be located in adrenergic postganglionic sympathetic nerve endings. The noradrenaline content is lost when the sympathetic nerve supply to the tissue is cut. Also, the release of free fatty acids by other agents (e.g. by prostaglandin) seems to depend on the presence of noradrenaline in the adipose tissue.

8. GENERAL METABOLISM. Oxygen consumption is increased by from 20 to 40 per cent, and

CO₂ production by from 30 to 50 per cent; the respiratory quotient is, therefore, raised. In man the increase in the basal metabolic rate occurs within a short time after the subcutaneous injection of 0.5 cc. of a 1:1000 solution; the temperature of the muscles rises. The effect of adrenaline upon heat production is known as its *calorigenic* action; it does not occur after removal of the liver (Soskin).

Boothby and Sandiford attributed the latter effect largely to stimulation of cellular oxidations throughout the tissues of the body generally, and in a major degree to the hyperglycemia ("carbohydrate plethora"), and the increased utilization of carbohydrate, that is, to the specific dynamic action of glucose. The extent to which each of these factors contribute to the increased heat production is a controversial question, but many authors consider increased carbohydrate utilization the predominant factor (see Griffith). However, recent work has suggested that the calorigenic effect is due to an increased metabolism of fatty acids released from adipose tissue. In particular, it has been suggested that "non-shivering thermogenesis" in animals (e.g. rats) acclimatized to a cold environment is due to an increased oxidation of free fatty acids released from adipose tissue under the influence of catechol amines (Hagen and Hagen). Cutaneous vasoconstriction leading to diminished heat loss and its effect upon metabolism, as well as increased muscular tone, are probably contributing factors. The calorigenic effect is not brought about through an action upon the thyroid since it is obtained after thyroidectomy. Moreover, the rise in metabolic rate commences within a few minutes and returns to normal within 2 hours or so, whereas the effect of thyroxine upon heat production does not commence for some hours and is prolonged for several days (p. 1530).

9. OTHER EFFECTS OF ADRENALINE (U.S.P.). (a) Secretion of saliva; (b) lacrymation; (c) sweating in such animals as horses and sheep, but in most other animals the sweat glands, though innervated by the sympathetic, are not excited by adrenaline. Sweating can be evoked in most human subjects by adrenaline or noradrenaline injected intradermally in very dilute solution; (d) contraction of the spleen (stimulation of the smooth muscle of its capsule and trabeculae) and consequent increase in the blood volume and in the red cell count; (e) increase in the coagulability of the blood; (f) small doses increase the flow of urine as a result of constriction of efferent glomerular vessels (larger doses constrict both afferent and efferent vessels) and through reduction of the renal blood flow diminish the urinary flow (p. 1679); (g) a fall, sometimes preceded by a rise, in the potassium of the blood; (h) contraction of melanophores of certain cold blooded animals, e.g., frog and horned toad (Redfield)[1]; (i) increased output of the adrenocorticotrophic hormone of the pituitary gland; (j) affects the transmission in nerve; (k) enhances or depresses, according to the dosage, the action of acetylcholine at synaptic junctions (ch. 71); and (l) intravenous injection of adrenaline causes arousal and anxiety in man, whereas injection of adrenaline into the cerebral ventricles gives signs of depression and drowsiness.

ASSAY OF ADRENALINE AND NORADRENALINE

The assay of adrenaline in blood, tissue fluids or extracts can be accomplished in many ways, and both biological and chemical methods are available. Since both adrenaline and noradrenaline are well established chemical entities, there is no international standard. All results are expressed in terms of the weight of pure amine.

With the growth of pharmacological knowledge it has been realised that the earlier methods are not specific and that they do not sufficiently distinguish between adrenaline and noradrenaline. Tissue extracts are often subjected to preliminary purification; for instance, the catechol amines can be concentrated and removed from an extract by absorption on to aluminium hydroxide, and they can subsequently be eluted. The amines can then be separated from each other either by paper chromatography or by ion-exchange chromatography.

Until recently, bioassay methods have generally been preferred, and they are still widely used. In recent years, however, the chemical methods have become more sensitive and also more reliable and they are used to an increasing extent. Moreover, dopamine is not easily determined by bioassay but it is readily assayed by chemical methods.

BIOASSAYS. These include:

Cat and rat blood pressure. An assay involving the pressor effect of catechol amines in the anesthetized or spinal cat has long been used. The re-

---

[1] The contraction of the melanophores of the horned toad which results from adrenaline administration, also occurs when the animal becomes excited. Since in the latter instance the effect is abolished if the circulation to the melanophores is occluded, but not when the skin nerves are cut, the effect must be due to a chemical substance, presumably adrenaline, in the blood.

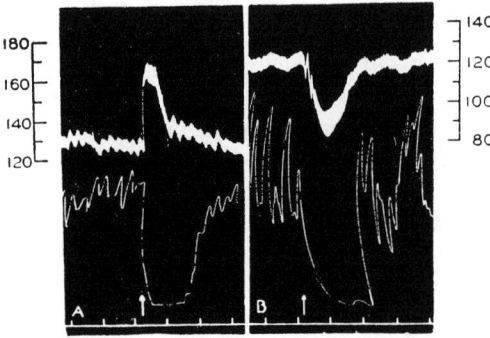

FIG. 76.4. Showing the effects of adrenaline upon the blood pressure and the uterus (*in situ*) of a pregnant cat before and after the administration of dibenamine. The intravenous injection of 2.5 mg. per kilogram is indicated by the arrows. (From Nickerson and Goodman.)

sponse to the sample and to standard solutions is measured and an attempt made to 'sandwich' the response of the unknown between a greater and a smaller dose of standard. The use of the hexamethonium treated rat provides a particularly sensitive preparation (Crawford and Outschoorn), and whereas the blood pressure of both the cat and rat is more sensitive to noradrenaline than to adrenaline, that of the rat is particularly so. Amounts of noradrenaline of the order of 0.050 of 1 μg. can be measured with accuracy.

Rat uterus. In this test the isolated rat uterus is suspended in a bath of modified Tyrode solution to which constant amounts of acetylcholine are added regularly. Contractions of the organ are induced which are readily inhibited by adrenaline. Unknown solutions are assayed by comparison of the effect observed with that produced by standard solutions. The rat uterus is much less sensitive to noradrenaline than to adrenaline and with good preparations less than 0.0001 of 1 μg. of adrenaline can be detected.

Vasoconstriction in rabbit ear. The vasoconstriction induced by adrenaline in the perfused rabbit ear provides by far the most sensitive assay for adrenaline available. The vessels are sensitized by denervation and the diameter of the central artery measured microscopically at intervals. Adrenaline can be detected in a concentration of 10^{-11} grams per milliliter or less. The rabbit ear is also sensitive to 5-hydroxytryptamine but this effect can be blocked with lysergic acid diethylamide.

Intestinal muscle. Catecholamines generally inhibit the smooth muscle of the gut and studies employing a segment of rabbit intestine were carried out over 40 years ago. Rat colon is particularly sensitive to noradrenaline, whereas the rectal cecum of the fowl is much better suited for the assay of adrenaline, since it is able to detect 0.002 of a microgram.

THE EFFECTS OF CERTAIN SUBSTANCES UPON THE ACTION OF ADRENALINE

Attempts to define the sites of action of the catechol amines in the excitable tissues have led to the belief that there are different types of "adrenergic receptors" in the tissues. One such classification, which goes back to Ahlquist, is based on the relative potencies of noradrenaline, adrenaline and isoprenaline in different tests. The so-called *α-receptors* are those sensitive principally to noradrenaline; adrenaline also acts on the α-receptors. Isoprenaline does not act on the α-receptors. On the other hand, β-receptors are acted upon by isoprenaline; adrenaline also acts on the β-receptors, but noradrenaline does not. The excitatory constrictor effects of the catechol amines on blood vessels are typical α-effects, the inhibitory dilator effects in vascular plain muscle are typical β-effects. Other β-effects include the bronchodilator actions. Although the concept of α- and β-receptors is inadequate to account for all our knowledge on the action of the catechol amines, it has been of use in the understanding of the so-called adrenergic blocking agents.

The first adrenergic blocking agents to be discovered were derivatives of ergot. *Ergotoxine* or *ergotamine* block the pressor effects of adrenaline and sympathetic stimulation, but the vasodilator action is not interfered with. For this reason certain effects of adrenaline administration or of sympathetic stimulation appear to be reversed by the ergot alkaloids. Thus, as just noted, only a depressor effect is obtainable with adrenaline if ergotoxine has been administered previously. Also, after ergotoxine, adrenaline causes expansion of the melanophores of the frog instead of the usual contraction. The hyperglycemic response to adrenaline is abolished after treatment with ergot alkaloids. Ergotoxine is made up of three alkaloids, ergocornine, ergocristine, and ergocryptine, which are derivatives of lysergic acid. These substances also markedly increase the motor activity of the uterus. This property is lost upon hydrogenation to, respectively, dehydroergocornine, -cristine, and -cryptine, but the cardiovascular effects are little affected. The action on the capillaries, blood pressure, and bronchioles of *histamine* and adrenaline are antagonistic, and adrenalectomized animals show an increased susceptibility to histamine administration. The blood concentrating effect of histamine administration is lessened or prevented by a previous injection of adrenaline. There is also some evidence that histamine increases the output of adrenaline from the medulla.

Other antagonists of adrenaline and of sympathetic effects have been discovered more recently. The β-halo-alkylamines (of which *dibenamine* and *dibenzyline* are examples) possess particularly powerful adrenergic blocking properties (see fig. 76.4). The blockade develops slowly, due to the *in vivo* formation of active intermediates, but is then highly specific and persistent. Dibenamine and dibenzyline reverse the pressor effect of adrenaline although, unlike ergotoxine, the hyperglycemic action of adrenaline is little affected. Nor are the inhibitory effects of adrenaline upon the virgin cat's uterus or the intestine modified by these drugs. Dibenamine (N,N-dibenzyl-β-chloroethylamine) and dibenzyline (phenoxybenzamine) have the structures shown below:

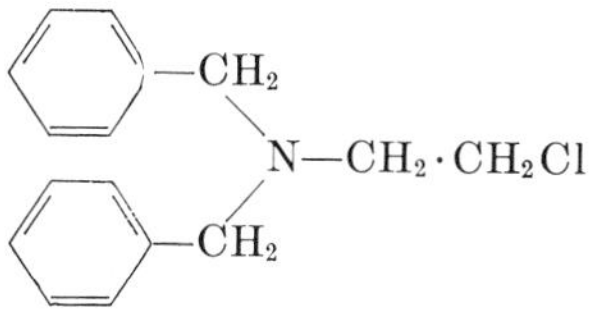

Dibenamine

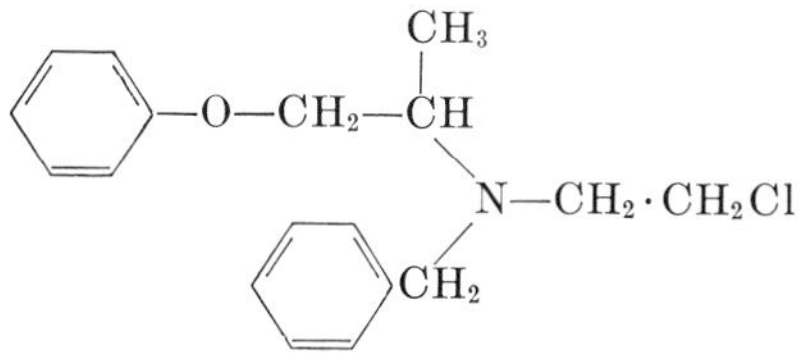

Dibenzyline

Adrenergic blocking activity is also possessed by the *benzodioxanes*, and the *imidazolines*. Of the imidazolines, tolazoline (priscoline, benzazoline, or priscol) and phentolamine (regitine) are best known. The blockade produced by both series is relatively transient and they are useful in the diagnosis of pheochromocytoma.

All the compounds thus far considered are so-called α-blockers; in other words, these drugs interfere with the interaction of the amines with the α-receptors. Such a concept accounts for the fact that these blocking agents unmark the vasodilator actions of adrenaline.

More recently, new blocking agents have been synthesized which appear to interfere selectively with the interaction of catechol amines and the β-receptors; these drugs are therefore called β-blockers. The first of these substances was the dichloro analogue of isoprenaline, dichloroisoproterenol (DCI). More recently, an even more selective β-blocking agent has been made; this is pronethanol:

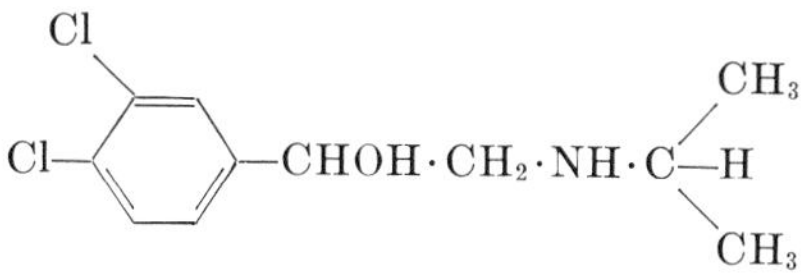

Dichloroisoproterenol

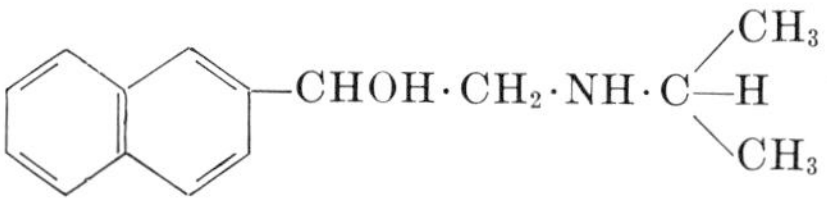

Pronethanol

GANGLIONIC BLOCKING AGENTS

Other compounds may be mentioned here which block ganglionic transmission. *Nicotine* acts by depolarizing the ganglion cell, which it first stimulates and then paralyzes. The *methonium compounds* (hexa- and decamethonium) compete with naturally formed acetylcholine for "possession" of the ganglion cells, that is for the specific chemical receptors of the cell. Once in position, the postsynaptic membrane is stabilized and depolarization rendered more difficult. This ability of the methonium compounds depends upon their resemblance to acetylcholine, being also quaternary nitrogen compounds. The methonium compounds are useful clinically for the reduction of blood pressure and for their curarelike action.

In addition, substances have recently been made which interfere specifically with the transmission of impulses in adrenergic neurones. These substances seem to act by different mechanism, *bretylium* mainly by interfering with the release of the adrenergic mediator, while *guanethidine* appears specifically to prevent the accumulation of newly-formed mediator in adrenergic neurones. Both types of compound have been used to control arterial hypertension in man.

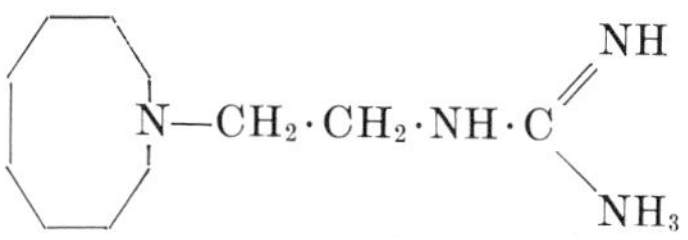

Guanethidine

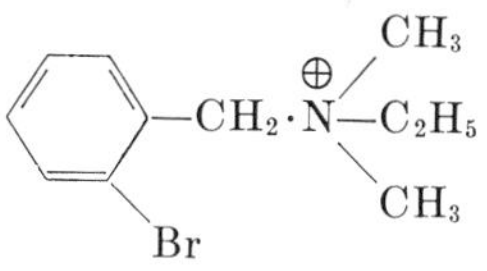

Bretylium

ADRENALINELIKE SUBSTANCES

An extract containing *ephedrine* has been used in Chinese medicine for thousands of years; the pure alkaloid was obtained by Nagai, who gave it its present name, in 1887. The chemical resemblance to adrenaline may be seen in the formula.

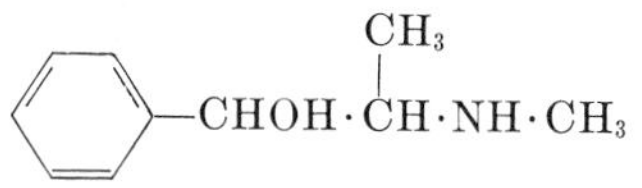

Ephedrine (1-hydroxy-1-phenyl-2-methylaminopropane)

This alkaloid is closely similar to adrenaline in its action, causing bronchiolar relaxation, vasoconstriction, hyperglycemia, inhibition of intestinal muscle, and excitation of other smooth muscle. It has also a calorigenic action; its pressor effect (Curtis) is reversed by ergotoxine and reduced by cocaine. Ephedrine is about 100 times less powerful than adrenaline, but its effects are more prolonged. Because of its more lasting effect, it is often combined with adrenaline in commercial preparations. Unlike adrenaline, it is active when taken by mouth. *Tyramine* is a sympathomimetic amine formed by the action of bacteria upon protein (decarboxylation of tyrosine). It is also secreted by the salivary glands of certain mollusks. It is chemically allied to adrenaline and resembles the latter in several of its actions, e.g., it elevates the blood pressure and stimulates the uterine muscle. Its structural formula is:

$$HO\langle\rangle CH_2NH_2$$

Tyramine (1-(4'-hydroxyphenyl)-2-amino ethane)

Amphetamine or *benzedrine* is a compound closely allied chemically to adrenaline, as shown in the following formula:

$$\underset{\text{—}CH\cdot NH_2}{\overset{CH_3}{|}}$$

Amphetamine (1-phenyl-2-aminopropane)

This sympathomimetic amine has also a stimulating action upon the mental processes somewhat like that of caffeine, inducing wakefulness, postponing mental fatigue, and relieving nervous depression.

Another important addition to the list therapeutically useful sympathomimetic amines is *isopropylnoradrenaline* (isopreneline).

$$HO\langle\rangle \overset{H}{\underset{OH}{\overset{|}{C}}}-CH_2\cdot NH\cdot CH\overset{CH_3}{\underset{CH_3}{\diagup}}$$

Isopropylnoradrenaline

It has a strong bronchodilator action which is not accompanied by a pressor effect, which makes it a valuable drug in the treatment of bronchial asthma.

A number of other sympathomimetic amines are known. Details of these should be sought in the review by Beyer and in current textbooks of pharmacology.

The skins of certain toads secrete substances (*bufotenine* and *bufotenedine*) similar in action to adrenaline; the secretion of these substances is increased during nervous excitement.

The Employment of Adrenaline in Medicine

Adrenaline is used (1) to staunch bleeding from accessible mucous surfaces (epistaxis, hematemesis) or from the skin. Because of its pressor effect it is of no value and may do harm in pulmonary hemorrhage and other forms of internal bleeding;

(2) to shrink mucous surfaces, especially those of the nose, and is then frequently used in combination with ephedrine; (3) to relax the muscle of the bronchioles in asthma, the relief following its use is very striking; (4) to combat certain allergic conditions, e.g., serum sickness, and to antagonize the effects of the histaminelike substances supposedly liberated in the skin in such conditions as urticaria and giant edema; (5) to stimulate the respiration or to resuscitate the heart which has ceased to beat; in the latter event it may be given by injection into the cardiac musculature. Adrenaline is of value in syncope due to Stokes-Adams disease (p. 193). It should be mentioned that the administration of adrenaline during chloroform anesthesia is attended by the danger of inducing ventricular fibrillation (p. 691); (6) to enhance and prolong the action of cocaine and similar local anesthetics; the vasoconstriction thus induced retards the absorption of these substances, thus prolonging their effects and reducing their toxicity. It is also used as an aid in spinal anesthesia; and (7) noradrenaline has been used in certain hypotensive states for its vasoconstrictor action.

The Regulation of the Secretions of the Adrenal Medulla

Under resting conditions the adrenal medulla releases very little secretion into the circulation; a recent estimate of the adrenaline equivalent for both adrenals in dogs is about 50 mμg. per kilogram per minute (Satake). On the other hand, in states of stress (see emergency function, below) or during stimulation of the splanchnic nerve, the output of pressor amine is greatly increased—to 50 to 75 μg. per minute per adrenal in the dog. Elliott in 1912, found that the content of pressor amines of innervated adrenals fell on stimulation of the splanchnic nerve. More detailed information has been obtained in the dog (Houssay and Rapela) for the output of adrenaline and noradrenaline under various conditions. The output of adrenaline at rest was 10 mμg. per kilogram per minute and 400 mμg. per kilogram per minute after stimulation of the splanchnic nerve. The corresponding figures for noradrenaline were 2 mμg. at rest and 80 mμg. per kilogram per minute after the nerve stimulation. Clearly the discharge of catechol amines is markedly increased.

There is little doubt that the activity of the adrenal medulla lies under direct nervous control. Denervation of the gland suppresses the release of hormone and the content of hormone declines. Procedures which normally cause the discharge of medullary hormone are ineffective in the denervated gland. Such factors as a fall in pressure in the carotid sinus, emotional excitement, asphyxia, and a fall in blood sugar appear to act reflexly upon the adrenal through centers in the diencephalon and midbrain. The location of these centers has been investigated by Ranson and Magoun. They found that electrical stimulation of various sites in the hypothalamus, midbrain, and medulla evoked signs of adrenal medullary activity, and it has since been shown by Vogt that these regions are characterized by a high content of noradrenaline. The diabetes which follows puncture of the floor of the fourth ventricle (Bernard) has been found to be due, at least in part, to increased adrenal medullary activity.

In simple terms, the adrenal medulla may be considered to respond to a circulatory stress tending to lower the blood pressure by releasing largely noradrenaline which constricts the arterioles and increases the peripheral resistance. Metabolic stresses, on the other hand, such as a sudden fall in the blood sugar level, are countered by the discharge of adrenaline which frees sugar from the liver and bars the uptake of sugar by the muscles. In order to respond appropriately to such stimuli it might be expected that a dual mechanism exists in the medulla for the release of adrenaline and/or noradrenaline. Information in favor of such a mechanism is accumulating. Measurement of the proportion of adrenaline and noradrenaline in adrenal vein blood has shown that the relative amounts change in accordance with the above concept. Scandinavian histologists have obtained evidence which indicates that some cells of the medulla contain mainly adrenaline, whereas others contain mainly noradrenaline. There may also be special islets of noradrenaline secretory cells. Chromaffin cell tumors in man may contain predominantly adrenaline or noradrenaline, and some exclusively noradrenaline. Further, it has been shown that electrical excitation of different regions of the hypothalamus may liberate preferentially adrenaline or noradrenaline.

Much has been learnt in recent years of the mode of storage and release of adrenaline and noradrenaline in the chromaffin cell. The amines are present in the cell but not evenly distributed through the cytoplasm, they are mainly present in a specific cell organelle, the *chromaffin granule*. These granules, which are kept intact when the adrenal medulla is homogenized in isotonic media, e.g., in sucrose, can be separated from other cell organelles, e.g., the mitochondria, by centrifugation. By this method it has been found that the amines are stored together with adenosine triphosphate (ATP), in stoichiometrical amounts, so that about 1 mole of ATP is associated with 4 moles of amine. When the gland is stimulated, the ATP and the amines are lost *pari passu*. The mechanism which releases the amines from the chromaffin granules when the cell is stimulated is not known, but it has recently been shown that stimulation of the splanchnic nerve will lead to a release of amines only when calcium ions are present.

Emotional excitement is a strong stimulus to sympathetic and adrenal medullary activity. Studies by Elmadjian and his colleagues on the human indicate that active, *aggressive* emotional displays are related to increased excretion of noradrenaline, whereas tense anxious, but *passive* emotional displays are related to increased excretion of adrenaline in the urine. There also seems to be a relationship between the adrenal content of noradrenaline and the typical behavior in different species. Aggressive animals (cat, lion) have large amounts of nonadrenaline in the adrenal medulla, whereas timid animals (rabbit, guinea pig) have little. The indication exists then, that aggressive excitement leads mainly to an increased blood concentration of noradrenaline, and that emotion of a restrained or defensive type affects mainly the blood content of adrenaline.

The adrenal medulla is supplied by preganglionic sympathetic nerve fibers and the medullary cells themselves replace the ordinary ganglion cells. Because of this relationship, stimuli are transmitted to the medulla cholinergically. The pressor effect of splanchnic stimulation in cats, or of the close arterial injection of acetylcholine, can be almost completely abolished by large doses of nicotine, whereas pretreatment with the anticholinesterase eserine enhances the effect of such stimulation.

The Role of the Adrenal Medulla in the Body

The adrenal medulla is not essential to life. In animals one adrenal may be removed completely and the medulla of the other excised without any apparent ill effect—the animal survives the operation indefinitely.

THE EMERGENCY THEORY OF ADRENAL FUNCTION. Cannon and his colleagues have furnished convincing evidence that the medulla liberates its secretion in significant amounts only under conditions which call for unusual effort on the part of the body to perform work, to prevent changes in its internal environment or to resist threatened dangers. In such times of stress the medullary secretion, it is believed, reinforces the sympathetic nervous system. Through this hormonal-nervous cooperation, the several bodily reactions associated with such states of emergency are raised to maximal efficiency. Cannon and his associates employed the denervated heart as an indicator of adrenaline liberation. The operation for denervation comprised section of the vagi and removal of the stellate and second thoracic ganglia of the sympathetic chain, so that the heart was completely isolated from nervous control. Inasmuch as in their experiments any effect due to a change in the temperature of the blood was excluded, a pronounced acceleration of a heart so prepared was taken to be the result of a chemical substance carried in the blood stream. Fright, rage, pain, asphyxia, anesthesia, muscular activity, exposure to cold, stimulation of a sensory nerve, and several other conditions, caused within 10 seconds an increase in heart rate of from 20 to 40 beats per minute. Removal of the adrenals, their denervation, or ligation of the adrenal veins, prevented this effect. The conclusion, therefore, is justified that the various conditions mentioned cause the reflex liberation of the medullary hormone. The denervated heart responds to as little as 1 part of adrenaline in 1400 million parts of blood. In some of Cannon's experiments, cats were frightened by the barking of a dog; the rate of the denervated heart increased by from 15 to 30 beats per minute. The cardiac acceleration was accompanied by pupillary dilation, erection of the hairs, and spitting. When motor activity, e.g., struggling in the animal holder, accompanied the emotional excitement, the cardiac acceleration was more pronounced (40 to 80 beats per minute). Even minor muscular movements without emotion, e.g., extending the legs, walking, or turning the body, caused an acceleration of from 5 to 20 beats per minute.

The hyperglycemia and glycosuria resulting from emotional excitement in man and animals is probably associated with the discharge of adrenaline, since it has been shown that the continued rise in blood sugar which occurs during the emotional reactions (sham rage) following removal of the cerebral cortex (p. 158) is dependent upon the adrenals. The blood sugar continues to rise after this operation, though the glycogen stores of the liver are removed from nervous control by sectioning the hepatic nerves. On the other hand, the effect does not occur after removal of the adrenals, even though the hepatic nerves are intact. In those instances in which the emotional state does not follow the operation of decortica-

tion, the hyperglycemic effect also fails to appear. Puncture of the floor of the fourth ventricle or stimulation of the adrenal nerves also causes hyperglycemia after the hepatic nerves have been previously cut.

Though direct evidence is difficult to obtain it is reasonable to assume that besides the effects mentioned above, adrenaline when secreted into the blood stream brings about other actions which we have seen to be characteristic of its action when injected.

A recapitulation of the actions of the sympathoadrenal system will show how useful these several actions are in fitting an animal for defense or flight; for attack or pursuit. (1) The rise in general blood pressure accompanied by dilation of the vessels of the contracting skeletal muscles, and of the coronary arteries, and the increased force and output of the heart, raise the circulatory system to a state of maximal efficiency. (2) Hyperglycemia indicates the mobilization of the carbohydrate stores of the liver: thus, an adequate supply of fuel for the active muscles is ensured; muscular fatigue occurs less readily. (3) Release of free fatty acids, and their increased concentration in the blood, serves as substrates for the muscles, especially cardiac muscle, in athletic effort. (4) Increased oxygen capacity of the blood is brought about by the discharge of red cells from the spleen. (5) Bronchiolar dilation and an increase in the rate and depth of respiration permit an increased oxygen intake to supply the tissue cells; at the same time the level of oxygen consumption of the latter is raised. (6) Shortened coagulation time of the blood lessens the danger from hemorrhage. (7) Finally, the emotional manifestations of man and the fighting attitudes or defense reactions of various animals are sympathoadrenal effects, e.g., pupillary dilation; and, possibly, the startled expression due to contraction of Mueller's orbital muscle which retracts the upper eyelid; cutaneous vasoconstriction; acceleration of the heart; contraction of smooth muscle in the skin causing "gooseflesh" in man, and the erection of the hairs, quills or feathers of animals; sweating; salivary secretion (cat),[2] and the color changes of some cold blooded animals.

However, it is important to bear in mind that

---

[2] It is an interesting and perhaps a significant fact that in the cat, in which spitting is a defense reaction, sympathetic stimulation causes a profuse watery flow of juice from the salivary glands. In other animals sympathetic stimulation causes a scanty flow of viscid saliva, a watery secretion being caused by parasympathetic excitation.

the above reactions are not *essential* to survival. In Cannon's studies, completely sympathectomized cats with denervated adrenal medullae lived entirely normal lives in the laboratory. Only when the animals were placed in an emergency situation did the effects of the operation become evident. Then the changes set out in the preceding paragraph were reduced in intensity or absent.

THE TONUS THEORY OF ADRENAL FUNCTION. It has been suggested that the medulloadrenal secretion maintains the sympathetic nerve endings in a state of sensitivity or tone and that the height of the normal blood pressure is dependent upon the continuous discharge of the hormone into the blood. Low blood pressure has been ascribed to adrenaline deficiency (so-called hypoadrenalemia) and essential hypertension to the liberation of adrenaline in excess (hyperadrenalemia). But the evidence against such conjectures is conclusive; the theory has been entirely discredited. For example, if one adrenal is excised and the other cureted or burned away, no fall in blood pressure occurs, so long as a sufficient amount of cortical tissue is left intact. Furthermore, we have seen that adrenaline does not increase the peripheral resistance (which is the basis of essential hypertension), and neither noradrenaline nor adrenaline is found in greater than usual amounts in the adrenals of hypertensive subjects. There are, however, certain types of hypertension, namely those associated with pheochromocytomata or adrenal hyperplasia, which are due to hypersecretion of the hormones of the adrenal medulla.

PHEOCHROMOCYTOMA AND HYPERPLASIA OF THE ADRENAL MEDULLA. Pheochromocytoma is a tumor composed of chromaffin tissue arising either in the adrenal medulla itself or in an outlying collection of chromaffin cells (paraganglia, Zuckerkandl's organ). The secretion of one of these growths, or of a simple hyperplasia of the adrenal medulla, is a rare cause of hypertension, though not as rare as it once was thought to be. The hypertension may be due to the presence in the circulation of unusual amounts of adrenaline, or of noradrenaline, or of both hormones, of which the tumor or hyperplastic medullary tissue contains excessive amounts. Noradrenaline rather than adrenaline is usually in greatest concentration and may constitute 90 per cent of the gland's hormone content. Both hormones have been found in excess in the urine of subjects of this type of arterial hypertension. Also an increased amount of vanilly mandelic acid (VMA) appears in the urine; it may amount to 9-90 mg. per mg. of creatinine. The hypertension may be paroxysmal, with sometimes a violent onset, or the excessive secretion of the hormones may be continuous, the high blood pressure then being sustained and indistinguishable, clinically, from essential hypertension. Hyperglycemia and glycosuria, especially when the disease is paroxysmal, may occur; pallor, rapid pulse and profuse sweating usually accompany the attack. Peripheral circulatory collapse may ensue during a paroxysm which is thought to be analogous to the shock in animals which follows the injection of large doses of adrenaline; or hypotension and circulatory collapse may result from surgical removal of the tumor. This is attributed to the depressed tone of the vasomotor center, made evident only after the abolition of the excessive adrenal secretion. Adrenal hypertension can be distinguished from essential and other hypertensive states by means of Goldenberg's benzodioxane test. Benzodioxanes temporarily abolish, through their adrenergic blocking action, hypertension of adrenal origin, but not that due to other causes. Alternatively, in cases of paroxysmal hypertension drugs which stimulate the adrenal medulla, such as histamine or methacholine, may be given in order to determine whether a paroxysm can be initiated.

SYMPATHIN

It has been mentioned that the *prompt* acceleration of the denervated heart does not occur in adrenalectomized animals during excitement, sensory nerve stimulation, etc. Cannon and his colleagues found, however, that a *slowly developing* acceleration of the denervated heart occurred during excitement or muscular activity though the adrenals had been extirpated. The increase in heart rate took about a minute to develop, reached its maximum in about 3 minutes and then gradually subsided. Its occurrence was not prevented by the removal of all accessory adrenal tissue, by hypophysectomy or by the excision of the thyroid, parathyroids, or gonads, or by denervation of the liver. It was abolished, however, by by removal of the sympathetic chains. It was also found that the characteristic slow acceleration of the heart occurred when the lower abdominal sympathetic chain was stimulated. The latter nerve contains fibers supplying the smooth muscle of the skin which are responsible for the erection of the tail hairs. Secretion of the denervated salivary glands, contraction of the nictitating membrane, a rise in blood pressure and of blood sugar also resulted from the stimulation of the abdominal sympathetic. These effects as well as the cardiac acceleration occurred though the cord had been divided in the thoracic region, and the sympathetic chain above this level removed. A material originating in the hind part of the animal was evidently conveyed in the blood stream to the heart and other structures mentioned. Blocking the blood flow returning from the area supplied

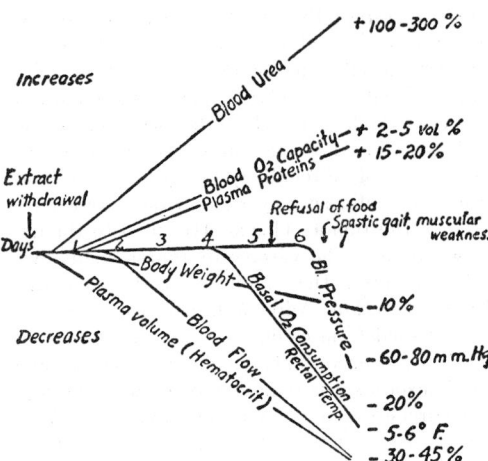

FIG. 76.5. Characteristic changes in metabolism, circulation, and blood concentration in a group of adrenalectomized dogs following withdrawal of extract. (From Harrop and associates.)

by the stimulated nerve or removal of the patch of skin prevented the cardiac response. As a result of these researches, Cannon and his associates concluded that during sympathetic stimulation a chemical substance resembling adrenaline in its action was liberated from the sympathetic endings supplying the smooth muscle of the skin. They named this substance *sympathin*. There is reason for believing that in most mammals noradrenaline and sympathin are identical.

There have been recent histochemical studies which have made it likely that adrenergic fibers occur in the brain-stem and hypothalamus. The method used is the observation in the fluororescence microscope of fluoridized sections treated with gaseous formaldehyde at very low temperature. Adrenergic fibers stand out by showing an intense green fluorescence. These findings are of particular importance in view of the occurrence of noradrenaline and dopamine in the hypothalamus and brain-stem. It is also known that dopamine and large amounts of noradrenaline occur in the caudate nucleus.

It is clear that noradrenaline rather than adrenaline is the predominant humor liberated at nerve endings, and in this context it is interesting to find that the excretion of noradrenaline in the urine is within normal limits in patients following bilateral adrenalectomy, whereas the content of adrenaline falls markedly.

The Adrenal Cortex

The cortex of the adrenal, unlike the medulla, is essential to life. Removal of more than about five-sixths of this part of the adrenal causes death in most species within a few days unless replacement therapy is instituted. Removal of the interrenal body of Elasmobranch fishes (p. 1055) is also fatal, but comparative work on the amphibia is complicated by the difficulty of complete removal of the organ without serious damage to the kidney. Stewart and Rogoff found that the average survival time of dogs after complete double adrenalectomy was 10 days and the maximal time 15 days. They observed that pregnant or pseudopregnant animals survived much longer and suggested that some substance formed at this time substituted for the adrenal hormone. The substance in question is probably progesterone (p. 1634), and, indeed, it has since been shown that progesterone administration prolongs the life of adrenalectomized dogs, rats, and ferrets. Numerous attempts were made to extract some substance from the adrenal gland which was able to maintain life, and in 1927, Stewart and Rogoff, and Hartman announced the preparation of suitable extracts. Both groups used watery extracts of the organ, but in 1930, Swingle and Pfiffner demonstrated that with the aid of lipid solvents a very potent substance could be extracted from the cortex which maintained adrenalectomized animals indefinitely and could be used successfully in the treatment of patients suffering from a deficiency of adrenal cortical hormone (Addison's disease). At this time it was thought by Hartman that the adrenal cortex produced a single hormone, and he called this *cortin*. Subsequent work has established the existence of a number of active adrenal hormones which, since they are steroid compounds, are termed *adrenal steroids*.

The Effects of Bilateral Adrenalectomy

During the short period of survival characteristic of the completely adrenalectomized animal, a variety of manifestations of adrenal cortical deficiency can be detected. These are also present in the "Addisonian" patient suffering from reduced adrenal function. There is a loss of appetite (particularly for fats), vomiting, diarrhea, rapid loss of weight, muscular weakness and prostration, hypotension, pronounced diuresis until the later stages, a fall in body temperature, and a reduction in the basal metabolic rate of about 20 per cent (fig. 76.5). Some of these effects are primary but many are the result of an impaired circulation: cardiac reserves are diminished and vessels become incapable of maintaining normal tone in response to humoral or nervous stimuli. The blood becomes concentrated (due to loss of plasma water) and shows a fall in the serum sodium and glucose, and a rise in nonprotein nitrogen, phosphate, calcium, and especially potassium. The urinary excretion of sodium is increased (see ch. 79) and that of potassium reduced. There is a reduced excretion of urinary nitrogen and there are other signs of renal failure. Although there is a spontaneous diuresis the elimination of ingested water is defective. The glycogen store of the liver and muscles is diminished. When placed in a cold environment, the metabolic response of the adrenalectomized animal is less than normal, and any form of stress is poorly met. Many of the above changes are detectable within 42 hours after the operation. Postmortem examination frequently shows congestion of the gastrointestinal tract and pancreas. There may be erosions in the mucosa of the stomach and intestine, and gastric ulcers may be observed; the gastric juice may lack hydrochloric acid—*achlorhydria.*

It will be seen that the adrenal cortex exerts an influence over many, if not all, bodily functions. As might be expected, the individual suffering from adrenal cortical insufficiency is extremely susceptible to the damaging effects of a wide variety of stimuli demanding compensatory responses, such as changes in the environmental temperature, fasting, haemorrhage, traumatic injuries, burns, severe muscular exercise, infections, and the administration, not only of obvious poisons, but of practically any drug—including all anaesthetics. Such stimuli may be grouped together as *stresses.* A supply of adrenal cortical hormones will greatly increase the resistance of an adrenalectomized individual to such noxious agents. One can understand the total lack of specificity of the beneficial action of cortical hormones if one considers that any stress will make demands for extra work on at least one, if not many organs, and that the metabolic processes enabling tissues to do more work require these steroids in order to proceed efficiently. In the intact animal, release of ACTH in response to stress supplies increased amounts of cortical hormones to the working tissue, and it is during stress that any deficiency in adrenal cortical function will become manifest. The relation of the adrenal cortical hormone to the development of renal hypertension is described in ch. 48, and the role of the adrenal cortex in lactation is mentioned in ch. 78.

Changes occurring after adrenalectomy can be prevented or reversed by the administration of adrenal cortical hormones, and even comatose animals can be restored to health. In treated adrenalectomized bitches, for example, heat will occur and pregnancy and lactation ensue normally. Adrenalectomized puppies given cortical extract will continue to grow.

The part played by adrenal hormones in salt and water metabolism merits a little more attention (see also ch. 79). In adrenalectomized animals, as well as in human adrenal insufficiency, there is a marked reduction in total base, due mainly to the loss of sodium, apparently through diminished reabsorption by the renal tubules, whereas the potassium concentration of the serum is raised above normal. The renal excretion of potassium is reduced and, perhaps most important, there is a shift of potassium from the intracellular to the extracellular fluids. In combination with an increased elimination of water by the kidney, marked dehydration results. Under these conditions, the administration of sodium chloride to adrenalectomized animals and a reduction in the potassium intake exert a remarkably beneficial effect. On the other hand, the withdrawal of salt from the diet increases the severity of the condition. The sodium, rather than the chloride ion, is the important factor.

The reduction of blood sodium was observed originally by Bauman and Kurland, and the effects of transfusions of saline in sustaining adrenalectomized animals were described by Stewart and Rogoff, and by Hartman, but the importance of sodium loss in the development of the symptoms was first pointed out by Loeb and his associates, and by Harrop. The value of a low potassium content of the diet in the survival of adrenalectomized animals was shown by Allers and his associates. Completely adrenalectomized rats and dogs can be maintained in good health without treatment by a cortical hormone if placed upon a diet low in potassium but high in sodium chloride and, in order to prevent the acidosis which otherwise develops, containing sodium citrate. The tendency to hypoglycemia is controlled by a high carbohydrate diet. These measures, however, do not completely restore an animal to a physiological state, for animals so treated are unable to withstand stress or to perform work with full efficiency.

THE PHYSIOLOGICAL ACTIONS OF ADRENAL CORTICAL EXTRACT

Extracts of the adrenal cortex contain a large number of steroids, of which only a minority are the active principles, and the remainder mainly precursors. In view of the wide spectrum of activity of the adrenal steroids it is convenient to classify them into three groups according to some characteristic action of each steroid. These are:

1. The *glucocorticoids*, which particularly affect protein, fat and carbohydrate metabolism.

2. A *mineralocorticoid*, which is highly active in the control of mineral and water metabolism.

3. The *androgenic corticoids*.

Before examining each group in more detail it must be pointed out that representatives of each group possess overlapping activities. Thus cortisol, which is classed as a glucocorticoid, also acts on salt and water metabolism, and conversely, aldosterone, the highly potent mineralocorticoid, possesses very definite glucocorticoid activity.

The *glucocorticoids* and the naturally occurring mineralocorticoid aldosterone are characterized by the presence of an oxygen atom at position 11 (p. 1573), either as a doubly-bound oxygen or as an hydroxyl group. In the absence of this grouping, there is little or no effect on carbohydrate, fat, or protein metabolism, whereas an hydroxyl group in addition at position 17, as in cortisone, enhances the activity of the steroid. Cortisol (Kendall's compound F) and corticosterone (compound B) are the main glucocorticoids secreted by all vertebrate adrenal glands, together with smaller quantities of the oxidized forms cortisone (compound E) and dehydrocorticosterone (compound A). Corticosterone was isolated by Reichstein and his associates, and by Kendall and his colleagues, in 1937, and was later synthesized by the former workers. The human, monkey, sheep, and guinea pig secrete primarily cortisol; the rabbit and rat primarily corticosterone; the dog and cat mainly cortisol with some corticosterone; and the ferret, ox, and cow a mixture of both in roughly equal parts. There is, however, a considerable variation within any one species.

The fundamental action of the glucocorticoids lies in the domain of glucose production and utilization, for in the salt-maintained adrenalectomized rat there is apparently little abnormality in the storage of carbohydrate until a period of fasting is instituted, when hypoglycemia develops and the store of glycogen in the liver is rapidly depleted. Administration of adrenal steroids is followed by a large increase in liver glycogen.

The glucocorticoids affect metabolism in a variety of ways. There is an increase in the catabolism of tissue protein, with the carbon fraction of the amino acids being used for the production of glucose. Because of this stimulation of gluconeogenesis, the glucocorticoids exert a marked anti-insulin action. Administration of these corticoids exacerbates diabetes and will induce diabetes in the force-fed normal individual; the diabetes so produced is ameliorated by insulin only with difficulty. There are indications that cortical extracts decrease the amount of glucose that is utilized. The daily administration of cortisone to rats fed a high carbohydrate diet results in a severe hyperglycemia and glycosuria, and the increased urinary nitrogen accounts for only a fraction of the glucose present in the urine (Ingle).

The glucocorticoids cause the mobilization of fat from the fat depots and increase the fat content of the liver. Nothing more need be said here concerning the role played by the adrenal cortex in the metabolism of carbohydrate and fat inasmuch as these subjects have been dealt with in chs. 67 and 68.

The point of action of the adrenal hormones in the metabolic processes touched upon above is not clear. Studies on the enzyme content of various tissues, before and after adrenalectomy, indicate that a variety of enzymes may be reduced in amount, but that is likely to be consequence rather than cause of a more fundamental disturbance of a fairly ubiquitous metabolic process. One current theory suggests that glucocorticoids (Greengard et al., 1963) and aldosterone (Edelman et al., 1963) stimulate the production of enzymes necessary for cell activity, and do so by activating a DNA-dependent synthesis of RNA; this, in turn, results in the accelerated formation of specific enzymes. There is analogy for this mode of action in the insect world, where the pupating hormone, the steroid *ecdysone*, acts on one gene in one chromosome, thus initiating a chain of events which leads to the production of the enzyme dopa-decarboxylase required for the chemical processes which transform the larval skin into the hard shell of the pupa (Karlson, 1964).

Under stressful conditions there is an increased liberation of glucocorticoids. This action is mediated *via* the adrenocorticotrophic hormone of the pituitary and does not occur in the hypophysectomized individual.Whereas the glucocorticoids are highly active in increasing resistance to stress, the mineralocorticoids are relatively ineffective. Allied to their protective action in stress is the effect the glucocorticoids exert on muscular efficiency. One characteristic of adrenal cortical insufficiency is the early onset of muscular weakness and fatigue. Administration of cortisone restores the normal work performance of muscles. This effect is complex and is due largely to improvement of cardiac action and of vascular reactivity.

The *mineralocorticoids* exert their most striking action upon the kidney, although there is increasing evidence for a generalized effect in the body, possibly on cell surfaces. In the adrenalectomized animal, there is an abnormally large excretion of sodium and chloride by the kidney and this phenomenon may be abolished by administration of adrenal cortical extract. Desoxycorticosterone, which is secreted by the mammalian adrenal in trace amounts, was the only known mineralocorticoid until 1952, when Simpson et al. combined paper chromatographic techniques and a sensitive bioassay in their search for the natural mineralocorticoid in adrenal gland extracts. In 1953, Simpson et al. announced the crystallization of a new steroid which was from 30 to 100 times more active than desoxycorticosterone in promoting sodium retention and was effective in the rat in amounts of 0.1 μg or less. Sodium retention in man can be demonstrated with doses of 100 μg. Initially the compound was termed electrocortin, but following the determination of the structure of the steroid, this name was replaced in 1954 by that of *aldosterone*. Aldosterone is unique among the adrenal steroids in possessing an aldehyde group at position 18 (p. 1573). Its main site of synthesis is the outer part of the adrenal cortex, the so-called *zona glomerulosa*, as first suggested by Deane and Greep (1946).

Desoxycorticosterone, mainly used in the form of the less soluble acetate ester, has been invaluable as the first synthetic steroid available as a life-saving drug in the Addisonian patient. It is still used as a supplement to cortisol in adrenal deficiency or in adrenalectomized patients. It exhibits the greatest influence on the kidney; it increases the concentration of sodium in the body fluids, but reduces the concentration of potassium. It also reduces the intracellular concentration of potassium and increases that of sodium (fig. 76.6) and with prolonged administration, the concentration of sodium may nearly equal that of potassium. The administration of potassium almost completely corrects the abnormal quantitative relationship of these electrolytes. Through its action in causing sodium and water retention, the administration of desoxycorti-

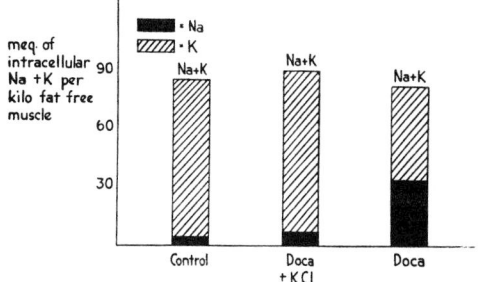

EFFECT OF DOCA UPON THE CONCENTRATION OF INTRACELLULAR Na AND K

FIG. 76.6. The replacement intracellularly of potassium and sodium in the muscles of normal dogs under the influence of desoxycorticosterone acetate (DOCA). The effect is inhibited by the administration of KCl. (From Loeb.)

costerone may be followed by a great increase in plasma volume and edema, especially if the intake of sodium is increased. With overdosage, more serious effects may result, such as hypertension, dilation of the right ventricle, and pulmonary congestion. Death from cardiac failure has resulted from its clinical use. Loeb and his associates have shown that administration of desoxycorticosterone to animals may lower the tissue potassium to the point where paralysis is produced.

The actions of aldosterone differ in some respects from those of desoxycorticosterone. A comparison of the relative potency of the two hormones shows that aldosterone is about 25 times as active as desoxycorticosterone in maintaining life in adrenalectomized dogs, and about 5 times as effective in promoting potassium excretion in adrenalectomized rats. In the maintenance of sodium and potassium balance in human adrenal insufficiency, aldosterone is the more potent by a factor of 30 or so. The amount secreted by the adrenal gland is approximately one-hundredth of the quantity of cortisol secreted. The sodium-retaining activity of aldosterone being about 1000 times that of cortisol, it follows that much of the sodium-sparing action of the adrenal cortex is due to its production of aldosterone. Prolonged administration of aldosterone does not, at present, appear to produce hypertension or edema though, like desoxycorticosterone, it results in chloride retention and increased potassium excretion.

The function of the *androgenic corticoids* produced by the adrenal gland has occasioned much controversy. Since normal sexual activity is maintained in rats given salt after adrenalectomy, it may be presumed that the adrenal steroids are not essential in reproductive processes. On the other hand, estrogens, androgens, and progesterone can be extracted from the adrenal cortex and are found, not only in normal urine, but that of eunuchs and of ovariectomized women. It is possible that the secretion of androgen by the adrenal is concerned in the persistence of libido after gonadal removal (p. 1620). There is some increase in the excretion of adrenal androgens in both boys and girls at puberty. Sexual abnormalities are a striking feature of the syndrome associated with certain tumors of the adrenal gland (p. 1578).

The adrenal glands of immature mice contain an *X-zone* of cells with an acidophilic cytoplasm and prominent basophilic nuclei; it immediately invests the medulla. In the male, the X-zone collapses as a result of the direct action of the androgens produced at puberty; if castration is performed, the X-zone persists and may enlarge. In the immature female, the X-zone continues to develop up to puberty and can then persist for several months until it too disappears, possibly under the influence of androgen. The function of the X-zone is not clear. A somewhat similar zone is distinguishable as the *fetal cortex* in the newborn human. In this case, the greater part of the cortex at birth (apart from a peripheral layer of cortical cells which develops into the definitive cortex) is destined to involute and disappear in the first months of extrauterine life. Despite considerable research, the function of the fetal cortex is also obscure, although it is speculated that the cells produce androgen. According to Benirschke, and Lanman, it would seem that the fetal cortex is trophically stimulated by chorionic gonadotrophin (p. 1640), and that upon withdrawal of this hormone at birth, involution occurs. The most likely function of adrenal androgens is a contribution, by their anabolic effect, to foetal growth and, after birth, to the development of musculature and other organs such as the kidneys.

The adrenal cortex possesses spheres of influence additional to those described above. Administration of adrenal cortical hormone, or the application of (stressful) stimuli leading to the discharge of cortical hormones, produces a *dissolution of lymphocytes and a fall in the lymphocyte count* in the blood. There is also an *eosinopenia*.

With high dosage of cortisone, there is an atrophy of the thymus, spleen, and lymph nodes; growth may be inhibited, and wound healing is retarded. Inflammation in many tissues (connective tissue, synovial membranes, reticulum), which is prominent in the so-called *collagen diseases*, is abruptly arrested by cortisone. Cortisone interferes with the formation of granulation tissue, with deposition of fibrin, and with some, but not all, immune responses and allergic phenomena. Cortisone also appears to inhibit the enzyme hyaluronidase (Opsahl) and thus to decrease cell permeability. All these actions are produced by doses of cortisol which exceed those secreted naturally. They are not seen with desoxycorticosterone which, in contrast, stimulates some inflammatory processes such as the growth of fibroblasts or the formation of ground substance.

OUTLINE OF THE BIOCHEMISTRY OF THE ADRENOCORTICAL HORMONES

The adrenal cortex is secreting continuously, and, in contrast to the intermittently active adrenal medulla, stores very little of the corticoids it synthesizes (Vogt, 1943). The amount of circulating ACTH released by the anterior lobe of the pituitary regulates the rate of secretion. The cortical hormones are produced in the adrenal from cholesterol, which is in turn synthesized from acetate. This is indicated by the finding that when an adrenal gland is perfused with C^{14}-labeled cholesterol, labeled corticosterone and cortisol are produced. Additionally, incubation of adrenal slices, or perfusion of isolated adrenal glands with labeled acetate, results in the formation of labeled cholesterol and corticosteroid. It has been found that the cholesterol content of the rat adrenal cortex is reduced by half by the injection of pituitary adrenocorticotrophic hormone, by trauma, or in states of stress (Long and associates). The fall is greatest some 5 to 6 hours after administration of ACTH and requires about 24 hours for the restoration of the normal level. No similar reduction in the cholesterol content of other organs has been observed to follow the injection of ACTH, so that the response appears to be specific to the adrenal cortex.

The ascorbic acid content of the rat adrenal is reduced by 50 per cent or more by ACTH or by trauma. The fall is maximal in about 1 hour. This fall has been much used as an index of the release of ACTH by various stimuli, and forms the basis of an assay method for ACTH. Nowadays, it is often replaced by estimation of the cortisol or corticosterone released into the adrenal vein or the general circulation. The significance of ascorbic acid with respect to adrenal

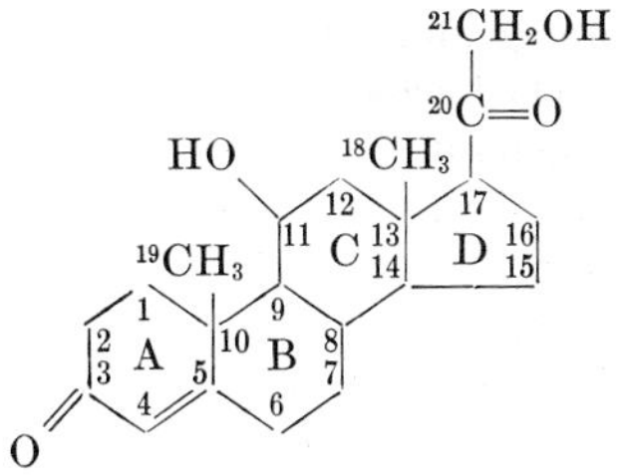

Corticosterone (Kendall's compound B)

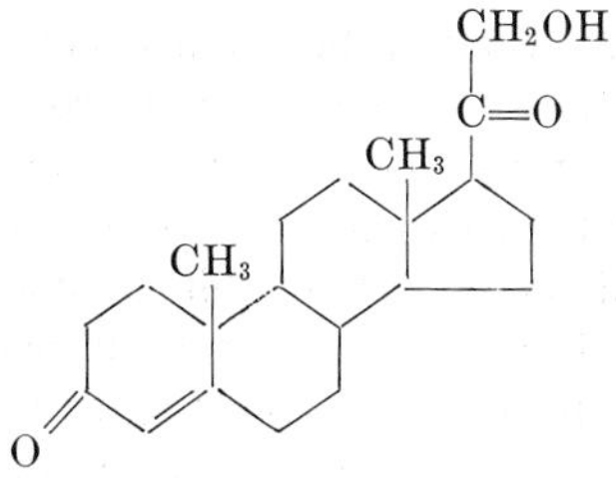

11-Desoxycorticosterone (DOC)

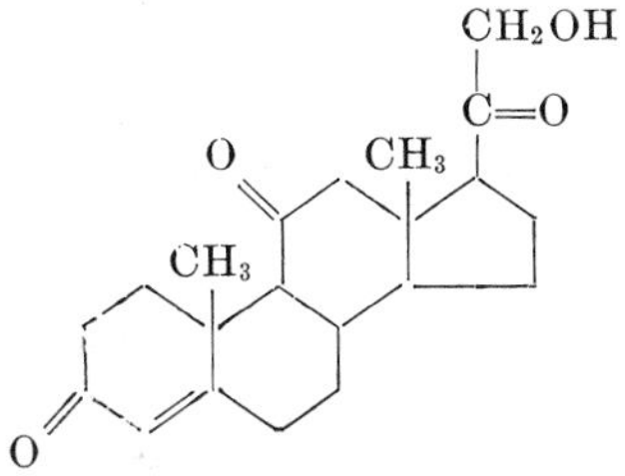

11-Dehydrocorticosterone
(Kendall's compound A)

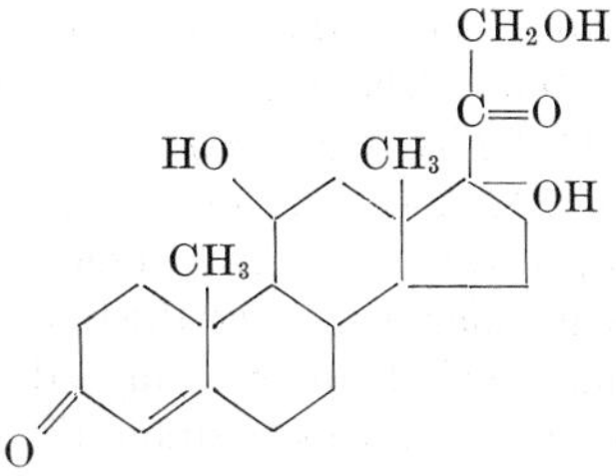

17-Hydroxycorticosterone
(Kendall's compound F;
cortisol)

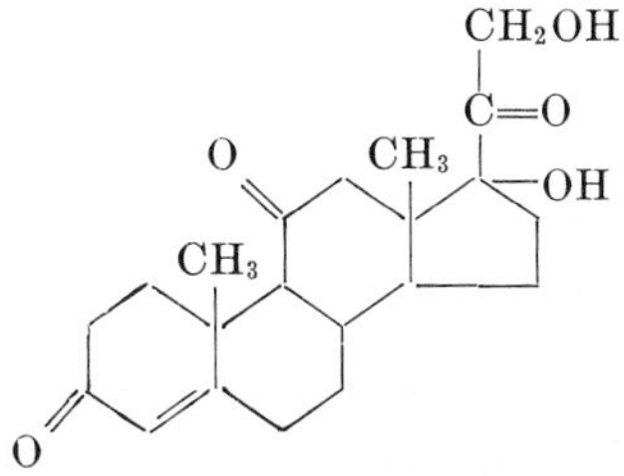

17-Hydroxy-11-dehydrocorticosterone
(Kendall's compound E; Reichstein's
compound Fa; cortisone)

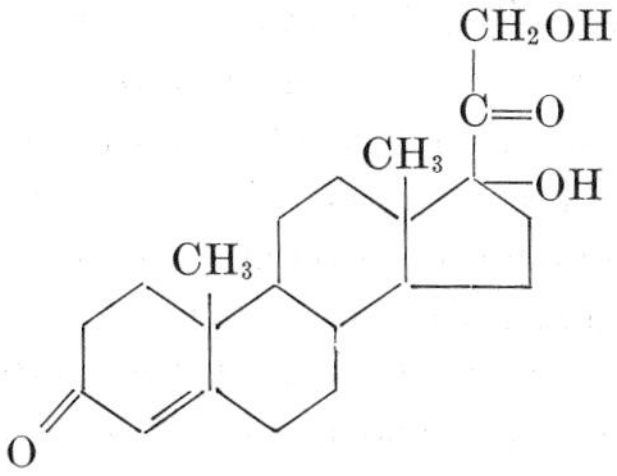

17-Hydroxy-11-desoxycorticosterone
(Reichstein's compound S; desoxycortisone)

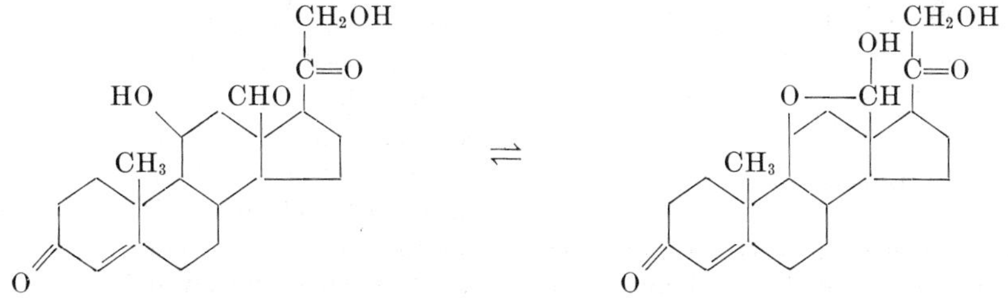

Aldosterone; electrocortin

CHART 76.1. Formula of adrenocortical principles.

cortical function is, however, unknown, since, in the guinea pig, elaboration of the adrenal corticoids has been found to continue in the scorbutic animal, that is, in the absence of ascorbic acid.

The adrenal corticoids (chart 76.1) belong to the group of C_{21}-steroids, that is, steroids with two methyl groups (at C_{10} and C_{13}) and a side-chain of two carbon atoms at C_{17}. They also have a Δ^4-3-ketone grouping believed to be essential for corticoid activity and a characteristic α-ketol (—CO—CH$_2$OH) grouping in the side-chain attached at C_{17}. All compounds of chart 76.1 are

known to be functionally important, except for desoxycortisone, which has little known physiological activity. As long as the only source of cortical steroids were adrenal extracts, which contain but small amounts of the active principles, therapy with these compounds was limited and progress in the study of structure-action relationship slow. Now, not only the naturally occurring cortical steroids, but also many synthetic analogues can be obtained by using chemical or microbiological processes in order to produce the desired compounds from steroids readily available in nature. As a result, there is not only an adequate supply of substances such as cortisol and cortisone, but also of more potent analogues, which may be particularly active in one therapeutically desired direction while producing less unwanted effects than the natural hormones. Progress in the understanding of structure-action relationships has been reviewed by Bush (1962).

As recorded earlier, the adrenal gland secretes steroids which might exert an effect upon the genital tract. These include *estrone, progesterone, 17-"β"-hydroxyprogesterone, Δ⁴-androstenedione-3-17* and *adrenosterone* (Δ⁴-androstenetrione-3,11,17). The last three of these compounds are androgenic, and the last two have no side-chain, and therefore only 19 carbon atoms, a ketone group at position 17, and are known as adrenal neutral *17-ketosteroids* (17-KS). Some of the 17-ketosteroids excreted in normal urine are *adrenosterone, dehydroepiandrosterone,* and *11-hydroxyepiandrosterone.* A stereoisomeride of the latter is also a metabolite of cortisol; other metabolites of cortisol have their C_{21} skeleton intact. These and the 17-KS are excreted in increased amount in adrenal tumors or following the administration of ACTH.

Adrenosterone is the most active androgen in the adrenal cortex, and has the formula:

Adrenosterone

URINARY EXCRETION AND ASSAY. A wide variety of steroids may be isolated from human urine. They are excreted both in the free form and following conjugation with glucuronic acid to form water-soluble glucuronides. Some may also be linked with sulfuric acid and excreted as sulfates. Before analysis of urine can be undertaken, it, therefore, becomes necessary to free the steroids from conjugation by hydrolysis with mineral acid or, better, by incubation with the enzyme β-glucuronidase. The steroids can then be extracted from the urine and subjected to analysis.

Chemical methods are now available for the estimation of all known corticoids, but bioassay may be required to test for biological activity of newly-found metabolites or synthetic analogues which are gaining increasing importance in medicine. The bioassays utilize effects such as the glycogen deposition induced in the livers of adrenalectomized mice, the action of adrenal corticoids in prolonging the lives of adrenalectomized rats subjected to cold environment, the fall in blood eosinophils induced by adrenal steroids in the adrenalectomized mouse, reduction of inflammatory responses to irritant chemicals, and elimination of radioactive sodium and potassium.

In the chemical analysis of urinary steroids, the *neutral 17-ketosteroids* may be studied, or attention given to metabolites of cortisol and corticosterone only, by testing either for the *reducing steroids, formaldehydogenic steroids, acetaldehydogenic steroids, 17-ketogenic steroids, total 17-hydroxysteroids, Porter-Silber chromogenic steroids,* and so on. In these procedures, a fraction of the urinary steroids is examined as an approximate index of adreno-cortical activity. The introduction of radioactive cortisol, labeled with C^{14} in ring A, has made possible a more direct method (Peterson and Wyngaarden, Cope and Black) for measuring the rate of production of endogenous cortisol.

The *neutral 17-ketosteroids* arise from precursors secreted largely by the adrenal cortex and testis, and only in a minor degree by the ovaries. In men, some two-thirds of the neutral 17-ketosteroids are derived from the adrenal cortex. Following the appropriate extraction procedure, the quantity of 17-ketosteroids is determined colorimetrically with the aid of the *Zimmerman reaction.* Here, steroids with a carbonyl group in position 17 give a purple color when treated with *m*-dinitrobenzene in the presence of alkali. The output of 17-ketosteroids is not constant throughout the life cycle. In both men and women it rises throughout infancy and adolescence, reaches a maximum at about 25 years of age (Hamburger), and subsequently slowly declines. The mean output in healthy 25-year-old males is 14 mg. per day, and in women of the same age 9 mg. per day. In cases of tumors of the adrenal cortex, the excretion of 17-ketosteroids is generally increased, and values of more than 1000 mg. per day have been found. In Addison's disease (p. 1576), the excretion of 17-ketosteroids is usually abnormally low.

THE REGULATION OF ADRENAL CORTICAL HORMONE SECRETION

The adrenal cortex, unlike the medulla, is under humoral and not nervous control. This is indicated by the marked adrenal atrophy which follows removal of the hypophysis, and the enlargement of the gland which is produced by administration of ACTH. However, the fact that complete adrenalectomy is fatal, whereas hypophysectomy is compatible with life, shows that the adrenal cortex of the hypophysectomized animal is functional to some extent.

1. *Androgenic corticoids.* Little is known regarding the factors regulating the secretion of these steroids. Wilkins observed that the virilizing effects associated with adrenal cortical hyperplasia in young girls could be controlled by cortisone administration, and suggested that the cortisone was acting by depressing the pituitary release of ACTH and, therefore, the adrenal cortical release of androgenic substances. Such a view implies a dependence of adrenal androgen secretion on ACTH.

3. *Glucocorticoids.* As indicated earlier, the secretion of corticosterone and cortisol is almost entirely dependent on the pituitary release of ACTH. Hypophysectomy severely reduces the glucocorticoid content of adrenal vein blood, whereas injection of ACTH gives a rapid and dramatic increase in the concentration of hormone in this blood. The regulation of secretion of the adrenal glucocorticoids becomes a question of the regulation of the secretion of pituitary ACTH (see ch. 74).

3. *Mineralocorticoid (aldosterone).* Unlike other adrenal corticoids, the secretion of aldosterone appears to be controlled by more than one factor, ACTH being only one of them. Aldosterone secretion decreases after hypophysectomy, particularly in the dog, but can be raised in such animals by lack of sodium in the diet or by a fall in the circulating blood volume; such falls may be produced, for example, by bleeding or by obstruction of the thoracic inferior vena cava, resulting in the formation of ascites. The agent believed to be responsible for stimulating aldosterone production in states of reduced blood volume is *renin*, an enzyme present in the kidneys and found in renal vein blood after haemorrhage. Renin, in turn, forms *angiotensin* in the blood stream, a polypeptide shown to stimulate secretion of aldosterone by direct action on the adrenal tissue (Davis et al.). Severe changes in blood electrolytes may act directly on adrenal tissue and elicit accelerated secretion of aldosterone (Denton, 1964). A sodium-deficient diet, however, is not necessarily associated with abnormal plasma sodium and potassium; how aldosterone secretion is stimulated under these circumstances is

not known for certain, but secretion of renin is one of the possibilities.

The role of the central nervous system, either through release of a *glomerulotrophin* (a substance stimulating the *zona glomerulosa* of the adrenal cortex), or through reflex action, in controlling output of aldosterone is controversial. It may be that the central nervous system acts only by influencing release of ACTH, and possibly, of renin, or by additional ways which are yet to be demonstrated beyond reasonable doubt.

Some Therapeutic Uses of Cortisone

Great interest was aroused by the dramatic discovery, in 1949, by Hench and his associates, of the therapeutic value of cortisone in acute rheumatism and rheumatoid arthritis, the first of the collagen diseases to be treated with a glucocorticoid. Used in acute rheumatism there is rapid reduction of fever, and of the swelling and pain in the joints, following oral or parenteral administration of cortisone. The high sedimentation rate which occurs in this disease is restored to normal. Cortisol and the adrenotrophic hormone of the hypophysis, ACTH (through its stimulation of the production of cortical hormones), have a similar beneficial effect.

The adrenal steroids suppress the signs of these arthritic diseases though there is no evidence of adrenal insufficiency. Inasmuch as such large doses are required, much greater than are employed in the treatment of Addison's disease, it is clear that these compounds do not act by correcting a hormone deficiency.

The *therapeutic* possibilities of cortisone and cortisol have been investigated in a large number of diseases. Many diseases upon whose course cortisone, cortisol, or ACTH have been found to have a favorable effect, though often this has been slight or evanescent, can be grouped under three main headings, as shown below:

Collagenous diseases (collagenoses)
   Acute rheumatism (rheumatic fever)
   Rheumatoid arthritis and spondylitis
   Psoriatic arthritis
   Scleroderma
   Periarteritis nodosa
   Dermatomyositis
Allergic diseases or diseases due to abnormal sensitivity of cells
   Bronchial asthma
   Allergic rhinitis (hay fever)
   Contact or atopic dermatitis
   Urticaria

Lymphatic and myelogenous diseases
  Acute and chronic lymphatic leukemias
  Lymphosarcoma
  Hodgkin's disease
  Lymphoid thyroiditis (struma lymphomatosa)
  Myelogenous leukemia
  Sarcoidosis
  Multiple myeloma

A number of other pathological states in which ACTH or cortisone has been employed with variable success, and which cannot be placed in any of the above categories, are: ulcerative colitis, acute inflammatory eye diseases, alcoholism with delirium tremens or Korsakoff's psychosis, and chronic nephrosis. The enthusiasm with which corticoid therapy was first hailed has been damped for two reasons: it soon became clear that the therapy, if successful, consisted in a suppression of the signs, not in a cure of the disease. This meant that therapy had to be continued indefinitely in all diseases which were not self-limiting, and this lead to the development of signs of hypercorticism, a damage against which the benefit derived from the treatment had to be carefully weighed. Thus, all signs of Cushing's disease (ch. 74), e.g., hirsutism, striae, diabetes, rounding of the facial contours, osteoporosis, kyphosis, and hypertension have been reported from the continued administration of ACTH or corticoids. Mental aberrations ranging from an exaggerated sense of well being (euphoria), moodiness, or mild anxiety states, to definite psychoses, e.g., paranoia, have been encountered following cortisone therapy. Wound healing may be delayed by cortisone, and resistance to certain infections is lowered. Hamsters can be infected with poliomyelitis virus by intraperitoneal injection, and develop a highly virulent form of the disease if pretreated with cortisone, but animals similarly injected, but not receiving the hormone, could not be infected (Shwartzman). The spread of a tuberculous infection from a previously localized focus is a serious complication which may follow cortisone therapy. Peptic ulcers are not uncommon with prolonged treatment, and perforation of the bowel in cases of ulcerative colitis has sometimes occurred. Prolonged cortisone therapy may lead to adrenocortical atrophy. Collapse and death from acute adrenal insufficiency may follow cessation of treatment.

Disease of the Adrenal Cortex in Man

Addison's Disease

The syndrome known today as Addison's disease was first described (in 1855) by Thomas Addison and ascribed by him to tuberculous disease of the adrenals. Experimental and clinical observations since that time have fully substantiated Addison's conclusion that the disease is due to adrenal destruction. Tuberculous disease of the gland is found, however, in only a proportion of the cases. It is now known that deficiency of the cortex and not of the medulla is the essential cause of the disease. The condition is most common between the ages of 30 and 50, and is found more often in men than in women. Its chief features, which closely resemble those seen in adrenalectomized animals, are: (a) muscular weakness and languor, (b) low blood pressure and reduced circulation rate, (c) gastrointestinal disturbances, loss of appetite (anorexia), hypochlorhydria, and vomiting, (d) pigmentation of the skin and mucous membranes, bronzing, or tanning—a dirty brown cutaneous discoloration being a classical symptom of the disease, (e) lowered metabolic rate, subnormal temperature, sodium loss and a rise in serum potassium, reduced blood volume (plasma loss), dehydration, and loss of weight, (f) renal insufficiency with consequent rise in blood nonprotein nitrogen, (g) depression of the sexual functions, (h) hypoglycemia, which may be an immediate cause of death, (i) abnormal electroencephalogram, slowing of α rhythm and reduced number of β waves, and (j) changes in the electrocardiogram, e.g., low voltage, flat or inverted T, prolongation of P-R and QRS, and depression of RS-T.

The pigmentation of the skin may be so deep that the patient is mistaken for a mulatto; it is most pronounced in those regions, nipples, abdomen, etc., where the normal pigmentation is greatest (fig. 76.7). The palms of the hands and soles of the feet remain pale. The discoloration is due to the excessive accumulation of the normal cutaneous pigment, *melanin*. This is deposited chiefly in the basal cells of the epidermis, but pigment granules are also found in the dermis. Bloch found that sections of normal skin became deeply pigmented when placed in a dilute solution of 3:4-dihydroxyphenylalanine; albino skin treated similarly remained unpigmented. Solutions of other aromatic compounds (e.g., tyrosine, tryptophane, pyrogallol, etc.) did not cause pigmentation of skin sections. Bloch concluded that *d*ihydroxyphenylalanine, which he called *dopa*, was the precursor of melanin, the conversion being brought about by an oxidizing enzyme (dopa oxidase) in the skin. Until recently, tyrosinase, present in potato, fungi, and other plants, and which is capable of catalyzing the conversion

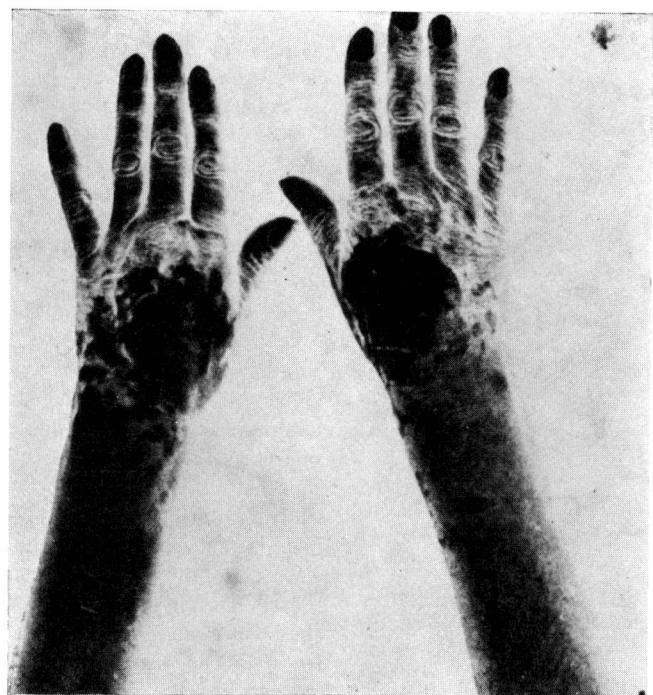

FIG. 76.7. Showing pigmentation of the skin together with patches of depigmentation in a patient with Addison's disease. (From Kepler.)

of tyrosine to "dopa," has been believed to be absent from mammalian tissues. But since its discovery in animals, this enzyme has been assigned the role of catalyzing the reactions, tyrosine to "dopa," and "dopa" to melanin (Lerner and Fitzpatrick). Tyrosinase is now thought to be identical with Bloch's dopa oxidase (see scheme below).

$$HO\hspace{-0.5em}\bighexagon\hspace{-0.5em}CH_2\!-\!CHNH_2\!-\!COOH$$

Tyrosine

↓

$$\underset{HO}{HO}\hspace{-0.5em}\bighexagon\hspace{-0.5em}CH_2\!-\!CHNH_2\!-\!COOH$$

3:4-Dihydroxyphenylalanine (dopa)

↓

Melanin

(left margin, vertical: *Tyrosinase*)

The increased pigmentation has been tentatively attributed to an excess of circulating melanocyte-stimulating hormone (MSH, Lerner et al. 1956). An increased excretion of MSH has been found in the urine, and therapy with cortisone may or may not reduce urinary MSH content, just as it may or may not decrease pigmentation. Administration of MSH may darken normal human skin, though the process involved in this darkening is not as clearly understood as in the amphibian skin with its large and active melanophores.

The reason for the increase in MSH in the Addisonian patient is not quite clear. It is well known that lack of cortical hormones leads to an excessive secretion of ACTH, a phenomenon considered to be part of the feedback mechanism between target hormone and pituitary hormone effective for a number of agents secreted from the anterior lobe. MSH, on the other hand, has no known target hormone in the mammal, and the increased melanocyte stimulating activity in adrenal insufficiency may arise from two causes: an excess synthesis of MSH, whenever excess ACTH is being produced in the pituitary, and a degree of intrinsic melanocyte-stimulating activity possessed by the ACTH molecule.

Addison's disease, before it was treated with cortical hormone and with a diet of high sodium and low potassium content, was almost invariably fatal. Now the treatment with cortisol or one of its synthetic substitutes, supplemented by DOCA or another synthetic mineralocorticoid, provides effective substitution therapy. It needs, however, adjusting in times of "stress" when the organism needs more cortical hormones than under basal

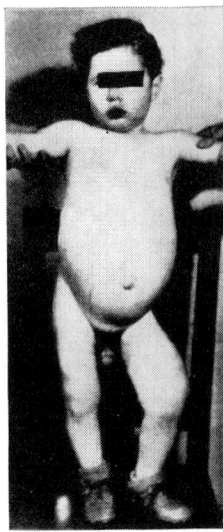

FIG. 76.8. Enlarged abdomen and precocious sexual development of a boy aged 30 months. A mass palpated in the abdomen was probably a suprarenal cortical tumor. (From Rowntree and Ball.)

conditions. The relative ease of such therapy, however, has enabled surgeons to carry out complete adrenalectomy in man, when such operations were indicated by certain forms of inoperable cancer or by malignant hypertension.

Tumors of the Adrenal Cortex. Adrenogenital Syndrome, Pseudohermaphroditism[4]

Tumors composed of cortical tissue, which secretes an excess of androgenic compounds, may arise in the adrenal itself or in aberrant collections of cortical cells (adrenal "rests") which are found in the broad ligament of the uterus, in the neighborhood of the testes, or in the retroperitoneal tissue of the abdomen or pelvis. Such growths, or a diffuse hyperplasia of the adrenal cortex, may occur in children or adults, and are associated with abnormalities of development, especially of the *accessory organs of sex* and of the *secondary sex characters* (p. 1615).

When cortical hyperplasia, or a tumor composed of cortical tissue, occurs in young children, puberty appears prematurely; a male child of 4 or 5 years, for example, may show the sexual development of an adult (fig. 76.8). The testes

[4] Pseudohermaphroditism is defined as a condition in which the gonads of one sex only are present, but the external genitalia combine features of both sexes, so that from inspection of them alone it is difficult or impossible to determine the sex. In true hermaphroditism, both ovarian and testicular tissues are present; it is an embryological aberration and not due to a hyperfunctional adrenal cortex (see also ch. 78).

and penis are enlarged, hair may appear upon the chest, pubis, and face, and there may be precocious sexual desire. Often there is also unusual muscular development or extreme obesity. There is early ossification of the epiphyses. Male children showing these characteristics have been described as resembling "an infant Hercules" (Herculean type of Weber), or "a burly brewer's drayman" (Guthrie). Growth is rapid as a rule, but the epiphyses fuse early; young subjects of the disease, therefore, do not reach full stature.

In little girls, the breasts hypertrophy, hair appears on the mons veneris and around the vulva, the uterus develops prematurely, the clitoris is hypertrophied, and there is sometimes precocious menstruation. In appearance such children resemble stout little women. Women who are subjects of this disease become masculine in appearance and disposition (virilism, fig. 76.9). The voice deepens, menstruation ceases, the breasts atrophy, and hair may grow upon the chest, face and limbs; baldness is a common feature. The urinary excretion of androgens (17-ketosteroids) is increased several fold. In some adult female subjects, the virilism is accompanied by glycosuria and decreased sugar tolerance, due apparently to an increased production of glucocorticoids. This type is known as the Achard-Tiers syndrome and was described by these authors as the "diabetes of bearded women." Adult male subjects of cortical tumors, as a rule, give no evidence of endocrine disturbances. In some, however, an exaggeration of the male characters is manifest, e.g., enlargement of the penis, a tendency to hirsutism, an increased sexual appetite. In others, the tumor secretes excessive amounts of estrogen when a certain degree of feminization is observed, e.g., enlargement of the mammae, atrophy of the testes, and a feminine distribution of fat.

It might be expected that with the increase in active adrenal cortical tissue, changes in electrolyte balance corresponding to those following injections of adrenal cortical hormone, namely, a rise in blood sodium and a fall in potassium, would be found. But actually such changes occur only in a proportion of cases and are, as a rule, moderate in degree. On the other hand, there may be an associated depression of adrenal salt retaining factors with the appearance of Addisonian symptoms, due to atrophy of the opposite adrenal. Surgical removal of the tumor or hyperplastic tissue is the preferred treatment when possible. Sometimes as a result of atrophy of the normal adrenal tissue, acute cortical insufficiency de-

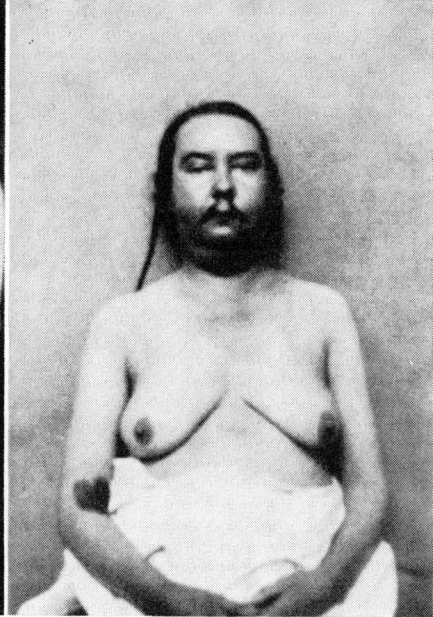

Fig. 76.9. Virilism due to adrenal tumor. On left, at age 28 years before the onset of the disease; on right, at age 35 years at the height of the disease. (From Lescher.)

velops after operation. In order to forestall such a crisis, treatment with a cortical hormone is instituted preoperatively. The administration of cortisone is sometimes successful in suppressing adrenal hyperplasia; the elevated blood level of this hormone tends to inhibit the output of ACTH and, as a consequence, to reduce its stimulating effect upon the hyperplastic tissue. This treatment, however, is of little benefit if the disease is due to a tumor whose activity is independent of pituitary control.

Broster and Vines have stated that hyperplastic adrenal cortical tissue or tumor tissue, in cases of virilism, contains large numbers of cells which have an affinity for fuchsin (fuchsinophil cells). Cells possessing this property are normally absent from the mature adrenal or present only in very small numbers. They are a characteristic feature, however, of the fetal adrenal of both sexes between the 10th and 17th weeks (in the case of the male) and between the 11th and 15th weeks (in the case of the female), but disappear thereafter. These observers suggest that virilism is due to the elaboration of a masculinizing hormone by the fuchsinophil cells, and that the female fetus normally passes through a male phase. The importance of the fuchsinophil cells in the production of hyperadrenocortical manifestations has been questioned, however, by Soffer.

Primary Aldosteronism

With the isolation of aldosterone as a highly potent mineralocorticoid, and with the develop-

ment of assays for this steroid, the existence of tumors primarily secreting aldosterone has been established. The syndrome of *'primary aldosteronism'* was first described by Conn in 1954, and many cases have now been detected. The major clinical manifestations of the syndrome consist of periodic severe muscular weakness, intermittent tetany and paresthesia, polyuria and polydipsia, and hypertension. The blood sodium level is raised, that of potassium lowered; there is an alkalosis. Only mineral metabolism appears to be affected. Surgical treatment is advised at present.

Clinical Tests of Adrenal Cortical Function

In mild or atypical cases of adrenocortical insufficiency the following tests may be employed for its detection:

1. Eosinopenic response to ACTH is one of the most sensitive tests. In normal persons, a 50 per cent reduction in circulating eosinophils results from the administration of a test dose of corticotrophin, whereas the response is absent or much reduced in adrenocortical insufficiency.

2. Robinson-Kepler-Power test to ingested water. Normally diuresis commences within 30 to 45 minutes after drinking water: in adrenal insufficiency the excretion of the excess water is much delayed.

3. Cutler-Power-Wilder test. The urinary excretion of sodium chloride during a 53 hour period of rigidly restricted salt intake accompanied by the administration of potassium. Normally less than 150 mg. per 190 cc. of urine is excreted in the last

4 hours of the test. The subject of adrenal insufficiency excretes a much larger quantity. This test is potentially dangerous, for unless the adrenal insufficiency is of mild or moderate degree, an adrenal crisis may be precipitated.

Other determinations are, the tendency to hypoglycemia during fasting, the sensitivity to insulin, estimation of urinary 17-KS (which are reduced in adrenal insufficiency and increased in normals by ACTH administration), and the uric acid-creatinine ratio which is normally increased by cortical stimulation.

REFERENCES

ADDISON, T. London, 1855. Reprinted by the New Sydenham Society, 1868.

ALDRICH, T. B. Am. J. Physiol., 1901, 5, 457.

ALDRICH, T. B. J. Am. Chem. Soc., 1905, 27, 1074.

ALLEN, W. J. AND ASSOCIATES. J. Physiol., 1946, 105, 255.

ALLERS, W. D. AND ASSOCIATES. Proc. Staff Meet. Mayo Clin., 1935, 10, 406.

ALLERS, W. D. AND ASSOCIATES. Proc. Staff Meet. Mayo Clin., 1936, 11, 283.

BACQ, M. M. Ann. physiol., 1934, 10, 467.

BAUMANN, E. J. AND KURLAND, S. J. Biol. Chem., 1926, 71, 281.

BEARN, A. G. AND ASSOCIATES. J. Physiol., 1951, 115, 430.

BENIRSCHKE, K. AND ASSOCIATES. Endocrinology, 1956, 58, 598.

BLASCHKO, H. J. Physiol., 1942, 101, 337.

BOOTHBY, W. M. AND SANDIFORD, I. Am. J. Physiol., 1923, 66, 93.

BRITTON, S. W. AND SILVETTE, H. Am. J. Physiol., 1932, 100, 701.

BRITTON, S. W. AND SILVETTE, H. Am. J. Physiol., 1934, 107, 190.

BROSTER, L. R. AND VINES, H. W. C. The adrenal cortex, a surgical and physiological study. Lewis, London, 1933.

BROSTER, L. R. Lancet, 1934, 1, 830.

BROWN-SÉQUARD, C. E. Compt. rend. Acad. sc., 1856, 43, 422.

BÜLBRING, E. J. Physiol., 1937, 91, 18P.

BÜLBRING, E. Brit. J. Pharmacol., 1949, 4, 234.

BÜLBRING, E. AND BURN, J. H. J. Physiol., 1941, 100, 337.

BÜLBRING, E. AND BURN, J. H. J. Physiol., 1949, 109, 11P.

CANNON, W. B. Am. J. Physiol., 1914, 33, 356.

CANNON, W. B. Am. J. Physiol., 1914, 34, 232, 243, 251.

CANNON, W. B. Am. J. Physiol., 1919, 50, 399.

CANNON, W. B. New England J. Med., 1928, 199, 593.

CANNON, W. B. Endocrinology, 1931, 15, 473.

CANNON, W. B. AND ASSOCIATES. Am. J. Physiol., 1911, 28, 64.

CANNON, W. B. AND ASSOCIATES. Am. J. Physiol., 1921, 58, 308, 338.

CANNON, W. B. AND ASSOCIATES. Am. J. Physiol., 1922, 61, 215.

CANNON, W. B. AND ASSOCIATES. Am. J. Physiol., 1925, 72, 283, 295.

CANNON, W. B. AND ASSOCIATES. Am. J. Physiol., 1926, 77, 326.

CANNON, W. B. AND ASSOCIATES. Am. J. Physiol., 1927, 79, 433, 466.

CANNON, W. B. AND ASSOCIATES. Am. J. Physiol., 1931, 96, 377, 392.

CANNON, W. B. AND ASSOCIATES. Am. J. Physiol., 1933, 104, 557.

CHAIKOFF, I. L. Quoted by C. N. H. LONG. Ciba Foundation Colloquia on Endocrinol., 1952, 4, 379.

CHEN, K. K. J. Am. Pharm. A., 1924, 14, 189.

CHEN, K. K. AND SCHMIDT, C. F. J. A. M. A., 1926, 87, 836.

CLEGHORN, R. A. AND ASSOCIATES. Am. J. Physiol., 1939, 126, 466.

CLEGHORN, R. A. AND ASSOCIATES. J. Physiol., 1939, 96, 146.

CONN, J. W. J. Lab. Clin. Med., 155, 45, 3, 661.

COPE, C. L. AND BLACK, E. Brit. Med. J., 1958, 1, 1020.

CORI, C. F. AND CORI, G. T. J. Biol. Chem., 1928, 79, 309.

DAKIN, H. E. J. Physiol., 1905, 32, xxxiv.

DAVIS, J. O., AYERS, C. R., AND CARPENTER, C. C. J., J. Clin. Invest., 1961, 40, 1466.

DEANE, H. W. AND GREEP, R. O. Am. J. Physiol., 1946, 79, 117.

DENTON, D. A. Australasian Ann. Med., 1964, 13, 121.

DUNLOP, H. A. J. Physiol., 1929, 67, 349.

EDELMAN, I. S., BOGOROCH, R., AND PORTER, G. A. Proc. Nat. Acad. Sci., 1963, 50, 1169.

ELLIOTT, T. R. J. Physiol., 1912, 44, 374.

ELLIOTT, T. R. J. Physiol., 1914, 49, 38.

VON EULER, U. S. Acta. med. scandinav., 1946, 12, 73.

GADDUM, J. H. AND KWIATKOWSKI, H. J. Physiol., 1938, 94, 87.

GOLDENBERG, M. AND ASSOCIATES. Science, 1949, 109, 534.

GREENGARD, O., WEBER, G., AND SINGHAL, R. L. Science, 1963, 141, 160.

GRIFFITH, F. R. Physiol. Rev., 1951, 31, 151.

GROLLMAN, A. AND FIROR, W. M. J. Biol. Chem., 1933, 100, 429.

GUTHRIE, L. AND EMERY, W. D'E. Tr. Clin. Soc. London, 1907, 40, 175.

HAMBURGER, C. Acta endocrinol., 1948, 1, 19.

HARROP, G. A. Bull. Johns Hopkins Hosp., 1936, 59, 11, 25.

HARROP, G. A. AND ASSOCIATES. J. Exper. Med., 1933, 58, 1.

HARROP, G. A. AND ASSOCIATES. J. Exper. Med., 1935, 61, 839.

HARTMAN, F. A. AND KILBORN, L. G. Am. J. Physiol., 1918, 45, 111.

HARTMAN, F. A. AND ASSOCIATES. Proc. Soc. Exper. Biol. & Med., 1927, 25, 69.

HARTMAN, F. A. AND ASSOCIATES. Am. J. Physiol., 1928, 86, 353.

HARTMAN, F. A. AND ASSOCIATES. Am. J. Physiol., 1930, 95, 670.

HARTMAN, F. A. AND ASSOCIATES. Proc. Soc. Exper. Biol. & Med., 1930, 28, 94.

HARTMAN, F. A. AND ASSOCIATES. Proc. Soc. Exper. Biol. & Med., 1933, 30, 560.

HARTMAN, F. A. AND ASSOCIATES. Am. J. Physiol., 1936, **117, 553.**

HECHTER, O. M. Transactions of the 3rd conference on the adrenal cortex, p. 115. Josiah Macy, Jr., Foundation, New York, 1951.

HENCH, P. S. AND ASSOCIATES. Proc. Staff Meet. Mayo Clin., 1949, **24,** 181, 277.

HENCH, P. S. AND ASSOCIATES. Ann. Rheumat. Dis., 1949, **8,** 90, 97.

HIMSWORTH, H. P. AND SCOTT, D. B. M. J. Physiol., 1938, **93,** 159.

HOSKINS, R. G. Am. J. Physiol., 1912, **29,** 363.

HOSKINS, R. G. J. A. M. A., 1927, **88,** 2011.

HOSKINS, R. G. AND MCCLURE, C. W. Arch. Int. Med., 1912, **10,** 343.

HOSKINS, R. G. AND MCCLURE, C. W. Am. J. Physiol., 1912, **30,** 192.

INGLE, D. J. Am. Pract. and Dig. of Treatment, 1953, **4,** 628.

INGLE, D. J. The Journal–Lancet, Minneapolis, 1953, **73,** 470.

KARLSON, P. Proc. 2nd Internat. Congr. Endocrin., 1964, Exc. Med. Found. Amsterdam, 1965.

KENDALL, E. C. Proc. Staff Meet. Mayo Clin., 1938, **13,** 519.

KENDALL, E. C. Proc. Staff Meet. Mayo Clin., 1949, **24,** 298.

KENDALL, E. C. AND ASSOCIATES. Proc. Staff Meet. Mayo Clin., 1934, **9, 245.**

KENDALL, E. C. AND ASSOCIATES. Proc. Staff Meet. Mayo Clin., 1936, **11,** 351.

KENDALL, E. C. AND ASSOCIATES. J. Biol. Chem., 1936, **114,** 613.

KENDALL, E. C. AND ASSOCIATES. Proc. Staff Meet. Mayo Clin., 1937, **12,** 136.

LANNAN, J. T. Endocrinology, 1957, **61, 684.**

LESCHER, F. G. Quart. J. Med., 1935, N.S. **4,** 23.

LI, C. H. AND ASSOCIATES. J. Biol. Chem., 1943, **149,** 413.

LI, C. H. AND ASSOCIATES. Harvey Lectures, 1951, **46,** 181.

LOEB, R. F. Proc. Soc. Exper. Biol. & Med., 1933, **30,** 808.

LOEB, R. F. J. A. M. A., 1935, **104, 2177.**

LOEB, R. F. Bull. New York Acad. Med., 1940, **16,** 347.

LOEB, R. F. AND ASSOCIATES. J. Exper. Med., 1933, **57,** 775.

LOEB, R. F. AND ASSOCIATES. Science, 1939, **90,** 496.

LONG, C. N. H. Bull. New York Acad. Med., 1947, **23,** 260.

LONG, C. N. H. Proc. Fed. Am. Soc. Exper. Biol., 1947, **6,** 461.

LONG, C. N. H., FRY, E. G. AND THOMPSON, K. W. Am. J. Physiol. Proc., 1938.

LONG, C. N. H. AND LUKENS, F. D. W. J. Exper. Med., 1936, **63,** 465.

MENKIN, V. Am. J. Physiol., 1940, **129,** 691.

NICKERSON, M. AND GOODMAN, L. S. Proc. Fed. Am. Soc. Exper. Biol., 1948, **7,** 397.

OLIVER, G. AND SCHÄFFER, E. A. J. Physiol., 1894, **16,** 1.

OLIVER, G. AND SCHÄFFER, E. A. J. Physiol., 1895, **18,** 230.

OPSAHL, J. C. Yale J. Biol. & Med., 1949, **21,** 255, **433.**

OPSAHL, J. C. Transactions of the 2nd conference on the adrenal cortex, Josiah Macy, Jr., Foundation, New York, 1950.

PETERSON, R. E. AND WYNGAARDEN, J. B. J. Clin. Invest., 1956, **35,** 552.

REDFIELD, A. C. J. Exper. Zool., 1918, **26,** 275.

REICHSTEIN, T. AND ASSOCIATES. Helvet. chim. acta, 1936, **19,** 1107.

REICHSTEIN, T. AND ASSOCIATES. Nature, 1937, **139,** 26, 925.

ROGOFF, J. M. Proc. California Acad. Med., 1930, **1, 7.**

ROGOFF, J. M. Canad. M. A. J., 1931, **24,** 43.

ROWNTREE, L. G. AND BALL, R. G. Endocrinology, 1933, **17,** 263.

SHWARTZMAN, G. Proc. Soc. Exper. Biol. & Med., 1952, **79,** 573.

SIMPSON, S. A., TAIT, J. F., AND BUSH, I. E. Lancet, 1952, **2,** 226.

SIMPSON, S. A., TAIT, J. F., WETTSTEIN, A., NEHER, R., VON EUW, J. AND REICHSTEIN, T. Experientia, 1953, **9,** 333.

SMITHWICK, R. H., FREEMAN, N. E. AND WHITE, J. C. Arch. Surg., 1934, **29,** 759.

SOFFER, L. J. Bull. New York Acad. Med., 1947, **23, 479.**

SOSKIN, A. Am. J. Physiol., 1927, **83,** 162.

STEWART, G. N. AND ROGOFF, J. M. Science, 1927, **66,** 327.

STEWART, G. N. AND ROGOFF, J. M. Am. J. Physiol., 1928, **84,** 660.

STEWART, G. N. AND ROGOFF, J. M. Am. J. Physiol., 1928, **86,** 20.

STEWART, G. N. AND ROGOFF, J. M. Am. J. Physiol., 1929, **88,** 162.

STEWART, G. N. AND ROGOFF, J. M. Am. J. Physiol., 1929, **91,** 254.

STEWART, G. N. AND ROGOFF, J. M. J. A. M. A., 1929, **92,** 1569.

STOLTZ, F. Ber. deutsch. chem. Gesellsch., 1904, **37,** 4149.

SWINGLE, W. W. AND ASSOCIATES. Science, 1930, **71,** 321, 489.

SWINGLE, W. W. AND ASSOCIATES. Science, 1930, **72,** 75, 483.

SWINGLE, W. W. AND ASSOCIATES. Am. J. Physiol., 1931, **96,** 153, 164.

SWINGLE, W. W. AND ASSOCIATES. Proc. Soc. Exper. Biol. & Med., 1932, **29,** 1267.

SWINGLE, W. W. AND ASSOCIATES. Am. J. M. Sc., 1932, **183,** 1.

SWINGLE, W. W. AND ASSOCIATES. J. Exper. Med., 1933, **58,** 17.

SWINGLE, W. W. AND ASSOCIATES. Science, 1933, **77,** 58.

SWINGLE, W. W. AND ASSOCIATES. Am. J. Physiol., 1934, **107,** 259.

SWINGLE, W. W. AND ASSOCIATES. Am. J. Physiol., 1934, **108,** 159.

SZENT-GYÖRGYI, A. Am. J. Physiol., 1929, **90, 536.**

SZENT-GYÖRGYI, A. Science, 1930, **72,** 125.

TAKAMINE, J. Am. J. Pharm., 1901, **73,** 523.

TAIT, J. F., SIMPSON, S. A. AND GRUNDY, H. M. Lancet, 1952, **1,** 122.

THORN, G. W. AND ASSOCIATES. Proc. Soc. Exper. Biol. & Med., 1936, **35,** 247.

VOGT, M. J. Physiol., 1943, **102,** 341.

VULPIAN, E. F. A. Compt. rend. Acad. sc., 1856, **43**, 663.

WELCH, A. D. Am. J. Physiol., 1934, **108**, 691.

WILDER, R. M. AND ASSOCIATES. J. A. M. A., 1938, **111**, 117.

WILKINS, L., BONGIOVANNI, A. M., CLAYTON, G. W., GRUMBACH, M. M. AND VAN WYK, J. Ciba Foundation Colloquia on Endocrinol., 1955, **8**, 460.

Monographs and Reviews

THE ADRENAL CORTEX, Brit. Med. Bull., 1962, **18**, No. 2.

BLAIR-WEST, J. R., COGHLAN, J. P., DENTON, D. A., GODING, J. R., WINTOUR, M. AND WRIGHT, R. D. Rec. Progr. Hormone Res., 1963, **19**, 311.

BUSH, I. E. Pharmacol. Rev., 1962, **14**, 317.

BURN, J. H. Physiol. Rev., 1945, **25**, 377.

CANNON, W. B. Bodily changes in pain, hunger, fear and rage. Appleton-Century-Crofts, New York, 1915.

CANNON, W. B. AND ROSENBLUETH, A. Autonomic neuro-effector systems. Macmillan, New York, 1937.

CONN, J. W. Arch. Int. Med., 1956, **97**, 135.

DAVIS, J. O., Rec. Progr. Hormone Res., 1961, **17**, 293.

DEANE, H. W. The adrenocortical hormones. Vol. 14, Pt. 1 of Supplement to Heffter's Handbuch der experimentellen Pharmakologie, ed. Eichler & Farah, Springer, Berlin, 1962.

DEANE, H. W. AND RUBIN, B. L. The adrenocortical hormones. Vol. 14, Pt. 2 of Supplement to Heffter's Handbuch der experimentellen Pharmakologie, ed. Eichler & Farah, Springer, Berlin, 1964.

ELMADJIAN, F., HOPE, J. M. AND LAMSON, E. T. Recent Progr. Hormone Res., 1958, **14**, 513.

VON EULER, U. S. Noradrenaline. Charles C Thomas, Springfield, Ill., 1956.

FARRELL, G. Physiol. Rev., 1958, **38**, 709.

GADDUM, J. H. AND HOLZBAUER, M. Vitamins & Hormones, 1957, **15**, 151.

HECHTER, O. AND PINCUS, G. Physiol. Rev., 1954, **34**, 459.

HOSKINS, R. G. Physiol. Rev., 1922, **2**, 343.

LERNER, A. B. AND FITZPATRICK, T. B. Physiol. Rev., 1950, **30**, 91.

LIEBERMAN, S. AND TEICH, S. Pharmacol. Rev., 1953, **5**, 285.

LOEB, R. F. Harvey Lectures, 1941–1942, **37**, 100.

LONG, C. N. H. Medicine, 1937, **16**, 215.

LORAINE, J. A. The clinical application of hormone assay. E. & S. Livingstone, Edinburgh, 1958.

NICKERSON, M. Pharmacol. Rev., 1949, **1**, 27.

PARKES, A. G. Physiol. Rev., 1945, **25**, 203.

SAYERS, G. Physiol. Rev., 1950, 30, 241.

SAYERS, G. Recent Progr. Hormone Research, 1948, **2**, 81.

SIMPSON, S. A. AND TAIT, J. F. Recent Progr. Hormone Res., 1955, **11**, 183.

See also references in chapter 75.

CHAPTER 77

The Parathyroid Glands

Development and Structure

The parathyroid glands are the smallest endocrine organs in the body. They remained unrecognized as structures distinct from the thyroid gland (to which they are often closely applied) until Sandström's description in 1880. Although Sandström was of the view that the structures represented remnants of embryonic thyroid tissue, and named them accordingly, the glands actually arise quite independently of the thyroid as outgrowths of the endoderm of the third and fourth pharyngeal pouches. Typically there are two pairs of glands, frequently called parathyroids III and IV to indicate the gill clefts of origin. Inasmuch as parathyroids III tend to follow the thymus during development, whereas parathyroids IV become associated with the thyroid gland, the position of the two pairs in the adult may become reversed from that in the embryo. This happens in the human, in whom the lower glands have also been called "parathymus," though occasionally a gland may be found in the mediastinum separate from the thymus. Parathyroids III are constantly found in all vertebrates above the fishes, whereas parathyroids IV are absent in some species.

In man, the number of glands is assumed to be 4, but in about 1 in 15 there are 5 glands. Reports claiming that more than 5 glands have been found have not been reliable. The upper pair of glands (IV) are usually more constant in position than the lower (III), and lie behind the upper poles of the thyroid gland among the upper branches of the inferior thyroid arteries. A lower parathyroid (III) usually also lies behind the thyroid, near the inferior thyroid artery from which it receives its blood supply. In this position it is near the upper tongue of the thymus which reaches from the mediastinum into the neck behind the lower pole of the thyroid. In about 10 per cent of normal persons, however, one or both of the lower parathyroids is mediastinal and may have a mediastinal blood supply. Branches of the recurrent and superior laryngeal nerves innervate the glands and are probably entirely vasomotor.

The human parathyroids are roughly oval in shape, about 6 mm. in length, and weigh between 30 and 35 mg. each. The combined weight is thus between 120 and 140 mg. Pathologically, glands weighing 50 grams have been reported. The colour of a normal gland varies with age. In children and older adults, a gland is browner because it contains less fat, while in adolescence and early adult life,

it is yellower, since the proportion of fat is greater. A large part of a normal adult gland is composed of groups of fat cells. The parathyroid cells are packed in masses, or sometimes cords, among the fat cells. Two main types of epithelial cell may be distinguished: the *chief*, or principal, cell which contains glycogen and possesses a clear cytoplasm, and the pale *oxyphil* cell which has a granular cytoplasm which stains intensely with acid dyes, and lacks glycogen. The large, round dark nucleus fills about half of the chief-cell and is a characteristic feature of parathyroid tissue. The chief-cells are, apparently, the essential secreting cells of the gland inasmuch as they are the only ones present in the human gland up to the age of 10 yr. and, indeed, are the only ones present at any age in most animals. There is little cytological evidence of secretory activity in these cells, although the physiologic evidence of an endocrine function is irrefutable. The oxyphil-cells gradually appear at puberty, and then increase in numbers with advancing age, and may form quite large islands. It is thought that the oxyphil-cell is an involuted chief-cell and, therefore, no longer has any function.

Early Studies and Concepts

The most prominent indication of inadequate function of the parathyroid glands is the occurrence of tetany. This symptom was long known to occur rather frequently after surgical thyroidectomy but was attributed to infection of the operation wound (Kocher), or to thyroid deficiency (Reverden). Attempts to induce tetany experimentally introduced complications, for in 1884, Schiff observed that thyroid removal in cats and dogs produced tetany and proved fatal, whereas little effect was observed in the rabbit. The difficulty was resolved by Gley in 1891, who pointed out that the inferior parathyroids lie caudal to the thyroid in the rabbit and that they were not affected by thyroidectomy. However, it was left to Vassale and Generale (1896) to differentiate between thyroid and parathyroid function by showing that removal of all the parathyroids, while leaving the thyroids intact, led to a fatal tetany. The cause of the tetany is a fall in the blood calcium level, as discovered by MacCallum and Voegtlin (1909). The same workers showed that administration of calcium salts could avert the convulsions.

For a number of years it was believed that the tetany occurring after parathyroidectomy was due to the accumulation of a toxin within the body, but this view was confounded, and the endocrine nature of the parathyroids established, when several independent workers, Hanson, Berman, and Collip, succeeded, around 1923, in obtaining consistently potent extracts of parathyroid hormone. It then became possible to relate clinical observations to the effects produced experimentally by overdosage with the extract.

Effects of Parathyroidectomy—Tetany

The effects observed following experimental removal of the parathyroid glands vary in intensity according to the species studied, although comparable metabolic changes occur in all. In general, young animals are more susceptible than older ones to the effects of parathyroid deprivation, and herbivores tolerate the operation better than carnivores. The existence of accessory parathyroids offers only a partial explanation, inasmuch as tetany is induced in the rat only with difficulty following complete parathyroidectomy. The high phosphate and low calcium content of the meat diet of carnivores probably accentuates the effects of parathyroidectomy.

In the dog, which has been studied most extensively, signs of parathyroid hormone deficiency may appear within 24 hours of operation. These include: (1) a *fall in plasma calcium* from the normal level of about 10 mg. per 100 ml. to 6 mg. or less. The fall may be very abrupt, reaching the latter value or lower in 24 hr., or may be delayed for 48 to 72 hr. or so. (2) A *rise in plasma inorganic phosphate* from a normal level of about 5 mg. per 100 ml. to 9 mg. or higher. (3) The *urinary excretion of calcium and phosphate* is reduced: this despite an increase in the blood level of the latter electrolyte. (4) *Fibrillary twitchings* of the muscles appear, followed by tonic or clonic (jerking) muscular contractions. The jaws are clenched and the limbs are either stiffly extended or jerk violently; the head is dorsiflexed. Sometimes there are automatic swimminglike movements of the forelimbs. (5) The skeletal muscles show *increased excitability* to a galvanic stimulus (p. 1053) and to mechanical excitation. Cardiac muscle also displays hyperirritability. The time constant of accommodation is increased. (6) The muscle *phosphocreatine* is reduced and its rate of resynthesis

slower than normal. (7) There is *rapid, noisy breathing* (hyperpnea), hyperpyrexia and tachycardia, and salivation. (8) *Death* usually follows in the dog, and is due to asphyxia through spasm of the laryngeal and thoracic muscles.

The signs of increased muscular excitability listed above are due to the hypocalcemia following parathyroidectomy and constitute the condition known as *tetany*. Because the complex can be produced in other ways, Erdheim designated it as *tetania parathyreopriva*. The severity of the tetany is closely related to the plasma calcium level. As this falls, the signs of tetany, mild at first (perhaps merely slight stiffness of the hind limbs), become gradually more severe, and when the plasma calcium has fallen to between 5 and 6 mg. per 100 ml., the tetanic state is usually fully developed. As might be expected, the tetanic convulsions can be relieved or averted by injection of calcium salts.

In man, in infants and very young children, tetany is usually seen in association with rickets. It may occur in the new-born due to a temporary inadequate production of parathyroid hormone. In the adult, tetany may follow accidental removal of the parathyroid glands during thyroidectomy, damage to the blood supply of the parathyroids at such an operation, or removal of a hyperfunctional adenoma. After such operations the tetany may not appear for several days; the symptoms are usually less intense than those seen in parathyroidectomized animals, and the condition runs a more chronic course. The plasma calcium lies usually between 6 and 7 mg. per 100 ml.; rapid respirations and high temperature are not usually seen. The outstanding feature is the heightened neuromuscular excitability. Though jerking movements and generalized convulsions may occur in children, they are unusual in adults. The hypertonic state of the muscles causes the hands and feet to be drawn into typical attitudes which are spoken of as *carpopedal spasm* (fig. 77.1). The hands are flexed at the wrists, and the fingers flexed at the metacarpophalangeal but extended at the interphalangeal joints. The thumb is adducted into the palm. This position constitutes the so-called *accoucheur's hand* of tetany. The feet are extended at the ankles and the toes plantarflexed. Spasms of the eye muscles may be seen, and, occasionally, spasmodic retention of urine occurs. In infantile tetany spasm of the muscles of the glottis is not uncommon, causing inspiratory stridor (*laryngismus stridulus*). When severe, the laryngeal spasm causes complete closure of the glottis for a time; cyanosis results and when asphyxiation seems imminent, a sharp inspiration occurs accompanied by a high pitched "crowing sound."

Parathyroid insufficiency. After operations on the thyroid gland or removal of hyperfunctioning parathyroid tissue, as well as with other causes of hypocalcemia such as "idiopathic hypoparathyroidism," the plasma calcium may lie just above the critical level at which definite tetanic symptoms appear. Emotion, any strain and particularly a strain in which there may be added difficulty in maintaining the plasma calcium level (such as lactation), or failure in taking an adequate diet of absorbable calcium, may, however, precipitate an attack of tetany in such patients with parathyroid insufficiency. Certain tests can be used to unmask the condition, besides estimating the plasma calcium level: (1) *Chvostek's sign,* tapping over the facial nerve in front of the ear causes twitching or spasm of the facial muscles; (2) *Trousseau's sign,* occlusion of the circulation in the arm by means of a blood pressure armlet causes the hand to assume the attitude seen in carpopedal spasm.

Other Forms of Tetany

These with the chief changes in blood chemistry are shown in table 77.1. Both metabolic and respiratory alkalosis may result in tetany, as well as hypocalcemia.

Idiopathic and infantile tetany. Spontaneous, or idiopathic, tetany may occur rarely in adults as a manifestation of defective parathyroid function, or hypoparathyroidism, with hypocalcemia. The tetany arising in this way does not differ from that following parathyroidectomy or damage to the blood supply of the parathyroids during operations on the neck. Tetany may occur during the first week of life, particularly in premature infants and in those born of diabetic mothers, and is characterised by paroxysms of generalised hyperactivity rather than by spasms of the muscles, though the first symptom of the disorder may be laryngeal stridor. There is a low plasma calcium level and the condition is attributed to a delay in the maturation of the parathyroid glands. Severe tetany in a newborn infant may lead to the diagnosis of hyperparathyroidism in the mother. Here the infant's parathyroid function is thought to have been suppressed by the high amount of circulating maternal parathormone.

However, the tetany of infants is usually not

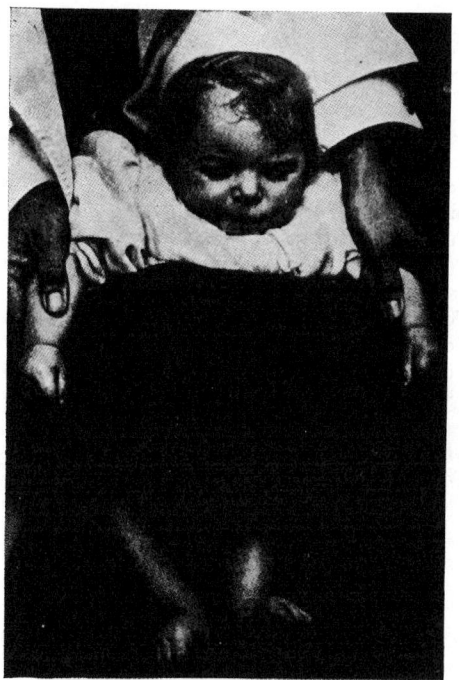

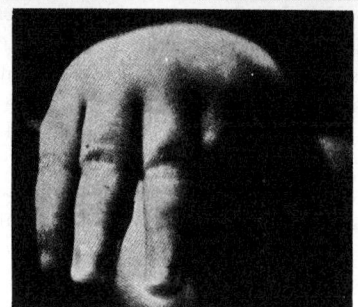

FIG. 77.1. Tetany (description in text). (Upper photograph from Purvis Stewart; lower photograph from Cabot.)

due to parathyroid hypofunction, but is an accompaniment of rickets. During the active stage of rickets, the plasma calcium is depressed little, if at all, but during the healing stage of the disease, bone may be laid down at such a rate that the plasma calcium falls and tetany may result. Tetany may also be produced in rachitic rats by placing them on an antirachitic diet.

Tetany in osteomalacia and sprue. Osteomalacia, a disease of the bones in adults, is produced, like rickets in the growing infant, by a lack of vitamin D. In both diseases there is a failure of calcium absorption, yet the plasma calcium level may be in the normal range. This is explained by assuming that the deficiency of calcium stimulates the parathyroids, which maintain a normal plasma calcium level by liberating the calcium

TABLE 77.1

Changes in the blood chemistry in the various types of tetany

	Plasma Calcium	Plasma Bicarbonate	Plasma Chloride	Blood pH	Plasma Inorganic Phosphate
Parathyroid insufficiency..............	Reduced	Normal	Normal	Normal	Increased
Idiopathic and infantile tetany........	Reduced	Normal		Normal	Increased
Tetany in rickets and osteomalacia....	Reduced	Normal		Normal	Reduced
Tetany in sprue and coeliac disease....	Reduced	Normal		Normal	Normal or reduced
Tetany in metabolic alkalosis.........	Normal	Increased	Reduced	Increased	Increased
Tetany in respiratory alkalosis........	Normal	Reduced		Increased	
Bicarbonate tetany..................	Normal	Increased	Reduced	Increased	
Phosphate (NA₂HPO₄) tetany.........	Reduced	Normal	Normal or increased	Normal or increased	Increased
Citrate and EDTA tetany............	Reduced				
Tetany in animals from magnesium deficiency........................	Normal or reduced				Normal

from bone. The plasma inorganic phosphate level is low in both osteomalacia and rickets, as a result of the parathyroid hormone diminishing the renal tubular reabsorption of phosphate. Sometimes in osteomalacia the plasma calcium level is low and then tetany may occur. The low plasma calcium then implies a failure of the parathyroids to respond to their normal stimulus, or failure of the parathormone to release calcium from bone, and thus to maintain the plasma calcium level at its normal concentration.

The condition of nontropical sprue, or idiopathic steatorrhoea, is the result of an intestinal disorder and is an important cause of osteomalacia. Idiopathic steatorrhoea in infancy, or coeliac disease, is complicated by rickets, but the florid features of rickets, such as tetany, do not appear until remission in the coeliac disease allows the child to grow. In the adult, steatorrhoea is due to malabsorption of fat and the defective absorption will thus include the fat-soluble vitamin D. With these, there is a poor net absorption of calcium (and probably of other substances such as glucose and iron), and the plasma calcium concentration may be low and tetany result. Tetany may also occur in tropical sprue.

Tetany associated with "alkalosis." So-called "metabolic alkalosis" may lead to tetany. Metabolic alkalosis is seen in patients with pyloric stenosis, or as a result of persistent vomiting from other causes, where the loss of chloride and of hydrogen ion in the vomitus causes an increase in blood buffer anion concentration and the blood

pH rises, as does the plasma bicarbonate level. "Respiratory alkalosis," which results from increased pulmonary ventilation, may also give tetany. In this condition there is an excessive elimination of carbon dioxide by the over-breathing, with lowering of the plasma bicarbonate level and a rise in the blood pH. "Alkalosis" is also apparently the cause of the tetany-like seizures which sometimes follow the administration of large quantities of sodium bicarbonate for therapeutic purposes.

Citrate, EDTA and phosphate tetany. Extracellular ionized calcium may be transiently diminished by the intravenous infusion of citrate, EDTA (ethylenediamine tetra-acetic acid) and phosphate, all of which form unionized complexes with calcium. Very large transfusions of stored blood, with added citrate to prevent clotting, may reduce the ionized calcium in the blood, especially in patients with liver failure who cannot metabolise citrate at the normal rate. For this reason, when massive blood transfusions are being given, calcium will also be injected— thus 10 ml. of a 10 per cent solution of calcium gluconate may be given for every 5 l. of blood— unless, of course, agents other than citrate have been used to prevent clotting of the stored blood. An intravenous injection of sodium citrate is not a certain way to induce experimental tetany, but in some animals typical convulsions follow within about 15 min. after the injection.

EDTA is a chelating agent and tetany can be induced on its injection. Tetany can also be produced experimentally by the intravenous injection of 0.5 g. per kg. of disodium hydrogen phosphate into animals, which causes a profound and rapid fall in the plasma calcium.

Experimental tetany due to calcium and vitamin D deficiency. The plasma calcium of rats on a diet lacking in calcium falls after a period of from 3 to 7 weeks to a low level, but tetany does not develop unless the diet is also devoid of vitamin D, and even then, tetany will not develop spontaneously. Typical convulsions can be induced with a galvanic current or by a sudden sound.

Milk fever. Hypocalcemia and tetany sometimes occur in cows after calving as a result of the loss of calcium in the milk. The condition is treated by inflating the udder with air, which suppresses milk secretion and causes a rise in the plasma calcium, or by the intravenous injection of calcium. A similar condition is seen in sheep after lambing and is then referred to as "lambing sickness" or "ewe distemper."

Magnesium deficiency tetany. The general features of this type of tetany are indistinguishable from those due to calcium deficiency. It has been produced in rats, dogs, and young cattle by feeding diets deficient in magnesium. Calves reared on whole milk, which has a low magnesium content (0.01 per 100 ml.), frequently show severe tetany and may die in convulsions. The blood calcium and inorganic phosphate are within normal limits but the magnesium is reduced to little more than half the normal value.

In man, hypomagnesemia in the absence of hypocalcemia probably never gives rise to tetany, though cases are known where the neuromuscular symptoms suggestive of tetany were not alleviated by the administration of calcium, but the patients then improved on receiving parenteral magnesium. Hypomagnesemia occurs in the human, in patients with severe steatorrhoea and with defective intestinal absorption as a result of excision of much of the small intestine. It may also occur with chronic malnutrition and in chronic renal failure when glomerular filtration predominates over tubular reabsorption. It is sometimes seen in patients with hyperparathyroidism and particularly after removal of the hyperfunctioning parathyroid tissue when there is a rapid laying-down of bone.

Pathogenesis of Tetany

MacCallum and Voegtlin discovered (1909) that the plasma calcium was invariably depressed in tetania parathyreopriva and that the condition was immediately relieved by the intravenous injection of calcium. In the years following the recognition of the connection between tetany and the parathyroids, and up to the work of Mac-

Callum and Voegtlin, the tetanic state was believed to be due to some endogenous toxic metabolite (e.g., guanidine) which was destroyed in some way by the parathyroids, but accumulated in the blood and tissues after parathyroidectomy.

With the general recognition of these facts the *calcium deficiency theory* of tetany came into being. The low plasma calcium found in other forms of tetany, that is, produced otherwise than by parathyroid deficiency, e.g., the tetanies of rickets, osteomalacia, and sprue, also indicates that calcium deficiency is the direct cause of the neuromuscular hyperexcitability in these conditions. Depression of the plasma calcium also explains the convulsions following the injection of phosphate. It is generally accepted that the determining factor in the production of tetany is the concentration of *ionized* calcium in the plasma and extracellular fluids of the body, rather than the *total calcium* concentration. For example, in nephritis with a low plasma protein, the total calcium of the plasma may be reduced to 3 or 4 mg. per 100 ml., yet tetany does not occur presumably because the concentration of ionic calcium has not been reduced to the critical level. As shown by the experiments of Loeb upon frog muscle, the sodium and potassium ions tend to increase neuromuscular excitability, the calcium and magnesium ions to depress it. The calcium concentration of the tissues themselves (muscle or brain) is not altered in tetany; the increased neuromuscular excitability appears to be due to a change in cell membrane potential, with decrease in the ionized calcium level, lowering the electrical resistance of the membrane and reducing end-plate potential (Brink, 1954).

It is difficult to assess the importance of hyperphosphatemia as a factor in the production of tetany, for a reciprocal relationship exists in the blood between the concentrations of calcium and phosphate. Phosphate retention or phosphate injection causes a fall in the calcium of the plasma; a rise in the concentration of the calcium of the plasma, on the other hand, tends to depress the blood inorganic phosphate. Nevertheless, tetany can result from a reduction in the plasma calcium as in infantile rickets and osteomalacia with a normal concentration of blood phosphate. Hyperphosphatemia, therefore, though undoubtedly increasing the severity of the tetanic symptoms, does not appear to play the primary role in their development.

The tetany of alkalosis cannot be explained upon the basis of calcium deficiency, inasmuch

as in this type, the plasma calcium is not significantly lowered. It has been suggested that the rise in blood pH could cause a reduction in the ionized fraction of the blood calcium without altering the concentration of the total plasma calcium, but it is not now thought that this effect could be large enough to produce tetany. In favor of this hypothesis, however, have been cited the beneficial effect upon tetany of the administration of an acidifying salt such as ammonium chloride, since it is not followed by a rise in the total plasma calcium, and the differing results of the intravenous injection, into dogs, of alkaline and acid phosphate solutions. As already mentioned, the alkaline salt will give tetany, but tetany does not follow after injection of the acid salt. A different interpretation of these observations could be the direct effect of change in pH. Both increase in the ionized calcium level and increase in pH raise the electrical resistance of cell membranes (Shanes, 1956), and it seems probable that lowering the pH will give the same change in cell membrane potential as decreasing the ionized calcium level. This will explain why the tetany of hypocalcemia may be lessened by giving acid salts, and it has been shown that with alkalosis (when the total plasma calcium is normal) the tetany promptly disappears with restoration of the blood pH to normal (Rasmussen and Reifenstein, 1962).

The question of the neuromuscular mechanisms responsible for the tetanic seizures has not received a decisive answer. D. N. Paton and his associates sectioned the cord in parathyroidectomized dogs and observed cessation of the clonic and tonic spasms, but the tremors and the fibrillary twitchings were abolished only by section of the peripheral nerves. These results indicated that the tonic and clonic spasms were supraspinal in origin whereas the finer movements were dependent upon spinal centers. West more recently concluded that the supraspinal centers were not involved, since the characteristic tonic and clonic spasms persisted after section of the cord in the upper thoracic region. The integrity of the spinal reflex arcs was, however, considered to be essential for the tonic and clonic manifestations since they were abolished after section of the dorsal roots. The fibrillary movements and the increased electrical excitability of the muscles appeared to be dependent upon a peripheral mechanism. They persisted for at least 24 hr., after section of both afferent and efferent nerves. In contradiction of West's conclusions, Greenberg and his colleagues state that in rats, tetanic movements of the hind limbs, but not of the forelimbs, are abolished by transection of the cord at the level of the seventh spinal segment. They conclude that activity of nervous centers above the spinal level is essential for the development of both the tonic and clonic seizures.

Hypoparathyroidism and Hypocalcemia

HYPOPARATHYROIDISM. Hypoparathyroidism disease results from a deficient quantity, or ineffective action, of the blood calcium-raising hormone secreted by the parathyroid glands, which is known as "parathormone." Beside the postsurgical causes of hypoparathyroidism, already mentioned, and idiopathic hypoparathyroidism, in which there is hypoplasia or absence of parathyroid tissue, there is a third form described, pseudohypoparathyroidism, in which it is postulated that the hormone is produced in sufficient quantity but is ineffective in its action, either because of unresponsiveness of the end organs, or because the hormone being produced is different from normal in some way. In this latter condition three are normal or hyperplastic parathyroid glands if the neck is explored. In hypoparathyroidism the plasma calcium level is low and the plasma inorganic phosphate level is raised, since there is a net decrease in bone resorption (see later) and diminished renal clearance of phosphate.

HYPOCALCEMIA. Tetany and convulsions are the outstanding symptoms of hypocalcemia, but there are other features of this biochemical alteration from normal. The causes of hypocalcemia have now been mentioned, either among the causes of tetany, or in the preceding paragraph.

The symptoms of hypocalcemia may be both motor and sensory. The motor symptoms are more dramatic, but the sensory symptoms are the first to appear. The secretory and autonomic nerves, as well as the higher centers, may also be abnormally excitable. With less severe hypocalcemia, there may be spontaneous discharges along sensory nerves producing "pins and needles," or paresthesias, which are particularly noted in the fingers and toes, or perhaps in the ears or the tip of the nose. Discharges along motor nerves may produce muscle spasms, or cramps, and these are particularly liable to occur after a voluntary contraction. The spasms may involve the diaphragm and the muscles of the abdomen, chest and back, and spasms of the muscles of respiration and of the glottis may lead to cyanosis and laryngeal stridor. A generalised spasm of voluntary muscles may make the patient fall to the ground without losing consciousness. Some of these motor manifestations have already been mentioned in the description of tetany, but a convulsion may be due to true epilepsy (usually grand mal in type) and this may be the sole symptom. Smooth muscle may also be hyper-excitable in hypocalcemia and there may be intestinal colic, bronchospasm and even biliary colic. Tetany may be accompanied by marked sweating.

Hypocalcemia may lead to mental changes such as depression, anxiety states and delusions. Mental retardation may be obvious. The electrocardiogram reflects hypocalcemia, with prolongation of the Q-T interval, and there may be changes on electroencephalography. With hypocalcemia, stimulation of a motor nerve (such as the median nerve in the human adult) with a galvanic current produces a muscular contraction with weaker currents than normal, and the contraction may be preferentially elicited by the anodal closing current rather than by the anodal closing current as is normally the case. A low plasma calcium level may result in metastatic calcification, involving the basal ganglia and the lens of the eye. Cataract is a complication in about 50 per cent of patients with hypoparathyroidism. Eczema and a variety of other skin conditions, including brittleness of the nails and loss of hair, may also complicate hypocalcemia. The teeth are not affected in the adult, but in the younger patient the teeth erupt late and fall out prematurely because the dentine and enamel are defective. Bone changes are variable. With reduced bone resorption in hypoparathyroidism, one would expect increased bone density, but, in fact, it may be normal, increased, or decreased.

TREATMENT OF HYPOCALCEMIA AND TETANY

Tetany is rapidly abolished by the intravenous injection of calcium gluconate, but the good effect only lasts for a short time. Calcium by mouth is little help with acute symptoms, but may be of advantage in chronic disease. Parathyroid gland extract (parathormone) relieves tetany, but only after a few hours, and has to be given parenterally. Its use is expensive and after 2 or 3 weeks patients stop responding to it, possibly because an immune reaction develops to the injected protein. Vitamin D by mouth, with supplemental oral calcium, will produce a rise in plasma calcium with control of any neuromuscular symptoms from hypocalcemia. This is not, however, the ideal treatment, since it may give marked hypercalciuria, and kidney stones may develop. The hypercalciuria may be difficult to

balance against the desired rise in plasma calcium, and vitamin D toxicity may develop. Vitamin D and oral calcium correct the neuromuscular symptoms, but it is less certain that this regime will benefit the ectopic calcifications, cataracts, mental disturbances, or epidermal manifestations. The oral calcium is best given with a low phosphate intake and this prevents milk being the ideal diet by which to gain a higher calcium absorption from the intestine. The treatment of chronic hypocalcemia remains difficult, and parathyroid transplantation has not yet been successful.

The Actions of Parathyroid Extracts

The belief in the calcium regulating function of the parathyroids, which followed naturally upon the discovery that hypocalcemia was an accompaniment of parathyroid deficiency, was confirmed in 1924, when Hanson obtained an active extract of the gland. At about the same time, Collip obtained an extract from beef parathyroids (parathormone) which also possessed a powerful hypercalcemic effect. The intravenous or subcutaneous administration of this extract to parathyroidectomized dogs will maintain the plasma calcium at the normal level. Violent tetanic symptoms are abolished within 3 or 4 hours after the injection of 10 or 20 units, and by the daily administration of considerably smaller doses than this the animal is maintained in good health indefinitely. If, after the calcium has been raised to normal, the administration of the hormone is continued in frequently repeated doses (10 to 20 units twice daily, or oftener) or if given in such dosage to a normal animal, overdosage effects are produced. These are: (1) *Early changes in blood chemistry.* The plasma calcium rises abruptly and within from 24 to 48 hours usually reaches a concentration of from 18 to 22 mg. per 100 ml. (fig. 77.2). During this time the inorganic phosphate shows a moderate fall followed by a return to normal and a small rise. There is a slight rise in the potassium and magnesium of the plasma. (2) *Early symptoms.* During the rise in plasma calcium there is loss of appetite, depression and weakness, polyuria, vomiting, diarrhea, and dehydration. (3) The *urinary excretion of calcium and phosphate* is greatly increased. The increased excretion of phosphate precedes the rise in plasma calcium and the increase in urinary calcium. There is little change in the fecal excretion of these elements. (4) *Later blood changes* are: a reduction in the hypercalcemia by 2 or 3 mg. per 100 ml.; a pronounced rise in the plasma

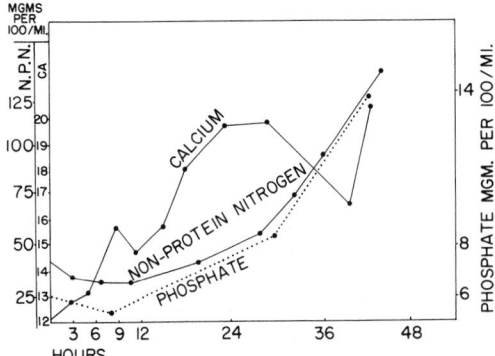

Fig. 77.2. Curves of plasma calcium, blood phosphate, and nonprotein nitrogen taken from Collip's article describing the effects of parathyroid extract. The curve representing the nonprotein nitrogen is not from the same animal as are the curves of plasma calcium and blood phosphate.

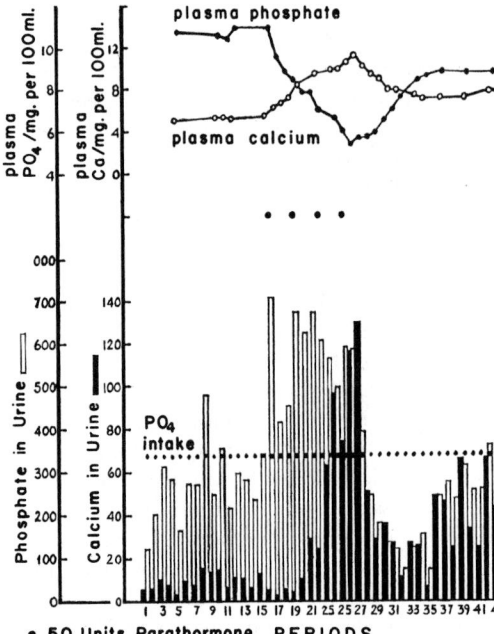

Fig. 77.3. Showing the effects of parathyroid hormone upon the plasma calcium and phosphate, and upon the urinary excretion of these minerals in a case of hypoparathyroidism. (From Albright and Ellsworth.)

inorganic phosphate; a 4-fold increase in blood nonprotein nitrogen; a reduction in blood volume by 15 per cent due to plasma loss and, in consequence, concentration of the blood and a great increase in its viscosity. (5) *Later symptoms.* At the time that these blood changes are occurring urgent symptoms appear—vomiting of bloody fluid and sometimes the passage of blood stained stools, signs of renal failure, and great

prostration ending in death. (6) *At autopsy* the gastrointestinal mucosa is found to be the seat of extensive hemorrhages, and the stomach and upper part of the intestinal canal contain a quantity of bloody fluid.

All the manifestations are intensified by a high calcium diet or the administration of calcium salts.

The preceding description applies chiefly to dogs. The plasma calcium of herbivorous animals, rats, mice, rabbits and guinea pigs, responds much less readily to the extract and the postmortem picture so characteristic of its effects in dogs and cats is not seen. In herbivorous animals, on the other hand, repeated doses cause the deposit of calcium in the soft tissues (metastatic calcification), particularly of the arterial tree; this is infrequent in dogs. In the human subject, hypercalcemia is produced about as easily as it is in dogs. In both man and dogs tolerance to the hormone not infrequently becomes established after a certain number of doses.

Therapeutic (physiological) doses administered to a normal man, or to a subject of hypoparathyroidism, cause a moderate increase in phosphate and calcium excretion, a fall in plasma phosphate, and a rise in plasma calcium, i.e., a complete reversal of the biochemical abnormalities caused by parathyroidectomy (fig. 77.3).

The excess calcium in the plasma following parathormone overdosage is mainly derived from the skeleton; there is initially an increased absorption of calcium from the gut, as well (Cramer, 1963).

Bauer, Aub, and Albright have shown that repeated doses of the extract to rabbits causes a reduction of the trabeculae of the epiphyses indicating that they serve as a store of calcium, which is rapidly mobilized by the hormone (fig. 77.4). By the administration of parathormone over long periods, a condition corresponding to osteitis fibrosa cystica of man (see below) has been produced by Bodansky and Jaffe in guinea pigs, and by others in rats and puppies. There is a marked demineralization and resorption of bone and replacement with fibrous tissue. Continued administration of the hormone to experimental animals results in gross and microscopical changes in the parathyroid glands; they become much reduced in size and their cells appear shrunken, show hydropic degeneration and a diminution in the number of mitotic figures. Such changes indicate that the administered hormone has depressed the functional activity of the glands.

In 1961, Copp and his colleagues reported some experiments which suggested that there is a second hormone produced by the parathyroid glands (see later) which lowers the blood calcium. Shortly afterwards (Copp and Cameron, 1961), it was noticed that there was hypocalcemic activity in a batch of commercial parathyroid extract (fig. 77.5). After intravenous injection of the extract into dogs there was a prompt drop in the blood calcium. The greatest fall occurred in 20 min. and then the usual rise followed that was expected on parathormone injection. Three subsequent batches showed no hypocalcemic activity, but a fifth again gave a hypocalcemic response in dogs and sheep. Extraction of fresh beef parathyroid glands for the calcium-lowering hormone, or calcitonin as it was named by Copp, was then carried out. It was found possible to obtain extracts rich either in parathormone or in calcitonin, or extracts with both parathormone and calcitonin activity (Copp *et al.*, 1962). It has already been mentioned that parathormone will increase the absorption of calcium from the small intestine, and it now appears that intravenous injection of an extract rich in calcitonin reduces the absorption of calcium from the ileum of the sheep, as well as giving a sharp fall in plasma calcium concentration (Care and Keynes, 1964). The reduction in absorption is greater than after thyro-parathyroidectomy.

Chemistry of the Parathyroid Hormones

Collip (1925) prepared the first effective extract of parathyroid tissue, but only in 1959 were the efforts to isolate parathormone successful. In that year, Aurbach (1959) reported extracting parathyroid glands with phenol and obtaining an active polypeptide, 90 per cent pure, in stable form in high yield. The crude extract was fractionated with salt, the hormone precipitated with trichloracetic acid, and the product purified by countercurrent distribution. The subsequent introduction by Rasmussen and Craig (1962) of the method of gel filtration of hormone preparations on columns of Sephadex G-50, made purification of parathormone practicable on a larger scale, with a biological activity in the range of 2500 to 3500 units per mg. dry weight.

From the reported chemical studies, it appears that parathormone is a single-chain polypeptide with a molecular weight of about 9000, and 75 residues in length (including two methionine, one tyrosine, and one tryptophan). Oxidation of the hormone by hydrogen peroxide mainly destroys its biological activity, but this may be

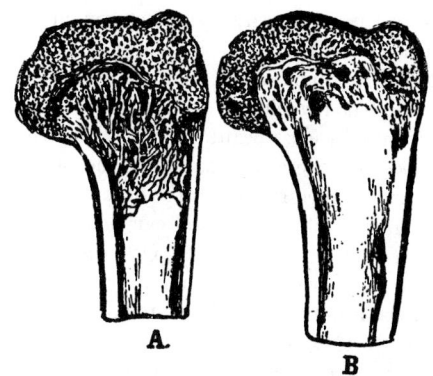

Fig. 77.4. Showing trabeculae of humeri of cat on (*A*) a high calcium diet and (*B*) on a low calcium diet. (Redrawn from Bauer, Aub, and Albright.)

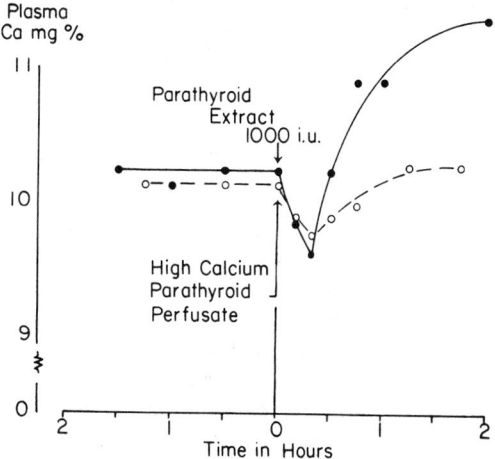

Fig. 77.5. Change in plasma calcium after intravenous injection of 1000 international units (I.U.) of commercial parathyroid gland extract (solid line), compared with that after intravenous injection of 50 ml. of plasma from perfusion of an isolated parathyroid with high calcium blood (dashed line). Experiment in a dog by Copp and Cameron (1961).

restored by reduction with cysteine in acid at elevated temperatures (Tashjian *et al.*, 1963). Work continues on the structure of parathormone and the parts of the polypeptide chain which are responsible for its biological activity. Other work is also being carried out to identify calcitonin, which appears to be a polypeptide of similar molecular weight to parathormone.

ASSAY. The classical assay for parathyroid hormone, which was developed by Collip and Clark (1925), was based on measurements of blood calcium in dogs. The method, although reliable, is cumbersome, and other biological assays have been devised. Munson (1955) observed that young rats depleted of calcium were more sensitive to parathyroidectomy and that parathormone retarded the onset of hypocalcemia, tetany, and death. Munson's assay measures the blood calcium 4 to 6 hr. after parathyroidectomy by electrocautery in rats immediately injected with the assay material. The blood calcium level is then related to the dose of parathormone given, and the method can detect as little as 3 units (1 μg.) of hormone. Other assays have used the radioactive calcium excretion of rats given the isotope many days previously, and the phosphaturic action of the hormone. At present, parathyroid extract, U.S.P., is still used most commonly as a reference standard; 100 U.S.P. units given to a 12-kg. dog causes a rise of 1 mg. per 100 ml. in the plasma calcium 18 hr. after injection.

In recent years, immunological methods have been successfully applied to tests for parathyroid hormone. Tashjian *et al.*, (1962) prepared a rabbit antiserum to parathormone which neutralized its activity and could be used to detect crude or purified hormone with a microcomplement fixation test. In 1963, Berson *et al.* developed a more sensitive immunoassay that measured human parathyroid hormone. This test used guinea pig antiserum and radioactive iodine-labeled pure parathyroid hormone as test antigen. The method has detected the hormone in the plasma of patients with hyperparathyroidism and in normal subjects, but not in the plasma of hypoparathyroid patients. This immunoassay gave similar results to those of bioassay when applied to the assay of parathyroid extracts.

Calcium, Phosphate and Magnesium Metabolism

Before proceeding to a discussion of the mode of action of parathyroid hormone, it will be advantageous at this point to review the metabolism of calcium, inorganic phosphate and magnesium.

Calcium is an indispensable mineral; it is a constituent of all animal fluids and solid tissues and is of importance in a variety of physiological processes. Among these may be listed: (1) coagulation of the blood (ch. 33), (2) formation of bone, (3) cardiac rhythmicity (ch. 35), (4) maintenance of normal neuromuscular excitability and (5) milk production.

The Distribution of Calcium in the Body

Calcium constitutes about 2 per cent of the weight of the adult body, and about 99 per cent of the total quantity is contained in the skeleton. The muscles contain about 8 mg. per 100 grams net weight, plasma or serum from 9 to 10.5 mg. per 100 ml. The red corpuscles contain only minute amounts, so that the content of whole blood is between 4.5 and 6 mg. per 100 ml. The other body fluids, e.g., lymph, aqueous humor, ascitic and edema fluids, etc., contain it in somewhat lower concentration, whereas the concentration in the cerebrospinal fluid is only about 5 mg. per 100 ml. Negligible amounts of calcium are deposited in the skeleton before the fifth month of intrauterine life, and nearly 70 per cent of the skeletal calcium of the new-born is the result of deposition during the last 2 months of prenatal life (fig. 77.6). The mother suffers a much greater loss of calcium to the suckling child. Whereas only about 20 g. of the element are lost during pregnancy, over 80 g. are secreted in the milk during a normal lactation period.

The State of the Calcium in the Blood

Practically all the calcium in the blood is contained in the plasma, and, since the ready availability of heparin as a cheap and effective anti-clotting agent, it is the plasma concentration which is used to give the total blood calcium. Before heparin, the substance which was used to stop blood clotting in laboratory work was oxalate, but, because this interferes with the chemical methods for measuring calcium, it could not be used in blood calcium estimations and the measurement was made on the serum (blood clot contains mere traces of calcium). Now, the plasma level is a more convenient estimation, and the normal range in the adult human is between 9 and 10.5 mg. per 100 ml. (4.5 to 5.2 mEq/l.). The exact calcium level will

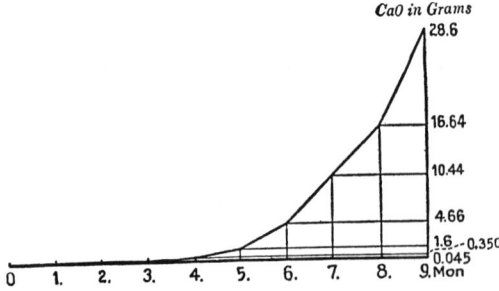

Ca0 in Grams

28.6

16.64

10.44

4.66

1.6 — 0.350
0.045

0 1. 2. 3. 4. 5. 6. 7. 8. 9.Mon

Fig. 77.6. Showing the increase in the calcium of human fetus in later months of gestation. (From Hess and Schmitz.)

vary a little, according to which method is used to measure it, and physical methods are now available as well as chemical methods.

Calcium is present in the plasma in three states, ionized, complexed and protein-bound. The protein-bound form is non-diffusible and attached to both the albumin and globulin fractions of the plasma proteins (but chiefly to the albumin) in the proportion of about 0.84 mg. per g. of protein. It remains in the plasma when the latter is dialyzed or subjected to ultrafiltration. The ionized and complexed calcium in plasma are diffusible and can be estimated by measurement of the total calcium in an ultrafiltrate and the ionised calcium in the same fluid. McLean and Hastings, in 1934, reported a biological method, described below, for the determination of calcium ions in normal human plasma. They found that the complexed calcium was less than 0.6 mg. per 100 ml. and that the range of ionized calcium was normally 4.25 to 5.25 mg. per 100 ml. Rose (1957) developed a chemical method for measuring the ionized calcium and with this, the range in normal plasma was 5.45 to 6.23 mg. per 100 ml., with a complexed fraction of less than 0.6 mg. per 100 ml. The range of the total diffusible calcium was 5.6 to 6.5 mg. per 100 ml. The non-diffusible, protein-bound calcium range was 3.0 to 4.4 mg. per 100 ml. (Fowler *et al.*, 1961).

Although the three fractions of calcium in the plasma are believed to be in equilibrium with one another, the level of the ionised calcium is regarded as most immediately related to the activity of the parathyroid glands. The ionised calcium in plasma is raised in hyperparathyroidism, and it has been found that, in this condition, but not with other causes of hypercalcemia, there is a reduced ability for the plasma proteins to bind calcium (Lloyd and Rose, 1958). Tetany has only been observed when the ionized calcium fell below a critical level of 4.3 mg. per 100 ml. (Rose, 1957). It is possible for a patient with hyperparathyroidism to have a normal total plasma calcium level, with normal plasma proteins and pH, but to have a high ionised fraction. A raised ionised calcium is probably more significant than a raised total calcium, and is the cause for the symptoms of hypercalcemia. When the total plasma calcium is definitely raised (for whatever reason), however, increase in the ionised level is to be expected. If the total plasma protein level is raised, then the total blood calcium will also be raised. The complexed calcium fraction is combined with citrate and

phosphate, and the level will be raised in renal failure as the blood urea mounts, and, as already mentioned, this calcium is diffusible but not ionised.

The nondiffusible calcium, as might be expected, varies with the protein concentration of the plasma. For example, in Bright's disease (with low plasma protein, and without phosphate retention) the decline in plasma calcium roughly parallels the fall in plasma albumin and the hypocalcemia is due mainly to a reduction in the nondiffusible fraction. Lymph, which has a lower concentration of protein than plasma, has also a lower calcium content.

The calcium of the cerebrospinal fluid, which is practically protein free, is almost entirely in the diffusible form, and has a concentration approximately equal to that of the diffusible fraction in the plasma. The calcium concentration of the cerebrospinal fluid has, therefore, been taken as an index of the diffusible fraction of the plasma calcium upon the assumption that the former fluid is simply an ultrafiltrate. This assumption is not warranted, inasmuch as it is more probable that the cerebrospinal fluid is *secreted* by the choroid plexus (ch. 11). Also, the administration of parathyroid extract or the injection of calcium salts, both of which raise the diffusible calcium of the plasma, causes little increase in the calcium concentration of the cerebrospinal fluid; it is little affected by parathyroidectomy.

McLean and Hastings (1934) devised a biological method for the determination of the ionized calcium of the body fluids based upon the sensitivity of the frog's heart to the calcium ion concentration. In this method a modified Straub cannula is passed through the aorta into the ventricle, tied into position, and then filled with the unknown fluid (serum, edema fluid, cerebrospinal fluid, etc.). The amplitude of the contraction of the heart is recorded on a moving drum, and the cannula emptied and refilled with one of a series of standard calcium chloride solutions graded in concentration by 0.1 mmole per liter. If the amplitude of contraction given by the unknown is greater than that given by the standard, then a standard of higher concentration is tried, and *vice versa*. The calcium solution giving a contraction which just matches that given with the unknown fluid is taken as having the same concentration as the unknown.

According to McLean and Hastings, the ionization of calcium in the body is determined primarily by an equilibrium between calcium and protein which may be expressed according to the law of mass action as:

$$\frac{(Ca^{++}) \times (Protein^=)}{(Ca\ Protein)} = K = 10^{-2.22}$$

(at 25° C. and pH 7.35)

In other words, the calcium in protein containing fluids is considered to be present as calcium proteinate which ionizes as a weak electrolyte into calcium and protein ions, with a residue of protein bound calcium—the nondiffusible calcium fraction. The above equation may be used for the calculation of the calcium ion concentration in human plasma or other protein containing fluids, providing that the total calcium and protein concentrations are known.

THE ABSORPTION AND EXCRETION OF CALCIUM—CALCIUM BALANCE

Calcium is found in food as both organic and inorganic compounds, but probably it is absorbed only in the inorganic form. Absorption occurs mainly from the upper part of the small intestine. The reaction of the intestinal contents is an important condition in the absorption of this mineral, its salts, for the most part, being readily soluble in acid but insoluble in alkaline media. Sugars, especially lactose, which in their fermentation yield organic acids in the intestine, favor absorption. Fats (free from vitamin D) reduce calcium absorption on a high calcium, low phosphate intake, owing most probably to the formation of insoluble calcium soaps; but for some reason, perhaps the production of soluble complexes with fatty acids, such fats increase the absorption of calcium on a diet with a low calcium-phosphate ratio. Protein food tends to increase the absorption of calcium inasmuch as the latter forms soluble complexes with certain amino acids. Soluble calcium salts, such as the chloride, carbonate, lactate, and gluconate, but not the relatively insoluble phosphate, are readily and, in moderate dosage, almost completely absorbed. After the ingestion of a large dose of a soluble calcium salt, the plasma calcium level rises, reaching its maximum value in about 2 hr. The normal plasma concentration is reached again about 3 hr later. It is not possible to maintain the calcium level above normal for any considerable time by the administration of calcium salts.

Milk is the best dietary source of calcium, but important amounts (up to 0.2 g. daily) of available calcium may be obtained from "hard" drinking water. The calcium of many vegetables is well utilized by the rat; the calcium of carrots (and probably of certain other vegetables as well) is readily absorbed by the human intestine, being nearly as valuable as that in milk. Spinach and other plant foods containing oxalic or benzoic acid, which form relatively insoluble compounds with calcium, reduce calcium absorption. In cereals (wheat, oatmeal), owing to their content of phytic acid (inositolhexaphosphoric acid) which combines with calcium and magnesium to form an insoluble salt, much of the mineral is unavailable. The action of phytic acid in the intestine depresses the absorption of calcium in other foods as well. Whole wheat flour has a higher phytic acid content than has white flour and, therefore, is a poorer source of absorbable calcium. As mentioned elsewhere (p. 1437) the phosphate of phytic acid is also largely unavailable. These facts explain the decalcifying action of certain cereals.

Calcium is secreted into the small intestine in various digestive juices, but little is eliminated through the wall of the colon. The excretion of calcium continues upon a calcium free diet or during a fast and, under these conditions, the body is in negative calcium balance. In man, on an ordinary mixed diet, the calcium of the feces amounts daily to from 0.4 to 0.8 g.; this, though a considerable amount is endogenous, is mainly the unabsorbable calcium of the food.

Smaller quantities of calcium are excreted in the urine, an average of 150 mg. being lost daily by this route, though there are rather wide variations. An increase or decrease in the absorption of calcium is reflected in parallel changes in the urinary excretion.

The *calcium balance*, that is the difference between the quantity of calcium ingested and that excreted in the urine and the feces, is *positive* (calcium retention) during *growth, pregnancy, acromegaly*, or after a period of *calcium starvation*. Sherman and Hawley found that children from 3 to 13 yr. of age, upon a daily calcium intake of from 0.74 to 1.02 g. of calcium, utilized (i.e., retained) from 0.15 to 0.62 g. per day; the quantity retained was in proportion to the size of the child (0.01 g., daily per kg.). In adults, Breiter and his colleagues found that the utilization of the calcium of milk varied from 15.3 to 30.3 per cent. A *negative calcium balance* is observed in *infantile rickets, celiac* and *renal rickets, sprue, osteomalacia, hyperparathyroidism, hyperthyroidism* (ch. 75), during *starvation* or *calcium deficiency*, and usually during *lactation*. In infantile rickets (p. 1437), celiac rickets, and osteomalacia, vitamin D administration reduces the negative balance, establishes calcium equilibrium, or induces a positive balance. The chief effect of the vitamin is to increase the absorption of calcium through the alimentary tract. It also augments the calcification of bone and cartilage. Vitamins A and C are also concerned in normal bone formation (ch. 71 and 72). The daily calcium requirement and the calcium content of various foods are given in chapter 73 (see also fig. 77.7).

Phosphate Metabolism

The adult body contains about 700 g. of phosphate, of which some 80 to 85 per cent is found in the bones and teeth. The daily requirement (1.2 g.) is 1.5 times that of calcium. The mineral may be obtained from a wide variety of foods. Because the foods containing most phosphate are also rich sources of calcium and protein, it can be assumed that a diet containing sufficient protein and calcium also contains sufficient phosphate. However, if an excess of calcium is present, the absorption of phosphate may be impeded due to the formation of insoluble calcium phosphates in the intestines.

Inorganic phosphates comprise about one-half of the total blood phosphate. In adults the normal blood level is 3.5 ± 0.5 mg. per 100 ml. In children the level is higher by 1 to 2 mg. per 100 ml. because of the activities of growth hormone. The plasma levels of phosphate and calcium are closely linked, the one varying inversely with the other. The relationship is such that the product of the total calcium in mg. per 100 ml. and inorganic phosphate in milligrams per 100 ml. is approximately constant. This *solubility product* ranges between 30 and 40 in adults and 40 and 55 in growing children. It was established by Howland and Kramer in 1922, that rickets occurs in children if the product falls below 35 and that healing takes place if it rises above 40. The plasma phosphate is also said to fluctuate directly with the blood sugar.

Magnesium Metabolism

The human body contains about 20 g. of magnesium, of which the greater part is found in muscle and bone. The normal plasma concentration ranges between 1.8 and 2.4 mg. per 100 ml., of which some is protein-bound. Mention has already been made, in the section on magnesium deficiency tetany, of the causes of hypomagnesemia. A low plasma magnesium concentration sometimes is found in patients with hyperparathyroidism, but usually without symptoms from this, and on metabolic study there is a negative

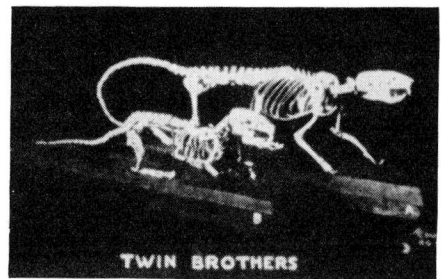

FIG. 77.7. Front and side views of skeletons of twin brothers (albino rats), one of which had received a diet of normal calcium content (wheat, meat, and milk) whereas the other had received a low calcium diet (wheat and meat). (From Sherman and MacLeod.)

balance. Besides tetany-like tremblings, hypomagnesemia may give mental confusion, and giving parenteral magnesium may be very beneficial.

The concentrations of calcium and magnesium in the diet affect the absorption and excretion of these cations. Thus, a low calcium intake will increase the absorption of magnesium, and *vice versa*, from the ileum. There is evidence that calcium and magnesium are absorbed via a common pathway (involving a common carrier system), and a low calcium or magnesium intake will decrease the urinary and fecal magnesium or calcium excretion, while high intake will have the reversed effect. Vitamin D does not seem to play much part in the absorption of magnesium.

Parathormone increases the absorption of magnesium from the intestine in the same way as it increases the absorption of calcium, and calcitonin has the reverse effect (Care and Keynes, 1964). Parathyroidectomy also lowers the absorption of magnesium and its urinary excretion. Parathyroid extract (parathormone), given parenterally to dogs, causes an increase in the urinary excretion of magnesium, and the plasma magnesium level may rise.

The Function of Parathormone

The primary concern of parathyroid hormone is the maintenance of a normal level of calcium in the blood. Following parathyroidectomy the blood calcium falls to a low level which is, however, maintained by residual homeostatic mechanisms. If the parathyroidectomized animal is subjected to bleeding and replacement with calcium free blood, then the blood calcium is restored to the low basal level. It is the function of parathormone to raise the blood calcium level to that prevailing normally.

The means by which parathyroid hormone is able to maintain a normal blood calcium level is not yet certain, although some features are becoming clear. At one time there was considerable argument over the question whether parathyroid hormone exerted its action mainly through the kidney, or by a direct effect on bone. It now appears that the hormone acts at both sites.

Because the first change observed following the administration of parathormone is a rise in the urinary excretion of phosphate, Albright and his associates adopted the view that the hormone exerted its primary action on phosphate metabolism. Ellsworth suggested that the reabsorption of phosphate from the kidney tubules was reduced, whereas in the opinion of Albright and Reifenstein, the phosphate dissolved in the tissue fluids was affected in such a way as to make it more readily excreted by the kidney. The ensuing fall in plasma phosphate and change in the calcium-phosphate solubility product produces reabsorption of bone salt to restore the equilibrium, and a rise in the level of plasma calcium to maintain the solubility product produced in the face of a low plasma phosphate. Since the hypercalcemia leads to a loss of calcium in the urine, there is a continued solution of bone salt.

Studies on nephrectomized animals have been prominent in experiments designed to test the above hypothesis. Thus, some workers (Tweedy, Neufeld, and Collip) found that parathyroid extracts were unable to raise the blood calcium level when given to dogs, cats, or rats following removal of both kidneys, ligation of the ureters, or ligation of the renal blood vessels. If the flow of urine was restored by opening the ureters, then the usual hypercalcemia followed injection of the hormone. Others (Ellsworth and Futcher, Stoerck, Monahan and Freeman, and Stewart and Bowen) have since recorded a characteristic hypercalcemia following intravenous parathyroid hormone administration to nephrectomized animals. Generally, when the kidneys are removed there is a steady rise in plasma phosphate which, through the solubility product, will tend to reduce the plasma calcium. When the parathyroids are further removed, there is a prompt fall in plasma calcium, indicating that endogenous parathyroid hormone is able to keep up the plasma calcium in the absence of the kidneys. The difficulties arising from the use of nephrectomized animals, and the reservations which must be made in the interpretation of the findings, are underlined by the work of Grollman, who found that if the blood levels of phosphate and calcium are maintained within normal limits by peritoneal dialysis, the nephrectomized dog will respond to parathyroid extract with an hypercalcemia. An extrarenal action of parathyroid hormone was thus established.

The evidence in favor of an extrarenal action of parathyroid hormone must not be taken to exclude a direct effect on the kidney, for recent work has shown that the reabsorption of phosphate is affected. Administration of parathormone depresses the tubular transfer maximum (ch. 79) of the kidney (Bartter, 1961).

The production of experimental osteitis fibrosa following parathyroid hormone administration drew attention to the possibility of a direct action of the hormone on bone. Selye found in rats that correlated with the hypercalcemia and hypercalciuria, there was an increase in the number of osteoclasts in bone (p. 1606). With continued treatment, the osteoblasts increase in number whereas the osteoclasts are reduced, a change which accords with increased calcification of bone and a return of the plasma calcium to normal. Osteoclast proliferation and resorption of bone have also been observed in nephrectomized animals following treatment with parathyroid hormone. Although nephrectomy itself elicits similar, though mild, bone changes, such changes are prevented by parathyroidectomy so that a direct action of the hormone on bone seems likely. Conclusive evidence to this effect was obtained by Barnicot, and subsequently by Chang. Barnicot transplanted pieces of parietal bone together with parathyroid tissue to the cranial cavity of mice. Intense osteoclastic activity and resorption of bone was observed; perforation of the bone sometimes occurred. Calciferol and Vitamin A, also known to affect bone metabolism, had a similar effect, but, as Chang showed, control grafts of cartilage, gastric mucosa, pancreas, bone marrow, thyroid, and other tissues had no effect. The histological changes in bone following parathyroid hormone administration occur quite rapidly; McLean and Bloom observed an extensive proliferation of osteoclasts and destruction of osteoblasts 6 hr. after the administration of a large dose of hormone to rats.

None of the effects of parathyroid hormone has been explained at the molecular level, but energy-yielding systems are presumably triggered by the hormone to regulate the transfer of calcium between the body fluids and bone, the intestine, and glomerular filtrate. Exchange of calcium isotopes with bone mineral occurs at more than one rate. A small fraction of bone calcium equilibrates rapidly with the extracellular fluids, but the major fraction (about 99 per cent, and consisting of older and densely crystallized tissue) exchanges at slower rates. Measurement of radiocalcium exchange has suggested that parathyroid hormone mainly affects older bone (Elliott and Talmage, 1958), and evidence is good that the bone supplies large amounts of calcium to the body fluids, even in parathyroidectomised animals (Copp, 1957; Sanderson *et al.* 1960; Talmage and Toft, 1961), though with intact parathyroids, bone releases calcium more rapidly toward equilibrium at a higher concentration of calcium.

In summary, it appears that secretions of the

parathyroid glands act directly on both bone and the kidney tubules (to explain the renal phosphaturic effect), and that there is accumulating evidence that the parathyroid hormones influence the intestinal absorption of calcium and magnesium (Care and Keynes, 1964).

Calcitonin and the Control of Parathyroid Gland Activity

The secretion of the parathyroid glands is not under nervous or pituitary control, and it is generally believed that the level of the ionised calcium in the blood directly regulates parathyroid hormone secretion (Talmage and Toft, 1961). In the past, reports have suggested that the plasma phosphate influenced parathyroid activity, but these studies have usually been based on alterations in the phosphate content in diets. High phosphate diets, however, inhibit, and diets low in phosphate enhance, intestinal calcium absorption. This secondary influence on calcium absorption probably explains the supposed direct effect of plasma phosphate on the parathyroids; the plasma phosphate level is greatly influenced by the amount of phosphate in the diet. Diets high in calcium and low in phosphate do not give parathyroid gland hyperplasia, but experimental hypocalcemic rickets resulting from low calcium intake does. The size of the glands appears to be inversely related to the level of the calcium in the blood, but not related to that of the phosphate (Stoerck and Carnes, 1945).

Patt and Luckhardt, in 1942, perfused the isolated thyroid-parathyroid glands of a dog with low-calcium containing blood, and then injected the perfusate into another animal previously parathyroidectomised. There was a rise, in the second animal of the blood calcium (with phosphaturia and, later, a rise in the plasma phosphate), similar to that obtained by injection of parathyroid extract. This work showed that the level of calcium in the blood is the primary determinant of parathyroid secretion, and it led to McLean (1957) proposing a negative "feed-back" mechanism for control of blood calcium. It was suggested that a fall in blood calcium would stimulate parathormone secretion, which would lead to increased calcium mobilization from bone, and thus restore the blood calcium to normal. Hypercalcemia would be controlled by suppression of parathormone production. Rasmussen (1961), however, pointed out that such a feed-back mechanism would lead to oscillations in plasma calcium, as parathormone has a relatively prolonged action, when the level in blood calcium remains, in fact, remarkably constant. Mean-

while, Sanderson *et al.* (1960) had shown that in dogs with intact parathyroids, the blood calcium returns to its initial level within a few hours after it has been artificially raised by infusion of calcium salts, or lowered by the injection of the chelating agent EDTA (ethylenediamine tetra-acetate). However, in parathyroidectomised dogs treated with similar injections, the plasma calcium did not return to the initial level, even 24 hr. after the injection. In these dogs, there were no parathyroids to release parathormone on the lowering of the blood calcium, but the difference in the response to induced hypercalcemia cannot be explained by suppression of parathyroid hormone output in the intact animals. If this were so, there should be a similar response to that shown in the parathyroidectomised dogs (in which parathyroid activity was inevitably completely suppressed). There is now accumulating evidence that there is an active hormone, released as a result of hypercalcemia, which lowers the blood calcium, and which would account for the lack of oscillation in the feed-back mechanism and for the findings of Sanderson and his colleagues.

Copp and his associates (1961) developed a technique for the perfusion of ioslated thyroparathyroids in dogs with high- or low-calcium containing blood, and then following the calcium concentrations in the systemic blood. Perfusion with EDTA caused systemic hypercalcemia, and perfusion with hypercalcemic blood gave systemic hypocalcemia (fig. 77.8), though if the parathyroids were removed there was systemic hypercalcemia (Copp *et al.*, 1962). These authors made the proposal that these results could be explained by the secretion of a quick-acting hormone, which induced hypocalcemia and was secreted in response to hypercalcemia. The hormone was called "calcitonin," and, in addition, these workers showed that injection of another animal with the perfusate from an isolated thyro-parathyroid, perfused with high-calcium blood, caused hypocalcemia in the recipient (fig. 77.5). They also obtained a hypocalcemic response on injecting an extract of parathyroid glands (fig. 77.5) (see section on the actions of parathyroid extracts).

In the dog, the inferior parathyroid glands are usually embedded in the thyroid lobes, with the superior glands sitting in the upper poles of the lobes. It is impossible to perfuse the parathyroids without, at the same time, perfusing the thyroid. This is important, since Hirsch *et al.* (1963) obtained evidence that there is a hypocalcemic-causing substance in the thyroid which is highly active in physiologic concentration and which

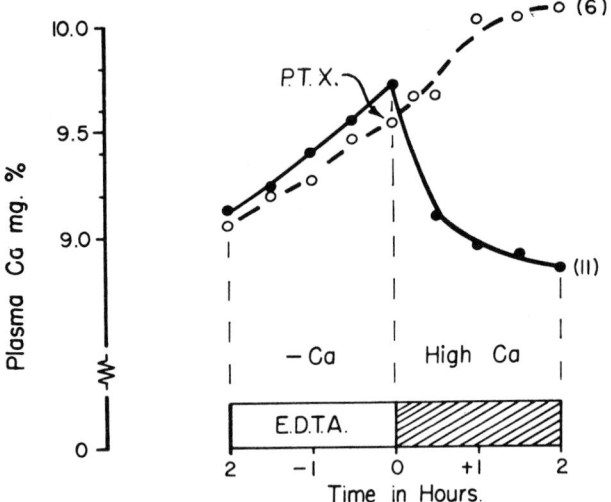

Fig. 77.8. Comparison of effect of parathyroidectomy with effect of hypercalcemic perfusion of parathyroids, in both cases after a period of parathyroid hypocalcemia. Number of dogs in each group in parentheses. Points represent average values. (Taken from Copp *et al.*, 1962.)

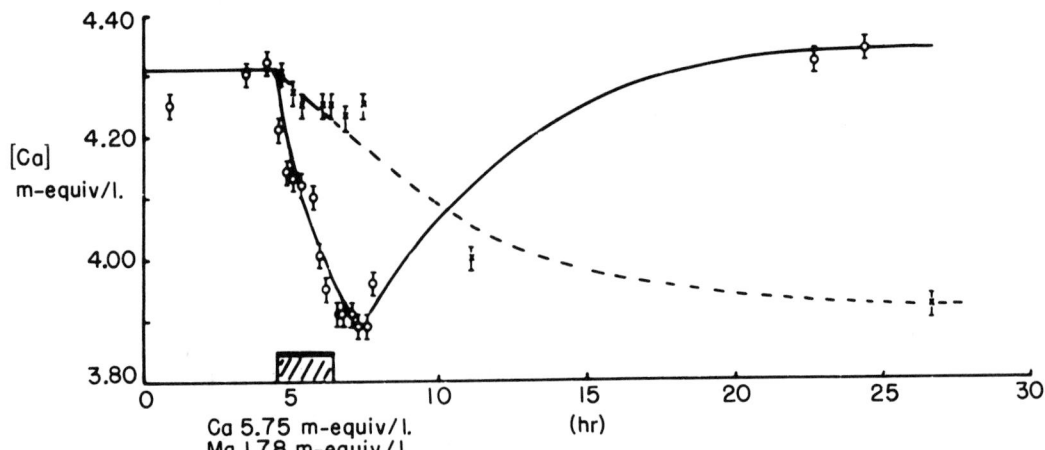

Fig. 77.9. Hypercalcemic perfusion (calcium 11.5 mg. per 100 ml.) of an isolated superior parathyroid gland in a conscious sheep. Solid line shows the effect of the perfusion on the systemic plasma calcium level, with its return to normal. The dotted line shows the plasma calcium fall on parathyroidectomy. This fall is slower than after perfusion when calcitonin is secreted by the gland. (Taken from Care and Keynes, 1965.)

can be extracted in nearly pure form (Hirsch and Munson, 1963). This substance they called "thyrocalcitonin."

It is not known whether there are two different calcium-lowering hormones, one produced by the parathyroids and one produced by the thyroid, or whether calcitonin and thyrocalcitonin are the same polypeptide. It appears that extracts of the two glands can both give hypocalcemia, and it

has been shown that perfusion of a single, isolated superior parathyroid in a conscious sheep (after removal of both thyroid lobes with the inferior parathyroids) with hypercalcemic blood, causes a systemic calcitonin-like response, while the perfusion is maintained (fig. 77.9) (in the sheep the superior parathyroid glands are separate from the thyroid lobes on each side), and that injection of the perfusate into another intact sheep gives a

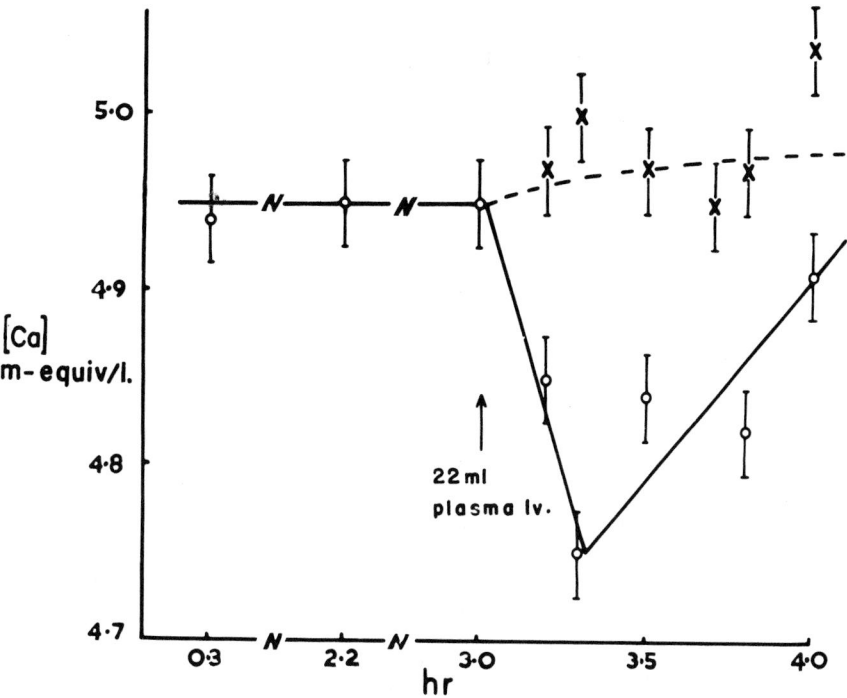

Fig. 77.10. Effect of intravenous injection into an intact sheep of 22 ml. of plasma from perfusion (same sheep as in fig. 77.9) of an isolated parathyroid gland with high calcium blood. Solid line shows fall in plasma calcium level similar to that seen in the systemic blood on hypercalcemic perfusion of an isolated gland. The dotted line shows that there is no hypocalcemic effect on crosstransfusion of a similar volume of systemic blood plasma. (Taken from Care and Keynes, 1965).

hypocalcemic response in that sheep (fig. 77.10) (Care and Keynes, 1965). The evidence that thyrocalcitonin is, in fact, a hormone is, as yet, a little less good than for calcitonin, but Care (1965) has perfused the thyroid in the pig, in which the parathyroids are separate from the thyroid, and obtained a hypocalcemic response to hypercalcemic perfusion in the same animal and also on crosstransfusion of the perfusate to another animal. There may be species differences to explain the differing results of different workers in this subject.

Hyperparathyroidism

In 4 out of 5 patients with *primary hyperparathyroidism* the disease is caused by a single adenoma of one of the parathyroid glands. In the remaining 20 per cent, more than half will have enlargements of all the glands, or hyperplasia, which is either chief-cell or clear-cell in type (Cope *et al.*, 1958). Cancer is a rare cause of hyperparathyroidism, and the remaining incidence has been due to adenomas in more than one gland. The disease is twice as common in women as it is in men, and the usual age of presentation is between the 30 and 60 yr. Enlargement of a parathyroid gland rarely gives a clinically palpable lump, but a tumour may displace or indent the esophagus or trachea on x-ray study. The first operation for removal of a parathyroid tumour was undertaken by Mandl in 1926, and in the years since then the understanding of primary hyperparathyroidism has widened considerably, though the disease still remains difficult of diagnosis as it depends on accurate biochemical estimations, which not only have to be correctly interpreted, but also have to be asked for by the clinician.

Primary hyperparathyroidism is proving more common than previously thought likely, and in recent years chance diagnoses have been made by the plasma calcium level being asked for for other reasons than because hyperparathyroidism was suspected. The biochemical diagnosis may be relatively easy with a clearly raised plasma calcium level, a lowered plasma phosphate level and hypercalciuria. Patients with borderline biochemical changes from normal may make diagnosis difficult, however, and an understanding of other possible causes for hypercalcemia, or bone changes on x-ray examination, or renal stones, may be helpful. The method of taking blood for estimation of plasma calcium and phosphate readings is important. Errors may arise from diurnal variations, from the effect of the previous diet, and from the possible effect of venous occlusion in raising the total plasma calcium level (by occlusion leading to an increase in the total plasma protein level). The blood levels should be measured in a fasting patient. Without precautions, hypercalcemia may seem to be found more readily than is actually the case.

A difficulty in the diagnosis of hyperparathyroidism is that the plasma calcium may not remain elevated all the time: a normal reading does not rule out the disease. The plasma phosphate level is not necessarily lowered, and, indeed, it may be raised if there is secondary renal impairment. A repeatedly raised plasma calcium level (above 10.5 mg. per 100 ml.) remains the most helpful single finding with which to make the diagnosis. Hypercalciuria is not necessarily present in hyperparathyroidism, even when renal stones are one of its complications. The urinary excretion of calcium depends on the degree of hypercalcemia and the state of renal function; an impaired function may lead to normal or reduced urinary calcium levels. Hypercalciuria is defined as being present when the calcium in a 24-hr. collection of urine is more than 200 mg. after the dietary intake of calcium has been less than 150 mg. for the previous 3 days. Hypercalciuria is unlikely to be present unless the urinary excretion of calcium is more than 300 mg. on a normal diet with normal activity.

In general, the presence of a complication is needed in order to suggest the diagnosis of primary hyperparathyroidism. However, it is not necessary that investigation of an initial complaint should unmask the presence of stone formation in the renal tract or typical bone disease, or, indeed, that one, or both, of these well-known complications has to be present, before the diagnosis can be made. The diagnosis depends on the finding of hypercalcemia, which can give symptoms and changes in the same way that hypocalcemia may give symptoms.

HYPERCALCEMIA

The symptoms of hypercalcemia are vague, and many of them are due to decreased muscular excitability, that is, the opposite effect of hypocalcemia. Increase in the ionised calcium raises the electrical resistance of the cell membrane and increases end-plate potential (Brink, 1954;

Shanes, 1956). Hypercalcemia may give lassitude, fatigue, backache and weakness from muscular hypotonia, difficulty in walking, and a waddling gait. Constipation, poor appetite, nausea, and vomiting may reflect smooth-muscle hypotonia, and a slow pulse rate with shortening of the Q-T interval of the electrocardiogram may be present. The nerve electrical reactions show decreased excitability. Headache, mental perturbation, depression, impaired concentration, and insomnia may be noted with hypercalcemia, and the mental disturbance may be sufficient to be called a psychosis. There may be accompanying changes on electroencephalography. Band keratopathy, which is a gray, granular, superficial opacity limited to either side of the paralimbal region of the cornea, may be visible to the naked eye. Hypercalcemia may lead to thirst and polyuria. The polyuria appears to be due to a direct effect on the renal tubular absorption, with increased excretion of calcium in the urine often being accompanied by increased losses of sodium, potassium, chloride and bicarbonate, as well as of water (Epstein *et al.*, 1959; Nordin, 1960). Hypokalemia may result from the potassium looses, and the urine tends to be alkaline with a low specific gravity

The changes outlined due to hypercalcemia have all led to the diagnosis of primary hyperparathyroidism. Hypercalcemia may, however, be due to other causes than hyperparathyrodism, and these other causes often have to be excluded before parathyroid disease becomes a biochemical, and thus a potential surgical, certainty. Hypercalcemia may be due to: faulty technique in collecting blood, osteolytic bone tumours and myeloma, certain malignant tumors of the bronchus which appear to secrete a substance identical to parathormone, vitamin D overdose, sensitivity to vitamin D (as in sarcoidosis), bed rest in patients with bone diseases such as Paget's disease, and, in patients with peptic ulcers, to medication with large doses of milk and bicarbonate of sodium. Fortunately, Dent (1956) discovered that hypercalcemia due to causes other than hyperparathyroidism can usually be suppressed by giving cortisone, 150 mg. daily, and this test may be very helpful to the clinician.

Parathyroid crisis, with a plasma calcium level greater than 17 mg. per 100 ml., may occur suddenly in patients with primary hyperparathyroidism, particularly possible after a high intake of calcium; these patients are usually very ill with cellular dehydration. A similar hypercalcemia is sometimes seen in patients with disseminated

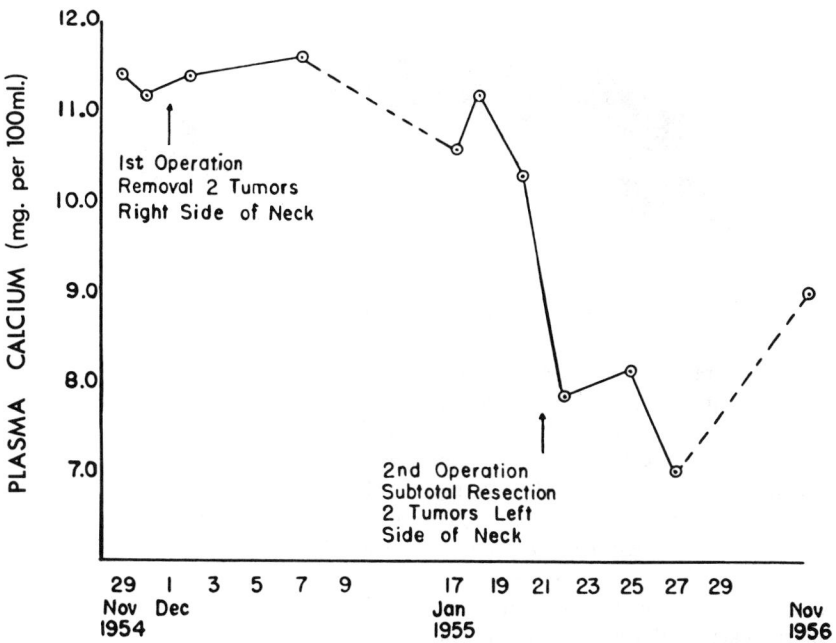

Fig. 77.11. Plasma calcium levels in a patient before and after two operations for cure of primary hyperparathyroidism due to primary chief-cell hyperplasia of the parathyroid glands. The first operation was inadequate, but the plasma calcium level promptly fell after the second. The plasma phosphate levels varied between 2.2 and 2.8 mg. per 100 ml. during the period of the graph. (Taken from Cope *et al.*, 1958.)

carcinoma of the breast. There is vomiting, tachycardia, high fever, and coma, with rising plasma phosphate and blood urea levels, and with oliguria. Emergency parathyroidectomy has been successful; usually efforts have to be made to resuscitate the patient first, and hydration is important in this. Often a chelating agent, such as EDTA, has been given in an effort to control the hypercalcemia, and limitation of the calcium intake is obvious. In patients with primary hyperparathyroidism, removal of sufficient over-active parathyroid tissue results in a fall in the plasma calcium level (fig. 77.11) to normal levels, and perhaps, as already mentioned in the section on tetany, to blood levels below normal.

Complications of Primary Hyperparathyroidism

The commonest complication of hyperparathyroidism is renal lithiasis, and about 70 per cent of patients have this. It may be the cause of the diagnosis, or be recognised on investigation of hypercalcemia. Impaired renal function in tests of maximum tubular absorption (Bartter, 1961) can be detected in most patients, and even when there is a raised blood urea present, these changes may be corrected by parathyroidectomy, though often the damage to the kidneys is permanent. Any calcium-containing stone in the urinary

tract may result from hyperparathyroidism, and nephrocalcinosis (though not common), strengthens the possibility of this diagnosis, where there are calcifications in the parenchyma of the kidney. Hypertension may be a consequence of renal damage in hyperparathyroidism.

The original complication to give the diagnosis of primary hyperparathyroidism was the bone disease named after von Recklinghausen. Bone changes are no longer so common and in recent reports only occurred in about a quarter of patients. The changes do not appear more often when the hyperparathyroidism has existed for longer periods, and the previous diet does not seem to be a factor in the incidence. It is not possible to say, if bone change is present, that the hyperparathyroidism is more severe. The bone change, when present, is associated with an elevated plasma alkaline phosphatase level, and consists of a *generalised* osteoporosis (with loss of matrix as well as mineral). To the osteoporosis may be added bone cysts and so-called "brown tumors" (which consist of groups of osteoclasts and hemorrhagic fibrous tissue), and these may be single or numerous (fig. 77.12). Fractures may occur as a result of the weakening of the bone by a cyst or brown tumor, and the patient may become deformed and shortened. Pain may be severe. On histological examination of the bone,

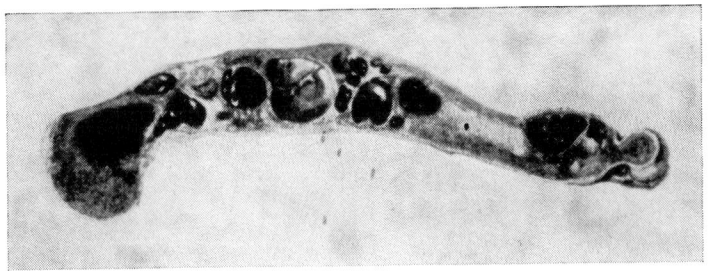

Fig. 77.12. Showing section of humerus from a case of generalized osteitis fibrosa. Bone cysts are obious. (From Hunter and Turnbull after Hill and Lucey.)

the surfaces of the trabeculae are irregular and osteoclasts are present in large numbers. There is extreme fibrosis between the trabeculae and this has given the name "osteitis fibrosa." Bone pain disappears within hours of a successful operation and the bone increases in density in time. The cysts are not replaced, although their surrounding cortex is thickened, but the brown tumors become solid bone. Low plasma calcium levels with tetany are particularly likely following operation, and the hypocalcemia may persist for some months and be difficult to alleviate as long as the bone is reforming.

There are two gastrointestinal complications of primary hyperparathyroidism, peptic ulcer and pancreatitis. About 10 to 15 per cent of patients with hyperparathyroidism have peptic ulcers; this is a greater incidence than expected for the general population (Ostrow *et al.*, 1960). The ulcers may be atypical, but are usually duodenal. Tests of gastric function before and after operation for hyperparathyroidism have not shown any change, and experimental studies on the influence of parathyroid hormone on gastric secretion have not been very conclusive. Indigestion has a greater incidence in patients with hyperparathyroidism than proved to be the case in peptic ulceration, and parathyroidectomy may improve this, and may also be followed by the healing of a proportion of the ulcers. Some of the indigestion may be due to pancreatitis, which occurs in about 10 per cent of patients with hyperparathyroidism (Mixter *et al.*, 1962). The pancreatitis may follow operation for hyperparathyroidism, but more frequently the symptoms subside after the operation. The pancreatitis may be acute, recurrent or relapsing, and pancreatic calcifications are not necessarily present. Studies on pancreatic secretion have so far not explained the relationship between pancreatitis and hyperparathyroidism.

Primary hyperparathyroidism has a relationship to disease in other endocrine glands, and has

now been reported in patients with Cushing's syndrome, hyperthyroidism, acromegaly, and in patients with islet-cell tumors of the pancreas which secrete a gastrin-like substance—the so-called Zollinger-Ellison syndrome. It is also part of a pluriglandular syndrome, which may be familial, involving the pituitary and pancreas as well as the parathyroids.

The three general categories of nonparathyroid disease which may simulate hyperparathyroidism are: various hypercalcemic states (already mentioned), nephrolithiasis, and various bone disorders. Careful history and physical examination, with details of the x-ray appearances and measurement of blood calcium, phosphate and alkaline phosphatase levels will usually distinguish the type of bone disease, but polyostotic fibrous dysplasia, Paget's disease of bone, and osteogenesis imperfecta can cause difficulty. Osteoporosis, osteomalacia, myeloma, sarcoidosis, and metastatic bone malignancy may also cause diagnostic problems. Idiopathic hypercalciuria and renal tubular acidosis are both diseases in which renal stones may occur and which can be difficult to separate from hyperparathyroidism. Aside from tests for phosphaturia, the cortisone suppression test, and quantitation of the hypercalciuria, a determination of the rate of calcium turnover in bone (using stable strontium (Fraser *et al.*, 1959) or radioactice calcium), may be helpful in the diagnosis of hyperparathyroidism. Unfortunately, there are probably some patients who never are shown to have hypercalcemia, and the diagnosis will remain difficult in such cases until a reliable assay of parathormone becomes available.

SECONDARY HYPERPARATHYROIDISM

Secondary hyperplasia, or enlargement of the parathyroid glands, secondary to a stimulus, such as a low intake of calcium in experimental animals, has often been confused in the past with secondary hyperparathyroidism. Such hyperparathyroidism should imply that there is an increased secretion of parathyroid hormone compared with normal, and probably the diagnosis of definite secondary hyperparathyroidism will only be possible when an accurate assay of the hormone is readily available. Enlargement of the glands does not necessarily mean a hypersecretion of the glands.

Patients with chronic azotemic renal disease, apparently euparathyroid until late in the course of the disease, may develop the symptoms and the x-ray changes of osteitis fibrosa. With these changes there is usually hyperphosphatemia with a raised blood pH. The plasma calcium is low or normal, and at autopsy the parathyroids are hyperplastic. The hyperplasia is chief-cell in type and in most of the reported examples there is no reason to believe that the cause of the renal failure is not primary glomerulonephritis. Enlargement of the parathyroids with osteitis fibrosa do not necessarily imply, however, hypersecretion of parathormone, and the assumption that there is a causal relationship between hyperphosphatemia, parathyroid hyperplasia, and bone disease has not yet been proved.

The Relation of Vitamin D to Parathyroid Function

The actions of parathyroid hormone and of vitamin D share many points in common. This is probably due to the fact that both agents act to maintain a normal blood calcium level. In the absence of vitamin D the parathyroid glands become hyperative. Higgins and Sheard found that the parathyroids of chicks deprived of ultraviolet light became hyperplastic, but were restored to normal appearance by the administration of cod liver oil. Also, the effects of overdosage of vitamin D are reduced by elimination of parathyroid function. Hess, Weinstock, and Rivkin found, in monkeys, that hypercalcemia is less readily induced by irradiated ergosterol after parathyroidectomy. In dogs, Taylor, Weld, Branion, and Kay found that the toxic overdosage effects of irradiated ergosterol were less severe than usual in parathyroidectomized dogs. They also showed that the overdosage effects of parathyroid hormone and irradiated ergosterol were similar in that both substances cause the same degree of hypercalcemia (fig. 77.13) and hyperphosphatemia, and a rise in the nonprotein nitrogen of the blood. The symptoms during life and the postmortem findings after poisoning with either material are identical and those species (herbivora) resistant to parathormone are similarly resistant to overdosage with vitamin D. It has also been shown that either parathyroid hor-

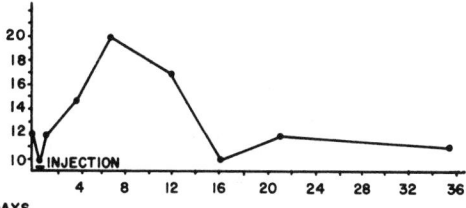

Fig. 77.13. Plasma calcium curve of a dog illustrating the effect of a large dose of irradiated ergosterol given intravenously in divided doses over a period of 4 hr. Note the prolonged effect upon the plasma calcium. (From Taylor, Weld, Branion, and Kay.)

mone or irradiated ergosterol gives rise to metastatic calcification and to bony changes analogous to osteitis fibrosa cystica. The effect of the vitamin upon the plasma calcium is slower to appear than that of the hormone. The hypercalcemia of the vitamin, once established, persists for weeks (fig. 77.13).

Clinically, a product of irradiated ergosterol, dihydrotachysterol (AT 10), has been used as a substitute for parathyroid hormone, since its effect does not diminish on repeated administration. Dihydrotachysterol, however, has now been shown to have no advantage over calciferol (vitamin D) which is cheaper and given in doses from 25,000 to 200,000 I.U., as well as oral calcium, like parathormone, from the intestine. If the absorption increases, then there is increased excretion of calcium in the urine; hypercalciuria may follow dosage with vitamin D and where there is undue sensitivity to normal amounts of vitamin D, as in the condition known as sarcoidosis.

Bone

The Composition of Bone

Osseous tissue freed from fatty marrow is composed of organic material (mainly protein), water, and minerals. The chief protein constituent is *ossein*, but there are also small quantities of *osseomucoid* and an *albuminoid*. Water constitutes about 25 per cent of the bone weight, 30 per cent organic material, and 45 per cent inorganic constituents. The minerals consist of calcium, phosphate, and magnesium, and small quantities of potassium, sodium, chlorine, fluorine, and iron. Citrate is present in bone; indeed, 70 per cent of the body's entire store of citrate is contained in the skeleton. The existence of a diffusible completed plasma calcium with citrate has been mentioned in the section on ionized calcium.

Calcium makes up from 15 to 18 per cent of the weight of fresh osseous tissue and from 20

TABLE 77.2

Calcium of bone (dog)

	Whole Bone		Bone Ash	Calcium-Phosphate Ratio
	Fresh	Dry, ether extracted		
Total calcium (per cent)	18	25	36	2.2:1
Residual calcium (per cent)	—	—	31	2:1

to 25 per cent of the weight of bone which has been dried and extracted with ether.

Bone calcium exists in two forms, calcium carbonate ($CaCo_3$) and tricalcium phosphate $Ca_3(PO_4)_2$.[1] The ash of bone amounts to about 6 per cent of its dry weight. Calcium constitutes about 36 per cent of the ash, phosphate about 16 per cent, magnesium 0.5 per cent, and CO_2 5.5 per cent. The ratio of calcium to phosphate is approximately 2.2:1. The ratio of residual calcium (i.e., calcium other than that present as carbonate) to residual phosphate (phosphate not combined with magnesium) is about 2:1. This is, approximately, the ratio of the two minerals in tricalcium phosphate. Magnesium is present mainly as $Mg_3(PO_4)_2$. The proportions of the three chief compounds in bone ash are $Ca_3(PO_4)_2$ 80 per cent, $CaCO_3$ 13 per cent, and $Mg_3(PO_4)_2$ 2 per cent. Some of the foregoing data are given in table 77.2.

Rickety bone contains a lower percentage of ash and larger proportions of water and organic material. The ratio of calcium to phosphate, however, remains unchanged whether the rickets (experimental) develops upon a low calcium or a low phosphate diet. The magnesium content of bone is said to be increased in rickets and in osteomalacia.

It is now generally believed that the calcium carbonate and calcium phosphate of bone are present not as separate compounds simply mixed together with smaller amounts of other mineral salts, but as a complex chemical structure.

From a comparison of the refractive indices and X-ray diffraction patterns of bone and dental enamel on the one hand, and certain crystalline minerals composed mainly of calcium and phosphate, Taylor and Sheard concluded that the inorganic solid phase of bone and of dental enamel resembled the apatite series (podolite, fluorapa-

---

[1] Small amounts of calcium chloride and calcium fluoride are also present.

tite, etc.). Fluorapatite, which many considered to be nearest in chemical structure to the bone salt, has the formula $Ca_{10}(PO_4)_6F_2$. In bone, *hydroxyapatite*, $Ca_{10}(PO_4)_6(OH)_2$ in which OH replaces F, or a closely similar compound, is very generally, though not unanimously, accepted as the predominant compound in bone. The bone salt is laid down in the form of minute crystals. Compounds in which sodium, magnesium, and other minerals are substituted for calcium are also found in bone.

Pathological calcifications, e.g., salivary calculi, arterial or pulmonary calcifications, are believed to be similar in chemical composition to bone. Hastings and his associates hold a similar view in respect to a crystalline compound related to the apatite series as being the main mineral constituent of bone.

It should be emphasized that adult bone is not simply an inert structural material, but living tissue whose mineral composition fluctuates under the influence of other body functions. The trabeculae of the bone, as shown by Aub and associates, constitute a calcium store readily available when necessary for the maintenance of the calcium requirements of other tissues when the exogenous supplies are deficient. For this reason, though calcium continues to be excreted when an animal is kept, even for a long period, upon a calcium free diet, no change in the plasma calcium level occurs. Parathyroid extract, as mentioned elsewhere, raised the plasma calcium through its action in mobilizing these calcium stores.

In birds, the extraordinary demand made upon calcium metabolism for the production of the egg shell has been provided for by the development of osseous tissue within the marrow spaces of the long bones. Weakening of the essential skeletal structure which otherwise might result from the withdrawal of the mineral during the egg laying season, is thus avoided. The growth of this so-called *medullary bone* is stimulated by estrogens. Normally, its growth appears to be under the control of the ovarian secretion; it is cyclical or seasonal in character, and is associated with other phenomena of the mating season of birds, e.g., the appearance of serum vitellin in the circulation, an increase in plasma fat and phospholipid, and pronounced hypercalcemia.

The bones also serve a detoxicating function, elements such as lead, radium, fluorine, and arsenic, being removed from circulation and deposited in the bones and teeth. "Mottled enamel" (chalky white patches upon the surfaces of the teeth) is attributed to an excess of fluorine in the food or drinking water, though smaller amounts of fluorine are said to be beneficial for the development of the teeth and to prevent dental caries. The mobilization of bone calcium plays a very minor role in maintaining the normal blood reaction against the ingestion or production of excess acid. Some reduction in bone calcium can be detected, however, in animals after the administration of hydrochloric acid.

BONE FORMATION

The Histology of Developing Bone

There are two types of ossification, *intramembranous* and *intracartilaginous* or *endochondral*. The bones of the cranial vault, the maxilla, and the mandible are formed through the ossification of membranes. The bones of the limbs and trunk, and the base of the skull are first modeled in cartilage which becomes transformed into bone by both endochondral and intramembranous (i.e., periosteal) forms of ossification. Studies with radioactive isotopes have shown that calcium and phosphate are first laid down in the epiphysis of the developing bone, and are later transferred to the shaft (diaphysis) where a *primary center* of ossification appears, and, enlarging, spreads toward both ends of the bone. Secondary centers appear subsequently in the epiphysis. The deposition of calcium is hastened by vitamin D. The cartilage cells just ahead of the spreading zone of calcification show active proliferation, and become arranged in longitudinal rows (fig. 77.14). The transformation of the calcified cartilage into true bone is brought about in the following fashion. The cells of the deeper layers of the membrane covering the cartilage (perichondrium) give off long processes to form a meshwork of interlacing fibers. These cells are referred to as *osteoblasts*. The fibrous framework thus laid down soon becomes impregnated with calcium salts with the formation of a layer of true bone just beneath the perichondrium, or periosteum as it must now be called. The subperiosteal process, which is essentially the same as that whereby the cranial bones are developed from membrane, is well advanced, whereas the interior of the bone still consists merely of calcified cartilage. The latter, however, soon becomes invaded by blood vessels from the periosteum and by large multinucleated cells (20 to 40 μ) known as *osteoclasts*. These cells, which have a pronounced eroding action upon the mineralized cartilage, probably through the production of an enzyme, tunnel channels through it for the conveyance of the blood vessels and excavate small cavities. The excavations in which the osteoclasts lie are known as *Howship's lacunae*. Osteoblasts which have advanced into the interior of the blood vessels cause the formation of true osseous tissue in the walls of the spaces formed by the osteoclasts.

At a somewhat later date than that at which the primary ossification center appears in the shaft, a

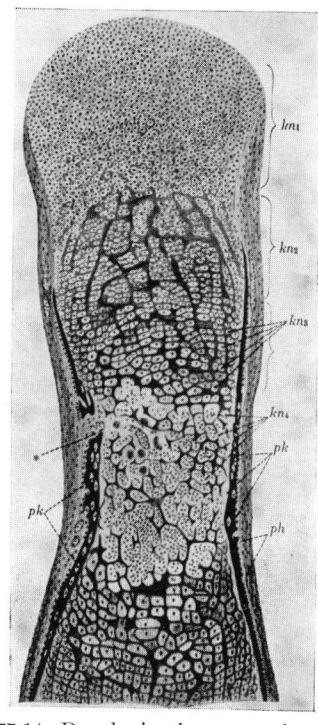

FIG. 77.14. Developing bone; proximal phalanx of a 3 month human fetus. kn_1, Unchanged cartilage; kn_2, columns of cartilage cells; kn_3, zone of calcifying cartilage; kn_4, vestiges of walls of broken down cartilage cavities; pk, perichondral (periosteal) bone (black); ph, perichondrium (periosteum); and *, connection between periosteum and primary marrow. As yet, no endochondral bone formation. (From Maximow and Bloom after Sobotta.)

secondary or epiphyseal center appears in one or both ends of the bone. The calcification process and subsequent ossification follow the same course as that described for the diaphysis. The epiphyseal and diaphyseal areas, however, remain separated from one another by a layer of uncalcified cartilage, the *epiphyseal plate*, until a certain age, which varies between different bones.

Through the combined action of osteoclasts and osteoblasts, a complete replacement of the calcified cartilage results, and the structure characteristic of bone gradually evolves. The center of the shaft becomes hollowed out to form the medullary canal. The spaces which have been formed by the osteoclasts in the shaft of the bone itself become joined together and constructed into the system of *Haversian canals* which serve as conduits for the transmission of blood vessels. In the ends of the bones the spaces are much larger and irregular; and becoming filled with red marrow constitute the characteristic spongy or cancellous bone of this region. The walls of these spaces appear in cross section as interlacing bars of osseous tissue and are usually referred to as trabeculae. The bone forming the walls of the Haversian canals is laid down in a series of concentric tubular lamellae. As each lamella is completed, it imprisons the osteoblasts within small lacunae from which numerous fine canals are given off; into these the processes of the osteoblasts penetrate. The osteoblasts in these situations lose their osteogenetic function but do not disappear. In the developed bone they are referred to simply as *osseous cells* or *osteocytes*.

A long bone grows in length at the junction of the epiphysis with the diaphysis, and in thickness through the activity of the osteoblasts of the deeper layers of the periosteum. The Haversian canals and the marrow cavity are also lined with a membrane (the *endosteum*) containing osteoblasts through which increased width of the bone is also brought about.

The osteoblasts and osteoclasts are concerned not only with the development and growth of bone, but are active throughout life and are responsible, it is believed, to a large extent at any rate, for the lability of adult osseous tissue (p. 1604). Healthy bone is constantly being broken down, resorbed, and repaired. Several conditions may alter the balance one way or the other between these two processes, e.g., the relation of the calcium intake to the calcium requirement and the activities of various ductless glands—parathyroid, thyroid, pituitary etc. Large numbers of osteoclasts are in evidence when bone resorption is taking place. Osteoclastic activity is, therefore, pronounced when remodeling of bone is occurring, as in the removal of excess callus or in the restoration to normal dimensions of the enlarged end of a bone in healing rickets, in certain bone diseases, and in wasting diseases. In old age also, the resorptive process outstrips the processes of repair; the bones become rarefied (*senile osteoporosis*) and more fragile. Ham and some other authorities deny that the osteoclasts are active agents in the removal of the bone tissue, claiming that the appearance of these cells is merely incidental or sequential to the resorption process.

When bone formation is in the ascendancy, as during the repair of a fracture, the osteoblasts show active proliferation.

Newly formed bone is stained selectively *in vivo* by madder, a red dye, or by alizarin, a derivative of it. These are, therefore, valuable agents for the investigation of the growth of bone in the living animal or of the action of parathyroid hormone and other influences upon bone metabolism. The dye, which is given orally, is deposited with the mineral constituents, calcium and phosphate.

A CONSIDERATION OF THE FACTORS UNDERLYING THE CALCIFICATION PROCESS. Several theories have been advanced in attempts to picture the process underlying the deposition of calcium salts in the cartilaginous matrix.

1. A protein constituent of cartilage, it has been supposed, adsorbs calcium, for which it exhibits a special affinity; the calcium subsequently combines with phosphate to form tricalcium phosphate. Wells showed, for example, that bone salts were deposited in a piece of boiled cartilage placed in the abdominal cavity.

2. The saturation of a solution with a salt such as calcium phosphate and the precipitation of the latter in solid form is determined by the product of the concentrations of the Ca^{++} and $PO_4^{=}$ ions in the solution, i.e., upon the *ion product* $(Ca^{++}) \times (PO_4^{=})$, and not upon the total quantities of calcium and phosphate present. The ion product at which the solution is just saturated is called the *solubility product*. The presence of protein in the solution reduces the degree of ionization, part of the calcium, as we have seen, becoming bound to form calcium proteinate, a weak electrolyte. The body fluids, are, therefore, capable of dissolving more calcium phosphate than is a protein free solution similar in its salt composition to that of plasma. The CO_2 dissolved in the body fluids also increases their ability to hold calcium salts in solution. Any reduction in the protein concentration or in the CO_2 tension in the body fluids would, therefore, be expected to favor the deposition of calcium salts.

An explanation of the calcification process upon a basis afforded by the foregoing considerations has been advanced by Howland. It is assumed that the fluids bathing the cartilage cells have, in common with other extravascular fluids, a lower protein concentration than has plama. It is further suggested that since the cartilaginous matrix has a low metabolism, the CO_2 tension of the fluids bathing its cells is lower than that of plasma; the pH of these fluids will, therefore, tend to be higher. Such conditions, it is argued, must favor the deposition of calcium salts. A low concentration of inorganic phosphate and of calcium in the plasma will, on the other hand, tend to retard calcification; this would be completely arrested it the ion product were below the value at which precipitation occurs. In practice, Howland and his associates have employed the product of the *total* calcium and inorganic phosphate, each expressed in milligrams per 100 ml., as an index of the calcification process in infantile rickets. They state that in children with active rickets the product is practically always below 40, and when the disease is severe, below 30, whereas in normal children it is between 50 and 60. It is obvious that a fall in either inorganic phosphate or calcium would tend to lower the $Ca \times PO_4$ product; actually two varieties of rickets were distinguished—a low phosphate and a low calcium type. It is now recognized, however, that these are simply different stages of the disease and that the level of the inorganic phosphate alone is a more useful criterion by which to judge the extent of the calcification defect than the Ca × PO$_4$ product. For example, when rickets is progressing, the inorganic phosphate of the plasma is lowered to between 3 and 4 mg. or less per 100 ml., but the plasma calcium is not far from the normal level. During the stage of healing, i.e., of active calcification, the inorganic phosphate of the blood tends to rise and the plasma calcium to fall; there might, therefore, be little change in the Ca × PO$_4$ product.

Another factor considered to be of importance in the calcification process is the *supersaturation* of the body fluids with calcium salts. That is, quite apart from the greater solubility of calcium salts in fluids containing protein and CO$_2$, the concentrations of calcium phosphate and calcium carbonate in the body fluids are constantly maintained above their saturation limits, owing to the extreme slowness with which final equilibrium between the solid and liquid phases is established. Precipitation of these salts from solution will continue so long as the ion product is above that of the saturation level.

Calcification, however, cannot be explained upon a physicochemical basis alone; the activity of living cells is also involved in the process. Shipley, Howland, and Kramer showed, for example, that in experiments *in vitro*, calcification was inhibited by a protoplasmic poison such as HCN. Two views have been expressed as to the nature of the vital processes concerned.

3. Watt, from a comparison of the shapes of calcium phosphate particles precipitated in certain inert colloids with those formed in bone, concluded that calcification was not a simple precipitation of calcium phosphate from solution but was due to the active *secretion* by the osteoblasts of bone salts derived from the calcium and phosphate of the blood.

4. According to Robison and his colleagues, calcification is primarily dependent upon enzyme action through which the fluids in immediate relation to cartilage cells become highly supersaturated with calcium phosphate. These observers have accumulated much evidence in favor of their view. They have demonstrated the presence in bone (and also in plasma and other tissues, see below) of an enzyme capable of hydrolyzing various phosphoric esters, e.g., hexosemonophosphate, glycerophosphate, etc. This enzyme is called *phosphatase*. It is believed to be a product of the osteoblasts, the proliferating cartilage cells and the cells of the inner layer of the periosteum. According to this conception of the calcification process, the enzyme liberates inorganic phosphate from phosphoric esters and raises, locally, the concentration of the PO$_4^{\equiv}$ ion. The product of the concentrations of Ca^{++} and PO$_4^{\equiv}$ ions then exceeds the solubility product of calcium phosphate, which is in consequence deposited in the cartilagenous matrix.

Evidence bearing upon this hypothesis is as follows:

1. It was shown by Robison that when the head of a bone from a rachitic rat was immersed in a solution of calcium hexosemonophosphate at body temperature, a deposit of calcium phosphate occurred in the zone of preparatory calcification. This was attributed to the liberation by phosphatase of inorganic phosphate from a phosphoric ester, thus raising the product of the concentrations of PO$_4^{\equiv}$ and Ca^{++} ions.

2. Shipley, Kramer, and Howland found that calcification of a rachitic bone occurred if placed in normal serum. Calcification also resulted if the bone were placed in a sterile solution of inorganic salts containing sodium chloride, sodium bicarbonate, and magnesium sulfate, together with calcium and inorganic phosphate in the same concentrations as in normal serum. They concluded that living processes were concerned, since calcification was inhibited by HCN. They believed, however, that phosphatase could have played no part in the process for the artificial solution did not, of course, contain a phosphoric ester.

3. Robison claimed that the result of the experiment just described was dependent upon the fact that in the solution used, the concentration of the calcium phosphate compound was near the point at which spontaneous precipitation might be expected to occur. In normal plasma, as already mentioned, calcium and phosphate remain in solution at these concentrations because it contains protein which depresses the ionization of calcium; the ion product upon which precipitation depends is, therefore, considerably lower. Robison and Soames showed that calcium phosphate precipitates after a few days from a solution such as that employed by Shipley and associates if simply allowed to stand. It was found indeed by the latter workers that the addition of protein to the extent of 1 or 2 per cent inhibited the calcification of the immersed bone. Robison and Soames showed later that though calcification of rachitic bone will occur when immersed in a solution containing calcium and phosphate if the concentrations are sufficiently high, i.e., Ca × PO$_4$ product over 40, calcification will not occur if the product is lower than this unless a phosphoric ester is added. Quite small amounts of the ester (glycerophosphate) were sufficient to cause calcification.

4. Phosphatase is present in bone in largest amounts when and where active calcification is taking place (see below), which strongly suggests that it plays an essential role in the calcification process.

5. Certain facts have been cited as opposed to the phosphatase hypothesis: (a) in rickets the phosphatase activity of bone and plasma is increased rather than the reverse, and in the blood of rachitic rats the percentage of phosphoric esters hydrolyzable by phosphatase is not below

normal; (b) normal plasma contains only very small quantities of phosphoric esters, which seem inadequate to supply the inorganic phosphate necessary for the calcification process; and (c) certain tissues which do not calcify normally are rich in phosphatase whereas other tissues, such as the arteries, which are frequently the site of pathological calcification, do not contain the enzyme.

Robison did not contend, however, that the phosphatase mechanism is the only one concerned in the calcification process for, as mentioned above, calcification will occur in the absence of a phosphoric ester provided the concentrations of calcium and inorganic phosphate are sufficiently high. He and his colleagues found that when bone slices were treated with KCN or with certain fat solvents (alcohol, chloroform, or acetone) before placing them in the supersaturated solution, calcification did not occur in the absence of glycerophosphate. These substances, however, exerted little or no inhibitory effect if glycerophosphate were present, i.e., the phosphatase mechanism was not paralyzed and calcification proceeded. Formalin, on the contrary, prevented calcification whether a phosphoric ester was present or not. These results, in Robison's view, point to two distinct mechanisms governing the calcification process. (1) The phosphatase mechanism, poisoned by formalin, which produces in the fluids bathing the cartilage cells a state of supersaturation in respect to bone salt. (2) A mechanism poisoned by several agents, especially cyanide, which is responsible for the deposition of bone salts from a supersaturated solution, whether this is the result of phosphatase action or is brought to the cartilage matrix from another source. The nature of the second mechanism is unknown. It may be due, Robison suggests, to a "slight increase in the pH of the matrix fluid brought about by some membrane equilibrium." Since this mechanism is inhibited or paralyzed by cyanide, it is evidently dependent also upon the activity of living cells.

At the present time a satisfactory description of the processes underlying the calcification of bone cannot be provided. Among the factors contributing to the prevailing uncertainty two are prominent:

1. There is no agreement concerning the precise structure of bone salt or of the identity of the mineral deposited during calcification. Although it is accepted that the material is of the general nature of an apatite, a complex of tricalcium phosphate and calcium hydroxide, there is also the presence of carbonate and its variable composition in different areas to be accounted for. Perhaps the bone salt may be precipitated in one form and then remodeled to another.

2. The function of alkaline phosphatase remains obscure. Although there is little doubt that the enzyme is concerned in some way with calcification, the view that the phosphatase may be concerned with the production and maturation of the bone matrix prior to calcification, rather than with the deposition of bone salt, is now thought possible. In this connection, it is of interest that ossifying areas of cartilage display a particular affinity for calcium and phosphate, even after boiling (Waldman).

Additional suggestions are that the enzyme might be concerned with the formation of a phosphate ester acting as a template for the catalytic crystallization of bone salt, or that it keeps the surface of bone crystals free of ester phosphate, thus permitting continued crystal growth.

THE DISTRIBUTION AND PROPERTIES OF "ALKALINE" PHOSPHATASE. Phosphatase[2] is present in greatest amount in ossifying cartilage, in smaller amount in formed bone, but is absent from resting epiphyseal cartilage and from nonossifying cartilage in other situations. It was shown by Robison to be absent from the patella before the appearance of the ossification center in this bone, but present thereafter. The teeth of young animals contain it in relatively large amounts. It is present in milk[3] and also in the floral parts of plants.

The optimum pH for phosphatase activity is around 9.0. Magnesium ions greatly increase the activity of the enzyme, whereas calcium ions are mildly inhibitory. Phosphatase activity has been demonstrated in a number of tissues (see table 77.3). The "alkaline" phosphatase in plasma, kidney, and intestine are not necessarily identical with that found in bone, inasmuch as the bone and kidney phosphatase, but not intestinal phosphatase, are inhibited by bile acids. Bone is apparently the main source of plasma phosphatase, since this is not appreciably reduced after the removal of various organs (intestine, kidney, spleen, pancreas, etc.). Phosphatase is excreted by the liver but is also secreted by it; a marked rise in plasma phosphatase occurs in obstructive jaundice and in jaundice due to liver damage, but not in the purely hemolytic type (ch. 59).

The pathological calcification of arteries such

---

[2] Phosphatase activity is expressed as the number of milligrams of inorganic phosphate liberated per gram of tissue from sodium β-glycerophosphate after 48 hours hydrolysis at the optimum pH and at a temperature of 38°C.

[3] Kay and Graham have introduced a test by which one may determine whether a given sample of milk has been properly pasteurized. The test is based upon the fact that the temperature used in the pasteurization process destroys the activity of the enzyme.

TABLE 77.3*

Relative phosphatase activity of tissue extracts prepared under similar conditions from various mammalian tissues†

Tissue	Forrai (1923)	Robison (1923)	Kay (1928)			Kay (1931)
	Man	Young rabbit	Adult			Adult rat —average of 4
			Rabbit	Cat	Man	
Intestine	100					
Duodenum			50‡	93‡	57‡	46
Jejunum			100‡	100‡	85‡	33
Ileum			53‡	81‡	100‡	15
Colon			17‡	34‡	27‡	6
Kidney	58	36	33	38	35	100
Ossifying cartilage		100				
Whole bone			20	10		76
Liver	16	43	12	4	6	4
Pancreas	8	11				
Lung			10	26	7	20
Blood		14				1
Testis	12					13
Brain cerebrum			3	3	4	7
Cardiac muscle			1	1		5
Skeletal muscle	4		1	1		2
Artery				Nil	Nil	

* Modified from Kay, H. D., Physiol. Rev., 1932, **12**, 388.

† The figures in each column are relative one to the other, but the different columns cannot be compared quantitatively.

‡ Mucosa only.

as the aorta, which Kay states does not contain the enzyme, cannot be satisfactorily explained upon the phosphatase hypothesis of Robison. The phosphatase in bone and the other solid tissues mentioned is reduced by the administration of irradiated ergosterol in amounts which cause the withdrawal of calcium from the bones and calcification of the tissues, whereas small doses cause an increase. On the other hand, it has been shown by Kay that the plasma phosphatase is increased, often markedly, in diseases involving extensive changes in bone structure (see table 77.4). Bone and certain other tissues, e.g., kidney, plasma, and semen, but especially the human prostate, contain an "acid" phosphatase. Its optimum pH is between 4 and 5.4. Its concentration in the plasma is increased in prostatic cancer with metastases.

Defects of Ossification and Pathological Calcifications

Diseases of Bone

Several of these have already been considered in other parts of the text—*infantile rickets,*

on page 1437, *osteomalacia* on page 1437, and *osteitis fibrosa* on page 1599.

The hardness, strength, and rigidity of healthy bone depend upon the proportions of the organic and inorganic constituents incorporated into its structure, much as the properties of a plaster bandage depend upon the impregnation of the cotton mesh with plaster of Paris. The mineral and fibrous components are of equal importance; each reinforces the other. The cotton bandage has a certain tensile strength but lacks rigidity; a cast of plaster of Paris alone has maximum rigidity, but is brittle and readily broken or crushed. In most bone diseases the normal proportions between these two components are altered. In rickets and osteomalacia, for example, the bone salts are reduced in relation to the organic material. In these diseases, as also in *osteitis fibrosa* the bones are in consequence softer and more yielding than the normal. In certain other bone conditions the proportion of mineral to organic material is increased. The bone as a result is brittle and easily fractured.

TABLE 77.4*

Changes in the phosphatase content of the plasma in disease

Disease	Number of Cases	Phosphatase Content of Plasma		
		Highest	Lowest	Mean
		unit	*unit*	*unit*
Arthritis without bony changes	11	0.33	0.11	0.17
Arthritis with bony changes	7	0.25	0.09	0.17
Exophthalmic goiter	7	0.75	0.27	0.47
	8†	0.53†	0.19†	0.36†
Osteomyelitis	8	0.41	0.14	0.27
Fragilitas osseum (infants or children)	6	0.66	0.16	0.41
Acromegaly	2	0.32	0.22	0.27
Rickets (infantile)‡	13	1.7	0.42	1.03
Rickets (renal)	2	1.5	0.9	1.2
Adolescent rickets	1			>2.4
Osteitis fibrosa (generalized)	3	>2.5	1.5	>1.8
	3†	1.8†	1.06†	>1.31†
Osteitis deformans	24	3.4	0.65	>1.7

* Modified from Kay H. D., Physiol. Rev., 1932, **12**, 412.

† Hunter (1930).

‡ Average for normal infants approximately same age = 0.32 arbitrary unit. Average for normal adults = 0.10 to 0.21 unit.

In other instances again there may be little change in the proportion of these two materials but the mass of the bone is increased or diminished with corresponding variations in strength.

Osteitis deformans (Paget's disease) is a disease of the skeleton involving mainly the bones of the skull, pelvis, limbs, and spine. The cranium is enlarged and its wall greatly thickened, the long bones of the limbs are massive and curved, the back is bowed (kyphosis) and its movements restricted. The organic matter of the bones is increased and the calcium content decreased, but the total amount of phosphate is not far from normal. Metabolic studies in this disease have yielded little information; the blood alkaline phosphatase level is high.

Fragilitas ossium (osteogenesis imperfecta) is a congenital disease characterized by thinness and extreme fragility of the skeleton, especially of the long bones and ribs. The cranium shows defective calcification. Fractures result from the most trivial injuries or may occur without any apparent cause. Union and healing of the fractures occur, however, as readily as in a normal bone. The bones have a low calcium content, the cortex is very thin, and the medullary cavity dilated.

Achondroplasia is a congenital disease in which endochondral ossification (p. 1604) of the limb bones, especially the humeri and femora, is defective. Periosteal ossification is active. The long bones are, therefore, much shorter and thicker than normal, strong, and dense. A characteristic type of dwarf results; short arms and legs with a

trunk and head of almost normal dimensions. The bones of the base of the skull fuse prematurely and the development of certain facial bones is abnormal. Achondroplastic dwarfs develop, as a result of these abnormalities, a distinctive facies; depressed nasal bridge (pug nose), a broad forehead, and prominent lower jaw.

Marble or chalky bone (Albers-Schönbergs disease). In this condition the density of the bone is greatly increased; the cancellous tissue is filled with a chalky material and the medullary canal may be almost obliterated by the concentric thickening of the shaft. The excessive calcification, however, renders the bones soft and brittle. Calcification ot soft tissues (arteries, lungs, tendons) is often a feature. The disease is exceedingly rare.

The cause or causes of the foregoing osseous abnormalities is unknown. The possibility of some endocrine disorder, of course, comes to mind, but there is little or no evidence of such.

Renal rickets, renal osteitis fibrosa. This is a condition commencing most usually in childhood and associated with chronic nephritis, rarefaction of the skeleton, dwarfism, low plasma calcium, and, sometimes, calcium deposits in the soft tissues, especially in the kidneys; there are also acidosis and phosphate retention. The parathyroids show hyperplasia. We have seen that a rise in plasma phosphate causes a reciprocal reduction in plasma calcium and it is often held that the hypocalcemia seen in this disease is due to the retention of phosphate resulting from the renal insufficiency. The hypocalcemia so produced causes, it is presumed, a drain of calcium from the bones. Increased excretion of phosphate into the intestine as a result of the diminished excretion by the kidney, with consequent depression of calcium absorption is possibly a contributory factor in the production of the low plasma calcium. Albright and his colleagues suggest that renal osteitis fibrosa is a more appropriate name for this disease than renal rickets inasmuch as the histological changes in the bones are indistinguishable from *primary* hyperparathyroidism (p. 1599). This brings up the question as to whether the demineralization of the skeleton is due to the hyperparathyroidism induced as a compensatory reaction to the low plasma calcium. In the opinion of Albright and his associates, the withdrawal of calcium from the skeleton is not directly due to the parathyroid hyperplasia, i.e., to the parathyroid hormone itself, but to the acidosis which results from the failure of the diseased renal tubules to produce ammonia. Calcium is used as a base for the neutralization of acid; the tendency toward a fall in plasma calcium is met by the withdrawal of calcium from the bones. Parathyroid hyperplasia occurs as a compensatory reaction to the hypocalcemia. The effect upon the bones was found to respond to measures which reduce the acidosis.

Calcification of Soft Tissues

Dystrophic calcification is the term applied to the deposition of calcium salts in dead, dying, or chronically inflamed tissues, and in areas of fatty or hyaline degeneration. Thus areas of necrosis, infarcts, scar tissue, caseous tuberculous areas, and degenerated nerve cells, tend to undergo calcification. Calcification also occurs in the infarcts of the placenta which appear in the later half of pregnancy. Many of the examples of pathological calcifications to be described are simply special examples of dystrophic calcification. The factors determining the deposition of calcium salts in devitalized tissues are obscure. It has been suggested that since the CO_2 production in such tissue is minimal or entirely absent they will have a more alkaline reaction; this, of course, would tend to cause the deposition of calcium salts.

Calcinosis is the name given to conditions in which (1) calcified areas are scattered throughout the skin and subcutaneous tissues (*calcinosis circumscripta*) or (2) a more generalized calcification of skin interstitial tissues, tendons, fascia, or muscles occurs (*calcinosis universalis*). When the calcification process involves predominantly the interstitial tissues of the muscles the condition is usually referred to as *myositis ossificans*. In calcinosis the calcium and phosphate levels of the blood are normal. Metabolic studies have in some instances revealed a retention of calcium. In the region of the calcified areas true bone formation may occur. Calcinosis of the superficial tissues is in many cases associated with scleroderma (a condition characterized by induration of the skin due to an increase in the intercellular collagenous tissue). The cause of calcinosis is obscure; the calcification process may be secondary to degenerative changes in the tissues themselves. There is no evidence that it is dependent upon an abnormality of parathyroid function, though Selye has reported a condition in rats resembling scleroderma following the administration of parathyroid extract.

ARTERIAL CALCIFICATION. *Arteriosclerosis* is seen in two main forms: (1) the *atherosclerosis* (athere = crushed grain, porridge) of *Marchand*, (2) the *medial sclerosis* of *Mönckeberg*.

METASTATIC CALCIFICATION. This term connotes a transference of calcium from the skeleton to the soft tissues. It occurs in animals treated with excessive doses of parathyroid extract or irradiated ergosterol. Though the calcium deposits may be found in any of the soft tissues, the arteries, kidneys, and lungs are especially susceptible to calcification. The fundus of the stomach is also a common site. It will be noted that the three last mentioned organs eliminate acid; and it has been suggested that since this will leave the cells more alkaline in reaction, a condition favorable to calcium deposition is created. Metastatic calcification also occurs occasionally clinically. It has been reported in hyperparathyroidism (p. 1599), renal rickets, and in certain bone diseases, e.g., multiple myelomata. It is very natural to assume that in conditions of disturbed calcium metabolism and destructive disease of bone the calcium deposits are simply the result of the excess calcium in the circulation. It is quite possible, however, that in some instances at any rate, it is secondary to tissue injury and may therefore be, in reality, a type of dystrophic calcification induced by a toxic agent. Parathyroid extract and irradiated ergosterol, for example, besides their effects upon calcium metabolism have a definitely toxic action. Furthermore, metastatic calcification is in some instances associated with hypocalcemia.

It is a fact of great interest that the calcium deposits in the arteries and in other soft tissues in the various types of pathological calcification have the same composition as the main mineral compounds of bone. Evidence obtained by both chemical and physical methods support this conclusion. In certain instances actual bone formation occurs, even to the extent of producing red marrow tissue. Areas of ossification have been observed in the aorta and in the neighborhood of calcium deposits in the necrotic kidney of the rabbit. Also, as shown by Huggins, if a section of the mucosa of the bladder be transplanted into the subcutaneous tissues it becomes the site of bone formation.

Renal calculi (nephrolithiasis, urolithiasis). Kidney and bladder stones composed largely of calcium phosphate have been produced in experimental animals (rats) by the administration of irradiated ergosterol or parathyroid extract in excess. They are apparently the result of the excretion in the urine of large amounts of calcium liberated from the bones.

Renal or vesical calculi are also associated with various bone diseases of a destructive nature; they are frequent in hyperparathyroidism. Renal calculi may be composed of calcium oxalate (in acid urine), or of calcium phosphate (in alkaline urine), or of urates, uric acid or cystine. There is a relationship between the urinary excretion of citrate and the production of calcium stones. Citrate excretion is reduced in those suffering from renal calcium deposits even though the intake of citrate is greatly increased. In normal persons, the urinary excretion of citrate runs parallel with the calcium excretion and varies with the calcium of the diet. It is suggested that citrate in some way reduces the tendency toward the precipitation of calcium. Nephrolithiasis is particularly prevalent in the tropics and the possibility has been suggested that hypervitaminosis D, due to overirradiation with ultraviolet light and, possibly, deficiency of vitamin A are causative factors. The production of renal calculi in animals by hypervitaminosis D, as mentioned above, occurs only, however, when doses are employed which cause bone resorption and an increased concentration of calcium in the urine. Such results have, therefore, little bearing upon the question of the production of urinary calculi in the human subject. Also, though there is some evidence that avitaminosis A is conducive to the development of urinary calculi in animals (the cornification of the epithelium of the urinary tract being, apparently, a predisposing factor), there is little warrant for applying the results of animal experiments to the question of urinary lithiasis in man.

Albright's syndrome (polyostotic fibrous dysplasia). This is a rare disease with bizarre manifestations, consisting of bone cysts, fractures, patches of brown pigmentation in the skin, outward bowing of the femur, and, in female children only, precocious puberty. The bony changes resemble those of osteitis fibrosa cystica but are more localized; they, as well as the cutaneous pigmentation, often show a segmental distribution, suggesting a neurological or developmental origin.

There is no evidence of parathyroid overactivity or of a fault in any other endocrine.

REFERENCES

ALBRIGHT, F., DRAKE, T. G., AND SULKOWITCH, H. W. Bull. Johns Hopkins Hosp., 1937, **60**, 377.

AUB, J. C. Medicine, 1925, **4**, 1.

AURBACH, G. D. J. Biol. Chem., 1959, **234**, 3179.

BARNICOT, N. A. Nature, 1948, **162**, 848.

BARTTER, F. C. In The parathyroids (ed. R. O. GREEP AND R. V. TALMAGE). Springfield, Illinois. C. C Thomas, 1961, pp. 388–405.

BAUER, W., AUB, J. C., AND ALBRIGHT, F. J. Exper. Med., 1929, **49**, 145.

BERSON, S. A., YALOW, R. S., AURBACH, G. D., AND POTTS, J. T., JR. Proc. Nat. Acad. Sci. U.S., 1963, **49**, 613.

BINGER, C. J. Pharmacol. & Exper. Therap., 1917, **10**, 105.

BODANSKY, A., BLAIR, J. E., AND JAFFE, H. L. J. Biol. Chem., 1930, **88**, 629.

BODANSKY, A. AND JAFFE, H. L. J. Exper. Med., 1931, **53**, 591.

BREITER, H. AND ASSOCIATES. J. Nutrition, 1941, **21**, 351.

CAMERON, A. T. AND MOORHOUSE, V. H. K. J. Biol. Chem., 1925, **63**, 687.

CAMERON, A. T. AND MOORHOUSE, V. H. K. Trans. Roy. Soc. Canada, 1925, **19**, section V, 39.

CARE, A. D. Nature, 1965.

CARE, A. D. AND KEYNES, W. M. Proc. Roy. Soc. Med., 1964, **57**, 867.

CARE, A. D. AND KEYNES, W. M. J. Endocrinol., 1965.

CHANG, H. Y. Anat. Rec., 1951, **111**, 23.

COLLIP, J. B. J. Biol. Chem., 1925, **63**, 395.

COLLIP, J. B. Medicine, 1926, **5**, 1.

COLLIP, J. B. AND CLARK, E. P. J. Biol. Chem., 1925, **64**, 485.

COLLIP, J. B., CLARK, E. P., AND SCOTT, J. W. J. Biol. Chem., 1925, **63**, 439.

COPE, O., KEYNES, W. M., ROTH, S. I., AND CASTLEMAN, B. Ann Surg., 1958, **148**, 375.

COPP, D. H. Am. J. Med., 1957, **22**, 275.

COPP, D. H. AND CAMERON, E. C. Science, 1961, **134**, 2038.

COPP, D. H., DAVIDSON, A. G. F., AND CHENEY, B. A., Proc. Can. Fed. Biol. Soc., 1961, **4**, 17.

COPP, D. H., CAMERON, E. C., CHENEY, B. A., DAVIDSON, A. G. F., AND HENZE, K. G. Endocrinol., 1962, **70**, 638.

CRAMER, C. F. Endocrinol., 1963, **72**, 192.

DENT, C. E. Brit. Med. J., 1956, **1**, 230.

ELLSWORTH, R. J. Clin. Invest., 1932, **11**, 1011.

EPSTEIN, F. H., BECK, D., CARONE, F. A., LEVITAN, H., AND MANITIUS, A. J. Clin. Invest., 1959, **38**, 1214.

FOWLER, D. I., FONE, D. J., AND COOKE, W. T. Lancet, 1961, **2**, 284.

FRASER, R., HARRISON, M., AND IBBERTSON, K. Quart. J. Med., 1959, **29**, 85.

GLEY, D. Arch. Physiol., 1893, **5**, 5 Serie, 766.

GREENBERG, D. M. AND ASSOCIATES. Am. J. Physiol., 1942, **137**, 459.

GREENWALD, I. J. Biol. Chem., 1924, **61**, 33.

GROLLMAN, A. Endocrinol., 1954, **55**, 166.

HAM, A. Cowdry's Special Cytol., 1932, **2**, 981.

HAM, A. J. Am. Dent. Assn., 1934, **21**, 3.

HARRISON, H. E. AND HARRISON, H. C. J. Clin. Invest., 1941, **20**, 47.

HASTINGS, A. B., ROSEBERRY, H. H., AND MORSE, J. K. J. Biol. Chem., 1931, **90**, 395.

HIGGINS, G. M. AND SHEARD, C. Am. J. Physiol., 1928, **85**, 299.

HIRSCH, P. F. AND MUNSON, P. L. Pharmacologist, 1963, **5**, 272.

HIRSCH, P. F., GAUTHIER, G. F., AND MUNSON, P. L. Endocrinol., 1963, **73**, 244.

HOLTZ, F. Klin. Wchnschr., 1934, **13**, 104.

HUGGINS, C. B. Arch. Surg., 1931, **22**, 377.

HUNTER, D. Lancet, 1930, **1**, 897, 947 and 999.

HUNTER, D. Brit. J. Surg., 1931, **19**, 203.

HUNTER, D. AND AUB, J. C. Quart. J. Med., 1926, **20**, 123.

IMRIE, C. G. AND JENKINSON, C. N. J. Physiol., 1933, **79**, 218.

JAFFE, H. L. AND BODANSKY, A. J. Exper. Med., 1930, **52**, 669.

JAFFE, H. L., BODANSKY, A., AND BLAIR, J. E. J. Exper. Med., 1932, **55**, 695.

KAY, H. D. J. Biol. Chem., 1930, **89**, 249.

KAY, H. D. AND GRAHAM, W. R. J. Dairy Res., 1933, 695.

LLOYD, H. M. AND ROSE, G. A. Lancet, 1958, **2**, 1258.

LOEB, J. Am. J. Physiol., 1900, **3**, 383.

LOEB, J. Am. J. Physiol., 1901, **5**, 362.

LOEB, J. J. Biol. Chem., 1915, **23**, 423.

MACCALLUM, W. G. AND VOEGTLIN, C. J. Exper. Med., 1909, **11**, 118.

McLEAN, F. C. Clin. Orthopaed., 1957, **9**, 46.

McLEAN, F. C. AND HASTINGS, A. B. J. Biol. Chem., 1934, **107**, 337.

McLEAN, F. C. AND HASTINGS, A. B. J. Biol. Chem., 1935, **108**, 285.

MacLEOD, J. J. R. AND TAYLOR, N. B. Trans. Roy. Soc. Can., 1925, **19**, Section V, 27.

MANDL, F. Zbl. Chir., 1926, **53**, 260.

MIXTER, C. G. JR., KEYNES, W. M., AND COPE, O. New Engl. J. Med., 1962, **266**, 265.

MUNSON, P. L. Ann. N. Y. Acad. Sci., 1955, **60**, 776.

NORDIN, B. E. C. Clin. Sci., 1960, **19**, 311.

OSTROW, J. D., BLANSHARD, G., AND GRAY, S. J. Am. J. Med., 1960, **29**, 769.

PATON, D. N. AND FINDLAY, J. Quart. J. Exper. Physiol., 1916, **10**, 203, 233, 315, and 377.

PATT, H. M. AND LUCKHARDT, A. B. Endocrinol., 1942, **31**, 384.

PUGSLEY, L. I. AND SELYE, H. J. J. Physiol., 1933, **79**, 113.

RASMUSSEN, H. AND CRAIG, L. C. Biochim. Biophys. Acta, 1962, **56**, 332.

RASMUSSEN, H. AND REIFENSTEIN, E. C., JR. In Textbook of endocrinology (ed., R. H. WILLIAMS). Philadelphia, Saunders, 1962, pp. 731–879.

ROBISON, R. Biochem. J. 1923, **17**, 286.

ROBISON, R. AND SOAMES, K. M. Biochem. J., 1924, **18**, 740.

ROBISON, R. AND SOAMES, K. M. Biochem. J., 1925, **19**, 153.

ROSE, G. A. Clin. Chim. Acta, 1957, **2**, 227.

SANDERSON, P. H., MARSHALL, F., AND WILSON, R. E. J. Clin. Invest., 1960, **39**, 662.

SCHOUR, I. AND HAM, A. Arch. Path., 1934, **17**, 22.

SELYE, H. Endocrinol., 1932, **16**, 547.

SELYE, H., Arch. Path., 1932, **14**, 60.

SELYE, H. J. A. M. A., 1932, **99**, 108.

SHERMAN, H. C. AND HAWLEY, E. J. Biol. Chem., 1922, **53**, 375.

SHIPLEY, P. G. AND HOLT, L. E. Bull. Johns Hopkins Hosp., 1927, **40**, 1.

SHIPLEY, P. G. AND HOLT, L. E. Bull. Johns Hopkins Hosp., 1927, **41**, 437.

SHIPLEY, P. G., KRAMER, B., AND HOWLAND, J. Biochem. J., 1926, **20**, 379.

SNAPPER, I. Arch. Int. Med., 1930, **46**, 506.

STOERCK, H. C. AND CARNES, W. H. J. Nutrition, 1945, **29**, 43.

TALMAGE, R. V. AND TOFT, R. J. In The parathyroids (ed., R. O. GREEP, AND R. V. TALMAGE). Springfield, Illinois, C. C Thomas, 1961, pp. 224–240.

TASHJIAN, A. H., JR., LEVINE, L., AND MUNSON, P. L. Biochem. Biophys. Res. Commun., 1962, **8**, 259.

TASHJIAN, A. H., JR., ONTJES, D. A., AND MUNSON, P. L. Fed. Proc., 1963, **22**, 520.

VASSALE, G. AND GENERALE, F. Riv. Pathol. Nervosa e Mentale, 1896, **1**, 95.

Monographs and Reviews

ALBRIGHT, F. AND REIFENSTEIN, E. C. (eds.). The parathyroid glands and metabolic bone disease. Baltimore: The Williams & Wilkins Co., 1948.

AUB, J. C. Harvey Lectures, 1928–1929, **24**, 151.

AURBACH, G. D. AND POTTS, J. T., JR. Chapter, The parathyroids, *in* Advances in metabolic disorders. New York, Academic Press, 1964, vol. 1.

BARR, D. P. Physiol. Rev., 1932, **12**, 593.

BOURNE, G. H. The biochemistry and physiology of bone. New York, Academic Press, 1956.

BRINK, F. Pharmacol. Rev., 1954, **6**, 243.

Ciba Foundation Symposium on Bone Structure and Metabolism (eds. G. E. C. WOLSTENHOLME AND C. M. O'CONNOR) London, J. & A. CHURCHILL, 1956.

COPP, D. H. Chapter, Parathyroids, calcitonin and control of plasma calcium, *in* Recent progress in hormone research. New York, Academic Press, 1964, vol. 20.

DRAGSTEDT, L. R. Physiol. Rev., 1927, **7**, 499.

FOURMAN, P. Calcium metabolism and the bone. Oxford, Blackwell, 1960.

HAM, A. W. Histology, 2nd. ed., ch. 16, London, Pitman Medical Publishing Co., 1953.

HESS, A. F. Rickets, including osteomalacia and tetany. Philadelphia, Lea & Febiger, 1929.

HUGGINS, C. Physiol. Rev., 1937, **17**, 119.

IRVING, J. T. Calcium metabolism. London, Methuen, 1957.

KAY, H. D. Physiol. Rev., 1932, **12**, 384.

KEYNES, W. M. The clinical diagnosis of primary hyperparathyroidism. Geriatrics, 1965, **20**, 65.

LOGAN, M. A. Physiol. Rev., 1940, **20**, 522.

MacCULLUM, W. G. Medicine, 1924, **3**, 137.

McLean, F. C. Ann. Rev. Physiol., 1943, **5**, 79.

McLean, F. C. and Bloom, W. Science, 1937, **85**, 24.

McLean, F. C. and Urist, M. R. Bone. Chicago, University of Chicago Press, 1955.

The parathyroids: Proceedings of a symposium on advances in parathyroid research (eds. R. O. Greep and R. V. Talmage). Springfield, Illinois, C. C Thomas, 1961.

Rasmussen, H. Parathyroid hormone: nature and mechanism of action. Am. J. Med., 1961, **30**, 112.

Robison, R. The significance of phosphoric esters in metabolism. New York, New York University Press, 1932.

Schmidt, C. L. A. and Greenberg, D. M. Physiol. Rev., 1935, **15**, 297.

Shanes, A. M. Electrochemical aspects of physiological and pharmacological action in excitable cells. Pharmacol. Rev., 1956, **10**, 59–273.

Thompson, D. L. and Collip, J. B. Physiol. Rev., 1932, **12**, 309.

Weinman, J. P. and Sicher, H. Bone and bones; fundamentals of bone biology, 2nd. ed. St. Louis, C. V. Mosby Co., 1955.

CHAPTER 78

The Endocrine Organs of Sex

The Genetic Basis of Sex

The sex glands—testes and ovaries—are known also as the *gonads* and are the *primary organs of sex*. They furnish the male or female sex cells (spermatozoa or ova) and the hormones upon which the *ultimate* maleness or femaleness of the individual depend. Associated with the sex glands are organs which are essential for procreation but whose activities are governed by the secretions of the sex glands. These are the *accessory sex organs* and include the external genitalia, as well as the uterus, fallopian tubes and vagina in the female and the seminal vesicles and prostate glands of the male. Certain sexual characteristics, the *secondary sex characters*, make their appearance at the time of sexual maturity (puberty). They include the occurrence of hair on the pubis of the human male or female, the deepening of the voice in men, the development of the mammary glands in women and the psychic manifestations in both sexes. In certain other forms the secondary sex characters differ even more noticeably, (e.g., the development of the antlers of stags, the distinctive plumage of birds, the comb and wattles of the cockerel).

The genetic sex of an animal is determined at the time of conjugation of the *gametes* (spermatozoon and ovum), and depends upon which one of two types of chromosome is contained in the sperm cell. The cells of the human body contain 23 pairs of chromosomes. During gametogenesis the pairs are split so that each gamete contains a single representative of each of the 23 pairs of chromosomes, in other words 23 chromosomes instead of 46. This is the process of *meiosis*. The partners in one pair of chromosomes of the male, the sex chromosomes, are dissimilar; one, X, is larger than the other, Y, and during meiosis these are separated so that one male gamete will contain an X-chromosome and the other a Y. In the female two X chromosomes are paired as the sex chromosomes, so that on meiotic division to form ova, each ovum comes to possess one X-chromosome. It will be seen that the chromosomes determining sex are carried by the gametes produced by the male. If an ovum is fertilized by a sperm bearing an X-chromosome then the combination XX will be produced and result in the development of a female. On the other hand, if the fertilizing sperm bears a Y-chromosome, then the XY combination produces a male. Perhaps it is worth noting that in birds the heterogametic sex (XY), is female, whereas the sex possessing two X-chromosomes (XX) is male.

In recent years, techniques have been developed for making preparations of human chromosomes in a routine manner so that these structures can be counted and examined in any individual. Generally, a specimen of skin or of blood leucocytes is cultured in order to obtain a collection of dividing cells. Completion of mitosis can be prevented by adding a mitotic inhibitor, such as colchicine, so that the number of cells in metaphase is increased. Next, the chromosomes are dispersed throughout the cytoplasm of the cell by exposing them to a hypotonic solution immediately before fixation and, finally, the chromosomes are spread over the surface of a slide by squashing the preparation or employing an air-drying technique. In determining the *karyotype*, or systematized array of chromosomes in a single cell, the chromosomes of that cell are often photographed or drawn; the individual chromosomes are identified, cut out of the picture, and arranged in pairs as shown in fig. 78.1. It is, of course, necessary to examine a large number of cells in this way in order to be certain of the karyotype of an individual.

Study of the karyotype in a variety of clinical conditions has greatly aided understanding of the genetic basis of certain diseases. So far as the sex chromosomes are concerned, it is evident that the presence of one Y chromosome confers "maleness" upon an individual, whilst full feminity requires two X chromosomes. However, variations on this theme are legion, and numerous combinations of sex chromosomes arising from abnormalities in meiosis are known. One such abnormality is known as *non-disjunction*, which arises from the failure of a pair of homologous chromosomes to separate during mitosis or a meiotic division so that both remain at the same nuclear pole. Because of this, an ovum resulting from a cell division of this kind will have either two X chromosomes (XX) or none (O). Equally, sperm will occur which possess both X and Y chromosomes (XY), or lack them (O). Fusion of an abnormal and normal gamete can then give rise to combinations such as XX + X, XX + Y, O + X and O + Y. Additional anomalies may arise so that the final result need not be of the simple type just discussed. Some combinations, such as zygotes with a YO or a YYO constitution, are considered to be non-viable since the X chromosome is said to carry genes essential for certain aspects of blood coagulation. The possession of extra sex chromosomes does not necessarily modify

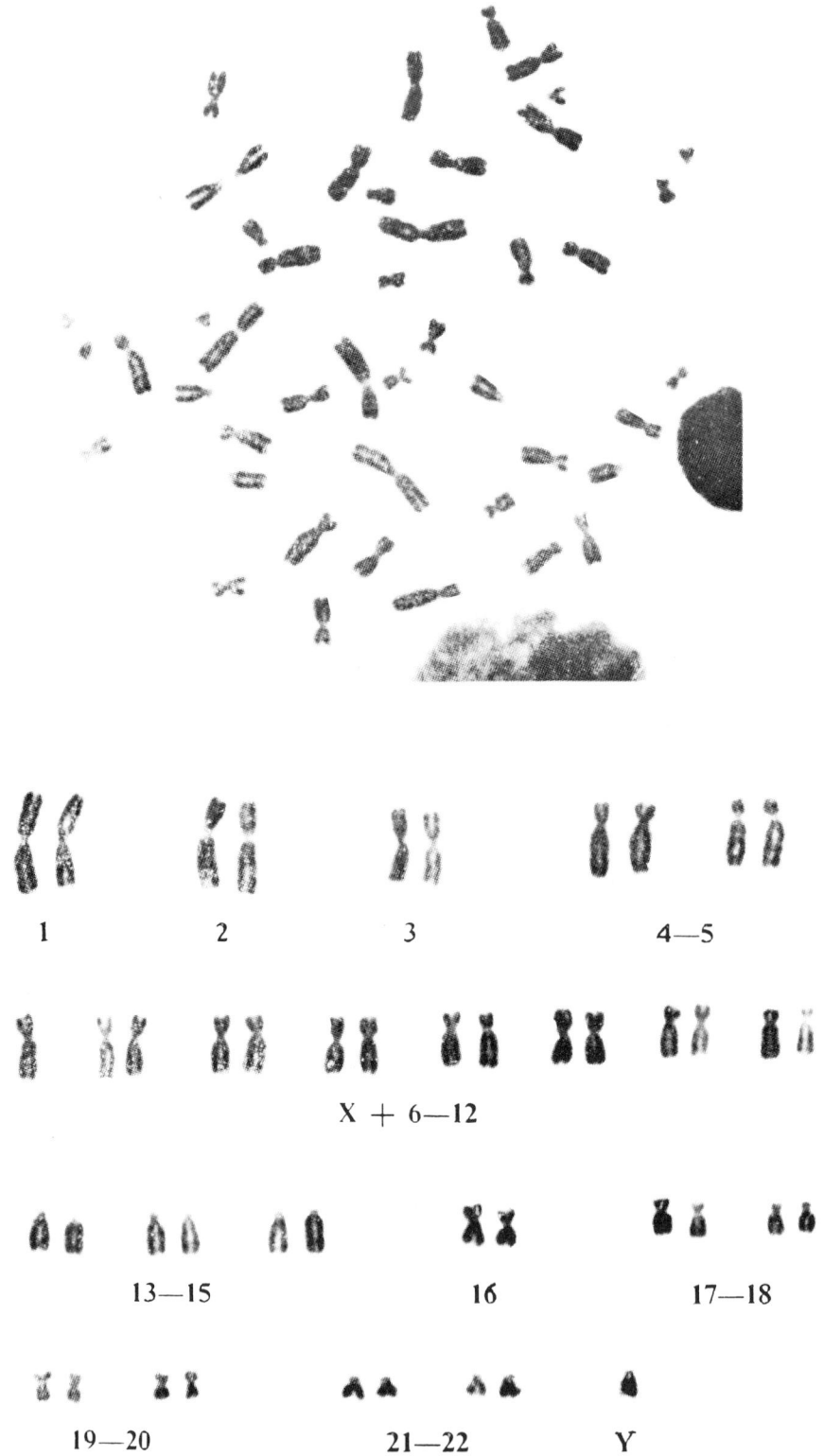

1

2

3

4—5

X + 6—12

13—15

16

17—18

19—20

21—22

Y

FIG. 78.1. A. Normal male cell, with karyotype, from a culture of lymphocytes. Note the X-chromosome at the left of the second row and the Y chromosome at the bottom right. The remainder of the chromosomes are paired.

B. Normal female cell, with karyotype, from a culture of lymphocytes. The pair of X chromosomes is placed at the left of the second row.

(From Court Brown, Harnden, Jacobs, McLean and Mantle, 1964. Her Majesty's Stationery Service.)

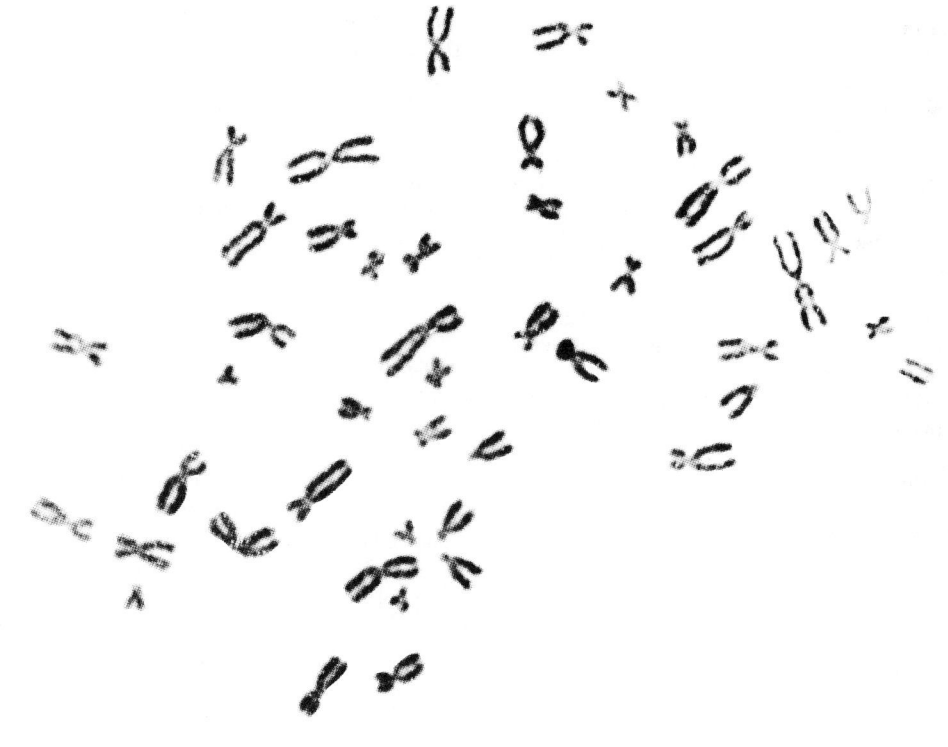

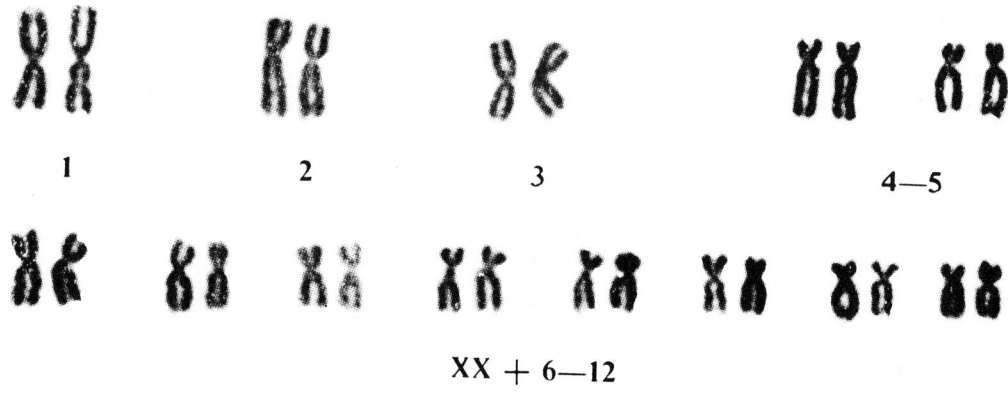

1   2   3   4—5

XX + 6—12

13—15   16   17—18

19—20   21—22

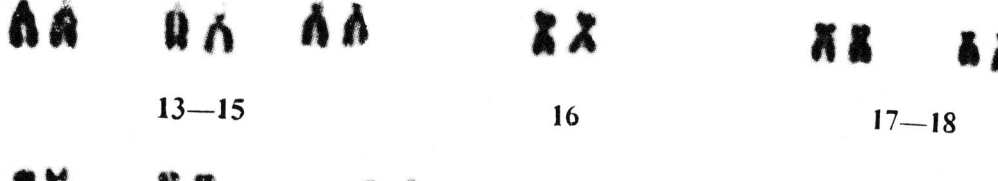

Fig. 78.1. B.

gonadal function: the term "super-female" is to be avoided when referring to patients with the sex chromosome constitution of XXXX.

Females with but a single X chromosome, of sex chromosome constitution designated XO, frequently present as cases of "Turner's syndrome" in which streaks of gonadal tissue occur in the place of normal ovaries; somatic malformations such as webbing of the neck, cubitus valgus, heart defects and renal anomalies may be found. The parallel condition in persons of male appearance (*Klinefelter's syndrome*) appears to arise from the presence of an XXY sex chromosome complement, which is associated with the presence of small testes lacking spermatogenesis and evidence of poor production of androgen. Other features of the syndrome, gynecomastia, abnormalities of hair distribution, and subnormal intelligence, are variable in extent.

Another class of genetic anomaly merits attention here: that of *mosaicism*. This can arise during embryonic development, or indeed at any time, when both members of a chromosome pair become included in the same daughter cell, or when one chromosome lags at anaphase and becomes effectively lost. In this way, stem lines and clones of cells may arise in an individual, each with different genetic constitution. In the human an XO/XX combination appears to be associated with gonadal dysgenesis of female phenotype, whilst with an XO/XY mosaic the phenotype varies. In cases of this nature, and particularly in more complex ones with XO/XX/XXX, XX/XY/XXY and so on, the chromosomal make-up of the cells of a tissue sample will vary in accordance with the source of the specimen.

Besides carrying the genes concerned with sex determination the sex chromosomes may also contain the genes controlling certain diseases and defects. Hemophilia, color-blindness and fishskin disease (ichthyosis) are examples of such abnormalities. Hemophilia and color-blindness are transmitted from grandfather to grandson, through the intermediary of a normal carrier female and are conveyed on the X-chromosome, whereas ichthyosis passes from father to son *via* the Y-chromosome. If a man afflicted with hemophilia marries a normal woman the disease is not transmitted to his sons (XY), for the X-chromosome received from the mother does not carry the defect and neither does the Y-chromosome received from the father. The daughters, however, have received an abnormal factor in the X-chromosome from the father as well as a normal one from the mother but remain free of the disease since the abnormal character is 'recessive' and is suppressed by the dominant normal character. Should the daughters marry and a Y-sperm fertilize an ovum, then a male (XY) zygote results and the child will show the disease for one of the

abnormal X-chromosomes of the mother has paired with the Y of the father. The Y-chromosome does not offset the effect of the abnormal X-chromosome. It should be remembered that since the mother possesses two X-chromosomes, a normal and an abnormal one, it is an even chance which one the child will receive. A classic series of cases of the disease may be found among the descendants of Queen Victoria who was a carrier. Eleven hemophilics are to be found in the three succeeding generations.

Sex chromatin. Since every cell of a male individual differs from that of a female, in that it possesses a dissimilar sex chromosome, it might be postulated that suitably refined cytological techniques would prove capable of distinguishing between male and female cells. Such is so. In 1949 Barr and Bertram reported the discovery of a sexual dimorphism in the neurone of the cat; since then their findings have been extended to a variety of tissues and a variety of species, including man. The difference between male and female cells lies in a special mass of chromatin, known as the *sex chromatin*, which is characteristic of the female. In man, skin biopsy preparations, smears from the oral mucous membrane, and blood films yield satisfactory preparations for study. Club-shaped appendages, "drum sticks," are present on the nuclei of some of the polymorphonuclear leucocytes of females. They occur in 1 to 17 per cent (mean, 2.6 per cent) of cells from females, but never in material collected from normal males. The sex chromatin is typically a plano-convex mass, about 1 micron in diameter lying close to or in contact with the nuclear membrane (fig. 78.2). It stains readily with basic dyes and is Feulgen-positive, indicating the presence of desoxyribose nucleic acid. The sex chromatin appears to be a chromosomal derivative since, like the chromosomes, it is consistently Feulgen-positive, whereas the nucleolus (with which the sex chromatin might be associated) is Fuelgen-negative. There is no evidence that the sex hormones influence the chromatin; typical sexual dimorphism has been found in the nuclei of individuals of all ages, from the early embryo to senility. It is possible that the sex chromatin of female cells represents certain regions of the two X-chromosomes that adhere together; it is also possible that a single X chromosome is responsible for the appearance of the body. The latter alternative has gained most acceptance since chromatin positive nuclei have been described in patients with an XO sex chromosome complex, since the number of sex chromatin bodies is usu-

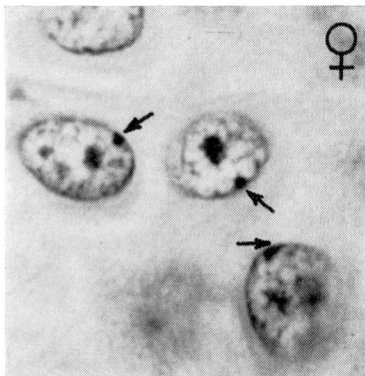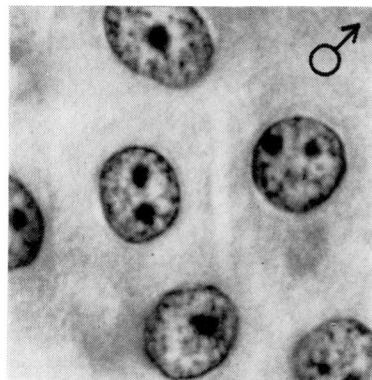

Fig. 78.2. Nuclei of cells in epidermal spinous cell layer of a chromosomal female (left) and chromosomal male (right). Note the sex chromatin indicated by arrows in the female. (From Grumbach and Barr.)

ally one less than the number of X chromosomes in cases of multiple X chromosome constitution, and since the two homologous X chromosomes of females show morphological and functional differences. The importance of the discovery of sex chromatin, apart from its theoretical significance, lies in the diagnosis of the genetic sex of individuals with sexual anomalies, such as in cases of pseudohermaphroditism, gonadal dysgenesis, etc.

Sex ratio. If spermatozoa carrying X-chromosomes and spermatozoa carrying Y-chromosomes are produced in equal numbers in the testis, and if each has an equal chance of fertilizing an ovum then equal numbers of male and female individuals should be conceived. In actual fact, in the human more male embryos than female develop; the *primary sex ratio* is greater than one. Precise figures are difficult to obtain for man, but in the pig Parkes concluded that the ratio must be about 160:100; in cattle it is about 130:100. Between conception and delivery there is an appreciable mortality which preferentially affects the male so that the proportion at birth, the *secondary sex ratio*, is lower, being in the pig about 105:100. In Britain the human secondary sex ratio is about 106:100. Through childhood and in adult life the male mortality exceeds that of the female so that numerical equality of the sexes is reached during adolescence, and thereafter the females outnumber the males. At around 85 years or so there are twice as many women as men. The cause of the primary sex ratio is uncertain. It has been suggested that the spermatozoa bearing the smaller Y-chromosomes are more active than those carrying the larger X-chromosome, so that more "male" spermatozoa than "female" reach the ovum. Alternatively the environment of the genital tract could favor one kind of spermatozoon—attempts to control the primary sex ratio have been made on this basis.

The Hormonal Factors in Development of the Genital System

Although the sex of an individual has been seen to be determined genetically, a variety of factors may intervene to modify embryonic sexual development. The gonads are derived from mesodermal primordia arising in the genital ridges along the dorsal surface of the celomic cavity. Essentially they are bipotential organs which can become testes or ovaries. The testicular and ovarian components are antagonistic, and the balance normally becomes tipped so that the resultant gonad conforms to the genetic sex of the individual. Experimentally, in lower forms such as amphibia and birds, treatment with sex hormones can reverse gonadal development so that a presumptive testis becomes an ovary, and vice versa. In mammals, complete gonadal reversal has not been achieved experimentally but evidence in favor of a hormonal effect on gonadal development has long been derived from the study of the bovine *freemartin*. Here a sterile female calf (a freemartin) is born as a twin with a normal male. The sexual abnormalities of the freemartin include a small undeveloped uterus and an enlarged clitoris. The gonads are intraabdominal and resemble testes to a variable extent. It is well established that the freemartin is a genetic female (this has been confirmed by sex chromatin studies) and that the condition is caused by a hormone that reaches the female embryo from the male twin through vascular anastomoses between the partially fused placentas. In the unusual case when fusion of the chorion does not occur the female embryo remains free from masculinization by the male and is normal. Modification of the development of the accessory sex structures is more easily achieved. Following castration of the male rabbit fetus the male tubular system (Wolffian ducts) regresses whereas the coexistent female (Müllerian) system persists and differentiates into a female reproductive tract together with female external genitalia. Removal of the fetal ovary, on the other hand, does not interfere with the differentiation of a female genital tract. Testosterone given to castrated males or to females stimulates the development of the masculine characters but does not inhibit the uterine horns or tubes. There is thus good evidence for the existence of a hormone secreted by the testis at a very early stage of development which results in the repression of the female primordia. The early observation of Bouin and Ancel that the interstitial cells (p. 1649) of the testis are well developed at this time supports this view, but the identity of the embryonic testicular hormone is unknown.

The facts summarized above are of importance in the study of a variety of sexual abnormalities. These include true and pseudohermaphroditism, and gonadal dysgenesis. In cases of *true hermaphroditism* the individual possesses both ovarian and testicular tissue. There is generally some degree of ambisexual development of the genital tract but this, and the development of the secondary sexual characteristics, is highly variable. The chromosomal sex may be male or female. In a number of cases mosaicism may be responsible for this condition. Two variations of *pseudohermaphroditism* exist: the male and the female type. In the male type the individual has testes only but exhibits development of the female genital duct system to a variable degree. The patients may appear male or female, but are genetically male. Female pseudohermaphrodites possess only ovaries and show variable masculine genital development. The sex chromatin is female. A variety of causes underlie these defects but, in the female, congenital virilizing adrenal hyperplasia is the most common. In typical cases of *gonadal dysgenesis*, the internal and external genital structures are female but remain infantile and there is little development of the secondary sexual characteristics. Following the description of a series of cases by H. H. Turner in 1938, the condition gained the name of Turner's syndrome and has been mentioned earlier as an example of the occurrence of the XO sex chromosome constitution. Sex chromatin is lacking in the nuclei of the cells of these patients. The nuclei of cells in many cases of gonadal dysgenesis in the male (Klinefelter's syndrome with XXY sex chromosome complement) are chromatin positive, in that the cell nuclei show the chromatin granule normally seen in the female. As a general rule, the number of sex-chromatin masses is usually one less than the number of X chromosomes. A tetra-X female would be expected to show a maximum of three sex chromatin masses in the nuclei, though some cells may contain two bodies and some only one.

The Effect of Excision of the Gonads

Removal of the gonads of a young animal inhibits the growth of the accessory sex organs and the secondary sex characters fail to develop. In the female, ovariectomy or *spaying* causes an atrophy of the uterus (figs. 78.3, 78.4) and regressive changes in the vagina and mammary glands. Orchidectomy or *castration* of the male exerts comparable effects. The effects of castration upon the secondary sex characters are evident even in such simple forms as the earthworm and hermit crab. Castration of the male frog prevents the appearance of the sexual changes which normally occur during the mating season. The thumb-pad and fore-limb muscles do not hypertrophy, the clasping reflex cannot be elicited and the animal does not emit its characteristic croak. The sexual development of birds is profoundly affected by castration. The castrated cockerel (capon), for example, has a greater proportion of body fat than the normal bird, whereas the comb and wattles, and the sex instincts, do not develop. Development of the spurs and of male plumage, however, is not prevented. Removal of the ovaries (spaying) causes the development of spurs, the growth of a comb resembling that of a cock, and male plumage. The spayed duck assumes the plumage of the drake. Male plumage is considered to be the basic or neutral type. Its development is suppressed by the female sex hormone, when the female type of plumage appears. Hence the male plumage appears after ovariectomy and persists after testicular removal.

The effects of castration upon young cattle, horses and stags are well known. Castration of young bulls causes an increase in the size of the skeleton and a greater deposition of fat. The mature development of the accessory organs is prevented. The antlers of young stags do not develop after castration. Castration of boys before puberty retards ossification of the epiphyses of the long bones with consequent enlargement of the stature due to disproportionate lengthening of the lower limbs. There is also adiposity, with a tendency toward a feminine distribution of the fat. The larynx is not prominent, as in the mature male, and the voice remains high-pitched. Hair fails to grow upon the face and body, but is unusually plentiful on the head. The penis remains

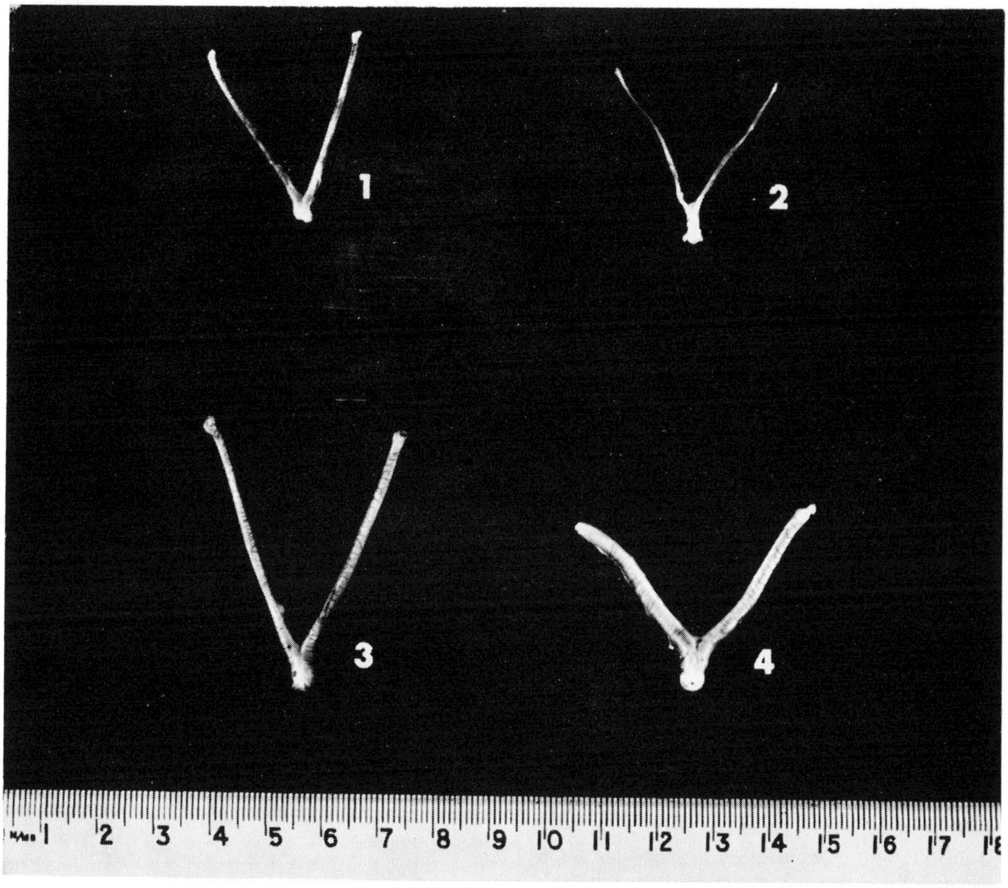

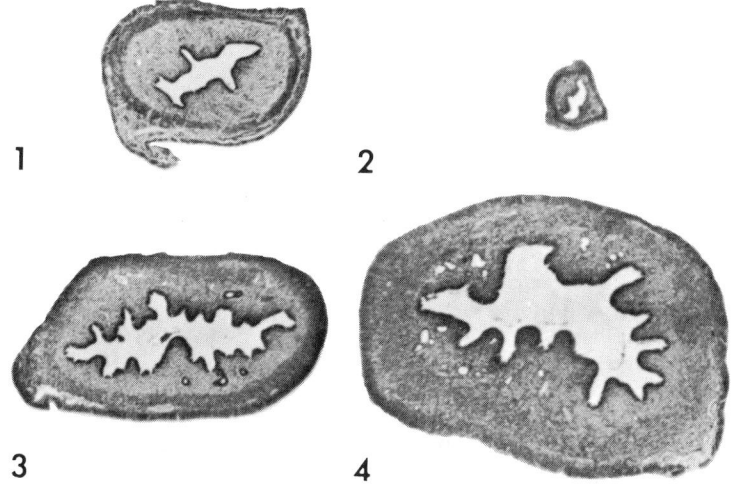

Fig. 78.3. The effect of ovariectomy and of estrogen treatment in the rat. Four litter-mate females were used at 32 days of age. Animal *1* was killed to provide an *initial control* uterus, *2* was spayed and killed 14 days later whilst *3* was *spayed and given 10 µg. estradiol benzoate* daily for 13 days and killed on the fourteenth day. Rat *4* was subjected to a blank operation (exposure of the ovaries) and killed 14 days later to serve as a *final control*. Note the atrophy of the uterus of rat *2*, and the approximately normal size of the uterus of rat *3* treated with estrogen. The dose of estrogen provided was greater than the minimal dose (1.0 µg. daily or less would have sufficed) yet the uterus did not display a supramaximal response.

Fig. 78.4. Sections of the uteri shown in fig. 78.3. *1*. Initial control, 32 days old. *2*. Littermate female, spayed at 32 days and killed 14 days later. *3*. Littermate female spayed at 32 days, given 10 µg. oestradiol benzoate daily for thirteen days and killed on the fourteenth day. *4*. Normal (Blank operated) 46-day old littermate female, final control. See also the legend of fig. 78.1.

infantile and sexual feeling is suppressed. Such a state is called *eunuchism*. Ovariectomy in women is followed by changes characteristic of the menopause (p. 1627), namely, amenorrhea, atrophy of the secondary sex organs and obesity. If performed before puberty the characteristic feminine attributes do not appear; the girl tends to become somewhat mannish in type for the accessory sex characteristics fail to develop fully and menstruation does not occur.

Sexual desire in higher animals and in the human subject is not necessarily entirely dependent upon the gonads, particularly in the male. Ovariectomized adult female chimpanzees show few signs of desire for intercourse, but ovariectomized women may show as much erotic behavior after the operation as was exhibited previously. Castration of male primates often produces no diminution in the capacity to mate or (in man) to achieve sexual climax during coitus. In lower mammals, such as the cat, removal of the ovaries abolishes sexual behavior. It may be recalled that following removal of the gonads, androgens produced by the adrenal gland may be responsible for some of the sexual responses observed.

Transplantation or grafting experiments. If the excised gonad (testis or ovary) is transplanted to another situation in the body and survives, the otherwise inevitable endocrine effects of castration are prevented. This fact, first demonstrated by Berthold in the cock in 1849, proves conclusively that the gonad furnishes an internal secretion. The studies of homotransplants show that feminization of the capon, or masculinization of the ovariectomized hen, can be induced by transplantation of the gonad of the opposite sex.

The Ovaries

Development of the ovaries. The ovaries, as well as the testes, arise from the celomic epithelium covering the inner aspect of the Wolffian body. The epithelial cells of this region assume a columnar form and proliferate to form several layers which constitute the *germinal epithelium*, whereas the mesenchymal stroma underlying the germinal epithelium becomes thickened to form the *genital ridge*. By means of a localized multiplication of cells in the germinal epithelium, fingerlike processes arise which penetrate into the mesenchymal stroma. These processes are known as the *primary sex cords* and contain both germinal and supporting tissue. Up to this point there is no difference in the differentiation of an ovary or testis. If the gonad is destined to become an ovary then the germinal epithelium remains thickened and pro-

liferates a set of *secondary sex cords* or *cortical cords* which form the definitive cortex of the adult ovary. The primary sex cords become the adult medulla. In the process of testis formation the germinal epithelium becomes reduced in thickness and the primary sex cords progress to become the seminiferous tubules. It is now generally believed that the gonial cells migrate to the presumptive gonad and do not arise from the germinal epithelium.

Structure of the ovary. The adult ovary is a flattened oval structure (about 3.4 cm. long) with one of its edges, the *hilus*, attached *via* the mesovarium to the broad ligament. It consists of a dense stroma of connective tissue which carries blood vessels and in which are embedded the oocytes and *Graafian follicles* in all stages of development. The stroma also contains smooth muscle fibers and small numbers of large polyhedral epithelial cells —the *interstitial cells*—which are prominent in other species but less obvious in the human. The surface of the ovary is covered with a layer of epithelial cells, the germinal epithelium, which is continuous with the epithelium of the general peritoneum.

The Graafian follicles. It is possible that the germinal epithelium covering the ovary retains its embryonic character and proclivities after birth—until the end of the reproductive period (to about the 45th year in women). However, the question of postnatal formation of ova has been subjected to intensive study and the balance of evidence has swung against this process. It now appears that the female mammal begins reproductive life with a finite stock of oöcytes which is not subsequently replenished. Accordingly, the oöcyte population of the human ovary (200,000–400,000) or that of the rat or mouse (10,000) declines with age. The ovaries of an aged, postmenopausal, woman generally lack ova, whilst those of an old rat may still contain oöcytes. A *primordial follicle* is formed by invagination of a cord of cell from the germinal epithelium (fig. 78.5). An island of cells becomes separated; one of the group develops into a *primitive ovum* whereas the rest form a surrounding layer of *granulosa cells*. At this time the primordial follicle is about 45 microns in diameter and becomes displaced towards the deeper regions of the cortex. It appears that the orderly arrangement of cells in the development of primordial follicles is governed by the ovum itself, for when the ova are destroyed by X-ray treatment the germinal epithelium forms cords and clumps instead of follicles.

The infantile ovary contains some 400,000 primordial follicles. As follicles develop two more layers of cells are produced from the ovarian stroma. The inner layer—the *theca interna*—is thought to be formed by some influence exerted upon the stroma cells by the granulosa cells.

This layer is vascular and more cellular than the outer layer—the *theca externa*—which is fibrous in character. At the same time that these changes are occurring the granulosa cells multiply to form a cell mass several layers deep, now known as the *membrana granulosa* in which two concentric zones can be distinguished. These become separated by the accumulation of fluid (liquor folliculi) and a cavity or *antrum* is formed. It is at this time that the follicle may be called a Graafian follicle. The cells of the inner zone of membrana granulosa surround the ovum and these are piled in pyramid fashion in contrast with part of the wall of the follicle. This mass protruding into the antrum of the follicle is the *cumulus oophorus*, or *discus proligerus*.

The growth of the follicle and the changes just described represent follicular maturation or ripening and during this process the follicle extends outwards so that when mature the follicular wall projects from the surface of the ovary. A mature follicle may have a diameter of up to 10 mm. and contains an ovum some 100 to 150 microns across, bounded by a clear membrane, the *zona pellucida*. Full maturity of the ovum is heralded by the extrusion of the first polar body and following this the follicular wall ruptures and the ovum, together with some discus proligerus cells forming the *corona radiata*, is discharged. It passes along the Fallopian tube to the uterus.

After discharge of the ovum the cavity of the ruptured Graafian follicle may become filled with a clot of blood. The small body formed in this way is sometimes spoken of as the *corpus hemorrhagicum*. The clot is soon largely replaced by a mass of cells containing a yellow lipid material (*luteal cells*). These are derived from the proliferation of the epithelial cells of the membrana granulosa (*granulosa lutein cells*) and of the theca interna (*theca lutein cells*). The follicle with its content of luteal cells constitutes the *corpus luteum*. The circumference of the follicle by this time has become more vascular and capillaries penetrate into the yellow cell mass. The transformed follicle may now be looked upon as a temporary organ of internal secretion. If fertilization of the ovum does not occur, the life of the corpus luteum is short. In the human it persists for about 10 days and then regresses. Its vessels become obliterated; the luteal cells disintegrate and are replaced by fibrous tissue; nothing then remains of the follicle but a pale scar—the *corpus albicans*. On the other hand, if fertilization of the ovum occurs the corpus luteum continues to grow and in women attains a diameter of three-quarters of an inch or more by the middle of pregnancy. It then commences to shrink and is finally absorbed by the seventh month.

Of the vast number of ova and primordial follicles in the ovary only a few ever reach the Gra-

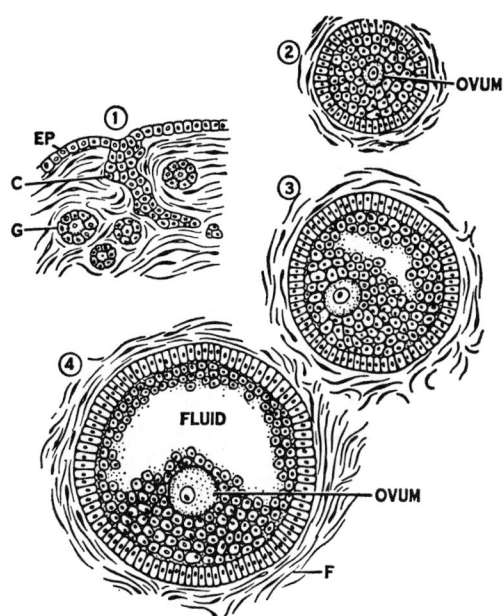

FIG. 78.5. Successive stages in the development of the ovum and Graafian follicle (diagrammatic). EP, germinal epithelium covering the surface of the ovary; C, a cord of cells growing from the germinal epithelium into the ovarian substance; G, primordial ovum encircled by a single layer of (granulosa) cells. In 4, the *membrana granulosa* and the *cumulus oophorus* are shown but the follicle has not yet reached full development; F, ovarian stroma.

afian follicle stage. In women, not more than one or two ova are as a rule discharged each month, or a total of 400 or so during the entire reproductive period. The remaining follicles develop to some extent and then undergo degenerative changes to become *atretic follicles*. Each of the latter is finally replaced by fibrous tissue derived from the theca and only a small scar, a *corpus atreticum*, remains.

The factors which determine the rupture of the ripe follicle are not definitely known but clearly involve the effects of the rhythmic secretions of the pituitary gland. The accumulation of fluid and the consequent increase in intrafollicular pressure is probably a factor in some animals, or the contraction of the smooth muscle fibers of the stroma may play a part. In most species, including man, the follicle ruptures "spontaneously," after being acted upon by sufficient gonadotrophin but in the rabbit, cat and ferret ovulation occurs only after copulation.

The Sexual Life of Females

Three sexual periods of different lengths occur in female mammals:

1. A single long period occupying the greater

part of the animal's life. It commences at *puberty*, at which time the first ovulation occurs. The accessory organs of reproduction mature, sex desire is aroused and the secondary sex characters develop. It ends with atrophic changes in the ovary and accessory organs. In women the termination of this period is called the *menopause* (p. 1627).

2. A period which recurs once or oftener each year, known as the *mating, sexual,* or *breeding season*. In most species it is only during this time, or during a part of it, that the female will receive the male.[1] The duration of the mating season and the number of times it occurs annually vary in different species. In the dog, for instance, it is generally said that two such periods of about six weeks' duration occur each year (spring and autumn), whereas in certain other species they occur more frequently, and in others again only once, and may be of long or short duration. In the human, reproduction is not confined to any one part of the year, although a study of birth statistics shows that fertility is greatest at certain periods (April to June). It has been suggested that in primitive man a mating season corresponding to this time of year did exist.

3. *The estrus cycles*. These are periods of sexual activity in animals which occur once or oftener in each breeding season. The first cycle commences at puberty. Animals such as the bitch, in which a single estrus cycle extends throughout the breeding season, are called *monestrus*. *Polyestrus* animals, on the other hand, are those such as the domestic cat, the mare, cow, sow, rat and mouse, in which cycles occur in succession during the breeding season. In a monestrus animal the following phases of the estrus cycle are distinguished. (a) *Proestrus*, or period of "coming on heat." This may be marked by swelling and congestion of the external genitalia together with growth and increased vascularity of the uterus. There is, as a rule, some enlargement of the mammary glands and, in the dog and mare, bleeding from the vagina. During this stage of the cycle the Graafian follicles are undergoing maturation preparatory to rupture. (b) *Estrus*,[2] or "period of desire." The female receives the male and ovulation occurs. The term "heat" is commonly applied to the combined periods, proestrus and estrus. (c) *Pseudopregnancy* or *pregnancy*. During

[1] The corresponding period which occurs in the males of some species is known as the *rutting season*. In many species however, the male is capable of copulation at any time.
[2] *Estrus*, L. = *gad-fly*, with figurative meaning of frenzy or intense desire.

this phase there occurs pronounced proliferation and secretory activity of the uterine glands, hypertrophy of the mucosa and a great increase of the uterine blood supply. It will be seen presently that these phenomena are dependent upon the formation of a corpus luteum. The growth of the mammary glands is stimulated. The uterine changes are looked upon as anticipating the arrival of, and providing nourishment for, a fertilized ovum. (d) *Anestrus* is the period of sexual quiescence between the mating seasons. In the cycle of those animals in which pseudopregnancy does not occur, the short period following estrus and during which the phenomena of estrus subside, is called *metestrus*. The monestrus cycle may be illustrated as follows.

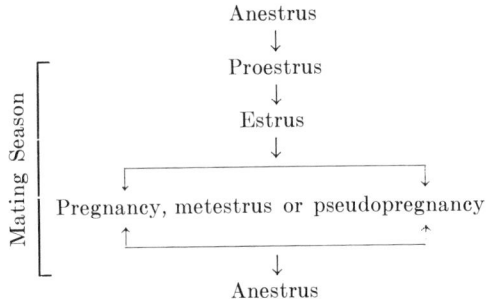

In polyestrus animals the short intervals of quiescence separating the estrous phases are called *diestrous* periods. The term anestrus, as in the case of monestrus species, refers to the longer periods of rest between the mating seasons.

Although the onset of estrus in some species is quite obvious, in others, such as the rodents, it is difficult to detect by the ordinary means. Stockard and Papanicolaou discovered that the vaginal mucosa of the guinea pig underwent certain changes (cornification of the epithelium) coinciding with estrus. Similar changes occur in the vagina of the rat and mouse as well as in the human vagina (fig. 78.6). By the examination of a smear of the vaginal secretions the stages of the estrus cycle can be readily followed in these animals. Leukocytes which are present in smears taken during the diestrus or anestrus period are absent from the vaginal secretions during proestrus and estrus, but large squamous (cornified) cells, with small pyknotic nuclei, appear. The intact vaginal epithelium becomes stratified squamous in character.

The menstrual cycle and sexual life in the human. The sexual cycle of primates is termed a *menstrual cycle*. This differs from that of lower forms in so far as the period of desire is not localized to any one phase of the cycle (such as estrus), and that external bleeding occurs roughly midway

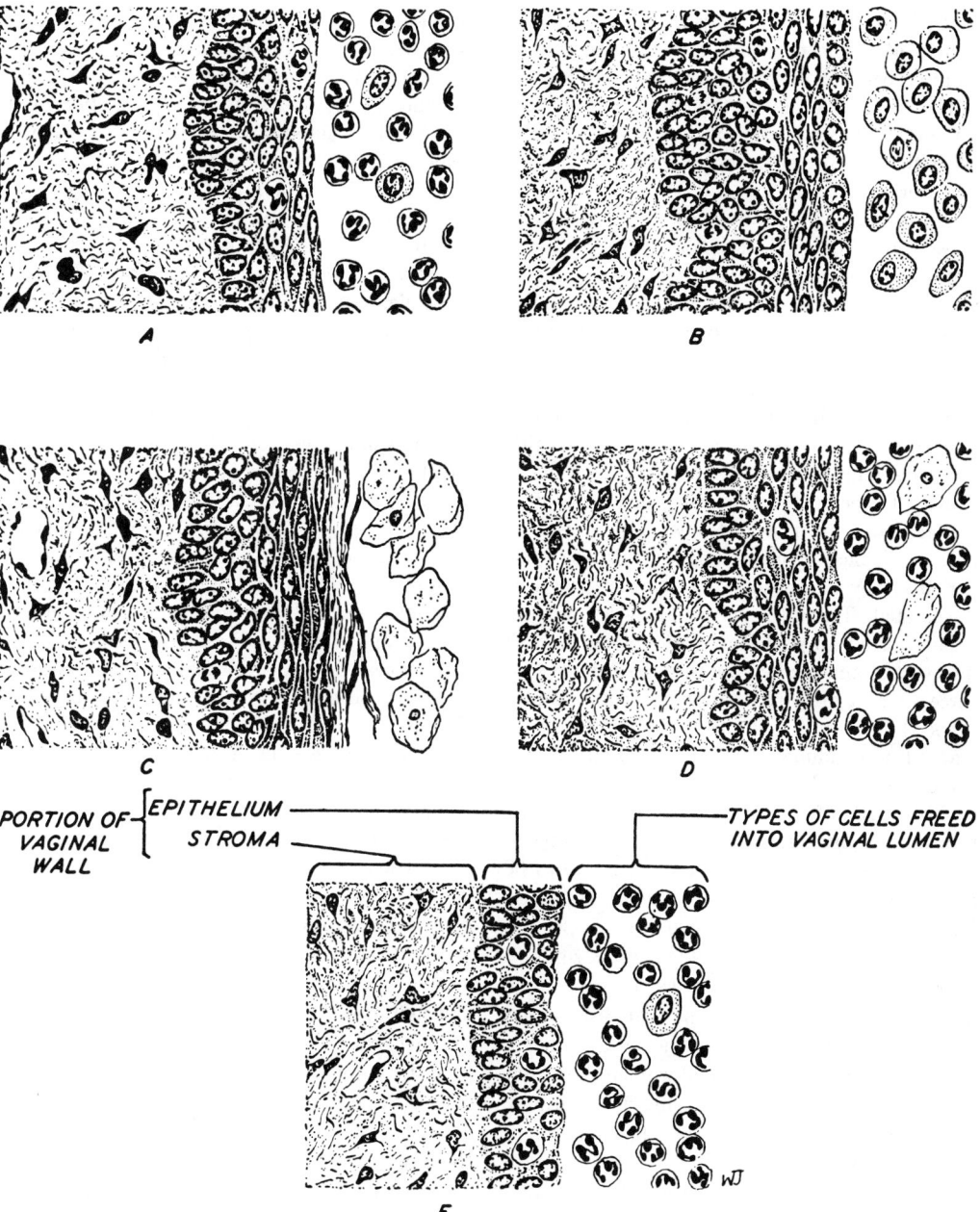

PORTION OF VAGINAL WALL — {EPITHELIUM — STROMA —} — TYPES OF CELLS FREED INTO VAGINAL LUMEN

FIG. 78.6. The vaginal epithelium and smear at various stages of the estrus cycle of the rat. A, diestrus; B, proestrus; C, estrus; D, metestrus; E, ovariectomized. (From Turner.)

between two ovulations rather than at the time of ovulation. Therefore in equating the typical 28-day menstrual cycle of the human with the estrous cycle of an animal such as the bitch, it may be said that the first 14 days of the menstrual cycle (day 1 being the first day of the flow) are represented by the phases of diestrus and proestrus during which follicular ripening occurs,

whereas the last 14 days of the menstrual cycle correspond to the phases of pseudopregnancy and metestrus associated with the development of corpora lutea. The ovarian and uterine changes which occur in the menstrual cycle, and the hormonal factors regulating the cycle, afford evidence in support of this relationship and are described further below (p. 1637). It may also be mentioned that slight bleeding does rarely occur in the human at about the time of ovulation, that is midway between the menstrual periods proper.

The sexual life of the human female usually commences between the 12th and 15th years, when the first menstruation or *menarche* occurs. This period of sexual awakening which is seen in animals and man of both sexes is referred to as *puberty*, with the periods before and after being called *pre-* and *postpubertal*, respectively. Some year or more before the appearance of the overt signs of puberty in girls gonadal hormone can be detected in the urine in amounts which are found to vary cyclically. At this time the ovaries show increased growth. The growth of the uterus is accelerated, the breasts enlarge and, in both girls and boys, hair appears upon the pubis and in the axillae. Deepening of the voice, enlargement of the genitalia (penis and testes) and growth of hair on the face are characteristic features of this period in boys. In both sexes, somatic growth is accelerated. The first menstrual cycles are frequently irregular and may be prolonged, with intervals of amenorrhea. During the next two or three years a menstrual rhythm becomes established but during this phase fertility has not reached the 'adult' level and the girl passes through a period of *"adolescent sterility."*

The length of the menstrual cycle has been measured on numerous occasions, with variable results. Most commonly the cycle lasts 25 to 30 days, with a mean close to 28 days. However, only about 15 per cent of menstrual cycles are exactly 28 days long and frequency distribution charts, plotting the number of cycles against the length of the cycle, show a normal distribution curve with cycles of 20 days and 40 days being recorded. Studies on individual women show that two consecutive cycles may differ in length by several days; this could be due to the operation of psychic factors.

Ovulation occurs usually, but not invariably, about the middle of the intermenstrual period, that is some 13 to 17 days after the first day of the last menstruation. Evidence in favor of this timing has been derived from the recovery of ova and early embryos from the tubes of women with known menstrual histories; from pregnancies following a single artificial insemination on a known day of the cycle; from the results of coitus at known times; from the occurrence of midmenstrual bleeding, which is associated with ovulation; and from the study of vaginal changes,

hormone excretion, and variations in basal temperature.

For a variety of reasons it is sometimes of importance to establish the day of ovulation in an individual. A number of approaches have been made to this problem. In 1935 it was discovered that ovulation in the rabbit is accompanied by a sharp rise in *electrical potential* across the pelvis just before rupture of the follicle, and this observation was confirmed in the human. However, subsequent work indicated that the effect was an indirect one only remotely due to ovarian influences, and unsuitable for the detection of ovulation. The *blood levels of hormones* and their excretion in the urine has been studied. Briefly, the maximum concentration of estrogen (p. 1627) in blood and urine occurs at about the time of ovulation, whereas a metabolic product of progesterone (p. 1634), pregnanediol, is demonstrable in the urine a day or so after ovulation. There is also an increase in the concentration of gonadotrophin (p. 1501) in the urine at about the time of ovulation. Studies of the *cervical mucus* have revealed cyclic changes in the character and composition of this secretion. It becomes less viscous and more plentiful about the time of ovulation, whereas on drying the mucus a characteristic crystallization pattern appears. By far the most convenient index of ovulation is the change in *basal temperature* that occurs about this time. The body temperature, recorded daily during the menstrual cycle and plotted upon a chart, may reach its lowest point at the time of ovulation. It then rises sharply and is maintained at a level about 0.8° F. above that seen during the first half of the cycle until the commencement of the menstrual flow. However, day-to-day variations in body temperature occurs, and for this reason the occurrence of a thermal shift can be defined with certainty only several days after this event.

Information concerning the time of ovulation in women has a practical value in contraception. The so-called "safe period" during which conception presumably cannot occur, has been placed in those parts of the cycle before and after ovulation. However, the time of ovulation varies considerably in different women and may occur several days before or after the 15th day of the cycle. The "safe period," therefore, cannot be predicted in any individual case without preliminary study although the least likely time for conception to occur is within the last eight days or so of the cycle, that is, eight days before menstruation.

Factors Concerned in the Fertilization of the Ovum

The ovum, if unfertilized, degenerates within a few hours after its discharge from the ovary, probably in the Fallopian tube. For this reason, and because only one ovum is discharged each cycle, the period during which fertilization can occur is very short, probably not longer than 6 or 7 hours. Yet the period during which coitus may lead to conception is relatively long, for the spermatozoa may retain their capacity to fertilize the ovum for some 48 hours or so, although this varies from species to species. In the rabbit the fertilizing capacity of sperm in the female tract may be retained for 32 hours, whereas in the mouse the corresponding period is only 6 hours. In the guinea pig this period is 22 hours, in the rat 14 hours, and perhaps remarkably, in the mare 5 to 6 days. The sperm shows motility for some time after it has lost its ability to fertilize. The former property is therefore not a reliable index of the latter.

Fertilization is effected in the Fallopian (uterine) tube and here also the earlier stages in the maturation of the ovum take place. When discharged, the ovum is surrounded by the *cumulus oophorus*. It has been thought that this covering could not be penetrated by the sperm, and must first be destroyed by the enzyme *hyaluronidase* contained in the sperm of most mammalian species; however, there has been a misconception in this regard for the mammalian spermatozoan can reach the ovum through an intact cumulus. It is possible, however, that the enzyme aids the sperm in some other way in its approach and penetration of the ovum. A hyaluronidase inhibitor, such as tri-gentisic acid (rehibin) added to rabbit semen before insemination was found by Parkes to prevent fertilization—an effect not due merely to a nonspecific spermicidal action. On the other hand, it has been argued that the rate of penetration of the cumulus by the sperm is too rapid to allow for any prerequisite enzyme action.

The menopause. Between the ages of 42 and 52 (average 47 years) the menstrual cycles become irregular and finally cease. This time is known as the *menopause* or *climacteric*. Retrogressive changes gradually set in in the accessory organs of reproduction, e.g., atrophy of the uterus, shortening and narrowing of the vagina with loss of its epithelium and replacement by fibrous tissue, and shrinkage of the mammary glands. These results are due to atrophic changes in the ovary—disappearance of the Graafian follicles together with a general fibrosis and shrinkage of the organ. Similar changes in the uterus and vagina follow the removal of the ovaries in earlier life, and constitute an *artificial menopause*. Psychic disturbances quite often occur during this "change of life" and occasionally may progress to melancholia and hysteria. Vasomotor and other autonomic disturbances, hot flushes, sweating, etc., are very common features of the climacteric. The effect of the natural menopause upon the sex libido varies in different subjects. In married women it shows little alteration as a rule. It would seem that the menopause occurs through a failure on the part of the ovary to secrete estrogen (see below).

The Ovarian Hormones

In addition to its gametogenic function the ovary produces hormones which regulate the reproductive processes. These are (1) the *estrogenic*, or follicular hormones; (2) the major hormone of the corpus luteum, *progesterone*, and (3) *relaxin*. The exact status of the latter hormone is doubtful since under certain conditions it can be formed by other parts of the reproductive tract. It has been isolated from the corpus luteum of the pig. The estrogenic hormones exert their effects primarily during the first part of the estrus cycle, whereas the corpus luteum hormone is concerned particularly with the latter part, with pseudopregnancy and pregnancy.

The Estrogenic Hormone

During the first twenty years of this century the evidence derived from ovariectomy and transplantation experiments had made it clear that the ovaries furnished an internal secretion which was responsible for the sexual development of the female. However the use of whole ovaries, and the use of rather uncertain biological indicators, confused the results available until the studies of Allen and Doisy in 1923. These workers aspirated the liquor folliculi from sows' ovaries and found that it was capable of inducing estrus in immature animals. The success of these workers was due to a large extent to the use of a precise method for the determination of estrus, namely the vaginal smear technique described above. Other investigators had mostly studied the effects of their extracts upon the uterus. With a sensitive test available the next step was to isolate the active constituent of follicular fluid. It was soon found that the material was extractable by fat solvents and could be concentrated, but another twelve years passed before the hormone was characterized. Meanwhile other estrogens had been isolated from the urine of pregnant women, pregnant mares, human placentas, and, surprisingly, the urine of stallions, and, in 1929, Doisy, Veler and Thayer, and Butenandt independently announced the crystallization of an oestrogen in pure form from the urine of pregnant women. It was believed at that time that there was only one estrogen and the workers concerned were generous in bestowing names upon it. Unfortunately, this led to confusion, particularly when the existence of other oestrogens came to light; therefore, many of the early names have been discarded and a formal nomenclature is now used.

The Origin and Distribution of Estrogen

The elements of the ovary responsible for the production of the follicular hormones are not definitely known. The presence of estrogen in high concentration in liquor folliculi, and the fact that follicular maturation coincides with the onset of estrus, point to the follicular cells (probably the theca interna) as being the chief source. Yet these cells cannot be solely responsible, for Parkes showed that estrus in mice continues to recur at regular intervals after the follicles have been completely destroyed by X-rays; moreover, the hormone can be extracted from the stroma alone. The interstitial cells in the latter situation may be a source of the hormone although it seems that co-operative action by the elements of the ovary is necessary for estrogen secretion. There is evidence that interstitial cells produce estrogen only in association with granulosal cells, whilst a study of the activity of fragments of rat ovary grafted to the eye indicated that secretion of estrogen occurred only when theca interna or interstitial cells were combined with granulosa or corpus luteum cells.

Estrogens are very widely distributed in normal tissues and occur in the ovaries of non-mammalian species of which the dogfish, cod, starfish sea urchin and molluscs are examples. The blood, urine, and feces, of both pregnant and non-pregnant female mamamls contain estrogens, as does the urine of adult males, with the testes and urine of stallions being among the richest known sources. As a consequence of the placental production of estrogen (see below), large amounts of

this class of hormone are excreted during pregnancy. In women, these total some 20–40 mg. daily in late pregnancy, whilst in the mare, values of the order of 100 mg. per liter of urine have been recorded.

Chemistry and Terminology

There are three well-established or "classic" estrogens. These are *estradiol, estrone* and *estriol*. Numerous other estrogens have been isolated from human pregnancy urine in recent years, but the most important and certainly the most abundant, ovarian estrogens are estrone and estradiol. Doisy and co-workers and Butenandt isolated estrone from the urine in 1929, whereas estradiol was obtained by MacCorquodale, Thayer and Doisy in 1935—after the use of 4 tons of ovaries as starting material. Estriol was first isolated in 1930 from human pregnancy urine independently by Doisy and associates and by Marrian. Estrone was named theelin by Doisy, and modifications of this name were subsequently applied to the compounds later discovered.

The estrogens possess a basic steroid nucleus like the hormones of the adrenal cortex. They differ from the cortical hormones in that ring A is benzenoid or aromatic in character, so that the phenolic hydroxyl group attached to carbon 3 has weakly acidic properties. This feature implies a solubility in alkaline solution and has been utilized in the separation of the hormones. In addition, the estrogens possess an oxygen or an hydroxyl group linked to carbon 17, and thus possess the capacity to exhibit stereoisomerism. By international agreement, the estrogens are considered to be derived from a parent substance, estrane, and are specifically named according to their relationship to the structure of that substance. The systematic names are informative and unequivocal but are unwieldy in daily use. Thus estra-1:3:5 (10)-triene-3-17β-diol is more simply known as estradiol-17β and the latter, trivial, name is generally preferred.

Estradiol. Estradiol was first obtained in the laboratory by reduction of the ketone group in estrone to an hydroxyl group, and was only later isolated from ovarian tissue. It is probably the major ovarian estrogen in the woman, cow and mare. Two steroisomers of estradiol are possible: estradiol-17α and estradiol-17β, depending on the stereoisomeric position of the hydroxyl group on the cyclopentane ring (ring D). There has been confusion over the relative biological activity of the two isomers but it is now established that the

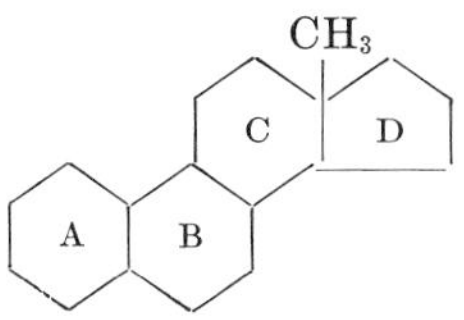

CH₃

Estrane

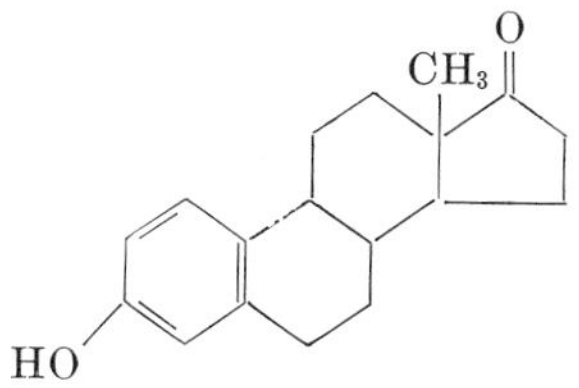

Estrone
3-Hydroxyestra-1:3:5(10)-triene-17-one

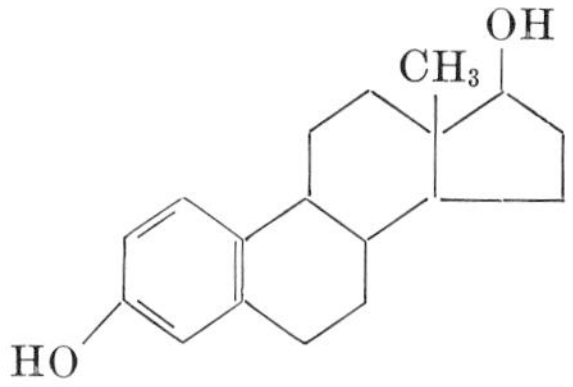

OH
CH₃

Estradiol-17β
Estra-1:3:5(10)-triene-3:17β-diol

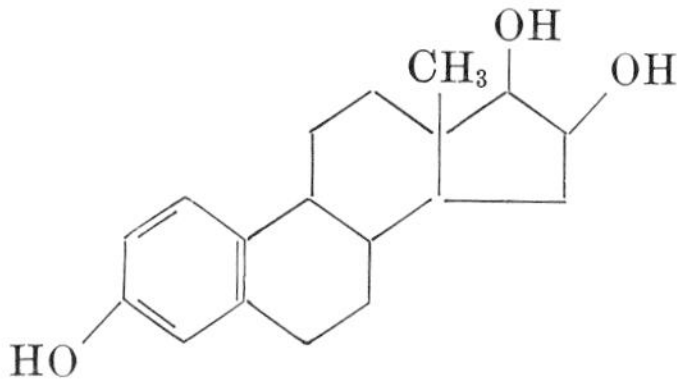

OH
CH₃   OH

Estriol
Estra-1:3:5(10)-triene-3:16α:17β-triol

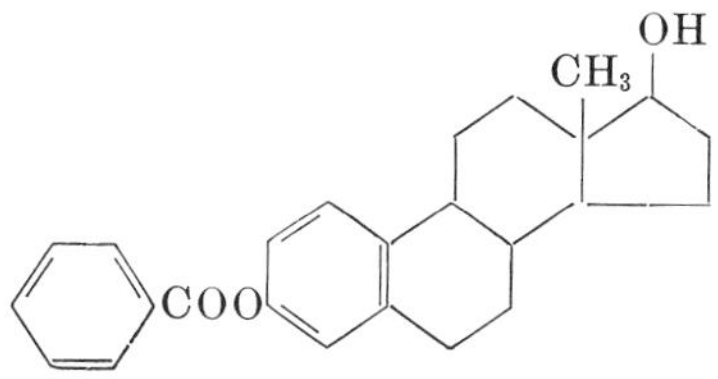

OH
CH₃

Estradiol benzoate
The formulae of some important estrogens

active one is estradiol-17β, or the cis form. Estradiol-17α does not appear to be excreted in the human but has been detected in the urine of the mare, stallion, cow and goat. The replacement of the hydroxyl group in the 3 position with benzoic acid, gives a product possessing more prolonged physiological action than the original compound, due to a slowed rate of inactivation. This compound, *estradiol benzoate*, is known commercially by various names. *Estradiol dipropionate* and *ethinyl estradiol* exert an even more prolonged effect.

Estrone. This was the first extrogen to be crystallized and was given a variety of names. These include *theelin, estrin, folliculin,* and *estrone.* It has been isolated from human blood, urine, placental tissue, bovine adrenal glands and the bile. It differs from estradiol in possessing an oxygen atom instead of an hydroxyl group at carbon-17.

Estriol has been obtained from human ovarian tissue, placenta and pregnancy urine. This hormone was once considered to be a characteristic product of the human species but this presumption has not been sustained. Since estriol contains three hydroxyl groups it is more soluble in water than the other estrogens.

The Metabolism of Estrogens

Like the adrenal cortical hormones, the estrogens are synthesized in the body from acetate, with cholesterol acting as a precursor. A fall in ovarian cholesterol occurs following stimulation with pituitary gonad-stimulating hormone and may be related to the synthesis of ovarian steroids. Cholesterol has been used as a starting material in the laboratory synthesis of estrogens. At this point it is appropriate to remark that there is a common pathway in the biosynthesis of steroids, which passes from acetate to cholesterol to pregnenolone to progesterone to the appropriate end products. In this way, steroids such as progesterone and testosterone serve both as active end products and intermediates in the manufacture of other, secreted, hormones. The progesterone produced in the adrenal, the testis and the ovarian follicle, and the testosterone found in the ovary are important in this way, as can be seen in fig. 78.7.

Following the administration of a pure estrogen labelled with radioactive carbon, a variety of metabolites appear in the urine and can be subjected to analysis. Alternatively, estrogens or estrogen precursors may be incubated with ovarian, placental or liver tissue *in vitro* and the transformation products isolated and identified. Experiments of this nature indicate that certain reactions can be brought about by the organ concerned, and by following the interconversions observed a variety of metabolic pathways for estrogens and other hormones can be traced. However, the physiological significance of the reactions observed is not always easy to gauge. Some metabolic transformations are plotted in fig. 78.8.

As indicated in fig. 78.8, the relationship between estradiol, estrone and estriol is of major importance. Administration of estradiol or estrone results in an increased excretion of estriol, whereas administration of estriol does not increase

the output of the other two hormones. Radioactive estrone and estradiol are converted to radioactive estriol. Estriol may be the main estrogen in human plasma; more estriol than estradiol or estrone tends to be excreted during the menstrual cycle.

The liver is of prime significance in the metabolism of estrogens, as well as of other steroids. Inactivation of estrogens occurs, as is shown by the loss of potency of the hormone when estradiol and estrone are incubated with liver slices. The use of a heart-lung-liver preparation has revealed a loss of estrogen in the perfusing fluid, whereas the activity was retained when the liver was excluded and the fluid circulated through a heart-lung preparation. Liver damage, such as follows the administration of carbon tetrachloride, is associated with an increased effect of estrogens, as well as a greater excretion of the steroids. Following the implantation of pellets of estrogen into the spleen of rats, so that the estrogen drains directly into the portal system, no estrogen activity is detected. But if the spleen is transplanted elsewhere in the body, or adhesions of the spleen to the stomach or body wall form, allowing escape of estrogens from the portal circulation, then full estrogenic activity appears. Clinical observations fully support the above experimental findings. Increased estrogen secretion often occurs in association with liver disease. Gynecomastia, loss of chest hair, testicular atrophy and loss of libido have all been described in men with cirrhosis of the liver, and can be attributed to interference with the mechanisms inactivating estrogens. The liver is concerned with the conjugation of estrogens with glucuronic acid or sulfate to form water-soluble

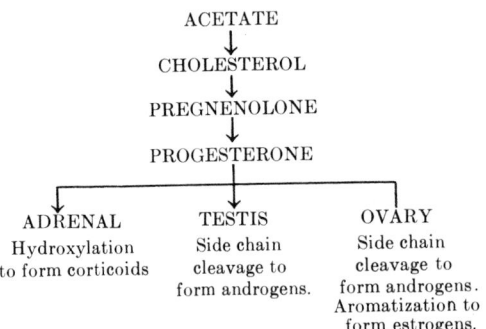

FIG. 78.7. The common pathway in the formation of steroid hormones. (After Ryan, Williams & Wilkins Co., 1963).

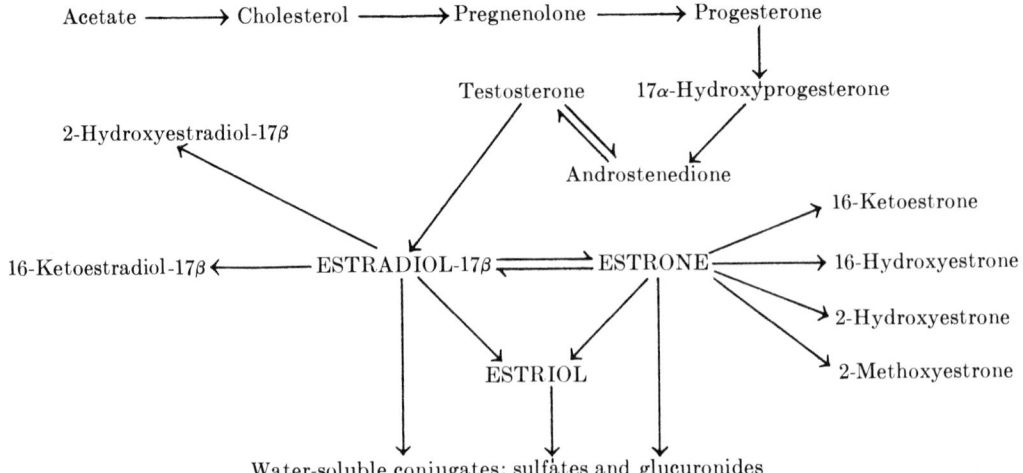

FIG. 78.8. Some metabolic transformations of estrogens

inert derivatives which may undergo further metabolic change without losing the sulfate group and which are excreted in the urine. Upon hydrolysis with acid, or enzymically with glucuronidase or phenol sulfatase, the conjugates are split and estrogenic activity reappears. Binding of estrogen to protein also takes place in the liver. Some 50 to 80 per cent of the estrogens present in blood are bound to the plasma proteins. The bile contains a relatively large quantity of free estrogens and biliary excretion may account for a significant proportion of the estrogen handled by the liver. Reabsorption of the steroids from the gastrointestinal tract probably occurs with an enterohepatic circulation coming into existence. Little estrogen is eliminated through the feces.

Synthetic estrogens. Estrogenic substances are not solely of animal origin. Estrogens can be obtained from petroleum, peat and lignite, rape seeds, palm kernels and pussy willow. Estrogen has been demonstrated in the mud at the bottom of the Dead Sea. It is not necessary for such substances to possess a similar chemical structure to that of the natural compounds. Miroestrol, from the roots of *Pueraria mirifica*, is highly active as an estrogen but is not a steroid. Dodds and his associates found active estrogens among the derivatives of diphenylethane and diphenylethylene and one of them *stilbestrol* (4,4'-dihydroxy-α-β-diethylstilbene), introduced in 1938, has been of great clinical value for many years. It is as active as the natural estrogens but, unlike the majority of them, retains its potency when given by mouth. The success of stilbestrol greatly stimulated work in this field and now a wide range of synthetic estrogens is available for clinical use. Two other synthetic compounds widely used clinically are *dihydroethylstilbestrol*, or *hexestrol*, and *dienestrol*.

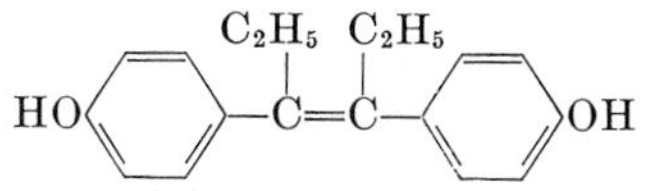

Diethylstilbestrol

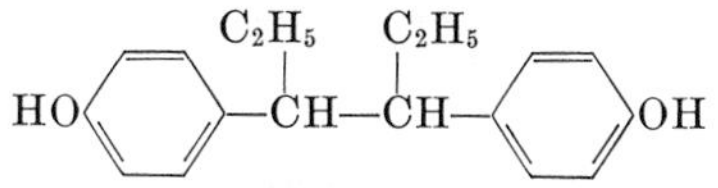

Hexestrol

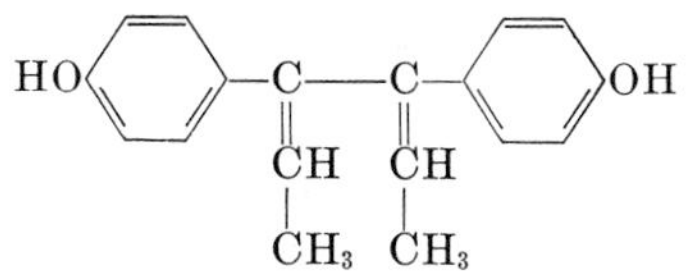

Dienestrol

The reasons underlying the estrogenic effect of the synthetic compounds are not well understood. One structural relationship between stilbestrol

and estradiol was pointed out by Dodds and is shown below, but when the structures are com-

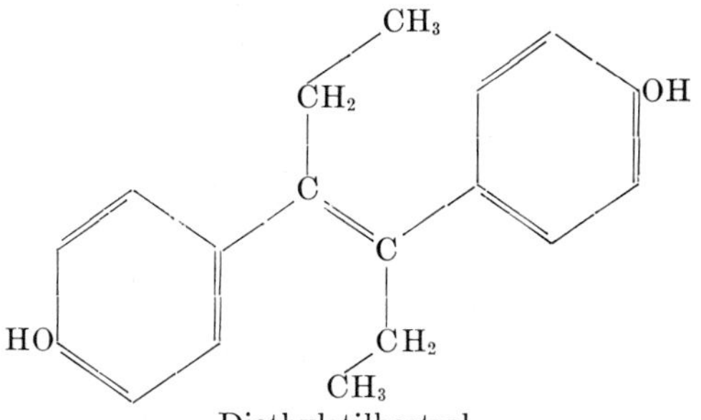

Diethylstilbestrol

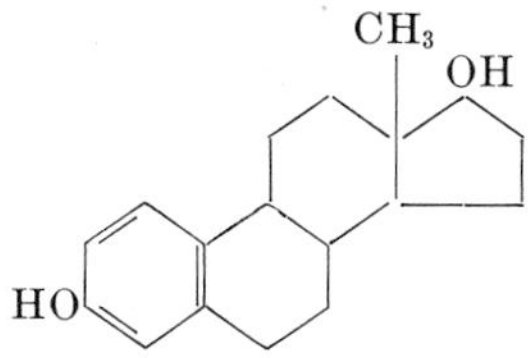

Estradiol

pared three-dimensionally there is not the same degree of similarity.

The Physiology of the Estrogens

For descriptive purposes, the actions of estradiol, estrone and estriol are identical, for these compounds differ only in relative potency. When used without qualification "estrogen" implies any substance which mimics the action of the natural estrogens. It is no longer associated with any special structural configuration. The actions of estrogens are many and varied. They may be divided into actions on the genital tract, on the accessory sex organs, and more generalised effects exerted elsewhere in the body.

Estrogens are of major importance in controlling *uterine function*. Removal of the source of estrogen, as after spaying, causes atrophy of the uterus which can be prevented by estrogen (figs. 78.3, 78.4). Estrogens cause hypertrophy of the uterus, which is associated with hyperemia, an increase in the wet and dry weight of the organ, and signs of anabolic activity such as the deposition of nitrogen and glycogen, an increased frequency of mitoses in the cells, and nucleic acid synthesis. This latter effect of estrogen is particularly marked during pregnancy. Under the influence of estrogen, a proliferative type of endometrium develops, and with prolonged treatment a pronounced hyperplasia of the endometrium ensues which parallels the clinical condition known as "Swiss cheese" endometrium. The uterus exhibits an increased motility with rhythmic movements in the presence of estrogen. This may be due in part to an increased sensitivity to oxytocin, as well as to an increase in the amount of actomyosin present in the myometrium with a rise in the isometric tension of the organ. At the end of pregnancy, when large amounts of estrogen are present in the body, a dose of estrogen which is normally ineffective will cause a powerful contraction of the uterus.

If, after menstruation has been abolished in monkeys by ovariectomy, a series of injections of an estrogen is given and then stopped abruptly, menstruation occurs a few days later. During the treatment of the spayed monkeys, phenomena appear which are analogous to those seen during the estrus period of lower animals, i.e. endometrial changes, reddening and swelling of the external genitalia and the production of a vaginal smear showing cornified cells and lacking leucocytes (fig. 78.6). Secretion of cervical mucus is also apparent. Induction of uterine bleeding by the above "estrogen withdrawal" is of value in the human, for artificial menstrual cycles can be produced in this way in women suffering from amenorrhea.

In the intact female, estrogens in high dosage prevent nidation of the fertilized ovum or induce abortion in early pregnancy.

Estrogens exert a direct effect upon the *ovary*. Since estrogen stimulates mitosis, the hormone present in the liquor folliculi itself promotes the growth of the follicle. Large doses of estrogen have been found to prevent ovarian atrophy in immature hypophysectomized rats. It has also been suggested that, on ovulation, the follicular fluid comes into contact with the germinal epithelium of the ovary and promotes a burst of mitoses which produces a new crop of follicles in readiness for a future cycle. With more moderate dosage and with chronic administration, estrogens induce ovarian atrophy, as well as testicular atrophy in the male, by suppressing the release of the pituitary gonadotrophins (ch. 74). However, estrogen is known to act, over a period of hours, on the hypothalamo-hypophysial system to cause the release of luteinizing hormone and hence ovulation.

Estrogens are responsible for the development of the *secondary sex characters*, which in some species are prominent features of the mature female. A variety of effects may be included under this heading, such as the altered location of fat depots, as compared to the male, a change in hair pattern with a thinning of the epidermis and skeletal changes which are particularly evident in the pelvis. The growth of the mammary glands is especially subject to the influence of estrogen, as discussed in connection with the physiology of lactation. Estrogens also promote the appearance of the psychic phenomena associated with "estrus," although they do not act alone in this respect, and the behavioral consequences of estrogen deprivation are not so well marked in the primate.

Of the *other actions* of estrogens which are manifest, that on water retention is of importance. This is brought about through increased retention of sodium and chloride, and is most evident at about the time of ovulation and just before menstruation when the blood concentration of estrogen is high. There may then be an increase in body weight associated with edema, thirst and a reduced output of urine. The blood volume is increased. With the onset of menstruation, there is a loss of the excess water and the body weight falls. Ovariectomy results in a loss of water and a diminished volume of blood, which is restored to normal by estrogen administration. Further information on the effects of estrogens will be found in the works listed at the end of this chapter.

In the *male*, estrogens in physiological dosage, or produced endogenously (testicular estrogen), may act synergistically with androgen in the development of the secondary sex characters. Protracted treatment with estrogen causes hypertrophy of the fibromuscular tissues of the prostate, but has little or no effect on the glandular elements. Growth of the male mammary glands may be stimulated. In young males other feminizing effects are produced.

Assay and Standardization of Estrogens

It has been the practice to assay the activity of estrogenic preparations upon ovariectomized rats or mice, with a unit being defined as the minimal quantity of the material required to induce estrus in 50 per cent of a group of test animals as shown by the vaginal smear. This is basically the technique of Allen and Doisy, but can be made quite sensitive by applying the estrogen directly to the vagina of the test animal. Alternatively, the increase of uterine weight produced by estrogen in ovariectomized or intact immature rats or mice has been used as an index of activity. Although there may be a linear relationship between the logarithm of the dose of estrogen and the increase in uterine weight, the dose-response curves of the separate estrogens differ one from the other, so that it becomes difficult to assay mixtures of estrogens, such as occur in the urine. Further, the use of such methods is complicated by the finding that results vary with the mode and frequency of administration of the hormone, as well as by the presence, in urine, of materials which may augment the action of estrogen.

Initially, in work on the assay of estrogens, a rat or mouse unit on the lines outlined above was used, but there were wide discrepancies between the results of different laboratories and in 1932 the Commission on Biological Standardization of the League of Nations defined an international unit. This was expressed in terms of estrone and was the activity exhibited by 0.1 μg. of the standard preparation. Later, with the use of esters of estrogen, an additional standard was set up, and one international unit was constituted by the activity of 0.1 μg. of estradiol-17β-monobenzoate.

Currently, most attention is being given to the development of chemical procedures for the assay of estrogen. These are essentially colorimetric or fluorimetric, in which the color or fluorescence is developed after a somewhat complex extraction and purification sequence. In the colorimetric method, when a pink color, which can be measured, is developed, the estrogens are heated with phenol and sulfuric acid, diluted with water and reheated. This is the Kober reaction, first described in 1931 and altered in detail since. The fluorimetric method is more sensitive but less specific than the colorimetric; it depends on the fact than an intense yellowish green fluorescence develops when an estrogen is heated with sulfuric or phosphoric acid.

Estrogens and Cancer

Since estrogens powerfully stimulate the growth of the uterus, vagina and mammary gland, it is not surprising that with continued administration benign proliferation may develop into malignant growth. As long ago as 1916, before the isolation of estrogens, Leo Loeb noted that spontaneous mammary cancer occurred in mice and was confined to the female; later, in 1932, Lacassagne succeeded in producing mammary cancer in the male mouse by the prolonged administration of estrogen. However, there are important species differences in the occurrence of mammary cancer. For instance, dogs and rabbits never develop breast cancer following administration of estrogen; neither does the rhesus monkey. But such a carcinoma can develop in dogs and rabbits following pregnancy toxemia which may damage the liver and interfere with the inactivation of estrogen. Rats never develop mammary cancer spontaneously, but will do so when subjected to treatment with estrogen. In women carcinoma of the breast is quite common but according to Bishop there is surprisingly little evidence that cancers develop with the administration of estrogen, particularly when the enormous number of women given estrogen at one time or other is taken into account.

From the present point of view there are two kinds of cancer; those that are *hormone-dependent* and those that are *hormone-independent*. As the classification implies, the hormone-dependent carcinoma requires a particular hormone or hormone complex for its development. Denial of this need frequently inhibits the growth and promotes regression. In the male, cancer of the prostate gland provides an instance of this class of tumor, which is dependent upon androgen for its continued growth. Removal of endogenous androgen by orchidectomy generally produces a remission although in some cases the adrenals may provide an alternative supply of androgen. *Hormone-independent* tumors are not subject to control by any endocrine secretion and develop in such tissues as the skin, stomach and lung. However, a hormone-dependent tumor can become independent of a particular hormone and so become autonomous. It should be pointed out that in a number of cases an optimal endocrine environment may be necessary for tumor growth. Thus it appears that following hypophysectomy certain chemical carcinogens failed to induce cancers of the liver, whereas they continue to do so in other parts of the body. The full carcinogenic effect is restored by ACTH or growth hormone administration.

The Luteal Hormone

The suspicion that the corpus luteum might be a gland of internal secretion which functions during gestation has long been held. Indeed, Corner relates that when Gustav Born lay dying in 1900 he imparted this idea to Ludwig Fraenkel for subsequent experimental test. Three years later (1903) Fraenkel reported that destruction of the corpora lutea in the ovaries of the rabbit was not compatible with the continuance of pregnancy, whereas Ancel and Bouin (1910) found that the cycle of growth and regression of the corpus luteum was closely linked with a series of (progestational) changes which take place in the uterus. Also about this time Loeb discovered (1909) that stimulation of the uterine mucosa of the non-pregnant guinea pig by means of a glass bead or a silk thread, or merely by scratching the endometrium with a needle during the development of the corpora lutea resulted in the growth of a small mass of decidual tissue (*deciduoma*) at the point of stimulation. This *Loeb reaction* could not be obtained after the corpora lutea had been excised or during a phase of the estrus cycle when they were absent. Even transplanted uterine tissue responded to stimulation if the ovary contained corpora lutea. Other observers have since obtained corresponding results in the rat, rabbit and dog. Thus it appears that the contact of the fertilized ovum with the endometrium is the natural stimulus which, in the presence of a corpus luteum, causes the formation of decidual tissue.

Corner first showed that the corpus luteum was necessary for the survival and implantation of the rabbit embryo and, in collaboration with W. M. Allen, he obtained a crude extract which was active in maintaining pregnancy in ovariectomized rabbits. Within five years (1934) the active constituent of the extract was obtained in chemically pure form by several groups of workers, and had been synthesized from stigmasterol by Butenandt and his associates. The hormone is now known as *progesterone*, with Corner's original name *progestin* being used as a general term for any substance possessing similar actions. A modern alternative to progestin is *gestagen*. Two derivatives of progesterone, 20α- and 20β-hydroxy progesterone, have since been isolated from human corpora lutea, follicular fluid and placentate. The corresponding tissues of other species appear to contain either the α or β isomer. Both substances exhibit less gestagenic activity than

oviparous and ovoviviparous selachians, teleosts and reptiles, and in mammals they first appear in the oviparous Monotremata. Further, any hormone produced is not necessarily progesterone.

Progesterone

Progesterone has the structure shown below. It occurs in two crystalline forms, the α and β, but these are about equal in physiological activity. Comparison with the estrogens (p. 1631) and the adrenal cortical hormones (p. 1573) shows that it is more closely allied to the adrenal hormones and that it belongs to the carbon-21 or pregnane group of steroids. This relationship is underlined by the fact that progesterone is an intermediate in the synthesis of adrenal, testicular and ovarian hormones. Progesterone has been isolated from ox adrenal tissue and from the adrenal venous blood of the sheep and cow. The fact that the administration of ACTH to ovariectomized women increases the urinary output of pregnanediol, a metabolic product of progesterone, further points to an adrenal origin of progesterone. Experiments with isotopically-labelled acetate and cholesterol indicate that these substances act as precursors in the formation of progesterone.

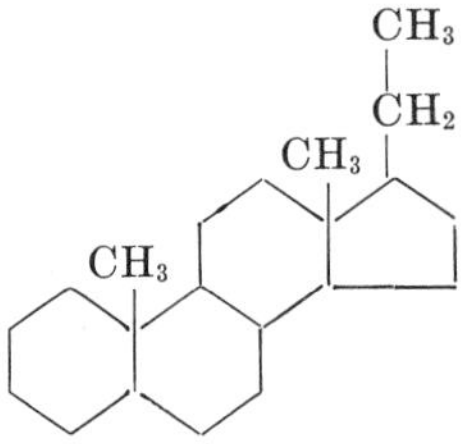

Pregnane

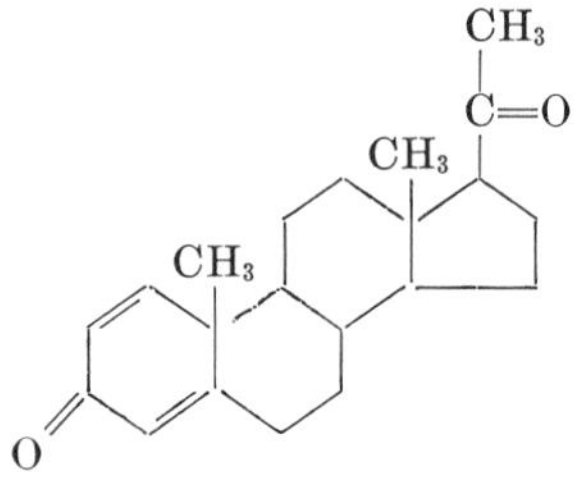

Progesterone

Pregn-4-ene-3:20-dione

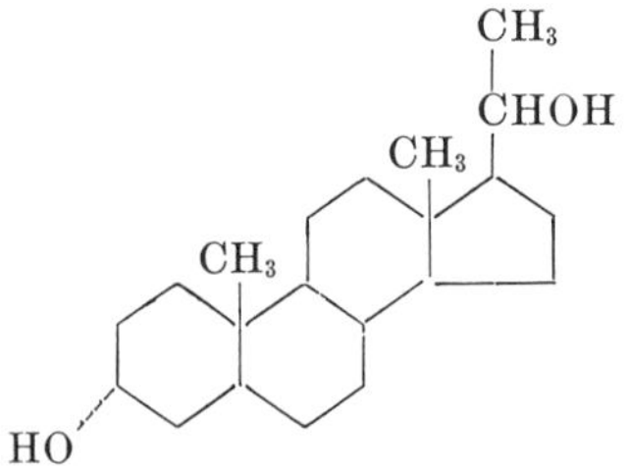

Pregnanediol

5β-pregnane-3α:20α-diol

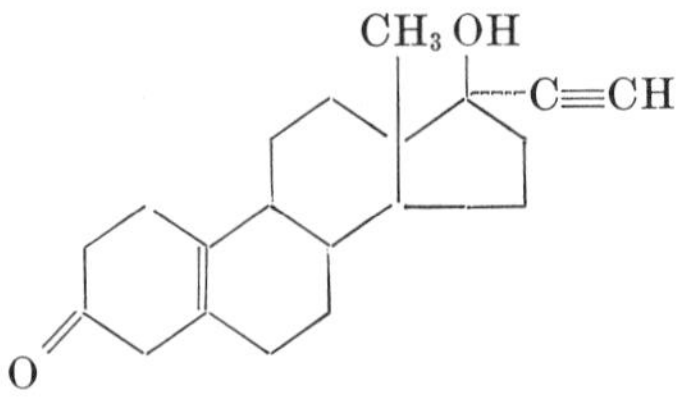

Norethynodrel

17α-ethynyl-17β-hydroxy-estr-5:10-en-3-one

The formulae of some important gestagens.

progesterone but this varies in degree, according to the test applied.

Corpora lutea are not restricted to the mammalia, nor are they invariably associated with viviparity since they have been described in

Progesterone is produced by luteal tissue, by the adrenal cortex and by the placenta. During pregnancy in women, the corpus luteum gradually ceases production of progesterone and the placenta takes over this function. For this reason, gestation can continue after ovariectomy if the latter operation is carried out after implantation. Clinical cases have been described in which the corpora lutea have been removed in the first month without causing abortion. A similar situation exists in the monkey, horse, ewe, cow and guinea pig, but in the rabbit and rat, abortion occurs if the corpora lutea are lost at any time during pregnancy.

Progesterone is rapidly metabolized *in vivo* and normally cannot be detected in the urine. The "turnover-time" of progesterone in the blood at the end of pregnancy (the period during which the amount of hormone in the blood can be considered to have been completely replaced) has been calculated to be about 3.3 minutes. Progesterone excretion is determined indirectly by measurement of its reduced form *pregnanediol*, which is physiologically inert and which appears as a water-soluble glucuronide. The concentration of this substance (and its isomers) provides a useful index of the rate of production of progesterone. However, caution is necessary in the interpretation of results since, according to Loraine, less than 20 per cent of a dose of administered progesterone may be excreted in the urine as pregnanediol. A rise in urinary pregnanediol has been reported to follow the administration of adrenal corticoids, and the pregnanediol output may also be increased in cases of adrenocortical hyperplasia or tumor, so the possible contribution of adrenal steroids should be borne in mind.

The liver is actively concerned with the conversion of progesterone to pregnanediol glucuronide and in the excretion of metabolites of progesterone in the bile. Following the administration of C^{14}-labelled progesterone to the cat, less than one per cent of the labelled material appeared in the urine in the ensuing six hours but up to sixty-seven per cent was excreted in the bile. The excretion of metabolites of progesterone in the feces may be considerable.

The Physiology of Progesterone

This hormone possesses a spectrum of activity which includes: (1) effects on the uterus, (2) the maintenance of pregnancy, (3) participation in the control of the growth of the mammary gland, and (4) suppression of estrus and ovulation. These actions will now be examined.

Effects on the uterus. It was early discovered that progesterone treatment develops the endometrium. In the rabbit, this is marked by a typical arborization of the glands, which is identical to that appearing during pregnancy or pseudopreg-

nancy. Corresponding changes have been observed in other species during treatment with progesterone, and under these conditions, deciduomas (p. 1633) are readily induced. In the immature rabbit, treatment with progesterone fails to produce the endometrial changes outlined above, nor is the treatment effective in adult rabbits which have been ovariectomized for some time. However, administration of estrogen for several days before the progesterone treatment results in the appearance of progestational changes. It is clear that the uterus must be "primed" with estrogen before it can respond to progesterone. This effect is not confined to the rabbit; it is also well marked in the monkey, where progesterone has little effect in the ovariectomized animal. When preceded by estrogen, progesterone will produce a typical premenstrual endometrium in 7 to 10 days. Two other aspects of this process must be emphasized. First, it is possible for progesterone to produce proliferative changes in the uterus by itself, but enormous doses must be given; and second, estrogen also antagonizes some effects of progesterone. This latter effect appears when the ratio of estrogen to progesterone, optimal for uterine development, is altered in favor of estrogen. Under these circumstances the action of progesterone is inhibited. Conversely, progesterone will block the action of estrogen; the coloration and edema of the sexual skin of a spayed monkey, developed by treatment with estrogen, is lost following a single injection of progesterone. It will be seen that, depending upon the relative amounts of these hormones, estrogen and progesterone can interact to produce a variety of effects. This is of importance in a number of reproductive processes. Thus, the deciduoma reaction (described previously) can be inhibited by treatment with estrogen.

In addition to the effects on the mucosa of the uterus, progesterone also exerts an action on the muscle. In the castrate rabbit the uterus is flaccid and quiescent and does not display any motility, although when estrogenized, regular rhythmic contractions appear. These are also seen in the estrous rabbit, rat or sow; however, administration of progesterone abolishes such activity. The activity of the uterus of the estrus animal is greatly increased by the oxytocic hormone. Following treatment with progesterone, oxytocin can no longer produce this effect upon the uterus which is then said to be "desensitized." Such phenomena would seem to be of value in the normal individual since a motile estrous uterus would aid the transport of sperm toward the ova, and the movement of ova along the tubes. In agreement with this concept oxytocin has been found to be released at coitus (p. 1518). Further, once the uterus contains blastocysts, the uterine contractions, which would be detrimental to their implantation and survival, are blocked by progesterone. Toward the end of pregnancy uterine reactivity to oxytocin reappears, possibly due to the increasing amounts of circulating estrogen, and discharge of the fetuses is facilitated.

Maintenance of pregnancy. This function of progesterone has previously been noted. In ovariectomized rabbits about 2 mg. of progesterone daily will compensate for the absence of corpora lutea and maintain pregnancy, although in the later stages up to 5 mg. may be necessary. In the rhesus monkey the corpus luteum may be removed as early as the 25th day without disturbing pregnancy, whereas in women gestation can continue following ovariectomy after the first weeks. In the latter species the placenta becomes responsible for the production of progesterone. Administration of progesterone toward the end of pregnancy in rabbits prolongs the gestation period and results in the delivery of larger young.

Suppression of estrus and ovulation. The estrous cycle or menstrual cycle does not continue during pregnancy; ovarian follicles do not mature and ovulation does not occur. This change is brought about by progesterone, which interrupts the normal sexual cycles in nonpregnant individuals. If the corpora lutea are removed during a pseudopregnancy then estrus and ovulation quickly follow; whereas if the corpora lutea are extirpated from the guinea pig ovary early in the estrous cycle then the next ovulation occurs sooner than usual. Elimination of the corpora lutea of the cow's ovary by manipulation through the rectum hastens the onset of the next estrous period. The ovulation which normally follows copulation in the rabbit is blocked by the administration of progesterone. Such effects are brought about by the inhibition of the secretion of gonadotrophin from the pituitary (p. 1501). The so-called "oral contraceptives" utilize this progestational effect in that they prevent ovulation by blocking the release of pituitary gonadotrophin. Unlike progesterone, they are active when taken by mouth; *norethynodrel* is an example of such a substance. During pregnancy or pseudopregnancy the superficial layer of cells in the vagina loses its squamous and cornified character and the cells become rounded and filled with a mucous-like substance. This change occurs under the

influence of progesterone, acting in cooperation with estrogen.

Growth of the mammary glands. The part played by progesterone in the development and function of the mammary glands will be discussed on p. 1643.

ASSAY AND STANDARDIZATION OF PROGESTERONE. The *international standard* of progesterone is defined as the progestational activity of 1 mg. of the international standard crystalline preparation. The test animal is an adult female rabbit which has been mated and then spayed, or an immature female rabbit which has been primed for 5 days previously with estrogen. These preparations are relatively insensitive and do not permit the detection of progesterone in blood. Hooker and Forbes (1947) used intrauterine injection of the hormone in ovariectomized mice and examined the endometrium histologically. This procedure will measure the total "progestogenic activity" in the blood of pregnant women but is not very specific. Recently Zander and Simmer (1954) have developed a chemical method, using ultraviolet spectroscopy, which will measure the progesterone concentration in blood.

Since pregnanediol is regarded as a metabolic product of progesterone and is present in relatively large amounts in the urine, assay of this steroid has been used as an index of progesterone production. The first method, described by Venning in 1937, involved extraction of the urine with butanol, precipitation with acetone, and weighing the precipitate. During the past 10 years a variety of procedures have been developed which generally involve chromatography and colorimetry. The technique of Klopper, Michie and Brown (1955) is sensitive enough to measure the pregnanediol produced by the adrenals of men.

RELAXIN

One of the many adaptive processes occurring in pregnancy is the relaxation of the ligaments of the symphysis pubis which takes place in a variety of species. This "pubic relaxation" occurs in women, monkeys, guinea pigs, mice, dogs, cows and ewes, among others. In 1926 Hisaw discovered that the blood serum of the pregnant rabbit contains a substance which produced this effect in nonpregnant guinea pigs. It was called *relaxin* and has now been detected in the serum of a wide variety of species. Relaxin differs from other ovarian hormones in that it appears to be peptide or polypeptide in nature, is readily soluble in water, and is destroyed by proteolytic enzymes. It has been extracted from the corpora lutea of sows, whole ovaries, blood serum, urine and placenta. The relaxin content of the sow ovary begins to increase early in pregnancy and reaches its highest concentration by the time the fetuses are from 12 to 15 cm. long.

For a time the existence of relaxin was questioned, for it was claimed by some workers that pubic relaxation could be induced by estrogen or progesterone or a combination of the two. Abramowitz and his associates found, however, that an extract prepared from sows' ovaries, when given in a dosage far below that necessary for an estrogenic or progestational effect caused relaxation of the pubic ligaments. It would seem that relaxin is formed in the uterus under the influence of estrogen and progesterone as removal of this organ greatly reduces the action of these steroids on the pelvis, whereas the potency of relaxin is retained. Even in the intact guinea pig relaxin acts much faster (within 12 hours) than progesterone or estrogen. Further, histological studies have shown that estrogen relaxes the pubic symphysis by promoting resorption of the bone, and a proliferation of loose fibrous connective tissue whereas relaxin produces a dissolution and splitting of the collagenous fibers into thin threads. The changes following progesterone treatment are similar to those induced by relaxin.

Whilst the existence of relaxin is well established, the physiological significance of this hormone in women is not yet clear. It is known that the concentration of relaxin in the blood rises steadily from the sixth week of pregnancy, to reach a peak at thirty-six weeks which is maintained until delivery, when a precipitous fall occurs. The hormone is not detectable in the serum twenty-four hours after parturition.

The Hormonal Control of the Menstrual Cycle

Although essentially similar to the estrous cycle of lower animals the menstrual cycle of primates possesses several features which must be examined. The hormonal basis of the process has also to be discussed.

Uterine Changes in the Menstrual Cycle

The occurrence of uterine bleeding marks the end of a menstrual cycle, although it is customary to describe the period of hemorrhage as days 1 to 4, i.e., the first stage of the cycle. The remainder of the cycle is usually divided into two stages—the stage of repair and proliferation (days 5 to 14) and the days of secretion (days 15 to 28). However since ovulation and any corpora lutea formed thereby exert a regulating influence on the succeeding menstrual flow, it is more logical to describe the cycle as commencing with the stage of repair and proliferation. The changes taking place in the endometrium of the rhesus monkey are illustrated in fig. 78.9.

The stage of repair and proliferation—follicular phase. During the 10 days or so after the end of the menstrual flow the epithelium of the endometrium which was shed at that time is restored by rapid outgrowths from the mouths of the glands. The epithelial lining then hypertrophies and the glands show proliferative changes. The uterus enlarges as a result of the accumulation of ground substance and as it becomes more vascular the arteries which supply the inner third of the endometrium—the *spiral arteries*—become coiled. In the ovary the Graafian follicle has been undergoing maturation and ovulation occurs at the end of the follicular phase. The proliferative changes in the uterus occur under the influence of estrogen.

The premenstrual, progestational or progravid stage—luteal phase. This stage, following the follicular phase, lasts for 13 or 14 days. Its length is more constant than that of the follicular phase. The uterine mucosa shows marked hypertrophy and is highly vascular; its glands become elongated and assume a coiled or corkscrew form. The glandular secretion becomes greatly increased and more mucoid in character and toward the end of the premenstrual stage the endometrium resembles the decidua of early pregnancy, with the appearance of typical decidual cells in the uterine stroma. During this phase the spiral arteries continue to lengthen disproportionately to the growth of the endometrium. Some time before menstruation there is a reduction in the blood supply to the endometrium which shrinks and compresses the spiral arteries. The blood is then further slowed until there is a state of stasis. Finally the spiral arteries constrict and ischemia of the endometrium occurs. The stage is set for menstruation.

The uterine changes occurring in the luteal phase are produced by progesterone secreted by the corpus luteum, and to this extent the stage corresponds to that of pseudopregnancy observed in some lower species. If fertilization of the ovum does not occur the corpus luteum does not persist, its influence upon the endometrium wanes, and this change is marked by shrinkage of the endometrium. At the end of the premenstrual stage swelling of the mammary glands may be noted and mild psychic disturbances (irritability, nervousness, depression, etc.) may appear.

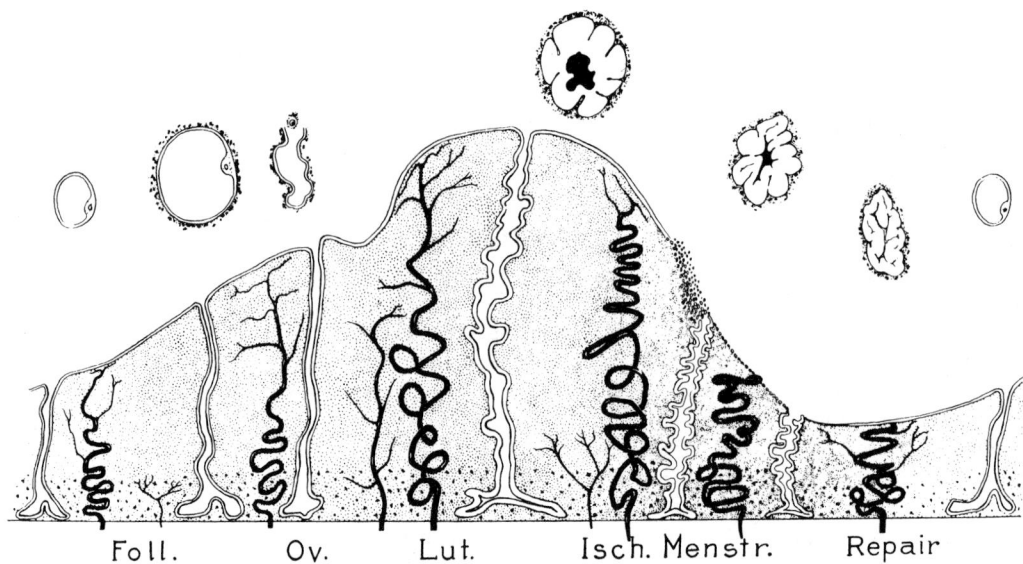

Foll.   Ov.   Lut.   Isch. Menstr.   Repair

Fig. 78.9. The correlated changes in ovary and endometrium during an ovulatory cycle in the rhesus monkey. Thickness of mucosa, density of stroma, gland form and three types of artery are indicated. There is a gradual increase in thickness up to the time of ovulation, marked by a brief thinning of the endometrium, which is followed by development of the progravid condition with accumulation of secretion in the glands due to relaxation of the myometrium. Then comes loss of ground substance from the stroma, which may be the primary factor in the premenstrual regression of the mucosa and the initiation of the schemic phase. There is further regression throughout menstruation. During repair, thickening of the endometrium is associated with increase in ground substance in the stroma and growth of the glands. (From Bartelmez, Am. J. Obst. & Gyn., 1957, 74, 931–955.)

The destructive stage or *stage of menstrual flow* lasts for about 4 days. After a period of ischemia of the endometrium individual spiral arteries relax and hemorrhage occurs through rupture of the wall of an arteriole or capillary. The blood may escape through the epithelium or may collect in the underlying tissues to form a hematoma which eventually discharges into the lumen of the uterus. Hemorrhage ceases locally through vasoconstriction of the spiral arteries, but constriction and relaxation of these vessels does not occur synchronously throughout the uterus so that some bleeding continues. During the process fragments of the epithelium become desquamated and blood vessels may be observed to project freely into the lumen. Gradually the vessels close permanently and an intact circulation becomes reestablished through the basal arteries. This heralds the end of menstruation and the commencement of a new follicular phase.

The blood discharged during menstruation differs from normal blood in that it does not clot. This is apparently due to its passage through the endometrium, for blood that escapes during arterial hemorrhage clots rapidly.

Markee has followed the process of menstruation microscopically in pieces of endometrium transplanted into the anterior chamber of the eye of monkeys. Bleeding occurred from the transplanted tissue during menstruation, but preceded the appearance of blood in the vagina by about 3 hours. His observations emphasize the essentially endocrine nature of the uterine changes occurring during the menstrual cycle. In the human subject patches or tumors of endometrial tissue are sometimes found in extrauterine situations, e.g., surface of the broad ligament or ovary, in the omentum, pelvic peritoneum or subcutaneous tissue of the vulva or perineum, or in the tissue in the neighborhood of a laparotomy scar. The ectopic tissue bleeds during menstruation. The condition is not uncommon and is known as *endometriosis*.

Effects of Estrogen—Progesterone Interactions on the Menstrual Cycle

It is evident that estrogen-progesterone interactions underly many of the changes observed during the menstrual cycle. However, although the changes seen are well accounted for on this basis, the precise mode of action of the ovarian hormones merits further examination.

It is not necessary for a luteal phase to precede menstruation. This is shown by the fact that in monkeys, as well as in women, ovariectomy during the follicular phase is followed in a few days by a premature menstrual period. Such postoperative bleeding can be postponed by administration of estrogen. Markee showed that an intraocular transplant of endometrium menstruated when a crystal of estrone inserted into that eye was removed, and also that while the crystal was present, the graft in that eye did not bleed at a time when the uterus did so. Also, in monkeys and young women, menstrual cycles can occur without ovulation and the formation of luteal tissue. In these cases cyclic changes in the blood level of estrogen alone presumably are responsible for the flow. Evidence for this view is the finding that ovariectomized monkeys, subjected to a course of estrogen treatment, menstruate soon after the withdrawal of the hormone. This is the estrogen withdrawal effect alluded to earlier (p. 1632). Bleeding may also follow if the dose of estrogen is suddenly reduced although continued at a low level.

Cessation of progesterone administration results in similar effects to estrogen withdrawal. If a short series of progesterone injections is superimposed upon a long course of treatment with estrogen in an ovariectomized monkey, then menstruation ensues shortly after the withdrawal of the progesterone. Alternatively progesterone will prevent estrogen-withdrawal bleeding when given immediately following the estrogen. On stopping the progesterone then a progesterone-withdrawal menstrual period ensues. Menstruation follows the end of progesterone treatment in a recently ovariectomized monkey not given estrogen. Progesterone delays menstruation when given during the normal menstrual cycle.

It would seem from the observations above that menstruation follows a reduction in the hormonal stimulus applied to the uterus—whether progestational or estrogenic. In the usual menstrual cycle bleeding normally follows a decline in the circulating level of progesterone for the urinary excretion of pregnanediol begins to fall a few days before the onset of menstruation. With regard to estrogen the observations of Brown on the excretion of the hormone during the menstrual cycle give the following picture: The excretion of estrogens increases steadily up to about the 13th day when an *ovulation peak* is reached. It then suddenly falls, remains low for several days, and thereafter slowly increases to reach a *luteal maximum* at about the 21st day. Finally, immediately prior to the onset

of menstruation the excretion of estrogen falls once more.

So far the menstrual cycle has been discussed as if it were a process lying entirely under the sway of the ovary. This is not so, for the participation of the gonadotrophic hormones of the pituitary gland in regulating the cyclic activity of the ovary has been neglected. These are discussed on page 1501, so that here the interactions may be tentatively summarized:

The estrogen content of the blood rises when the ovary is stimulated by the follicle-stimulating hormone of the pituitary, and when the concentration of this ovarian hormone reaches a certain level it, in turn, acts to suppress the output of follicle-stimulating hormone and excite the release of luteinizing hormone. The concentration of estrogen upon which the proliferative stage of menstruation depends is thus reduced. Next the hypophysis releases its luteinizing principle which stimulates the development of the corpus luteum, but as the concentration of progesterone in the blood rises the production of the luteinizing principle is in turn suppressed, with the result that the integrity of the luteal tissue cannot be maintained. With the fall in the concentration of estrogen and progesterone menstrual bleeding occurs and the secretion of follicle-stimulating hormone is then resumed—with commencement of another cycle.

Menstrual Irregularities

The nonoccurrence of the menstrual periods in postpubertal life is called *amenorrhea*; except during pregnancy, when suppression of the menses is a physiological phenomenon, the failure of the menstrual cycles at any time between puberty and the menopause is abnormal. Amenorrhea may be either *primary* or *secondary*. In the former instance the menses have never occurred, in the latter they appeared but were subsequently suppressed. Primary amenorrhea is in many instances associated with arrested development of the reproductive organs. Scanty menstruation is termed *oligomenorrhea*, whereas *menorrhagia* is excessive bleeding. *Metrorrhagia* is the loss of blood from the uterus in the intermenstrual periods. A large proportion of these menstrual irregularities, when unaccompanied by some gross disease (e.g., tumor in the uterus), have an endocrine basis.

Amenorrhea is frequently the result of ovarian hypofunction. *Dysmenorrhea*, painful menstruation, is the result of irregular and spasmodic contractions of the uterine muscle which may in many cases have an hormonal origin. In the past, excessive bleeding in the absence of some obvious uterine disease has been put down to inflammation of the uterine mucosa (endometritis). Before the physiological changes in the endometrium were correlated with the stages of the ovarian cycle (p. 1637) the normal premenstrual characters of the uterine mucosa were considered to be pathological evidence of endometritis!

With the knowledge currently available it is clear that disorders of the menstrual cycle, such as amenorrhea, can result from a variety of causes which will operate through the ovaries or through the pituitary. The operation of psychological or neurological factors which act on the pituitary gland through the hypothalamus must not be neglected in this regard. It is well known that *gross* diseases of the anterior pituitary gland such as acromegaly, Simmond's disease, and dystrophia adiposogenitalis are associated with menstrual irregularities which usually appear as oligomenorrhea or amenorrhea. Amenorrhea also occurs as an accompaniment of hyperthyroidism and as a symptom of several general diseases, notably anemia, tuberculosis and malnutrition.

The treatment of menstrual disorders depends, of course, upon the nature of the factors precipitating the condition.

The Endocrine Functions of the Placenta

The human placenta has been found to contain many hormones and undoubtedly acts as an endocrine gland. However, conclusive evidence exists only for the production of chorionic gonadotrophin, estrogen and progesterone.

Human Chorionic Gonadotrophin (HCG)

The existence of a gonadotrophic principle in the blood and urine of pregnant women was established in 1927 by Ascheim and Zondek, but it was left to later workers to show that the substance was derived from the placenta. Besides its presence in the organ the following evidence demonstrates that HCG is produced by the placenta: Gonadotrophin is detectable in the urine and body fluids in all conditions in which normal or abnormal chorionic tissue is present and disappears with its complete removal. In cases in which the placenta is retained after expulsion of the fetus, gonadotrophin secretion continues, so excluding a fetal origin of the hormone. Chorionepitheliomas of the uterus, or of the testis, are also characterized by the excretion of chorionic gonadotrophin in the urine, as is hydatiform mole (a cystic degenerative disease of chorionic tissue). Grafts of human chorionic villi inserted into the anterior chamber of the eye of the rabbit produce gonadotrophin, as shown by changes in the ovaries of the host which parallel those caused by injection of HCG. Confirmatory findings have been made in other species. Chorionic tissue maintained in tissue culture has been shown to manufacture gonadotrophin and not simply to store the hormone.

The excretion of HCG has been found to be within normal limits in the hypophysectomized woman and this fact, together with the findings showing that the physicochemical and biological properties of HCG differ from those of the pituitary gonadotrophins, make it unlikely that the hypophysis is concerned in the production of this hormone. The hormonal secretions of the pituitary are required during pregnancy in the rabbit and dog whereas in other species (monkey, ewe, horse and cow) pregnancy is interrupted only if pituitary ablation is performed early.

While it is generally considered that the Langhans cells of the fetal chorion produce HCG, complete agreement has yet to be reached. In the human, the hormone can be detected in the blood serum or urine as early as the 24th day of the menstrual cycle. From about the 40th day, the concentration rises extremely rapidly to reach a peak at about 60 days which is maintained for some 10 days, when an equally rapid fall begins. A relatively low concentration is found by the 100th day of gestation and this level is maintained until delivery. In the monkey and chimpanzee, chorionic gonadotrophin is excreted for only a short time during pregnancy.

The actions of chorionic gonadotrophin differ from those of any of the pituitary gonadotrophins but most closely parallel those of the luteinizing hormone (LH). When immature female rats are treated with chorionic gonadotrophin prepared from human placenta, placental implants, or extracts of human pregnancy urine, follicular maturation, estrus and the formation of corpora lutea ensue; the luteinizing action is the predominant effect. LH is ineffective in immature animals. The failure of the pituitary principle is probably due to the lack of sufficient follicle-stimulating hormone (FSH), whose synergistic action is required by both LH and HCG, for the placental hormone appears able to stimulate the release of FSH from the hypophysis of the rat, whereas the pituitary hormone can not. Accordingly, removal of the hypophysis of the immature rat abolishes the overall stimulating effect of HCG upon the ovary but the interstitial cells are maintained in good condition.

In women, HCG, in the presence of FSH, has been found to induce corpus luteum formation and increase the output of pregnanediol. It is also active in supporting the secretory activity of pre-existing corpora lutea in women and in monkeys. In males, HCG has been shown to stimulate the production of androgen by the Leydig cells of the testis. This effect occurs in immature, adult and hypophysectomized individuals. The hormone will also maintain the integrity of the seminiferous tubules of hypophysectomized males, possibly through the mediation of the raised output of androgen. These actions of HCG are of clinical value in the treatment of undescended testes and of eunuchoidism.

The physiological function of chorionic gonadotrophin is not entirely clear. It would seem that the hormone is concerned with the prolongation of corpus luteum function during the first weeks of gestation, but once past this stage the ovaries can be removed from women without inducing abortion. The reason for the production of large quantities of HCG in the later stages of pregnancy is not at all apparent.

A wide variety of techniques has been used in the assay of human chorionic gonadotrophin. Those performed on the rat include the increase in ovarian weight after treatment with the hormone, the production of ovarian hyperemia, increase in uterine weight, changes in the vaginal smear, and increase in the weight of the accessory reproductive organs of the male. The production of ovulation in the rabbit and toad, as well as spermiation in the male toad, are also used. For comparative purposes, the international unit represents the activity contained in 0.1 mg. of the international standard preparation.

Pregnancy Tests

Quite apart from strictly quantitative or assay purposes, a number of the tests noted above are of value in the diagnosis of pregnancy. Since chorionic gonadotrophin appears in the urine some 2 or 3 weeks after conception, detection of the hormone permits an early diagnosis of the presence or absence of pregnancy. Such tests are also of importance in cases of suspected chorionepithelioma and hydatidiform mole.

The more important pregnancy tests are:

1. *The Ascheim-Zondek test.* This was the first procedure devised and depends on the changes induced by HCG in the ovaries of immature mice. Two milliliters of urine are given over 2 days and the ovaries examined on the 5th day. The presence of hemorrhagic and luteinized follicles indicates that the urine contains chorionic gonadotrophin.

2. *The Kupperman test.* In order to save time the immature rat may be used. Here 2 ml. of urine are injected subcutaneously into each of three immature females, which are killed 6 hours later. If the urine contains HCG a marked hyperemia of the ovaries is observed. Alternatively, the response may be read after 2 hours following intra-peritoneal administration of the hormone.

3. *The Friedman test* depends on the production of ovulation in the rabbit following the intravenous injection of 10 to 15 ml. of urine. The ovaries are examined 24 to 48 hours later.

4. *The Hogben test* utilizes the South African clawed toad, *Xenopus laevis*. A mature female is isolated and a concentrate, prepared from 20 to 30 ml. of urine, is instilled into the dorsal lymph sac. If the urine contains HCG ovulation follows between 6 and 12 hours later.

5. *The Galli-Mainini test* employs the male amphibian and is the most recently developed method. It depends upon the expulsion of spermatozoa and the result can usually be read within 2 hours. A variety of species may be used, including *Bufo arenarum* (which was the first tested), *Rana pipiens*, *Bufo bufo*, *Bufo marinus* and *Xenopus laevis*.

Finally, it is perhaps worth recalling that as Ascheim has pointed out, tests for pregnancy are not a modern innovation. In an Egyptian papyrus some 3000 or 4000 years old it is directed that should a woman wish to know whether she is pregnant she should place some earth and barley in a vessel and add a little of her urine each day. Should the barley grow she is pregnant. It has since been found that estrogen, which is present in quite high concentration in the urine after the first month or two of pregnancy, is a stimulant to plant growth.

Pregnant mare serum gonadotrophin. The existence of a gonadotrophin in the serum of the pregnant mare was discovered in 1930 by Cole and Hart. This hormone appears about the time of implantation of the blastocyst and its concentration in the blood reaches a peak at about the 80th day, although, unlike HCG, only very small amounts appear in the urine. It seems fairly clear that pregnant mare serum gonadotrophin (PMS) is produced by specialized structures in the mucosa of the uterus—the endometrial cups, and the production of PMS may be correlated with the appearance of a number of accessory corpora lutea in the ovary.

In hypophysectomized rats, PMS causes a marked increase in ovarian weight, follicular growth, and, with large doses, luteinization. The interstitial cells in the testes of the male are markedly stimulated.

The hormone is seldom used clinically in view

of its limited effect on the human gonad and the ease with which antigenic reactions are stimulated.

Estrogen. Large quantities of estrogen are excreted in the urine of pregnant women and it is quite evident that this comes from the placenta. Bilateral ovariectomy, carried out as early as the sixth to tenth week of pregnancy, does not interfere with the output of this hormone and so excludes the ovaries as a possible source. The increased urinary excretion of estrogen is matched by the increasing size of the placenta and falls rapidly upon delivery of this organ. Although removal of a foetus reduces the production of estrogen by a retained placenta, it has been found that perfusion of the placenta from the foetal side will restore the estrogen secretion to normal. In this case, it is apparent that an adequate circulation to the placenta is important for estrogen production. Like chroionic gonadotrophin, estrogen is secreted by intraocular implants of fragments of full-term human placenta introduced into the anterior eye chamber of ovariectomized rabbits. This is indicated by the occurrence of an estrogenic stimulation of the reproductive tract. Isolated placental tissue has been found capable of synthesizing estrogens. Current evidence, largely based on histochemistry and tissue culture studies, indicates that the syncytial cells of the trophoblast are responsible for the secretion of estrogen.

Numerous estrogens have been isolated from the placenta. *Estrone, estradiol and estriol* are produced in greatest quantity. The placenta is unique in manufacturing estriol; other endocrine glands secrete estrone and/or estradiol. In the course of the thousand-fold increase in estrogen secretion during pregnancy, the ratio of estriol to estrone to estradiol becomes approximately 30:2:1. Estriol is unquestionably excreted in greatest amount, and at term the 24-hour discharge of the various estrogens is approximately: estriol, 30 mg; estrone, 2.0 mg.; estradiol, 0.75 mg., whilst 2 mg. of hydroxyestrone and 0.75 mg. epiestrol are also eliminated. However, it has been calculated that the total daily secretion of the three major estrogens during the latter half of pregnancy is of the order of 40–100 mg. Such large amounts of estrogen are not excreted in the free form but are conjugated with glucuronic acid. Toward the end of pregnancy, it has been found that the proportion of combined to free estrogen, normally of the order of 99:1, falls as more free estrogen appears in the urine. At delivery, with expulsion of the placenta, the urinary output of estrogen falls sharply to the levels found in non-pregnant individuals.

The physiological significance of the estrogen produced by the placenta has not been settled. A variety of possibilities have been advanced: that estrogen is concerned with the growth of the uterus during pregnancy, that estrogen is concerned with the increasing contractility of the uterus and sensitivity to oxytocin seen near delivery, that estrogen is provided for mammary growth and that estrogen synergizes with and counteracts some of the actions of, progesterone.

Progesterone. The excretory product of progesterone, pregnanediol, was first obtained from human pregnancy urine in 1929, but the metabolic link between these two substances was not established until 1936. Only then did it become evident that the placenta might elaborate progesterone. The occurrence or continuation of normal pregnancy, with normal pregnanediol excretion, in the ovariectomized or adrenalectomized woman, excludes the ovaries or adrenals from providing a major supply of progesterone during gestation. In cases of intrauterine fetal death, or removal of the fetus with the placenta remaining intact, pregnanediol excretion continues, but falls to nonpregnant levels upon elimination of the placenta. The concentration of progesterone in uterine vein blood in pregnancy is higher than that in peripheral blood, whilst progesterone has been extracted from, and found to be synthesized by, placental tissue. Placental tissue can also produce other gestagens, including 20α-hydroxypregn-4-ene-3-one and 20β-hydroxypregn-4-ene-3-one, which are measured in biological assays such as the Hooker-Forbes test, but escape when progesterone is determined by physicochemical means. For this reason, biological assays for gestagens frequently result in higher values than a biochemical procedure. It is most likely that the syncytial cells of the cytotrophoblast produce progesterone as well as estrogen.

During pregnancy, the output of pregnanediol increases from 5 or 10 gm. per day to some 40 mg. per day at term, although individual variations are considerable. A plateau in pregnanediol excretion may be reached about the thirty-second week. Only about 35 per cent of the progesterone produced is excreted as pregnanediol in the urine; another 30 per cent is disposed of in the feces. It has been estimated that about 0.25 g. of progesterone is synthesized daily in late pregnancy.

Progesterone is indispensable for normal pregnancy. It depresses the contractility of the myometrium and stimulates growth of the uterus but these effects may only partially explain the need for this hormone during pregnancy. Progesterone is frequently given clinically in cases of threatened abortion. In lower forms, parturition can be inhibited and gestation prolonged by this means.

Other placental hormones. It has been reported that ACTH, MSH, growth hormone, prolactin and relaxin occur in the placenta and proof of the production of these hormones, as opposed to storage, is being sought.

The Structure and Development of the Mammary Glands and the Secretion of Milk

The Structure of the Mammary Glands

The secretory tissue of the mammary glands consists of elongated slender sacs or ducts—the *alveolar ducts*—whose walls show numerous pouches—the *alveoli*. The walls of the alveoli are composed of a basement membrane, a layer of myoepithelial cells, and an inner layer of columnar epithelium. The epithelial cells are the secreting elements.

The gland is composed of some 15 to 25 lobes marked off by connective tissue septa containing much fat and derived from the mantle of adipose tissue which envelops it. A lobe is subdivided into lobules which are variable in size, shape and number. Each lobule gives rise to a narrow duct which is the continuation of an alveolar duct but whose wall is quite devoid of alveoli. By the successive junctions of these lobular ducts a single *lactiferous duct* is formed which serves an entire lobe; it is lined by stratified epithelium. The lactiferous ducts converge toward the nipple, become dilated beneath the areola and then constrict again. Near the base of the nipple they turn abruptly to run vertically toward the skin surface. Each opens separately at the apex of the nipple by a minute mouth called the *galactopore*. In the nonlactating gland few alveoli, if any, are to be found and the gland consists of ducts, connective tissue and fat. Preparatory to lactation the glandular tissue shows active growth, leading to the development of the lobular-alveolar system which completely transforms the histological appearance.

The nipple and an area of the skin (the *areola*) surrounding it are darkly pigmented. The pigmentation deepens in the early months of pregnancy, a sign recognized from the earliest times, and only partially fades after gestation. As in other cutaneous pigmented areas the color is due mainly to the accumulation of granules of pigment in the squamous epithelial cells of the skin; but the actual production of pigment is a function of cells called *melanoblasts* lying just below the epithelial layers. These are the cells which give the "dopa" reaction (p. 1576), but they themselves may contain little pigment. The function of this pigment is unknown but its increase during pregnancy appears to be causally related to the functional activity of the underlying gland.

The nipple contains smooth muscle which is arranged circularly as well as vertically. The vertical fibers are in close relation to the lactiferous ducts. The stiffening and erection of the nipple which results from mild stimulation is caused by the contraction of these strands of muscle. The nipple is one of the most richly innervated structures in the body. Both somatic and sympathetic nerve fibers are found in the profusion in and beneath the skin, and especially in relation to the openings of the lactiferous ducts. In the dermis, nerve fibers form a loose open network without encapsulation, or enter end-organs of various forms. Pacinian and Meissner's corpuscles commonly found in other cutaneous and subcutaneous areas are few, and Krause's end-organs are scarce.

The Roles of the Ovaries and Anterior Pituitary in Mammary Development

There are three phases in the development and activity of the mammary glands. These are seen as (a) the period up to and including puberty, (b) the phase during which the action of the corpus luteum is prominent, that is during pregnancy and pseudopregnancy, and (c) the final secretory phase of lactation when milk is secreted and discharged.

The building of the framework upon which the mechanism of lactation is to be hung begins before puberty, for it has been shown that growth of the mammary glands of the rat becomes faster than that of the body as a whole at about the 22nd day. At this time it would appear that estrogen is largely responsible for the growth changes seen. It is generally true that estrogen is responsible for the growth of the mammary duct system whereas progesterone, acting synergistically with estrogen, promotes full alveolar development. But the above is a generalization and in the mouse, rat and monkey progesterone alone, in sufficiently high dosage, will cause alveolar development in spayed animals lacking estrogen. Further, it is possible to group various species according to the effect estrogen has on the undeveloped mammary gland. In some species, the dog and probably the ferret, estrogen alone causes little or no mammary development, whereas in the next group, which includes the mouse, rat, rabbit and cat, estrogen in physiological dosage evokes primarily and mainly duct growth. In the third group, which includes the monkey, guinea pig, cow and goat, estrogen produces extensive growth of the alveolar system—lobular-alveolar development—as well as of the ducts.

Surprisingly little is known about the relative roles of estrogen and progesterone in the development of the human mammary gland. Mammary development has been produced clinically by the topical administration of estrogen. A number of workers have described cyclic changes in the tissues of the breast during the menstrual cycle, with growth occurring in the luteal phase and regression after menstruation. However such reports have been contested. Physiologically, the enlargement of the mammary glands seen during pregnancy is due to corpus luteum and placental activity which superimposes the alveolar developing action of progesterone upon the basically ductal action of estrogen.

It has long been thought that an intact anterior pituitary gland is essential for the stimulating actions of the ovarian hormones on the mammary gland. In hypophysectomized rats, mice or guinea pigs, estrogen exerts little or no effect upon duct development unless anterior pituitary replacement therapy is initiated. The nature of the pituitary principle necessary for the response to estrogen and progesterone was once a controversial topic. Turner and his associates produced evidence for the view that the pituitary produced two mammogenic principles, distinct from any known hormone. *Mammogen I* was thought to stimulate the duct system and to be liberated under the influence of estrogen; and *Mammogen II*, was believed to produce the growth of the lobular-alveolar system and to be secreted under the influence of progesterone. Thus the ovarian hormones acted, not directly on the mammary gland, but through the hypophysis. Though the concept of special hormones has not been validated, the importance of the pituitary gland is unquestionable. It is possible to obtain full mammary development, typical of late pregnancy, in the hypophysectomized rat by giving estrogen, progesterone and the anterior pituitary hormones, prolactin, growth hormone and adrenocorticotrophin. Further, it has been shown that if insulin is supplied to the hypophysectomized immature female rat (together with estrogen and progesterone), then mammary growth and differentiation will follow. This observation underlines the importance of general metabolic activities in mammary development.

The direct action of prolactin in promoting mammary growth (as distinct from its lactogenic effect described below) has been shown by Lyons and others who have induced localized hyperplasia of the glandular epithelium by injections of prolactin into the mammary ducts of rabbits previously treated with ovarian hormones.

Prolactin

The existence of a lactogenic hormone in the pituitary has already been mentioned, and is discussed elsewhere, in chapter 74. However, certain points are of interest here. The first evidence of the existence of such a hormone was provided by Stricker and Grueter in 1928 who found that crude anterior pituitary extracts induced lactation in ovariectomized, pseudopregnant rabbits. The material would also restore lactation in rabbits which had ceased lactating 10 to 15 days previously, and was later found to act similarly in bitches. In 1930 Corner showed that injections of anterior lobe extract caused enlargement of the mammary glands and lactation in ovariectomized virgin rabbits. Many workers quickly confirmed that anterior pituitary extracts were able to initiate lactation in the adequately developed glands of a wide variety of species. Within a few years it was established that the extracts contained a separate hormone which had pronounced lactogenic effects, and was called *prolactin, galacin,* or *mammotropin.*

The Role of the Placenta in Mammary Growth

The extensive studies of Lyons on the hypophysectomized rat have also shown that mammary development can be induced in animals given placental extracts instead of prolactin. This finding is accord with the results of rather different work performed somewhat earlier. It was then found that removal of the ovaries and fetuses from rats together with hypophysectomy caused mammary regression if the placentas were also removed, but that mammary growth continued if the placentas were left. It appears then that the placenta can substitute for the ovaries as well as the pituitary. The production of estrogen and progesterone by the placenta should be recalled in this connection (see also p. 1642). Studies using monkeys hypophysectomized during pregnancy support this idea, for good development of alveolar lobules was apparent at term and secretion appeared during the first few days after delivery.

The Initiation of Lactation

Although lactation is generally held to start at the end of pregnancy, the secretion of milk sets in long before this, at about the fifth month. Nevertheless the initiation of a copious lactation is a striking consequence of delivery.

The factors underlying this event have excited comment for many years, and a variety of explanations have been put forward. Thus it was supposed that lactation resulted as a natural consequence of the end of pregnancy and mammary development, so that when the growth stimulus was removed, secretion began. Support for this view came from experiments in which, for example, lactation followed the end of a course of estrogen injections in the guinea pig. With the discovery of prolactin, attention was directed to the pituitary gland, as well as to the endocrine activities of the placenta, and Nelson in 1936 put forward a new concept. This was that during pregnancy the ovarian hormones induced proliferative changes in the mammary glands and in addition, and particularly during the latter half, inhibited the actual secretion of milk. The restraining influence was visualized as acting (a) by suppressing the secretion or release of the pituitary lactogenic hormone, and (b) by a direct inhibitory effect on the mammary glands. Thus the high ovarian hormone levels during pregnancy would promote glandular development, whereas the sharp fall in concentration at parturition would permit lactation to begin. It is known that lactation is inhibited in most animals by estrogen, or by measures which stimulate estrogen liberation, and is also promptly suppressed by human chorionic gonadotropin (HCG) which stimulates the production of luteal tissue. Collip and his colleagues reported that if the luteinized ovaries induced in virgin rats by the administration of HCG were removed, then the hypertrophied mammae secreted profusely. Removal of the pituitary, however, together with the ovaries prevented this result. When lactating cows become pregnant, milk production declines progressively during gestation but rises abruptly after calving. In guinea pigs, removal of the ovaries and embryos, although leaving the placentas intact, does not induce lactation, but lactation occurs following expulsion of the placentas. Observations of the above nature lend strong support to the view of Nelson. Evans also explained the milk secretion which occasionally occurs in the child shortly after birth ("witches milk") on this basis, for the fetus is exposed to ovarian hormones and the elimination of these after birth might result in the liberation of prolactin from the pituitary of the infant.

The theory as described above, with an emphasis on the inhibitory action of estrogen, has limitations. Thus the amounts of estrogen required to suppress established lactation probably are greater than those produced during pregnancy, and the typical signs of high estrogen levels (cornified vagina, estrous behavior) are not seen during pregnancy. Further, low doses of estrogen actually stimulate mammary secretion in some forms (goat and cow). It was to account for difficulties of this nature that Meites and Turner in 1942 drew attention to the possible role of progesterone. These workers suggested that during pregnancy progesterone inhibited a stimulating effect of estrogen on the secretion of prolactin, but at the time of parturition estrogen became dominant and was able to evoke a quick rise in the output of prolactin and so initiate lactation. In support of this view it was found that in rats and guinea pigs the prolactin content of the hypophysis began to rise a few days before the birth of the young, and that the urinary excretion of prolactin after parturition was from 8 to 16 times greater than that during pregnancy. Estrogen was found to increase the content of prolactin in the hypophysis, so that the low prolactin content during pregnancy was attributed to the relatively high progestin content of the blood, and its antagonistic effect on the action of estrogen. It was found that estrogen and progesterone given in appropriate proportion had no effect on the prolactin content of the pituitary.

In turn, the view of Meites and Turner has been subjected to criticism, notably by Folley, who was not convinced that increases in pituitary prolactin content (assumed to reflect pituitary secretion rate by Meites and Turner) were accompanied by an increased secretion of prolactin into the blood, and who objected to the key position assigned to prolactin in the initiation of lactation. He suggested, as a modification of the Nelson theory, that low levels of circulating estrogen stimulate the secretion of anterior pituitary hormones concerned in lactogenesis, whereas high levels inhibit such secretion. At about the time of parturition the level of circulating estrogen, previously above the threshold for pituitary inhibition, falls and in passing through the range between the two thresholds causes functional activation of the anterior pituitary with respect to the production of lactogenic hormones and so initiates full lactation.

More recently it has been found that estrogen and progesterone exert an antagonistic effect toward prolactin at the mammary gland level. Thus the ability of a moderate dose of prolactin to initiate milk secretion in ovariectomized rabbits with well developed glands could be effectively inhibited if optimal mammary growth-promoting doses of estrone and progesterone were given at the same time. In the absence of either or both steroids prolactin elicited a good lactational response. Variation of the amounts of gonadal or hypophysial hormones given showed that the occurrence of mammary growth (or of lactation) depended on the balance achieved. In the light of this work it is clear that to focus attention solely upon the hypophysis at the onset of lactation is to neglect other important factors. Although retaining his "double threshold" theory, Folley later took these observations into account and considered that 'lactogenic' doses of estrogen might be deprived of their lactogenic action by suitable doses of progesterone, and that the combination of the two hormones might act as a potent inhibitor of lactation during pregnancy. At parturition the fall in the ratio of progesterone to estrogen would remove the inhibition, and the positive "lactogenic" effect of estrogen would act unopposed.

An entirely different viewpoint is that of Petersen, who did not concern himself with estrogen-progesterone-prolactin interrelationships. It is now clear that milk production, i.e., the formation of milk and its secretion into the alveoli, begins some time before parturition. The question, therefore, is not a matter of *secretion* after childbirth, but of the discharge or *ejection* of milk from the gland. As pointed out by Petersen, the low water content of the first milk secreted, the *colostrum*, strongly suggests a retained secretion which tends by distention of the alveoli to depress secretory activity, but with the emptying of the alveoli the inhibitory effect of distention is removed and a continuous profuse secretion is maintained by the lactogenic hormone. The effects of the stimulus of suckling should also be taken into account (see below).

The Maintenance of Lactation

With parturition the operation of a number of as yet imperfectly understood factors results in lactation, a process which is maintained in many forms for months.

Neural factors. The mechanism underlying the continuance of lactation is not clear, although it is certain that the pituitary is involved since lactation is arrested abruptly by hypophysectomy. It is common knowledge that weaning is followed by rapid involution of the mammary gland and cessation of milk production. This might be due to the retention of milk within the gland, with consequent deleterious effects on its secretory activity, or to loss of a stimulus which promotes lactation—the stimulus of suckling. The latter alternative is more likely, for there are numerous cases in which suckling has been shown to induce lactation in male individuals of various species (bull, goat, wether, man). Lactation has often been induced in this way in virgin girls, as well as experimentally in the rat. Selye and his coworkers showed that suckling tended to delay the involution of the mammary glands in rats in which the

galactophores were tied (to prevent the egress of milk), and suggested that the suckling stimulus caused a nervous reflex release of lactogenic hormone from the pituitary which maintained lactation. In lactating mice deprived of their litters the mammary involution which normally occurs may be retarded by painting the nipples with an irritant such as turpentine. The prolactin content of the hypophysis of lactating rats has been observed to fall over a 30-minute nursing period. In nonpuerperal women lactation may follow extensive operations involving the thoracic wall, probably through irritation of the intercostal nerves. Such observations indicate that nervous factors play an important part in the maintenance of lactation. The operation of psychic factors in women is not to be neglected; their operation is well seen in relation to milk ejection (see below).

Hormonal factors. The precise nature of the hormonal systems activated by neural stimuli has not been elucidated. It is presumed that the stimulus is transmitted to the hypothalamus and from there to the hypophysis by the portal vessels. But the nature of the response of the anterior pituitary gland is not certain although the secretion of prolactin and ACTH may be promoted. With the availability of purified pituitary hormones the maintenance of lactation in hypophysectomized rats has been attempted. Cowie found that, using growth hormone, prolactin and ACTH singly and in combination, the best result was given by prolactin plus ACTH. Oxytocin was also given to make certain that the litters obtained any milk produced. Lyons, in rather similar work, found that prolactin and hydrocortisone together were able to raise the milk production to about half of normal.

When pure pituitary hormones are given to lactating animals, and the effect on the milk output is studied, it is found that growth hormone augments the secretion of milk (*galactopoiesis*) to the greatest extent. This effect can be observed, not only toward the the end of lactation, when the milk yield is declining, but also at the height of milk secretion. It is further significant that upon cessation of treatment the milk yield does not fall below the expected level—the action of growth hormone is thus not due to mobilization of reserves. Prolactin exerts very little galactopoietic activity although its continued secretion is probably necessary for the maintenance of lactation. Injection of ACTH in cows has been found to temporarily depress the milk yield, although it is evident from work involving adrenalectomy and replacement therapy that the adrenal corticoids are essential for the maintenance of lactation. In adrenalectomized rats cortisone and desoxycorticosterone acetate together provided the best maintenance of lactation, whereas later work showed that chlorohydrocortisone gave virtually complete maintenance. The effects of thyroidectomy on lactation, although depressive, do not appear to be particularly striking. It was found more than 60 years ago that thyroid feeding increased the milk yield of women and cows. This has been confirmed, and similar responses demonstrated in the rat. Pituitary thyrotrophic hormone is also active in this regard. Besides increasing the weight of milk produced, L-thyroxine increases the percentage of fat and nonfatty solids in the milk, whereas the concentration of alkaline phosphatase drops markedly. Triiodothyronine (ch. 75) is about twice as active as L-thyroxine. Unlike thyroxine, triiodothyronine is not effective when given orally to cows. Dried thyroid and L-thyroxine have been used with benefit in the treatment of human hypogalactia, but cannot be regarded as a panacea.

Milk Ejection

The production of milk by the maternal mammary gland forms only one step in the process of lactation. For lactation to be successful the milk must be transferred to the young. It is not possible to empty a mammary gland passively, by compression or by suction, since the milk is retained in the small ducts and alveoli. Physiologically, emptying of the gland is achieved by the operation of a neurohormonal reflex referred to as the milk ejection reflex. It consists of an afferent nervous pathway, which begins with the sensory end-organs in the nipple and areola, passes up the spinal cord to the hypothalamus, and to the posterior lobe of the hypophysis through the supraoptico-hypophysial tract. That is the neural part of the reflex. In the posterior pituitary the neurohypophysial hormone, oxytocin, is discharged into the blood stream whence it is carried to cause the contraction of myoepithelial cells embracing the alveoli. There is little doubt that this is the reflex activated by milking in cattle which results in *"let-down,"* or by suckling in women, which results in the *"draught."* The reflex is highly susceptible to conditioning, and is easily inhibited by fright or, in women, by embarrassment. Experimentally, milk ejection can be produced by electrical stimulation of the supraopticohypophysial tract, and blocked by lesions of this nerve pathway. In the latter case milk ejection may be restored by injection of oxytocin.

It follows from the above that interference with the process of milk ejection will stop or prevent lactation just as surely as disturbance of the formation of milk. Neglect of this consideration has in the past led to much confusion in both experimental and clinical investigations.

The fact that both oxytocic hormone and lactogenic hormone are secreted in response to the same physiological stimuli has led several investigators to suggest that oxytocin released from the neurohypophysis acts on the anterior pituitary to cause the release of lactogenic hormone. However, this view has not been sustained in the light of work which demonstrated that prolactin is released from the hypophysis isolated from neural influences by transplantation away from the sella turcica. It is now considered likely that some agent is released from the hypothalamus into the hypophysial portal vessels to *inhibit* the secretion of prolactin by the hypophysis (see ch. 74).

The Composition of Milk, the Origin and Secretion of Its Constituents

With the onset of lactation, the epithelial cells lining the alveoli become loaded with fine droplets of fat which soon coalesce to form large globules in the part of the cell lying next to the alveolar lumen. The fat, with other constituents of the milk, may then be discharged into the alveolus as droplets, or the inner part of the cell pinched off, as it were, from the larger portion and freed into the lumen. The latter represents the process of *apocrine* secretion.

Colostrum. At the end of pregnancy and the beginning of lactation the secretion contained in the mammary gland is unlike normal milk. It is known as *colostrum.* Colostrum contains numerous globules and cell fragments, together with free-fat droplets, lymphocytes, monocytes, histiocytes, desquamated epithelial cells and colostrum corpuscles or bodies of Donné. These latter are large cells containing a variety of inclusions. Colostrum contains little fat, but a larger amount of antibodies than are present in milk proper. It is presumed that colostrum formation occurs when there is an imbalance between the secretion of milk and its removal. Thus it is found at the end of pregnancy and at the end of lactation.

Milk. Milk consists essentially of an emulsion of fat globules in a colloidal solution of protein, together with crystalloids in true solution. It contains two substances not found elsewhere in the body, casein and lactose; the combination of glycerides forming milk fat is peculiar to it.

The composition of human milk is compared

TABLE 78.1.

The composition of cow and human milk

Average values per 100 ml whole milk. (After Macy and Kelly).

	Energy Kcal	Total Solids g	Fat g	Lactose g	Ash g	Calcium mg	Potassium mg	Protein g	Casein g	Lacto-albumin g	Lacto-globulin g
Cow's milk..............	69	12.7	3.7	4.8	0.72	125	138	3.3	2.8	0.4	0.2
Mature human milk........	71	12.4	3.8	7.0	0.21	33	55	1.2	0.4	0.3	0.2

with that of cow's milk in Table 78.1. The quantity of protein in cow's milk is more than double that in human milk; the difference is largely confied to the casein content. The sugar and fat content of cow's milk is lower than that of the human. Calcium is the mineral present in largest amount. Both human milk and cow's milk vary greatly in composition and in quality due to the operation of many factors; psychic, dietary, hormonal, period of lactation, time of day (greater volume during night), etc. The daily output increases up to a maximum of from 1000 to 3000 ml. at about the 25th week after childbirth and then gradually declines. Human milk of good quality contains all the elements essential for building body tissue, and adequate amounts of vitamins A (as well as carotene), the B complex and C. Vitamins B_1 and D are in low concentration and may be present in inadequate amounts. Raising the protein in the diet tends to increase the total milk yield, as does a high fat diet, which also raises the fat content of the milk. Carbohydrates, if in high proportion in the diet, reduce both the yield and the quality of the milk.

The milk protein. The proteins of milk consist largely of casein, lactalbumin and lactoglobulin. Since the phosphoprotein, casein, occurs in no place other than the mammary gland, it is clear that it must be synthesized there. The details of the synthesis have not yet been worked out. According to Folley, milk protein may be synthesized entirely from the amino acids of the circulating blood, or partly from these and partly from degradation of plasma protein in the mammary gland. Alternatively the milk proteins might arise from plasma proteins by rearrangement of peptide chains, or partly in this manner and partly from blood amino acids. From measurement of the arteriovenous difference of blood amino acids in the lactating udder it is clear that some amino acids are utilized by the mammary gland. Recent work with udder perfusion methods and with labelled amino acids indicates that casein is indeed synthesized from plasma amino acids, and that a similar conclusion may well be reached in the

case of lactoglobulin. Experiments carried out on the goat, indicate that much of the globulin fraction of colostrum is probably synthesized by plasma cells in the mammary gland from the free amino acids of the blood.

Milk fat. Milk fat differs in composition from the neutral fat of the blood in that it contains a relatively high proportion of short chain fatty acids of the series C_4 to C_{12}. The fatty acids, e.g., butyric, caproic, caprylic, lauric, and myristic, constitute about 30 per cent of the total fat of milk. The fat of milk therefore cannot be simply neutral fat transferred from the circulation to the gland and there concentrated. Of the long chain fatty acids, oleic (35 per cent) and palmitic (30 per cent) are present in greatest quantity. Stearic acid constitutes only about 2 per cent. Much of our knowledge of the synthesis of milk fat is derived from work on the ruminant, where it is probable that most of the fatty acids up to, and including, palmitic acid are formed in the udder from acetate. The acetate, in turn, is derived from the metabolism of carbohydrates. Some proportion of the fatty acids in the milk probably still arises from circulating preformed fatty acids.

Lactose. Like the other constituents of milk just discussed, lactose is found only in the mammary gland. This disaccharide, galactose-glucose, must therefore be formed in that organ. Lactose could be produced from small molecules taken up from the blood, like lactic acid and pyruvate, or from the blood glucose. Most evidence favors glucose as a precursor. Thus perfusion of a bovine udder with blood containing labelled glucose, followed by extraction and hydrolysis of the lactose resulted in isolation of labelled glucose and galactose. This result implies that galactose is derived from glucose and is supported by experiments in which slices of mammary tissue, incubated with glucose, formed lactose. It has also proved possible to synthesize lactose from glucose in homogenates of mammary gland tissue. It is perhaps worth noting here that procedures which lower the blood sugar tend to decrease the concentration of lactose in milk whereas hyperglycemic procedures have the reverse effect.

The Testes

THE STRUCTURE OF THE TESTES

The testes are ovoid glands suspended in the scrotum by the spermatic cords. Each is surrounded by a firm, thick capsule—the *tunica albuginea*, which is in turn enclosed by a double layer of peritoneum. The layers of the *tunica vaginalis communis* slide freely upon one another, enabling the testis to move easily within its scrotal sac.

The substance of the testis consists of a mass of coiled tubules, the *convoluted seminiferous tubules*, bound together by a stroma of connective tissue. Each seminiferous tubule is a rather closely coiled tube between 35 and 70 cm. long and from 150 to 300 microns in diameter. They are held in wedge-shaped compartments or *lobules* by incomplete connective tissue septa. Through the gaps in the septa they are joined to one another by short tubular connections. The combined length of the convoluted tubules of man has been estimated at over 300 yards. At the apices of the lobules the seminiferous tubules join the first elements of the excretory duct system. These are narrow straight tubules—the *tubuli recti*—which in turn empty into a system of irregular cavernous spaces, the *rete testis* in the hilum or mediastinum in the posterior part of the testis. At the upper part of the rete testis some dozen or more ducts, the *ductuli efferentes*, arise; passing to the upper part or *caput* of the epididymis, these ducts become confluent to form the *ductus epididymis*. The latter is a long, greatly tortuous tube which forms the body and tail of the epididymis. At the lower extremity of the epididymis the ductus bends abruptly upon itself to be continued as the *vas* or *ductus deferens*. The vas deferens on each side, after a devious course, is joined by the duct of the corresponding seminal vesicle, and terminates as an *ejaculatory duct* which opens into the urethra.

The convoluted tubules are lined by several layers of cells, the *spermatogenic* cells, which produce the spermatozoa. Among the spermatogenic or sex cells are a small number of *cells of Sertoli*— long cells attached perpendicularly to the basement membrane. The spermatogenic cells undergo well defined changes in the course of transformation into spermatozoa. In the mature testis these can be distinguished, for the primitive stages lie close to the basement membrane and develop on passage toward the lumen of the tubule. Initially the germ cells are large round cells at the periphery of the tubule and are called *spermatogonia*. They alone are present in the immature testis. Spermatogonia multiply mitotically, giving rise to *primary spermatocytes*. These are larger than the

spermatogonia. Each divides into two smaller *secondary spermatocytes*, and each of these in turn divides to produce two *spermatids*. The latter transformation involves a *reduction* or *meiotic division* of the nucleus, so that each spermatid contains only half the normal number of chromosomes in its nucleus. The spermatids which are found near the lumen of the tubule are transformed directly, i.e., without division, into free *spermatozoa*. About half the number of spermatids or spermatozoa contain a Y-chromosome and half an X-chromosome. Modern cytological studies, using biopsies taken from the testes of normal men, have established that the stages of spermatogenesis can be broken down into more steps than indicated by the synopsis just given. These are illustrated in fig. 78.10.

Sertoli cells. The Sertoli or sustentacular cells occur fairly regularly at intervals around the tubules. The nucleus of a Sertoli cell is large, but division has not been seen under normal conditions. In the human testis, the Sertoli cell contains a spindle-shaped crystalloid near the nucleus. The Sertoli cells are believed to perform a nutritive and supporting function toward the developing spermatozoa; the spermatids are found to be attached to them. Unlike the spermatogenic cells, the cells of Sertoli are highly resistant toward a variety of noxious factors. To judge from the findings in cases of Sertoli cell tumors of the testis, the sustentacular cells may secrete estrogen.

The interstitial cells. The tubules of the testis lie in a stroma of connective tissue, and in this connective tissue are found clumps of irregularly polyhedral cells—the *interstitial cells of Leydig*. The Leydig cells appear to be differentiated from fibroblasts, and contain many granules of lipoid material and pigment. In the fetus and newborn the Leydig cells are remarkably prominent due to stimulation by chorionic gonadotrophin. After birth they atrophy but become conspicuous once more at puberty. The Leydig cells are known to secrete androgen.

The accessory sex glands. Linked in functional association with the testis are a number of glands which produce secretions which, with the sperm of the testis, together make up the *semen*. They are functionally dependent upon the endocrine secretion of the testis, for they display atrophy in its absence. The most important are the *seminal vesicles, prostate gland*, and the *bulbo-urethral or Cowper's glands*.

The *seminal vesicles* are paired organs lying dorsal to the bladder; their ducts join the vas deferens. They are absent in many mammals

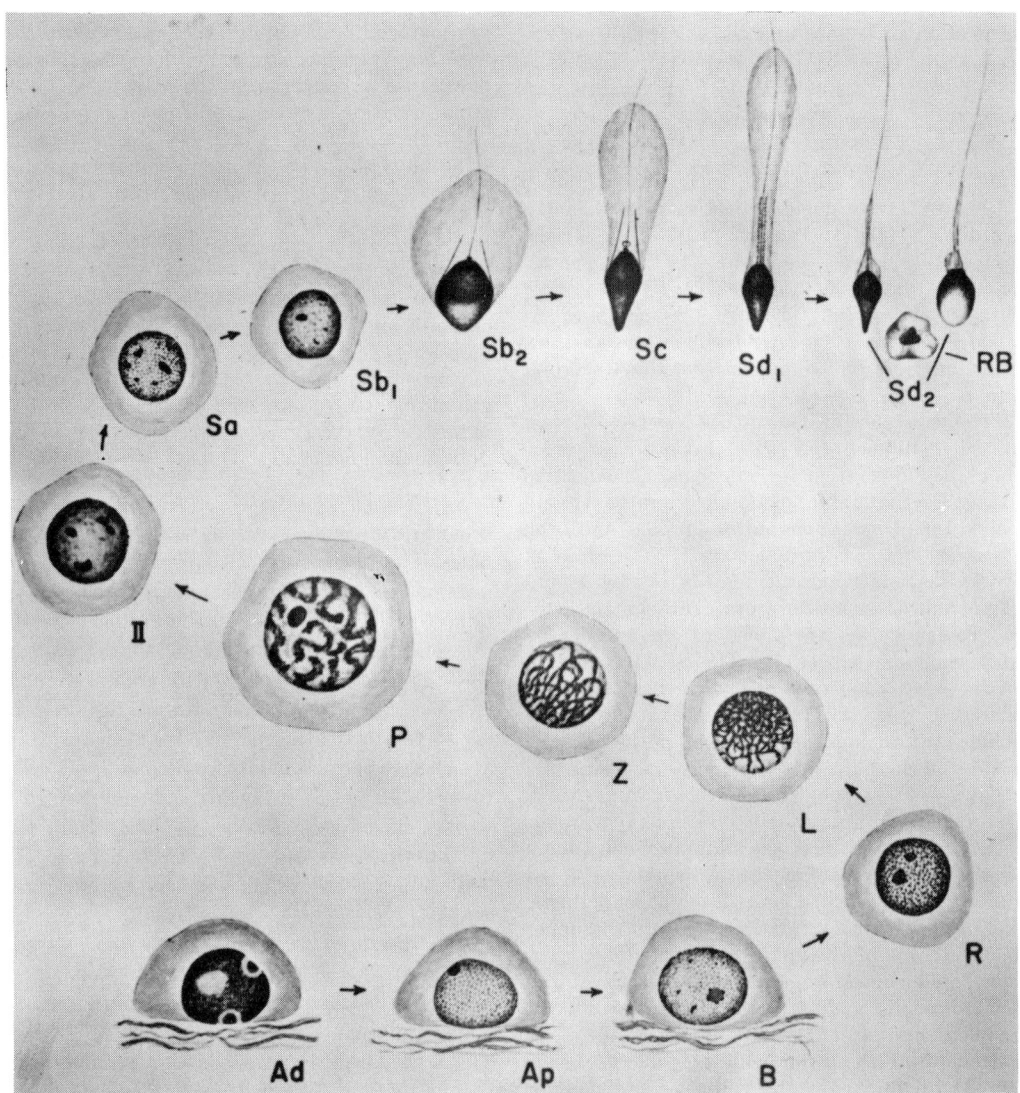

FIG. 78.10. Drawings illustrating the main steps of spermatogenesis in man. Spermatogenesis starts at the bottom left with the dark, type A, spermatogonium (Ad) considered as the stem cell and terminates with the step d_2 (Sd₂) spermatid or spermatozoon at the top right. In sequence the other elements are: Ap, pole type A spermatogium; B, type B spermatogium; R, resting (or preleptotene) spermatocytes; L, leptotene seprmatocyte; Z, zygotene spermatocyte; P, pachytene spermatocyte; II, secondary spermatocyte; Sa, Sb₁, Sb₂, Sc, Sd₁, spermatids at various steps of spermiogenesis. (From Heller and Clermont, Recent Progress in Hormone Research, 1964. Academic Pres.)

(e.g., the whale and dog) and so are not considered essential in reproduction. On the other hand they are greatly developed in boars, hedgehogs, rats and guinea pigs, and their secretion increases the volume of the ejaculate in these species. They do not act as reservoirs for the spermatozoa. The secretion of the seminal vesicles is a yellowish viscous fluid which is marked by its content of fructose and of reducing substances such as ascorbic acid and ergothionine. The level of fructose is closely associated with the blood titer of male sex hormone, and falls sharply in its absence (as after castration). The fructose appears to be derived from blood glucose since it is increased in diabetic rabbits or in humans, and falls after the administration of insulin.

The semen. The fluid ejaculated from the male genital tract is known as *semen.* It contains about 60,000,000 spermatozoa per cu. ml., although the normal limits range from 25,000,000 to 225,000,000. In the assessment of fertility from a sample of semen the motility and viability are often regarded as more important than the sperm count. The average volume of an ejaculate is about 3 ml. and immediately after expulsion the semen coagulates, to liquefy again in a few minutes. The spermatozoa in the seminiferous tubules are non-motile and appear to be carried along the ductuli efferentia by the cilia of the cells lining these channels. They are stored in the epididymis. Ejaculation of the semen during coitus is brought about by contractions of the deferentia and the ejaculatory ducts.

The Physiology of the Testis

The function of the testis is two-fold, namely, the production of germ cells, *spermatogenesis*, and the elaboration of the male sex hormone, its *endocrine function*.

The Gametogenic Function of the Testis

In man the production of spermatozoa in the testes is carried on continuously throughout adult life, with the formation of an astronomical number of germ cells. In some other species the production of sperm occurs seasonally, at a time when conception of young will lead to their delivery at an auspicious time of the year. The sheep, deer, ferret and many classes of birds display this condition; sheep, for example, breed in autumn and the young are delivered in spring. During the remainder of the year, outside the breeding season, little sign of germinal activity is seen in the testis. Experimentally, however, spermatogenesis may be promoted by administration of pituitary gonadotrophic hormones. Spermatogenesis can also be advanced in seasonally breeding species by modifying the external environment, such as by altering the period of illumination during the day. This latter effect is mediated by the nervous system which brings about an increase in the secretion of pituitary hormones.

The testis, like the ovary, is functionally dependent on the pituitary gland. The removal of the hypophysis is followed by arrest of spermatogenesis and testicular atrophy; these changes can be reversed by implantation of pituitary tissue or suitable extracts of anterior pituitary glands. Upon hypophysectomy the testes soften and lose weight. Differentiation of the gametes does not proceed and spermatids and spermatozoa disappear from the organ. The Leydig cells become inactive and androgen production ceases, with consequent atrophy of the accessory sexual organs and accessory sex characters. Implantation of pituitary tissue or injection of gonadotrophic

extracts of the pituitary speedily results in the onset of spermatogenesis in the immature individual, whether mouse or man. The effect is sometimes seen clinically in cases where pituitary overactivity advances puberty in boys. It is believed that the follicle-stimulating hormone (FSH) of the hypophysis is mainly concerned with spermatogenesis, as injection of purified FSH into hypophysectomized male rats prevents atrophy of the seminiferous tubules and will restore gametogenic activity. Similar effects have been reported in studies employing purified FSH in man. The luteinizing hormone (LH) of the pituitary also exerts an effect on spermatogenesis. Here it is believed, mainly from studies on rats, that the action is initially on the Leydig cells to promote androgen secretion, which in turn stimulates sperm formation. It has been found that androgen (testosterone) will support gametogenesis in the hypophysectomized male rat but it should be borne in mind that in normal individuals large doses of testosterone suppress spermatogenesis and, *via* its suppressive action of the secretion of pituitary gonadotrophin, causes testicular atrophy.

In man and many other mammals, but not in the sloth, whale or elephant, the testes are contained extraabdominally in the scrotum. In many of these the testes descend into the scrotum at puberty and remain there permanently; in others again the testes occupy a scrotal position only during the breeding season. It is now evident that the scrotum exerts a thermo-regulating function. This has been established in a variety of studies. In the developmental anomaly known as *cryptorchidism* the testis fails to descend into the scrotum and spermatogenesis does not occur in the undescended organ. This condition can be reproduced experimentally by returning the testis of the normal adult animal from the scrotum to the abdomen; degeneration of the seminiferous tubules will follow in a few days. Upon replacement of the testis in the scrotum there is a restoration of normal testicular appearance and function provided that the stay in the abdomen has not been too long. It is possible to produce this effect in the ram by enclosing the testis in a bag of heat-insulating material which raises the temperature of the testis by a few degrees. Such an observation ensures that the result of moving the testis to the abdomen was not an artifact due to operative procedures. Measurement of the temperature of the scrotum has shown that it is several degrees lower than that of the abdomen. It has also been found that exposure for 15 minutes or so to a temperature of 6° C. above the normal body temperature leads within some 10 days to degeneration of the sperm producing cells. The human testis may suffer in febrile illnesses, as a result of the high temperature, but as a rule the loss of function is only temporary. The requirement for a lower temperature than that prevailing in the rest of the body explains why testicular transplantation has seldom been associated with continuing spermatogenesis, unless a cool location (such as the anterior chamber of the eye) is chosen. Normally it appears that the descent of the testis is dependent upon the secretion of androgen, although in cases of cryptorchidism gonadotrophin is used to produce descent in order to avoid the depressive effects on the pituitary of androgen alone.

Ligation of the vas deferens has been stated by some (e.g., Steinach) to cause degeneration of the spermatogenic cells, and further, to increase the production of sex hormone. These claims have been conclusively disproved. Vasoligation has been advocated as a means of increasing the output of male hormone and so causing "rejuvenation," but it is based on error. It exerts no lasting effect upon either the sperm-producing cells or upon those of internal secretion. Ligation, or resection of a portion of the vas deferens, results in sterility by preventing the egress of the male germ cells but does not interfere with the sexual drive of the male.

The spermatogenic function of the testis is affected adversely by several conditions, such as exposure to ionising radiation, alcoholism, vitamin deficiency and (in some species) close confinement. Following irradiation of the testes there is a marked destruction of spermatogonia whereas the Sertoli and Leydig cells survive. This effect would seem to be due to the operation of the principle that the most actively dividing cells are those most adversely affected by ionizing radiations. The effect of vitamin deficiency may be exerted through the pituitary, though conclusive information is difficult to obtain, whereas lack of vitamin E would seem to act directly on the testis. Testicular function is depressed in cases of simple starvation.

The Endocrine Function of the Testis

The effects of castration have long been known. Aristotle described the changes following castration in the bird more than 2000 years ago, and before that testicular tissue was used as a treatment for impotence in India. More recently John Hunter showed that the normal function of the prostate and seminal vesicles was maintained only in the presence of the testes, and Berthold,

in 1849, demonstrated that the testes discharged some material into the blood stream essential for the growth of the cock's comb. Among the first to attempt the preparation of an active material was the noted physiologist Brown-Séquard (1889) who administered testicular extracts to himself and thought that he acquired an increase of vigor and a greater capacity for work after the treatment. This concept was later revived by Voronoff in France and Steinach in Germany who believed that senescence was related to testicular atrophy and consequent reduction or loss of male hormone. However this idea has been discredited and it is only necessary to point out that although in the female ovarian function ceases at the menopause (p. 1627) senile changes are not prominent at this time. Eunuchs did not show premature senility, and, in any case, the sexual functions in the male often continue well into old age.

The effects of castration have been discussed at the beginning of this chapter (p. 1615), and it will be recalled that in the male the accessory sexual organs are developed and maintained under the influence of androgen, as are certain characters, including the pattern of pubic and facial hair, and the pitch of the voice. In lower mammals other features can be studied, such as the presence of horns in the stag, the cape of long hair in the male baboon, and the male odor of the billy goat. These male features may be maintained in the castrated animal by the transplantation of testicular tissue, or androgen therapy.

When the testes are transplanted from the scrotum to a situation elsewhere in the body germinal activity ceases (p. 1651) but the endocrine function continues. A similar finding is made following destruction of the germinal elements with X-rays and it then becomes evident that germinal cells are not concerned with the production of androgen. This function is exercised by the Leydig cells. Apart from the evidence which denies this function to other testicular constituents it has been found that in rats with vitamin B deficiency there is a loss of androgenic activity and the interstitial cells are atrophic, but normal production of sperm continues. Injection of homogenized testicular tissue together with an adjuvant, has been found to cause an immune reaction which destroyed the germinal epithelium of the testes of the male but left the Leydig cells (and the production of androgen) unharmed. In man, tumors of the interstitial tissue of the testis produce excessive quantities of androgen and, in boys, cause a premature appearance of masculine characteristics.

An active androgen-containing extract of testis was obtained by Pézard in 1911 who produced comb growth in capons with a saline extract. McGee in 1927 obtained an active lipoid extract of bull's testes, but it was not until 1935 that the pure hormone, *testosterone*, was separated in crystalline form by Laqueur and his colleagues. Meanwhile more success had been achieved with extracts of human urine for between 1931 and 1934 two androgenic substances had been isolated. These were androsterone and dehydroandrosterone, and were found to differ from the hormone in

established from experiments involving study of perfused testes, testis homogenates, and testis slices, as well as in similar investigations using ovarian or adrenal tissue.

The hypothetical parent substance of the androgens is androstane, shown below. Since the hydrogen atom at C_5 may be either *cis* or *trans* in relation to the angle methyl groups, two isomers are possible. The *cis* form is known as etiocholane, and the *trans* form as androstane; derivates of the androgens may be related to either parent substance.

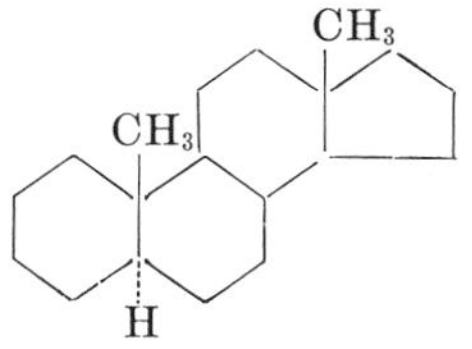

Androstane

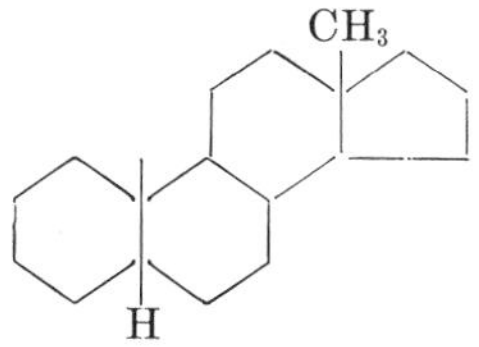

Etiocholane

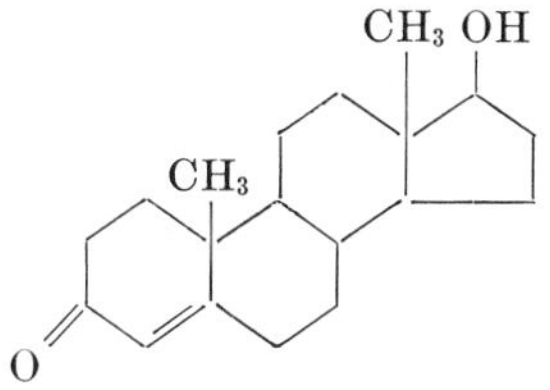

Testosterone
17-β-Hydroxyandrost-4-ene-3-one

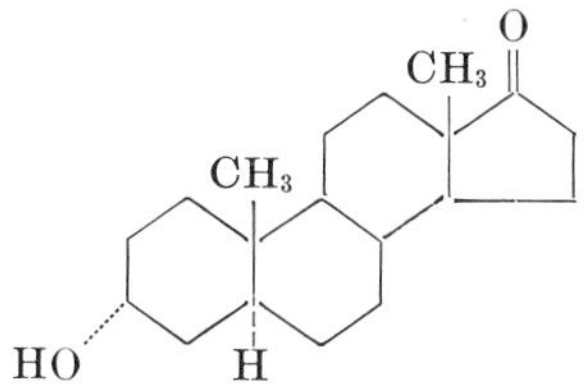

Androsterone
3α-Hydroxy-5α-androstan-17-one

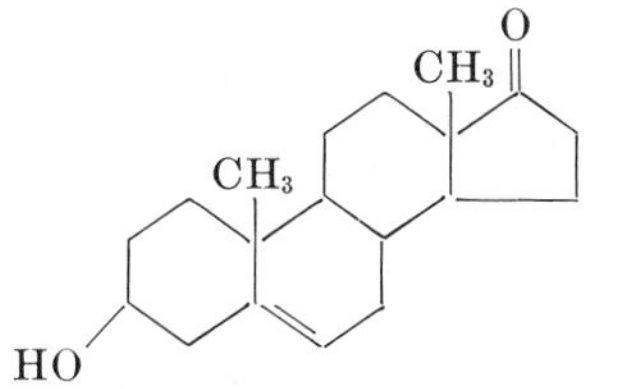

Dehydroepiandrosterone
3β-Hydroxyandrost-5-en-17-one
The formulae of some important androgens.

testicular extracts in being less potent and more stable to alkali.

THE ANDROGENS. In recent years the efforts of the biochemists in isolating steroids from organs such as the adrenal cortex, ovary and testis have resulted in the identification of a wide variety of androgens.

Of the steroids isolated from the testis, *testosterone* is the most important and is regarded as the true male hormone. The conversion of acetate to testosterone and other androgens has been observed on many occasions, and the pathway of androgen synthesis, involving cholesterol, pregnenolone, and progesterone (fig. 78.7) is well

The urine provides a ready source of androgens. Here the first androgen isolated, *androsterone*, is also the principal androgen, and it is about one-tenth as potent as testosterone. It was synthesized from cholesterol by Ruzicka and coworkers. Two isomers of androsterone exist and are found in urine. Epiandrosterone is about five times less active than androsterone, whereas the other isomer, etiocholan-3α-ol-17-one is almost inactive. It has been shown that the principal metabolites of testosterone in urine are androsterone and its isomers. The testicular androgen androst-4-ene-3:17-dione is also found in urine alongside both free and conjugated testosterone. A further androgen, dehydroepiandrosterone, with an activity of the order of that of epiandrosterone, also occurs in urine.

Most of the androgens found in the urine possess a ketone group attached to carbon-17, and are thus *17-ketosteroids*. On the other hand, certain urinary 17-ketosteroids which possess a ketone group at this site lack androgenic activity. Etiocholan-3α-ol-17-one and dehydroepiandrosterone are examples of such compounds. This is in part due to the fact that the adrenal makes a major contribution to the output of 17-ketosteroids. Therefore measurement of these compounds by chemical methods (Zimmerman reaction) does not necessarily coincide with the amounts as measured by biological assay of androgenic activity. However a reasonable correlation exists between the results of the two methods.

Only very small amounts of androgens or 17-ketosteroids are found in the urine of children. At puberty the output increases and it reaches a maximum in men of about 25 years of age when the excretion is 12 to 17 mg. of 17-ketosteroids daily. In women the daily excretion is 7 to 12 mg. per day, much of which comes from the adrenal, and which does not exert any androgenic effect physiologically. Androgen has been extracted from ovarian tissue and the production of androgens by the ovaries has been demonstrated experimentally. Clinically, virilism (p. 1578) has been found in association with several kinds of ovarian tumors (arrhenoblastoma, "Leydig cell" tumor, "theca cell" tumor, "lipoid cell" tumor). These tumors thus seem to produce androgens, and this has been confirmed by study of the metabolism of the tumors, and investigation of the substances excreted in the urine.

In general the actions of androgen may be summarized as follows.

1. They promote the growth of many tissues. Besides that of the accessory sex organs such as the seminal vesicles and prostate glands, there is a general increase in body mass with growth of muscle, kidneys and bone. This action is marked by an increased blood supply to the various organs, which obviously follows application of androgen in the cock's comb.

2. Perhaps as part of the growth-promoting action, androgens are remarkably anabolic and cause nitrogen retention. This response is of clinical value and compounds allied to testosterone are being studied in the hope of finding one with high anabolic activity but little androgenic potency.

3. They act directly upon the nervous system to shape the sexual behavior of the individual. This is clearly shown by the effects of castration

on masculine sexual behavior and the return to normal with androgen treatment, perhaps before effects on the sex accessories are observed. In the intact female androgens may result in a bisexual pattern of behavior. In women, moderate doses of androgen appear to heighten, but not alter, the sexual interests.

The actions of androgens. Androgens exert an effect upon the genital system from the earliest period of life. When frog larvae (or tadpoles) are treated with testosterone, genetic females are transformed into apparently normal males which will produce normal spermatozoa. In the mammalian fetus, such as that of the rat, the injection of androgens markedly stimulates the Wolffian (male) structures, both in the male and female, without promoting the disappearance of the Müllerian system. This effect can also be observed when large amounts of male sex hormone are given to the pregnant cat or mouse. Here also, alongside the development of the Wolffian system in the female, the Müllerian ducts persist.

The effects of androgen in the fowl have been long studied. In the castrated cock, or capon, androgens restore the size of the comb and wattles, and enlarge those of the female (figure 78.11). The ability to crow is regained and male sexual behavior becomes manifest. Continued administration of androgen to hens enables them to assume dominance over other members of the flock and so assume a higher rank in the "social scale" or peck-order.

Castration atrophy of the accessory male organs (seminal vesicles, prostate gland, Cowper's glands, scrotum and penis) is prevented by testosterone or other androgens (figure 78.12). The epithelium of the seminal vesicles is restored to its normal condition and the level of fructose in the gland is raised. Involution of the prostate gland is prevented and there is stimulation of the secretion of the gland with elevation of the concentration of acid phosphatase.

The effect of androgens upon the testis seems to be largely dependent upon the amount given. With a moderate dose there is testicular atrophy together with arrest of spermatogenesis and atrophy of the Leydig cells. The pituitary is involved in this response, for when gonadotrophic hormone is given with the androgen there is no atrophy. High doses of androgen stimulate the seminiferous tubules and will partially prevent the results of hypophysectomy, but the Leydig cells still undergo degeneration, for they are solely under the control of the hypophysis. Androgens do not exhibit the seminiferous tubule maintenance to the

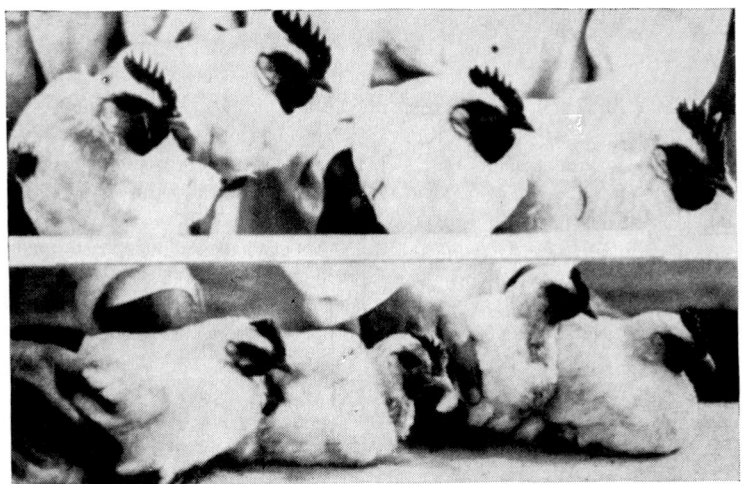

FIG. 78.11. Showing the effect of testis hormone (from urine) upon the comb growth of capons. The birds in the upper photograph received daily injections over a period of 15 days. Lower photograph, untreated controls. (After Funk, Harrow and Lejwa.)

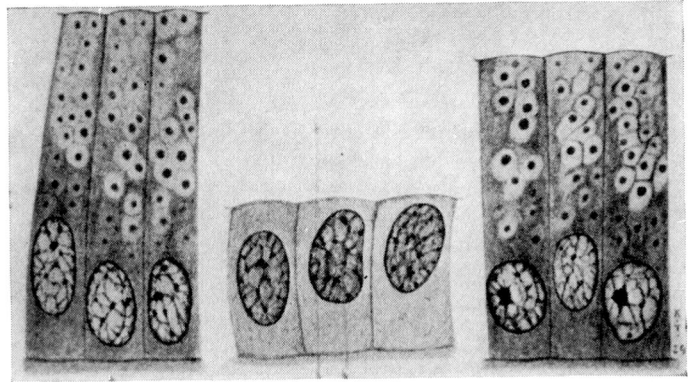

FIG. 78.12. Effect of castration and testis hormone on epithelium of seminal vesicles. (Moore, Hughes and Gallagher.) 1, cells from normal animal, showing secretion granules; 2, cells from 20-day castrate; 3, cells from 20-day castrate treated with male hormone.

same degree. The most potent in this regard is 17-methyl-Δ^5-androstene-3β,17β-diol (methylandrostenediol), whereas testosterone is much less effective.

In the female small doses of testosterone modify the secretion of gonadotrophin by the pituitary in favor of FSH so that mainly follicular activity is observed in the ovaries. When testicular tissue is implanted into an intact female rat within a few days of birth, or testosterone is administered, the animal displays constant estrus on reaching sexual maturity. This effect of male hormone would seem to be exerted at an hypothalamic level. Transplantation of the pituitary of a male rat under the median eminence of an hypophysectomized female is compatible with the restoration of normal estrous cycles. In large doses androgens inhibit the gonadotrophic func-

tion of the hypophysis and so produce ovarian atrophy. Testosterone exhibits progesteronelike effects in the female, as seen by the changes induced in the endometrium of the uterus. However, deciduomas cannot be produced or pregnancy maintained.

Regulation of Testicular Function

There is much evidence to show that the testis and pituitary interact with one another. Besides the striking effect of hypophysectomy upon the testis (p. 1491) it is well known that removal of the testes results in enlargement of the hypophysis and the appearance of characteristic signet ring cells or *castration cells*. This change is prevented by the administration of androgen. Further, assay of the gonadotrophic hormone in the urine after castration shows that the excretion of gonadotrophic hormone is increased, but can be reduced by the administration of sex hormones. This phenomenon is observed clinically in cases of primary testicular deficiency in which the gonad is defective. Here too the output of pituitary hormone can be limited by administration of testosterone.

However, a variety of observations indicate that the normal regulation of testicular function is not a simple matter of a depressive action of testosterone on the pituitary. For example, in cases of primary testicular failure more testosterone is required to inhibit the secretion of gonadotrophin than to restore the secondary sex characters. Mottram and Cramer in 1923 found that although radium treatment caused atrophy of the the tubular epithelium of the rat testis without apparently harming the interstitial cells, castration cells nevertheless appeared in the hypophysis. This observation indicated that the tubular epithelium might produce a hormone which inhibited the pituitary, and search for it began. Although an aqueous extract which caused disappearance of castration cells in the hypophysis without stimulating the accessory sex organs was prepared and was called "inhibin," this work has not been confirmed. Albright and his colleagues directed attention to a close analogy between testis-pituitary and ovary-pituitary function. In their view an "X-hormone" produced by the Sertoli cells of the testis takes the place of the estrogen secreted by the analogous follicular structures of the ovary. The identity of the postulated "X-hormone" is not established although it is likely that the Sertoli cells produce estrogen (p. 1649). Estrogen will inhibit the secretion of gonadotrophin in the male in smaller dosage than testosterone. Nelson and his coworkers found little to favor in the inhibitory concept. Although they agree that the testis produces estrogen (but locate its origin in the Leydig cells) they put forward the hypothesis that the germinal cells inactivate pituitary gonadotrophin during spermatogenesis and so keep down the level of hormone in the blood. They suggest that when spermatogenesis stops, as in radiation damage, cryptorchidism, or castration, the gonadotrophins are not removed from the blood, accumulate and are then excreted in the urine in abnormal quantity. Evidence in favor of each theory has been brought forward by its supporters, and at the present time both find adherents.

It is important not to disregard the brain in considering the control of testicular function. In lower animals, the breeding season is often subject to control by day length, and a reflex involving the eyes, the hypothalamus, and the pituitary gland, and leading to the secretion of gonadotrophin exists. In dogs and rats, the local application of testosterone to the hypothalamus has been found to cause testicular atrophy.

ASSAY OF ANDROGENS. Androgen may be assayed biologically, using the growth of the comb of the fowl or changes in the accessory sex organs of mammals, or it may be assayed chemically by measurement of the 17-ketosteroids although the three most abundant urinary 11-deoxy-17-ketosteroids, dehydroisoandrosterone, androsterone and etiocholanolone are principally derived from dehydroisoandrosterone. In the assays utilizing the fowl, the capon or chick is used, and the test material is given intramuscularly or applied directly to the comb. Measurement of the blood or urinary neutral 17-ketosteroids is more frequently used as an index of androgenic activity, but it should be borne in mind that the androgenic potency of a given urine extract will not necessarily parallel 17-ketosteroid concentration. In a method developed for the measurement of testosterone in plasma, a testosterone-containing extract is treated with a placental enzyme to convert the androgen to estradiol-17β, and the amount of this steroid determined after correction for losses during the procedure. With this technique, the mean testosterone level for normal men was found to be 0.56 μg./100 ml. plasma, and 0.12 μg/100 ml. plasma for normal women.

HYPOGONADISM AND HYPERGONADISM IN THE MALE. Tumors of the testis in young boys may result in the precocious development of the secondary sex characters—growth of hair upon the pubis, in the axillae and over the face, deepening of the voice and enlargement of the penis. These effects are evidently due to hypersecretion of the male hormone, for they tend to subside after excision of the tumor. Hypergenitalism with closely similar features occurs as a result of hyperfunction of the adrenal cortex. Failure of development of the accessory male sex organs and of the secondary sexual characters, a condition referred to as hypogonadism or eunuchoidism, is in most cases due primarily to a pituitary disorder. This can be tested by measurement of the FSH excreted in the urine, which will be low. In other instances of eunuchoidism, the testes are the primary site of disease, e.g., destructive new growth, mumps, typhoid fever, syphilis, etc. Here, in the postpubertal individual, the output of FSH in the urine will be higher than normal. Testicular atrophy occasionally results from prolonged and severe inanition or vitamin B$_1$ deficiency. Hypofunctioning of the testes may commence at any time during postpubertal life as a result of pituitary disease or of any of the conditions just mentioned. In this deferred type of eunuchoidism, regressive changes may result, although usually of mild degree in the accessory organs of sex and in the secondary sex characters.

The Prostate Gland and Seminal Vesicles

The *prostate gland*, which surrounds the first inch or so of the urethra, is composed of branched tubulo-alveolar glands grouped into about 20 lobules. Its stroma is fibroelastic in nature and contains many bundles of smooth muscle. The alveoli of these glands drain into some 20 ducts which discharge into the urethra. There are indications, largely based upon the response to hormone administration, that the anterior portion of the prostate differs in function from the posterior. Prostatic carcinoma occurs more frequently in the posterior region of the gland than in the anterior. The gland is traversed by the ejaculatory ducts. Within the lumina of some of the alveoli, small bodies may be found. These include corpora amylacea, which are concentrically laminated bodies probably composed of desquamated epithelial cells and prostatic secretion, and prostatic calculi or concretions which normally are of a millimeter or so in diameter but can increase in size, particularly in elderly men, to become prostatic stones. Analysis of prostatic stones has shown them to be composed of calcium and magnesium phosphates and carbonates together with organic matter.

Glands lying in relation to the wall of the upper part of the urethra are present in the female. They are analogous to the male organ and are referred to as the female prostate.

The prostate gland does not appear to have any endocrine function. It secretes small amounts of fluid continuously into the urethra (from 0.5 to 2 ml. per hour in man), and much larger amounts during coitus. Prostatic fluid contains proteolytic enzymes, β-glucuronidase, citric acid and acid phosphatase. The prostate gland is unusual in containing a relatively high concentration of zinc, which can be increased by androgens and reduced by castration.

The *seminal vesicles* represent evaginations of the ductus deferens, and are elongated, hollow bodies with a mucosa displaying many folds and pockets. They do not store sperm and are lacking in monotremes, marsupials and carnivores. The secretion of the seminal vesicles contains a high concentration of potassium and has a considerable content of reducing substances such as ergothioneine, ascorbic acid and fructose, which are added to the semen. The fructose content of the semen is directly controlled by circulating androgen and provides a sensitive index of androgenic activity.

Prostatic fluid, and that derived from the seminal vesicles, contributes to the seminal plasma and provides ingredients, such as fructose, that are utilized by the sperm. However, these secretions are not indispensible for fertility. Sperm taken from the epididymis are entirely adequate for artificial insemination purposes whilst the seminal vesicles or the prostate glands can be removed from rats with the continuance of normal mating and the induction of pregnancy. Nevertheless, the importance of the secretions of the accessory sex glands in providing a physiological diluent for the sperm should not be overlooked.

The secretion of prostatic fluid is increased by stimulation of the nerve erigentes (parasympathetic), whilst discharge of the secretion from the gland is brought about by the hypogastric nerves (sympathetic).

PROSTATIC NEOPLASMS. Two common forms of prostatic neoplasm can be distinguished: benign and carcinomatous. Benign prostatic hypertrophy is common in old men but is generally restricted to the medullary region of the gland. Since it does not occur after early castration, androgens are presumably concerned with its development, although castration is of little benefit once the condition is manifest. Prostatic cancer is also common in the elderly human male, though rare in rodents. In this case, removal of androgen, by castration or by treatment with estrogen, is of value in promoting regression of the tumor but the effect is not permanent.

HORMONAL TREATMENT OF MALE SEX DISORDERS. Although the testis hormone, in accordance with the principles of hormone action, does not stimulate the interstitial cells of the testes, it provides the perfect substitution therapy in cases of underdevelopment or regression of the accessory male sex organs. Testosterone, methyl testosterone or testosteronecyclopentenyl propionate may all be used.

Chorionic gonadotrophin has been employed to stimulate spermatogenesis in an undeveloped testis or to restore normal spermatogenic function. It has also proved of value in the treatment of cryptorchidism, with descent of the testes being induced. The use of pituitary gonadotrophins does not appear to be practicable in view of the development of antihormones.

Erection and Ejaculation

In order to carry to completion the sexual function of the male, semen must be deposited in the female genital tract. For this purpose the flaccid penis is converted into a rigid intromittent organ and at the orgasm, expulsion of semen occurs through it. Thus two phases can be distinguished: erection and ejaculation. Both provide good examples of sympathetic-parasympathetic interaction although, since the nerve plexuses involved contain both sympathetic and parasympathetic fibers, it is difficult to study each system in isolation.

Erection is brought about by a vascular engorgement of the penis, produced by dilation of the arteries which supply the spongelike erectile tissue in the corpora cavernosa penis and the corpus cavernosum urethrae. This reaction was observed a hundred years ago by Eckhard (1863) who found that electrical stimulation of the visceral rami of the sacral nerves in the dog induced penile erection *via* the vasodilator action. He called these fibers the "nervi erigentes" and the name has been retained. However, the integrity of the nervi erigentes is not essential for erection, for in the dog and cat destruction of the origin of the nervi erigentes in the spinal cord does not prevent erection following suitable stimuli such as manipulation of the glans or psychic stimulation. In the latter case erection does not occur when the lumbar part of the spinal cord is destroyed. It would seem that, in addition to the action of the parasympathetic nervi erigentes, sympathetic fibers arising in the lumbar cord are involved in the erectile process, although sympathetic stimulation, by its vasoconstrictor effect, may interfere with erection. Eckhard also found that mechanical stimulation of the glans would bring about erection only if the pudendal nerve was intact. Thus the pudendal nerve is afferent to glans stimulation. Efferent fibers from the hypogastric plexus also pass in the pudendal nerve to exert a vasoconstrictor action on the penis.

Ejaculation of semen is a frequent accompaniment of erection although the *emission* of semen can occur through a flaccid penis. In man stimulation of the pelvic sympathetic nerves produces discharge of semen from the ejaculating ducts due to seminal vesicle and prostatic contraction. Following lumbar sympathectomy semen is no longer discharged from the urethra. Ejaculation still occurs but the semen may enter the bladder instead of the urethra because of nonclosure of the internal vesical sphincter. During physiological ejaculation the smooth muscle of the genital system is probably constricted by both parasympathetic and sympathetic impulses propagated under the control of the spinal cord. Contraction of the voluntary muscles, such as the bulbo-cavernosus and ischio-cavernosus muscles also occurs at this time.

Sexual Behavior

The gonadal hormones, in addition to their actions upon the reproductive system, act upon the nervous system to elicit characteristic patterns of behavior—sexual behavior. It may perhaps be taken for granted that the sexual behavior is invariably associated with fully functional gonads. Such may be deduced from the fact that the term "estrous cycle" has a behavioral basis. However, in the sheep one or more estrous cycles—*silent heats*—may pass at the commencement of the breeding season before the occurrence of overt estrous behavior. In the monkey, ovulation may not occur during the summer, although the menstrual cycles continue. Sexual activity does not appear to be diminished.

There is no question that the removal of the gonads may depress sexual activity, although to an extent which varies between the sexes and from one species to another. In the female rat sexual activity is abolished whereas in the female rabbit coitus may occasionally take place. In the ovariectomized chimpanzee there is little sign of desire for intercourse but it is said that ovariectomized women may show as much erotic behavior after the operation as before. With regard to the male primate, castration often fails to diminish the capacity to mate (chimpanzee) or to abolish the orgasm (man).

Full sexual activity in the ovariectomized or castrated individual may be restored by treatment with the appropriate sex hormones. Further, it is possible to evoke components of the pattern of sexual behavior of the opposite sex by administration of androgen, e.g., to a spayed female, and *vice versa*. Basically, overt sexual behavior does not appear to depend upon a learned response but is due to a fundamental action of the sex hormones upon the nervous system. (Young has shown that in guinea pigs the performance of the male is improved by experience; the sexual activity of males reared in isolation is inferior to that of animals reared in a group, and may be permanently impaired.)

The gonadal hormones might produce their behavioral actions either by an effect on the peripheral receptors, or by a direct action on some integrating center in the central nervous system. In the former case the hormone could act by sensitizing the genitalia to excitation, but this possibility has been eliminated by the finding that removal or denervation of the genitalia does not inhibit sexual behavior or reduce sexual aggression.

The second possibility, that of a direct action of the gonadal hormones upon the central nervous system, has received detailed examination. It is now clear that "normal" estrous behavior can continue in the cat, rabbit, guinea pig and rat following removal of the cerebral cortex, although none appears in the spinal animal. It may therefore be presumed that some subcortical but supraspinal neural structure is involved in the behavioral mechanism. Dempsey and Rioch in 1939 studied the guinea pig and found that a transection of the brain which passed through the rostral end of the mammillary bodies did not abolish estrous reflexes, but that transection posterior to the mammillary bodies did cause lose of these reflexes. This observation implies that some area in the region of the hypothalamus may be concerned in the production of sexual behavior in the guinea pig, and since that time evidence has accrued which indicates that the hypothalamus itself is of importance. Among the salient observations we may note that (a) sexual behavior may be abolished by hypothalamic lesions, (b) reproducible electrical activity has been recorded in the hypothalamus following artificial stimulation of the vagina of the cat, and (c) the application of estrogen to the posterior hypothalamus of the spayed cat has been found to induce full and typical sexual behavior at a time when no effects of the estrogen upon the reproductive organs could be found. The insertion of similar amounts of estrogen into the cerebellum, preoptic region, caudate nucleus, thalamus or amygdaloid nucleus did not evoke sexual behavior in similar circumstances.

In summary, it appears that some integrating mechanism exists in the upper midbrain or hypothalamus which is sensitive to the blood concentration of gonadal hormones. If these hormones are present in amounts above a certain threshold level, then specific sensory stimuli (e.g., visual, auditory, olfactory), normally derived from a possible mate, act through this mechanism to excite reflexly the pattern of sexual behavior typical of the species. In the human, it seems that this basic neural mechanism has become largely dominated by cortical factors, so that learning and conditioning play an increasingly important role. The continuance of active sexual behavior after castration in the adult human may well be dependent on this latter fact.

The Pineal Body or Epiphysis

ORIGIN AND STRUCTURE. This is a small gland-like structure (about 10 mm. long in man) somewhat resembling a pine cone (pinea) in shape, situated just beneath the splenium of the corpus callosum and resting in the groove between the superior colliculi. The pineal arises as a diverticulum of the roof of the third ventricle. The cavity of the original pouch eventually disappears, the fully developed gland being composed of a solid mass of cells. The histological features of the pineal are very diverse, the picture varying from species to species and with age. In general however, it may be said to have a pseudoalveolar structure, the cells being arranged in masses or lobules surrounded by a highly vascular connective tissue.

Involutionary changes are said to commence in the human pineal body of about the seventh year. In children past the age of seven, laminated bodies composed of phosphates and carbonates of calcium and magnesium—the so-called "brain sand" —make their appearance.

The functions of the pineal body are unknown. Its structure has suggested an endocrine function but there is really little definite evidence from which such a conclusion may be drawn. Recent work has tended to imply that the pineal gland exerts an action which is antagonistic to that brought about by gonadotrophic hormone. This represents a revival of an earlier view that fell into disrepute.

REFERENCES

It is no longer advisable to give chapter and verse for every salient observation quoted in this chapter; the list would be far too long. Alternatively, selection of the most significant publications would probably reflect the interest of the writer more than the importance of the work in question. For such reasons the ensuing list is restricted to monographs and reviews.

Two works are of particular value when seeking information concerning the physiology of reproduction. These are "Sex and Internal Secretions," edited by W. C. Young, and "Marshall's Physiology of Reproduction," edited by A. S. Parkes. Three series of volumes merit special mention because of their continuing importance: Recent Progress in Hormone Research, Vitamins and Hormones, and the Ciba Foundation Colloquia in Endocrinology.

ALLEN, E. (ed.) Sex and internal secretions. 2nd ed. Baltimore: Williams & Wilkins. 1939.

ASDELL, S. A. The growth and function of the corpus luteum. Physiol. Rev., **8**, 313–345, 1928.

BARD, P. The hypothalamus and sexual behavior. Res. Publ. Ass. Nerv. Ment. Dis., **20**, 551–576, 1940.

BARTELMEZ, G. W. Menstruation. Physiol. Rev., **17**, 28–72, 1937.

BARTELMEZ, G. W. The phases of the menstrual cycle and their interpretation in terms of the pregnancy cycle. Am. J. Obstet. Gynecol. **74**, 931–955, 1957.

BIELSCHOWSKY, F. AND HORNING, E. S. Aspects of endocrine carcinogenesis. Brit. Med. Bull. **14**, 106–151, 1958.

BISHOP, P. M. F. Recent advances in endocrinology. 7th ed. New York: Blakiston. 1954.

BREUER, H. The metabolism of the natural estrogens. Vitamins and Hormones, **20**, 285–335, 1962.

BROWN, J. B. Estrogen excretion in normal and abnormal menstrual cycles, *In* Recent progress in the endocrinology of reproduction (ed. LLOYD, C. W.). New York, Academic Press. 1959.

CHANG, M. C. AND PINCUS, G. Physiology of fertilization in mammals. *Physiol. Rev.*, **31**, 1–26, 1951.

COLE, H. H. AND CUPPS, P. T. (Eds.) Reproduction in Domestic Animals. New York, Academic Press. 1959.

CORNER, G. W. Oestrus, ovulation and menstruation. Physiol. Rev., **3**, 457–482, 1923.

CORNER, G. W. The sites of formation of estrogenic substances in the animal body. Physiol. Rev., **18**, 154–172, 1938.

CORNER, G. W. The hormones in reproduction. Princeton, Princeton University Press. 1942.

CORNER, G. W. The early history of the oestrogenic hormones. J. Endocrinol., **31**, iii–xviii, 1965.

COURT BROWN, W. M., HARNDEN, D. G., JACOBS, P. A., MACLEAN, N., AND MANTLE, D. J., Abnormalities of the sex chromosome complement in man. Medical Research Council Special Report Series, No. 305. London: Her Majesty's Stationery Office, 1964.

CSAPO, A. Function and regulation of the myometrium. Ann. N. Y. Acad. Sci., **75**, 790–808, 1959.

DICZFALUSY, E. AND TROEN, P. Endocrine functions of the human placenta. Vitamins and hormones, **19**, 229–311, 1961.

DODDS, C. Synthetic oestrogens. Brit. Med. Bull., **11**, 131–134, 1955.

DOISY, E. A. The estrogenic substances. Harvey lectures, **29**, 158–175, 1933–34.

DORFMAN, R. I., FORCHIELLI, E., AND GUT, M. Androgen biosynthesis and related studies. Recent Progr. Hormone Res., **19**, 251–267, 1963.

DORFMAN, R. I., AND SHIPLEY, R. A. Androgens, biochemistry, physiology and clinical significance. New York, John Wiley, 1956.

FALCK, B. Site of production of oestrogen in rat ovary as studied in micro-transplants. Acta Physiol. Scand., **47**, Suppl. 163, 1959.

FOLLEY, S. J. Endocrine control of the mmamary gland. Brit. Med. Bull. **5**, 130–148, 1947.

FOLLEY, S. J. Lactation, *in* Marshall's physiology of reproduction. 3rd ed. **2**, (ed., PARKES, A. S.) London, Longmans Green, 1952.

FOLLEY, S. J. The physiology and biochemistry of lactation. Edinburgh, Oliver and Boyd, 1956.

FRIEDEN, E. H. AND HISAW, F. L. The biochemistry of relaxin. Recent Progr. Hormone Res., **8**, 333–372, 1953.

FUNK, C., HARROW, B. AND LEJWA, A. The male hormone. *Amer. J. Physiol.*, **92**, 440–449, 1930.

GARCIA, C. AND ROCK, J. Ovulation *in* Essentials of human reproduction (ed. VELARDO, J. T.) New York, Oxford University Press, 1958.

GOREMAN, B. (ed.). Comparative endocrinology. New York, John Wiley, 1959.

GRADY, H. G. AND SMITH, D. E. (eds.) The ovary. Baltimore, Williams & Wilkins, 1963.

GRAY, C. H. AND BACHARACH, A. L. (eds.) Hormones in blood. London, Academic Press, 1961.

GRUMBACH, M. M. AND BARR, M. L. Cytologic tests of chromosomal sex in relation to sexual anomalies in man. Recent Progr. Hormone Res. **14**, 255–342, 1958.

HAMERTON, J. L. (ed.) Chromosomes in medicine. Little Club Clinics in Developmental Medicine, No. 5 London, Heinemann, 1962.

HARRIS, G. W., MICHAEL, R. P., AND SCOTT, P. P. Neurological site of action of stilboestrol in eliciting sexual behaviour. Ciba Foundation Sympos. on the Neurological Basis of Behaviour, London: Churchill, 1958.

HARTMAN, C. G. (ed.) Mechanisms concerned with conception. Oxford, Pergamon Press, 1963.

HISAW, F. L. Development of the Graafian follicle and ovulation. Physiol. Rev., **27**, 95–119, 1947.

HISAW, F. L. AND ZARROW, M. X. The physiology of relaxin. Vitamins and Hormones, **8**, 151–178, 1950.

HUGGINS, C. The physiology of the prostate gland. Physiol. Rev. **25**, 281–295, 1945.

JOST, A. Problems of fetal endocrinology: the gonadal and hypophyseal hormones. Recent Progr. Hormone Res. **8**, 379–413, 1953.

KITAY, J. I. AND ALTSCHULE, M. D. The pineal gland. Cambridge, Mass., Harvard Univ. Press, 1954.

KOCH, F. C. The male sex hormones. Physiol. Rev. **17**, 153–238, 1937.

KON, S. K. AND COWIE, A. T. (Eds.) Milk: The mammary gland and its secretion. New York, Academic Press, 1961.

LEATHEM, J. H. Nutritional effects on endocrine secretions *in* Sex and internal secretions (ed., YOUNG, W. C.), 3rd ed., Baltimore, Williams & Wilkins, 1961.

LINZELL, J. L. Physiology of the mammary glands. *Physiol. Rev.* **39**, 534–576, 1959.

LIPSCHUTZ, A. The internal secretions of the sex glands. Baltimore, Williams & Wilkins, 1924.

LLOYD, C. W. (ed.) Recent progress in the endocrinology of reproduction. New York, Academic Press, 1959.

LLOYD, C. W. (ed.) Human Reproduction and sexual behavior. Philadelphia, Lea & Febiger, 1964.

LONG, J. A. AND EVANS, H. M. The oestrous cycle in the rat and its associated phenomena. Memoirs Univ. California. **6**, 1–148, 1922.

LORAINE, J. A. (1958). The clinical application of hormone assay. Edinburgh, Livingstone, 1958.

LYONS, W. R., LI, C. H., AND JOHNSON, R. E. The hormonal control of mammary growth and lactation. Recent Progr. Hormone Res. 14, 219–248, 1958.

McCULLAGH, E. P. AND SCHAFFENBURG, C. A. The testes *in* Glandular physiology and therapy. 5th ed. Philadelphia, Lippincott, 1954.

MACY, I. G. AND KELLY, H. J. Human milk and cow's milk in infant nutrition *in* Milk: The mammary gland and its secretion (eds. KON, S. K. AND COWIE, A. T.) New York, Academic Press, 1961.

MANN, T. The biochemistry of semen and of the male reproductive tract. London, Methuen, 1964.

MARRIAN, G. F. Recent advances in the chemistry and biological assay of oestrin. Physiol. Rev. 13, 185–221, 1933.

MARSHALL, F. H. A. The physiology of reproduction. 2nd ed. London, Longmans, 1922.

MARTIN, G. J. AND SCHOENBACH, V. Historical aspects of relaxin. Ann. N. Y. Acad. Sci. 75, 923–930.

MERRILL, R. C. Estriol: a review. Physiol. Rev. 38, 463–480, 1958.

MOORE, C. R., HUGHES, W. AND GALLAGHER, T. F. Rat seminal-vesicle cytology as a testis-hormone indicator and the prevention of castration changes by testis-extract injection. Amer. J. Anat. 45, 109–135, 1930.

NELSON, W. O. Endocrine control of the mammary gland. Physiol. Rev. 16, 488–526, 1936.

PARKES, A. S. (ed.) Marshall's physiology of reproduction, London, Longmans, Green, 1952, 1956, 1960.

PARKES, A. S. (ed.) Hormones in reproduction. Brit. Med. Bull. 11, No. 2, 1955.

PETERSEN, W. E. Lactation. Physiol. Rev. 24, 340–371, 1944.

PETERSEN, W. E. The hormonal control of lactation. Recent Progr. Hormone Res. 2, 133–158, 1948.

RIDDLE, O. AND BATES, R. W. The preparation, assay and actions of lactogenic hormone *in* Sex and internal secretions (ed., ALLEN E.) 2nd ed., Baltimore, Williams & Wilkins, 1938.

ROBERTS, S. AND SZEGO, C. M. Steroid interaction in the metabolism of reproductive target organs. Physiol. Rev. 33, 593–629, 1953.

ROBSON, J. M. Recent advances in sex and reproductive physiology. 3rd Ed. London, Churchill, 1947.

RYAN, K. J. Synthesis of hormones in the ovary *in* The ovary (eds., GRADY, H. G. AND SMITH, D. E.) Baltimore, Williams & Wilkins, 1963.

SOHVAL, A. R. The anatomy and endocrine physiology of the male reproductive system *in* The endocrinology of reproduction, (ed., VELARDO, J. T.) New York: Oxford University Press.

SOHVAL, A. R. Chromosomes and sex chromatin in normal and anomalous sexual development. Physiol. Rev. 43, 306–356, 1963.

STOCKARD, C. R. AND PAPANICOLAOU, G. N. The existence of a typical oestrous cycle in the guinea pig with a study of its histological and physiological changes. Amer. J. Anat. 22, 225–283, 1917.

STONE, M. L. Effects of relaxin in the human *in* Recent progress in the endocrinology of reproduction (ed., LLOYD, C. W.) New York, Academic Press, 1959.

TURNER, C. D. General endocrinology. 1st ed. Philadelphia, Saunders, 1948.

VAN OORDT, G. J. Male gonadal hormones *in* Comparative endocrinology (eds., VON EULER, U. S. AND HELLER, H.) New York, Academic Press, 1963.

VANDE WIELE, R. L., MacDONALD, P. C., GURPIDE, E. AND LIEBERMAN, S. Studies on the secretion and interconversion of androgens. Recent Progr. Hormone Res., 19, 275–305, 1963.

VELARDO, J. T. (ed.) The endocrinology of reproduction. New York, Oxford University Press, 1958.

VELARDO, J. T. (ed.) Essentials of human reproduction. New York, Oxford University Press, 1958.

VELLE, W. Female gonadal hormones *in* Comparative endocrinology (eds., VON EULER, U. S. AND HELLER, H.) New York, Academic Press, 1963.

VENNING, E. H. Clinical value of hormone estimations. Brit. Med. Bull. 11, 140–144, 1955.

WILKINS, L. The diagnosis and treatment of endocrine disorders in childhood and adolescence. Springfield, Thomas, 1950.

YOUNG, W. C. Genetic and psychological determination of sexual behavior pattern *in* Hormones, brain function and behaviour (ed., HOAGLAND, H.) New York, Academic Press, 1957.

YOUNG, W. C. (ed.) Sex and internal secretions. 3rd ed. Baltimore, Williams & Wilkins, 1961.

ZANDER, J. Gestagens in human pregnancy *in* Recent progress in the endocrinology of reproduction (ed., LLOYD, C. W.) New York, Academic Press. 1959.

ZARROW, M. X. Gestation *in* Sex and internal secretions. 3rd ed. (ed. YOUNG, W. C.) Baltimore, Williams & Wilkins, 1961.

ZUCKERMAN, S. The regenerative capacity of ovarian tissue. In Ciba Foundation Colloquia on Ageing, 2, (eds., WOLSTENHOLME, G. E. W. AND MILLAR, E. C. P.) London, Churchill, 1956.

ZUCKERMAN, S. (ed.) The ovary. New York, Academic Press, 1962.

X

THE EXCRETION OF URINE

CHAPTER 79

Urine Formation

The Structure of the Kidney; Theories of Renal Function

THE STRUCTURE OF THE HUMAN KIDNEY

The functional unit of the kidney is the *nephron*, each kidney being composed of approximately one million such units. The nephron begins at a blind end enclosing a leash of capillaries. In this structure, known as the *glomerulus (renal corpuscle, Malpighian corpuscle)*, urine formation begins by the separation, from the blood perfusing the glomerular capillaries, of an essentially protein-free filtrate of plasma. The glomerular space or *Bowman's capsule* is continuous with the lumen of the *renal tubule*, a long coiled structure structurally and functionally divisible into three segments: proximal convoluted tubule, loop of Henle and distal convoluted tubule. The nephron as an individual unit ends with the distal convoluted tubule but groups of distal convoluted tubules empty into a series of *collecting tubules*, which in turn coalesce to form *collecting ducts*. The collecting ducts in turn empty into the short *papillary ducts of Bellini* which open into the renal calyces at the tips of the papillae.

THE GLOMERULUS consists of a leash of capillaries interconnected by short anastamotic channels. These capillaries are invaginated into and covered on their outer surfaces by the visceral layer of the epithelium of Bowman's capsule. This layer of flattened cells is continuous with the parietal layer of epithelium and with the lining cells of the renal tubules. Blood enters the glomerulus from the short afferent arteriole, and the coalescence of the glomerular capillaries forms the efferent arteriole; the glomerular capillaries are thus unique in being interposed between two arterioles. The glomerulus averages about 200 μ in diameter and the total surface of glomerular capillaries in the two human kidneys is estimated to be about 1.5 square meters. The glomeruli are found only in the cortex.

THE PROXIMAL CONVOLUTED TUBULE is a tortuous structure averaging about 55 μ in diameter and 14 mm. in length. It lies in the renal cortex usually in close proximity to the glomerulus to which it is conjoined. It is lined with a single layer of cuboidal cells, each interdigitated with the adjoining cells in a highly complex manner. The border facing the tubule lumen is characterized and distinguished from that of other segments by delicate striations perpendicular to the free edge and known as the brush border. The terminal portion of the proximal tubule becomes straight and dips toward the medulla to become the loop of Henle.

THE LOOP OF HENLE commences with a descending limb which dips down into the medulla. As it does so, the cuboidal cells are suddenly replaced by the flattened cells of the *thin segment*. The loop penetrates into the medulla for a varying distance, the depth depending upon the location of the glomerulus from which the tubule is derived. Those loops derived from tubules with glomeruli situated near the surface of the kidney penetrate only a short distance into the medulla before turning back toward the cortex; those arising from tubules with glomeruli close to the cortico-medullary junction (*juxtamedullary glomeruli*) penetrate deeply to near the tip of the papilla before turning back (see fig. 79.1). The first part of the ascending limb does not differ in appearance from the thin portion of the descending limb, but as the ascending limb reaches the outer medullary zone it widens and becomes lined with a cuboidal epithelium which continues into the distal tubule. The tubule continues into the cortex and comes into contact with the glomerulus from which it arose, this contact being marked by a region of closely packed nuclei designated as the *macula densa*.

THE DISTAL CONVOLUTED TUBULE may be defined as beginning at the macula densa. Like the proximal tubule with which its loops are generally entwined, the distal convoluted tubule lies in the cortex. It is distinguished by the fact that its lining epithelium is somewhat lower, less complex and lacks the brush border. The distal convoluted tubules empty into collecting tubules. The collecting tubules empty into collecting ducts which pass through the medulla and papilla to empty into the pelvis.

BLOOD SUPPLY. The renal artery upon entering the hilum of the kidney breaks up into numerous branches, the *interlobular arteries*, which pass outward between the renal pyramids to the junction

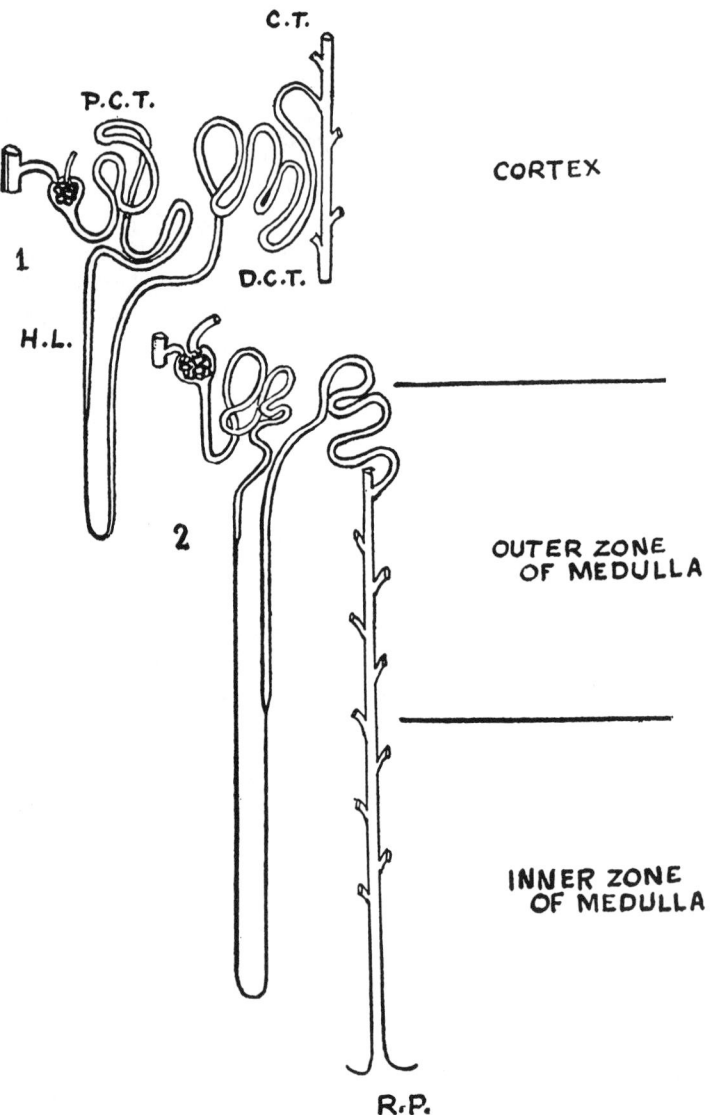

FIG. 79.1. Diagram of a cortical (1) and of a juxtamedullary (2) nephron. P.C.T., proximal convoluted tubule; D.C.T., distal convoluted tubule; C.T., collecting tubule; H.L., Henle's loop; R.P., renal pelvis.

of the cortex with the medulla. Here they turn to follow a more horizontal course and form arterial arches (the *arcuate arteries*) across the bases of the pyramids. From the arcuate arteries arise the *interlobular arteries* which run outward through the cortex. From the interlobular arteries the afferent arterioles carry blood to the glomeruli.

The short muscular *afferent arteriole* enters the glomerulus and breaks up into the leash of glomerular capillaries. The latter again coalesce to empty into the *efferent arteriole* which is usually appreciably smaller in diameter than the afferent arteriole (fig. 79.2).

The efferent arterioles derived from most glomeruli break up into a network of capillaries surrounding the convoluted tubules as they lie in the cortex. This capillar network is drained by veins which follow a course close to the arteries and empty into the renal vein (fig. 79.3).

The efferent arterioles derived from the *juxtamedullary glomeruli* close to the cortico-medullary junction do not feed into the peritubular capillary plexus. Instead each divides into a group of straight vessels, the *vasa recta* which descend into the medulla, following a course similar to the loops of Henle, and then turn to return to the cortex and enter the venous system. As they pass through the cortico-medullary junction, the vasa recta tend to become gathered into groups, the *vascular bundles*, and in these groups the descending and ascending limbs of the vasa recta lie closely intermingled in an arrangement ideally suited for diffusional exchanges between inflowing and outflowing blood.

SUMMARY OF DEVELOPMENT OF CURRENT CONCEPTS

The development of our present understanding of the function of the kidney can be considered to date from 1842 when Bowman described the structure of the glomerulus, particularly showing the continuity of the space of the Malpighian corpuscle with the lumen of the tubule. Bowman recognized the structural characteristics which suggested its function as a filter. He supposed that the filtration process provided only the urinary water and that the solutes of the urine were added by the secretory activity of the cells of the renal tubules. The process of glomerular filtration thus served merely to wash the solutes through the tubules.

Ludwig in 1844 proposed that glomerular filtration provided all of the water and solutes of the urine and that the function of the tubules was to concentrate the solutes by the reabsorption of water. It was recognized that this concentration would lead to some loss of solute by diffusion. Heidenhain (1874) from observations on the accumulation of dyes in the renal tubule cells returned to a theory close to that of Bowman, placing the burden of urinary excretion on secretion of solutes by the tubule cells.

In 1917, Cushny, in an attempt to simplify what had by then become a complex and confused subject, proposed what he termed the "modern theory of renal function." Totally rejecting any secretion by the renal tubules, Cushny hypothesized that urine formation began with the formation of a protein-free ultrafiltrate of plasma in the glomeruli. From this flow of fluid the tubules were assumed to reabsorb a solution of constant and unvarying composition. This solution was presumed to have the composition of an ultrafiltrate of normal plasma and Cushny proposed that the "fluid reabsorbed is always the same, whatever the needs of the organism at the moment."

The development of knowledge concerning the function of the kidney has shown that each of the above theories contains some parts which are correct and others which are not. The existence of secretion by the tubules was definitively shown by Marshall and his associates.

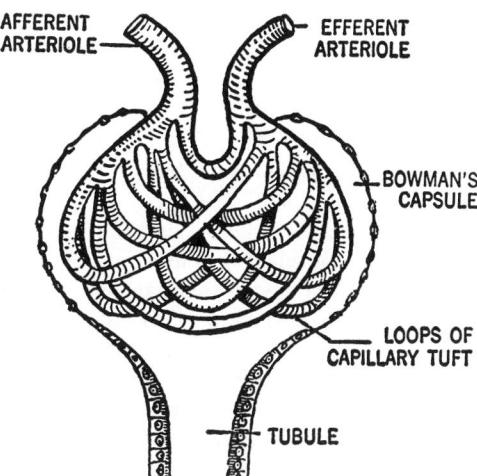

FIG. 79.2. Diagramatic representation of the glomerulus.

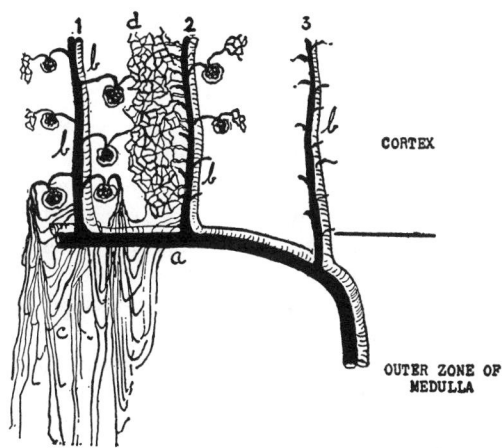

FIG. 79.3. Diagram of the renal circulation; *a*, arcuate vessels; *b*, interlobular vessels (1, 2 and 3), arteries *black*, veins *shaded*; *c*, vasa recta; *d*, peritubular plexus of vessels. In 2 and 3 peritubular plexus and all but two glomeruli are omitted.

In the development of renal physiology which has taken place in the last 30 years, leading to the physiological picture presented in the following pages, two experimental techniques have played a central role. The micropuncture techniques developed by A. N. Richards and his many important associates provided means for collecting fluid from accurately located regions of the nephron and for the analysis of this fluid by microchemical methods. This has provided invaluable information on the nature and localization of events in the renal tubule. The clearance methods, with measurement of the rate of glomerular filtration, in connection with which the names of Rehberg, Homer Smith and Shannon stand out, has provided a tool for the evaluation of many processes in the intact unanesthetized animal or in man, under conditions approaching normal.

General Nature of Urine Formation

Although the two human kidneys are made up of some two million nephron units, it is convenient for most purposes to consider the two kidneys as constituting a single huge nephron. Such a model is accurate to the extent that each nephron is similar in its functional proportions to every other and to the extent that each nephron functions in parallel with and independent of every other. These assumptions may be accepted as first approximations. The consequences of heterogeneity of nephron function and of interdependence of nephrons will be considered in subsequent sections. For present purposes we may speak of *the* glomerulus and *the* proximal convoluted tubule, etc., as if the kidneys represented a single unit, and referring to the sum of the functions of the several million units.

The processes of renal function are initiated in the glomerulus by the separation from the plasma of an essentially protein-free ultrafiltrate. The ultrafiltrate delivered from the glomerular capillaries into the space of Bowman's capsule enters the lumen of the proximal tubule. As the result of the net filtration pressure, the separated fluid flows through the tubule. As it passes through the various tubule segments, the fluid is drastically modified both in volume and composition by a series of operations performed upon it by the lining epithelium of the tubules. Many of the constituents of the fluid originally filtered into the glomerular space are removed from the fluid as it traverses the renal tubules and are returned to the blood to be retained within the body. Some components of the glomerular filtrate such as glucose and the amino acids are virtually completely reabsorbed, appearing in the final urine only under unusual circumstances. Other constituents such as urea, are reabsorbed to only a limited extent while still others are excreted and reabsorbed to an extent which is regulated so as to maintain the normal composition of body fluids. Among the substances reabsorbed to a major but variable extent is water itself, so that the volume flow of urine is always but a fraction of the flow of glomerular filtrate. In addition to reabsorbing many substances from the fluid flowing through the tubule, the tubule epithelium also removes certain substances from the peritubular blood and deposits them in the fluid within the lumen. Thus three individual processes, glomerular filtration, tubular reabsorption (from lumen to blood) and tubular secretion (from blood to lumen) are involved in the process of urine formation. These three processes will be considered in detail in subsequent sections.

GLOMERULAR FILTRATION

The idea that the glomerulus is a device for filtering fluid from the blood perfusing the glomerular capillaries goes back to Bowman who in 1842 first described the relationship of the glomerular capsule to the renal tubules. Bowman believed that only the water of the urine was contributed by this filtration process, the solutes being added by secretion in the tubule. Shortly thereafter Ludwig (1844) offered the view, which has since been amply confirmed, that the glomerulus acts as an ultrafilter, separating from the plasma a solution which contains all of the solutes of plasma except the proteins and each at a concentration identical to that in the plasma water except as modified by the absence of protein. The cornerstones of the evidence indicating that the glomerulus is indeed an ultrafilter were supplied by A. N. Richards and his associates who showed that the composition of fluid collected from glomeruli in amphibians was, with respect to an extensive list of constituents, that required of a plasma ultrafiltrate. (The studies were later extended, with respect to a limited number of substances, to fluid collected directly from mammalian glomeruli by Walker, Bott, Oliver and MacDowell.) In addition it was shown that the hydrostatic pressure in the glomerular capillaries is sufficient to supply the driving force for the filtration process.

As in the case of other capillary beds, and in accord with the Starling hypothesis, the rate of filtration through the walls of the glomerular capillaries is determined by a balance of forces favoring and opposing filtration. The main driving force is the hydrostatic pressure—the intracapillary blood pressure (P_b). Opposing filtration is the osmotic pressure exerted by the plasma proteins (π_b) and the hydrostatic pressure of the fluid in Bowman's capsule (P_c). The rate of glomerular filtration (GFR) may thus be expressed as

$$\text{GFR} = K_p([P_b - P_c] - \pi_b) \qquad (1)$$

where K_p is a constant relating net filtration pressure to filtration rate and thus related to the area and the permeability of the glomerular capillary walls.

The glomerular capillaries differ from those of other capillary beds in being interposed between two arterioles, in maintaining a higher hydrostatic pressure, and in having a higher permeability. Pappenheimer and his associates have estimated that the permeability of glomerular capillaries is approximately one hundred times that of the capillaries in the limbs (muscles); the difference is presumably largely in the fraction of the total capillary surface occupied by the pores through which filtration actually occurs. The membrane which constitutes the significant filtration resistance and which is penetrated by the pores of critical size is probably the capillary basement membrane.

Some idea of the size of the pores can be obtained from the characteristics of those solutes that are filtered through the glomerular capillary membrane as compared with those that are not. The normal glomerular membrane is virtually completely impermeable to the proteins of plasma. The smallest of these, albumin, has a molecular weight of about 70,000 and appears in the glomerular filtrate either not at all or at a very low concentration (less than 0.2–0.3 % of its concentration in plasma). Recent measurements in samples from the early part of the dog proximal tubule indicate that the concentration is usually less than 5 mg per cent. Hemoglobin (molecular weight 68,000) on the other hand is excreted at a rate which would indicate that it appears in glomerular filtrate at a concentration equal to about 5 per cent of its concentration in the plasma. (The concentration referred to is that not combined, in the plasma, with larger protein molecules.) The hemoglobin molecule is somewhat less elongated than the albumin molecule, but the difference is relatively small. In any case, it is clear that the pores in the glomerular membranes can not be far removed in size from the dimensions of these molecules.

Also pertinent is the passage through the glomerular membrane of certain polysaccharides. Most important among these is inulin, a polymer of fructose, which has found a central role in the study of renal function. Its molecular weight is usually estimated to be 5200, but different inulin molecules probably differ in size, some being smaller, others larger. In addition, the molecule is greatly elongated, a characteristic which reduces its diffusibility and filtrability compared to a compact molecule of the same molecular weight. Nevertheless, the glomerular membrane appears to offer no hindrance to the passage of inulin, and its concentration in glomerular filtrate is the same as in the plasma from which the filtrate is derived. Dextrans (polysaccharides composed of glucose)

of a molecular weight approximately equal to that of inulin have been found to pass the glomerular membrane freely, but their passage is progressively restricted as their molecular weight increases and those with molecular weights above 55,000 do not appear in the urine from normal kidneys (i.e., kidneys producing protein-free urine).

Although different theoretical treatments will yield different dimensions for the size of the pores in the glomerular membrane, the permeability can be interpreted as attributable to pores approximately 100 Å in diameter.

Equation (1) indicates that glomerular filtration is a function of three variables as well as the area and permeability of the glomerular membrane. It is important to consider the possible contribution of changes in each of these to the physiological regulation of glomerular filtration.

1. THE GLOMERULAR MEMBRANE. (a) *Permeability*. The permeability of the glomerular membrane per unit of functioning surface is presumably fixed by its anatomical nature and not subject to physiological variation. Although changes do occur with disease, the effect of change in permeability as opposed to change in effective filtering area is difficult to evaluate. The diseased membrane may permit the passage of molecules larger than those which normally penetrate, but the predominant effect appears to be a decreased permeability.

(b) *Area*. The effective area available for filtration depends upon the number of glomeruli active at any time and the number of functioning capillaries in each glomerulus. The weight of evidence favors the view that, in the mammalian kidney under physiological conditions, all glomeruli are continuously active. This interpretation is not universally accepted and there are those who believe that variation in the number of glomeruli contributing to urine formation is a major factor in determining the rate of glomerular filtration. Subsequent treatment of the subject in this section will be based on the assumption that all the glomeruli are continuously involved in the formation of glomerular filtrate.

2. CAPILLARY BLOOD PRESSURE (P_b). The major variable in the regulation of the rate of glomerular filtration is the pressure within the glomerular capillaries. The pressure at which blood enters the afferent arterioles is not much lower than that in the aorta; the decrease in pressure between aorta and glomerular capillaries is largely determined by the resistance of the afferent arterioles. Thus, other factors remaining equal, constriction of the afferent arterioles will decrease and dilata-

tion will increase glomerular filtration. The effect of changes in the caliber of the efferent vessels is in general the converse of parallel changes in the afferent vessels.

It is to be noted that it is the *pressure, not the blood or plasma flow*, in the glomerular capillaries which determines glomerular filtration rate. Thus the rate of glomerular filtration need not bear any particular relationship to the cardiac output. A low level of cardiac output is, at least in theory, quite compatible with a normal rate of filtration provided this output is sufficient to maintain a normal blood pressure and provided that renal vasoconstriction is not a part of the general vasoconstriction necessary to maintain the normal arterial pressure.

Although the renal nerves play a role in the regulation of the renal arteriolar resistances and thus in the maintenance of a stable rate of glomerular filtration (and, particularly in man, this function is maintained at a remarkably constant level under normal conditions), the nerves are not essential to this stability. The kidney even when totally isolated, shows only slight changes in glomerular filtration rate (and blood flow) as perfusion pressure is varied over a wide range. This process, frequently designated by the term *autoregulation*, has attracted considerable interest among physiologists. It is probably attributable to spontaneous adjustments of the arteriolar resistances.

3. INTRACAPSULAR HYDROSTATIC PRESSURE (P_c). Under ordinary conditions variations in the pressure within Bowman's capsule probably contribute little to changing glomerular filtration rate. With ureteral obstruction this pressure may rise until the rate of filtration is reduced to negligible levels, but such obstruction does not, of course, occur under normal circumstances. It is also likely that in the extremes of solute diuresis produced experimentally the pressure required to drive the greatly increased flow of urine against the resistance offered by the tubules may be sufficient to reduce filtration.

4. COLLOID OSMOTIC PRESSURE OF THE PLASMA PROTEINS (π_c). The osmotic effect of the plasma proteins is the equivalent of a hydrostatic pressure of some 25 to 30 mm. Hg opposed to glomerular filtration. Glomerular filtration must, therefore, cease when the net hydrostatic pressure across the capillary membrane falls to this level. Although this osmotic effect is large enough for changes to exert appreciable effects on net filtration pressure, it is doubtful whether such changes contribute significantly to the physiological regulation of glomerular filtration. Experimentally, it can be shown that sudden dilution of the plasma proteins by the administration of isotonic sodium chloride solution produces an increase in glomerular filtration and urine flow (dilution diuresis), but the changes are small compared to those which can be produced experimentally in other ways.

The Measurement of Glomerular Filtration Rate

The difference between the rate at which a substance is filtered at the glomeruli and the rate at which it is excreted in the urine represents the rate at which the substance is removed from or added to the urine as the latter traverses the renal tubules. The rate at which a substance is filtered is given by the product of its concentration in the plasma (or more accurately, the concentration of unbound substance in the plasma water) and the rate of formation of glomerular filtrate. The rate of excretion is easily determined as the product of urine flow and the concentration in the urine of the substance in question. Thus the measurement of glomerular filtration rate plays a central role not only in the evaluation of glomerular filtration itself, but in the assessment of the processes of reabsorption and secretion as well.

The rate of glomerular filtration can be determined if there is some substance which is neither reabsorbed nor secreted by the tubules and if the concentration of this substance in the glomerular filtrate can be deduced from its concentration in the plasma. If a substance is neither reabsorbed nor secreted as the urine flows through the tubules, then, in the steady state, the rate of excretion of the substance must be the same as the rate at which it is filtered. Given the rate at which the substance is filtered and its concentration in the filtrate, the volume of the filtrate can be calculated.

For example, consider some substance X which we will assume has the requisite characteristics of (1) being freely filterable at the glomeruli, (2) being neither reabsorbed from nor excreted into the tubule lumen. Suppose we measure the flow of urine over a 10-minute period during which 20 ml. of urine are collected to yield a flow (V) of 2 ml. per minute.

The concentration (U_x) of substance X in the urine is determined and found to be 120 mg. per ml.

The rate of excretion, then, is given by the product of flow and concentration

$$U_x V = 120 \text{ mg./ml.} \times 2 \text{ ml./min.}$$

$$= 240 \text{ mg./min.}$$

Since for substances which are neither reabsorbed nor secreted the rate of excretion is equal to the rate of filtration, the rate of filtration of substance X is also 240 mg. per minute. But the rate of filtration of a substance is equal to the product of the rate of formation of filtrate (GFR) times the concentration of the substance in the filtrate which, in this case, is defined above as being the same as the concentration in the plasma (P_x). Assume the concentration in the plasma in this case is determined and found to be 2 mg./ml.

Thus the rate of filtration of X is the product $GFR \cdot P_x = U_x V$ and

$$GFR = \frac{U_x V}{P_x} = \frac{240 \text{ mg./min.}}{2 \text{ mg./ml.}} = 120 \text{ ml./min.}$$

The desirability, for the evaluation of renal function, of a substance which fulfills the criteria for measuring glomerular filtration is apparent. It is now generally accepted that *inulin*, a starchlike polymer of fructose obtained from dahlia tubers, has the requisite characteristics and can be used for the measurement of glomerular filtration in all vertebrates including man.

THE USE OF THE TERM CLEARANCE. The expression $U_x V / P_x$ denotes a quantity which is generally referred to as the *clearance* of substance X and abbreviated C_x. As can be seen, it is the volume of plasma needed each minute to supply the substance in question at the rate at which it is excreted in the urine. It is thus a measure of the efficiency of the kidney in the excretion of a particular substance; the larger the value of its clearance, the more effectively it is excreted. The term is derived from the fact that one may consider the clearance to be that volume of plasma which completely yields its content for excretion and is thus cleared of the particular substance each minute. Some confusion arises when the latter concept of clearance is used since the volume cleared of a particular substance is usually virtual rather than real. The same clearance is obtained if 50 ml. of plasma yield all of their content, if 100 ml. lose half or 200 ml. yield one-fourth.

The clearance of a substance such as inulin is the volume flow of glomerular filtrate. By comparison of the clearance of any other substance with that of inulin we may infer the nature of the processes involved in its excretion. If it is filtered but neither reabsorbed nor excreted by the tubules, its clearance must be identical with that of inulin. If its clearance is lower, it must be reabsorbed from the tubules; if higher, it must be secreted by them.

Thus if P_x is the concentration of X filterable in the plasma, T_x the amount of X which is secreted into or reabsorbed from the tubule each minute and C_{In} the inulin clearance taken as equal to the rate of formation of glomerular filtrate, then,

$$C_{In} P_x = \text{filtered X}$$

$$C_{In} P_x + T_x = \text{excreted X} = U_x V$$

(where T_x will have a negative value if X is reabsorbed from the tubules).

Then

$$C_{In} + \frac{T_x}{P_x} = \frac{U_x V}{P_x} = C_x \qquad (2)$$

It can be seen from equation (2) that if for any reason the capacity of the tubule (T_x) to reabsorb or secrete a particular substance is limited, the clearance of that substance will approach the rate of glomerular filtration as the plasma concentration is progressively increased, since as P_x approaches infinity, the term T_x/P_x approaches zero. It will be shown that this is the case with most substances transported by the renal tubules.

THE RATE OF GLOMERULAR FILTRATION IN MAN. The clearance of inulin in a man of average size under normal basal conditions (except for the water usually administered during the determination of such clearances) averages slightly in excess of 125 ml. per minute. It is customary, in order to compare individuals of varying size, to normalize the clearance values by "correcting" them to what is generally considered an average normal value of body surface area, 1.73 square meters. Women have glomerular filtration rates some 10 per cent lower than those found in men even after "correction" to the same value of surface area.

The large value for the rate of formation of glomerular filtrate emphasizes the similarly great magnitude of many of the processes of reabsorption carried on by the renal tubules. Thus if we assume that the rate of 125 ml. per minute is maintained throughout the day we may calculate that some 7.5 liters are filtered each hour or 180 liters per day in an individual of normal size. Since ordinarily such an individual will excrete only a liter or two of urine in a day, it is clear that an amount approaching 180 liters is also reabsorbed. The total body water of a 70 kilogram man is of the order of 45 liters, so that on the average all of the body water is filtered into the renal tubules and reabsorbed four times each day. On the same basis we may calculate that the extracellular fluid (approximately 12 liters) is filtered and reabsorbed some 15 times per day,

TABLE 79.1

Filtration, reabsorption and excretion of certain normal constituents of plasma

	Filtered per 24 Hours		Excreted* per 24 Hours		Reabsorbed per 24 Hours	
	grams	*m.eq. or mmole†*	*grams*	*m.eq. or mmole*	*grams*	*m.eq. or mmole*
Sodium	540	24,500	3.3	150	537	24,350
Chloride	630	17,850	5.3	150	625	17,700
Bicarbonate	300	4,900	0.3	1	300	4,900
Potassium	28	700	3.9	100	24	600
Glucose	140	780	0	0	140	780
Urea	53	870	25	410	28	460
Creatinine	1.4	12	1.4	12	0	0
Uric Acid	8.5	50	0.8	5	7.7	45

* These are typical normal values. Wide variation is found depending on diet.

† Milliequivalents or millimoles.

the plasma volume (roughly 3 liters) some 60 times.

We may further multiply this volume by its content of the various filtrable solutes of plasma to estimate the amounts of these filtered and by comparison with the amounts excreted in the urine, calculate the amounts of each reabsorbed. Illustrative data are indicated in table 79.1. It is apparent from this table that very large quantities are turned over by the kidney each day and that only a small percentage departure from normal in the process of reabsorption could result in very large changes in excretion.

OTHER MEASURES OF GLOMERULAR FILTRATION. In man, except for inulin, no substance has been found which can be considered to give an accurate and reliable value for the rate of glomerular filtration. Approximations can be made using one of several substances, and such approximations are useful for comparative purposes but not for the evaluation of tubular reabsorptive and secretory processes. Most commonly the creatinine clearance is used and gives a value, under most conditions, not too different from the clearance of inulin.

This is probably the result of compensating errors, since creatinine is excreted into the lumen by the tubules of the human kidney. It is possible that it is also reabsorbed and in addition the methods usually used for determining the concentration of creatinine in plasma are not specific and include small amounts of other substances which apparently are reabsorbed. Under some conditions, particularly in the presence of renal disease, the departure of the creatinine clearance from the rate of glomerular filtration may be considerable.

Other substances which have been used to approximate the rate of glomerular filtration in man are certain hexitols (mannitol, sorbitol, dulcitol), particularly mannitol, and allantoin. The mannitol clearance is about 10 per cent lower than the clearance of inulin, indicating that about 10 per cent of the filtered mannitol is, on the average, reabsorbed.

In many lower mammals, as well as in amphibians, the creatinine clearance does not have the limitations which reduce its usefulness in man. The clearance of creatinine is, for practical purposes, identical with the clearance of inulin in the dog, cat and rabbit.

TUBULAR REABSORPTION

The quantitative importance of the process of reabsorption in the renal tubules has been indicated above by the magnitude of the amounts of material involved. An understanding of the nature of the mechanisms by which this reabsorption is effected is essential to a grasp of the function of the kidney.

The processes involved in tubular reabsorption are divided into two categories, passive and active.

1. *Passive reabsorption.* It is clear that the volume of the urine is greatly reduced as it flows through the tubules. If, in the course of this reduction in volume, some solute is retained in the lumen to a greater extent than water, its concentration will rise above that in the glomerular filtrate and above the concentration in the plasma and interstitial fluid which surround the tubules. A concentration gradient for the substance is thus created between the lumen and the environment of the tubule and, provided the tubule is permeable to some extent to the substance in question, it will diffuse from the lumen of the tubule to interstitial fluid and blood. This type of process is designated by the term *passive reabsorption* and is typified by the reabsorption of urea, the excretion of which will be considered in more detail later.

More generally, the movement of any substance across a biological membrane (in this case the complex membrane is the renal tubule epithelium) is considered *passive* when it can be explained entirely by gradients of concentration and/or (in the case of charged particles) gradients of electrical potential. In such a context, the movement of urea is a passive process requiring no mechanism in the tubule cells specific for urea and no expenditure of energy by the tubule cells for the movement of urea itself. However, it should be noted that work must be done to raise the urea concentration so that it may diffuse out passively. It will be shown that in this instance the primary active process is the removal of salt from the lumen by the activity of the tubule cells; the movement of water is the passive consequence of the transport of salt and the movement of urea is in turn secondary to the movement of water.

2. *Active reabsorption.* The reabsorption of many substances from the renal tubules can not be explained by gradients of concentration or electrical potential. The process involved in the movement of these solutes is designated as *active reabsorption.* The best known and possibly simplest example of an active reabsorptive process is probably that for glucose. A consideration of glucose reabsorption will illustrate the characteristics of these mechanisms.

Active Reabsorption: The Reabsorption of Glucose

Under normal conditions approximately 100 mg. of glucose are filtered at the glomerulus each minute. Of this, none but the merest trace is excreted in the urine. Clearly, the transport of glucose is effected against a *concentration gradient* and, since glucose carries no electrical charge, its transport is, by definition, *active.*

If the concentration of glucose in the plasma is progressively increased, it is found that, for a time, the urine remains free of glucose. However, when a sufficiently high plasma glucose concentration is reached, glucose appears in the urine in appreciable quantities. Further increments in plasma glucose concentration are then accompanied by proportional increments of glucose excretion. The basis for the relationship of plasma glucose concentration and glucose excretion becomes clear when the glomerular and tubular events are analyzed by the simultaneous determination of glomerular filtration rate (inulin clearance). From the product of inulin clearance and plasma glucose concentration,[1] the filtered glucose is calculated; the difference between filtered and excreted glucose is the amount reabsorbed. It is then found that as the plasma glucose concentration increases (the filtered glucose, of

[1] In determining the amount filtered in the case of substances, such as glucose, which are rapidly metabolized by the tissues, it is important to measure the arterial plasma concentration, since the venous concentration may be appreciably lower and since it is arterial plasma from which glomerular filtrate is derived.

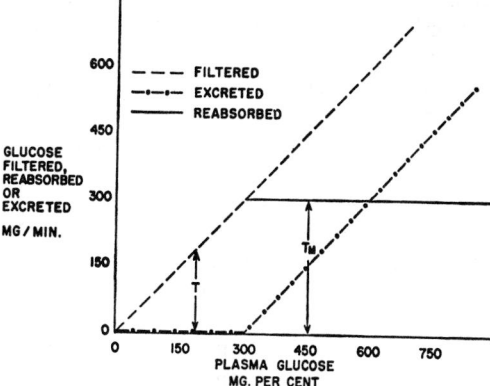

FIG. 79.4. Diagramatic and idealized representation of the relationship among filtration, reabsorption and excretion of glucose. The figures are calculated on the assumption that glomerular filtration rate was 100 ml per minute.

course, increasing proportionately) the reabsorbed glucose increases, remaining equal to the filtered, until a limiting value of glucose reabsorption is reached. As the filtered glucose increases beyond this level there is no further increase in glucose reabsorption and the excess glucose is excreted in the urine. These relationships are illustrated in figure 79.4. The relationship among the various quantities is expressed by the equation:

$$U_G V = C_{In} P_G - T_G$$

where T represents the amount reabsorbed per minute from the tubule and the subscripts G and In refer to glucose and inulin respectively.

T_G is seen to increase, remaining equal to the filtered glucose (frequently referred to as the *load* or *filtered load*), until T_G reaches a maximum. This maximum, which represents the capacity of the tubules to transport glucose, is conventionally designated as the glucose T_m or T_{mG}. The existence of such a limited capacity subject to saturation is a characteristic feature of active transport processes and is one of the criteria by which they may be identified.

The limitation which characterizes the transport mechanism involved in glucose reabsorption and other similar mechanisms is believed to derive from the involvement of a "carrier" in the process. In this view, the tubule cell membrane is virtually impermeable to glucose in the free state. However, the membrane contains certain molecules which can combine reversibly with glucose, and in this state the glucose, now in combination with its carrier, is able to penetrate the membrane. Having reached the inside of the tubule cell, the carrier-glucose complex dissociates releasing free glucose which, we may assume, is free to diffuse out of the cell into the peritubular fluid and blood. The carrier is then available to repeat the process.

The reactions involved may be represented:

$$A + B \overset{(1)}{\rightleftharpoons} AB \overset{(2)}{\rightarrow} T + B$$

where A is glucose in the tubule lumen, B the carrier, AB the glucose-carrier complex and T the glucose which has been transported (e.g., into the tubule cell). Some step in the process requires an input of energy since the expenditure of energy is necessary to drive the reaction "uphill" from the low concentration in the lumen to the higher one in the cell. This energy might be involved in driving reaction (2) or possibly the carrier might be modified in the transport process and require activation before it can again combine with glucose in the lumen. When the mechanism is saturated all of the carrier is interpreted as in the combined state AB and the maximum rate of transport (T_m) reflects the total amount of carrier in the tubule cells and the rate constant for the dissociation of AB to yield B and T. Although, theoretically, the rate of such transport processes could be limited by the amount of energy available to drive them, there is no evidence that this actually occurs, and the same tubule cells are able simultaneously to carry out the transport of a number of solutes among which there is no mutual interference.

Although the existence of carriers with the properties described is fairly generally accepted, it should be noted that none has ever been isolated or identified chemically. The interaction between carrier and transported substance may be considered analogous to that between an enzyme and its substrate; in fact the reactions suggested above correspond to those to which the kinetic behavior of enzymatic reactions are attributed. Transport reactions also show certain other characteristics of enzymatic reactions, particularly in being subject to inhibition, both competitive and noncompetitive.

The glucose transport mechanism is fairly specificially inhibited by the glycoside, *phlorizin*. The administration of this inhibitor in adequate dosage completely abolishes glucose transport so that the clearance of glucose becomes equal to the glomerular filtration rate. This property is also shared by the glycoside of the adrenocortical steroid, desoxycorticosterone. Several monosaccharides (e.g., xylose, fructose and galactose) are reabsorbed to some extent apparently by the same transport mechanism responsible for the reabsorption of glucose, and their reabsorption is also inhibited by phlorizin.

Micropuncture studies have clearly shown that the reabsorption of glucose occurs high in the proximal convoluted tubule and that when the plasma glucose concentration is normal the glucose has largely been removed before the urine reaches the middle of the proximal tubule.

In human beings, the normal capacity to reabsorb glucose (glucose T_m) averages approximately 375 and 300 mg. per minute per 1.73M^2 of body surface area in men and women respectively. If we compare the capacity to reabsorb glucose with the rate of glomerular filtration we may deduce what concentration of glucose in the plasma would be required to yield enough filtered glucose to saturate the glucose T_m. Since the average normal rate of glomerular filtration is 125 ml. per minute it is apparent that a plasma glucose concentration of 3 mg. per ml. or 300 mg. per cent is required to yield a filtered load equal to reabsorptive capacity of 375 mg. per minute. From the idealized and oversimplified diagram of excretion and reabsorption versus load plotted in figure 34.4 it would be predicted that *no* glucose should appear in the urine until the plasma glucose is 300 mg. per cent; at that point, filtered load should be exactly equal to reabsorptive capacity and reabsorptive capacity should be fully saturated. Further increases in plasma glucose should give no increase in glucose reabsorption. In actual practice this is not the case. In figure 79.5 is reproduced the observed relationship between plasma glucose (filtered glucose) and excretion and reabsorption in normal man. It is seen that glucose begins to appear in the urine when the filtered glucose is only about three-fourths of the capacity of the tubules to reabsorb and that the reabsorption does not reach its maximum rate until the amount filtered is some 50 per cent greater than this maximum.

The departure from the idealized relationship is due to two factors. Two assumptions are implicit in the construction of the idealized relationship, and neither is completely valid: (1) Each tubule reabsorbs all the glucose presented to it until its capacity is fully saturated, and *none* of the filtered glucose escapes reabsorption until saturation is achieved; and (2) all of the tubules are functionally identical so that the kidney may be looked upon as a single nephron. We may now consider why these assumptions are valid only as first approximations.

1. The hypothetical basis of transport in terms of the formation of a substrate-carrier complex was presented above. The initial reaction is visualized as the reversible formation of the complex:

$$A + B \rightleftharpoons AB$$

If we write the mass action expression for this reaction, we obtain:

$$K = \frac{[A][B]}{[AB]}$$

where the brackets signify concentration and K is the dissociation constant for the substrate-carrier complex. The smaller the value of K, the greater the affinity of the carrier for the transported substance.

It is apparent from this that the residual (unreabsorbed) substrate will be very small only (1) if the value of K is very small or (2) when there remains an appreciable concentration of unsaturated carrier (B). Conversely (once the total A available is equal to the total transport capacity) there will be negligible unutilized transport capacity only (1) when K is very small or (2) when there remains a considerable amount of unreabsorbed substrate. Thus, the relationship will approach the ideal as the value of K becomes infinitely small and for any finite value of K there will be some departure from the ideal (fig. 79.4). Actually among the various substances actively reabsorbed by the renal tubules there are varying degrees of departure from ideality presumably reflecting differences in the value of K. The departure from ideality in the case of glucose is small compared to that for many other substances, suggesting a low value for the dissociation of the glucose-carrier complex.

The type of relationship plotted in figure 79.5 is commonly referred to as a *titration curve,* and the departure from the sharp break of the ideal relationship is called the *splay* of the titration curve.

2. The nephrons are clearly not all identical nor is it reasonable to expect them to be so. The heterogeneity of the nephron population which is pertinent to the shape of reabsorptive titration curves is heterogeneity of what is called *glomerulo-tubular* balance, that is, the relationship between the filtering capacity of the glomerulus and the reabsorptive capacity of the tubule attached to that particular glomerulus. Thus if we deal with a tubule with an average capacity to reabsorb glucose but a filtration rate of twice the average, it will become saturated with glucose when the

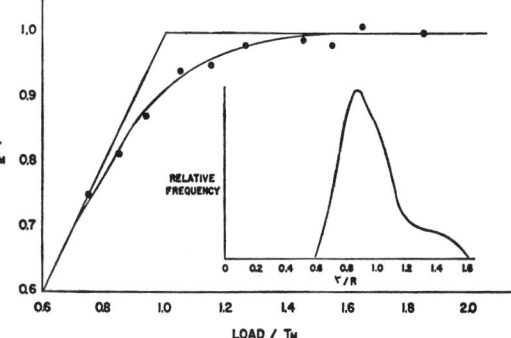

FIG. 79.5. Titration of the capacity to reabsorb glucose. Based on average data from ten normal individuals. The ordinate (T/T_m) is the ratio of glucose reabsorbed at a particular value of filtered glucose to the maximum capacity to reabsorb glucose in the same individual. It is thus the fractional saturation of glucose reabsorptive capacity. The abscissa (load/T_m) is the amount of glucose available for reabsorption, again related to the capacity of the individual to reabsorb glucose.

The frequency distribution curve shows the proportion of nephrons having various ratios (r) of filtration rate to reabsorptive capacity as related to the average of this ratio (R) for the two kidneys as a unit.

The data are those of Smith, Goldring, Chasis, Ranges and Bradley (J. Mt. Sinai Hosp., 10:59, 1943).

plasma glucose concentration is only half that required to saturate the average nephron. Conversely nephrons with small glomerular filtering capacity and large reabsorptive capacity will become saturated only when the plasma glucose is much higher than that which would saturate the average nephron.

The titration curve in figure 79.5 can be analyzed to yield the distribution of glomerular activity in relation to glucose reabsorptive capacity if it is assumed that the titration curve in each individual nephron is ideal (that is, if the kinetic contribution to splay is disregarded). What is obtained is a distribution of the ratios of filtration to reabsorption for the nephron population as these ratios relate to the average ratio for the kidneys taken as a unit. This distribution curve, included in figure 79.5 indicates that in the normal human kidney no appreciable number of nephrons has a ratio of filtration to reabsorption of glucose departing more than 50 per cent from the average.

The earlier literature on the physiology of the kidney divides substances which may appear in the urine into *threshold* and *no-threshold substances.* A threshold substance was one which did not appear in the urine until its concentration in the blood exceeded some value, this value being designated as the renal threshold. No-threshold substances were those which appeared in the urine at all concentrations in the plasma. Clearly glucose (and most other substances actively reabsorbed by the tubules) would fall in the category of "threshold" substances. However, with improvements in the methods of study of renal function, this terminology has in large measure lost its usefulness, and it is greatly preferable to consider the specific mechanisms involved in the excretion of a particular substance and the quantitative aspects, formerly subsumed in the "threshold," in terms of the rates of filtration, reabsorption and secretion.

OTHER SUBSTANCES ACTIVELY REABSORBED BY THE TUBULES. The reabsorption of glucose is the prototype of a number of reabsorptive processes which are qualitatively similar. In several instances the site of reabsorption has been identified, and in each case the proximal tubule is the segment concerned. It is probable that, except for those mechanisms involved in the movements of the more important monovalent electrolytes and water (these will be considered separately later), the active reabsorptive (and secretory) processes are confined to the proximal convoluted tubules.

The normal urine contains only traces of *amino acids* although, of course, a number of amino acids are present in plasma. Several separate transport mechanisms are involved in their reabsorption. The basic amino acids arginine, lysine and histidine appear to share the same mechanism since elevation of the plasma concentration of any one depresses the reabsorption of the others. Reabsorptive T_m's have been demonstrated for lysine and arginine but not for histidine, the reabsorption of which is still increasing at the highest levels produced experimentally. A second transport mechanism is responsible for the reabsorption of leucine and isoleucine which compete, but the capacity for reabsorption is so high that no T_m has been demonstrated. Glycine appears to be reabsorbed by a separate mechanism which also is involved in the transport of proline and hydroxyproline. In those instances in which T_m's have been demonstrated, there is considerable excretion of the amino acid when the reabsorptive capacity is far from saturated. Presumably this represents a relatively high degree of dissociation of the carrier-substrate complex. *Creatine* is reabsorbed by a mechanism closely related to, if not identical with, that involved in glycine reabsorption.

Phosphate is reabsorbed by an active process

which can be saturated on elevation of the plasma concentration. The transport mechanism seems to be modified by a number of factors. It is probable, that parathyroid hormone depresses the phosphate transport system. Acidosis increases phosphate excretion in part by what appears to be an increase in the splay of the titration curve.

Sulfate reabsorption is effected by a mechanism which becomes saturated with only a slight increase in the plasma concentration above the normal level. The reabsorption of sulfate can be depressed by the administration of thiosulfate which competes for reabsorption by the same mechanism.

The study of *uric acid* reabsorption is complicated by the fact that uric acid is probably also secreted by the tubules. The reabsorptive capacity for urate is far greater than the amount normally contained in the glomerular filtrate and it is therefore almost certain that this capacity is never saturated in the normal individual. The source of the urate normally excreted in the urine is therefore somewhat uncertain; although it might be urate which escapes reabsorption by virtue of the great splay in the reabsorptive titration curve, it is generally believed that it represents urate secreted into the tubules by a secretory process of low capacity. Whatever may be its role in regulating excretion under normal conditions, urate reabsorption is remarkable for the number of substances known to inhibit it and thereby to yield marked increases in urate excretion. These inhibitors include other reabsorbed compounds, such as glycine, as well as a number of drugs which are best known for their ability to inhibit the secretion of organic anions by the tubules (e.g. carinamide, probenecid, phenylbutazone).

Among other substances actively reabsorbed by the tubules are *ascorbic acid* and *betahydroxybutyric* and *acetoacetic acids*.

TUBULAR SECRETION

The processes by which materials are removed from the peritubular fluid and transferred to the tubule lumen are designated by the term *tubular secretion*. The term *tubular excretion* is often used synonymously. In the present section the secretion of the monovalent ions potassium, hydrogen and ammonium will be omitted, and the discussion will be concerned with the somewhat simpler transport processes involved in the secretion of certain organic electrolytes.

The first substance for which tubular secretion was demonstrated was phenol red (phenolsulfonphthalein, PSP). The critical experiment was that of Marshall who showed that as much as 75 per cent of the phenol red contained in the arterial blood could be removed as the blood traversed the kidney, whereas, because of a high degree of binding of phenol red to plasma proteins, only 20 to 25 per cent of the phenol red in the arterial plasma is free and filterable. Clearly, no matter what fraction of the plasma was converted to glomerular filtrate, filtration alone could not account for the excretion of phenol red. These experiments put an end to a prolonged controversy over the existence of tubular secretory processes.

A large number of substances are now recognized to be transported into the tubules by the same mechanism responsible for the secretion of phenol red. Among these are *hippuric acid* and a variety of its iodo-, hydroxy-, and amino derivatives, *penicillin*, 5-hydroxyindoleacetic acid (a metabolite of serotonin), a number of *sulfonphthaleins* in addition to phenol red, several of the iodinated compounds which have been used for X-ray contrast study (intravenous pyelography) of the urinary tract (Diodrast, Iopax, Neoiopax, Skiodan).[2] Also, although their tubular secretion in man has not been identified, it has been shown that glucuronides and ethereal sulfates are so transported in other animals, and the same is probably true in man. It is notable that the list contains no normal constituents of the body, but under normal conditions it seems likely that the mechanism serves for the rapid excretion of the conjugates of ingested foreign substances, these conjugates being in the form of hippurates, glucuronides and sulfates.

The tubular secretory process, which is also located in the proximal tubule, resembles those involved in reabsorption in many respects, except for the reversal of direction:

At low concentrations of the transported substance the mechanism is able to transport all of the material presented to it. The most commonly studied substance, p-aminohippuric acid (PAH) may be used, as an example. If PAH is administered intravenously in small amounts, so as to maintain a low concentration in the arterial plasma, it is found that the blood leaving the kidney in the renal vein may be almost free of PAH. An average of some 90 per cent of the PAH reach-

[2] While the iodine is important for X-ray density, it is not related to the susceptibility to transport which undoubtedly derives from the organic structures to which the iodine is attached. The first three of those mentioned are derivatives of pyridine-N-acetic acid; the last is an organic sulfate.

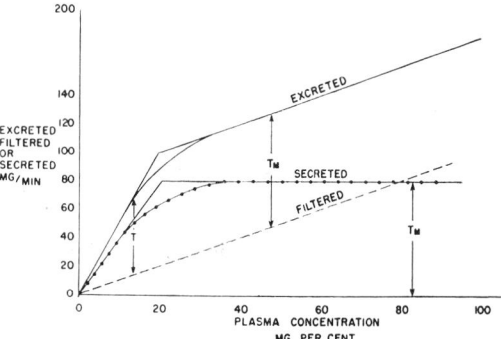

FIG. 79.6. Relationship between plasma concentration and filtered, secreted and excreted amounts of a substance excreted by tubule secretion. See text for details.

ing the kidney in the plasma is removed. Since some of the blood reaching the renal vein has probably perfused tissue which does not transport PAH, it is apparent that very little can be left over from that plasma which passes through the active areas. This extremely effective *extraction* of PAH is the basis of the use of this substance for the estimation of renal plasma flow which is considered below.

As the plasma concentration of the transported substance is increased, the rate of tubular excretion increases until a maximum is reached and no further augmentation of secretion occurs. The relationship between plasma PAH concentration and PAH excretion in the urine is illustrated in figure 79.6. The dotted line passing through the intercept is the amount of PAH filtered at the glomeruli calculated from the product of inulin clearance and the plasma concentration of free PAH. (Since PAH is, to a small extent, bound to plasma albumin the total concentration must be corrected for this binding to obtain the filtered amount.) At every level of plasma PAH the rate of excretion exceeds the rate of filtration.

$$U_{PAH}V = C_{In}P_{PAH}f + T_{PAH}$$

where f is the fraction of the plasma PAH which is filterable. As the plasma PAH is increased the rate of excretion at first increases sharply, the slope of the line relating excretion to plasma concentration being equal to the renal plasma flow. When the plasma concentration is further increased, the rate of excretion increases less rapidly, and it is found that the excess of excreted over filtered has become constant. This excess represents the maximum rate of tubular secretion and is designated as T_{mPAH}.

If the rate of tubular secretion is determined

by subtracting the filtered from the total excretion the relationship shown in figure 79.6 is obtained. Again, the actually observed titration curve differs from the idealized intersection of two straight lines and for reasons analogous to those involved in tubular reabsorption: (1) the dissociation of substrate-carrier complex and (2) heterogeneity of nephron function. The pertinent heterogeneity in this case, however, is in the ratio of perfusion to transport capacity since it is blood supply, rather than glomerular filtration, which along with plasma concentration will determine the amount available for secretion by the tubules.

Any of the various substances listed above as being secreted by this particular transport mechanism can be shown to compete with the others. Thus a high concentration of one will reduce the secretion of another and vice versa. Presumably they share a common carrier, and when some of the carrier sites are occupied by one, it has less capacity for the transport of another.

Several substances which are effective inhibitors of this mechanism have been discovered (carinamide, probenecid, phenylbutazone). These compounds are competitive inhibitors but are themselves only slowly excreted because subsequent to their secretion into the tubule they are reabsorbed by the process known as *non-ionic diffusion* (see p. 1699). (It is interesting to note that these inhibitors have found their major practical application as inhibitors of the *reabsorption* of urate in the treatment of gout.)

The mechanism is also inhibited by dinitrophenol and by mercurial diuretics. The effect of dinitrophenol has been attributed to the property of this substance of uncoupling phosphorylation from oxidation and has been interpreted as indicating that phosphate bond energy is important in the transport process. However, the recent finding that the dinitrophenol inhibition appears to be competitive casts doubt on this interpretation. The effect of mercurial diuretics is non-competitive and, for unknown reasons, is striking in man but entirely absent in the dog.

The transport of PAH is enhanced by acetate and lactate and inhibited by a number of the dicarboxylic acid intermediates of the Krebs cycle.

All of the substrates of the secretory process responsible for the tubular excretion of PAH are weak organic anions. A separate and distinct mechanism is capable of transporting a variety of organic bases including N-methylnicotinamide, tetraethylammonium ion and priscoline. These compete with each other but show no interaction with the organic anions. The normal substrate for this mechanism has not been recognized.

The Utilization of Tubular Secretion for the Measurement of Renal Blood Flow

As was noted above, several substances which undergo tubular excretion are very nearly completely removed from the blood which perfuses the kidney. This has made them singularly useful for the estimation of renal blood flow. Diodrast and *p*-aminohippurate (PAH), because they are well adapted to chemical analysis, have particularly been used for this purpose, and we will consider the use of PAH as an example.

In accord with the Fick principle, if the rate of removal of a substance from the blood as it flows through an organ is known, and if the concentration in the blood entering and leaving the organ can be determined, the blood flow can be calculated:

$$F = \frac{R}{A - V}$$

where F is the flow, R the rate of removal, and A and V the concentration in arterial and venous blood respectively.

In applying this to the measurement of renal blood flow using PAH, the following experimental facts are important: (1) there is no metabolism, production nor storage of PAH in the kidney; all of the PAH removed from the blood is excreted in the urine; (2) all of the PAH removed from the blood is removed from the plasma; the concentration in the red blood cells does not change significantly as blood passes through the kidney. Then the above equation can be modified to yield:

$$RPF = \frac{U_{PAH}V}{P^{A}_{PAH} - P^{RV}_{PAH}}$$

where RPF represents renal plasma flow and P^{A}_{PAH} and P^{RV}_{PAH} represent concentrations of PAH in arterial and renal venous plasma respectively.

Now, as it stands in this form the determination of renal plasma flow would require measurement of the rate of excretion of PAH and the concentrations in arterial and renal venous blood plasma. All of these are feasible in man, but the collection of renal venous blood is considerably more difficult than the remainder of the procedures. However, since we know that at low concentrations of PAH in the arterial plasma the removal of PAH as blood passes through the kidney is very nearly complete, we may as a first approximation consider the concentration in renal venous plasma to be zero and write

$$\text{ERPF} = \frac{\text{U}_{\text{PAH}}\text{V}}{\text{P}_{\text{PAH}}^{\text{A}}} = \text{C}_{\text{PAH}}$$

or that the *effective renal plasma flow* is equal to the PAH clearance. In practice it is not necessary to measure arterial plasma PAH since, when arterial concentration is constant, there is no measurable removal of PAH by peripheral tissues, and the PAH in peripheral venous plasma is the same as that in arterial plasma. Therefore, the effective renal plasma flow can be simply estimated by measurement of the plasma PAH clearance when the plasma PAH is maintained at a low level. (As plasma PAH is increased, the extraction becomes less complete and the clearance falls further below the true plasma flow.) From the effective renal plasma flow the corresponding renal blood flow can be calculated if the hematocrit is known.

$$\text{ERBF} = \frac{\text{ERPF}}{1 - \text{Hct}}$$

It is interesting to note that Homer Smith and his associates deduced that the clearance of diodrast could be used to measure renal plasma flow in man before the technique for obtaining renal venous blood by venous catheterization had been devised and the virtually total extraction of diodrast confirmed.[3] This was based on the very high value (approximately 650 ml. per minute) of the diodrast clearance; thus plasma flow of at least 650 ml. per minute was required to supply the diodrast at the rate it was excreted. It was reasoned that this was already such a large volume flow that the true plasma flow could not be much higher.

Renal Blood Flow and Filtration Fraction in Man

The remarkably high value of the renal plasma flow has been mentioned above. A plasma flow of 650 ml. per minute corresponds to a blood flow of about 1200 ml. per minute, an amount approximately equal to one-fourth of the cardiac output

[3] It should also be noted that if, for some reason, renal venous blood is collected so that true plasma and blood flow can be determined, PAH and similar substances lose their unique value. Then any substance which is removed by, but not produced, metabolized or stored in the kidney can be used for the measurement, since the Fick principle can be applied directly. A high degree of extraction, under these conditions, has only the virtue of minimizing experimental error.

under basal conditions. The ratio of the renal blood flow to cardiac output is frequently referred to as the *renal fraction* of the cardiac output.

The demonstrated equivalence of PAH clearance and (effective) renal plasma flow has made it possible to measure the renal blood flow in man with a minimum of manipulation and disturbance. Thus, it has been possible to measure changes in blood flow with disease as well as to determine the effects of various changes in physiological state and the effects of drugs, etc.

In considering changes in the renal plasma and blood flows, it is pertinent to take account of the fraction of the plasma lost as glomerular filtrate as the plasma flows through the glomerular capillaries. Since all of the renal blood flow under normal conditions passes through the glomeruli, the volume given up as glomerular filtrate is derived from the total plasma flow and the ratio of filtration rate to plasma flow (inulin clearance to PAH clearance) is a measure of the extent to which, in the average glomerulus, the plasma volume is reduced, and the plasma protein concentration increased by the process of glomerular filtration. The ratio of filtration rate to plasma flow is known as the *filtration fraction*.

While, as was noted in an earlier section, the rate of glomerular filtration is a remarkably stable function, the renal blood flow manifests a fairly marked degree of lability, and may be modified by any of a number of stimuli. Most of the changes are mediated via the sympathetic nerve supply and are in the direction of decreases. In fact, although the subject has long been debated and no consensus has been achieved, the only physiological effects clearly shown to be mediated by the nerve supply to the kidneys are vasoconstrictor, and the renal nerves have not been shown to play a significant role in the regulation of transport processes in the renal tubules.

The renal blood flow is diminished by fright, pain, exercise, epinephrine, norepinephrine and stimulation of several areas of the central nervous system, and by a number of other stimuli. In general, anything which lowers blood pressure will reduce renal blood flow, not so much because of the reduction in perfusion pressure, but because the kidney takes part in the general vasoconstriction which is the homeostatic response to a lowering of blood pressure. Thus there may be a marked decrease in renal blood flow with only a trivial reduction in aortic blood pressure. Drugs which reduce blood pressure also reduce the renal blood flow. However, in general, the reduction in flow is less than with equivalent reductions in blood pressure due to, for instance, hemorrhage or orthostasis, since the blood pressure reducing drugs usually inhibit renal as well as peripheral vasoconstriction. A special case appears to be hydrazinophthalazine which may increase renal blood flow while reducing systemic blood pressure, probably through a specific renal vasodilator action.

A more or less unique phenomenon is the marked renal vasodilation and hyperemia produced by the pyrogenic reaction. The latter phenomenon, the most striking clinical feature of which is chills and fever, is most often a response to bacterial products (certain bacterial polysaccharides, typhoid vaccine). It is accompanied by intense hyperemia of the kidney, and the renal blood flow may reach twice it normally very high value. Interestingly the renal response to pyrogenic materials is not abolished by the administration of antipyretic drugs although the latter may completely suppress the chills and fever.

With all of the above changes in renal blood flow there are frequently only slight changes in glomerular filtration rate and such changes are frequently entirely absent. Thus the changes in filtration fraction are the inverse of the changes in blood flow.

The Reabsorption and Excretion of Water

One of the most striking features of the function of the mammalian kidney is the capacity to excrete urine differing in osmotic pressure from the blood from which it is derived. It is through this capacity to excrete concentrated or dilute urine that the solute concentration (osmotic pressure) of the body fluids is maintained within remarkably narrow limits despite wide variation in the intake of solute and water. When, because of water loss or solute gain, the solute concentration of body fluids rises, the urine becomes concentrated, solute is excreted with less than the equivalent amount of water, and the solute concentration of the body fluids is restored to normal. Conversely, when the body fluids become diluted by water intake or solute loss, a dilute urine containing an excess of water is excreted, and the osmotic pressure of body fluids is returned to normal. Before considering the mechanisms by which the renal tubules effect these changes, it may be helpful to digress briefly to review the concept of osmotic pressure and its measurement.

If two solutions containing different concentrations of solute are separated by a membrane

permeable to the solvent (water in all cases with which we are concerned) but not the solute, there will be a movement of water from the more dilute to the more concentrated of the solutions. The movement of water is due to the fact that the presence of solute reduces the chemical activity of water, and water will move from the solution in which its activity (analogous to concentration) is high to one where it is lower. Water will move from dilute to concentrated solution until both have the same solute concentration or, if the movement of water is opposed by the application of a hydrostatic pressure, until the hydrostatic pressure balances the concentration difference. The hydrostatic pressure which would be required to maintain a solution at constant volume when it is separated by an ideal semipermeable membrane[4] from pure water is the osmotic pressure of that solution. The term osmotic pressure is applied although the osmotic pressure is never actually determined. Instead, some other property of the solution dependent upon total solute concentration is measured: most commonly the freezing point, occasionally the vapor pressure.

The *colligative properties* (osmotic pressure, freezing point depression, vapor pressure depression) depend on the ratio of the total number of solute particles to the number of mols of solvent. The nature of the solute is, to a large extent, indifferent; ideally, a protein molecule of molecular weight 100,000 has an effect equal to that of a sodium ion of weight 23, and a mol of sodium chloride, since it dissociates to yield two particles, has twice the effect of a mol of urea or glucose. One mol of ideal solute dissolved in a kilogram of water depresses the freezing point of the solution by 1.86°C. Such a solution is defined as an *osmolal* solution and is said to contain one osmol per kilogram of water. Since most biological fluids are considerably more dilute, it is convenient, in order to avoid decimals, to deal with *milliosmols* or *micro-osmols*, one milliosmol being one one-thousandth of an osmol, one micro-osmol one thousandth of a milliosmol. The milliosmolality of a solution is defined as its freezing point depression in degrees Centigrade divided by 0.00186. Thus normal plasma is about 285 milliosmolal (abbreviated 285 mOs) and has a freezing point of about −0.53°C.[5]

---

[4] An ideal semipermeable membrane is one permeable to solvent but impermeable to all solute.

[5] Note that osmotic pressure depends on the number of solute particles per unit of solvent. The amount of water in a given *volume of solution* will vary with concentration as well as with the

It will facilitate consideration of the processes which take place between the filtration of an isotonic fluid (one which has the same osmotic pressure as blood plasma) and the excretion of dilute and concentrated urine, if we first consider the gross behavior of water excretion and its extrarenal control. Under basal conditions the urine is usually moderately concentrated and the urine flow is small. If under such conditions an individual ingests a moderately large volume of water, e.g., one liter, it is found that after an interval of some 15 to 20 minutes the urine flow begins to rise. The flow increases rapidly to reach a peak of some 12 to 15 ml. per minute at 40 minute to 1 hour, and, when an amount approximately equal to that ingested has been excreted, returns to the same low level as obtained before the water ingestion. (Of course, if the water ingestion is continued so that a positive balance is maintained, the high rate of flow may continue for prolonged periods.) If these events are analyzed more carefully, it is found (1) that the osmotic pressure of the blood shows a distinct drop (though only a few per cent) well before the onset of the increase in urine flow (*diuresis*); (2) that the change in urine flow is almost entirely due to a change in the amount of water excreted, manifested by a shift in urine osmolality from hypertonic to markedly hypotonic to plasma; solute excretion shows little or no change; (3) if glomerular filtration has been measured it is found that the increase in urine flow occurs without or with only trivial changes in the rate of formation of glomerular filtrate; the change in water excretion is due to a change in the absorption of water in the renal tubules; (4) if at the peak of the urine flow, additional water is ingested, the urine flow does not increase further but remains at a value of some 12 to 15 per cent of the volume of the glomerular filtrate; (5) if, at any point in the course of the diuresis, vasopressin, the antidiuretic hormone of the posterior pituitary, is administered, the diuresis is immediately interrupted, and the urine again becomes more concentrated than the blood.

The concentration of the urine is normally continuously regulated by the secretion of antidiuretic hormone (ADH) by the posterior lobe of the pituitary gland. This hormone is believed to be produced in the supraoptic nuclei of the hypothalamus and to migrate via the supraoptico-hypophyseal tracts to the posterior lobe of the pituitary where it is stored and released into the blood in response to stimuli mediated from the hypothalamus via the same tract system. Within the supraoptic nuclei certain cells (*osmoreceptors*) are believed to behave as tiny osmometers, taking up water and swelling when the osmotic pressure of the surrounding body fluids is reduced and giving up water as the osmotic pressure of the bathing fluid rises. The swelling and shrinking of these cells is believed to lead to the transmission of nervous impulses which modulate the release of antidiuretic hormone from the posterior pituitary. Thus a reduction of the osmotic pressure of the blood leads to inhibition of ADH release;[6] an increase of osmotic pressure stimulates ADH secretion. In turn, the ADH is carried by the blood to the kidney, and in the kidney ADH regulates the reabsorption and excretion of water.

The work of Verney, to whom we owe much of our understanding of the pituitary control of water excretion, showed that injection into the internal carotid artery of the dog of enough sodium chloride to raise the osmotic pressure of the blood by about 2 per cent resulted in immediate inhibition of water excretion. Injection of the same amount into a peripheral vessel had no such effect since it was then diluted with a large volume of blood before being delivered to the sensitive area in the brain. Injection of the osmotically equivalent amount of urea into the internal carotid was also virtually without effect. In this case the ineffectiveness is presumably due to the fact that urea readily penetrates cells. When the urea concentration of their environment is raised, the osmoreceptor cells take up urea rather than lose water. Since the receptors do not shrink, there is no induction of ADH secretion. Thus, *only those solutes to which cells are relatively impermeable make up the effective osmotic pressure in response to which ADH secretion is regulated.*[7]

Our knowledge of the location in the renal tubule and the nature of the processes by which water excretion is regulated is due largely to the application of the micropuncture technique—in

---

nature of the solute. There is, therefore, no simple way to convert from osmolality to a number of solute particles per unit volume of solution. It is, however, the practice to disregard the inaccuracy involved and multiply volume by osmolality to obtain the approximate amount of solute in a given volume.

[6] The latent period from water ingestion to onset of diuresis is attributable 1) to the time required for water absorption to produce sufficient dilution of the body fluids and thus inhibit ADH secretion, 2) for the circulating ADH to disappear.

[7] The above describes the normal control of ADH secretion. A number of other stimuli such as fear, trauma, nausea, certain drugs, and many others may produce secretion of ADH under conditions unrelated to the osmotic pressure of the body fluids.

amphibians by Richards and his associates and in mammals by Walker, Bott, Oliver, and Mac-Dowell and more recently and extensively by Wirz and Gottschalk.

The glomerular filtrate has the same osmotic pressure as the plasma except for the absence of the plasma proteins.[8] As the fluid flows through the proximal tubule, its volume is reduced to a fraction of that which enters the glomerular space. Although, because of inaccessibility from the kidney surface no samples have been collected from the last 40 per cent of the proximal tubule, it is generally estimated that approximately one-fifth of the filtered volume reaches the end of the proximal tubule and enters the loop of Henle. This reduction of volume occurs *without change in osmotic pressure* whether the urine being produced is dilute or concentrated. Thus the large fraction of fluid reabsorbed in the proximal tubule does not take part in the concentration and dilution processes, and, in fact, is lost to the process of osmoregulation. The water thus reabsorbed in the proximal segment has been termed by Smith *obligatory water reabsorption* to distinguish it from the *facultative water reabsorption* in the more distal portions of the nephron where water reabsorption is subject to regulation in accordance with the excess or deficit of water in the body fluids.

A considerable body of evidence indicates that the water reabsorption in the proximal tubule is entirely a passive process and that the active process which underlies it is the transport of salt (predominantly sodium salts) out of the tubule lumen. As sodium salts are transferred from lumen to peritubular fluid, there is a tendency to produce dilution of the tubule contents and hypertonicity of the surroundings. The proximal tubule is highly permeable to water and, in response to the osmotic gradient, water follows the salt out of the tubule. Within the limits of the determinations the proximal tubule contents are always isotonic with the blood.

The exact course of events in the loop of Henle is not completely established because of inaccessibility to direct puncture (except at the tip). How-ever, from more indirect evidence it is quite probable that the descending limb of the loop retains the high water permeability which characterizes the proximal tubule and that the fluid within the descending limb retains the same osmotic pressure as the surrounding interstitial fluid. The high water permeability is, however, lost in the ascending limb and now the continued removal of salt leaves the fluid dilute. The urine emerges into the distal convoluted tubule with its osmotic pressure reduced to about half that of plasma whether the final urine is to be dilute or hypertonic.

The changes which take place in the distal tubule depend upon whether a dilute or concentrated urine is to be produced. In the *formation of dilute urine*, the dilute fluid which enters the distal tubule is further diluted by the continued removal of salt, and the salt removal probably continues through the collecting system. The urine is thus rendered hypotonic by the active reabsorption of salt in a region which clearly has a low permeability to water. (Otherwise the osmotic gradient would be dissipated, as it is in the proximal tubule, by the escape of water to the more concentrated surroundings.) The low permeability to water which characterizes the distal convoluted tubule and collecting system during the formation of dilute urine is dependent upon the absence of ADH.

In the *formation of concentrated urine*, the events are similar up to the point at which the fluid enters the distal convoluted tubule. In the presence of antidiuretic hormone, however, the distal convoluted tubule and collecting ducts become permeable to water.[9] Consequently, as it flows through the distal tubule the osmotic gradient, established by the reabsorption of sodium and chloride, is dissipated, and, despite additional salt removal in the distal tubule, the dilute character of the urine is lost so that it regains isotonicity before it enters the collecting system. It is important to emphasize that it enters the collecting system isotonic, never hypertonic. The additional water loss which renders the urine more concentrated than blood occurs in the collecting system.

The nature of the mechanism by which urine is rendered hypertonic to the body fluids has long been one of the more intriguing problems of renal physiology, and its apparent elucidation, largely

---

[8] It is important to make a clear distinction between the total osmotic pressure, with which we are concerned in the processes of urine dilution and concentration, and the colloid osmotic pressure or oncotic pressure due to the plasma proteins which play such an important role in the distribution of fluid across capillary membranes (because the latter are so highly permeable to all the other solutes). The colloid osmotic pressure of plasma is equivalent to about 25 mm. Hg (1 to 2 mOs.) while the total osmotic pressure is of the order of 6 atmospheres (285 mOs.).

[9] Antidiuretic hormone has been shown to have the property of increasing water permeability in isolated membranes (frog skin, toad skin, toad bladder) by causing the dilation of water-filled pores. Presumably the effect on the distal tubule epithelium is similar.

through the efforts of Wirz and his associates, is one of the more important recent achievements. Although some of the details of the mechanism are relatively complex, the essentials are quite simple and directly related to the anatomical organization of the kidney. The convoluted tubules are cortical structures; the loops of Henle and the collecting ducts lie in the medulla. The latter structures are thus relatively isolated from the cortical structures in which most of the transport activity of the kidney takes place. In addition, the blood supply of medulla and papilla forms a looplike system derived from the efferent vessels of the juxtamedullary glomeruli, running down into the medulla, and looping back to the cortex. Thus both loop of Henle and the blood supply of the medullary region form *countercurrent* systems in which the outflowing fluid flows counter to and in proximity to inflowing fluid. We will for the moment defer consideration of the importance of this particular arrangement.

As was noted above, as fluid flows through the ascending limb of the loop sodium and chloride are removed while the water remains behind in the tubule lumen and the urine becomes diluted. The sodium and chloride removed are transferred to the interstitial fluid of the medulla, increasing the osmotic pressure of this fluid. The diluted urine emerges into the cortex where, in the presence of ADH, it loses its excess of water and is further reduced in volume as solute is removed in the distal tubule. This water loss occurs in the cortex, spatially separated from the salt left behind in the medulla, and in an area where, because of the very large flow of blood, the excess water produces only a minimal change in osmotic pressure. Now the remaining urine, greatly reduced in volume and isotonic with the blood, enters the collecting system and flows through the medulla. The interstitial fluid of the medulla, however, has a high osmotic pressure because of the salt transported by the loop and, the collecting duct being permeable to water in the presence of ADH, the urine loses water to attain the same osmotic pressure as the interstitial fluid. Thus the hypertonicity of the urine is produced. These events are illustrated diagramatically in figure 79.7. Because the volume flow through the loop is several times larger than that in the collecting ducts, a relatively small change in concentration in the loop is sufficient to yield enough solute to raise the concentration of the urine in the collecting ducts severalfold.

If the sodium salts transported into the medullary interstitial fluid are to raise the osmotic pressure of the latter, they must not be immediately carried away by the blood flowing through the area. The retention of excess solute in the medullary interstitial fluid is made possible by the arrangement of the blood flow which constitutes a countercurrent exchanger. The principle of the countercurrent exchanger is illustrated in figure 79.8. Outflowing blood tends to lose its solute to the inflowing blood. As a result, solute

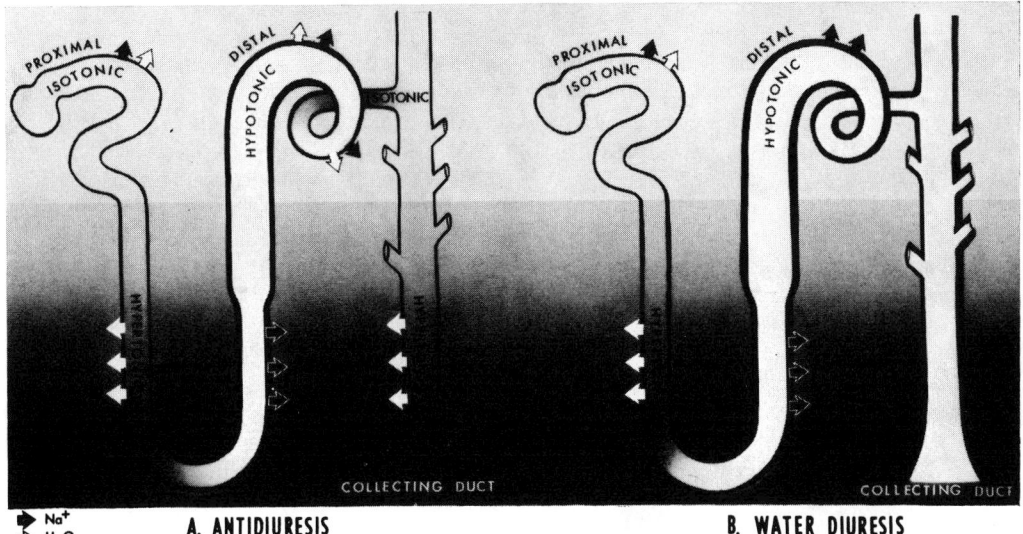

A. ANTIDIURESIS　　　　　　　　　　　　　B. WATER DIURESIS

Na⁺

H₂O

Fɪɢ. 79.7. Diagramatic representation of changes in the tonicity of fluid in the tubules during the formation of concentrated and dilute urine. Dark and light arrows indicate movements of sodium chloride and water respectively, and the relative permeability of the tubule wall to water is indicated by its thickness.

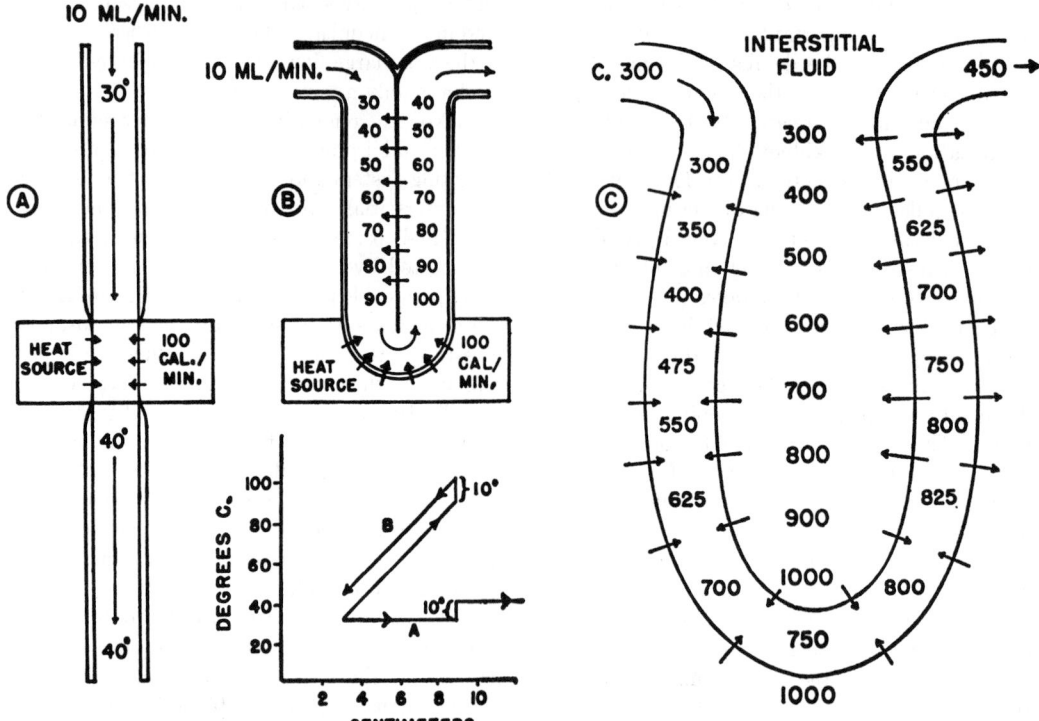

Fig. 79.8. Principle of the countercurrent exchanger. A and B, 100 calories per minute raise the temperature of 10 ml. per minute of water 10 degrees in both A (straight flow) and B (countercurrent flow). However, since the incoming water is heated by the outgoing water in B, the *maximum temperature* attained in the countercurrent system is considerably higher than with straight flow. The graph compares the temperature along the flow tubes in each system. C, countercurrent flow as applied to the capillary loop, showing that it is not necessary for the limbs of the loop to be in direct contact. In the *hypothetical* illustration given, both limbs are in contact with the same interstitial fluid, of progressively increasing concentration. Sodium salts (arrows) at first enter the capillary blood, later partly return to the interstitial fluid. Note the analogy between B, in which heat is recirculated, and C, in which sodium salts are similarly retained in an area.

is recirculated in the medulla. This characteristic makes it possible not only to retain sodium salts but to trap urea as well; the special role of urea in the concentration process is considered with the excretion of urea.

The loop arrangement has an additional physiological advantage. As the fluid flows down the descending limb of the loop of Henle into an environment made hypertonic by the activity of the ascending limb, it loses water so as to retain the same osmotic pressure as the environment. The loss of water raises the concentration of sodium salts in the loop contents so that the transport of sodium salts out of the ascending limb is against only a small gradient of concentration despite the very high concentration of sodium salts in the interstitial fluid surrounding the loop. This arrangement is that of a *countercurrent multiplier,* so called because the small concentration gradient from the loop contents to environment

is multiplied in the longitudinal direction from cortex to tip of papilla.

The highest concentration achieved by the human kidney is generally about 1200 to 1400 mOs. (a relatively modest maximum compared with some other mammals, e.g., dog 2300 to 2500 mOs., rat 3000 to 3200 mOs., kangaroo rat over 5000 mOs.); the lowest concentrations observed are of the order of 30 to 40 mOs. Thus the kidney is able to produce urine four to five times more concentrated than or one-seventh to one-tenth as concentrated as the blood (roughly 300 mOs.).

In clinical practice, the specific gravity, rather than the osmolality, is generally used as an index of concentration and dilution. Urine of specific gravity 1.008 to 1.010 is approximately isotonic with plasma, but the two scales are not directly interchangeable since the specific gravity depends not only on the concentration of solute but also on the latter's nature. The chief value of the specific gravity lies in the simplicity of its determination.

The highest and lowest concentrations are produced only when solute excretion is at a relatively low level; as solute excretion increases dilute urines become less dilute and concentrated urines less concentrated. The basis for this change can be deduced from the mechanisms for dilution and concentration described above and is more easily understood if the urine flow is considered to be divided into two parts as suggested by Smith. One fraction is considered to contain all of the solute excreted at the same concentration as plasma; the other fraction is the amount of water contained in excess of this isotonic fraction. The isotonic fraction is calculated by dividing total solute excretion by the osmolality of plasma. Solute excretion is given by the product of urine flow and urine osmolality $U_{os}V$ and when this is divided by the plasma osmolality, the resulting value has the dimensions of a clearance and is generally called the osmolal clearance (C_{os})

$$C_{os} = \frac{U_{os}V}{P_{os}}$$

When the urine is dilute the flow exceeds the osmolal clearance by an amount which Smith has designated the *free water clearance* (C_{H_2O}). This is the volume of water which must be removed from one minute's flow of urine to return the urine to isotonicity. Thus

$$V - \frac{U_{os}V}{P_{os}} = C_{H_2O} ; \quad C_{H_2O} = V - C_{os}$$

From the mechanism described above it may be seen that, provided no water has escaped from distal tubule or collecting duct, C_{H_2O} is the volume of water which originally contained the salt reabsorbed in ascending limb, distal tubule and collecting duct. The capacity of these segments to reabsorb sodium salts, therefore, sets the limit on the amount of water which can be excreted above that containing the urinary solutes in isotonic solution. It is this limited capacity to excrete water freed of solute which accounts for the increasing concentration of dilute urine as solute excretion increases, the isotonic portion of the urine flow (C_{os}) constituting an ever larger fraction of the total flow (V). Actually C_{H_2O} may be less than maximal 1) because insufficient sodium salts are delivered to the distal portions of the tubule to saturate the reabsorptive capacity or

2) because some of the water "freed" by salt removal diffuses out of the distal tubule. Even in the total absence of ADH some permeability to water persists, and this permeability may be increased by amounts of ADH which are too small to yield a maximal effect and thus a concentrated urine.

When the urine is concentrated the flow is smaller than the osmolal clearance; that is,—water must be *added* to the urine to render it isotonic. Thus C_{H_2O} assumes a negative value; this has been designated as $T^c_{H_2O}$ by Smith. The driving force for the removal of water from urine flowing through the collecting ducts is provided by the salt transported out of the ascending limb of the loop of Henle. Therefore the amount of water thus removed ($T^c_{H_2O}$) can not be greater than the osmotic equivalent of the salt deposited in the medulla by the loop.[10] Since the value of $T^c_{H_2O}$ is limited, as solute excretion increases the urine concentration falls, again because the isotonic portion of the urine (C_{os}) constitutes an even greater fraction of the total (V). (V = C_{os} − $T^c_{H_2O}$.) The flows and concentrations of dilute and concentrated urines as solute excretion is varied are illustrated in figures 79.9a and 79.9b.

In considering the effects of antidiuretic hormone and the change from dilute to concentrated urine, it is important to emphasize that by far the most important effect is that in the distal tubule which involves the change from dilute to isotonic urine. The relative quantitative importance of the dilution and concentration processes can be illustrated in a person excreting enough solute to require the excretion of 2 liters of isotonic urine in 24 hours. If he were to produce maximally dilute urine for this period, he would excrete approximately 20 liters of urine. Therefore, if ADH were to effect a rise in urine concentration only to isotonicity with plasma, some 18 liters of water would be conserved. If, on the other hand, the same solute were to be excreted in a maximally concentrated urine, the volume would be reduced to about 500 ml., a further saving of about 1.5 liters. Clearly, the water saved in not putting out a dilute urine is quantitatively much more important than that conserved in forming a concentrated urine.

[10] This is equivalent to saying that the production of a concentrated fluid (urine) in the medulla must be just balanced by the production of a dilute one (the fluid emerging from the ascending limb of the loop).

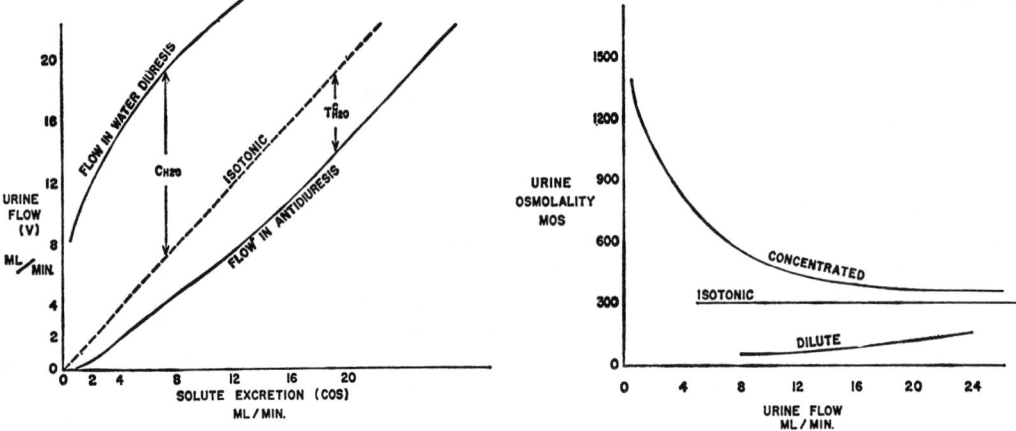

Fig. 79.9a (left). Relationship between urine flow and solute excretion in water diuresis and during the formation of concentrated urine.

Fig. 79.9b (right). Relationship between urine flow and urine osmolality when urine flow is modified by changing solute excretion. See text for explanation.

The Reabsorption and Excretion of Sodium and Chloride

The regulation of the osmotic pressure of body fluids tends to adjust the amount of water in the body to the amount of solute in the body fluids. Thus, so long as osmotic pressure regulation remains normal, the volume of the body fluids will depend on the amount of solute in the body. Since sodium salts constitute some 90 per cent or more of the solute of extracellular fluid, the volume of the extracellular fluid is largely dependent on the regulation of renal sodium excretion.

We have already considered, in relation to the regulation of water excretion, how sodium reabsorption is distributed in the renal tubule. It has been pointed out that a major fraction of the filtered solute and water are reabsorbed in the proximal tubule. Since most of this solute is composed of sodium salts and since the fluid remains isotonic in the process of this reabsorption, there is ordinarily little reduction of sodium concentration in the proximal tubule. However, the reabsorption involves active sodium transport since (1) the reabsorption occurs despite an electrical potential (20 mv., lumen negative to interstitial fluid) opposing the movement of sodium, and (2) if some nonreabsorbable solute (e.g., mannitol) is present, the sodium concentration does fall well below that of the peritubular fluid as sodium is reabsorbed. (However, because of a relatively high permeability the gradient of sodium concentration which can be established is limited because of diffusion from peritubular fluid.) Since chloride reabsorption is favored by the electrical potential, there is no reason to believe any specific transport mechanism for chloride reabsorption

is present. In essence, the chloride is pulled by its electrical charge as a result of the active transport of sodium.

The reabsorption of sodium in the more distal segments of the nephron does result in the establishment of gradients of sodium concentration which may, indeed, be very steep since sodium may be virtually absent from the urine. The difference between proximal and distal tubules probably resides not in the character of the transport mechanism, but in the passive permeability of the tubule epithelium; there is less tendency, in the distal area, for the sodium to diffuse back into the lumen and dissipate the gradient. However, there is evidence that in the distal convoluted tubule the removal of chloride may be the consequence of an active transport process since the concentration may fall to levels too low to be accounted for by the electrical force provided by the sodium transport.

In addition, in the distal tubule, not all of the reabsorption of sodium is accompanied by reabsorption of anion. Some of the sodium reabsorbed in the distal segment is replaced by potassium, and some is replaced by hydrogen and ammonium ions. These aspects of the sodium reabsorptive mechanism will be considered in relation to potassium excretion and the renal regulation of acid-base balance in later sections of this chapter.

The mechanism by which sodium is transferred from lumen to peritubular fluid is poorly understood. It is probably very closely related to that mechanism (also poorly understood) common to virtually every cell of the body, by which sodium is extruded from and potassium maintained at a high concentration in the intracellular fluid. The process probably involves a negatively charged carrier and an exchange of sodium ions for other cations (potassium and/or hydrogen), but no entirely satisfactory and generally applicable model is available.

The Regulation of Sodium Excretion

A number of circumstances are known to influence the rate of sodium excretion. The way in which these factors are integrated to determine and regulate the rate of sodium excretion is not so well known. To say that the rate of sodium excretion is determined by the balance between filtration of sodium at the glomeruli and reabsorption of sodium by the renal tubules is merely to state the obvious. What is required is a knowledge of how these two processes are interrelated and modified to maintain a normal body sodium content. Although we can indicate qualitatively some of the determinants of sodium excretion, they can not be put together as, for instance, in the case of glucose, to predict the rate of salt excretion.

1. GLOMERULAR FILTRATION. Under average normal conditions only a very small fraction of the sodium contained in the glomerular filtrate is excreted in the urine—a person on an average salt intake puts out only about one-half of one per cent of the amount filtered. It is clear, therefore, that an increase of only one per cent in the rate of glomerular filtration[11] supplies enough additional sodium in the filtrate to double or triple the sodium excretion were none of the extra sodium reabsorbed by the tubules. It is also clear, however, that when the glomerular filtration rate increases, the increment of filtered sodium is never quantitatively excreted. In fact, unlike the situation with respect to the reabsorption of such substances as glucose and phosphate, changes in the rate of glomerular filtration are attended by parallel changes in the rate of sodium reabsorption. When glomerular filtration increases, sodium reabsorption increases; when filtration decreases, reabsorption likewise decreases. When changes in glomerular filtration occur the reabsorption of salt in the proximal convoluted tubule changes very nearly in exact proportion. However, because similar changes do not take place in reabsorption in the remainder of the nephron, changes in the filtration of sodium are not accompanied

by proportional changes in excretion. As a matter of fact, acute changes in the filtration of sodium produce relatively very large changes in sodium excretion. However, if the filtration rate changes are maintained for a protracted period compensatory changes in reabsorption occur so as to restore sodium balance.

These circumstances are very clearly demonstrated by the experiments of Mueller and his associates. In dogs operated upon to make it possible to collect the urine from each kidney separately, these investigators placed constricting clamps on one renal artery. It was found that if the artery was constricted so as to produce a barely detectable decrease in glomerular filtration rate, there was a marked drop in the amount of sodium excreted by the affected kidney. Such a kidney might excrete only 10 to 20 per cent of the daily sodium intake, the remainder being excreted by the normal control kidney so as to maintain sodium balance. This situation might persist indefinitely. If, however, the normal kidney was then removed there was a prompt increase in the salt excreted by the kidney with the constricted artery. When the full load of maintaining sodium balance was placed on the experimental kidney, compensatory adjustments of reabsorption overcame the effects of reduced glomerular filtration.

2. ADRENOCORTICAL STEROIDS. The best known of the influences which modify tubular reabsorption of sodium is that exerted by the steroid hormones of the adrenal cortex. The natural hormone with the greatest effect on sodium reabsorption is aldosterone, but similar effects are produced by desoxycorticosterone, cortisol, cortisone and others, as well as a number of synthetic steroids. All of the active steroids exert qualitatively identical effects on sodium transport by the renal tubules, increasing reabsorption in all its forms—that is, sodium reabsorption accompanied by chloride reabsorption as well as sodium exchange for potassium and hydrogen ions. However, the various steroids may produce differing effects on sodium *excretion* not only because they differ in potency with respect to their capacity to modify sodium transport, but because glucocorticoid activity is associated with the specific property of increasing the rate of glomerular filtration.

The control of salt excretion by the adrenal cortex is probably mediated by the secretion of aldosterone. The secretion of aldosterone appears to be stimulated by angiotensin, a small peptide hormone formed in the blood from a circulating precursor globulin by the action of the enzyme renin. Renin is secreted by the juxtaglomerular

---

[11] Changes in the amount of sodium filtered are generally due largely to changes in the rate of glomerular filtration since the plasma sodium concentration is normally maintained within a very narrow range, reflecting the constancy of osmotic pressure to which sodium salts contribute such a major share.

apparatus of the kidney in response to a stimulus which has not been clearly established, but which appears to be related in some way to the effective circulating blood volume. Contraction of blood volume leads to increased secretion of renin which in turn yields increased formation of angiotensin and, in turn, increased secretion of aldosterone, increased reabsorption of sodium (and chloride) and secondarily, by an increase in the retention of water, to expansion of volume.

The action of aldosterone is to increase the formation of a protein which plays some as yet unidentified role in the sodium transport process.

It should be clearly understood that the transport process proceeds very well in the absence of the corticosteroids; the effect of the hormones is, in a sense, the fine adjustment of a process which is largely autonomous.

When adrenal salt-retention hormones are administered to normal animals there is a brief period of salt retention but the decreased salt excretion is relatively short-lived. After retaining a modest amount of salt, the animal comes back into balance. This does not indicate the development of resistance to the effect of steroid on sodium transport but compensation for this effect by other factors including, but not limited to, an increase in glomerular filtration.

3. It has recently been shown that expansion of the blood and extracellular fluid volume by the administration of saline solutions has a very striking effect in reducing sodium reabsorption in the proximal convoluted tubules. This depression is great enough to cause an increase in salt excretion even if the usual increase in glomerular filtration rate is prevented or reversed. The mechanism involved in this depressed salt reabsorption has not yet been clarified but it appears to be attributable to the secretion of some humoral agent by an unidentified organ in response to a stimulus which also remains to be identified. Whatever its nature, this mechanism is one of the more important regulators of salt excretion. It appears to be largely responsible for the escape from the salt-retaining effects of adrenal steroids described above.

4. OSMOTIC DIURESIS. The excretion of sodium is increased by any circumstance which leads to an increase in the excretion of solute. Perhaps the most common such event is elevation of the blood glucose to levels at which the reabsorptive capacity of the tubules is saturated and glucose is excreted in the urine. The same effect may be produced by the administration of poorly reabsorbed substances such as urea or mannitol. This

phenomenon is known as *osmotic diuresis*. Sodium excretion is increased because the presence of the other solute depresses sodium reabsorption in the proximal tubule. As sodium is reabsorbed, the other solute, which remains behind in the tubule, forms a larger and larger fraction of the total solute. Since the fluid retains the same total solute concentration as the blood, the sodium concentration must fall; the decrease in concentration impairs reabsorption.

5. EXCRETION OF POORLY REABSORBED ANIONS OR ANIONS SUBJECT TO TUBULAR EXCRETION. When large amounts of some anion are excreted in the urine, there must be an equivalent amount of cation excreted. To some extent sodium may be substituted for by potassium, ammonium or hydrogen ions, but the capacity to do this is limited. Thus under conditions where large amounts of sulfate, phosphate, p-aminohippurate (PAH), etc., are excreted, sodium excretion is increased.

6. SPECIFIC INHIBITION OF SODIUM TRANSPORT. The commonly used diuretics,—organic mercurials, chlorothiazide and related compounds, carbonic anhydrase inhibitors, etc., all owe their efficacy to the capacity to depress sodium transport by the renal tubules.

The Excretion of Potassium

Potassium holds a unique place among the normal constituents of the blood and urine in being subject to both reabsorption and secretion by the tubules. The average rate at which potassium is excreted in the urine is only about 15 per cent of the rate at which it is filtered at the glomeruli; on the other hand, if large amounts of potassium salts are administered, or if the secretion of hydrogen ion is inhibited, the rate of excretion of potassium may rise to levels equivalent to twice the rate at which it is filtered. There is considerable evidence to support the view that, even when the amount excreted is less than that filtered, the potassium in the urine is derived largely from tubular secretion.

Potassium reabsorption occurs largely in the proximal tubule. The process involves active transport since, although the concentration of potassium is generally reduced only slightly, the potassium movement occurs against the electrical force provided by the negativity of the tubule lumen relative to the peritubular interstitial fluid. Reabsorption continues beyond the convoluted portion of the proximal tubule since only a small fraction of the filtered potassium remains when the fluid enters the distal convoluted tubule.

The potassium secretory process begins in the distal convoluted tubules and continues into the collecting system. The process is, in effect, an exchange of potassium ions for sodium ions, the reabsorption of sodium setting up an electrical gradient with the lumen of the tubule strongly negative. This electrical gradient causes potassium ions to diffuse into the lumen through the distal tubule lining which has a high permeability to potassium. Thus sodium reabsorption provides the driving force for potassium secretion. This driving force is opposed by active transport of potassium out of the lumen, the actual amount of potassium at any point along the distal system being determined by the balance of these two processes. When the supply of sodium is exhausted before the end of the nephron, the driving force provided by sodium reabsorption falls off and potassium is reabsorbed sometimes to very low levels.

The rate of potassium excretion is determined by several factors:

1. The concentration of potassium in cells, particularly the renal tubule cells. The concentration of potassium in the plasma has little influence on potassium excretion except insofar as cell potassium concentration tends to vary with plasma concentration. Such an arrangement is highly reasonable since potassium is primarily an intracellular ion, and it is, therefore, the cell potassium to which excretion should be related.

2. The amount of sodium remaining as the end of the distal tubule system is reached. Thus paradoxically, since sodium is reabsorbed as potassium is secreted, sodium and potassium excretion frequently vary in parallel rather than inversely.

3. The rate of secretion of hydrogen ion by the tubules. The secretion of hydrogen ion tends to reduce the electrical potential gradient produced by sodium transport and, thus, the driving force for secretion of potassium into the lumen. Anything which tends to enhance the secretion of hydrogen ion, depresses tubular excretion of potassium; anything which inhibits tubular secretion of hydrogen ion, enhances excretion of potassium.

4. The capacity of the exchange mechanism. Provided sufficient sodium is delivered to the exchange mechanism potassium excretion is enhanced by conditions which enhance sodium reabsorption (adrenocortical steroids) and depressed by inhibitors of the mechanism (mercurial diuretics).

5. Tolerance to potassium. For reasons that are not entirely clear potassium excretion is facilitated by repeated administration of potassium.

RENAL REGULATION OF ACID-BASE BALANCE

Under normal conditions the diet provides a number of sources of potential acid. The organic phosphorus of proteins and phospholipids is converted to phosphoric acid; the sulfur of the sulfur-containing amino acids is converted to sulfuric acid. When ammonium chloride is ingested, the ammonium ion is converted to urea and hydrogen ion leaving hydrochloric acid as the end product. If calcium chloride is ingested, the calcium may be excreted in the stool as the insoluble salts of organic acids (such as fatty acids), and hydrochloric acid is absorbed. Under abnormal conditions (starvation, diabetic ketosis) large amounts of organic acid may be produced, well beyond the capacity of the body to oxidize this acid to carbon dioxide.

In the usual dietary circumstances the dietary sources of acid predominate over the sources of alkali, but the latter may be in excess with certain intakes. Fruits and vegetables abound in the salts of organic acids. The organic anions are oxidized to CO_2 leaving the bicarbonates of sodium and potassium. In addition the intake may include sodium or potassium bicarbonate as such.

Acid or alkali entering the body fluids react with the buffers of these fluids and the pH change which occurs is thereby minimized. The most abundant buffer system of extracellular fluid is that made up of bicarbonate and carbonic acid and the bulk of the extracellular buffering is therefore involved with this system. Because it must provide the major part of the alkali to neutralize any acid gaining access to the extracellular fluid, the bicarbonate concentration has been designated the *alkali reserve* and can be considered a measure of the degree of acidosis or alkalosis (even though, by respiratory compensation, changes of bicarbonate concentration may be accompanied by only minimal changes in pH).

Acid added to extracellular fluid reacts chiefly with bicarbonate to yield carbonic acid and the salt of the acid. The carbonic acid in turn yields CO_2 which is excreted in the lungs.

$$H^+A^- + Na^+HCO_3^- \leftrightarrows$$
$$NA^+A^- + H_2CO_3 \leftrightarrows H_2O + CO_2$$

The result is the replacement, in the extracellular

fluid, of one equivalent of bicarbonate with one equivalent of the anion of the acid. The anion (A^-) will eventually be excreted in the urine. If it is excreted as the sodium salt, the form in which it exists in plasma, the over-all result will have been the disappearance from the extracellular fluid of one mol of sodium bicarbonate for each mol of HA added.

The buffer capacity of the extracellular fluid can be restored only by regaining a mol of sodium bicarbonate. This might be done, if, instead of excreting the sodium salt (NaA) in the urine, the kidney were able to dispose of the free acid HA thus regenerating sodium bicarbonate. This would amount to a reversal of the reactions above:

$$H_2O + CO_2 \rightarrow H_2CO_3 + Na^+A^- \rightarrow$$

$$Na^+HCO^-_3 + HA \rightarrow (urine)$$

This, in fact, the kidney is able to do by virtue of its capacity to produce urine considerably more acid (down almost to pH 4) than the blood (pH 7.40). Thus, to the extent that any acid is un-ionized at the pH of the urine, that acid may be disposed of directly, with regeneration and recovery of the bicarbonate by which it was temporarily buffered in the extracellular fluid.

The extent to which an acid is un-ionized at a given pH can be deduced from the Henderson-Hasselbalch equation

$$pH = pK + \log \frac{[A^-]}{[HA]}$$

This may be rearranged in the form $pK - pH = \log [HA] - \log [A^-]$ to indicate more clearly that when the pH is lower than the pK of the acid concerned there will be more un-ionized acid than salt. Thus any acid which has a pK higher, *or not much lower* than the pH of the urine,[12] can be excreted to an appreciable extent in un-ionized form. Acids with pK's high enough to appear in the urine in undissociated form to an appreciable extent are monobasic phosphate ($H_2PO_4^- \rightleftharpoons HPO_4^{--} + H^+$), pK 6.80; β-hydroxybutyric acid, pK 4.7 and creatinine ($CrH^+ \rightleftharpoons Cr + H^+$), pK 5.0.

For most acids which enter the extracellular fluid, excretion as the undissociated acid is impossible. Hydrochloric and sulfuric acids are completely dissociated at all pH's. At a urine pH as low as 4.0, the concentration of hydrochloric or sulfuric acid would be only 10^{-4} N or 0.1 m.eq. per liter. Even *weak* acids having pK's much be-

low 5 must be excreted almost entirely as salts. In the excretion of such acids, then, some other mechanism is required if bicarbonate is to be regained to replace that originally lost in neutralizing them. This is accomplished by the generation of ammonium ion from neutral precursors and the substitution of ammonium ion for sodium ion in the urine. The acids are excreted as ammonium salts; the sodium is returned to the extracellular fluid as sodium bicarbonate. The overall reaction may be considered to be the following:

$$RNH_2 + HOH \rightarrow NH_3 + ROH \text{ (which may}$$

then be oxidized to CO_2 and H_2O)

$$NH_3 + Na^+A^- + H_2CO_3 \rightarrow$$

$$NH_4^+A^- \text{ (to urine)} + Na^+HCO_3^-$$

Neither of these reactions nor those indicated above should be interpreted as indicating the actual processes which take place in the kidney. They represent the net results of a series of reactions.

Thus acids are disposed of without loss of alkali reserve (1) by excretion of weak acids in their un-ionized form and (2) by the substitution of ammonium ion for sodium ion in the excretion of their salts. The disposal of excess alkali is more direct. Alkali appears in the extracellular fluid as bicarbonate ($B^+OH^- + CO_2 \rightleftharpoons B^+HCO_3^-$) and is excreted in the urine as that bicarbonate which escapes reabsorption in the tubules. This background concerning the nature of the overall processes will serve as an introduction to the renal mechanisms which determine the excretion of acid or alkali.

Three processes are important in regulating the amount of acid or alkali excreted: (1) the filtration of bicarbonate at the glomeruli, (2) the transport mechanism by which bicarbonate is reabsorbed and the urine rendered acid, and (3) the synthesis of ammonia by the cells of the renal tubule.

The glomerular filtrate contains bicarbonate at a concentration essentially identical to that in plasma.[13] Micropuncture studies have shown that there is some variation in the pH and bicarbonate concentration as the fluid flows through the proximal convoluted tubule. Under normal con-

---

[12] Although more acid urine *can* be formed, the urine pH is not often below 5.0 and is more commonly around 6.

[13] Because the plasma proteins are nonfilterable anions, a Donnan equilibrium is set up across the glomerular membrane, and all monovalent filterable anions, including bicarbonate, are about 5 per cent more concentrated in glomerular filtrate than in plasma water. All monovalent filterable cations, including H^+, are about 5 per cent less concentrated.

ditions in the dog, the bicarbonate concentration, and hence the pH, is close to that in plasma. When plasma bicarbonate is reduced by acidosis, the bicarbonate concentration falls in the proximal tubule to levels one-half to one-quarter that in plasma while when the plasma bicarbonate is elevated in metabolic alkalosis, the concentration of bicarbonate rises in the proximal tubule as fluid is reabsorbed relatively more rapidly than bicarbonate. Since the tubule has a very high permeability to CO_2, the carbon dioxide tension and, hence, the carbonic acid concentration in the lumen are very close to those of plasma. Thus the denominator in the Henderson-Hasselbalch equation,

$$pH = 6.1 + \log ([HCO_3^-]/[H_2CO_3]),$$

remains constant and pH varies directly with the log $[HCO_3^-]$. It should be noted that even though the bicarbonate concentration may change but little in the proximal tubule, most of the filtered bicarbonate is usually reabsorbed in this segment as a consequence of the reabsorption of a large fraction of the filtered volume.

In the distal tubule the urine is further acidified, and the process continues into the collecting ducts. The major reduction in pH occurs in the distal parts of the nephron, but this does not necessarily indicate that the reabsorption of base occurs predominantly in the latter segments. As bicarbonate is removed from the tubule lumen, changes in the pH of the remaining fluid will depend upon the changes in volume of the remaining fluid. If bicarbonate removal proceeds more rapidly than volume decreases, the bicarbonate concentration falls and the pH likewise falls since the concentration of carbonic acid remains constant (see above). If the volume of the remaining tubular fluid diminishes more rapidly than does the amount of bicarbonate remaining, the pH of the fluid will rise. Thus, the degree to which the urine is acidified depends not only upon the rate of bicarbonate removal, but on the relationship of the removal rate to the rate of removal of water. Consequently, the production of urine more alkaline than plasma requires only that a greater fraction of the filtered water than of the filtered bicarbonate be reabsorbed.

Mechanism of Urine Acidification

Largely as the result of the studies of Pitts and his associates the process by which bicarbonate removal is effected is generally accepted as being one in which hydrogen ion is secreted by the cells

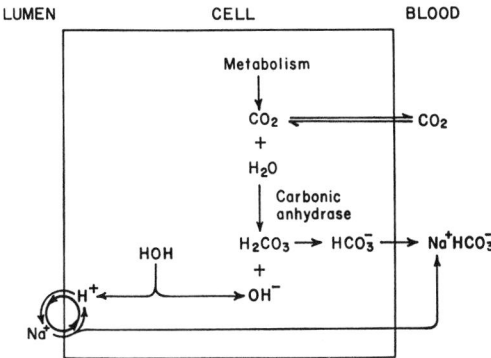

FIG. 79.10. Hypothetical cellular processes in the secretion of hydrogen ion in exchange for sodium.

of the renal tubule in exchange for sodium ions. The mechanism may be conveniently depicted as follows (fig. 79.10): In the renal tubule cell, as a result of energy-requiring processes, hydrogen ion and hydroxyl ion are generated from water in spatially separated loci. The hydrogen ion enters the tubule lumen in exchange for a sodium ion which is taken into the cell. Meanwhile the hydroxyl ion is buffered within the cell by reacting with carbonic acid to yield bicarbonate ion and water. The bicarbonate and sodium ions are extruded into the extracellular fluid. The carbonic acid is regenerated by the hydration of carbon dioxide; the latter may be derived from either the metabolic processes within the cell or from the carbon dioxide of the blood and extracellular fluid.

The regeneration of the carbonic acid proceeds rapidly only in the presence of the enzyme *carbonic anhydrase* and this step may become rate-limiting in the overall process. When the production of carbonic acid is impaired by inhibition of the enzyme, the concentration of carbonic acid in the cell falls and with it the hydrogen ion concentration. Since the rate at which hydrogen ion is extruded in exchange for sodium ion is related to the hydrogen ion concentration in the cell, the rate of secretion of hydrogen ion is diminished. Thus *inhibition of carbonic anhydrase diminishes the secretion of hydrogen ion* and all of the processes dependent upon the secretion of hydrogen ion.

It should be noted that in the above process, for each hydrogen ion extruded one equivalent of sodium as the bicarbonate is added to the extracellular fluid and this result is independent of the fate of the hydrogen ion in the tubule lumen (fig. 79.11). The fate of the hydrogen ion which enters the lumen in exchange for a sodium ion depends upon the composition of the fluid which it enters.

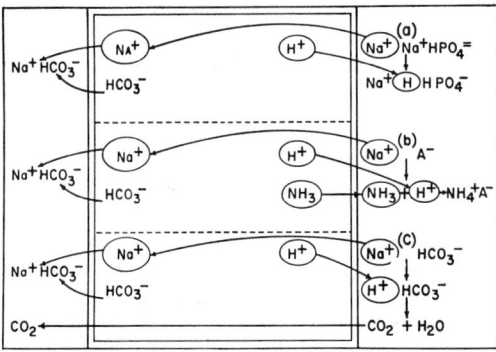

Fig. 79.11. Fate of hydrogen ion secreted into tubule lumen in exchange for sodium. a) Formation of titratable acid; b) formation of ammonium ion; c) reabsorption of filtered bicarbonate. Modified from figure of Orloff (Yale J. Biol. & Med., 29:211, 1956).

Acid added to any buffered solution is distributed among the buffers of that solution in a predictable way depending upon the relative concentrations of the buffers and their pK values. Any change in hydrogen ion concentration must affect all the buffers present since all must satisfy their ionization constants. The amount of hydrogen ion distributed to each buffer will be directly proportional to the concentration of the buffer and inversely related to the difference between the pH of the solution and the pK of the buffer.

We may consider as an example the secretion of hydrogen ion into the proximal renal tubule. The buffers contained in the glomerular filtrate may be considered to be bicarbonate (pK' 6.1) at a concentration of about 27 mmole per liter and phosphate (pK 6.8) at a concentration of about 1.5 mmole per liter. Because it is present in much higher concentration, bicarbonate will take up most of the hydrogen ion secreted even though the pH of the fluid (7.4) is closer to the pK of phosphate. Thus in the proximal tubule most of the added hydrogen ion reacts with bicarbonate.

$$H^+ + HCO_3^- \rightleftarrows H_2CO_3 \rightleftarrows H_2O + CO_2$$

The result of hydrogen ion addition, then, is the conversion of bicarbonate ion to CO_2 and water, and the CO_2 diffuses out of the tubule lumen to extracellular fluid. Thus the exchange of a mol of sodium ion for a mol of hydrogen ion has resulted in the removal of a mol of sodium bicarbonate from the glomerular filtrate even though no bicarbonate ion has crossed the membrane separat-

ing lumen from tubule cell. Instead, the bicarbonate ion which enters the extracellular fluid is generated independently in the tubule cell.

In the distal tubule the situation may be quite different. Suppose that the proximal tubule capacity for phosphate reabsorption has been saturated so that half of the filtered phosphate has escaped reabsorption and reaches the distal tubule. At the same time the volume of the fluid flowing through the tubule has been greatly diminished by the processes of reabsorption, so that we may assume that at some point in the distal tubule only 5 per cent of the glomerular filtrate remains. The phosphate concentration in the fluid will then have reached a value ten times that in the glomerular filtrate or 15 mmole per liter. Now the hydrogen ion secreted into the fluid will to a very considerable extent react with dibasic phosphate, converting it to monobasic phosphate:

$$H^+ + HPO_4^= \rightleftarrows H_2PO_4^-$$

As the pH falls, the concentration of bicarbonate diminishing rapidly, a greater proportion of the hydrogen ion will be taken up by other buffers. At pH 6.1, the bicarbonate concentration will be only about 1.4 m.eq. per liter, at 5.1 about 0.14 m. eq. per liter.

It is important to note that as hydrogen ion reacts with bicarbonate the resulting undissociated acid (H_2CO_3) disappears from the urine (as CO_2). The hydrogen ion which reacts with other weak acids, however, remains and can be detected in the final urine in the form of *titratable acid*. The amount of the latter can be determined as the amount of alkali required to titrate the urine back to the pH of plasma, and is equal to the amount of hydrogen ion expended and sodium bicarbonate regenerated in the conversion of the buffer salt (as it existed in plasma) to the buffer acid as it appears in the urine. The titratable acid, therefore, is a very poor measure of the amount of hydrogen ion secreted by the renal tubules since most of the acid produced by this secretion is carbonic acid which is dissipated.

However, from the standpoint of the regulation of the acid-base balance of the body, the situation is reversed. That part of the secretion of hydrogen ion which is expended in reabsorbing bicarbonate from the glomerular filtrate serves an important conservative role in preventing loss of bicarbonate from the body, but its overall effect is only to return to the extracellular fluid that which it previously had lost for a time into the glomerular filtrate. The excretion of titratable acid, however, represents the addition of extra sodium bicarbonate to the extracellular fluid, replacing the neutral salt (Na^+A^-) which it had previously contained. This, then, is an addition to the alkali reserve and as such can be used to balance off the acid products of ingestion and metabolism.

The excretion of titratable acid is a process in which there is a net gain of alkali reserve, but it is a process of limited potentiality, limited by the capacity of the kidney to reduce the pH of the urine and by the amount of weak acid of suitable pK excreted in the urine. This process alone would be unable to maintain the alkali reserve against the continued addition to extracellular fluid of even most of those acids which can be excreted to a considerable extent in un-ionized form. Thus, β-hydroxybutyric acid can be excreted about half as the free acid, half as the salt. The excretion of titratable acid can therefore diminish the attrition of body buffer by about one-half, but the continued production of this acid would eventually exhaust the extracellular bicarbonate supply. Of course, the production of titratable acid contributes nothing to balancing off the effects of the ingestion or production of strong mineral acids. The latter effects are overcome by the production and excretion of ammonium ion in place of so-called "fixed cation" (largely sodium and potassium).

EXCRETION OF AMMONIA. The source of urinary ammonia was the subject of debate for many years. That the ammonia is produced in the kidney was established by the studies of Nash and Benedict who showed that more ammonia left the kidney in renal venous blood than entered in the arterial blood. The experiments of Van Slyke and his associates demonstrated that a major fraction of the urinary ammonia was derived from the amide nitrogen of glutamine.

Glutamine $\rightarrow NH_3$ + glutamic acid

The more recent work of Pitts has shown that much of the remainder is derived from the amino group of glutamine. Ammonia can also be produced by the oxidative deamination of a number of amino acids (glycine, alanine, leucine, aspartic acid) but under ordinary conditions the urinary ammonia appears to be derived from glutamine and asparagine with smaller contributions from glycine, citrulline, tryptophan, and proline.

Ammonia, produced in the cells of the renal tubules, enters and accumulates in the renal tubules by simple diffusion. The nature of the process by which this accumulation takes place may be understood from a consideration of the nature of cell membranes and the solubility characteristics of weak electrolytes.

Most cell membranes that have been studied have the characteristics of lipid layers permeated by aqueous pores which occupy only a very small part of the total surface area. Substances which are highly soluble in lipid can penetrate the entire surface of the cell, while those which are highly water-soluble and lipid-insoluble can penetrate only through the aqueous pores. Lipid soluble materials, therefore, diffuse in and out of cells very much more rapidly than water soluble substances. Among the latter are most ions; ionized compounds are, in general, highly water soluble and poorly soluble in lipid. On the other hand many un-ionized substances are highly soluble in lipids (provided they are not highly polar compounds, e.g., sugars, urea, short-chain alcohols, etc.). In accord with these generalizations, the ammonium ion (NH_4^+) is highly water soluble and would be expected to penetrate cell membranes poorly; on the other hand, free ammonia (NH_3) is highly lipid-soluble and penetrates cells quite readily.

Now suppose we have two aqueous solutions of different pH separated by a membrane having the characteristics of the lipid layer discussed above. To such a system ammonia is added. The ammonia, being highly lipid soluble, will penetrate the membrane readily and will reach equilibrium when the concentration of the free ammonia (NH_3) is the same on both sides of the membrane. However, in each solution ammonia will react with hydrogen ion to yield ammonium ion:

$$NH_3 + H^+ \rightleftharpoons NH_4^+$$

This reaction will be continuously at the equilibrium required by the dissociation equation:

$$K_A = \frac{[H^+][NH_3]}{[NH_4^+]}$$

or

$$pH = pK_A + \log \frac{[NH_3]}{[NH_4^+]}; \qquad pK_A = 8.9$$

Since $[NH_3]$ is the same on both sides of the membrane, the numerator of last term may be considered a constant and the log $[NH_4^+]$ will vary inversely with the pH. Thus a decrease in pH of one unit will yield a tenfold increase in ammonium ion concentration. Since the free ammonia constitutes a very small part of the total ($NH_3 + NH_4^+$) the total will vary pretty much as the concentration of ammonium ion.

This model may be considered to approximate the situation in the kidney where the solution on one side of the membrane represents the contents of the renal tubule cells in which ammonia is produced and the other side of the membrane, the fluid in the lumen. We may consider the pH of the intracellular fluid and its ammonia concentration to be maintained relatively constant and ammonia to accumulate in the lumen until the free ammonia concentration is approximately the same on both sides and the ammonium ion concentration in the lumen that required by the urinary pH. The concentration of ammonium ion will therefore increase as urine pH decreases.

Because several assumptions involved in this model are only approximations, the actual ammonia excretion varies with pH appreciably less than would be predicted. A urinary pH change of two to two and a half units is required to yield a tenfold change in ammonia excretion. (The idealized model would indicate a tenfold change with each pH unit.) It should be noted that as NH_3 diffuses into the urine, hydrogen ion is titrated and the pH of the urine tends to become elevated; the pH difference would disappear if it were not maintained by the continuous secretion of hydrogen ion.

Ammonia appears in the tubule lumen wherever the tubule fluid has a pH low enough to permit the trapping of ammonia as ammonium ion. It thus appears in the proximal tubule when the pH falls appreciably below that of plasma (normally in the rat, in metabolic acidosis in the dog). As urine pH approaches its minimum in the distal nephron, each hydrogen ion secreted into the lumen must be neutralized by capture of NH_3 to form an ammonium ion before another hydrogen ion can be secreted.

The excretion of ammonia like the excretion of titratable acid represents replenishment of the body's alkali reserve. Quantitatively it represents, under most conditions, the more important contribution to the maintenance of the acid-base balance of the body. The sum of titratable acid and urinary ammonium ion represent the net gain of sodium bicarbonate for the body fluids as a result of the process of urine formation. (In estimating body balance, it is necessary to subtract from this total any bicarbonate excreted in the urine.)

A striking and unique feature of ammonia formation and excretion is the phenomenon of *adaptation*. If an individual is given an acidifying regimen (such as the administration of ammonium or calcium chloride or the feeding of a strongly acid-ash diet), there is a gradual increase, over a period of three to five days, of the excretion of ammonia in the urine. This increase is independent of changes in urinary pH (which occur very much more rapidly) and the amount of ammonia in the urine is eventually greater at each pH than it was before the acidifying stimulus was started. The administration of alkali has an effect exactly the reverse of the administration of acid. Neither the nature nor the immediate stimulus to this adaptation are too clearly established. It undoubtedly involves a modification in the enzymatic mechanism by which ammonia is produced and presumably a rise in the concentration of ammonia in the cells in which it is produced.

In the rat, but not in the dog, it can be shown that glutaminase activity is increased. The overall behavior of ammonia excretion in man resembles that in the dog more closely than in the rat. For instance, if acidosis is produced by the administration of inhibitors of carbonic anhydrase which cause massive loss of bicarbonate in the urine, ammonia excretion and glutaminase activity increase markedly in the rat, but ammonia excretion remains at a level related only to urine pH in both man and dog. There is no evidence of adaptation of the sort produced by the administration of acidifying salts.

The stimulus to adaptation is also not clear. It is obviously in some way related to the intake of acid, but it does not appear to depend on the degree of acidosis, ammonia excretion remaining high when, as a result of the adaptation, plasma bicarbonate has been restored essentially to normal.

QUANTITATIVE ASPECTS OF URINE ACIDIFICATION. As with all processes of urinary excretion, the urinary acidification is dependent upon the balance between glomerular filtration and tubular reabsorption. In this case, the important characteristic of the filtrate is its bicarbonate concentration. We will postpone consideration of those factors which modify the secretion of hydrogen ion by the renal tubules and consider first the effect of changes in plasma bicarbonate concentration.

We must first take note of the fact that for reasons that have not been determined, the capacity of the tubules to reabsorb bicarbonate varies with the rate of glomerular filtration but not with the plasma bicarbonate concentration. The concentration of bicarbonate in the glomerular filtrate is therefore a far more important determinant of bicarbonate excretion than the total amount of bicarbonate filtered. To take this into account and to present the reabsorption and excretion of bicarbonate as an orderly, predictable phenomenon, it is the practice to divide the amounts filtered, reabsorbed and excreted by the rate of glomerular filtration and to present the data as the amount reabsorbed, etc., per 100 ml. or per liter of glomerular filtrate.

When the plasma bicarbonate concentration is low the urine is acid and essentially free of bicarbonate; all of the filtered bicarbonate is reabsorbed. As the plasma bicarbonate concentration is increased, the urine remains essentially free of bicarbonate until the concentration approaches approximately 28 m.eq. per liter. Bicarbonate then begins to appear in the urine and as the plasma concentration increases further bicarbonate reabsorption remains virtually constant at 28 m.eq. per liter of glomerular filtrate, and the excess is excreted in the urine. This is illustrated in figure 79.12. This tends to produce stabilization of the plasma bicarbonate concentration at its normal level of 27 to 28 m.eq. per liter. When the plasma bicarbonate falls below this level, the filtered bicarbonate is completely reabsorbed and conserved. If the plasma bicarbonate rises appreciably above 28 m.eq. per liter, the excess is excreted and the plasma bicarbonate tends to return rapidly to normal.

It should be noted that, to the extent that the capacity of the tubule to secrete hydrogen ion is expended in the reabsorption of bicarbonate, no appreciable amount is available to appear as titratable acid or ammonia. Thus when the plasma bicarbonate is close to 28 m.eq. per liter, essentially all of the filtered bicarbonate will be reabsorbed but there will be little titratable acid and ammonia in the urine (reflecting the fact that the urine pH will not be very low). However, when the plasma bicarbonate drops lower the bicarbonate of the glomerular filtrate may be exhausted before the capacity to secrete hydrogen ion is fully utilized, and a variable part of the remaining capacity will appear as titratable acid (depending on the rate of excretion of buffer acid) or as ammonium ion (depending upon the rate of production of ammonia).

It is also noteworthy that the amount of titratable acid and ammonia in the urine is a poor indication of the capacity of the tubules to secrete hydrogen ion because, if plasma bicarbonate is low, hydrogen ion secretion stops when the urine pH gets too low and before all the capacity for hydrogen-sodium exchange is utilized. Thus the *capacity* to secrete hydrogen ion can be evaluated only when there is bicarbonate left over from the process—that is, when the urine is alkaline.

FACTORS MODIFYING THE RATE OF SECRETION OF HYDROGEN ION. Under ordinary conditions of acid-base balance, with a normal carbon dioxide tension in the blood, a normal cell potassium concentration, etc., the capacity to secrete hydrogen ion in exchange for sodium is about 28 m.eq. per liter of glomerular filtrate as indicated in the preceding discussion. This tends to maintain the

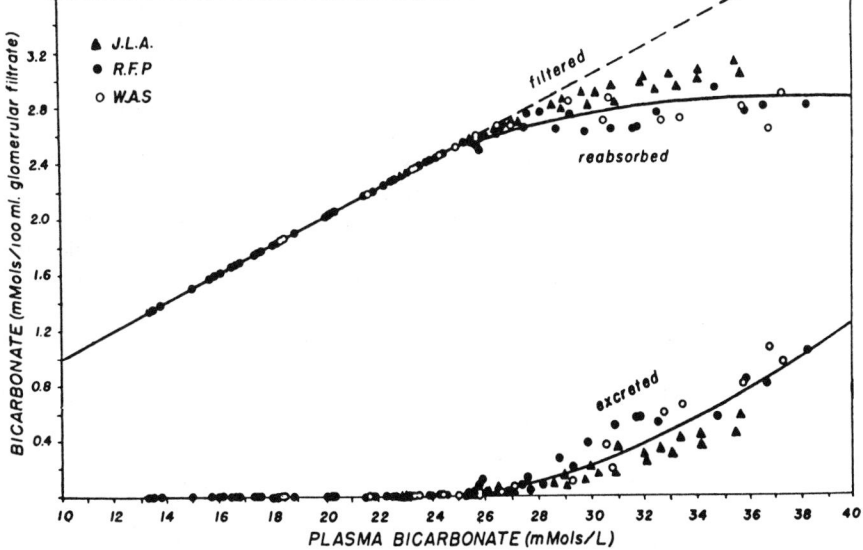

FIG. 79.12. Relationship between plasma bicarbonate and reabsorption and excretion of bicarbonate in man. (Pitts, Ayer and Schiess, J. Clin. Invest., 28: 35, 1949).

plasma bicarbonate concentration at about 28 m.eq. per liter. The capacity to secrete hydrogen ion may be varied in response to several factors:

1. Carbon dioxide tension. When the carbon dioxide tension is increased (respiratory acidosis) the plasma bicarbonate concentration increases by titration of the blood buffers, and the pH change attributable to the increased carbonic acid concentration is minimized. The elevated plasma bicarbonate concentration persists, and the maintenance implies an increase in bicarbonate reabsorption (hydrogen ion secretion) by the renal tubules. Indeed, such an increase in bicarbonate reabsorption is demonstrable immediately upon elevation of the carbon dioxide tension. If elevation of the carbon dioxide tension is maintained for extended periods there is a further increase in the capacity to secrete hydrogen ion; the nature of this further adaptation is unknown. Decreases in carbon dioxide tension (respiratory alkalosis) have exactly the opposite effects, reducing renal bicarbonate reabsorption (hydrogen ion secretion) and causing stabilization of the plasma bicarbonate concentration at a reduced level.

The effects of changes in carbon dioxide tension on hydrogen ion secretion are readily interpreted in terms of the hypothesis that the rate of secretion of hydrogen ion is directly related to the hydrogen ion concentration of the tubule cells. The concentration of dissolved CO_2 is directly related to the carbon dioxide tension (pCO_2) and the concentration of carbonic acid (H_2CO_3) is directly proportional to the pCO_2. Since cell membranes have a very high permeability to CO_2, all changes in extracellular pCO_2 are reflected by similar changes in intracellular pCO_2. Thus intracellular pH falls when extracellular pCO_2 is elevated and vice versa. (On the other hand, changes in extracellular bicarbonate concentration are probably *not* regularly reflected by parallel changes in intracellular bicarbonate and pH.)

2. Potassium metabolism. The secretion of hydrogen ion is depressed when potassium is administered so that the urine frequently becomes alkaline even though the plasma bicarbonate concentration is low. Conversely, in the presence of potassium depletion the rate of secretion of hydrogen ion is enhanced so that the plasma bicarbonate concentration becomes stabilized at an elevated level.

The effects of potassium on hydrogen ion secretion presumably reflect the fact that the rate of secretion of hydrogen ion is dependent upon the pH of the secreting cells and that when cells lose potassium they become more acid while when they gain potassium they become less acid.

3. Chloride balance. When loss of chloride has been incurred in the course of elevation of the plasma bicarbonate, the excretion of the excess bicarbonate must lead to a contraction of extracellular fluid volume unless chloride is available from the intake to replace the bicarbonate. In the absence of such chloride intake, urine acidification continues at a high level.

4. Carbonic anhydrase. The role of carbonic anhydrase and the effect of inhibition of this enzyme have been discussed earlier. Under normal conditions the activity of carbonic anhydrase is not rate-limiting in hydrogen ion secretion although it may become so when inhibited. There is no evidence that adaptation to acid loads involves an increase in kidney carbonic anhydrase.

5. Adrenal steroids. The secretion of hydrogen ion participates in the enhancement of sodium reabsorption produced by aldosterone and other steroids with similar effects on electrolyte metabolism.

Passive Reabsorption; The Excretion of Urea

Because passive reabsorption is the result of the active reabsorption of other constituents of the glomerular filtrate, it is appropriate to consider this relatively simple mechanism last. The reabsorption of urea has long been considered a typical example of this process.[14] Certainly as the most abundant constituent of the urine and as one which fits in unique fashion into the formation of highly concentrated urine, urea requires separate consideration.

Cell membranes generally have a high permeability to urea. It is therefore not surprising that as the filtrate is reabsorbed from the renal tubules, tending to concentrate the urea in the remaining fluid, urea tends to diffuse out of the lumen. What is more remarkable is the very considerable extent to which the urea concentration can be raised in the urine. This appears to be due to two factors: (1) in unusually low permeability to urea of the cells lining some segments of the renal tubules (it is to be remembered that much of the tubule

---

[14] There is evidence that in ruminants (sheep, camel) there is some sort of active renal conservation of urea when the animal receives a low protein intake. Active reabsorption from the collecting duct has also been demonstrated. While it has also been suggested that there is a similar mechanism in man, the evidence is not convincing, and for the sake of didactic clarity, any such process will be disregarded.

lining membrane also has a uniquely low permeability to water, especially in the absence of antidiuretic hormone); and (2) a mechanism for maintaining a high urea concentration in the interstitial fluid (of the medulla) surrounding those portions of the nephron containing fluid with the highest urea concentrations (the collecting ducts); in the latter case the concentration gradient driving the diffusion of urea out of the urine is minimized.

As is characteristic of substances excreted by mechanisms involving passive reabsorption, the fraction of the filtered urea excreted in the urine varies with the urine flow. The fraction of the filtered urea excreted is given by the ratio of the urea clearance (C_U) to the glomerular filtration rate. At urine flows in excess of about 2 ml. per minute in individuals with normal renal function, there is relatively little further increase in the urea clearance with further elevation of urine flow up to the limits of *water diuresis*. At this time the urea clearance averages about 60 to 70 per cent of the inulin clearance, i.e., about 30 to 40 per cent of the filtered urea is reabsorbed. If *osmotic diuresis* is superimposed, the urine flow can be further increased, and under these conditions the excreted fraction of filtered urea increases further along a curve which may be extrapolated to suggest that no urea would be reabsorbed when no water was reabsorbed. Conversely, as urine flow decreases in antidiuresis the excreted urea diminishes to what may be only 15 or 20 per cent of the

filtered. These phenomena are illustrated in figure 79.13 from the data of Shannon obtained in the dog.

As was noted earlier, in the discussion of water excretion and reabsorption, the change from the low flow of concentrated urine to the high flow of water diuresis involves primarily modifications in the flow in the distal portions of the nephron. The reabsorption of water which occurs in the proximal tubule is relatively unaffected. Thus, the additional urea which is reabsorbed when water diuresis is interrupted is logically considered to be reabsorbed in the distal tubule and collecting system. Furthermore, since in the absence of antidiuretic hormone these portions of the nephron have a low permeability to water they may be expected to have a low permeability to urea as well. It is thus logical to attribute the reabsorption of some 30 to 40 per cent of the filtered urea to losses from the proximal tubule as water is reabsorbed from that segment and to consider the losses from the distal portions of the nephron to be negligible in water diuresis. As the fraction of the filtrate reabsorbed in the proximal tubule is diminished in osmotic diuresis, the urea is concentrated to a lesser extent and less than the usual 30 to 40 per cent is reabsorbed.

In antidiuresis, the reabsorption of water in the distal tubule is markedly increased; at the same time, it is highly probable that the permeability of the collecting duct to urea is also enhanced. Both of these factors lead to an increase in the

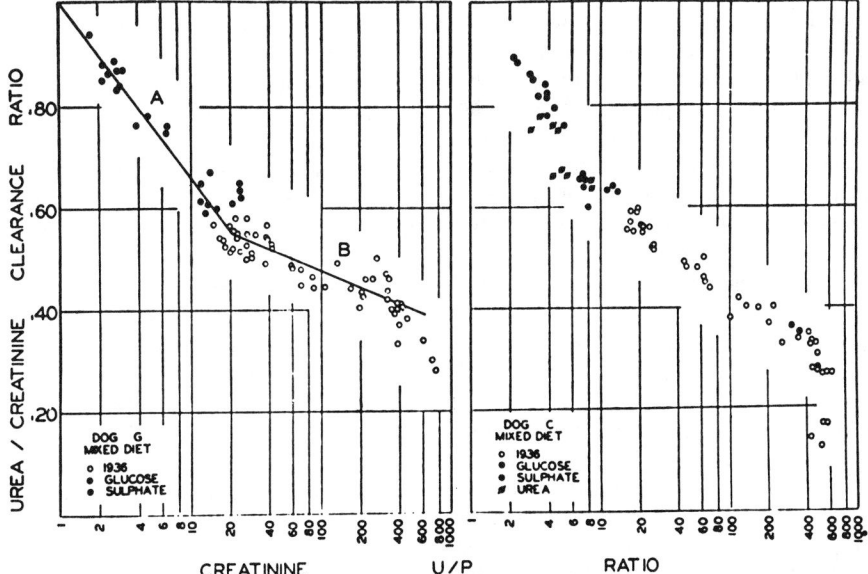

FIG. 79.13. The ratio of urea clearance to creatinine clearance. (Fraction of the filtered urea excreted in relation to the reabsorption of water as indicated by the U/P ratio of creatinine.) (Shannon, Am. J. Physiol., **122**: 782, 1938).

diffusion of urea out of the urine in the distal portions of the nephron and account for the rapid falling off of the urea clearance as urine flow decreases to low levels.

Because the arrangement of the blood supply in the medulla constitutes a countercurrent exchanger, urea escaping from the collecting ducts is not easily carried away in the blood, as it is in the cortex. Instead, even a relatively slow leak of urea from the collecting ducts is sufficient to yield a high urea concentration in the peritubular region. As a result, the urea concentration in the interstitial space of the papilla is almost as high as in the urine. This has several important consequences: (1) the amount of urea lost from the urine is reduced because the concentration gradient is small. (2) The osmotic effect of the urea in the collecting duct urine is counterbalanced largely by urea in the interstitial space; the sodium chloride of the interstitial space, which initiates the urine concentrating process can be utilized to balance the osmotic effect of the nonurea solute, the urea being simply added to both sides of the intervening membrane. Consequently the urine can be made considerably more concentrated when urea is a major part of the excreted solute, and urea, the major product of protein catabolism, and, in fact, by far the most abundant product of metabolism requiring urinary excretion can thus be excreted largely in water already obligated for the excretion of other urinary solutes. (3) Some of the urea enters the descending limb of the loop of Henle and recirculates through the distal tubule and collecting system. In fact, the micropuncture studies of Lassiter, Gottschalk and Mylle have shown that, in the antidiuretic rat, the urine flowing through the loops of Henle gains an amount of urea equivalent to about half of the amount filtered so that it would appear that a large part of the urea which escapes the collecting ducts recirculates through the distal tubule and that very little can leave the medulla via the blood in the vasa recta.

Because the level of the blood urea and the urea clearance are frequently used for the clinical evaluation of renal function, a brief discussion of these clinical indices is warranted. Since the concentration of urea in red blood cell water is the same as in the plasma, the concentration of urea in whole blood is only slightly lower than in plasma, the difference being due to the larger fraction of solids in the red cells. Consequently, it has been the usual practice to base the clinical estimation of urea clearance on the measurement of urea in whole blood (although glomerular filtration operates only on plasma). Because of the variation of urea clearance with urine flow some account must be taken of this factor. The convention which has been adopted has been to arbitrarily divide urea clearances into two classes. When the urine flow exceeds 2 ml. per minute, the clearance of urea is calculated in the conventional fashion except for the substitution of B, the concentration in whole blood, for P, the concentration in plasma. The figure (UV)/B obtained is called the *maximal urea clearance* and a value of 75 ml. per minute is accepted as the average normal. It is sometimes the practice to divide the clearance obtained by 75 and express the result as a per cent of normal.

When the urine flow is less than 2 ml. per minute, some correction is necessary to take into account the marked effect of urine flow change on urea excretion. It has been found empirically that, in normal individuals, if the clearance is divided by the square root of the urine flow ($\sqrt{V}$) the value obtained is relatively independent of urine flow provided the latter is less than 2 ml. per minute. This figure is referred to as the *standard urea clearance* and is equal to

$$\frac{UV}{B} \times \frac{1}{\sqrt{V}} = \frac{U\sqrt{V}}{B}.$$

It has an average normal value of 54 and, again, the result obtained is often expressed as a per cent of the normal value.

When urea clearances are measured, every attempt should be made to assure a urine flow in excess of 2 ml. per minute since the maximal urea clearance is more clearly related to the value which one wishes to estimate, the rate of glomerular filtration.

The blood urea concentration is also, in a rough way, related to the rate of glomerular filtration. However, it is subject to modification by factors which do not affect the urea clearance, namely the intake and metabolism of protein and other nitrogen sources. For this reason the urea clearance is a much more reliable index of renal function.

For the individual in nitrogen balance, almost the entire nitrogen intake is excreted in the form of urea. The excretion of urea is in the long term equal to the formation of urea. Therefore, if we were to consider the daily excretion of urea as a sort of 24-hour determination of urea clearance we would have

$$C_U = \frac{UV}{B} = \frac{\text{rate of nitrogen turnover}}{B}$$

and

$$B = \frac{\text{rate of nitrogen turnover}}{C_U}$$

Thus we see that the blood urea is inversely related to the filtration rate to the extent that the urea clearance is related to the filtration rate, but in addition it is also directly proportional to the nitrogen turnover. The latter factor is eliminated when the urea clearance is determined.

NON-IONIC DIFFUSION. The excretion of weak electrolytes is frequently modified by diffusion dependent upon the dissociation characteristics of the substance concerned. The phenomenon is entirely analogous to that involved in the entrance of ammonia into the urine, a process which was discussed in some detail above. It was pointed out that un-ionized weak electrolytes frequently penetrate cell membranes very much more readily than their ions. As a result when cell membranes separate two aqueous phases of differing pH, the weak electrolyte accumulates in that phase in which the pH requires that the ratio of ionized to un-ionized weak electrolyte is higher. The same considerations apply to a number of other weak electrolytes, not only weak bases such as ammonia but weak acids as well. Most of the substances the excretion of which has been shown to involve this type of mechanism are foreign to the body, but it is highly probable that a number of normal constituents are also involved although they have not been studied in detail. Some of those drugs which have been shown to be excreted by mechanisms involving processes of nonionic diffusion are: bases (quinine, atabrine, neutral red, mecamylamine) and acids (salicylates, phenobarbital). As opposed to the situation with respect to ammonia, which is produced in the tubule cells, the two phases of differing pH involved in excretion of these foreign materials are the urine and the peritubular interstitial space.

The effect of pH on the excretion of weak acids is exactly the opposite of its effect on that of weak bases. This is due to the fact that the ratio of ion to un-ionized fraction increases with pH in the case of weak acids, as indicated by the equation

$$pH = pK_A + \log \frac{[A^-]}{[HA]}$$

while in the case of weak bases the ratio of ionized to un-ionized decreases with rising pH as indicated by the dissociation equation for a base

$$pH = pK_A + \log \frac{[RNH_2]}{[RNH_3^+]}$$

The effect of pH on the excretion of weak bases is appreciable only when the pH of the urine is lower than the pK_A of the base, since it is only when pH is less than pK that the amount of ion is the major fraction of the total. For similar reasons pH change has an appreciable effect on acid excretion only when the urine pH is higher than the pK of the acid.

The bases and acids noted above as being excreted by mechanisms involving non-ionic diffusion are each secreted into the proximal tubule by active transport processes and escape to a variable extent, depending on urine pH, by non-ionic diffusion in the more distal segments of the nephron.

REFERENCES

ANDERSEN, B. AND USSING, H. H. Solvent drag on nonelectrolytes during osmotic flow through isolated toad skin and its response to antidiuretic hormone. Acta Physiol. scandinav., 1957, **39**, 228.

BERGER, E. Y., FARBER, S. J., AND EARLE, D. P., JR. Renal excretion of mannitol. Proc. Soc. Exper. Biol. & Med., 1947, **66**, 62.

BERLINER, R. W. Renal secretion of potassium and hydrogen ions. Fed. Proc., 1952, **11**, 695.

BERLINER, R. W. AND KENNEDY, T. J., JR. Renal tubular secretion of potassium in the normal dog. Proc. Soc. Exper. Biol. & Med., 1948, **67**, 542.

BERLINER, R. W., KENNEDY, T. J., JR., AND HILTON, J. G. Renal mechanisms for excretion of potassium. Am. J. Physiol., 1950, **162**, 348.

BERLINER, R. W., KENNEDY, T. J., JR., AND ORLOFF, J. Relationship between acidification of the urine and potassium metabolism. Effect of carbonic anhydrase inhibition on potassium excretion. Am. J. Med., 1951, **11**, 274.

BEYER, K. H., WRIGHT, L. D., SKEGGS, H. R., RUSSO, H. F., AND SHANER, G. A. Renal clearance of essential amino acids: their competition for reabsorption by the renal tubules. Am. J. Physiol., 1947, **151**, 202.

BRAZEAU, P., AND GILMAN, A. Effect of plasma CO_2 tension on renal tubular reabsorption of bicarbonate. Am. J. Physiol., 1953, **175**, 33.

CHASIS, H., RANGES, H. A., GOLDRING, W., AND SMITH, H. W. The control of renal blood flow and glomerular filtration in normal man. J. Clin. Invest., 1938, **17**, 683.

DAVIDSON, D. G., LEVINSKY, N. G., AND BERLINER, R. W. Maintenance of potassium excretion despite reduction of glomerular filtration during sodium diuresis, J. Clin. Invest., 1958, **37**, 548.

DAVIES, B. M. A., AND YUDKIN, J. Studies in biochemical adaptation. The origin of urinary ammonia as indicated by the effect of chronic acidosis and alkalosis on some renal enzymes in the rat. Biochem. J., 1952, **52**, 407.

DAVIS, J. O., HOWELL, D. S., AND SOUTHWORTH, J. L. Mechanisms of fluid and electrolyte retention in experimental preparations in dogs. III. Effect of adrenalectomy and subsequent desoxycorticosterone acetate administration on ascites formation. Circulation Res., 1953, 1, 260.

FINDLEY, T., JR. AND WHITE, H. L. The response of normal individuals and patients with diabetes insipidus to the ingestion of water. J. Clin. Invest., 1937, 16, 197.

GAMBLE, J. L., McKHANN, C. F., BUTLER, A. M., AND TUTHILL, E. An economy of water in renal function referable to urea. Am. J. Physiol., 1934, 109, 139.

GOMEZ, D. M. Evaluation of renal resistances, with special reference to changes in essential hypertension. J. Clin. Invest., 1951, 30, 1143.

GOTTSCHALK, C. W., AND MYLLE, M. Micropuncture study of the mammalian urinary concentrating mechanism: evidence for the countercurrent hypothesis. Am. J. Physiol., 1959, 196, 927.

GUTMAN, A. B., YU, T. F., AND BERGER, L. Tubular secretion of urate in man. J. Clin. Invest., 1959, 38, 1778.

HILGER, H. H., KLUMPER, J. D., AND ULLRICH, K. J. Wasserruckresorption und Ionentransport durch die Sammelrohrzellen der Saugetierniere. Arch. ges. Physiol., 1958, 267, 218.

HOBER, R. Effect of some sulfanilamides on renal secretion. Proc. Soc. Exper. Biol. & Med., 1942. 49, 87.

KANDEL, A. AND PETERS, L. Observations concerning the renal tubular transport characteristics of three quaternary bases in dogs. J. Pharmacol. & Exper. Therap., 1957, 119, 550.

KOEFOED-JOHNSEN, V. AND USSING, H. H. The nature of the frog skin potential. Acta Physiol. scandinav., 1958, 42, 298.

LEVINSKY, N. G. AND BERLINER, R. W. The role of urea in the urine concentrating mechanism. J. Clin. Invest., 1959, 38, 741.

LEVINSKY, N. G., DAVIDSON, D. G., AND BERLINER, R. W. Effects of reduced glomerular filtration on urine concentration in the presence of antidiuretic hormone, J. Clin. Invest., 1959, 38, 730.

LOTSPEICH, W. D. Renal tubular reabsorption of inorganic sulfate in the normal dog. Am. J. Physiol., 1947, 151, 311.

MARSHALL, E. K., JR. AND VICKERS, J. L. The mechanism of the elimination of phenolsulphonphthalein by the kidney; a proof of secretion by the convoluted tubules. Bull. Johns Hopkins Hosp., 1923, 34, 1.

MOLLER, E., McINTOSH, J. F., AND VAN SLYKE, D. D. Studies of urea excretion. II. Relationship between urine volume and the rate of urea excretion by normal adults. J. Clin. Invest., 1929, 6, 427.

MONTGOMERY, H. AND PIERCE. J. A. The site of acidification of the urine within the renal tubule in Amphibia. Am. J. Physiol., 1937, 118, 144.

MUDGE, G. H., AMES, A., FOULKS, J., AND GILMAN, A. Effect of drugs on renal excretion of potassium in the dog. Am. J. Physiol., 1950, 161, 151.

MUDGE, G. H., FOULKS, J., AND GILMAN, A. The renal excretion of potassium. Proc. Soc. Exper. Biol. & Med., 1948, 67, 545.

MUELLER, C. B., SURTSHIN, A., CARLIN, M. R., AND WHITE, H. L. Glomerular and tubular influences on sodium and water excretion. Am. J. Physiol., 1951, 165, 411.

NASH, T. P. AND BENEDICT, S. R. The ammonia content of the blood and its bearing on the mechanism of acid neutralization in the animal organism. J. Biol. Chem., 1921, 48, 463.

ORLOFF, J. AND BERLINER, R. W. The mechanism of the excretion of ammonia in the dog. J. Clin. Invest., 1956, 35, 223.

ORLOFF, J., KENNEDY, T. J., JR., AND BERLINER, R. W. The effect of potassium in nephrectomized rats with hypokalemic alkalosis. J. Clin. Invest., 1953, 32, 538.

PAPPENHEIMER, J. R., RENKIN, E. M., AND BORRERO, L. M. Filtration, diffusion and molecular sieving through peripheral capillary membranes. A contribution to the pore theory of capillary permeability. Am. J. Physiol., 1951, 167, 13.

PITTS, R. F. A comparison of the renal reabsorptive processes for several amino acids. Am. J. Physiol., 1944, 140, 535.

PITTS, R. F. AND ALEXANDER, R. S. The renal reabsorptive mechanism for inorganic phosphate in normal and acidotic dogs. Am. J. Physiol., 1944, 142, 648.

PITTS, R. F. AND ALEXANDER, R. S. The nature of the renal tubular mechanism for acidifying the urine. Am. J. Physiol., 1945, 144, 239.

PITTS, R. F. AND LOTSPEICH, W. D. Bicarbonate and the renal regulation of acid-base balance. Am. J. Physiol., 1946 147, 138.

PITTS, R. F., LOTSPEICH, W. D., SCHIESS, W. A., AND AYER, J. L. The renal regulation of acid-base balance in man. I. The nature of the mechanism for acidifying the urine. J. Clin. Invest., 1948, 27, 48.

RECTOR, F. C., JR. AND ORLOFF, J. The effect of the administration of sodium bicarbonate and ammonium chloride on the excretion and production of ammonia. The absence of alterations in the activity of renal ammonia-producing enzymes in the dog. J. Clin. Invest., 1959, 38, 366.

REHBERG, P. B. Studies on kidney function. I. The rate of filtration and reabsorption in the human kidney. Biochem. J., 1926, 20, 447.

RELMAN, A. S., ETSTEN, B., AND SCHWARTZ, W. B. The regulation of renal bicarbonate reabsorption by plasma carbon dioxide tension. J. Clin. Invest., 1953, 32, 972.

RICHARDS, A. N., BOTT, P. A., AND WESTFALL, B. B. Experiments concerning the possibility that inulin is secreted by the renal tubules. Am. J. Physiol., 1938, 123, 281.

RICHARDS, A. N. AND WALKER, A. M. Methods of collecting fluid from known regions of the renal tubules of Amphibia and of perfusing the lumen of a single tubule. Am. J. Physiol., 1936, 118, 111.

SARTORIUS, O. W., ROEMMELT, J. C., AND PITTS,

R. F. The renal regulation of acid-base balance in man. IV. The nature of the renal compensations in ammonium chloride acidosis, J. Clin. Invest., 1949, **28**, 423.

SAWYER, W. H. Increased renal reabsorption of osmotically free water by the toad (*Bufo marinus*) in response to neurohypophysial hormones. Am. J. Physiol., 1957, **189**, 564.

SHANNON, J. A. The excretion of inulin by the dog. Am. J. Physiol., 1935, **112**, 405.

SHANNON, J. A. Glomerular filtration and urea excretion in relation to urine flow in the dog. Am. J. Physiol., 1936, **117**, 206.

SHANNON, J. A. Urea excretion in the normal dog during forced diuresis. Am. J. Physiol., 1938, **122**, 782.

SHANNON, J. A. Renal tubular excretion. Physiol. Rev., 1939, **19**, 63.

SHANNON, J. A. AND FISHER, S. The renal tubular reabsorption of glucose in the normal dog. Am. J. Physiol., 1938, **122**, 765.

SHANNON, J. A. AND SMITH, H. W. The excretion of inulin, xylose, and urea by normal and phlorizinized man. J. Clin. Invest., 1935, **14**, 393.

SHIPLEY, R. E. AND STUDY, R. S. Changes in renal blood flow, extraction of inulin, glomerular filtration rate, tissue pressure and urine flow with acute alterations of renal artery blood pressure. Am. J. Physiol., 1951, **167**, 676.

SMITH, H. W. The physiology of the kidney. Oxford University Press, New York, 1937.

SMITH, H. W. Lectures on the kidney. University Extension Division, University of Kansas, Lawrence, Kansas, 1943.

SMITH, H. W. Renal excretion of sodium and water. Fed. Proc., 1952, **11**, 701.

SMITH, H. W., FINKELSTEIN, N., ALIMINOSA, L., CRAWFORD, B., AND GRABER, M. The renal clearances of substituted hippuric acid derivatives and other aromatic acids in dog and man. J. Clin. Invest., 1945, **24**, 388.

SMITH, H. W., GOLDRING, W., AND CHASIS, H. The measurement of the tubular excretory mass, effective blood flow, and filtration rate in the normal human kidney. J. Clin. Invest., 1938, **17**, 263.

SMITH, W. W., FINKELSTEIN, N. AND SMITH, H. W. Renal excretion of hexitols (sorbitol, mannitol, and dulcitol) and their derivatives (sorbitan, isomannide, and sorbide) and of endogenous creatinine-like chromogen in dog and man. J. Biol. Chem., 1940, **135**, 231.

SULLIVAN, W. J. AND DORMAN, P. J. The renal response to chronic respiratory acidosis, J. Clin. Invest., 1955, **34**, 268.

TAGGART, J. V. Tubular transport mechanisms. Am. J. Med., 1950, **9**, 678.

TAGGART, J. V. Mechanisms of renal tubular transport. Am. J. Med., 1958, **24**, 774.

THATCHER, J. S. AND RADIKE, A. W. Tolerance to potassium intoxication in the albino rat. Am. J. Physiol., 1947, **151**, 138.

ULLRICH, K. J., HILGER, H. H., AND KLUMPER, J. D. Sekretion von Ammoniumionen in den

Sammelrohren der Saugetierniere. Arch. ges. Physiol., 1958, **267**, 244.

USSING, H. H. The distinction by means of tracers between active transport and diffusion. The transfer of iodide across the isolated frog skin. Acta Physiol. scandinav., 1949, **19**, 43.

VAN SLYKE, D. D., PHILLIPS, R. A., HAMILTON, P. B., ARCHIBALD, R. M., FUTCHER, P. H., AND HILLER, A. Glutamine as source material of urinary ammonia. J. Biol. Chem., 1943, **150**, 481.

VERNEY, E. G. Antidiuretic hormone and the factors which determine its release. Proc. Roy. Soc. London, 1947, **B135**, 25.

WALKER, A. M. Comparisons of total molecular concentration of glomerular urine and blood plasma from the frog and from Necturus. J. Biol. Chem., 1930, **87**, 499.

WALKER, A. M., BOTT, P. A., OLIVER, J., AND MacDOWELL, M. C. The collection and analysis of fluid from single nephrons of the mammalian kidney. Am. J. Physiol., 1941, **134**, 580.

WALKER, A. M., HUDSON, C. L., FINDLEY, T., JR., AND RICHARDS, A. N. The total molecular concentration and the chloride concentration of fluid from different segments of the renal tubule of Amphibia: the site of chloride reabsorption. Am. J. Physiol., 1937, **118**, 121.

WALLENIUS, G. Renal clearance of dextran as a measure of glomerular permeability. Acta Societatis Medicorum Upsaliensis, 1954, Supplement 4 to Volume 59.

WESSON, L. G., JR. AND ANSLOW, W. P. Excretion of sodium and water during osmotic diuresis in the dog. Am. J. Physiol., 1948, **153**, 465.

WILBRANDT, W. Secretion and transport of nonelectrolytes. In Active Transport. SEB Symposia VIII, Academic Press, New York, 1954, p. 136.

WINDHAGER, E., WHITTEMBURY, G., OKEN, D. E., SCHATZMANN, H. J., AND SOLOMON, A. K. Single proximal tubules of the Necturus kidney. III. Dependence of H_2O movement on NaCl concentration. Am. J. Physiol., 1959, **197**, 313.

WIRZ, H. Der osmotische Druck in den corticalen Tubuli der Rattenniere. Helvet. Physiol. et Pharmacol. Acta, 1956, **14**, 353.

Monographs and Reviews

BERLINER, R. W. Renal mechanisms for potassium excretion. Harvey Lectures, 1961, Series 55, 141.

BERLINER, R. W., LEVINSKY, N. G., DAVIDSON, D. G., AND EDEN, M. Dilution and concentration of the urine and the action of antidiuretic hormone. Am. J. Med., 1958, **24**, 730.

CUSHNY, A. R. The secretion of urine. Longmans, Green Co., London, 1926.

GIEBISCH, G. AND WINDHAGER, E. E. Renal tubular transfer of sodium, chloride and potassium. Am. J. Med., 1964, **36**, 643.

GOTTSCHALK, C. W. Renal tubular function: Lessons from micropuncture. Harvey Lectures, 1963, Series 58, 99.

MARSHALL, E. K., JR. The comparative physiology of the kidney in relation to theories of renal secretion. Physiol. Rev., 1934, **14**, 133.

ORLOFF, J. The role of the kidney in the regulation of acid-base balance. Yale J. Biol. & Med., 1956, **29,** 211.

PITTS, R. F. Renal excretion of acid. Fed. Proc., 1948, **7,** 418.

PITTS, R. F. Some reflections on mechanisms of action of diuretics. Am. J. Med., 1958, **24,** 745.

RICHARDS, A. N. The Croonian Lecture: Processes of urine formation. Proc. Roy. Soc. London, 1938, **126,** 398.

SMITH, H. W. The kidney. Structure and function in health and disease. Oxford University Press, New York, 1951.

WEINER, I. M. AND MUDGE, G. H. Renal tubular mechanisms for excretion of organic acids and bases. Am. J. Med., 1964, **36,** 743.

CHAPTER 80

The Pathological Physiology of the Kidney. Micturition

The Clinical Evaluation of Renal Function

Examination of the Urine

The first step in the evaluation of the functional status of the kidney and frequently the source of the first clue to the presence of renal disease is usually the clinical pathological examination of the urine. This has the unique advantage of extreme simplicity, requiring only a minimum of time and the simplest of equipment. Furthermore, the presence of renal disease is usually manifested by some abnormality of the urine. However, it is important to note that an apparently normal urine does not exclude the presence of certain diseases of the kidney nor impairment of renal function of even very marked degree.

Although the full routine examination of the urine includes several other tests usually intended to detect nonrenal metabolic abnormalities (diabetes, ketosis, etc.), those particularly related to diseases of the kidney itself are tests for protein and examination of the urinary sediment. In addition, determination of the specific gravity and acidity may, under certain conditions, be revealing of disorders of kidney function. Certain specific defects of renal function may be detected by analysis of urine for amino acids.

Tests Involving Examination of the Blood Only

The most commonly used test intended to evaluate the functional state of the kidney is the determination of the blood urea. (The results of this determination are commonly reported as the blood urea nitrogen; since nitrogen makes up just under half of the molecular weight of urea, the blood urea concentration is approximately twice the concentration of blood urea nitrogen.) The concentration of urea in the blood is directly proportional to the nitrogen turnover and inversely proportional to the renal clearance of urea. Its relationship to the nitrogen turnover and to glomerular filtration are fully discussed in the preceding chapter.

Since the blood urea concentration is only partially related to the rate of glomerular filtration and to the functional status of the kidney, it is hardly surprising that there is a wide range of normal values for the blood urea concentration and it is likely to be unequivocally elevated only when renal function is reduced by about half or more.

Nonprotein nitrogen. Under normal conditions urea contributes about half of the nonprotein nitrogen of plasma (or serum). The remainder is made up of the nitrogen of a heterogeneous group of substances: creatine, creatinine, uric acid, amino acids, etc. As renal function is depressed the nonprotein nitrogen concentration of plasma rises, largely because of increasing urea concentration, though some of the other components also accumulate. The nonprotein nitrogen determination is thus subject to very much the same interpretation and qualifications as the blood urea analysis.

Creatinine. The plasma creatinine concentration is a somewhat more reliable index of renal function than the blood urea concentration because the rate of formation of creatinine in the body is much more stable than the formation of urea. However, some reservation is required because the usual analysis of plasma for creatinine involves a chemical method affected by other constituents of the plasma.

Tests Involving Collection of Urine

A general comment and caution concerning these tests as a group is warranted. These tests (except for the concentration test) involve determination of the rate of excretion of some substance. They thus require a *timed collection of urine* and can be no more accurate than the timing and completeness of collection. In the case of substances such as urea or creatinine which are normal constituents of the urine, the urine formed before the actual period of the test will contain the test substance and it is, therefore, just as important that the bladder be completely emptied at the start of the test period as that all of the urine be collected at the end. Failure to empty the bladder before the test period will give a result that is misleadingly high just as failure to empty at the conclusion of the test will give an erroneously low value. Failure to give due care and consideration to this point frequently vitiates the usefulness of what is fundamentally a valuable method for assessing kidney function.

Urea clearance. The mechanism of urea excretion has been considered in detail in the preceding chapter, and little need be added here. The test is useful for the information it gives concerning the level of glomerular filtration. In contradistinction to the simple determination of blood urea, the urea clearance is not dependent upon the rate of formation of urea so that this source of variation is eliminated. The urea clearance depends only upon the rate of glomerular filtration and the urine flow. When the test is carefully performed it is a very useful index of glomerular filtration rate.

Creatinine clearance. The clearance of endogenous creatinine is frequently a valuable index of glomerular filtration. As compared with the urea clearance it has the advantage of being unaffected by the rate of urine flow.[1] However, for reasons that have not been fully elucidated, the clearance of endogenous creatinine is sometimes considerably greater than the glomerular filtration rate and sometimes lower. This is particularly true in the presence of renal disease. The creatinine clearance can therefore be considered only a rough approximation of the rate of glomerular filtration.

Excretion of phenolsulfonphthalein (PSP, phenol red). Phenolsulfonphthalein (PSP) is one of that group of organic acids rapidly secreted into the urine by the renal tubules (see preceding chapter). In contrast to some of the other substances in this group, PSP is *not* completely removed from the blood which perfuses the kidney. Nevertheless, the rate at which it is excreted by the kidney is determined largely by the rate at which PSP is delivered to the kidney by the flow of blood. The excretion of PSP is, therefore, reduced when the renal blood flow is diminished. The greatest virtue of the test is its simplicity; PSP is a dye which, in alkaline solution, has an intense red color, and its concentration in the urine is easily estimated.

A number of different procedures for the performance of the PSP test have been used, involving various routes of administration of the dye and varying time periods for the collection of the urine. Procedures involving intravenous administration of the dye and relatively short periods for the collection of the urine are to be preferred as most sensitive to changes in kidney function. Low results can be obtained because of retention of PSP in the bladder as well as because of poor renal function.

Concentration test. The concentration test is a measure of the ability of the kidneys to form hypertonic urine. Because the test as usually performed involves determination of the urine specific gravity, it can be considered only a rather crude index of this particular function.[2] The determina-

tion of specific gravity is, however, such a simple procedure that it is unlikely that it will soon be replaced by an estimation of osmolality by the determination of the freezing point depression.

In the performance of the test, it is usual to determine the specific gravity of the urine formed after all fluids have been withheld for 10 to 24 hours. Normally the specific gravity should be greater than 1.025 although a specific gravity between 1.020 and 1.025 can not be interpreted as a clear indication of abnormality.

Clearances of inulin and p-aminohippurate. Properly performed these measurements yield accurate estimates of glomerular filtration rate and renal blood flow and hence are highly valuable in accurately defining the status of renal function. The theoretical basis of the measurements is discussed in the preceding chapter. Unfortunately the determination of inulin and p-aminohippurate clearances requires the administration of continuous intravenous infusions at constant rate. The desired and attainable accuracy can be achieved only with meticulous care in the collection of the urine, usually with bladder catheterization and washout of the bladder at the termination of each collection period. Finally, the chemical analysis, particularly that for inulin, is relatively involved. For these reasons these tests are rarely used for routine clinical purposes; for most such situations one or more of the approximation procedures discussed above will suffice.

Measurement of Tubular Reabsorptive and Secretory Capacity

These indices of renal function determined, respectively, as the maximum capacity to reabsorb glucose (Tm_G) and to secrete p-aminohippurate (Tm_{PAH}) are, like the measurement of inulin and PAH clearances, more or less definitive measurements of renal function (see preceding chapter). Like the latter determinations, the procedures are involved, poorly suited to routine use, and rarely performed for purely clinical purposes.

Disturbances of Renal Function

CLASSIFICATION

Disturbances of renal function may be separated into two groups—those due to disease of the kidney itself and those due to nonrenal disturbances. In the latter group fall abnormalities of renal function due to circulatory disorders and to disturbed hormonal balance with loss or excess of endocrine factors which modify the function of the kidney. Among disturbances due to disease of the kidney itself two groups may be recognized: (1) disorders due to specific abnormalities of one or more of the transport mechanisms of the renal tubule; although these are particularly interesting

---

[1] However, as in any test involving the collection of urine, the *errors* due to incomplete or inaccurate collection of the urine are minimized if the rate of flow is high.

[2] In the formation of hypertonic urine the nature of the urinary solute is more or less a matter of indifference, the process being involved with modifying the urine osmotic pressure to which each solute particle, independent of its nature, contributes equally. However, each solute particle does not modify the specific gravity in the same way; one molal solutions of different solutes may vary widely in specific gravity.

from the point of view of clinicophysiological correlations, they are neither as frequent nor as important as (2) the inflammatory and degenerative diseases which involve the kidney more diffusely, affecting entire nephrons or nephron segments and their functions.

In the group of diseases which produce such diffuse involvement of the kidney, a few warrant brief discussion here to provide a background for some of the correlations between disturbances of physiology and renal disease. By far the most important of these from the standpoint of frequency of occurrence are glomerulonephritis, arteriolar nephrosclerosis, and pyelonephritis.

Glomerulonephritis

Glomerulonephritis is a diffuse inflammatory disease involving primarily the glomeruli and secondarily, with loss of glomerular function, degeneration of the conjoined tubules. A number of classifications of glomerulonephritis, based largely on pathological distinction, have been proposed and a number of variants are recognized by some workers. For present purposes it is sufficient to note that glomerulonephritis can be divided into two forms which may or may not represent different stages of the same disease.

ACUTE GLOMERULONEPHRITIS is characterized by a more or less sudden onset with proteinuria and hematuria, and varying degrees of edema, hypertension and renal insufficiency. The onset of the disease can usually be related to an antecedent infection most often with Group A, β-hemolytic streptococcus. Glomerulonephritis is generally believed to be a disease involving, in some still obscure fashion, an antigen-antibody reaction which produces damage to the glomerular capillaries. Acute glomerulonephritis has a relatively low mortality. The great majority of cases recover completely, with no residual evidence of renal disease or of significant functional loss. A small proportion do not recover, but show persisting evidence of active renal disease and progressive loss of renal function with an eventually fatal outcome.

CHRONIC GLOMERULONEPHRITIS is a progressive disease characterized by proteinuria, hypertension and diminution of renal function. Whether or not it is the progressive form of the same disease recognized as acute glomerulonephritis is disputed. In most patients with the chronic form no episode of acute glomerulonephritis is recognized. The rate of progress of the disease is extremely variable; some patients have a rapid downhill course with a precipitous decline in renal func-

tion. Others may, for years, have proteinuria as the only evidence of smoldering disease.

The Nephrotic Syndrome

The nephrotic syndrome is characterized by massive proteinuria leading to a marked reduction of the plasma protein (particularly albumin) concentration, with edema, frequently massive, and generally a marked increase in the concentration of lipids, particularly cholesterol, in the plasma. Hematuria and hypertension are usually not prominent. A small proportion of instances of the nephrotic syndrome are clearly due to recognizable causes such as *amyloidosis* of the kidney, *lupus erythematosus, syphilis,* etc., but in most cases the underlying cause is not recognizable. No unanimity exists as to whether or not the idiopathic nephrotic syndrome represents a stage of chronic glomerulonephritis. A certain number of patients with the nephrotic syndrome do not recover, but show progressive loss of renal function with the development of hypertension and renal insufficiency in a fashion not distinguishable from chronic glomerulonephritis. On the other hand, with antibiotic treatment and prevention of intercurrent infection and with control of the disease with adrenocortical steroids, a considerable proportion of patients with the idiopathic nephrotic syndrome recover completely.

Whereas it was formerly believed that in true nephrosis the glomeruli were normal and the disease limited to degenerative changes in the tubule epithelium, this is now recognized as being the exact reverse of the true situation. The primary defect is in the capillary basement membrane, permitting the escape of protein into the glomerular filtrate. The striking changes in the appearance of the tubule cells on microscopic examination are probably secondary to the high concentration of protein in the glomerular filtrate with protein uptake from the tubule lumen.

Arteriolar Nephrosclerosis

Arteriolar nephrosclerosis is the manifestation of renal damage due to hypertension. It is characterized by thickening and hyalinization and sometimes necrosis of the renal arterioles. There is progressive loss of glomeruli and the function of the tubules to which they are attached. Clinically it is characterized by proteinuria and progressive impairment of renal function which in some instances ("malignant nephrosclerosis") may be remarkably rapid. Some degree of nephrosclerosis occurs in most cases of hypertension of long standing. The progressive form leading to renal insufficiency occurs in some five to ten per cent of patients with so-called "essential" hypertension.

In contrast to the diffuse involvement of the kidney in *arteriolar*sclerosis (arteriolar nephrosclerosis) *arterio*sclerotic involvement of the larger vessels may lead to patchy ischemic degeneration of portions of the kidney. This type of involvement is relatively benign and rarely leads to significant functional disturbance.

Pyelonephritis

Pyelonephritis is an inflammatory disease of the kidney resulting from infection of the urinary tract (pelvis) with invasion of the kidney interstitium. Single acute attacks may subside without significant sequelae, but repeated or longstanding infections lead to scarring and contraction of the kidney and what may be extensive loss of renal tissue. The loss of renal function may be accelerated as changes due to hypertension (itself initiated by the chronic pyelonephritis) are superimposed on the results of infection and scarring. Proteinuria is usually not prominent and may be absent.

DISTURBANCES OF FUNCTION IN DIFFUSE RENAL DISEASE

PROTEINURIA (ALBUMINURIA). Perhaps the commonest manifestation of renal disease is the presence of increased amounts of protein in the urine. Normally only traces of protein are present in the urine, less than 100 mg. being excreted in a 24-hour period. In the presence of renal disease the amounts excreted may vary widely and reach figures of many grams. Whereas protein may gain access to the urine with exudation or bleeding into any part of the urinary tract, the glomeruli are the most pertinent source of urinary protein. Among the proteins of the urine albumin predominates, but despite the fact that urinary protein is frequently referred to as albumin, the other plasma proteins are also represented. However, it is true that the relative abundance of albumin is greater in the urine than the plasma.

An increased concentration of protein in the glomerular filtrate, the result of an abnormal increase in the permeability of the glomerular capillaries to plasma protein, is generally accepted as the cause of proteinuria in most instances of renal disease and is one of the major features of the nephrotic syndrome, of glomerulonephritis and of arteriolar nephrosclerosis.

It is worth noting that decreased reabsorption of normally filtered protein has been seriously considered as a possibly significant factor in producing proteinuria. This possibility is based on the uncertainty concerning the amount of protein normally contained in the glomerular filtrate in man. At a concentration of only 10 mg per cent, some 18 grams/day might be excreted in the urine if none were reabsorbed. It may be dangerous to assume that the concentration in human glomerular filtrate is the same as that in the dog but it is worth noting that recent micropuncture studies in the dog revealed albumin concentrations in the proximal tubule averaging less than 5 mg per cent.

On the other hand, there is good evidence not only that there is an increased filtration of protein in the presence of proteinuria but that there is also an increase in the reabsorption of protein by the tubules under these conditions and that, in all probability, it is this increased protein uptake that is responsible for the histological changes in renal tubule cells in such disorders as the nephrotic syndrome.

Aside from its importance as a clue to the presence of renal disease, proteinuria may, when of sufficient intensity, lead to significant depletion of the plasma proteins. In the nephrotic syndrome largely as a result of urinary losses, the plasma albumin concentration may be reduced to 20 per cent or less of its normal value. This is a significant factor in the development of nephrotic edema.

The presence of proteinuria is not always a sign of significant organic disease of the kidney. It may be produced in otherwise normal individuals, for example, by fever or by violent exercise. Particularly likely to be misleading is the benign condition known as *orthostatic albuminuria* or *postural proteinuria*. This is characterized by the occurrence, especially in young people, of proteinuria when the individual assumes the upright position. The urine, after a night's rest in bed, is protein free. The production of proteinuria is presumably attributable to some sort of circulatory disturbance associated with the erect posture. It is important chiefly because it is frequently mistakenly interpreted as indicating the presence of latent glomerulonephritis.

CYLINDRURIA. *Casts* are collections of protein which has precipitated in the tubules or ducts of the kidney and has been molded in the form of the structure in which it was precipitated. Cylindruria or the presence of increased number of casts in the urine is commonly associated with proteinuria of glomerular origin. Aside from the diagnostic information derivable from the nature of the casts, the detection of casts is most significant as an indication that the protein in the urine has arisen from the nephrons. The casts may consist of protein only (hyaline casts) or may have incorporated into them red or white blood cells, epithelial cells, etc. The normal urine does not contain more than 2000 casts per 24 hours.

HEMATURIA. Red blood cells may be present in the urine in increased numbers (normal: less than 130,000 per 24 hours) because of bleeding anywhere into the urinary tract. Of greatest importance in the present context is that, with inflammatory disease of the glomeruli, red cells as well as protein may penetrate the glomerular capillaries. Marked hematuria is particularly characteristic of acute glomerulonephritis.

IMPAIRMENT OF URINARY CONCENTRATION, POLYURIA, NOCTURIA. Two types of impairment of urine concentrating capacity are recognizable: (1) due to impairment of the process by which water is removed to produce urine hypertonic to plasma and (2) due to the excretion of increased amounts of solute per functioning nephron. Both types of defect contribute to the impairment of urine concentrating power observed in the presence of renal disease. Specific defects in the process which renders the urine hypertonic are present in *potassium depletion* and *hypercalciuria*. Since the processes responsible for rendering the urine more concentrated than plasma are located in the renal medulla, disease which disrupts the structure and/or function of this portion of the kidney, such as pyelonephritis and hydronephrosis, may be expected to have particularly marked effects on the concentrating process.

On the other hand, as renal function becomes progressively impaired by any nephron-destroying disease process, impaired ability to produce concentrated urine must inevitably result. Indeed, it has been shown experimentally that removal of one kidney and part of the other results in impaired ability of the remaining kidney to produce concentrated urine. The situation here is quite analogous to that observed as solute excretion is markedly increased (osmotic diuresis) in the individual with normal kidneys (see previous chapter, fig. 79.9b). As renal function becomes progressively diminished, the rate of excretion of solute must, over the long run, remain essentially unchanged reflecting the maintenance of salt balance and the excretion of products of metabolism. However, as the number of nephrons involved in urine formation becomes smaller, the amount of solute excreted by each of those remaining becomes greater in proportion. Thus the volume of

isotonic fluid in each nephron reaching the site of formation of hypertonic urine is increased and even the removal of a normal amount of water changes the concentration only to a limited extent.

As the ability to form concentrated urine is impaired, the volume of urine excreted must increase. The formation of increased volumes of urine is known as *polyuria*, a common manifestation of impaired renal function. The production of excessive amounts of urine may cause the patient to awake at night to void, a symptom designated as *nocturia*. (Of course, the ingestion of large volumes of fluid may lead to polyuria and nocturia in the absence of renal disease.)

OLIGURIA, ANURIA. Oliguria is the excretion of a markedly reduced volume of urine; anuria is the complete suppression of urine formation. Oliguria may, at times, be physiological—that is, a normal response to dehydration and the characteristic manifestation of the formation of highly concentrated urine. A particularly low urine flow is found when dehydration is accompanied by a low rate of solute excretion. This combination is likely to be encountered in the individual who is excreting very little salt because of a low salt intake, because of antecedent salt loss (sweating, diarrhea, vomiting, induced diuresis) or because salt excretion is suppressed for other reasons as in the individual who is developing edema (see discussion of edema).

On the other hand, oliguria or its extreme, anuria, may be a manifestation of a severe disorder of renal function. It may occur as a complication of severe acute nephritis or as a terminal event in chronic glomerulonephritis or other chronic renal disease. Most often, however, anuria or severe oliguria is a manifestation of some acute renal insult—a circumstance commonly known as *acute renal insufficiency* or *acute renal failure*. Such severe acute damage may be produced by a variety of injuries and nephrotoxic substances, particularly with traumatic shock (in which circumstance it has been called the *crush syndrome*), hemorrhagic shock, incompatible blood transfusion, and mercury or carbon tetrachloride poisoning. This list is far from inclusive, and acute renal insufficiency may be caused by any condition which produces prolonged hypotension and/or intense renal vasoconstriction. Renal ischemia seems a major factor in the production of acute renal insufficiency in those situations in which chemical nephrotoxins can not be implicated.

The methods by which glomerular filtration is

measured are not applicable in the presence of anuria, so that it is not possible to say with certainty whether, in acute renal failure, glomerular filtration ceases, or whether it continues but that complete reabsorption of the filtered fluid occurs through disrupted tubule walls. Both theories have their supporters. In either case, it is clear, *effective* glomerular filtration is zero.

It has also been proposed that in the anuria following trauma the renal blood flow is not reduced, but actually increased, the blood being shunted away from the cortex and through the juxtamedullary and medullary regions by dilation in the latter areas. This concept has been largely discredited. In the presence of anuria there is a marked reduction in the renal blood flow. The preferential injection of the juxtamedullary circulation which can be demonstrated under these conditions (Trueta) is due to the lesser involvement of this part of the renal circulation in the generally intense renal vasoconstriction.

EDEMA. The accumulation of sufficient excess of extracellular fluid to produce detectable swelling of distensible tissues (edema) is a common feature of many renal diseases. Since edema fluid is extracellular fluid, it has the composition of plasma except for its lower protein concentration. Like plasma, then, its major constituents are sodium chloride and water. Except for localized and limited amounts of edema which can be produced by redistribution of the normal volume of extracellular fluid, the production of edema requires that an excess of both salt and water be retained within the body and, conversely, edema may be produced by any circumstance which yields a sufficient increase of the salt and water content of the body. Actually in the production of edema, it is the salt retention which is primary, water being retained to maintain the normal osmotic pressure of body fluids, and, further, in the salt, it is specifically the sodium ion which plays the predominant role; in the edematous individual, edema is increased by sodium bicarbonate (or, of course, sodium chloride) but not by ammonium or potassium chloride.

In patients with renal disease, edema may be traced to three types of disturbance: (1) to impairment of sodium excretion due to the direct effect of disease on renal processes involved in salt excretion, (2) to hypoproteinemia, and (3) to cardiac insufficiency, a common complication of renal disease particularly in the presence of long-standing hypertension.

The edema of acute glomerulonephritis is primarily of the first type, due to the effect of disease on the renal processes involved in salt excretion; salt intake exceeds the capacity of the kidney to excrete it, and edema results. The predominant mechanism is probably a sudden and sharp reduction in the rate of glomerular filtration without an equivalent impairment of the capacity of the tubules to reabsorb sodium salts, a condition frequently called "glomerulotubular imbalance." Through much of the course of chronic glomerulonephritis, a new balance is struck so that, despite reduction of the rate of glomerular filtration, sodium reabsorption by the tubules is reduced to an equivalent extent, and adequate excretion of salt is maintained. In the course of chronic glomerulonephritis, edema may appear as a result of any of the mechanisms noted above, because of the development of hypoproteinemia or, particularly late in the course of the disease, because glomerular filtration is reduced to such low levels that it is no longer possible to maintain more than a very low rate of salt excretion and finally because cardiac insufficiency may be superimposed.

In acute renal insufficiency the capacity to excrete salt may be entirely lost. Thus any salt and fluid intake is retained in the form of edema, except to the extent to which they may be lost by extrarenal routes. This situation represents the extreme of edema formation due to impairment of the renal processes for salt excretion.

The classic example of edema resulting primarily from hypoproteinemia is that which characterizes the nephrotic syndrome. In this disorder the continuous loss of large amounts of protein, particularly albumin, in the urine taxes the capacity of the body mechanisms to synthesize albumin and the plasma protein concentration falls. As the plasma protein concentration is reduced, the colloid osmotic pressure is lowered, particularly since most of the colloid osmotic pressure of plasma is normally attributable to its albumin concentration. The lowering of the plasma colloid osmotic pressure favors redistribution of fluid volume from plasma to interstitial space in accord with the Starling hypothesis (see ch. 24). It is important to note that although this series of events favors expansion of the interstitial fluid volume at the expense of the intravascular volume, no significant quantity of edema can be attributed to this series of events *alone*; the intravascular volume is not large enough to yield a significant volume of edema without disastrously compromising the circulation. The production of hypoproteinemic edema, then, requires, as does all edema formation, retention of excess salt and water. The reduced intravascular volume favored by the reduction of colloid osmotic pressure is, in all probability, the stimulus for renal salt retention mediated in part by the secretion of salt retention steroid (aldosterone) by the adrenal cortex and, probably to a major extent, by the as yet poorly understood system which controls the reabsorption of salt in the proximal convoluted tubule. A low rate of glomerular filtration may be a contributory factor.

That hypoproteinemia alone is not a sufficient cause of edema in the nephrotic syndrome is indicated by the results of steroid treatment in this disorder. When fully successful, treatment with large doses of adrenocortical steroids produces disappearance of proteinuria, restoration of the plasma protein concentration, and diuresis with disappearance of the edema. However, in a number of instances in which the steroid is without apparent effect on proteinuria or plasma protein concentration, withdrawal of steroid therapy is accompanied by diuresis and loss of the edema, although the plasma protein concentration remains at its previous low level. Spontaneous diuresis without increase of the plasma protein concentration may also occur.

The edema of cardiac failure, whether a complication of renal disease (hypertension) or not, depends on renal retention of excess salt. Thus, edema of any origin is a manifestation of disordered kidney function, in the case of heart failure secondary to an abnormality of cardiac function. Although the sequence of events leading to edema in heart failure is disputed, the salt retention which occurs is the result of a complex of factors including: increased secretion of salt-active adrenocortical steroids, some reduction of renal blood flow and glomerular filtration in many instances and, almost certainly, the poorly understood factor or factors mentioned above. The latter is manifested by the following observations: The administration of salt-active steroids to normal experimental animals leads to only very little retention of sodium (much of which replaces potassium which is lost) and no edema. If, however, because of borderline cardiac insufficiency or elevation of venous pressure in a major segment of the circulation, the experimental animal is prone to the development of edema, sodium will be retained and edema will form—without reduction of the rate of glomerular filtration. The difference between edema formation and no edema formation in these two experimental situations is neither in glomerular filtration nor the amount of adrenocortical steroid

administered indicating involvement of the additional unidentified factors.

ACIDOSIS. Inability to maintain a normal level of plasma bicarbonate (alkali reserve) in the face of an acidifying intake is a common feature of advanced renal disease of any type. The most important factor responsible for the acidosis is deficient ability to form and excrete ammonia and thus maintain the plasma bicarbonate concentration in the face of the acid load provided by the acidifying components of the normal diet. Usually there is no defect in the ability of the kidney to render the urine acid and highly acid urines are frequently observed in even the most advanced renal failure. Since there is no major change in the excretion of weak acids, the output of titratable acid is not depressed. However, the reduced number of nephrons is not adequate to form and put out ammonia at a normal rate in the face of even the usual, much less any increased, demands. Thus the strong acids derived from dietary sources are excreted as the sodium or potassium, rather than the ammonium salt and the blood bicarbonate (alkali reserve) is depleted. In some cases an additional factor may contribute to the acidosis in the form of a deficient ability to reabsorb bicarbonate completely when the plasma bicarbonate concentration is at normal or only slightly lowered levels.

If bicarbonate is added to render the intake effectively neutral, the acidosis of renal failure may be absent. In fact, if bicarbonate intake is much more than that necessary for a neutral intake, alkalosis may be relatively easily produced since the capacity to excrete bicarbonate at a rapid rate is limited as a consequence of the reduction of the rate of glomerular filtration.

As opposed to the tendency to the development of acidosis which is almost universal in advanced renal disease of any type, acidosis of renal origin may occur as the result of a more or less specific defect of renal function with renal function remaining relatively intact in other respects. This relatively uncommon condition is known as *renal tubular acidosis*. In contrast to the acidosis of renal insufficiency it appears to be due specifically to an inability to render the urine normally acid and not to a deficient capacity to form ammonia. In some such cases the maximum capacity to secrete hydrogen ion in exchange for sodium can be shown to be normal, since there is a normal maximum rate of bicarbonate reabsorption when bicarbonate is administered. Under these conditions the urine is alkaline and the secretion of hydrogen ion which effects bicarbonate reabsorption occurs against only a very limited concentration gradient (see ch. 79, p. 1682 ff). However, as the bicarbonate concentration is reduced to normal or below, the tubules are unable to effect the complete removal of bicarbonate, this requiring that the urine be rendered highly acid. Hence bicarbonate escapes in the urine. The defect appears to be in the ability to secrete hydrogen ion against any considerable concentration gradient. Since the urine does not become acid, the excretion of ammonia remains low despite what is probably a normal ability to produce ammonia in the renal tubules (see p. 1693).

RENAL INSUFFICIENCY; UREMIA. Renal insufficiency is the general term for reduction of the function of the kidney. It is manifested by many of those physiological disturbances already described—impaired concentrating capacity, polyuria, nocturia, acidosis and a general loss of flexibility in the maintenance of normal body composition in the face of the stress of departure of the intake from ideal. *Uremia* is the complex of symptoms and signs which accompany advanced renal insufficiency. It is characterized by anemia, nausea, vomiting, weakness, twitching, frequently convulsions and terminally stupor and coma. Although it derives its name from the elevated blood urea concentration which is a universal finding in the presence of the syndrome, the urea retention is not primarily responsible for the symptoms.

That urea itself is not responsible for the abnormalities associated with uremia is shown by several observations. Urea may be administered to normal individuals without producing significant disturbances. In the uremic individual, the blood urea can be considerably reduced by restriction of the protein intake without otherwise affecting the course of the disorder. The improvement which can be produced in the uremic patient by dialysis with the "artificial kidney" is not lost when urea is included in the dialysis bath so that the blood urea is not removed by the dialysis.

Disturbances of acid-base balance and fluid and electrolyte metabolism are also commonly present in uremia, and may, at times, contribute to or be responsible for certain of the symptoms. Nevertheless, these electrolyte imbalances can not be considered to be the major contributor to the picture of uremia, and the factor or factors primarily responsible for the symptoms and signs remains unidentified. It is generally believed that toxic products of metabolism may, in the presence of depressed renal function, accumulate in the body fluids till toxic concentrations are reached.

These substances, if they exist, have never been adequately identified.

Intrinsic Defects of Renal Tubular Function

As opposed to the disturbances of renal function attributable to diffuse inflammatory or degenerative kidney disease, there are a number of abnormalities due to deficiency of certain transport mechanisms or groups of transport mechanisms. Many of these defects are familial or congenital though some may be acquired. They are for the most part uncommon, but warrant brief mention because of their unusual physiological interest.

One such defect, *renal tubular acidosis*, has been mentioned above and the impairment of sodium-hydrogen ion exchange described. The disorder is, at least in some instances, familial. It is frequently associated with nephrocalcinosis and pyelonephritis, but these are quite probably secondary rather than the cause of the renal abnormality.

NEPHROGENIC DIABETES INSIPIDUS is a rare congenital familial disorder most often encountered in males and characterized by the continuous obligatory excretion of dilute urine, and consequently intense polyuria and secondarily polydipsia. The abnormality is apparently due to inability of the distal portions of the renal tubules to respond to pituitary antidiuretic hormone by a decrease in the permeability to water. Thus the urine, diluted by salt removal in the distal portions of the nephron, fails to give up the excess of water in the tubules, and the water is lost in the urine. True or *pituitary diabetes insipidus* is characterized by the same symptoms and signs but is due to a lack of antidiuretic hormone secretion. The tubules are normally responsive to antidiuretic hormone in this disorder which is much more frequent than the nephrogenic type. Pituitary diabetes insipidus is usually an acquired abnormality secondary to injury to the pituitary and/or hypothalamus.

RENAL GLYCOSURIA is characterized by the excretion of glucose in the urine when the concentration in the plasma is normal or low. The abnormality is a defect in the mechanism by which glucose is reabsorbed in the proximal tubule; other proximal tubule functions may be normal. The specific nature of the derangement is not known. There is some depression of the maximum capacity to reabsorb glucose (Tm_G), but there is also considerable excretion of glucose when the concentration is below that required to saturate the reabsorptive mechanism. The possible interpretations of this "splay in the titration curve" are discussed on pages 1673 to 1675 of the preceding chapter.

RENAL HYPOPHOSPHATEMIA (or Vitamin D resistant rickets) is a familial disorder characterized by excretion of phosphate in the urine when the plasma concentration is low. It is attributable to a defect of the phosphate reabsorptive mechanism analogous to that for glucose in renal glycosuria.

AMINO-ACIDURIA. Defects of amino acid reabsorption occur as specific defects of certain transport mechanisms and as part of more generalized disorders of renal tubular function. An example of the specific type is that known as *essential cystinuria* in which the abnormality is limited to diminished reabsorption of cystine, lysine, arginine and ornithine. The chief hazard derives from the formation of stones from the poorly soluble cystine. Abnormalities involving certain other specific amino acids or groups of amino acids are also known. In addition defects of amino acid reabsorption may occur in several other disorders including, among others, Wilson's disease (fundamentally a disturbance of copper metabolism), heavy metal poisoning, and the Fanconi syndrome in which amino-aciduria is associated with defective reabsorption of glucose and phosphate and sometimes with renal tubular acidosis.

DISTURBANCES OF RENAL FUNCTION OF EXTRARENAL ORIGIN

The function of the kidney is dependent, for the maintenance of glomerular filtration, on the adequacy of the circulation. The effect of shock, leading as it may to sustained damage to the kidney, has already been discussed. In addition several of the renal transport systems for electrolytes and water are regulated by the activity of endocrine organs. The function of these systems is therefore subject to disturbance through abnormal activity of the endocrine organs in the form of either deficient or excessive secretion of hormones acting on the kidney. Two such abnormalities have already been described in relation to intrinsic renal disorders which they resemble or to which they are related.

1. *Pituitary diabetes insipidus* in which, because of deficiency of antidiuretic hormone secretion, renal water reabsorption is diminished and a dilute urine is continuously formed. The converse of this disorder may occur and a concentrated urine be formed when a reduced osmotic pressure of body fluids would ordinarily lead to the formation of dilute urine; most often this is due to the induction of antidiuretic hormone secretion by non-osmotic stimuli.

2. The excessive reabsorption of salt which characterizes *edema formation* and the contribution of hypersecretion of aldosterone have been discussed in relation to edema. Excessive secretion of aldosterone leads to accumulation of edema only in the presence of factors predisposing to edema formation. In the absence of such factors, the increased sodium reabsorption is limited, and the major manifestation of hypersecretion of aldosterone is *potassium loss* resulting from stimulation of secretion of potassium ion in exchange for reabsorbed sodium. If potassium loss due to intrinsic renal disease with defective potassium reabsorption exists, it has not been demonstrated, and excessive renal potassium excretion appears to be due to excessive secretion of potassium by the renal tubules generally stimulated by excess adrenocortical hormone.

In the absence of adrenocortical hormones (*adrenal insufficiency*, Addison's disease) reabsorption of sodium and secretion of potassium by the renal tubules are defective. Sodium loss in the urine proceeds despite contraction of the extracellular fluid volume, which may become markedly reduced. The potassium concentration of body fluids becomes elevated. Abnormal loss of sodium in the urine despite sodium depletion may occasionally result from renal disease, and may be produced by inhibitors of sodium reabsorption (diuretics).

The reabsorption of phosphate by the renal tubules is regulated by parathyroid hormone. Excessive secretion of parathyroid hormone (*hyperparathyroidism*) is associated with loss of phosphate in the urine; loss of parathyroid function (*hypoparathyroidism*) leads to elevation of the plasma phosphate concentration without an equivalent increase in urinary excretion.

The Urinary Bladder

ANATOMIC CONSIDERATIONS

Urine leaving the tips of the renal papillae passes through three functionally distinct divisions of the urinary tract in its course to the exterior. The first of these, termed the upper urinary tract, is made up of the minor and major calyces of the two kidneys, the renal pelves, and the ureters. It functions as a low-pressure, actively propulsive conduit with a small, fixed capacity, transmitting urine rapidly to the urinary bladder by peristaltic wave motion. The second division, the urinary bladder, acts as a reservoir, storing urine at low pressures and periodically discharging it at much higher pressures. The third division, comprising the male urethra below the urogenital diaphragm, serves as a passive conduit for the urinary stream and, except for the intrinsic resistance offered to the flow of fluid, plays no part in the mechanics of voiding. This structure has no homologue in the female, a fact which underscores its role as an essential male genital organ, associated anatomically rather than functionally with the urinary tract.

Several valves located in relation to the urinary bladder control the direction and flow of urine during its filling and emptying phases. Between the bladder and ureters, the uretero-vesical junctions prevent reflux of urine into the upper urinary tracts. At the internal urethral orifice, the bladder neck (comprising the prostatic urethra in males and the entire urethra in females) maintains urinary continence. In males, a striated muscular sphincter rests between the layers of the urogenital diaphragm at the distal end of the prostatic urethra, surrounding the membranous urethra. Known as the external sphincter (sphincter urethrae membranacae), and under voluntary control, it can abruptly stop the voiding stream once initiated. This structure is far less well developed in females, and its function is, therefore, less well performed in that sex.

The entire urinary tract is lined by transitional epithelium as far distally as the membranous urethra. This epithelium, 5 to 7 cells thick when the urinary organs are empty, rests on a fibro-elastic lamina propria which is commonly but incorrectly designated the submucosa. (A muscularis mucosae is not present in the urinary system, and, therefore, a true submucous coat which by definition lies deep to this muscular layer cannot be present. The term "submucosa" will nevertheless be retained, since it is honoured by long and extensive usage.) Transitional cells have the ability to slide over one another, thereby increasing their surface area at the expense of the thickness of the cell layer without breaking the continuity of the epithelium. Deep mucosal folds or rugae are present in the collapsed ureter and bladder, which, together with the unique properties of the epithelial coat, permit the considerable dilatation which these structures undergo in the course of urine transportation and storage. The submucosa rests on a smooth muscle coat, the muscularis, and is in turn surrounded by a loose areolar adventitia which in no way limits distensibility.

Anatomic adaptation to function resides chiefly in the muscularis of the urinary tract. It was formerly believed that the smooth muscle of the upper tract and bladder was disposed in three layers of unvarying thickness, an inner longitudinal, a middle circular, and an outer longitudinal. This concept is not supported by anatomic microdissections, and fails to explain the pattern of motility of these organs. The muscularis of the upper urinary tract is now believed to be arranged as interlacing bands of smooth muscle fibres, spiralling in both a clockwise and counter-clockwise direction from the necks of the minor calyces to the trigone of the bladder. In the calyces and renal pelvis, the majority of spirals have a shallow angle of ascent, and the majority of the muscle in this area appears circular. Near the uretero-pelvic junction and in the upper few centimeters of the ureter, the spirals wind much less sharply and the muscle bundles appear predominantly longitudinal. The major length of the ureter is again supported mainly by tightly wound spirals with only a few longitudinally arranged bundles, but, in the lowermost portion of the ureter, where it passes through the bladder wall, the muscular spirals disappear and the intramural ureter is surrounded only by a thin coat of entirely longitudinal muscle. These fibres are continued beyond the ureteral orifices, where they fan out and mingle with their opposite numbers to form the bulk of the trigonal muscle.

The individual smooth muscle cells of the upper urinary tract are linked by intercellular bridges, forming a syncytium capable of conducting an action potential without the necessity of extrinsic nervous mechanisms. The force and direction of the resulting muscular contraction depends on the predominant directional arrangement of the muscle bundles at any given level.

The lower ends of the ureters enter the postero-lateral angles of the bladder wall and, pursuing an oblique course, first through an hiatus in the vesical muscle, and then within the vesical submucosa, terminate in orifices at the lateral angles of the trigone. The total length of ureter enclosed by the bladder in the adult is approximately 2 cm., with an average diameter of 3.5 mm. Terminally, the ureter is anchored firmly to the trigone by continuation of its longitudinal muscular coat, and by fusion of its roof with the mucous membrane of the bladder. Where it passes through the ureteral hiatus, however, there is only the loosest of areolar connections between vesical and ureteral muscle, in order that the bladder may "slide up" around the ureter as it fills with urine. There is thus no anatomic basis of a circular muscular sphincter in this area, known as the uretero-vesical junction, which might prevent reflux of urine from the bladder

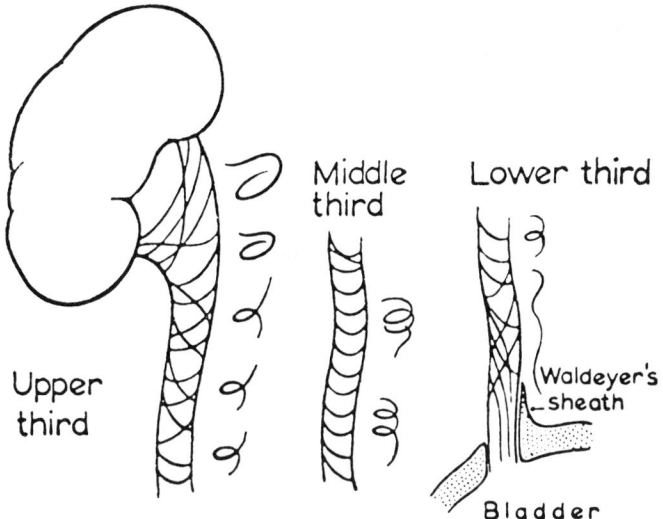

FIG. 80.1. Interlacing spirals of smooth muscle of varying obliquity support the entire upper urinary tract. (Source: Urology, ed. by M. F. Campbell, W. B. Saunders Co., Phila., 1963. P. 355, Figs. 8–19.)

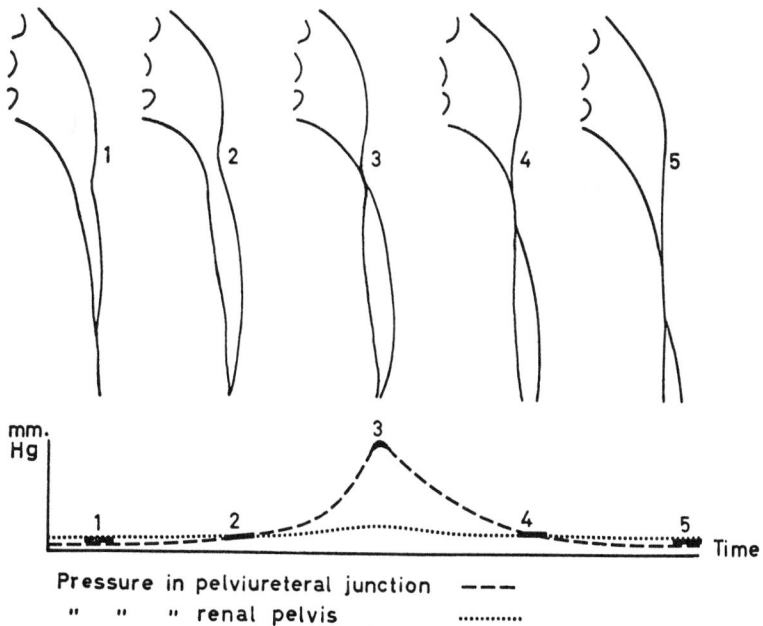

FIG. 80.2. (Source: Urology, Ed. by M. F. Campbell, p. 100, figs. 3–6. W. B. Saunders Co., Phila., 1963.)

to the upper urinary tract. The uretero-vesical junction nevertheless remains closed except when urine is flowing into the bladder. Reflux is prevented by the long oblique course of the ureter through the bladder wall, which is in turn maintained by three factors—the firm terminal anchoring of the ureter, the firm support of its posterior wall by the detrusor muscle of the bladder, and by Waldeyer's sheath, a flesh bundle of vesical muscle fibres blending with the antero-superior aspect of the ureteral wall just outside the bladder. When intravesical pressure exceeds ureteral pressure, as in voiding, the flexible anterior wall of the submucosal ureter is collapsed against the firm posterior muscular supports. Waldeyer's sheath draws the ureter tightly against the roof of the ureteral hiatus, collapsing its submucosal portion, while fixation to the trigone maintains its length. The resistance to flow through a tube of zero diameter is infinitely high, and reflux cannot occur.

The muscularis body of the urinary bladder, known as the detrusor muscle, is composed of an interwoven network of decussating smooth muscle bundles, coursing in random fashion in all directions and at all depths in the bladder wall. There is no evidence for the three concentric layers of fibres formerly believed to be present. At the internal urethral orifice, fibres from the detrusor arch obliquely over the bladder outlet, creating a ridge of muscular fibres which at first glance appear to be circularly disposed in the manner of a sphincter; indeed, this area was for a long time known as "the internal sphincter." It is not, however, a sphincter at all, but the proximal portion of a tubular structure known as the bladder neck, formed by the detrusor fibres continuing uninterrupted, along the length of the prostatic urethra in the male and the entire urethra in the female. An anatomic sphincter at the internal urethral orifice does not exist.

The trigone is separate from the detrusor both embryologically (it is derived from the mesonephric duct) and anatomically, being separated from the detrusor by an areolar plane of cleavage. It sends fibres over the posterior lip of the bladder neck to mingle with the detrusor fibres. It plays no definite role in voiding, but probably closes the internal urethral orifice during ejaculation.

The structure of the external sphincter and its role in voluntary compression of the urethra has been briefly considered. Urethral compression is also exerted to a minor extent by the levator ani muscles, and the small muscles of the peri-

neum, notably the bulbo-cavernosus, which is also capable of stripping the male urethra following micturition.

Neuroanatomic Considerations

The Upper Urinary Tract

Nerve fibres and ganglion cells are present in the adventitia, muscular and submucosal coats of the ureter, originating from the sympathetic and parasympathetic divisions of the autonomic nervous system. The presence of this ennervation is unnecessary for the maintainence of muscular tone, or for the initiation, maintainence and variation of pelvi-ureteric contractions. Drugs affecting the autonomic nervous system at all synaptic levels have no effect on ureteral motility in pharmacologic doses, whether administered systemically or applied directly to the ureteral wall. Ureteral denervation, likewise, has no effect. The best available evidence indicates that ureteral motility is an autonomous function, dependent on normal ureteral metabolism, and coordinated via the intercellular smooth muscle bridges of the muscularis. The stimulus to contraction is stretching of the muscle fibres. The ureter is richly supplied with visceral afferent fibres terminating in the L1 and T12 segments of the spinal cord. Acute ureteral distension is the adequate stimulus, giving rise to ureteral pain, referred along the corresponding cutaneous dermatomes. This pain may be abolished by section of the ureteral nerves without interfering in any way with peristalsis or tone.

Bladder, Bladder Neck and External Sphincter

These structures function as a unit in the maintainence of continence and the act of micturition. Their nerve supply is, therefore, functionally integrated, and can be logically considered under a single heading. Ennervation is both motor and sensory, derived from the somatic and autonomic nervous systems, with integration on both segmental reflex and suprasegmental levels.

MOTOR INNERVATION. Sympathetic white rami arising from the lowest thoracic and upper two lumbar segments of the intermedio-lateral column of grey matter of the spinal cord pass through the sympathetic chain to synapse in the celiac and mesenteric ganglia, from which grey rami flow into the pelvis as part of the superior hypogastric plexus (presacral nerve). At the promontory of the sacrum the plexus bifurcates, to form

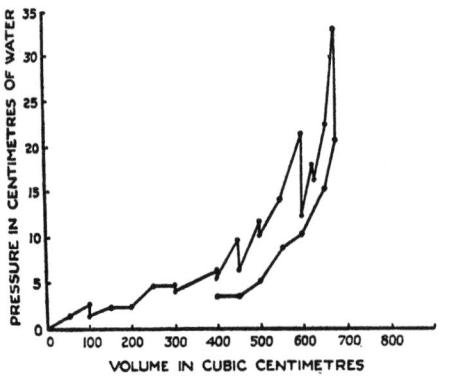

Fig. 80.3. Curve of pressure changes in human bladder during filling and emptying. Involuntary contractions and sharply rising pressures above 450–500 ml. indicate filling beyond physiologic capacity.

the right and left inferior hypogastric plexi (hypogastric nerves) which run deep into the pelvis to form the pelvic plexus. From here, fibres pass to smaller plexi surrounding the bladder, prostate and posterior urethra. These efferents, contrary to previous teaching, have no known effect on vesical and bladder neck function; through their action on the trigone and urethral crest, however, they may close the bladder neck during ejaculation.

Parasympathetic motor fibres to bladder and bladder neck arise in the intermedio-lateral column in the second, third and fourth segments of the sacral cord, and travel as medullated fibres in the pelvic nerves (N. erigentes) to the pelvic plexus. Synapses occur with post-ganglionic neurons either here, or with ganglion cells within the bladder wall, with grey rami taking a short, direct course to the vesical muscle. The parasympathetic division is the sole motor supply of the detrusor, both body and neck. The time-honoured theory of dual antagonistic ennervation of the body and neck of the bladder, in which sympathetic impulses relaxed the detrusor and constricted the internal sphincter (syn. = bladder neck), and parasympathetic impulses produced the reverse, is not supported by experimental evidence. Presacral nerve section in the human has no effect on micturition, nor do sympathomimetic drugs. Bilateral pelvic nerve section causes complete detrusor paralysis, with urinary retention and overflow incontinence, while their stimulation causes immediate detrusor contraction.

The somatic motor supply of the striated muscles of the perineum, including the external sphincter, is carried via the pudendal nerves from the anterior horn cells of sacral segments 2, 3 and 4. These fibres maintain tonic contraction of the external sphincter except when reflexly inhibited during micturition. Their bilateral section causes total relaxation and degeneration of the external sphincter muscle. Continence is not affected, but rather, the ability is lost to rapidly and voluntarily arrest the urinary stream, once initiated.

SENSORY INNERVATION. Afferent fibres, both visceral and somatic, follow the three routes taken by the efferent fibres of bladder, urethra and perineum.

Some sensory fibres arising from bladder and posterior urethra follow sympathetic efferent pathways to cell stations in the dorsal root ganglia. The lower limit of their central connections is at L2, while their upper limit has been variously placed from T11 to as high as T6, following clinical observations on patients with transections of the spinal cord. The exact role of these fibres is obscure. They probably carry pain and some proprioceptive and temperature sensation, but their section produces no significant deficit. They are said to account for the vague, often painful sensations due to vesical overdistension and spasm experienced by paraplegics with spinal cord transections below T12.

All the important afferent fibres of the bladder, and posterior urethra, especially those associated with sensation of fullness and desire to void but which are also useful thresholds of pain and temperature sensation, follow the pelvic nerves to the dorsal root ganglia of S2–4. Section of these nerves results in the loss of all useful vesical sensation.

The pudendal nerves carry superficial and deep somatic sensation from the distal bladder neck, and adjacent perineal structures.

REFLEX CENTRES AND SUPRASEGMENTAL-PATHWAYS. Centres for the control and integration of micturition are situated in sacral spinal cord, brain stem, and cerebral cortex.

A spinal centre for the reflex control of micturition exists in the second, third and fourth segments of the spinal cord. Two important reflexes are served. Visceral afferent impulses from stretch receptors in the bladder wall travel via the pelvic nerves to the micturition centre, which, unless inhibited by higher centres, sends efferent impulses via the pelvic nerves resulting in detrusor contraction. This has the effect of forcing urine into the posterior urethra, initiating a second reflex. Visceral afferent endings in the posterior urethra, stimulated by the presence of urine, send impulses via the pelvic nerves to the spinal micturition centre, which transmits inhibitory impulses to the anterior horn cells of S2–4, decreasing the frequency of impulses in the pudendal nerve, and thereby causing relaxation of the external sphincter.

The activity of the spinal micturition centre is modified by a higher reflex centre in the brain stem, and by cortical activity under the control of the will. Pain and temperature afferents reach these centers via the crossed spino-thalamic tracts after synapse in the dorsal horn cells at the appropriate segmental level. Proprioceptive sensations, especially the desire to void and the feeling of fullness, turn into the ipsi-lateral funiculus gracilis without synapse, reach the medulla where they effect synapse in the Nucleus Gracilis, and then cross the midline to join the spino-thalamic tracts and follow the great sensory pathways to the brain-stem and cortical centres for micturition. Regulatory pathways descend from these centres, via the crossed and uncrossed pyramidal and extrapyramidal tracts, to modify the activity of the spinal micturition centre.

The location of the brain-step centre for micturition is uncertain in man, but probably resides in the pons. It exerts both facilitory and inhibitory effects of the spinal centre. It is responsible for sustaining detrusor contraction and external sphincter relaxation until the bladder is completely emptied; this is necessary because, after partial emptying of the bladder, proprioceptive afferent impulses to the spinal centre fall below the threshold necessary to maintain the micturition reflex. The brain stem probably also inhibits the spinal micturition reflex at an unconscious level, even when the bladder is adequately filled.

The cerebral cortex receives vesical representation at the extreme medial aspect of the sensory-motor strip (paracentral lobule). Here the degree of fullness of the bladder, the slight burning felt on initiating voiding and the pain of vesical spasm is consciously appreciated. Here too, voluntary control is exerted over the lower micturition centres. Thus, although micturition can proceed normally in the absence of cortical control, the cortex inhibits lower centres until a suitable time and place for voiding can be found. Voiding is then allowed to proceed automatically by removing cortical inhibition. Micturition can also be voluntarily initiated by the cerebral cortex in the absence of a desire to void or, once interrupted at any time.

Mechanical Considerations

The urinary system is a series of pipes and reservoirs transmitting and storing fluid, and as such is subject to the laws of fluid mechanics. Most important of these is LaPlace's law, which states:

$$P = 2T/R \text{ in a sphere,}$$

and

$$P = T/R \text{ in a tube,}$$

where

P = intraluminal pressure (sphere); resistance to flow (tube), (provided external pressure is constant)

T = tension on the wall of the sphere or tube (ie., the sum of the force of active tension developed by muscular contrac-

tion plus the passive tension exerted by the elastic properties of the wall)

R = radius of the tube or sphere.

These relationships hold good, regardless of the characteristics of the wall of the viscus, provided the system is at equilibrium.

Certain corrolaries of this law provide a mechanical explanation for the behaviour of the upper urinary tract and bladder, and will be emphasized in the appropriate sections below. One example will be recalled, namely, the absence of reflux when the intravesical ureter is collapsed. Under these conditions, the radius (R) is very small, so that for any given tension on the ureteral wall, the resistance to flow (P) in the ureter is extremely high, certainly higher than the intravesical pressure.

Urinary Transport in the upper Urinary Tract

Distension is the adequate stimulus to contraction throughout the entire upper urinary tract. Urine flowing into the minor calyces creates distension, triggering a calyceal contraction which, because of the predominantly circular muscle in the area, causes narrowing of the calyx and forces urine into the renal pelvis. Calyceal contractions occur independently of one another and of renal pelvic contractions. Calyceal pressures follow renal pelvic pressures, because the two are in free communication at all times.

The renal pelvis is relatively indistensible beyond its fairly low capacity of 3–10 l. Like the calyces it undergoes rhythmic dilatation and contraction, referred to as diastole and systole respectively. It fills passively from the calyces under very low pressures during diastole, and then contracts, expressing only a small percentage of its volume into the upper end of the ureter. The normal intrapelvic pressure seldom exceeds more than a few cm. of water, even in systole, but tends to be higher in the narrow, ureter-like pelvis than in the large, ampullary-type pelvis—a direct result of LaPlace's law.

Efforts to locate a pelvi-ureteric pacemaker have failed, but the contraction wave begins somewhere in the region of the pelvi-calyceal junction and sweeps distally at a relatively constant rate of about 3 cm./sec. The pelvis is comprised of both circular and longitudinal muscle, and in systole, therefore, it decreases in volume and approximates itself toward the kidney.

The upper end of the ureter is in communication with, and fills with, the renal pelvis during diastole, the uretero-pelvic junction remaining open during this phase, and the pelvis and upper together forming the functional renal pelvis. Contraction of the renal pelvis and closure of the ureteropelvic junction occur almost simultaneously, trapping urine within the renal pelvis, above, and within the uppermost ureter below the ureteropelvic junction. The ureteropelvic junction may be defined, physiologically, as the most proximal point of closure of the ureter during systole of the renal pelvis, and its localization varies somewhat with the volume of urine flow.

The ureteral cone is the segment of ureter in open communication with the renal pelvis during diastole. Its proximal limit is the pelvi-ureteric junction, but its size, shape and distal limit depends on the rate of urine flow and the body position, filling being reduced in the supine position.

The frequency of pelvi-ureteric contractions ranges from 1–5 per min. at normal rates of flow, tending to occur at regular intervals, although at different rates on the two sides. Sudden reduction of urine formation may or may not result in a transient decrease in the frequency of contractions, following which the rate returns to its normal frequency, even in the presence of complete anuria. Higher than normal rates of urine flow increase the amplitude of contractions, provided the ureteral cone is capable of coping with the increased volumes. If, however, renal pelvic distension occurs, the frequency of contractions increases. At the highest flow rates, the entire pelvis and ureter remain open, urine transport being a function of the pelvi-vesical pressure gradient.

The closure of the pelvi-ureteric junction marks the origin of a peristaltic wave which sweeps down the ureter, transporting the urine trapped in the ureteral cone ahead of it. A single peristaltic wave rarely strips the ureter of urine completely, but leaves behind from one to four tapered columns of urine of varying length, called urine spindles, separated by lengths of contracted, empty ureter. Spindles tend to be formed under conditions causing resistance to urine flow, such as recumbency, high urine flow rates, and high intravesical pressure, which lead to retention of urine in the upper tract. Small spindles fill from above and empty from below as the peristaltic wave sweeps over them, but large spindles can contract as a unit, rapidly expelling urine toward the bladder. Spindle formation is a more efficient

method of emptying the ureter than peristalsis; the transition from the latter to the former method of urine propulsion occurs smoothly, and is a function of the volume retained in the upper tract.

Circular muscle is absent in the intravesical ureter, which, therefore, plays a passive role in urine transport. Urine is forced in intermittent jets through this portion of the upper tract, ahead of the contraction waves descending from above. Just as the spurt of urine ceases, the longitudinal muscle of the submucosal ureter contracts, drawing the lateral angle of the trigone slightly upwards and outwards.

Pressures in the ureter rise progressively as the bladder is approached being normally about 15 cm. of water in the upper ureter, and 30 cm. in the pelvic ureter during systole. These pressures are not transmitted to the kidney as long as the ureter distal to the ureteral cone remains closed, and are quite sufficient to maintain a uretero-vesical pressure gradient under normal conditions.

Vesical Physiology

Filling of the Bladder

The normal bladder is completely empty at the end of micturition; the intravesical pressure is equal to the intra-abdominal pressure. As the bladder fills, it adjusts its tone to its capacity, so that minimal alterations of intravesical pressure occur over a wide range of intravesical volumes. This phenomenon, sometimes called adaptation, is an inherent property of the smooth muscle of the detrusor, and is not dependent on nervous mechanisms. It is, therefore, present in denervated bladders, but not after death. The adaptation is not to a constant pressure, but always to a pressure slightly higher than existed before the addition of the fluid increment.

In the adult, direct measurements show a gradual smooth increase in intravesical pressure to about 10 cm. of water at a capacity of approximately 400 ml. The first sensation of bladder filling generally occurs at a capacity of 100–150 ml., and the first desire to void at between 150 and 250 ml. The physiologic capacity of the bladder, that is, the maximum intravesical volume tolerated without undue discomfort and at which micturition is normally effected, ranges between 250 and 450 ml.

Filling of the bladder beyond its physiologic capacity is associated with progressive failure of adaptation, and intravesical pressure rises

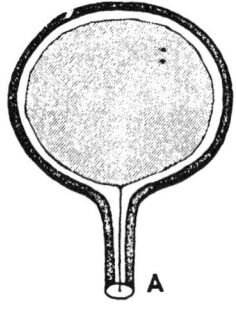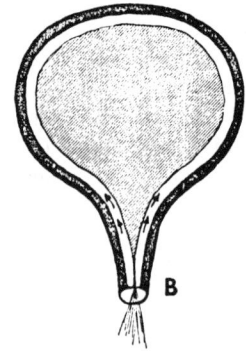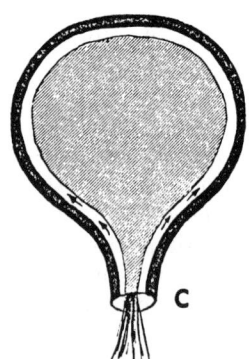

FIG. 80.4. The bladder neck in continence and micturition. Detrusor contraction decreases urethral resistance by shortening and widening the bladder neck. (Source: Urology, ed. M. F. Campbell, p. 134, fig. 4–5. W. B. Saunders Co., Phila., 1963.)

much more sharply relative to the increase in intravesical volume. Despite strong cortical inhibition, efferent impulses reach the detrusor, causing involuntary contractions. At first these are of low pressure and not associated with conscious sensation, but, as filling continues, they are associated with sharp rises in pressure, and felt consciously as an acute urge to void. These may for a time be inhibited voluntarily, but eventually reflex micturition will occur despite all efforts at voluntary control.

The physiologic bladder capacity varies greatly with age and psychic factors. At birth it ranges from 20 to 50 ml., increasing four times during the first year of life. In the adult it can be as high as 600 ml., especially in persons whose occupations make access to lavatory facilities difficult. In all cases, the capacity is about twice that at which the first desire to void is felt. The anatomic capacity of the bladder—the capacity just before rupture occurs—is well above one litre, and is never approached under physiologic conditions.

Continence

In addition to accepting urine from the ureters, and periodically discharging urine under voluntary control, the bladder must also retain urine. Continence under physiologic conditions is dependent almost entirely upon the detrusor muscle. Reference has been made previously to the bladder neck, a tubular structure corresponding to the prostatic urethra in males and the entire urethra in females, the muscularis of which is continuous with the body of the detrusor. Except during micturition, the tone inherent in the smooth muscle and elastic tissue of the bladder neck holds its walls in firm apposition. Since, according to LaPlace's law, the resistance to flow

through a tube varies inversely to its radius, the tone in its walls being constant, it follows that the urethral resistance approaches infinity as the radius of the bladder neck approaches zero. Put more simply, the intravesical pressure, aided by accommodation, never exceeds the intraurethral pressure under resting conditions.

The external sphincter is not normally necessary to continence, and its paralysis does not cause leakage of urine, provided the bladder neck is intact. If, however, the bladder neck is destroyed, leakage of urine is prevented by the tonic contraction of the external sphincter. Under conditions of sudden increase of intra-abdominal pressure, such as occur with coughing, intravesical pressure may reach 50–80 cm. of water, forcing urine into the bladder neck. Leakage is prevented under these circumstances by reflex contraction of the perineal and levator ani muscles.

Urine normally enters the bladder neck only when the detrusor contracts. The muscularis of the bladder neck, being part of the detrusor, contracts longitudinally. This has the effect of decreasing urethral resistance by decreasing the constrictive tone inherent in the posterior urethra, shortening the posterior urethra, and widening the bladder neck. At the same time, the intravesical pressure rises as the muscular network of the body of the detrusor increases its tone. Intravesical pressure exceeds urethral resistance at a pressure somewhere between 18 and 43 cm. of water, and urine flows through the internal urethral orifice.

Micturition

Micturition may be defined as the periodic complete emptying of the urinary bladder, under voluntary control except in infancy. The nervous, muscular and mechanical factors essential to the act have all been discussed, and must now be integrated.

At the end of voiding, the bladder is empty, the bladder neck is closed, and the intravesical pressure is close to zero. The bladder slowly fills as ureteral peristalsis forces jets of urine through the aperistaltic intramural ureter. Despite a rising intravesical volume, the intravesical pressure remains low, due to the phenomenon of accommodation inherent in the smooth muscle of the vesical wall, and at no time does it exceed either the intraureteral pressure at the uretero-vesical junction, or the urethral resistance provided by the closed bladder neck.

As the bladder radius increases, the tension on the vesical wall increases, even though the intravesical pressure remains almost constant (Laplace's law). Tension is the adequate stimulus for the proprioceptive end organs in the vesical wall which send visceral afferent impulses via the pelvic nerves to terminate in the spinal reflex centre for micturition (S2–4), and also in the fasciculus gracilis to the reflex centre for micturition in the brain step (pons?) and in the voluntary centre for micturition in the paracentral lobule of cerebral cortex. The first feeling of filling of the bladder is generally appreciated at a capacity of 100–150 ml., and the first desire to void, accompanied by a vague feeling in the penis or perineum, at 150–250 ml. At this stage, the spinal reflex centre for micturition is inhibited by impulses from the brain stem centre via the cortico-regulatory tracts, preventing efferent impulses from leaving the spinal centre. If micturition is unduly postponed, a feeling of fullness, then discomfort, and finally pain results. The latter sensation is transmitted to the cortex via the crossed spinothalamic tracts. Under these conditions, voiding is inhibited by cortical impulses blocking the discharge of the spinal center.

When an opportunity is found to empty the bladder, the voluntary restraint placed upon the spinal micturition center is lifted, and micturition proceeds automatically. The cessation of inhibitory impulses from the cerebral cortex (in the case of a full bladder), or the facilatory impulses from the cortex (in the case of low intravesical volume), permit the discharge of parasympathetic efferent impulses along the pelvic nerves to synapses in the pelvic plexi and bladder wall, and thence via postganglionic rami to the body of the detrusor muscle and the bladder neck. A voiding contraction of the detrusor results, generating pressures of 50–150 cm. of water

within the bladder. At the same time, the detrusor contraction shortens and widens the bladder neck while decreasing its tone. The effect is to increase intravesical pressure and decrease urethral resistance, and a bolus of urine is forced into the posterior urethra. Urine in the posterior urethra stimulates parasympathetic visceral afferents which send impulses via the pelvic nerves to the spinal centre. This reflexly relaxes the external sphincter by decreasing the frequency of efferent impulses which normally travel from the anterior horn cells of S2–4 via the pudendal nerves to keep the external sphincter in a state of tonic contraction. Urine flows through the membranous urethra and then, in the male, through a passive conduit, the spongy urethra, to the exterior.

Certain muscular movements not essential to micturition commonly accompany the act. At the onset of micturition the levatores ani and perineal muscles are relaxed, thereby decreasing somewhat urethral resistance. At the same time the glottis closes, the diaphragm descends and the abdominal wall muscles contract, accelerating the flow of urine by raising intravesical pressure.

A voiding contraction, once initiated, is normally maintained until all the urine has been discharged from the urinary bladder. This is a function of facilitory impulses from the brain stem. The bladder contracts in all directions like a toy balloon deflating from its neck. When the bladder and posterior urethra have emptied, the external sphincter closes, the detrusor relaxes, and finally the bladder neck closes gradually.

Arrest of the voiding stream, once initiated, is accomplished by a powerful voluntary contraction of the external sphincter and perineal muscles, and is associated with a sense of burning and urgency due to stimulation of somatic afferents in the region of the membranous urethra. If the contraction is sustained, urine is forced backwards into the bladder by collapse of the posterior urethra, associated with gradual relaxation of the detrusor muscle.

Micturition begins in the fifth intrauterine month with the onset of urinary secretion. It remains a reflex act until approximately 2½ years of age, at which time it begins to come under cortical control. Complete continence is usually achieved by the age of 3.

Nocturnal enuresis, or the passage of urine during sleep, occurs in young children up to an age which varies considerably, and may be attributed to the undeveloped state of the neural mechanism through which the act of micturition is voluntarily inhibited. But enuresis during sleep sometimes persists beyond the usual time and even to adult age. It may then be associated with some definite organic abnormality, e.g., in the lumbo-sacral vertebrae, e.g., spina bifida occulta, but nocturnal enuresis in the adult is usually related to some functional neurological disorder, or to psychological factors. Evidence of pelvic autonomic dysfunction or psychiatric conditions in the subject's immediate family are present in a large proportion of such persons. In others there is definite mental deficiency.

REFERENCES

GREENE, L. F. AND EMMETT, J. L. *in* Urology (ed. by M. F. Campbell) pp. 118–147, W. B. Saunders, Phila. 1963.

KIIL, F. The Function of the Ureter and Renal Pelvis. W. B. Saunders Co., 1957.

HUTCH, J. A. The Ureterovesical Junction. Univ. of California Press, Los Angeles, 1958.

INDEX

A

Abdomen, nerve plexus of, 247
Abdominal cavity, lymphatic system of, 505
Abdominal muscle. *See* Muscle, abdominal
Abdominal reflex, discussion of, 141
Abducent nerve, 370
Absorption, **1373**
  fate of amino acids after, **1296**
  homeostasis at the end of, 1391
  in gall bladder, 1160
  intestinal, **1172, 1178**
    of amino acids, 1185
    of calcium salts 1181
    of carbohydrates, 1182
    of cholesterol, 1191
      role of bile in, 1191
      role of pancreatic juice in, 1191
    of disaccharides, 1183
    of fat, 1187
      impairment of, following bilateral adrenalectomy, 1191
      site of, 1190
      theories of, 1187
        lipolytic, 1187, 1188
        partition, 1187, 1188
    of glucose, 1182
    of inorganic salts, 1180
    of monosaccharides, 1182
    of native protein, 1186
    of peptidases, 1186
    of phosphate, 1181
    of protein, 1185
    of proteoses, 1186
    of salt, mechanism of, 1181
    of sugars, 1183
    of triglycerides, 1188
    of vitamin A, 1192
    of vitamin B₁₂, 1192
    of vitamins, 1192
    study of, methods, 1179
    transamination during, 1186
  of calcium, 1594
    from intestine, 1437
  of carotene, by intestines, 1434
  of fats, 1373
    defective, causes of, 1376
    disturbances in, 1376
    in intestine, schematic outline of, 1375
    relation of portal-biliary circulation of bile salts to, 1144
    role of bile in, 1373
    role of pancreatic juice in, 1373
  of fatty acids, 1373

of fluids, factors influencing, 1179
of glucose, from gut, 1334
of lipids, subdivision of oil droplets into micelles in, 1374
of medium-chain fatty acids, 1375
of protein, **1295**
of urobilinogen C¹⁴, 1146
of vitamin A by intestine, 1433
of vitamin K from gut, 1443
of water
  in intestine, 1179
  mechanism of, 1181
transport of dietary lipids during, 1391
Acapnia, 1031
Acceleration
  angular, 901
  centripetal, 900, 901
    effects of, 902
  effects of, on circulation, 900
  horizontal linear, 901
  linear, 900
  negative, 901
  positive, 901
  physiological effects of, 902
Accessory nerves
  central connections of, **127**
  spinal
    bulbar root of, 132
    spinal root of, 132
Accommodation
  amplitude of, 345
    changes in, 346
  dynamics of, 344
  mechanism of, 342
    diagram, 343, 344
  of the eye, **340**
    relation between distance and effort, 370
  range of, 345
  visual axes and pupillary diameter during, 345
Accoucheur's hand of tetany, 1584
Acetate, active, generated in liver cells, utilization of, 1384
Acetoacetate, ability of liver to produce, 1384
Acetoacetic acids, reabsorption of, by renal tubules, 1676
Acetylation
  coenzyme of, 1456
    chemical structure of, 1456
    function of, 1456
  general discussion on, 1382
  metabolism of, 1383
  role of, in fatty acid metabolism, 1382

Acetylcholine
  as an intermediary of parasympathetic effects to the alimentary tract and bladder, 253
  as humoral mediator, 258
  as mediator of autonomic ganglia, 251
  as transmitter of effects of sweat glands, 254
  effect of
    on cardiac output, 800
    on coronary circulation, 823
    on salivary secretion, 1078
  free, instability of, 251
  in synaptic transmission, 259
  in transmission of nervous effects, 253
  liberation of
    during discharge of adrenaline, 254
    from parasympathetic endings in iris, 253
    from sympathetic preganglionic fibers, 254
  synthesis of, by cholineacetylase, 251
  uneven distribution of, in central nervous system, 260
Acetylcholinesterase
  in cholinergic nerves, 251
  in erythrocytes, 251 (footnote)
Achalasia, 1208
Achard-Tiers syndrome, **1578**
Achlorhydria, 1569
  in pernicious anemia, 548
  in thiamine deficiency, 1103
Achromatic interval, 301
Achondroplasia, 1610
Acid
  See specific acid
  -base balance
    disturbances of
      due to dehydration, 496
      "mixed," 619
      nature and severity of, 618
      types of, 614
    effect of hemoglobin on, 521
    renal regulation of, 1689
    Brønsted-Lowry concept of, 595
    desoxyribonucleic. *See* Desoxyribonucleic acid
    discussion of, 595
    effect of
      on gastric emptying, 1217
      on gastric secretion, 1103
    excretion of, factors affecting, 1690

Bold-face numbers indicate major discussion

Bold-face numbers indicate major discussion

Bold-face numbers indicate major discussion

Bold-face numbers indicate major discussion

Bold-face numbers indicate major discussion

Bold-face numbers indicate major discussion

Bold-face numbers indicate major discussion

Blood—*cont.*
  volume—*cont.*
    increase in—*cont.*
      pathological states as-
        sociated with, 501
    measurement of
      empiric methods for, 711
      from plasma volume and
        hematocrit reading,
        489
      in conjunction with
        measurement of
        pressure and flow,
        728
    of cavity, measurement of,
      716
    of organ, measurement of,
      716
    of packed cell, 489
    of region, measurement of,
      716
    of vessel, measurement of,
      716
    reduction of, 500
      causes of, 500
      in anhydremia, 500
      in pernicious anemia, 548
      pathological states as-
        sociated with, 501
    regional
      calculation of, 716
      determination of
        by dilution technique,
          717
        by plethysmography,
          717
      distribution of, 718
    splanchnic, reduction of,
      during hemorrhage,
      868
    stroke, 804
      factors affecting, 804
    systolic, role of, as cardiac
      reserve, 808
    total
      determination of, 490
      effects of changing, 648
      variations in, role of, in
        regulation of body
        temperature, 1415
    ventricular, 731, 804
      diastolic, 932
    water loss from, pathological
      variations in plasma
      proteins in, 475
    water, loss of, effect of, on
      blood volume, 500
  whole
    constituents of, 473
      inorganic, 473
    loss of, effect on blood
      volume, 500
    phosphorus in, 474
    volume of, normal values
      obtained for, **490**
Blood-brain barrier, penetration of, **240**
Blood-cerebrospinal fluid barrier, penetration of,
  240
Body
  fluid
    See also Body water; Water
      balance

acidity of, importance of,
  594
alterations in hydrogen ion
  concentration of
  compensatory reac-
  tions, 612
and blood plasma, distribution of sodium and
  potassium between,
  492
electrolytes in, concentrations of, 600
electrolytic concentration
  of, 495
extracellular, and tissue
  cells, 608
fatty acids of, 1368
functions of
  excretory, 471
  maintenance of water
    content of tissues,
    471
  nutritive, 471
  protective, 472
  regulation of body tem-
    peratures, 471
  regulatory, 472
  respiratory, 471
hydrogen ion concentration
  of, 594, 600, **605**
  physicochemical princi-
    ples, 594
  regulation of, **594**
isotonicity of, 494
loss of, in hemorrhage, replacement of, 503
osmotic pressure of, regulation of, 1686
reaction of, 594
  range of, 602
  regulation of, 594
heat
See also Body temperature
  conservation of, factors
    affecting, 1415
  environmental temperature
    and, 1414
  loss of
    by convection, 1416
    by radiation, 1415
    by vaporization, 1419
    factors affecting, 1414,
      1415
    routes of, 1414
  production of, 1413
    by basal metabolic rate,
      1414
    by metabolic activity,
      1413
    factors influencing, 1419
    low environmental
      temperature, 1419
    role of liver in, 1419
    role of muscle tissue in,
      1419
  regulation of
    centers for, 1421
    factors affecting, 1421
    disturbances of, **1422**
    mechanisms for, 1414
    depression of, 1422
  sources of, 1419
  storage of, 1420
temperature, **1413**
See also Body heat

effects of
  on blood flow of forearm,
    845
  on skin temperature, 845
excessive, effects of, 1423
factors affecting, 1415
  water, by conduction,
    1419
fever. *See* Fever
general discussion on, 1413
hypothermia, 1426
limits of, upper and lower,
  1414
normal, 1413
of homoiothermic animals,
  1413
of poikilothermic animals,
  1413
regulation of, **1413**
  by diet, 1420
  by evaporation of water,
    1416
  by sweating, 1418
  role of the endocrines in,
    1422
  rise in, due to dehydration,
    496
  variation in, in different
    types of animals,
    1414
water, **490**
See also Water balance;
  Body fluids
content of various tissues,
  491
decrease in, thirst aroused
  by, 493
extracellular, 491
  constituents of, 491
formation of, by poly-
  merization, 493
increase in, by sodium carbonate administra-
  tion, 494
intracellular, 491
  amount of, determina-
    tion of, 491
replenishment of, methods
  of, 493
total
  effects of diet changes
    on, 494
  lost in dehydration, 492
  mean value of, in man,
    490
volume of, 492
  mechanism regulating,
    492
relation of electrolyte concentration and tissue
  changes to, 494
total, 490
  determination of, 490
Bohr integration, **990**
Bone, **1603**
  calcification of. *See* Calcifica-
    tion
  calcium in, 1604
    forms of, 1604
  composition of, 1603
  conduction
    audiometry, 412
    compression, 412
    in testing cochlear mecha-
      nism, 412

Bold-face numbers indicate major discussion

Bold-face numbers indicate major discussion

Bold-face numbers indicate major discussion

Bold-face numbers indicate major discussion

Bold-face numbers indicate major discussion

Bold-face numbers indicate major discussion

Bold-face numbers indicate major discussion

Bold-face numbers indicate major discussion

Bold-face numbers indicate major discussion

Bold-face numbers indicate major discussion

influence of, on carbohydrate metabolism, **1357**
structure of, 1481
study of, methods of, 1485
verification of organs as, 1485
organs, of sex, **1615**
system, and nervous system, relationship between, 1483
Endogenous protein, 1185
Endolymph, 378, 379
Endolymphatic duct, 98
Endolymphatic sac, 98
Endometrium, relationship of, to anterior pituitary and ovary, 1502
Endoplasmic reticulum, 1384
Endosmosis, 497
Energy
economy of, 87
expenditure of, increase in, in treatment of obesity, 1411
law of conservation of, 1264, 1276
output of, and foot intake, balance between, regulation of, 1251
Energy balance, 1279, 1285
Energy content
by bomb calorimetry, of some fuels, foods and metabolic products, 1265
of substances, general discussion on, 1272
Engram, 200
Enterochromaffine cells, 1173
Enterocrinin, 1176
Enterogastric reflex, 1218, 1219
Enterogastrone, 1219
effect of, on gastric secretion, 1105
inhibition of gastric secretion by, 1099
production of, 1219
release of, from mucosa of upper small bowel, 1093
Enterokinase, 1126
secretion of, in small intestine, 1175
Entoptic phenomena, 339
Enuresis, nocturnal, 1719
Enzyme
gastric, 1088
in intestinal secretion, source of, 1175
involved in the formation of catecholamines, 1557
pancreatic, 1125
production of, 1128
secretion of, 1128
proteolytic, 1126
in gastric juice, 1088
secretion of, regulation of, 1177
synthesis of, 1129
amino acids essential for, 1128
system, that synthesizes long-chain fatty acids, 1378

Eosinophil, 556
functions of, 559
Eosinophilia, 561
discussion of, 563
Ephedrine
chemical structure of, 1563
resemblance to adrenaline, 1564
Epilepsy, **183**
clonic stage, 183
cryptogenic, 184
grand mal, 183
idiopathic, 184
Jacksonian
caused by lesions of sensory cortex, 176
indicative of abnormality in brain, 184
localized, 184
petit mal, 183
psychomotor, 183
seizures caused by disturbances in temporal lobe, 184
status epilepticus, 183
tonic stage, 183
Epinephrine
See also Adrenaline
effects of
on coronary circulation, 823
on glucose output by liver, 1337
on renal circulation, 875
glycosuria produced by, 1357
metabolism, pathways of, 255
stimulation of α- and β-receptors by, 255
Epiphyseal plate, 1605
Epiphysis, **1659**
origin of, 1659
structure of, 1659
Epithelium
corneal, 267
germinal, 1622
stratified, squamous, of salivary glands, 1063
two-layered, of salivary ducts, 1063
Epitympanic recess, 377
EPSP (excitatory postsynaptic potential), 72
origin of, 73
Equilibratory sense, 176
Equilibrium, physiological mechanisms governing, 84
Erection, **1658**
Ergosterol, chemical structure of, 1436
Ergot, effect of, on salivary secretion, 1078
Ergotamine, 1562
Ergotoxine, 1562
Erythrocyte
addition of hemoglobin to, 537
agglutination of, 529
buffer systems in, 607
changes in, in disease, 486
composition of, diagram of, 481
concentrations of, estimation of, 485
constituents of, 480

count, in emphysema, 1041
destruction of
by burns, 529
by snake venom, 529
by toxic substances, 529
developing, profile sketch of, 1056
diameter of, distribution curve of, 481
dimensions of, diagram of, 481
effect of high altitudes on, 1033
formation of, 537
materials necessary for, 537
fragility of
factors affecting, 527
in certain diseases, 528
test for, 527
interior of, alkalinity of, 1034
life span of, 536, 568
average, 537
measurement of, 536
methods of, 536, 537
membrane of, permeability properties of, 528
normal, resistance of, to disintegrating effect of hypotonic solutions, 527
number of, **481**
alterations in pathological states, 483
counting, methods of, 485
decreases in, apparent, 485
effect of altitude on, 482
increases in
apparent, 485
causes of
conditions that lower oxygen tension of arterial blood, 483
emotional states, 483
heightened environmental temperature, 483
high altitude, 482
muscular exercise, 483
in pathological conditions, 483
permanent, 483
physiological variations in, 482
permeability of membrane of, 528
production of
hormonal effect on, 482
stimulus to, 575
red blood, human, 2
reduction
effect of, on blood volume, 500
in number of, in pernicious anemia, 548
reticulated, 483
role of, in transport of carbon dioxide, 608
sedimentation rate of, 531
factors affecting, 531
lecithin-cholesterol ratio, 532
protein constitution of plasma, 532
red cell concentration, 532

Bold-face numbers indicate major discussion

Bold-face numbers indicate major discussion

Bold-face numbers indicate major discussion

Bold-face numbers indicate major discussion

Bold-face numbers indicate major discussion

Bold-face numbers indicate major discussion

Gastric tissue and the anti-anemic principle, **551**
Gastric ulcers. *See* Ulcers, gastric
Gastrin, 1096
 function of, 1097
 nature of, 1097
 release of, from gastric antrum, 1085, 1093
Gastrocnemius, components of, 464
Gastrocolic reflex, 1232
Gastroduodenal pressure cycle, 1215
 correlation of, with motility cycle, 1216
Gastroileal reflex, 1230, 1232
Gastrointestinal stimuli, effect of, on food intake, 1256
Gastrointestinal tract
 effects of altitude on, 1034
 innervation of, **1242**
 sensations arising in, effect of, on food intake, 1255
 visceral sensations of, **1242**
Gaucher's disease, enlargement of spleen in, 535
Gay Lussac's law, 965
Gelatin, 1316
 amino acid content of, 1317
Gelatinase, 1089
Gellé test for hearing impairment, 420
Generator potential, 61
Geniculate
 medial, 176, 387
 neurons of, 406
Geniculate body
 lateral, 360
 cells of, 360
Geniculocalcarine pathway, 361
Genital ridge, 1622
Genital system, development of, hormonal factors in, **1619**
Germinal epithelium, 1622
Gestagen, 1634
Gigantism
 acromegalic, 1521
 causes of, 1522
 general discussion of, 1522
Gland
 See also specific gland
 Brunner's, 1173
  secretion of, 1175
 bulbo-urethral, 1649
 cardiac, 1082
 ceruminous, 375
 digestive
  See also Salivary glands
  secretion of, methods of regulating, 1071
 ductless. *See* Endocrine gland
 Ebner's, 1061
 fundic, cells of, 1082, 1083
 intestinal, 1173
 lacrimal, 265
 lingual mucous, 1061
 lingual serous, 1061
 maxillary, respiratory quotient of, 1066
 of Bowman, 428

oral mucous, 1061
pyloric, location of, 1083
racemose, 1061
sex, accessory, 1649
suprarenal. *See* Adrenal glands
Glandular fever, leukocytosis in, **563**, 565
Glare
 blinding, 324
 classification of, 324
 dazzling, 324
 veiling, 324
Glaucoma, 355
 compensated, 355
 decompensated, 355
 inflammatory, 355
 primary, 355
 secondary, 355
Gliadin, 1316
 amino acid content of, 1317
 characteristics of, 1293
 examples of, 1293
Globin, structure of, 522
Globulin
 as a factor in growth, 1320
 characteristics of, 1293
 example of, 1293
 subdivision of, into α, β, and γ-globulins, 476
γ-Globulin
 increase of, in certain conditions, 476
 production of, effects of undernutrition on, 1408
Globus pallidus, 144
 destruction of, associated with tremor at rest of parkinsonism, 149
Glomerular filtrate, increased concentration of protein in, 1706
Glomerular filtration
 colloid osmotic pressure of the plasma proteins in, 1670
 discussion of, 1668
 in regulation of sodium excretion, 1687
 measurement of, 1672
 rate of
  factors determining, 1670
  in anuria, 1707
  in man, 1671
  measurement of, 1670
  reduction of, in congestive heart failure, 920
  relation to blood urea concentration, 1703
  substances used for approximation of, 1672
 rate of blood urea concentration to, 1698
 role of intracapsular hydrostatic pressure in, 1670
Glomerular membrane, 1669
Glomerulonephritis
 acute, 1705
 edema of, 1708
 chronic, 1705
 discussion of, 1705
Glomerulotubular balance, 1675

Glomerulus
 description of, 1665
 diagrammatic representation of, 1667
 juxtamedullary, 1665, 1666
Glossitis, in pernicious anemia, 548
Glossopalatine nerve, 129
Glossopharyngeal nerve, 131, 1064
 afferent nerve fibers in, 1065
 central connections of, **127**
 parasympathetic fibers of, 248
 role of, in sense of taste, 423
Glucagon, **1362**
 effect of, on glucose output by liver, 1337
 estimation of, by immunoassay method, 1362
 metabolic rate of rats treated with, 1362
Glucocorticoids
 effects of, on metabolism, 1570
 fundamental action of, 1570
 general discussion on, 1570
 regulation of, 1575
Gluconeogenesis, definition of, 1298
Glucose
 See also Carbohydrates
 absence of, in saliva, 1070
 absorbed, fate of, 1335
 absorption of, from gut, 1334
 acetyl derivatives of, role of, in detoxifying actions of liver, 1329
 administration of
  intravenous, 1338
  oral, 1338
 compartmental analysis of, 1334
 continuous intravenous injection of, effect of, on blood sugar, 1345
 conversion of glycogen to, 1385
 conversion of, to galactose in mammary gland, 1329
 degradation, energy yield in, 457
 derivatives of, 1329
 entrance of, into blood, 1334
 entrance of, into cells, 1335
 excess, conversion of, to fats or glycogen, 1329
 excretion of, diagrammatic representation of, 1673
 filtration of, diagrammatic representation of, 1673
 formation of, **1333**
 in blood
  elevated levels of, stimulation of insulin secretion by, 1343
  increase in, effect of, on blood insulin level, 1345
 in supply of energy for brain tissue, 1329

Bold-face numbers indicate major discussion

Bold-face numbers indicate major discussion

Bold-face numbers indicate major discussion

Bold-face numbers indicate major discussion

Bold-face numbers indicate major discussion

Hypothalamus, **156**
anterior, functions of, 849
connections of, diagram of, 156
disorders of, 160
disturbances in fat, carbohydrate or water metabolism, 160
emotional manifestations, 160
phenomena attributable to sympathetic or parasympathetic stimulation, 160
sexual function, 160
sleep, 160
electrical stimulation of various sites in, 1509
function of, 157
"heat loss center" in, 748
in control of vasoconstriction, 748
nuclei of, 156
diagram of, 156
dorsomedial, 157
fiber connections of, 157
paraventricular, 156
physiology of, 157
posterior group of, 156
preoptic, 156
supraoptic, 156
ventromedial, 157
nucleus tuber of, 157
regulation of pituitary secretion of thyrotrophic hormone by, 1497
relationship of, to endocrine system, 1483
role of
in emotional states, 157
in regulation of food intake, 157, 1253
stimulation of, effects of, 1505
Hypothermia, 1426
and renal blood flow, 876
effects of, on coronary circulation, 825
Hypothyroidism, **1548**
after treatment with thyroid extract, 1551
before treatment with thyroid extract, 1551
compensated, 1547
congenital, sporadic, 1549
in adults, 1550
in childhood, 1550
laboratory tests in, 1552
onset of, 1548
oxygen consumption in, 1530
primary, origin of, 1550
secondary, origin of, 1550
spontaneous, 1550
treatment of, 1552
untreated, end result of, 1550
Hypotonia, 175
Hypotonus, 1220
Hypoventilation, **898**
Hypovolemia, 501
Hypoxia, **992**
alveolar ventilation, insufficient, as a cause of, 986
anemic, 1030
normal arterial oxygen tension in, 1031

arterial, 1030
acute, circulatory adjustments to, 1032
changes associated with acclimatization, 1033
effect of altitude on, **1031**
lowering of oxygen tension and volumes per cent of oxygen in, 1031
signs and symptoms of, 1032
at high altitudes, 899
cardiac output increased by, 899
combination of, with hypercapnia, 1030
effects of
on cardiac output, 791
on electroencephalogram, 186
on pulmonary arterial pressure, 791
on renal vessels, 874
hypokinetic, 1030
oxygen tension and volumes per cent of oxygen in arterial blood in, 1031
in pneumonia, causes of, 1036
in stimulation of erythrocyte production, 575
role of low ventilation-perfusion ratios with increased admixture in, 989
types of, **1030**

I

Icterus neonatorum, 1151
Ileocolic valve, 1230
anatomy of, 1230
functions of, 1230
Ileus
paralytic, 1229
postoperative
causes of, 1229
prevention of, 1229
Illumination
differences in, 296
intensity of, in relation to visual acuity, 322
measurement of, 281
retinal unit of, 282
Image
false, 373
formation of
by spherical mirrors, 329
on the retina, 334
full-sized erect, 329
real inverted, 329
true, 373
virtual erect, 329
Imidazolines, adrenergic blocking by, 1563
Immersion foot, 858
Immune response, 579, 581
Incisura angularis, 1210
Incus, 377
long crus of, 376
Infantilism, 1523
Lorain type, 1523
Infection
bacterial, role of, in production of ulcer, 1114

susceptibility to, in pancreatic diabetes, 1339
Infundibular process, 1487
Infundibular stem, 1487
Infundibulum, 1487
Inhibitory postsynaptic potentials, 74
currents responsible for, 74
Injury, current of, 30
Innervation, 384
reciprocal, principle of, 68
Inositol
chemistry of, 1462
function of, 1462
general discussion on, 1462
requirements of, 1462
sources of, 1462
Insight problems, 220
Inspiration
accessory muscles of, 1007
control of, **1007**
difficulty in, in bronchial asthma, 1038
during eupnea, 1007
primary muscles of, 1007
rhythm of, 1009
nervous connections responsible for control of, 1009
rhythmic, mechanism of, 965
Inspiratory center, 1008
location of, 1009
methods used for localizing, 1010
role of, in spontaneous respiratory activity, 1010
stimulation of, effects of, 1009
Insulin, **1341**
absence of, 1392
acidified, stability of, 1347
action of, 1350
on cell permeability, 1351
on fat metabolism, 1350
on glycogen storage, 1350
interference with, 1352
by anesthetics, 1353
by toxic products, 1352
mechanism of, 1349
on oxidation of sugar, 1351
on phosphate, 1351
on potassium, 1351
on protein metabolism, 1350
administration of, 1353
induction of hunger contractions by, 1255
antagonism, types of, 1340
antibodies, production of diabetes by, 1340
beef, structure of, 1347
breakdown of, in tissues, 1352
chemistry of, 1346
content, of pancreas
factors affecting
age, 1356
anterior pituitary extracts, 1356
starvation, 1356
under different conditions, **1355**
crystalline zinc, 1354
decrease in plasma by, 1389
deficiency of, 1392
effects of

Bold-face numbers indicate major discussion

Bold-face numbers indicate major discussion

Bold-face numbers indicate major discussion

Bold-face numbers indicate major discussion

Bold-face numbers indicate major discussion

Bold-face numbers indicate major discussion

Bold-face numbers indicate major discussion

Bold-face numbers indicate major discussion

Bold-face numbers indicate major discussion

Bold-face numbers indicate major discussion

Bold-face numbers indicate major discussion

Bold-face numbers indicate major discussion

Bold-face numbers indicate major discussion

Bold-face numbers indicate major discussion

Bold-face numbers indicate major discussion

Bold-face numbers indicate major discussion

Ulcer—*cont.*
  site of, 1113
  stomal, 1112
  treatment of, diet to reduce gastric stimulation, 1117
Umbilical arteries, 1043
Umbilical vein, 1042
Umbo, of ear, 375
Uncinate seizures, resulting from lesions in the anterior temporal region, 177
Undernutrition, 1407
  See also Semistarvation
  and carbohydrate metabolism, **1362**
  general discussion of, **1407**
  severe, effects of, 1408
Unresponsiveness, immunological, 581
Urea
  clearance of
    as index of renal function, 1703
    maximal, 1698
    ratio of, to creatinine clearance, 1697
    standard, 1698
    use of, in clinical evaluation of renal function, 1698
  concentration of, in blood, relation to glomerular filtration rate, 1703
  decomposition of, 1303
  distribution of, in body, 1303
  excretion of, 1303, 1696
  filtered, fraction of, excreted in urine, variation in, with urine flow, 1697
  in saliva, 1070
  nitrogen, excretion of, in starvation, 1406
  production of
    from arginine, 1302
    site of, 1303
  role of, in uremia, 1710
  -urease-ammonia mechanism, in gastric secretion, 1114
Urease, 1089
Uremia
  discussion of, 1710
  disturbance of acid-base balance in, 1710
  disturbances of fluid and electrolyte metabolism in, 1710
  role of urea in, 1710
Ureter, pressures in, 1717
Ureteral cone, 1717
Urethra, posterior, sensory innervation of, 1715
Uric acid
  amount of, in body, calculation of, 1327
  distribution of, in biologic fluids, 1327
  excess nitrogen eliminated as, 1323
  excretion of, in normal man, 1327

function of, 1325
  in saliva, 1070
  pKa of, 1327
  production of, 1302
    increase in, 1328
    decrease in, 1328
  reabsorption of, by renal tubules, 1676
  synthesis of, 1325
Urinary tract
  mechanical considerations of, 1716
  muscularis of, role of, in anatomic adaptation to function, 1712
  transitional epithelium of, 1712
  upper
    neuroanatomic considerations of, 1714
    smooth muscle cells of, 1712
    urinary transport in, 1716
Urine
  acidification of, 1694
    mechanism of, 1691
  acidity of, in low plasma bicarbonate concentration, 1695
  amino acids in, traces of, 1676
  collection of, timing and completeness in, 1703
  composition of, effect of dietary protein on, 1306
  concentrated, formation, 1682
  concentration of, effects of, on relation of flow to osmolal clearance, 1685
    impairment of, 1707
    high, production of, 1685
    low, production of, 1685
    regulation of, 1681
  dilute, formation of, 1682
  examination of, 1703
  flow of
    relationship of
      to solute excretion, in water diuresis and during the formation of concentrated urine, 1686
      to urine osmolality, when solute excretion changes, 1686
  formation of, **1665**
    general nature of, **1668**
  hypertonic
    concentration test for, 1704
    formation of, 1704 (footnote)
  hypertonicity of, mechanism of, 1682
  no-threshold substances in, 1675
  proteolytic activity in, 1088
  threshold substances in, 1675
  transport of, in upper urinary tract, 1716
Urobilin, 1145
  definition of, 1144
  effect of, on color of feces, 1236
  in urine, in pernicious anemia, 548

Urobilinogen, 1144
  absorption of, 1146
  circulation of, 1145
  excreted in urine, quantity of, 1155
  formation of, 1145
    from bilirubin, 1146
    sites of, 1147
Urolithiasis, 1612
Uropepsin, increase in, 1104
Urticaria, factitious, 847
Uterus
  changes in
    during luteal phase of menstrual cycle, 1637
    in menstrual cycle, 1637
  effects of progesterone on, 1635
  factors affecting, whole posterior pituitary extract, 1511
  function of, role of estrogens in, 1631
  oxytocic action of posterior pituitary extracts on, 1517
Utricle, 96, 378
  communication of, with saccule, 98
  macula of, 98
  of ear, 375
  role of, in static reflexes, 111
Utriculo-saccular duct, 98
Uvula, functions of, 232

V

Vagectomy, in treatment of duodenal ulcers, 1117
Vagotomy, double, in treatment of duodenal ulcers, 1117
Vagotonia, 1220
  association of, with hypotonus, 1220
Vagus nerve, 795
  afferent fibers of, 249
  central connections of, **127**
  parasympathetic fibers of, 249
  role of, in sense of taste, 423
  stimulation of, effect of, on gastric and intestinal smooth muscle, 1245
  tone of, 796
    reflex nature of, 797
Valine
  chemical structure of, 1296
  nutritional defects in rats deprived of, 1317
  requirements of, average minimal, 1475
  role of, in nitrogen equilibrium, 1318
Vallate papillae, 423
Vallecula, of cerebellum, 223
Valve, of Heister, 1157
Valvula coli. *See* Ileocolic valve
Van den Bergh reaction
  direct, 1154
  indirect, 1154
  quantitative estimation of bilirubin, 1154
Van Slyke-Neill manometric apparatus, use of, for

Bold-face numbers indicate major discussion

Bold-face numbers indicate major discussion

similarity of properties of, to phthiocol, 1442
toxicity of, 1443
Vitamin K$_1$, 1443
chemical structure of, 1442
Vitamin M. *See* Pteroylglutamic acid
Vitreous body
anatomical structure of, 352
location of, 352
Vitreous humor, absorptive properties of, 282
"Voltage clamp" method of determining ionic flow, 45
Volume conduction, 42
Vomeronasal organ, 428 (footnote)
Vomiting, 1220
and nausea, 1221
antiperistaltic waves during, 1221
causes of, 1220
motion, 1220
center controlling, 1220
central, 1220
induction of, 1220
mechanism of, 1221
of pregnancy, causes of, 1221
projectile, 1221
psychic, 1220
reflex, 1220
relaxation of cardia during, 1222
relaxation of esophagus during, 1222
Von Gierke's disease, 1332, 1333
enlargement of spleen in, 536
Von Jaksch's disease, enlargement of spleen in, 536

W

Wakefulness, humoral mechanisms of, 191
Waldeyer's sheath, 1713
Water
balance, **492**
See also Body fluids; Body water
negative, 492, 495
positive, 492
principle, 1512
regulation of, function of, 1078
evaporation of, role of, in regulation of body temperature, 1416

excretion of
by kidneys, 1680
in congestive heart failure, 920
regulation of, 1686
intake of
See also Thirst
daily average, 493
daily requirements, 493
from metabolism of food, 493
regulation of, 493, **1251**
neural mechanisms for, 1257
intestinal absorption of, 1179
mechanism of, 1181
intoxication
causes of, 496
effects of, 496
intramolecular, definition of, 1276
ionic product of, 598
loss of
average daily, 493
by insensible perspiration, 493
effect of, on blood volume, 501
in saliva, 493
insensible
measurement of, 493
salt loss accompanied by, 494
through skin and lungs, 493
mean values of, in normal subjects, 1371
metabolism of
in fever, 1425
role of adrenal hormones in, 1569
output
See also Water loss
daily loss, average, 493
reabsorption of, 1680
facultative, 1682
in proximal tubule, 1682
obligatory, 1682
retention
factors affecting
estrogen, 1632
reduction of caloric value of diet on, 495
tension, 967
thermal conductivity of, 472
Water-brash, 1079
Wave, peristalic, 1213

Weber test for hearing impairment, 420
Weber's paralysis, 136
Weight
loss of
due to dehydration, 496
rate of, effect of diet on, 1412
Weightlessness, effects of, on circulation, **900**
Wernicke's hemianopic pupillary reaction, 366
Wharton's duct, 1062
White
photopic, 303
scotopic, 303
White matter, of spinal cord, 116
Wills factor. *See* Pteroylglutamic acid
Wolff-Parkinson-White syndrome, **683**
causes of, 683
electrocardiography in, 683
Wrisberg, nervus intermedius of, 129, 1064

X, Y, Z

Xanthophore, 1513
Xerostomia, 1078
difficulty of masticating and swallowing food in, 1079
X-ray
kymography, 712
therapy, effects of, on salivary secretion, 1079

Yeast, vitamin content of, 1450
Yellow, indicator, 283

Zein, 1316
amino acid content of, 1317
Zimmerman reaction, 1574
Zinn, zonula of, 342
Zona fasciculata, 1555
Zona glomerulosa, 1555, 1571
Zona pellucida, 1623
Zonula ciliaris, 353
Zwitter hypothesis, 1294
Zwitterion theory, 1294
Zymogen
granule
of pancreatic cells, 1129
intracellular route of flow of, 1056

Bold-face numbers indicate major discussion

tive and may become inactive as a result of hyperventilation. This is also a characteristic of the neuronal system which is concerned with maintaining steady state activity in abdominal muscles (Youmans et al., 1953).

Among the best evidence for reflex influences on abdominal muscle tonus elicited from a cardiac chamber, is that reported by Turner (1961), who demonstrated that distention of the left atrium produces inhibition of tonus of abdominal muscles in dogs being artificially respired and having the systemic and pulmonary circulation maintained constant by means of a pump. This would seem to implicate the left atrium as at least one site from which tonus of abdominal muscles can be influenced, but it does not rule out the possibility of influences from still other sites in the heart or pulmonary circuit.

Reflexes Initiated in Other Parts of the Body

The experiments of Churchill and Cope show that a reflex increase in the respiratory rate results from distention of the pulmonary vascular bed. When the vessels of the lung, which was isolated from the body except for its nerves, were injected with fluid to cause overfilling of the vascular bed, rapid shallow breathing immediately ensued. Section of the vagal fibers abolished the response.

Stimulation of almost any afferent nerve may bring about a reflex change in respiration. Stimulation of pain fibers is especially potent in this regard, and the respiratory effects of the excitation of the cutaneous nerves by extremes of heat or cold are well known. The thermal effect upon respiration is apparent in the panting of the dog. The increased pulmonary ventilation in fever is also partly due to the stimulation of receptors (*thermoreceptors*) responsive to a rise in temperature. The thermoreceptors are situated periph-

erally, especially in the skin, and centrally in the hypothalamus; the latter, being stimulated through the rise in temperature of the blood, set up impulses which are transmitted to the respiratory centers, the pneumotaxic center in particular. The great increase in pulmonary ventilation occurring in muscular exercise is dependent in part upon reflexes originating in the active muscles and moving joints. Proprioceptive impulses from the diaphragm and other respiratory muscles during one respiratory movement exert an important influence upon the succeeding movement. Stimulation of sensory nerves in the respiratory tract, as by ether anesthesia, or of the abdominal viscera, either during surgical operations or as the result of disease may cause profound changes in breathing. Also, as pointed out by Harrison and his associates, stimulation of afferent nerve endings in the great veins and right auricle by the rise in venous pressure is a possible factor in the hyperpnea of exercise or in the dyspnea of cardiac failure. The glossopharyngeal nerve contains afferent fibers which inhibit respiration during the second stage of the act of swallowing. Abrupt inhibition of respiration is also caused by the inhalation of an irritant gas through stimulation of nasal branches of the 5th nerve. In other instances irritation of these endings may cause sneezing—a modified respiratory act. Coughing, though it can be brought about by a voluntary effort, is most commonly reflex in character, and initiated by the stimulation of afferent nerve endings in the trachea and larynx.

Also, there are receptors in the heart, which notably are activated by veratridine injected into the coronary arteries, and elicit inhibition of respiration—along with a decrease in heart rate and inhibition of arteriolar tonus. The physiologic role of these receptors is not known, but stretching of the cardiac chambers by overfilling elicits a similar response and it is possible that these receptors are concerned in this reflex.

Regulation of Pulmonary Ventilation

Respiratory Adjustments to CO_2

The CO_2 content of inspired air is negligible, as far as human physiology is concerned, and can be increased somewhat without causing an increase in RMV. Its concentration at sea level can be increased by about 1% (7.6 mm. Hg) before a measurable increase in pulmonary ventilation occurs. If 4% CO_2 is breathed, the RMV is approximately doubled on the average, but the effect may be scarcely noticed by the subject.

Any further increase in CO_2 from 4% up to 10% produces a correspondingly greater RMV, and at the latter level it may be 8 to 10 times the resting level. Also the subject may have symptoms of dizziness, faintness and headache. Increasing the CO_2 percentage beyond 10 does not result in significantly greater increases in RMV, and at levels above 20% the RMV may begin to show a decrease. Also, these levels cause convulsive seizures. From the practical standpoint it